SECOND CANADIAN EDITION

CAMPBELL
BIOLOGY

SECOND CANADIAN EDITION

CAMPBELL
BIOLOGY

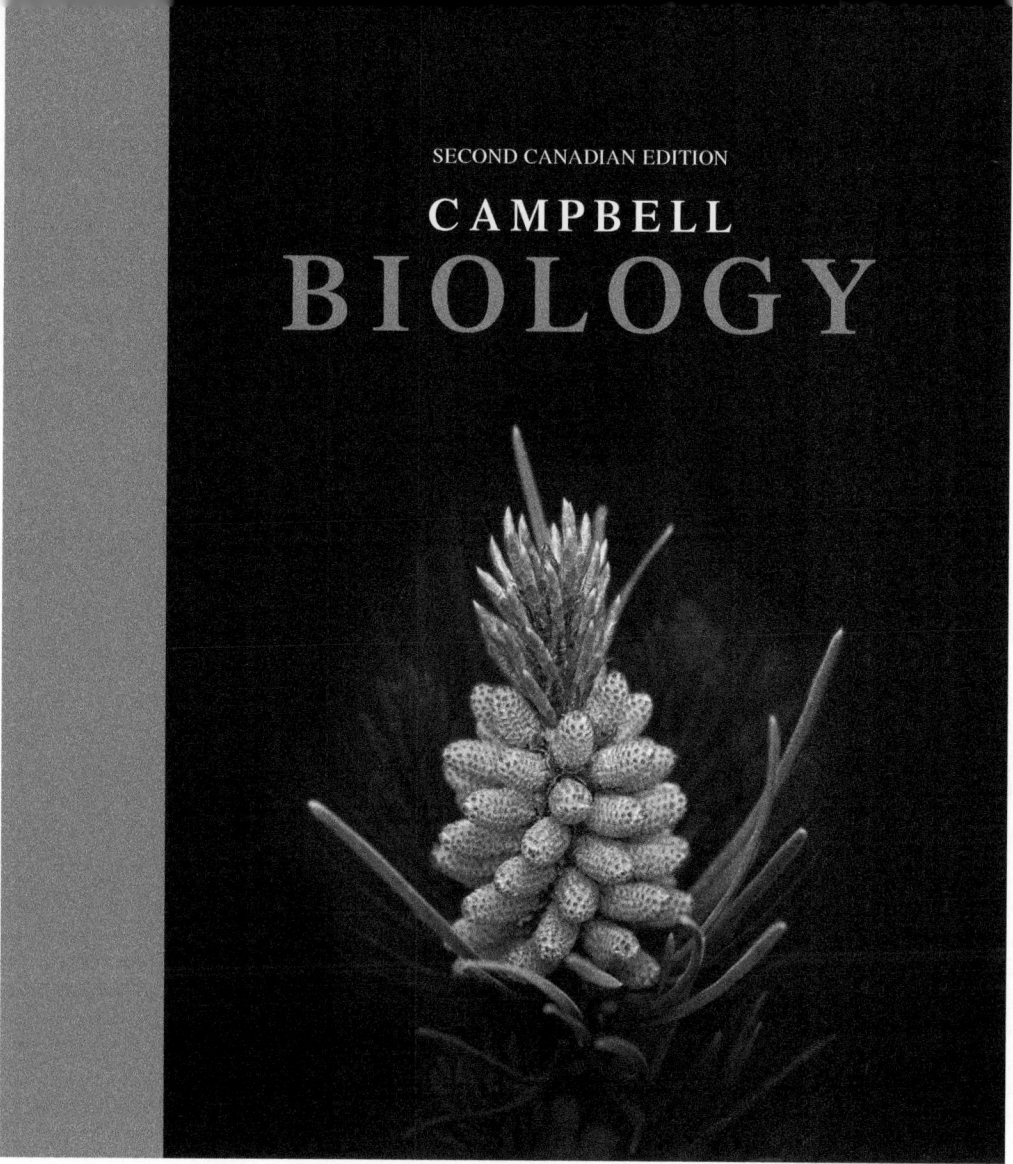

Jane B. Reece
Berkeley, California

Lisa A. Urry
Mills College, Oakland, California

Michael L. Cain
Bowdoin College, Brunswick, Maine

Steven A. Wasserman
University of California, San Diego

Peter V. Minorsky
Mercy College, Dobbs Ferry, New York

Robert B. Jackson
Stanford University, Stanford, California

Fiona E. Rawle
University of Toronto Mississauga, Mississauga, Ontario

Dion G. Durnford
University of New Brunswick, Fredericton, New Brunswick

Chris D. Moyes
Queen's University, Kingston, Ontario

Kevin Scott
University of Manitoba, Winnipeg, Manitoba

Sandra J. Walde
Dalhousie University, Halifax, Nova Scotia

EDITORIAL DIRECTOR: Claudine O'Donnell
EXECUTIVE ACQUISITIONS EDITOR: Cathleen Sullivan
SENIOR MARKETING MANAGER: Kimberly Teska
PROGRAM MANAGER: Kamilah Reid-Burrell
MANAGER, PROJECT MANAGEMENT: Avinash Chandra
SENIOR PROJECT MANAGER: Jessica Hellen
MANAGER OF CONTENT DEVELOPMENT: Suzanne Schaan
DEVELOPMENTAL EDITOR: Jennifer Murray
MEDIA EDITORS: Daniella Balabuk and Tamara Capar

MEDIA DEVELOPER: Shalin Banjara
PRODUCTION SERVICES: Cenveo® Publisher Services
PERMISSIONS PROJECT MANAGERS: Alison Derry, Sarah Horsfall, Joanne Tang
PHOTO PERMISSIONS RESEARCH: Integra Publishing Services
TEXT PERMISSIONS RESEARCH: Integra Publishing Services
INTERIOR AND COVER DESIGNER: Anthony Leung
COVER IMAGE: Ed Reschke/Getty Images
VP, CROSS MEDIA AND PUBLISHING SERVICES: Gary Bennett

Pearson Canada Inc., 26 Prince Andrew Place, Don Mills, Ontario M3C 2T8.

ISBN-13: 978-0-13-418911-6

4   18

Library and Archives Canada Cataloguing in Publication

Reece, Jane B., author
    Campbell biology / Jane B. Reece, Lisa A. Urry, Michael L. Cain, Steven A. Wasserman, Peter V. Minorsky, Robert B. Jackson, Fiona Rawle, Dion Durnford, Chris Moyes, Sandra Walde, Kevin Scott.—Second Canadian edition.

Includes index.
ISBN 978-0-13-418911-6 (hardback)

    1. Biology—Textbooks. 2. Textbooks. I. Title. II. Title: Biology.

QH308.2 R44 2017   570   C2016-906935-4

Cover image Caption: MALES CONES (PRODUCE POLLEN). LODGEPOLE PINE. Pinus contorta. The male cones produce copious amounts of pollen in the spring. Rocky Mountains, Yellowstone NP

KV 10.05.2018 1850

About the Authors

Jane B. Reece

Jane Reece was Neil Campbell's longtime collaborator, and she has participated in every edition of *CAMPBELL BIOLOGY*. Earlier, Jane taught biology at Middlesex County College and Queensborough Community College. She holds an A.B. in biology from Harvard University, an M.S. in microbiology from Rutgers University, and a Ph.D. in bacteriology from the University of California, Berkeley. Jane's research as a doctoral student at UC Berkeley and postdoctoral fellow at Stanford University focused on genetic recombination in bacteria. Besides her work on *CAMPBELL BIOLOGY*, she has been a co-author on *Campbell Biology in Focus, Campbell Biology: Concepts & Connections, Campbell Essential Biology,* and *The World of the Cell.*

Lisa A. Urry

Lisa Urry is Professor of Biology and Chair of the Biology Department at Mills College in Oakland, California, and a Visiting Scholar at the University of California, Berkeley. After graduating from Tufts University with a double major in biology and French, Lisa completed her Ph.D. in molecular and developmental biology at the Massachusetts Institute of Technology (MIT) in the MIT/Woods Hole Oceanographic Institution Joint Program. She has published a number of research papers, most of them focused on gene expression during embryonic and larval development in sea urchins. Lisa has taught a variety of courses, from introductory biology to developmental biology and senior seminar. As a part of her mission to increase understanding of evolution, Lisa also teaches a nonmajors course called Evolution for Future Presidents and is on the Teacher Advisory Board for the Understanding Evolution website developed by the University of California Museum of Paleontology. Lisa is also deeply committed to promoting opportunities in science for women and underrepresented minorities. Lisa is also a co-author of *Campbell Biology in Focus.*

Michael L. Cain

Michael Cain is an ecologist and evolutionary biologist who is now writing full-time. Michael earned a joint degree in biology and math at Bowdoin College, an M.Sc. from Brown University, and a Ph.D. in ecology and evolutionary biology from Cornell University. As a faculty member at New Mexico State University and Rose-Hulman Institute of Technology, he taught a wide range of courses, including introductory biology, ecology, evolution, botany, and conservation biology. Michael is the author of dozens of scientific papers on topics that include foraging behaviour in insects and plants, long-distance seed dispersal, and speciation in crickets. In addition to his work on *CAMPBELL BIOLOGY* and *Campbell Biology in Focus,* Michael is the lead author of an ecology textbook.

Steven A. Wasserman

Steve Wasserman is Professor of Biology at the University of California, San Diego (UCSD). He earned his A.B. in biology from Harvard University and his Ph.D. in biological sciences from MIT. Through his research on regulatory pathway mechanisms in the fruit fly *Drosophila,* Steve has contributed to the fields of developmental biology, reproduction, and immunity. As a faculty member at the University of Texas Southwestern Medical Center and UCSD, he has taught genetics, development, and physiology to undergraduate, graduate, and medical students. He currently focuses on teaching introductory biology. He has also served as the research mentor for more than a dozen doctoral students and more than 50 aspiring scientists at the undergraduate and high school levels. Steve has been the recipient of distinguished scholar awards from both the Markey Charitable Trust and the David and Lucile Packard Foundation. In 2007, he received UCSD's Distinguished Teaching Award for undergraduate teaching. Steve is also a co-author of *Campbell Biology in Focus.*

Peter V. Minorsky

Peter Minorsky is Professor of Biology at Mercy College in New York, where he teaches introductory biology, evolution, ecology, and botany. He received his A.B. in biology from Vassar College and his Ph.D. in plant physiology from Cornell University. He is also the science writer for the journal *Plant Physiology*. After a postdoctoral fellowship at the University of Wisconsin at Madison, Peter taught at Kenyon College, Union College, Western Connecticut State University, and Vassar College. His research interests concern how plants sense environmental change. Peter received the 2008 Award for Teaching Excellence at Mercy College. Peter is also a co-author of *Campbell Biology in Focus*.

Robert B. Jackson

Rob Jackson is the Douglas Professor of Environment and Energy in the Department of Environmental Earth System Science at Stanford University. Rob holds a B.S. in chemical engineering from Rice University, as well as M.S. degrees in ecology and statistics and a Ph.D. in ecology from Utah State University. While a biology professor at Duke University, Rob directed the university's Program in Ecology and was Vice President of Science for the Ecological Society of America. He has received numerous awards, including a Presidential Early Career Award in Science and Engineering from the National Science Foundation. Rob is a Fellow of both the Ecological Society of America and the American Geophysical Union. He also enjoys popular writing, having published a trade book about the environment, *The Earth Remains Forever*, and two books of poetry for children, *Animal Mischief* and *Weekend Mischief*. Rob is also a co-author of *Campbell Biology in Focus*.

Neil A. Campbell

Neil Campbell (1946–2004) combined the investigative nature of a research scientist with the soul of an experienced and caring teacher. He earned his M.A. in zoology from the University of California, Los Angeles, and his Ph.D. in plant biology from the University of California, Riverside, where he received the Distinguished Alumnus Award in 2001. Neil published numerous research articles on desert and coastal plants and how the sensitive plant (*Mimosa*) and other legumes move their leaves. His 30 years of teaching in diverse environments included introductory biology courses at Cornell University, Pomona College, and San Bernardino Valley College, where he received the college's first Outstanding Professor Award in 1986. Neil was a visiting scholar in the Department of Botany and Plant Sciences at the University of California, Riverside.

Fiona Rawle

Fiona Rawle: (Units 1-3; editor Units 1-8) received her Ph.D. from Queen's University in Kingston, Ontario. She is an Associate Professor, Teaching Stream, at the University of Toronto Mississauga, where she teaches Introduction to Evolution and Evolutionary Genetics, Introductory Genetics, and Molecular Basis of Disease. Fiona's teaching and pedagogical research interests focus on several areas: (1) the development of case studies to immerse students in real-world biological challenges and allow students to connect with material from different perspectives; (2) the development of active learning techniques that can be used in large class settings; and (3) the development of scientific literacy interventions that can be used across the undergraduate biology curriculum. Fiona was the recipient of the 2016 University of Toronto Mississauga Teaching Excellence Award, a 2015 University of Toronto Early Career Teaching Award, and a 2010 Faculty Award for Teaching Excellence while at Wilfrid Laurier University.

Dion Durnford

Dion Durnford (Unit 5) is a professor at the University of New Brunswick, in Fredericton. He earned a B.Sc. in Biology from Dalhousie University and a Ph.D. in Botany from the University of British Columbia. His research has focused on the evolution of light-harvesting antenna systems and the role of these proteins in light harvesting and photo-protection in microalgae. His recent work is examining how microalgae age and their strategies for increasing longevity. Dion was the recipient of the 2002 Faculty of Science Excellence in Teaching award and the 2010 Allan P. Stewart Award for Excellence in Teaching.

Chris Moyes

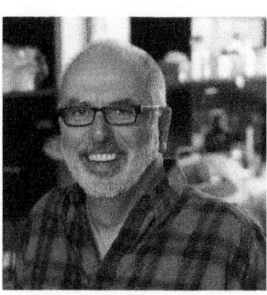

Chris Moyes (Unit 7) is a comparative physiologist, focusing on the muscle biochemistry and energetics. He received his Ph.D. in Zoology from the University of British Columbia (1991) and is currently a Professor in the Department of Biology, Queen's University. He has published more than 100 research papers and contributed to four books. He is co-author of *Principles of Animal Physiology,* first published in 2006.

Kevin Scott

Kevin Scott (Units 4 and 6) is a senior instructor at the University of Manitoba where he teaches introductory biology for both biology majors and nonbiology majors; human physiology; and environmental physiology of animal laboratories. In the past, he has also taught courses in ecology for nonbiology majors, immunology, parasitology, and microbiology. He received a B.Sc. in Zoology and a Ph.D. joint between Zoology and Cellular, Molecular, and Microbial Biology at the University of Calgary. As an educator, Dr. Scott's career is centred on teaching and the classroom, where he shares his excitement for biology. His interest in plant biology has grown during his professional career and is a favourite topic in his classroom. Kevin was a co-author of *Campbell Biology: Concepts and Connections*, Canadian Edition.

Sandra Walde

Sandra Walde (Unit 8) is a professor of biology and associate dean of science at Dalhousie University. She received her B.Sc. in Biology and Ph.D. in Ecology from the University of Calgary, and then went to the University of California, Santa Barbara, as a post-doctoral fellow. At Dalhousie, she teaches general ecology to first- and second-year students and population ecology to upper-year students. Sandy's research has focused on dispersal and ecological interactions in aquatic and terrestrial communities. She feels lucky that her field work has taken her to some beautiful places, including studies of stream invertebrate communities in Alberta and Nova Scotia, and research on native fishes in the lakes of the Patagonian Andes.

Brief Contents

1 Evolution, the Themes of Biology, and Scientific Inquiry 1

THE CHEMISTRY OF LIFE 29

2 The Chemical Context of Life 32
3 Water and Life 49
4 Carbon and the Molecular Diversity of Life 63
5 The Structure and Function of Large Biological Molecules 74

THE CELL 101

6 A Tour of the Cell 104
7 Membrane Structure and Function 136
8 An Introduction to Metabolism 154
9 Cellular Respiration and Fermentation 175
10 Photosynthesis 198
11 Cell Communication 221
12 The Cell Cycle 243

GENETICS 263

13 Meiosis and Sexual Life Cycles 266
14 Mendel and the Gene Idea 281
15 The Chromosomal Basis of Inheritance 307
16 The Molecular Basis of Inheritance 329
17 Gene Expression: From Gene to Protein 351
18 Regulation of Gene Expression 380
19 Viruses 414
20 DNA Tools and Biotechnology 433
21 Genomes and Their Evolution 463

MECHANISMS OF EVOLUTION 489

22 Descent with Modification: A Darwinian View of Life 492
23 The Evolution of Populations 510
24 The Origin of Species 530
25 The History of Life on Earth 550

THE EVOLUTIONARY HISTORY OF BIOLOGICAL DIVERSITY 579

26 Phylogeny and the Tree of Life 582
27 Bacteria and Archaea 603
28 Protists 625
29 Plant Diversity I: How Plants Colonized Land 652

30 Plant Diversity II: The Evolution of Seed Plants 672
31 Fungi 692
32 An Overview of Animal Diversity 712
33 An Introduction to Invertebrates 726
34 The Origin and Evolution of Vertebrates 759

PLANT FORM AND FUNCTION 799

35 Plant Structure, Growth, and Development 802
36 Resource Acquisition and Transport in Vascular Plants 828
37 Soil and Plant Nutrition 849
38 Angiosperm Reproduction and Biotechnology 866
39 Plant Responses to Internal and External Signals 888

ANIMAL FORM AND FUNCTION 917

40 Basic Principles of Animal Form and Function 920
41 Animal Nutrition 943
42 Circulation and Gas Exchange 966
43 The Immune System 999
44 Osmoregulation and Excretion 1025
45 Hormones and the Endocrine System 1048
46 Animal Reproduction 1070
47 Animal Development 1095
48 Neurons, Synapses, and Signalling 1120
49 Nervous System 1139
50 Sensory and Motor Mechanisms 1162
51 Animal Behaviour 1196

ECOLOGY 1221

52 An Introduction to Ecology and the Biosphere 1224
53 Population Ecology 1250
54 Community Ecology 1273
55 Ecosystems and Restoration Ecology 1299
56 Conservation Biology and Global Change 1320

Detailed Contents

1 Evolution, the Themes of Biology, and Scientific Inquiry 1

Inquiring About Life 1
CONCEPT 1.1 The study of life reveals common themes 3
    Theme: New Properties Emerge at Successive Levels of Biological Organization 3
    Theme: Life's Processes Involve the Expression and Transmission of Genetic Information 6
    Theme: Life Requires the Transfer and Transformation of Energy and Matter 8
    Theme: From Molecules to Ecosystems, Interactions Are Important in Biological Systems 9
CONCEPT 1.2 The Core Theme: Evolution accounts for the unity and diversity of life 11
    Classifying the Diversity of Life 11
    The Tree of Life 16
CONCEPT 1.3 In studying nature, scientists make observations and form and test hypotheses 17
    Making Observations 18
    Forming and Testing Hypotheses 18
    The Flexibility of the Scientific Process 20
    A Case Study in Scientific Inquiry: Investigating Coat Colouration in Mouse Populations 21
    Theories in Science 23
CONCEPT 1.4 Science benefits from a cooperative approach and diverse viewpoints 23
    Building on the Work of Others 23
    Science, Technology, and Society 25
    The Value of Diverse Viewpoints in Science 26

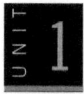

UNIT 1 THE CHEMISTRY OF LIFE 29

2 The Chemical Context of Life 32

A Chemical Connection to Biology 32
CONCEPT 2.1 Matter consists of chemical elements in pure form and in combinations called compounds 33
    Elements and Compounds 33
    The Elements of Life 33
    Case Study: Evolution of Tolerance to Toxic Elements 33
CONCEPT 2.2 An element's properties depend on the structure of its atoms 34
    Subatomic Particles 34
    Atomic Number and Atomic Mass 35
    Isotopes 35
    The Energy Levels of Electrons 36
    Electron Distribution and Chemical Properties 38
    Electron Orbitals 39
CONCEPT 2.3 The formation and function of molecules depend on chemical bonding between atoms 40
    Covalent Bonds 40
    Ionic Bonds 42
    Weak Chemical Bonds 43
    Molecular Shape and Function 44
CONCEPT 2.4 Chemical reactions make and break chemical bonds 45

3 Water and Life 49

The Molecule That Supports All of Life 49
CONCEPT 3.1 Polar covalent bonds in water molecules result in hydrogen bonding 50
CONCEPT 3.2 Four emergent properties of water contribute to Earth's suitability for life 50
    Cohesion of Water Molecules 50
    Moderation of Temperature by Water 51
    Floating of Ice on Liquid Water 53
    Water: The Solvent of Life 54
    Possible Evolution of Life on Other Planets 56
CONCEPT 3.3 Acidic and basic conditions affect living organisms 56
    Acids and Bases 57
    The pH Scale 57
    Buffers 58
    Acidification: A Threat to Water Quality 59

4 Carbon and the Molecular Diversity of Life 63

Carbon: The Backbone of Life 63
CONCEPT 4.1 Organic chemistry is the study of carbon compounds 64
    Organic Molecules and the Origin of Life on Earth 64
CONCEPT 4.2 Carbon atoms can form diverse molecules by bonding to four other atoms 66
    The Formation of Bonds with Carbon 66
    Molecular Diversity Arising from Variation in Carbon Skeletons 67
CONCEPT 4.3 A few chemical groups are key to molecular function 69
    The Chemical Groups Most Important in the Processes of Life 69
    ATP: An Important Source of Energy for Cellular Processes 70
    The Chemical Elements of Life: *A Review* 70

5 The Structure and Function of Large Biological Molecules 74

The Molecules of Life 74
CONCEPT 5.1 Macromolecules are polymers, built from monomers 75
    The Synthesis and Breakdown of Polymers 75
    The Diversity of Polymers 75
CONCEPT 5.2 Carbohydrates serve as fuel and building material 76
    Sugars 76
    Polysaccharides 78
CONCEPT 5.3 Lipids are a diverse group of hydrophobic molecules 80
    Fats 80

Phospholipids 82
Steroids 83
CONCEPT 5.4 Proteins include a diversity of structures, resulting in a wide range of functions 83
Amino Acid Monomers 83
Polypeptides (Amino Acid Polymers) 86
Protein Structure and Function 86
CONCEPT 5.5 Nucleic acids store, transmit, and help express hereditary information 92
The Roles of Nucleic Acids 92
The Components of Nucleic Acids 93
Nucleotide Polymers 94
The Structures of DNA and RNA Molecules 94
CONCEPT 5.6 Genomics and proteomics have transformed biological inquiry and applications 96
DNA and Proteins as Tape Measures of Evolution 96

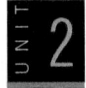

UNIT 2 THE CELL 101

6 A Tour of the Cell 104

The Fundamental Units of Life 104
CONCEPT 6.1 Biologists use microscopes and the tools of biochemistry to study cells 105
Microscopy 105
Cell Fractionation 107
CONCEPT 6.2 Eukaryotic cells have internal membranes that compartmentalize their functions 108
Comparing Prokaryotic and Eukaryotic Cells 108
A Panoramic View of the Eukaryotic Cell 110
CONCEPT 6.3 The eukaryotic cell's genetic instructions are housed in the nucleus and carried out by the ribosomes 111
The Nucleus: Information Central 111
Ribosomes: Protein Factories 111
CONCEPT 6.4 The endomembrane system regulates protein traffic and performs metabolic functions in the cell 115
The Endoplasmic Reticulum: Biosynthetic Factory 115
The Golgi Apparatus: Shipping and Receiving Centre 116
Lysosomes: Digestive Compartments 118
Vacuoles: Diverse Maintenance Compartments 119
The Endomembrane System: A Review 119
CONCEPT 6.5 Mitochondria and chloroplasts change energy from one form to another 120
The Evolutionary Origins of Mitochondria and Chloroplasts 120
Mitochondria: Chemical Energy Conversion 121
Chloroplasts: Capture of Light Energy 122
Peroxisomes: Oxidation 123
CONCEPT 6.6 The cytoskeleton is a network of fibres that organizes structures and activities in the cell 123
Roles of the Cytoskeleton: Support and Motility 124
Components of the Cytoskeleton 125
CONCEPT 6.7 Extracellular components and connections between cells help coordinate cellular activities 129
Cell Walls of Plants 129
The Extracellular Matrix (ECM) of Animal Cells 130
Cell Junctions 131
The Cell: A Living Unit Greater Than the Sum of Its Parts 131

7 Membrane Structure and Function 136

Life at the Edge 136
CONCEPT 7.1 Cellular membranes are fluid mosaics of lipids and proteins 137
The Fluidity of Membranes 137
Evolution of Differences in Membrane Lipid Composition 139
Membrane Proteins and Their Functions 139
The Role of Membrane Carbohydrates in Cell-Cell Recognition 141
Synthesis and Sidedness of Membranes 141
CONCEPT 7.2 Membrane structure results in selective permeability 142
The Permeability of the Lipid Bilayer 142
Transport Proteins 142
CONCEPT 7.3 Passive transport is diffusion of a substance across a membrane with no energy investment 143
Effects of Osmosis on Water Balance 143
Facilitated Diffusion: Passive Transport Aided by Proteins 145
CONCEPT 7.4 Active transport uses energy to move solutes against their gradients 146
The Need for Energy in Active Transport 147
How Ion Pumps Maintain Membrane Potential 147
Cotransport: Coupled Transport by a Membrane Protein 148
CONCEPT 7.5 Bulk transport across the plasma membrane occurs by exocytosis and endocytosis 149
Exocytosis 149
Endocytosis 149

8 An Introduction to Metabolism 154

The Energy of Life 154
CONCEPT 8.1 An organism's metabolism transforms matter and energy, subject to the laws of thermodynamics 155
Organization of the Chemistry of Life into Metabolic Pathways 155
Forms of Energy 155
The Laws of Energy Transformation 156
CONCEPT 8.2 The free-energy change of a reaction tells us whether or not the reaction occurs spontaneously 158
Free Energy Change, ΔG 158
Free Energy, Stability, and Equilibrium 158
Free Energy and Metabolism 159
CONCEPT 8.3 ATP powers cellular work by coupling exergonic reactions to endergonic reactions 161
The Structure and Hydrolysis of ATP 162
How the Hydrolysis of ATP Performs Work 162
The Regeneration of ATP 164
CONCEPT 8.4 Enzymes speed up metabolic reactions by lowering energy barriers 164
The Activation Energy Barrier 164
How Enzymes Speed Up Reactions 165
Substrate Specificity of Enzymes 166
Catalysis in the Enzyme's Active Site 167
Effects of Local Conditions on Enzyme Activity 168
The Evolution of Enzymes 170
CONCEPT 8.5 Regulation of enzyme activity helps control metabolism 170
Allosteric Regulation of Enzymes 170
Localization of Enzymes within the Cell 172

9 Cellular Respiration and Fermentation 175

Life Is Work 175
CONCEPT 9.1 Catabolic pathways yield energy by oxidizing organic fuels 176
    Catabolic Pathways and Production of ATP 176
    Redox Reactions: Oxidation and Reduction 176
    The Stages of Cellular Respiration: *A Preview* 179
CONCEPT 9.2 Glycolysis harvests chemical energy by oxidizing glucose to pyruvate 181
CONCEPT 9.3 After pyruvate is oxidized, the citric acid cycle completes the energy-yielding oxidation of organic molecules 181
    Oxidation of Pyruvate to Acetyl CoA 181
    The Citric Acid Cycle 182
CONCEPT 9.4 During oxidative phosphorylation, chemiosmosis couples electron transport to ATP synthesis 185
    The Pathway of Electron Transport 185
    Chemiosmosis: The Energy-Coupling Mechanism 187
    An Accounting of ATP Production by Cellular Respiration 188
CONCEPT 9.5 Fermentation and anaerobic respiration enable cells to produce ATP without the use of oxygen 191
    Types of Fermentation 191
    Comparing Fermentation with Anaerobic and Aerobic Respiration 192
    The Evolutionary Significance of Glycolysis 193
CONCEPT 9.6 Glycolysis and the citric acid cycle connect to many other metabolic pathways 193
    The Versatility of Catabolism 193
    Biosynthesis (Anabolic Pathways) 194
    Regulation of Cellular Respiration via Feedback Mechanisms 194

10 Photosynthesis 198

The Process That Feeds the Biosphere 198
CONCEPT 10.1 Photosynthesis converts light energy to the chemical energy of food 200
    Chloroplasts: The Sites of Photosynthesis in Plants 200
    Tracking Atoms Through Photosynthesis: *Scientific Inquiry* 201
    The Two Stages of Photosynthesis: *A Preview* 202
CONCEPT 10.2 The light reactions convert solar energy to the chemical energy of ATP and NADPH 203
    The Nature of Sunlight 203
    Photosynthetic Pigments: The Light Receptors 204
    Excitation of Chlorophyll by Light 206
    A Photosystem: A Reaction-Centre Complex Associated with Light-Harvesting Complexes 206
    Linear Electron Flow 208
    Cyclic Electron Flow 209
    A Comparison of Chemiosmosis in Chloroplasts and Mitochondria 210
CONCEPT 10.3 The Calvin cycle uses the chemical energy of ATP and NADPH to reduce CO_2 to sugar 212
CONCEPT 10.4 Alternative mechanisms of carbon fixation have evolved in hot, arid climates 214
    Photorespiration: An Evolutionary Relic? 214
    C_4 Plants 214
    CAM Plants 216
    The Importance of Photosynthesis: *A Review* 217

11 Cell Communication 221

Cellular Messaging 221
CONCEPT 11.1 External signals are converted to responses within the cell 222
    Evolution of Cell Signalling 222
    Local and Long-Distance Signalling 223
    The Three Stages of Cell Signalling: *A Preview* 224
CONCEPT 11.2 Reception: A signalling molecule binds to a receptor protein, causing it to change shape 225
    Receptors in the Plasma Membrane 225
    Intracellular Receptors 228
CONCEPT 11.3 Transduction: Cascades of molecular interactions relay signals from receptors to target molecules in the cell 229
    Signal Transduction Pathways 229
    Protein Phosphorylation and Dephosphorylation 230
    Small Molecules and Ions as Second Messengers 231
CONCEPT 11.4 Response: Cell signalling leads to regulation of transcription or cytoplasmic activities 234
    Nuclear and Cytoplasmic Responses 234
    Regulation of the Response 234
CONCEPT 11.5 Apoptosis integrates multiple cell-signalling pathways 238
    Apoptosis in the Soil Worm *Caenorhabditis elegans* 239
    Apoptotic Pathways and the Signals That Trigger Them 239

12 The Cell Cycle 243

The Key Roles of Cell Division 243
CONCEPT 12.1 Most cell division results in genetically identical daughter cells 244
    Cellular Organization of the Genetic Material 244
    Distribution of Chromosomes during Eukaryotic Cell Division 245
CONCEPT 12.2 The mitotic phase alternates with interphase in the cell cycle 246
    Phases of the Cell Cycle 246
    The Mitotic Spindle: *A Closer Look* 249
    Cytokinesis: *A Closer Look* 250
    Binary Fission in Bacteria 251
    The Evolution of Mitosis 252
CONCEPT 12.3 The eukaryotic cell cycle is regulated by a molecular control system 253
    The Cell Cycle Control System 254
    Loss of Cell Cycle Controls in Cancer Cells 258

UNIT 3 GENETICS 263

13 Meiosis and Sexual Life Cycles 266

Variations on a Theme 266
CONCEPT 13.1 Offspring acquire genes from parents by inheriting chromosomes 267
    Inheritance of Genes 267
    Comparison of Asexual and Sexual Reproduction 267
CONCEPT 13.2 Fertilization and meiosis alternate in sexual life cycles 268
    Sets of Chromosomes in Human Cells 268
    Behaviour of Chromosome Sets in the Human Life Cycle 269
    The Variety of Sexual Life Cycles 270

CONCEPT 13.3 Meiosis reduces the number of chromosome sets from diploid to haploid 271

The Stages of Meiosis 271

Crossing Over and Synapsis During Prophase I 274

A Comparison of Mitosis and Meiosis 274

CONCEPT 13.4 Genetic variation produced in sexual life cycles contributes to evolution 277

Origins of Genetic Variation Among Offspring 277

The Evolutionary Significance of Genetic Variation Within Populations 278

14 Mendel and the Gene Idea 281

Drawing from the Deck of Genes 281

CONCEPT 14.1 Mendel used the scientific approach to identify two laws of inheritance 282

Mendel's Experimental, Quantitative Approach 282

The Law of Segregation 283

The Law of Independent Assortment 286

CONCEPT 14.2 Probability laws govern Mendelian inheritance 288

The Multiplication and Addition Rules Applied to Monohybrid Crosses 289

Solving Complex Genetics Problems with the Rules of Probability 289

CONCEPT 14.3 Inheritance patterns are often more complex than predicted by simple Mendelian genetics 290

Extending Mendelian Genetics for a Single Gene 290

Extending Mendelian Genetics for Two or More Genes 293

Nature and Nurture: The Environmental Impact on Phenotype 295

A Mendelian View of Heredity and Variation 295

CONCEPT 14.4 Many human traits follow Mendelian patterns of inheritance 296

Pedigree Analysis 296

Recessively Inherited Disorders 297

Dominantly Inherited Disorders 299

Multifactorial Disorders 300

Genetic Testing and Counselling 300

15 The Chromosomal Basis of Inheritance 307

Locating Genes Along Chromosomes 307

CONCEPT 15.1 Morgan showed that Mendelian inheritance has its physical basis in the behaviour of chromosomes: Scientific Inquiry 309

CONCEPT 15.2 Sex-linked genes exhibit unique patterns of inheritance 311

The Chromosomal Basis of Sex 311

Inheritance of X-Linked Genes 312

X Inactivation in Female Mammals 313

CONCEPT 15.3 Linked genes tend to be inherited together because they are located near each other on the same chromosome 314

How Linkage Affects Inheritance 314

Genetic Recombination and Linkage 316

Mapping the Distance Between Genes Using Recombination Data: Scientific Inquiry 317

CONCEPT 15.4 Alterations of chromosome number or structure cause some genetic disorders 321

Abnormal Chromosome Number 321

Alterations of Chromosome Structure 322

Human Disorders Due to Chromosomal Alterations 322

CONCEPT 15.5 Some inheritance patterns are exceptions to standard Mendelian inheritance 324

Genomic Imprinting 324

Inheritance of Organelle Genes 325

16 The Molecular Basis of Inheritance 329

Life's Operating Instructions 329

CONCEPT 16.1 DNA is the genetic material 330

The Search for the Genetic Material: Scientific Inquiry 330

Building a Structural Model of DNA: Scientific Inquiry 333

CONCEPT 16.2 Many proteins work together in DNA replication and repair 335

The Basic Principle: Base Pairing to a Template Strand 335

DNA Replication: A Closer Look 337

Proofreading and Repairing DNA 342

Evolutionary Significance of Altered DNA Nucleotides 343

Replicating the Ends of DNA Molecules 343

CONCEPT 16.3 A chromosome consists of a DNA molecule packed together with proteins 345

17 Gene Expression: From Gene to Protein 351

The Flow of Genetic Information 351

CONCEPT 17.1 Genes specify proteins via transcription and translation 352

Evidence from the Study of Metabolic Defects 352

Basic Principles of Transcription and Translation 353

The Genetic Code 355

CONCEPT 17.2 Transcription is the DNA-directed synthesis of RNA: A closer look 358

Molecular Components of Transcription 358

Synthesis of an RNA Transcript 358

CONCEPT 17.3 Eukaryotic cells modify RNA after transcription 361

Alteration of mRNA Ends 361

Split Genes and RNA Splicing 361

CONCEPT 17.4 Translation is the RNA-directed synthesis of a polypeptide: A closer look 363

Molecular Components of Translation 363

Building a Polypeptide 366

Completing and Targeting the Functional Protein 369

Making Multiple Polypeptides in Bacteria and Eukaryotes 371

CONCEPT 17.5 Mutations of one or a few nucleotides can affect protein structure and function 372

Types of Small-Scale Mutations 374

New Mutations and Mutagens 375

What Is a Gene? Revisiting the Question 376

18 Regulation of Gene Expression 380

Beauty in the Eye of the Beholder 380

CONCEPT 18.1 Bacteria often respond to environmental change by regulating transcription 381

Operons: The Basic Concept 381

Repressible and Inducible Operons: Two Types of Negative Gene Regulation 383

Positive Gene Regulation 384

CONCEPT 18.2 Eukaryotic gene expression is regulated at many stages 385

Differential Gene Expression 385
Regulation of Chromatin Structure 385
Regulation of Transcription Initiation 387
Mechanisms of Post-Transcriptional Regulation 392
CONCEPT 18.3 Noncoding RNAs play multiple roles in controlling gene expression 394
Effects on mRNAs by MicroRNAs and Small Interfering RNAs 394
Chromatin Remodelling by ncRNAs 395
The Evolutionary Significance of Small ncRNAs 396
CONCEPT 18.4 A program of differential gene expression leads to the different cell types in a multicellular organism 397
A Genetic Program for Embryonic Development 397
Cytoplasmic Determinants and Inductive Signals 397
Sequential Regulation of Gene Expression During Cellular Differentiation 398
Pattern Formation: Setting Up the Body Plan 400
CONCEPT 18.5 Cancer results from genetic changes that affect cell cycle control 404
Types of Genes Associated with Cancer 404
Interference with Normal Cell-Signalling Pathways 405
The Multistep Model of Cancer Development 406
Inherited Predisposition and Environmental Factors Contributing to Cancer 407
The Role of Viruses in Cancer 410

19 Viruses 414

A Borrowed Life 414
CONCEPT 19.1 A virus consists of a nucleic acid surrounded by a protein coat 415
The Discovery of Viruses: *Scientific Inquiry* 415
Structure of Viruses 416
CONCEPT 19.2 Viruses replicate only in host cells 418
General Features of Viral Replicative Cycles 418
Replicative Cycles of Phages 419
Replicative Cycles of Animal Viruses 421
Evolution of Viruses 425
CONCEPT 19.3 Viruses and prions are formidable pathogens in animals and plants 425
Viral Diseases in Animals 426
Emerging Viruses 426
Viral Diseases in Plants 430
Prions: Proteins as Infectious Agents 430

20 DNA Tools and Biotechnology 433

The DNA Toolbox 433
CONCEPT 20.1 DNA sequencing and DNA cloning are valuable tools for genetic engineering and biological inquiry 434
DNA Sequencing 434
Making Multiple Copies of a Gene or Other DNA Segment 437
Using Restriction Enzymes to Make a Recombinant DNA Plasmid 438
Amplifying DNA: The Polymerase Chain Reaction (PCR) and Its Use in DNA Cloning 440
Expressing Cloned Eukaryotic Genes 441
CONCEPT 20.2 Biologists use DNA technology to study gene expression and function 442
Analyzing Gene Expression 443
Determining Gene Function 446

CONCEPT 20.3 Cloned organisms and stem cells are useful for basic research and other applications 448
Cloning Plants: Single-Cell Cultures 449
Cloning Animals: Nuclear Transplantation 449
Stem Cells of Animals 451
CONCEPT 20.4 The practical applications of DNA-based biotechnology affect our lives in many ways 454
Medical Applications 454
Forensic Evidence and Genetic Profiles 457
Environmental Cleanup 458
Agricultural Applications 459
Safety and Ethical Questions Raised by DNA Technology 459

21 Genomes and Their Evolution 463

Reading the Leaves from the Tree of Life 463
CONCEPT 21.1 The Human Genome Project fostered development of faster, less expensive sequencing techniques 464
CONCEPT 21.2 Scientists use bioinformatics to analyze genomes and their functions 465
Centralized Resources for Analyzing Genome Sequences 465
Identifying Protein-Coding Genes and Understanding Their Functions 466
Understanding Genes and Gene Expression at the Systems Level 467
CONCEPT 21.3 Genomes vary in size, number of genes, and gene density 469
Genome Size 469
Number of Genes 470
Gene Density and Noncoding DNA 471
CONCEPT 21.4 Multicellular eukaryotes have a lot of noncoding DNA and many multigene families 472
Transposable Elements and Related Sequences 473
Other Repetitive DNA, Including Simple Sequence DNA 474
Genes and Multigene Families 474
CONCEPT 21.5 Duplication, rearrangement, and mutation of DNA contribute to genome evolution 476
Duplication of Entire Chromosome Sets 476
Alterations of Chromosome Structure 476
Duplication and Divergence of Gene-Sized Regions of DNA 477
Rearrangements of Parts of Genes: Exon Duplication and Exon Shuffling 478
How Transposable Elements Contribute to Genome Evolution 480
CONCEPT 21.6 Comparing genome sequences provides clues to evolution and development 481
Comparing Genomes 481

UNIT 4 MECHANISMS OF EVOLUTION 489

22 Descent with Modification: A Darwinian View of Life 492

"Endless Forms Most Beautiful"—Charles Darwin 492
CONCEPT 22.1 The Darwinian revolution challenged traditional views of a young Earth inhabited by unchanging species 493
Scala Naturae and Classification of Species 494

Ideas about Change over Time 494
Lamarck's Hypothesis of Evolution 494

CONCEPT 22.2 Descent with modification by natural selection explains the adaptations of organisms and the unity and diversity of life 495
Darwin's Research 495

CONCEPT 22.3 Evolution is supported by an overwhelming amount of scientific evidence 500
Direct Observations of Evolutionary Change 501
Homology 503
The Fossil Record 505
Biogeography 506
What Is Theoretical About Darwin's View of Life? 507

23 The Evolution of Populations 510

The Smallest Unit of Evolution 510

CONCEPT 23.1 Genetic variation makes evolution possible 511
Genetic Variation 511
Sources of Genetic Variation 512

CONCEPT 23.2 The Hardy-Weinberg equation can be used to test whether a population is evolving 514
Gene Pools and Allele Frequencies 514
The Hardy-Weinberg Equation 514

CONCEPT 23.3 Natural selection, genetic drift, and gene flow can alter allele frequencies in a population 518
Natural Selection 518
Genetic Drift 518
Gene Flow 521

CONCEPT 23.4 Natural selection is the only mechanism that consistently causes adaptive evolution 522
Natural Selection: *A Closer Look* 522
The Key Role of Natural Selection in Adaptive Evolution 523
Sexual Selection 524
Balancing Selection 524
Heterozygote Advantage 525
Frequency-Dependent Selection 525
Why Natural Selection Cannot Fashion Perfect Organisms 526

24 The Origin of Species 530

That "Mystery of Mysteries" 530

CONCEPT 24.1 The biological species concept emphasizes reproductive isolation 531
The Biological Species Concept 531
Other Definitions of Species 534

CONCEPT 24.2 Speciation can take place with or without geographic separation 535
Allopatric ("Other Country") Speciation 535
Sympatric ("Same Country") Speciation 538
Allopatric and Sympatric Speciation: *A Review* 540

CONCEPT 24.3 Hybrid zones reveal factors that cause reproductive isolation 540
Patterns Within Hybrid Zones 541
Hybrid Zones over Time 542

CONCEPT 24.4 Speciation can occur rapidly or slowly and can result from changes in few or many genes 544
The Time Course of Speciation 544
Studying the Genetics of Speciation 546
From Speciation to Macroevolution 547

25 The History of Life on Earth 550

Dinosaurs of a Feather 550

CONCEPT 25.1 Conditions on early Earth made the origin of life possible 551
Synthesis of Organic Compounds on Early Earth 551
Abiotic Synthesis of Macromolecules 552
Protocells 552
Self-Replicating RNA 553

CONCEPT 25.2 The fossil record documents the history of life 554
The Fossil Record 554
How Rocks and Fossils Are Dated 554
The Origin of New Groups of Organisms 556

CONCEPT 25.3 Key events in life's history include the origins of single-celled and multicelled organisms and the colonization of land 556
The First Single-Celled Organisms 559
The Origin of Multicellularity 560
The Colonization of Land 562

CONCEPT 25.4 The rise and fall of groups of organisms reflect differences in speciation and extinction rates 563
Plate Tectonics 563
Mass Extinctions 565
Adaptive Radiations 568

CONCEPT 25.5 Major changes in body form can result from changes in the sequences and regulation of developmental genes 570
Effects of Developmental Genes 570
The Evolution of Development 571

CONCEPT 25.6 Evolution is not goal oriented 574
Evolutionary Novelties 574
Evolutionary Trends 575

UNIT 5 THE EVOLUTIONARY HISTORY OF BIOLOGICAL DIVERSITY 579

26 Phylogeny and the Tree of Life 582

Investigating the Tree of Life 582

CONCEPT 26.1 Phylogenies show evolutionary relationships 584
Binomial Nomenclature 584
Hierarchical Classification 584
Linking Classification and Phylogeny 585

CONCEPT 26.2 Phylogenies are inferred from morphological and molecular data 586
Morphological and Molecular Homologies 586
Sorting Homology from Analogy 586
Evaluating Molecular Homologies 587

CONCEPT 26.3 Shared characters are used to construct phylogenetic trees 588
Cladistics 588
Maximum Parsimony and Maximum Likelihood 589
Interpreting Phylogenetic Trees 590
Applying Phylogenies 593

CONCEPT 26.4 An organism's evolutionary history is documented in its genome 595
Gene Duplications and Gene Families 595
Genome Evolution 596

CONCEPT 26.5 Molecular clocks help track evolutionary time 596
Molecular Clocks 596
Applying a Molecular Clock: The Origin of HIV 597

CONCEPT 26.6 Our understanding of the tree of life continues to change based on new data 598
From Two Kingdoms to Three Domains 598
The Important Role of Horizontal Gene Transfer 599

27 Bacteria and Archaea 603

Masters of Adaptation 603
CONCEPT 27.1 Structural and functional adaptations contribute to prokaryotic success 604
Cell-Surface Structures 604
Endospores 606
Motility 606
Internal Organization and DNA 607
Reproduction 608
CONCEPT 27.2 Rapid reproduction, mutation, and genetic recombination promote genetic diversity in prokaryotes 608
Rapid Reproduction and Mutation 608
Genetic Recombination 609
CONCEPT 27.3 Diverse nutritional and metabolic adaptations have evolved in prokaryotes 612
The Role of Oxygen in Metabolism 612
Nitrogen Metabolism 612
Metabolic Cooperation 613
CONCEPT 27.4 Prokaryotes have radiated into a diverse set of lineages 613
An Overview of Prokaryotic Diversity 614
Bacteria 614
Archaea 614
CONCEPT 27.5 Prokaryotes play crucial roles in the biosphere 618
Chemical Recycling 618
Ecological Interactions 618
CONCEPT 27.6 Prokaryotes have both beneficial and harmful impacts on humans 619
Mutualistic Bacteria 619
Pathogenic Bacteria 620
Prokaryotes in Research and Technology 621

28 Protists 625

The Hidden Diversity 625
CONCEPT 28.1 Protists are a diverse group of eukaryotes that span all four supergroups 626
Structural and Functional Diversity in Protists 626
Four Supergroups of Eukaryotes 626
Endosymbiosis and the Spread of Photosynthesis During Protist Evolution 627
How Do You Create an Organelle Through Endosymbiosis? 631
CONCEPT 28.2 Excavates include protists with modified mitochondria and protists with unique flagella 632
Diplomonads and Parabasalids 632
Euglenozoans 632
CONCEPT 28.3 The SAR clade is a highly diverse group of protists defined by DNA similarities 634
Stramenopiles 634
Alveolates 637
Rhizarians 639
CONCEPT 28.4 Red algae and green algae are the closest relatives of land plants 642
Red Algae 642
Green Algae 643

CONCEPT 28.5 Unikonts include protists that are closely related to fungi and animals 644
Amoebozoans 645
Opisthokonts 646
CONCEPT 28.6 Protists play key roles in ecological communities 647
Symbiotic Protists 647
Photosynthetic Protists 648

29 Plant Diversity I: How Plants Colonized Land 652

The Greening of Earth 652
CONCEPT 29.1 Land plants evolved from green algae 653
Morphological and Molecular Evidence 653
Adaptations Enabling the Move to Land 653
Derived Traits of Plants 654
The Origin and Diversification of Plants 654
CONCEPT 29.2 Mosses and other nonvascular plants have life cycles dominated by gametophytes 658
Bryophyte Gametophytes 659
Bryophyte Sporophytes 660
The Ecological and Economic Importance of Mosses 661
CONCEPT 29.3 Ferns and other seedless vascular plants were the first plants to grow tall 664
Origins and Traits of Vascular Plants 664
Classification of Seedless Vascular Plants 666
The Significance of Seedless Vascular Plants 669

30 Plant Diversity II: The Evolution of Seed Plants 672

Transforming the World 672
CONCEPT 30.1 Seeds and pollen grains are key adaptations for life on land 673
Advantages of Reduced Gametophytes 673
Heterospory: The Rule Among Seed Plants 673
Ovules and Production of Eggs 673
Pollen and Production of Sperm 673
The Evolutionary Advantage of Seeds 675
Evolution of the Seed 676
CONCEPT 30.2 Gymnosperms bear "naked" seeds, typically on cones 676
The Life Cycle of a Pine 676
Evolution of Gymnosperms 677
Gymnosperm Diversity 678
CONCEPT 30.3 The reproductive adaptations of angiosperms include flowers and fruits 678
Characteristics of Angiosperms 678
Angiosperm Evolution 684
Evolutionary Links Between Angiosperms and Animals 685
Angiosperm Diversity 686
CONCEPT 30.4 Human welfare depends greatly on seed plants 688
Products from Seed Plants 688
Threats to Plant Diversity 689

31 Fungi 692

Brewer's Yeast and Climate Change 692
CONCEPT 31.1 Fungi are heterotrophs that feed by absorption 693
Nutrition and Ecology 693
Body Structure 693
Specialized Hyphae in Mycorrhizal Fungi 694

CONCEPT 31.2 Fungi produce spores through sexual or asexual life cycles 695

Sexual Reproduction 695
Asexual Reproduction 697

CONCEPT 31.3 The ancestor of fungi was an aquatic, single-celled, flagellated protist 698

Early-Diverging Fungal Groups 698
The Move to Land 698

CONCEPT 31.4 Fungi have radiated into a diverse set of lineages 699

Chytrids 699
Zygomycetes 699
Glomeromycetes 701
Ascomycetes 702
Basidiomycetes 704

CONCEPT 31.5 Fungi play key roles in nutrient cycling, ecological interactions, and human welfare 704

Fungi as Decomposers (Saprotrophs) 705
Fungi as Mutualists 706
Fungi as Pathogens 708
Practical Uses of Fungi 709

32 An Overview of Animal Diversity 712

Welcome to Your Kingdom 712
CONCEPT 32.1 Animals are multicellular, heterotrophic eukaryotes with tissues that develop from embryonic layers 713

Nutritional Mode 713
Cell Structure and Specialization 713
Reproduction and Development 713

CONCEPT 32.2 The history of animals spans more than half a billion years 714

Neoproterozoic Era (1 Billion–542 Million Years Ago) 714
Paleozoic Era (542–251 Million Years Ago) 716
Mesozoic Era (251–65.5 Million Years Ago) 717
Cenozoic Era (65.5 Million Years Ago to the Present) 717

CONCEPT 32.3 Animals can be characterized by "body plans" 719

Symmetry 719
Tissues 719
Body Cavities 720
Protostome and Deuterostome Development 720

CONCEPT 32.4 Views of animal phylogeny continue to be shaped by new molecular and morphological data 722

The Diversification of Animals 722
Future Directions in Animal Systematics 723

33 An Introduction to Invertebrates 726

Life Without a Backbone 726
CONCEPT 33.1 Sponges are basal animals that lack true tissues 730
CONCEPT 33.2 Cnidarians are an ancient phylum of eumetazoans 731

Medusozoans 732
Anthozoans 733

CONCEPT 33.3 Lophotrochozoans, a clade identified by molecular data, have the widest range of animal body forms 734

Flatworms 734
Rotifers 737
Lophophorates: Ectoprocts and Brachiopods 738
Molluscs 738
Annelids 742

CONCEPT 33.4 Ecdysozoans are the most species-rich animal group 745

Nematodes 745
Arthropods 746

CONCEPT 33.5 Echinoderms and chordates are deuterostomes 754

Echinoderms 754
Chordates 756

34 The Origin and Evolution of Vertebrates 759

Half a Billion Years of Backbones 759
CONCEPT 34.1 Chordates have a notochord and a dorsal, hollow nerve cord 760

Derived Characters of Chordates 761
Lancelets 761
Tunicates 762
Early Chordate Evolution 762

CONCEPT 34.2 Vertebrates are chordates that have a backbone 763

Derived Characters of Vertebrates 764
Hagfishes and Lampreys 764
Hagfishes 764
Lampreys 764
Early Vertebrate Evolution 765
Origins of Bone and Teeth 766

CONCEPT 34.3 Gnathostomes are vertebrates that have jaws 767

Derived Characters of Gnathostomes 767
Fossil Gnathostomes 767
Chondrichthyans (Sharks, Rays, and Their Relatives) 767
Ray-Finned Fishes and Lobe-Fins 769

CONCEPT 34.4 Tetrapods are gnathostomes that have limbs 771

Derived Characters of Tetrapods 771
The Origin of Tetrapods 772
Amphibians 773
Salamanders 773
Frogs 773
Caecilians 774
Lifestyle and Ecology of Amphibians 774

CONCEPT 34.5 Amniotes are tetrapods that have a terrestrially adapted egg 775

Derived Characters of Amniotes 775
Early Amniotes 776
Reptiles 777

CONCEPT 34.6 Mammals are amniotes that have hair and produce milk 783

Derived Characters of Mammals 783
Early Evolution of Mammals 783
Monotremes 784
Marsupials 784
Eutherians (Placental Mammals) 785

CONCEPT 34.7 Humans are mammals that have a large brain and bipedal locomotion 790

Derived Characters of Humans 790
The Earliest Hominins 790
Australopiths 791
Bipedalism 792
Tool Use 792
Early *Homo* 794
Neanderthals 794
Homo sapiens 795

UNIT 6 PLANT FORM AND FUNCTION 799

35 Plant Structure, Growth, and Development 802

A Plant's Growth is Directed by Environmental Cues 802
CONCEPT 35.1 Plants have a hierarchical organization consisting of organs, tissues, and cells 803
    The Three Basic Plant Organs: Roots, Stems, and Leaves 803
    Dermal, Vascular, and Ground Plant Tissues 806
    Common Types of Plant Cells 807
CONCEPT 35.2 Different meristems generate cells for primary and secondary growth 810
CONCEPT 35.3 Primary growth lengthens roots and shoots 811
    Primary Growth of Roots 811
    Primary Growth of Shoots 813
CONCEPT 35.4 Secondary growth increases the diameter of stems and roots in woody plants 815
    The Vascular Cambium and Secondary Vascular Tissue 815
    The Cork Cambium and the Production of Periderm 818
    Evolution of Secondary Growth 818
    Wood Development 818
CONCEPT 35.5 Growth, morphogenesis, and cell differentiation produce the plant body 819
    Model Organisms: Revolutionizing the Study of Plants 820
    Growth: Cell Division and Cell Expansion 821
    Morphogenesis and Pattern Formation 822
    Gene Expression and Control of Cell Differentiation 823
    Shifts in Development: Phase Changes 823
    Genetic Control of Flowering 824

36 Resource Acquisition and Transport in Vascular Plants 828

Natural Bonsai Trees 828
CONCEPT 36.1 Adaptations for acquiring resources were key steps in the evolution of vascular plants 829
    Shoot Architecture and Light Capture 830
    Root Architecture and Acquisition of Water and Minerals 831
CONCEPT 36.2 Different mechanisms transport substances over short or long distances 831
    The Apoplast and Symplast: Transport Continuums 831
    Short-Distance Transport of Solutes Across Plasma Membranes 832
    Short-Distance Transport of Water Across Plasma Membranes 832
    Long-Distance Transport: The Role of Bulk Flow 835
CONCEPT 36.3 Transpiration drives the transport of water and minerals from roots to shoots via the xylem 836
    Absorption of Water and Minerals by Root Epidermal Cells 836
    Transport of Water and Minerals into the Xylem 836
    Bulk Flow Transport via the Xylem 836
    Xylem Sap Ascent by Bulk Flow: *A Review* 840
CONCEPT 36.4 The rate of transpiration is regulated by stomata 840
    Stomata: Major Pathways for Water Loss 841
    Mechanisms of Stomatal Opening and Closing 841
    Stimuli for Stomatal Opening and Closing 842

    Effects of Transpiration on Wilting and Leaf Temperature 842
    Adaptations That Reduce Evaporative Water Loss 842
CONCEPT 36.5 Sugars are transported from sources to sinks via the phloem 843
    Movement from Sugar Sources to Sugar Sinks 843
    Bulk Flow by Positive Pressure: The Mechanism of Translocation in Angiosperms 844
CONCEPT 36.6 The symplast is highly dynamic 846
    Changes in Plasmodesmata 846
    Phloem: An Information Superhighway 846
    Electrical Signalling in the Phloem 846

37 Soil and Plant Nutrition 849

The Corkscrew Carnivore 849
CONCEPT 37.1 Soil contains a living, complex ecosystem 850
    Soil Texture 850
    Topsoil Composition 850
    Soil Conservation and Sustainable Agriculture 851
CONCEPT 37.2 Plants require essential elements to complete their life cycle 854
    Essential Elements 855
    Symptoms of Mineral Deficiency 856
    Improving Plant Nutrition by Genetic Modification 856
CONCEPT 37.3 Plant nutrition often involves relationships with other organisms 857
    Bacteria and Plant Nutrition 857
    Fungi and Plant Nutrition 861
    Epiphytes, Parasitic Plants, and Carnivorous Plants 862

38 Angiosperm Reproduction and Biotechnology 866

Canola (Canadian Oil Low Acid): A Canadian Invention 866
CONCEPT 38.1 Flowers, double fertilization, and fruits are unique features of the angiosperm life cycle 867
    Flower Structure and Function 867
    The Angiosperm Life Cycle: An Overview 869
    Methods of Pollination 870
    From Seed to Flowering Plant: A Closer Look 872
    Fruit Form and Function 876
CONCEPT 38.2 Flowering plants reproduce sexually, asexually, or both 877
    Mechanisms of Asexual Reproduction 877
    Advantages and Disadvantages of Asexual versus Sexual Reproduction 877
    Mechanisms That Prevent Self-Fertilization 879
    Totipotency, Vegetative Reproduction, and Tissue Culture 881
CONCEPT 38.3 People modify crops by breeding and genetic engineering 882
    Plant Breeding 882
    Plant Biotechnology and Genetic Engineering 883
    The Debate over Plant Biotechnology 885

39 Plant Responses to Internal and External Signals 888

Stimuli and a Stationary Life 888
CONCEPT 39.1 Signal transduction pathways link signal reception to response 889
    Reception 890
    Transduction 890
    Response 891

CONCEPT 39.2 Plant hormones help coordinate growth, development, and responses to stimuli 892

A Survey of Plant Hormones 892

Auxin 893

More Recently Discovered Plant Hormones 900

CONCEPT 39.3 Responses to light are critical for plant success 901

Blue-Light Photoreceptors 901

Phytochromes as Photoreceptors 902

Biological Clocks and Circadian Rhythms 903

The Effect of Light on the Biological Clock 904

Photoperiodism and Responses to Seasons 905

CONCEPT 39.4 Plants respond to a wide variety of stimuli other than light 907

Gravity 907

Mechanical Stimuli 908

Environmental Stresses 908

CONCEPT 39.5 Plants respond to attacks by herbivores and pathogens 912

Defences Against Herbivores 912

Defences Against Pathogens 912

Immune Responses of Plants 912

The Hypersensitive Response 913

Systemic Acquired Resistance 913

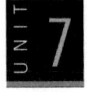

UNIT 7 ANIMAL FORM AND FUNCTION 917

40 Basic Principles of Animal Form and Function 920

Diverse Forms, Common Challenges 920

CONCEPT 40.1 Animal form and function are correlated at all levels of organization 921

Evolution of Animal Size and Shape 921

Exchange with the Environment 921

Hierarchical Organization of Body Plans 923

Coordination and Control 927

CONCEPT 40.2 Feedback control maintains the internal environment in many animals 928

Regulating and Conforming 928

Homeostasis 928

CONCEPT 40.3 Homeostatic processes for thermoregulation involve form, function, and behaviour 930

Endothermy and Ectothermy 931

Variation in Body Temperature 931

Balancing Heat Loss and Gain 932

Acclimation and Acclimatization 934

Physiological Thermostats and Fever 935

CONCEPT 40.4 Energy requirements are related to animal size, activity, and environment 936

Energy Allocation and Use 937

Quantifying Energy Use 937

Minimum Metabolic Rate and Thermoregulation 937

Influences on Metabolic Rate 938

Torpor and Energy Conservation 939

41 Animal Nutrition 943

The Need to Feed 943

CONCEPT 41.1 An animal's diet must supply chemical energy, organic molecules, and essential nutrients 944

Essential Nutrients 944

Dietary Deficiencies 947

Assessing Nutritional Needs 947

CONCEPT 41.2 The main stages of food processing are ingestion, digestion, absorption, and elimination 948

Digestive Compartments 950

CONCEPT 41.3 Organs specialized for sequential stages of food processing form the mammalian digestive system 951

The Oral Cavity, Pharynx, and Esophagus 951

Digestion in the Stomach 953

Digestion in the Small Intestine 954

Absorption in the Small Intestine 955

Absorption in the Large Intestine 956

CONCEPT 41.4 Evolutionary adaptations of vertebrate digestive systems correlate with diet 957

Dental Adaptations 957

Stomach and Intestinal Adaptations 958

Mutualistic Adaptations 958

Mutualistic Adaptations in Herbivores 958

CONCEPT 41.5 Feedback circuits regulate digestion, energy storage, and appetite 960

Regulation of Digestion 960

Regulation of Energy Storage 961

Regulation of Appetite and Consumption 961

Obesity and Evolution 962

42 Circulation and Gas Exchange 966

Trading Places 966

CONCEPT 42.1 Circulatory systems link exchange surfaces with cells throughout the body 967

Gastrovascular Cavities 967

Evolutionary Variation in Circulatory Systems 968

Evolution of Vertebrate Circulatory Systems 969

CONCEPT 42.2 Coordinated cycles of heart contraction drive double circulation in mammals 972

Mammalian Circulation 972

The Mammalian Heart: *A Closer Look* 972

Maintaining the Heart's Rhythmic Beat 974

CONCEPT 42.3 Patterns of blood pressure and flow reflect the structure and arrangement of blood vessels 975

Blood Vessel Structure and Function 975

Blood Flow Velocity 975

Blood Pressure 976

Capillary Function 978

Fluid Return by the Lymphatic System 979

CONCEPT 42.4 Blood components function in exchange, transport, and defence 980

Blood Composition and Function 980

Cardiovascular Disease 983

CONCEPT 42.5 Gas exchange occurs across specialized respiratory surfaces 985

Partial Pressure Gradients in Gas Exchange 985

Respiratory Media 986

Respiratory Surfaces 986
Gills in Aquatic Animals 986
Tracheal Systems in Insects 988
Lungs 988
CONCEPT 42.6 Breathing ventilates the lungs 990
How an Amphibian Breathes 990
How a Bird Breathes 990
How a Mammal Breathes 990
Control of Breathing in Humans 992
CONCEPT 42.7 Adaptations for gas exchange include pigments that bind and transport gases 992
Coordination of Circulation and Gas Exchange 993
Respiratory Pigments 993
Respiratory Adaptations of Diving Mammals 995

43 The Immune System 999

Recognition and Response 999
CONCEPT 43.1 In innate immunity, recognition and response rely on traits common to groups of pathogens 1000
Innate Immunity of Invertebrates 1001
Innate Immunity of Vertebrates 1001
Evasion of Innate Immunity by Pathogens 1005
CONCEPT 43.2 In adaptive immunity, receptors provide pathogen-specific recognition 1005
Antigen Recognition by B Cells and Antibodies 1006
Antigen Recognition by T Cells 1006
B Cell and T Cell Development 1007
CONCEPT 43.3 Adaptive immunity defends against infection of body fluids and body cells 1011
Helper T Cells: A Response to Nearly All Antigens 1012
Cytotoxic T Cells: A Response to Infected Cells 1012
B Cells and Antibodies: A Response to Extracellular Pathogens 1013
Summary of the Humoral and Cell-Mediated Immune Responses 1015
Active and Passive Immunization 1015
Antibodies as Tools 1017
Immune Rejection 1017
CONCEPT 43.4 Disruptions in immune system function can elicit or exacerbate disease 1018
Exaggerated, Self-Directed, and Diminished Immune Responses 1018
Evolutionary Adaptations of Pathogens That Underlie Immune System Avoidance 1020
Cancer and Immunity 1022

44 Osmoregulation and Excretion 1025

A Balancing Act 1025
CONCEPT 44.1 Osmoregulation balances the uptake and loss of water and solutes 1026
Osmosis and Osmolarity 1026
Osmotic Challenges 1026
Energetics of Osmoregulation 1029
Transport Epithelia in Osmoregulation 1030
CONCEPT 44.2 An animal's nitrogenous wastes reflect its phylogeny and habitat 1030

Forms of Nitrogenous Waste 1031
The Influence of Evolution and Environment on Nitrogenous Wastes 1032
CONCEPT 44.3 Diverse excretory systems are variations on a tubular theme 1032
Excretory Processes 1033
Survey of Excretory Systems 1033
CONCEPT 44.4 The nephron is organized for stepwise processing of blood filtrate 1035
From Blood Filtrate to Urine: *A Closer Look* 1035
Solute Gradients and Water Conservation 1038
Adaptations of the Vertebrate Kidney to Diverse Environments 1040
CONCEPT 44.5 Hormonal circuits link kidney function, water balance, and blood pressure 1043
Antidiuretic Hormone 1043
The Renin-Angiotensin-Aldosterone System 1044
Homeostatic Regulation of the Kidney 1045

45 Hormones and the Endocrine System 1048

The Body's Long-Distance Regulators 1048
CONCEPT 45.1 Hormones and other signalling molecules bind to target receptors, triggering specific response pathways 1049
Intercellular Communication 1049
Cellular Response Pathways 1051
Multiple Effects of Hormones 1053
CONCEPT 45.2 Feedback regulation and antagonistic hormone pairs are common in endocrine systems 1055
Simple Hormone Pathways 1055
Feedback Regulation 1055
Control of Blood Glucose By Antagonistic Hormones 1056
CONCEPT 45.3 Vertebrate hormones regulate homeostasis, development, and behaviour 1059
The Hypothalamus-Pituitary Axis 1059
Thyroid Hormone Regulation 1061
Growth Hormone 1062
Parathyroid Hormone and Vitamin D: Control of Blood Calcium 1063
Adrenal Hormones: Response to Stress 1064
Sex Hormones 1065
Melatonin and Biorhythms 1067

46 Animal Reproduction 1070

Pairing Up for Sexual Reproduction 1070
CONCEPT 46.1 Both asexual and sexual reproduction occur in the animal kingdom 1071
Mechanisms of Asexual Reproduction 1071
Sexual Reproduction: An Evolutionary Enigma 1071
Reproductive Cycles 1072
Variation in Patterns of Sexual Reproduction 1073
CONCEPT 46.2 Fertilization depends on mechanisms that bring together sperm and eggs of the same species 1074
Ensuring the Survival of Offspring 1074
Gamete Production and Delivery 1075
CONCEPT 46.3 Reproductive organs produce and transport gametes 1077

Female Reproductive Anatomy 1077
Male Reproductive Anatomy 1078
Gametogenesis 1079
CONCEPT 46.4 The interplay of tropic and sex hormones regulates mammalian reproduction 1082
Hormonal Control of Female Reproductive Cycles 1083
Hormonal Control of the Male Reproductive System 1085
Human Sexual Response 1085
CONCEPT 46.5 In placental mammals, an embryo develops fully within the mother's uterus 1086
Conception, Embryonic Development, and Birth 1086
Maternal Immune Tolerance of the Embryo and Fetus 1089
Contraception and Abortion 1089
Modern Reproductive Technologies 1091

47 Animal Development 1095

A Body-Building Plan 1095
CONCEPT 47.1 Fertilization and cleavage initiate embryonic development 1096
Fertilization 1096
Cleavage 1099
CONCEPT 47.2 Morphogenesis in animals involves specific changes in cell shape, position, and survival 1102
Gastrulation 1102
Extraembryonic Membranes of Amniotes 1106
Organogenesis 1106
Cellular Mechanisms in Morphogenesis 1108
CONCEPT 47.3 Cytoplasmic determinants and inductive signals contribute to cell fate specification 1110
Fate Mapping 1110
Cell Fate Determination and Pattern Formation by Inductive Signals 1114

48 Neurons, Synapses, and Signalling 1120

Lines of Communication 1120
CONCEPT 48.1 Neuron organization and structure reflect function in information transfer 1121
Neuron Structure and Function 1121
Introduction to Information Processing 1122
CONCEPT 48.2 Ion gradients and ion channels establish the resting membrane potential of a neuron 1123
The Resting Membrane Potential 1123
Determining the Resting Membrane Potential 1124
CONCEPT 48.3 Action potentials are the signals conducted by axons 1125
Hyperpolarization and Depolarization 1125
Graded Potentials and Action Potentials 1126
Generation of Action Potentials: A Closer Look 1127
Conduction of Action Potentials 1128
CONCEPT 48.4 Neurons communicate with other cells at synapses 1130
Generation of Postsynaptic Potentials 1132
Summation of Postsynaptic Potentials 1132
Modulated Signalling at Synapses 1133
Neurotransmitters 1133

49 Nervous Systems 1139

Command and Control Centre 1139
CONCEPT 49.1 Nervous systems consist of circuits of neurons and supporting cells 1140
Glia 1141
Organization of the Vertebrate Nervous System 1142
The Peripheral Nervous System 1143
CONCEPT 49.2 The vertebrate brain is regionally specialized 1145
Arousal and Sleep 1148
Biological Clock Regulation 1149
Emotions 1150
Functional Imaging of the Brain 1150
CONCEPT 49.3 The cerebral cortex controls voluntary movement and cognitive functions 1151
Information Processing 1151
Language and Speech 1152
Frontal Lobe Function 1152
Evolution of Cognition in Vertebrates 1153
CONCEPT 49.4 Changes in synaptic connections underlie memory and learning 1154
Neural Plasticity 1154
Memory and Learning 1155
Long-Term Potentiation 1156
CONCEPT 49.5 Many nervous system disorders can be explained in molecular terms 1157
Schizophrenia 1157
Depression 1158
The Brain's Reward System and Drug Addiction 1158
Alzheimer's Disease 1159
Parkinson's Disease 1159

50 Sensory and Motor Mechanisms 1162

Sensing and Acting 1162
CONCEPT 50.1 Sensory receptors transduce stimulus energy and transmit signals to the central nervous system 1163
Sensory Pathways 1163
Types of Sensory Receptors 1165
CONCEPT 50.2 The mechanoreceptors responsible for hearing and equilibrium detect moving fluid or settling particles 1167
Sensing of Gravity and Sound in Invertebrates 1167
Hearing and Equilibrium in Mammals 1167
Hearing and Equilibrium in Other Vertebrates 1171
CONCEPT 50.3 Visual receptors in diverse animals depend on light-absorbing pigments 1172
Evolution of Visual Perception 1172
The Vertebrate Visual System 1174
CONCEPT 50.4 The senses of taste and smell rely on similar sets of sensory receptors 1179
Taste in Mammals 1179
Smell in Humans 1180
CONCEPT 50.5 The physical interaction of protein filaments is required for muscle function 1181
Vertebrate Skeletal Muscle 1181
Other Types of Muscle 1187
CONCEPT 50.6 Skeletal systems transform muscle contraction into locomotion 1188
Types of Skeletal Systems 1189
Types of Locomotion 1191

51 Animal Behaviour 1196

The How and Why of Animal Activity 1196
CONCEPT 51.1 Discrete sensory inputs can stimulate both simple and complex behaviours 1197
  Fixed Action Patterns 1197
  Migration 1197
  Behavioural Rhythms 1198
  Animal Signals and Communication 1198
CONCEPT 51.2 Learning establishes specific links between experience and behaviour 1201
  Experience and Behaviour 1201
  Learning 1201
CONCEPT 51.3 Selection for individual survival and reproductive success can explain most behaviours 1206
  Foraging Behaviour 1206
  Mating Behaviour and Mate Choice 1207
CONCEPT 51.4 Genetic analyses and the concept of inclusive fitness provide a basis for studying the evolution of behaviour 1213
  Genetic Basis of Behaviour 1213
  Genetic Variation and the Evolution of Behaviour 1213
  Altruism 1214
  Inclusive Fitness 1216
  Evolution and Human Culture 1217

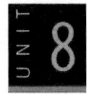

UNIT 8 ECOLOGY 1221

52 An Introduction to Ecology and the Biosphere 1224

Discovering Ecology 1224
CONCEPT 52.1 Earth's climate varies by latitude and season and is changing rapidly 1225
  Global Climate Patterns 1225
  Regional and Local Effects on Climate 1225
  Microclimate 1229
  Global Climate Change 1230
CONCEPT 52.2 The structure and distribution of terrestrial biomes are controlled by climate and disturbance 1231
  Climate and Terrestrial Biomes 1231
  General Features of Terrestrial Biomes 1232
  Disturbance and Terrestrial Biomes 1233
CONCEPT 52.3 Aquatic biomes are diverse and dynamic systems that cover most of Earth 1238
  Zonation in Aquatic Biomes 1238
CONCEPT 52.4 Interactions between organisms and the environment limit the distribution of species 1239
  Dispersal and Distribution 1244
  Abiotic Factors 1245
  Biotic Factors 1246

53 Population Ecology 1250

Counting Sheep 1250
CONCEPT 53.1 Dynamic biological processes influence population density, dispersion, and demographics 1251
  Density and Dispersion 1251
  Demographics 1253
CONCEPT 53.2 The exponential model describes population growth in an idealized, unlimited environment 1255
  Change in Population Size 1255
  Exponential Growth 1256
CONCEPT 53.3 The logistic model describes how a population grows more slowly as it nears its carrying capacity 1257
  The Logistic Growth Model 1257
  The Logistic Model and Real Populations 1258
CONCEPT 53.4 Life history traits are products of natural selection 1260
  Evolution and Life History Diversity 1260
  "Trade-offs" and Life Histories 1261
CONCEPT 53.5 Many factors that regulate population growth are density dependent 1262
  Population Dynamics 1263
CONCEPT 53.6 The human population is no longer growing exponentially but is still increasing rapidly 1267
  The Global Human Population 1267
  Global Carrying Capacity 1268

54 Community Ecology 1273

Dynamic Communities 1273
CONCEPT 54.1 Community interactions are classified by whether they help, harm, or have no effect on the species involved 1274
  Competition 1274
  Predation 1276
  Herbivory 1279
  Symbiosis 1279
  Facilitation 1281
CONCEPT 54.2 Diversity and trophic structure characterize biological communities 1282
  Species Diversity 1282
  Diversity and Community Stability 1282
  Trophic Structure 1283
  Species with a Large Impact 1285
  Bottom-Up and Top-Down Controls 1287
CONCEPT 54.3 Disturbance influences species diversity and composition 1289
  Characterizing Disturbance 1289
  Ecological Succession 1290
  Human Disturbance 1292
CONCEPT 54.4 Biogeographic factors affect community diversity 1292
  Latitudinal Gradients 1292
  Area Effects 1293
  Island Equilibrium Model 1293
CONCEPT 54.5 Pathogens alter community structure locally and globally 1294
  Pathogens and Communities 1295
  Community Ecology and Zoonotic Diseases 1295

55 Ecosystems and Restoration Ecology 1299

In the Deep, Dark Sea 1299
CONCEPT 55.1 Physical laws govern energy flow and chemical cycling in ecosystems 1300
  Conservation of Energy 1300
  Conservation of Mass 1301
  Energy, Mass, and Trophic Levels 1301

CONCEPT 55.2 Energy and other limiting factors control primary production in ecosystems 1302

Ecosystem Energy Budgets 1302
Primary Production in Aquatic Ecosystems 1304
Primary Production in Terrestrial Ecosystems 1306

CONCEPT 55.3 Energy transfer between trophic levels is typically only 10% efficient 1307

Production Efficiency 1307
Trophic Efficiency and Ecological Pyramids 1308

CONCEPT 55.4 Biological and geochemical processes cycle nutrients and water in ecosystems 1309

Biogeochemical Cycles 1309
Decomposition and Nutrient Cycling Rates 1309

CONCEPT 55.5 Restoration ecologists help return degraded ecosystems to a more natural state 1313

Bioremediation 1314
Biological Augmentation 1314
Restoration Projects Worldwide 1315

56 Conservation Biology and Global Change 1320

An Odd Fish 1320

CONCEPT 56.1 Human activities threaten Earth's biodiversity 1321

Three Levels of Biodiversity 1321
Biodiversity and Human Welfare 1323
Threats to Biodiversity 1324
Can Extinct Species Be Resurrected? 1326

CONCEPT 56.2 Population conservation focuses on population size, genetic diversity, and critical habitat 1327

Small-Population Approach 1327

Field Study: *The Greater Prairie Chicken and the Extinction Vortex* 1327
Field Study: *Analysis of Grizzly Bear Populations* 1329
Declining-Population Approach 1329
Field Study: *Decline of the Rufa Red Knot* 1330
Weighing Conflicting Demands 1331

CONCEPT 56.3 Landscape and regional conservation help sustain biodiversity 1331

Landscape Structure and Biodiversity 1331
Establishing Protected Areas 1332
Urban Ecology 1335

CONCEPT 56.4 Earth is changing rapidly as a result of human actions 1335

Acid Precipitation 1335
Nutrient Enrichment 1335
Toxic Compounds in the Environment 1337
Greenhouse Gases and Climate Change 1338
Depletion of Atmospheric Ozone 1341

CONCEPT 56.5 Sustainable development can improve human lives while conserving biodiversity 1342

Sustainable Development 1343
Field Study: *Sustainable Development in Costa Rica* 1343
The Future of the Biosphere 1343

APPENDIX A   Answers A-1
APPENDIX B   B-1
APPENDIX C   C-1
APPENDIX D   D-1
APPENDIX E   E-1
GLOSSARY   G-1
INDEX   I-1

Preface

We are honoured to present the Second Canadian Edition of *CAMPBELL BIOLOGY*. For the last three decades, *CAMPBELL BIOLOGY* has been the leading university text in the biological sciences. It has been translated into more than a dozen languages and has provided millions of students with a solid foundation in university-level biology. This success is a testament not only to Neil Campbell's original vision but also to the dedication of thousands of reviewers, who, together with editors, artists, and contributors, have shaped and inspired this work.

Our goals for the Second Canadian Edition include:

- increasing visual literacy through figures, tutorials, and problems that guide students to a deeper understanding of the ways in which figures represent biological structure and function.
- giving students a strong foundation in **scientific thinking and quantitative reasoning skills**
- inspiring students with the excitement and relevance of modern biology, particularly in the realm of **genomics**

Our starting point, as always, is our commitment to crafting text and visuals that are accurate, current, and reflect our passion for teaching and learning about biology.

New to This Edition

Here we provide an overview of the new features that we have developed for the Second Canadian Edition; we invite you to explore pages xxviii–xxxv for more information and examples.

- **Scientific Skills Exercises** in every chapter use real data to help students learn and practise data interpretation, graphing, experimental design, and math skills. Scientific Skills Exercises have assignable, automatically graded versions in **MasteringBiology**.
- **Interpret the Data Questions** throughout the text engage students in scientific inquiry by asking them to interpret data presented in a graph, figure, or table. The Interpret the Data

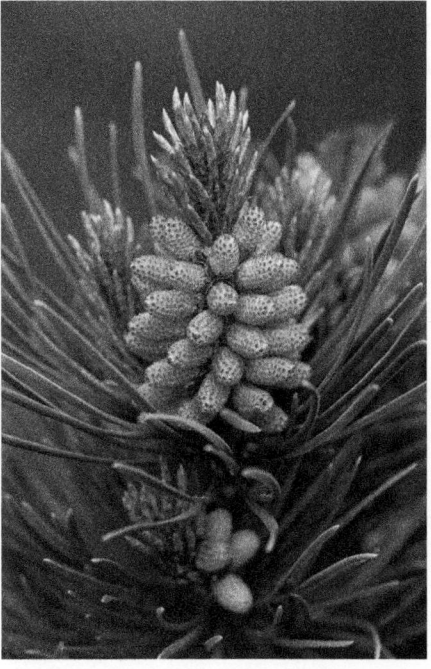

Questions can be assigned and automatically graded in **MasteringBiology**.

- **The impact of genomics across biology** is explored throughout the Second Canadian Edition with examples that reveal how our ability to rapidly sequence DNA and proteins on a massive scale is transforming all areas of biology, from molecular and cell biology to phylogenetics, physiology, and ecology.
- **Synthesize Your Knowledge Questions** at the end of each chapter ask students to synthesize the material in the chapter and demonstrate their big-picture understanding. A striking, thought-provoking photograph leads to a question that helps students realize that what they have learned in the chapter connects to their world and provides understanding and insight into natural phenomena.
- **The impact of climate change** is explored throughout the text, starting with an introduction in Chapter 1, and concluding with the Exploring Climate Change Figure 56.27.
- **The Second Canadian Edition provides a range of new practice and Assessment Opportunities in MasteringBiology®**. Besides the Scientific Skills Exercises and Interpret the Data Questions, **Solve It Tutorials** in MasteringBiology engage students in a multistep investigation of a "mystery" or open question. Acting as scientists, students must analyze real data and work through a simulated investigation. In addition, students can use the **Dynamic Study Modules** to study anytime and anywhere with their smartphone, tablet, or computer.
  - **Learning Catalytics™** allows students to use their smartphone, tablet, or laptop to respond to questions in class.
  - As in each new edition of *CAMPBELL BIOLOGY*, the Second Canadian Edition incorporates **new content** and **organizational improvements**. These are summarized on pp. xxv–xxvii, following this Preface. Additional content updates reflect rapid, ongoing changes in technology and knowledge in the fields of genomics, gene editing technology (CRISPR), and more.

Our Hallmark Features

Teachers of general biology face a daunting challenge: to help students acquire a conceptual framework for organizing an ever-expanding amount of information. The hallmark features of *CAMPBELL BIOLOGY* provide such a framework while promoting a deeper understanding of biology and the process of science. Chief among the themes of *CAMPBELL BIOLOGY* is **evolution.** Chapters throughout the text include at least one Evolution section that explicitly focuses on evolutionary aspects of the chapter material, and chapters end with an Evolution Connection Question and a Write about a Theme Question.

To help students distinguish the "forest from the trees," each chapter is organized around a framework of three to seven carefully chosen **Key Concepts.** The text, Concept Check Questions, Summary of Key Concepts, and MasteringBiology all reinforce these main ideas and essential facts.

Because text and illustrations are equally important for learning biology, **integration of text and figures** has been a hallmark of this text since the first edition. The Exploring Figures and Make Connections Figures epitomize this approach. Each Exploring Figure is a learning unit of core content that brings together related illustrations and text, whereas Make Connections Figures use art and text to illustrate how key ideas link together what might appear to be discrete and disparate topics in introductory biology.

To encourage **active reading** of the text, *CAMPBELL BIOLOGY* includes numerous opportunities for students to stop and think about what they are reading, often by putting pencil to paper to draw a sketch, annotate a figure, or graph data. Active reading questions include Make Connections Questions, What If? Questions, Figure Legend Questions, Draw It Questions, Summary Questions, and the new Synthesize Your Knowledge and Interpret the Data Questions. The answers to most of these questions require students to write as well as think and thus help develop the core competency of communicating science.

Finally, *CAMPBELL BIOLOGY* has always featured **scientific inquiry**, an essential component of any biology course. Complementing stories of scientific discovery in the text narrative, the unit-opening interviews, and our standard-setting Inquiry Figures all deepen the ability of students to understand how we know what we know. Scientific Inquiry Questions give students opportunities to practise scientific thinking, along with the new Scientific Skills Exercises and Interpret the Data Questions. Together, these activities provide students practice both in applying the process of science and in using quantitative reasoning.

MasteringBiology®

MasteringBiology, the most widely used online assessment and tutorial program for biology, provides an extensive library of homework assignments that are graded automatically. In addition to the new Scientific Skills Exercises, Interpret the Data Questions, Solve It Tutorials, Adaptive Follow-Up Assignments, and Dynamic Study Modules, MasteringBiology offers BioFlix® Tutorials with 3-D Animations, Experimental Inquiry Tutorials, Interpreting Data Tutorials, Visualizing the Concept activities, Video Field Trips, HHMI Short Files, Make Connections Tutorials, Activities, Reading Quiz Questions, Student Misconception Questions, 4,500 Test Bank Questions, and MasteringBiology Virtual Labs. MasteringBiology also includes the *CAMPBELL BIOLOGY* eText, Study Area, and Instructor Resources. See pages xxxvi–xxxix and www.masteringbiology.com for more details.

Our Partnership with Instructors and Students

A core value underlying our work is our belief in the importance of a partnership with instructors and students. One primary way of serving instructors and students, of course, is providing a text that teaches biology well. In addition, Pearson Education offers a rich variety of instructor and student resources, in both print and electronic form (see pp. xl–xli). In our continuing efforts to improve the book and its supplements, we benefit tremendously from instructor and student feedback, not only in formal reviews from hundreds of scientists, but also via e-mail and other forms of informal communication.

The real test of any textbook is how well it helps instructors teach and students learn. We welcome comments from both students and instructors. Please address your suggestions to Fiona Rawle, Lead Author, at fiona.rawle@utoronto.ca, and Cathleen Sullivan, Executive Acquisitions Editor, cathleen.sullivan@pearsoned.com

New and Featured Content

This section highlights selected new content and organizational changes in CAMPBELL BIOLOGY, Second Canadian Edition.

CHAPTER 1 Evolution, the Themes of Biology, and Scientific Inquiry

To help students focus on the big ideas of biology, we now emphasize five themes: Organization, Information, Energy and Matter, Interactions, and the core theme of Evolution. A new figure on gene expression (Figure 1.9) equips students from the outset with an understanding of how gene sequences determine an organism's characteristics. Concept 1.3 has been reframed to more accurately reflect the scientific process, including a new figure on the complexity of the practice of science (Figure 1.26). A new case study (Figures 1.27 and 1.28) examines research on evolution of colouration in mice.

UNIT 1 The Chemistry of Life

In Unit 1, new content engages students in learning this foundational material. In Chapter 3, the discussion of organisms affected by loss of Arctic sea ice has been expanded. Chapter 5 has updates on trans fats, the effects of diet on blood cholesterol, protein sequences and structures, and intrinsically disordered proteins. The Make Connections Figure, "Contributions of Genomics and Proteomics to Biology" (Figure 5.26) has also been revised. Unit 1 also highlights research by the Department of Fisheries and Oceans, work of David Wishart at the University of Alberta on characterizing small molecules in the human body, as well as work by Edward Fon and Kalle Gehring from McGill University on the structure of the parkin protein.

UNIT 2 The Cell

Our main goal in this unit was to make the material more accessible and inviting to students. We have streamlined coverage of the cytoskeleton in Chapter 6 and historical aspects of the membrane model in Chapter 7. We have revised the photosynthesis summary figure (Figure 10.22) to incorporate the big-picture context of photosynthesis. Concept 12.3 has been streamlined, with a new Figure 12.17 that covers the M checkpoint as well as the G_1 checkpoint. Unit 2 also features the identification of LHON mutations by Eric Shoubridge at McGill University; the International Cancer Genome Consortium, co-founded by Thomas Hudson, Scientific Director of the Ontario Institute of Cancer Research; work on membrane proteins by Frances Sharom at the University of Guelph; and work on the impact of environment on metabolism by Helga Guderley at Université Laval.

UNIT 3 Genetics

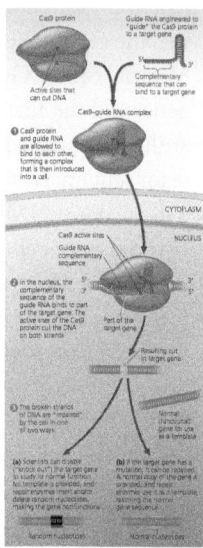

In Chapters 13–17, we have incorporated changes that help students grasp the more abstract concepts of genetics and their molecular underpinnings. For example, Chapter 13 includes a new figure (Figure 13.9) showing details of crossing over during prophase. Figure 14.4, showing alleles on chromosomes, has been enhanced to show the DNA sequences of both alleles, along with their biochemical and phenotypic consequences. A new figure on sickle-cell disease also connects these levels (Figure 14.17). In Chapter 17 material on coupled transcription and translation in bacteria has been united with coverage of polyribosomes.

Chapters 18–21 are extensively updated, with the changes driven by exciting new discoveries based on DNA sequencing and gene-editing technology. Chapter 18 includes a new figure (Figure 18.15) on the role of siRNAs in chromatin remodelling. A new Make Connections Figure (Figure 18.27) details four subtypes of breast cancer that have recently been proposed, based on gene expression in tumour cells. Chapter 19 features a new section that covers bacterial defences against bacteriophages and describes the CRISPR–Cas9 system (Figure 19.7). In Chapter 20, techniques that are less commonly used have been pruned, and the chapter has been reorganized to emphasize the important role of sequencing. A new figure (Figure 20.4) illustrates next-generation sequencing. A new section titled Editing Genes and Genomes has been added describing the CRISPR–Cas9 system (Figure 20.14) that has been developed to edit genes in living cells. Information has also been added later in the chapter on use of the CRISPR–Cas9 system, including a study in which a genetic mutation for the disease tyrosinemia was corrected in mice. Finally, the discussion of ethical considerations has been updated to include a recent report of scientists using the CRISPR–Cas9 system to edit a gene in human embryos, along with a discussion of the ethical questions raised by such experiments, such as its usage along with the gene drive approach to combat carrying of diseases by mosquitoes. Chapter 21 has been updated to reflect new research, including the ENCODE project and the Cancer Genome Atlas. A new figure (Figure 21.15) compares the 3-D structures of lysozyme and α-lactalbumin and their amino acid sequences, providing support for the common evolutionary origin of these proteins.

Unit 3 also features the work of Stephen Scherer, who produced a detailed annotated map and DNA sequence of human chromosome 7; Calvin Harley and the discovery of telomeres; Michael Houghton, whose research team recently developed a vaccine for the hepatitis C virus at the University of Alberta; the Michael Smith Genome Sciences Centre in Vancouver, which generated the first genome sequence of SARS; Frank Plummer at the National Microbiology Laboratory in Winnipeg, whose team sequenced the full genome of H1N1 flu samples; James Till and Ernest McCulloch, the Canadian scientists who discovered stem cells; Michael Rudnicki, who led the team that discovered adult muscle stem cells at the Sprott Centre for Stem Cell Research in Ottawa; and Charlie Boone, from the University of Toronto, who maps genetic interactions in yeast. In addition, a range of genomics research in Canada is featured in the updated Exploring Figure 21.6.

Mechanisms of Evolution

One goal of this revision was to highlight connections among fundamental evolutionary concepts. For example, new material connects Darwin's ideas to what can be learned from phylogenetic trees, and a new figure (Figure 25.13) and text illustrate how the combined effects of speciation and extinction determine the number of species in different groups of organisms. The unit also features new material on nucleotide variability within genetic loci, including a new figure (Figure 23.3) that shows variability at the level of DNA. Updates include revised discussions of the events and underlying causes of the Cambrian explosion and the Permian mass extinction, as well as new figures providing fossil evidence of key evolutionary events, such as the formation of plant-fungi symbioses (Figure 25.12).

Unit 4 includes updated data on MRSA incidence at Canadian hospitals, and profiles the research of Darla Zelenitsky at the University of Calgary on the discovery of a winged dinosaur with feathers in the Badlands of Alberta, the research of Hans Larsson from McGill University on phenotype plasticity in tetrapods, and the research of Charles Henderson and others who pinpointed the end-Permian mass extinction.

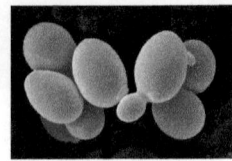 The Evolutionary History of Biological Diversity

In keeping with our Second Canadian Edition goals, we have expanded the coverage of genomic and other molecular studies and how they inform our understanding of phylogeny. Examples include a new Inquiry Figure (Figure 34.50) on the Neanderthal genome and presentation of new evidence that mutualistic interactions between plants and fungi are ancient. In addition, many phylogenies have been revised to reflect recent miRNA and genomic data. The unit also contains new material on tree-thinking, such as a new figure (Figure 26.11) that distinguishes between paraphyletic and polyphyletic taxa.

This unit also highlights research on mycorrhizal networks by Suzanne Simard at the University of British Columbia; research on early eukaryotic evolution by Patrick Keeling at the University of British Columbia; data from COSEWIC (Committee on the Status of Endangered Wildlife in Canada), a profile of the Banff spring snail, and endangered species; the Hydrocarbon Metagenome projects run out of the University of Calgary and the University of Alberta, and the Wildlife DNA Forensic Laboratory at Trent University.

Plant Form and Function

In developing the Second Canadian Edition, we have continued to provide students with a basic understanding of plant anatomy and function while highlighting dynamic areas of plant research and the many important connections between plants and other organisms. To underscore the relevance of plant biology to society, there is now expanded coverage of plant biotechnology and the development of biofuels in Chapter 38. Other updates include expanded coverage of bacterial components of the rhizosphere (Figure 37.9), plant mineral deficiency symptoms (Table 37.1), evolutionary trends in floral morphology (Chapter 38), and chemical communication between plants (Chapter 39). Amongst others, we highlight the work of Rob Guy at the University of British Columbia on balsam poplar trees; Doug Larson at the University of Guelph on cedars growing out of the rock face of the Niagara Escarpment; R. Keith Downey at the Ministry of Agriculture in Saskatoon and Baldur Stefansson at the University of Manitoba in Winnipeg on canola oil, and Mark Belmonte at the University of Manitoba on disease resistance in plants. An Inquiry Figure features the work of Bruce Greenberg and Bernie Glick at the University of Waterloo on the possible effects of soil bacteria.

UNIT 7 Animal Form and Function

In revising this unit, we strove to enhance student appreciation of the core concepts and ideas that apply across diverse organisms and varied organ systems. To help students recognize the central concept of homeostasis, figures were revised across six chapters to provide a consistent organization that facilitates interpretation of individual hormone pathways as well as the comparison of pathways across organisms. Homeostasis and endocrine regulation are highlighted by a revised presentation of the variation in target cell responses to a hormone (Figure 45.8) and a new figure integrating art and text on human endocrine glands and hormones (Figure 45.9). Throughout the unit, new state-of-the-art images and material on current and compelling topics—such as the human stomach microbiome (Figure 41.18) and the identification of the complete set of human taste receptors (Chapter 50)—will help engage students and encourage them to make connections beyond the text.

An Inquiry Figure features the work of Sarah Iverson at Dalhousie University on the analysis of lipid profiles to dissect food webs in free-roaming animals, and an Impact Figure features Ralph Steinman's Nobel Prize work on dendritic cells. There is a description of the work of Brenda Milner, the McGill researcher who introduced the world of neuropsychology to patient HM. Additional research highlighted in this unit includes Janet Rossant at the University of Toronto on cell fate determination; Naweed Syed at the University of Calgary on synaptic repair; University of British Columbia researchers exploring the impact of global warming trends on salmon; University of Manitoba research that explores structure/function relationships in hemoglobin of woolly mammoths; Karen Kidd at the University of New Brunswick on environmental estrogens; Barrie Frost of Queen's University, who explored the navigational mechanisms used by monarch butterflies; and Suzie Currie of Mount Allison University on phenotypic plasticity and environmental stress.

UNIT 8 Ecology

Unit 8 focuses on how ecologists apply biological knowledge and ecological theory to understand and solve problems in the world around them. The Second Canadian Edition introduces the global nature of climate and its effects on life in Chapter 52, providing a logical foundation for the rest of this unit, and the science behind climate change is explored throughout the Unit, including an Exploring Figure dedicated to climate change. In addition, Chapter 52 highlights blacklegged ticks and Lyme disease, and includes a new Inquiry figure on sugar maple and climate change. Chapter 53 profiles research on moose and wolf populations on Isle Royal. In Chapter 54, text and a figure (Figure 54.6) examine the mimic octopus, a recently discovered species that illustrates how predators use mimicry. This chapter also profiles an arctic tundra food web, the mountain pine beetle outbreak and lodgepole pine, and has a new Research Method figure on studying winter ecology of Arctic foxes. Chapter 55 has a new Impact figure on the Canadian oil sands. Chapter 56 highlights the emerging fields of urban ecology and conservation biology, including the technical and ethical challenges of resurrecting extinct species. It also examines the threat of pharmaceuticals in the environment, and incorporates a new Concept section (Concept 56.4) on global change as a result of human actions. Unit 8 also profiles the research of David Schindler from the University of Alberta, and Verena Tunnicliffe from the University of Victoria. The book ends on a hopeful note, charging students to use biological knowledge to help solve problems and improve life on Earth.

See the Big Picture

KEY CONCEPTS

Each chapter is organized around a framework of 3 to 7
Key Concepts that focus on the big picture and provide
a context for the supporting details.

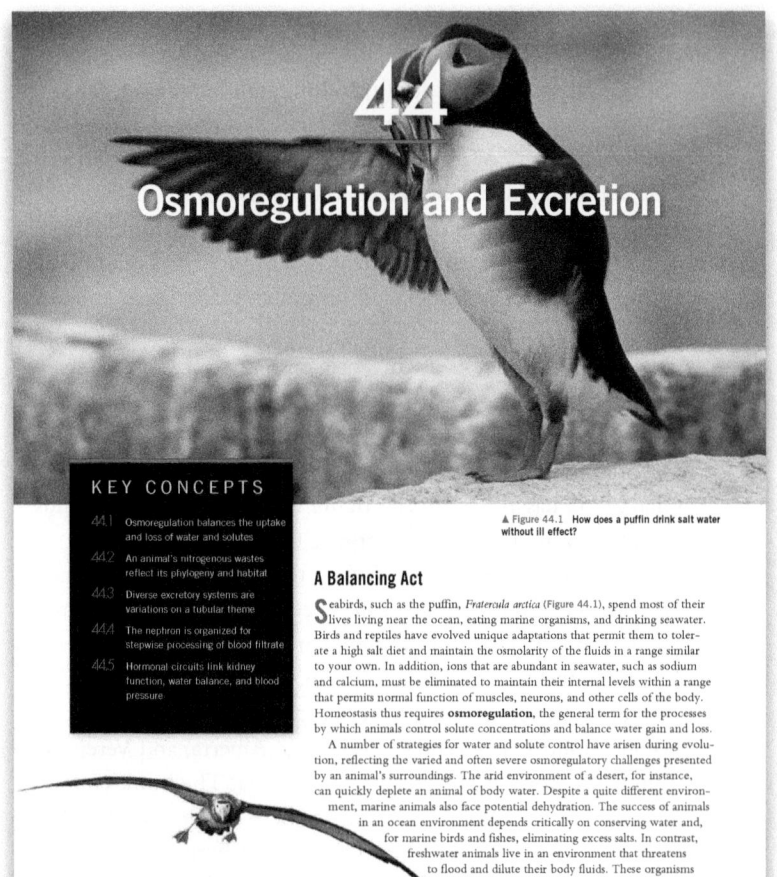

KEY CONCEPTS

44.1 Osmoregulation balances the uptake and loss of water and solutes

44.2 An animal's nitrogenous wastes reflect its phylogeny and habitat

44.3 Diverse excretory systems are variations on a tubular theme

44.4 The nephron is organized for stepwise processing of blood filtrate

44.5 Hormonal circuits link kidney function, water balance, and blood pressure

▲ Figure 44.1 **How does a puffin drink salt water without ill effect?**

A Balancing Act

Seabirds, such as the puffin, *Fratercula arctica* (Figure 44.1), spend most of their lives living near the ocean, eating marine organisms, and drinking seawater. Birds and reptiles have evolved unique adaptations that permit them to tolerate a high salt diet and maintain the osmolarity of the fluids in a range similar to your own. In addition, ions that are abundant in seawater, such as sodium and calcium, must be eliminated to maintain their internal levels within a range that permits normal function of muscles, neurons, and other cells of the body. Homeostasis thus requires **osmoregulation,** the general term for the processes by which animals control solute concentrations and balance water gain and loss.

A number of strategies for water and solute control have arisen during evolution, reflecting the varied and often severe osmoregulatory challenges presented by an animal's surroundings. The arid environment of a desert, for instance, can quickly deplete an animal of body water. Despite a quite different environment, marine animals also face potential dehydration. The success of animals in an ocean environment depends critically on conserving water and, for marine birds and fishes, eliminating excess salts. In contrast, freshwater animals live in an environment that threatens to flood and dilute their body fluids. These organisms

◀ Every chapter opens with a visually dynamic **photo** accompanied by an **intriguing question** that invites students into the chapter.

▲ The **List of Key Concepts** introduces the big ideas covered in the chapter.

After reading a Key Concept section, students can check their understanding using the **Concept Check Questions.**

What if? Questions ask students ▶ to apply what they've learned.

Make Connections Questions ▶ ask students to relate content in the chapter to material presented earlier in the course.

CONCEPT CHECK 44.5

1. How does alcohol affect regulation of water balance in the body?

2. Why could it be dangerous to drink a very large amount of water in a short period of time?

3. **WHAT IF?** Conn's syndrome is a condition caused by tumours of the adrenal cortex that secrete high amounts of aldosterone in an unregulated manner. What would you expect to be the major symptom of this disorder?

4. **MAKE CONNECTIONS** Compare the activity of renin and ACE in the renin-angiotensin-aldosterone system with that of the protein kinases in a phosphorylation cascade, such as the one shown in Figure 11.10. How are the roles of these enzymes similar and different in the two regulated response pathways?

For suggested answers, see Appendix A.

◀ Questions throughout the chapter encourage students to **read the text actively.**

The **Summary of Key Concepts** refocuses students on the main points of the chapter.

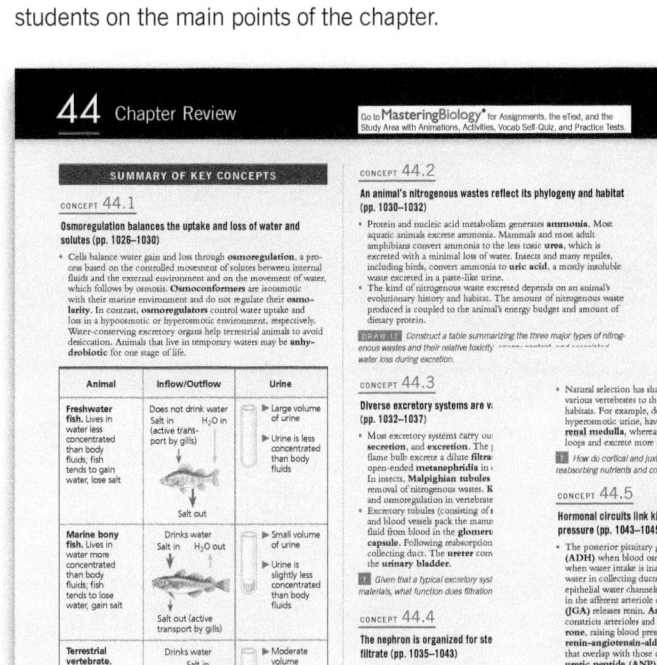

▲ **Summary Figures** recap key information in a visual way. **Summary of Key Concepts Questions** check students' understanding of a key idea from each concept.

▼ **Test Your Understanding Questions** at the end of each chapter are organized into three levels based on **Bloom's Taxonomy**:

- Level 1: Knowledge/Comprehension
- Level 2: Application/Analysis
- Level 3: Synthesis/Evaluation

Test Bank questions and multiple-choice questions in MasteringBiology® are also categorized by Bloom's Taxonomy.

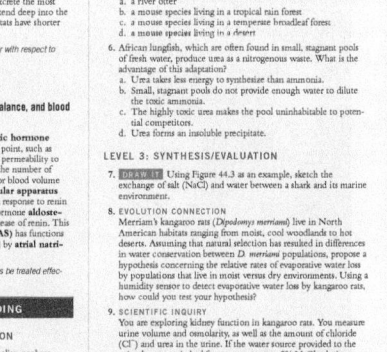

◀ **NEW! Synthesize Your Knowledge Questions** ask students to apply their understanding of the chapter content to explain an intriguing photo.

THEMES

To help students focus on the big ideas of biology, five **themes** are introduced in Chapter 1 and woven throughout the text:

- Evolution
- Organization
- Information
- Energy and Matter
- Interactions

▲ To reinforce the themes, every chapter ends with an **Evolution Connection Question** and a **Write About a Theme Question**.

Every chapter has a section ▶ explicitly relating the chapter content to **evolution**, the fundamental theme of biology.

> **EVOLUTION** Mitochondria and chloroplasts display similarities with bacteria that led to the **endosymbiont theory**, illustrated in Figure 6.16. This theory states that an early ancestor of eukaryotic cells engulfed an oxygen-using non-photosynthetic prokaryotic cell. Eventually, the engulfed cell formed a relationship with the host cell in which it was enclosed, becoming an *endosymbiont* (a cell living within another cell). Indeed, over the course of evolution, the host cell and its endosymbiont merged into a single organism, a eukaryotic cell with a mitochondrion. At least one of these cells may have then taken up a photosynthetic prokaryote, becoming the ancestor of eukaryotic cells that contain chloroplasts.
>
> This a widely accepted theory, which we will discuss in more detail in Chapter 25. This theory is consistent with many structural features of mitochondria and chloroplasts. First, rather than being bounded by a single membrane like organelles of the endomembrane system, mitochondria and typical chloroplasts have two membranes surrounding them. (Chloroplasts also have an internal system of membranous sacs.) There is evidence that the ancestral engulfed

Make Connections Visually

Make Connections Figures pull together content from different chapters, providing a visual representation of "big picture" relationships.

Make Connections Figures include:

Unit 1 Properties of Water p. 30

Figure 5.26 Contributions of Genomics and Proteomics to Biology p. 97

Unit 2 The Working Cell p. 102

Unit 3 Mutations and Inheritance of Cystic Fibrosis p. 264

Figure 18.27 Genomics, Cell Signalling, and Cancer p. 408

Unit 4 The Sickle-Cell Allele p. 490

Unit 5 Evolutionary History of Biological Diversity p. 580

Unit 6 Levels of Plant Defences Against Herbivores p. 800

Unit 7 Life Challenges and Solutions p. 918

Figure 44.18 Ion Movement and Gradients p. 1042

Unit 8 The Working Ecosystem p. 1222

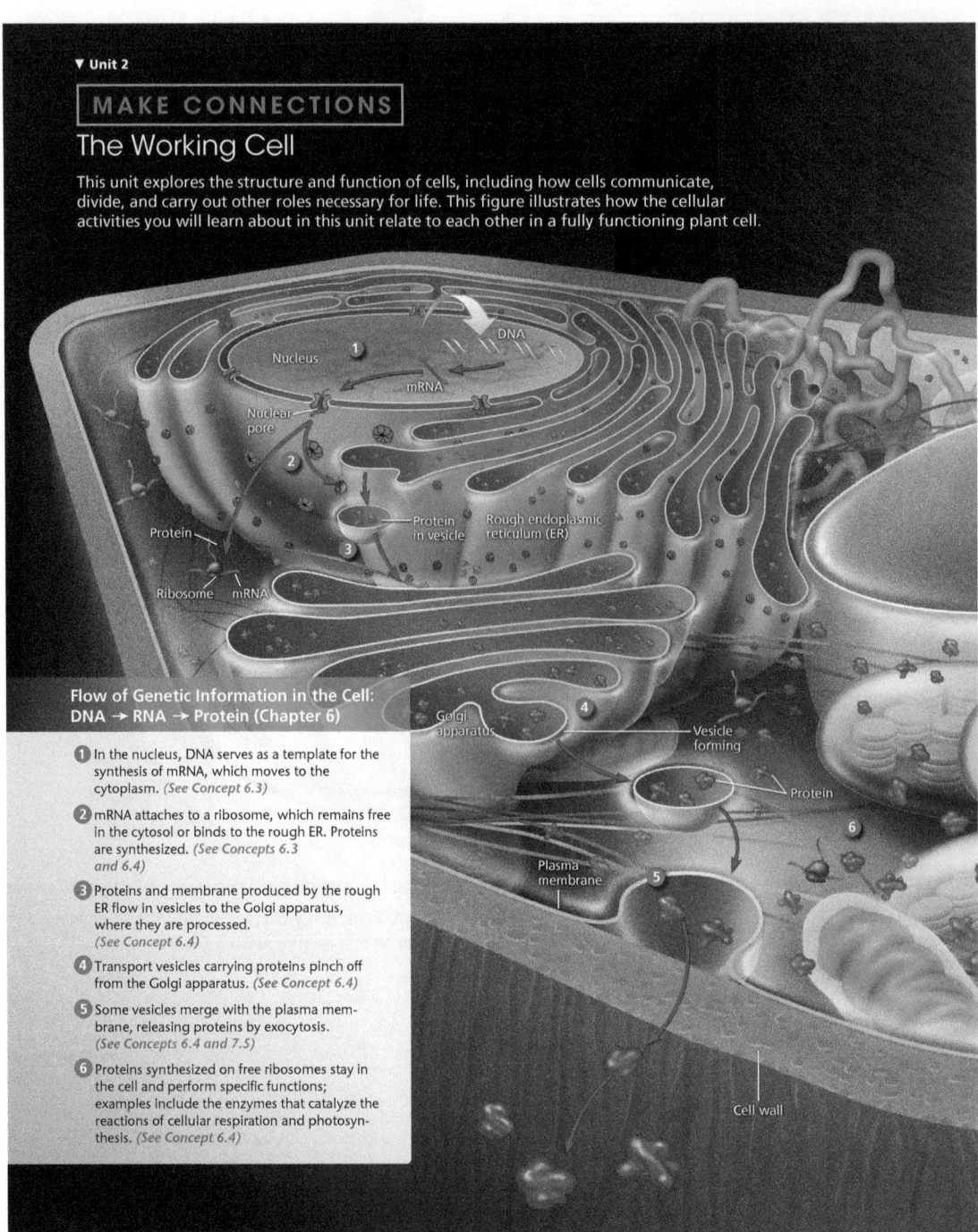

▼ Unit 2

MAKE CONNECTIONS

The Working Cell

This unit explores the structure and function of cells, including how cells communicate, divide, and carry out other roles necessary for life. This figure illustrates how the cellular activities you will learn about in this unit relate to each other in a fully functioning plant cell.

Flow of Genetic Information in the Cell: DNA → RNA → Protein (Chapter 6)

1. In the nucleus, DNA serves as a template for the synthesis of mRNA, which moves to the cytoplasm. (See Concept 6.3)

2. mRNA attaches to a ribosome, which remains free in the cytosol or binds to the rough ER. Proteins are synthesized. (See Concepts 6.3 and 6.4)

3. Proteins and membrane produced by the rough ER flow in vesicles to the Golgi apparatus, where they are processed. (See Concept 6.4)

4. Transport vesicles carrying proteins pinch off from the Golgi apparatus. (See Concept 6.4)

5. Some vesicles merge with the plasma membrane, releasing proteins by exocytosis. (See Concepts 6.4 and 7.5)

6. Proteins synthesized on free ribosomes stay in the cell and perform specific functions; examples include the enzymes that catalyze the reactions of cellular respiration and photosynthesis. (See Concept 6.4)

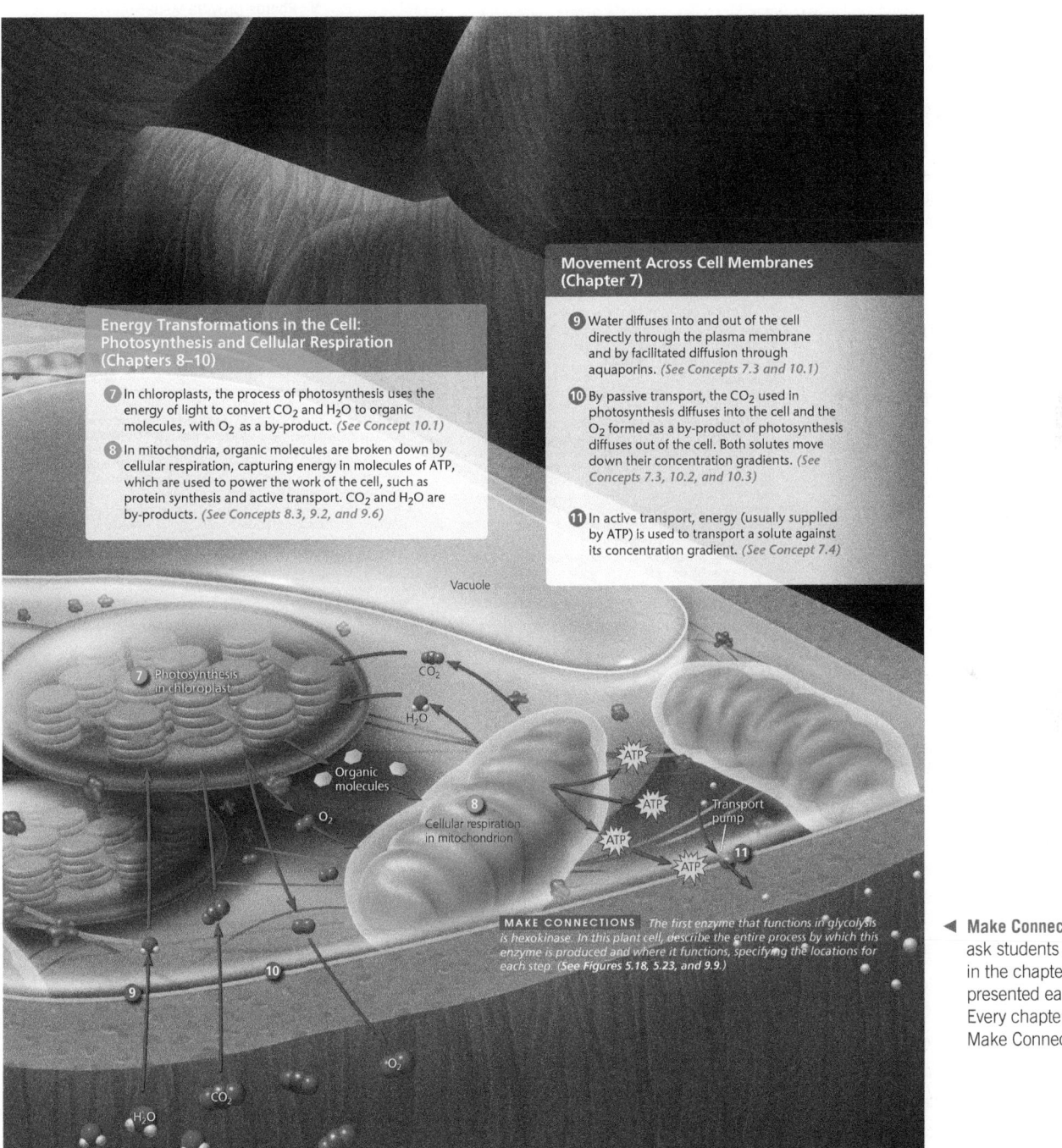

**Energy Transformations in the Cell:
Photosynthesis and Cellular Respiration
(Chapters 8–10)**

7 In chloroplasts, the process of photosynthesis uses the energy of light to convert CO_2 and H_2O to organic molecules, with O_2 as a by-product. *(See Concept 10.1)*

8 In mitochondria, organic molecules are broken down by cellular respiration, capturing energy in molecules of ATP, which are used to power the work of the cell, such as protein synthesis and active transport. CO_2 and H_2O are by-products. *(See Concepts 8.3, 9.2, and 9.6)*

**Movement Across Cell Membranes
(Chapter 7)**

9 Water diffuses into and out of the cell directly through the plasma membrane and by facilitated diffusion through aquaporins. *(See Concepts 7.3 and 10.1)*

10 By passive transport, the CO_2 used in photosynthesis diffuses into the cell and the O_2 formed as a by-product of photosynthesis diffuses out of the cell. Both solutes move down their concentration gradients. *(See Concepts 7.3, 10.2, and 10.3)*

11 In active transport, energy (usually supplied by ATP) is used to transport a solute against its concentration gradient. *(See Concept 7.4)*

Vacuole

7 Photosynthesis in chloroplast

CO_2

H_2O

Organic molecules

O_2

8 Cellular respiration in mitochondrion

ATP

ATP

ATP

ATP

Transport pump

11

9

10

O_2

CO_2

H_2O

MAKE CONNECTIONS *The first enzyme that functions in glycolysis is hexokinase. In this plant cell, describe the entire process by which this enzyme is produced and where it functions, specifying the locations for each step. (See Figures 5.18, 5.23, and 9.9.)*

◀ **Make Connections Questions** ask students to relate content in the chapter to material presented earlier in the course. Every chapter has at least three Make Connections Questions.

Practise Scientific Skills

▼ **Photos** provide visual interest and context.

Each Scientific Skills Exercise is ▶ based on an **experiment related to the chapter content.**

SCIENTIFIC SKILLS EXERCISE

Interpreting a Scatter Plot with a Regression Line

How Does the Carbonate Ion Concentration of Seawater Affect the Calcification Rate of a Coral Reef? Scientists predict that acidification of the ocean due to higher levels of atmospheric CO_2 will lower the concentration of dissolved carbonate ions, which living corals use to build calcium carbonate reef structures. In this exercise, you will analyze data from a controlled experiment that examined the effect of carbonate ion concentration ($[CO_3^{2-}]$) on calcium carbonate deposition, a process called calcification.

How the Experiment Was Done The Biosphere 2 aquarium in Arizona contains a large coral reef system that behaves like a natural reef. For several years, a group of researchers measured the rate of calcification by the reef organisms and examined how the calcification rate changed with differing amounts of dissolved carbonate ions in the seawater.

Most Scientific Skills Exercises ▶ use **data from published research.**

Data from the Experiment The black data points in the graph form a scatter plot. The red line, known as a linear regression line, is the best-fitting straight line for these points.

Interpret the Data

Questions build in difficulty, ▶ walking students through new skills step by step and providing opportunities for higher-level critical thinking.

1. When presented with a graph of experimental data, the first step in analysis is to determine what each axis represents. (a) In words, explain what is being shown on the x-axis. Be sure to include the units. (b) What is being shown on the y-axis (including units)? (c) Which variable is the independent variable—the variable that was *manipulated* by the researchers? (d) Which variable is the dependent variable—the variable that responded to or depended on the treatment, which was *measured* by the researchers? (For additional information about graphs, see the Scientific Skills Review in Appendix E and in the Study Area in MasteringBiology.)

2. Based on the data shown in the graph, describe in words the relationship between carbonate ion concentration and calcification rate.

3. (a) If the seawater carbonate ion concentration is 270 μmol/kg, what is the approximate rate of calcification, and approximately how many days would it take 1 square metre of reef to accumulate 30 mmol of

calcium carbonate ($CaCO_3$)? (b) If the seawater carbonate ion concentration is 250 μmol/kg, what is the approximate rate of calcification, and approximately how many days would it take 1 square metre of reef to accumulate 30 mmol of calcium carbonate? (c) If carbonate ion concentration decreases, how does the calcification rate change, and how does that affect the time it takes coral to grow?

4. (a) Referring to the equations in Figure 3.12, determine which step of the process is measured in this experiment. (b) Are the results of this experiment consistent with the hypothesis that increased atmospheric $[CO_2]$ will slow the growth of coral reefs? Why or why not?

Data from C. Langdon et al., Effect of calcium carbonate saturation state on the calcification rate of an experimental coral reef, *Global Biogeochemical Cycles* 14:639–654 (2000).

▲ Each Scientific Skills Exercise **cites the published research.**

Every chapter has a Scientific Skills Exercise

1. Interpreting a Pair of Bar Graphs, p. 24
2. Calibrating a Standard Radioactive Isotope Decay Curve and Interpreting Data, p. 37
3. Interpreting a Scatter Plot with a Regression Line, p. 60
4. Working with Moles and Molar Ratios, p. 65
5. Analyzing Polypeptide Sequence Data, p. 98
6. Using a Scale Bar to Calculate Volume and Surface Area of a Cell, p. 110
7. Interpreting a Scatter Plot with Two Sets of Data, p. 146
8. Making a Line Graph and Calculating a Slope, p. 168
9. Making a Bar Graph and Evaluating a Hypothesis, p. 190
10. Making Scatter Plots with Regression Lines, p. 216
11. Using Experiments to Test a Model, p. 237
12. Interpreting Histograms, p. 259
13. Making a Line Graph and Converting Between Units of Data, p. 276
14. Making a Histogram and Analyzing a Distribution Pattern, p. 294

15. Using the Chi-Square Test, p. 318
16. Working with Data in a Table, p. 333
17. Interpreting a Sequence Logo, p. 368
18. Analyzing DNA Deletion Experiments, p. 390
19. Analyzing a Sequence-Based Phylogenetic Tree to Understand Viral Evolution, p. 429
20. Analyzing Quantitative and Spatial Gene Expression Data, p. 445
21. Reading an Amino Acid Sequence Identity Table, p. 479
22. Making and Testing Predictions, p. 507
23. Using the Hardy-Weinberg Equation to Interpret Data and Make Predictions, p. 517
24. Identifying Independent and Dependent Variables, Making a Scatter Plot, and Interpreting Data, p. 537
25. Estimating Quantitative Data from a Graph and Developing Hypotheses, p. 564
26. Using Protein Sequence Data to Test an Evolutionary Hypothesis, p. 600

NEW! **Scientific Skills Exercises** from the text have assignable, interactive versions in **MasteringBiology** that are automatically graded.

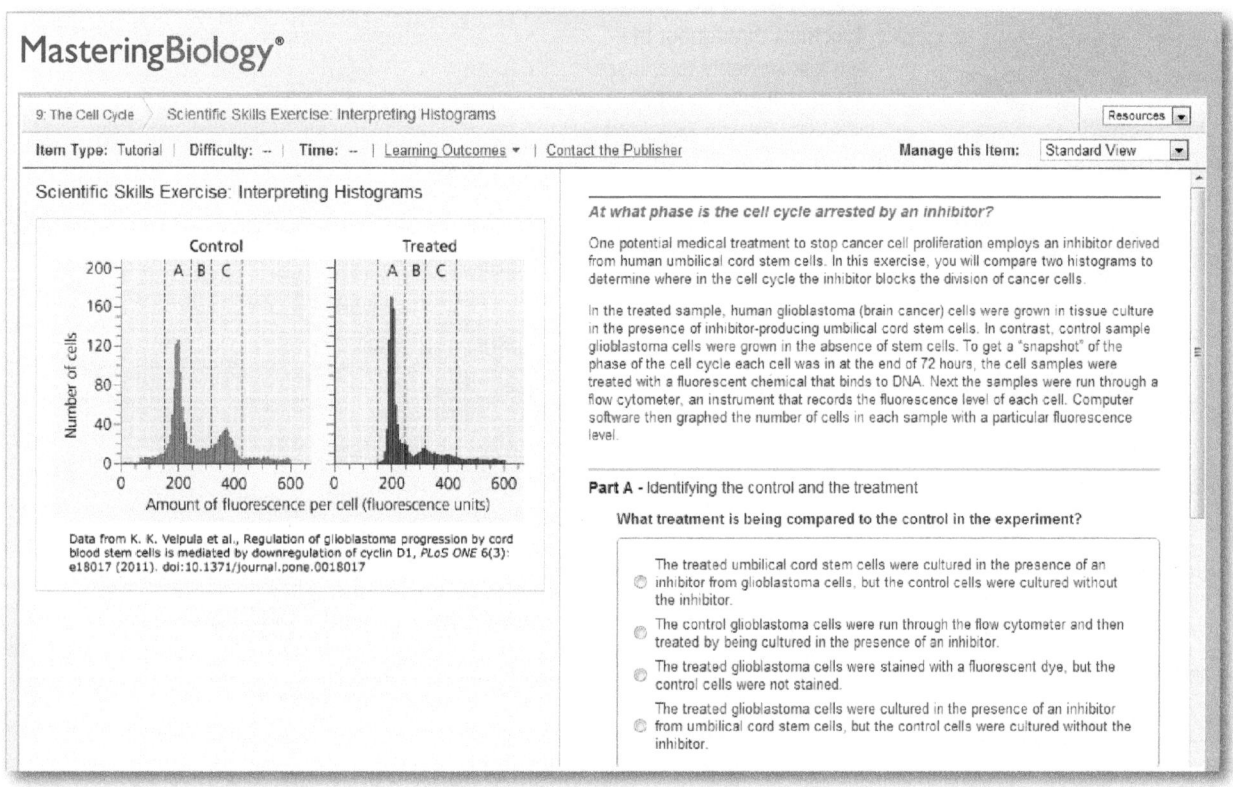

MasteringBiology®

To learn more, visit www.masteringbiology.com

27. Making a Bar Graph and Interpreting Data, p. 622
28. Interpreting Comparisons of Genetic Sequences, p. 631
29. Making Bar Graphs and Interpreting Data, p. 663
30. Using Natural Logarithms to Interpret Data, p. 675
31. Interpreting Genomic Data and Generating Hypotheses, p. 696
32. Calculating and Interpreting Correlation Coefficients, p. 718
33. Understanding Experimental Design and Interpreting Data, p. 740
34. Determining the Equation of a Regression Line, p. 793
35. Using Bar Graphs to Interpret Data, p. 806
36. Calculating and Interpreting Temperature Coefficients, p. 834
37. Making Observations, p. 857
38. Using Positive and Negative Correlations to Interpret Data, p. 880
39. Interpreting Experimental Results from a Bar Graph, p. 910
40. Interpreting Pie Charts, p. 939
41. Interpreting Data from Experiments with Genetic Mutants, p. 963

42. Making and Interpreting Histograms, p. 985
43. Comparing Two Variables on a Common x-Axis, p. 1021
44. Describing and Interpreting Quantitative Data, p. 1029
45. Designing a Controlled Experiment, p. 1066
46. Making Inferences and Designing an Experiment, p. 1082
47. Interpreting a Change in Slope, p. 1101
48. Interpreting Data Values Expressed in Scientific Notation, p. 1136
49. Designing an Experiment Using Genetic Mutants, p. 1149
50. Interpreting a Graph with Log Scales, p. 1192
51. Testing a Hypothesis with a Quantitative Model, p. 1208
52. Making and Interpreting Line and Scatterplot Graphs, p. 1247
53. Using the Logistic Equation to Model Population Growth, p. 1259
54. Graphing and Interpreting Experimental Data, p. 1277
55. Using Tabular Data to Calculate Net Ecosystem Production, p. 1304
56. Graphing Cyclic Data, p. 1341

Interpret Data

Campbell BIOLOGY, Second Canadian Edition, and MasteringBiology® offer a wide variety of ways for students to move beyond memorization and **think like a scientist.**

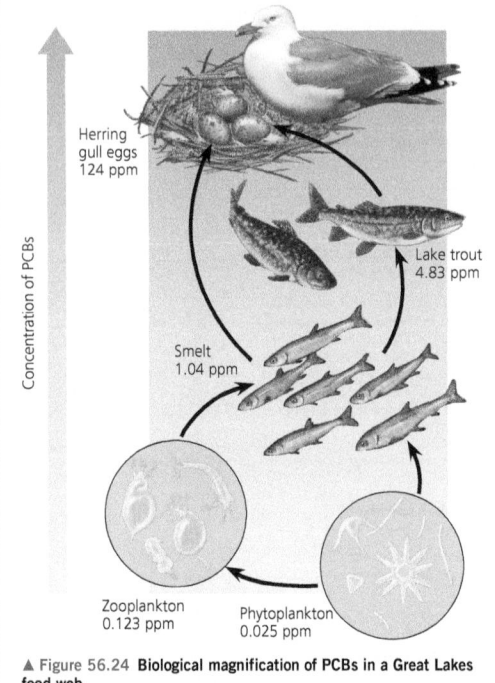

▲ Figure 56.24 **Biological magnification of PCBs in a Great Lakes food web.**

INTERPRET THE DATA *If a typical smelt weighs 225 g, what is the total mass of PCBs in a smelt in the Great Lakes? If an average lake trout weighs 4500 g, what is the total mass of PCBs in a trout in the Great Lakes? Assume that a lake trout from an unpolluted source is introduced into the Great Lakes and smelt are the only source of PCBs in the trout's diet. How many smelt would the new trout have to consume to attain a pcb level equivalent to existing trout in the Great University. (Assume that the trout retains 100% of the PCBs it consumes.)*

◀ **NEW!** Interpret the Data Questions throughout the text ask students to analyze a graph, figure, or table.

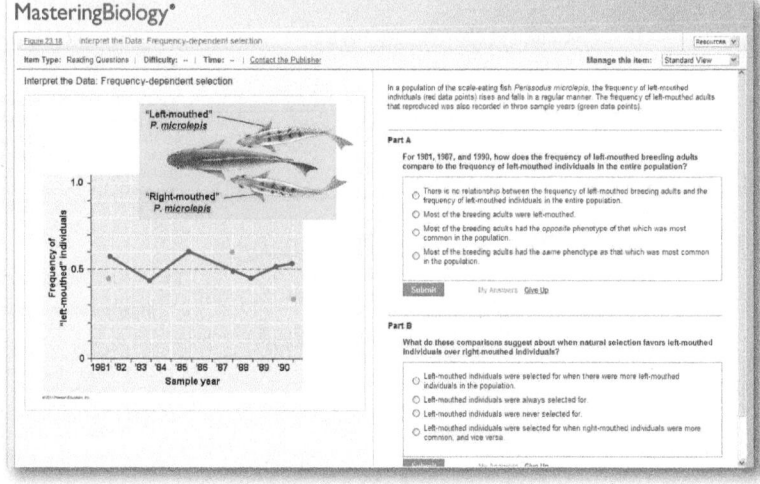

▲ **NEW!** Interpret the Data Question from the text is assignable in **MasteringBiology**.

MasteringBiology®
Learn more at
www.masteringbiology.com

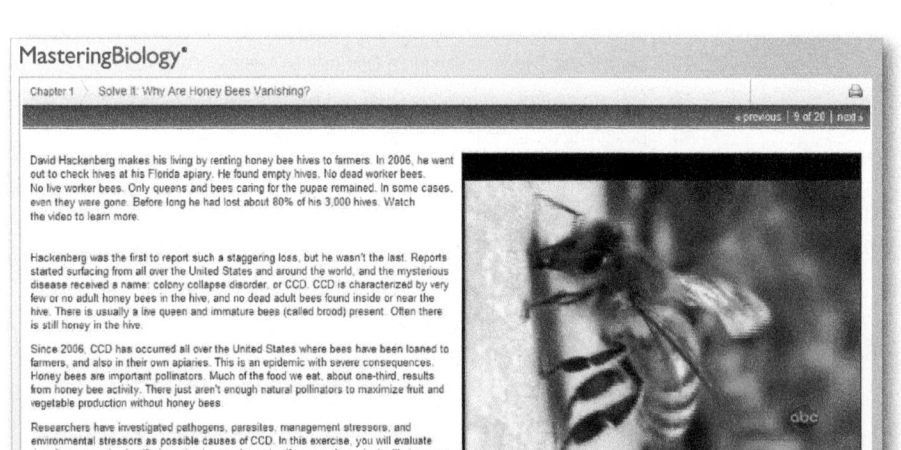

◀ **NEW!** Solve It Tutorials engage students in a multistep investigation of a "mystery" or open question in which they must analyze real data. These are assignable in **MasteringBiology**.

Topics include:

- Is It Possible to Treat Bacterial Infections Without Traditional Antibiotics?
- Are You Getting the Fish You Paid For?
- Why Are Honey Bees Vanishing?
- Which Biofuel Has the Most Potential to Reduce our Dependence on Fossil Fuels?
- Which Insulin Mutations May Result in Disease?
- What Is Causing Episodes of Muscle Weakness in a Patient?

Explore the Impact of Genomics

Throughout the Second Canadian Edition, new examples show students how our ability to **sequence DNA and proteins rapidly and inexpensively** is transforming every subfield of biology, from cell biology to physiology to ecology.

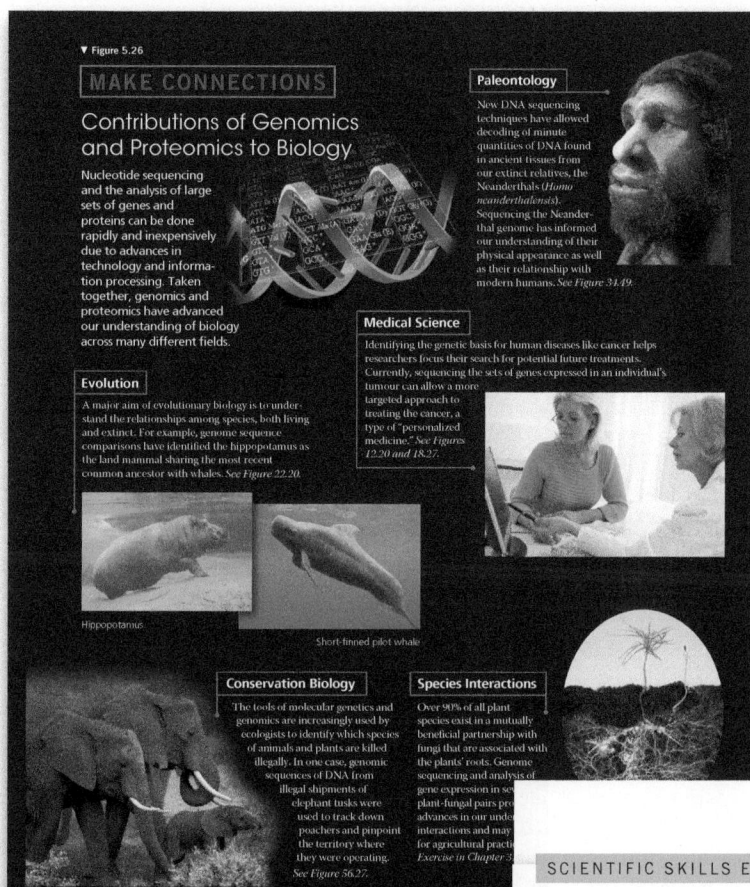

▼ Figure 5.26

MAKE CONNECTIONS

Contributions of Genomics and Proteomics to Biology

Nucleotide sequencing and the analysis of large sets of genes and proteins can be done rapidly and inexpensively due to advances in technology and information processing. Taken together, genomics and proteomics have advanced our understanding of biology across many different fields.

Paleontology

New DNA sequencing techniques have allowed decoding of minute quantities of DNA found in ancient tissues from our extinct relatives, the Neanderthals (*Homo neanderthalensis*). Sequencing the Neanderthal genome has informed our understanding of their physical appearance as well as their relationship with modern humans. *See Figure 34.49.*

Evolution

A major aim of evolutionary biology is to understand the relationships among species, both living and extinct. For example, genome sequence comparisons have identified the hippopotamus as the land mammal sharing the most recent common ancestor with whales. *See Figure 22.20.*

Hippopotamus

Short-finned pilot whale

Medical Science

Identifying the genetic basis for human diseases like cancer helps researchers focus their search for potential future treatments. Currently, sequencing the sets of genes expressed in an individual's tumour can allow a targeted approach to treating the cancer, a type of "personalized medicine." *See Figures 12.20 and 18.27.*

Conservation Biology

The tools of molecular genetics and genomics are increasingly used by ecologists to identify which species of animals and plants are killed illegally. In one case, genomic sequences of DNA from illegal shipments of elephant tusks were used to track down poachers and pinpoint the territory where they were operating. *See Figure 56.27.*

Species Interactions

Over 90% of all plant species exist in a mutually beneficial partnership with fungi that are associated with the plants' roots. Genome sequencing and analysis of gene expression in several plant-fungal pairs provide advances in our understanding of these interactions and may provide ideas for agricultural practices. *See the Exercise in Chapter 31.*

◄ This **Make Connections Figure** in Chapter 5 previews some examples of how genomics and proteomics have helped shed light on diverse biological questions. These examples are explored in greater depth later in the text.

SCIENTIFIC SKILLS EXERCISE

Analyzing Polypeptide Sequence Data

▶ Human ▶ Rhesus monkey ▶ Gibbon

Are Rhesus Monkeys or Gibbons More Closely Related to Humans? DNA and polypeptide sequences from closely related species are more similar to each other than are sequences from more distantly related species. In this exercise, you will look at amino acid sequence data for the β polypeptide chain of hemoglobin, often called β-globin. You will then interpret the data to hypothesize whether the monkey or the gibbon is more closely related to humans.

How Such Experiments Are Done Researchers can isolate the polypeptide of interest from an organism and then determine the amino acid sequence. More frequently, the DNA of the relevant gene is sequenced, and the amino acid sequence of the polypeptide is deduced from the DNA sequence of its gene.

Data from the Experiments In the data below, the letters give the sequence of the 146 amino acids in β-globin from humans, rhesus monkeys, and gibbons. Because a complete sequence would not fit on one line here, the sequences are broken into three segments. The sequences for the three different species are aligned so that you can compare them easily. For example, you can see that for all three species, the first amino acid is V (valine) and the 146th amino acid is H (histidine).

Interpret the Data

1. Scan the monkey and gibbon sequences, letter by letter, circling any amino acids that do not match the human sequence. (a) How many amino acids differ between the monkey and the human sequences? (b) Between the gibbon and human?

2. For each nonhuman species, what percent of its amino acids are identical to the human sequence of β-globin?

3. Based on these data alone, state a hypothesis for which of these two species is more closely related to humans. What is your reasoning?

4. What other evidence could you use to support your hypothesis?

 A version of this Scientific Skills Exercise can be assigned in MasteringBiology.

Data from Human: http://www.ncbi.nlm.nih.gov/protein/AAA21113.1; rhesus monkey: http://www.ncbi.nlm.nih.gov/protein/122634; gibbon: http://www.ncbi.nlm.nih.gov/protein/122616

◄ Selected Scientific Skills Exercises involve **working with DNA or protein sequences.**

Species	Alignment of Amino Acid Sequences of β-globin				
Human	1 VHLTPEEKSA	VTALWGKVNV	DEVGGEALGR	LLVVYPWTQR	FFESFGDLST
Monkey	1 VHLTPEEKNA	VTTLWGKVNV	DEVGGEALGR	LLLVYPWTQR	FFESFGDLSS
Gibbon	1 VHLTPEEKSA	VTALWGKVNV	DEVGGEALGR	LLVVYPWTQR	FFESFGDLST
Human	51 PDAVMGNPKV	KAHGKKVLGA	FSDGLAHLDN	LKGTFATLSE	LHCDKLHVDP
Monkey	51 PDAVMGNPKV	KAHGKKVLGA	FSDGLNHLDN	LKGTFAQLSE	LHCDKLHVDP
Gibbon	51 PDAVMGNPKV	KAHGKKVLGA	FSDGLAHLDN	LKGTFAQLSE	LHCDKLHVDP
Human	101 ENFRLLGNVL	VCVLAHHFGK	EFTPPVQAAY	QKVVAGVANA	LAHKYH
Monkey	101 ENFKLLGNVL	VCVLAHHFGK	EFTPQVQAAY	QKVVAGVANA	LAHKYH
Gibbon	101 ENFRLLGNVL	VCVLAHHFGK	EFTPQVQAAY	QKVVAGVANA	LAHKYH

MasteringBiology®

eTEXT

Access the complete **textbook online!**

Pearson eText. The Pearson eText gives students access to their textbook anytime, anywhere. In addition to note taking, highlighting, and bookmarking, the Pearson eText offers interactive and sharing features. Instructors can share their comments or highlights, and students can add their own, creating a tight community of learners within the class.

STUDY AREA

Students can access the **Study Area** for use on their own or in a study group.

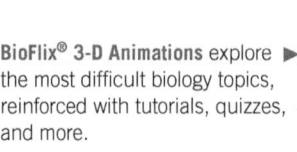

▶ **BioFlix® 3-D Animations** explore the most difficult biology topics, reinforced with tutorials, quizzes, and more.

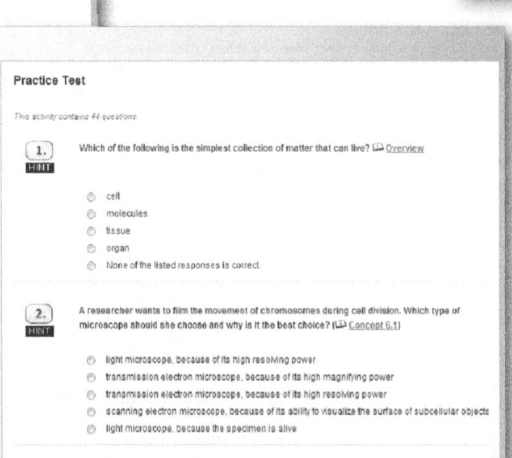

▲ **Get Ready for Biology** helps students get up to speed for their course by covering study skills, basic math, terminology, chemistry, and biology basics.

◀ **Practice Tests** help students assess their understanding of each chapter, providing feedback for right and wrong answers.

The **Study Area** also includes: MP3 Tutor Sessions, Videos, Activities, Investigations, Audio Glossary, Word Roots, Key Terms, Flashcards, and Art.

DYNAMIC STUDY MODULES

NEW! **Dynamic Study Modules**, designed to enable students to study effectively on their own, help students quickly access and learn the information they need to be more successful on quizzes and exams.

How it works:

1. Students receive an initial **set of questions**.

◄ A unique answer format asks students to indicate how **confident** they are about their answer.

2. After answering each set of questions, students **review their answers**.

3. Each answer has an **explanation** using material that is taken directly **from the textbook**.

◄ These modules can be accessed on smartphones, tablets, and computers. Results can be tracked in the MasteringBiology Gradebook.

4. Once students review the explanations from the textbook, they are presented with a new set of questions. Students cycle through this **dynamic process of test–learn–retest** until they achieve mastery of the textbook material.

Learn more at www.masteringbiology.com

Learn Through Assessment

Instructors can assign **self-paced MasteringBiology tutorials** that provide students with individualized coaching with specific hints and feedback on the toughest topics in the course.

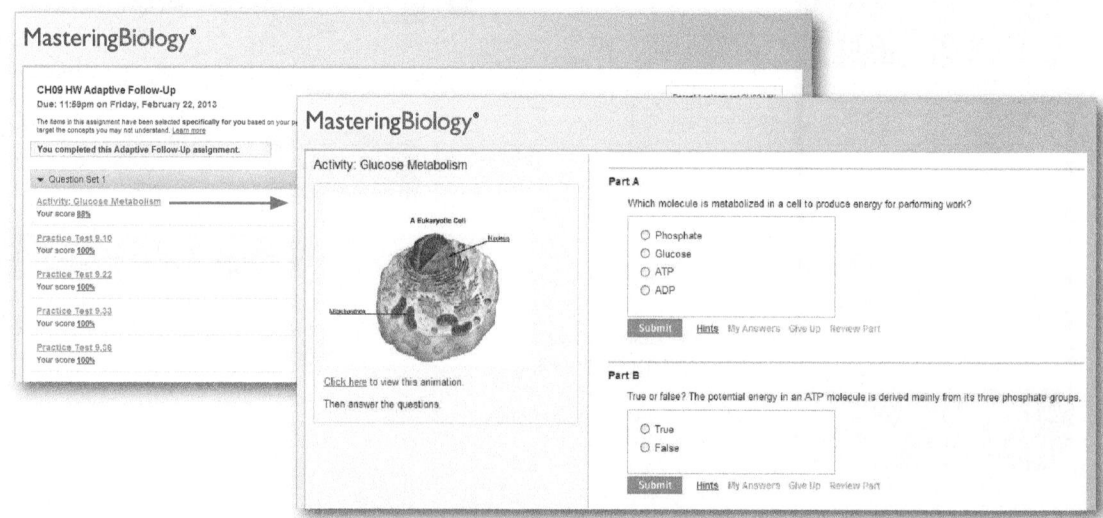

MasteringBiology®

Learn more at
www.masteringbiology.com

1. If a student gets stuck ...

2. specific wrong-answer **feedback** appears in the purple feedback box.

3. **Hints** coach the student to the correct response.

4. Optional **Adaptive Follow-Up Assignments** are based on each student's performance on the original homework assignment and provide additional coaching and practice as needed.

▼

Question sets in the Adaptive ▶ Follow-Up Assignments **continuously adapt** to each student's needs, making efficient use of study time.

The MasteringBiology® Gradebook provides instructors with quick results and easy-to-interpret insights into student performance. Every assignment is automatically graded. Shades of red highlight vulnerable students and challenging assignments.

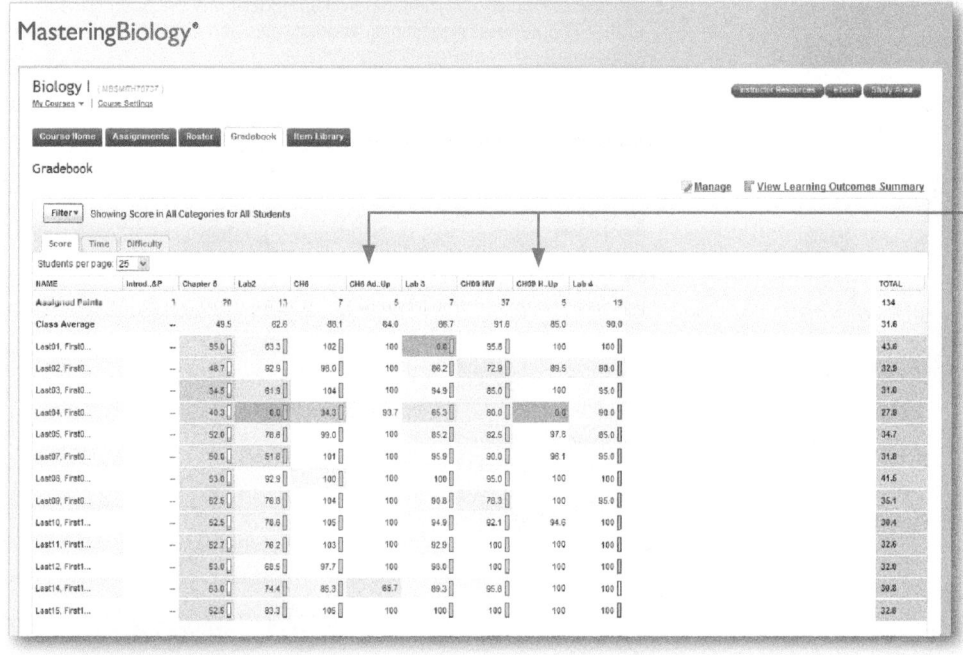

Student scores on the optional **Adaptive Follow-Up Assignments** are recorded in the gradebook and offer additional diagnostic information for instructors to monitor learning outcomes and more.

MasteringBiology offers a wide variety of tutorials that can be assigned as homework. For example, **BioFlix Tutorials** use 3-D, movie-quality **Animations** and coaching exercises to help students master tough topics outside of class. Animations can also be shown in class.

BioFlix Tutorials and 3-D Animations include:

- A Tour of the Animal Cell
- A Tour of the Plant Cell
- Membrane Transport
- Cellular Respiration
- Photosynthesis
- Mitosis
- Meiosis

- DNA Replication
- Protein Synthesis
- Mechanisms of Evolution
- Water Transport in Plants
- Homeostasis: Regulating Blood Sugar
- Gas Exchange

- How Neurons Work
- How Synapses Work
- Muscle Contraction
- Population Ecology
- The Carbon Cycle

Supplements

FOR INSTRUCTORS

Learning Catalytics™ allows students to use their smartphone, tablet, or laptop to respond to questions in class.
Visit www.learningcatalytics.com.

Instructor Resources Area in MasteringBiology

This area includes:

- PowerPoint Lecture Presentations
- Videos and Animations, including BioFlix®
- JPEG Images of most Art and Photos (labelled and unlabelled)
- Test Bank Files
- **NEW!** Ready To Go Teaching Modules on key topics provide instructors with assignments to use before and after class, as well as in-class activities that use clickers or Learning Catalytics™ for assessment.
- Instructor Guides for Supplements
- Rubric and Tips for Grading Short-Answer Essays
- Solutions to Special Topics includes suggested answers and teaching tips for the Scientific Skills Exercises, Interpret the Data Questions, and the Short-Answer Essay Questions.

Instructor Resources for Flipped Classrooms

- Lecture videos can be posted on MasteringBiology for students to view before class.
- Homework can be assigned in MasteringBiology so students come to class prepared.
- In-class resources: Learning Catalytics, Student Misconception Questions, end-of-chapter essay questions, and activities and case studies from the student supplements.

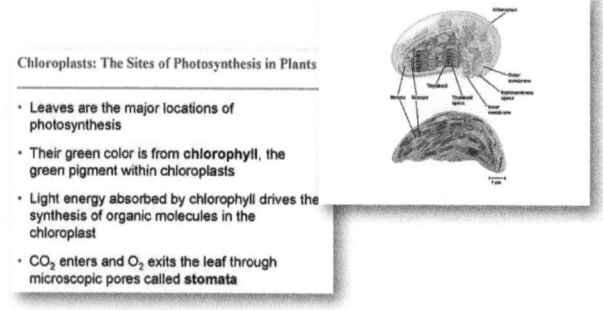

▲ **Customizable PowerPoints** provide a jumpstart for each lecture.

▲ **Art, graphs, and photos from the book**
More than 1600 photos from the text and other sources are included.

Test Bank

This invaluable resource contains more than 4500 questions, including scenario-based questions and art, graph, and data interpretation questions. In addition, Pearson's computerized test banks allow instructors to filter and select questions to create quizzes, tests or homework. Instructors can revise questions or add their own, and may be able to choose print or online options.

FOR STUDENTS

Study Guide, Second Canadian Edition
by Martha R. Taylor, *Ithaca, New York,* and Vivian Deyah, *University of Waterloo*
978-0-134-57044-0 / 0-134-57044-8
This popular study aid provides concept maps, chapter summaries, word roots, and a variety of interactive activities including multiple-choice, short-answer essay, art labelling, and graph-interpretation questions.

Inquiry in Action: Interpreting Scientific Papers, Third Edition*
by Ruth Buskirk, *University of Texas at Austin,* and Christopher M. Gillen, *Kenyon College*
978-0-321-83417-1 / 0-321-83417-8
This guide helps students learn how to read and understand primary research articles. Part A presents complete articles accompanied by questions that help students analyze the article. Related Inquiry Figures are included in the supplement. Part B covers every part of a research paper, explaining the aim of the sections and how the paper works as a whole.

Practicing Biology: A Student Workbook, Fifth Edition*
by Jean Heitz and Cynthia Giffen, *University of Wisconsin, Madison*
978-0-321-87705-5 / 0-321-87705-5
This workbook offers a variety of activities to suit different learning styles. Activities such as modelling and concept mapping allow students to visualize and understand biological processes. Other activities focus on basic skills, such as reading and drawing graphs.

Biological Inquiry: A Workbook of Investigative Cases, Fourth Edition*
by Margaret Waterman, *Southeast Missouri State University,* and Ethel Stanley, *BioQUEST Curriculum Consortium and Beloit College*
978-0-321-83391-4 / 0-321-83391-0
This workbook offers ten investigative cases. Each case study requires students to synthesize information from multiple chapters of the text and apply that knowledge to a real-world scenario as they pose hypotheses, gather new information, analyze evidence, graph data, and draw conclusions. A link to a student website is in the Study Area in MasteringBiology.

Into the Jungle: Great Adventures in the Search for Evolution
by Sean B. Carroll, *University of Wisconsin, Madison*
978-0-321-55671-4 / 0-321-55671-2
These nine short tales vividly depict key discoveries in evolutionary biology and the excitement of the scientific process. Online resources available at www.aw-bc.com/carroll.

Get Ready for Biology
978-0-321-50057-1 / 0-321-50057-1
This engaging workbook helps students brush up on important math and study skills and get up to speed on biological terminology and the basics of chemistry and cell biology.

A Short Guide to Writing About Biology, Ninth Edition
by Jan A. Pechenik, *Tufts University*
978-0-032198425-8/0-321-98425-0
This best-selling writing guide teaches students to think as biologists and to express ideas clearly and concisely through their writing.

An Introduction to Chemistry for Biology Students, Ninth Edition
by George I. Sackheim, *University of Illinois, Chicago*
978-0-8053-9571-6 / 0-8053-9571-7
This text/workbook helps students review and master all the basic facts, concepts, and terminology of chemistry that they need for their life science course.

FOR LAB

Pearson Collections Custom Library gives instructors the power to create custom lab manuals using Pearson Content as well as original materials. Learn more at pearsonhighered.com/ collections

MasteringBiology® Virtual Labs
www.masteringbiology.com
This online environment promotes critical thinking skills using virtual experiments and explorations that may be difficult to perform in a wet lab environment due to time, cost, or safety concerns. Designed to supplement or substitute for existing wet labs, this product offers students unique learning experiences and critical thinking exercises in the areas of microscopy, molecular biology, genetics, ecology, and systematics.

*An Instructor Guide is available for download in the Instructor Resources Area in MasteringBiology

Featured Figures

Make Connections Figures

Unit 1   Properties of Water 30
5.26   Contributions of Genomics and Proteomics to Biology 97
Unit 2   The Working Cell 102
Unit 3   Mutations and Inheritance of Cystic Fibrosis 264
18.27   Genomics, Cell Signalling, and Cancer 408
Unit 4   The Sickle-Cell Allele 490
Unit 5   Evolutionary History of Biological Diversity 580
Unit 6   Levels of Plant Defences Against Herbivores 800
Unit 7   Life Challenges and Solutions 918
44.18   Ion Movement and Gradients 1042
Unit 8   The Working Ecosystem 1222

Exploring Figures

1.4   Levels of Biological Organization 4
5.18   Levels of Protein Structure 88
6.3   Microscopy 106
6.8   Eukaryotic Cells 112
6.30   Cell Junctions in Animal Tissues 132
7.19   Endocytosis in Animal Cells 150
11.8   Cell-Surface Transmembrane Receptors 226
12.7   Mitosis in an Animal Cell 247
13.8   Meiosis in an Animal Cell 272
16.23   Chromatin Packing in a Eukaryotic Chromosome 346
21.6   Genomics Research in Canada 470
24.3   Reproductive Barriers 532
25.7   The Origin of Mammals 557
27.16   Selected Major Groups of Bacteria 616
28.2   Protistan Diversity 628
29.4   Derived Traits of Land Plants 655
29.9   Bryophyte Diversity 662
29.14   Seedless Vascular Plant Diversity 667
30.7   Gymnosperm Diversity 679
30.17   Angiosperm Diversity 687
31.10   Fungal Diversity 700
33.3   Invertebrate Diversity 727
33.43   Insect Diversity 753
34.41   Mammalian Diversity 786
35.10   Examples of Differentiated Plant Cells 808
37.15   Unusual Nutritional Adaptations in Plants 863
38.3   Trends in the Evolution of Flowers 868
38.5   Flower Pollination 871
38.12   Fruit and Seed Dispersal 878

40.5   Structure and Function in Animal Tissues 924
41.5   Four Main Feeding Mechanisms of Animals 949
44.13   The Mammalian Excretory System 1036
46.12   Human Gametogenesis 1080
49.11   The Organization of the Human Brain 1146
50.10   The Structure of the Human Ear 1168
50.18   The Structure of the Human Eye 1174
50.31   The Regulation of Skeletal Muscle Contraction 1185
52.2   The Scope of Ecological Research 1226
52.3   Global Climate Patterns 1227
52.11   Terrestrial Biomes 1234
52.14   Aquatic Biomes 1240
53.17   Mechanisms of Density-Dependent Regulation 1264
55.13   Water and Nutrient Cycling 1310
55.18   Restoration Ecology Worldwide 1316
56.27   Climate Change 1339

Inquiry Figures

1.28   Does camouflage affect predation rates on two populations of mice? 22
4.2   Can organic molecules form under conditions estimated to simulate those on the early Earth? 64
5.22   What can the 3-D shape of the enzyme RNA polymerase II tell us about its function? 92
7.4   Do membrane proteins move? 138
10.10   Which wavelengths of light are most effective in driving photosynthesis? 205
12.9   At which end do kinetochore microtubules shorten during anaphase? 250
12.14   Do molecular signals in the cytoplasm regulate the cell cycle? 254
14.3   When F_1 hybrid pea plants self- or cross-pollinate, which traits appear in the F_2 generation? 283
14.8   Do the alleles for one character assort into gametes dependently or independently of the alleles for a different character? 288
15.4   In a cross between a wild-type female fruit fly and a mutant white-eyed male, what colour eyes will the F_1 and F_2 offspring have? 310
15.9   How does linkage between two genes affect inheritance of characters? 315
16.2   Can a genetic trait be transferred between different bacterial strains? 330
16.4   Is protein or DNA the genetic material of phage T2? 331
16.11   Does DNA replication follow the conservative, semiconservative, or dispersive model? 337
17.2   Do individual genes specify the enzymes that function in a biochemical pathway? 354
18.22   Could Bicoid be a morphogen that determines the anterior end of a fruit fly? 403

19.3   What causes tobacco mosaic disease? *416*

20.16   Can the nucleus from a differentiated animal cell direct development of an organism? *449*

20.22   Can a fully differentiated human cell be "deprogrammed" to become a stem cell? *453*

21.18   What is the function of a gene (*FOXP2*) that is rapidly evolving in the human lineage? *483*

22.13   Can a change in a population's food source result in evolution by natural selection? *501*

23.15   Do females select mates based on traits indicative of "good genes"? *525*

24.7   Can divergence of allopatric populations lead to reproductive isolation? *536*

24.11   Does sexual selection in cichlids result in reproductive isolation? *540*

24.18   How does hybridization lead to speciation in sunflowers? *546*

25.27   What causes the loss of spines in lake stickleback fish? *573*

27.10   Can prokaryotes evolve rapidly in response to environmental change? *609*

28.25   What is the root of the eukaryotic tree? *645*

29.8   Do animals facilitate fertilization in mosses? *661*

31.20   Do endophytes benefit a woody plant? *706*

33.30   Did the arthropod body plan result from new *Hox* genes? *747*

34.50   Did gene flow occur between Neanderthals and humans? *795*

36.18   Does phloem sap contain more sugar near sources than sinks? *845*

37.9   How variable are the compositions of bacterial communities inside and outside of roots? *858*

37.14   Can soil bacteria make plants more resistant to a stressful environment? *862*

39.5   What part of a grass coleoptile senses light, and how is the signal transmitted? *893*

39.6   What causes polar movement of auxin from shoot tip to base? *894*

39.16   How does the order of red and far-red illumination affect seed germination? *903*

40.15   How does thermal history affect thermal tolerance? *935*

40.20   What happens to the circadian clock during hibernation? *940*

41.2   What do polar bears eat? *945*

42.5   Temperature adaptation in salmon *971*

42.30   Mammoth hemoglobin is less sensitive to changes in temperature *995*

43.5   Can a single antimicrobial peptide protect fruit flies against infection? *1002*

44.8   Fishes living in alkaline lakes switch from ammonia to urea as their nitrogenous waste *1031*

44.21   Can aquaporin mutations cause diabetes? *1044*

46.9   Why is sperm usage biased when female fruit flies mate twice? *1076*

47.4   Does the distribution of Ca^{2+} in an egg correlate with formation of the fertilization envelope? *1098*

47.23   How does distribution of the grey crescent affect the developmental potential of the first two daughter cells? *1114*

47.24   Can the dorsal lip of the blastopore induce cells in another part of the amphibian embryo to change their developmental fate? *1115*

47.26   What role does the zone of polarizing activity (ZPA) play in limb pattern formation in vertebrates? *1116*

48.16   Can a damaged neuron reform synaptic connections? *1132*

50.15   How do monarch butterflies know which way to fly? *1172*

50.24   How do mammals detect different tastes? *1180*

51.8   Does a digger wasp use landmarks to find her nest? *1203*

51.24   Are differences in migratory orientation within a species genetically determined? *1215*

52.7   Will the distribution of sugar maple "keep up" with global warming? *1230*

53.13   Do common eiders "pay" for raising many offspring? *1261*

53.20   The sensitive snowshoe hare: Does stress from predators affect reproduction? *1266*

54.3   Can a species' niche be influenced by interspecific competition? *1275*

54.19   Is *Pisaster ochraceus* a keystone predator? *1287*

54.30   How does species richness relate to area? *1294*

55.7   Which nutrient limits phytoplankton production along the coast of Long Island? *1305*

55.14   How does temperature influence decomposition rates in Canadian soils? *1312*

56.8   Can we slow species invasions? *1325*

56.12   What caused the near-extirpation of the Illinois greater prairie chicken population? *1328*

Research Method Figures

6.4   Cell Fractionation *107*

10.9   Determining an Absorption Spectrum *204*

13.3   Preparing a Karyotype *268*

14.2   Crossing Pea Plants *282*

14.7   The Testcross *287*

15.11   Constructing a Linkage Map *319*

20.3   Dideoxy Chain Termination Method for Sequencing DNA *435*

20.8   The Polymerase Chain Reaction (PCR) *440*

20.12   RT-PCR Analysis of the Expression of Single Genes *444*

26.13   Applying Parsimony to a Problem in Molecular Systematics *591*

26.16   Using a Molecular Marker for Universal Species Identification *594*

35.21   Using Dendrochronology to Study Climate *817*

35.25   Using the Ti Plasmid to Produce Transgenic Plants *820*

37.7   Hydroponic Culture *854*

48.8   Intracellular Recording *1126*

53.2   Determining Population Size Using the Mark-Recapture Method *1251*

54.17   Using Traditional Ecological Knowledge to Study the Winter Ecology of Arctic Foxes *1286*

55.5   Determining Primary Production with Satellites *1303*

Impact Figures

3.13   The Threat of Ocean Acidification to Marine Life *60*

9.14   What Happens When One of the Proteins Involved in Oxidative Phosphorylation Doesn't Function Properly? *186*

10.3   Alternative Fuels from Plants and Algae *199*

12.21   The International Cancer Genome Consortium (ICGC) *260*

14.19   Prenatal Genetic Testing *301*

15.13   Chromosome 7 Decoded *320*

16.22   The Ticking Telomere Clock *345*

16.24   Painting Chromosomes *348*

17.26   Mutation-Specific Disease Treatment *375*

18.28   Analyzing the Genomic Evolution of Breast Cancer *409*

19.11   Sequencing the SARS Genome *427*

20.19   Stem Cells: A Canadian Discovery *451*

20.23   Inducing stem cell growth to treat disease *454*

22.14   The Rise of MRSA *502*

25.18   Pinpointing the End-Permian Mass Extinction *567*

27.20   The Human Microbiome and Health *620*

28.17   Will the Study of Protist Diversity Lead to a Treatment for Malaria? *639*

28.31   Marine Protists in a Warmer World *649*

29.15   The First Forests Were Composed of Seedless Vascular Plants That Eventually Became Coal *668*

30.18   Modern Agriculture and Honeybee Colony Losses *688*

31.25   Demise of North American, Cave-Hibernating Bats *709*

32.7   The Burgess Shale and *Anomalocaris canadensis* *717*

33.22   Invertebrates: Loss of biodiversity *742*

34.20   Discovery of a "Fishapod": *Tiktaalik* *772*

38.19   Cellulosic Biofuels *884*

43.16   Discovery of Dendritic Cells *1011*

45.13   Discovery and Use of Purified Insulin *1057*

46.4   Global Warming and Arctic Mammals *1072*

49.21   What regions of the brain control short-term memory? *1155*

52.17   Range Expansion: The Adaptable Coyote *1245*

54.23   Overfishing and Trophic Cascades in the Sea *1288*

54.32   Lyme Disease Dynamics—Understanding Ecological Complexity *1296*

55.8   Lake Erie—A Near Death Experience *1306*

55.16   Can this ecosystem be restored? *1314*

Interviews

UNIT 1

THE CHEMISTRY OF LIFE 29

David Wishart
Departments of Biological
Sciences and Computing
Science,
University of Alberta

UNIT 2

THE CELL 101

Helga Guderley
Department of Biology,
Université Laval

UNIT 3

GENETICS 263

Charlie Boone
Department of Molecular
Genetics,
University of Toronto

UNIT 4

MECHANISMS OF EVOLUTION 489

Hans Larsson
Redpath Museum,
McGill University

UNIT 5

THE EVOLUTIONARY HISTORY OF BIOLOGICAL DIVERSITY 579

Patrick Keeling
Department of Botany,
University of British
Columbia

UNIT 6

PLANT FORM AND FUNCTION 799

Mark Belmonte
Department of Biology,
University of Manitoba

UNIT 7

ANIMAL FORM AND FUNCTION 917

Suzie Currie
Department of Biology,
Mount Allison University

UNIT 8

ECOLOGY 1221

Verena Tunnicliffe
School of Earth and Ocean
Sciences,
University of Victoria

Acknowledgments

The authors wish to express their gratitude to the global community of instructors, researchers, students, and publishing professionals who have contributed to this edition.

As authors of this text, we are mindful of the daunting challenge of keeping up to date in all areas of our rapidly expanding subject. We are grateful to the many scientists who helped shape this text by discussing their research fields with us, answering specific questions in their areas of expertise, and sharing their ideas about biology education. We are especially grateful to the following, listed alphabetically: Monika Abedin, John Archibald, Chris Austin, Kristian Axelsen, Jamie Bascom, Ethan Bier, Jorg Bohlmann, Barbara Bowman, Daniel Boyce, Jean DeSaix, Amy Dobberteen, Graham Forbes, Ira Greenbaum, Ken Halanych, Robert Hebbel, Erin Irish, Duncan Irschick, Azarias Karamanlidis, Patrick Keeling, Nikos Kyrpides, Teri Liegler, Gene Likens, Tom Owens, Kevin Peterson, Michael Pollock, Amy Rappaport, Andrew Roger, Andrew Roth, Andrew Schaffner, Thomas Schneider, Alastair Simpson, Doug Soltis, Pamela Soltis, Anna Thanukos, Elisabeth Wade, Phillip Zamore, and Christine Zardecki. In addition, the biologists listed on page xlv provided detailed reviews, helping us ensure the text's scientific accuracy and improve its pedagogical effectiveness. We thank Marty Taylor, author of the Study Guide, for her many contributions to the accuracy, clarity, and consistency of the text; and we thank Carolyn Wetzel, Ruth Buskirk, Joan Sharp, Jennifer Yeh, and Charlene D'Avanzo for their contributions to the Scientific Skills Exercises.

Thanks also to the other professors and students, from all over the world, who contacted the authors directly with useful suggestions. We alone bear the responsibility for any errors that remain, but the dedication of our consultants, reviewers, and other correspondents makes us confident in the accuracy and effectiveness of this text.

Interviews with prominent scientists have been a hallmark of CAMPBELL BIOLOGY since its inception, and conducting these interviews was again one of the great pleasures of revising the book. To open the eight units of this edition, we are proud to include interviews with David Wishart, Helga Guderley, Charlie Boone, Hans Larsson, Patrick Keeling, Mark Belmonte, Suzie Currie, and Verena Tunnicliffe.

This Second Canadian Edition of CAMPBELL BIOLOGY is the result of the combined efforts of many talented and hardworking people. We wish to extend our heartfelt appreciation to the authors of the U.S. Edition: Jane Reece, Lisa Urry, Michael Cain, Peter Minorsky, Steve Wasserman, and Robert Jackson.

CAMPBELL BIOLOGY, Second Canadian Edition, results from an unusually strong synergy between a team of scientists and a team of publishing professionals. Our editorial team at Pearson Canada demonstrated unmatched talents, commitment, and pedagogical insights. Claudine O'Donnell, Editorial Director, Cathleen Sullivan, Executive Acquisitions Editor, Kimberly Teska, Senior Marketing Manager, Kamilah Reid-Burrell, Program Manager, Jennifer Murray, Developmental Editor, Ben Zaporozan, Digital Process Content Editor, Jessica Hellen, Senior Project Manager, Susan Bindernagel, Copyeditor, Anthony Leung, Senior Designer, Sarah Horsfall, Project Manager, Permissions.

We likewise appreciate the commitment of the biologists who conducted a meticulous quality check of the textbook's pages. We thank Mike Weber, Michael Durrant, Reehan Mirza, Rachel Krause, Agata Becalska, Sanja-Hinic Frlog, and Sean Modesto. Their subject matter expertise and attention to detail helped the publisher maintain CAMPBELL BIOLOGY's tradition of accuracy.

The Pearson sales team, which represents CAMPBELL BIOLOGY on campus, is an essential link to the users of the text. They tell us what you like and don't like about the text, communicate the features of the text, and provide prompt service. We thank them for their hard work and professionalism. For representing our text to our international audience, we thank our sales and marketing partners throughout the world. They are all strong allies in biology education.

Finally, we wish to thank our families and friends for their encouragement and patience throughout this long project. Our special thanks to Adrian, Lucas, Anna, and Emmie (F.R.); Dax and Dana (D.D.); Daniel (S.W.); and Janice, Eleanor, and Amelia (K.S.).

Fiona Rawle, Dion Durnford,
Chris Moyes, Sandra Walde, and Kevin Scott

Reviewers

Canadian Edition Reviewers

Ron Aiken, *Mount Allison University*
Eric Alcorn, *Acadia University*
Edward William Awad, *Vanier College*
Greg Beaulieu, *University of Victoria*
Todd Bishop, *Dalhousie University*
Richard Calve, *Dawson College*
Bruce Campbell, *Okanagan College*
Priscila Castillo-Ruiz, *Champlain Regional College*
Dora Cavallo-Medved, *University of Windsor*
Brett Couch, *University of British Columbia*
David Creasey, *University of Victoria*
Leslie Dafoe, *Sault College of Applied Arts & Technology*
Mrinal Das, *Grant MacEwan University*
Kathy Davies, *Grant MacEwan University*
Vivian Dayeh, *University of Waterloo*
Rajinder Dhindsa, *McGill University*
Heidi Engelhardt, *University of Waterloo*
Kerri Finlay, *University of Regina*
Kevin Friesen, *Grant MacEwan University*
Sheryl Gares, *University of Alberta*
Chris Garside, *University of Toronto*
Sharon Gillies, *University of the Fraser Valley*
Lawrence Hale, *University of Prince Edward Island*
Jonathan Horsman, *Medicine Hat College*
Anna Hicks, *Memorial University*
William Huddleston, *University of Calgary*
Mariola Maja Janowicz, *Concordia University, College of Alberta*
Joan Kearvell, *Champlain Regional College*
Carson Keever, *Kwantlen Polytechnic University*
Blaine Legaree, *Keyano College*

Vett Lloyd, *Mount Allison University*
Elaine Dodge Lynch, *Memorial University*
Sharon Mansiere, *Okanagan College*
Paul McMillan, *Capilano University*
Ann Meitz, *Capilano University*
Reehan Mirza, *Nipissing University*
Ivona Mladenovic, *Simon Fraser University*
Betty Mosher, *College of the Rockies*
Michael Mucz, *University of Alberta*
Kirsten Muller, *University of Waterloo*
Ken Naumann, *Langara College*
Tracy O'Connor, *Mount Royal University*
Mary Olaveson, *University of Toronto Scarborough*
Robin Owen, *Mount Royal University*
William Paton, *Brandon University*
Carol Pollock, *University of British Columbia*
Melanie Rathburn, *Mount Royal University*
Scott Reid, *University of British Columbia*
Heidi Richter, *University of the Fraser Valley*
Tatiana Rogasevskaia, *Mount Royal University*
Owen Rowland, *Carleton University*
Eleftherios (Terry) Saropoulos, *Vanier College*
Ross Shaw, *Grant MacEwan University*
Andrew Taylor, *Keyano College*
Sophia Ushinsky, *Concordia University*
Patrick von Aderkas, *University of Victoria*
Richard Walker, *University of Calgary*
Michael Weber, *Carleton University*
Frank Williams, *Langara College*
Tony Williams, *Simon Fraser University*
Sherry Wilson, *Kwantlen Polytechnic University*
Jonathan Wright, *Dalhousie University*

1

Evolution, the Themes of Biology, and Scientific Inquiry

▲ Figure 1.1 **How is the lodgepole pine adapted to its environment?**

KEY CONCEPTS

1.1 The study of life reveals common themes

1.2 The Core Theme: Evolution accounts for the unity and diversity of life

1.3 In studying nature, scientists make observations and form and test hypotheses

1.4 Science benefits from a cooperative approach and diverse viewpoints

Inquiring About Life

The lodgepole pine (*Pinus contorta*, subspecies *latifolia*) tree is found extensively throughout western North America. This tree's male cones, shown in Figure 1.1, produce massive amounts of pollen, which travel by air to the female cones, also called seed cones (Figure 1.2). Interestingly, some lodgepole pines produce seed cones that are adapted to fire and are sealed with a hard resin. The mature cones will only open if they are exposed to temperatures greater than 45°C, causing the resin bond to melt. The subsequent seed release allows for rapid tree regrowth after a fire, and could be an evolutionary adaptation to forest fires. Currently, lodgepole pine forests are experiencing extensive tree mortality due to mountain pine beetle outbreaks, which you'll learn more about in Chapters 31 and 54.

An organism's adaptations to its environment, such as adaptations for seed survival and dispersal, are the result of **evolution**, the process of change over time that has resulted in the astounding array of organisms found on Earth. Evolution is the fundamental principle of biology; it is the core theme of this text.

Although biologists know a great deal about life on Earth, many mysteries remain. Posing questions about the living world and seeking answers through scientific inquiry are the central activities of **biology**, the scientific study of life.

▲ Release of pollen by a lodgepole pine.

1

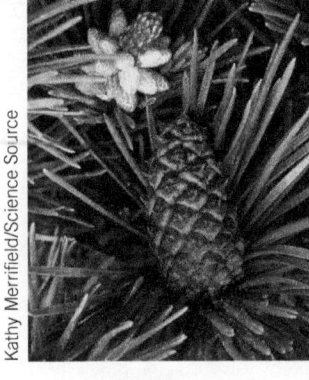
Kathy Merrifield/Science Source

◀ Figure 1.2 **Lodgepole pine pollen cones (above) and seed cone (below).**

Biologists' questions can be ambitious. They may ask how a dog or a tree develops from a single cell, how the human mind works, or how the different forms of life in a forest interact. When questions occur to you as you observe the natural world, you are thinking like a biologist. More than anything else, biology is a quest, an ongoing inquiry about the nature of life.

At the most fundamental level, we may ask, "What is life?" Even a child realizes that a dog or a plant is alive, while a rock or a car is not. Yet the phenomenon we call life defies a simple, one-sentence definition. We recognize life by what living things do. **Figure 1.3** highlights some of the properties and processes we associate with life.

While limited to a handful of images, Figure 1.3 reminds us that the living world is wondrously varied. How do

▼ **Order.** This close-up of a sunflower illustrates the highly ordered structure that characterizes life.

R. Dirscherl/OceanPhoto/Frank Lane Picture Agency Limited

Tim Gainey/Alamy Stock Photo

▲ **Evolutionary adaptation.** The appearance of this pygmy seahorse camouflages the animal in its environment. Such adaptations evolve over many generations by the reproductive success of those individuals with heritable traits that are best suited to their environments.

Henry Ausloos/Photononstop/Getty Images

▲ **Regulation.** The regulation of blood flow through the blood vessels of this white-tailed jackrabbit's ears helps maintain a constant body temperature by adjusting heat exchange with the surrounding air.

ondrejprosicky/Fotolia

▲ **Energy processing.** This hummingbird obtains fuel in the form of nectar from flowers. The hummingbird will use chemical energy stored in its food to power flight and other work.

▼ **Reproduction.** Organisms (living things) reproduce their own kind. Here, two baby polar bear cubs rest by their mother.

Anup Shah/Getty Images

▶ **Response to the environment.** Venus fly trap with trapped insect prey.

Nature Production/Nature Picture Library

Francois Gohier/Science Source

▲ **Growth and development.** Inherited information carried by genes controls the pattern of growth and development of organisms, such as this Nile crocodile.

▲ Figure 1.3 **Some properties of life.**

biologists make sense of this diversity and complexity? This opening chapter sets up a framework for answering this question. The first part of the chapter provides a panoramic view of the biological "landscape," organized around some unifying themes. We then focus on biology's core theme, evolution, which accounts for life's unity and diversity. Next, we look at scientific inquiry—how scientists ask and attempt to answer questions about the natural world. Finally, we address the culture of science and its effects on society.

CONCEPT 1.1

The study of life reveals common themes

Biology is a subject of enormous scope, and exciting new biological discoveries are being made every day. How can you organize into a comprehensible framework all the information you'll encounter as you study biology? Focusing on a few big ideas—ways of thinking about life that will still hold true decades from now—will help. Here, we'll describe five unifying themes to serve as touchstones as you proceed through this text:

- Organization
- Information
- Energy and Matter
- Interactions
- Evolution

Theme: New Properties Emerge at Successive Levels of Biological Organization

ORGANIZATION The study of life extends from the microscopic scale of the molecules and cells that make up organisms to the global scale of the entire living planet. As biologists, we can divide this enormous range into different levels of biological organization.

Imagine zooming in from space to take a closer and closer look at life on Earth. It is spring in Ontario, Canada, and our destination is a local forest, where we will eventually narrow our focus down to the molecules that make up a maple leaf. **Figure 1.4** narrates this journey into life, as the numbers guide you through photographs illustrating the hierarchy of biological organization.

Zooming in at ever-finer resolution illustrates an approach called *reductionism*, which reduces complex systems to simpler components that are more manageable to study. Reductionism is a powerful strategy in biology. For example, by studying the molecular structure of DNA that had been extracted from cells, James Watson and Francis

Crick inferred the chemical basis of biological inheritance. Although it has propelled many major discoveries, reductionism provides a necessarily incomplete view of life on Earth, as we'll discuss next.

Emergent Properties

Let's reexamine Figure 1.4, beginning this time at the molecular level and then zooming out. Viewed this way, we see that at each level, novel properties emerge that are absent from the preceding level. These **emergent properties** are due to the arrangement and interactions of parts as complexity increases. For example, although photosynthesis occurs in an intact chloroplast, it will not take place in a disorganized test-tube mixture of chlorophyll and other chloroplast molecules. The coordinated processes of photosynthesis require a specific organization of these molecules in the chloroplast. Isolated components of living systems, serving as the objects of study in a reductionist approach to biology, lack a number of significant properties that emerge at higher levels of organization.

Emergent properties are not unique to life. A box of bicycle parts won't transport you anywhere, but if they are arranged in a certain way, you can pedal to your chosen destination. Compared to such nonliving examples, furthermore, biological systems are far more complex, making the emergent properties of life especially challenging to study.

To explore emergent properties more fully, biologists today complement reductionism with **systems biology**, the exploration of a biological system by analyzing the interactions among its parts. In this context, a single leaf cell can be considered a system, as can a frog, an ant colony, or a desert ecosystem. By examining and modelling the dynamic behaviour of an integrated network of components, systems biology enables us to pose new kinds of questions. For example, we can ask how a drug that lowers blood pressure affects the functioning of organs throughout the human body. At a larger scale, how does a gradual increase in atmospheric carbon dioxide alter ecosystems and the entire biosphere? Systems biology can be used to study life at all levels.

Structure and Function

At each level of the biological hierarchy, we find a correlation of structure and function. Consider the leaf shown in Figure 1.4: Its thin, flat shape maximizes the capture of sunlight by chloroplasts. More generally, analyzing a biological structure gives us clues about what it does and how it works. Conversely, knowing the function of something provides insight into its structure and organization. Many examples from the animal kingdom show a correlation between structure and function. For example, the hummingbird's anatomy allows the wings to rotate at the shoulder, so hummingbirds have the ability, unique among birds, to fly backward or hover in place. While hovering, the birds can extend their long, slender beaks into flowers and feed on nectar. The elegant match of form and function in the structures of life is explained by natural selection, which we'll explore shortly.

The Cell: An Organism's Basic Unit of Structure and Function

In life's structural hierarchy, the cell is the smallest unit of organization that can perform all required activities. In fact, the actions of organisms are all based on the functions of cells. For instance, the movement of your eyes as you read this sentence results from the activities of muscle and nerve cells. Even a

▼ Figure 1.4

Exploring Levels of Biological Organization

WorldSat International Inc./Science Source

◄ 1 The Biosphere

Even from space, we can see signs of Earth's life—in the green mosaic of the forests, for example. We can also see the scale of the entire biosphere, which consists of all life on Earth and all the places where life exists: most regions of land, most bodies of water, the atmosphere to an altitude of several kilometres, and even sediments far below the ocean floor.

Bill Brooks/Alamy Stock Photo

◄ 2 Ecosystems

Our first scale change brings us to a North American forest with many deciduous trees (trees that lose their leaves and grow new ones each year). A deciduous forest is an example of an ecosystem, as are grasslands, deserts, and coral reefs. An ecosystem consists of all the living things in a particular area, along with all the nonliving components of the environment with which life interacts, such as soil, water, atmospheric gases, and light.

► 3 Communities

The array of organisms inhabiting a particular ecosystem is called a biological community. The community in our forest ecosystem includes many kinds of trees and other plants, various animals, mushrooms and other fungi, and enormous numbers of diverse microorganisms, which are living forms, such as bacteria, that are too small to see without a microscope. Each of these forms of life is called a *species*.

Linda Freshwaters Arndt/Alamy Stock Photo

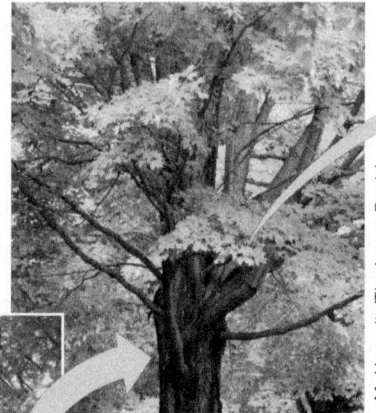

Ross M. Horowitz/The Image Bank/ Getty Images

► 4 Populations

A population consists of all the individuals of a species living within the bounds of a specified area. For example, our forest includes a population of sugar maple trees and a population of white-tailed deer. A community is therefore the set of populations that inhabit a particular area.

Michael Orton/Photographer's Choice/Getty Images

▲ 5 Organisms

Individual living things are called organisms. Each of the maple trees and other plants in the forest is an organism, and so is each deer, frog, beetle, and other forest animals. The soil teems with microorganisms such as bacteria.

process that occurs on a global scale, such as the recycling of carbon atoms, is the product of cellular functions, including the photosynthetic activity of chloroplasts in leaf cells.

All cells share certain characteristics. For instance, every cell is enclosed by a membrane that regulates the passage of materials between the cell and its surroundings.

Nevertheless, we recognize two main forms of cells: prokaryotic and eukaryotic. The cells of two groups of single-celled microorganisms—bacteria (singular, *bacterium*) and archaea (singular, *archaean*)—are prokaryotic. All other forms of life, including plants and animals, are composed of eukaryotic cells.

▼ 6 Organs and Organ Systems

The structural hierarchy of life continues to unfold as we explore the architecture of more complex organisms. A maple leaf is an example of an organ, a body part that carries out a particular function in the body. Stems and roots are the other major organs of plants. The organs of complex animals and plants are organized into organ systems, each a team of organs that cooperate in a larger function. Organs consist of multiple tissues.

▶ 10 Molecules

Our last scale change drops us into a chloroplast for a view of life at the molecular level. A molecule is a chemical structure consisting of two or more units called atoms, represented as balls in this computer graphic of a chlorophyll molecule. Chlorophyll is the pigment molecule that makes a maple leaf green, and it absorbs sunlight during photosynthesis. Within each chloroplast, millions of chlorophyll molecules are organized into systems that convert light energy to the chemical energy of food.

Atoms

Chlorophyll molecule

▶ 9 Organelles

Chloroplasts are examples of organelles, the various functional components present in cells. This image, taken by a powerful microscope, shows a single chloroplast.

Chloroplast

1 μm

50 μm

Cell 10 μm

◀ 7 Tissues

Viewing the tissues of a leaf requires a microscope. Each tissue is a group of cells that work together, performing a specialized function. The leaf shown here has been cut on an angle. The honeycombed tissue in the interior of the leaf (left side of photo) is the main location of photosynthesis, the process that converts light energy to the chemical energy of sugar. The jigsaw puzzle–like "skin" on the surface of the leaf is a tissue called epidermis (right side of photo). The pores through the epidermis allow entry of the gas CO_2, a raw material for sugar production.

▲ 8 Cells

The cell is life's fundamental unit of structure and function. Some organisms are single cells, while others are multicellular. A single cell performs all the functions of life, while a multicellular organism has a division of labour among specialized cells. Here we see a magnified view of cells in a leaf tissue. One cell is about 40 micrometres (μm) across—about 500 of them would reach across a small coin. As tiny as these cells are, you can see that each contains numerous green structures called chloroplasts, which are responsible for photosynthesis.

Eukaryotic cell

Prokaryotic cell

Membrane

Cytoplasm

DNA (no nucleus)

Membrane

Nucleus (membrane-enclosed)

Membrane-enclosed organelles

DNA (throughout nucleus)

1 μm

S. C. Holt/Biological Photo Service

Steve Gschmeissner/Science Source

▲ Figure 1.5 **Contrasting eukaryotic and prokaryotic cells in size and complexity.**

A **eukaryotic cell** contains membrane-enclosed organelles (Figure 1.5). Some organelles, such as the DNA-containing nucleus, are found in the cells of all eukaryotes; other organelles are specific to particular cell types. For example, the chloroplast in Figure 1.4 is an organelle found only in eukaryotic cells that carry out photosynthesis. In contrast to eukaryotic cells, a **prokaryotic cell** lacks a nucleus and other membrane-enclosed organelles. Another distinction is that prokaryotic cells are generally smaller than eukaryotic cells, as shown in Figure 1.5.

Theme: Life's Processes Involve the Expression and Transmission of Genetic Information

INFORMATION Within cells, structures called chromosomes contain genetic material in the form of **DNA (deoxyribonucleic acid)**. In cells that are preparing to divide, the chromosomes may be made visible using a dye that appears blue when bound to the DNA (Figure 1.6).

DNA, the Genetic Material

Each time a cell divides, the DNA is first replicated, or copied, and each of the two cellular offspring inherits a complete set of chromosomes, identical to that of the parent cell. Each chromosome contains one very long DNA molecule with hundreds or thousands of **genes**, each a stretch of DNA that is part of the chromosome. Transmitted from parents to offspring, genes are the units of inheritance. They encode the information necessary to build all of the molecules synthesized within a cell, which in turn

25 μm

Conly L. Rieder, Ph.D.

Conly L. Rieder, Ph.D.

▲ Figure 1.6 **A lung cell from a newt divides into two smaller cells that will grow and divide again.**

establish that cell's identity and function. Each of us began as a single cell stocked with DNA inherited from our parents. The replication of that DNA during each round of cell division transmitted copies of the DNA to what eventually became the trillions of cells of our body. As the cells grew and divided, the genetic information encoded by the DNA directed our development (Figure 1.7).

The molecular structure of DNA accounts for its ability to store information. A DNA molecule is made up of two long chains, called strands, arranged in a double helix. Each chain is made up of four kinds of chemical building blocks called nucleotides, abbreviated A, T, C, and G (Figure 1.8). The way DNA encodes information is analogous to how we arrange the letters of the alphabet into words and phrases with specific meanings. The word *rat*, for example, evokes a rodent; the words *tar* and *art*, which contain the same letters, mean very different things. We can think of nucleotides as a four-letter alphabet. Specific sequences of these four nucleotides encode the information in genes.

Nuclei containing DNA

Sperm cell

Egg cell

Fertilized egg with DNA from both parents

Embryo's cells with copies of inherited DNA

Offspring with traits inherited from both parents

Camille Tokerud/Getty Images

▲ Figure 1.7 **Inherited DNA directs development of an organism.**

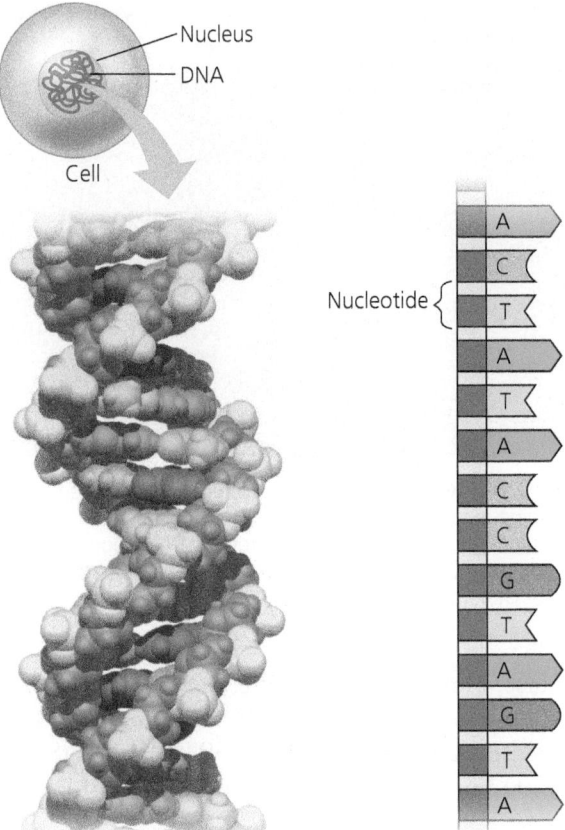

(a) DNA double helix. This model shows the atoms in a segment of DNA. Made up of two long chains (strands) of building blocks called nucleotides, a DNA molecule takes the three-dimensional form of a double helix.

(b) Single strand of DNA. These geometric shapes and letters are simple symbols for the nucleotides in a small section of one strand of a DNA molecule. Genetic information is encoded in specific sequences of the four types of nucleotides. Their names are abbreviated A, T, C, and G.

▲ Figure 1.8 **DNA: The genetic material.**

Many genes provide the blueprints for making proteins, which are the major players in building and maintaining the cell and carrying out its activities. For instance, a given bacterial gene may specify a particular protein (an enzyme) required to break down a certain sugar molecule, while a human gene may denote a different protein (an antibody) that helps fight off infection.

Genes control protein production indirectly, using a related molecule called ribonucleic acid (RNA) as an intermediary (Figure 1.9). The sequence of nucleotides along a gene is transcribed into RNA, which is then translated into a linked series of protein building blocks called amino acids. Together, this results in a specific protein with a unique shape and function. This entire process, by which the information in a gene directs the manufacture of a cellular product, is called **gene expression**.

In translating genes into proteins, all forms of life employ essentially the same genetic code: A particular sequence of nucleotides says the same thing in one organism as it does

(a) The lens of the eye (behind the pupil) is able to focus light because lens cells are tightly packed with transparent proteins called crystallin.

Lens cell

(b) How do lens cells make crystallin proteins?

The crystallin gene is a section of DNA in a chromosome.

Crystallin gene

DNA (part of the crystallin gene)

Using the information in the sequence of DNA nucleotides, the cell makes (transcribes) a specific RNA molecule called messenger RNA (mRNA).

TRANSCRIPTION

mRNA

The cell translates the information in the sequence of mRNA nucleotides to make a protein, a series of linked amino acids.

TRANSLATION

Chain of amino acids

PROTEIN FOLDING

Protein

The chain of amino acids folds into the specific shape of a crystallin protein. Crystallin proteins can then pack together and focus light, allowing the eye to see.

Crystallin protein

▲ Figure 1.9 **Gene expression: The transfer of information from a gene results in a functional protein.**

in another. Differences among organisms reflect differences among their nucleotide sequences rather than among their genetic codes. Comparing the sequences in several species for a gene that codes for a particular protein can provide valuable information both about the protein and about the relationship of the species to each other, as you will see.

In addition to RNA molecules that are translated into proteins, some RNAs in the cell carry out other important tasks. For example, we have known for decades that some types of RNA are actually components of the cellular machinery that manufactures proteins. Recently, scientists have discovered whole new classes of RNA that play other roles in the cell, such as regulating the functioning of protein-coding genes. All of these RNAs are specified by genes, and the production of these RNAs is also referred to as gene expression. By carrying the instructions for making proteins and RNAs and by replicating with each cell division, DNA ensures faithful inheritance of genetic information from generation to generation.

Genomics: Large-Scale Analysis of DNA Sequences

The entire "library" of genetic instructions that an organism inherits is called its **genome**. A typical human cell has two similar sets of chromosomes, and each set has approximately 3 billion nucleotide pairs of DNA. If the one-letter abbreviations for the nucleotides of one strand in a set were written in letters the size of those you are now reading, the genetic text would fill about 700 biology textbooks.

Since the early 1990s, the pace at which researchers can determine the sequence of a genome has accelerated at an almost unbelievable rate, enabled by a revolution in technology. The entire sequence of nucleotides in the human genome is now known, along with the genome sequences of many other organisms, including other animals and numerous plants, fungi, bacteria, and archaea. To make sense of the deluge of data from genome-sequencing projects and the growing catalogue of known gene functions, scientists are applying a systems biology approach at the cellular and molecular levels. Rather than investigating a single gene at a time, researchers study whole sets of genes in one or more species—an approach called **genomics**. Along similar lines, the term **proteomics** refers to the study of whole sets of proteins encoded by the genome (known as **proteomes**) and their interactions.

Three important research developments have made the genomic and proteomic approaches possible. One is "high-throughput" technology that can analyze many biological samples very rapidly (Figure 1.10). The second major development is **bioinformatics**, the use of computational tools to store, organize, and analyze the huge volume of data that results from high-throughput methods. The third development is the formation of interdisciplinary research teams—groups of diverse specialists that may include computer scientists, mathematicians, engineers, chemists, physicists,

▲ Figure 1.10 **Biology as an information science.** Automatic DNA-sequencing machines and abundant computing power make the sequencing of genomes possible. This robotic DNA-sequencing machine is selecting DNA fragments for sequencing at Canada's Michael Smith Genome Sciences Centre in British Columbia.

and, of course, biologists from a variety of fields. Researchers in such teams aim to learn how the activities of all the proteins and non-translated RNAs encoded by the DNA are coordinated in cells and in whole organisms.

Theme: Life Requires the Transfer and Transformation of Energy and Matter

ENERGY AND MATTER A fundamental characteristic of living organisms is their use of energy to carry out life's activities. Moving, growing, reproducing, and the various cellular activities of life are work, and work requires energy. The input of energy, primarily from the sun, and the transformation of energy from one form to another make life possible. A plant's leaves absorb sunlight, and chlorophyll molecules within the leaves convert the energy of sunlight to the chemical energy of food, such as sugars, produced during photosynthesis. The chemical energy in the food molecules is then passed along by plants and other photosynthetic organisms (**producers**) to consumers. **Consumers** are organisms, such as animals, that feed on producers and other consumers.

When an organism uses chemical energy to perform work, such as muscle cells moving or cells dividing, some of that energy is lost to the surroundings as heat. As a result, energy flows one way *through* an ecosystem, usually entering as light and exiting as heat. In contrast, chemicals are recycled *within* an ecosystem (Figure 1.11). Chemicals that a plant absorbs from the air or soil may be incorporated into the plant's body, and then passed to an animal that eats the plant. Eventually, these chemicals will be returned to the environment by decomposers, such as bacteria and fungi, that break down waste products, organic debris, and the bodies of dead organisms. The chemicals are then available to be taken up by plants again, thereby completing the cycle.

▶ Figure 1.11 **Energy flow and chemical cycling.** There is a one-way flow of energy in an ecosystem: During photosynthesis, plants convert energy from sunlight to chemical energy (stored in food molecules such as sugars), which is used by plants and other organisms to do work and is eventually lost from the ecosystem as heat. In contrast, chemicals cycle between organisms and the physical environment.

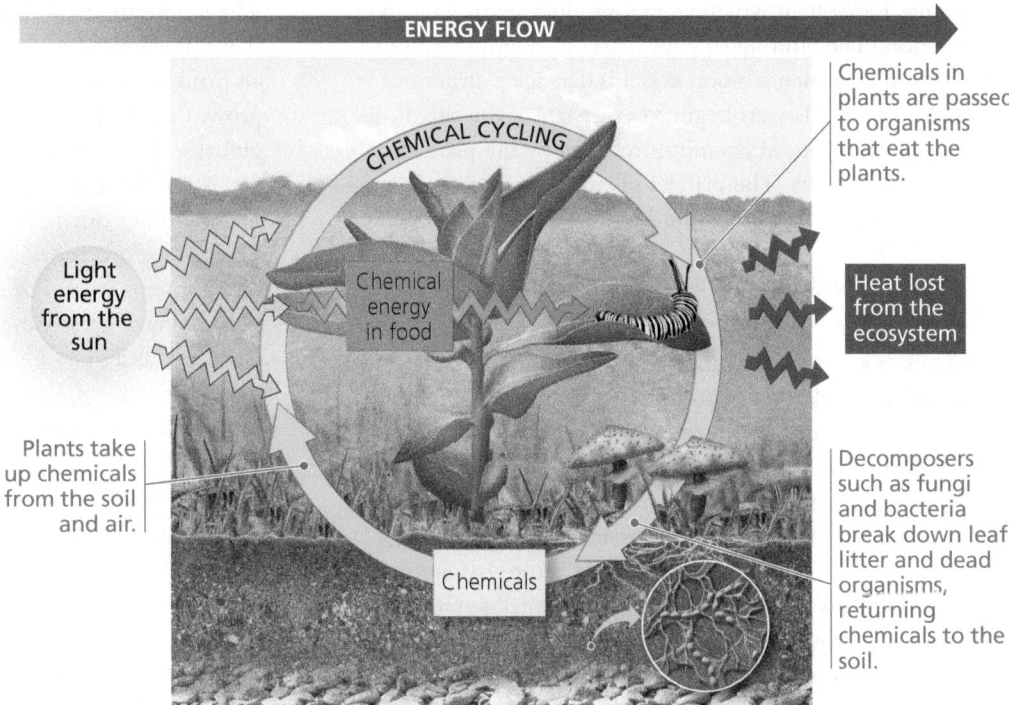

ENERGY FLOW

CHEMICAL CYCLING

Chemicals in plants are passed to organisms that eat the plants.

Light energy from the sun

Chemical energy in food

Heat lost from the ecosystem

Plants take up chemicals from the soil and air.

Chemicals

Decomposers such as fungi and bacteria break down leaf litter and dead organisms, returning chemicals to the soil.

Theme: From Molecules to Ecosystems, Interactions Are Important in Biological Systems

INTERACTIONS At any level of the biological hierarchy, interactions between the components of the system ensure smooth integration of all the parts, such that they function as a whole. This holds true equally well for molecules in a cell and the components of an ecosystem; we'll discuss both as examples.

Molecules: Interactions Within Organisms

At lower levels of organization, the interactions between components that make up living organisms—organs, tissues, cells, and molecules—are crucial to their smooth operation. Consider the regulation of blood sugar levels, for instance. Cells in the body must match the supply of fuel (sugar) to demand, regulating the opposing processes of sugar breakdown and storage. The key is the ability of many biological processes to self-regulate by a mechanism called feedback.

In **feedback regulation**, the output or product of a process regulates that very process. The most common form of regulation in living systems is *negative feedback*, a loop in which the response reduces the initial stimulus. As seen in the example of insulin signalling (Figure 1.12), after a meal the level of the sugar glucose in your blood rises, which stimulates cells of the pancreas to secrete insulin. Insulin, in turn, causes body cells to take up glucose, thus decreasing blood glucose levels. This eliminates the stimulus for insulin secretion, shutting off the pathway. Thus, the output of the process negatively regulates that process.

Though less common than processes regulated by negative feedback, there are also many biological processes regulated

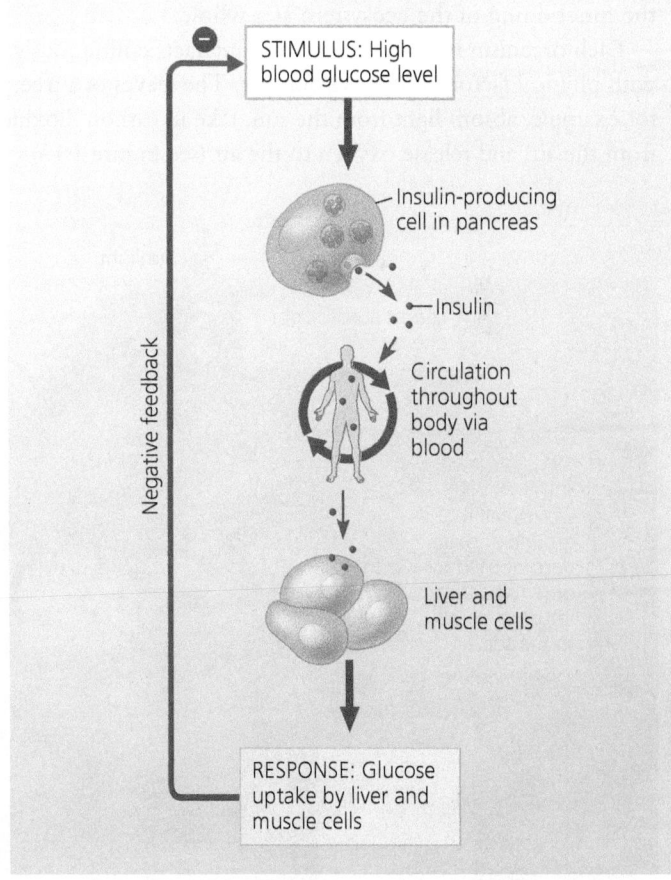

STIMULUS: High blood glucose level

Insulin-producing cell in pancreas

Insulin

Circulation throughout body via blood

Negative feedback

Liver and muscle cells

RESPONSE: Glucose uptake by liver and muscle cells

▲ Figure 1.12 **Feedback regulation.** The human body regulates the use and storage of glucose, a major cellular fuel derived from food. This figure shows negative feedback: The response (glucose uptake by cells) decreases the high glucose levels that provide the stimulus for insulin secretion, thus negatively regulating the process.

by *positive feedback*, in which an end product *speeds up* its own production. The clotting of your blood in response to injury is an example. When a blood vessel is damaged, structures in the blood called platelets begin to aggregate at the site. Positive feedback occurs as chemicals released by the platelets attract *more* platelets. The platelet pileup then initiates a complex process that seals the wound with a clot.

Ecosystems: An Organism's Interactions with Other Organisms and the Physical Environment

Feedback is a regulatory motif common to life at all levels, from the molecular level through ecosystems and the biosphere. At the ecosystem level, every organism interacts with other organisms. For instance, an acacia tree interacts with soil microorganisms associated with its roots, insects that live on it, and animals that eat its leaves and fruit (Figure 1.13). Interactions between organisms include those that are mutually beneficial (as when "cleaner fish" eat small parasites on a turtle), and those in which one species benefits and the other is harmed (as when a lion kills and eats a zebra). In some interactions between species, both are harmed—for example, when two plants compete for a soil resource that is in short supply. Interactions among organisms help regulate the functioning of the ecosystem as a whole.

Each organism in an ecosystem also interacts continuously with physical factors in its environment. The leaves of a tree, for example, absorb light from the sun, take in carbon dioxide from the air, and release oxygen to the air (see Figure 1.13).

The environment is also affected by the organisms living there. For instance, in addition to taking up water and minerals from the soil, the roots of a plant break up rocks as they grow, thereby contributing to the formation of soil. On a global scale, plants and other photosynthetic organisms have generated all the oxygen in the atmosphere.

Like other organisms, we humans interact with our environment. Unfortunately, our interactions sometimes have dire consequences. For example, over the past 150 years, humans have greatly increased the burning of fossil fuels (coal, oil, and gas). This practice releases large amounts of carbon dioxide (CO_2) and other gases into the atmosphere, causing heat to be trapped close to the Earth's surface (see Figure 56.27). Scientists calculate that the CO_2 that human activities have added to the atmosphere has increased the average temperature of the planet by about 1°C since 1900. At the current rates that CO_2 and other gases are being added to the atmosphere, global models predict an additional rise of at least 3°C before the end of this century.

This ongoing global warming is a major aspect of **climate change**, a directional change to the global climate that lasts for three decades or more (as opposed to short-term changes in the weather). But global warming is not the only way the climate is changing: wind and precipitation patterns are also shifting, and extreme weather events such as storms and droughts are occurring more often. Climate change has already affected organisms and their habitats all over the planet. For example, polar bears have lost much of the ice platform from which they hunt, leading to food shortages and increased mortality rates. As habitats deteriorate, hundreds of plant and animal species are shifting their ranges to more suitable locations—but for some, there is insufficient suitable habitat, or they may not be able to migrate quickly enough. As a result, the populations of many species are shrinking in size or even disappearing. This trend can result in extinction, the permanent loss of a species. As we'll discuss in greater detail in Concept 56.4, the consequences of these changes for humans and other organisms may be profound.

Take, for example, the ivory gull (*Pagophila eburnean*), a small seabird that nests in Nunavut (Figure 1.14). Its population numbers have decreased by more than 80% over the last 30 years. Because the ivory gull is associated year-round with Arctic pack ice, scientists suspect climate change could be a key contributor to this population decline, along with illegal hunting by humans and natural predation by Arctic

Sunlight

Leaves absorb light energy from the sun.

Leaves take in carbon dioxide from the air and release oxygen.

CO_2

O_2

Leaves fall to the ground and are decomposed by organisms that return minerals to the soil.

Water and minerals in the soil are taken up by the tree through its roots.

Animals eat leaves and fruit from the tree, returning nutrients and minerals to the soil in their waste products.

James Balog/Aurora/Getty Images

▲ Figure 1.13 **Interactions of an African acacia tree with other organisms and the physical environment.**

▲ Figure 1.14 **An ivory gull (*Pagophila eburnea*).** The population numbers of ivory gulls have decreased by over 80% in the last 30 years. The ivory gull is protected under Canada's *Species at Risk Act.*

foxes. Researchers also suspect that climate change is playing a role in mountain pine beetle (*Dendroctonus ponderosae*) outbreaks that have damaged large areas of pine forest in British Columbia and Alberta (see Figure 56.27, Exploring Climate Change). Warmer weather is more conducive to mountain pine beetle survival, and insect outbreaks in general are expected to become more common with global warming.

Having considered four of the unifying themes that run through this text (organization, information, energy and matter, and interactions), let's now turn to evolution. There is consensus among biologists that evolution is the core theme of biology, and it is discussed in detail in the next section.

CONCEPT CHECK 1.1

1. For each biological level in Figure 1.4, write a sentence that includes components from the previous (lower) level of biological organization, for example: "A community consists of populations of the various species inhabiting a certain area."

2. Identify the theme or themes exemplified by (a) the sharp quills of a porcupine, (b) the development of a multicellular organism from a single fertilized egg, and (c) a hummingbird using sugar to power its flight.

3. **WHAT IF?** For each theme discussed in this section, give an example not mentioned in the text.

For suggested answers, see Appendix A.

CONCEPT 1.2

The Core Theme: Evolution accounts for the unity and diversity of life

EVOLUTION Evolution is the one idea that makes logical sense of everything we know about living organisms. As the fossil record clearly shows, life has been evolving on Earth for billions of years, resulting in a vast diversity of past and present organisms. But along with the diversity there is also unity. For example, while seahorses, jackrabbits, hummingbirds, and polar bears all look very different, their skeletons are organized in the same basic way.

The scientific explanation for the unity and diversity of organisms—as well as for the adaptation of organisms to their particular environments—is evolution: the concept that the organisms living on Earth today are the modified descendants of common ancestors. As a result of descent with modification, two species share certain traits (unity) simply because they have descended from a common ancestor. Furthermore, we can account for differences between two species (diversity) with the idea that certain heritable changes occurred after the two species diverged from their common ancestor. An abundance of evidence of different types supports the occurrence of evolution and the theory that describes how it takes place, which we'll discuss in detail in Chapters 22–25. To quote one of the founders of modern evolutionary theory, Theodosius Dobzhansky, "Nothing in biology makes sense except in the light of evolution." To understand Dobzhansky's statement, we need to discuss how biologists think about the vast diversity of life on the planet.

Classifying the Diversity of Life

Diversity is a hallmark of life. Biologists have so far identified and named about 1.8 million species of organisms. Each species is given a two-part name: The first part is the name of the genus (plural, *genera*) to which the species belongs, and the second part is unique to the species within the genus. (For example, *Homo sapiens* is the name of our species.)

To date, this diversity of life is known to include at least 100 000 species of fungi, 290 000 plant species, 57 000 vertebrate species (animals with backbones), and 1 million insect species (more than half of all known forms of life)—not to mention the myriad types of single-celled organisms. Researchers identify thousands of additional species each year. Estimates of the total number of species range from about 10 million to over 100 million. Whatever the actual number, the enormous variety of life gives biology a very broad scope. Biologists face a major challenge in attempting to make sense of this variety.

Grouping Species: The Basic Idea

There is a human tendency to group diverse items according to their similarities and their relationships to each other. For instance, we may speak of "squirrels" and "butterflies," though we recognize that many different species belong to each group. We may even sort groups into broader categories, such as rodents (which include squirrels) and insects (which include butterflies). Taxonomy, the branch of biology that names and classifies species, formalizes this

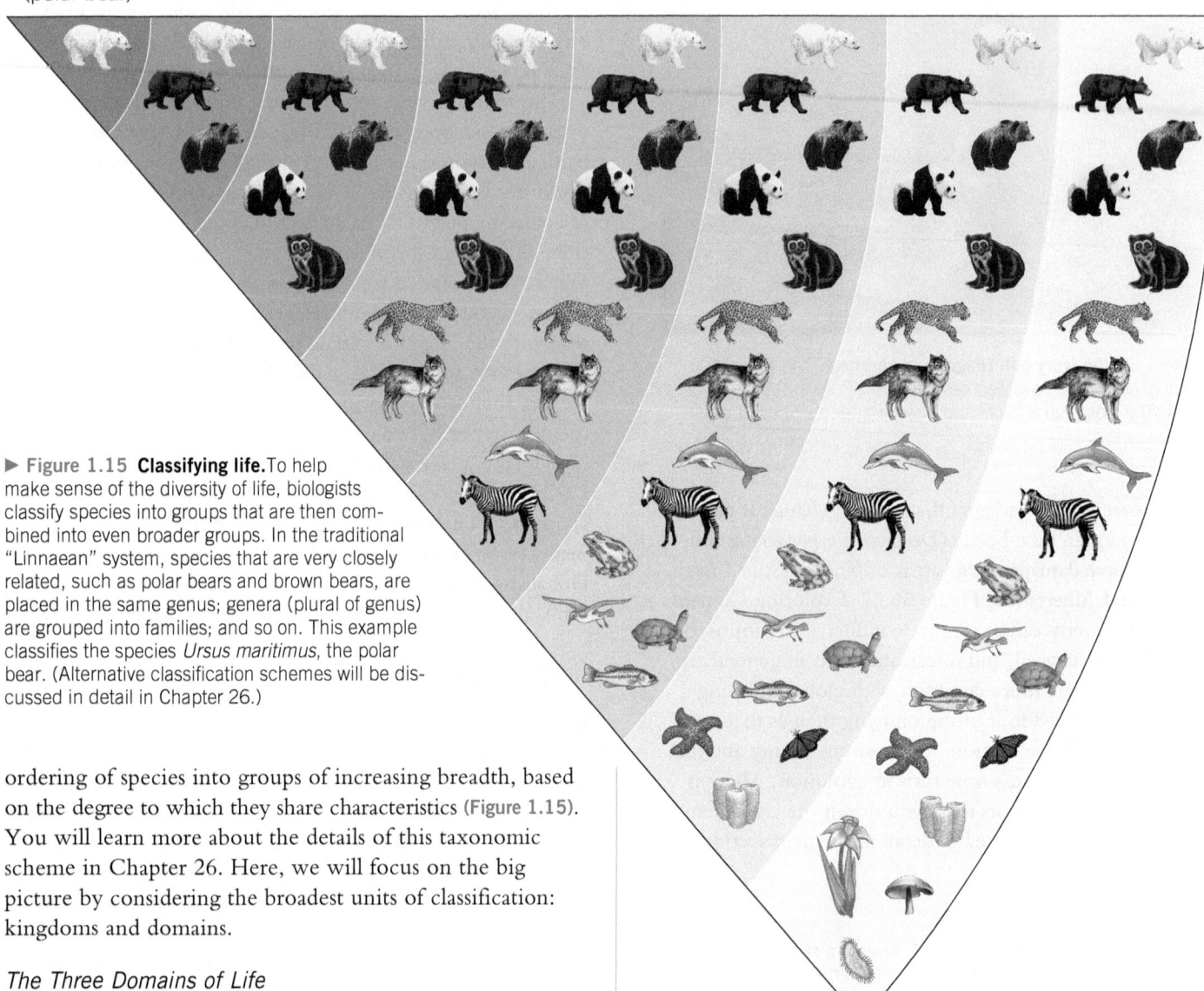

Species *Ursus maritimus* (polar bear)	Genus *Ursus*	Family Ursidae	Order Carnivora	Class Mammalia	Phylum Chordata	Kingdom Animalia	Domain Eukarya

▶ Figure 1.15 **Classifying life.** To help make sense of the diversity of life, biologists classify species into groups that are then combined into even broader groups. In the traditional "Linnaean" system, species that are very closely related, such as polar bears and brown bears, are placed in the same genus; genera (plural of genus) are grouped into families; and so on. This example classifies the species *Ursus maritimus*, the polar bear. (Alternative classification schemes will be discussed in detail in Chapter 26.)

ordering of species into groups of increasing breadth, based on the degree to which they share characteristics (Figure 1.15). You will learn more about the details of this taxonomic scheme in Chapter 26. Here, we will focus on the big picture by considering the broadest units of classification: kingdoms and domains.

The Three Domains of Life

Historically, scientists have classified the diversity of life-forms into species and broader groupings by careful comparisons of structure, function, and other obvious features. In the last few decades, new methods of assessing species relationships, such as comparisons of DNA sequences, have led to a reevaluation of the classification of life. Although this reevaluation is ongoing, biologists currently divide all organisms into three groups called domains: Bacteria, Archaea, and Eukarya (Figure 1.16).

As you read earlier, organisms making up two of the three domains—**Bacteria** and **Archaea**—are all prokaryotic. All the eukaryotes (organisms with eukaryotic cells) are now grouped in domain **Eukarya**. This domain includes four subgroups: kingdom Plantae, kingdom Fungi, kingdom Animalia, and the protists. The three kingdoms are distinguished partly by their modes of nutrition: Plants produce their own sugars and other food molecules by photosynthesis, fungi absorb dissolved nutrients from their surroundings, and animals obtain food by eating and digesting other organisms. Animalia is, of course, the kingdom to which we belong.

The most diverse eukaryotes are the protists, which are mostly single-celled organisms. Although protists were once placed in a single kingdom, they are now classified into several groups. One major reason for this change is the recent DNA evidence showing that some protists are less closely related to other protists than they are to plants, animals, or fungi.

Unity in the Diversity of Life

As diverse as life is, it also displays remarkable unity. Consider, for example, the similar skeletons of different animals and the universal genetic language of DNA (the genetic code), both mentioned earlier. In fact, similarities between organisms are evident at all levels of the biological hierarchy. For example, unity is obvious in many

▼ Figure 1.16 **The three domains of life.**

(a) Domain Bacteria

Eye of Science/Science Source

Bacteria are the most diverse and widespread prokaryotes and are now classified into multiple kingdoms. Each rod-shaped structure in this photo is a bacterial cell.

(b) Domain Archaea

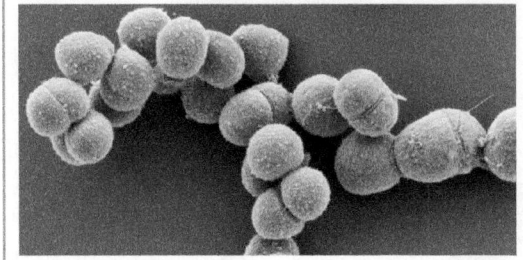

Eye of Science/Science Source

Many of the prokaryotes known as **archaea** live in Earth's extreme environments, such as salty lakes and boiling hot springs. Domain Archaea includes multiple kingdoms. Each round structure in this photo is an archaeal cell.

(c) Domain Eukarya

Kunst Scheidulin/AGE Fotostock

Peter Lilja/Getty Images

Anup Shah/Nature Picture Library

◄ **Kingdom Animalia** consists of multicellular eukaryotes that ingest other organisms.

100 μm

D.P. Wilson/Science Source

▲ **Kingdom Plantae** consists of terrestrial multicellular eukaryotes (land plants) that carry out photosynthesis, the conversion of light energy to the chemical energy in food.

► **Kingdom Fungi** is defined in part by the nutritional mode of its members (such as this mushroom), which absorb nutrients from outside their bodies.

► **Protists** are mostly unicellular eukaryotes and some relatively simple multicellular relatives. Pictured here is an assortment of protists inhabiting pond water. Scientists are currently debating how to classify protists in a way that accurately reflects their evolutionary relationships.

features of cell structure, even among distantly related organisms (Figure 1.17).

How can we account for life's dual nature of unity and diversity? The process of evolution, explained next, illuminates both the similarities and differences in the world of life and introduces another dimension of biology: the passage of time. The history of life, as documented by fossils and other evidence, is the saga of a changing Earth billions of years old, inhabited by an evolving cast of living forms (Figure 1.18).

Charles Darwin and the Theory of Natural Selection

An evolutionary view of life came into sharp focus in November 1859, when Charles Robert Darwin published one of the most important and influential books ever written, *On the Origin of Species by Means of Natural Selection* (Figure 1.19). *The Origin of Species* articulated two main points. The first point was that contemporary species arose from a succession of ancestors that differed from them. Darwin called this process "descent with modification." This insightful phrase captured the duality of life's unity and diversity—unity in the kinship among species that descended from common ancestors and diversity in the modifications that evolved as species branched from their common ancestors (Figure 1.20). Darwin's second main point was his proposal that "natural selection" is the primary cause of this descent with modification.

Darwin developed his theory of natural selection from observations that by themselves were neither new nor profound. While others had described the pieces of the puzzle,

15 μm

5 μm

Cross section of a cilium, as viewed with an electron microscope

0.1 μm

Cilia of *Paramecium*. The cilia of the single-celled *Paramecium* propel the organism through pond water.

Cilia of windpipe cells. The cells that line the human windpipe are equipped with cilia that help keep the lungs clean by sweeping a film of debris-trapping mucus upward.

▲ Figure 1.17 **An example of unity underlying the diversity of life: the architecture of cilia in eukaryotes.** Cilia (singular, *cilium*) are extensions of cells that function in locomotion. They occur in eukaryotes as diverse as *Paramecium* and humans. Even organisms so different share a common architecture for their cilia, which have an elaborate system of tubules that is striking in cross-sectional views.

▲ Figure 1.18 **Dr. Philip Currie and colleagues.** Dr. Philip Currie, centre, and Eva Koppelhus, right, from the University of Alberta are working in Patagonia to excavate several bones of *Austroraptor cabazai*, a Late Cretaceous meat-eating dinosaur.

▲ Figure 1.19 **Charles Darwin as a young man.** His revolutionary book *On the Origin of Species* was first published in 1859.

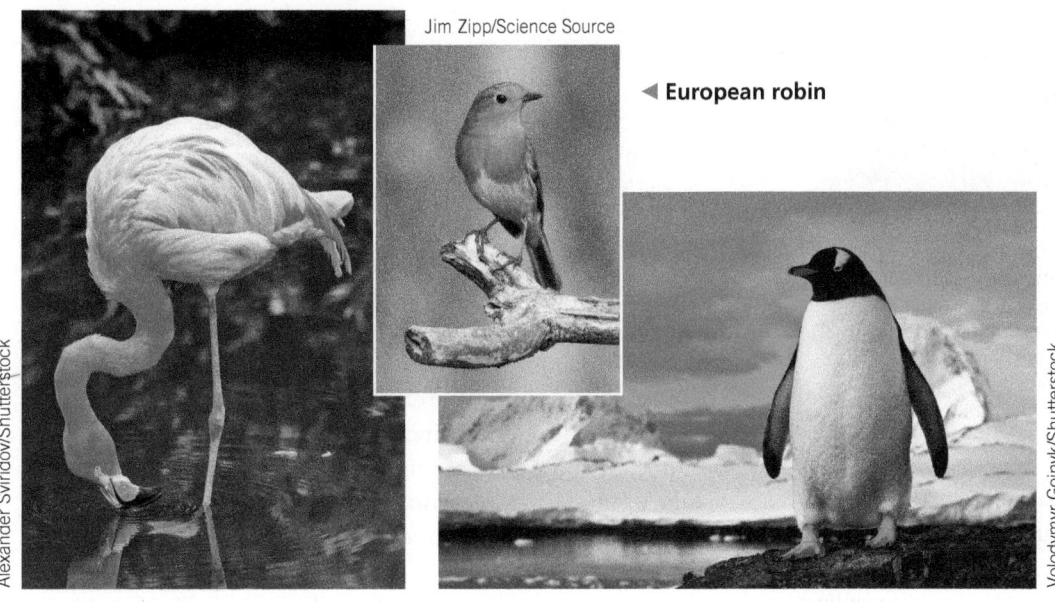

Jim Zipp/Science Source

◄ **European robin**

Alexander Sviridov/Shutterstock

Volodymyr Goinyk/Shutterstock

▲ **American flamingo** ▲ **Gentoo penguin**

◄ **Figure 1.20 Unity and diversity among birds.** These three different species of birds are variations on a common body plan. For example, each has feathers, a beak, and wings—although these features are highly specialized for the birds' diverse lifestyles.

it was Darwin who saw how they fit together. He started with the following three observations from nature: First, individuals in a population vary in their traits, many of which seem to be heritable (passed on from parents to offspring). Second, a population can produce far more offspring than can survive to produce offspring of their own. With more individuals than the environment is able to support, competition is inevitable. Third, species generally are suited to their environments—in other words, they are adapted to their environments. For instance, a common adaptation among birds that eat mostly hard seeds is an especially hard beak.

By making inferences from these three observations, Darwin arrived at his theory of evolution. He reasoned that individuals with inherited traits that are better suited to the local environment are more likely to survive and reproduce than less-well-suited individuals. Over many generations, a higher and higher proportion of individuals in a population will have the advantageous traits. Evolution occurs as the unequal reproductive success of individuals ultimately leads to adaptation to their environment, as long as the environment remains the same.

Darwin called this mechanism of evolutionary adaptation **natural selection** because the natural environment consistently "selects" for the propagation of certain traits among naturally occurring variant traits in the population. The example in **Figure 1.21** illustrates the ability of natural selection to "edit" a population's heritable variations

❶ Population with varied inherited traits

❷ Elimination of individuals with certain traits

❸ Reproduction of survivors

❹ Increasing frequency of traits that enhance survival and reproductive success

▲ **Figure 1.21 Natural selection.** This imaginary beetle population has colonized a locale where the soil has been blackened by a recent brush fire. Initially, the population varies extensively in the inherited colouration of the individuals, from very light grey to charcoal. For hungry birds that prey on the beetles, it is easiest to spot the beetles that are lightest in colour.

▲ Figure 1.22 **Evolutionary adaptation.** Bats, the only mammals capable of active flight, have wings with webbing between extended "fingers." In the Darwinian view of life, such adaptations are refined over time by natural selection.

in colour. We see the products of natural selection in the exquisite adaptations of various organisms to the special circumstances of their way of life and their environment. The wings of the bat shown in Figure 1.22 are an excellent example of adaptation.

The Tree of Life

Take another look at the skeletal architecture of the bat's wings in Figure 1.22. These wings are not like those of feathered birds; the bat is a mammal. The bat's forelimbs, though adapted for flight, actually have all the same bones, joints, nerves, and blood vessels found in other limbs as diverse as the human arm, the foreleg of a horse, and the flipper of a whale. Indeed, all mammalian forelimbs are anatomical variations of a common architecture. According to the Darwinian concept of descent with modification, the shared anatomy of mammalian limbs reflects inheritance of the limb structure from a common ancestor—the "prototype" mammal from which all other mammals descended. The diversity of mammalian forelimbs results from modification by natural selection operating over millions of years in different environmental contexts. Fossils and other evidence corroborate anatomical unity in supporting this view of mammalian descent from a common ancestor.

Darwin proposed that natural selection, by its cumulative effects over long periods of time, could cause an ancestral species to give rise to two or more descendant species. This could occur, for example, if one population fragmented into several subpopulations isolated in different environments. In these separate arenas of natural selection, one species could gradually radiate into multiple species as the geographically isolated populations adapted over many generations to different sets of environmental factors.

The "family tree" of 14 finches in Figure 1.23 illustrates a famous example of adaptive radiation of new species

from a common ancestor. Darwin collected specimens of these birds during his 1835 visit to the remote Galápagos Islands, 900 kilometres (km) off the Pacific coast of South America. These relatively young, volcanic islands are home to many species of plants and animals found nowhere else in the world, though many Galápagos organisms are clearly related to species on the South American mainland. After volcanoes built up the Galápagos several million years ago, finches probably diversified on the various islands from an ancestral finch species that by chance reached the archipelago from elsewhere. Years after Darwin collected the Galápagos finches, researchers began to sort out the relationships among these finch species, first from anatomical and geographic data and more recently with the help of DNA sequence comparisons.

Biologists' diagrams of evolutionary relationships generally take treelike forms, though the trees are often turned sideways, as in Figure 1.23. Tree diagrams make sense: Just as an individual has a genealogy that can be diagrammed as a family tree, each species is one twig of a branching tree of life extending back in time through ancestral species more and more remote. Species that are very similar, such as the Galápagos finches, share a common ancestor at a relatively recent branch point on the tree of life. But through an ancestor that lived much farther back in time, finches are related to sparrows, hawks, penguins, and all other birds. And birds, mammals, and all other vertebrates share a common ancestor even more ancient. Trace life back far enough, and we reach the early prokaryotes that inhabited Earth over 3.5 billion years ago. We can recognize their vestiges in our own cells—in the universal genetic code, for example. Indeed, all of life is connected through its long evolutionary history.

CONCEPT CHECK 1.2

1. How is a mailing address analogous to biology's hierarchical taxonomic system?

2. Explain why "editing" is an appropriate metaphor for how natural selection acts on a population's heritable variation.

3. **WHAT IF?** The three domains you learned about in Concept 1.2 can be represented in the tree of life as the three main branches, with three subbranches on the eukaryotic branch being the kingdoms Plantae, Fungi, and Animalia. What if fungi and animals are more closely related to each other than either of these kingdoms is to plants—as recent evidence strongly suggests? Draw a simple branching pattern that symbolizes the proposed relationship between these three eukaryotic kingdoms.

For suggested answers, see Appendix A.

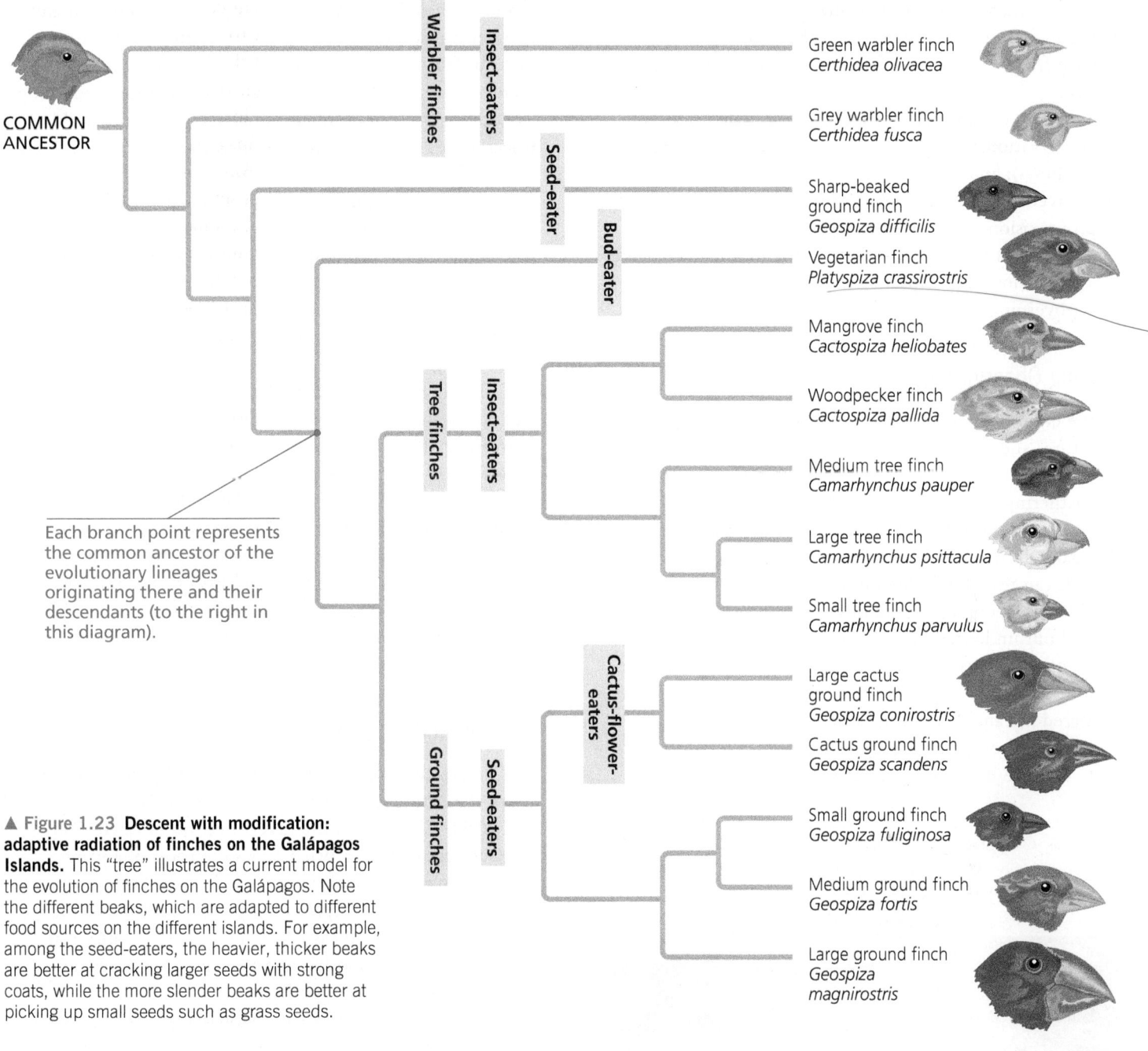

▲ Figure 1.23 **Descent with modification: adaptive radiation of finches on the Galápagos Islands.** This "tree" illustrates a current model for the evolution of finches on the Galápagos. Note the different beaks, which are adapted to different food sources on the different islands. For example, among the seed-eaters, the heavier, thicker beaks are better at cracking larger seeds with strong coats, while the more slender beaks are better at picking up small seeds such as grass seeds.

Each branch point represents the common ancestor of the evolutionary lineages originating there and their descendants (to the right in this diagram).

In studying nature, scientists make observations and form and test hypotheses

Science is a way of knowing—an approach to understanding the natural world. It developed out of our curiosity about ourselves, other life-forms, our planet, and the universe. The word is derived from a Latin verb meaning "to know." Striving to understand seems to be one of our basic urges.

At the heart of science is **inquiry**, a search for information and explanations of natural phenomena. There is no formula for successful scientific inquiry, no single scientific method that researchers must rigidly follow. As in all quests, science includes elements of challenge, adventure, and luck, along with careful planning, reasoning, creativity, patience, and the persistence to overcome setbacks. Such diverse elements of inquiry make science far less structured than most people realize. That said, it is possible to highlight certain characteristics that help to distinguish science from other ways of describing and explaining nature.

Scientists use a process of inquiry that includes making observations; forming logical, testable explanations (hypotheses); and testing them. The process is necessarily repetitive: In testing a hypothesis, more observations may inspire revision of the original hypothesis or formation of a new one, thus leading to further testing. In this way, scientists circle closer and closer to their best estimation of the laws governing nature.

Making Observations

In the course of their work, scientists describe natural structures and processes as accurately as possible through careful observation and analysis of data. Observation is the gathering of information, either through direct use of the senses or with the help of tools such as microscopes, thermometers, and balances that extend our senses. Observations can reveal valuable information about the natural world. For example, a series of detailed observations have shaped our understanding of cell structure, and another set of observations is currently expanding our databases of genomes of diverse species and of genes whose expression is altered in cancer and other diseases.

Recorded observations are called **data**. Put another way, data are items of information on which scientific

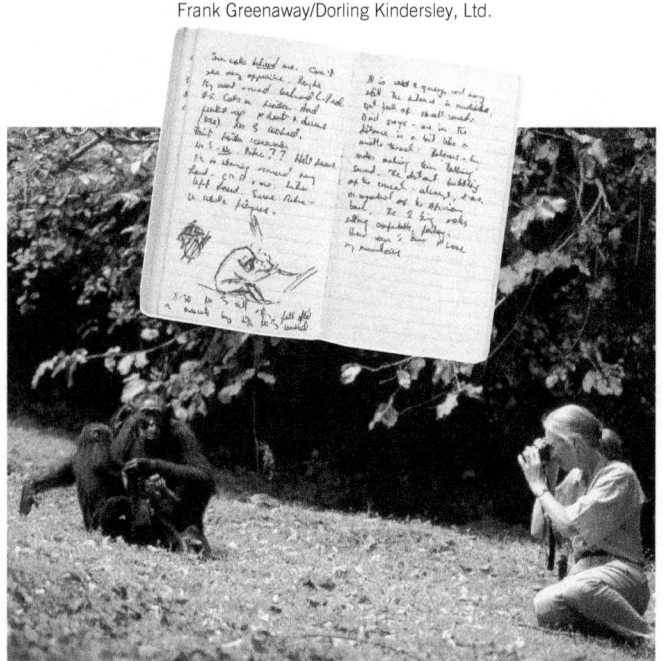

Frank Greenaway/Dorling Kindersley, Ltd.

Karl Ammann/Corbis Images

▲ Figure 1.24 **Jane Goodall collecting qualitative data on chimpanzee behaviour.** Goodall recorded her observations in field notebooks, often with sketches of the animals' behaviour.

inquiry is based. The term *data* implies numbers to many people. But some data are *qualitative*, often in the form of recorded descriptions rather than numerical measurements. For example, Jane Goodall spent decades recording her observations of chimpanzee behaviour during field research in a Tanzanian jungle (Figure 1.24). She also documented her observations with photographs and movies. Along with these qualitative data, Goodall enriched the field of animal behaviour with volumes of *quantitative* data, such as the frequency and duration of specific behaviours for different members of a group of chimpanzees in a variety of situations. Qualitative data are generally expressed as numerical measurements and are often organized into tables and graphs.

Collecting and analyzing observations can lead to important conclusions based on a type of logic called **inductive reasoning**. Through induction, we derive generalizations from a large number of specific observations. "The sun always rises in the east" is an example. And so is "All organisms are made of cells." The latter generalization, part of the so-called cell theory, was based on two centuries of microscopic observations by biologists of cells in diverse biological specimens. Careful observations and data analyses, along with generalizations reached by induction, are fundamental to our understanding of nature.

Forming and Testing Hypotheses

Our innate curiosity often stimulates us to pose questions about the natural basis for the phenomena we observe in the world. What *caused* the diversification of finches on the Galápagos Islands? What *causes* the roots of a plant seedling to grow downward and the leaf-bearing shoot to grow upward? What *explains* the generalization that the sun always rises in the east? In science, such inquiry usually involves the proposing and testing of hypothetical explanations—that is, hypotheses.

In science, a **hypothesis** is a tentative answer to a well-framed question—an explanation on trial. It is usually a rational account for a set of observations, based on the available data and guided by inductive reasoning. A scientific hypothesis must lead to predictions that can be tested by making additional observations or by performing experiments. An *experiment* is a scientific test carried out under controlled conditions.

We all use observations and develop questions and hypotheses in solving everyday problems. Let's say, for example, that your flashlight fails while you are camping. That's an observation. The question is obvious: Why doesn't the flashlight work? Two reasonable hypotheses based on your experience are that (1) the batteries in the flashlight are dead or (2) the bulb is burnt out. Each of these alternative hypotheses leads to predictions you can

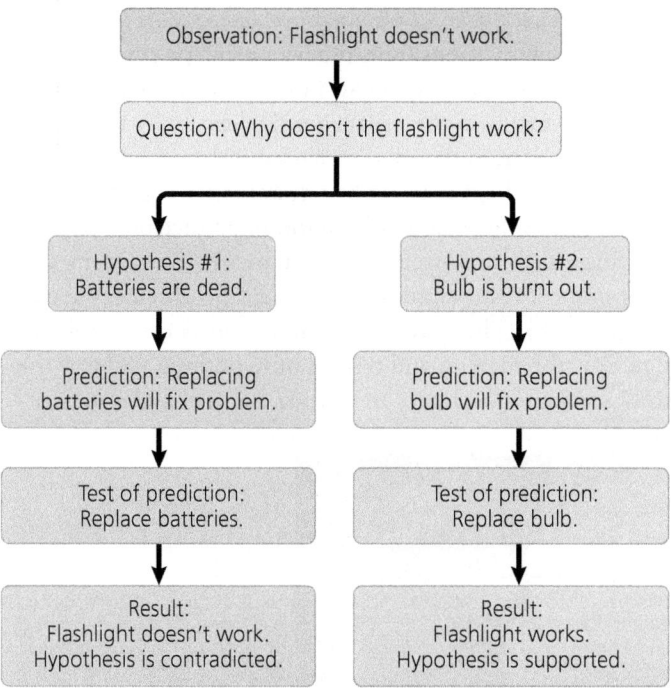

▲ Figure 1.25 **A simplified view of the scientific process.** The idealized process sometimes called the "scientific method" is shown in this flow chart, using a campground example of hypothesis testing.

test with informal experiments. For example, the dead-battery hypothesis predicts that replacing the batteries will fix the problem. **Figure 1.25** diagrams this campground inquiry. Figuring things out like this, by systematic trial and error, is a hypothesis-based approach.

Sometimes we can't carry out an experiment but can test a hypothesis using observations. Let's say you don't have a spare bulb or spare batteries. How could you figure out which hypothesis is more likely? You could examine the bulb to see if it looks burnt out. You could also check the expiration date on the battery. Experiments are great ways to test hypotheses, but when experiments aren't possible, we can often test a hypothesis in other ways.

Deductive Reasoning

A type of logic called deduction is also built into the use of hypotheses in science. While induction entails reasoning from a set of specific observations to reach a general conclusion, **deductive reasoning** involves logic that flows in the opposite direction, from the general to the specific. From general premises, we extrapolate to the specific results we should expect if the premises are true. In the scientific process, deductions usually take the form of predictions of results that will be found if a particular hypothesis (premise) is correct. We then test the hypothesis by carrying out experiments or observations to see whether or not the results are as predicted. This deductive testing takes the form of "If . . . then" logic. In the case of the flashlight

example: *If* the dead-battery hypothesis is correct, *then* the flashlight should work if you replace the batteries with new ones.

The flashlight inquiry demonstrates two other key points about the use of hypotheses in science. First, the initial observations may give rise to multiple hypotheses. The ideal plan is to design experiments to test all these possible candidate explanations. For instance, another of the many possible alternative hypotheses to explain our dead flashlight is that *both* the batteries *and* the bulb are bad, and you could design an experiment to test this.

Second, we can never *prove* that a hypothesis is true. Based on the experiments shown in Figure 1.25, the burnt-out bulb hypothesis stands out as the most likely explanation. The results support that hypothesis but do not absolutely prove it is correct. Perhaps the first bulb was simply loose, so it wasn't making electrical contact, and the new bulb was inserted correctly. We could attempt to test the burnt-out bulb hypothesis again by trying another experiment—removing the original bulb and carefully reinstalling it. If the flashlight still doesn't work, the burnt-out bulb hypothesis is supported by another line of evidence—but still not proven. For example, the bulb may have another defect not related to being burnt out. Testing a hypothesis in various ways with different sorts of data can increase our confidence in it tremendously (or strongly suggest that it is incorrect), but no amount of experimental testing can *prove* a hypothesis beyond a shadow of doubt.

Questions That Can and Cannot Be Addressed by Science

Scientific inquiry is a powerful way to learn about nature, but there are limitations to the kinds of questions it can answer. A scientific hypothesis must be *testable*; there must be some observation or experiment that could reveal if such an idea is likely to be true or false. The hypothesis that dead batteries are the sole cause of the broken flashlight could be (and was) tested by replacing the old batteries with new ones.

Not all hypotheses meet the criteria of science: You wouldn't be able to test the hypothesis that invisible campground ghosts are fooling with your flashlight! Because science only deals with natural, testable explanations for natural phenomena, it can neither support nor contradict the invisible ghost hypothesis, nor whether spirits, elves, or fairies, either benevolent or evil, cause storms, rainbows, illnesses, or cures. Such supernatural explanations, because they cannot be tested, are simply outside the bounds of science. For the same reason, science does not deal with religious matters, which are issues of personal faith. Science and religion are not mutually exclusive or contradictory; they are simply concerned with different issues.

The Flexibility of the Scientific Process

The flashlight example of Figure 1.25 traces an idealized process of inquiry sometimes called *the scientific method*. We can recognize the elements of this process in most of the research articles published by scientists, but rarely in such structured form. Very few scientific inquiries adhere rigidly to the sequence of steps prescribed by the "textbook" scientific method, which is often applied in hindsight, after the experiment or study is completed. For example, a scientist may start to design an experiment, but then backtrack after realizing that more preliminary observations are necessary.

In other cases, puzzling observations simply don't prompt well-defined questions until other research places those observations in a new context. For example, Darwin collected specimens of the Galápagos finches, but it wasn't until years later, as the idea of natural selection began to gel, that biologists began asking key questions about the history of those birds. Science is a lot more unpredictable—and exciting—than lock-step adherence to any five-step method.

A more realistic model of the scientific process is shown in Figure 1.26. The core activity (the central circle in the figure) is the making and testing of hypotheses. This is the most fundamental aspect of science and is the reason that

► Figure 1.26 **The process of science: A more realistic model.** In reality, the process of science is not linear, but is more circular, involving backtracking, repetitions, and interactions of different parts of the process. This illustration is based on a model (How Science Works) from the website called Understanding Science (understandingscience.org).

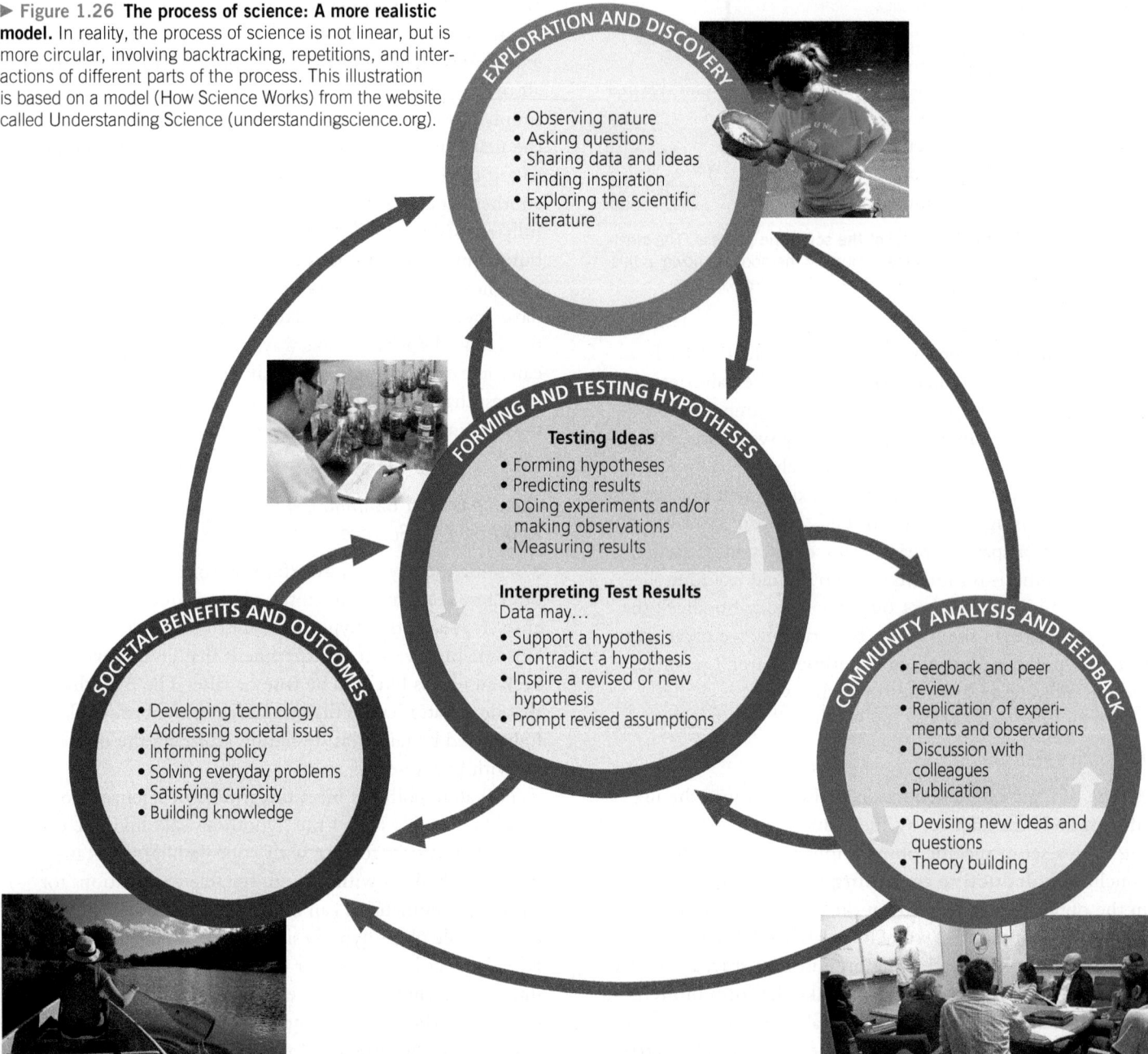

EXPLORATION AND DISCOVERY
- Observing nature
- Asking questions
- Sharing data and ideas
- Finding inspiration
- Exploring the scientific literature

FORMING AND TESTING HYPOTHESES

Testing Ideas
- Forming hypotheses
- Predicting results
- Doing experiments and/or making observations
- Measuring results

Interpreting Test Results
Data may…
- Support a hypothesis
- Contradict a hypothesis
- Inspire a revised or new hypothesis
- Prompt revised assumptions

SOCIETAL BENEFITS AND OUTCOMES
- Developing technology
- Addressing societal issues
- Informing policy
- Solving everyday problems
- Satisfying curiosity
- Building knowledge

COMMUNITY ANALYSIS AND FEEDBACK
- Feedback and peer review
- Replication of experiments and observations
- Discussion with colleagues
- Publication

- Devising new ideas and questions
- Theory building

Source: Adaptation of figure from "The real process of science," from *Understanding Science* website. Copyright © 2013 by The University of California Museum of Paleontology, Berkeley, and the Regents of the University of California. Material used courtesy of the UC Museum of Paleontology. ucmp.berkeley.edu.

science does such a reliable job of explaining phenomena in the natural world. However, there is much more to the scientific process than just testing. The choice of ideas to test, the interpretation and evaluation of results, and the decision about which ideas to pursue for further study are influenced by three other arenas as well.

First, well-framed questions, new hypotheses, and good study designs do not spring to life out of thin air; they are inspired and nurtured by the sorts of endeavours associated with exploration and discovery (the upper circle in the figure). Second, testing is not performed in a social vacuum; community analysis and feedback play an important role (lower right circle). Interactions within the scientific community influence which hypotheses are tested and how, provoke reinterpretations of test results, provide independent assessments of the validity of study designs, and much more. Finally, the process of science is interwoven with the fabric of society (the lower left circle of the figure). A societal need—for example, to understand the process of climate change—may inspire a flurry of hypotheses and studies. Similarly, well-supported hypotheses may wind up enabling an important technological innovation or encouraging a particular policy, which may, in turn, inspire new scientific questions. Though evidence and testing are at the heart of science, these pursuits represent only part of the picture.

The laboratory inquiries in your biology course may be formulated around the scientific method because it captures the core logic of testing scientific ideas (the central circle in Figure 1.26). Such exercises can be great practice for you, but it is important to remember that they do not represent how science really works. Performing research does not involve a lock-step adherence to the scientific method.

A Case Study in Scientific Inquiry: Investigating Coat Colouration in Mouse Populations

Now that we have highlighted the key features of scientific inquiry—making observations and forming and testing hypotheses—you should be able to recognize these features in a case study of actual scientific research.

The story begins with a set of observations and inductive generalizations. Colour patterns of animals vary widely in nature, sometimes even among members of the same species. What accounts for such variation? An illustrative example is found in two populations of mice that belong to the same species (*Peromyscus polionotus*) but have different colour patterns and reside in different environments (Figure 1.27). The beach mouse lives along the Florida seashore, a habitat of brilliant white sand dunes with sparse clumps of beach grass. The inland mouse lives on

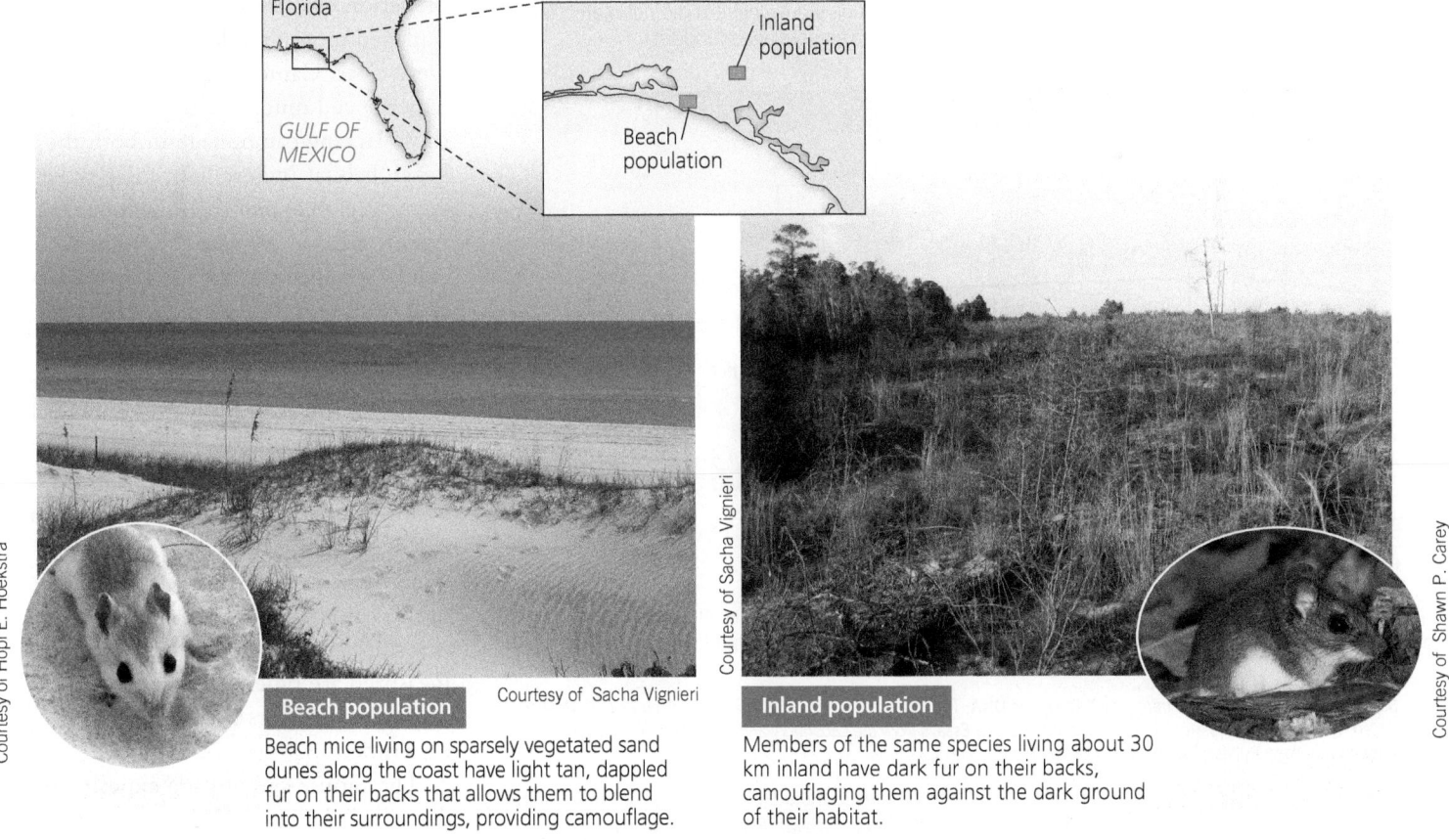

Courtesy of Hopi E. Hoekstra

Courtesy of Sacha Vignieri

Courtesy of Sacha Vignieri

Courtesy of Shawn P. Carey

Beach population

Beach mice living on sparsely vegetated sand dunes along the coast have light tan, dappled fur on their backs that allows them to blend into their surroundings, providing camouflage.

Inland population

Members of the same species living about 30 km inland have dark fur on their backs, camouflaging them against the dark ground of their habitat.

▲ Figure 1.27 **Different colouration in beach and inland populations of *Peromyscus polionotus*.**

darker, more fertile soil farther inland. Even a brief glance at the photographs in Figure 1.27 reveals a striking match of mouse colouration to its habitat. The natural predators of these mice, including hawks, owls, foxes, and coyotes, are all visual hunters (they use their eyes to look for prey). It was logical, therefore, for Francis Bertody Sumner, a naturalist studying populations of these mice in the 1920s, to form the hypothesis that their colouration patterns had evolved as adaptations that camouflage the mice in their native environments, protecting them from predation.

As obvious as the camouflage hypothesis may seem, it still required testing. In 2010, biologist Hopi Hoekstra of Harvard University and a group of her students headed to Florida to test the prediction that mice with colouration that did not match their habitat would be preyed on more heavily than the native, well-matched mice. Figure 1.28

summarizes this field experiment, introducing a format we will use throughout the book to walk through other examples of biological inquiry.

The researchers built hundreds of plasticine models of mice and spray-painted them to resemble either beach mice (light coloured) or inland mice (darker coloured), so that the models differed only in their colour patterns. The researchers placed equal numbers of these model mice randomly in both habitats and left them overnight. The mouse models resembling the native mice in the habitat were the *control* group (for instance, light-coloured beach mouse models in the beach habitat), while the mouse models with the non-native colouration were the *experimental* group (for example, darker-coloured inland mouse models in the beach habitat). The following morning, the team counted and recorded signs of predation events, which ranged from bites and gouge marks on some models to the outright disappearance of others. Judging by the shape of the predator's bites and the tracks surrounding the experimental sites, the predators appeared to be split fairly evenly between mammals (such as foxes and coyotes) and birds (such as owls, herons, and hawks).

For each environment, the researchers then calculated the fraction of predation events that targeted camouflaged mouse models. The results were clear: Camouflaged models experienced much less predation than those lacking camouflage in both the beach habitat (where light mice were less vulnerable) and the inland habitat (where dark mice were less vulnerable). The data thus fit the key prediction of the camouflage hypothesis.

Experimental Variables and Controls

Earlier in this section, we described an experiment as a scientific test carried out under controlled conditions. More specifically, an **experiment** also involves manipulation of one factor in a system in order to see the effects of its changing. Both the factor that is manipulated and the effects that are measured are types of experimental **variables**—factors that vary in an experiment.

The mouse camouflage experiment described in Figure 1.28 is an example of a **controlled experiment**, one that is designed to compare an experimental

▼ Figure 1.28 | **Inquiry**

Does camouflage affect predation rates on two populations of mice?

Experiment Hopi Hoekstra and colleagues wanted to test the hypothesis that colouration of beach and inland mice (*Peromyscus polionotus*) provides camouflage that protects them from predation in their respective habitats. The researchers spray-painted mouse models with either light or dark colour patterns that matched those of the beach and inland mice and then placed models with both patterns in each of the habitats. The next morning, they counted damaged or missing models.

Results For each habitat, the researchers calculated the percentage of attacked models that were camouflaged or non-camouflaged. In both habitats, the models whose pattern did not match their surroundings suffered much higher "predation" than did the camouflaged models.

Conclusion The results are consistent with the researchers' prediction: that mouse models with camouflage colouration would be preyed on less often than non-camouflaged mouse models. Thus, the experiment supports the camouflage hypothesis.

Source: Adaptation of figure 3 from "From Darwin to DNA: The Genetic Basis of Color Adaptations" by Hopi E. Hoekstra, edited by Jonathan Losos, from *In The Light of Evolution: Essays from the Laboratory and Field.* Copyright © 2011 by Roberts Company Publishers, Inc. Reprinted with permission.

INTERPRET THE DATA *The bars indicate the percentage of the attacked models that were either light or dark. Assume 100 mouse models were attacked in each habitat. For the beach habitat, how many were light models? Dark models? Answer the same questions for the inland habitat.*

group (the non-camouflaged mice, in this case) with a control group (the camouflaged mice normally resident in that area). Ideally, the experimental and control groups are designed to differ only in the one factor the experiment is testing—in our example, mouse colouration and its effect on the behaviour of predators. Here, mouse colour is the **independent variable**, the factor manipulated by the researchers, and the amount of predation is the **dependent variable**, a factor that is measured in the experiment. Without the control group, the researchers would not have been able to rule out other factors as causes of the more frequent attacks on the non-camouflaged mice—such as different numbers of predators or different temperatures in the different test areas. The clever experimental design left colouration as the only factor that could account for the low predation rate on the camouflaged mice placed in their normal environment.

A common misconception is that the term *controlled experiment* means that scientists control the experimental environment to keep everything strictly constant except the one variable being tested. But that's impossible in field research and not realistic even in highly regulated laboratory environments. Researchers usually "control" unwanted variables not by *eliminating* them through environmental regulation, but by *cancelling out* their effects by using control groups.

Theories in Science

Our everyday use of the term *theory* often implies an untested speculation: "It's just a theory!" But the term *theory* has a different meaning in science. What is a scientific theory, and how is it different from a hypothesis or from mere speculation?

First, a scientific **theory** is much broader in scope than a hypothesis. This is a hypothesis: "Having fur colouration well-matched to their habitat is an adaptation that protects mice from predators." But *this* is a theory: "Evolutionary adaptations arise by natural selection." This theory proposes that natural selection is the evolutionary mechanism that accounts for an enormous variety of adaptations, of which coat colour in mice is one example. The theory of natural selection has been supported by a vast quantity of evidence, with more being found every day, and has not been contradicted by any scientific data. Other similarly supported theories include the theory of gravity and the theory that the Earth revolves around the sun.

Second, a theory is general enough to spin off many new, specific hypotheses that can be tested. For example, two researchers at Princeton University, Peter and Rosemary Grant, were motivated by the theory of natural selection to test the specific hypothesis that the beaks of Galápagos finches evolve in response to changes in the types of available food. (Their results supported their hypothesis.)

And third, compared to any one hypothesis, a theory is generally supported by a much greater body of evidence. Those theories that become widely adopted in science (such as the theory of natural selection or the theory of gravity) explain a great range of observations and are supported by a vast accumulation of evidence. In fact, scrutiny of theories continues through testing of the specific hypotheses they generate.

In spite of the body of evidence supporting a widely accepted theory, scientists will modify or even reject theories when new research produces results that don't fit. For example, the theory of biological diversity that lumped bacteria and archaea together as a kingdom of prokaryotes began to erode when new methods for comparing cells and molecules made it possible to test some of the hypothetical relationships between organisms that were based on the theory. If there is "truth" in science, it is at best conditional, based on the preponderance of available evidence.

CONCEPT CHECK 1.3

1. Contrast inductive reasoning with deductive reasoning.
2. In the mouse camouflage experiment, what is the independent variable? The dependent variable?
3. Why is natural selection called a theory?
4. **WHAT IF?** In the deserts of the Southwestern United States, the soils are mostly sandy, with occasional large regions of black rock derived from lava flows that occurred 1.7 million years ago. Mice are found in both sandy and rocky areas, and owls are known predators. What might you expect about coat colour in these two mouse populations? Explain. How would you use this ecosystem to further test the camouflage hypothesis?

For suggested answers, see Appendix A.

CONCEPT 1.4

Science benefits from a cooperative approach and diverse viewpoints

Movies and cartoons sometimes portray scientists as loners working in isolated labs. In reality, science is an intensely social activity. Most scientists work in teams, which often include both graduate and undergraduate students. And to succeed in science, it helps to be a good communicator. Research results have no impact until shared with a community of peers through seminars, publications, and websites.

Building on the Work of Others

The great scientist Sir Isaac Newton once said: "To explain all nature is too difficult a task for any one man or even for any one age. 'Tis much better to do a little with certainty, and leave the rest for others that come after you. . . ." Anyone who becomes a scientist, driven by curiosity about how nature works, is sure to benefit greatly from the rich storehouse of discoveries by others who have come before.

Science is rarely perfectly objective, but is continuously vetted through the expectation that observations and experiments be repeatable. Scientists working in the same research field often check one another's claims by attempting to confirm observations or repeat experiments. In fact, Hopi Hoekstra's experiment benefited from the work of another researcher, D. W. Kaufman, 40 years earlier. You can study the design of Kaufman's experiment and interpret the results in the Scientific Skills Exercise.

If experimental results cannot be repeated by scientific colleagues, this failure may reflect some underlying weakness in the original claim, which will then have to be revised. In this sense, science polices itself. Integrity and adherence to high professional standards in reporting results are central to the scientific endeavour. After all, the validity of experimental data is key to designing further lines of inquiry.

It is not unusual for several scientists to converge on the same research question. Some scientists enjoy the challenge of being first with an important discovery or key

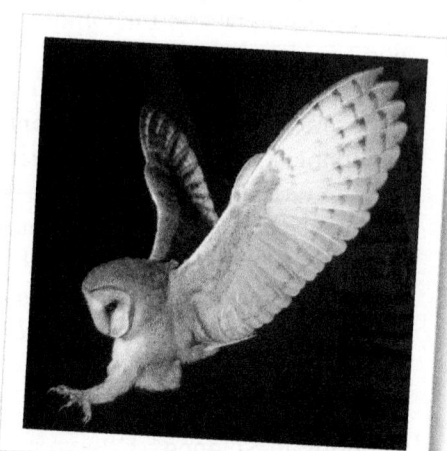

SCIENTIFIC SKILLS EXERCISE

Interpreting a Pair of Bar Graphs

How Much Does Camouflage Affect Predation on Mice by Owls with and without Moonlight? D. W. Kaufman investigated the effect of prey camouflage on predation. Kaufman tested the hypothesis that the amount of contrast between the coat colour of a mouse and the colour of its surroundings would affect the rate of nighttime predation by owls. He also hypothesized that the colour contrast would be affected by the amount of moonlight. In this exercise, you will analyze data from his owl–mouse predation studies.

How the Experiment Was Done Pairs of mice (*Peromyscus polionotus*) with different coat colours, one light brown and one dark brown, were released simultaneously into an enclosure that contained a hungry owl. The researcher recorded the colour of the mouse that was first caught by the owl. If the owl did not catch either mouse within 15 minutes, the test was recorded as a zero. The release trials were repeated multiple times in enclosures with either a dark-coloured soil surface or a light-coloured soil surface. The presence or absence of moonlight during each assay was recorded.

Data from the Experiment

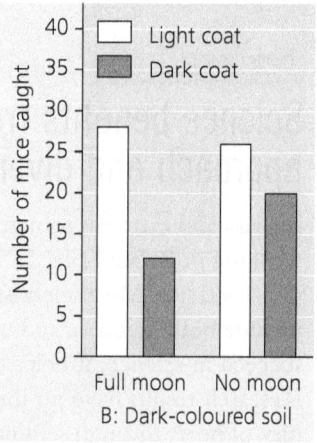

Interpret the Data

1. First, make sure you understand how the graphs are set up. Graph A shows data from the light-coloured soil enclosure and graph B from the dark-coloured enclosure, but in all other respects the graphs are the same. (a) There is more than one independent variable in these graphs. What are the independent variables, the variables that were tested by the researcher? Which axis of the graphs has the independent variables? (b) What is the dependent variable, the response to the variables being tested? Which axis of the graphs has the dependent variable?

2. (a) How many dark brown mice were caught in the light-coloured soil enclosure on a moonlit night? (b) How many dark brown mice were caught in the dark-coloured soil enclosure on a moonlit night? (c) On a moonlit night, would a dark brown mouse be more likely to escape predation by owls on dark- or light-coloured soil? Explain your answer.

3. (a) Is a dark brown mouse on dark-coloured soil more likely to escape predation under a full moon or with no moon? (b) A light brown mouse on light-coloured soil? Explain.

4. (a) Under which conditions would a dark brown mouse be most likely to escape predation at night? (b) A light brown mouse?

5. (a) What combination of independent variables led to the highest predation level in enclosures with light-coloured soil? (b) What combination of independent variables led to the highest predation level in enclosures with dark-coloured soil? (c) What relationship, if any, do you see in your answers to parts (a) and (b)?

6. What conditions are most deadly for both colours of mice?

7. Combining the data shown in both graphs, estimate the total number of mice caught in moonlight versus no-moonlight conditions. Which condition is optimal for predation by the owl on mice? Explain your answer.

Data from "Adaptive Coloration in Peromyscus polionotus: Experimental Selection by Owls" by Donald W. Kaufman, from *Journal of Mammology*, May 1974, Volume 55(2). © Jane B Reece.

experiment, while others derive more satisfaction from cooperating with fellow scientists working on the same problem.

Cooperation is facilitated when scientists use the same organism. Often it is a widely used **model organism**—a species that is easy to grow in the lab and lends itself particularly well to the questions being investigated. Because all species are evolutionarily related, such an organism may be viewed as a model for understanding the biology of other species (including humans) and their diseases. For example, genetic studies of the fruit fly *Drosophila melanogaster* have taught us a lot about how genes work in other species, even humans. Some other popular model organisms are the mustard plant *Arabidopsis thaliana*, the soil worm *Caenorhabditis elegans*, the zebrafish *Danio rerio*, the mouse *Mus musculus*, and the bacterium *Escherichia coli*. As you read through this text, note the many contributions that these and other model organisms have made to the study of life.

Biologists may approach interesting questions from different angles. Some biologists focus on ecosystems, while others study natural phenomena at the level of organisms or cells. This text is divided into units that look at biology focusing on different details. Yet any given problem can be addressed from many perspectives, which in fact complement each other.

For example, Hoekstra's work uncovered at least one genetic mutation that underlies the differences between beach and inland mouse colouration. Her lab includes biologists with different specialties, allowing links to be made between evolutionary adaptations she focuses on and their molecular basis in DNA sequences.

As a biology student, you can benefit from making connections among the different levels of biology. You can develop this skill by noticing when certain topics crop up again and again in different units. One such topic is sickle-cell disease, a well-understood genetic condition that is prevalent among native inhabitants of Africa and other warm regions and their descendants. Another topic viewed at different levels in this book is global climate change, mentioned earlier in this chapter. Sickle-cell disease and global climate change will appear in several units of the book, each time with a focus on different details. In addition, we have designed a number of figures that make connections between the content in different chapters, as well as questions that ask you to make the connections yourselves. We hope these features will help you integrate the material you're learning and enhance your enjoyment of biology by encouraging you to keep the "big picture" in mind.

Science, Technology, and Society

The research community is part of society at large, and the relationship of science to society becomes clearer when we add technology to the picture. Though science and technology sometimes employ similar inquiry patterns, their basic goals differ. The goal of science is to understand natural phenomena, while that of **technology** is to apply scientific knowledge for some specific purpose. Biologists and other scientists usually speak of "discoveries," while engineers and other technologists more often speak of "inventions." Because scientists put new technology to work in their research, science and technology are interdependent.

The potent combination of science and technology can have dramatic effects on society. Sometimes, the applications of basic research that turn out to be the most beneficial come out of the blue, from completely unanticipated observations in the course of scientific exploration. For example, discovery of the structure of DNA by Watson and Crick 60 years ago and subsequent achievements in DNA science led to the technologies of DNA manipulation that are transforming applied fields such as medicine, agriculture, and forensics (Figure 1.29). Perhaps Watson and Crick envisioned that their discovery would someday lead to important applications, but it is unlikely that they could have predicted exactly what all those applications would be.

The directions that technology takes depend less on the curiosity that drives basic science than on the current needs and wants of people and on the social environment of the times. Debates about technology centre more on "*should* we do it" than "*can* we do it." With advances in technology come difficult choices. For example, under what circumstances is it acceptable to use DNA technology to find out if particular people have genes for hereditary diseases? Should such tests always be voluntary, or are there circumstances when genetic testing should be mandatory? Should insurance companies or employers have access to the information, as

▲ Figure 1.29 **DNA technology and crime scene investigation.** David Milgaard, pictured here with his mother, spent 22 years in jail for the 1969 murder of a nursing aide from Saskatoon. The Supreme Court of Canada set aside his conviction in 1992, and he was subsequently cleared by DNA evidence in 1997. The details of forensic analysis of DNA will be described in Chapter 20.

they do for many other types of personal health data? These questions are becoming much more urgent as the sequencing of individual genomes becomes quicker and cheaper.

Ethical issues raised by such questions have as much to do with politics, economics, and cultural values as with science and technology. All citizens—not only professional scientists—have a responsibility to be informed about how science works and about the potential benefits and risks of technology. The relationship between science, technology, and society increases the significance and value of any biology course.

The Value of Diverse Viewpoints in Science

Many of the technological innovations with the most profound impact on human society originated in settlements along trade routes, where a rich mix of different cultures ignited new ideas. For example, the printing press, which helped spread knowledge to all social classes and ultimately led to the book in your hands, was invented by the German Johannes Gutenberg around 1440. This invention relied on several innovations from China, including paper and ink. Paper travelled along trade routes from China to Baghdad, where technology was developed for its mass production. This technology then migrated to Europe, as did water-based ink from China, which was modified by Gutenberg to become oil-based ink. We have the cross-fertilization of diverse cultures to thank for the printing press, and the same can be said for other important inventions.

Along similar lines, science stands to gain much from embracing a diversity of backgrounds and viewpoints among its practitioners. But just how diverse a population are scientists in relation to gender, race, ethnicity, and other attributes?

The scientific community reflects the cultural standards and behaviours of the society around it. It is therefore not surprising that until recently, women and certain minorities have faced huge obstacles in their pursuit to become professional scientists in many countries around the world. Over the past 50 years, changing attitudes about career choices have increased the proportion of women in biology and some other sciences, so that now women constitute roughly half of undergraduate biology majors and biology Ph.D. students. The pace has been slow at higher levels in the profession, however, and women and many racial and ethnic groups are still significantly underrepresented in many branches of science. This lack of diversity hampers the progress of science. The more voices that are heard at the table, the more robust, valuable, and productive the scientific interchange will be. The authors of this text welcome all students to the community of biologists, wishing you the joys and satisfactions of this exciting field of science.

CONCEPT CHECK 1.4

1. How does science differ from technology?

2. **WHAT IF?** The gene that causes sickle-cell disease is present in a higher percentage of residents of sub-Saharan Africa than it is among those of African descent living in Canada or the United States. The presence of this gene provides some protection from malaria, a serious disease that is widespread in sub-Saharan Africa. Discuss an evolutionary process that could account for the different percentages among residents of these regions.

For suggested answers, see Appendix A.

---

1 | Chapter Review

Go to **MasteringBiology®** for Assignments, the eText, and the Study Area with Animations, Activities, Vocab Self-Quiz, and Practice Tests.

SUMMARY OF KEY CONCEPTS

CONCEPT 1.1

The study of life reveals common themes (pp. 3–11)

Organization Theme: New Properties Emerge at Successive Levels of Biological Organization

- The hierarchy of life unfolds as follows: biosphere > ecosystem > community > population > organism > organ system > organ > tissue > cell > organelle > molecule > atom. With each step upward from atoms, new **emergent properties** result from interactions among components at the lower levels. In an approach called reductionism, complex systems are broken down to simpler components that are more manageable to study. In **systems biology**, scientists attempt to model the dynamic behaviour of whole biological systems based on a study of the interactions among the system's parts.

- The structure and function of biological components are interrelated. The cell, an organism's basic unit of structure and function, is the lowest level of organization that can perform all activities required for life. Cells are either prokaryotic or eukaryotic. **Eukaryotic cells** contain membrane-enclosed organelles, including a DNA-containing nucleus. **Prokaryotic cells** lack such organelles.

Information Theme: Life's Processes Involve the Expression and Transmission of Genetic Information

- Genetic information is encoded in the nucleotide sequences of **DNA**. It is DNA that transmits heritable information from parents to offspring. DNA sequences (called **genes**) program a cell's protein production by being transcribed into RNA and then translated into specific proteins, a process called **gene expression**. Gene expression also results in RNAs that are not translated into protein but serve other important functions. **Genomics** is the large-scale analysis of the DNA sequences within a species (its **genome**) as well as the comparison of genomes between species. **Bioinformatics** uses computational tools to deal with the huge volume of sequence data.

Energy and Matter Theme: Life Requires the Transfer and Transformation of Energy and Matter

- Energy flows through an ecosystem. All organisms must perform work, which requires energy. Producers convert energy from sunlight to chemical energy, some of which is then passed on to consumers. (The rest is lost as heat energy.) Chemicals cycle between organisms and the environment.

Interactions Theme: From Ecosystems to Molecules, Interactions Are Important in Biological Systems

- Organisms interact continuously with physical factors. Plants take up nutrients from the soil and chemicals from the air and use energy from the sun. Interactions among plants, animals, and other organisms affect the participants in varying ways.

- In **feedback regulation,** a process is regulated by its output or end product. In negative feedback, the physiological response to a stimulus limits the effects of the stimulus. Feedback is a type of regulation common to life at all levels, from molecules to ecosystems.

Evolution, the Core Theme of Biology

- Evolution accounts for the unity and diversity of life and also for the match of organisms to their environments.

? *Why is evolution considered the core theme of biology?*

CONCEPT 1.2

The Core Theme: Evolution accounts for the unity and diversity of life (pp. 11–16)

- Biologists classify species according to a system of broader and broader groups. Domain **Bacteria** and domain **Archaea** consist

of prokaryotes. Domain **Eukarya**, the eukaryotes, includes various groups of protists and the kingdoms Plantae, Fungi, and Animalia. As diverse as life is, there is also evidence of remarkable unity, which is revealed in the similarities between different kinds of organisms.

- Darwin proposed **natural selection** as the mechanism for evolutionary adaptation of populations to their environments.

- Each species is one twig of a branching tree of life extending back in time through ancestral species more and more remote. All of life is connected through its long evolutionary history.

? *How could natural selection have led to the evolution of adaptations such as the white-tailed jackrabbit's ears shown in Figure 1.3?*

CONCEPT 1.3

In studying nature, scientists make observations and form and test hypotheses (pp. 17–23)

- In scientific **inquiry**, scientists make observations (collect **data**) and use **inductive reasoning** to draw a general conclusion, which can be developed into a testable **hypothesis**. **Deductive reasoning** makes predictions that can be used to test hypotheses. Hypotheses must be testable; science can address neither the possibility of supernatural phenomena nor the validity of religious beliefs. Hypotheses can be tested by experimentation or, when that is not possible, by making observations. In the process of science, the core activity is testing ideas. This endeavour is informed by three arenas: exploration and discovery, community analysis and feedback, and societal benefits and outcomes. Testing ideas, in turn, affects each of these three pursuits as well.
- **Controlled experiments**, such as the study investigating coat colouration in mouse populations, are designed to demonstrate the effect of one variable by testing control groups and experimental groups that differ in only that one variable.
- A scientific **theory** is broad in scope, generates new hypotheses, and is supported by a large body of evidence.

? *What are the roles of gathering and interpreting data in the process of scientific inquiry?*

CONCEPT 1.4

Science benefits from a cooperative approach and diverse viewpoints (pp. 23–26)

- Science is a social activity. The work of each scientist builds on the work of others that have come before. Scientists must be able to repeat each other's results, so integrity is key. Biologists approach questions at different levels; their approaches complement each other.

- **Technology** consists of any method or device that applies scientific knowledge for some specific purpose that affects society. The ultimate impact of basic research is not always immediately obvious.
- Diversity among scientists promotes progress in science.

? *Explain why different approaches and diverse backgrounds among scientists are important.*

TEST YOUR UNDERSTANDING

LEVEL 1: KNOWLEDGE/COMPREHENSION

1. All the organisms on your campus make up
   a. an ecosystem.
   b. a community.
   c. a population.
   d. a taxonomic domain.

2. Which of the following is a correct sequence of levels in life's hierarchy, proceeding downward from an individual animal?
   a. organism, brain, organ system, nerve cell
   b. organ system, nervous tissue, brain, nerve cell
   c. organism, organ system, tissue, cell, organ
   d. nervous system, brain, nervous tissue, nerve cell

3. Which of the following is *not* an observation or inference on which Darwin's theory of natural selection is based?
   a. Poorly adapted individuals never produce offspring.
   b. There is heritable variation among individuals.
   c. Because of overproduction of offspring, there is competition for limited resources.
   d. A population can become adapted to its environment over time.

4. Systems biology is mainly an attempt to
   a. analyze genomes from different species.
   b. simplify complex problems by reducing the system into smaller, less complex units.
   c. understand the behaviour of entire biological systems by studying interactions among its component parts.
   d. build high-throughput machines for the rapid acquisition of biological data.

5. Protists and bacteria are grouped into different domains because
   a. protists eat bacteria.
   b. bacteria are not made of cells.
   c. protists have a membrane-bounded nucleus.
   d. protists are photosynthetic.

6. Which of the following best demonstrates the unity among all organisms?
   a. emergent properties
   b. descent with modification
   c. the structure and function of DNA
   d. natural selection

7. A controlled experiment is one that
   a. proceeds slowly enough that a scientist can make careful records of the results.
   b. tests experimental and control groups in parallel.
   c. is repeated many times to make sure the results are accurate.
   d. keeps all variables constant.

8. Which of the following statements best distinguishes hypotheses from theories in science?
   a. Theories are hypotheses that have been proved.
   b. Hypotheses are guesses; theories are correct answers.
   c. Hypotheses usually are relatively narrow in scope; theories have broad explanatory power.
   d. Theories are proved true; hypotheses are often contradicted by experimental results.

LEVEL 2: APPLICATION/ANALYSIS

9. Which of the following is an example of qualitative data?
   a. The fish swam in a zigzag motion.
   b. The contents of the stomach are mixed every 20 seconds.
   c. The temperature decreased from 20°C to 15°C.
   d. The six pairs of robins hatched an average of three chicks each.

10. Which of the following best describes the logic of scientific inquiry?
    a. If I generate a testable hypothesis, tests and observations will support it.
    b. If my prediction is correct, it will lead to a testable hypothesis.
    c. If my observations are accurate, they will support my hypothesis.
    d. If my hypothesis is correct, I can expect certain test results.

11. **DRAW IT** With rough sketches, draw a biological hierarchy similar to the one in Figure 1.4 but using a coral reef as the ecosystem, a fish as the organism, its stomach as the organ, and DNA as the molecule. Include all levels in the hierarchy.

LEVEL 3: SYNTHESIS/EVALUATION

12. **EVOLUTION CONNECTION**
    A typical prokaryotic cell has about 3000 genes in its DNA, while a human cell has about 20 500 genes. About 1000 of these genes are present in both types of cells. Based on your understanding of evolution, explain how such different organisms could have this same subset of genes. What sorts of functions might these shared genes have?

13. **SCIENTIFIC INQUIRY**
    Based on the results of the mouse colouration case study, suggest another hypothesis researchers might use to extend the investigation.

14. **WRITE ABOUT A THEME: EVOLUTION**
    In a short essay (100–150 words), discuss Darwin's view of how natural selection resulted in both unity and diversity of life on Earth. Include in your discussion some of his evidence. (See a suggested grading rubric and tips for writing good essays in the Study Area of MasteringBiology under "Write About a Theme.")

15. **SYNTHESIZE YOUR KNOWLEDGE**

Chris Mattison/Alamy Stock Photo

Can you pick out the mossy leaf-tailed gecko lying against the tree trunk in this photo? How is the appearance of the gecko a benefit in terms of survival? Given what you learned about evolution, natural selection, and genetic information in this chapter, describe how the gecko's colouration might have evolved.

For selected answers, see Appendix A.

THE CHEMISTRY OF LIFE

AN INTERVIEW WITH
David Wishart

David Wishart was born in Edmonton, completed a B.Sc. at the University of Alberta, and did his Ph.D. at Yale University. He is currently a Professor in the Departments of Biological Sciences and Computing Science at the University of Alberta. He is also a Senior Research Officer at the National Research Council's National Institute for Nanotechnology.

How did you become interested in science?
I think it runs in the family as my dad is a scientist. The seminal moment was when we went fossil hunting in the Badlands of Alberta. Within 15 minutes of getting out of the car, we found several exceptional fossils. That was this eureka moment—when I, as just a kid, discovered something ancient but also exceptional.

> " The usual quote is that scientists stand on the shoulders of giants—but in fact, they stand on a very large pyramid. Everyone stands on every other scientist's shoulders. "

What are you focusing on in your research?
Right now, we are focusing on completely characterizing all the small molecules in the human body—the human metabolome. My focus is to go from the genome to the proteome to the metabolome, which is essentially a way of looking at biochemistry in a new and different way, and realizing how little we actually know.

We are working in areas of human disease, such as neurodegenerative diseases, heart disease, diabetes, as well as perinatal conditions like preeclampsia, and we are trying to understand a bit about the biochemistry of how those diseases develop.

We are also working on projects to characterize protein structures very rapidly, which will allow us to answer more questions about the proteome. To look at protein structure, we use nuclear magnetic spectroscopy and mass spectrometry and we are developing computer programs that allow us to work with micromolecular information—like chemical shifts—to figure out the structures of proteins. We are combining experimental methods with computer programs to make the process faster and simpler.

What do you like most about your life as a scientist?
Scientists are fundamentally curious and are passionate about their subject. I think some people take a job so that it can pay for their hobby. But in my case science has been my hobby since I was a kid, and I still get a chance to play in the lab or take on projects that are really interesting. As a scientist I am my own boss, set my own hours, and to some extent I get to choose what to work on and how long I get to work on it. Not many jobs in the world are quite like that. Going back to that eureka moment I had as a kid—that happens in my group every couple of months, and I get to share that with my students.

Can you comment on the value of collaboration in science?
The usual quote is that scientists stand on the shoulders of giants—but in fact, they stand on a very large pyramid. Everyone stands on every other scientist's shoulders. We depend on each other, not only to lift our research up, but also to share our ideas. In science we sometimes forget that almost all scientists are publicly funded; in that regard they are doing a public service. And that service is to help, in the end, lead to the betterment of humanity. Collaboration means sharing ideas openly, sharing results openly, working as a team, and thinking as a team. Collaborations are also really critical for allowing us to move forward. Science is like a village where everyone is a member and has to carry their weight, but also has to teach the younger members of the community.

What advice would you give to a biology student just starting out at university?
If there is something that you pursue as a hobby, to some extent that should help guide you to where your interests ultimately lie and perhaps where your career choices could be too. Some people are told they have to be a physician or a dentist. But you don't have to be anything. You can go where your heart takes you or where your passion leads you.

Source: Interview with David Wishart. Used with permission from David Wishart.

▲ David Wishart and colleagues established the Human Metabolome Database, which contains information about the body's small molecule metabolites.

MAKE CONNECTIONS

Properties of Water

Life depends on the unique properties of water.
These unique properties exist primarily due to the polar covalent bonds
within the water molecule, and the hydrogen bonds that water can form
with other molecules. (See Concepts 2.3, 3.1, and 3.2)

Hydrogen
bond

$\delta-$

$\delta+$

H

O

H

$\delta+$ · · · · $\delta-$

$\delta-$

$\delta+$

Property 1: Water molecules like to "stick" together.
Water molecules stay close to each other as a result of hydrogen
bonding, constantly breaking and forming bonds with other molecules.

Alamy

Water has a high surface tension because
water molecules are hydrogen-bonded to
one another and to the water below. This
high surface tension allows some animals,
such as the basilisk lizard, pictured above,
to walk or run on water. (See Figure 3.4)

pmphoto/Shutterstock

Cohesion due to hydrogen bonding
contributes to the transport of water
against gravity in this redwood tree.
Evaporation from leaves pulls water
upward from the roots. (See Figure 3.3)

Property 4: Water is an excellent solvent.
Water's polar molecules are attracted to charged and polar substances
capable of forming hydrogen bonds. (See Figures 3.8 and 3.9)

Biological fluids, such as blood,
the sap of plants, and the
liquid within cells, contain
many different dissolved polar
compounds and ions.

Image Source/Alamy

Oxygen and hydrogen have different electronegativities, resulting in polar covalent bonds between the atoms and partial charges. These partial charges allow the water molecule to form hydrogen bonds with other molecules, including other molecules of water. (See Concepts 2.3 and 3.1)

Polar covalent bonds

δ+

δ−

Property 2: Water can moderate temperature.

Water has a high specific heat because of its ability to form hydrogen bonds. Heat must be absorbed in order to break these hydrogen bonds, and heat is released when hydrogen bonds form.

Large bodies of water, such as the Great Lakes, absorb and store heat from the sun during the day and can warm the air at night, which can minimize temperature fluctuations. (See Figure 3.5)

Rich Lam/Getty Images

Water has a high heat of vaporization, which contributes to water's evaporative cooling effect. This is what allows evaporation of sweat from human skin to dissipate body heat.

NASA/Corbis

Property 3: Ice is less dense than liquid water.

Ice floats on liquid water because as the temperature drops, water molecules move too slowly to break hydrogen bonds, resulting in a crystalline lattice structure. This results in ice being less dense than liquid water, causing the ice to float. (See Figures 3.6 and 3.7)

Floating ice provides a habitat for many animals, including polar bears. Also, floating ice insulates the liquid below and will prevent bodies of water from freezing, allowing life to exist underneath the ice.

Liquid Water

Hydrogen bonds break and re-form

Yvonne Pijnenburg Schonewille/Shutterstock

MAKE CONNECTIONS *Ocean temperatures have increased about 1/10 of a degree over the last two decades. Do you consider this to be strong evidence for global warming? Why or why not?* (Refer to Figure 56.27)

ICE

Hydrogen bonds are stable

2

The Chemical Context of Life

KEY CONCEPTS

2.1 Matter consists of chemical elements in pure form and in combinations called compounds

2.2 An element's properties depend on the structure of its atoms

2.3 The formation and function of molecules depend on chemical bonding between atoms

2.4 Chemical reactions make and break chemical bonds

© Warren Photographic

▲ Figure 2.1 **What weapon are these ants shooting into the air?**

A Chemical Connection to Biology

Like other animals, ants have structures and mechanisms that defend them from attack. Wood ants live in colonies, and the colony as a whole has a particularly effective mechanism for dealing with enemies. When threatened, the ants—which may number in the hundreds or even thousands—shoot formic acid into the air from their abdomens, causing a deluge of this irritating acid to rain down upon the potential invaders **(Figure 2.1)**. This substance is produced by many species of ants, and in fact got its name from the Latin word for ant, *formica*, although most species do not shoot volleys of the acid into the air like wood ants do. For quite a few ant species, the formic acid probably serves as a disinfectant that protects the ants against microbial parasites. Scientists have long known that chemicals play a major role in insect communication, the attraction of mates, and defence against predators. The ants featured above are red wood ants (*Formica lugubris*), which are found predominantly in Europe and Asia. In 1971, this ant species was purposely established in Eastern Canada with the goal of acting as a pest control and preventing other insects from damaging conifer trees. More than 45 years later, the imported ant population is thriving.

Research on ants and other insects is only one example of how relevant chemistry is to the study of life. Unlike university courses, nature is not neatly packaged into individual sciences—biology, chemistry, physics, and so forth. Biologists specialize in the study of life, but organisms and their environments are natural systems to which the concepts of chemistry and physics apply. Biology is multidisciplinary.

This unit of chapters introduces some basic concepts of chemistry that apply to the study of life. Somewhere in the transition from molecules to cells, we will cross the blurry boundary between nonlife and life. This chapter focuses on the chemical components that make up all matter.

CONCEPT 2.1

Matter consists of chemical elements in pure form and in combinations called compounds

Organisms are composed of **matter**, which is anything that takes up space and has mass.★ Matter exists in many forms. Rocks, metals, oils, gases, and living organisms are a few examples of what seems to be an endless assortment of matter.

Elements and Compounds

Matter is made up of elements. An **element** is a substance that cannot be broken down to other substances by chemical reactions. Today, chemists recognize 92 elements occurring in nature; gold, copper, carbon, and oxygen are examples. Each element has a symbol, usually the first letter or two of its name. Some symbols are derived from Latin or German; for instance, the symbol for sodium is Na, from the Latin word *natrium*.

A **compound** is a substance consisting of two or more different elements combined in a fixed ratio. Table salt, for example, is sodium chloride (NaCl), a compound composed of the elements sodium (Na) and chlorine (Cl) in a 1:1 ratio. Pure sodium is a metal, and pure chlorine is a poisonous gas. When chemically combined, however, sodium and chlorine form an edible compound. Water (H_2O), another compound, consists of the elements hydrogen (H) and oxygen (O) in a 2:1 ratio. These are simple examples of organized matter having emergent properties: A compound has characteristics different from those of its elements (Figure 2.2).

The Elements of Life

Of the 92 natural elements, about 20–25% are **essential elements** that an organism needs to live a healthy life and

Sodium   **Chlorine**   **Sodium chloride**

▲ Figure 2.2 **The emergent properties of a compound.** The metal sodium combines with the poisonous gas chlorine, forming the edible compound sodium chloride, or table salt.

reproduce. The essential elements are similar among organisms, but there is some variation—for example, humans need 25 elements, but plants need only 17.

Just four elements—oxygen (O), carbon (C), hydrogen (H), and nitrogen (N)—make up 96% of living matter. Calcium (Ca), phosphorus (P), potassium (K), sulphur (S), and a few other elements account for most of the remaining 4% of an organism's mass. **Trace elements** are required by an organism in only minute quantities. Some trace elements, such as iron (Fe), are needed by all forms of life; others are required only by certain species. For example, in vertebrates (animals with backbones), the element iodine (I) is an essential ingredient of a hormone produced by the thyroid gland. A daily intake of only 0.15 milligram (mg) of iodine is adequate for normal activity of the human thyroid. An iodine deficiency in the diet causes the thyroid gland to grow to abnormal size, a condition called goiter. Where it is available, eating seafood or iodized salt reduces the incidence of goiter. All the elements needed by the human body are listed in Table 2.1.

Some naturally occurring elements are toxic to organisms. In humans, for instance, the element arsenic has been linked to numerous diseases and can be lethal. In some areas of the world, arsenic occurs naturally and can make its way into the groundwater. As a result of using water from drilled wells in southern Asia, millions of people have been inadvertently exposed to arsenic-laden water. Efforts are under way to reduce arsenic levels in their water supply.

Case Study: Evolution of Tolerance to Toxic Elements

EVOLUTION Some species have become adapted to environments containing elements that are usually toxic; an example is serpentine plant communities. Serpentine is a jade-like mineral that contains elevated concentrations of elements such as chromium, nickel, and cobalt. Although most plants cannot survive in soil that forms from serpentine rock, a small number of plant species have adaptations

---

★In everyday language we tend to substitute the term *weight* for *mass*, although the two are not identical. *Mass* is the amount of matter in an object, whereas the *weight* of an object is how strongly that mass is pulled by gravity. The weight of an astronaut walking on the moon is approximately $\frac{1}{6}$ the astronaut's weight on Earth, but his or her mass is the same. However, as long as we are earthbound, the weight of an object is a measure of its mass; in everyday language, therefore, we tend to use the terms interchangeably.

Table 2.1 Elements in the Human Body

Element	Symbol	Percentage of Body Mass (including water)	
Oxygen	O	65.0%	
Carbon	C	18.5%	96.3%
Hydrogen	H	9.5%	
Nitrogen	N	3.3%	
Calcium	Ca	1.5%	
Phosphorus	P	1.0%	
Potassium	K	0.4%	
Sulphur	S	0.3%	3.7%
Sodium	Na	0.2%	
Chlorine	Cl	0.2%	
Magnesium	Mg	0.1%	

Trace elements (less than 0.01% of mass): Boron (B), chromium (Cr), cobalt (Co), copper (Cu), fluorine (F), iodine (I), iron (Fe), manganese (Mn), molybdenum (Mo), selenium (Se), silicon (Si), tin (Sn), vanadium (V), zinc (Zn)

INTERPRET THE DATA *Given what you know about the human body, what do you think could account for the high percentage of oxygen (65.0%)?*

that allow them to do so (**Figure 2.3**). Presumably, variants of ancestral, nonserpentine species arose that could survive in serpentine soils, and subsequent natural selection resulted in the distinctive array of species we see in these areas today. Researchers are studying whether serpentine-adapted plants could take up toxic heavy metals in contaminated areas, concentrating them for safer disposal.

Michael C. Hogan

California Native Plant Society

Andrew Alden

▲ **Figure 2.3 Serpentine plant community.**
These plants are growing on serpentine soil, which contains elements that are usually toxic to plants. The insets show a close-up of serpentine rock and one of the plants, a Tiburon Mariposa lily.

1. **MAKE CONNECTIONS** Explain how table salt has emergent properties. (See Concept 1.1.)
2. Is a trace element an essential element? Explain.
3. **WHAT IF?** In humans, iron is a trace element required for the proper functioning of hemoglobin, the molecule that carries oxygen in red blood cells. What might be the effects of an iron deficiency?
4. **MAKE CONNECTIONS** Explain how natural selection might have played a role in the evolution of species that are tolerant of serpentine soils. (Review Concept 1.2.)

For suggested answers, see Appendix A.

CONCEPT 2.2

An element's properties depend on the structure of its atoms

Each element consists of a certain type of atom that is different from the atoms of any other element. An **atom** is the smallest unit of matter that still retains the properties of an element. Atoms are so small that it would take about a million of them to stretch across the period printed at the end of this sentence. We symbolize atoms with the same abbreviation used for the element that is made up of those atoms. For example, the symbol C stands for both the element carbon and a single carbon atom.

Subatomic Particles

Although the atom is the smallest unit having the properties of an element, these tiny bits of matter are composed of even smaller parts, called *subatomic particles*. Using high-energy collisions, physicists have produced more than a hundred types of particles from the atom, but only three kinds of particles are relevant here: **neutrons**, **protons**, and **electrons**. Protons and electrons are electrically charged. Each proton has one unit of positive charge, and each electron has one unit of negative charge. A neutron, as its name implies, is electrically neutral.

Protons and neutrons are packed together tightly in a dense core, or **atomic nucleus**, at the centre of an atom; protons give the nucleus a positive charge. The rapidly moving electrons form a "cloud" of negative charge around the nucleus, and it is the attraction between opposite charges that keeps the electrons in the vicinity of the nucleus. **Figure 2.4** shows two commonly used models of the structure of the helium atom as an example.

The neutron and proton are almost identical in mass, each about 1.7×10^{-24} gram (g). Grams and other conventional units are not very useful for describing the mass of objects so minuscule. Thus, for atoms and subatomic

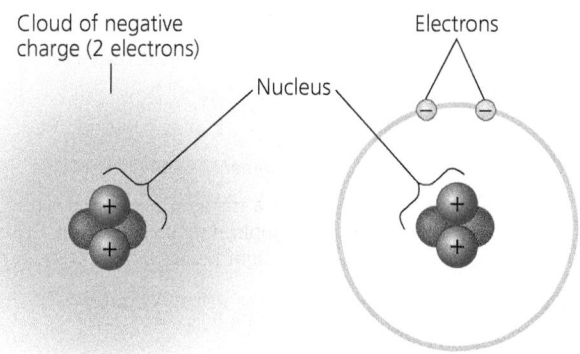

Cloud of negative charge (2 electrons)

Nucleus

Electrons

(a) This model represents the two electrons as a cloud of negative charge.

(b) In this more simplified model, the electrons are shown as two small yellow spheres on a circle around the nucleus.

▲ Figure 2.4 **Simplified models of a helium (He) atom.** The helium nucleus consists of 2 neutrons (brown) and 2 protons (pink). Two electrons (yellow) exist outside the nucleus. These models are not to scale; they greatly overestimate the size of the nucleus in relation to the electron cloud.

particles (and for molecules, too), we use a unit of measurement called the **dalton**, in honour of John Dalton, the British scientist who helped develop atomic theory around 1800. (The dalton is the same as the *atomic mass unit,* or *amu,* a unit you may have encountered elsewhere.) Neutrons and protons have masses close to 1 dalton. Because the mass of an electron is only about 1/2000 that of a neutron or proton, we can ignore electrons when computing the total mass of an atom.

Atomic Number and Atomic Mass

Atoms of the various elements differ in their number of subatomic particles. All atoms of a particular element have the same number of protons in their nuclei. This number of protons, which is unique to that element, is called the **atomic number** and is written as a subscript to the left of the symbol for the element. The abbreviation $_2$He, for example, tells us that an atom of the element helium has 2 protons in its nucleus. Unless otherwise indicated, an atom is neutral in electrical charge, which means that its protons must be balanced by an equal number of electrons. Therefore, the atomic number tells us the number of protons and also the number of electrons in an electrically neutral atom.

We can deduce the number of neutrons from a second quantity, the **mass number**, which is the sum of protons plus neutrons in the nucleus of an atom. The mass number is written as a superscript to the left of an element's symbol. For example, we can use this shorthand to write an atom of helium as $_2^4$He. Because the atomic number indicates how many protons there are, we can determine the number of neutrons by subtracting the atomic number from the mass

number: Accordingly, the helium atom, $_2^4$He, has 2 neutrons. For sodium (Na):

$$_{11}^{23}\text{Na}$$

Mass number = number of protons + neutrons
= 23 for sodium

Atomic number = number of protons
= number of electrons in a neutral atom
= 11 for sodium

Number of neutrons = mass number − atomic number
= 23 − 11 = 12 for sodium

The simplest atom is hydrogen, $_1^1$H, which has no neutrons; it consists of a single proton with a single electron.

Because the contribution of electrons to mass is negligible, almost all of an atom's mass is concentrated in its nucleus. And since neutrons and protons each have a mass very close to 1 dalton, the mass number is an approximation of the total mass of an atom, called its **atomic mass**. So we might say that the atomic mass of sodium ($_{11}^{23}$Na) is 23 daltons, although more precisely it is 22.9898 daltons.

Isotopes

All atoms of a given element have the same number of protons, but some atoms have more neutrons than other atoms of the same element and therefore have greater mass. These different atomic forms of the same element are called **isotopes** of the element. In nature, an element occurs as a mixture of its isotopes. As an explanatory example, let's consider the three naturally occurring isotopes of the element carbon, which has the atomic number 6. The most common isotope is carbon-12, $_6^{12}$C, which accounts for about 99% of the carbon in nature. The isotope $_6^{12}$C has 6 neutrons. Most of the remaining 1% of carbon consists of atoms of the isotope $_6^{13}$C, with 7 neutrons. A third, even rarer isotope, $_6^{14}$C, has 8 neutrons. Notice that all three isotopes of carbon have 6 protons; otherwise, they would not be carbon. Although the isotopes of an element have slightly different masses, they behave identically in chemical reactions. (The number usually given as the atomic mass of an element, such as 12.01 daltons for carbon, is actually an average of the atomic masses of all the element's naturally occurring isotopes, weighted according to the abundance of each.)

Both ^{12}C and ^{13}C are stable isotopes, meaning that their nuclei do not have a tendency to lose subatomic particles, a process called decay. The isotope ^{14}C, however, is unstable, or radioactive. A **radioactive isotope** is one in which the nucleus decays spontaneously, giving off particles and energy. When the radioactive decay leads to a change in the number of protons, it transforms the atom to an atom of a different element. For example, when an atom of carbon-14 (^{14}C) decays, it becomes an atom of nitrogen (^{14}N). Radioactive isotopes have many useful applications in biology.

◀ Figure 2.5 **A PET scan, a medical use for radioactive isotopes.** PET, an acronym for positron-emission tomography, detects locations of intense chemical activity in the body. The bright yellow spot marks an area with an elevated level of radioactively labelled glucose, which in turn indicates high metabolic activity, a hallmark of cancerous tissue.

Cancerous throat tissue

Radioactive Tracers

Radioactive isotopes are often used as diagnostic tools in medicine. Cells can use radioactive isotopes just as they would use nonradioactive isotopes of the same element. The radioactive isotopes are incorporated into biologically active molecules, which are then used as tracers to track atoms during metabolism, the chemical processes of an organism. For example, certain kidney disorders are diagnosed by injecting small doses radioactively labelled substances into the blood and then analyzing the tracer molecules excreted in the urine. Radioactive tracers are also used in combination with sophisticated imaging instruments, such as PET scanners that can monitor growth and metabolism of cancers in the body (**Figure 2.5**).

Although radioactive isotopes are very useful in biological research and medicine, radiation from decaying isotopes also poses a hazard to life by damaging cellular molecules. The severity of this damage depends on the type and amount of radiation an organism absorbs. One of the most serious environmental threats is radioactive fallout from nuclear accidents. The doses of most isotopes used in medical diagnosis, however, are relatively safe.

Radiometric Dating

EVOLUTION Researchers measure radioactive decay in fossils to date these relics of past life. Fossils provide a large body of evidence for evolution, documenting differences between organisms from the past and those living at present, and giving us insight into species that have disappeared over time. While the layering of fossil beds establishes that deeper fossils are older than more shallow ones, the actual age (in years) of the fossils in each layer cannot be determined by position alone. This is where radioactive isotopes come in.

A "parent" isotope decays into its "daughter" isotope at a fixed rate, expressed as the **half-life** of the isotope—the time it takes for 50% of the parent isotope to decay. Each radioactive isotope has a characteristic half-life that is not affected by temperature, pressure, or any other

environmental variable. Using a process called **radiometric dating**, scientists measure the ratio of different isotopes and calculate how many half-lives (in years) have passed since an organism was fossilized or a rock was formed. Half-life values range from very short for some isotopes, measured in seconds or days, to extremely long—uranium-238 has a half-life of 4.5 billion years! Each isotope can best "measure" a particular range of years: Uranium-238 was used to determine that moon rocks are approximately 4.5 billion years old, similar to the estimated age of Earth. In the Scientific Skills Exercise, you can work with data from an experiment that used carbon-14 to determine the age of an important fossil. (You'll learn more about radiometric dating of fossils in Chapter 25.)

The Energy Levels of Electrons

The simplified models of the atom in Figure 2.4 greatly exaggerate the size of the nucleus relative to that of the whole atom. If an atom of helium were the size of a typical football stadium, the nucleus would be the size of a pencil eraser in the centre of the field. Moreover, the electrons would be like two tiny gnats buzzing around the stadium. Atoms are mostly empty space.

When two atoms approach each other during a chemical reaction, their nuclei do not come close enough to interact. Of the three kinds of subatomic particles we have discussed, only electrons are directly involved in the chemical reactions between atoms.

(a) A ball bouncing down a flight of stairs provides an analogy for energy levels of electrons, because the ball can come to rest only on each step, not between steps.

Third shell (highest energy level in this model)

Second shell (higher energy level)

First shell (lowest energy level)

Energy absorbed

Energy lost

Atomic nucleus

(b) An electron can move from one shell to another only if the energy it gains or loses is exactly equal to the difference in energy between the energy levels of the two shells. Arrows in this model indicate some of the stepwise changes in potential energy that are possible.

▲ Figure 2.6 **Energy levels of an atom's electrons.** Electrons exist only at fixed levels of potential energy called electron shells.

Calibrating a Standard Radioactive Isotope Decay Curve and Interpreting Data

When Did Neanderthals Become Extinct? Neanderthals (*Homo neanderthalensis*) were living in Europe by 350 000 years ago, perhaps coexisting with early *Homo sapiens* in parts of Eurasia for hundreds or thousands of years. Researchers sought to more accurately determine the extent of their overlap by pinning down when Neanderthals became extinct. They used carbon-14 dating to determine the age of a Neanderthal fossil from the most recent (uppermost) archaeological layer containing Neanderthal bones. In this exercise you will calibrate a standard carbon-14 decay curve and use it to determine the age of this Neanderthal fossil. The age will help you approximate the last time the two species may have coexisted at the site where this fossil was collected.

How the Experiment Was Done Carbon-14 (^{14}C) is a radioactive isotope of carbon that decays to ^{14}N at a constant rate. ^{14}C is present in the atmosphere in small amounts at a constant ratio with both ^{13}C and ^{12}C, two other isotopes of carbon. When carbon is taken up from the atmosphere by a plant during photosynthesis, ^{12}C, ^{13}C, and ^{14}C isotopes are incorporated into the plant in the same proportions in which they were present in the atmosphere. These proportions remain the same in the tissues of an animal that eats the plant. While an organism is alive, the ^{14}C in its body constantly decays to ^{14}N but is constantly replaced by new carbon from the environment. Once an organism dies, it stops taking in new ^{14}C, but the ^{14}C in its tissues continues to decay, while the ^{12}C in its tissues remains the same because it is not radioactive and does not decay. Thus, scientists can calculate how long the pool of original ^{14}C has been decaying in a fossil by measuring the ratio of ^{14}C to ^{12}C and comparing it to the ratio of ^{14}C to ^{12}C present originally in the atmosphere. The fraction of ^{14}C in a fossil compared to the original fraction of ^{14}C can be converted to years because we know that the half-life of ^{14}C is 5730 years—in other words, half of the ^{14}C in a fossil decays every 5730 years.

Data from the Experiment The researchers found that the Neanderthal fossil had approximately 0.0078 (or, in scientific notation, 7.8×10^{-3}) as much ^{14}C as the atmosphere. The questions will guide you through translating this fraction into the age of the fossil.

Interpret the Data

1. A standard graph of radioactive isotope decay is shown at the top of the right column. The graph line shows the fraction of the radioactive isotope over time (before present) in units of half-lives. Recall that a half-life is the amount of time it takes for half of the radioactive isotope to decay. Labelling each data point with the corresponding fractions will help orient you to this graph. Draw an arrow to the data point for half-life = 1 and write the fraction of ^{14}C that will remain after one half-life. Calculate the fraction of ^{14}C remaining at each half-life and write the fractions on the graph near arrows pointing to the data points. Convert each fraction to a decimal number and round off to a maximum of three significant digits (zeros at the beginning of the number

Pascal Goetgheluck/Science Source

▶ **Neanderthal fossils**

[Graph: y-axis "Fraction of isotope remaining in fossil" from 0 to 1.0; x-axis "Time before present (half-lives)" from 0 to 10]

do not count as significant digits). Also write each decimal number in scientific notation.

2. Recall that ^{14}C has a half-life of 5730 years. To calibrate the x-axis for ^{14}C decay, write the time before present in years below each half-life.

3. The researchers found that the Neanderthal fossil had approximately 0.0078 as much ^{14}C as found originally in the atmosphere. (a) Using the numbers on your graph, determine how many half-lives have passed since the Neanderthal died. (b) Using your ^{14}C calibration on the x-axis, what is the approximate age of the Neanderthal fossil in years (round off to the nearest thousand)? (c) Approximately when did Neanderthals become extinct according to this study? (d) The researchers cite evidence that modern humans (*H. sapiens*) became established in the same region as the last Neanderthals approximately 39 000–42 000 years ago. What does this suggest about the overlap of Neanderthals and modern humans?

4. Carbon-14 dating works for fossils up to about 75 000 years old; fossils older than that contain too little ^{14}C to be detected. Most dinosaurs went extinct 65.5 million years ago. (a) Can ^{14}C be used to date dinosaur bones? Explain. (b) Radioactive uranium-235 has a half-life of 704 million years. If it was incorporated into dinosaur bones, could it be used to date the dinosaur fossils? Explain.

Data from "Revised Age of Late Neanderthal Occupation and the End of the Middle Paleolithic in the Northern Caucasus" by Ron Pinhasi et al., *Proceedings of the National Academy of Sciences of the United States of America*, 2011, Volume 108(21). © Jane B Reece.

An atom's electrons vary in the amount of energy they possess. **Energy** is defined as the capacity to cause change—for instance, by doing work. **Potential energy** is the energy that matter possesses because of its location or structure. For example, water in a reservoir on a hill has potential energy because of its altitude. When the gates of the reservoir's dam are opened and the water runs downhill, the energy can be used to do work, such as moving the blades of turbines to generate electricity. Because energy has been expended, the water has less energy at the

bottom of the hill than it did in the reservoir. Matter has a natural tendency to move toward the lowest possible state of potential energy; in our example, the water runs downhill. To restore the potential energy of a reservoir, work must be done to elevate the water against gravity.

The electrons of an atom have potential energy due to their distance from the nucleus (**Figure 2.6**). The negatively charged electrons are attracted to the positively charged nucleus. It takes work to move a given electron farther away from the nucleus, so the more distant an electron is from the nucleus, the greater its potential energy. Unlike the continuous flow of water downhill, changes in the potential energy of electrons can occur only in steps of fixed amounts. An electron having a certain amount of energy is something like a ball on a staircase (Figure 2.6a). The ball can have different amounts of potential energy, depending on which step it is on, but it cannot spend much time between the steps. Similarly, an electron's potential energy is determined by its energy level. An electron can exist only at certain energy levels, not between them.

An electron's energy level is correlated with its average distance from the nucleus. Electrons are found in different **electron shells**, each with a characteristic average distance and energy level. In diagrams, shells can be represented by concentric circles (Figure 2.6b). The first shell is closest to the nucleus, and electrons in this shell have the lowest potential energy. Electrons in the second shell have more energy, and electrons in the third shell even more energy. An electron can move from one shell to another, but only by absorbing or losing an amount of energy equal to the difference in potential energy between its position in the old shell and that in the new shell. When an electron absorbs energy, it moves to a shell farther out

from the nucleus. For example, light energy can excite an electron to a higher energy level. (Indeed, this is the first step taken when plants harness the energy of sunlight for photosynthesis, the process that produces food from carbon dioxide and water. You'll learn more about photosynthesis in Chapter 10.) When an electron loses energy, it "falls back" to a shell closer to the nucleus, and the lost energy is usually released to the environment as heat. For example, sunlight excites electrons in the surface of a car to higher energy levels. When the electrons fall back to their original levels, the car's surface heats up. This thermal energy can be transferred to the air or to your hand if you touch the car.

Electron Distribution and Chemical Properties

The chemical behaviour of an atom is determined by the distribution of electrons in the atom's electron shells. Beginning with hydrogen, the simplest atom, we can imagine building the atoms of the other elements by adding 1 proton and 1 electron at a time (along with an appropriate number of neutrons). **Figure 2.7**, an abbreviated version of what is called the *periodic table of the elements*, shows this distribution of electrons for the first 18 elements, from

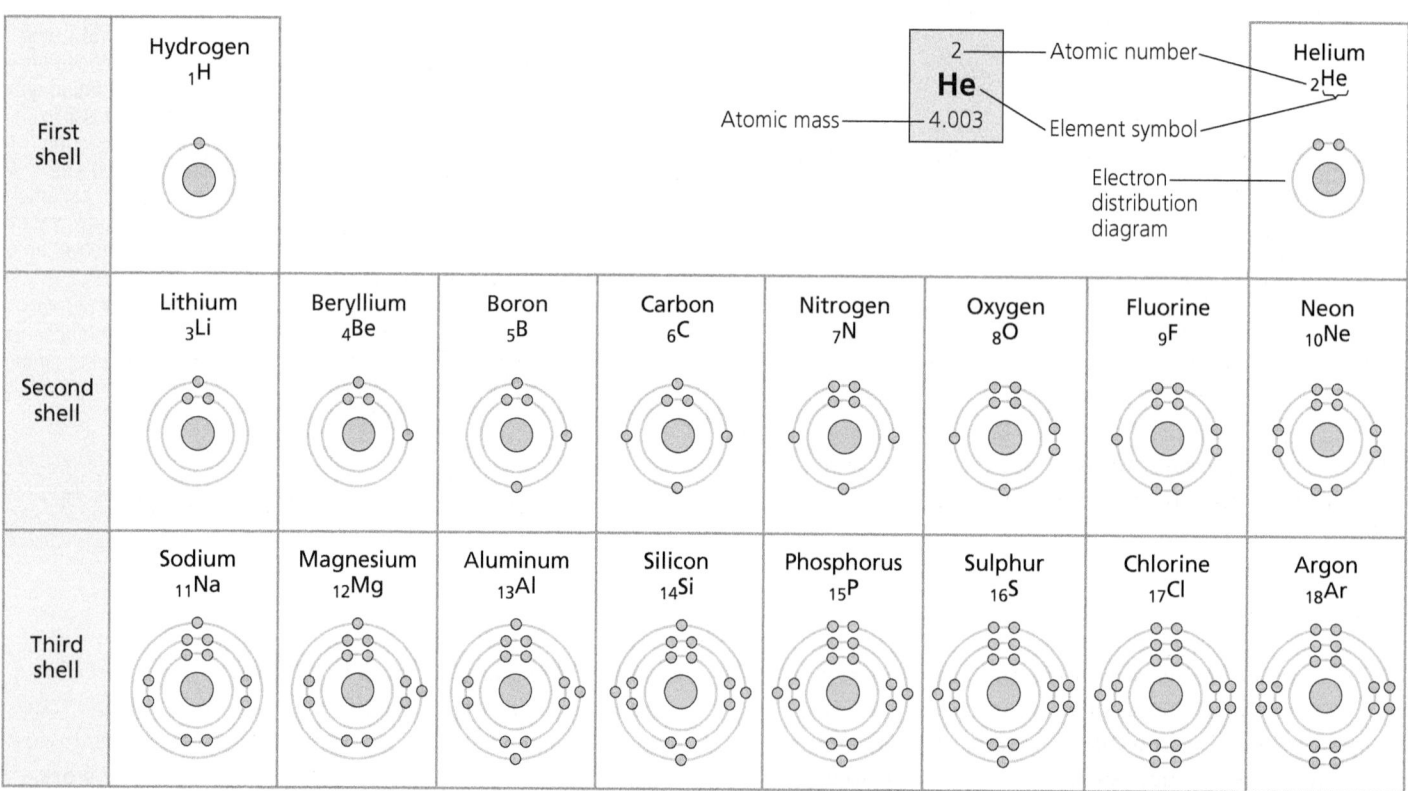

▲ **Figure 2.7 Electron distribution diagrams for the first 18 elements in the periodic table.** In a standard periodic table (see Appendix B), information for each element is presented as shown for helium in the inset. In the diagrams in this table, electrons are represented as yellow dots and electron shells as concentric circles. These diagrams are a convenient way to picture the distribution of an atom's electrons among its electron shells, but these simplified models do not accurately represent the shape of the atom or the location of its electrons. The elements are arranged in rows, each representing the filling of an electron shell. As electrons are added, they occupy the lowest available shell.

? *What is the atomic number of magnesium? How many protons and electrons does it have? How many electron shells? How many valence electrons?*

hydrogen ($_1$H) to argon ($_{18}$Ar). The elements are arranged in three rows, or periods, corresponding to the number of electron shells in their atoms. The left-to-right sequence of elements in each row corresponds to the sequential addition of electrons and protons. (See Appendix B for the complete periodic table.)

Hydrogen's 1 electron and helium's 2 electrons are located in the first shell. Electrons, like all matter, tend to exist in the lowest available state of potential energy. In an atom, this state is in the first shell. However, the first shell can hold no more than 2 electrons; thus, hydrogen and helium are the only elements in the first row of the table. In an atom with more than 2 electrons, the additional electrons must occupy higher shells because the first shell is full. The next element, lithium, has 3 electrons. Two of these electrons fill the first shell, while the third electron occupies the second shell. The second shell holds a maximum of 8 electrons. Neon, at the end of the second row, has 8 electrons in the second shell, giving it a total of 10 electrons.

The chemical behaviour of an atom depends mostly on the number of electrons in its *outermost* shell. We call those outer electrons **valence electrons** and the outermost electron shell the **valence shell**. In the case of lithium, there is only 1 valence electron, and the second shell is the valence shell. Atoms with the same number of electrons in their valence shells exhibit similar chemical behaviour. For example, fluorine (F) and chlorine (Cl) both have 7 valence electrons, and both form compounds when combined with the element sodium (Na): Sodium fluoride (NaF) is commonly added to toothpaste to prevent tooth decay, and, as described earlier, NaCl is table salt (see Figure 2.2). An atom with a completed valence shell is unreactive; that is, it will not interact readily with other atoms. At the far right of the periodic table are helium, neon, and argon, the only three elements shown in Figure 2.7 that have full valence shells. These elements are said to be inert, meaning chemically unreactive. All the other atoms in Figure 2.7 are chemically reactive because they have incomplete valence shells.

Electron Orbitals

In the early 1900s, the electron shells of an atom were visualized as concentric paths of electrons orbiting the nucleus, somewhat like planets orbiting the sun. It is still convenient to use two-dimensional concentric-circle diagrams, as in Figure 2.7, to symbolize three-dimensional electron shells. However, you need to remember that each concentric circle represents only the *average* distance between an electron in that shell and the nucleus. Accordingly, the concentric-circle diagrams do not give a real picture of an atom. In reality, we can never know the exact location of

an electron. What we can do instead is describe the space in which an electron spends most of its time. The three-dimensional space where an electron is found 90% of the time is called an **orbital**.

Each electron shell contains electrons at a particular energy level, distributed among a specific number of orbitals of distinctive shapes and orientations. Figure 2.8 shows the orbitals of neon as an example, with its electron

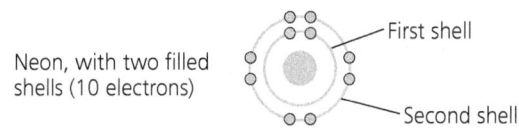

Neon, with two filled shells (10 electrons)
First shell
Second shell

(a) Electron distribution diagram. An electron distribution diagram is shown here for a neon atom, which has a total of 10 electrons. Each concentric circle represents an electron shell, which can be subdivided into electron orbitals.

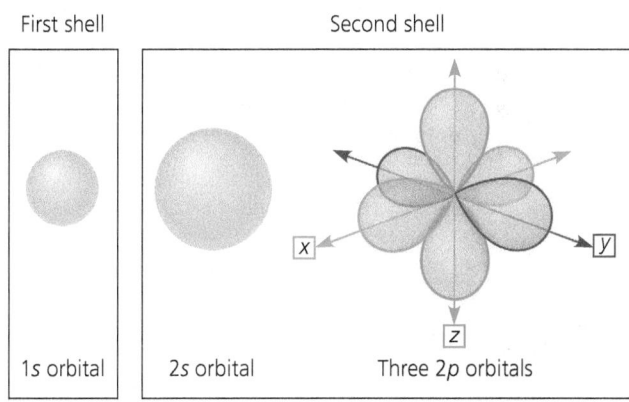

First shell
Second shell
1s orbital
2s orbital
Three 2p orbitals

(b) Separate electron orbitals. The three-dimensional shapes represent electron orbitals—the volumes of space where the electrons of an atom are most likely to be found. Each orbital holds a maximum of 2 electrons. The first electron shell, on the left, has one spherical (*s*) orbital, designated 1*s*. The second shell, on the right, has one larger *s* orbital (designated 2*s* for the second shell) plus three dumbbell-shaped orbitals called *p* orbitals (2*p* for the second shell). The three 2*p* orbitals lie at right angles to one another along imaginary *x*-, *y*-, and *z*-axes of the atom. Each 2*p* orbital is outlined here in a different colour.

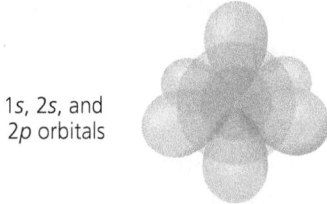

1s, 2s, and 2p orbitals

(c) Superimposed electron orbitals. To reveal the complete picture of the electron orbitals of neon, we superimpose the 1*s* orbital of the first shell and the 2*s* and three 2*p* orbitals of the second shell.

▲ Figure 2.8 **Electron orbitals.**

distribution diagram for reference. You can think of an orbital as a component of an electron shell. The first electron shell has only one spherical *s* orbital (called 1*s*), but the second shell has four orbitals: one large spherical *s* orbital (called 2*s*) and three dumbbell-shaped *p* orbitals (called 2*p* orbitals). (The third shell and other higher electron shells also have *s* and *p* orbitals, as well as orbitals of more complex shapes.)

No more than 2 electrons can occupy a single orbital. The first electron shell can therefore accommodate up to 2 electrons in its *s* orbital. The lone electron of a hydrogen atom occupies the 1*s* orbital, as do the 2 electrons of a helium atom. The four orbitals of the second electron shell can hold up to 8 electrons, 2 in each orbital. Electrons in each of the four orbitals have nearly the same energy, but they move in different volumes of space.

The reactivity of an atom arises from the presence of unpaired electrons in one or more orbitals of its valence shell. As you will see in the next section, atoms interact in a way that completes their valence shells. When they do so, it is the *unpaired* electrons that are involved.

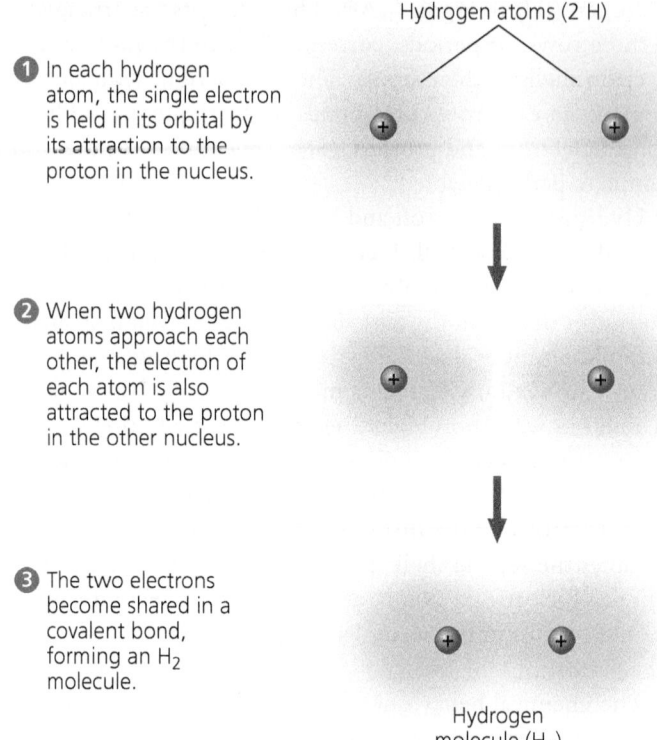

① In each hydrogen atom, the single electron is held in its orbital by its attraction to the proton in the nucleus.

② When two hydrogen atoms approach each other, the electron of each atom is also attracted to the proton in the other nucleus.

③ The two electrons become shared in a covalent bond, forming an H_2 molecule.

Hydrogen atoms (2 H)

Hydrogen molecule (H_2)

▲ Figure 2.9 **Formation of a covalent bond.**

CONCEPT CHECK 2.2

1. A lithium atom has 3 protons and 4 neutrons. What is its mass number?

2. A nitrogen atom has 7 protons, and the most common isotope of nitrogen has 7 neutrons. A radioactive isotope of nitrogen has 8 neutrons. Write the atomic number and mass number of this radioactive nitrogen as a chemical symbol with a subscript and superscript.

3. How many electrons does fluorine have? How many electron shells? Name the orbitals that are occupied. How many electrons are needed to fill the valence shell?

4. **WHAT IF?** In Figure 2.7, if two or more elements are in the same row, what do they have in common? If two or more elements are in the same column, what do they have in common?

For suggested answers, see Appendix A.

CONCEPT **2.3**

The formation and function of molecules depend on chemical bonding between atoms

Now that we have looked at the structure of atoms, we can move up the hierarchy of organization and see how atoms combine to form molecules and ionic compounds. Atoms with incomplete valence shells can interact with certain other atoms in such a way that each partner completes its valence shell: The atoms either share or transfer valence electrons. These interactions usually result in atoms staying close together, held by attractions called **chemical bonds**.

The strongest kinds of chemical bonds are covalent bonds and ionic bonds (when in dry ionic compounds).

Covalent Bonds

A **covalent bond** is the sharing of a pair of valence electrons by two atoms. For example, let's consider what happens when two hydrogen atoms approach each other. Recall that hydrogen has 1 valence electron in the first shell, but the shell's capacity is 2 electrons. When the two hydrogen atoms come close enough for their 1*s* orbitals to overlap, they can share their electrons (Figure 2.9). Each hydrogen atom is now associated with 2 electrons in what amounts to a completed valence shell. Two or more atoms held together by covalent bonds constitute a **molecule**, in this case a hydrogen molecule.

Figure 2.10a shows several ways of representing a hydrogen molecule. Its *molecular formula*, H_2, simply indicates that the molecule consists of two atoms of hydrogen. Electron sharing can be depicted by an electron distribution diagram or by a *Lewis dot structure*, in which element symbols are surrounded by dots that represent the valence electrons (H:H). We can also use a *structural formula*, H—H, where the line represents a **single bond**, a pair of shared electrons. A space-filling model comes closest to representing the actual shape of the molecule. You may also be familiar with ball-and-stick models, which are shown in Figure 2.15.

Oxygen has 6 electrons in its second electron shell and therefore needs 2 more electrons to complete its valence

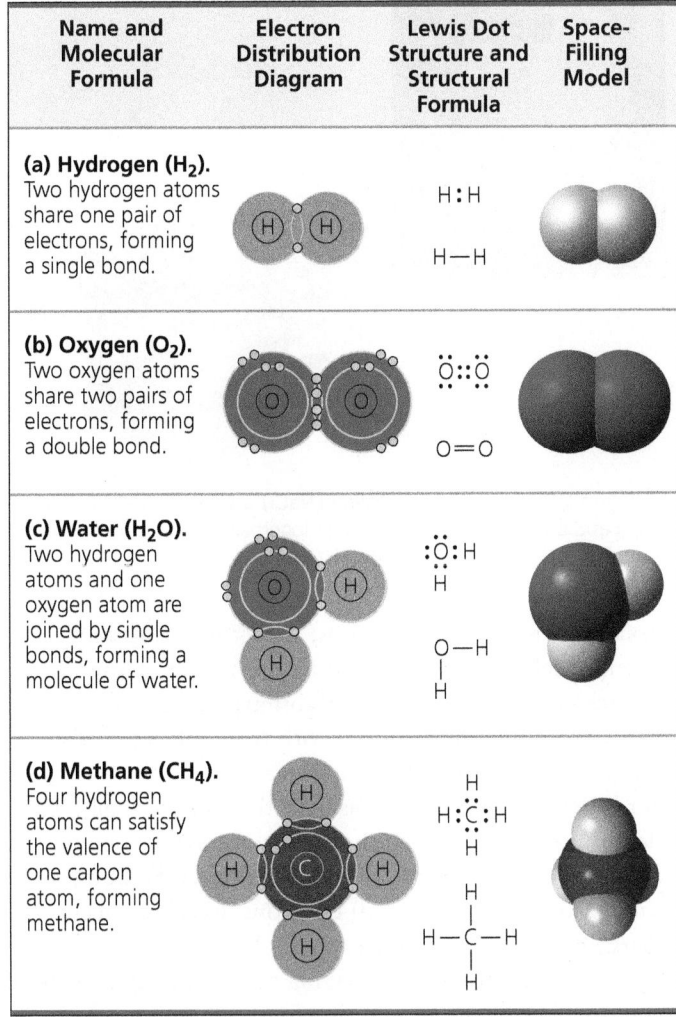

Name and Molecular Formula	Electron Distribution Diagram	Lewis Dot Structure and Structural Formula	Space-Filling Model
(a) Hydrogen (H₂). Two hydrogen atoms share one pair of electrons, forming a single bond.		H:H H—H	
(b) Oxygen (O₂). Two oxygen atoms share two pairs of electrons, forming a double bond.		Ö::Ö O=O	
(c) Water (H₂O). Two hydrogen atoms and one oxygen atom are joined by single bonds, forming a molecule of water.		:Ö:H H O—H H	
(d) Methane (CH₄). Four hydrogen atoms can satisfy the valence of one carbon atom, forming methane.		H H:C:H H H H—C—H H	

▲ Figure 2.10 **Covalent bonding in four molecules.** The number of electrons required to complete an atom's valence shell generally determines how many covalent bonds that atom will form. This figure shows several ways of indicating covalent bonds.

shell. Two oxygen atoms form a molecule by sharing two pairs of valence electrons (**Figure 2.10b**). The atoms are thus joined by what is called a **double bond** (O=O).

Each atom that can share valence electrons has a bonding capacity corresponding to the number of covalent bonds the atom can form. When the bonds form, they give the atom a full complement of electrons in the valence shell. The bonding capacity of oxygen, for example, is 2. This bonding capacity is called the atom's **valence** and usually equals the number of unpaired electrons required to complete the atom's outermost (valence) shell. See if you can determine the valences of hydrogen, oxygen, nitrogen, and carbon by studying the electron distribution diagrams in Figure 2.7. You can see that the valence of hydrogen is 1; oxygen, 2; nitrogen, 3; and carbon, 4. However, the situation is more complicated for elements in the third row of the periodic table. Phosphorus, for example, can have a valence of 3, as we would predict from the presence of

3 unpaired electrons in its valence shell. In some molecules that are biologically important, however, phosphorus can form three single bonds and one double bond. Therefore, it can also have a valence of 5.

The molecules H₂ and O₂ are pure elements rather than compounds because a compound is a combination of two or more *different* elements. Water, with the molecular formula H₂O, is a compound. Two atoms of hydrogen are needed to satisfy the valence of one oxygen atom. **Figure 2.10c** shows the structure of a water molecule. (Water is so important to life that Chapter 3 is devoted entirely to its structure and behaviour.)

Methane, the main component of natural gas, is a compound with the molecular formula CH₄. It takes four hydrogen atoms, each with a valence of 1, to complement one atom of carbon, with its valence of 4 (**Figure 2.10d**). We will look at many other compounds of carbon in Chapter 4.

Atoms in a molecule attract shared bonding electrons to varying degrees, depending on the element. The attraction of a particular atom for the electrons of a covalent bond is called its **electronegativity**. The more electronegative an atom is, the more strongly it pulls shared electrons toward itself. In a covalent bond between two atoms of the same element, the electrons are shared equally because the two atoms have the same electronegativity—the tug-of-war is at a standoff. Such a bond is called a **nonpolar covalent bond**. For example, the single bond of H₂ is nonpolar, as is the double bond of O₂. However, when an atom is bonded to a more electronegative atom, the electrons of the bond are not shared equally. This type of bond is called a **polar covalent bond**. Such bonds vary in their polarity, depending on the relative electronegativity of the two atoms. For example, the bonds between the oxygen and hydrogen atoms of a water molecule are quite polar (**Figure 2.11**).

Oxygen is one of the most electronegative elements, attracting shared electrons much more strongly than hydrogen does. In a covalent bond between oxygen and hydrogen, the electrons spend more time near the oxygen nucleus than they do near the hydrogen nucleus. Because

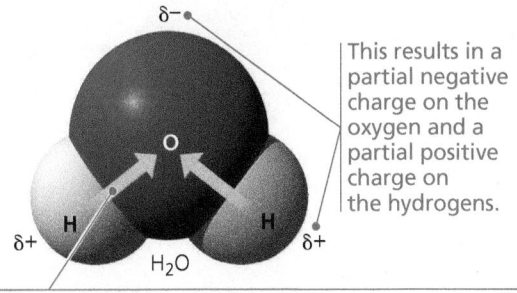

This results in a partial negative charge on the oxygen and a partial positive charge on the hydrogens.

Because oxygen (O) is more electronegative than hydrogen (H), shared electrons are pulled more toward oxygen.

▲ Figure 2.11 **Polar covalent bonds in a water molecule.**

electrons have a negative charge and are pulled toward oxygen in a water molecule, the oxygen atom has a partial negative charge (indicated by the Greek letter δ with a minus sign, δ–, or "delta minus"), and each hydrogen atom has a partial positive charge (δ+, or "delta plus"). In contrast, the individual bonds of methane (CH_4) are much less polar because the electronegativities of carbon and hydrogen are similar. You may find it useful to memorize the relative electronegativities of the most common elements in the human body, including oxygen, carbon, hydrogen, and nitrogen. The relative electronegativities of these elements are: **O>N>C≃H**. (The actual electronegativities are O = 3.44, N = 3.04, C = 2.55, and H = 2.20.) This will be useful as you identify the behaviour of amino acids based on their molecular structure in Chapter 5.

Ionic Bonds

In some cases, two atoms are so unequal in their attraction for valence electrons that the more electronegative atom strips an electron completely away from its partner. The two resulting oppositely charged atoms (or molecules) are called **ions**. A positively charged ion is called a **cation**, while a negatively charged ion is called an **anion**. Because of their opposite charges, cations and anions attract each other; this attraction is called an ionic bond. Note that the transfer of an electron is not, by itself, the formation of a bond; rather, it allows a bond to form because it results in two ions of opposite charge. Any two ions of opposite charge can form an **ionic bond**. The ions do not need to have acquired their charge by an electron transfer with each other.

This is what happens when an atom of sodium ($_{11}Na$) encounters an atom of chlorine ($_{17}Cl$) (**Figure 2.12**). A sodium atom has a total of 11 electrons, with its single valence electron in the third electron shell. A chlorine

▲ **Figure 2.13 A sodium chloride (NaCl) crystal.** The sodium ions (Na^+) and chloride ions (Cl^-) are held together by ionic bonds. The formula NaCl tells us that the ratio of Na^+ to Cl^- is 1:1.

atom has a total of 17 electrons, with 7 electrons in its valence shell. When these two atoms meet, the lone valence electron of sodium is transferred to the chlorine atom, and both atoms end up with their valence shells complete. (Because sodium no longer has an electron in the third shell, the second shell is now the valence shell.) The electron transfer between the two atoms moves one unit of negative charge from sodium to chlorine. Sodium, now with 11 protons but only 10 electrons, has a net electrical charge of 1+: The sodium atom has become a cation. Conversely, the chlorine atom, having gained an extra electron, now has 17 protons and 18 electrons, giving it a net electrical charge of 1–: an anion.

Compounds formed by ionic bonds are called **ionic compounds**, or **salts**. We know the ionic compound sodium chloride (NaCl) as table salt (**Figure 2.13**). Salts are often found in nature as crystals of various sizes and shapes. Each salt crystal is an aggregate of vast numbers of cations and anions bonded by their electrical attraction and arranged in a three-dimensional lattice. Unlike a covalent compound, which consists of molecules having a definite size and number of atoms, an ionic compound does not consist of molecules. The formula for an ionic compound, such as NaCl, indicates only the ratio of elements in a crystal of the salt. "NaCl" by itself is not a molecule.

Not all salts have equal numbers of cations and anions. For example, the ionic compound magnesium chloride ($MgCl_2$) has two chloride ions for each magnesium ion. Magnesium ($_{12}Mg$) must lose 2 outer electrons if the atom

1 The lone valence electron of a sodium atom is transferred to join the 7 valence electrons of a chlorine atom.

2 Each resulting ion has a completed valence shell. An ionic bond can form between the oppositely charged ions.

Na
Sodium atom

Cl
Chlorine atom

Na^+
Sodium ion
(a cation)

Cl^-
Chloride ion
(an anion)

Sodium chloride (NaCl)

▲ **Figure 2.12 Electron transfer and ionic bonding.** The attraction between oppositely charged atoms, or ions, is an ionic bond. An ionic bond can form between any two oppositely charged ions, even if they have not been formed by transfer of an electron from one to the other.

is to have a complete valence shell, so it has a tendency to become a cation with a net charge of 2+ (Mg^{2+}). One magnesium cation can therefore form ionic bonds with two chloride anions.

The term *ion* also applies to entire molecules that are electrically charged. In the salt ammonium chloride (NH_4Cl), for instance, the anion is a single chloride ion (Cl^-), but the cation is ammonium (NH_4^+), a nitrogen atom covalently bonded to four hydrogen atoms. The whole ammonium ion has an electrical charge of 1+ because it has given up 1 electron and thus is 1 electron short.

Environment affects the strength of ionic bonds. In a dry salt crystal, the bonds are so strong that it takes a hammer and chisel to break enough of them to crack the crystal in two. If the same salt crystal is dissolved in water, however, the ionic bonds are much weaker because each ion is partially shielded by its interactions with water molecules. Most drugs are manufactured as salts because they are quite stable when dry but can dissociate (come apart) easily in water. (In the next chapter, you will learn how water dissolves salts.)

Weak Chemical Bonds

In organisms, most of the strongest chemical bonds are covalent bonds, which link atoms to form a cell's molecules. But weaker bonding within and between molecules is also indispensable, contributing greatly to the emergent properties of life. Many large biological molecules are held in their functional form by weak bonds. In addition, when two molecules in the cell make contact, they may adhere temporarily by weak bonds. The reversibility of weak bonding can be an advantage: Two molecules can come together, respond to one another in some way, and then separate.

Several types of weak chemical bonds are important in organisms. One is the ionic bond as it exists between ions dissociated in water, which we just discussed. Hydrogen bonds and van der Waals interactions are also crucial to life.

Hydrogen Bonds

Among weak chemical bonds, hydrogen bonds are so central to the chemistry of life that they deserve special attention. When a hydrogen atom is covalently bonded to an electronegative atom, the hydrogen atom has a partial positive charge that allows it to be attracted to a different electronegative atom nearby. This attraction between a hydrogen and an electronegative atom is called a **hydrogen bond**. In living cells, the electronegative partners are usually oxygen or nitrogen atoms. Refer to **Figure 2.14** to examine the simple case of hydrogen bonding between water (H_2O) and ammonia (NH_3). (You will learn more

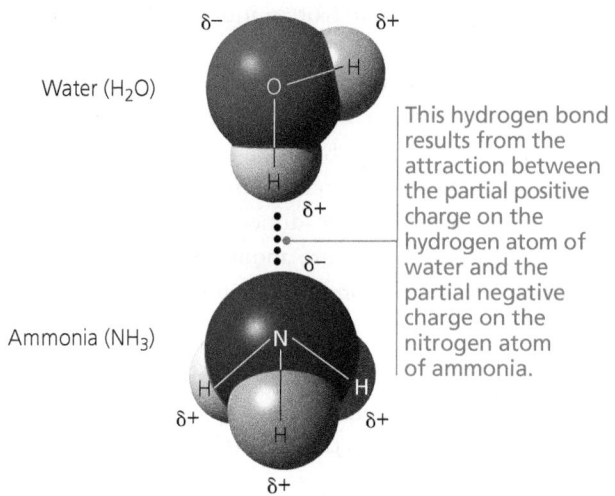

This hydrogen bond results from the attraction between the partial positive charge on the hydrogen atom of water and the partial negative charge on the nitrogen atom of ammonia.

▲ **Figure 2.14 A hydrogen bond.**

DRAW IT *Draw five water molecules. (Use structural formulas; show partial charges.) Show how they make hydrogen bonds with each other.*

about the biological importance of hydrogen bonds and their role in the structure of the DNA double helix in Chapter 16.)

Van der Waals Interactions

Even a molecule with nonpolar covalent bonds may have positively and negatively charged regions. Electrons are not always evenly distributed; at any instant, they may accumulate by chance in one part of a molecule or another. The results are ever-changing regions of positive and negative charge that enable all atoms and molecules to stick to one another. These **van der Waals interactions** are individually weak and occur only when atoms and molecules are very close together. When many such interactions occur simultaneously, however, they can be powerful: Van der Waals interactions allow a gecko lizard (below) to walk straight up a wall! The anatomy of the gecko's foot—including many minuscule hair-like projections from the toes and the strong tendons underlying the skin—strikes a balance between maximum surface contact with the wall and necessary stiffness of the foot. The van der Waals interactions between the foot molecules and the molecules of the wall's surface are so numerous that, despite their individual weakness, together they can support the gecko's body weight. This discovery has inspired development of an artificial adhesive called

Martin Harvey/Photolibrary/Getty Images

"Geckskin": A patch the size of an index card can hold a 320 kg weight to a wall!

Van der Waals interactions, hydrogen bonds, ionic bonds in water, and other weak bonds may form not only between molecules but also between parts of a large molecule, such as a protein. The cumulative effect of weak bonds is to reinforce the three-dimensional shape of the molecule. (You will learn more about the very important biological roles of weak bonds in Chapter 5.)

Molecular Shape and Function

A molecule has a characteristic size and precise shape, which are crucial to its function in the living cell. A molecule consisting of two atoms, such as H_2 or O_2, is always linear, but most molecules with more than two atoms have more complicated shapes. These shapes are determined by the positions of the atoms' orbitals (Figure 2.15). When an atom forms covalent bonds, the orbitals in its valence shell

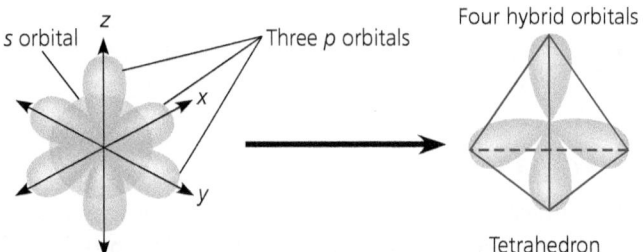

(a) **Hybridization of orbitals.** The single s and three p orbitals of a valence shell involved in covalent bonding combine to form four teardrop-shaped hybrid orbitals. These orbitals extend to the four corners of an imaginary tetrahedron (outlined in pink).

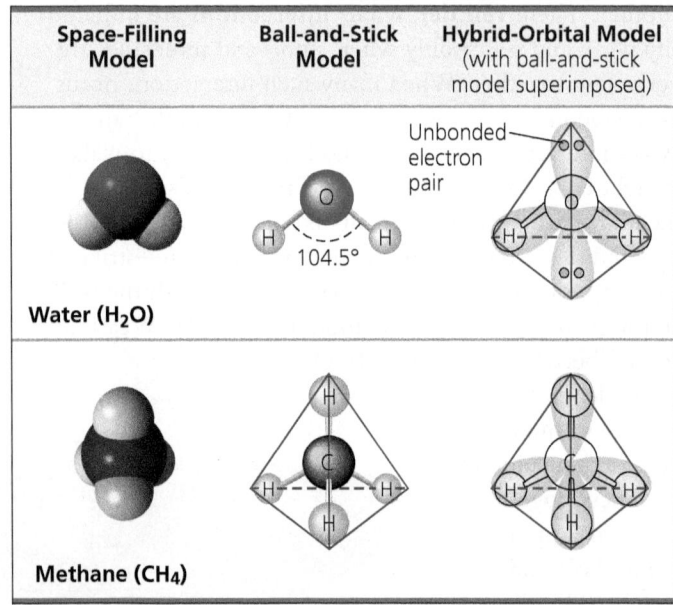

Space-Filling Model	Ball-and-Stick Model	Hybrid-Orbital Model (with ball-and-stick model superimposed)

Water (H_2O)

Methane (CH_4)

(b) **Molecular-shape models.** Three models representing molecular shape are shown for water and methane. The positions of the hybrid orbitals determine the shapes of the molecules.

▲ Figure 2.15 **Molecular shapes due to hybrid orbitals.**

undergo rearrangement. For atoms with valence electrons in both s and p orbitals (review Figure 2.8), the single s and three p orbitals form four new hybrid orbitals shaped like identical teardrops extending from the region of the atomic nucleus (Figure 2.15a). If we connect the larger ends of the teardrops with lines, we have the outline of a geometric shape called a tetrahedron, a pyramid with a triangular base.

For water molecules (H_2O), two of the hybrid orbitals in the oxygen's valence shell are shared with hydrogens (Figure 2.15b). The result is a molecule shaped roughly like a V, with its two covalent bonds spread apart at an angle of 104.5°.

The methane molecule (CH_4) has the shape of a completed tetrahedron because all four hybrid orbitals of the carbon atom are shared with hydrogen atoms (see Figure 2.15b). The carbon nucleus is at the centre, with its four covalent bonds radiating to hydrogen nuclei at the corners of the tetrahedron. Larger molecules containing multiple carbon atoms, including many of the molecules that make up living matter, have more complex overall shapes. However, the tetrahedral shape of a carbon atom bonded to four other atoms is often a repeating motif within such molecules.

Molecular shape is crucial: It determines how biological molecules recognize and respond to one another with specificity. Biological molecules often bind temporarily to each other by forming weak bonds, but this can happen only if their shapes are complementary. Consider the effects of opiates, drugs such as morphine and heroin derived from opium. Opiates relieve pain and alter mood by weakly binding to specific receptor molecules on the surfaces of brain cells. Why would brain cells carry receptors for opiates, compounds that are not made by the body? In 1975, the discovery of endorphins answered this question. Endorphins are signalling molecules made by the pituitary gland that bind to the receptors, relieving pain and producing euphoria during times of stress, such as intense exercise. Opiates have shapes similar to endorphins and mimic them by binding to endorphin receptors in the brain. That is why opiates and endorphins have similar effects (Figure 2.16). The role of molecular shape in brain chemistry illustrates how biological organization leads to a match between structure and function, one of biology's unifying themes.

CONCEPT CHECK 2.3

1. Why does the structure H—C=C—H fail to make sense chemically?

2. What holds the atoms together in a crystal of magnesium chloride ($MgCl_2$)?

3. **WHAT IF?** If you were a pharmaceutical researcher, why would you want to learn the three-dimensional shapes of naturally occurring signalling molecules?

For suggested answers, see Appendix A.

Natural endorphin

Morphine

(a) Structures of endorphin and morphine. The boxed portion of the endorphin molecule (left) binds to receptor molecules on target cells in the brain. The boxed portion of the morphine molecule (right) is a close match.

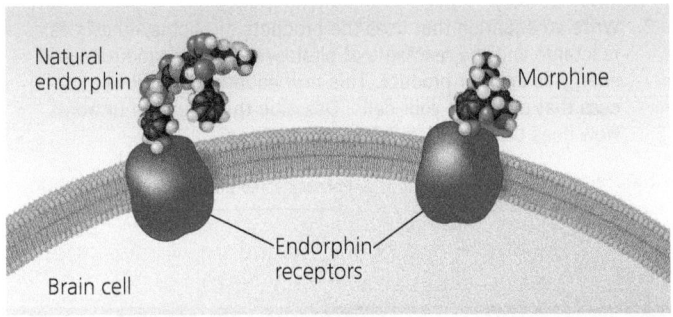

Natural endorphin

Morphine

Endorphin receptors

Brain cell

(b) Binding to endorphin receptors. Both endorphin and morphine can bind to endorphin receptors on the surface of a brain cell.

▲ Figure 2.16 **A molecular mimic.** Morphine affects pain perception and emotional state by mimicking the brain's natural endorphins.

CONCEPT 2.4

Chemical reactions make and break chemical bonds

The making and breaking of chemical bonds, leading to changes in the composition of matter, are called **chemical reactions**. An example is the reaction between hydrogen and oxygen molecules that forms water:

$$2 H_2 + O_2 \longrightarrow 2 H_2O$$

Reactants   **Reaction**   **Products**

This reaction breaks the covalent bonds of H_2 and O_2 and forms the new bonds of H_2O. When we write a chemical reaction, we use an arrow to indicate the conversion of the starting materials, called the **reactants**, to the **products**. The coefficients indicate the number of molecules involved; for example, the coefficient 2 in front of the H_2 means that the reaction starts with two molecules of hydrogen. Notice that all atoms of the reactants must be accounted for in the products. Matter is conserved in a chemical reaction: Reactions cannot create or destroy atoms but can only rearrange (redistribute) the electrons among them.

Photosynthesis, which takes place within the cells of green plant tissues, is an important biological example of how chemical reactions rearrange matter. Humans and other animals ultimately depend on photosynthesis for food and oxygen, and this process is at the foundation of almost all ecosystems. The following chemical shorthand summarizes the process of photosynthesis:

$$6 CO_2 + 6 H_2O \longrightarrow C_6H_{12}O_6 + 6 O_2$$

The raw materials of photosynthesis are carbon dioxide (CO_2), which is taken from the air, and water (H_2O), which is absorbed from the soil. Within the plant cells, sunlight powers the conversion of these ingredients to a sugar called glucose ($C_6H_{12}O_6$) and oxygen molecules (O_2), a by-product that the plant releases into the surroundings (**Figure 2.17**). Although

▲ Figure 2.17 **Photosynthesis: a solar-powered rearrangement of matter.** Elodea, a freshwater plant, produces sugar by rearranging the atoms of carbon dioxide and water in the chemical process known as photosynthesis, which is powered by sunlight. Much of the sugar is then converted to other food molecules. Oxygen gas (O_2) is a by-product of photosynthesis; notice the bubbles of O_2-containing gas escaping from the leaves in the photo.

[?] *Explain how this photo relates to the reactants and products in the equation for photosynthesis given in the text. (You will learn more about photosynthesis in Chapter 10.)*

Nigel Cattlin/Science Source

photosynthesis is actually a sequence of many chemical reactions, we still end up with the same number and types of atoms that we had when we started. Matter has simply been rearranged, with an input of energy provided by sunlight.

All chemical reactions are reversible, with the products of the forward reaction becoming the reactants for the reverse reaction. For example, hydrogen and nitrogen molecules can combine to form ammonia, but ammonia can also decompose to regenerate hydrogen and nitrogen:

$$3\,H_2 + N_2 \rightleftharpoons 2\,NH_3$$

The two opposite-headed arrows indicate that the reaction is reversible.

One of the factors affecting the rate of a reaction is the concentration of reactants. The greater the concentration of reactant molecules, the more frequently they collide with one another and have an opportunity to react and form products. The same holds true for products. As products accumulate, collisions resulting in the reverse reaction become more frequent. Eventually, the forward and reverse reactions occur at the same rate, and the relative concentrations of products and reactants stop changing. The point at which the reactions offset one another exactly is called **chemical equilibrium**. This is a dynamic equilibrium; reactions are still going on, but with no net effect on the concentrations of reactants and products. Equilibrium does *not* mean that the reactants and products are equal in concentration, but only that their

concentrations have stabilized at a particular ratio. The reaction involving ammonia reaches equilibrium when ammonia decomposes as rapidly as it forms. In some chemical reactions, the equilibrium point may lie so far to the right that these reactions go essentially to completion; that is, virtually all the reactants are converted to products.

We will return to the subject of chemical reactions after more detailed study of the various types of molecules that are important to life. In the next chapter, we focus on water, the substance in which all the chemical processes of organisms occur.

CONCEPT CHECK 2.4

1. **MAKE CONNECTIONS** Consider the reaction between hydrogen and oxygen that forms water, shown with ball-and-stick models at the beginning of Concept 2.4. Study Figure 2.10 and draw the Lewis dot structures representing this reaction.

2. Which type of chemical reaction occurs faster at equilibrium: the formation of products from reactants or reactants from products?

3. Write an equation that uses the products of photosynthesis as reactants and the reactants of photosynthesis as products. Add energy as another product. This new equation describes a process that occurs in your cells. Describe this equation in words. How does this equation relate to breathing?

For suggested answers, see Appendix A.

---

2 Chapter Review

Go to **MasteringBiology®** for Assignments, the eText, and the Study Area with Animations, Activities, Vocab Self-Quiz, and Practice Tests.

SUMMARY OF KEY CONCEPTS

CONCEPT 2.1

Matter consists of chemical elements in pure form and in combinations called compounds (pp. 33–34)

- **Elements** cannot be broken down chemically to other substances. A **compound** contains two or more different elements in a fixed ratio. Oxygen, carbon, hydrogen, and nitrogen make up approximately 96% of living matter.

  ? *In what way does the need for iodine or iron in your diet differ from your need for calcium or phosphorus?*

CONCEPT 2.2

An element's properties depend on the structure of its atoms (pp. 34–40)

- An **atom**, the smallest unit of an element, has the following components:

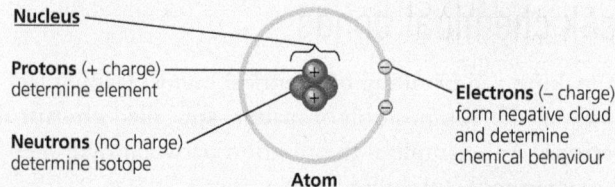

Nucleus

Protons (+ charge) determine element

Neutrons (no charge) determine isotope

Electrons (– charge) form negative cloud and determine chemical behaviour

Atom

- An electrically neutral atom has equal numbers of electrons and protons; the number of protons determines the **atomic number**. The **atomic mass** is measured in **daltons** and is roughly equal to the mass number, the sum of protons plus neutrons. **Isotopes** of an element differ from each other in neutron number and therefore mass. Unstable isotopes give off particles and energy as radioactivity.
- In an atom, electrons occupy specific **electron shells**; the electrons in a shell have a characteristic energy level. Electron distribution in shells determines the chemical behaviour of an atom. The outer shell is called the **valence shell**. If it is incomplete, the atom is reactive.

- Electrons exist in **orbitals**, three-dimensional spaces with specific shapes that are components of electron shells.

DRAW IT *Draw the electron distribution diagrams for neon ($_{10}$Ne) and argon ($_{18}$Ar). Use these diagrams to explain why these elements are chemically unreactive.*

CONCEPT 2.3

The formation and function of molecules depend on chemical bonding between atoms (pp. 40–45)

- **Chemical bonds** form when atoms interact and complete their valence shells. **Covalent bonds** form when pairs of electrons are shared.

$$H\cdot + H\cdot \longrightarrow H:H$$
Single covalent bond

$$:\ddot{O}\cdot + \cdot\ddot{O}: \longrightarrow \ddot{O}::\ddot{O}$$
Double covalent bond

- **Molecules** consist of two or more covalently bonded atoms. The attraction of an atom for the electrons of a covalent bond is its **electronegativity**. If both atoms are the same, they have the same electronegativity and share a **nonpolar covalent bond**. Electrons of a **polar covalent bond** are pulled closer to the more electronegative atom.
- An **ion** forms when an atom or molecule gains or loses an electron and becomes charged. An **ionic bond** is the attraction between two oppositely charged ions.

Ionic bond

Electron transfer forms ions

| **Na** Sodium atom | **Cl** Chlorine atom | **Na⁺** Sodium ion (a cation) | **Cl⁻** Chloride ion (an anion) |

- Weak bonds reinforce the shapes of large molecules and help molecules adhere to each other. A **hydrogen bond** is an attraction between a hydrogen atom carrying a partial positive charge ($\delta+$) and an electronegative atom ($\delta-$). **Van der Waals interactions** occur between transiently positive and negative regions of molecules.
- A molecule's shape is determined by the positions of its atoms' valence orbitals. Covalent bonds result in hybrid orbitals, which are responsible for the shapes of H_2O, CH_4, and many more complex biological molecules. Shape is usually the basis for the recognition of one biological molecule by another.

? *In terms of electron sharing between atoms, compare nonpolar covalent bonds, polar covalent bonds, and the formation of ions.*

CONCEPT 2.4

Chemical reactions make and break chemical bonds (pp. 45–46)

- **Chemical reactions** change **reactants** into **products** while conserving matter. All chemical reactions are theoretically reversible. **Chemical equilibrium** is reached when the forward and reverse reaction rates are equal.

? *What would happen to the concentration of products if more reactants were added to a reaction that was in chemical equilibrium? How would this addition affect the equilibrium?*

LEVEL 1: KNOWLEDGE/COMPREHENSION

1. In the term *trace element*, the adjective *trace* means that
   a. the element is required in very small amounts.
   b. the element can be used as a label to trace atoms through an organism's metabolism.
   c. the element is very rare on Earth.
   d. the element enhances health but is not essential for the organism's long-term survival.

2. Compared with ^{31}P, the radioactive isotope ^{32}P has
   a. a different atomic number.
   b. one more proton.
   c. one more electron.
   d. one more neutron.

3. The reactivity of an atom arises from
   a. the average distance of the outermost electron shell from the nucleus.
   b. the existence of unpaired electrons in the valence shell.
   c. the sum of the potential energies of all the electron shells.
   d. the potential energy of the valence shell.

4. Which statement is true of all atoms that are anions?
   a. The atom has more electrons than protons.
   b. The atom has more protons than electrons.
   c. The atom has fewer protons than does a neutral atom of the same element.
   d. The atom has more neutrons than protons.

5. Which of the following statements correctly describes any chemical reaction that has reached equilibrium?
   a. The concentrations of products and reactants are equal.
   b. The reaction is now irreversible.
   c. Both forward and reverse reactions have halted.
   d. The rates of the forward and reverse reactions are equal.

LEVEL 2: APPLICATION/ANALYSIS

6. We can represent atoms by listing the number of protons, neutrons, and electrons—for example, $2p^+$, $2n^0$, $2e^-$ for helium. Which of the following represents the ^{18}O isotope of oxygen?
   a. $7p^+$, $2n^0$, $9e^-$
   b. $8p^+$, $10n^0$, $8e^-$
   c. $9p^+$, $9n^0$, $9e^-$
   d. $10p^+$, $8n^0$, $9e^-$

7. The atomic number of sulphur is 16. Sulphur combines with hydrogen by covalent bonding to form a compound, hydrogen sulphide. Based on the number of valence electrons in a sulphur atom, predict the molecular formula of the compound.
   a. HS
   b. HS_2
   c. H_2S
   d. H_4S

8. What coefficients must be placed in the following blanks so that all atoms are accounted for in the products?

   $$C_6H_{12}O_6 \rightarrow \underline{\quad} C_2H_6O + \underline{\quad} CO_2$$

   a. 2; 1
   b. 3; 1
   c. 1; 3
   d. 2; 2

9. **DRAW IT** Draw Lewis dot structures for each hypothetical molecule shown below, using the correct number of valence electrons for each atom. Determine which molecule makes sense because each atom has a complete valence shell and each bond has the correct number of electrons. Explain what makes the other molecules nonsensical, considering the number of bonds each type of atom can make.

   (a)
   $$H-O-\underset{\underset{H}{|}}{\overset{\overset{H}{|}}{C}}-\underset{\underset{H}{|}}{\overset{\overset{H}{|}}{C}}=O$$

   (b)
   $$H-\underset{\underset{H}{|}}{\overset{\overset{H}{|}}{C}}-H-\underset{\underset{H}{|}}{\overset{\overset{H}{|}}{C}}=O$$

LEVEL 3: SYNTHESIS/EVALUATION

10. **EVOLUTION CONNECTION** The percentages of naturally occurring elements making up the human body (see Table 2.1) are similar to the percentages of these elements found in other organisms. How could you account for this similarity among organisms?

11. **SCIENTIFIC INQUIRY** Female silkworm moths (*Bombyx mori*) attract males by emitting chemical signals that spread through the air. A male hundreds of metres away can detect these molecules and fly toward their source. The sensory organs responsible for this behaviour are the comblike antennae visible in the photo-

graph shown here. Each filament of an antenna is equipped with thousands of receptor cells that detect the sex attractant. Based on what you learned in this chapter, propose a hypothesis to account for the ability of the male moth to detect a specific molecule in the presence of many other molecules in the air. What predictions does your hypothesis make? Design an experiment to test one of these predictions.

12. **WRITE ABOUT A THEME: ORGANIZATION** While waiting at an airport, Neil Campbell once overheard this claim: "It's paranoid and ignorant to worry about industry or agriculture contaminating the environment with their chemical wastes. After all, this stuff is just made of the same atoms that were already present in our environment." Drawing on your knowledge of electron distribution, bonding, and the theme of emergent properties (p. 3), write a short essay (100–150 words) countering this argument.

13. **SYNTHESIZE YOUR KNOWLEDGE**

This bombardier beetle is spraying a boiling hot liquid that contains irritating chemicals used as a defence mechanism against its enemies. The beetle stores two sets of chemicals separately in its glands. Using what you learned about chemistry in this chapter, propose a possible explanation for why the beetle is not harmed by the chemicals it stores and what causes the explosive discharge.

For selected answers, see Appendix A.

3

Water and Life

▲ Polar bears use ice as a hunting platform.

KEY CONCEPTS

3.1 Polar covalent bonds in water molecules result in hydrogen bonding

3.2 Four emergent properties of water contribute to Earth's suitability for life

3.3 Acidic and basic conditions affect living organisms

KPG_Payless/Shutterstock

▲ Figure 3.1 **How does the life of a harp seal depend on the chemistry of water?**

The Molecule That Supports All of Life

Life on Earth began in water and evolved there for 3 billion years before spreading onto land. Water is the substance that makes possible life as we know it here on Earth. All organisms familiar to us are made mostly of water and live in an environment dominated by water. Water is the biological medium here on Earth, and possibly on other planets as well.

Three-quarters of Earth's surface is covered by water. Although most of this water is in liquid form, water is also present on Earth as a solid (ice) and a gas (water vapour). Water is the only common substance to exist in the natural environment in all three physical states of matter. Furthermore, the solid state of water floats on the liquid, a rare property emerging from the chemistry of the water molecule. Ice can thus provide a pupping platform for harp seals to give birth and nurse pups (Figures 3.1 and 3.7), and a hunting platform for the polar bear (left).

As the Earth is warming from climate change (see Concept 1.1), the ratio of ice to liquid water is changing. Arctic sea ice and glaciers are melting, affecting life around them. In the Arctic, warmer waters and the smaller ice pack have a negative impact on organisms that depend on Arctic ice.

In this chapter, you will learn how the structure of a water molecule allows it to interact with other molecules, including other water molecules. This ability leads to water's unique emergent properties that help make Earth suitable for life.

Alexander/Fotolia

49

CONCEPT 3.1

Polar covalent bonds in water molecules result in hydrogen bonding

Water is so familiar to us that it is easy to overlook its many extraordinary qualities. Following the theme of emergent properties, we can trace water's unique behaviour to the structure and interactions of its molecules.

Studied on its own, the water molecule is deceptively simple. It is shaped like a wide V, with its two hydrogen atoms joined to the oxygen atom by single covalent bonds. Oxygen is more electronegative than hydrogen, so the electrons of the covalent bonds spend more time closer to oxygen than to hydrogen; these are **polar covalent bonds** (see Figure 2.11). This unequal sharing of electrons and water's V-like shape make it a **polar molecule**, meaning that its overall charge is unevenly distributed. In water, the oxygen region of the molecule has a partial negative charge ($\delta-$), and each hydrogen has a partial positive charge ($\delta+$).

The properties of water arise from attractions between oppositely charged atoms of different water molecules: The partially positive hydrogen of one molecule is attracted to the partially negative oxygen of a nearby molecule. The two molecules are thus held together by a hydrogen bond (**Figure 3.2**). When water is in its liquid form, its hydrogen bonds are very fragile, each only about 1/20 as strong as a covalent bond. The hydrogen bonds form, break, and re-form with great frequency. Each lasts only a few trillionths of a second, but the molecules are constantly forming new hydrogen bonds with a succession of partners. Therefore, at any instant, most of the water molecules are hydrogen-bonded to their neighbours. The extraordinary properties of water emerge from this hydrogen bonding, which organizes water molecules into a higher level of structural order.

CONCEPT CHECK 3.1

1. **MAKE CONNECTIONS** What is electronegativity, and how does it affect interactions between water molecules? (Review Figure 2.11.)

2. Why is it unlikely that two neighbouring water molecules would be arranged like this?

$$O \underset{\diagdown H \;\; H \diagup}{\overset{\diagup H \;\; H \diagdown}{}} O$$

3. **WHAT IF?** What would be the effect on the properties of the water molecule if oxygen and hydrogen had equal electronegativity?

For suggested answers, see Appendix A.

CONCEPT 3.2

Four emergent properties of water contribute to Earth's suitability for life

We will examine four emergent properties of water that contribute to Earth's suitability as an environment for life: cohesive behaviour, ability to moderate temperature, expansion upon freezing, and versatility as a solvent.

Cohesion of Water Molecules

Water molecules stay close to each other as a result of hydrogen bonding. Although the arrangement of molecules in a sample of liquid water is constantly changing, at any given moment many of the molecules are linked by multiple hydrogen bonds. These linkages make water more structured than most other liquids. Collectively, the hydrogen bonds hold the substance together, a phenomenon called **cohesion**.

Cohesion due to hydrogen bonding contributes to the transport of water and dissolved nutrients against gravity in plants. Water from the roots reaches the leaves

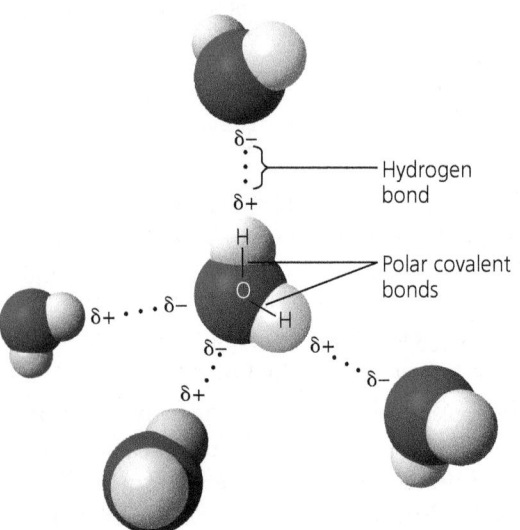

▲ Figure 3.2 **Hydrogen bonds between water molecules.** The charged regions in a water molecule are due to its polar covalent bonds. Oppositely charged regions of neighbouring water molecules are attracted to each other, forming hydrogen bonds. Each molecule can hydrogen-bond to multiple partners, and these associations are constantly changing.

DRAW IT *Draw partial charges on all the atoms of the water molecule on the far left, and draw two more water molecules hydrogen-bonded to it.*

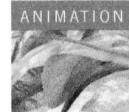

▲ **Figure 3.3 Water transport in plants.** Evaporation from leaves pulls water upward from the roots through water-conducting cells. Because of the properties of cohesion and adhesion, the tallest trees can transport water more than 100 m upward—approximately one-fifth the height of the CN Tower in Toronto.

ANIMATION **BioFlix** Visit the Study Area at **MasteringBiology** for the BioFlix® 3-D Animation on Water Transport in Plants.

through a network of water-conducting cells (**Figure 3.3**). As water evaporates from a leaf, hydrogen bonds cause water molecules leaving the veins to tug on molecules farther down, and the upward pull is transmitted through the water-conducting cells all the way to the roots. **Adhesion**, the clinging of one substance to another, also plays a role. Adhesion of water by hydrogen bonds to the molecules of cell walls helps counter the downward pull of gravity.

Related to cohesion is **surface tension**, a measure of how difficult it is to stretch or break the surface of a liquid. At the interface between water and air is an ordered

▼ **Figure 3.4 Walking on water.** The high surface tension of water, resulting from the collective strength of its hydrogen bonds, allows this raft spider to walk on the surface of a pond.

AlasdairJames/Getty Images

arrangement of water molecules, hydrogen-bonded to one another and to the water below. This gives water an unusually high surface tension, making it behave as though it were coated with an invisible film. You can observe the surface tension of water by slightly overfilling a drinking glass; the water will stand above the rim. The spider in **Figure 3.4** takes advantage of the surface tension of water to walk across a pond without breaking the surface.

Moderation of Temperature by Water

Water moderates air temperature by absorbing heat from air that is warmer and releasing the stored heat to air that is cooler. Water is effective as a heat bank because it can absorb or release a relatively large amount of heat with only a slight change in its own temperature. To understand this capability of water, let's first look at temperature and heat.

Temperature and Heat

Anything that moves has **kinetic energy**, the energy of motion. Atoms and molecules have kinetic energy because they are always moving, although not necessarily in any particular direction. The faster a molecule moves, the greater its kinetic energy. The kinetic energy associated with the random movement of atoms or molecules is called **thermal energy**. Thermal energy is related to temperature, but they are not the same thing. **Temperature** is a measure of energy that represents the average kinetic energy of the molecules in a body of matter, regardless of volume, whereas the total thermal energy depends in part on the matter's volume. When water is heated in a coffeemaker, the average speed of the molecules increases, and the thermometer records this as a rise in temperature of the liquid. The total amount of thermal energy also increases in this case. Note, however, that although the pot of coffee has a much higher temperature than, say, the water in a swimming pool, the swimming pool contains more thermal energy because of its much greater volume.

Whenever two objects of different temperature are brought together, thermal energy passes from the warmer to the cooler object until the two are the same temperature. Molecules in the cooler object speed up at the expense of the thermal energy of the warmer object. An ice cube cools a drink not by adding coldness to the liquid, but by absorbing thermal energy from the liquid as the ice itself melts. Thermal energy in transfer from one body of matter to another is defined as **heat**.

According to the International System of Units, heat energy is measured in joules (J); however, historically heat has also been measured in calories. A calorie is the amount of heat it takes to raise the temperature of 1 g of water by 1°C. Conversely, a calorie is also the amount of heat that 1 g of water releases when it cools by

1°C. A **kilocalorie (kcal)**, 1000 cal, is the quantity of heat required to raise the temperature of 1 kilogram (kg) of water by 1°C. (The "calories" on food packages are actually kilocalories.) One joule equals 0.239 cal; one calorie equals 4.184 J.

Water's High Specific Heat

The ability of water to stabilize temperature stems from its relatively high specific heat. The **specific heat** of a substance is defined as the amount of heat that must be absorbed or lost for 1 g of that substance to change its temperature by 1°C. The specific heat of water is 4.18 joules per gram and per degree Celsius, abbreviated as 4.18 J/g·°C. Compared with most other substances, water has an unusually high specific heat. For example, ethyl alcohol, the type of alcohol in alcoholic beverages, has a specific heat of 2.46 J/g·°C; that is, only 2.46 joules is required to raise the temperature of 1 g of ethyl alcohol by 1°C.

Because of the high specific heat of water relative to other materials, water will change its temperature less than other liquids when it absorbs or loses a given amount of heat. The reason you can burn your fingers by touching the side of an iron pot on the stove when the water in the pot is still lukewarm is that the specific heat of water is ten times greater than that of iron. In other words, the same amount of heat will raise the temperature of 1 g of the iron much faster than it will raise the temperature of 1 g of the water. Specific heat can be thought of as a measure of how well a substance resists changing its temperature when it absorbs or releases heat. Water resists changing its temperature; when it does change its temperature, it absorbs or loses a relatively large quantity of heat for each degree of change.

We can trace water's high specific heat, like many of its other properties, to hydrogen bonding. Heat must be absorbed in order to break hydrogen bonds; by the same token, heat is released when hydrogen bonds form. A few joules of heat cause a relatively small change in the temperature of water because much of the heat is used to disrupt hydrogen bonds before the water molecules can begin moving faster. And when the temperature of water drops slightly, many additional hydrogen bonds form, releasing a considerable amount of energy in the form of heat.

What is the relevance of water's high specific heat to life on Earth? A large body of water can absorb and store a huge amount of heat from the sun in the daytime and during summer while warming up only a few degrees. At night and during winter, the gradually cooling water can warm the air. This capability of water serves to moderate air temperatures in coastal areas (Figure 3.5). The high specific heat of water also tends to stabilize ocean temperatures, creating a favourable environment for marine life. Thus, because of its high specific heat, the water that covers most of Earth keeps temperature

▲ Figure 3.5 **Temperature for the Pacific Ocean and Southern California on an August day.**

INTERPRET THE DATA *Explain the pattern of temperatures shown in this diagram.*

fluctuations on land and in water within limits that permit life. Also, because organisms are made primarily of water, they are better able to resist changes in their own temperature than if they were made of a liquid with a lower specific heat.

Evaporative Cooling

Molecules of any liquid stay close together because they are attracted to one another. Molecules moving fast enough to overcome these attractions can depart the liquid and enter the air as a gas (vapour). This transformation from a liquid to a gas is called *vaporization*, or *evaporation*. Recall that the speed of molecular movement varies and that temperature is the average kinetic energy of molecules. Even at low temperatures, the speediest molecules can escape into the air. Some evaporation occurs at any temperature; a glass of water at room temperature, for example, will eventually evaporate completely. If a liquid is heated, the average kinetic energy of molecules increases and the liquid evaporates more rapidly.

Heat of vaporization is the quantity of heat a liquid must absorb for 1 g of it to be converted from the liquid to the gaseous state. For the same reason that water has a high specific heat, it also has a high heat of vaporization relative to most other liquids. To evaporate 1 g of water at 25°C, about 2427 joules of heat is needed—nearly double the amount needed to vaporize a gram of alcohol or ammonia. Water's high heat of vaporization is another emergent property resulting from the strength of its hydrogen bonds, which must be broken before the molecules can exit from the liquid in the form of water vapour.

The high amount of energy required to vaporize water has a wide range of effects. On a global scale, for example, it helps moderate Earth's climate. A considerable amount of solar heat absorbed by tropical seas is consumed during the evaporation of surface water. Then, as moist tropical air circulates poleward, it releases heat as it condenses and forms rain. On an organismal level, water's high heat of vaporization accounts for the severity of steam burns. These burns are caused by the heat energy released when steam condenses into liquid on the skin.

As a liquid evaporates, the surface of the liquid that remains behind cools down (its temperature decreases). This **evaporative cooling** occurs because the "hottest" molecules, those with the greatest kinetic energy, are the most likely to leave as gas. It is as if the hundred fastest runners at a university transferred to another school; the average speed of the remaining students would decline.

Evaporative cooling of water contributes to the stability of temperature in lakes and ponds and also provides a mechanism that prevents terrestrial organisms from overheating. For example, evaporation of water from the leaves of a plant helps keep the tissues in the leaves from becoming too warm in the sunlight. Evaporation of sweat from human skin dissipates body heat and helps prevent overheating on a hot day or when excess heat is generated by strenuous activity. High humidity on a hot day increases discomfort because the high concentration of water vapour in the air inhibits the evaporation of sweat from the body.

Floating of Ice on Liquid Water

Water is one of the few substances that are less dense as a solid than as a liquid. In other words, ice floats on liquid water. While other materials contract and become denser when they solidify, water expands. The cause of this exotic behaviour is, once again, hydrogen bonding. At temperatures above 4°C, water behaves like other liquids, expanding as it warms and contracting as it cools. As the temperature falls from 4°C to 0°C, water begins to freeze because more and more of its molecules are moving too slowly to break hydrogen bonds. At 0°C, the molecules become locked into a crystalline lattice, each water molecule hydrogen-bonded to four partners (Figure 3.6). The hydrogen bonds keep the

molecules at "arm's length," far enough apart to make ice about 10% less dense (10% fewer molecules for the same volume) than liquid water at 4°C. When ice absorbs enough heat for its temperature to rise above 0°C, hydrogen bonds between molecules are disrupted. As the crystal collapses, the ice melts, and molecules are free to slip closer together. Water reaches its greatest density at 4°C and then begins to expand as the molecules move faster. Even in liquid water, many of the molecules are connected by hydrogen bonds, though only transiently: The hydrogen bonds are constantly breaking and re-forming.

The ability of ice to float due to its lower density is an important factor in the suitability of the environment for life. If ice sank, then eventually all ponds, lakes, and even oceans would freeze solid, making life as we know it impossible on Earth. During summer, only the upper few inches of the ocean would thaw. Instead, when a deep body of water cools, the floating ice insulates the liquid water below, preventing it from freezing and allowing life to exist under the frozen surface, as shown in the photo in Figure 3.6. Besides insulating the water below, ice also provides solid habitat for some animals, such as polar bears and seals (see Figures 3.1 and 3.7).

Many scientists are worried that these bodies of ice are at risk of disappearing. Global warming, which is caused by carbon dioxide and other "greenhouse" gases in the atmosphere, is having a profound effect on icy environments around the globe. In the Arctic, the average air temperature has risen 1.4°C just since 1961. This temperature increase has affected the seasonal balance between Arctic sea ice and liquid water, causing ice to form later in the year, to melt earlier, and to cover a smaller area. The alarming rate at which glaciers and Arctic sea ice are disappearing is posing

▶ Figure 3.6 **Ice: crystalline structure and floating barrier.** In ice, each molecule is hydrogen-bonded to four neighbours in a three-dimensional crystal. Because the crystal is spacious, ice has fewer molecules than an equal volume of liquid water. In other words, ice is less dense than liquid water. Floating ice becomes a barrier that protects the liquid water below from the colder air. The marine organism shown here is a type of shrimp called krill; it was photographed beneath floating ice in the Southern Ocean near Antarctica.

WHAT IF? *If water did not form hydrogen bonds, what would happen to the shrimp's habitat, shown here?*

Hydrogen bond

Ice:
Hydrogen bonds
are stable

Liquid water:
Hydrogen bonds
break and re-form

Jan van Franeker/Alfred-Wegener-Institut fur
Polar-und Meeresforschung, Germany

▲ Figure 3.7 **Marine mammals that depend on Arctic ice.** Many Arctic marine mammals rely on sea ice for hunting, travel, and/or birthing. (a) Polar bears use the ice for hunting and travel. (b) Harp seals use the ice as a pupping platform to give birth and nurse pups. (c) Walruses seasonally feed from the edge of sea-ice platforms. (d) Bearded seals use the ice as a pupping platform, and also for moulting.

an extreme challenge to animals, such as those depicted in Figure 3.7, that depend on ice for their survival.

Water: The Solvent of Life

A sugar cube placed in a glass of water will dissolve with a little stirring. The glass will then contain a uniform mixture of sugar and water; the concentration of dissolved sugar will be the same everywhere in the mixture. A liquid that is a completely homogeneous mixture of two or more substances is called a **solution**. The dissolving agent of a solution is the **solvent**, and the substance that is dissolved is the **solute**. In this case, water is the solvent and sugar is the solute. An **aqueous solution** is one in which the solute is dissolved in water; water is the solvent.

Water is a very versatile solvent, a quality we can trace to the polarity of the water molecule. Suppose, for example, that a spoonful of table salt, the ionic compound sodium chloride (NaCl), is placed in water (**Figure 3.8**). At the surface of each grain, or crystal, of salt, the sodium and chloride ions are exposed to the solvent. These ions and regions of the water molecules are attracted to each other due to their opposite charges. The oxygen regions of the water molecules are negatively charged and are attracted to sodium cations.

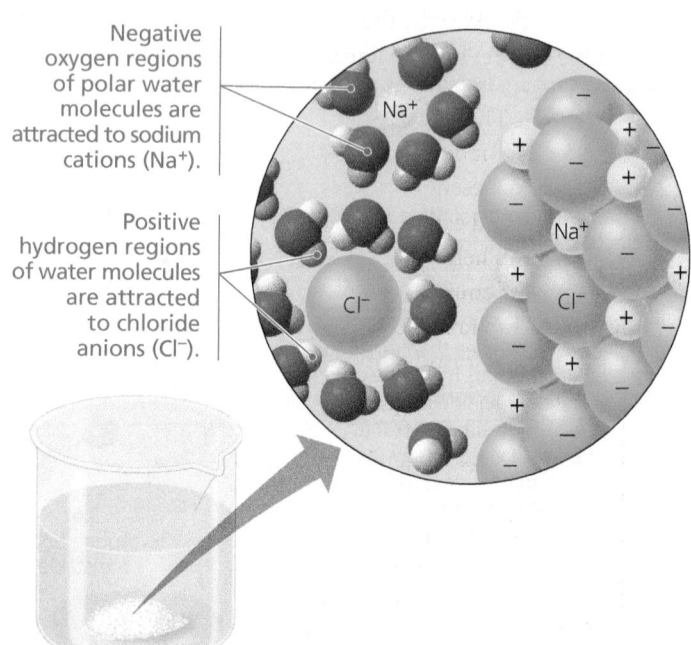

Negative oxygen regions of polar water molecules are attracted to sodium cations (Na⁺).

Positive hydrogen regions of water molecules are attracted to chloride anions (Cl⁻).

▲ Figure 3.8 **Table salt dissolving in water.** A sphere of water molecules, called a hydration shell, surrounds each solute ion.

WHAT IF? *What would happen if you heated this solution for a long time?*

The hydrogen regions are positively charged and are attracted to chloride anions. As a result, water molecules surround the individual sodium and chloride ions, separating and shielding them from one another. The sphere of water molecules around each dissolved ion is called a **hydration shell**. Working inward from the surface of each salt crystal, water eventually dissolves all the ions. The result is a solution of two solutes, sodium cations and chloride anions, homogeneously mixed with water, the solvent. Other ionic compounds also dissolve in water. Seawater, for instance, contains a great variety of dissolved ions, as do living cells.

A compound does not need to be ionic to dissolve in water; many compounds made up of nonionic polar molecules, such as the sugar in the sugar cube mentioned earlier, are also water-soluble. Such compounds dissolve when water molecules surround each of the solute molecules, forming hydrogen bonds with them. Even molecules as large as proteins can dissolve in water if they have ionic and polar regions on their surface (Figure 3.9). Many different kinds of polar compounds are dissolved (along with ions) in the water of such biological fluids as blood, the sap of plants, and the liquid within all cells. Water is the solvent of life.

Hydrophilic and Hydrophobic Substances

Any substance that has an affinity for water is said to be **hydrophilic** (from the Greek *hydro*, water, and *philos*, loving). In some cases, substances can be hydrophilic without actually dissolving. For example, some molecules in cells are so large that they do not dissolve. Another example of a hydrophilic substance that does not dissolve is cotton, a plant product. Cotton consists of giant molecules of cellulose, a compound with numerous regions of partial positive and partial negative charges that can form hydrogen bonds with water. Water adheres to the cellulose fibres. Thus, a cotton towel does a great job of drying the body, yet it does not dissolve in the washing machine. Cellulose is also present in the walls of water-conducting cells in a plant; you read earlier how the adhesion of water to these hydrophilic walls helps water move up the plant against gravity.

There are, of course, substances that do not have an affinity for water. Substances that are nonionic and nonpolar (or otherwise cannot form hydrogen bonds) actually seem to repel water; these substances are said to be **hydrophobic** (from the Greek *phobos*, fearing). An example from the kitchen is vegetable oil, which, as you know, does not mix stably with water-based substances such as vinegar. The hydrophobic behaviour of the oil molecules results from a prevalence of relatively nonpolar covalent bonds, in this case bonds between carbon and hydrogen, which

▶ **Figure 3.9 A water-soluble protein.** Human lysozyme is a protein found in tears and saliva that has antibacterial action. This model shows the lysozyme molecule (purple) in an aqueous environment. Ionic and polar regions on the protein's surface attract water molecules.

Source: Based on "Stimulating Water and the Molecules of Life" by Mark Gerstein and Michael Levitt, from *Scientific American*, November 1998. © Jane B Reece.

share electrons almost equally. Hydrophobic molecules related to oils are major ingredients of cell membranes. (Imagine what would happen to a cell if its membrane dissolved!)

Solute Concentration in Aqueous Solutions

Most of the chemical reactions in organisms involve solutes dissolved in water. To understand such reactions, we must know how many atoms and molecules are involved and be able to calculate the concentration of solutes in an aqueous solution (the number of solute molecules in a volume of solution).

When carrying out experiments, we must first calculate the **molecular mass**, which is the sum of the masses of all the atoms in a molecule. As an example, let's calculate the molecular mass of table sugar (sucrose), which has the molecular formula $C_{12}H_{22}O_{11}$. In round numbers of daltons, the mass of a carbon atom is 12, the mass of a hydrogen atom is 1, and the mass of an oxygen atom is 16. Thus, sucrose has a molecular mass of $(12 \times 12) + (22 \times 1) + (11 \times 16) = 342$ daltons. Because we can't weigh out small numbers of molecules, we usually measure substances in units called moles. Just as a dozen always means 12 objects, a **mole (mol)** represents an exact number of objects: 6.02×10^{23}, which is called Avogadro's number. Because of the way in which Avogadro's number and the unit *dalton* were originally defined, there are 6.02×10^{23} daltons in 1 g. This is significant because once we determine the molecular mass of a molecule such as sucrose, we can use the same number (342), but with the unit *gram*, to represent the mass of 6.02×10^{23} molecules of sucrose, or 1 mol of sucrose (this is sometimes called the *molar mass*). To obtain 1 mol of sucrose in the lab, therefore, we weigh out 342 g.

The practical advantage of measuring a quantity of chemicals in moles is that a mole of one substance has exactly the same number of molecules as a mole of any other substance. If the molecular mass of substance A is 342 daltons and that of substance B is 10 daltons, then 342 g of A will have the same

This oxygen is attracted to a slight positive charge on the lysozyme molecule.

This hydrogen is attracted to a slight negative charge on the lysozyme molecule.

number of molecules as 10 g of B. A mole of ethyl alcohol (C_2H_6O) also contains 6.02×10^{23} molecules, but its mass is only 46 g because the mass of a molecule of ethyl alcohol is less than that of a molecule of sucrose. Measuring in moles makes it convenient for scientists working in the laboratory to combine substances in fixed ratios of molecules.

How would we make a litre (L) of solution consisting of 1 mol of sucrose dissolved in water? We would measure out 342 g of sucrose and then gradually add water, while stirring, until the sugar was completely dissolved. We would then add enough water to bring the total volume of the solution up to 1 L. At that point, we would have a 1-molar (1 M) solution of sucrose. **Molarity**—the number of moles of solute per litre of solution—is the unit of concentration most often used by biologists for aqueous solutions.

Water's capacity as a versatile solvent complements the other properties discussed in this chapter. Since these remarkable properties allow water to support life on Earth so well, scientists who seek life elsewhere in the universe look for water as a sign that a planet might sustain life.

Possible Evolution of Life on Other Planets

EVOLUTION Biologists who look for life elsewhere in the universe (known as **astrobiologists**) have concentrated their search on planets that might have water. More than 800 planets have been found outside our solar system, and there is evidence for the presence of water vapour on a few of them. In our own solar system, Mars has been a focus of study. Like Earth, Mars has an ice cap at both poles. Images from spacecraft sent to Mars show that ice is present just under the surface of Mars and enough water vapour exists in its atmosphere for frost to form. In 2015, scientists found evidence of water flowing on Mars (Figure 3.10), and other studies suggested conditions existed that could have supported microorganismal life. Drilling below the surface may be the next step in the search for signs of life on Mars. If any life-forms or fossils are found, their study will shed light on the process of evolution from an entirely new perspective.

CONCEPT CHECK 3.2

1. Describe how properties of water contribute to the upward movement of water in a tree.
2. Explain the saying "It's not the heat; it's the humidity."
3. How can the freezing of water crack boulders?
4. **WHAT IF?** A water strider (which can walk on water) has legs that are coated with a hydrophobic substance. What might be the benefit? What would happen if the substance were hydrophilic?
5. **INTERPRET THE DATA** The concentration of the appetite-regulating hormone ghrelin is about 1.3×10^{-10} M in the blood of a fasting person. How many molecules of ghrelin are in 1 L of blood?

For suggested answers, see Appendix A.

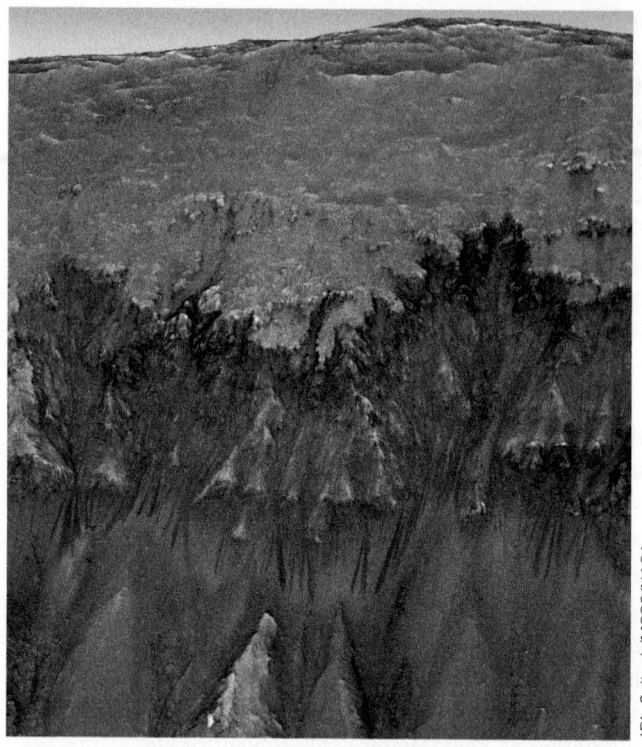

▲ Figure 3.10 **Evidence for liquid water on Mars.** Water appears to be involved in the formation of these dark streaks that run downhill during the Martian summer. NASA scientists found evidence of hydrated salts on the slopes, indicating the presence of water.

CONCEPT 3.3

Acidic and basic conditions affect living organisms

Occasionally, a hydrogen atom participating in a hydrogen bond between two water molecules shifts from one molecule to the other. When this happens, the hydrogen atom leaves its electron behind, and what is actually transferred is a **hydrogen ion** (H^+), a single proton with a charge of 1+. The water molecule that lost a proton is now a **hydroxide ion** (OH^-), which has a charge of 1−. The proton binds to the other water molecule, making that molecule a **hydronium ion** (H_3O^+). We can picture the chemical reaction as follows:

2 H_2O Hydronium ion (H_3O^+)   Hydroxide ion (OH^-)

By convention, H^+ (the hydrogen ion) is used to represent H_3O^+ (the hydronium ion), and we follow that practice in this text. Keep in mind, though, that H^+ does not exist on its own in an aqueous solution. It is always associated with a water molecule in the form of H_3O^+.

As indicated by the double arrows, this is a reversible reaction that reaches a state of dynamic equilibrium when water molecules dissociate at the same rate that they are being re-formed from H^+ and OH^-. At this equilibrium point, the concentration of water molecules greatly exceeds the concentrations of H^+ and OH^-. In pure water, only one water molecule in every 554 million is dissociated; the concentration of each ion in pure water is 10^{-7} M (at 25°C). This means there is only one ten-millionth of a mole of hydrogen ions per litre of pure water and an equal number of hydroxide ions. (Even so, this is a huge number—over 60 000 *trillion*—of each ion.)

Although the dissociation of water is reversible and statistically rare, it is exceedingly important in the chemistry of life. H^+ and OH^- are very reactive. Changes in their concentrations can drastically affect a cell's proteins and other complex molecules. As we have seen, the concentrations of H^+ and OH^- are equal in pure water, but adding certain kinds of solutes, called acids and bases, disrupts this balance. Biologists use something called the pH scale to describe how acidic or basic (the opposite of acidic) a solution is. In the remainder of this chapter, you will learn about acids, bases, and pH and why changes in pH can adversely affect organisms.

Acids and Bases

What would cause an aqueous solution to have an imbalance in H^+ and OH^- concentrations? When acids dissolve in water, they donate additional H^+ to the solution. An **acid** is a substance that increases the hydrogen ion concentration of a solution. For example, when hydrochloric acid (HCl) is added to water, hydrogen ions dissociate from chloride ions:

$$HCl \rightarrow H^+ + Cl^-$$

This source of H^+ (dissociation of water is the other source) results in an acidic solution—one having more H^+ than OH^-.

A substance that reduces the hydrogen ion concentration of a solution is called a **base**. Some bases reduce the H^+ concentration directly by accepting hydrogen ions. Ammonia (NH_3), for instance, acts as a base when the unshared electron pair in nitrogen's valence shell attracts a hydrogen ion from the solution, resulting in an ammonium ion (NH_4^+):

$$NH_3 + H^+ \leftrightharpoons NH_4^+$$

Other bases reduce the H^+ concentration indirectly by dissociating to form hydroxide ions, which combine with hydrogen ions and form water. One such base is sodium hydroxide (NaOH), which in water dissociates into its ions:

$$NaOH \rightarrow Na^+ + OH^-$$

In either case, the base reduces the H^+ concentration. Solutions with a higher concentration of OH^- than H^+ are known as basic solutions. A solution in which the H^+ and OH^- concentrations are equal is said to be neutral.

Notice that single arrows were used in the reactions for HCl and NaOH. These compounds dissociate completely when mixed with water, so hydrochloric acid is called a strong acid and sodium hydroxide a strong base. In contrast, ammonia is a weak base. The double arrows in the reaction for ammonia indicate that the binding and release of hydrogen ions are reversible reactions, although at equilibrium there will be a fixed ratio of NH_4^+ to NH_3.

Weak acids are acids that reversibly release and accept back hydrogen ions. An example is carbonic acid:

$$\underset{\substack{\text{Carbonic} \\ \text{acid}}}{H_2CO_3} \quad \leftrightharpoons \quad \underset{\substack{\text{Bicarbonate} \\ \text{ion}}}{HCO_3^-} \quad + \quad \underset{\substack{\text{Hydrogen} \\ \text{ion}}}{H^+}$$

Here the equilibrium so favours the reaction in the left direction that when carbonic acid is added to pure water, only 1% of the molecules are dissociated at any particular time. Still, that is enough to shift the balance of H^+ and OH^- from neutrality.

The pH Scale

In any aqueous solution at 25°C, the product of the H^+ and OH^- concentrations is constant at 10^{-14}. This can be written

$$[H^+][OH^-] = 10^{-14}$$

In such an equation, brackets indicate molar concentration. In a neutral solution at 25°C (close to room temperature), $[H^+] = 10^{-7}$ and $[OH^-] = 10^{-7}$, so in this case, 10^{-14} is the product of $10^{-7} \times 10^{-7}$. If enough acid is added to a solution to increase $[H^+]$ to 10^{-5} M, then $[OH^-]$ will decline by an equivalent factor to 10^{-9} M (note that $10^{-5} \times 10^{-9} = 10^{-14}$). This constant relationship expresses the behaviour of acids and bases in an aqueous solution. An acid not only adds hydrogen ions to a solution, but also removes hydroxide ions because of the tendency for H^+ to combine with OH^-, forming water. A base has the opposite effect, increasing OH^- concentration but also reducing H^+ concentration by the formation of water. If enough of a base is added to raise the OH^- concentration to 10^{-4} M, it will cause the H^+ concentration

pH Scale

- 0
- 1 Battery acid
- 2 Gastric juice, lemon juice
- 3 Vinegar, wine, cola
- 4 Tomato juice Beer
- 5 Black coffee

  Rainwater
- 6 Urine

  Saliva
- 7 **Pure water**

  Human blood, tears
- 8 Seawater

  Inside of small intestine
- 9
- 10

  Milk of magnesia
- 11

  Household ammonia
- 12
- 13 Household bleach

  Oven cleaner
- 14

Increasingly **Acidic** [H$^+$] > [OH$^-$]

Neutral [H$^+$] = [OH$^-$]

Increasingly **Basic** [H$^+$] < [OH$^-$]

Acidic solution
H$^+$ H$^+$
H$^+$ OH$^-$ H$^+$
OH$^-$ H$^+$ H$^+$
H$^+$ H$^+$

Neutral solution
OH$^-$ OH$^-$
H$^+$ H$^+$ OH$^-$
OH$^-$ OH$^-$
H$^+$ H$^+$ H$^+$

Basic solution
OH$^-$ OH$^-$
OH$^-$ H$^+$ OH$^-$
OH$^-$ OH$^-$
H$^+$ OH$^-$

Jsemeniuk/Getty Images

Getty Images

Humonia/Getty Images

Beth Van Trees/Shutterstock

▲ **Figure 3.11 The pH scale and pH values of some aqueous solutions.**

to drop to 10^{-10} M. Whenever we know the concentration of either H$^+$ or OH$^-$ in an aqueous solution, we can deduce the concentration of the other ion.

Because the H$^+$ and OH$^-$ concentrations of solutions can vary by a factor of 100 trillion or more, scientists have developed a way to express this variation more conveniently than in moles per litre. The pH scale (**Figure 3.11**) compresses the range of H$^+$ and OH$^-$ concentrations by employing logarithms. The **pH** of a solution is defined as the negative logarithm (base 10) of the hydrogen ion concentration:

$$pH = -\log [H^+]$$

For a neutral aqueous solution, [H$^+$] is 10^{-7} M, giving us

$$-\log 10^{-7} = -(-7) = 7$$

Notice that pH *declines* as H$^+$ concentration increases. Notice, too, that although the pH scale is based on H$^+$ concentration, it also implies OH$^-$ concentration. A

solution of pH 10 has a hydrogen ion concentration of 10^{-10} M and a hydroxide ion concentration of 10^{-4} M.

The pH of a neutral aqueous solution at 25°C is 7, the midpoint of the pH scale. A pH value less than 7 denotes an acidic solution; the lower the number, the more acidic the solution. The pH for basic solutions is above 7. Most biological fluids, such as blood and saliva, are within the range of pH 6–8. There are a few exceptions, however, including the strongly acidic digestive juice of the human stomach, which has a pH of about 2.

Remember that each pH unit represents a tenfold difference in H$^+$ and OH$^-$ concentrations. It is this mathematical feature that makes the pH scale so compact. A solution of pH 3 is not twice as acidic as a solution of pH 6, but a thousand times ($10 \times 10 \times 10$) more acidic. When the pH of a solution changes slightly, the actual concentrations of H$^+$ and OH$^-$ in the solution change substantially.

Buffers

The internal pH of most living cells is close to 7. Even a slight change in pH can be harmful, because the chemical processes of the cell are very sensitive to the concentrations of hydrogen and hydroxide ions. The pH of human blood is very close to 7.4, which is slightly basic. A person cannot survive for more than a few minutes if the blood pH drops to 7 or rises to 7.8, and a chemical system exists in the blood that maintains a stable pH. If 0.01 mol of a strong acid is added to a litre of pure water, the pH drops from 7.0 to 2.0. If the same amount of acid is added to a litre of blood, however, the pH decrease is only from 7.4 to 7.3. Why does the addition of acid have so much less of an effect on the pH of blood than it does on the pH of water?

The presence of substances called buffers allows biological fluids to maintain a relatively constant pH despite the addition of acids or bases. A **buffer** is a substance that minimizes changes in the concentrations of H$^+$ and OH$^-$ in a solution. It does so by accepting hydrogen ions from the solution when they are in excess and donating hydrogen ions to the solution when they have been depleted. Most buffer solutions contain a weak acid and its corresponding base, which combine reversibly with hydrogen ions.

There are several buffers that contribute to pH stability in human blood and many other biological solutions. One of these is carbonic acid (H$_2$CO$_3$), formed when CO$_2$ reacts with water in blood plasma. As mentioned earlier, carbonic acid dissociates to yield a bicarbonate ion (HCO$_3^-$) and a hydrogen ion (H$^+$):

	Response to a rise in pH		
H$_2$CO$_3$	⇌	HCO$_3^-$ $+$	H$^+$
H$^+$ donor (acid)	Response to a drop in pH	H$^+$ acceptor (base)	Hydrogen ion

The chemical equilibrium between carbonic acid and bicarbonate acts as a pH regulator, the reaction shifting left or right as other processes in the solution add or remove hydrogen ions. If the H^+ concentration in blood begins to fall (that is, if pH rises), the reaction proceeds to the right and more carbonic acid dissociates, replenishing hydrogen ions. But when H^+ concentration in blood begins to rise (when pH drops), the reaction proceeds to the left, with HCO_3^- (the base) removing the hydrogen ions from the solution and forming H_2CO_3. Thus, the carbonic acid–bicarbonate buffering system consists of an acid and a base in equilibrium with each other. Most other buffers are also acid-base pairs.

Acidification: A Threat to Water Quality

Among the many threats to water quality posed by human activities is the burning of fossil fuels, which releases CO_2 into the atmosphere. The resulting increase in atmospheric CO_2 levels has caused global warming and other aspects of climate change (see Figure 56.27). In addition, 25% of human-generated CO_2 is absorbed by the oceans. In spite of the huge volume of water in the oceans, scientists worry that the absorption of so much CO_2 will harm marine ecosystems.

Recent data have shown that such fears are well founded. When CO_2 dissolves in seawater, it reacts with water to form carbonic acid, which lowers ocean pH. This process, known as **ocean acidification**, alters the delicate balance of conditions for life in the oceans (Figure 3.12).

Based on measurements of CO_2 levels in air bubbles trapped in ice over thousands of years, scientists calculate that the pH of the oceans is 0.1 pH unit lower now than at any time in the past 420 000 years. Recent studies predict that it will drop another 0.3–0.5 pH unit by the end of this century.

As seawater acidifies, the extra hydrogen ions combine with carbonate ions (CO_3^{2-}) to form bicarbonate ions (HCO_3^-), thereby reducing the carbonate ion concentration (see Figure 3.12). Scientists predict that ocean acidification will cause the carbonate ion concentration to decrease by 40% by the year 2100. This is of great concern because carbonate ions are required for calcification, the production of calcium carbonate ($CaCO_3$) by many marine organisms, including reef-building corals and animals that build shells. The Scientific Skills Exercise allows you to work with data from an experiment examining the effect of carbonate ion concentration on coral reefs. Coral reefs are sensitive ecosystems that act as havens for a great diversity of marine life (Figure 3.13). The disappearance of coral reef ecosystems would be a tragic loss of biological diversity.

Some carbon dioxide (CO_2) in the atmosphere dissolves in the ocean, where it reacts with water to form carbonic acid (H_2CO_3).

$CO_2 + H_2O \rightarrow H_2CO_3$

Carbonic acid dissociates into hydrogen ions (H^+) and bicarbonate ions (HCO_3^-).

$H_2CO_3 \rightarrow H^+ + HCO_3^-$

The added H^+ combines with carbonate ions (CO_3^{2-}), forming more HCO_3^-.

$H^+ + CO_3^{2-} \rightarrow HCO_3^-$

Less CO_3^{2-} is available for calcification—the formation of calcium carbonate ($CaCO_3$)—by marine organisms such as corals.

$CO_3^{2-} + Ca^{2+} \rightarrow CaCO_3$

▲ Figure 3.12 **Atmospheric CO_2 from human activities and its fate in the ocean.**

If there is any reason for optimism about the future quality of water resources on our planet, it is that we have made progress in learning about the delicate chemical balances in oceans, lakes, and rivers. Continued progress can come only from the actions of informed individuals, like yourselves, who are concerned about environmental quality. This requires understanding the crucial role that water plays in the suitability of the environment for continued life on Earth.

CONCEPT CHECK 3.3

1. Compared with a basic solution at pH 9, the same volume of an acidic solution at pH 4 has _____ times as many hydrogen ions (H^+).

2. HCl is a strong acid that dissociates in water: $HCl \rightarrow H^+ + Cl^-$. What is the pH of 0.01 M HCl?

3. Acetic acid (CH_3COOH) can be a buffer, similar to carbonic acid. Write the dissociation reaction, identifying the acid, base, H^+ acceptor, and H^+ donor.

4. **WHAT IF?** Given a litre of pure water and a litre solution of acetic acid, what would happen to the pH if you added 0.01 mol of a strong acid to each? Use the reaction equation from question 3 to explain the result.

For suggested answers, see Appendix A.

Interpreting a Scatter Plot with a Regression Line

How Does the Carbonate Ion Concentration of Seawater Affect the Calcification Rate of a Coral Reef? Scientists predict that acidification of the ocean due to higher levels of atmospheric CO_2 will lower the concentration of dissolved carbonate ions, which living corals use to build calcium carbonate reef structures. In this exercise, you will analyze data from a controlled experiment that examined the effect of carbonate ion concentration ($[CO_3^{2-}]$) on calcium carbonate deposition, a process called calcification.

How the Experiment Was Done The Biosphere 2 aquarium in Arizona contains a large coral reef system that behaves like a natural reef. For several years, a group of researchers measured the rate of calcification by the reef organisms and examined how the calcification rate changed with differing amounts of dissolved carbonate ions in the seawater.

Data from the Experiment The black data points in the graph form a scatter plot. The red line, known as a linear regression line, is the best-fitting straight line for these points.

Interpret the Data

1. When presented with a graph of experimental data, the first step in analysis is to determine what each axis represents. (a) In words, explain what is being shown on the x-axis. Be sure to include the units. (b) What is being shown on the y-axis (including units)? (c) Which variable is the independent variable—the variable that was *manipulated* by the researchers? (d) Which variable is the dependent variable—the variable that responded to or depended on the treatment, which was *measured* by the researchers? (For additional information about graphs, see the Scientific Skills Review in Appendix E and in the Study Area in MasteringBiology.)

2. Based on the data shown in the graph, describe in words the relationship between carbonate ion concentration and calcification rate.

3. (a) If the seawater carbonate ion concentration is 270 μmol/kg, what is the approximate rate of calcification, and approximately how many days would it take 1 square metre of reef to accumulate 30 mmol of calcium carbonate ($CaCO_3$)? (b) If the seawater carbonate ion concentration is 250 μmol/kg, what is the approximate rate of calcification, and approximately how many days would it take 1 square metre of reef to accumulate 30 mmol of calcium carbonate? (c) If carbonate ion concentration decreases, how does the calcification rate change, and how does that affect the time it takes coral to grow?

4. (a) Referring to the equations in Figure 3.12, determine which step of the process is measured in this experiment. (b) Are the results of this experiment consistent with the hypothesis that increased atmospheric $[CO_2]$ will slow the growth of coral reefs? Why or why not?

Data from Data from "Effect of Calcium Carbonate Saturation State on the Calcification Rate of an Experimental Coral Reef" by Chris Langdon, et al., from *Global Biogeochemical Cycles,* June 2000, Volume 14(2). © Jane B Reece.

▼ Figure 3.13 | **Impact**

The Threat of Ocean Acidification to Marine Life

Currently, scientists from Canada's Department of Fisheries and Oceans are studying ocean acidification, the process in which oceans become more acidic due to increased atmospheric carbon dioxide levels (see Figure 3.12), on all three of Canada's coasts. Ocean acidification results in a decreased ability of organisms, such as coral, calcareous phytoplankton, sea urchins, and some molluscs, to form calcium carbonate ($CaCO_3$) shells and skeletons. Also, some invertebrates and fish may suffer from acidosis due to carbonic acid buildup in tissues, thus resulting in decreased blood pH. Cold-water corals (also known as deep-water corals), and tropical and sub-tropical coral reefs are seriously affected by ocean acidification. An international team of scientists has defined three scenarios for coral reefs during this century, depending on whether the concentration of atmospheric

CO₂ (a) stays at today's level, (b) increases at the current rate, or (c) increases more rapidly. The photographs below show coral reefs resembling those predicted under each scenario.

The healthy coral reef in **(a)** supports a highly diverse group of species and bears little resemblance to the damaged coral reef in **(c)**.

Why It Matters The disappearance of cold-water, tropical, and sub-tropical coral ecosystems would be a tragic loss of biological diversity. Many commercially valuable fish depend on fragile cold-water coral communities. Also, tropical and sub-tropical coral reefs provide shoreline protection, a feeding ground for commercial fishery species, and a popular tourist draw, so coastal human communities would suffer from greater wave damage, collapsed fisheries, and reduced tourism with the destruction and disappearance of these reefs. When decreased calcification due to ocean acidification is combined with coral bleaching caused by increased ocean temperatures (see Chapter 56), the impact on coral reef ecosystems is likely to be considerable.

Further Reading O. Hoegh-Guldberg et al., Coral reefs under rapid climate change and ocean acidification, *Science* 318:1737–1742 (2007). S. C. Doney, The dangers of ocean acidification, *Scientific American*, March 2006, 58–65.

WHAT IF? *Would lowering the ocean's carbonate concentration have any effect, even indirectly, on organisms that don't form $CaCO_3$? Explain.*

 (a) (b) (c)

The University of Queensland, Australia

3 Chapter Review

Go to **MasteringBiology**® for Assignments, the eText, and the
Study Area with Animations, Activities, Vocab Self-Quiz, and Practice Tests.

SUMMARY OF KEY CONCEPTS

CONCEPT 3.1

Polar covalent bonds in water molecules result in hydrogen bonding (p. 50)

- Water is a polar molecule. A hydrogen bond forms when the slightly negatively charged oxygen of one water molecule is attracted to the slightly positively charged hydrogen of a nearby water molecule. Hydrogen bonding between water molecules is the basis for water's properties.

 Label a hydrogen bond and a polar covalent bond in this figure. Is a hydrogen bond a covalent bond? Explain.

CONCEPT 3.2

Four emergent properties of water contribute to Earth's suitability for life (pp. 50–56)

- Hydrogen bonding keeps water molecules close to each other, and this **cohesion** helps pull water upward in the microscopic water-conducting cells of plants. Hydrogen bonding is also responsible for water's **surface tension**.
- Water has a high **specific heat:** Heat is absorbed when hydrogen bonds break and is released when hydrogen bonds form. This helps keep temperatures relatively steady, within limits that permit life. **Evaporative cooling** is based on water's high **heat of vaporization**. The evaporative loss of the most energetic water molecules cools a surface.
- Ice floats because it is less dense than liquid water. This property allows life to exist under the frozen surfaces of lakes and polar seas.
- Water is an unusually versatile **solvent** because its polar molecules are attracted to ions and polar substances that can form hydrogen bonds. **Hydrophilic** substances have an affinity for water; **hydrophobic** substances do not. **Molarity**, the number of moles of **solute** per litre of **solution**, is used as a measure of solute concentration in solutions. A **mole** is a certain number of molecules of a substance. The mass of a mole of a substance in grams is the same as the **molecular mass** in daltons.
- The emergent properties of water support life on Earth and may contribute to the potential for life to have evolved on other planets.

? *Describe how different types of solutes dissolve in water. Explain what a solution is.*

CONCEPT 3.3

Acidic and basic conditions affect living organisms (pp. 56–60)

- A water molecule can transfer an H^+ to another water molecule to form H_3O^+ (represented simply by H^+) and OH^-.
- The concentration of H^+ is expressed as **pH**; $pH = -\log [H^+]$. **Buffers** in biological fluids resist changes in pH. A buffer consists of an acid-base pair that combines reversibly with hydrogen ions, allowing it to resist pH changes.

- The burning of fossil fuels increases the amount of CO_2 in the atmosphere. Some CO_2 dissolves in the oceans, causing **ocean acidification**, which has potentially grave consequences for coral reefs.

Acids donate H^+ in aqueous solutions.

Bases donate OH^- or accept H^+ in aqueous solutions.

? *Explain how increasing amounts of CO_2 dissolving in the ocean leads to ocean acidification. How does this change in pH affect carbonate ion concentration and the rate of calcification?*

TEST YOUR UNDERSTANDING

LEVEL 1: KNOWLEDGE/COMPREHENSION

1. Which of the following is a hydrophobic material?
   a. paper   c. wax
   b. table salt   d. sugar

2. We can be sure that a mole of table sugar and a mole of vitamin C are equal in their
   a. mass.   c. number of atoms.
   b. volume.   d. number of molecules.

3. Measurements show that the pH of a particular lake is 4.0. What is the hydrogen ion concentration of the lake?
   a. 4.0 M   c. 10^{-4} M
   b. 10^{-10} M   d. 10^4 M

4. What is the hydroxide ion concentration of the lake described in question 3?
   a. 10^{-10} M   c. 10^{-7} M
   b. 10^{-4} M   d. 10.0 M

LEVEL 2: APPLICATION/ANALYSIS

5. A slice of pizza has 2092 kJ. If we could burn the pizza and use all the heat to warm a 50-L container of cold water, what would be the approximate increase in the temperature of the water? (Note: A litre of cold water weighs about 1 kg.)
   a. 50°C   b. 5°C   c. 100°C   d. 10°C

6. **DRAW IT** Draw the hydration shells that form around a potassium ion and a chloride ion when potassium chloride (KCl) dissolves in water. Label the positive, negative, and partial charges on the atoms.

7. **MAKE CONNECTIONS** What do global warming (see Chapter 1, p. 10) and ocean acidification have in common?

LEVEL 3: SYNTHESIS/EVALUATION

8. In agricultural areas, farmers pay close attention to the weather forecast. Right before a predicted overnight freeze, farmers spray water on crops to protect the plants. Use the properties of water to explain how this method works. Be sure to mention why hydrogen bonds are responsible for this phenomenon.

9. **EVOLUTION CONNECTION**
   This chapter explains how the emergent properties of water contribute to the suitability of the environment for life. Until fairly recently, scientists assumed that other physical requirements for life included a moderate range of temperature, pH, atmospheric pressure, and salinity, as well as low levels of toxic chemicals. That view has changed with the discovery of organisms known as extremophiles, which have been found flourishing in hot, acidic sulphur springs, around hydrothermal vents deep in the ocean, and in soils with high levels of toxic metals. Why would astrobiologists be interested in studying extremophiles? What does the existence of life in such extreme environments say about the possibility of life on other planets?

10. **SCIENTIFIC INQUIRY**
    Design a controlled experiment to test the hypothesis that acid precipitation inhibits the growth of *Elodea*, a common freshwater plant (see Figure 2.17, p. 45).

11. **SCIENTIFIC INQUIRY**
    A 2000 study by Langdon et al. used an artificial coral reef system to test the effect of carbonate concentration on the rate of calcification by reef organisms. The graph below presents one set of their results. Describe what these data show. How do these results relate to the ocean acidification that is associated with increasing atmospheric CO_2 levels?

12. **WRITE ABOUT A THEME: EMERGENT PROPERTIES**
    Several emergent properties of water contribute to the suitability of the environment for life. In a short essay (100–150 words), describe how the ability of water to function as a versatile solvent arises from the structure of water molecules.

13. **SYNTHESIZE YOUR KNOWLEDGE**

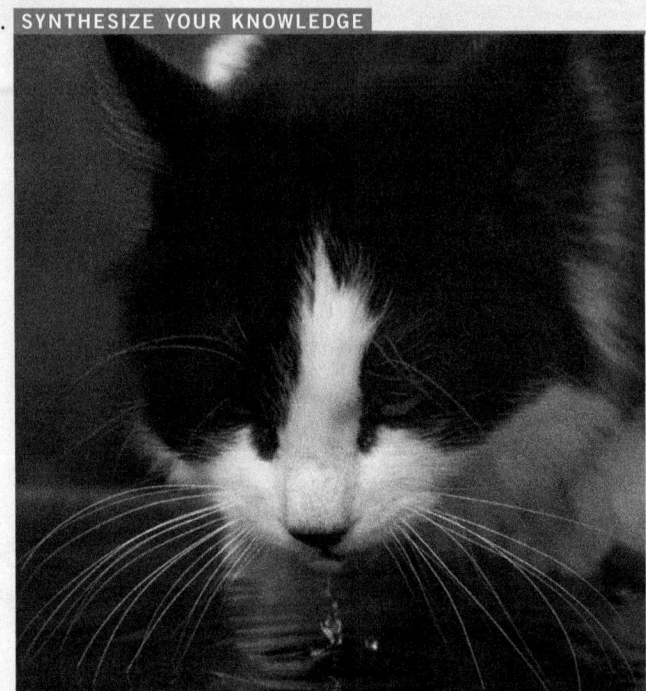

How do cats drink? While dogs form their tongues into spoons and scoop water into their mouths, scientists using high-speed video have shown that cats use a different technique to drink aqueous substances like water and milk. Four times a second, the cat touches the tip of its tongue to the water and draws a column of water up into its mouth (as you can see in the photo), which then shuts before gravity can pull the water back down. Describe how the properties of water allow cats to drink in this fashion, including how water's molecular structure contributes to the process.

For selected answers, see Appendix A.

4

Carbon and the Molecular Diversity of Life

KEY CONCEPTS

4.1 Organic chemistry is the study of carbon compounds

4.2 Carbon atoms can form diverse molecules by bonding to four other atoms

4.3 A few chemical groups are key to molecular function

▲ Figure 4.1 **What properties make carbon the basis of all life?**

Carbon: The Backbone of Life

Living organisms, such as the plants and the tadpoles found in Cedar Lake on Vancouver Island and shown in Figure 4.1, are made up of chemicals based mostly on the element carbon. Carbon enters the biosphere through the action of plants and other photosynthetic organisms. Plants use solar energy to transform atmospheric CO_2 into the molecules of life, which are then taken in by plant-eating animals.

Of all the chemical elements, carbon is unparalleled in its ability to form molecules that are large, complex, and varied, making possible the diversity of organisms that have evolved on Earth. Proteins, DNA, carbohydrates, and other molecules that distinguish living matter from inanimate material are all composed of carbon atoms bonded to one another and to atoms of other elements. Hydrogen (H), oxygen (O), nitrogen (N), sulphur (S), and phosphorus (P) are other common ingredients of these compounds, but it is the element carbon (C) that accounts for the enormous variety of biological molecules.

Large biological molecules, such as proteins, are the main focus of Chapter 5. In this chapter, we investigate the properties of smaller molecules. We will use these small molecules to illustrate concepts of molecular architecture that will help explain why carbon is so important to life, at the same time highlighting the theme that emergent properties arise from the organization of matter in living organisms.

▲ Carbon can bond to four other atoms or groups of atoms, making a large variety of molecules possible.

63

Organic chemistry is the study of carbon compounds

For historical reasons, compounds containing carbon are said to be organic, and their study is called **organic chemistry**.

By the early 1800s, chemists had learned to make simple compounds in the laboratory by combining elements under the right conditions. Artificial synthesis of the complex molecules extracted from living matter seemed impossible, however. Organic compounds were thought to arise only in living organisms, which were believed to contain a life force beyond the jurisdiction of physical and chemical laws.

Chemists began to chip away at this notion when they learned to synthesize organic compounds in the laboratory. In 1828, Friedrich Wöhler, a German chemist, tried to make an "inorganic" salt, ammonium cyanate, by mixing solutions of ammonium ions (NH_4^+) and cyanate ions (CNO^-). Wöhler was astonished to find that instead he had made urea, an organic compound present in the urine of animals.

The next few decades saw laboratory synthesis of increasingly complex organic compounds, supporting the view that physical and chemical laws govern the processes of life. Organic chemistry was redefined as the study of carbon compounds, regardless of origin. Organic compounds range from simple molecules, such as methane (CH_4), to colossal ones, such as proteins, with thousands of atoms.

Organic Molecules and the Origin of Life on Earth

EVOLUTION In 1953, Stanley Miller, a graduate student of Harold Urey's at the University of Chicago, helped bring the abiotic (nonliving) synthesis of organic compounds into the context of evolution. Study Figure 4.2 to learn about his classic experiment. From his results, Miller concluded that complex organic molecules could arise spontaneously under conditions thought at that time to have existed on the early Earth.

You can work with the data from a related experiment in the Scientific Skills Exercise. These experiments support the idea that abiotic synthesis of organic compounds, perhaps near volcanoes, could have been an early stage in the origin of life (see Chapter 25).

The overall percentages of the major elements of life—C, H, O, N, S, and P—are quite uniform from one organism to another, reflecting the common evolutionary origin of all life. Because of carbon's ability to form four

▼ Figure 4.2 | **Inquiry**

Can organic molecules form under conditions estimated to simulate those on the early Earth?

Experiment In 1953, Stanley Miller set up a closed system to mimic conditions thought to have existed on the early Earth. A flask of water simulated the primeval sea. The water was heated so that some vaporized and moved into a second, higher flask containing the "atmosphere"—a mixture of gases. Sparks were discharged in the synthetic atmosphere to mimic lightning.

Results Miller identified a variety of organic molecules that are common in organisms. These included simple compounds, such as formaldehyde (CH_2O) and hydrogen cyanide (HCN), and more complex molecules, such as amino acids and long chains of carbon and hydrogen known as hydrocarbons.

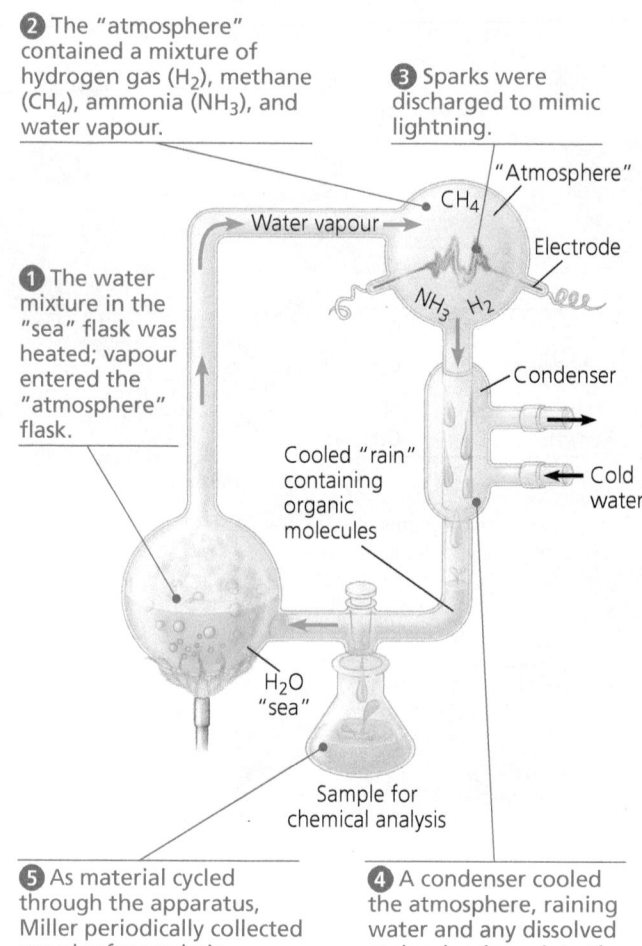

❷ The "atmosphere" contained a mixture of hydrogen gas (H_2), methane (CH_4), ammonia (NH_3), and water vapour.

❸ Sparks were discharged to mimic lightning.

"Atmosphere"

CH_4

Water vapour

Electrode

❶ The water mixture in the "sea" flask was heated; vapour entered the "atmosphere" flask.

NH_3 H_2

Condenser

Cooled "rain" containing organic molecules

Cold water

H_2O "sea"

Sample for chemical analysis

❺ As material cycled through the apparatus, Miller periodically collected samples for analysis.

❹ A condenser cooled the atmosphere, raining water and any dissolved molecules down into the sea flask.

Conclusion Organic molecules, a first step in the origin of life, may have been synthesized abiotically on the early Earth. (We will explore this hypothesis in more detail in Chapter 25.)

Source: Based on "A Production of Amino Acids under Possible Primitive Earth Conditions" by Stanley L. Miller, from, *Science* New Series, May 15, 1953, Volume 117(3046). © Jane B Reece.

WHAT IF? *If Miller had increased the concentration of NH_3 in his experiment, how might the relative amounts of the products HCN and CH_2O have differed?*

Working with Moles and Molar Ratios

Could the First Biological Molecules Have Formed Near Volcanoes on Early Earth? In 2007, Jeffrey Bada, a former graduate student of Stanley Miller's, discovered some vials of samples that had never been analyzed from an experiment performed by Miller in 1958. In this experiment, Miller used hydrogen sulphide gas (H_2S) as one of the gases in the reactant mixture. Since H_2S is released by volcanoes, the H_2S experiment was designed to mimic conditions near volcanoes on early Earth. In 2011, Bada and colleagues published the results of their analysis of these "lost" samples. In this exercise, you will make calculations using the molar ratios of reactants and products from the H_2S experiment.

How the Experiment Was Done According to his laboratory notebook, Miller used the same apparatus as in his original experiment (see Figure 4.2), but the mixture of gaseous reactants included methane (CH_4), carbon dioxide (CO_2), hydrogen sulphide (H_2S), and ammonia (NH_3). After three days of simulated volcanic activity, he collected samples of the liquid, partially purified the chemicals, and sealed the samples in sterile vials. In 2011, Bada's research team used modern analytical methods to analyze the products in the vials for the presence of amino acids, the building blocks of proteins.

Data from the Experiment The table below shows four of the 23 amino acids detected in the samples from Miller's 1958 H_2S experiment:

Product Compound	Molecular Formula	Molar Ratio (Relative to Glycine)
Glycine	$C_2H_5NO_2$	1.0
Serine	$C_3H_7NO_3$	3.0×10^{-2}
Methionine	$C_5H_{11}NO_2S$	1.8×10^{-3}
Alanine	$C_3H_7NO_2$	1.1

Interpret the Data

1. A *mole* is the number of grams of a substance that equals its molecular (or atomic) mass in daltons. There are 6.02×10^{23} molecules (or atoms) in 1.0 mole (Avogadro's number; see Concept 3.2). The data table shows the "molar ratios" of some of the products from the Miller H_2S experiment. In a molar ratio, each unitless value is expressed relative to a standard for that experiment. Here, the standard is the number of moles of the amino acid glycine, which is set to a value of 1.0. For instance, serine has a molar ratio of 3.0×10^{-2}, meaning that for every mole of glycine, there is 3.0×10^{-2} mole of serine. (a) Give the molar ratio of methionine to glycine and explain what it means. (b) How many molecules of glycine are present in 1.0 mole? (c) For every 1.0 mole of glycine in the sample, how many molecules of methionine

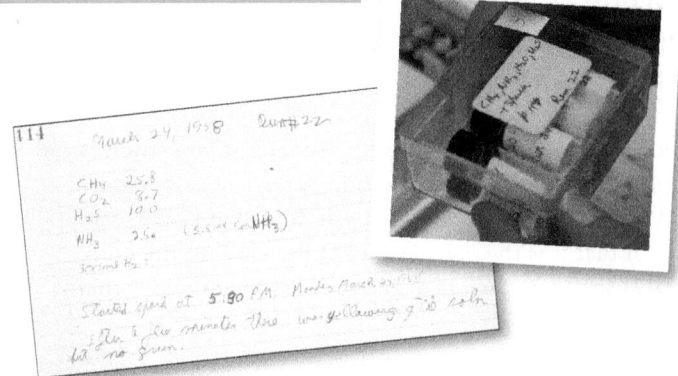

The Register of Stanley Miller Papers (Laboratory Notebook 2, page 114, Serial number 655, MSS642, Box 122), Mandeville Special Collections Library, UC San Diego.

▲ Some of Stanley Miller's notes from his 1958 hydrogen sulphide (H_2S) experiment along with his original vials.

are present? (Recall that to multiply two numbers with exponents, you add their exponents; to divide them, you subtract the exponent in the denominator from that in the numerator.)

2. (a) Which amino acid is present in higher amounts than glycine? (b) How many more molecules of that amino acid are present than the number of molecules in 1.0 mole of glycine?

3. The synthesis of products is limited by the amount of reactants. (a) If one mole each of CH_4, NH_3, H_2S, and CO_2 is added to 1 litre of water ($\times$ 55.5 moles of H_2O) in a flask, how many moles of hydrogen, carbon, oxygen, nitrogen, and sulphur are in the flask? (b) Looking at the molecular formula in the table, how many moles of each element would be needed to make 1.0 mole of glycine? (c) What is the maximum number of moles of glycine that could be made in that flask, with the specified ingredients, if no other molecules were made? Explain. (d) If serine or methionine were made individually, which element(s) would be used up first for each? How much of each product could be made?

4. The earlier published experiment carried out by Miller did not include H_2S in the reactants (see Figure 4.2). Which of the compounds shown in the data table can be made in the H_2S experiment but could not be made in the earlier experiment?

Data from E. T. Parker et al., Primordial synthesis of amines and amino acids in a 1958 Miller H_2S-rich spark discharge experiment, *Proceedings of the National Academy of Sciences USA* 108:5526–5531 (2011). www.pnas.org/cgi/doi/10.1073/pnas.1019191108.

bonds, however, this limited assortment of atomic building blocks can be used to build an inexhaustible variety of organic molecules. Different species of organisms, and different individuals within a species, are distinguished by variations in the types of organic molecules they make. In a sense, the great diversity of living organisms we see on the planet (and in fossil remains) is made possible by the unique chemical versatility of the element carbon.

CONCEPT CHECK 4.1

1. Why was Wöhler astonished to find he had made urea?

2. **WHAT IF?** When Miller tried his experiment without the electrical discharge, no organic compounds were found. What might explain this result?

For suggested answers, see Appendix A.

CONCEPT 4.2

Carbon atoms can form diverse molecules by bonding to four other atoms

The key to an atom's chemical characteristics is its electron configuration. This configuration determines the kinds and number of bonds an atom will form with other atoms. Recall that it is the valence electrons, those in the outermost shell, that are available to form bonds with other atoms.

The Formation of Bonds with Carbon

Carbon has 6 electrons, with 2 in the first electron shell and 4 in the second shell; thus, it has 4 valence electrons in a shell that can hold up to 8 electrons. A carbon atom usually completes its valence shell by sharing its 4 electrons with other atoms so that 8 electrons are present. Each pair of shared electrons constitutes a covalent bond (see Figure 2.10d). In organic molecules, carbon usually forms single or double covalent bonds. Each carbon atom acts as an intersection point from which a molecule can branch off in as many as four directions. This enables carbon to form large, complex molecules.

When a carbon atom forms four single covalent bonds, the arrangement of its four hybrid orbitals causes the bonds to angle toward the corners of an imaginary tetrahedron.

The bond angles in methane (CH_4) are 109.5° (Figure 4.3a), and they are roughly the same in any group of atoms where carbon has four single bonds. For example, ethane (C_2H_6) is shaped like two overlapping tetrahedrons (Figure 4.3b). In molecules with more carbons, every grouping of a carbon bonded to four other atoms has a tetrahedral shape. But when two carbon atoms are joined by a double bond, as in ethene (C_2H_4), the bonds from both carbons are all in the same plane, so the atoms joined to those carbons are in the same plane as well (Figure 4.3c). We find it convenient to write molecules as structural formulas, as if the molecules being represented are two-dimensional, but keep in mind that molecules are three-dimensional and that the shape of a molecule is central to its function.

The electron configuration of carbon gives it covalent compatibility with many different elements. Figure 4.4 shows the valences of carbon and its most frequent bonding partners—hydrogen, oxygen, and nitrogen. These are the four major atomic components of organic molecules. These valences are the basis for the rules of covalent bonding in organic chemistry—the building code for the architecture of organic molecules.

How do the rules of covalent bonding apply to carbon atoms with partners other than hydrogen? We'll look at two examples, the simple molecules carbon dioxide and urea.

In the carbon dioxide molecule (CO_2), a single carbon atom is joined to two atoms of oxygen by double covalent bonds. The structural formula for CO_2 is shown here:

$$O=C=O$$

Name and Comment	Molecular Formula	Structural Formula	Ball-and-Stick Model (molecular shape in pink)	Space-Filling Model
(a) Methane. When a carbon atom has four single bonds to other atoms, the molecule is tetrahedral.	CH_4			
(b) Ethane. A molecule may have more than one tetrahedral group of single-bonded atoms. (Ethane consists of two such groups.)	C_2H_6			
(c) Ethene (ethylene). When two carbon atoms are joined by a double bond, all atoms attached to those carbons are in the same plane; the molecule is flat.	C_2H_4			

▲ Figure 4.3 **The shapes of three simple organic molecules.**

Hydrogen (valence = 1)   **Oxygen** (valence = 2)   **Nitrogen** (valence = 3)   **Carbon** (valence = 4)

H·   ·Ö: ·N̈·   ·C̈·

▲ **Figure 4.4 Valences of the major elements of organic molecules.** Valence is the number of covalent bonds an atom can form. It is generally equal to the number of electrons required to complete the valence (outermost) shell (see Figure 2.7). All the electrons are shown for each atom in the electron distribution diagrams (top). Only the valence shell electrons are shown in the Lewis dot structures (bottom). Note that carbon can form four bonds.

MAKE CONNECTIONS *Draw the Lewis dot structures for sodium, phosphorus, sulphur, and chlorine. (Refer to Figure 2.7.)*

Each line in a structural formula represents a pair of shared electrons. Thus, the two double bonds in CO_2 have the same number of shared electrons as four single bonds. The arrangement completes the valence shells of all atoms in the molecule. Because CO_2 is a very simple molecule and lacks hydrogen, it is often considered inorganic, even though it contains carbon. Whether we call CO_2 organic or inorganic, however, it is clearly important to the living world as the source of carbon for all organic molecules in organisms.

Urea, $CO(NH_2)_2$, is the organic compound found in urine that Wöhler synthesized in the early 1800s. Again, each atom has the required number of covalent bonds. In this case, one carbon atom participates in both single and double bonds.

Urea and carbon dioxide are molecules with only one carbon atom. But as Figure 4.3 shows, a carbon atom can also use one or more valence electrons to form covalent bonds to other carbon atoms, each of which can also form four bonds. Thus, the atoms can be linked into chains of seemingly infinite variety.

Urea

Molecular Diversity Arising from Variation in Carbon Skeletons

Carbon chains form the skeletons of most organic molecules. The skeletons vary in length and may be straight, branched, or arranged in closed rings (Figure 4.5). Some carbon skeletons have double bonds, which vary in number and location. Such variation in carbon skeletons is one important source of the molecular complexity and diversity that characterize living matter. In addition, atoms of other elements can be bonded to the skeletons at available sites.

Hydrocarbons

All of the molecules that are shown in Figures 4.3 and 4.5 are **hydrocarbons**, organic molecules consisting of only carbon

▼ Figure 4.5 **Four ways that carbon skeletons can vary.**

(a) Length

Ethane   Propane

Carbon skeletons vary in length.

(b) Branching

Butane   2-Methylpropane (commonly called isobutane)

Skeletons may be unbranched or branched.

(c) Double bond position

1-Butene   2-Butene

The skeleton may have double bonds, which can vary in location.

(d) Presence of rings

Cyclohexane   Benzene

Some carbon skeletons are arranged in rings. In the abbreviated structural formula for each compound (at the right), each corner represents a carbon and its attached hydrogens.

and hydrogen. Atoms of hydrogen are attached to the carbon skeleton wherever electrons are available for covalent bonding. Hydrocarbons are the major components of petroleum, which is called a fossil fuel because it consists of the partially decomposed remains of organisms that lived millions of years ago.

Although hydrocarbons are not prevalent in most living organisms, many of a cell's organic molecules have regions consisting of only carbon and hydrogen. For example, the molecules known as fats have long hydrocarbon tails attached to a nonhydrocarbon component (Figure 4.6). Neither petroleum nor fat dissolves in water; both are hydrophobic compounds because the great majority of their

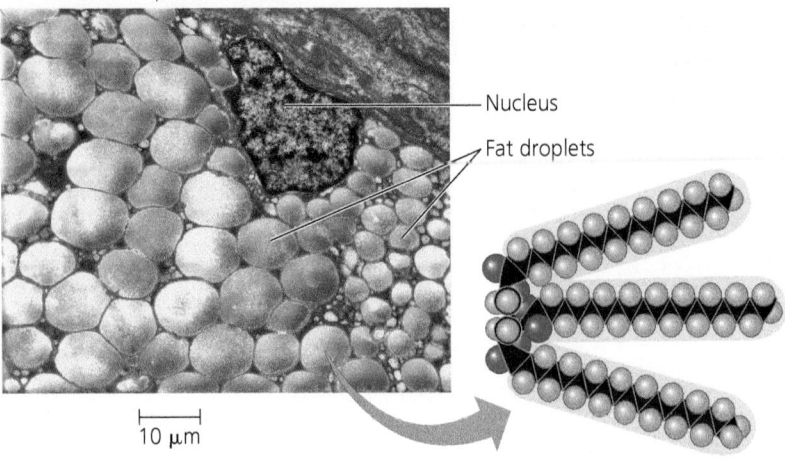

— Nucleus

— Fat droplets

10 µm

(a) Part of a human adipose cell   **(b) A fat molecule**

▲ Figure 4.6 **The role of hydrocarbons in fats. (a)** Mammalian adipose cells stockpile fat molecules as a fuel reserve. This colourized micrograph shows part of a human adipose cell with many fat droplets, each containing a large number of fat molecules. **(b)** A fat molecule consists of a small, nonhydrocarbon component joined to three hydrocarbon tails that account for the hydrophobic behaviour of fats. The tails can be broken down to provide energy. (Black = carbon; grey = hydrogen; red = oxygen.)

Source: Figure adapted from *Biochemistry*, 2nd Edition, by Christopher K. Mathews and Kensal E. Van Holde. Copyright © 1996 by Pearson Education, Inc. Adapted and electronically reproduced by permission of Pearson Education, Inc., Upper Saddle River, New Jersey.

MAKE CONNECTIONS   *How do the tails account for the hydrophobic nature of fats? (See Concept 3.2.)*

bonds are relatively nonpolar carbon-to-hydrogen linkages. Another characteristic of hydrocarbons is that they can undergo reactions that release a relatively large amount of energy. The gasoline that fuels a car consists of hydrocarbons, and the hydrocarbon tails of fats serve as stored fuel for plant embryos (seeds) and animals.

Isomers

Variation in the architecture of organic molecules can be seen in **isomers**, compounds that have the same numbers of atoms of the same elements but different structures and hence different properties. We will examine three types of isomers: structural isomers, *cis-trans* isomers, and enantiomers.

Structural isomers differ in the covalent arrangements of their atoms. Compare, for example, the two five-carbon compounds in **Figure 4.7a**. Both have the molecular formula C_5H_{12}, but they differ in the covalent arrangement of their carbon skeletons. The skeleton is straight in one compound but branched in the other. The number of possible isomers increases tremendously as carbon skeletons increase in size. There are only three forms of C_5H_{12} (two of which are shown in Figure 4.7a), but there are 18 variations of C_8H_{18} and 366 319 possible structural isomers of $C_{20}H_{42}$. Structural isomers may also differ in the location of double bonds.

▼ Figure 4.7 **Three types of isomers, compounds with the same molecular formula but different structures.**

(a) Structural isomers

Pentane   2-methyl butane

Structural isomers differ in covalent partners, as shown in this example of two isomers of C_5H_{12}: pentane (left) and 2-methyl butane (right).

(b) *Cis-trans* isomers

cis isomer: The two Xs are on the same side.   *trans* isomer: The two Xs are on opposite sides.

Cis-trans isomers differ in arrangement about a double bond. In these diagrams, X represents an atom or group of atoms attached to a double-bonded carbon.

(c) Enantiomers

CO₂H   CO₂H

H   NH₂   NH₂   H

CH₃   CH₃

L isomer   D isomer

Enantiomers differ in spatial arrangement around an asymmetric carbon, resulting in molecules that are mirror images, like left and right hands. The two isomers here are designated the L and D isomers from the Latin for "left" and "right" (*levo* and *dextro*). Enantiomers cannot be superimposed on each other.

© Pearson Education, Inc.

Source: Figure adapted from *The World Of The Cell*, 3rd Edition, by Wayne M. Becker, Jane B. Reece, and Martin F. Poenie. Copyright © 1996 by Pearson Education, Inc. Adapted and electronically reproduced by permission of Pearson Education, Inc., Upper Saddle River, New Jersey.

DRAW IT   *There are three structural isomers of C_5H_{12}; draw the one not shown in (a).*

In *cis-trans* **isomers** (formerly called geometric isomers), carbons have covalent bonds to the same atoms, but these atoms differ in their spatial arrangements due to the inflexibility of double bonds. Single bonds allow the atoms they join to rotate freely about the bond axis without changing the compound. In contrast, double bonds do not permit such rotation. If a double bond joins two carbon atoms, and each C also has two different atoms (or groups of atoms) attached to it, then two distinct *cis-trans* isomers are possible. Consider a simple molecule with two double-bonded carbons, each of which has an H and an X attached to it (Figure 4.7b). The arrangement with both Xs on the same side of the double bond is called a *cis* isomer, and that with the Xs on opposite sides is called a *trans* isomer. The subtle difference in shape between such isomers can dramatically affect the biological activities of organic molecules. For example, the biochemistry of vision involves a light-induced change of retinal, a chemical compound in the eye, from the *cis* isomer to the *trans* isomer (see Figure 50.17). Another example involves *trans* fats, which are discussed in Chapter 5.

Enantiomers are isomers that are mirror images of each other and that differ in shape due to the presence of an asymmetric carbon, one that is attached to four different atoms or groups of atoms. (See the middle carbon in the ball-and-stick models shown in Figure 4.7c.) The four groups can be arranged in space around the asymmetric carbon in two different ways that are mirror images. Enantiomers are, in a way, left-handed and right-handed versions of the molecule. Just as your right hand won't fit into a left-handed glove, a "right-handed" molecule won't fit into the same space as the "left-handed" version. Usually, only one isomer is biologically active because only that form can bind to specific molecules in an organism.

The concept of enantiomers is important in the pharmaceutical industry because the two enantiomers of a drug may not be equally effective, as is the case for both ibuprofen and the asthma medication albuterol (Figure 4.8).

Drug	Condition	Effective Enantiomer	Ineffective Enantiomer
Ibuprofen	Pain; inflammation	*S*-Ibuprofen	*R*-Ibuprofen
Albuterol	Asthma	*R*-Albuterol	*S*-Albuterol

▲ Figure 4.8 **The pharmacological importance of enantiomers.** Ibuprofen and albuterol are examples of drugs whose enantiomers have different effects. (*S* and *R* are letters used in one system to distinguish between enantiomers.) They are commonly sold as a mixture of the two enantiomers. The *S* enantiomer is 100 times more effective than the other. Albuterol is used to relax bronchial muscles, improving airflow in asthma patients. Only *R*-albuterol is synthesized and sold as a drug; the *S* form counteracts the active *R* form.

Methamphetamine also occurs in two enantiomers that have very different effects. One enantiomer is the highly addictive stimulant drug known as "crank," sold illegally in the street drug trade. The other has a much weaker effect and is the active ingredient in an over-the-counter vapour inhaler for treatment of nasal congestion. The differing effects of enantiomers in the body demonstrate that organisms are sensitive to even the most subtle variations in molecular architecture. Once again, we see that molecules have emergent properties that depend on the specific arrangement of their atoms.

CONCEPT CHECK 4.2

1. **DRAW IT** (a) Draw a structural formula for C_2H_4. (b) Draw the *trans* isomer of $C_2H_2Cl_2$.
2. Which molecules in Figure 4.5 are isomers? For each pair, identify the type of isomer.
3. How are gasoline and fat chemically similar?
4. Can propane (C_3H_8) form isomers? Explain.

For suggested answers, see Appendix A.

CONCEPT 4.3

A few chemical groups are key to molecular function

The distinctive properties of an organic molecule depend not only on the arrangement of its carbon skeleton but also on the chemical groups attached to that skeleton. We can think of hydrocarbons, the simplest organic molecules, as the underlying framework for more complex organic molecules. A number of chemical groups can replace one or more of the hydrogens bonded to the carbon skeleton of the hydrocarbon. These groups may participate in chemical reactions or may contribute to function indirectly by their effects on molecular shape; they help give each molecule its unique properties.

The Chemical Groups Most Important in the Processes of Life

Consider the differences between estradiol (a type of estrogen) and testosterone. These compounds are female and male sex hormones, respectively, in humans and other vertebrates. Both are steroids, organic molecules with a common carbon skeleton in the form of four fused rings. They differ only in the chemical groups attached to the rings (shown here in abbreviated form); the distinctions in molecular architecture are shaded in blue:

Estradiol

Testosterone

The different actions of these two molecules on many targets throughout the body are the basis of gender, producing the contrasting features of male and female vertebrates.

In this case, chemical groups are important because they affect molecular shape, contributing to function.

In other cases, chemical groups are directly involved in chemical reactions; such groups are known as **functional groups**. Each has certain properties, such as shape and charge, that cause it to participate in chemical reactions in a characteristic way.

The seven chemical groups most important in biological processes are the hydroxyl, carbonyl, carboxyl, amino, sulfhydryl, phosphate, and methyl groups. The first six groups can be chemically reactive; all of these, except the sulfhydryl group, are also hydrophilic and thus increase the solubility of organic compounds in water. The methyl group is not reactive, but instead often serves as a recognizable tag on biological molecules. Study Figure 4.9 to become familiar with these biologically important chemical groups.

ATP: An Important Source of Energy for Cellular Processes

The "Phosphate group" row in Figure 4.9 shows a simple example of an organic phosphate molecule. A more complicated organic phosphate, **adenosine triphosphate**, or **ATP**, is worth mentioning here because its function in the cell is so important. ATP consists of an organic molecule called adenosine attached to a string of three phosphate groups:

Where three phosphates are present in series, as in ATP, one phosphate may be split off as a result of a reaction with water. This inorganic phosphate ion, $HOPO_3^{2-}$, is often abbreviated $\textcircled{P}_i$ in this book, and a phosphate group in an organic molecule is often written as $\textcircled{P}$. Having lost one phosphate, ATP becomes adenosine diphosphate, or ADP. Although ATP is sometimes said to store energy, it is more accurate to think of it as storing the potential to react with water. This reaction releases energy that can be used by the cell. You will learn about this in more detail in Chapter 8.

CONCEPT CHECK 4.3

1. What does the term *amino acid* signify about the structure of such a molecule?

2. What chemical change occurs to ATP when it reacts with water and releases energy?

3. **WHAT IF?** Suppose you had an organic molecule such as cysteine (see Figure 4.9, sulfhydryl group example), and you chemically removed the —NH2 group and replaced it with —COOH. Draw the structural formula for this molecule and speculate about its chemical properties. Is the central carbon asymmetric before the change? After?

For suggested answers, see Appendix A.

The Chemical Elements of Life: *A Review*

Living matter, as you have learned, consists mainly of carbon, oxygen, hydrogen, and nitrogen, with smaller amounts of sulphur and phosphorus. These elements all form strong covalent bonds, an essential characteristic in the architecture of complex organic molecules. Of all these elements, carbon is the virtuoso of the covalent bond. The versatility of carbon makes possible the great diversity of organic molecules, each with particular properties that emerge from the unique arrangement of its carbon skeleton and the chemical groups appended to that skeleton. This variation at the molecular level provides the foundation for the rich biological diversity found on our planet.

Chemical Group	Group Properties and Compound Name	Examples	
Hydroxyl group (—OH) (may be written HO—)	Is polar due to electronegative oxygen. Forms hydrogen bonds with water, helping dissolve compounds such as sugars. Compound name: Alcohol (specific name usually ends in -ol)	**Ethanol**, the alcohol present in alcoholic beverages	
Carbonyl group ($>$C$=$O)	Sugars with ketone groups are called ketoses; those with aldehydes are called aldoses. Compound name: Ketone (carbonyl group is within a carbon skeleton) or aldehyde (carbonyl group is at the end of a carbon skeleton)	**Acetone**, the simplest ketone	**Propanal**, an aldehyde
Carboxyl group (—COOH)	Acts as an acid (can donate H$^+$) because the covalent bond between oxygen and hydrogen is so polar. Compound name: Carboxylic acid, or organic acid	**Acetic acid**, which gives vinegar its sour taste	Ionized form of —COOH (carboxylate ion), found in cells
Amino group (—NH$_2$)	Acts as a base; can pick up an H$^+$ from the surrounding solution (water, in living organisms). Compound name: Amine	**Glycine**, an amino acid (note its carboxyl group)	Ionized form of —NH$_2$, found in cells
Sulfhydryl group (—SH) (may be written HS —)	Two — SH groups can react, forming a "cross-link" that helps stabilize protein structure. Hair protein cross-links maintain the straightness or curliness of hair; in hair salons, permanent treatments break cross-links, then re-form them while the hair is in the desired shape. Compound name: Thiol	**Cysteine**, a sulphur-containing amino acid	
Phosphate group (—OPO$_3$$^{2-}$)	Contributes negative charge (1– when positioned inside a chain of phosphates; 2– when at the end). When attached, confers on a molecule the ability to react with water, releasing energy. Compound name: Organic phosphate	**Glycerol phosphate**, which takes part in many important chemical reactions in cells	
Methyl group (—CH$_3$)	Affects the expression of genes when on DNA or on proteins bound to DNA. Affects the shape and function of male and female sex hormones. Compound name: Methylated compound	**5-Methyl cytosine**, a component of DNA that has been modified by addition of a methyl group	

4 Chapter Review

Go to **MasteringBiology**® for Assignments, the eText, and the Study Area with Animations, Activities, Vocab Self-Quiz, and Practice Tests.

SUMMARY OF KEY CONCEPTS

CONCEPT 4.1

Organic chemistry is the study of carbon compounds (pp. 64–65)

- Organic compounds, once thought to arise only within living organisms, were finally synthesized in the laboratory.
- Living matter is made mostly of carbon, oxygen, hydrogen, and nitrogen. Biological diversity results from carbon's ability to form a huge number of molecules with particular shapes and properties.

? *How did Stanley Miller's experiments support the idea that, even at life's origins, physical and chemical laws govern the processes of life?*

CONCEPT 4.2

Carbon atoms can form diverse molecules by bonding to four other atoms (pp. 66–69)

- Carbon, with a valence of 4, can bond to various other atoms, including O, H, and N. Carbon can also bond to other carbon atoms, forming the carbon skeletons of organic compounds. These skeletons vary in length and shape and have bonding sites for atoms of other elements.
- **Hydrocarbons** consist only of carbon and hydrogen.
- **Isomers** are compounds that have the same molecular formula but different structures and therefore different properties. Three types of isomers are **structural isomers**, *cis-trans* **isomers**, and **enantiomers**.

? *Refer back to Figure 4.9. What type of isomers are acetone and propanal? How many asymmetric carbons are present in acetic acid, glycine, and glycerol phosphate? Can these three molecules exist as forms that are enantiomers?*

CONCEPT 4.3

A few chemical groups are key to molecular function (pp. 69–71)

- Chemical groups attached to the carbon skeletons of organic molecules participate in chemical reactions (**functional groups**) or contribute to function by affecting molecular shape (see Figure 4.9).
- **ATP (adenosine triphosphate)** consists of adenosine attached to three phosphate groups. ATP can react with water, forming inorganic phosphate and ADP (adenosine diphosphate). This reaction releases energy that can be used by the cell (see the following equation).

? *In what ways does a methyl group differ chemically from the other six important chemical groups shown in Figure 4.9?*

TEST YOUR UNDERSTANDING

LEVEL 1: KNOWLEDGE/COMPREHENSION

1. Organic chemistry is currently defined as
   a. the study of compounds made only by living cells.
   b. the study of carbon compounds.
   c. the study of natural (as opposed to synthetic) compounds.
   d. the study of hydrocarbons.

2. Which functional group is not present in this molecule?
   a. carboxyl
   b. sulfhydryl
   c. hydroxyl
   d. amino

3. **MAKE CONNECTIONS** Which chemical group is most likely to be responsible for an organic molecule behaving as a base (see Concept 3.3, p. 57)?
   a. hydroxyl
   b. carbonyl
   c. amino
   d. phosphate

LEVEL 2: APPLICATION/ANALYSIS

4. Which of the following hydrocarbons has a double bond in its carbon skeleton?
   a. C_3H_8
   b. C_2H_6
   c. C_2H_4
   d. C_2H_2

5. Choose the term that correctly describes the relationship between these two sugar molecules:
   a. structural isomers
   b. *cis-trans* isomers
   c. enantiomers
   d. isotopes

6. Identify the asymmetric carbon in this molecule:

7. Which action could produce a carbonyl group?
   a. the replacement of the —OH of a carboxyl group with hydrogen
   b. the addition of a thiol to a hydroxyl
   c. the addition of a hydroxyl to a phosphate
   d. the replacement of the nitrogen of an amine with oxygen

8. Which of the molecules shown in question 5 has an asymmetric carbon? Which carbon is asymmetric?

LEVEL 3: SYNTHESIS/EVALUATION

9. EVOLUTION CONNECTION

DRAW IT Some scientists think that life elsewhere in the universe might be based on the element silicon, rather than on carbon, as on Earth. Look at the electron distribution diagram for silicon in Figure 2.7 and draw the Lewis dot structure for silicon. What properties does silicon share with carbon that would make silicon-based life more likely than, say, neon-based life or aluminum-based life?

10. SCIENTIFIC INQUIRY

Thalidomide achieved notoriety 50 years ago because of a wave of birth defects among children born to women who took this drug during pregnancy as a treatment for morning sickness. Thalidomide is a mixture of two enantiomers; one reduces morning sickness, but the other causes severe birth defects. (Although the beneficial enantiomer can be synthesized and given to patients, it is converted in the body to the harmful enantiomer.) The U.S. Food and Drug Administration (FDA) withheld approval of thalidomide in 1960 (although it was widely prescribed in Canada until 1962). Since then, however, the FDA has approved this drug for the treatment of conditions associated with Hansen's disease (leprosy) and newly diagnosed multiple myeloma, a blood and bone marrow cancer. In clinical trials, thalidomide also shows promise as a treatment for AIDS, tuberculosis, inflammatory diseases, and some other types of cancer. Assuming that molecules related to thalidomide could be synthesized in the laboratory, describe in a broad way the type of experiments you would do to improve the benefits of this drug and minimize its harmful effects.

11. WRITE ABOUT A THEME: ORGANIZATION

In 1918, an epidemic of sleeping sickness caused an unusual rigid paralysis in some survivors, similar to symptoms of advanced Parkinson's disease. Years later, L-dopa (below, left), a chemical used to treat Parkinson's disease, was given to some of these patients, as dramatized in the 1990 movie *Awakenings*, starring Robin Williams. L-dopa was remarkably effective at eliminating the paralysis, at least temporarily. However, its enantiomer, D-dopa (right), was subsequently shown to have no effect at all, as is the case for Parkinson's disease. In a short essay (100–150 words), discuss how the effectiveness of one enantiomer and not the other illustrates the theme of structure and function.

L-dopa   **D-dopa**

12. SYNTHESIZE YOUR KNOWLEDGE

Danita Delimont/Alamy Stock Photo

Explain how the chemical structure of the carbon atom accounts for the differences between the male and female moose seen in the photo.

For selected answers, see Appendix A.

5

The Structure and Function of Large Biological Molecules

KEY CONCEPTS

5.1 Macromolecules are polymers, built from monomers

5.2 Carbohydrates serve as fuel and building material

5.3 Lipids are a diverse group of hydrophobic molecules

5.4 Proteins include a diversity of structures, resulting in a wide range of functions

5.5 Nucleic acids store, transmit, and help express hereditary information

5.6 Genomics and proteomics have transformed biological inquiry and applications

▲ **Figure 5.1 Why is the structure of a protein important for its function?**

The Molecules of Life

Given the rich complexity of life on Earth it might surprise you that the most important large molecules found in all living things—from bacteria to elephants—can be sorted into just four main classes: carbohydrates, lipids, proteins, and nucleic acids. On the molecular scale, members of three of these classes—carbohydrates, proteins, and nucleic acids—are huge and are therefore called **macromolecules**. For example, a protein may consist of thousands of atoms that form a molecular colossus with a mass well over 100 000 daltons. Considering the size and complexity of macromolecules, it is noteworthy that biochemists have determined the detailed structure of so many of them. The image in Figure 5.1 depicts a molecular model of a protein called parkin. Dr. Edward A. Fon from the Montreal Neurological Institute and Hospital, and Dr. Kalle Gehring from the Department of Biochemistry in the Faculty of Medicine at McGill University, discovered the 3-D structure of this protein in 2015. Parkin is a protein involved in protecting neurons from cell death, and mutations in this protein can cause a hereditary, albeit rare, form of Parkinson's disease.

The architecture of a large biological molecule plays an essential role in its function. Like water and simple organic molecules, large biological molecules exhibit unique emergent properties arising from the orderly arrangement of their atoms.

In this chapter, we'll first consider how macromolecules are built. Then we'll examine the structure and function of all four classes of large biological molecules: carbohydrates, lipids, proteins, and nucleic acids.

CONCEPT 5.1

Macromolecules are polymers, built from monomers

The macromolecules in three of the four classes of life's organic compounds—carbohydrates, proteins, and nucleic acids, all except lipids—are chain-like molecules called polymers (from the Greek *polys*, many, and *meros*, part). A **polymer** is a long molecule consisting of many similar or identical building blocks linked by covalent bonds, much as a train consists of a chain of cars. The repeating units that serve as the building blocks of a polymer are smaller molecules called **monomers** (from the Greek *monos*, single). Some monomers also have other functions of their own.

The Synthesis and Breakdown of Polymers

Although each class of polymer is made up of a different type of monomer, the chemical mechanisms by which cells make and break down polymers are basically the same in all cases. In cells, these processes are facilitated by **enzymes**, specialized macromolecules that speed up chemical reactions. Monomers are connected by a reaction in which two molecules are covalently bonded to each other, with the loss of a water molecule; this is known as a **dehydration reaction** (Figure 5.2a). When a bond forms between two monomers, each monomer contributes part of the water molecule that is released during the reaction: One monomer provides a hydroxyl group (—OH), while the other provides a hydrogen (—H). This reaction is repeated as monomers are added to the chain one by one, making a polymer.

Polymers are disassembled to monomers by **hydrolysis**, a process that is essentially the reverse of the dehydration reaction (Figure 5.2b). Hydrolysis means water breakage (from the Greek *hydro*, water, and *lysis*, break). The bond between monomers is broken by the addition of a water molecule, with a hydrogen from water attaching to one monomer and the hydroxyl group attaching to the other. An example of hydrolysis within our bodies is the process of digestion. The bulk of the organic material in our food is in the form of polymers that are much too large to enter our cells. Within the digestive tract, various enzymes attack the polymers, speeding up hydrolysis. Released monomers are then absorbed into the bloodstream for distribution to all body cells. Those cells can then use dehydration reactions to assemble the monomers into new, different polymers that can perform specific functions required by the cell.

▼ Figure 5.2 **The synthesis and breakdown of polymers.**

(a) Dehydration reaction: synthesizing a polymer

Short polymer · Unlinked monomer

Dehydration removes a water molecule, forming a new bond.

H_2O

Longer polymer

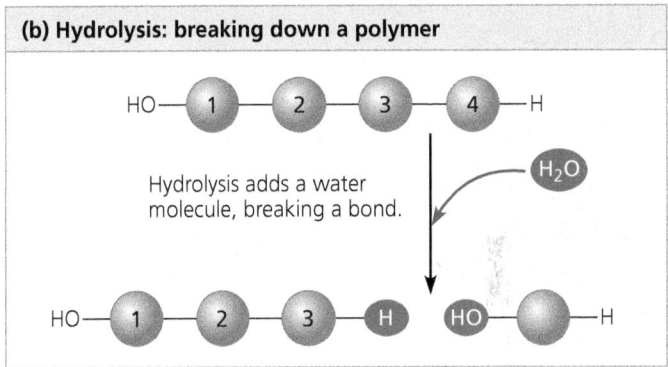

(b) Hydrolysis: breaking down a polymer

Hydrolysis adds a water molecule, breaking a bond.

H_2O

The Diversity of Polymers

A cell has thousands of different macromolecules; the collection varies from one type of cell to another. The inherited differences between close relatives such as human siblings reflect small variations in polymers, particularly DNA and proteins. Molecular differences between unrelated individuals are more extensive, and those between species greater still. The diversity of macromolecules in the living world is vast, and the possible variety is effectively limitless.

What is the basis for such diversity in life's polymers? These molecules are constructed from only 40 to 50 common monomers and some others that occur rarely. Building a huge variety of polymers from such a limited number of monomers is analogous to constructing hundreds of thousands of words from only 26 letters of the alphabet. The key is arrangement—the particular linear sequence that the units follow. However, this analogy falls far short of describing the great diversity of macromolecules because most biological polymers have many more monomers than the number of letters in a word, even the longest ones. Proteins, for example, are built from 20 kinds of amino acids arranged in chains that are typically hundreds of amino acids long. The molecular logic of life is simple but elegant: Small molecules common to all organisms are ordered into unique macromolecules.

Despite this immense diversity, molecular structure and function can still be grouped roughly by class. Let's

CHAPTER 5 The Structure and Function of Large Biological Molecules 75 examine each of the four major classes of large biological molecules. For each class, the large molecules have emergent properties not found in their individual building blocks.

CONCEPT CHECK 5.1

1. What are the four main classes of large biological molecules? Which class does not consist of polymers?

2. How many molecules of water are needed to completely hydrolyze a polymer that is 10 monomers long?

3. **WHAT IF?** If you eat a piece of fish, what reactions must occur for the amino acid monomers in the protein of the fish to be converted to new proteins in your body?

For suggested answers, see Appendix A.

CONCEPT 5.2

Carbohydrates serve as fuel and building material

Carbohydrates include sugars and polymers of sugars. The simplest carbohydrates are the monosaccharides, or simple sugars; these are the monomers from which more complex carbohydrates are built. Disaccharides are double sugars, consisting of two monosaccharides joined by a covalent bond. Carbohydrate macromolecules are polymers called polysaccharides, composed of many sugar building blocks.

Sugars

Monosaccharides (from the Greek *monos*, single, and *sacchar*, sugar) generally have molecular formulas that are some multiple of the unit CH_2O. Glucose ($C_6H_{12}O_6$), the most common monosaccharide, is of central importance in the chemistry of life. In the structure of glucose, we can see the trademarks of a sugar: The molecule has a carbonyl group ($C=O$) and multiple hydroxyl groups ($-OH$) **(Figure 5.3)**. Depending on the location of the carbonyl group, a sugar is either an aldose (aldehyde sugar) or a ketose (ketone sugar). Glucose, for example, is an aldose; fructose, an isomer of glucose, is a ketose. (Most names for sugars end in -*ose*.) Another criterion for classifying sugars is the size of the carbon skeleton, which ranges from three to seven carbons long. Glucose, fructose, and other sugars that have six carbons are called hexoses. Trioses (three–carbon sugars) and pentoses (five-carbon sugars) are also common.

Still another source of diversity for simple sugars is in the spatial arrangement of their parts around asymmetric carbons. (Recall that an asymmetric carbon is a carbon attached to four different atoms or groups of atoms. See Concept 4.2.) Glucose and galactose, for example, differ only in the placement of parts around one asymmetric carbon (see the purple boxes in Figure 5.3). What seems like a small difference is

Aldoses (Aldehyde Sugars) Carbonyl group at end of carbon skeleton	Ketoses (Ketone Sugars) Carbonyl group within carbon skeleton
Trioses: 3-carbon sugars ($C_3H_6O_3$)	
Glyceraldehyde An initial breakdown product of glucose	**Dihydroxyacetone** An initial breakdown product of glucose
Pentoses: 5-carbon sugars ($C_5H_{10}O_5$)	
Ribose A component of RNA	**Ribulose** An intermediate in photosynthesis
Hexoses: 6-carbon sugars ($C_6H_{12}O_6$)	
Glucose **Galactose** Energy sources for organisms	**Fructose** An energy source for organisms

▲ **Figure 5.3 The structure and classification of some monosaccharides.** Sugars vary in the location of their carbonyl groups (orange), the length of their carbon skeletons, and the spatial arrangement around asymmetric carbons (compare, for example, the purple portions of glucose and galactose).

MAKE CONNECTIONS *In the 1970s, a process was developed that converts the glucose in corn syrup to its sweeter isomer, fructose. High-fructose corn syrup, a common ingredient in soft drinks and processed food, is a mixture of glucose and fructose. What type of isomers are glucose and fructose? See Figure 4.7.*

(a) **Linear and ring forms.** Chemical equilibrium between the linear and ring structures greatly favours the formation of rings. The carbons of the sugar are numbered 1 to 6, as shown. To form the glucose ring, carbon 1 bonds to the oxygen attached to carbon 5.

(b) **Abbreviated ring structure.** Each corner represents a carbon. The ring's thicker edge indicates that you are looking at the ring edge-on; the components attached to the ring lie above or below the plane of the ring.

▲ Figure 5.4 **Linear and ring forms of glucose.**

DRAW IT *Start with the linear form of fructose (see Figure 5.3) and draw the formation of the fructose ring in two steps. First, number the carbons starting at the top of the linear structure. Then attach carbon 5 via its oxygen to carbon 2. Compare the number of carbons in the fructose and glucose rings.*

significant enough to give the two sugars distinctive shapes and binding activities, thus different behaviours.

Although it is convenient to draw glucose with a linear carbon skeleton, this representation is not completely accurate. In aqueous solutions, glucose molecules, as well as most other five- and six-carbon sugars, form rings (Figure 5.4).

Monosaccharides, particularly glucose, are major nutrients for cells. In the process known as cellular respiration, cells extract energy from glucose molecules by breaking them down in a series of reactions. Not only are simple-sugar molecules a major fuel for cellular work, but their carbon skeletons also serve as raw material for the synthesis of other types of small organic molecules, such as amino

acids and fatty acids. Sugar molecules that are not immediately used in these ways are generally incorporated as monomers into disaccharides or polysaccharides.

A **disaccharide** consists of two monosaccharides joined by a **glycosidic linkage**, a covalent bond formed between two monosaccharides by a dehydration reaction. For example, maltose is a disaccharide formed by the linking of two molecules of glucose (Figure 5.5a). Also known as malt sugar, maltose is an ingredient used in brewing beer. The most prevalent disaccharide is sucrose, which is table sugar. Its two monomers are glucose and fructose (Figure 5.5b). Plants generally transport carbohydrates from leaves to roots and other nonphotosynthetic organs in the form of

(a) Dehydration reaction in the synthesis of maltose. The bonding of two glucose units forms maltose. The glycosidic linkage joins the number 1 carbon of one glucose to the number 4 carbon of the second glucose. Joining the glucose monomers in a different way would result in a different disaccharide.

Glucose   Glucose   Maltose

(b) Dehydration reaction in the synthesis of sucrose. Sucrose is a disaccharide formed from glucose and fructose. Notice that fructose, though a hexose like glucose, forms a five-sided ring.

Glucose   Fructose   Sucrose

▲ Figure 5.5 **Examples of disaccharide synthesis.**

DRAW IT *Referring to Figure 5.4, number the carbons in each sugar in this figure. Show how the numbering is consistent with the name of the glycosidic linkage in each disaccharide.*

sucrose. Lactose, the sugar present in milk, is another disaccharide, in this case a glucose molecule joined to a galactose molecule.

Polysaccharides

Polysaccharides are macromolecules, polymers with a few hundred to a few thousand monosaccharides joined by glycosidic linkages. Some polysaccharides serve as storage material, hydrolyzed as needed to provide sugar for cells. Other polysaccharides serve as building material for structures that protect the cell or the whole organism. The architecture and function of a polysaccharide are determined by its sugar monomers and by the positions of its glycosidic linkages.

Storage Polysaccharides

Both plants and animals store sugars for later use in the form of storage polysaccharides (Figure 5.6). Plants store **starch**, a polymer of glucose monomers, as granules within cellular structures known as plastids, which include chloroplasts. Synthesizing starch enables the plant to stockpile surplus glucose. Because glucose is a major cellular fuel, starch represents stored energy. The sugar can later be withdrawn from this carbohydrate "bank" by hydrolysis, which breaks the bonds between the glucose monomers. Most animals, including humans, also have enzymes that can hydrolyze plant starch, making glucose available as a nutrient for cells. Rice, maize (corn), wheat, and potato tubers are major sources of starch in the human diet.

Most of the glucose monomers in starch are joined by 1–4 linkages (number 1 carbon to number 4 carbon), like the glucose units in maltose (see Figure 5.5a). The simplest form of starch, amylose, is unbranched. Amylopectin, a more complex starch, is a branched polymer with 1–6 linkages at the branch points. Both of these starches are shown in Figure 5.6a.

Animals store a polysaccharide called **glycogen**, a polymer of glucose that is like amylopectin but more extensively branched (Figure 5.6b). Humans and other vertebrates store glycogen mainly in liver and muscle cells. Hydrolysis of glycogen in these cells releases glucose when the demand for sugar increases. (The extensively branched structure of glycogen fits its function: More free ends are available for

▲ Figure 5.6 **Polysaccharides of plants and animals.** Starch stored in plant cells **(a)**, glycogen stored in muscle cells **(b)**, and structural cellulose fibres in plant cell walls **(c)** are all polysaccharides composed entirely of glucose monomers (green hexagons). In starch and glycogen, the polymer chains tend to form helices in unbranched regions because of the angle of the linkages between glucose molecules. Starch consists of two kinds of polysaccharide, amylose and amylopectin. Cellulose, with a different kind of glucose linkage (to be discussed shortly), is always unbranched.

hydrolysis.) This stored fuel cannot sustain an animal for long, however. In humans, for example, glycogen stores are depleted in about a day unless they are replenished by eating. This is an issue of concern in low-carbohydrate diets, which can result in weakness and fatigue.

Structural Polysaccharides

Organisms build strong materials from structural polysaccharides. For example, the polysaccharide called **cellulose** is a major component of the tough walls that enclose plant cells (Figure 5.6c). On a global scale, plants produce almost 10^{14} kg (100 billion tonnes) of cellulose per year; it is the most abundant organic compound on Earth.

Like starch, cellulose is a polymer of glucose, but the glycosidic linkages in these two polymers differ. The difference is based on the fact that there are actually two slightly different ring structures for glucose (Figure 5.7a). When glucose forms a ring, the hydroxyl group attached to the number 1 carbon is positioned either below or above the plane of the ring. These two ring forms for glucose are called alpha (α) and beta (β), respectively. (Greek letters are often used as a "numbering" system for different versions of biological structures, much as we use the letters a, b, c, and so on for the parts of a question or a figure.) In starch, all the glucose monomers are in the α configuration (Figure 5.7b), the arrangement we saw in Figures 5.4 and 5.5. In contrast, the glucose monomers of cellulose are all in the β configuration, making every glucose monomer "upside down" with respect to its neighbours (Figure 5.7c; see also Figure 5.6c).

The differing glycosidic linkages in starch and cellulose give the two molecules distinct three-dimensional shapes. Whereas certain starch molecules are largely helical, a cellulose molecule is straight. Cellulose is never branched, and some hydroxyl groups on its glucose monomers are free to hydrogen-bond with the hydroxyls of other cellulose molecules lying parallel to it. In plant cell walls, parallel cellulose molecules held together in this way are grouped into units called microfibrils (see Figure 5.6c). These cable-like microfibrils are a strong building material for plants and an important substance for humans because cellulose is the major constituent of paper and the only component of cotton.

Enzymes that digest starch by hydrolyzing its α linkages are unable to hydrolyze the β linkages of cellulose due to the distinctly different shapes of these two molecules. In fact, few organisms possess enzymes that can digest cellulose. Almost all animals, including humans, do not; the cellulose in our food passes through the digestive tract and is eliminated with the feces. Along the way, the cellulose abrades the wall of the digestive tract and stimulates the lining to secrete mucus, which aids in the smooth passage of food through the tract. Thus, although cellulose is not a nutrient for humans, it is an important part of a healthful diet. Most fruits, vegetables, and whole grains are rich in cellulose. On food packages, "insoluble fibre" refers mainly to cellulose.

Some microorganisms can digest cellulose, breaking it down into glucose monomers. A cow harbours cellulose-digesting prokaryotes and protists in its gut. These microbes

(a) α and β glucose ring structures. These two interconvertible forms of glucose differ in the placement of the hydroxyl group (highlighted in blue) attached to the number 1 carbon.

α Glucose

β Glucose

(b) Starch: 1–4 linkage of α glucose monomers. All monomers are in the same orientation. Compare the positions of the —OH groups highlighted in yellow with those in cellulose (c).

(c) Cellulose: 1–4 linkage of β glucose monomers. In cellulose, every β glucose monomer is upside down with respect to its neighbours.

▲ Figure 5.7 **Starch and cellulose structures.**

F. Collet/Science Source

CH$_2$OH

◄ The structure of the chitin monomer

◄ Chitin forms the exoskeleton of arthropods. This cicada is moulting, shedding its old exoskeleton and emerging in adult form.

► Chitin is used to make a strong and flexible surgical thread that decomposes after the wound or incision heals.

Corbis

▲ Figure 5.8 **Chitin, a structural polysaccharide.**

hydrolyze the cellulose of hay and grass and convert the glucose to other compounds that nourish the cow. Similarly, a termite, which is unable to digest cellulose by itself, has prokaryotes or protists living in its gut that can make a meal of wood. Some fungi can digest cellulose in soil and elsewhere, thereby helping recycle chemical elements within Earth's ecosystems.

Another important structural polysaccharide is **chitin**, the carbohydrate used by arthropods (insects, spiders, crustaceans, and related animals) to build their exoskeletons (Figure 5.8). An exoskeleton is a hard case that surrounds the soft parts of an animal. Made up of chitin embedded in a layer of proteins, the case is leathery and flexible at first, but becomes hardened when the proteins are chemically linked to each other (as in insects) or encrusted with calcium carbonate (as in crabs). Chitin is also found in fungi, which use this polysaccharide rather than cellulose as the building material for their cell walls. Chitin is similar to cellulose, with β linkages, except that the glucose monomer of chitin has a nitrogen-containing appendage (see Figure 5.8).

CONCEPT 5.3

Lipids are a diverse group of hydrophobic molecules

Lipids are the one class of large biological molecules that does not include true polymers, and they are generally not big enough to be considered macromolecules. The compounds called **lipids** are grouped with each other because they share one important trait: They mix poorly, if at all, with water. The hydrophobic behaviour of lipids is based on their molecular structure. Although they may have some polar bonds associated with oxygen, lipids consist mostly of hydrocarbon regions. Lipids are varied in form and function. They include waxes and certain pigments, but we will focus on the types of lipids that are most biologically important: fats, phospholipids, and steroids.

Fats

Although fats are not polymers, they are large molecules assembled from smaller molecules by dehydration reactions. A **fat** is constructed from two kinds of smaller molecules: glycerol and fatty acids (Figure 5.9a). Glycerol is an alcohol; each of its three carbons bears a hydroxyl group. A **fatty acid** has a long carbon skeleton, usually 16 or 18 carbon atoms in length. The carbon at one end of the skeleton is part of a carboxyl group, the functional group that gives these molecules the name fatty *acid*. The rest of the skeleton consists of a hydrocarbon chain. The relatively nonpolar C—H bonds in the hydrocarbon chains of fatty acids are the reason fats are hydrophobic. Fats separate from water because the water molecules hydrogen-bond to one another and exclude the fats. This is the reason that vegetable oil (a liquid fat) separates from the aqueous vinegar solution in a bottle of salad dressing.

In making a fat, three fatty acid molecules are each joined to glycerol by an ester linkage, a bond formed by a dehydration reaction between a hydroxyl group and a carboxyl group. The resulting fat, also called a **triacylglycerol**, thus consists of three fatty acids linked to one glycerol molecule. (Still another name for a fat is *triglyceride*, a word often found in the list of ingredients on packaged foods.)

Fatty acid
(in this case, palmitic acid)

Glycerol

(a) One of three dehydration reactions in the synthesis of a fat

Ester linkage

(b) Fat molecule (triacylglycerol)

▲ **Figure 5.9** **The synthesis and structure of a fat, or triacyl-glycerol.** The molecular building blocks of a fat are one molecule of glycerol and three molecules of fatty acids. **(a)** One water molecule is removed for each fatty acid joined to the glycerol. **(b)** A fat molecule with three fatty acid units, two of them identical. The carbons of the fatty acids are arranged zigzag to suggest the actual orientations of the four single bonds extending from each carbon (see Figure 4.3a).

The fatty acids in a fat can all be the same, or they can be of two or three different kinds, as in **Figure 5.9b**.

The terms *saturated fats* and *unsaturated fats* are commonly used in the context of nutrition (**Figure 5.10**). These terms refer to the structure of the hydrocarbon chains of the fatty acids. If there are no double bonds between carbon atoms composing a chain, then as many hydrogen atoms as possible are bonded to the carbon skeleton. Such a structure is said to be *saturated* with hydrogen, and the resulting fatty acid is therefore called a **saturated fatty acid** (Figure 5.10a). An **unsaturated fatty acid** has one or more double bonds, with one fewer hydrogen atom on each double-bonded carbon. Nearly all double bonds in naturally occurring fatty acids are *cis* double bonds, which cause a kink in the hydrocarbon chain wherever they occur (Figure 5.10b). (See Figure 4.7b to remind yourself about *cis* and *trans* double bonds.)

A fat made from saturated fatty acids is called a saturated fat. Most animal fats are saturated: The hydrocarbon chains of their fatty acids—the "tails" of the fat molecules—lack double bonds, and their flexibility allows the fat molecules to pack together tightly. Saturated animal fats—such as lard and butter—are solid at room temperature. In contrast, the

▼ Figure 5.10 **Saturated and unsaturated fats and fatty acids.**

(a) Saturated fat

At room temperature, the molecules of a saturated fat, such as the fat in butter, are packed closely together, forming a solid.

Structural formula of a saturated fat molecule (Each hydrocarbon chain is represented as a zigzag line, where each bend represents a carbon atom and hydrogens are not shown.)

Space-filling model of stearic acid, a saturated fatty acid (red = oxygen, black = carbon, grey = hydrogen)

(b) Unsaturated fat

At room temperature, the molecules of an unsaturated fat, such as olive oil, cannot pack together closely enough to solidify because of the kinks in some of their fatty acid hydrocarbon chains.

Structural formula of an unsaturated fat molecule

Space-filling model of oleic acid, an unsaturated fatty acid

Cis double bond causes bending.

fats of plants and fishes are generally unsaturated, meaning that they are built of one or more types of unsaturated fatty acids. Usually liquid at room temperature, plant and fish fats are referred to as oils—olive oil and cod liver oil are examples. The kinks where the *cis* double bonds are located prevent the molecules from packing together closely enough to solidify at room temperature. The phrase "hydrogenated vegetable oils" on food labels means that unsaturated fats have been synthetically converted to saturated fats by adding hydrogen. Peanut butter, margarine, and many other products are hydrogenated to prevent lipids from separating out in liquid (oil) form.

A diet rich in saturated fats is one of several factors that may contribute to the cardiovascular disease known as atherosclerosis. In this condition, deposits called plaques develop within the walls of blood vessels, causing inward bulges that impede blood flow and reduce the resilience of the vessels. Recent studies have shown that the process of hydrogenating vegetable oils produces not only saturated fats but also unsaturated fats with *trans* double bonds. It appears that ***trans* fats** can contribute to coronary heart disease (see Concept 42.4). Because *trans* fats are especially common in baked goods and processed foods, Health Canada and the U.S. Food and Drug Administration (FDA) require nutritional labels to include information on *trans* fat content. In addition, the FDA has ordered *trans* fats to be removed from the U.S. food supply by 2018. Some countries, such as Denmark, Switzerland, and Hungary, have already banned *trans* fats in foods.

The major function of fats is energy storage. The hydrocarbon chains of fats are similar to gasoline molecules and just as rich in energy. A gram of fat stores more than twice as much energy as a gram of a polysaccharide, such as starch. Because plants are relatively immobile, they can function with bulky energy storage in the form of starch. (Vegetable oils are generally obtained from seeds, where more compact storage is an asset to the plant.) Animals, however, must carry their energy stores with them, so there is an advantage to having a more compact reservoir of fuel—fat. Humans and other mammals stock their long-term food reserves in adipose cells (see Figure 4.6a), which swell and shrink as fat is deposited and withdrawn from storage. In addition to storing energy, adipose tissue also cushions such vital organs as the kidneys, and a layer of fat beneath the skin insulates the body. This subcutaneous layer is especially thick in whales, seals, and most other marine mammals, protecting them from cold ocean water.

Phospholipids

Cells as we know them could not exist without another type of lipid—**phospholipids.** Phospholipids are essential for cells because they are major constituents of cell membranes. Their structure provides a classic example of how form fits function at the molecular level. As shown in Figure 5.11, a phospholipid is similar to a fat molecule but has only two fatty acids attached to glycerol rather than three. The third hydroxyl group of glycerol is joined to a phosphate group, which has a negative electrical charge in the cell. Typically, an additional small charged or polar molecule is also linked to the phosphate group. Choline is one such molecule (see Figure 5.11), but there are many others as well, allowing formation of a variety of phospholipids that differ from each other.

The two ends of phospholipids show different behaviour toward water. The hydrocarbon tails are hydrophobic and are excluded from water. However, the phosphate group and its attachments form a hydrophilic head that has an affinity for water. When phospholipids are added to water, they self-assemble into double-layered structures called "bilayers," shielding their hydrophobic portions from water (Figure 5.11d).

◀ **Figure 5.11** **The structure of a phospholipid.** A phospholipid has a hydrophilic (polar) head and two hydrophobic (nonpolar) tails. This particular phospholipid, called a phosphatidylcholine, has a choline attached to a phosphate group. Shown here are **(a)** the structural formula, **(b)** the space-filling model (yellow = phosphorus, blue = nitrogen), **(c)** the symbol for a phospholipid that will appear throughout this book, and **(d)** the bilayer structure formed by self-assembly of phospholipids in an aqueous environment.

Source: Figure adapted from Biology: The Science of Life:, *3rd Edition, by Robert Wallace, Gerald Sanders, and Robert Ferl. Copyright © 1991 by Pearson Education, Inc. Adapted and electronically reproduced by permission of Pearson Education, Inc., Upper Saddle River, New Jersey.*

DRAW IT *Draw an oval around the hydrophilic head of the space-filling model.*

Hydrophilic head

Choline

Phosphate

Glycerol

Fatty acids

Kink due to *cis* double bond

Hydrophobic tails

(a) Structural formula

(b) Space-filling model

Hydrophilic head

Hydrophobic tails

(c) Phospholipid symbol

(d) Phospholipid bilayer

At the surface of a cell, phospholipids are arranged in a similar bilayer. The hydrophilic heads of the molecules are on the outside of the bilayer, in contact with the aqueous solutions inside and outside of the cell. The hydrophobic tails point toward the interior of the bilayer, away from the water. The phospholipid bilayer forms a boundary between the cell and its external environment; in fact, the existence of cells depends on the properties of phospholipids.

Steroids

Steroids are lipids characterized by a carbon skeleton consisting of four fused rings. Different steroids are distinguished by the particular chemical groups attached to this ensemble of rings (Figure 5.12). **Cholesterol**, a type of steroid, is a crucial molecule in animals. It is a common component of animal cell membranes and is also the precursor from which other steroids, such as the vertebrate sex hormones, are synthesized. In vertebrates, cholesterol is synthesized in the liver and is also obtained from the diet. A high level of cholesterol in the blood may contribute to atherosclerosis, although some researchers are questioning the roles of cholesterol and saturated fats in the development of this condition.

▲ **Figure 5.12 Cholesterol, a steroid.** Cholesterol is the molecule from which other steroids, including the sex hormones, are synthesized. Steroids vary in the chemical groups attached to their four interconnected rings (shown in gold).

MAKE CONNECTIONS   *Compare cholesterol with the sex hormones shown in Concept 4.3. Circle the chemical groups that cholesterol has in common with estradiol; put a square around the chemical groups that cholesterol has in common with testosterone.*

CONCEPT CHECK 5.3

1. Compare the structure of a fat (triglyceride) with that of a phospholipid.

2. Why are human sex hormones considered lipids?

3. **WHAT IF?** Suppose a membrane surrounded an oil droplet, as it does in the cells of plant seeds and in some animal cells. Describe and explain the form it might take.

For suggested answers, see Appendix A.

Proteins include a diversity of structures, resulting in a wide range of functions

Nearly every dynamic function of a living being depends on proteins. In fact, the importance of proteins is underscored by their name, which comes from the Greek word *proteios*, meaning "first," or "primary." Proteins account for more than 50% of the dry mass of most cells, and they are instrumental in almost everything organisms do. Some proteins speed up chemical reactions, while others play a role in defence, storage, transport, cellular communication, movement, or structural support. Figure 5.13 shows examples of proteins with these functions, which you'll learn more about in later chapters.

Life would not be possible without enzymes, most of which are proteins. Enzymatic proteins regulate metabolism by acting as **catalysts**, chemical agents that selectively speed up chemical reactions without being consumed by the reaction. Because an enzyme can perform its function over and over again, these molecules can be thought of as workhorses that keep cells running by carrying out the processes of life.

A human has tens of thousands of different proteins, each with a specific structure and function; proteins, in fact, are the most structurally sophisticated molecules known. Consistent with their diverse functions, they vary extensively in structure, each type of protein having a unique three-dimensional shape.

Diverse as proteins are, they are all constructed from the same set of 20 amino acids, linked in unbranched polymers. The bond between amino acids is called a **peptide bond**, so a polymer of amino acids is called a **polypeptide**. A **protein** is a biologically functional molecule made up of one or more polypeptides, each folded and coiled into a specific three-dimensional structure.

Amino Acid Monomers

All amino acids share a common structure. An **amino acid** is an organic molecule with both an amino group and a carboxyl group (see Figure 4.9). The illustration at the right shows the general formula for an amino acid. At the centre of the amino acid is an asymmetric carbon atom called the *alpha* (α) *carbon*. Its four different partners are an amino group, a carboxyl group, a hydrogen atom, and a variable group symbolized by R. The R group, also called the side chain, differs with each amino acid.

Side chain (R group)

α carbon

Amino group

Carboxyl group

Enzymatic proteins

Function: Selective acceleration of chemical reactions

Example: Digestive enzymes catalyze the hydrolysis of bonds in food molecules.

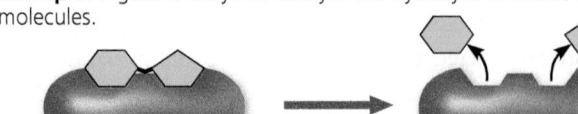

Defensive proteins

Function: Protection against disease

Example: Antibodies inactivate and help destroy viruses and bacteria.

Storage proteins

Function: Storage of amino acids

Examples: Casein, the protein of milk, is the major source of amino acids for baby mammals. Plants have storage proteins in their seeds. Ovalbumin is the protein of egg white, used as an amino acid source for the developing embryo.

Transport proteins

Function: Transport of substances

Examples: Hemoglobin, the iron-containing protein of vertebrate blood, transports oxygen from the lungs to other parts of the body. Other proteins transport molecules across membranes, as shown here.

Hormonal proteins

Function: Coordination of an organism's activities

Example: Insulin, a hormone secreted by the pancreas, causes other tissues to take up glucose, thus regulating blood sugar concentration.

Receptor proteins

Function: Response of cell to chemical stimuli

Example: Receptors built into the membrane of a nerve cell detect signalling molecules released by other nerve cells.

Contractile and motor proteins

Function: Movement

Examples: Motor proteins are responsible for the undulations of cilia and flagella. Actin and myosin proteins are responsible for the contraction of muscles.

Structural proteins

Function: Support

Examples: Keratin is the protein of hair, horns, feathers, and other skin appendages. Insects and spiders use silk fibres to make their cocoons and webs, respectively. Collagen and elastin proteins provide a fibrous framework in animal connective tissues.

Source: Protein Data Bank ID 1CGD: "Hydration Structure of a Collagen Peptide" by Jordi Bella et al., from *Structure*, September 1995, Volume 3(9).

Figure 5.14 shows the 20 amino acids that cells use to build their thousands of proteins. Here the amino groups and carboxyl groups are all depicted in ionized form, the way they usually exist at the pH found in a cell.

The physical and chemical properties of the side chain determine the unique characteristics of a particular amino acid, thus affecting its functional role in a polypeptide. In Figure 5.14, the amino acids are grouped according to the properties of their side chains. One group consists of amino acids with nonpolar side chains, which are hydrophobic.

Another group consists of amino acids with polar side chains, which are hydrophilic. Acidic amino acids are those with side chains that are generally negative in charge due to the presence of a carboxyl group, which is usually dissociated (ionized) at cellular pH. Basic amino acids have amino groups in their side chains that are generally positive in charge. (Notice that *all* amino acids have carboxyl groups and amino groups; the terms *acidic* and *basic* in this context refer only to groups in the side chains.) Because they are charged, acidic and basic side chains are also hydrophilic.

▼ Figure 5.14 **The 20 amino acids of proteins.** The amino acids are grouped here according to the properties of their side chains (R groups) and shown in their prevailing ionic forms at pH 7.2, the pH within a cell. The three-letter and one-letter abbreviations for the amino acids are in parentheses. All amino acids used in proteins are L enantiomers, the form shown here (see Figure 4.7).

Nonpolar side chains; hydrophobic

Polar side chains; hydrophilic

Electrically charged side chains; hydrophilic

Polypeptides (Amino Acid Polymers)

Now that we have examined amino acids, let's see how they are linked to form polymers (Figure 5.15). When two amino acids are positioned so that the carboxyl group of one is adjacent to the amino group of the other, they can become joined by a dehydration reaction, with the removal of a water molecule. The resulting covalent bond is called a peptide bond. Repeated over and over, this process yields a polypeptide, a polymer of many amino acids linked by peptide bonds. You'll learn more about how cells synthesize polypeptides in Chapter 17.

The repeating sequence of atoms highlighted in purple in Figure 5.15 is called the *polypeptide backbone*. Extending from this backbone are the different side chains (R groups) of the amino acids. Polypeptides range in length from a few amino acids to a thousand or more. Each specific polypeptide has a unique linear sequence of amino acids. Note that

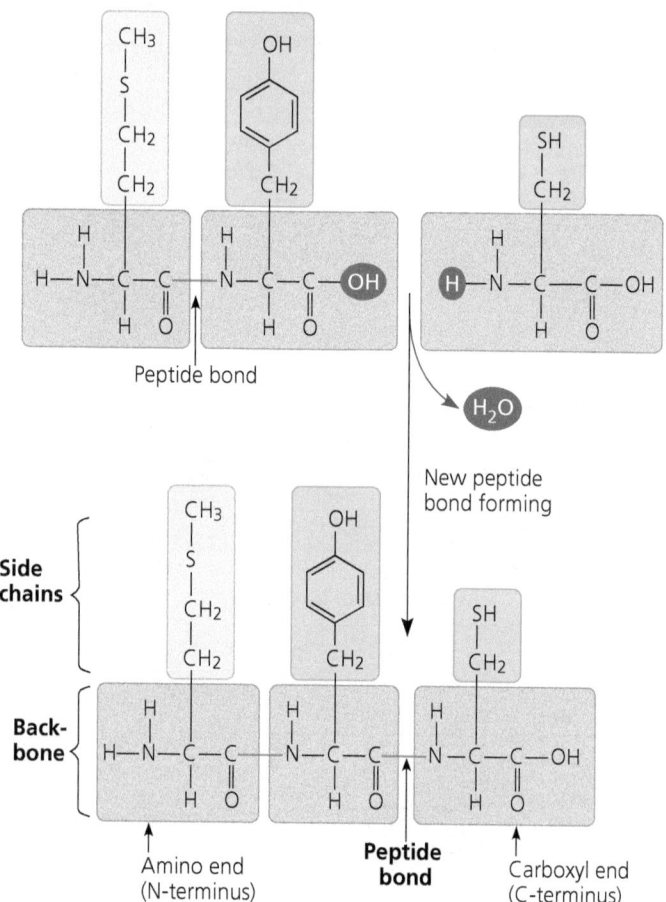

Side chains

Backbone

Peptide bond

New peptide bond forming

H_2O

Amino end (N-terminus)

Peptide bond

Carboxyl end (C-terminus)

▲ Figure 5.15 **Making a polypeptide chain.** Peptide bonds are formed by dehydration reactions, which link the carboxyl group of one amino acid to the amino group of the next. The peptide bonds are formed one at a time, starting with the amino acid at the amino end (N-terminus). The polypeptide has a repetitive backbone (purple) to which the amino acid side chains (yellow and green) are attached.

DRAW IT *Label the three amino acids in the upper part of the figure using three-letter and one-letter codes. Circle and label the carboxyl and amino groups that will form the new peptide bond.*

one end of the polypeptide chain has a free amino group, while the opposite end has a free carboxyl group. Thus, a polypeptide of any length has a single amino end (N-terminus) and a single carboxyl end (C-terminus). In a polypeptide of any significant size, the side chains far outnumber the terminal groups, so the chemical nature of the molecule as a whole is determined by the kind and sequence of the side chains. The immense variety of polypeptides in nature illustrates an important concept introduced earlier—that cells can make many different polymers by linking a limited set of monomers into diverse sequences.

Protein Structure and Function

The specific activities of proteins result from their intricate three-dimensional architecture, the simplest level of which is the sequence of their amino acids. The pioneer in determining the amino acid sequence of proteins was Frederick Sanger, who, with his colleagues at Cambridge University in England, worked on the hormone insulin in the late 1940s and early 1950s. He used agents that break polypeptides at specific places, followed by chemical methods to determine the amino acid sequence in these small fragments. Sanger and his co-workers were able, after years of effort, to reconstruct the complete amino acid sequence of insulin. Since then, the steps involved in sequencing a polypeptide have been automated.

Once we have learned the amino acid sequence of a polypeptide, what can it tell us about the three-dimensional structure (commonly referred to simply as the "structure") of the protein and its function? The term *polypeptide* is not synonymous with the term *protein*. Even for a protein consisting of a single polypeptide, the relationship is somewhat analogous to that between a long strand of yarn and a sweater of particular size and shape that can be knit from the yarn. A functional protein is not *just* a polypeptide chain, but one or more polypeptides precisely twisted, folded, and coiled into a molecule of unique shape, which can be shown in several different types of models (Figure 5.16). It is the amino acid sequence of each polypeptide that determines what three-dimensional structure the protein will have under normal cellular conditions.

When a cell synthesizes a polypeptide, the chain may fold spontaneously, assuming the functional structure for that protein. This folding is driven and reinforced by the formation of various bonds between parts of the chain, which in turn depends on the sequence of amino acids. Many proteins are roughly spherical (*globular proteins*), while others are shaped like long fibres (*fibrous proteins*). Even within these broad categories, countless variations exist.

A protein's specific structure determines how it works. In almost every case, the function of a protein depends on its ability to recognize and bind to some other molecule. In an especially striking example of the marriage of form and

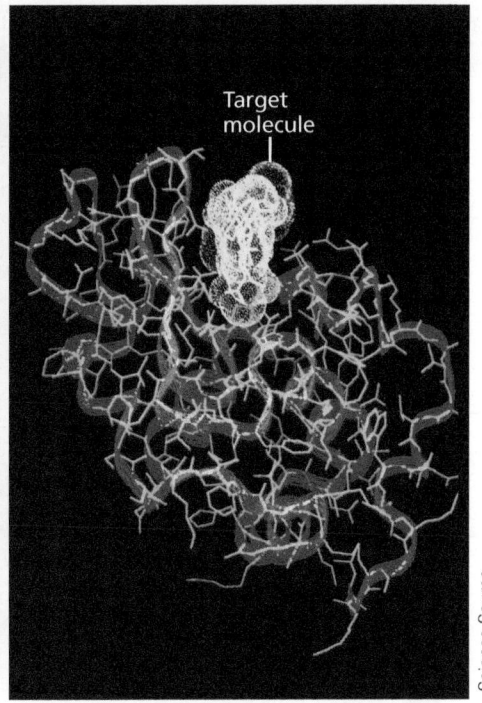

(a) A **ribbon model** shows how the single polypeptide chain folds and coils to form the functional protein. (The yellow lines represent disulphide bridges that stabilize the protein's shape; see Figure 5.18.)

(b) A **space-filling model** shows more clearly the globular shape seen in many proteins, as well as the specific three-dimensional structure unique to lysozyme.

(c) In this view, a ribbon model is superimposed on a **wireframe model**, which shows the backbone with the side chains extending from it. The yellow structure is the target molecule.

▲ Figure 5.16 **Structure of a protein, the enzyme lysozyme.** Present in our sweat, tears, and saliva, lysozyme is an enzyme that helps prevent infection by binding to and destroying specific molecules on the surface of many kinds of bacteria. The groove is the part of the protein that recognizes and binds to the target molecules on bacterial walls.

Source: 5.16(a), (b), Figure adapted from "How Amino-Acid Insertions Are Allowed in an Alpha-helix of T4 Lysozyme" by D. W. Heinz et al., from, February 1993, Volume 362(6412). Copyright © 1993 by Macmillan Publishers Ltd. Reprinted with permission.

function, Figure 5.17 shows the exact match of shape between an antibody (a protein in the body) and the particular foreign substance on a flu virus that the antibody binds to and marks for destruction. In Chapter 43, you'll learn more about how the immune system generates antibodies that match the shapes of specific foreign molecules so well. Also, you may recall from Chapter 2 that natural signalling molecules called endorphins bind to specific receptor proteins on the surface of brain cells in humans, producing euphoria and relieving pain. Morphine, heroin, and other opiate drugs are able to mimic endorphins because they all share a similar shape with endorphins and can thus fit into and bind to endorphin receptors in the brain. This fit is very specific, something like a lock and key (see Figure 2.16). Thus, the function of a protein—for instance, the ability of a receptor protein to bind to a particular pain-relieving signalling molecule—is an emergent property resulting from exquisite molecular order.

Four Levels of Protein Structure

With the goal of understanding the function of a protein, learning about its structure is often productive. In spite of their great diversity, all proteins share three superimposed levels of structure, known as primary, secondary,

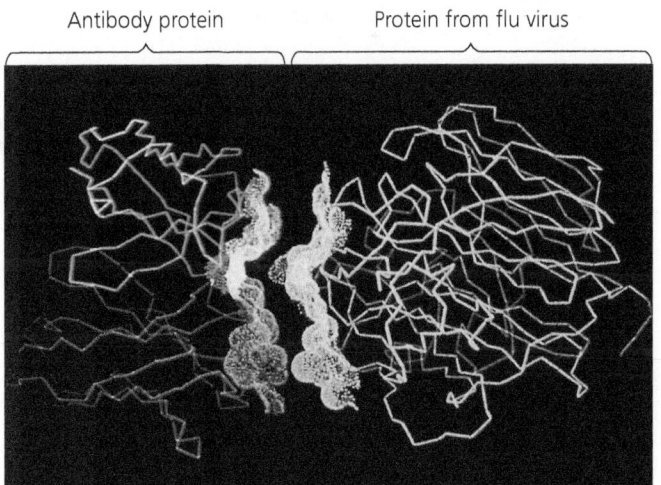

▲ Figure 5.17 **An antibody binding to a protein from a flu virus.** A technique called X-ray crystallography was used to generate a computer model of an antibody protein (blue and orange, left) bound to a flu virus protein (green and yellow, right). Computer software was then used to back the images away from each other, revealing the exact complementarity of shape between the two protein surfaces.

and tertiary structure. A fourth level, quaternary structure, arises when a protein consists of two or more polypeptide chains. Figure 5.18 describes these four levels of protein

Exploring Levels of Protein Structure

Linear chain of amino acids

Amino acids

Primary structure of transthyretin

^+H_3N — Amino end

Carboxyl end

Regions stabilized by hydrogen bonds between atoms of the polypeptide backbone

α helix

Hydrogen bond

β pleated sheet

β strand, often shown as a flat arrow pointing toward the carboxyl end (here, shown folded)

Hydrogen bond

The **primary structure** of a protein is its sequence of amino acids. As an example, let's consider transthyretin, a globular blood protein that transports vitamin A and one of the thyroid hormones throughout the body. Transthyretin is made up of four identical polypeptide chains, each composed of 127 amino acids. Shown here is one of these chains unravelled for a closer look at its primary structure. Each of the 127 positions along the chain is occupied by one of the 20 amino acids, indicated here by its three-letter abbreviation.

The primary structure is like the order of letters in a very long word. If left to chance, there would be 20^{127} different ways of making a polypeptide chain 127 amino acids long. However, the precise primary structure of a protein is determined not by the random linking of amino acids, but by inherited genetic information. The primary structure in turn dictates secondary and tertiary structure, due to the chemical nature of the backbone and the side chains (R groups) of the amino acids along the polypeptide.

Most proteins have segments of their polypeptide chains repeatedly coiled or folded in patterns that contribute to the protein's overall shape. These coils and folds, collectively referred to as **secondary structure**, are the result of hydrogen bonds between the repeating constituents of the polypeptide backbone (not the amino acid side chains). Within the backbone, the oxygen atoms have a partial negative charge, and the hydrogen atoms attached to the nitrogens have a partial positive charge (see Figure 2.14); therefore, hydrogen bonds can form between these atoms. Individually, these hydrogen bonds are weak, but because there are so many of them over a relatively long region of the polypeptide chain, they can support a particular shape for that part of the protein.

One such secondary structure is the **α helix**, a delicate coil held together by hydrogen bonding between every fourth amino acid, as shown above. Although each transthyretin polypeptide has only one α helix region (see tertiary structure), other globular proteins have multiple stretches of α helix separated by nonhelical regions (see hemoglobin on the next page). Some fibrous proteins, such as α-keratin, the structural protein of hair, have the α helix structure over most of their length.

The other main type of secondary structure is the **β pleated sheet**. As shown above, in this structure two or more segments of the polypeptide chain lying side by side (called β strands) are connected by hydrogen bonds between parts of the two parallel segments of the polypeptide backbone. β pleated sheets make up the core of many globular proteins, as is the case for transthyretin (see tertiary structure), and dominate some fibrous proteins, including the silk protein of a spider's web. The teamwork of so many hydrogen bonds makes each spider silk fibre stronger than a steel strand of the same weight.

▼ Spiders secrete silk fibres made of a structural protein containing β pleated sheets, which allow the spider web to stretch and recoil.

<table>
<tr><td>

Tertiary Structure

Three-dimensional shape stabilized by interactions between side chains

</td><td>

Quaternary Structure

Association of two or more polypeptides (some proteins only)

</td></tr>
</table>

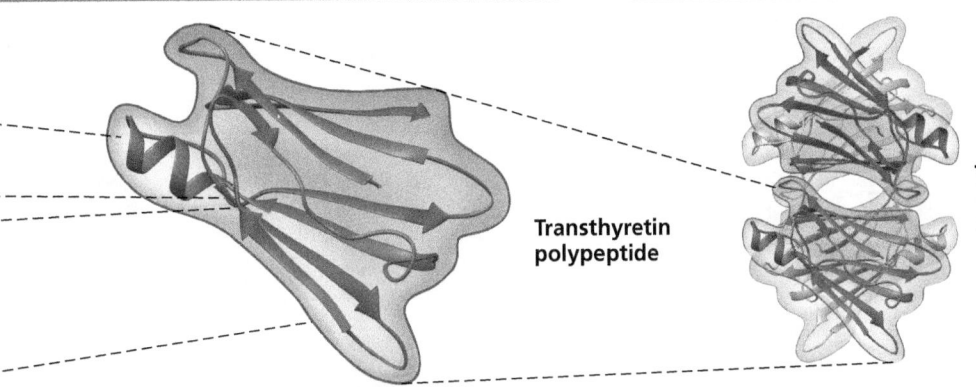

Transthyretin polypeptide

Transthyretin protein (four identical polypeptides)

Based on Protein Data Bank ID 3GS0: "Novel Transthyretin Amyloid Fibril Formation Inhibitors: Synthesis, Biological Evaluation, and X-ray Structural Analysis" by Satheesh K. Palaninathan et al., from *PLOS ONE* , July 21, 2009, Volume 4(7). © Jane B Reece.

Superimposed on the patterns of secondary structure is a protein's tertiary structure, shown above in a ribbon model of the transthyretin polypeptide. While secondary structure involves interactions between backbone constituents, **tertiary structure** is the overall shape of a polypeptide resulting from interactions between the side chains (R groups) of the various amino acids. One type of interaction that contributes to tertiary structure is called—somewhat misleadingly— a **hydrophobic interaction**. As a polypeptide folds into its functional shape, amino acids with hydrophobic (nonpolar) side chains usually end up in clusters at the core of the protein, out of contact with water. Thus, a "hydrophobic interaction" is actually caused by the exclusion of nonpolar substances by water molecules. Once nonpolar amino acid side chains are close together, van der Waals interactions help hold them together. Meanwhile, hydrogen bonds between polar side chains and ionic bonds between positively and negatively charged side chains also help stabilize tertiary structure. These are all weak interactions in the aqueous cellular environment, but their cumulative effect helps give the protein a unique shape.

Covalent bonds called **disulphide bridges** may further reinforce the shape of a protein. Disulphide bridges form where two cysteine monomers, which have sulfhydryl groups (—SH) on their side chains (see Figure 4.9), are brought close together by the folding of the protein. The sulphur of one cysteine bonds to the sulphur of the second, and the disulfide bridge (—S—S—) rivets parts of the protein together (see the yellow lines in Figure 5.16a). All of these different kinds of interactions can contribute to the tertiary structure of a protein, as shown here in a small part of a hypothetical protein:

Some proteins consist of two or more polypeptide chains aggregated into one functional macromolecule. **Quaternary structure** is the overall protein structure that results from the aggregation of these polypeptide subunits. For example, shown above is the complete globular transthyretin protein, made up of its four polypeptides.

Another example is collagen, shown below, which is a fibrous protein that has three identical helical polypeptides intertwined into a larger triple helix, giving the long fibres great strength. This suits collagen fibres to their function as the girders of connective tissue in skin, bone, tendons, ligaments, and other body parts. (Collagen accounts for 40% of the protein in a human body.)

Collagen

Protein Data Bank ID 1CGD: "Hydration Structure of a Collagen Peptide" by Jordi Bella et al., from *Structure*, September 1995, Volume 3(9).

Hemoglobin, the oxygen-binding protein of red blood cells, shown below, is another example of a globular protein with quaternary structure. It consists of four polypeptide subunits, two of one kind (α) and two of another kind (β). Both α and β subunits consist primarily of α-helical secondary structure. Each subunit has a nonpolypeptide component, called heme, with an iron atom that binds oxygen.

Red blood cells

Hydrogen bond

Hydrophobic interactions and van der Waals interactions

Disulfide bridge

Ionic bond

Polypeptide backbone

Heme
Iron
β subunit
α subunit
α subunit
β subunit

Hemoglobin

Based on Protein Data Bank ID 2HHB: "The Crystal Structure of Human Deoxyhaemoglobin at 1.74 A Resolution" by G. Fermi et al., from *Journal of Molecular Biology*, May 1984, Volume 175(2). © Jane B Reece.

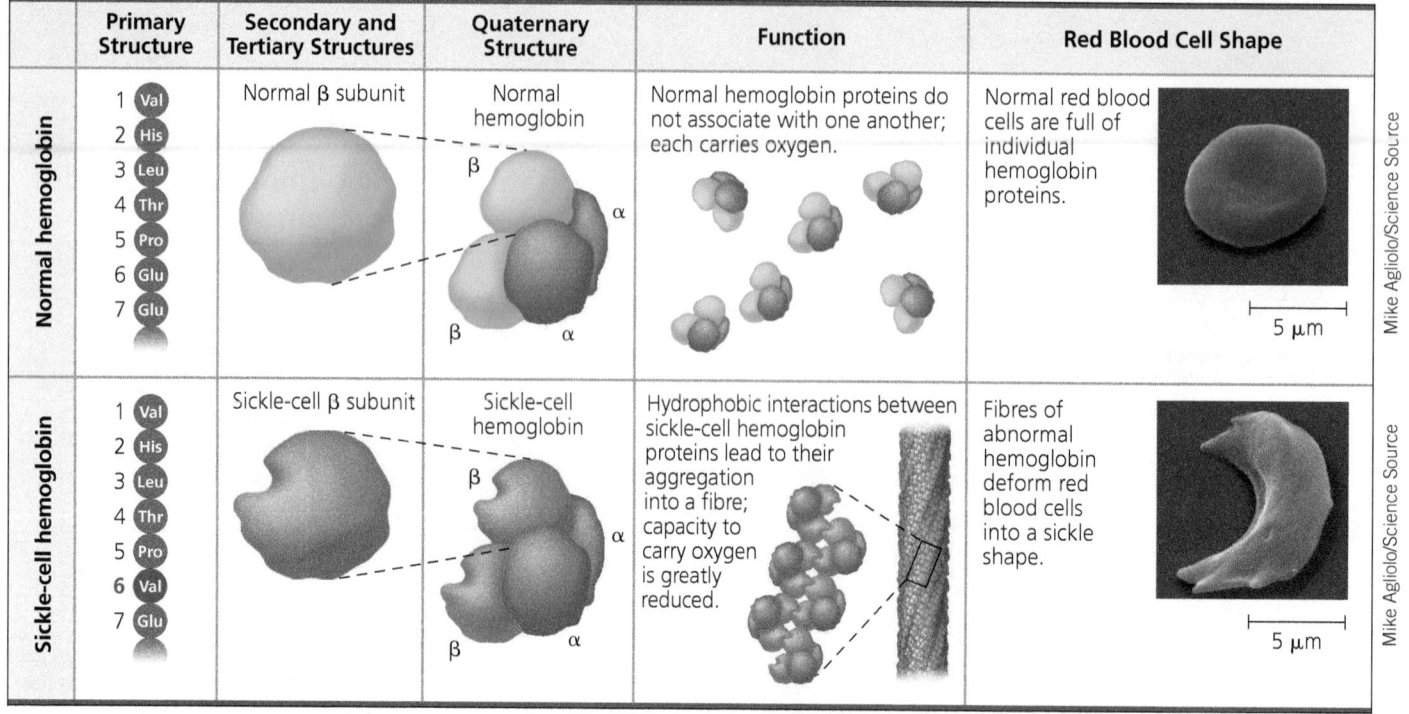

	Primary Structure	Secondary and Tertiary Structures	Quaternary Structure	Function	Red Blood Cell Shape
Normal hemoglobin	1 Val 2 His 3 Leu 4 Thr 5 Pro 6 Glu 7 Glu	Normal β subunit	Normal hemoglobin β α β α	Normal hemoglobin proteins do not associate with one another; each carries oxygen.	Normal red blood cells are full of individual hemoglobin proteins. 5 μm *Mike Agliolo/Science Source*
Sickle-cell hemoglobin	1 Val 2 His 3 Leu 4 Thr 5 Pro 6 Val 7 Glu	Sickle-cell β subunit	Sickle-cell hemoglobin β α β α	Hydrophobic interactions between sickle-cell hemoglobin proteins lead to their aggregation into a fibre; capacity to carry oxygen is greatly reduced.	Fibres of abnormal hemoglobin deform red blood cells into a sickle shape. 5 μm *Mike Agliolo/Science Source*

▲ Figure 5.19 **A single amino acid substitution in a protein causes sickle-cell disease.**

MAKE CONNECTIONS *Considering the chemical characteristics of the amino acids valine and glutamic acid (see Figure 5.14), propose a possible explanation for the dramatic effect on protein function that occurs when valine is substituted for glutamic acid.*

structure. Be sure to study this figure thoroughly before going on to the next section.

Sickle-Cell Disease: A Change in Primary Structure

Even a slight change in primary structure can affect a protein's shape and ability to function. For instance, **sickle-cell disease**, an inherited blood disorder, is caused by the substitution of one amino acid (valine) for the normal one (glutamic acid) at a particular position in the primary structure of hemoglobin, the protein that carries oxygen in red blood cells. Normal red blood cells are disk-shaped, but in sickle-cell disease, the abnormal hemoglobin molecules tend to aggregate into chains, deforming some of the cells into a sickle shape (Figure 5.19). A person with the disease has periodic "sickle-cell crises" when the angular cells clog tiny blood vessels, impeding blood flow. The toll taken on such patients is a dramatic example of how a simple change in protein structure can have devastating effects on protein function.

What Determines Protein Structure?

You've learned that a unique shape endows each protein with a specific function. But what are the key factors determining protein structure? You already know most of the answer: A polypeptide chain of a given amino acid sequence can be arranged into a three-dimensional shape determined by the interactions responsible for secondary and tertiary structure. This folding normally occurs as the protein is being synthesized in the crowded environment within a cell, aided by other proteins. However, protein structure also depends on the physical and chemical conditions of the protein's environment. If the pH, salt concentration, temperature, or other aspects of its environment are altered, the weak chemical bonds and interactions within a protein may be destroyed, causing the protein to unravel and lose its native shape, a change called **denaturation** (Figure 5.20). Because it is misshapen, the denatured protein is biologically inactive.

Normal protein — Denaturation → Denatured protein
Renaturation

▲ Figure 5.20 **Denaturation and renaturation of a protein.** High temperatures or various chemical treatments will denature a protein, causing it to lose its shape and hence its ability to function. If the denatured protein remains dissolved, it can often renature when the chemical and physical aspects of its environment are restored to normal.

Cap

Hollow cylinder

Nature Magazine

Chaperonin
(fully assembled)

Polypeptide

1 An unfolded poly-peptide enters the cylinder from one end.

2 Cap attachment causes the cylinder to change shape, creating a hydrophilic environ-ment for polypeptide folding.

Correctly folded protein

3 The cap comes off, and the properly folded protein is released.

▲ **Figure 5.21   A chaperonin in action.** The computer graphic (left) shows a large chaperonin protein complex from the bacterium *E. coli*. It has an interior space that provides a shelter for the proper folding of newly made polypeptides. The complex consists of two proteins: One protein is a hollow cylinder; the other is a cap that can fit on either end.

Most proteins become denatured if they are transferred from an aqueous environment to a nonpolar solvent, such as ether or chloroform; the polypeptide chain refolds so that its hydrophobic regions face outward toward the solvent. Other denaturation agents include chemicals that disrupt the hydrogen bonds, ionic bonds, and disulphide bridges that maintain a protein's shape. Denaturation can also result from excessive heat, which agitates the polypeptide chain enough to overpower the weak interactions that stabilize the structure. The white of an egg becomes opaque during cooking because the denatured proteins are insoluble and solidify. This also explains why excessively high fevers can be fatal: Proteins in the blood tend to denature at very high body temperatures.

When a protein in a test-tube solution has been denatured by heat or chemicals, it can sometimes return to its functional shape when the denaturing agent is removed. (Sometimes this is not possible: For example, a fried egg will not become liquefied when placed back into the refrigerator!) We can conclude that the information for building specific shape is intrinsic to the protein's primary structure. The sequence of amino acids determines the protein's shape—where an α helix can form, where β pleated sheets can exist, where disulphide bridges are located, where ionic bonds can form, and so on. But how does protein folding occur in the cell?

Protein Folding in the Cell

Biochemists now know the amino acid sequence for more than 24 million proteins, with about 1 million added each month, and the three-dimensional shape for more than 25 000. Researchers have tried to correlate the primary structure of many proteins with their three-dimensional structure to discover the rules of protein folding. Unfortunately, however, the protein-folding process is not that simple. Most proteins probably go through several intermediate structures on their way to a stable shape, and looking at the mature structure does not reveal the stages of folding required to achieve that form. However, biochemists have developed methods for tracking a protein through such stages.

Crucial to the folding process are **chaperonins** (also called chaperone proteins), protein molecules that assist in the proper folding of other proteins (Figure 5.21). Chaperonins do not specify the final structure of a polypeptide. Instead, they keep the new polypeptide segregated from disruptive chemical conditions in the cytoplasmic environment while it folds spontaneously. The chaperonin shown in Figure 5.21, from the bacterium *E. coli*, is a giant multiprotein complex shaped like a hollow cylinder. The cavity provides a shelter for folding polypeptides, and recent research suggests that minute amounts of water are present, ensuring a hydrophilic environment that aids the folding process. Molecular systems have been identified that interact with chaperonins and check whether proper folding has occurred. Such systems either refold the misfolded proteins correctly or mark them for destruction.

Misfolding of polypeptides is a serious problem in cells that has come under increasing scrutiny by medical researchers. Many diseases—such as cystic fibrosis, Alzheimer's, Parkinson's, and mad cow disease—are associated with an accumulation of misfolded proteins. In fact, misfolded versions of the transthyretin protein featured in Figure 5.18 have been implicated in several diseases, including one form of senile dementia.

Even when scientists have a correctly folded protein in hand, determining its exact three-dimensional structure is not simple, for a single protein molecule has thousands of atoms. The first 3-D structures were worked out in the late 1950s for hemoglobin and a related protein called myoglobin. The method that made these feats possible was **X-ray crystallography**, which has since been used to determine the 3-D structure of many other proteins. In a recent example, Roger Kornberg and his colleagues at Stanford University used this method to elucidate the structure of RNA polymerase, an enzyme that plays a crucial role in the expression of genes (Figure 5.22). Another

What can the 3-D shape of the enzyme RNA polymerase II tell us about its function?

Experiment In 2006, Roger Kornberg was awarded the Nobel Prize in Chemistry for using X-ray crystallography to determine the 3-D shape of RNA polymerase II, which binds to the DNA double helix and synthesizes RNA. After crystallizing a complex of all three components, Kornberg and his colleagues aimed an X-ray beam through the crystal. The atoms of the crystal diffracted (bent) the X-rays into an orderly array that a digital detector recorded as a pattern of spots called an X-ray diffraction pattern.

Results Using data from X-ray diffraction patterns, as well as the amino acid sequence determined by chemical methods, Kornberg and colleagues built a 3-D model of the complex with the help of computer software.

Conclusion By analyzing their model, the researchers developed a hypothesis about the functions of different regions of RNA polymerase II. For example, the region above the DNA may act as a clamp that holds the nucleic acids in place. (You'll learn more about this enzyme in Chapter 17.)

Source: Adaptation of figure 2c from "Structural Basis of Transcription: An RNA Polymerase II Elongation Complex at 3.3 Resolution" by Averell L. Gnatt et al., from *Science*, June 2001, Volume 292(5523). Copyright © 2001 by AAAS. Reprinted with permission

WHAT IF? *If you were an author of the paper and were describing the model, what type of protein structure would you call the small polypeptide spirals in RNA polymerase II?*

method for analyzing protein structure is nuclear magnetic resonance (NMR) spectroscopy, which does not require protein crystallization. A still newer approach employs bioinformatics (see Concept 5.6) to predict the 3-D structure of polypeptides from their amino acid sequence. X-ray crystallography, NMR spectroscopy, and bioinformatics are complementary approaches to understanding protein structure and function.

The structure of some proteins is difficult to determine for a simple reason: A growing body of biochemical research has revealed that a significant number of proteins, or regions of proteins, do not have a distinct 3-D structure until they interact with a target protein or other molecule. Their flexibility and indefinite structure is important for their function, which may require binding with different targets at different times. These proteins, which may account for 20 to 30% of mammalian proteins, are called *intrinsically disordered proteins* and are the focus of current research.

CONCEPT CHECK 5.4

1. Why does a denatured protein no longer function normally?
2. What parts of a polypeptide participate in the bonds that hold together secondary structure? Tertiary structure?
3. **WHAT IF?** Where would you expect a polypeptide region that is rich in the amino acids valine, leucine, and isoleucine to be located in the folded polypeptide? Explain.

For suggested answers, see Appendix A.

CONCEPT 5.5

Nucleic acids store, transmit, and help express hereditary information

If the primary structure of polypeptides determines a protein's shape, what determines primary structure? The amino acid sequence of a polypeptide is programmed by a discrete unit of inheritance known as a **gene**. Genes consist of DNA, which belongs to the class of compounds called nucleic acids. **Nucleic acids** are polymers made of monomers called *nucleotides*.

The Roles of Nucleic Acids

The two types of nucleic acids, **deoxyribonucleic acid (DNA)** and **ribonucleic acid (RNA)**, enable living organisms to reproduce their complex components from one generation to the next. Unique among molecules, DNA provides directions for its own replication. DNA also directs RNA synthesis and, through RNA, controls protein synthesis; this entire process is called gene expression (Figure 5.23).

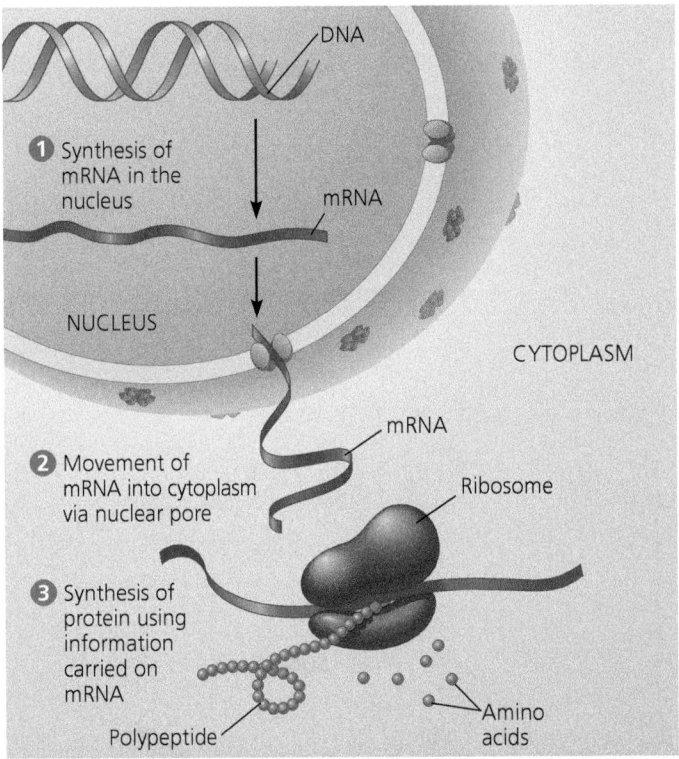

① Synthesis of mRNA in the nucleus

② Movement of mRNA into cytoplasm via nuclear pore

③ Synthesis of protein using information carried on mRNA

DNA

mRNA

NUCLEUS

CYTOPLASM

mRNA

Ribosome

Polypeptide

Amino acids

▲ Figure 5.23 **DNA → RNA → protein.** In a eukaryotic cell, DNA in the nucleus programs protein production in the cytoplasm by dictating synthesis of messenger RNA (mRNA). (The cell nucleus is actually much larger relative to the other elements of this figure.)

DNA is the genetic material that organisms inherit from their parents. Each chromosome contains one long DNA molecule, usually carrying several hundred or more genes. When a cell reproduces itself by dividing, its DNA molecules are copied and passed along from one generation of cells to the next. Encoded in the structure of DNA is the information that programs all the cell's activities. The DNA, however, is not directly involved in running the operations of the cell, any more than computer software by itself can read the bar code on a box of cereal. Just as a scanner is needed to read a bar code, proteins are required to implement genetic programs. The molecular hardware of the cell—the tools for biological functions—consists mostly of proteins. For example, the oxygen carrier in red blood cells is the protein hemoglobin, which you saw earlier (see Figure 5.18), not the DNA that specifies its structure.

How does RNA, the other type of nucleic acid, fit into gene expression, the flow of genetic information from DNA to proteins? Each gene along a DNA molecule directs synthesis of a type of RNA called *messenger RNA* (*mRNA*). The mRNA molecule interacts with the cell's protein-synthesizing machinery to direct production of a polypeptide, which folds into all or part of a protein. We

can summarize the flow of genetic information as DNA → RNA → protein (see Figure 5.23). The sites of protein synthesis are cellular structures called ribosomes. In a eukaryotic cell, ribosomes are in the region between the nucleus and the plasma membrane (the cytoplasm), but DNA resides in the nucleus. Messenger RNA conveys genetic instructions for building proteins from the nucleus to the cytoplasm. Prokaryotic cells lack nuclei but still use mRNA to convey a message from the DNA to ribosomes and other cellular equipment that translate the coded information into amino acid sequences. In Chapter 18, you'll read about other functions of some recently discovered RNA molecules.

The Components of Nucleic Acids

Nucleic acids are macromolecules that exist as polymers called **polynucleotides** (Figure 5.24a). As indicated by the name, each polynucleotide consists of monomers called **nucleotides**. A nucleotide, in general, is composed of three parts: a nitrogen-containing (nitrogenous) base, a five-carbon sugar (a pentose), and one or more phosphate groups (Figure 5.24b). In a polynucleotide, each monomer has only one phosphate group. The portion of a nucleotide without any phosphate groups is called a *nucleoside*.

To build a nucleotide, let's first consider the nitrogenous bases (Figure 5.24c). Each nitrogenous base has one or two rings that include nitrogen atoms. (They are called nitrogenous *bases* because the nitrogen atoms tend to take up H^+ from solution, thus acting as bases.) There are two families of nitrogenous bases: pyrimidines and purines. A **pyrimidine** has one six-membered ring of carbon and nitrogen atoms. The members of the pyrimidine family are cytosine (C), thymine (T), and uracil (U). **Purines** are larger, with a six-membered ring fused to a five-membered ring. The purines are adenine (A) and guanine (G). The specific pyrimidines and purines differ in the chemical groups attached to the rings. Adenine, guanine, and cytosine are found in both DNA and RNA; thymine is found only in DNA and uracil only in RNA.

Now let's add the sugar to which the nitrogenous base is attached. In DNA the sugar is **deoxyribose**; in RNA it is **ribose** (see Figure 5.24c). The only difference between these two sugars is that deoxyribose lacks an oxygen atom on the second carbon in the ring; hence the name *deoxyribose*. To distinguish the numbers of the sugar carbons from those used for the ring atoms of the attached nitrogenous base, the sugar carbon numbers of a nucleoside or nucleotide have a prime (′) after them. Thus, the second carbon in the sugar ring is the 2′ ("2 prime") carbon, and the carbon that sticks up from the ring is called the 5′ carbon.

▼ **Figure 5.24 Components of nucleic acids. (a)** A polynucleotide has a sugar-phosphate backbone with variable appendages, the nitrogenous bases. **(b)** A nucleotide monomer includes a nitrogenous base, a sugar, and a phosphate group. Note that carbon numbers in the sugar include primes ('). **(c)** A nucleoside includes a nitrogenous base (purine or pyrimidine) and a five-carbon sugar (deoxyribose or ribose).

(a) Polynucleotide, or nucleic acid

(b) Nucleotide

(c) Nucleoside components

So far, we have built a nucleoside (nitrogenous base plus sugar). To complete the construction of a nucleotide, we attach a phosphate group to the 5' carbon of the sugar (see Figure 5.24b). The molecule is now a nucleoside monophosphate, more often called a nucleotide.

Nucleotide Polymers

The linkage of nucleotides into a polynucleotide involves a dehydration reaction. (You will learn the details in Chapter 16.) In the polynucleotide, adjacent nucleotides are joined by a phosphodiester linkage, which consists of a phosphate group that links the sugars of two nucleotides. This bonding results in a repeating pattern of sugar-phosphate units called the *sugar-phosphate backbone* (see Figure 5.24a). (Note that the nitrogenous bases are not part of the backbone.) The two free ends of the polymer are distinctly different from each other. One end has a phosphate attached to a 5' carbon, and the other end has a hydroxyl group on a 3' carbon; we refer to these as the 5' end and the 3' end, respectively. We can say that a polynucleotide has a built-in directionality along its sugar-phosphate backbone, from

5' to 3', somewhat like a one-way street. All along this sugar-phosphate backbone are appendages consisting of the nitrogenous bases.

The sequence of bases along a DNA (or mRNA) polymer is unique for each gene and provides very specific information to the cell. Because genes are hundreds to thousands of nucleotides long, the number of possible base sequences is effectively limitless. A gene's meaning to the cell is encoded in its specific sequence of the four DNA bases. For example, the sequence 5'-AGGTAACTT-3' means one thing, whereas the sequence 5'-CGCTTTAAC-3' has a different meaning. (Entire genes, of course, are much longer.) The linear order of bases in a gene specifies the amino acid sequence—the primary structure—of a protein, which in turn specifies that protein's three-dimensional structure and its function in the cell.

The Structures of DNA and RNA Molecules

DNA molecules have two polynucleotides, or "strands," that wind around an imaginary axis, forming a **double**

5′ 3′
Sugar-phosphate backbones
Hydrogen bonds

T ···· A
G ··· C
C ··· G
A ··· T
C ··· G

3′ 5′
Base pair joined by hydrogen bonding

(a) DNA

Base pair joined by hydrogen bonding

G ··· C
G ··· C
U ··· A

(b) Transfer RNA

▲ **Figure 5.25** **The structures of DNA and tRNA molecules. (a)** The DNA molecule is usually a double helix, with the sugar-phosphate backbones of the antiparallel polynucleotide strands (symbolized here by blue ribbons) on the outside of the helix. Hydrogen bonds between pairs of nitrogenous bases hold the two strands together. As illustrated here with symbolic shapes for the bases, adenine (A) can pair only with thymine (T), and guanine (G) can pair only with cytosine (C). Each DNA strand in this figure is the structural equivalent of the polynucleotide diagrammed in Figure 5.24a. **(b)** A tRNA molecule has a roughly L-shaped structure, with complementary base pairing of antiparallel stretches of RNA. In RNA, A pairs with U.

helix (Figure 5.25a). The two sugar-phosphate backbones run in opposite $5' \rightarrow 3'$ directions from each other; this arrangement is referred to as **antiparallel**, somewhat like a divided highway. The sugar-phosphate backbones are on the outside of the helix, and the nitrogenous bases are paired in the interior of the helix. The two strands are held together by hydrogen bonds between the paired bases (see Figure 5.25a). Most DNA molecules are very long, with thousands or even millions of base pairs. For example, the one long DNA double helix in a eukaryotic chromosome includes many genes, each one a particular segment of the molecule.

In base pairing, only certain bases in the double helix are compatible with each other. Adenine (A) in one strand always pairs with thymine (T) in the other, and guanine (G) always pairs with cytosine (C). Reading the sequence of bases along one strand of the double helix would tell us the sequence of bases along the other strand. If a stretch of one strand has the base sequence 5′-AGGTCCG-3′, then the base-pairing rules tell us that the same stretch of the other strand must have the sequence 3′-TCCAGGC-5′. The two strands of the double helix are *complementary*, each the predictable counterpart of the other. It is this feature of DNA that makes it possible to generate two identical copies of each DNA molecule in a cell that is preparing to

divide. When the cell divides, the copies are distributed to the daughter cells, making them genetically identical to the parent cell. Thus, the structure of DNA accounts for its function of transmitting genetic information whenever a cell reproduces.

RNA molecules, by contrast, exist as single strands. Complementary base pairing can occur, however, between regions of two RNA molecules or even between two stretches of nucleotides in the *same* RNA molecule. In fact, base pairing within an RNA molecule allows it to take on the particular three-dimensional shape necessary for its function. Consider, for example, the type of RNA called *transfer RNA (tRNA)*, which brings amino acids to the ribosome during the synthesis of a polypeptide. A tRNA molecule is about 80 nucleotides in length. Its functional shape results from base pairing between nucleotides where complementary stretches of the molecule can run antiparallel to each other (Figure 5.25b).

Note that in RNA, adenine (A) pairs with uracil (U); thymine (T) is not present in RNA. Another difference between RNA and DNA is that DNA almost always exists as a double helix, whereas RNA molecules are more variable in shape. RNAs are very versatile molecules, and many biologists believe RNA may have preceded DNA as the carrier of genetic information in early forms of life.

1. **DRAW IT** Go to Figure 5.24a and, for the top three nucleotides, number all the carbons in the sugars, circle the nitrogenous bases, and star the phosphates.

2. **DRAW IT** In a DNA double helix, a region along one DNA strand has this sequence of nitrogenous bases: 5′-TAGGCCT-3′. Copy this sequence, and write down its complementary strand, clearly indicating the 5′ and 3′ ends of the complementary strand.

For suggested answers, see Appendix A.

CONCEPT 5.6

Genomics and proteomics have transformed biological inquiry and applications

Experimental work in the first half of the 20th century established the role of DNA as the bearer of genetic information, passed from generation to generation, that specified the functioning of living cells and organisms. Once the structure of the DNA molecule was described in 1953, and the linear sequence of nucleotide bases was understood to specify the amino acid sequence of proteins, biologists sought to "decode" genes by learning their base sequences.

The first chemical techniques for *DNA sequencing*, or determining the sequence of nucleotides along a DNA strand, one by one, were developed in the 1970s. Researchers began to study gene sequences, gene by gene, and the more they learned the more questions they had: How was expression of genes regulated? Genes and their protein products clearly interacted with each other, but how? What was the function, if any, of the DNA that is not part of genes? To fully understand the genetic functioning of a living organism, the entire sequence of the full complement of DNA, the organism's *genome*, would be most enlightening. In spite of the apparent impracticality of this idea, in the late 1980s several prominent biologists put forth an audacious proposal to launch a project that would sequence the entire human genome—all 3 billion bases of it! This endeavour began in 1990 and was effectively completed in the early 2000s.

An unplanned but profound side benefit of this project—the Human Genome Project—was the rapid development of faster and less expensive methods of sequencing. This trend has continued apace: The cost for sequencing 1 million bases in 2001, well over $5000, had decreased to less than $0.08 in 2014. And a human genome, the first of which took over 10 years to sequence, could be completed at today's pace in just a few days. The number of genomes that have been fully sequenced has burgeoned, generating reams of data and prompting development of *bioinformatics*, the use of computer software and other computational tools that can handle and analyze these large data sets.

The reverberations of these developments have transformed the study of biology and related fields. Biologists often look at problems by analyzing large sets of genes or even comparing whole genomes of different species, an approach called **genomics**. A similar analysis of large sets of proteins, including their sequences, is called **proteomics**. (Protein sequences can be determined either by using biochemical techniques or by translating the DNA sequences that code for them.) These approaches permeate all fields of biology, some examples of which are shown in **Figure 5.26**. In the interview at the start of Unit 1, we also learned about the Human Metabolome Database, which was established by David Wishart and colleagues. **Metabolomics** is the analysis of small molecules called metabolites (intermediate and end products of metabolism).

Perhaps the most significant impact of genomics and proteomics on the field of biology as a whole has been their contributions to our understanding of evolution. To quote one of the founders of modern evolutionary theory, Theodosius Dobzhansky, "Nothing in biology makes sense except in the light of evolution." In addition to confirming evidence for evolution from the study of fossils and characteristics of currently existing species, genomics has helped us tease out relationships among different groups of organisms that had not been resolved by previous types of evidence, and thus infer evolutionary history.

DNA and Proteins as Tape Measures of Evolution

EVOLUTION We are accustomed to thinking of shared traits, such as hair and milk production in mammals, as evidence of shared ancestry. Because DNA carries heritable information in the form of genes, sequences of genes and their protein products document the hereditary background of an organism. The linear sequences of nucleotides in DNA molecules are passed from parents to offspring; these sequences determine the amino acid sequences of proteins. As a result, siblings have greater similarity in their DNA and proteins than do unrelated individuals of the same species.

Given our evolutionary view of life, we can extend this concept of "molecular genealogy" to relationships between species: We would expect two species that appear to be closely related based on anatomical evidence (and possibly

Contributions of Genomics and Proteomics to Biology

Nucleotide sequencing and the analysis of large sets of genes and proteins can be done rapidly and inexpensively due to advances in technology and information processing. Taken together, genomics and proteomics have advanced our understanding of biology across many different fields.

Paleontology

New DNA sequencing techniques have allowed decoding of minute quantities of DNA found in ancient tissues from our extinct relatives, the Neanderthals (*Homo neanderthalensis*). Sequencing the Neanderthal genome has informed our understanding of their physical appearance as well as their relationship with modern humans. See Figure 34.49.

Viktor Deak

Medical Science

Identifying the genetic basis for human diseases like cancer helps researchers focus their search for potential future treatments. Currently, sequencing the sets of genes expressed in an individual's tumour can allow a more targeted approach to treating the cancer, a type of "personalized medicine." See Figures 12.20 and 18.27.

Chassenet/BSIP SA/Alamy Stock Photo

Evolution

A major aim of evolutionary biology is to understand the relationships among species, both living and extinct. For example, genome sequence comparisons have identified the hippopotamus as the land mammal sharing the most recent common ancestor with whales. See Figure 22.20.

Frontline Photography/Alamy Stock photo

Hippopotamus

WaterFrame/Alamy Stock Photo

Short-finned pilot whale

Conservation Biology

The tools of molecular genetics and genomics are increasingly used by ecologists to identify which species of animals and plants are killed illegally. In one case, genomic sequences of DNA from illegal shipments of elephant tusks were used to track down poachers and pinpoint the territory where they were operating.

Species Interactions

Over 90% of all plant species exist in a mutually beneficial partnership with fungi that are associated with the plants' roots. Genome sequencing and analysis of gene expression in several plant-fungal pairs promise major advances in our understanding of such interactions and may have implications for agricultural practices. (See the Scientific Skills Exercise in Chapter 31.)

David Read, Department of Animal and Plant Sciences, University of Sheffield, UK

ImageBroker/Frank Lane Picture Agency Limited

SCIENTIFIC SKILLS EXERCISE

Analyzing Polypeptide Sequence Data

 ► Human

 ► Rhesus monkey

 ► Gibbon

Are Rhesus Monkeys or Gibbons More Closely Related to Humans? DNA and polypeptide sequences from closely related species are more similar to each other than are sequences from more distantly related species. In this exercise, you will look at amino acid sequence data for the β polypeptide chain of hemoglobin, often called β-globin. You will then interpret the data to hypothesize whether the monkey or the gibbon is more closely related to humans.

How Such Experiments Are Done Researchers can isolate the polypeptide of interest from an organism and then determine the amino acid sequence. More frequently, the DNA of the relevant gene is sequenced, and the amino acid sequence of the polypeptide is deduced from the DNA sequence of its gene.

Data from the Experiments In the data below, the letters give the sequence of the 146 amino acids in β-globin from humans, rhesus monkeys, and gibbons. Because a complete sequence would not fit on one line here, the sequences are broken into three segments. The sequences for the three different species are aligned so that you can compare them easily. For example, you can see that for all three species, the first amino acid is V (valine) and the 146th amino acid is H (histidine).

Interpret the Data

1. Scan the monkey and gibbon sequences, letter by letter, circling any amino acids that do not match the human sequence. (a) How many amino acids differ between the monkey and the human sequences? (b) Between the gibbon and human?

2. For each nonhuman species, what percent of its amino acids are identical to the human sequence of β-globin?

3. Based on these data alone, state a hypothesis for which of these two species is more closely related to humans. What is your reasoning?

4. What other evidence could you use to support your hypothesis?

Data from "Molecular and Population Genetic Analysis of Allelic Sequence Diversity at the Human Beta-globin Locus" by S. M. Fullerton et al., from *Proceedings of the National Academy of Sciences USA*, March 1994, Volume 91(5); Data for rhesus from "The Primary Structure of the Alpha and Beta Polypeptide Chains of Adult Hemoglobin of the Rhesus Monkey (Macaca mulatta). Biochemical Studies on Hemoglobins and Myoglobins. IV" by Genji Matsuda et al., from *International Journal of Protein Research*, December 1970, Volume 2(1–4); data for gibbon from "Primate Hemoglobins: Some Sequences and Some Proposals Concerning the Character of Evolution and Mutation" by Samuel H. Boyer et al.

Species	Alignment of Amino Acid Sequences of β-globin
Human	1 VHLTPEEKSA VTALWGKVNV DEVGGEALGR LLVVYPWTQR FFESFGDLST
Monkey	1 VHLTPEEKNA VTTLWGKVNV DEVGGEALGR LLLVYPWTQR FFESFGDLSS
Gibbon	1 VHLTPEEKSA VTALWGKVNV DEVGGEALGR LLVVYPWTQR FFESFGDLST
Human	51 PDAVMGNPKV KAHGKKVLGA FSDGLAHLDN LKGTFATLSE LHCDKLHVDP
Monkey	51 PDAVMGNPKV KAHGKKVLGA FSDGLNHLDN LKGTFAQLSE LHCDKLHVDP
Gibbon	51 PDAVMGNPKV KAHGKKVLGA FSDGLAHLDN LKGTFAQLSE LHCDKLHVDP
Human	101 ENFRLLGNVL VCVLAHHFGK EFTPPVQAAY QKVVAGVANA LAHKYH
Monkey	101 ENFKLLGNVL VCVLAHHFGK EFTPQVQAAY QKVVAGVANA LAHKYH
Gibbon	101 ENFRLLGNVL VCVLAHHFGK EFTPQVQAAY QKVVAGVANA LAHKYH

fossil evidence) to also share a greater proportion of their DNA and protein sequences than do less closely related species. In fact, that is the case. An example is the comparison of the β polypeptide chain of human hemoglobin with the corresponding hemoglobin polypeptide in other vertebrates. In this chain of 146 amino acids, humans and gorillas differ in just 1 amino acid, while humans and frogs, more distantly related, differ in 67 amino acids. In the Scientific Skills Exercise, you can apply this sort of reasoning to additional species. And this conclusion holds true as well when comparing whole genomes: The human genome is 95–98% identical to that of the chimpanzee, but only roughly 85% identical to that of the mouse, a more distant

evolutionary relative. Molecular biology has added a new tape measure to the toolkit biologists use to assess evolutionary kinship.

CONCEPT CHECK 5.6

1. How would sequencing the entire genome of an extinct organism help scientists understand how that organism functioned?

2. Given the function of DNA, why would you expect two species with very similar traits to also have very similar genomes?

For suggested answers, see Appendix A.

5 Chapter Review

SUMMARY OF KEY CONCEPTS

CONCEPT 5.1

Macromolecules are polymers, built from monomers (pp. 75–76)

- Large carbohydrates (polysaccharides), proteins, and nucleic acids are **polymers**, which are chains of **monomers**. The components of lipids vary. Monomers form larger molecules by **dehydration reactions**, in which water molecules are released. Polymers can disassemble by the reverse process, **hydrolysis**. An immense variety of polymers can be built from a small set of monomers.

? *What is the fundamental basis for the differences between large carbohydrates, proteins, and nucleic acids?*

Large Biological Molecules	Components	Examples	Functions
CONCEPT 5.2 **Carbohydrates serve as fuel and building material (pp. 76–80)** **?** *Compare the composition, structure, and function of starch and cellulose. What role do starch and cellulose play in the human body?*	Monosaccharide monomer	**Monosaccharides:** glucose, fructose	Fuel; carbon sources that can be converted to other molecules or combined into polymers
		Disaccharides: lactose, sucrose	
		Polysaccharides: • Cellulose (plants) • Starch (plants) • Glycogen (animals) • Chitin (animals and fungi)	• Strengthens plant cell walls • Stores glucose for energy • Strengthens exoskeletons and fungal cell walls
CONCEPT 5.3 **Lipids are a diverse group of hydrophobic molecules (pp. 80–83)** **?** *Why are lipids not considered to be macromolecules or polymers?*	Glycerol / 3 fatty acids	**Triacylglycerols** (fats or oils): glycerol + 3 fatty acids	Important energy source
	Head with Ⓟ / 2 fatty acids	**Phospholipids:** glycerol + phosphate group + 2 fatty acids	Lipid bilayers of membranes
	Steroid backbone	**Steroids:** four fused rings with attached chemical groups	• Component of cell membranes (cholesterol) • Signalling molecules that travel through the body (hormones)
CONCEPT 5.4 **Proteins include a diversity of structures, resulting in a wide range of functions (pp. 83–92)** **?** *Explain the basis for the great diversity of proteins.*	Amino acid monomer (20 types)	• Enzymes • Structural proteins • Storage proteins • Transport proteins • Hormones • Receptor proteins • Motor proteins • Defensive proteins	• Catalyze chemical reactions • Provide structural support • Store amino acids • Transport substances • Coordinate organismal responses • Receive signals from outside cell • Function in cell movement • Protect against disease
CONCEPT 5.5 **Nucleic acids store, transmit, and help express hereditary information (pp. 92–96)** **?** *What role does complementary base pairing play in the functions of nucleic acids?*	Nucleotide monomer	**DNA:** • Sugar = deoxyribose • Nitrogenous bases = C, G, A, T • Usually double-stranded	Stores hereditary information
		RNA: • Sugar = ribose • Nitrogenous bases = C, G, A, U • Usually single-stranded	Various functions in gene expression, including carrying instructions from DNA to ribosomes

CONCEPT 5.6

Genomics and proteomics have transformed biological inquiry and applications (pp. 96–98)

- Recent technological advances in DNA sequencing have given rise to **genomics**, an approach that analyzes large sets of genes or whole genomes, and **proteomics**, a similar approach for large sets of proteins. Bioinformatics is the use of computational tools and computer software to analyze these large data sets.
- The more closely two species are related evolutionarily, the more similar their DNA sequences are. DNA sequence data confirms models of evolution based on fossils and other anatomical evidence.

? *Given the sequences of a particular gene in fruit flies, fish, mice, and humans, predict the relative similarity of the human sequence to that of each of the other species.*

TEST YOUR UNDERSTANDING

LEVEL 1: KNOWLEDGE/COMPREHENSION

1. Which of the following categories includes all others in the list?
   a. monosaccharide
   b. polysaccharide
   c. starch
   d. carbohydrate

2. The enzyme amylase can break glycosidic linkages between glucose monomers only if the monomers are in the α form. Which of the following could amylase break down?
   a. glycogen, starch, and amylopectin
   b. glycogen and cellulose
   c. cellulose and chitin
   d. starch, chitin, and cellulose

3. Which of the following statements is true of *unsaturated* fats?
   a. They are more common in animals than in plants.
   b. They have double bonds in the carbon chains of their fatty acids.
   c. They generally solidify at room temperature.
   d. They contain more hydrogen than do saturated fats having the same number of carbon atoms.

4. The structural level of a protein *least* affected by a disruption in hydrogen bonding is the
   a. primary level.
   b. secondary level.
   c. tertiary level
   d. quaternary level.

5. Enzymes that break down DNA catalyze the hydrolysis of the covalent bonds that join nucleotides together. What would happen to DNA molecules treated with these enzymes?
   a. The two strands of the double helix would separate.
   b. The phosphodiester linkages of the polynucleotide backbone would be broken.
   c. The pyrimidines would be separated from the deoxyribose sugars.
   d. All bases would be separated from the deoxyribose sugars.

LEVEL 2: APPLICATION/ANALYSIS

6. The molecular formula for glucose is $C_6H_{12}O_6$. What would be the molecular formula for a polymer made by linking 10 glucose molecules together by dehydration reactions?
   a. $C_{60}H_{120}O_{60}$
   b. $C_{60}H_{102}O_{51}$
   c. $C_{60}H_{100}O_{50}$
   d. $C_{60}H_{111}O_{51}$

7. Which of the following pairs of base sequences could form a short stretch of a normal double helix of DNA?
   a. 5′-purine-pyrimidine-purine-pyrimidine-3′ with 3′-purine-pyrimidine-purine-pyrimidine-5′
   b. 5′-AGCT-3′ with 5′-TCGA-3′
   c. 5′-ATGC-3′ with 5′-GCAT-3′
   d. All of these pairs are correct.

8. Construct a table that organizes the following terms, and label the columns and rows.

phosphodiester linkages	polypeptides	monosaccharides
peptide bonds	triacylglycerols	nucleotides
glycosidic linkages	polynucleotides	amino acids
ester linkages	polysaccharides	fatty acids

9. **DRAW IT** Copy the polynucleotide strand in Figure 5.24a and label the bases G, T, C, and T, starting from the 5′ end. Assuming this is a DNA polynucleotide, now draw the complementary strand, using the same symbols for phosphates (circles), sugars (pentagons), and bases. Label the bases. Draw arrows showing the 5′ → 3′ direction of each strand. Use the arrows to make sure the second strand is antiparallel to the first. *Hint*: After you draw the first strand vertically, turn the paper upside down; it is easier to draw the second strand from the 5′ toward the 3′ direction as you go from top to bottom.

LEVEL 3: SYNTHESIS/EVALUATION

10. **EVOLUTION CONNECTION**
    Comparisons of amino acid sequences can shed light on the evolutionary divergence of related species. If you were comparing two living species, would you expect all proteins to show the same degree of divergence? Why or why not?

11. **SCIENTIFIC INQUIRY**
    Suppose you are a research assistant in a lab studying DNA-binding proteins. You have been given the amino acid sequences of all the proteins encoded by the genome of a certain species and have been asked to find candidate proteins that could bind DNA. What type of amino acids would you expect to see in such proteins? Why?

12. **WRITE ABOUT A THEME: ORGANIZATION**
    Proteins, which have diverse functions in a cell, are all polymers of the same subunits—amino acids. Write a short essay (100–150 words) that discusses how the structure of amino acids allows this one type of polymer to perform so many functions.

13. **SYNTHESIZE YOUR KNOWLEDGE**

Andrey Stratilatov/Shutterstock

Given that the function of egg yolk is to nourish and support the developing chick, explain why egg yolks are so high in fat, protein, and cholesterol.

For selected answers, see Appendix A.

AN INTERVIEW WITH

Helga Guderley

Helga Guderley was born in Dayton, Ohio, did a Ph.D. at UBC, later became Full Professor at Université Laval, and is the former president of the Canadian Society of Zoologists. She retired in 2010, after publishing more than 170 scientific articles.

How did you become interested in science?

My father was an aerodynamicist and his influence was central in bringing me to science. After my BA in Chemistry, I got an offer to do graduate work with Peter Hochachka at UBC. He wrote me from a research cruise in Alaska where he was working with king crabs. I decided to accept because his approach of looking at how the environment shapes biochemical processes within organisms really intrigued me, and I liked that he signed his letter "your travelling biologist."

What were the main questions you were trying to answer in your research?

My primary interest is in the cellular underpinnings of organismal performance. I looked at what muscle can do biochemically and how this links to exercise performance in animals, ranging from scallops to cod to mice. For example, in scallops, I looked at the impact of reproductive effort on escape responses: When scallops reproduce their gonad becomes bigger than their muscle, and many macromolecules are removed from muscle. Similar changes happen in other broadcast spawning organisms. In scallops, reproductive investment decreases repeat escape response performance, thus potentially reducing survival. For cod, our results indicate that the impact of food loss on swimming capacities helps explain the loss of cod stocks. In mice, selection for wheel running changes fibre-type composition in hindlimb muscles.

> " The fascinating thing about membranes is that they are largely composed of dietary lipids—so diet could have major effects on cellular physiology. "

◄ Scallops can use jet propulsion to escape from predators, but this escape response is diminished when there is reproductive investment.

Mark Webster/Oxford Scientific/Getty Images

What would the relevance of your research be to an undergraduate student just learning about metabolism?

The environment affects metabolism both directly and indirectly. A major question I was interested in was how temperature impacts function. In ectothermal organisms, temperature modifies reaction rates and changes protein structures, with disproportionate effects on membranes. Phospholipids change from gel to liquid with marked warming, thus affecting the activity of membrane proteins. For ectothermal animals to maintain membrane function over a wide range of temperatures, they need mechanisms modifying membrane properties.

The fascinating thing about membranes is that they are largely composed of dietary lipids, so diet could have major effects on cellular physiology. Mitochondria, the powerhouses of cells, the source of virtually all ATP, rely on a transmembrane gradient to produce ATP. This gradient requires membrane protein mobility. To examine the effect of dietary lipid composition on mitochondrial function, we fed trout diets that had different levels of saturated lipids, and watched how the composition and function of mitochondrial membranes changed. Interestingly, specific aspects of membrane composition changed radically, but function *didn't*. Rates of oxygen uptake and ATP synthesis were largely maintained despite the many specific changes in membrane composition. A closer examination of membrane phospholipids showed that many overall parameters were maintained, such as the proportions of saturated, monounsaturated, and polyunsaturated fatty acids. The proportions of specific classes of phospholipids changed, presumably to counteract the influence of the modified fatty acid composition. Thus, although diet influences membrane composition, this change is regulated. Animals are capable of an amazing amount of regulation.

What is the key "take-home" message for students about your research?

Animals can adjust tremendously to environmental conditions, but there are limits. Unfortunately, you can't extrapolate from one species to another to identify these limits. The metabolic capacities and physiological capacities of animals need to be examined in the context of the environment in which they evolved.

What advice would you give to a biology student just starting out at university?

Don't worry—just follow your interests. You have to take one step at a time, identify your passions, develop them, and be willing to go in new directions. I started out in chemistry in the United States and ended up in biology in Quebec, teaching in French. Life can be full of wonderful surprises if you recognize the opportunities that present themselves.

Source: Interview with Helga Guderley. Used with permission from Helga Guderley.

The Working Cell

This unit explores the structure and function of cells, including how cells communicate, divide, and carry out other roles necessary for life. This figure illustrates how the cellular activities you will learn about in this unit relate to each other in a fully functioning plant cell.

Nucleus

DNA

mRNA

Nuclear pore

Protein

Ribosome

mRNA

Protein in vesicle

Rough endoplasmic reticulum (ER)

Golgi apparatus

Vesicle forming

Protein

Plasma membrane

Cell wall

Flow of Genetic Information in the Cell: DNA → RNA → Protein (Chapter 6)

1 In the nucleus, DNA serves as a template for the synthesis of mRNA, which moves to the cytoplasm. (See Concept 6.3)

2 mRNA attaches to a ribosome, which remains free in the cytosol or binds to the rough ER. Proteins are synthesized. (See Concepts 6.3 and 6.4)

3 Proteins and membrane produced by the rough ER flow in vesicles to the Golgi apparatus, where they are processed. (See Concept 6.4)

4 Transport vesicles carrying proteins pinch off from the Golgi apparatus. (See Concept 6.4)

5 Some vesicles merge with the plasma membrane, releasing proteins by exocytosis. (See Concepts 6.4 and 7.5)

6 Proteins synthesized on free ribosomes stay in the cell and perform specific functions; examples include the enzymes that catalyze the reactions of cellular respiration and photosynthesis. (See Concept 6.4)

Movement Across Cell Membranes (Chapter 7)

9 Water diffuses into and out of the cell directly through the plasma membrane and by facilitated diffusion through aquaporins. (See Concepts 7.3 and 10.1)

10 By passive transport, the CO_2 used in photosynthesis diffuses into the cell and the O_2 formed as a by-product of photosynthesis diffuses out of the cell. Both solutes move down their concentration gradients. (See Concepts 7.3, 10.2, and 10.3)

11 In active transport, energy (usually supplied by ATP) is used to transport a solute against its concentration gradient. (See Concept 7.4)

Energy Transformations in the Cell: Photosynthesis and Cellular Respiration (Chapters 8–10)

7 In chloroplasts, the process of photosynthesis uses the energy of light to convert CO_2 and H_2O to organic molecules, with O_2 as a by-product. (See Concept 10.1)

8 In mitochondria, organic molecules are broken down by cellular respiration, capturing energy in molecules of ATP, which are used to power the work of the cell, such as protein synthesis and active transport. CO_2 and H_2O are by-products. (See Concepts 8.3, 9.2, and 9.6)

Vacuole

7 Photosynthesis in chloroplast

CO_2

H_2O

Organic molecules

O_2

8 Cellular respiration in mitochondrion

ATP

ATP

ATP

ATP

Transport pump

11

10

9

O_2

CO_2

H_2O

MAKE CONNECTIONS *The first enzyme that functions in glycolysis is hexokinase. In this plant cell, describe the entire process by which this enzyme is produced and where it functions, specifying the locations for each step.* **(See Figures 5.18, 5.23, and 9.9.)**

6

A Tour of the Cell

KEY CONCEPTS

6.1 Biologists use microscopes and the tools of biochemistry to study cells

6.2 Eukaryotic cells have internal membranes that compartmentalize their functions

6.3 The eukaryotic cell's genetic instructions are housed in the nucleus and carried out by the ribosomes

6.4 The endomembrane system regulates protein traffic and performs metabolic functions in the cell

6.5 Mitochondria and chloroplasts change energy from one form to another

6.6 The cytoskeleton is a network of fibres that organizes structures and activities in the cell

6.7 Extracellular components and connections between cells help coordinate cellular activities

Steve Gschmeissner/Science Source

▲ **Figure 6.1 How do the cells in your retina communicate with other cells to help you learn about biology?**

The Fundamental Units of Life

Cells are as fundamental to the living systems of biology as the atom is to chemistry. Photoreceptor cells in your eyes allow you to see the scanning electron micrograph in **Figure 6.1**. The image depicts rods (pale yellow) and cones (green) in the human retina, which are capable of converting light into a signal via phototransduction. The words on the page are translated into signals that nerve cells then carry to your brain, where they are passed on to other nerve cells. As you study, you are making cell connections like these that solidify memories and permit learning to occur.

All organisms are made of cells. In the hierarchy of biological organization, the cell is the simplest collection of matter that can be alive. Indeed, many forms of life exist as single-celled organisms. Larger, more complex organisms, including plants and animals, are multicellular; their bodies are cooperatives of many kinds of specialized cells that could not survive for long on their own. Even when cells are arranged into higher levels of organization, such as tissues and organs, the cell remains the organism's basic unit of structure and function.

All cells are related by their descent from earlier cells. During the long evolutionary history of life on Earth, cells have been modified in many different ways. But although cells can differ substantially from one another, they share common features. In this chapter, we'll first examine the tools and techniques that allow us to understand cells, then tour the cell and become acquainted with its components.

Biologists use microscopes and the tools of biochemistry to study cells

How can cell biologists investigate the inner workings of a cell, usually too small to be seen by the unaided eye? Before we tour the cell, it will be helpful to learn how cells are studied.

Microscopy

The development of instruments that extend the human senses has allowed the discovery and early study of cells. Microscopes were invented in 1590 and were further refined during the 1600s. Cell walls were first seen by Robert Hooke in 1665 as he looked through a microscope at dead cells from the bark of an oak tree. But it took the wonderfully crafted lenses of Antoni van Leeuwenhoek to visualize living cells. Imagine Hooke's awe when he visited van Leeuwenhoek in 1674 and the world of microorganisms—what his host called "very little animalcules"—was revealed to him.

The microscopes first used by Renaissance scientists, as well as the microscopes you are likely to use in the laboratory, are all light microscopes. In a **light microscope (LM)**, visible light is passed through the specimen and then through glass lenses. The lenses refract (bend) the light in such a way that the image of the specimen is magnified as it is projected into the eye or into a camera (see Appendix C).

Three important parameters in microscopy are magnification, resolution, and contrast. *Magnification* is the ratio of an object's image size to its real size. Light microscopes can magnify effectively to about 1000 times the actual size of the specimen; at greater magnifications, additional details cannot be seen clearly. *Resolution* is a measure of the clarity of the image; it is the minimum distance two points can be separated and still be distinguished as separate points. For example, what appears to the unaided eye as one star in the sky may be resolved as twin stars with a telescope, which has a higher resolving ability than the eye. Similarly, using standard techniques, the light microscope cannot resolve detail finer than about 0.2 micrometre (μm), or 200 nanometres (nm), regardless of the magnification (Figure 6.2). The third parameter, *contrast*, is the difference in brightness between the light and dark areas of an image. Methods for enhancing contrast include staining or labelling cell components to stand out visually. Figure 6.3 shows some different types of microscopy; study this figure as you read the rest of this section.

Until recently, the resolution barrier prevented cell biologists from using standard light microscopy when studying **organelles**, the membrane-enclosed structures within eukaryotic cells. To see these structures in any detail required the development of a new instrument. In the 1950s, the electron microscope was introduced to biology. Rather than focusing light, the **electron microscope (EM)**

1 centimetre (cm) = 10^{-2} metre (m)
1 millimetre (mm) = 10^{-3} m
1 micrometre (μm) = 10^{-3} mm = 10^{-6} m
1 nanometre (nm) = 10^{-3} μm = 10^{-9} m

▲ Figure 6.2 **The size range of cells.** Most cells are between 1 and 100 μm in diameter (yellow region of chart) and their components are even smaller, as are viruses. Notice that the scale along the left side is logarithmic, to accommodate the range of sizes shown. Starting at the top of the scale with 10 m and going down, each reference measurement marks a tenfold decrease in diameter or length.

focuses a beam of electrons through the specimen or onto its surface (see Appendix C). Resolution is inversely related to the wavelength of the light (or electrons) a microscope uses for imaging, and electron beams have much shorter wavelengths than visible light. Modern electron microscopes can theoretically achieve a resolution of about 0.002 nm, though in practice they usually cannot resolve structures smaller than about 2 nm across. Still, this is a 100-fold improvement over the standard light microscope.

The **scanning electron microscope (SEM)** is especially useful for detailed study of the topography of a specimen (see Figure 6.3). The electron beam scans the surface of

Exploring Microscopy

Light Microscopy (LM)

Brightfield (unstained specimen). Light passes directly through the specimen. Unless the cell is naturally pigmented or artificially stained, the image has little contrast. (The first four light micrographs show human cheek epithelial cells; the scale bar pertains to all four micrographs.)

Elisabeth Pierson/Pearson Education

50 μm

Brightfield (stained specimen). Staining with various dyes enhances contrast. Most staining procedures require that cells be fixed (preserved), thereby killing them.

Elisabeth Pierson/Pearson Education

Phase-contrast. Variations in density within the specimen are amplified to enhance contrast in unstained cells; this is especially useful for examining living, unpigmented cells.

Elisabeth Pierson/Pearson Education

Differential-interference-contrast (Nomarski). As in phase-contrast microscopy, optical modifications are used to exaggerate differences in density; the image appears almost 3-D.

Elisabeth Pierson/Pearson Education

Fluorescence. The locations of specific molecules in the cell can be revealed by labelling the molecules with fluorescent dyes or antibodies; some cells have molecules that fluoresce on their own. Fluorescent substances absorb ultraviolet radiation and emit visible light. In this fluorescently labelled uterine cell, nuclear material is blue, organelles called mitochondria are orange, and the cell's "skeleton" is green.

Michael W. Davidson/ The Florida State University Research Foundation

10 μm

Confocal. The top image is a standard fluorescence micrograph of fluorescently labelled nervous tissue (nerve cells are green, support cells are orange, and regions of overlap are yellow); below it is a confocal image of the same tissue. Using a laser, this "optical sectioning" technique eliminates out-of-focus light from a thick sample, creating a single plane of fluorescence in the image. By capturing sharp images at many different planes, a 3-D reconstruction can be created. The standard image is blurry because out-of-focus light is not excluded.

Karl Garsha

Karl Garsha

50 μm

Deconvolution. The top of this split image is a compilation of standard fluorescence micrographs through the depth of a white blood cell. Below is an image of the same cell reconstructed from many blurry images at different planes, each of which was processed using deconvolution software. This process digitally removes out-of-focus light and reassigns it to its source, creating a much sharper 3-D image.

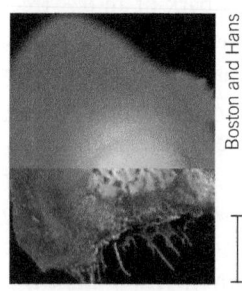

Boston and Hans van der Voort SVI

10 μm

Super-resolution. On the top is a confocal image of part of a nerve cell, using a fluorescent label that binds to a molecule clustered in small sacs in the cell (vesicles) that are 40 nm in diameter. The greenish-yellow spots are blurry because 40 nm is below the 200-nm limit of resolution for standard light microscopy. Below is an image of the same part of the cell, seen using a new super-resolution technique. Sophisticated equipment is used to light up individual fluorescent molecules and record their position. Combining information from many molecules in different places "breaks" the limit of resolution, resulting in the sharp greenish-yellow dots seen here. (Each dot is a 40-nm vesicle.)

MPI for Biophysical Chemistry

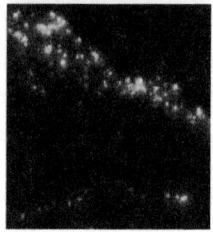

MPI for Biophysical Chemistry

1 μm

Electron Microscopy (EM)

Scanning electron microscopy (SEM). Micrographs taken with a scanning electron microscope show a 3-D image of the surface of a specimen. This SEM shows the surface of a cell from a trachea (windpipe) covered with cilia. Beating of the cilia helps move inhaled debris upward toward the throat. Electron micrographs are black and white, but are often artificially colourized to highlight particular structures, as has been done with both micrographs (SEM and TEM) shown here.

Abbreviations used in figure legends in this book:
LM = Light Micrograph
SEM = Scanning Electron Micrograph
TEM = Transmission Electron Micrograph

Cilia

Longitudinal section of cilium

Cross section of cilium

Molecular Expressions

2 μm

Thomas Moninger/ MPI for Biophysical Chemistry

2 μm

Transmission electron microscopy (TEM). A transmission electron microscope profiles a thin section of a specimen. Here we see a section through a tracheal cell, revealing its internal structure. In preparing the specimen, some cilia were cut along their lengths, creating longitudinal sections, while other cilia were cut straight across, creating cross-sections.

the sample, usually coated with a thin film of gold. The beam excites electrons on the surface, and these secondary electrons are detected by a device that translates the pattern of electrons into an electronic signal sent to a video screen. The result is an image of the specimen's surface that appears three-dimensional.

The **transmission electron microscope (TEM)** is used to study the internal structure of cells (see Figure 6.3). The TEM aims an electron beam through a very thin section of the specimen, much as a light microscope aims light through a sample on a slide. For the TEM, the specimen has been stained with atoms of heavy metals, which attach to certain cellular structures, thus enhancing the electron density of some parts of the cell more than others. The electrons passing through the specimen are scattered more in the denser regions, so fewer are transmitted. The image displays the pattern of transmitted electrons. Instead of using glass lenses, both the SEM and TEM use electromagnets as lenses to bend the paths of the electrons, ultimately focusing the image onto a monitor for viewing.

Electron microscopes have revealed many subcellular structures that were impossible to resolve with the light microscope. But the light microscope offers advantages, especially in studying living cells. A disadvantage of electron microscopy is that the methods used to prepare the specimen kill the cells. Specimen preparation for any type of microscopy can introduce artifacts, structural features seen in micrographs that do not exist in the living cell.

In the past several decades, light microscopy has been revitalized by major technical advances (see Figure 6.3). Labelling individual cellular molecules or structures with fluorescent markers has made it possible to see such structures with increasing detail. In addition, both confocal and deconvolution microscopy have produced sharper images of three-dimensional tissues and cells. Finally, a group of new techniques and labelling molecules developed in recent years have allowed researchers to "break" the resolution barrier and distinguish subcellular structures as small as 10–20 nm across. As this *super-resolution microscopy* becomes more widespread, the images we see of living cells are proving as awe-inspiring to us as van Leeuwenhoek's were to Robert Hooke 350 years ago.

Microscopes are the most important tools of *cytology*, the study of cell structure. Understanding the function of each structure, however, required the integration of cytology and *biochemistry*, the study of the chemical processes (metabolism) of cells.

Cell Fractionation

A useful technique for studying cell structure and function is **cell fractionation** (Figure 6.4), which takes cells apart and separates major organelles and other subcellular structures

▼ Figure 6.4 **Research Method**

Cell Fractionation

Application Cell fractionation is used to isolate (fractionate) cell components based on size and density.

Technique Cells are homogenized in a blender to break them up. The resulting mixture (homogenate) is centrifuged. The supernatant (liquid) is poured into another tube and centrifuged at a higher speed for a longer time. This process is repeated several times. This "differential centrifugation" results in a series of pellets, each containing different cell components.

Homogenization

Tissue cells

Homogenate

Centrifugation

Centrifuged at 1000 g (1000 times the force of gravity) for 10 min

Supernatant poured into next tube

Differential centrifugation

20 000 g 20 min

80 000 g 60 min

150 000 g 3 hr

Pellet rich in nuclei and cellular debris

Pellet rich in mitochondria (and chloroplasts if cells are from a plant)

Pellet rich in "microsomes" (pieces of plasma membranes and cells' internal membranes)

Pellet rich in ribosomes

Results In early experiments, researchers used microscopy to identify the organelles in each pellet and biochemical methods to determine their metabolic functions. These identifications established a baseline for this method, enabling today's researchers to know which cell fraction they should collect in order to isolate and study particular organelles.

from one another. The piece of equipment that is used for this task is the centrifuge, which spins test tubes holding mixtures of disrupted cells at a series of increasing speeds. At each speed, the resulting force causes a subset of the cell components to settle to the bottom of the tube, forming a pellet. At lower speeds, the pellet consists of larger components, and higher speeds result in a pellet with smaller components.

Cell fractionation enables researchers to prepare specific cell components in bulk and identify their functions, a task not usually possible with intact cells. For example, on one of the cell fractions, biochemical tests showed the presence of enzymes involved in cellular respiration, while electron microscopy revealed large numbers of the organelles called mitochondria. Together, these data helped biologists determine that mitochondria are the sites of cellular respiration. Biochemistry and cytology thus complement each other in correlating cell function with structure.

CONCEPT CHECK 6.1

1. How do stains used for light microscopy compare with those used for electron microscopy?
2. **WHAT IF?** Which type of microscope would you use to study (a) the changes in shape of a living white blood cell and (b) the details of surface texture of a hair?

For suggested answers, see Appendix A.

CONCEPT 6.2

Eukaryotic cells have internal membranes that compartmentalize their functions

Cells—the basic structural and functional units of every organism—are of two distinct types: prokaryotic and eukaryotic. Organisms of the domains Bacteria and Archaea consist of prokaryotic cells. Protists, fungi, animals, and plants all consist of eukaryotic cells. (*Protist* is an informal term referring to a group of mostly unicellular eukaryotes.)

Comparing Prokaryotic and Eukaryotic Cells

All cells share certain basic features: They are all bounded by a selective barrier, called the *plasma membrane*. Inside all cells is a semifluid, jellylike substance called **cytosol**, in which subcellular components are suspended. All cells contain *chromosomes*, which carry genes in the form of DNA. And all cells have *ribosomes*, tiny complexes that make proteins according to instructions from the genes.

A major difference between prokaryotic and eukaryotic cells is the location of their DNA. In a **eukaryotic cell**, most of the DNA is in an organelle called the *nucleus*, which is bounded by a double membrane (see Figure 6.8). In a **prokaryotic cell**, the DNA is concentrated in a region that is not membrane-enclosed, called the **nucleoid** (Figure 6.5).

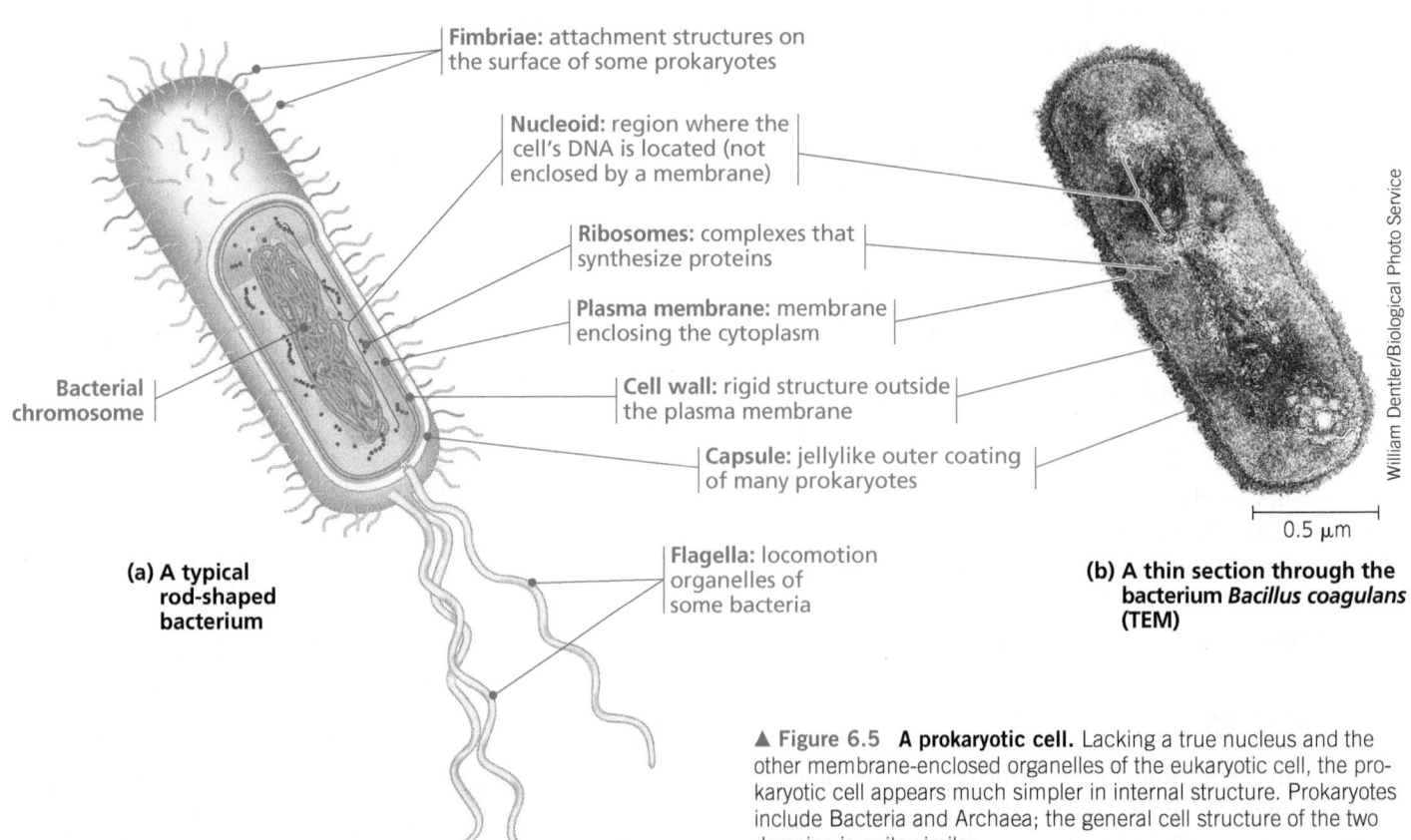

Fimbriae: attachment structures on the surface of some prokaryotes

Nucleoid: region where the cell's DNA is located (not enclosed by a membrane)

Ribosomes: complexes that synthesize proteins

Plasma membrane: membrane enclosing the cytoplasm

Cell wall: rigid structure outside the plasma membrane

Capsule: jellylike outer coating of many prokaryotes

Flagella: locomotion organelles of some bacteria

Bacterial chromosome

(a) A typical rod-shaped bacterium

(b) A thin section through the bacterium *Bacillus coagulans* (TEM)

0.5 μm

William Dentler/Biological Photo Service

▲ **Figure 6.5** **A prokaryotic cell.** Lacking a true nucleus and the other membrane-enclosed organelles of the eukaryotic cell, the prokaryotic cell appears much simpler in internal structure. Prokaryotes include Bacteria and Archaea; the general cell structure of the two domains is quite similar.

Eukaryotic means "true nucleus" (from the Greek *eu*, true, and *karyon*, kernel, here referring to the nucleus), and the word *prokaryotic* means "before nucleus" (from the Greek *pro*, before), reflecting the earlier evolution of prokaryotic cells.

The interior of either type of cell is called the **cytoplasm**; in eukaryotic cells, this term refers only to the region between the nucleus and the plasma membrane. Within the cytoplasm of a eukaryotic cell, suspended in cytosol, are a variety of organelles of specialized form and function. These membrane-bounded structures are absent in prokaryotic cells, another distinction between prokaryotic and eukaryotic cells. However, in spite of the absence of organelles, the prokaryotic cytoplasm is not a formless soup of cytoplasm, but appears to be organized into different regions.

Eukaryotic cells are generally much larger than prokaryotic cells (see Figure 6.2). Size is a general feature of cell structure that relates to function. The logistics of carrying out cellular metabolism sets limits on cell size. At the lower limit, the smallest cells known are bacteria called mycoplasmas, which have diameters between 0.1 and 1.0 μm. These are perhaps the smallest packages with enough DNA to program metabolism and enough enzymes and other cellular equipment to carry out the activities necessary for a cell to sustain itself and reproduce. Typical bacteria are 1–5 μm in diameter, about 10 times the size of mycoplasmas. Eukaryotic cells are typically 10–100 μm in diameter.

Metabolic requirements also impose theoretical upper limits on the size that is practical for a single cell. At the boundary of every cell, the **plasma membrane** functions as a selective barrier that allows passage of enough nutrients and wastes to service the entire cell (**Figure 6.6**). For each square micrometre of membrane, only a limited amount of a particular substance can cross per second, so the ratio of surface area to volume is critical. As a cell (or any other object) increases in size, its surface area grows proportionately less than its volume. (Area is proportional to a linear dimension squared, whereas volume is proportional to the linear dimension cubed.) Thus, a smaller object has a greater ratio of surface area to volume (**Figure 6.7**). The Scientific Skills Exercise gives you a chance to calculate the volumes and surface areas of two actual cells: a mature yeast cell and a cell budding from it.

The need for a surface area sufficiently large to accommodate the volume helps explain the microscopic size of most cells and the narrow, elongated shapes of others, such as nerve cells. Larger organisms do not generally have *larger* cells than smaller organisms—they simply have *more* cells (see Figure 6.7). A sufficiently high ratio of surface area to volume is especially important in cells that exchange a lot of material with their surroundings, such as intestinal cells. Such cells may have many long, thin projections from their surface called *microvilli*, which increase surface area without an appreciable increase in volume.

(a) TEM of a plasma membrane. The plasma membrane, here in a red blood cell, appears as a pair of dark bands separated by a light band.

Outside of cell

Inside of cell 0.1 μm

Daniel S. Friend

Carbohydrate side chains

Hydrophilic region

Hydrophobic region

Hydrophilic region

Phospholipid

Proteins

(b) Structure of the plasma membrane

▲ **Figure 6.6 The plasma membrane.** The plasma membrane and the membranes of organelles consist of a double layer (bilayer) of phospholipids with various proteins attached to or embedded in it. The hydrophobic parts of phospholipids and membrane proteins are found in the interior of the membrane, while the hydrophilic parts are in contact with the aqueous solutions on either side. Carbohydrate side chains may be attached to proteins or lipids on the outer surface of the plasma membrane.

Source: Figure 6.6(b), Figure adapted from *The World of the Cell,* 3rd Edition, by Wayne M. Becker, Jane B. Reece, and Martin F. Poenie. Copyright © 1996 by Pearson Education, Inc. Adapted and electronically reproduced by permission of Pearson Education, Inc., Upper Saddle River, New Jersey.

MAKE CONNECTIONS *Review Figure 5.11 and describe the characteristics of a phospholipid that allow it to function as the major component in the plasma membrane.*

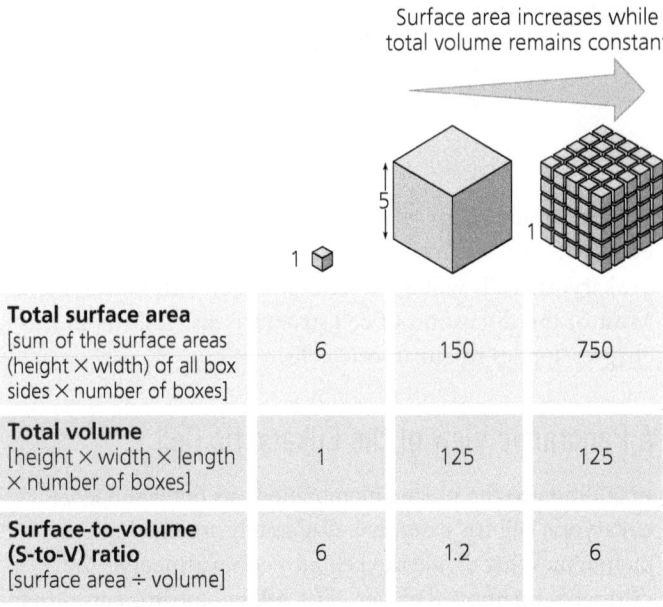

Surface area increases while total volume remains constant

Total surface area [sum of the surface areas (height × width) of all box sides × number of boxes]	6	150	750
Total volume [height × width × length × number of boxes]	1	125	125
Surface-to-volume (S-to-V) ratio [surface area ÷ volume]	6	1.2	6

▲ **Figure 6.7 Geometric relationships between surface area and volume.** In this diagram, cells are represented as boxes. Using arbitrary units of length, we can calculate the cell's surface area (in square units, or units^2), volume (in cubic units, or units^3), and ratio of surface area to volume. A high surface-to-volume ratio facilitates the exchange of materials between a cell and its environment.

Using a Scale Bar to Calculate Volume and Surface Area of a Cell

How Much New Cytoplasm and Plasma Membrane Are Made by a Growing Yeast Cell? The unicellular yeast *Saccharomyces cerevisiae* divides by budding off a small new cell that then grows to full size (see the yeast cells at the bottom of Figure 6.8). During its growth, the new cell synthesizes new cytoplasm, which increases its volume, and new plasma membrane, which increases its surface area. In this exercise, you will use a scale bar to determine the sizes of a mature parent yeast cell and a cell budding from it. You will then calculate the volume and surface area of each cell. You will use your calculations to determine how much cytoplasm and plasma membrane the new cell needs to synthesize to grow to full size.

How the Experiment Was Done Yeast cells were grown under conditions that promoted division by budding. The cells were then viewed with a differential interference contrast light microscope and photographed.

Data from the Experiment This light micrograph shows a budding yeast cell about to be released from the mature parent cell:

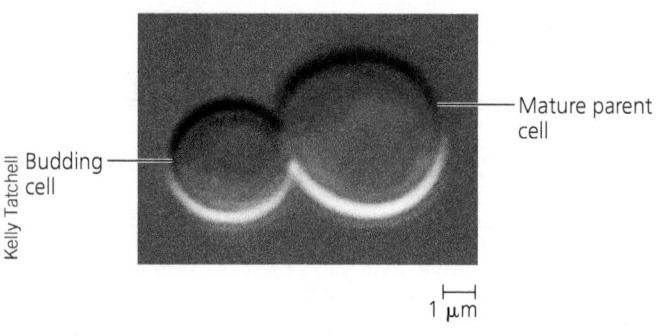

Budding cell

Mature parent cell

Kelly Tatchell

1 μm

Interpret the Data

1. Examine the micrograph of the yeast cells. The scale bar under the photo is labelled 1 μm. The scale bar works in the same way as a scale on a map, where, for example, 1 centimetre equals 1 kilometre. In this case the bar represents one thousandth of a millimetre. Using the scale bar as a basic unit, determine the diameter of the mature parent cell and the new cell. Start by measuring the scale bar and then the diameter of each cell. The units you use are irrelevant, but working in millimetres is convenient. Divide each diameter by the length of the scale bar and then multiply by the scale bar's length value to give you the diameter in micrometres.

2. The shape of a yeast cell can be approximated by a sphere. (a) Calculate the volume of each cell using the formula for the volume of a sphere:

$$V = \frac{4}{3}\pi r^3$$

Note that π (the Greek letter pi) is a constant with an approximate value of 3.14, d stands for diameter, and r stands for radius, which is half the diameter. (b) How much new cytoplasm will the new cell have to synthesize as it matures? To determine this, calculate the difference between the volume of the full-sized cell and the volume of the new cell.

3. As the new cell grows, its plasma membrane needs to expand to contain the increased volume of the cell. (a) Calculate the surface area of each cell using the formula for the surface area of a sphere: $A = 4\pi r^2$. (b) How much area of new plasma membrane will the new cell have to synthesize as it matures?

4. When the new cell matures, it will be approximately how many times greater in volume and how many times greater in surface area than its current size?

Micrograph from Kelly Tatchell, using yeast cells grown for experiments described in L. Kozubowski et al., Role of the septin ring in the asymmetric localization of proteins at the mother-bud neck in *Saccharomyces cerevisiae*, *Molecular Biology of the Cell* 16:3455–3466 (2005).

The evolutionary relationships between prokaryotic and eukaryotic cells will be discussed later in this chapter, and prokaryotic cells will be described in detail in Chapter 27. Most of the discussion of cell structure that follows in this chapter applies to eukaryotic cells.

A Panoramic View of the Eukaryotic Cell

In addition to the plasma membrane at its outer surface, a eukaryotic cell has extensive, elaborately arranged internal membranes that divide the cell into compartments—the organelles mentioned earlier. The cell's compartments provide different local environments that support specific metabolic functions, so incompatible processes can occur simultaneously in a single cell. The plasma membrane and organelle membranes also participate directly in the cell's metabolism, because many enzymes are built right into the membranes.

The basic fabric of most biological membranes is a double layer of phospholipids and other lipids. Embedded in this lipid bilayer or attached to its surfaces are diverse proteins (see Figure 6.6). However, each type of membrane has a unique composition of lipids and proteins suited to that membrane's specific functions. For example, enzymes embedded in the membranes of the organelles called mitochondria function in cellular respiration. Because membranes are so fundamental to the organization of the cell, Chapter 7 will discuss them in detail.

Before continuing with this chapter, examine the eukaryotic cells in **Figure 6.8** on pages 112–113. The generalized diagrams of an animal cell and a plant cell introduce the various organelles and show the key differences between animal and plant cells. The micrographs at the bottom of the figure give you a glimpse of cells from different types of eukaryotic organisms.

1. Briefly describe the structure and function of the nucleus, the mitochondrion, the chloroplast, and the endoplasmic reticulum.

2. **WHAT IF?** Imagine an elongated cell (such as a nerve cell) that measures 125 × 1 × 1 arbitrary units. Predict how its surface-to-volume ratio would compare with those in Figure 6.7. Then calculate the ratio and check your prediction.

For suggested answers, see Appendix A.

CONCEPT 6.3

The eukaryotic cell's genetic instructions are housed in the nucleus and carried out by the ribosomes

On the first stop of our detailed tour of the eukaryotic cell, let's look at two cellular components involved in the genetic control of the cell: the nucleus, which houses most of the cell's DNA, and the ribosomes, which use information from the DNA to make proteins.

The Nucleus: Information Central

The **nucleus** contains most of the genes in the eukaryotic cell. (Some genes are located in mitochondria and chloroplasts.) It is generally the most conspicuous organelle, averaging about 5 μm in diameter. The **nuclear envelope** encloses the nucleus (**Figure 6.9**), separating its contents from the cytoplasm.

The nuclear envelope is a *double* membrane. The two membranes, each a lipid bilayer with associated proteins, are separated by a space of 20–40 nm. The envelope is perforated by pore structures that are about 100 nm in diameter. At the lip of each pore, the inner and outer membranes of the nuclear envelope are continuous. An intricate protein structure called a *pore complex* lines each pore and plays an important role in the cell by regulating the entry and exit of proteins and RNAs, as well as large complexes of macromolecules. Except at the pores, the nuclear side of the envelope is lined by the **nuclear lamina**, a netlike array of protein filaments that maintains the shape of the nucleus by mechanically supporting the nuclear envelope. There is also much evidence for a *nuclear matrix*, a framework of protein fibres extending throughout the nuclear interior. The nuclear lamina and matrix may help organize the genetic material so it functions efficiently.

Within the nucleus, the DNA is organized into discrete units called **chromosomes**, structures that carry the genetic

Thomas Deerinck/Mark Ellisman/NCMIR

Nucleus

5 μm

information. Each chromosome contains one long DNA molecule associated with many proteins. Some of the proteins help coil the DNA molecule of each chromosome, reducing its length and allowing it to fit into the nucleus. The complex of DNA and proteins making up chromosomes is called **chromatin**. When a cell is not dividing, stained chromatin appears as a diffuse mass in micrographs, and the chromosomes cannot be distinguished from one another, even though discrete chromosomes are present. As a cell prepares to divide, however, the chromosomes coil (condense) further, becoming thick enough to be distinguished in a microscope as separate structures. Each eukaryotic species has a characteristic number of chromosomes. For example, a typical human cell has 46 chromosomes in its nucleus; the exceptions are the sex cells (eggs and sperm), which have only 23 chromosomes in humans. A fruit fly cell has 8 chromosomes in most cells and 4 in the sex cells.

A prominent structure within the nondividing nucleus is the **nucleolus** (plural, *nucleoli*), which appears through the electron microscope as a mass of densely stained granules and fibres adjoining part of the chromatin. Here a type of RNA called *ribosomal RNA* (rRNA) is synthesized from instructions in the DNA. Also in the nucleolus, proteins imported from the cytoplasm are assembled with rRNA into large and small subunits of ribosomes. These subunits then exit the nucleus through the nuclear pores to the cytoplasm, where a large and a small subunit can assemble into a ribosome. Sometimes there are two or more nucleoli; the number depends on the species and the stage in the cell's reproductive cycle.

As we saw in Figure 5.23, the nucleus directs protein synthesis by synthesizing messenger RNA (mRNA) according to instructions provided by the DNA. The mRNA is then transported to the cytoplasm via the nuclear pores. Once an mRNA molecule reaches the cytoplasm, ribosomes translate the mRNA's genetic message into the primary structure of a specific polypeptide. (This process of transcribing and translating genetic information is described in detail in Chapter 17.)

Ribosomes: Protein Factories

Ribosomes, which are complexes made of ribosomal RNA and protein, are the cellular components that carry out protein synthesis (**Figure 6.10**). (Note that ribosomes are not membrane-bounded and thus are not considered organelles.) Cells that have high rates of protein synthesis have particularly large numbers of ribosomes. For example, a

Exploring Eukaryotic Cells

Animal Cell (cutaway view of generalized cell)

Flagellum: motility structure present in some animal cells, composed of a cluster of microtubules within an extension of the plasma membrane

ENDOPLASMIC RETICULUM (ER): network of membranous sacs and tubes; active in membrane synthesis and other synthetic and metabolic processes; has rough (ribosome-studded) and smooth regions

Rough ER   **Smooth ER**

Nuclear envelope: double membrane enclosing the nucleus; perforated by pores; continuous with ER

Nucleolus: nonmembranous structure involved in production of ribosomes; a nucleus has one or more nucleoli

Chromatin: material consisting of DNA and proteins; visible in a dividing cell as individual condensed chromosomes

NUCLEUS

Centrosome: region where the cell's microtubules are initiated; contains a pair of centrioles

Plasma membrane: membrane enclosing the cell

CYTOSKELETON: reinforces cell's shape; functions in cell movement; components are made of protein. Includes:

Microfilaments |-

Intermediate filaments |-

Microtubules |-

Ribosomes (small brown dots): complexes that make proteins; free in cytosol or bound to rough ER or nuclear envelope

Microvilli: projections that increase the cell's surface area

Golgi apparatus: organelle active in synthesis, modification, sorting, and secretion of cell products

Mitochondrion: organelle where cellular respiration occurs and most ATP is generated

Peroxisome: organelle with various specialized metabolic functions; produces hydrogen peroxide as a by-product, then converts it to water

Lysosome: digestive organelle where macromolecules are hydrolyzed

Animal Cells

10 µm

Cell

Nucleus

Nucleolus

Human cells from lining of uterus (colourized TEM)

Fungal Cells

Parent cell

Buds

5 µm

1 µm

Cell wall

Vacuole

Nucleus

Mitochondrion

Yeast cells: reproducing by budding (above, colourized SEM) and a single cell (right, colourized TEM)

Plant Cell (cutaway view of generalized cell)

ANIMATION *BioFlix* Visit the Study Area in **MasteringBiology** for the BioFlix® 3-D Animations Tour of an Animal Cell and Tour of a Plant Cell.

NUCLEUS
- Nuclear envelope
- Nucleolus
- Chromatin

Rough endoplasmic reticulum

Smooth endoplasmic reticulum

Ribosomes (small brown dots)

Central vacuole: prominent organelle in older plant cells; functions include storage, breakdown of waste products, hydrolysis of macromolecules; enlargement of vacuole is a major mechanism of plant growth

Golgi apparatus

CYTOSKELETON
- Microfilaments
- Intermediate filaments
- Microtubules

Mitochondrion

Peroxisome

Plasma membrane

Cell wall: outer layer that maintains cell's shape and protects cell from mechanical damage; made of cellulose, other polysaccharides, and protein

Wall of adjacent cell

Chloroplast: photosynthetic organelle; converts energy of sunlight to chemical energy stored in sugar molecules

Plasmodesmata: cytoplasmic channels through cell walls that connect the cytoplasms of adjacent cells

Plant Cells

Biophoto Associates/Science Source

5 μm

- Cell
- Cell wall
- Chloroplast
- Mitochondrion
- Nucleus
- Nucleolus

Cells from duckweed (*Spirodela oligorrhiza*), a floating plant (colourized TEM)

Unicellular Eukaryotes

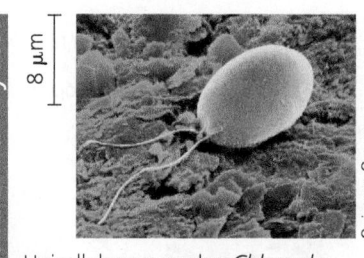

8 μm

Science Source

Unicellular green alga *Chlamydomonas* (above, colourized SEM; right, colourized TEM)

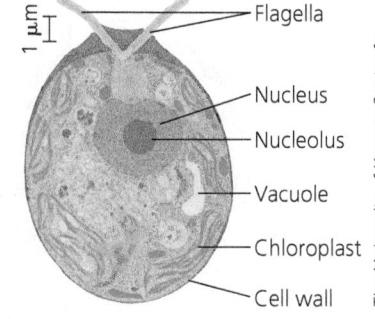

1 μm

- Flagella
- Nucleus
- Nucleolus
- Vacuole
- Chloroplast
- Cell wall

The University of Kansas Center for Bioinformatics

Source: Adaptation of figure 3.2 from *Human Anatomy and Physiology*, 8th Edition, by Elaine N. Marieb and Katja N. Hoehn, 2010. Copyright © 2010 by Pearson Education, Inc. Reprinted and electronically reproduced by permission of Pearson Education, Inc. Upper Saddle River, New Jersey.

1 μm

Nucleus

Nucleus

Nucleolus

Chromatin

Nuclear envelope:

Inner membrane

Outer membrane

Nuclear pore

Rough ER

▲ **Surface of nuclear envelope (TEM)**. This specimen was prepared by a technique known as freeze-fracture.

Pore complex

Ribosome

0.25 μm

◀ **Close-up of nuclear envelope**

▲ **Chromatin.** This segment of a chromosome from a non-dividing cell shows two states of coiling of the DNA (blue) and protein (purple) complex. The thicker form is sometimes also organized into long loops.

▲ **Pore complexes (TEM).** Each pore is ringed by protein particles.

0.5 μm

Nature Magazine

◀ **Nuclear lamina (TEM).** The netlike lamina lines the inner surface of the nuclear envelope.

▲ **Figure 6.9 The nucleus and its envelope.** Within the nucleus are the chromosomes, which appear as a mass of chromatin (DNA and associated proteins), and one or more nucleoli (singular, *nucleolus*), which function in ribosome synthesis. The nuclear envelope, which consists of two membranes separated by a narrow space, is perforated with pores and lined by the nuclear lamina.

Source: Adaptation of figure 3.29 from *Human Anatomy and Physiology,* 8th Edition, by Elaine N. Marieb and Katja N. Hoehn, 2010. Copyright © 2010 by Pearson Education, Inc. Reprinted and electronically reproduced by permission of Pearson Education, Inc. Upper Saddle River, New Jersey.

MAKE CONNECTIONS *Since the chromosomes contain the genetic material and reside in the nucleus, how does the rest of the cell get access to the information they carry? See Figure 5.23, page 93.*

Ribosomes

ER

0.25 μm

Free ribosomes in cytosol

Endoplasmic reticulum (ER)

Ribosomes bound to ER

Large subunit

Small subunit

TEM showing ER and ribosomes

Diagram of a ribosome

◀ **Figure 6.10 Ribosomes.** This electron micrograph of part of a pancreas cell shows many ribosomes, both free (in the cytosol) and bound (to the endoplasmic reticulum). The simplified diagram of a ribosome shows its two subunits.

Source: Adaptation of figure 3.2 from *Human Anatomy and Physiology,* 8th Edition, by Elaine N. Marieb and Katja N. Hoehn, 2010. Copyright © 2010 by Pearson Education, Inc. Reprinted and electronically reproduced by permission of Pearson Education, Inc. Upper Saddle River, New Jersey.

DRAW IT *After you have read the section on ribosomes, circle a ribosome in the micrograph that might be making a protein that will be secreted.*

human pancreas cell, which makes many digestive enzymes, has a few million ribosomes. Not surprisingly, cells active in protein synthesis also have prominent nucleoli.

Ribosomes build proteins in two cytoplasmic locales. At any given time, *free ribosomes* are suspended in the cytosol, while *bound ribosomes* are attached to the outside of the endoplasmic reticulum or nuclear envelope (see Figure 6.10). Bound and free ribosomes are structurally identical, and ribosomes can alternate between the two roles. Most of the proteins made on free ribosomes function within the cytosol; examples are enzymes that catalyze the first steps of sugar breakdown. Bound ribosomes generally make proteins that are destined for insertion into membranes, for packaging within certain organelles such as lysosomes (see Figure 6.8), or for export from the cell (secretion). Cells that specialize in protein secretion—for instance, the cells of the pancreas that secrete digestive enzymes—frequently have a high proportion of bound ribosomes. (You will learn more about ribosome structure and function in Chapter 17.)

CONCEPT CHECK 6.3

1. What role do ribosomes play in carrying out genetic instructions?
2. Describe the molecular composition of nucleoli and explain their function.
3. **WHAT IF?** As a cell begins the process of dividing, its chromosomes become shorter, thicker, and individually visible under a light microscope. Explain what is happening at the molecular level.

For suggested answers, see Appendix A.

CONCEPT 6.4

The endomembrane system regulates protein traffic and performs metabolic functions in the cell

Many of the different membranes of the eukaryotic cell are part of the **endomembrane system**, which includes the nuclear envelope, the endoplasmic reticulum, the Golgi apparatus, lysosomes, various kinds of vesicles and vacuoles, and the plasma membrane. This system carries out a variety of tasks in the cell, including synthesis of proteins, transport of proteins into membranes and organelles or out of the cell, metabolism and movement of lipids, and detoxification of poisons. The membranes of this system are related either through direct physical continuity or by the transfer of membrane segments as tiny **vesicles** (sacs made of membrane). Despite these relationships, the various membranes are not identical in structure and function. Moreover, the thickness, molecular composition, and types of chemical

reactions carried out in a given membrane are not fixed, but may be modified several times during the membrane's life. Having already discussed the nuclear envelope, we will now focus on the endoplasmic reticulum and the other endomembranes to which the endoplasmic reticulum gives rise.

The Endoplasmic Reticulum: Biosynthetic Factory

The **endoplasmic reticulum (ER)** is such an extensive network of membranes that it accounts for more than half the total membrane in many eukaryotic cells. (The word *endoplasmic* means "within the cytoplasm," and *reticulum* is Latin for "little net.") The ER consists of a network of membranous tubules and sacs called cisternae (from the Latin *cisterna*, a reservoir for a liquid). The ER membrane separates the internal compartment of the ER, called the *ER lumen* (cavity) or cisternal space, from the cytosol. And because the ER membrane is continuous with the nuclear envelope, the space between the two membranes of the envelope is continuous with the lumen of the ER (Figure 6.11).

There are two distinct, though connected, regions of the ER that differ in structure and function: smooth ER and rough ER. **Smooth ER** is so named because its outer surface lacks ribosomes. **Rough ER** is studded with ribosomes on the outer surface of the membrane and thus appears rough through the electron microscope. As already mentioned, ribosomes are also attached to the cytoplasmic side of the nuclear envelope's outer membrane, which is continuous with rough ER.

Functions of Smooth ER

The smooth ER functions in diverse metabolic processes, which vary with cell type. These processes include synthesis of lipids, metabolism of carbohydrates, detoxification of drugs and poisons, and storage of calcium ions.

Enzymes of the smooth ER are important in the synthesis of lipids, including oils, steroids, and new membrane phospholipids. Among the steroids produced by the smooth ER in animal cells are the sex hormones of vertebrates and the various steroid hormones secreted by the adrenal glands. The cells that synthesize and secrete these hormones—in the testes and ovaries, for example—are rich in smooth ER, a structural feature that fits the function of these cells.

Other enzymes of the smooth ER help detoxify drugs and poisons, especially in liver cells. Detoxification usually involves adding hydroxyl groups to drug molecules, making them more soluble and easier to flush from the body. The sedative phenobarbital and other barbiturates are examples of drugs metabolized in this manner by smooth ER in liver cells. In fact, barbiturates, alcohol, and many other drugs induce the proliferation of smooth ER and its

Smooth ER

Rough ER

Nuclear envelope

ER lumen

Cisternae

Ribosomes

Transitional ER

Transport vesicle

Smooth ER

Rough ER

0.20 μm

R.W. Bolender/Don Fawcett/Science Source

▲ **Figure 6.11** **Endoplasmic reticulum (ER).** A membranous system of interconnected tubules and flattened sacs called cisternae, the ER is also continuous with the nuclear envelope, as shown in the cutaway diagram at the top. The membrane of the ER encloses a continuous compartment called the ER lumen (or cisternal space). Rough ER, which is studded on its outer surface with ribosomes, can be distinguished from smooth ER in the electron micrograph (TEM). Transport vesicles bud off from a region of the rough ER called transitional ER and travel to the Golgi apparatus and other destinations.

Source: Adaptation of figure 3.18 from *Human Anatomy and Physiology*, 8th Edition, by Elaine N. Marieb and Katja N. Hoehn, 2010. Copyright © 2010 by Pearson Education, Inc. Reprinted and electronically reproduced by permission of Pearson Education, Inc. Upper Saddle River, New Jersey.

associated detoxification enzymes, thus increasing the rate of detoxification. This, in turn, increases tolerance to the drugs, meaning that higher doses are required to achieve a particular effect, such as sedation. Also, because some of the detoxification enzymes have relatively broad action, the proliferation of smooth ER in response to one drug can increase the need for higher dosages of other drugs as well. Barbiturate abuse, for example, can decrease the effectiveness of certain antibiotics and other useful drugs.

The smooth ER also stores calcium ions. In muscle cells, for example, the smooth ER membrane pumps calcium ions from the cytosol into the ER lumen. When a muscle cell is stimulated by a nerve impulse, calcium ions rush back across the ER membrane into the cytosol and trigger contraction of the muscle cell. In other cell types, calcium ion release from the smooth ER triggers different responses, such as secretion of vesicles carrying newly synthesized proteins.

Functions of Rough ER

Many cells secrete proteins that are produced by ribosomes attached to rough ER. For example, certain pancreatic cells synthesize the protein insulin in the ER and secrete this hormone into the bloodstream. As a polypeptide chain grows from a bound ribosome, the chain is threaded into the ER lumen through a pore formed by a protein complex in the ER membrane. The new polypeptide folds into its functional shape as it enters the ER lumen. Most secretory proteins are **glycoproteins**, proteins with carbohydrates covalently bonded to them. The carbohydrates are attached to the proteins in the ER lumen by enzymes built into the ER membrane.

After secretory proteins are formed, the ER membrane keeps them separate from proteins that are produced by free ribosomes and that will remain in the cytosol. Secretory proteins depart from the ER wrapped in the membranes of vesicles that bud like bubbles from a specialized region called transitional ER (see Figure 6.11). Vesicles in transit from one part of the cell to another are called **transport vesicles**; we will discuss their fate shortly.

In addition to making secretory proteins, rough ER is a membrane factory for the cell; it grows in place by adding membrane proteins and phospholipids to its own membrane. As polypeptides destined to be membrane proteins grow from the ribosomes, they are inserted into the ER membrane itself and anchored there by their hydrophobic portions. Like the smooth ER, the rough ER also makes membrane phospholipids; enzymes built into the ER membrane assemble phospholipids from precursors in the cytosol. The ER membrane expands and portions of it are transferred in the form of transport vesicles to other components of the endomembrane system.

The Golgi Apparatus: Shipping and Receiving Centre

After leaving the ER, many transport vesicles travel to the **Golgi apparatus**. We can think of the Golgi as a warehouse for receiving, sorting, shipping, and even some manufacturing. Here, products of the ER, such as proteins, are modified and stored and then sent to other destinations. Not surprisingly, the Golgi apparatus is especially extensive in cells specialized for secretion.

The Golgi apparatus consists of flattened membranous sacs—cisternae—looking like a stack of pita bread (Figure 6.12). A cell may have many, even hundreds, of these stacks. The membrane of each cisterna in a stack separates its internal space from the cytosol. Vesicles concentrated in the vicinity of the Golgi apparatus are engaged in the transfer of material between parts of the Golgi and other structures.

A Golgi stack has a distinct structural directionality, with the membranes of cisternae on opposite sides of the stack differing in thickness and molecular composition. The two sides of a Golgi stack are referred to as the *cis* face and the *trans* face; these act, respectively, as the receiving and shipping departments of the Golgi apparatus. The term *cis* means "on the same side," and the *cis* face is usually located near the ER. Transport vesicles move material from the ER to the Golgi apparatus. A vesicle that buds from the ER can add its membrane and the contents of its lumen to the *cis* face by fusing with a Golgi membrane. The *trans* face ("on the opposite side") gives rise to vesicles that pinch off and travel to other sites.

Products of the endoplasmic reticulum are usually modified during their transit from the *cis* region to the *trans* region of the Golgi apparatus. For example, glycoproteins formed in the ER have their carbohydrates modified, first in the ER itself, then as they pass through the Golgi. The Golgi removes some sugar monomers and substitutes others, producing a large variety of carbohydrates. Membrane phospholipids may also be altered in the Golgi.

In addition to its finishing work, the Golgi apparatus also manufactures some macromolecules. Many polysaccharides secreted by cells are Golgi products. For example, pectins and certain other noncellulose polysaccharides are made in the Golgi of plant cells and then incorporated along with cellulose into their cell walls. Like secretory proteins, nonprotein Golgi products that will be secreted depart from the *trans* face of the Golgi inside transport vesicles that eventually fuse with the plasma membrane.

The Golgi manufactures and refines its products in stages, with different cisternae containing unique teams of enzymes. Until recently, biologists viewed the Golgi as a static structure, with products in various stages of processing transferred from one cisterna to the next by vesicles. While this may occur, research from several labs has given rise to a new model of the Golgi as a more dynamic

▼ Figure 6.12 **The Golgi apparatus.** The Golgi apparatus consists of stacks of flattened sacs, or cisternae, which (unlike ER cisternae) are not physically connected, as you can see in the cutaway diagram. A Golgi stack receives and dispatches transport vesicles and the products they contain. A Golgi stack has a structural and functional directionality, with a *cis* face that receives vesicles containing ER products and a *trans* face that dispatches vesicles. The cisternal maturation model proposes that the Golgi cisternae themselves "mature," moving from the *cis* to the *trans* face while carrying some proteins along. In addition, some vesicles recycle enzymes that had been carried forward in moving cisternae, transporting them "backward" to a less mature region where their functions are needed.

Source: Adaptation of figure 3.19 from Human Anatomy and Physiology, 8th Edition, by Elaine N. Marieb and Katja N. Hoehn, 2010. Copyright © 2010 by Pearson Education, Inc. Reprinted and electronically reproduced by permission of Pearson Education, Inc. Upper Saddle River, New Jersey.

Golgi apparatus

cis **face** ("receiving" side of Golgi apparatus)

❶ Vesicles move from ER to Golgi.

❷ Vesicles coalesce to form new *cis* Golgi cisternae.

❻ Vesicles also transport certain proteins back to ER, their site of function.

Cisternae

❸ Cisternal maturation: Golgi cisternae move in a *cis*-to-*trans* direction.

❹ Vesicles form and leave Golgi, carrying specific products to other locations or to the plasma membrane for secretion.

❺ Vesicles transport some proteins backward to less mature Golgi cisternae, where they function.

trans **face** ("shipping" side of Golgi apparatus)

© Pearson Education, Inc.

0.1 μm

TEM of Golgi apparatus

Science Source

structure. According to the *cisternal maturation model*, the cisternae of the Golgi actually progress forward from the *cis* to the *trans* face, carrying and modifying their cargo as they move. Figure 6.12 shows the details of this model.

Before a Golgi stack dispatches its products by budding vesicles from the *trans* face, it sorts these products and targets them for various parts of the cell. Molecular identification tags, such as phosphate groups added to the Golgi products, aid in sorting by acting like postal codes on mailing labels. Finally, transport vesicles budded from the Golgi may have external molecules on their membranes that recognize "docking sites" on the surface of specific organelles or on the plasma membrane, thus targeting the vesicles appropriately.

Lysosomes: Digestive Compartments

A **lysosome** is a membranous sac of hydrolytic enzymes that many eukaryotic cells use to digest (hydrolyze) macromolecules. Lysosomal enzymes work best in the acidic environment found in lysosomes. If a lysosome breaks open or leaks its contents, the released enzymes are not very active because the cytosol has a near-neutral pH. However, excessive leakage from a large number of lysosomes can destroy a cell by self-digestion.

Hydrolytic enzymes and lysosomal membrane are made by rough ER and then transferred to the Golgi apparatus for further processing. At least some lysosomes probably arise by budding from the *trans* face of the Golgi apparatus (see Figure 6.12). How are the proteins of the inner surface of the lysosomal membrane and the digestive enzymes themselves spared from destruction? Apparently, the three-dimensional shapes of these proteins protect vulnerable bonds from enzymatic attack.

Lysosomes carry out intracellular digestion in a variety of circumstances. Amoebas and many other unicellular eukaryotes eat by engulfing smaller organisms or food particles, a process called **phagocytosis** (from the Greek *phagein*, to eat, and *kytos*, vessel, referring here to the cell). The *food vacuole* formed in this way then fuses with a lysosome, whose enzymes digest the food (**Figure 6.13a**, bottom). Digestion products, including simple sugars, amino acids, and other monomers, pass into the cytosol and

(a) Phagocytosis: lysosome digesting food

1 Lysosome contains active hydrolytic enzymes.

2 Lysosome fuses with food vacuole.

3 Hydrolytic enzymes digest food particles.

Digestive enzymes

Lysosome

Plasma membrane

Food vacuole

Digestion

(b) Autophagy: lysosome breaking down damaged organelles

1 Lysosome fuses with vesicle containing damaged organelles.

2 Hydrolytic enzymes digest organelle components.

Lysosome

Peroxisome

Vesicle

Mitochondrion

Digestion

▲ **Figure 6.13 Lysosomes.** Lysosomes digest (hydrolyze) materials taken into the cell and recycle intracellular materials. **(a)** *Top*: In this macrophage (a type of white blood cell) from a rat, the lysosomes are very dark because of a stain that reacts with one of the products of digestion inside the lysosome (TEM). Macrophages ingest bacteria and viruses and destroy them using lysosomes. *Bottom*: This diagram shows a lysosome fusing with a food vacuole during the process of phagocytosis by a unicellular eukaryote. **(b)** *Top*: In the cytoplasm of this rat liver cell is a vesicle containing two disabled organelles (TEM). The vesicle will fuse with a lysosome in the process of autophagy. *Bottom*: This diagram shows fusion of such a vesicle with a lysosome. This type of vesicle has a double membrane of unknown origin. The outer membrane fuses with the lysosome, and the inner membrane is degraded along with the damaged organelles.

Source: Figure 6.13(a), Adaptation of figure 3.2 from *Human Anatomy and Physiology*, 8th Edition, by Elaine N. Marieb and Katja N. Hoehn, 2010. Copyright © 2010 by Pearson Education, Inc. Reprinted and electronically reproduced by permission of Pearson Education, Inc. Upper Saddle River, New Jersey.

become nutrients for the cell. Some human cells also carry out phagocytosis. Among them are macrophages, a type of white blood cell that helps defend the body by engulfing and destroying bacteria and other invaders (see Figure 6.13a, top, and Figure 6.31).

Lysosomes also use their hydrolytic enzymes to recycle the cell's own organic material, a process called *autophagy*. During autophagy, a damaged organelle or small amount of cytosol becomes surrounded by a double membrane (of unknown origin), and a lysosome fuses with the outer membrane of this vesicle (Figure 6.13b). The lysosomal enzymes dismantle the enclosed material, and the resulting small organic compounds are released to the cytosol for reuse. With the help of lysosomes, the cell continually renews itself. A human liver cell, for example, recycles half of its macromolecules each week.

The cells of people with inherited lysosomal storage diseases lack a functioning hydrolytic enzyme normally present in lysosomes. The lysosomes become engorged with indigestible material, which begins to interfere with other cellular activities. In Tay-Sachs disease, for example, a lipid-digesting enzyme is missing or inactive, and the brain becomes impaired by an accumulation of lipids in the cells. Fortunately, lysosomal storage diseases are rare in the general population.

Vacuoles: Diverse Maintenance Compartments

Vacuoles are large vesicles derived from the endoplasmic reticulum and Golgi apparatus. Thus, vacuoles are an integral part of a cell's endomembrane system. Like all cellular membranes, the vacuolar membrane is selective in transporting solutes; as a result, the solution inside a vacuole differs in composition from the cytosol.

Vacuoles perform a variety of functions in different kinds of cells. **Food vacuoles**, formed by phagocytosis, have already been mentioned (see Figure 6.13a). Many unicellular eukaryotes living in fresh water have **contractile vacuoles** that pump excess water out of the cell, thereby maintaining a suitable concentration of ions and molecules inside the cell (see Figure 7.13). In plants and fungi, certain vacuoles carry out enzymatic hydrolysis, a function shared by lysosomes in animal cells. (In fact, some biologists consider these hydrolytic vacuoles to be a type of lysosome.) In plants, small vacuoles can hold reserves of important organic compounds, such as the proteins stockpiled in the storage cells in seeds. Vacuoles may also help protect the plant against herbivores by storing compounds that are poisonous or unpalatable to animals. Some plant vacuoles contain pigments, such as the red and blue pigments of petals that help attract pollinating insects to flowers.

Mature plant cells generally contain a large **central vacuole** (Figure 6.14), which develops by the coalescence of smaller vacuoles. The solution inside the central vacuole,

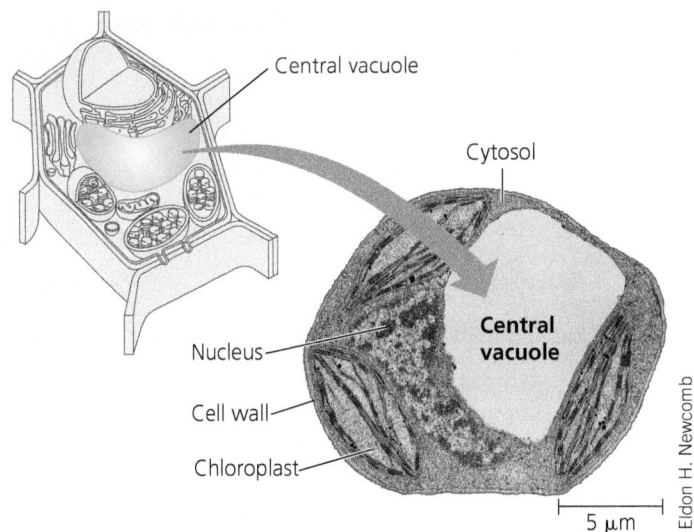

▲ **Figure 6.14** **The plant cell vacuole.** The central vacuole is usually the largest compartment in a plant cell; the rest of the cytoplasm is often confined to a narrow zone between the vacuolar membrane and the plasma membrane (TEM).

called cell sap, is the plant cell's main repository of inorganic ions, including potassium and chloride. The central vacuole plays a major role in the growth of plant cells, which enlarge as the vacuole absorbs water, enabling the cell to become larger with a minimal investment in new cytoplasm. The cytosol often occupies only a thin layer between the central vacuole and the plasma membrane, so the ratio of plasma membrane surface to cytosolic volume is sufficient, even for a large plant cell.

The Endomembrane System: *A Review*

Figure 6.15 reviews the endomembrane system, showing the flow of membrane lipids and proteins through the various organelles. As the membrane moves from the ER to the Golgi and then elsewhere, its molecular composition and metabolic functions are modified, along with those of its contents. The endomembrane system is a complex and dynamic player in the cell's compartmental organization.

We'll continue our tour of the cell with some organelles that are not closely related to the endomembrane system but play crucial roles in the energy transformations carried out by cells.

CONCEPT CHECK 6.4

1. Describe the structural and functional distinctions between rough and smooth ER.

2. Describe how transport vesicles integrate the endomembrane system.

3. **WHAT IF?** Imagine a protein that functions in the ER but requires modification in the Golgi apparatus before it can achieve that function. Describe the protein's path through the cell, starting with the mRNA molecule that specifies the protein.

For suggested answers, see Appendix A.

① Nuclear envelope is connected to rough ER, which is also continuous with smooth ER.

Nucleus

② Membranes and proteins produced by the ER flow in the form of transport vesicles to the Golgi.

Smooth ER

Rough ER

cis Golgi

③ Golgi pinches off transport vesicles and other vesicles that give rise to lysosomes, other types of specialized vesicles, and vacuoles.

trans Golgi

Plasma membrane

④ Lysosome is available for fusion with another vesicle for digestion.

⑤ Transport vesicle carries proteins to plasma membrane for secretion.

⑥ Plasma membrane expands by fusion of vesicles; proteins are secreted from cell.

▲ Figure 6.15 **Review: relationships among organelles of the endomembrane system.** The red arrows show some of the migration pathways for membranes and the materials they enclose.

Source: Adaptation of figure 3.20 from *Human Anatomy and Physiology,* 8th Edition, by Elaine N. Marieb and Katja N. Hoehn, 2010. Copyright © 2010 by Pearson Education, Inc. Reprinted and electronically reproduced by permission of Pearson Education, Inc. Upper Saddle River, New Jersey.

CONCEPT 6.5

Mitochondria and chloroplasts change energy from one form to another

Organisms transform the energy they acquire from their surroundings. In eukaryotic cells, mitochondria and chloroplasts are the organelles that convert energy to forms that cells can use for work. **Mitochondria** (singular, *mitochondrion*) are the sites of cellular respiration, the metabolic process that uses oxygen to drive the generation of ATP by extracting energy from sugars, fats, and other fuels. **Chloroplasts**, found in plants and algae, are the sites of photosynthesis. This process in chloroplasts converts solar energy to chemical energy by absorbing sunlight and using it to drive the synthesis of organic compounds such as sugars from carbon dioxide and water.

In addition to having related functions, mitochondria and chloroplasts share similar evolutionary origins, which we'll discuss briefly before describing their structures. In this section, we will also consider the peroxisome, an oxidative organelle. The evolutionary origin of the peroxisome, as well as its relation to other organelles, is still a matter of some debate.

The Evolutionary Origins of Mitochondria and Chloroplasts

EVOLUTION   Mitochondria and chloroplasts display similarities with bacteria that led to the **endosymbiont theory**, illustrated in **Figure 6.16**. This theory states that an early ancestor of eukaryotic cells engulfed an oxygen-using nonphotosynthetic prokaryotic cell. Eventually, the engulfed cell formed a relationship with the host cell in which it was enclosed, becoming an *endosymbiont* (a cell living within another cell). Indeed, over the course of evolution, the host cell and its endosymbiont merged into a single organism, a eukaryotic cell with a mitochondrion. At least one of these cells may have then taken up a photosynthetic prokaryote, becoming the ancestor of eukaryotic cells that contain chloroplasts.

This a widely accepted theory, which we will discuss in more detail in Chapter 25. This theory is consistent with many structural features of mitochondria and chloroplasts. First, rather than being bounded by a single membrane like organelles of the endomembrane system, mitochondria and typical chloroplasts have two membranes surrounding them. (Chloroplasts also have an internal system of membranous sacs.) There is evidence that the ancestral engulfed

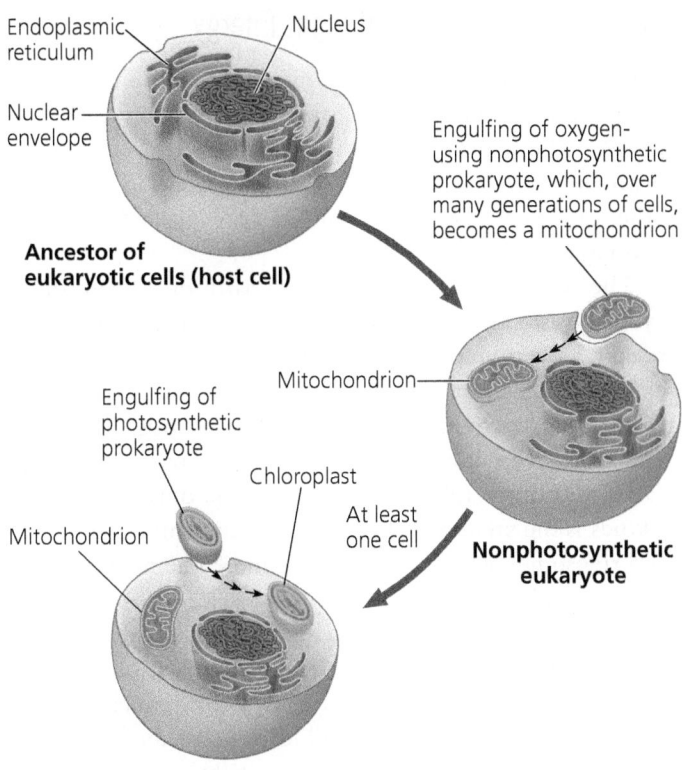

Endoplasmic reticulum

Nucleus

Nuclear envelope

Ancestor of eukaryotic cells (host cell)

Engulfing of oxygen-using nonphotosynthetic prokaryote, which, over many generations of cells, becomes a mitochondrion

Mitochondrion

Nonphotosynthetic eukaryote

Engulfing of photosynthetic prokaryote

Chloroplast

At least one cell

Mitochondrion

Photosynthetic eukaryote

▲ Figure 6.16 **The endosymbiont theory of the origin of mitochondria and chloroplasts in eukaryotic cells.** According to this theory, the proposed ancestors of mitochondria were oxygen-using nonphotosynthetic prokaryotes, while the proposed ancestors of chloroplasts were photosynthetic prokaryotes. The large arrows represent change over evolutionary time; the small arrows inside the cells show the process of the endosymbiont becoming an organelle, also over long periods of time.

prokaryotes had two outer membranes, which became the double membranes of mitochondria and chloroplasts. Second, like prokaryotes, mitochondria and chloroplasts contain ribosomes, as well as multiple circular DNA molecules associated with their inner membranes. The DNA in these organelles programs the synthesis of some organelle proteins on ribosomes that have been synthesized and assembled there as well. Third, also consistent with their probable evolutionary origins as cells, mitochondria and chloroplasts are autonomous (somewhat independent) organelles that grow and reproduce within the cell.

Next, we focus on the structures of mitochondria and chloroplasts, while providing an overview of their structures and functions. (In Chapters 9 and 10, we will examine their roles as energy transformers.)

Mitochondria: Chemical Energy Conversion

Mitochondria are found in nearly all eukaryotic cells, including those of plants, animals, fungi, and most unicellular eukaryotes. Some cells have a single large mitochondrion, but more often a cell has hundreds or even thousands of mitochondria; the number correlates with the cell's level of metabolic activity. For example, cells that move or contract have proportionally more mitochondria per volume than less active cells.

Each of the two membranes enclosing the mitochondrion is a phospholipid bilayer with a unique collection of embedded proteins (**Figure 6.17**). The outer membrane

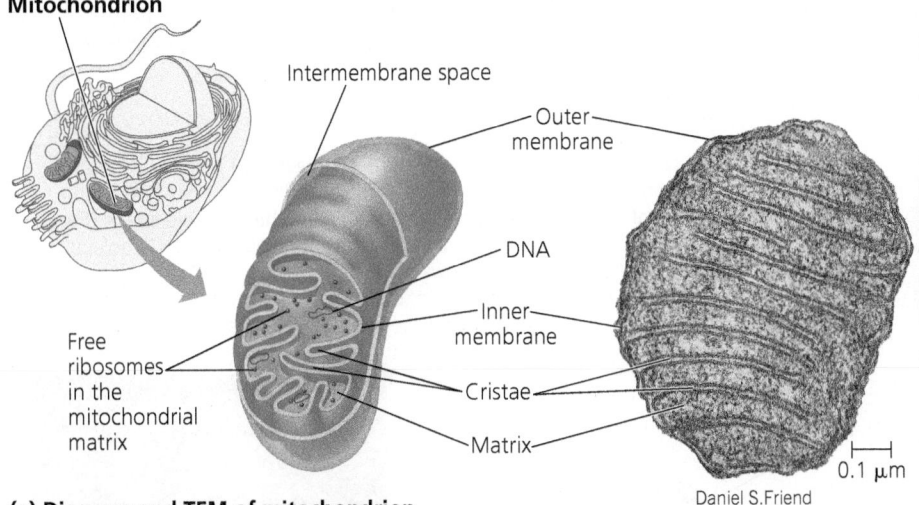

Mitochondrion

Intermembrane space

Outer membrane

DNA

Inner membrane

Cristae

Matrix

Free ribosomes in the mitochondrial matrix

Daniel S. Friend

0.1 μm

(a) Diagram and TEM of mitochondrion

10 μm

Mitochondria

Mitochondrial DNA

Nuclear DNA

Niigata University, Japan

(b) Network of mitochondria in *Euglena* (LM)

▲ Figure 6.17 **The mitochondrion, site of cellular respiration. (a)** The inner and outer membranes of the mitochondrion are evident in the drawing and electron micrograph (TEM). The cristae are infoldings of the inner membrane, which increase its surface area. The cutaway drawing shows the two compartments bounded by the membranes: the intermembrane space and the mitochondrial matrix. Many respiratory enzymes are found in the inner membrane and the matrix. Free ribosomes are also present in the matrix. The DNA molecules are usually circular and are attached to the inner mitochondrial membrane. **(b)** The light micrograph shows an entire unicellular eukaryote (*Euglena gracilis*) at a much lower magnification than the TEM. The mitochondrial matrix has been stained green. The mitochondria form a branched tubular network. The nuclear DNA is stained red, and the molecules of mitochondrial DNA appear as bright yellow spots.

Source: Adaptation of figure 3.17 from *Human Anatomy and Physiology,* 8th Edition, by Elaine N. Marieb and Katja N. Hoehn, 2010. Copyright © 2010 by Pearson Education, Inc. Reprinted and electronically reproduced by permission of Pearson Education, Inc. Upper Saddle River, New Jersey.

is smooth, but the inner membrane is convoluted, with infoldings called **cristae**. The inner membrane divides the mitochondrion into two internal compartments. The first is the intermembrane space, the narrow region between the inner and outer membranes. The second compartment, the **mitochondrial matrix**, is enclosed by the inner membrane. The matrix contains many different enzymes as well as the mitochondrial DNA and ribosomes. Enzymes in the matrix catalyze some of the steps of cellular respiration. Other proteins that function in respiration, including the enzyme that makes ATP, are built into the inner membrane. As highly folded surfaces, the cristae give the inner mitochondrial membrane a large surface area, thus enhancing the productivity of cellular respiration. This is another example of structure fitting function.

Disease-causing mutations that have been identified in some mitochondrial genes also reveal information about the function of mitochondrial proteins and the mitochondrion. Defects in one or more of the proteins described above, that participate in cellular respiration, decrease the amount of ATP the cell can make. An example of an inherited mitochondrial disorder is mitochondrial myopathy (Chapter 15), which causes weakness, intolerance of exercise, and muscle deterioration.

Mitochondria are generally in the range of 1–10 µm long. Time-lapse films of living cells reveal mitochondria moving around, changing their shapes, and fusing or dividing in two, unlike the static structures seen in electron micrographs of dead cells. These observations helped cell biologists understand that mitochondria in a living cell form a branched tubular network, seen in a whole cell in Figure 6.17, that is in a dynamic state of flux.

Chloroplasts: Capture of Light Energy

Chloroplasts contain the green pigment chlorophyll, along with enzymes and other molecules that function in the photosynthetic production of sugar. These lens-shaped organelles, about 3–6 µm in length, are found in leaves and other green organs of plants and in algae (Figure 6.18; see also Figure 6.26c).

The contents of a chloroplast are partitioned from the cytosol by an envelope consisting of two membranes separated by a very narrow intermembrane space. Inside the chloroplast is another membranous system in the form of flattened, interconnected sacs called **thylakoids**. In some regions thylakoids are stacked like poker chips; each stack is called a **granum** (plural, *grana*). The fluid outside the thylakoids is the **stroma**, which contains the chloroplast DNA and ribosomes as well as many enzymes. The membranes of the chloroplast divide the chloroplast space into three compartments: the intermembrane space, the stroma, and the thylakoid space. This compartmental organization enables the chloroplast to convert light energy to chemical energy during photosynthesis (You will learn more about photosynthesis in Chapter 10.)

Note that chloroplasts also possess nonphotosynthetic functions. Some examples of these functions include nitrogen assimilation and the synthesis of fatty acids, hormones, amino acids, heme, and vitamins. Although photosynthesis is the dominant and most recognizable function of the plastid, there are many other essential cellular functions of this organelle. This explains why plastids are retained in nonphotosynthetic organisms, such as in parasitic plants (Chapter 37) and members of the apicoplastida (Chapter 28).

▼ Figure 6.18 **The chloroplast, site of photosynthesis. (a)** Many plants have disk-shaped choloroplasts, as shown here. A typical chloroplast has three compartments: the intermembrane space, the stroma, and the thylakoid space. Free ribosomes are present in the stroma, as are copies of chloroplast DNA molecules. **(b)** This fluorescence micrograph shows a cell of the green alga *Spirogyra crassa*, which is named for its spiral chloroplasts. Under natural light the chloroplasts appear green, but under ultraviolet light they naturally fluoresce red, as shown here.

Chloroplast

Ribosomes

Stroma

Inner and outer membranes

Granum

DNA

Thylakoid

Intermembrane space

(a) Diagram and TEM of chloroplast

E. H. Newcomb/W. P. Wergin/Biological Photo Service

1 µm

50 µm

Chloroplasts (red)

Franz Grolig

(b) Chloroplasts in an algal cell

As with mitochondria, the static and rigid appearance of chloroplasts in micrographs or schematic diagrams is not true to their dynamic behaviour in the living cell. Their shape is changeable, and they grow and occasionally pinch in two, reproducing themselves. They are mobile and, with mitochondria and other organelles, move around the cell along tracks of the cytoskeleton, a structural network we will consider later in this chapter.

The chloroplast is a specialized member of a family of closely related plant organelles called **plastids**. One type of plastid, the *amyloplast*, is a colourless organelle that stores starch (amylose), particularly in roots and tubers. Another is the *chromoplast*, which has pigments that give fruits and flowers their orange and yellow hues.

Peroxisomes: Oxidation

The **peroxisome** is a specialized metabolic compartment bounded by a single membrane (**Figure 6.19**). Peroxisomes contain enzymes that remove hydrogen atoms from various substrates and transfer them to oxygen (O_2), producing hydrogen peroxide (H_2O_2) as a by-product (from which the organelle derives its name). These reactions have many different functions. Some peroxisomes use oxygen to break fatty acids down into smaller molecules that are transported to mitochondria and used as fuel for cellular respiration. Peroxisomes in the liver detoxify alcohol and other harmful compounds by transferring hydrogen from the poisons to oxygen. The H_2O_2 formed by peroxisomes is itself toxic, but the organelle also contains an enzyme that converts H_2O_2 to water. This is an excellent example of how the cell's compartmental structure is crucial to its functions: The enzymes that produce H_2O_2 and those that dispose of this toxic compound are sequestered away from other cellular components that could be damaged.

Specialized peroxisomes called *glyoxysomes* are found in the fat-storing tissues of plant seeds. These organelles contain enzymes that initiate the conversion of fatty acids to sugar, which the emerging seedling uses as a source of energy and carbon until it can produce its own sugar by photosynthesis.

How peroxisomes are related to other organelles is still an open question. They grow larger by incorporating proteins made in the cytosol and ER, as well as lipids made in the ER and within the peroxisome itself. Peroxisomes may increase in number by splitting in two when they reach a certain size, sparking the suggestion of an endosymbiotic evolutionary origin, but others argue against this scenario. Discussion of this issue is ongoing.

CONCEPT CHECK 6.5

1. Describe two common characteristics of chloroplasts and mitochondria. Consider both function and membrane structure.
2. Do plant cells have mitochondria? Explain.
3. **WHAT IF?** A classmate proposes that mitochondria and chloroplasts should be classified in the endomembrane system. Argue against the proposal.

For suggested answers, see Appendix A.

CONCEPT **6.6**

The cytoskeleton is a network of fibres that organizes structures and activities in the cell

In the early days of electron microscopy, biologists thought that the organelles of a eukaryotic cell floated freely in the cytosol. But improvements in both light microscopy and electron microscopy have revealed the **cytoskeleton**, a network of fibres extending throughout the cytoplasm (**Figure 6.20**).

▲ Figure 6.20 **The cytoskeleton.** As shown in this fluorescence micrograph, the cytoskeleton extends throughout the cell. The cytoskeletal elements have been tagged with different fluorescent molecules: green for microtubules and reddish orange for microfilaments. A third component of the cytoskeleton, intermediate filaments, is not evident here. (The blue colour tags the DNA in the nucleus.)

Albert Tousson

▶ Figure 6.19 **A peroxisome.** Peroxisomes are roughly spherical and often have a granular or crystalline core that is thought to be a dense collection of enzyme molecules. Chloroplasts and mitochondria cooperate with peroxisomes in certain metabolic functions (TEM).

Peroxisome

Mitochondrion

Chloroplasts

1 μm

Eldon H. Newcomb

Bacterial cells also have fibres that form a type of cytoskeleton, constructed of proteins similar to eukaryotic ones, but here we will concentrate on eukaryotes. The eukaryotic cytoskeleton, which plays a major role in organizing the structures and activities of the cell, is composed of three types of molecular structures: microtubules, microfilaments, and intermediate filaments.

Roles of the Cytoskeleton: Support and Motility

The most obvious function of the cytoskeleton is to give mechanical support to the cell and maintain its shape. This is especially important for animal cells, which lack walls. The remarkable strength and resilience of the cytoskeleton as a whole are based on its architecture. Like a dome tent, the cytoskeleton is stabilized by a balance between opposing forces exerted by its elements. And just as the skeleton of an animal helps fix the positions of other body parts, the cytoskeleton provides anchorage for many organelles and even cytosolic enzyme molecules. The cytoskeleton is more dynamic than an animal skeleton, however. It can be quickly dismantled in one part of the cell and reassembled in a new location, changing the shape of the cell.

(a) Motor proteins that attach to receptors on vesicles can "walk" the vesicles along microtubules or, in some cases, along microfilaments.

Bruce J. Schnapp

(b) In this SEM of a squid giant axon (a nerve cell extension), two vesicles containing neurotransmitters move toward the axon's tip.

▲ Figure 6.21 **Motor proteins and the cytoskeleton.**

Table 6.1 The Structure and Function of the Cytoskeleton			
Property	**Microtubules (Tubulin Polymers)**	**Microfilaments (Actin Filaments)**	**Intermediate Filaments**
Structure	Hollow tubes	Two intertwined strands of actin	Fibrous proteins coiled into cables
Diameter	25 nm with 15-nm lumen	7 nm	8–12 nm
Protein subunits	Tubulin, a dimer consisting of α-tubulin and β-tubulin	Actin	One of several different proteins (such as keratins)
Main functions	Maintenance of cell shape (compression-resisting "girders"); cell motility (as in cilia or flagella); chromosome movements in cell division; organelle movements	Maintenance of cell shape (tension-bearing elements); changes in cell shape; muscle contraction; cytoplasmic streaming in plant cells; cell motility (as in amoeboid movement); division of animal cells	Maintenance of cell shape (tension-bearing elements); anchorage of nucleus and certain other organelles; formation of nuclear lamina
Fluorescence micrographs of fibroblasts. Fibroblasts are a favourite cell type for cell biology studies. In each, the structure of interest has been tagged with fluorescent molecules. The DNA in the nucleus has also been tagged in the first micrograph (blue) and third micrograph (orange).	10 μm — Dr. Mary Osborn — Column of tubulin dimers — 25 nm — α β — Tubulin dimer	10 μm — Frank Solomon — Actin subunit — 7 nm	5 μm — Mark Ladinsky — Keratin proteins — Fibrous subunit (keratins coiled together) — 8–12 nm

Source: Adaptation of table 15.1 from *Becker's World of the Cell*, 8th Edition, by Jeff Hardin et al. Copyright © 1996 by Pearson Education, Inc. Reprinted and electronically reproduced by permission of Pearson Education, Inc. Upper Saddle River, New Jersey.

Some types of cell motility (movement) also involve the cytoskeleton. The term *cell motility* includes both changes in cell location and movements of cell parts. Cell motility generally requires interaction of the cytoskeleton with **motor proteins**. There are many such examples: Cytoskeletal elements and motor proteins work together with plasma membrane molecules to allow whole cells to move along fibres outside the cell. Inside the cell, vesicles and other organelles often use motor protein "feet" to "walk" to their destinations along a track provided by the cytoskeleton. For example, this is how vesicles containing neurotransmitter molecules migrate to the tips of axons, the long extensions of nerve cells that release these molecules as chemical signals to adjacent nerve cells (Figure 6.21). The cytoskeleton also manipulates the plasma membrane, bending it inward to form food vacuoles or other phagocytic vesicles.

Components of the Cytoskeleton

Now let's look more closely at the three main types of fibres that make up the cytoskeleton: *Microtubules* are the thickest of the three types; *microfilaments* (also called actin filaments) are the thinnest; and *intermediate filaments* are fibres with diameters in a middle range (Table 6.1).

Microtubules

All eukaryotic cells have **microtubules**, hollow rods constructed from a globular protein called tubulin. Each tubulin protein is a *dimer*, a molecule made up of two subunits. A tubulin dimer consists of two slightly different polypeptides, α-tubulin and β-tubulin. Microtubules grow in length by adding tubulin dimers; they can also be disassembled and their tubulin used to build microtubules elsewhere in the cell. Because of the orientation of tubulin dimers, the two ends of a microtubule are slightly different. One end can accumulate or release tubulin dimers at a much higher rate than the other, thus growing and shrinking significantly during cellular activities. (This is called the "plus end," not because it can only add tubulin proteins but because it's the end where both "on" and "off" rates are much higher.)

Microtubules shape and support the cell and also serve as tracks along which organelles equipped with motor proteins can move. In addition to the example in Figure 6.21, microtubules guide vesicles from the ER to the Golgi apparatus and from the Golgi to the plasma membrane. Microtubules are also involved in the separation of chromosomes during cell division, which will be discussed in Chapter 12.

Centrosomes and Centrioles In animal cells, microtubules grow out from a **centrosome**, a region that is often located near the nucleus. These microtubules function as compression-resisting girders of the cytoskeleton. Within the

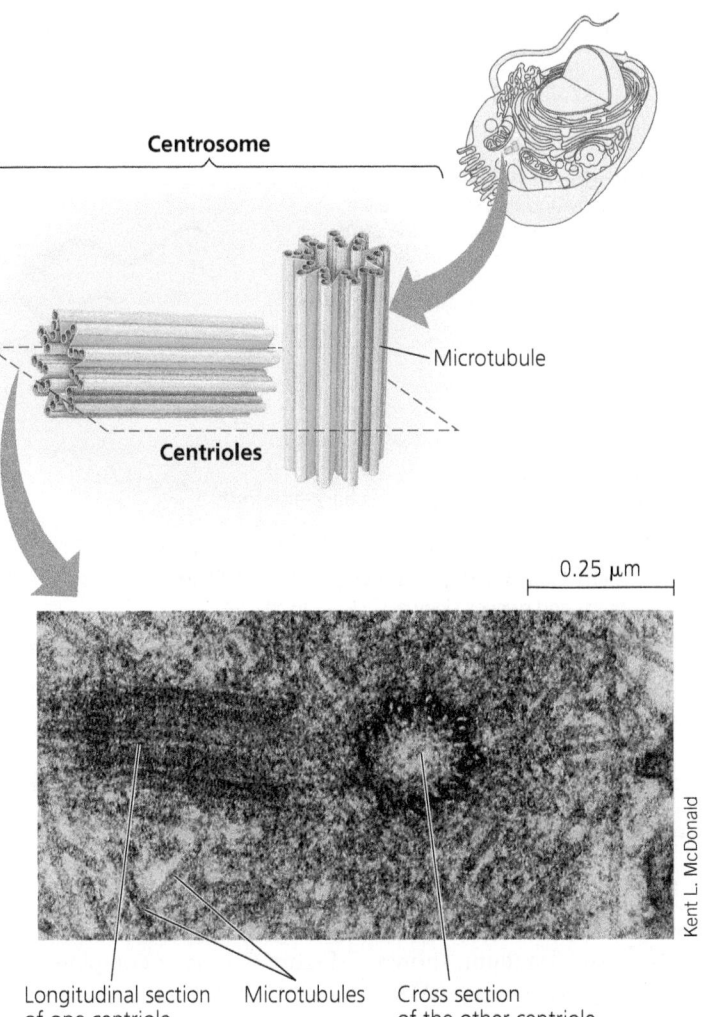

▲ Figure 6.22 **Centrosome containing a pair of centrioles.** Most animal cells have a centrosome, a region near the nucleus where the cell's microtubules are initiated. Within the centrosome is a pair of centrioles, each about 250 nm (0.25 µm) in diameter. The two centrioles are at right angles to each other, and each is made up of nine sets of three microtubules. The blue portions of the drawing represent nontubulin proteins that connect the microtubule triplets.

Source: Adaptation of figure 3.25 from , 8th Edition, by Elaine N. Marieb and Katja N. Hoehn, 2010. Copyright © 2010 by Pearson Education, Inc. Reprinted and electronically reproduced by permission of Pearson Education, Inc. Upper Saddle River, New Jersey.

? *How many microtubules are in a centrosome? In the drawing, circle and label one microtubule and describe its structure. Circle and label a triplet.*

centrosome is a pair of **centrioles**, each composed of nine sets of triplet microtubules arranged in a ring (Figure 6.22). Although centrosomes with centrioles may help organize microtubule assembly in animal cells, many other eukaryotic cells lack centrosomes with centrioles and instead organize microtubules by other means.

Cilia and Flagella In eukaryotes, a specialized arrangement of microtubules is responsible for the beating of **flagella** (singular, *flagellum*) and **cilia** (singular, *cilium*), microtubule-containing extensions that project from some cells. (The

(a) Motion of flagella. A flagellum usually undulates, its snakelike motion driving a cell in the same direction as the axis of the flagellum. Propulsion of a human sperm cell is an example of flagellate locomotion (LM).

Direction of swimming

5 μm

Biophoto Associates/Science Source

(b) Motion of cilia. Cilia have a back-and-forth motion. The rapid power stroke moves the cell in a direction perpendicular to the axis of the cilium. Then, during the slower recovery stroke, the cilium bends and sweeps sideways, closer to the cell surface. A dense carpet of cilia, beating at a rate of about 40 to 60 strokes a second, covers this *Colpidium*, a freshwater protist (colourized SEM).

Direction of organism's movement

Power stroke   Recovery stroke

15 μm

Science Source

▲ Figure 6.23 **A comparison of the beating of flagella and motile cilia.**

bacterial flagellum, shown in Figure 6.5, has a completely different structure.) Many unicellular eukaryotes are propelled through water by cilia or flagella that act as locomotor appendages, and the sperm of animals, algae, and some plants have flagella. When cilia or flagella extend from cells that are held in place as part of a tissue layer, they can move fluid over the surface of the tissue. For example, the ciliated lining of the trachea (windpipe) sweeps mucus containing trapped debris out of the lungs (see the EMs in Figure 6.3). In a woman's reproductive tract, the cilia lining the oviducts help move an egg toward the uterus.

Motile cilia usually occur in large numbers on the cell surface. Flagella are usually limited to just one or a few per cell, and they are longer than cilia. Flagella and cilia differ in their beating patterns (Figure 6.23). A flagellum has an undulating motion like the tail of a fish. In contrast, cilia work more like oars, with alternating power and recovery strokes, much like the oars of a racing crew boat.

A cilium may also act as a signal-receiving "antenna" for the cell. Cilia that have this function are generally nonmotile, and there is only one per cell. (In fact, in vertebrate animals, it appears that almost all cells have such a cilium, which is called a *primary cilium*.) Membrane proteins on this kind of cilium transmit molecular signals from the cell's environment to its interior, triggering signalling pathways that may lead to changes in the cell's activities.

Cilium-based signalling appears to be crucial to brain function and to embryonic development.

Though different in length, number per cell, and beating pattern, motile cilia or flagella share a common structure. Each motile cilium and flagellum has a group of microtubules sheathed in an extension of the plasma membrane (Figure 6.24). Nine doublets of microtubules are arranged in a ring; in the centre of the ring are two single microtubules. This arrangement, referred to as the "9 + 2" pattern, is found in nearly all eukaryotic flagella and motile cilia. (Nonmotile primary cilia have a "9 + 0" pattern, lacking the central pair of microtubules.) The microtubule assembly of a cilium or flagellum is anchored in the cell by a **basal body**, which is structurally very similar to a centriole, with microtubule triplets in a "9 + 0" pattern. In fact, in many animals (including humans), the basal body of the fertilizing sperm's flagellum enters the egg and becomes a centriole.

How does the microtubule assembly produce the bending movements of flagella and motile cilia? Bending involves large motor proteins called **dyneins** (red in the diagram in Figure 6.24) that are attached along each outer microtubule doublet. A typical dynein protein has two "feet" that "walk" along the microtubule of the adjacent doublet, using ATP for energy. One foot maintains contact while the other releases and reattaches one step farther along the microtubule (see Figure 6.21). The outer doublets and two

0.1 μm

Outer microtubule doublet

Plasma membrane

Motor proteins (dyneins)

Central microtubule

Radial spoke

Cross-linking proteins between outer doublets

(b) A cross section through a motile cilium shows the "9 + 2" arrangement of microtubules (TEM). The outer microtubule doublets are held together with the two central microtubules by flexible cross-linking proteins (blue in art), including the radial spokes. The doublets also have attached motor proteins called dyneins (red in art).

Microtubules

Plasma membrane

Basal body

Omikron/Science Source

0.5 μm

(a) A longitudinal section of a motile cilium shows microtubules running the length of the membrane-sheathed structure (TEM).

(c) Basal body: The nine outer doublets of a cilium or flagellum extend into the basal body, where each doublet joins another microtubule to form a ring of nine triplets. Each triplet is connected to the next by nontubulin proteins (thinner blue lines in diagram). This is a "9 + 0" arrangement: The two central microtubules are not present because they terminate above the basal body (TEM).

0.1 μm

Triplet

Cross section of basal body

From: Functional protofilament numbering of ciliary, flagellar, and centriolar microtubules. R. W. Linck, R. E. Stephens. *Cell Motil. Cytoskeleton.* 2007 Jul; 64(7):489–95, Fig. 1B Reproduced by permission of Rockefeller University Press

▲ **Figure 6.24   Structure of a flagellum or motile cilium.**

Source: Adaptation of figures 3.2 and 3.26 from *Human Anatomy and Physiology,* 8th Edition, by Elaine N. Marieb and Katja N. Hoehn, 2010. Copyright © 2010 by Pearson Education, Inc. Reprinted and electronically reproduced by permission of Pearson Education, Inc. Upper Saddle River, New Jersey.

DRAW IT   *In (a) and (b), circle the central pair of microtubules. In (a), show where they terminate, and explain why they aren't seen in the cross section of the basal body in (c).*

central microtubules are held together by flexible cross-linking proteins (blue in the diagram in Figure 6.24), and the walking movement is coordinated so that it happens on one side of the circle at a time. If the doublets were not held in place, the walking action would make them slide past each other. Instead, the movements of the dynein feet cause the microtubules—and the organelle as a whole—to bend.

Microfilaments (Actin Filaments)

Microfilaments are thin solid rods. They are also called actin filaments because they are built from molecules of **actin**, a globular protein. A microfilament is a twisted double chain of actin subunits (see Table 6.1). Besides occurring as linear filaments, microfilaments can form structural networks when certain proteins bind along the side of such a filament and allow a new filament to extend as a branch. Like microtubules, microfilaments seem to be present in all eukaryotic cells.

In contrast to the compression-resisting role of microtubules, the structural role of microfilaments in the cytoskeleton is to bear tension (pulling forces). A three-dimensional network formed by microfilaments just inside the plasma membrane (*cortical microfilaments*) helps support the cell's shape (see Figure 6.8). This network gives the outer cytoplasmic layer of a cell, called the **cortex**, the semisolid consistency of a gel, in contrast with the more fluid state of the interior cytoplasm. In some kinds of animal cells, such as nutrient-absorbing intestinal cells, bundles of microfilaments make up the core of microvilli, delicate projections that increase the cell's surface area (**Figure 6.25**).

Microfilaments are well known for their role in cell motility; some examples are shown in **Figure 6.26**. Thousands of actin filaments and thicker filaments made of a protein called **myosin** interact to cause contraction of muscle cells (see Figure 6.26a; muscle contraction is described in detail in

Microvillus

Plasma membrane

Microfilaments (actin filaments)

Intermediate filaments

From: Cross-linker system between neurofilaments, microtubules, and membranous organelles in frog axons revealed by the quick-freeze, deep-etching method. Hirokawa Nobutaka. *Journal of Cell Biology* 94(1): 129–142, 1982. Reproduced by permission of Rockefeller University Press.

0.25 μm

▲ **Figure 6.25 A structural role of microfilaments.** The surface area of this nutrient-absorbing intestinal cell is increased by its many microvilli (singular, *microvillus*), cellular extensions reinforced by bundles of microfilaments. These actin filaments are anchored to a network of intermediate filaments (TEM).

Chapter 50). In the unicellular eukaryote *Amoeba* and some of our white blood cells, localized contractions brought about by actin and myosin are involved in the amoeboid (crawling) movement of the cells (see Figure 6.26b). The cell crawls along a surface by extending cellular extensions called **pseudopodia** (from the Greek *pseudes*, false, and *pod*, foot) and moving toward them. In plant cells, both actin-myosin interactions contribute to **cytoplasmic streaming**, a circular flow of cytoplasm within cells (see Figure 6.26c). This movement, which is especially common in large plant cells, speeds the distribution of materials within the cell.

Intermediate Filaments

Intermediate filaments are named for their diameter, which, at 8–12 nm, is larger than the diameter of microfilaments but smaller than that of microtubules (see Table 6.1). Unlike microtubules and microfilaments, which are found in all eukaryotic cells, intermediate filaments are only found in the cells of some animals, including vertebrates. Specialized for bearing tension (like microfilaments), intermediate filaments are a diverse class of cytoskeletal elements. Each type is constructed from a particular molecular subunit belonging to a family of proteins whose members include the keratins. Microtubules and microfilaments, in contrast, are consistent in diameter and composition in all eukaryotic cells.

Intermediate filaments are more permanent fixtures of cells than are microfilaments and microtubules, which are often

Muscle cell

0.5 μm

Clara Franzini-Armstrong/ University of Pennsylvania

Actin filament

Myosin filament

Myosin head

(a) Myosin motors in muscle cell contraction. The "walking" of myosin projections (the so-called heads) drives the parallel myosin and actin filaments past each other so that the actin filaments approach each other in the middle (red arrows). This shortens the muscle cell. Muscle contraction involves the shortening of many muscle cells at the same time (TEM).

Cortex (outer cytoplasm): gel with actin network

Inner cytoplasm (more fluid)

100 μm

Extending pseudopodium

M I Walker/Science Source

(b) Amoeboid movement. Interaction of actin filaments with myosin causes contraction of the cell, pulling the cell's trailing end (at left) forward (to the right) (LM).

Chloroplast

30 μm

Michael Clayton/University of Wisconsin

(c) Cytoplasmic streaming in plant cells. A layer of cytoplasm cycles around the cell, moving over a carpet of parallel actin filaments. Myosin motors attached to organelles in the fluid cytosol may drive the streaming by interacting with the actin (LM).

▲ **Figure 6.26 Microfilaments and motility.** In these three examples, interactions between actin filaments and motor proteins bring about cell movement.

disassembled and reassembled in various parts of a cell. Even after cells die, intermediate filament networks often persist; for example, the outer layer of our skin consists of dead skin cells full of keratin filaments. Chemical treatments that remove microfilaments and microtubules from the cytoplasm of living cells leave a web of intermediate filaments that retains its original shape. Such experiments suggest that intermediate filaments are especially sturdy and that they play an important role in reinforcing the shape of a cell and fixing the position of certain organelles. For instance, the nucleus typically sits within a cage made of intermediate filaments, fixed in location by branches of the filaments that extend into the cytoplasm. Other intermediate filaments make up the nuclear lamina, which lines the interior of the nuclear envelope (see Figure 6.9). By supporting a cell's shape, intermediate filaments help the cell carry out its specific function. For example, the network of intermediate filaments shown in Figure 6.25 help anchor the microfilaments supporting the intestinal microvilli. Thus, the various kinds of intermediate filaments may function together as the permanent framework of the entire cell.

CONCEPT CHECK 6.6

1. Describe shared features of microtubule-based motion of flagella and microfilament-based muscle contraction.

2. **WHAT IF?** Males afflicted with Kartagener's syndrome are sterile because of immotile sperm, and they tend to suffer from lung infections. This disorder has a genetic basis. Suggest what the underlying defect might be.

For suggested answers, see Appendix A.

CONCEPT 6.7

Extracellular components and connections between cells help coordinate cellular activities

Having crisscrossed the cell to explore its interior components, we complete our tour of the cell by returning to the surface of this microscopic world, where there are additional structures with important functions. The plasma membrane is usually regarded as the boundary of the living cell, but most cells synthesize and secrete materials that are then extracellular, or external to the plasma membrane. Although these materials and the structures they form are outside the cell, their study is important to cell biology because they are involved in a great many important cellular functions.

Cell Walls of Plants

The **cell wall** is an extracellular structure of plant cells that distinguishes them from animal cells (see Figure 6.8). The wall protects the plant cell, maintains its shape, and prevents excessive uptake of water. On the level of the whole plant, the strong walls of specialized cells hold the plant up against the force of gravity. Prokaryotes, fungi, and some unicellular eukaryotes also have cell walls, as you saw in Figures 6.5 and 6.8, but we will postpone discussion of them until Unit Five.

Plant cell walls are much thicker than the plasma membrane, ranging from 0.1 μm to several micrometres. The exact chemical composition of the wall varies from species to species and even from one cell type to another in the same plant, but the basic design of the wall is consistent. Microfibrils made of the polysaccharide cellulose (see Figure 5.6) are synthesized by an enzyme called cellulose synthase and secreted to the extracellular space, where they become embedded in a matrix of other polysaccharides and proteins. This combination of materials, strong fibres in a "ground substance" (matrix), is the same basic architectural design found in steel-reinforced concrete and in fibreglass.

A young plant cell first secretes a relatively thin and flexible wall called the **primary cell wall** (Figure 6.27).

▲ **Figure 6.27 Plant cell walls.** The drawing shows several cells, each with a large vacuole, a nucleus, and several chloroplasts and mitochondria. The transmission electron micrograph shows the cell walls where two cells come together. The multilayered partition between plant cells consists of adjoining walls individually secreted by the cells.

Between primary walls of adjacent cells is the **middle lamella**, a thin layer rich in sticky polysaccharides called pectins. The middle lamella glues adjacent cells together. (Pectin is used in cooking as a thickening agent in jams and jellies.) When the cell matures and stops growing, it strengthens its wall. Some plant cells do this simply by secreting hardening substances into the primary wall. Other cells add a **secondary cell wall** between the plasma membrane and the primary wall. The secondary wall, often deposited in several laminated layers, has a strong and durable matrix that affords the cell protection and support. Wood, for example, consists mainly of secondary walls. Plant cell walls are usually perforated by channels between adjacent cells called plasmodesmata (see Figure 6.27), which will be discussed shortly.

The Extracellular Matrix (ECM) of Animal Cells

Although animal cells lack walls akin to those of plant cells, they do have an elaborate **extracellular matrix (ECM)**. The main ingredients of the ECM are glycoproteins and other carbohydrate-containing molecules secreted by the cells. (Recall that glycoproteins are proteins with covalently bonded carbohydrates, usually short chains of sugars.) The most abundant glycoprotein in the ECM of most animal cells is **collagen**, which forms strong fibres outside the cells

(see Figure 5.18). In fact, collagen accounts for about 40% of the total protein in the human body. The collagen fibres are embedded in a network woven out of **proteoglycans** secreted by cells (**Figure 6.28**). A proteoglycan molecule consists of a small core protein with many carbohydrate chains covalently attached, so that it may be up to 95% carbohydrate. Large proteoglycan complexes can form when hundreds of proteoglycan molecules become noncovalently attached to a single long polysaccharide molecule, as shown in Figure 6.28. Some cells are attached to the ECM by ECM glycoproteins such as **fibronectin**. Fibronectin and other ECM proteins bind to cell-surface receptor proteins called **integrins** that are built into the plasma membrane. Integrins span the membrane and bind on their cytoplasmic side to associated proteins attached to microfilaments of the cytoskeleton. The name *integrin* is based on the word *integrate*: Integrins are in a position to transmit signals between the ECM and the cytoskeleton and thus to integrate changes occurring outside and inside the cell.

Current research on fibronectin, other ECM molecules, and integrins is revealing the influential role of the ECM in the lives of cells. By communicating with a cell through integrins, the ECM can regulate a cell's behaviour. For example, some cells in a developing embryo migrate along specific pathways by matching the orientation of their microfilaments to the "grain" of fibres in the extracellular

Collagen fibres are embedded in a web of proteoglycan complexes.

EXTRACELLULAR FLUID

A **proteoglycan complex** consists of hundreds of proteoglycan molecules attached noncovalently to a single long polysaccharide molecule.

Polysaccharide molecule

Carbohydrates

Core protein

Fibronectin attaches the ECM to integrins embedded in the plasma membrane.

Plasma membrane

Microfilaments

CYTOPLASM

Integrins, membrane proteins with two subunits, bind to the ECM on the outside and to associated proteins attached to microfilaments on the inside. This linkage can transmit signals between the cell's external environment and its interior and can result in changes in cell behaviour.

Proteoglycan molecule

Proteoglycan complex

▲ Figure 6.28 **Extracellular matrix (ECM) of an animal cell.** The molecular composition and structure of the ECM vary from one cell type to another. In this example, three different types of ECM molecules are present: proteoglycans, collagen, and fibronectin.

matrix. Researchers have also learned that the extracellular matrix around a cell can influence the activity of genes in the nucleus. Information about the ECM probably reaches the nucleus by a combination of mechanical and chemical signalling pathways. Mechanical signalling involves fibronectin, integrins, and microfilaments of the cytoskeleton. Changes in the cytoskeleton may in turn trigger chemical signalling pathways inside the cell, leading to changes in the set of proteins being made by the cell and therefore changes in the cell's function. In this way, the extracellular matrix of a particular tissue may help coordinate the behaviour of all the cells of that tissue. Direct connections between cells also function in this coordination, as we discuss next.

Cell Junctions

Cells in an animal or plant are organized into tissues, organs, and organ systems. Neighbouring cells often adhere, interact, and communicate via sites of direct physical contact.

Plasmodesmata in Plant Cells

It might seem that the nonliving cell walls of plants would isolate plant cells from one another. But in fact, as shown in **Figure 6.29**, cell walls are perforated with **plasmodesmata** (singular, *plasmodesma*; from the Greek *desma*, to bond), channels that connect cells. Cytosol passing through the plasmodesmata joins the internal chemical environments of adjacent cells. These connections unify most of the plant into one living continuum. The plasma membranes of adjacent cells line the channel of each plasmodesma and thus are continuous. Water and small solutes can pass freely from cell to cell, and recent experiments have shown that, in some circumstances, certain proteins and RNA molecules can do this as well (see Concept 36.5). The macromolecules transported to neighbouring cells appear to reach the plasmodesmata by moving along fibres of the cytoskeleton.

Wm. P. Wergin, courtesy of Eldon H. Newcomb

Cell walls

Interior of cell

Interior of cell

0.5 μm

Plasmodesmata   Plasma membranes

▲ **Figure 6.29 Plasmodesmata between plant cells.** Cytoplasm of one plant cell is continuous with the cytoplasm of its neighbours via plasmodesmata, cytoplasmic channels through the cell walls (TEM).

Tight Junctions, Desmosomes, and Gap Junctions in Animal Cells

In animals, there are three main types of cell junctions: *tight junctions*, *desmosomes*, and *gap junctions*. (Gap junctions are most like the plasmodesmata of plants, although gap junction pores are not lined with membrane.) All three types of cell junctions are especially common in epithelial tissue, which lines the external and internal surfaces of the body. **Figure 6.30** uses epithelial cells of the intestinal lining to illustrate these junctions.

CONCEPT CHECK 6.7

1. In what way are the cells of plants and animals structurally different from single-celled eukaryotes?
2. **WHAT IF?** If the plant cell wall or the animal extracellular matrix were impermeable, what effect would this have on cell function?
3. **MAKE CONNECTIONS** The polypeptide chain that makes up a tight junction weaves back and forth through the membrane four times, with two extracellular loops, and one loop plus short C-terminal and N-terminal tails in the cytoplasm. Looking at Figure 5.14, what would you predict about the amino acid sequence of the tight-junction protein?

For suggested answers, see Appendix A.

The Cell: A Living Unit Greater Than the Sum of Its Parts

From our panoramic view of the cell's compartmental organization to our close-up inspection of each organelle's architecture, this tour of the cell has provided many opportunities to correlate structure with function. (This would be a good time to review cell structure by returning to Figure 6.8.) But even as we dissect the cell, remember that none of its components works alone. As an example of cellular integration, consider the microscopic scene in **Figure 6.31**. The large cell is a macrophage (see Figure 6.13a). It helps defend the mammalian body against infections by ingesting bacteria (the smaller cells) into phagocytic vesicles. The macrophage crawls along a surface and reaches out to the bacteria with thin pseudopodia (specifically, filopodia). Actin filaments interact with other elements of the cytoskeleton in these movements. After the macrophage engulfs the bacteria, they are destroyed by lysosomes. The elaborate endomembrane system produces the lysosomes. The digestive enzymes of the lysosomes and the proteins of the cytoskeleton are all made by ribosomes. And the synthesis of these proteins is programmed by genetic messages dispatched from the DNA in the nucleus. All these processes require energy, which mitochondria supply in the form of ATP. Cellular functions arise from cellular order: The cell is a living unit greater than the sum of its parts.

Exploring Cell Junctions in Animal Tissues

From: Fine structure of desmosomes., hemidesmosomes, and an adepidermal globular layer in developing newt epidermis. DE Kelly. *Journal of Cell Biology* 1966 Jan; 28(1):51–72. Fig. 7. Reproduced by permission of Rockefeller University Press

Tight junctions prevent fluid from moving across a layer of cells.

Tight junction

TEM
0.5 μm

Tight junction

Intermediate filaments

Desmosome

Gap junction

Ions or small molecules

Plasma membranes of adjacent cells

Space between cells

Extracellular matrix

Tight Junctions

At **tight junctions**, the plasma membranes of neighbouring cells are very tightly pressed against each other, bound together by specific proteins (purple). Forming continuous seals around the cells, tight junctions establish a barrier that prevents leakage of extracellular fluid across a layer of epithelial cells (see red dashed arrow). For example, tight junctions between skin cells make us watertight.

Reproduced with permission from *Freeze-Etch Histology*, by L. Orci and A. Perrelet, Springer-Verlag, Heidelberg, 1975.

Desmosomes

Desmosomes (also called *anchoring junctions*) function like rivets, fastening cells together into strong sheets. Intermediate filaments made of sturdy keratin proteins anchor desmosomes in the cytoplasm. Desmosomes attach muscle cells to each other in a muscle. Some "muscle tears" involve the rupture of desmosomes.

TEM
1 μm

Gap Junctions

Gap junctions (also called *communicating junctions*) provide cytoplasmic channels from one cell to an adjacent cell and in this way are similar in their function to the plasmodesmata in plants. Gap junctions consist of membrane proteins that surround a pore through which ions, sugars, amino acids, and other small molecules may pass. Gap junctions are necessary for communication between cells in many types of tissues, such as heart muscle, and in animal embryos.

TEM
0.1 μm

From: Low resistance junctions in crayfish. Structural changes with functional uncoupling. C. Peracchia and A. F. Dulhunty, The Journal of Cell Biology. 1976 Aug; 70(2 pt 1):419–39. Fig. 6. Reproduced by permission of Rockefeller University Press.

◄ **Figure 6.31 The emergence of cellular functions.** The ability of this macrophage (brown) to recognize, apprehend, and destroy bacteria (yellow) is a coordinated activity of the whole cell. Its cytoskeleton, lysosomes, and plasma membrane are among the components that function in phagocytosis (colourized SEM).

Lennart Nilsson/Scanpix Sweden AB

5 μm

6 Chapter Review

Go to **MasteringBiology**® for Assignments, the eText, and the Study Area with Animations, Activities, Vocab Self-Quiz, and Practice Tests.

SUMMARY OF KEY CONCEPTS

CONCEPT 6.1

Biologists use microscopes and the tools of biochemistry to study cells (pp. 105–108)

- Improvements in microscopy that affect the parameters of magnification, resolution, and contrast have catalyzed progress in the study of cell structure. **Light microscopy** (LM) and **electron microscopy** (EM), as well as other types, remain important tools.
- Cell biologists can obtain pellets enriched in particular cellular components by centrifuging disrupted cells at sequential speeds, a process known as **cell fractionation**. Larger cellular components are in the pellet after lower-speed centrifugation, and smaller components are in the pellet after higher-speed centrifugation.

? *How do microscopy and biochemistry complement each other to reveal cell structure and function?*

CONCEPT 6.2

Eukaryotic cells have internal membranes that compartmentalize their functions (pp. 108–111)

- All living cells are bounded by a **plasma membrane**.
- **Prokaryotic cells** lack nuclei and other membrane-enclosed **organelles**, while **eukaryotic cells** have internal membranes that compartmentalize cellular functions.
- The surface-to-volume ratio is an important parameter affecting cell size and shape.
- Plant and animal cells have most of the same organelles: a nucleus, endoplasmic reticulum, Golgi apparatus, and mitochondria. Chloroplasts are present only in cells of photosynthetic eukaryotes.

? *Explain how the compartmental organization of a eukaryotic cell contributes to its biochemical functioning.*

	Cell Component	Structure	Function
CONCEPT 6.3 **The eukaryotic cell's genetic instructions are housed in the nucleus and carried out by the ribosomes (pp. 111–115)** **?** *Describe the relationship between the nucleus and ribosomes.*	Nucleus (ER)	Surrounded by nuclear envelope (double membrane) perforated by nuclear pores; nuclear envelope continuous with endoplasmic reticulum (ER)	Houses chromosomes, which are made of chromatin (DNA and proteins); contains nucleoli, where ribosomal subunits are made; pores regulate entry and exit of materials
	Ribosome	Two subunits made of ribosomal RNA and proteins; can be free in cytosol or bound to ER	Protein synthesis
CONCEPT 6.4 **The endomembrane system regulates protein traffic and performs metabolic functions in the cell (pp. 115–120)** **?** *Describe the key role played by transport vesicles in the endomembrane system.*	Endoplasmic reticulum (Nuclear envelope)	Extensive network of membrane-bounded tubules and sacs; membrane separates lumen from cytosol; continuous with nuclear envelope	Smooth ER: synthesis of lipids, metabolism of carbohydrates, Ca^+ storage, detoxification of drugs and poisons Rough ER: aids in synthesis of secretory and other proteins from bound ribosomes; adds carbohydrates to proteins to make glycoproteins; produces new membrane
	Golgi apparatus	Stacks of flattened membranous sacs; has polarity (*cis* and *trans* faces)	Modification of proteins, carbohydrates on proteins, and phospholipids; synthesis of many polysaccharides; sorting of ER and Golgi products, which are then released in vesicles

(Continued)

Cell Component	Structure	Function
Lysosome	Membranous sac of hydrolytic enzymes (in animal cells)	Breakdown of ingested substances, cell macromolecules, and damaged organelles for recycling
Vacuole	Large membrane-bounded vesicle	Digestion, storage, waste disposal, water balance, cell growth, and protection
Mitochondrion	Bounded by double membrane; inner membrane has infoldings (cristae)	Cellular respiration
Chloroplast	Typically two membranes around fluid stroma, which contains thylakoids stacked into grana (in cells of photosynthetic eukaryotes, including plants)	Photosynthesis (non-photosynthetic functions include the assimilation of nitrogen and the synthesis of fatty acids, hormones, amino acids, heme and vitamins)
Peroxisome	Specialized metabolic compartment bounded by a single membrane	Contains enzymes that transfer hydrogen atoms from substrates to oxygen, producing hydrogen peroxide (H_2O_2) as a by-product; H_2O_2 is converted to water by another enzyme

CONCEPT 6.5

Mitochondria and chloroplasts change energy from one form to another (pp. 120–123)

? *What is the endosymbiont theory?*

Source: Adaptation of figure 3.2 from Human Anatomy and Physiology, 8th Edition, by Elaine N. Marieb and Katja N. Hoehn, 2010. Copyright © 2010 by Pearson Education, Inc. Reprinted and electronically reproduced by permission of Pearson Education, Inc. Upper Saddle River, New Jersey.

CONCEPT 6.6

The cytoskeleton is a network of fibres that organizes structures and activities in the cell (pp. 123–129)

- The **cytoskeleton** functions in structural support for the cell and in motility and signal transmission.
- **Microtubules** shape the cell, guide organelle movement, and separate chromosomes in dividing cells. **Cilia** and **flagella** are motile appendages containing microtubules. Primary cilia also play sensory and signalling roles. **Microfilaments** are thin rods that function in muscle contraction, amoeboid movement, **cytoplasmic streaming**, and support of microvilli. **Intermediate filaments**, present in some animal cells, support cell shape and fix organelles in place.

? *Describe the role of motor proteins inside the eukaryotic cell and in whole-cell movement.*

CONCEPT 6.7

Extracellular components and connections between cells help coordinate cellular activities (pp. 129–132)

- Plant **cell walls** are made of cellulose fibres embedded in other polysaccharides and proteins.
- Animal cells secrete glycoproteins and proteoglycans that form the **extracellular matrix (ECM)**, which functions in support, adhesion, movement, and regulation.

- Cell junctions connect neighbouring cells in plants and animals. Plants have **plasmodesmata** that pass through adjoining cell walls. Animal cells have **tight junctions, desmosomes**, and **gap junctions**.

? *Compare the composition and functions of a plant cell wall and the extracellular matrix of an animal cell.*

TEST YOUR UNDERSTANDING

LEVEL 1: KNOWLEDGE/COMPREHENSION

1. Which structure is *not* part of the endomembrane system?
   a. nuclear envelope
   b. chloroplast
   c. Golgi apparatus
   d. plasma membrane

2. Which structure is common to plant *and* animal cells?
   a. chloroplast
   b. central vacuole
   c. mitochondrion
   d. centriole

3. Which of the following is present in a prokaryotic cell?
   a. mitochondrion
   b. ribosome
   c. chloroplast
   d. ER

4. Which structure-function pair is *mismatched*?
   a. microtubule; muscle contraction
   b. ribosome; protein synthesis
   c. Golgi; protein trafficking
   d. nucleolus; production of ribosomal subunits

LEVEL 2: APPLICATION/ANALYSIS

5. Cyanide binds to at least one molecule involved in producing ATP. If a cell is exposed to cyanide, most of the cyanide will be found within the
   a. mitochondria.
   b. ribosomes.
   c. peroxisomes.
   d. lysosomes.

6. What is the most likely pathway taken by a newly synthesized protein that will be secreted by a cell?
   a. Golgi → ER → lysosome
   b. nucleus → ER → Golgi
   c. ER → Golgi → vesicles that fuse with plasma membrane
   d. ER → lysosomes → vesicles that fuse with plasma membrane

7. Which cell would be best for studying lysosomes?
   a. muscle cell
   b. nerve cell
   c. phagocytic white blood cell
   d. bacterial cell

8. **DRAW IT** From memory, draw two eukaryotic cells, labelling the structures listed here and showing any physical connections between the internal structures of each cell: nucleus, rough ER, smooth ER, mitochondrion, centrosome, chloroplast, vacuole, lysosome, microtubule, cell wall, ECM, microfilament, Golgi apparatus, intermediate filament, plasma membrane, peroxisome, ribosome, nucleolus, nuclear pore, vesicle, flagellum, microvilli, plasmodesma.

LEVEL 3: SYNTHESIS/EVALUATION

9. **EVOLUTION CONNECTION**
   Which aspects of cell structure best reveal evolutionary unity? What are some examples of specialized modifications?

10. **SCIENTIFIC INQUIRY**
    Imagine protein X, destined to span the plasma membrane. Assume that the mRNA carrying the genetic message for protein X has already been translated by ribosomes in a cell culture. If you fractionate the cells, in which fraction would you find protein X? Explain by describing its transit through the cell.

11. **WRITE ABOUT A THEME: ORGANIZATION**
    Considering some of the characteristics that define life and drawing on your new knowledge of cellular structures and functions, write a short essay (100–150 words) that discusses this statement: Life is an emergent property that appears at the level of the cell. (Review p. 3 in Chapter 1.)

12. **SYNTHESIZE YOUR KNOWLEDGE**

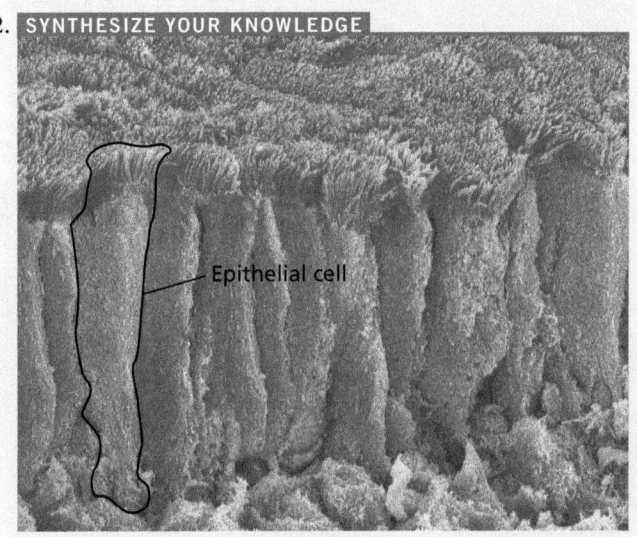

Epithelial cell

Susumu Nishinaga/Science Source

The cells in this SEM are epithelial cells from the small intestine. Discuss how aspects of their structure contribute to their specialized functions of nutrient absorption and as a barrier between the intestinal contents and the blood supply on the other side of the sheet of epithelial cells.

For selected answers, see Appendix A.

7

Membrane Structure and Function

KEY CONCEPTS

7.1 Cellular membranes are fluid mosaics of lipids and proteins

7.2 Membrane structure results in selective permeability

7.3 Passive transport is diffusion of a substance across a membrane with no energy investment

7.4 Active transport uses energy to move solutes against their gradients

7.5 Bulk transport across the plasma membrane occurs by exocytosis and endocytosis

▲ Figure 7.1 **Why is the surface of this plasma membrane bumpy?**

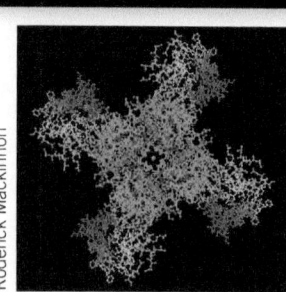

◄ **How do cell membrane proteins help regulate chemical traffic?**

Life at the Edge

The plasma membrane is the edge of life, the boundary that separates the living cell from its surroundings. A remarkable film only about 8 nm thick— it would take over 8000 plasma membranes to equal the thickness of this page— the plasma membrane controls traffic into and out of the cell it surrounds. Like all biological membranes, the plasma membrane exhibits **selective permeability**; that is, it acts as a gatekeeper and allows some substances to cross it more easily than others. One of the earliest episodes in the evolution of life may have been the formation of a membrane that enclosed a solution different from the surrounding solution while still permitting the uptake of nutrients and elimination of waste products. The ability of the cell to discriminate in its chemical exchanges with its environment is fundamental to life, and it is the plasma membrane and its component molecules that make this selectivity possible.

In this chapter, you will learn how cellular membranes control the passage of substances. The surface of a plasma membrane is complex, and the "bumps" you see in the colourized atomic force micrograph in **Figure 7.1** are membrane proteins rising from the membrane surface. Membrane proteins are integral to cellular function and can also play roles in disease, such as cancer and genetic disorders. Dr. Frances Sharom from the University of Guelph isolates membrane proteins involved in the transport of substances across the plasma membrane, such as the P-glycoprotein multidrug transporter. This membrane protein is an ATP-powered pump which removes various substances from cells, including crucial chemotherapy drugs. By studying the P-glycoprotein transporter, it may be possible to design drugs that cannot be pumped out of a cell. To understand how membranes work, we'll begin by examining their structure. Then, in the rest of the chapter, we'll describe in some detail how plasma membranes control transport into and out of cells.

CONCEPT 7.1

Cellular membranes are fluid mosaics of lipids and proteins

Lipids and proteins are the staple ingredients of membranes, although carbohydrates are also important. The most abundant lipids in most membranes are phospholipids. The ability of phospholipids to form membranes is inherent in their molecular structure. A phospholipid is an **amphipathic** molecule, meaning it has both a hydrophilic region and a hydrophobic region (see Figure 5.11). Other types of membrane lipids are also amphipathic. A phospholipid bilayer can exist as a stable boundary between two aqueous compartments because the molecular arrangement shelters the hydrophobic tails of the phospholipids from water while exposing the hydrophilic heads to water (**Figure 7.2**).

Like membrane lipids, most membrane proteins are amphipathic. Such proteins can reside in the phospholipid

▼ Figure 7.2 **Phospholipid bilayer (cross section).**

Hydrophilic head

Hydrophobic tail

WATER

WATER

MAKE CONNECTIONS *Consulting Figure 5.11, circle the hydrophilic and hydrophobic portions of the enlarged phospholipids on the right. Explain what each portion contacts when the phospholipids are in the plasma membrane.*

bilayer with their hydrophilic regions protruding. This molecular orientation maximizes contact of hydrophilic regions of proteins with water in the cytosol and extracellular fluid, while providing their hydrophobic parts with a nonaqueous environment.

Figure 7.3 shows the currently accepted model of the arrangement of molecules in the plasma membrane of an animal cell. In this **fluid mosaic model**, the membrane is a mosaic of protein molecules bobbing in a fluid bilayer of phospholipids. The proteins are not randomly distributed in the membrane, however. Groups of proteins are often associated in long-lasting, specialized patches, where they carry out common functions. The lipids themselves appear to form defined regions as well. Also, in some regions the membrane may be much more packed with proteins than shown in Figure 7.3. Like all models, the fluid mosaic model is continually being refined as new research reveals more about membrane structure.

The Fluidity of Membranes

Membranes are not static sheets of molecules locked rigidly in place. A membrane is held together primarily by hydrophobic interactions, which are much weaker than covalent bonds (see Figure 5.18). Most of the lipids and some of the proteins can shift about laterally—that is, in the plane of the membrane, like partygoers elbowing their way through a crowded room. Very rarely, also, a lipid may flip-flop across the membrane, switching from one phospholipid layer to the other.

The lateral movement of phospholipids within the membrane is rapid. Adjacent phospholipids switch positions about 10^7 times per second, which means that a phospholipid can travel about 2 μm—the length of many bacterial cells—in 1 second. Proteins are much larger than lipids and move more slowly, but some membrane proteins do drift, as shown in a classic experiment described in **Figure 7.4**. Some membrane proteins seem to move in a highly directed manner, perhaps driven along cytoskeletal fibres in the cell by motor proteins connected to the membrane proteins' cytoplasmic regions. However, many other membrane proteins seem to be held immobile by their attachment to the cytoskeleton or to the extracellular matrix (see Figure 7.3).

We learned from Helga Guderley, in the Unit 2 Interview, that temperature can have an impact on membrane fluidity. A membrane remains fluid as temperature decreases until the phospholipids settle into a closely packed arrangement and the membrane solidifies, much as bacon grease forms lard when it cools. The temperature at which a membrane solidifies depends on the types of lipids it is made of. The membrane remains fluid to a lower temperature if it is rich in phospholipids with unsaturated

Fibres of extra-
cellular matrix (ECM)

Glyco-
protein

Carbohydrate

Glycolipid

EXTRACELLULAR
SIDE OF
MEMBRANE

Cholesterol

Microfilaments
of cytoskeleton

Peripheral
proteins

Integral
protein

CYTOPLASMIC SIDE
OF MEMBRANE

▲ Figure 7.3 **Updated model of an animal cell's plasma membrane (cutaway view).**

▼ Figure 7.4

Inquiry

Do membrane proteins move?

Experiment Larry Frye and Michael Edidin, at Johns Hopkins University, labelled the plasma membrane proteins of a mouse cell and a human cell with two different markers and fused the cells. Using a microscope, they observed the markers on the hybrid cell.

Results

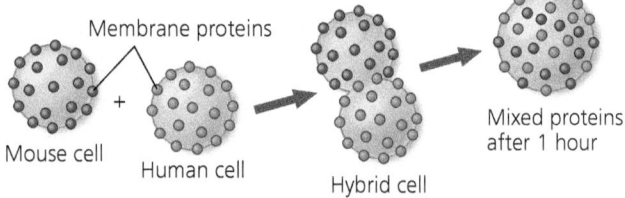

Membrane proteins

Mouse cell

+

Human cell

Hybrid cell

Mixed proteins
after 1 hour

Conclusion The mixing of the mouse and human membrane proteins indicates that at least some membrane proteins move sideways within the plane of the plasma membrane.

Source: Based on "The Rapid Intermixing of Cell Surface Antigens After Formation of Mouse-Human Heterokaryons" by L. D. Frye and M. Edidin, from , September 1970, Volume 7. © Jane B Reece.

WHAT IF? *Suppose the proteins did not mix in the hybrid cell, even many hours after fusion. Would you be able to conclude that proteins don't move within the membrane? What other explanation could there be?*

hydrocarbon tails (see Figures 5.10 and 5.11). Because of kinks in the tails where double bonds are located, unsaturated hydrocarbon tails cannot pack together as closely as saturated hydrocarbon tails, making the membrane more fluid (**Figure 7.5a**).

The steroid cholesterol, which is wedged between phospholipid molecules in the plasma membranes of animal cells, has different effects on membrane fluidity at different temperatures (**Figure 7.5b**). At moderately high temperatures—at 37°C, the body temperature of humans, for example—cholesterol makes the membrane less fluid by restraining phospholipid movement. However, because cholesterol also hinders the close packing of phospholipids, it lowers the temperature required for the membrane to solidify. Thus, cholesterol can be thought of as a "fluidity buffer" for the membrane, resisting changes in membrane fluidity that can be caused by changes in temperature.

Membranes must be fluid to work properly; the fluidity of a membrane affects both its permeability and the ability of membrane proteins to move to where their function is needed. Usually, membranes are about as fluid as salad oil. When a membrane solidifies, its permeability changes, and enzymatic proteins in the membrane may become inactive if their activity requires movement within the membrane.

▼ Figure 7.5 **Factors that affect membrane fluidity.**

(a) Unsaturated versus saturated hydrocarbon tails.

Fluid	Viscous

Unsaturated hydrocarbon tails (kinked) prevent packing, enhancing membrane fluidity.

Saturated hydrocarbon tails pack together, increasing membrane viscosity.

(b) Cholesterol within the animal cell membrane.

Cholesterol reduces membrane fluidity at moderate temperatures by reducing phospholipid movement, but at low temperatures it hinders solidification by disrupting the regular packing of phospholipids.

Cholesterol

However, membranes that are too fluid cannot support protein function either. Therefore, extreme environments pose a challenge for life, resulting in evolutionary adaptations that include differences in membrane lipid composition.

Evolution of Differences in Membrane Lipid Composition

EVOLUTION   Variations in the cell membrane lipid compositions of many species appear to be evolutionary adaptations that maintain the appropriate membrane fluidity under specific environmental conditions. For instance, fishes that live in extreme cold have membranes with a high proportion of unsaturated hydrocarbon tails, enabling their membranes to remain fluid (see Figure 7.5a). At the other extreme, some bacteria and archaea thrive at temperatures greater than 90°C in thermal hot springs and geysers. Their membranes include unusual lipids that may prevent excessive fluidity at such high temperatures.

The ability to change the lipid composition of cell membranes in response to changing temperatures has evolved in organisms that live where temperatures vary. In many plants that tolerate extreme cold, such as winter wheat, the percentage of unsaturated phospholipids increases in autumn, an adjustment that keeps the membranes from solidifying during winter. Certain bacteria and archaea can also change the proportion of unsaturated phospholipids in their cell membranes, depending on the temperature at which they are

growing. Overall, natural selection has apparently favoured organisms whose mix of membrane lipids ensures an appropriate level of membrane fluidity for their environment.

Membrane Proteins and Their Functions

Now we come to the *mosaic* aspect of the fluid mosaic model. Somewhat like a tile mosaic, a membrane is a collage of different proteins, often clustered together in groups, embedded in the fluid matrix of the lipid bilayer (see Figure 7.3). In the plasma membrane of red blood cells alone, for example, more than 50 kinds of proteins have been found so far. Phospholipids form the main fabric of the membrane, but proteins determine most of the membrane's functions. Different types of cells contain different sets of membrane proteins, and the various membranes within a cell each have a unique collection of proteins.

Notice in Figure 7.3 that there are two major populations of membrane proteins: integral proteins and peripheral proteins. **Integral proteins** penetrate the hydrophobic interior of the lipid bilayer. The majority are *transmembrane proteins*, which span the membrane; other integral proteins extend only partway into the hydrophobic interior. The hydrophobic regions of an integral protein consist of one or more stretches of nonpolar amino acids (see Figure 5.14), usually coiled into α helices (**Figure 7.6**). The hydrophilic parts of the molecule are exposed to the aqueous solutions on either side of the membrane. Some proteins also have one or more hydrophilic channels that allow passage through the membrane of hydrophilic substances. **Peripheral proteins** are not embedded in the lipid bilayer at all; they are appendages loosely bound to the surface of the membrane, often to exposed parts of integral proteins (see Figure 7.3).

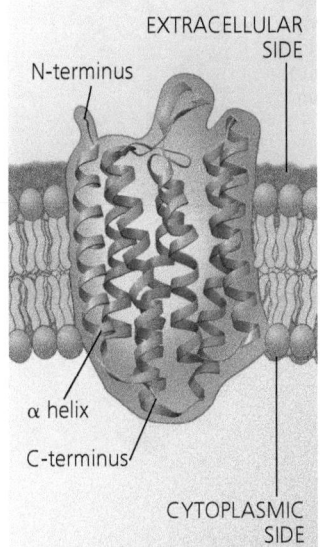

EXTRACELLULAR SIDE

N-terminus

α helix

C-terminus

CYTOPLASMIC SIDE

◀ Figure 7.6 **The structure of a transmembrane protein.** Bacteriorhodopsin (a bacterial transport protein) has a distinct orientation in the membrane, with its N-terminus outside the cell and its C-terminus inside. This ribbon model highlights the α-helical secondary structure of the hydrophobic parts, which lie mostly within the hydrophobic interior of the membrane. The protein includes seven transmembrane helices. The nonhelical hydrophilic segments are in contact with the aqueous solutions on the extracellular and cytoplasmic sides of the membrane. Although shown as simple purple shapes in many figures in this book, each protein has its own unique structure.

Source: Protein Data Bank ID 3HAO: "Similar Energetic Contributions of Packing in the Core of Membrane and Water-Soluble Proteins" by Nathan H. Joh et al., from *Journal of the American Chemical Society*, Volume 131(31).

(a) Transport. *Left:* A protein that spans the membrane may provide a hydrophilic channel across the membrane that is selective for a particular solute. *Right:* Other transport proteins shuttle a substance from one side to the other by changing shape (see Figure 7.14b). Some of these proteins hydrolyze ATP as an energy source to actively pump substances across the membrane.

(b) Enzymatic activity. A protein built into the membrane may be an enzyme with its active site exposed to substances in the adjacent solution. In some cases, several enzymes in a membrane are organized as a team that carries out sequential steps of a metabolic pathway.

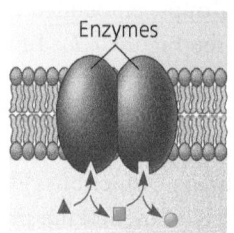

Enzymes

(c) Signal transduction. A membrane protein (receptor) may have a binding site with a specific shape that fits the shape of a chemical messenger, such as a hormone. The external messenger (signalling molecule) may cause the protein to change shape, allowing it to relay the message to the inside of the cell, usually by binding to a cytoplasmic protein (see Figure 11.6).

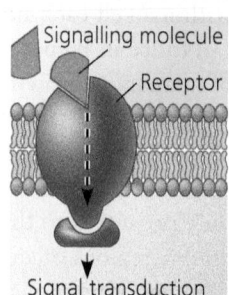

Signalling molecule

Receptor

Signal transduction

(d) Cell-cell recognition. Some glycoproteins serve as identification tags that are specifically recognized by membrane proteins of other cells. This type of cell-cell binding is usually short-lived compared to that shown in (e).

Glyco-protein

(e) Intercellular joining. Membrane proteins of adjacent cells may hook together in various kinds of junctions, such as gap junctions or tight junctions (see Figure 6.30). This type of binding is more long-lasting than that shown in (d).

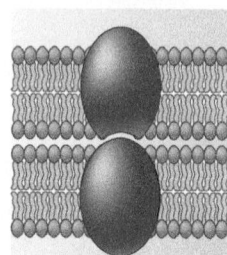

(f) Attachment to the cytoskeleton and extracellular matrix (ECM). Microfilaments or other elements of the cytoskeleton may be noncovalently bound to membrane proteins, a function that helps maintain cell shape and stabilizes the location of certain membrane proteins. Proteins that can bind to ECM molecules can coordinate extracellular and intracellular changes (see Figure 6.28).

▲ **Figure 7.7 Some functions of membrane proteins.** In many cases, a single protein performs multiple tasks.

? *Some transmembrane proteins can bind to a particular ECM molecule and, when bound, transmit a signal into the cell. Use the proteins shown here to explain how this might occur.*

On the cytoplasmic side of the plasma membrane, some membrane proteins are held in place by attachment to the cytoskeleton. And on the extracellular side, certain membrane proteins are attached to fibres of the extracellular matrix (see Figure 6.28; *integrins* are one type of integral transmembrane protein). These attachments combine to give animal cells a stronger framework than the plasma membrane alone could provide.

Figure 7.7 gives an overview of six major functions performed by proteins of the plasma membrane. A single cell may have membrane proteins carrying out several of these functions, and a single membrane protein may have multiple functions. In this way, the membrane is a functional mosaic as well as a structural one.

Proteins on a cell's surface are important in the medical field. For example, a protein called CD4 on the surface of immune cells helps the human immunodeficiency virus (HIV) infect these cells, leading to acquired immune deficiency syndrome (AIDS). Despite multiple exposures to HIV, however, a small number of people do not develop AIDS and show no evidence of HIV-infected cells. Comparing their genes with the genes of infected individuals, researchers learned that resistant people have an unusual form of a gene that codes for an immune cell-surface protein called CCR5. Further work showed although CD4 is the main HIV receptor, HIV must also bind to CCR5 as a "co-receptor" to infect most cells **(Figure 7.8a)**. An absence of CCR5 on the cells of resistant individuals, due to the gene alteration, prevents the virus from entering the cells **(Figure 7.8b)**.

This information has been key to developing a treatment for HIV infection. Interfering with CD4 could cause dangerous side effects because it performs many important functions in cells. Discovery of the CCR5 co-receptor provided a safer target for development of drugs that mask this protein and block HIV entry. One such drug, maraviroc

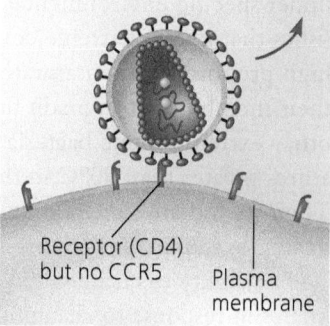

HIV

Receptor (CD4)

Co-receptor (CCR5)

Receptor (CD4) but no CCR5

Plasma membrane

(a)   (b)

▲ **Figure 7.8 The genetic basis for HIV resistance. (a)** HIV can infect a cell with CCR5 on its surface, as in most people. **(b)** HIV cannot infect a cell lacking CCR5 on its surface, as in resistant individuals.

MAKE CONNECTIONS *Study Figures 2.16 and 5.17, both of which show pairs of molecules binding to each other. What would you predict about CCR5 that would allow HIV to bind to it? How could a drug molecule interfere with this binding?*

(brand name Selzentry), was approved for treatment of HIV in 2007 and is still being used today. A clinical trial began in 2012 to test whether this drug might also work to prevent HIV infection in uninfected at-risk patients.

The Role of Membrane Carbohydrates in Cell-Cell Recognition

Cell-cell recognition, a cell's ability to distinguish one type of neighbouring cell from another, is crucial to the functioning of an organism. It is important, for example, in the sorting of cells into tissues and organs in an animal embryo. It is also the basis for the rejection of foreign cells by the immune system, an important line of defence in vertebrate animals (see Chapter 43). Cells recognize other cells by binding to molecules, often containing carbohydrates, on the extracellular surface of the plasma membrane (see Figure 7.7d).

Membrane carbohydrates are usually short, branched chains of fewer than 15 sugar units. Some are covalently bonded to lipids, forming molecules called **glycolipids**. (Recall that *glyco* refers to the presence of carbohydrate.) However, most are covalently bonded to proteins, which are thereby **glycoproteins** (see Figure 7.3).

The carbohydrates on the extracellular side of the plasma membrane vary from species to species, among individuals of the same species, and even from one cell type to another in a single individual. The diversity of the molecules and their location on the cell's surface enable membrane carbohydrates to function as markers that distinguish one cell from another. For example, the four human blood types designated A, B, AB, and O reflect variation in the carbohydrate part of glycoproteins on the surface of red blood cells.

Synthesis and Sidedness of Membranes

Membranes have distinct inside and outside faces. The two lipid layers may differ in specific lipid composition, and each protein has directional orientation in the membrane (see Figure 7.6). Figure 7.9 shows how membrane sidedness arises: The asymmetrical arrangement of proteins, lipids, and their associated carbohydrates in the plasma membrane is determined as the membrane is being built by the endoplasmic reticulum (ER) and Golgi apparatus, components of the endomembrane system (see Figure 6.15).

CONCEPT CHECK 7.1

1. Plasma membrane proteins have carbohydrates attached to them in the ER and Golgi apparatus, then are transported in vesicles to the cell surface. On which side of the vesicle membrane are the carbohydrates?

2. **WHAT IF?** How would the membrane lipid composition of a native grass found in very warm soil around hot springs compare with that of a native grass found in cooler soil? Explain.

For suggested answers, see Appendix A.

▼ Figure 7.9 **Synthesis of membrane components and their orientation in the membrane.** The cytoplasmic (orange) face of the plasma membrane differs from the extracellular (aqua) face. The latter arises from the inside face of ER, Golgi, and vesicle membranes.

1 Membrane proteins and lipids are synthesized in the endoplasmic reticulum (ER). Carbohydrates (green) are added to the transmembrane proteins (purple dumbbells), making them glycoproteins. The carbohydrate portions may then be modified.

2 Inside the Golgi apparatus, the glycoproteins undergo further carbohydrate modification, and lipids acquire carbohydrates, becoming glycolipids.

3 The glycoproteins, glycolipids, and secretory proteins (purple spheres) are transported in vesicles to the plasma membrane.

4 As vesicles fuse with the plasma membrane, the outside face of the vesicle becomes continuous with the inside (cytoplasmic) face of the plasma membrane. This releases the secretory proteins from the cell, a process called *exocytosis*, and positions the carbohydrates of membrane glycoproteins and glycolipids on the outside (extracellular) face of the plasma membrane.

DRAW IT *Draw an integral membrane protein extending from partway through the ER membrane into the ER lumen. Next, draw the protein where it would be located in a series of numbered steps ending at the plasma membrane. Would the protein contact the cytoplasm or the extracellular fluid?*

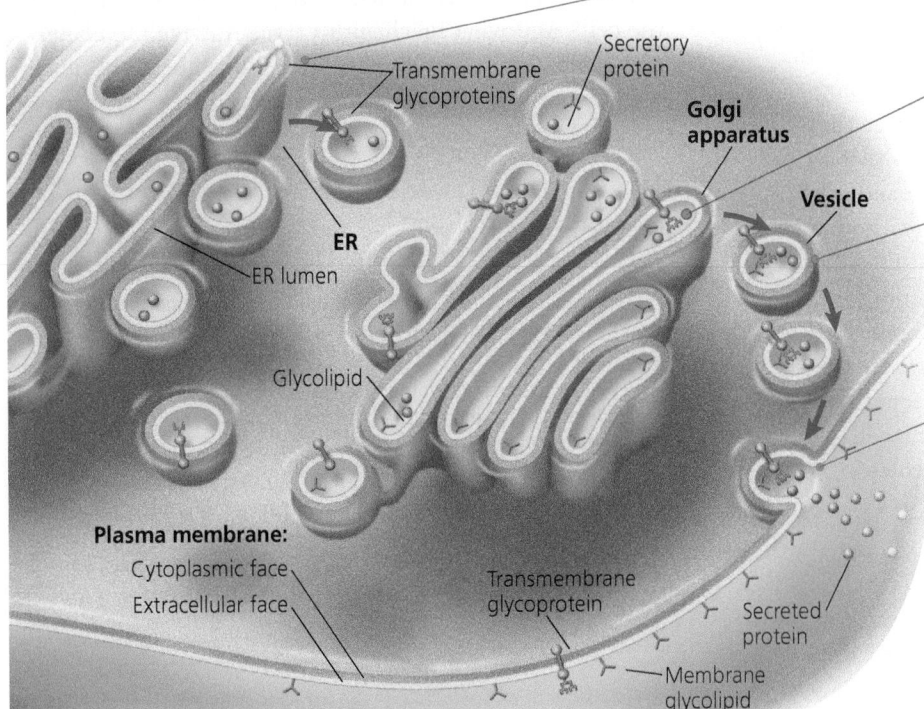

Membrane structure results in selective permeability

The biological membrane is an exquisite example of a supramolecular structure—many molecules ordered into a higher level of organization—with emergent properties beyond those of the individual molecules. The remainder of this chapter focuses on one of the most important of those properties: the ability to act as a gatekeeper and regulate transport across cellular boundaries, a function essential to the cell's existence. We will see once again that form fits function: The fluid mosaic model helps explain how membranes regulate the cell's molecular traffic.

A steady traffic of small molecules and ions moves across the plasma membrane in both directions. Consider the chemical exchanges between a muscle cell and the extracellular fluid that bathes it. Sugars, amino acids, and other nutrients enter the cell, and metabolic waste products leave it. The cell takes in O_2 for use in cellular respiration and expels CO_2. Also, the cell regulates its concentrations of inorganic ions, such as Na^+, K^+, Ca^{2+}, and Cl^-, by shuttling them one way or the other across the plasma membrane. Although the heavy traffic through them may seem to suggest otherwise, cell membranes are selectively permeable, and substances do not cross the barrier indiscriminately. The cell is able to take up some small molecules and ions and exclude others.

The Permeability of the Lipid Bilayer

Nonpolar molecules, such as hydrocarbons, CO_2, and O_2, are hydrophobic. They can therefore dissolve in the lipid bilayer of the membrane and cross it easily, without the aid of membrane proteins. However, the hydrophobic interior of the membrane impedes direct passage through the membrane of ions and polar molecules, which are hydrophilic. Polar molecules such as glucose and other sugars pass only slowly through a lipid bilayer, and even water, a very small polar molecule, does not cross rapidly. A charged atom or molecule and its surrounding shell of water (see Figure 3.8) are even less likely to penetrate the hydrophobic interior of the membrane. Furthermore, the lipid bilayer is only one aspect of the gatekeeper system responsible for the selective permeability of a cell. Proteins built into the membrane play key roles in regulating transport.

Transport Proteins

Specific ions and a variety of polar molecules can't move through cell membranes on their own; however, these hydrophilic substances can avoid contact with the lipid bilayer by passing through **transport proteins** that span the membrane.

Some transport proteins, called *channel proteins*, function by having a hydrophilic channel that certain molecules or atomic ions use as a tunnel through the membrane (see Figure 7.7a, left). For example, the passage of water molecules through the membrane in certain cells is greatly facilitated by channel proteins known as **aquaporins**. Each aquaporin allows entry of up to *3 billion* (3×10^9) water molecules per second, passing single file through its central channel, which fits 10 at a time. Without aquaporins, only a tiny fraction of these water molecules would pass through the same area of the cell membrane in a second, so the channel protein brings about a tremendous increase in rate. Other transport proteins, called *carrier proteins*, hold onto their passengers and change shape in a way that shuttles them across the membrane (see Figure 7.7a, right).

A transport protein is specific for the substance it translocates (moves), allowing only a certain substance (or a small group of related substances) to cross the membrane. For example, a specific carrier protein in the plasma membrane of red blood cells transports glucose across the membrane 50 000 times faster than glucose can pass through on its own. This "glucose transporter" is so selective that it even rejects fructose, a structural isomer of glucose.

Thus, the **selective permeability** of a membrane depends on both the discriminating barrier of the lipid bilayer and the specific transport proteins built into the membrane. But what establishes the *direction* of traffic across a membrane? At a given time, what determines whether a particular substance will enter the cell or leave the cell? And what mechanisms actually drive molecules across membranes? We will address these questions next as we explore two modes of membrane traffic: passive transport and active transport.

CONCEPT CHECK 7.2

1. Two molecules that can cross a lipid bilayer without help from membrane proteins are O_2 and CO_2. What property allows this to occur?

2. Why is a transport protein needed to move water molecules rapidly and in large quantities across a membrane?

3. **MAKE CONNECTIONS** Aquaporins exclude passage of hydronium ions (H_3O^+; see pp. 56–57). Recent research on fat metabolism has shown that some aquaporins allow passage of glycerol, a three-carbon alcohol (see Figure 5.9), as well as H_2O. Since H_3O^+ is much closer in size to water than is glycerol, what might be the basis of this selectivity?

For suggested answers, see Appendix A.

Passive transport is diffusion of a substance across a membrane with no energy investment

Molecules have a type of energy called thermal energy, due to their constant motion (see Concept 3.2). One result of this motion is **diffusion**, the movement of particles of any substance so that they spread out into the available space. Each molecule moves randomly, yet diffusion of a *population* of molecules may be directional. To understand this process, let's imagine a synthetic membrane separating pure water from a solution of a dye in water. Study **Figure 7.10a** carefully to appreciate how diffusion would result in both solutions having equal concentrations of the dye molecules. Once that point is reached, there will be a dynamic equilibrium, with roughly as many dye molecules crossing the membrane each second in one direction as in the other.

(a) Diffusion of one solute. The membrane has pores large enough for molecules of dye to pass through. Random movement of dye molecules will cause some to pass through the pores; this will happen more often on the side with more dye molecules. The dye diffuses from where it is more concentrated to where it is less concentrated (called diffusing down a concentration gradient). This leads to a dynamic equilibrium: The solute molecules continue to cross the membrane, but at equal rates in both directions.

(b) Diffusion of two solutes. Solutions of two different dyes are separated by a membrane that is permeable to both. Each dye diffuses down its own concentration gradient. There will be a net diffusion of the purple dye toward the left, even though the *total* solute concentration was initially greater on the left side.

▲ **Figure 7.10 The diffusion of solutes across a synthetic membrane.** Each of the large arrows under the diagrams shows the net diffusion of the dye molecules of that colour.

We can now state a simple rule of diffusion: In the absence of other forces, a substance will diffuse from where it is more concentrated to where it is less concentrated. Put another way, any substance will diffuse down its **concentration gradient**, the region along which the density of a chemical substance increases or decreases (in this case, decreases). No work must be done to make this happen; diffusion is a spontaneous process, needing no input of energy. Note that each substance diffuses down its *own* concentration gradient, unaffected by the concentration gradients of other substances (**Figure 7.10b**).

Much of the traffic across cell membranes occurs by diffusion. When a substance is more concentrated on one side of a membrane than on the other, there is a tendency for the substance to diffuse across the membrane down its concentration gradient (assuming that the membrane is permeable to that substance). One important example is the uptake of oxygen by a cell performing cellular respiration. Dissolved oxygen diffuses into the cell across the plasma membrane. As long as cellular respiration consumes the O_2 as it enters, diffusion into the cell will continue because the concentration gradient favours movement in that direction.

The diffusion of a substance across a biological membrane is called **passive transport** because the cell does not have to expend energy to make it happen. The concentration gradient itself represents potential energy (see Concept 2.2 and Figure 8.5b) and drives diffusion. Remember, however, that membranes are selectively permeable and therefore have different effects on the rates of diffusion of various molecules. In the case of water, aquaporins allow water to diffuse very rapidly across the membranes of certain cells. As we'll see next, the movement of water across the plasma membrane has important consequences for cells.

Effects of Osmosis on Water Balance

To see how two solutions with different solute concentrations interact, picture a U-shaped glass tube with a selectively permeable artificial membrane separating two sugar solutions (**Figure 7.11**). Pores in this synthetic membrane are too small for sugar molecules to pass through but large enough for water molecules. However, tight clustering of water molecules around the hydrophilic solute molecules makes some of the water unavailable to cross the membrane. As a result, the solution with a higher solute concentration has a lower *free* water concentration. Water diffuses across the membrane from the region of higher free water concentration (lower solute concentration) to that of lower free water concentration (higher solute concentration) until the solute concentrations on both sides of the membrane are more nearly equal. The diffusion of

Lower concentration of solute (sugar) Higher concentration of solute

Same concentration of solute

Sugar molecule

H_2O

Selectively permeable membrane

Water molecules can pass through pores, but sugar molecules cannot.

Water molecules cluster around sugar molecules.

This side has fewer solute molecules, more free water molecules.

This side has more solute molecules, fewer free water molecules.

Osmosis

Water moves from an area of higher to lower free water concentration (lower to higher solute concentration).

▲ Figure 7.11 **Osmosis.** Two sugar solutions of different concentrations are separated by a membrane that the solvent (water) can pass through but the solute (sugar) cannot. Water molecules move randomly and may cross in either direction, but overall, water diffuses from the solution with less concentrated solute to that with more concentrated solute. This diffusion of water, or osmosis, equalizes the sugar concentrations on both sides.

WHAT IF? *If an orange dye capable of passing through the membrane were added to the left side of the tube above, how would it be distributed at the end of the experiment? (See Figure 7.10.) Would the final solution levels in the tube be affected?*

free water across a selectively permeable membrane, whether artificial or cellular, is called **osmosis**. The movement of water across cell membranes and the balance of water between the cell and its environment are crucial to organisms. Let's now apply what we have learned about this system to living cells.

Water Balance of Cells Without Cell Walls

To explain the behaviour of a cell in a solution, we must consider both solute concentration and membrane permeability. Both factors are taken into account in the concept of **tonicity**, the ability of a surrounding solution to cause a cell to gain or lose water. The tonicity of a solution depends in part on its concentration of solutes that cannot cross the

membrane (nonpenetrating solutes) relative to that inside the cell. If there is a higher concentration of nonpenetrating solutes in the surrounding solution, water will tend to leave the cell, and vice versa.

If a cell without a cell wall, such as an animal cell, is immersed in an environment that is **isotonic** to the cell (*iso* means "same"), there will be no *net* movement of water across the plasma membrane. Water diffuses across the membrane, but at the same rate in both directions. In an isotonic environment, the volume of an animal cell is stable (Figure 7.12a).

Let's transfer the cell to a solution that is **hypertonic** to the cell (*hyper* means "more," in this case referring to nonpenetrating solutes). The cell will lose water, shrivel, and probably die. This is why an increase in the salinity (saltiness) of a lake can kill the animals there; if the lake water becomes hypertonic to the animals' cells, they might shrivel and die. However, taking up too much water can be just as hazardous to an animal cell as losing water. If we place the cell in a solution that is **hypotonic** to the cell (*hypo* means "less"), water will enter the cell faster than it leaves, and the cell will swell and lyse (burst) like an overfilled water balloon.

A cell without rigid cell walls can tolerate neither excessive uptake nor excessive loss of water. This problem of water balance is automatically solved if such a cell lives in isotonic surroundings. Seawater is isotonic to many marine invertebrates. The cells of most terrestrial (land-dwelling) animals are bathed in an extracellular fluid that is isotonic to the cells. In hypertonic or hypotonic environments,

(a) Animal cell. An animal cell fares best in an isotonic environment unless it has special adaptations that offset the osmotic uptake or loss of water.

(b) Plant cell. Plant cells are turgid (firm) and generally healthiest in a hypotonic environment, where the uptake of water is eventually balanced by the wall pushing back on the cell.

Hypotonic solution   Isotonic solution   Hypertonic solution

H_2O H_2O H_2O H_2O

Lysed   Normal   Shrivelled

Plasma membrane   Cell wall

H_2O H_2O H_2O Plasma membrane H_2O

Turgid (normal)   Flaccid   Plasmolyzed

▲ Figure 7.12 **The water balance of living cells.** How living cells react to changes in the solute concentration of their environment depends on whether or not they have cell walls. **(a)** Animal cells, such as this red blood cell, do not have cell walls. **(b)** Plant cells do. (Arrows indicate net water movement after the cells were first placed in these solutions.)

however, organisms that lack rigid cell walls must have other adaptations for **osmoregulation**, the control of solute concentrations and water balance. For example, the unicellular protist *Paramecium caudatum* lives in pond water, which is hypotonic to the cell. *P. caudatum* has a plasma membrane that is much less permeable to water than the membranes of most other cells, but this only slows the uptake of water, which continually enters the cell. The *P. caudatum* cell doesn't burst because it is also equipped with a contractile vacuole, an organelle that functions as a bilge pump to force water out of the cell as fast as it enters by osmosis (Figure 7.13). We will examine other evolutionary adaptations for osmoregulation in Chapter 44.

Water Balance of Cells with Cell Walls

The cells of plants, prokaryotes, fungi, and some protists are surrounded by cell walls (see Figure 6.27). When such a cell is immersed in a hypotonic solution—bathed in rainwater, for example—the cell wall helps maintain the cell's water balance. Consider a plant cell. Like an animal cell, the plant cell swells as water enters by osmosis (Figure 7.12b). However, the relatively inelastic cell wall will expand only so much before it exerts a back pressure on the cell, called *turgor pressure*, that opposes further water uptake. At this point, the cell is **turgid** (very firm), which is the healthy state for most plant cells. Plants that are not woody, such as most houseplants, depend for mechanical support on cells kept turgid by a surrounding hypotonic solution. If a plant's cells and their surroundings are isotonic, there is no net tendency for water to enter, and the cells become **flaccid** (limp).

However, a cell wall is of no advantage if the cell is immersed in a hypertonic environment. In this case, a plant cell, like an animal cell, will lose water to its surroundings and shrink. As the plant cell shrivels, its plasma membrane pulls away from the cell wall at multiple places. This phenomenon, called **plasmolysis**, causes the plant to wilt and can lead to plant death. The walled cells of bacteria and fungi also plasmolyze in hypertonic environments.

Facilitated Diffusion: Passive Transport Aided by Proteins

Let's look more closely at how water and certain hydrophilic solutes cross a membrane. As mentioned earlier, many polar molecules and ions impeded by the lipid bilayer of the membrane diffuse passively with the help of transport proteins that span the membrane. This phenomenon is called **facilitated diffusion**. Cell biologists are still trying to learn exactly how various transport proteins facilitate diffusion. Most transport proteins are very specific: They transport some substances but not others.

As mentioned earlier, the two types of transport proteins are channel proteins and carrier proteins. Channel proteins simply provide corridors that allow specific molecules or ions to cross the membrane (Figure 7.14a). The hydrophilic passageways provided by these proteins can allow water molecules or small ions to diffuse very quickly from one side of the membrane to the other. Aquaporins, the water channel proteins, facilitate the massive amounts of diffusion that occur in plant cells and in animal cells such as red blood cells (see Figure 7.12). Certain kidney cells also have a high number of aquaporins, allowing them to reclaim water from urine before it is excreted. If the kidneys did not perform this function, you would excrete about 180 L of urine per day—and have to drink an equal volume of water!

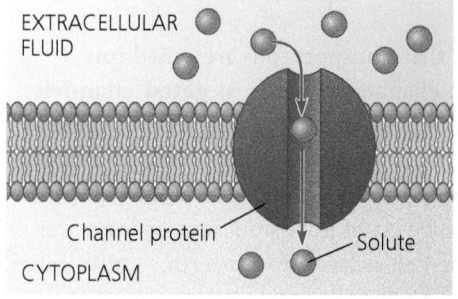

(a) A channel protein (purple) has a channel through which water molecules or a specific solute can pass.

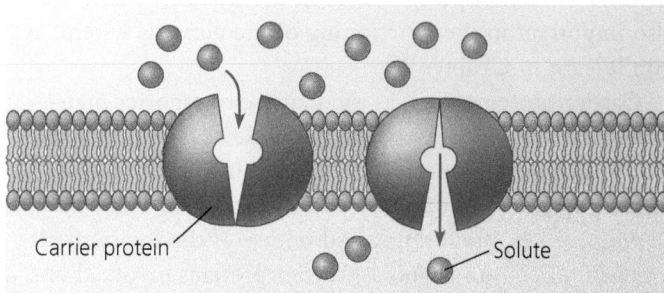

(b) A carrier protein alternates between two shapes, moving a solute across the membrane during the shape change.

▲ Figure 7.14 **Two types of transport proteins that carry out facilitated diffusion.** In both cases, the protein can transport the solute in either direction, but the net movement is down the concentration gradient of the solute.

▲ Figure 7.13 **The contractile vacuole of *Paramecium caudatum*.** The vacuole collects fluid from a system of canals in the cytoplasm. When full, the vacuole and canals contract, expelling fluid from the cell (LM).

Interpreting a Scatter Plot with Two Sets of Data

Is Glucose Uptake into Cells Affected by Age? Glucose, an important energy source for animals, is transported into cells by facilitated diffusion using protein carriers. In this exercise, you will interpret a graph with two sets of data from an experiment that examined glucose uptake over time in red blood cells from guinea pigs of different ages. You will determine if the age of the guinea pigs affected their cells' rate of glucose uptake.

How the Experiment Was Done Researchers incubated guinea pig red blood cells in a 300 mM (millimolar) radioactive glucose solution at pH 7.4 at 25°C. Every 10 or 15 minutes, they removed a sample of cells and measured the concentration of radioactive glucose inside those cells. The cells came from either a 15-day-old or 1-month-old guinea pig.

Data from the Experiment When you have multiple sets of data, it can be useful to plot them on the same graph for comparison. In the graph here, each set of dots (of the same colour) forms a *scatter plot*, in which every data point represents two numerical values, one for each variable. For each data set, a curve that best fits the points has been drawn to make it easier to see the trends. (For additional information about graphs, see the Scientific Skills Review in Appendix E and in the Study Area in MasteringBiology.)

Interpret the Data

1. First make sure you understand the parts of the graph. (a) Which variable is the independent variable—the variable controlled by the researchers? (b) Which variable is the dependent variable—the variable that depended on the treatment and was measured by the researchers? (c) What do the red dots represent? (d) the blue dots?

2. From the data points on the graph, construct a table of the data. Put "Incubation Time (min)" in the left column of the table.

Glucose Uptake over Time in Guinea Pig Red Blood Cells

3. What does the graph show? Compare and contrast glucose uptake in red blood cells from 15-day-old and 1-month-old guinea pigs.

4. Develop a hypothesis to explain the difference between glucose uptake in red blood cells from 15-day-old and 1-month-old guinea pigs. (Think about how glucose gets into cells.)

5. Design an experiment to test your hypothesis.

Adaptation of Figure 1 from "Developmental Changes in Glucose Transport of Guinea Pig Erythrocytes" by Takahito Kondo and Ernest Beutler, from , January 1980, Volume 65(1). Copyright © by American Society for Clinical Investigation. Permission to reprint conveyed through Copyright Clearance Center, Inc.

Channel proteins that transport ions are called **ion channels**. Many ion channels function as **gated channels**, which open or close in response to a stimulus. For some gated channels, the stimulus is electrical. In a nerve cell, for example, an ion channel opens in response to an electrical stimulus, allowing a stream of potassium ions to leave the cell. This restores the cell's ability to fire again. Other gated channels open or close when a specific substance other than the one to be transported binds to the channel. These are also important in the functioning of the nervous system, as you'll learn in Chapter 48.

Carrier proteins, such as the glucose transporter mentioned earlier, seem to undergo a subtle change in shape that somehow translocates the solute-binding site across the membrane (**Figure 7.14b**). Such a change in shape may be triggered by the binding and release of the transported molecule. Like ion channels, carrier proteins involved in facilitated diffusion result in the net movement of a substance down its concentration gradient. No energy input is thus required: This is passive transport.

The Scientific Skills Exercise gives you an opportunity to work with data from an experiment related to glucose transport.

CONCEPT CHECK 7.3

1. How do you think a cell performing cellular respiration rids itself of the resulting CO_2?

2. **WHAT IF?** If a *Paramecium caudatum* swims from a hypotonic to an isotonic environment, will its contractile vacuole become more active or less? Why?

For suggested answers, see Appendix A.

CONCEPT 7.4

Active transport uses energy to move solutes against their gradients

Despite the help of transport proteins, facilitated diffusion is considered passive transport because the solute is moving down its concentration gradient, a process that requires no energy. Facilitated diffusion speeds transport of a solute by providing efficient passage through the membrane, but it does not alter the direction of transport. Some other transport proteins, however, can move solutes against their

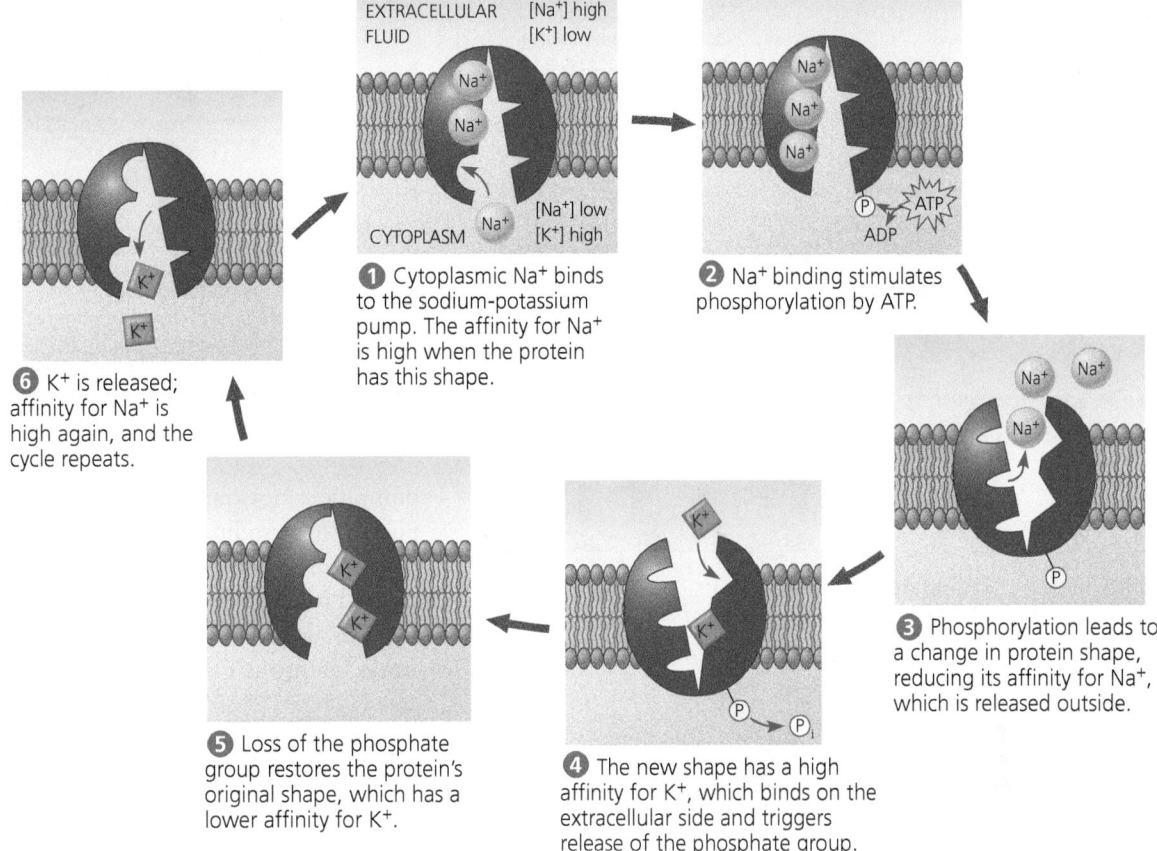

► Figure 7.15 **The sodium-potassium pump: a specific case of active transport.** This transport system pumps ions against steep concentration gradients: Sodium ion concentration ($[Na^+]$) is high outside the cell and low inside, while potassium ion concentration ($[K^+]$) is low outside the cell and high inside. The pump oscillates between two shapes in a cycle that moves 3 Na^+ out of the cell for every 2 K^+ pumped into the cell. The two shapes have different affinities for Na^+ and K^+. ATP powers the shape change by transferring a phosphate group to the transport protein (phosphorylating the protein).

EXTRACELLULAR FLUID $[Na^+]$ high $[K^+]$ low

CYTOPLASM $[Na^+]$ low $[K^+]$ high

1 Cytoplasmic Na^+ binds to the sodium-potassium pump. The affinity for Na^+ is high when the protein has this shape.

2 Na^+ binding stimulates phosphorylation by ATP.

3 Phosphorylation leads to a change in protein shape, reducing its affinity for Na^+, which is released outside.

4 The new shape has a high affinity for K^+, which binds on the extracellular side and triggers release of the phosphate group.

5 Loss of the phosphate group restores the protein's original shape, which has a lower affinity for K^+.

6 K^+ is released; affinity for Na^+ is high again, and the cycle repeats.

concentration gradients, across the plasma membrane from the side where they are less concentrated (whether inside or outside) to the side where they are more concentrated.

The Need for Energy in Active Transport

To pump a solute across a membrane against its gradient requires work; the cell must expend energy. Therefore, this type of membrane traffic is called **active transport**. The transport proteins that move solutes against their concentration gradients are all carrier proteins rather than channel proteins. This makes sense because when channel proteins are open, they merely allow solutes to diffuse down their concentration gradients rather than picking them up and transporting them against their gradients.

Active transport enables a cell to maintain internal concentrations of small solutes that differ from concentrations in its environment. For example, compared with its surroundings, an animal cell has a much higher concentration of potassium ions (K^+) and a much lower concentration of sodium ions (Na^+). The plasma membrane helps maintain these steep gradients by pumping Na^+ out of the cell and K^+ into the cell.

As in other types of cellular work, ATP supplies the energy for most active transport. One way ATP can power active transport is by transferring its terminal phosphate group directly to the transport protein. This can induce

the protein to change its shape in a manner that translocates a solute bound to the protein across the membrane. One transport system that works this way is the **sodium-potassium pump**, which exchanges Na^+ for K^+ across the plasma membrane of animal cells (Figure 7.15). The distinction between passive transport and active transport is reviewed in **Figure 7.16**.

How Ion Pumps Maintain Membrane Potential

All cells have voltages across their plasma membranes. Voltage is electrical potential energy—a separation of opposite charges. The cytoplasmic side of the membrane is negative in charge relative to the extracellular side because of an unequal distribution of anions and cations on the two sides. The voltage across a membrane, called a **membrane potential**, ranges from about −50 to −200 millivolts (mV). (The minus sign indicates that the inside of the cell is negative relative to the outside.)

The membrane potential acts like a battery, an energy source that affects the traffic of all charged substances across the membrane. Because the inside of the cell is negative compared with the outside, the membrane potential favours the passive transport of cations into the cell and anions out of the cell. Thus, *two* forces drive the diffusion of ions across a membrane: a chemical force (the ion's concentration gradient) and an electrical force (the effect

▼ **Figure 7.16 Review: passive and active transport.**

Passive transport. Substances diffuse spontaneously down their concentration gradients, crossing a membrane with no expenditure of energy by the cell. The rate of diffusion can be greatly increased by transport proteins in the membrane.

Active transport. Some transport proteins act as pumps, moving substances across a membrane against their concentration (or electrochemical) gradients. Energy for this work is usually supplied by ATP.

Diffusion. Hydrophobic molecules and (at a slow rate) very small uncharged polar molecules can diffuse through the lipid bilayer.

Facilitated diffusion. Many hydrophilic substances diffuse through membranes with the assistance of transport proteins, either channel proteins (left) or carrier proteins (right).

? *For each solute in the right panel, describe its direction of movement, and state whether it is going with or against its concentration gradient.*

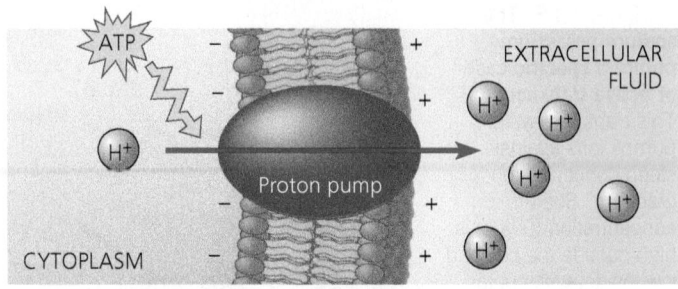

▲ **Figure 7.17 A proton pump.** Proton pumps are electrogenic pumps that store energy by generating voltage (charge separation) across membranes. A proton pump translocates positive charge in the form of hydrogen ions. The voltage and H^+ concentration gradient represent a dual energy source that can drive other processes, such as the uptake of nutrients. Most proton pumps are powered by ATP.

of the membrane potential on the ion's movement). This combination of forces acting on an ion is called the **electrochemical gradient**.

In the case of ions, then, we must refine our concept of passive transport: An ion diffuses not simply down its *concentration* gradient but, more exactly, down its *electrochemical* gradient. For example, the concentration of Na^+ inside a resting nerve cell is much lower than outside it. When the cell is stimulated, gated channels open that facilitate Na^+ diffusion. Sodium ions then "fall" down their electrochemical gradient, driven by the concentration gradient of Na^+ and by the attraction of these cations to the negative side (inside) of the membrane. In this example, both electrical and chemical contributions to the electrochemical gradient act in the same direction across the membrane, but this is not always so. In cases where electrical forces due to the membrane potential oppose the simple diffusion of an ion down its concentration gradient, active transport may be necessary. In Chapter 48, you'll learn about the importance of electrochemical gradients and membrane potentials in the transmission of nerve impulses.

Some membrane proteins that actively transport ions contribute to the membrane potential. An example is the sodium-potassium pump. Notice in Figure 7.15 that the

pump does not translocate Na^+ and K^+ one for one, but pumps three sodium ions out of the cell for every two potassium ions it pumps into the cell. With each "crank" of the pump, there is a net transfer of one positive charge from the cytoplasm to the extracellular fluid, a process that stores energy as voltage. A transport protein that generates voltage across a membrane is called an **electrogenic pump**. The sodium-potassium pump appears to be the major electrogenic pump of animal cells. The main electrogenic pump of plants, fungi, and bacteria is a **proton pump**, which actively transports protons (hydrogen ions, H^+) out of the cell. The pumping of H^+ transfers positive charge from the cytoplasm to the extracellular solution (**Figure 7.17**). By generating voltage across membranes, electrogenic pumps help store energy that can be tapped for cellular work. One important use of proton gradients in the cell is for ATP synthesis during cellular respiration, as you will see in Chapter 9. Another is a type of membrane traffic called cotransport.

Cotransport: Coupled Transport by a Membrane Protein

A solute that exists in different concentrations across a membrane can do work as it moves across that membrane by diffusion down its concentration gradient. This is analogous to water that has been pumped uphill and performs work as it flows back down. In a mechanism called **cotransport**, a transport protein (a cotransporter) can couple the "downhill" diffusion of the solute to the "uphill" transport of a second substance against its own concentration gradient. For instance, a plant cell uses the gradient of H^+ generated by its ATP-powered proton pumps to drive the active transport of amino acids, sugars, and several other nutrients into the cell. In the example shown in **Figure 7.18**, a cotransporter couples the return of H^+ to the transport of sucrose into the cell. This protein can translocate sucrose into the cell against its concentration gradient, but only if the sucrose molecule travels in the company

▲ **Figure 7.18 Cotransport: active transport driven by a concentration gradient.** A carrier protein, such as this sucrose-H⁺ cotransporter in a plant cell, is able to use the diffusion of H⁺ down its electrochemical gradient into the cell to drive the uptake of sucrose. The H⁺ gradient is maintained by an ATP-driven proton pump that concentrates H⁺ outside the cell, thus storing potential energy that can be used for active transport, in this case of sucrose. Thus, ATP indirectly provides the energy necessary for cotransport. (The cell wall is not shown.)

of an H⁺. The H⁺ uses the transport protein as an avenue to diffuse down its own electrochemical gradient, which is maintained by the proton pump. Plants use sucrose-H⁺ cotransport to load sucrose produced by photosynthesis into cells in the veins of leaves. The vascular tissue of the plant can then distribute the sugar to nonphotosynthetic organs, such as roots.

What we know about cotransport proteins in animal cells has helped us find more effective treatments for diarrhea, a serious problem in developing countries. Normally, sodium in waste is reabsorbed in the colon, maintaining constant levels in the body, but diarrhea expels waste so rapidly that reabsorption is not possible, and sodium levels fall precipitously. To treat this life-threatening condition, patients are given a solution to drink containing high concentrations of salt (NaCl) and glucose. The solutes are taken up by sodium-glucose cotransporters on the surface of intestinal cells and passed through the cells into the blood. This simple treatment has lowered infant mortality worldwide.

CONCEPT CHECK 7.4

1. Sodium-potassium pumps help nerve cells establish a voltage across their plasma membranes. Do these pumps use ATP or produce ATP? Explain.

2. Explain why the sodium-potassium pump in Figure 7.15 would not be considered a cotransporter.

3. **MAKE CONNECTIONS** Review the characteristics of the lysosome in Concept 6.4. Given the internal environment of a lysosome, what transport protein might you expect to see in its membrane?

For suggested answers, see Appendix A.

CONCEPT 7.5

Bulk transport across the plasma membrane occurs by exocytosis and endocytosis

Water and small solutes enter and leave the cell by diffusing through the lipid bilayer of the plasma membrane or by being pumped or moved across the membrane by transport proteins. However, large molecules—such as proteins and polysaccharides, as well as larger particles—generally cross the membrane in bulk, packaged in vesicles. Like active transport, these processes require energy.

Exocytosis

As seen in Chapter 6, the cell secretes certain biological molecules by the fusion of vesicles with the plasma membrane; this process is called **exocytosis**. A transport vesicle that has budded from the Golgi apparatus moves along microtubules of the cytoskeleton to the plasma membrane. When the vesicle membrane and plasma membrane come into contact, specific proteins rearrange the lipid molecules of the two bilayers so that the two membranes fuse. The contents of the vesicle spill out of the cell, and the vesicle membrane becomes part of the plasma membrane (see Figure 7.9, step 4).

Many secretory cells use exocytosis to export products. For example, the cells in the pancreas that make insulin secrete it into the extracellular fluid by exocytosis. In another example, neurons (nerve cells) use exocytosis to release neurotransmitters that signal other neurons or muscle cells. When plant cells are making cell walls, exocytosis delivers proteins and carbohydrates from Golgi vesicles to the outside of the cell.

Endocytosis

In **endocytosis**, the cell takes in molecules and particulate matter by forming new vesicles from the plasma membrane. Although the proteins involved in the processes are different, the events of endocytosis look like the reverse of exocytosis. A small area of the plasma membrane sinks inward to form a pocket. Then, as the pocket deepens, it pinches in, forming a vesicle containing material that had been outside the cell. Study **Figure 7.19** carefully to understand the three types of endocytosis: phagocytosis ("cellular eating"), pinocytosis ("cellular drinking"), and receptor-mediated endocytosis (which is considered a form of pinocytosis).

Human cells use receptor-mediated endocytosis to take in cholesterol for membrane synthesis and the synthesis of other steroids. Cholesterol travels in the blood in particles

Exploring Endocytosis in Animal Cells

Phagocytosis

EXTRACELLULAR FLUID

Solutes

Pseudopodium

"Food" or other particle

Food vacuole

CYTOPLASM

In **phagocytosis**, a cell engulfs a particle by extending pseudopodia (singular, *pseudopodium*) around it and packaging it within a membranous sac called a food vacuole. The particle will be digested after the food vacuole fuses with a lysosome (see Figure 6.13a).

Pseudopodium of amoeba

Bacterium

Food vacuole

1 µm

Biological Photo Service

An amoeba engulfing a bacterium via phagocytosis (TEM).

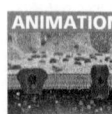

BioFlix Visit the Study Area in **MasteringBiology** for the BioFlix® 3-D Animation on Membrane Transport. BioFlix Tutorials can also be assigned in MasteringBiology.

Pinocytosis

Plasma membrane

Coat protein

Coated pit

Coated vesicle

In **pinocytosis**, a cell continually "gulps" droplets of extracellular fluid into tiny vesicles, formed by infoldings of the plasma membrane. In this way, the cell obtains molecules dissolved in the droplets. Because any and all solutes are taken into the cell, pinocytosis as shown here is nonspecific for the substances it transports. In many cases, as above, the parts of the plasma membrane that form vesicles are lined on their cytoplasmic side by a fuzzy layer of coat protein; the "pits" and resulting vesicles are said to be "coated."

Science Source

0.25 µm

Pinocytotic vesicles forming (TEMs).

Receptor-Mediated Endocytosis

Receptor

Receptor-mediated endocytosis is a specialized type of pinocytosis that enables the cell to acquire bulk quantities of specific substances, even though those substances may not be very concentrated in the extracellular fluid. Embedded in the plasma membrane are proteins with receptor sites exposed to the extracellular fluid. Specific solutes bind to the sites. The receptor proteins then cluster in coated pits, and each coated pit forms a vesicle containing the bound molecules. Notice that there are relatively more bound molecules (purple triangles) inside the vesicle, but other molecules (green balls) are also present. After the ingested material is liberated from the vesicle, the emptied receptors are recycled to the plasma membrane by the same vesicle (not shown).

Plasma membrane

Coat protein

0.25 µm

From: M.M. Perry and A.B. Gilbert, *Journal of Cell Science 39*: 257–272, Fig. 11 (1979). © 1979 The Company of Biologists Ltd.

Top: A coated pit. *Bottom*: A coated vesicle forming during receptor-mediated endocytosis (TEMs).

called low-density lipoproteins (LDLs), each a complex of lipids and a protein. LDLs bind to LDL receptors on plasma membranes and then enter the cells by endocytosis. (LDLs thus act as **ligands,** a term for any molecule that binds specifically to a receptor site on another molecule.) In the inherited disease familial hypercholesterolemia, characterized by a very high level of cholesterol in the blood, LDLs cannot enter cells because the LDL receptor proteins are defective or missing. Consequently, cholesterol accumulates in the blood, where it contributes to early atherosclerosis, the buildup of lipid deposits within the walls of blood vessels. This buildup narrows the space in the vessels and impedes blood flow, and can result in heart damage and stroke.

Vesicles not only transport substances to be released from the cell but also provide a mechanism for rejuvenating or remodelling the plasma membrane. Endocytosis and exocytosis occur continually in most eukaryotic cells, yet the amount of plasma membrane in a nongrowing cell remains fairly constant. The addition of membrane by one process appears to offset the loss of membrane by the other.

Energy and cellular work have figured prominently in our study of membranes. We have seen, for example, that active transport is powered by ATP. In the next three chapters, you will learn more about how cells acquire chemical energy to do the work of life.

CONCEPT CHECK 7.5

1. As a cell grows, its plasma membrane expands. Does this involve endocytosis or exocytosis? Explain.

2. **DRAW IT** Return to Figure 7.9, and circle a patch of plasma membrane that is coming from a vesicle involved in exocytosis.

3. **MAKE CONNECTIONS** In Concept 6.7, you learned that animal cells make an extracellular matrix (ECM). Describe the cellular pathway of synthesis and deposition of an ECM glycoprotein.

For suggested answers, see Appendix A.

7 Chapter Review

Go to **MasteringBiology®** for Assignments, the eText, and the Study Area with Animations, Activities, Vocab Self-Quiz, and Practice Tests.

SUMMARY OF KEY CONCEPTS

CONCEPT 7.1

Cellular membranes are fluid mosaics of lipids and proteins (pp. 137–141)

- In the **fluid mosaic model**, **amphipathic** proteins are embedded in the phospholipid bilayer. Proteins with related functions often cluster in patches.
- Phospholipids and some proteins move laterally within the membrane. The unsaturated hydrocarbon tails of some phospholipids keep membranes fluid at lower temperatures, while cholesterol helps membranes resist changes in fluidity caused by temperature changes. Differences in membrane lipid composition, as well as the ability to change lipid composition, are evolutionary adaptations that ensure membrane fluidity.
- **Integral proteins** are embedded in the lipid bilayer; **peripheral proteins** are attached to the membrane surface. The functions of membrane proteins include transport, enzymatic activity, signal transduction, cell-cell recognition, intercellular joining, and attachment to the cytoskeleton and extracellular matrix. Short chains of sugars linked to proteins (in **glycoproteins**) and lipids (in **glycolipids**) on the exterior side of the plasma membrane interact with surface molecules of other cells.
- Membrane proteins and lipids are synthesized in the ER and modified in the ER and Golgi apparatus. The inside and outside faces of membranes differ in molecular composition.

? *In what ways are membranes crucial to life?*

CONCEPT 7.2

Membrane structure results in selective permeability (p. 142)

- A cell must exchange molecules and ions with its surroundings, a process controlled by the **selective permeability** of the plasma membrane. Hydrophobic substances are soluble in lipids and pass through membranes rapidly, whereas polar molecules and ions generally require specific **transport proteins** to cross the membrane.

? *How do **aquaporins** affect the permeability of a membrane?*

CONCEPT 7.3

Passive transport is diffusion of a substance across a membrane with no energy investment (pp. 143–146)

- **Diffusion** is the spontaneous movement of a substance down its **concentration gradient**. Water diffuses out through the permeable membrane of a cell (**osmosis**) if the solution outside has a higher solute concentration (**hypertonic**) than the cytosol; water enters the cell if the solution has a lower solute concentration (**hypotonic**). If the concentrations are equal (**isotonic**), no net osmosis occurs. Cell survival depends on balancing water uptake and loss. Cells lacking cell walls (as in animals and some protists) are isotonic with their environments or have adaptations for **osmoregulation**. Plants, prokaryotes, fungi, and some protists have relatively inelastic cell walls, so the cells don't burst in a hypotonic environment.

- In a type of **passive transport** called **facilitated diffusion**, a transport protein speeds the movement of water or a solute across a membrane down its concentration gradient. **Ion channels**, some of which are **gated channels**, facilitate the diffusion of ions across a membrane. Carrier proteins can undergo changes in shape that translocate bound solutes across the membrane.

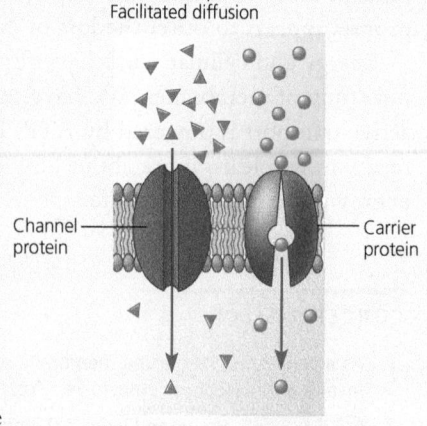

Passive transport: Facilitated diffusion

Channel protein

Carrier protein

? *What happens to a cell placed in a hypertonic solution? Describe the free water concentration inside and out.*

CONCEPT 7.4

Active transport uses energy to move solutes against their gradients (pp. 146–149)

- Specific membrane proteins use energy, usually in the form of ATP, to do the work of **active transport**. One example of such a protein is the **sodium-potassium pump**.
- Ions can have both a concentration (chemical) gradient and an electrical (voltage) gradient. These gradients combine in the **electrochemical gradient**, which determines the net direction of ionic diffusion. **Electrogenic pumps**, such as the sodium-potassium pump and **proton pumps**, are transport proteins that contribute to electrochemical gradients.
- **Cotransport** of two solutes occurs when a membrane protein enables the "downhill" diffusion of one solute to drive the "uphill" transport of the other.

Active transport

ATP

? *ATP is not directly involved in the functioning of a cotransporter. Why, then, is cotransport considered active transport?*

CONCEPT 7.5

Bulk transport across the plasma membrane occurs by exocytosis and endocytosis (pp. 149–151)

- In **exocytosis**, transport vesicles migrate to the plasma membrane, fuse with it, and release their contents. In **endocytosis**, molecules enter cells within vesicles that pinch inward from the plasma membrane. The three types of endocytosis are **phagocytosis**, **pinocytosis**, and **receptor-mediated endocytosis**.

? *Which type of endocytosis involves ligands? What does this type of transport enable a cell to do?*

TEST YOUR UNDERSTANDING

LEVEL 1: KNOWLEDGE/COMPREHENSION

1. In what way do the membranes of a eukaryotic cell vary?
   a. Phospholipids are found only in certain membranes.
   b. Certain proteins are unique to each membrane.
   c. Only certain membranes of the cell are selectively permeable.
   d. Only certain membranes are constructed from amphipathic molecules.

2. According to the fluid mosaic model of membrane structure, proteins of the membrane are mostly
   a. spread in a continuous layer over the inner and outer surfaces of the membrane.
   b. confined to the hydrophobic interior of the membrane.
   c. embedded in a lipid bilayer.
   d. randomly oriented in the membrane, with no fixed inside-outside polarity.

3. Which of the following factors would tend to increase membrane fluidity?
   a. a greater proportion of unsaturated phospholipids
   b. a greater proportion of saturated phospholipids
   c. a lower temperature
   d. a relatively high protein content in the membrane

LEVEL 2: APPLICATION/ANALYSIS

4. Which of the following processes includes all others?
   a. osmosis
   b. diffusion of a solute across a membrane
   c. passive transport
   d. transport of an ion down its electrochemical gradient

5. Based on Figure 7.18, which of these experimental treatments would increase the rate of sucrose transport into the cell?
   a. decreasing extracellular sucrose concentration
   b. decreasing extracellular pH
   c. decreasing cytoplasmic pH
   d. adding a substance that makes the membrane more permeable to hydrogen ions

6. **DRAW IT** An artificial "cell" consisting of an aqueous solution enclosed in a selectively permeable membrane is immersed in a beaker containing a different solution, the "environment," as shown below. The membrane is permeable to water and to the simple sugars glucose and fructose but impermeable to the disaccharide sucrose.
   a. Draw solid arrows to indicate the net movement of solutes into and/or out of the cell.
   b. Is the solution outside the cell isotonic, hypotonic, or hypertonic?
   c. Draw a dashed arrow to show the net osmosis, if any.
   d. Will the artificial cell become more flaccid, more turgid, or stay the same?
   e. Eventually, will the two solutions have the same or different solute concentrations?

"Cell"
0.03 M sucrose
0.02 M glucose

"Environment"
0.01 M sucrose
0.01 M glucose
0.01 M fructose

LEVEL 3: SYNTHESIS/EVALUATION

7. **EVOLUTION CONNECTION**
   Paramecium and other protists that live in hypotonic environments have cell membranes that limit water uptake, while those living in isotonic environments have membranes that are more permeable to water. What water regulation adaptations might have evolved in protists in hypertonic habitats such as Great Salt Lake? In habitats with changing salt concentration?

8. **SCIENTIFIC INQUIRY**
An experiment is designed to study the mechanism of sucrose uptake by plant cells. Cells are immersed in a sucrose solution, and the pH of the solution is monitored. Samples of the cells are taken at intervals, and their sucrose concentration is measured. After a decrease in the pH of the solution to a steady, slightly acidic level, sucrose uptake begins. Propose a hypothesis for these results. What do you think would happen if an inhibitor of ATP regeneration by the cell were added to the beaker once the pH is at a steady level? Explain.

9. **SCIENCE, TECHNOLOGY, AND SOCIETY**
Extensive irrigation in arid regions causes salts to accumulate in the soil. (When water evaporates, salts that were dissolved in the water are left behind in the soil.) Based on what you learned about water balance in plant cells, explain why increased soil salinity (saltiness) might be harmful to crops. Suggest ways to minimize damage. What costs are attached to your solutions?

10. **WRITE ABOUT A THEME: INTERACTION**
A human pancreatic cell obtains O_2, fuel molecules such as glucose, and building materials such as amino acids and cholesterol from its environment, and it releases CO_2 as a waste product of cellular respiration. In response to hormonal signals, the cell secretes digestive enzymes. It also regulates its ion concentrations by exchange with its environment. Based on what you have just learned about the structure and function of cellular membranes, write a short essay (100–150 words) that describes how such a cell accomplishes these interactions with its environment.

11. **SYNTHESIZE YOUR KNOWLEDGE**

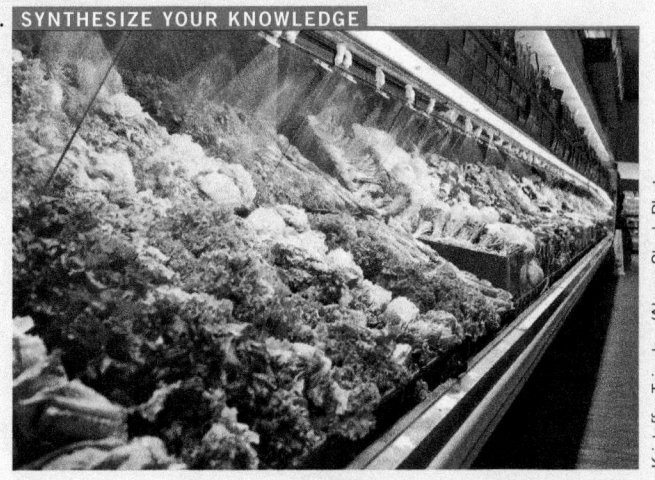

Kristoffer Tripplaar/Alamy Stock Photo

In the supermarket, lettuce and other produce are often sprayed with water. Explain why this makes vegetables crisp.

For selected answers, see Appendix A.

8

An Introduction to Metabolism

KEY CONCEPTS

8.1 An organism's metabolism transforms matter and energy, subject to the laws of thermodynamics

8.2 The free-energy change of a reaction tells us whether or not the reaction occurs spontaneously

8.3 ATP powers cellular work by coupling exergonic reactions to endergonic reactions

8.4 Enzymes speed up metabolic reactions by lowering energy barriers

8.5 Regulation of enzyme activity helps control metabolism

Chad J. Tamis Photography

▲ Figure 8.1 **What causes this comb jelly to glow?**

The Energy of Life

The living cell is a chemical factory in miniature, where thousands of reactions occur within a microscopic space. Sugars can be converted to amino acids that are linked together into proteins when needed. Conversely, when food is digested, proteins are dismantled into amino acids that can be converted to sugars. In multicellular organisms, many cells export chemical products that are used in other parts of the organism. The process called cellular respiration drives this cellular economy by extracting the energy stored in sugars and other fuels. Cells apply this energy to perform various types of work, such as the transport of solutes across the plasma membrane, which we discussed in Chapter 7. In a more exotic example, the photo of a *Leucothea pluchra* comb jelly taken in Barkley Sound on the west coast of Vancouver Island (Figure 8.1) is brightly illuminated. Cells in this comb jelly enable this "glow" by converting the energy stored in certain organic molecules to light, a process called bioluminescence. Most bioluminescent organisms are found in the oceans, but some exist on land, such as the bioluminescent fungus seen at the lower left. Bioluminescence and other metabolic activities carried out by a cell are precisely coordinated and controlled. In its complexity, its efficiency, and its responsiveness to subtle changes, the cell is peerless as a chemical factory. The concepts of metabolism that you learn in this chapter will help you understand how matter and energy flow during life's processes and how that flow is regulated.

Ocean Research & Conservation Association, Inc.

An organism's metabolism transforms matter and energy, subject to the laws of thermodynamics

The totality of an organism's chemical reactions is called **metabolism** (from the Greek *metabole*, change). Metabolism is an emergent property of life that arises from orderly interactions between molecules.

Organization of the Chemistry of Life into Metabolic Pathways

We can picture a cell's metabolism as an elaborate road map of the thousands of chemical reactions that occur in a cell, arranged as intersecting metabolic pathways. A **metabolic pathway** begins with a specific molecule, which is then altered in a series of defined steps, resulting in a certain product. Each step of the pathway is catalyzed by a specific enzyme:

Analogous to the red, yellow, and green stoplights that control the flow of automobile traffic, mechanisms that regulate enzymes balance metabolic supply and demand.

Metabolism as a whole manages the material and energy resources of the cell. Some metabolic pathways release energy by breaking down complex molecules to simpler compounds. These degradative processes are called **catabolic pathways**, or breakdown pathways. A major pathway of catabolism is cellular respiration, in which the sugar glucose and other organic fuels are broken down in the presence of oxygen to carbon dioxide and water. (Pathways can have more than one starting molecule and/or product.) Energy that was stored in the organic molecules becomes available to do the work of the cell, such as ciliary beating or membrane transport. **Anabolic pathways**, in contrast, consume energy to build complicated molecules from simpler ones; they are sometimes called biosynthetic pathways. Examples of anabolism are the synthesis of an amino acid from simpler molecules and the synthesis of a protein from amino acids. Catabolic and anabolic pathways are the "downhill" and "uphill" avenues of the metabolic landscape. Energy released from the downhill reactions of catabolic pathways can be stored and then used to drive the uphill reactions of anabolic pathways.

In this chapter, we will focus on mechanisms common to metabolic pathways. Because energy is fundamental to all metabolic processes, a basic knowledge of energy is necessary to understand how the living cell works. Although we will use some nonliving examples to study energy, the concepts demonstrated by these examples also apply to **bioenergetics**, the study of how energy flows through living organisms.

Forms of Energy

Energy is the capacity to cause change. In everyday life, energy is important because some forms of energy can be used to do work—that is, to move matter against opposing forces, such as gravity and friction. Put another way, energy is the ability to rearrange a collection of matter. For example, you expend energy to turn the pages of this book, and your cells expend energy in transporting certain substances across membranes. Energy exists in various forms, and the work of life depends on the ability of cells to transform energy from one form to another.

Energy can be associated with the relative motion of objects; this energy is called **kinetic energy**. Moving objects can perform work by imparting motion to other matter: A pool player uses the motion of the cue stick to push the cue ball, which in turn moves the other balls; water gushing through a dam turns turbines; and the contraction of leg muscles pushes bicycle pedals. **Thermal energy** is kinetic energy associated with the random movement of atoms or molecules; thermal energy transferred from one object to another is called **heat**. Light is also a type of energy that can be harnessed to perform work, such as powering photosynthesis in green plants.

An object not presently moving may still possess energy. Energy that is not kinetic is called **potential energy**; it is energy that matter possesses because of its location or structure. Water behind a dam, for instance, possesses energy because of its altitude above sea level. Molecules possess energy because of the arrangement of electrons in the bonds between their atoms. **Chemical energy** is a term used by biologists to refer to the potential energy available for release in a chemical reaction. Recall that catabolic pathways release energy by breaking down complex molecules. Biologists say that these complex molecules, such as glucose, are high in chemical energy. During a catabolic reaction, some bonds are broken and others formed, releasing energy and resulting in lower-energy breakdown products. This transformation also occurs, for example, in the engine of a car when the hydrocarbons of gasoline react explosively with oxygen, releasing the energy that pushes the pistons and producing exhaust. Although less explosive, a similar reaction of food molecules with oxygen provides chemical energy in biological systems, producing carbon dioxide and water as waste products. Biochemical pathways, carried out in the context of cellular structures, enable cells to release chemical energy from food molecules and use the energy to power life processes.

How is energy converted from one form to another? Consider the divers in **Figure 8.2**. The young woman climbing the ladder to the diving platform is releasing chemical energy from the food she ate for lunch and using some of that energy to perform the work of climbing. The kinetic energy of muscle movement is thus being transformed into potential energy due to her increasing height above the water. The young man diving is converting his potential energy to kinetic energy, which is then transferred to the water as he enters it. A small amount of energy is lost as heat due to friction.

Now let's consider the original source of the organic food molecules that provided the necessary chemical energy for the diver to climb the steps. This chemical energy was itself derived from light energy by plants during photosynthesis. Organisms are energy transformers.

The Laws of Energy Transformation

The study of the energy transformations that occur in a collection of matter is called **thermodynamics**. Scientists use the word *system* to denote the matter under study; they refer to the rest of the universe—everything outside the system—as the *surroundings*. A completely *isolated system* is unable to exchange either energy or matter with its surroundings; this can be approximated by a thermos bottle that partially isolates the contents from the surroundings. In an *open system*, energy and matter can be transferred between the system and its surroundings. Organisms are open systems. They absorb energy—for instance, light energy or chemical energy in the form of organic molecules—and release heat and metabolic waste products, such as carbon dioxide, to the surroundings. Two laws of thermodynamics govern energy transformations in organisms and all other collections of matter.

A diver has more potential energy on the platform than in the water.

Diving converts potential energy to kinetic energy.

Climbing up converts the kinetic energy of muscle movement to potential energy.

A diver has less potential energy in the water than on the platform.

Stephen Simpson/Photolibrary/Getty Images

▲ Figure 8.2 **Transformations between potential and kinetic energy.**

The First Law of Thermodynamics

According to the **first law of thermodynamics**, the energy of the universe is constant: *Energy can be transferred and transformed, but it cannot be created or destroyed.* The first law is also known as the *principle of conservation of energy*. The electric company does not make energy, but merely converts it to a form that is convenient for us to use. By converting sunlight to chemical energy, a plant acts as an energy transformer, not an energy producer.

The brown bear in **Figure 8.3a** will convert the chemical energy of the organic molecules in its food to kinetic and

Chemical energy

Robert N. Johnson/RnJ Photography

Heat

CO_2
+
H_2O

RnJ Photography

(a) First law of thermodynamics: Energy can be transferred or transformed but neither created nor destroyed. For example, chemical reactions in this brown bear (*Ursus arctos*) will convert the chemical (potential) energy in the fish into the kinetic energy of running, shown in (b).

(b) Second law of thermodynamics: Every energy transfer or transformation increases the disorder (entropy) of the universe. For example, as it runs, disorder is increased around the bear by the release of heat and small molecules that are the by-products of metabolism. A brown bear can run at speeds up to 56 km/hr—as fast as a racehorse.

▲ Figure 8.3 **The two laws of thermodynamics.**

other forms of energy as it carries out biological processes. What happens to this energy after it has performed work? The second law of thermodynamics helps to answer this question.

The Second Law of Thermodynamics

If energy cannot be destroyed, why can't organisms simply recycle their energy over and over again? It turns out that during every energy transfer or transformation, some energy becomes unavailable to do work. In most energy transformations, more usable forms of energy are at least partly converted to thermal energy and released as heat. Only a small fraction of the chemical energy from the food in Figure 8.3a is transformed into the motion of the brown bear shown in **Figure 8.3b**; most is lost as heat, which dissipates rapidly through the surroundings.

In the process of carrying out chemical reactions that perform various kinds of work, living cells unavoidably convert other forms of energy to heat. A system can put this energy to work only when there is a temperature difference that results in thermal energy flowing as heat from a warmer location to a cooler one. If temperature is uniform, as it is in a living cell, then the heat generated during a chemical reaction will simply warm a body of matter, such as the organism. (This can make a room crowded with people uncomfortably warm, as each person is carrying out a multitude of chemical reactions!)

A logical consequence of the loss of usable energy as heat to the surroundings is that each energy transfer or transformation makes the universe more disordered. Scientists use a quantity called **entropy** as a measure of disorder, or randomness. The more randomly arranged a collection of matter is, the greater its entropy. We can now state the **second law of thermodynamics**: *Every energy transfer or transformation increases the entropy of the universe.* Although order can increase locally, there is an unstoppable trend toward randomization of the universe as a whole.

In many cases, increased entropy is evident in the physical disintegration of a system's organized structure. For example, you can observe increasing entropy in the gradual decay of an unmaintained building. Much of the increasing entropy of the universe is less obvious, however, because it takes the form of increasing amounts of heat and less ordered forms of matter. As the bear in Figure 8.3b converts chemical energy to kinetic energy, it is also increasing the disorder of its surroundings by producing heat and small molecules, such as the CO_2 it exhales, that are the breakdown products of food.

The concept of entropy helps us understand why certain processes are energetically favourable and occur on their own. It turns out that if a given process, by itself, leads to an increase in entropy, that process can proceed without requiring an input of energy. Such a process is called a **spontaneous process**. Note that as we're using it here, the word *spontaneous* does not imply that the process would occur quickly; rather, the word signifies that it is energetically favourable. (In fact, it may be helpful for you to think of the phrase "energetically favourable" when you read the formal term "spontaneous.") Some spontaneous processes, such as an explosion, may be virtually instantaneous, while others, such as the rusting of an old car over time, are much slower.

A process that, considered on its own, leads to a decrease in entropy is said to be nonspontaneous: It will happen only if energy is supplied. We know from experience that certain events occur spontaneously and others do not. For instance, we know that water flows downhill spontaneously but moves uphill only with an input of energy, such as when a machine pumps the water against gravity. Some energy is inevitably lost as heat, increasing entropy in the surroundings, so usage of energy ensures that a nonspontaneous process also leads to an increase in the entropy of the universe as a whole.

Biological Order and Disorder

Living systems increase the entropy of their surroundings, as predicted by thermodynamic law. It is true that cells create ordered structures from less organized starting materials. For example, simpler molecules are ordered into the more complex structure of an amino acid, and amino acids are ordered into polypeptide chains. At the organismal level as well, complex and beautifully ordered structures result from biological processes that use simpler starting materials (Figure 8.4). However, an organism also takes in organized

Georgette Douwman/Nature Picture Library

asharkyu/Shutterstock

▲ Figure 8.4 **Order as a characteristic of life.** Order is evident in the detailed structures of the sea urchin skeleton and the succulent plant shown here. As open systems, organisms can increase their order as long as the order of their surroundings decreases.

forms of matter and energy from the surroundings and replaces them with less ordered forms. For example, an animal obtains starch, proteins, and other complex molecules from the food it eats. As catabolic pathways break these molecules down, the animal releases carbon dioxide and water—small molecules that possess less chemical energy than the food did. (See Figure 8.3b.) The depletion of chemical energy is accounted for by heat generated during metabolism. On a larger scale, energy flows into most ecosystems in the form of light and exits in the form of heat (see Figure 1.11).

During the early history of life, complex organisms evolved from simpler ancestors. For instance, we can trace the ancestry of the plant kingdom from much simpler organisms called green algae to more complex flowering plants. However, this increase in organization over time in no way violates the second law. The entropy of a particular system, such as an organism, may actually decrease as long as the total entropy of the *universe*—the system plus its surroundings—increases. Thus, organisms are islands of low entropy in an increasingly random universe. The evolution of biological order is perfectly consistent with the laws of thermodynamics.

CONCEPT CHECK 8.1

1. **MAKE CONNECTIONS** How does the second law of thermodynamics help explain the diffusion of a substance across a membrane? See Figure 7.11.

2. Describe the forms of energy found in an apple as it grows on a tree, then falls, then is digested by someone who eats it.

3. **WHAT IF?** If you place a teaspoon of sugar in the bottom of a glass of water, it will dissolve completely over time. Left longer, eventually the water will disappear and the sugar crystals will reappear. Explain these observations in terms of entropy.

For suggested answers, see Appendix A.

CONCEPT 8.2

The free-energy change of a reaction tells us whether or not the reaction occurs spontaneously

The laws of thermodynamics that we've just discussed apply to the universe as a whole. As biologists, we want to understand the chemical reactions of life—for example, which reactions occur spontaneously and which ones require some input of energy from outside. But how can we know this without assessing the energy and entropy changes in the entire universe for each separate reaction?

Free Energy Change, ΔG

Recall that the universe is really equivalent to "the system" plus "the surroundings." In 1878, J. Willard Gibbs, a professor at Yale, defined a very useful function called the Gibbs free energy of a system (without considering its surroundings), symbolized by the letter G. We'll refer to the Gibbs free energy simply as free energy. **Free energy** is the portion of a system's energy that can perform work when temperature and pressure are uniform throughout the system, as in a living cell. Let's consider how we determine the free-energy change that occurs when a system changes—for example, during a chemical reaction.

The change in free energy, ΔG, can be calculated for a chemical reaction by applying the following equation:

$$\Delta G = \Delta H - T\Delta S$$

This equation uses only properties of the system (the reaction) itself: ΔH symbolizes the change in the system's *enthalpy* (in biological systems, equivalent to total energy); ΔS is the change in the system's entropy; and T is the absolute temperature in Kelvin (K) units (K = °C + 273).

Once we know the value of ΔG for a process, we can use it to predict whether the process will be spontaneous (that is, whether it is energetically favourable and will occur without an input of energy). More than a century of experiments has shown that only processes with a negative ΔG are spontaneous. For ΔG to be negative, either ΔH must be negative (the system gives up enthalpy and H decreases) or $T\Delta S$ must be positive (the system gives up order and S increases), or both: When ΔH and $T\Delta S$ are tallied, ΔG has a negative value ($\Delta G < 0$) for all spontaneous processes. In other words, every spontaneous process decreases the system's free energy, and processes that have a positive or zero ΔG are never spontaneous.

This information is immensely interesting to biologists, for it gives us the power to predict which kinds of change can happen without an input of energy. Such spontaneous changes can be harnessed to perform work. This principle is very important in the study of metabolism, where a major goal is to determine which reactions can supply energy for cellular work.

Free Energy, Stability, and Equilibrium

As we saw in the previous section, when a process occurs spontaneously in a system, we can be sure that ΔG is negative. Another way to think of ΔG is to realize that it represents the difference between the free energy of the final state and the free energy of the initial state:

$$\Delta G = G_{\text{final state}} - G_{\text{initial state}}$$

Thus, ΔG can be negative only when the process involves a loss of free energy during the change from initial state to final state. Because it has less free energy, the system in its final state is less likely to change and is therefore more stable than it was previously.

We can think of free energy as a measure of a system's instability—its tendency to change to a more stable state. Unstable systems (higher G) tend to change in such a way that they become more stable (lower G). For example, a diver on top of a platform is less stable (more likely to fall) than when floating in the water; a drop of concentrated dye is less stable (more likely to disperse) than when the dye is spread randomly through the liquid; and a glucose molecule is less stable (more likely to break down) than the simpler molecules into which it can be split (Figure 8.5). Unless something prevents it, each of these systems will move toward greater stability: The diver falls, the solution becomes uniformly coloured, and the glucose molecule is broken down into smaller molecules.

Another term that describes a state of maximum stability is *equilibrium*, which you learned about in Chapter 2 in connection with chemical reactions. There is an important relationship between free energy and equilibrium, including chemical equilibrium. Recall that most chemical reactions are reversible and proceed to a point at which the forward and backward reactions occur at the same rate. The reaction is then said to be at chemical equilibrium, and

there is no further net change in the relative concentration of products and reactants.

As a reaction proceeds toward equilibrium, the free energy of the mixture of reactants and products decreases. Free energy increases when a reaction is somehow pushed away from equilibrium, perhaps by removing some of the products (and thus changing their concentration relative to that of the reactants). For a system at equilibrium, G is at its lowest possible value in that system. We can think of the equilibrium state as a free-energy valley. Any change from the equilibrium position will have a positive ΔG and will not be spontaneous. For this reason, systems never spontaneously move away from equilibrium. Because a system at equilibrium cannot spontaneously change, it can do no work. *A process is spontaneous and can perform work only when it is moving toward equilibrium.*

Free Energy and Metabolism

We can now apply the free-energy concept more specifically to the chemistry of life's processes.

Exergonic and Endergonic Reactions in Metabolism

Based on their free-energy changes, chemical reactions can be classified as either exergonic ("energy outward")

- More free energy (higher *G*)
- Less stable
- Greater work capacity

In a **spontaneous change**
- The free energy of the system decreases ($\Delta G < 0$)
- The system becomes more stable
- The released free energy can be harnessed to do work

- Less free energy (lower *G*)
- More stable
- Less work capacity

(a) Gravitational motion. Objects move spontaneously from a higher altitude to a lower one.

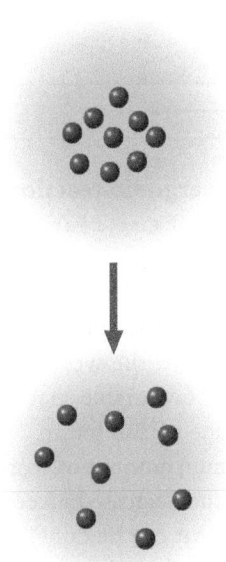

(b) Diffusion. Molecules in a drop of dye diffuse until they are randomly dispersed.

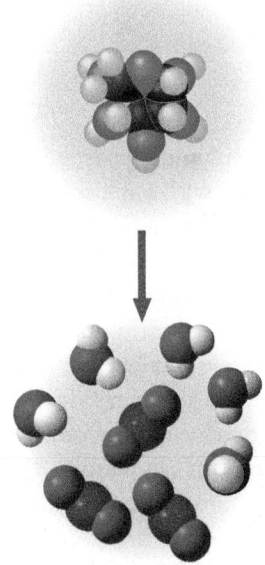

(c) Chemical reaction. In a cell, a glucose molecule is broken down into simpler molecules.

▲ Figure 8.5 **The relationship of free energy to stability, work capacity, and spontaneous change.** Unstable systems (top) are rich in free energy, *G*. They have a tendency to change spontaneously to a more stable state (bottom), and it is possible to harness this "downhill" change to perform work.

MAKE CONNECTIONS *Compare the redistribution of molecules shown in (b) to the transport of hydrogen ions (H^+) across a membrane by a proton pump, creating a concentration gradient, as shown in Figure 7.17. Which process(es) result(s) in higher free energy? Which system(s) can do work?*

(a) Exergonic reaction: energy released, spontaneous

(b) Endergonic reaction: energy required, nonspontaneous

or endergonic ("energy inward"). An **exergonic reaction** proceeds with a net release of free energy (Figure 8.6a). Because the chemical mixture loses free energy (G decreases), ΔG is negative for an exergonic reaction. Using ΔG as a standard for spontaneity, exergonic reactions are those that occur spontaneously. (Remember, the word *spontaneous* implies that it is energetically favourable, not that it will occur rapidly.) The magnitude of ΔG for an exergonic reaction represents the maximum amount of work the reaction can perform.★ The greater the decrease in free energy, the greater the amount of work that can be done.

We can use the overall reaction for cellular respiration as an example:

$$C_6H_{12}O_6 + 6\ O_2 \rightarrow 6\ CO_2 + 6\ H_2O$$
$$\Delta G = -2870\ kJ/mol$$

For each mole (180 g) of glucose broken down by respiration under what are called "standard conditions" (1 M of

each reactant and product, 25°C, pH 7), 2870 kJ of energy are made available for work. Because energy must be conserved, the chemical products of respiration store 2870 kJ less free energy per mole than the reactants. The products are, in a sense, the spent exhaust of a process that tapped the free energy stored in the bonds of the sugar molecules.

It is important to realize that the breaking of bonds does not release energy; on the contrary, as you will soon see, it requires energy. The phrase "energy stored in bonds" is shorthand for the potential energy that can be released when new bonds are formed after the original bonds break, as long as the products are of lower free energy than the reactants.

An **endergonic reaction** is one that absorbs free energy from its surroundings (Figure 8.6b). Because this kind of reaction essentially *stores* free energy in molecules (G increases), ΔG is positive. Such reactions are nonspontaneous, and the magnitude of ΔG is the quantity of energy required to drive the reaction. If a chemical process is exergonic (downhill), releasing energy in one direction, then the reverse process must be endergonic (uphill), using energy. A reversible process cannot be downhill in both directions. If $\Delta G = -2870\ kJ/mol$ for respiration, which converts glucose and oxygen to carbon dioxide and water, then the reverse process—the conversion of carbon dioxide and water to glucose and oxygen—must be strongly endergonic, with $\Delta G = +2870\ kJ/mol$. Such a reaction would never happen by itself.

How, then, do plants make the sugar that organisms use for energy? Plants get the required energy—2870 kJ to make a mole of glucose—from the environment by capturing light and converting its energy to chemical energy. Next, in a long series of exergonic steps, they gradually spend that chemical energy to assemble glucose molecules.

Equilibrium and Metabolism

Reactions in an isolated system eventually reach equilibrium and can then do no work, as illustrated by the isolated hydroelectric system in Figure 8.7. The chemical reactions of metabolism are reversible, and they, too, would reach

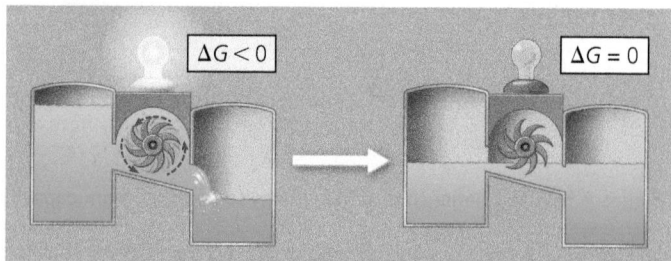

▲ Figure 8.7 **Equilibrium and work in an isolated hydroelectric system.** Water flowing downhill turns a turbine that drives a generator providing electricity to a lightbulb, but only until the system reaches equilibrium.

★The word maximum qualifies this statement, because some of the free energy is released as heat and cannot do work. Therefore, ΔG represents a theoretical upper limit of available energy.

equilibrium if they occurred in the isolation of a test tube. Because systems at equilibrium are at a minimum of *G* and can do no work, a cell that has reached metabolic equilibrium is dead! The fact that metabolism as a whole is never at equilibrium is one of the defining features of life.

Like most systems, a living cell is not in equilibrium. The constant flow of materials in and out of the cell keeps the metabolic pathways from ever reaching equilibrium, and the cell continues to do work throughout its life. This principle is illustrated by the open (and more realistic) hydroelectric system in **Figure 8.8a**. However, unlike this simple system in which water flowing downhill turns a single turbine, a catabolic pathway in a cell releases free energy in a series of reactions. An example is cellular respiration, illustrated by analogy in **Figure 8.8b**. Some of the reversible reactions of respiration are constantly "pulled" in one direction—that is, they are kept out of equilibrium. The key to maintaining this lack of equilibrium is that the product of a reaction does not accumulate but instead becomes a reactant in the next step; finally, waste products are expelled from the cell. The overall sequence of reactions is kept going by the huge free-energy difference between glucose and oxygen at the top of the energy "hill" and carbon dioxide and water at the "downhill" end. As long as our cells have a steady supply of glucose or other fuels and oxygen and are able to expel waste products to the surroundings, their metabolic pathways never reach equilibrium and can continue to do the work of life.

Stepping back to look at the big picture, we see once again how important it is to think of organisms as open systems. Sunlight provides a daily source of free energy for an ecosystem's plants and other photosynthetic organisms. Animals and other nonphotosynthetic organisms in an ecosystem must have a source of free energy in the form of the organic products of photosynthesis. Now that we have applied the free-energy concept to metabolism, we are ready to see how a cell actually performs the work of life.

CONCEPT CHECK 8.2

1. Cellular respiration uses glucose and oxygen, which have high levels of free energy, and releases CO_2 and water, which have low levels of free energy. Is cellular respiration spontaneous or not? Is it exergonic or endergonic? What happens to the energy released from glucose?

2. How would the processes of catabolism and anabolism relate to Figure 8.5c?

3. **WHAT IF?** Some night-time partygoers wear glow-in-the-dark necklaces. The necklaces start glowing once they are "activated" by snapping the necklace in a way that allows two chemicals to react and emit light in the form of chemiluminescence. Is the chemical reaction exergonic or endergonic? Explain your answer.

For suggested answers, see Appendix A.

CONCEPT 8.3

ATP powers cellular work by coupling exergonic reactions to endergonic reactions

A cell does three main kinds of work:

- *Chemical work*, the pushing of endergonic reactions that would not occur spontaneously, such as the synthesis of polymers from monomers (chemical work will be discussed further here and in Chapters 9 and 10)
- *Transport work*, the pumping of substances across membranes against the direction of spontaneous movement (see Chapter 7)
- *Mechanical work*, such as the beating of cilia (see Chapter 6), the contraction of muscle cells, and the movement of chromosomes during cellular reproduction

A key feature in the way cells manage their energy resources to do this work is **energy coupling**, the use of an exergonic process to drive an endergonic one. ATP is responsible for mediating most energy coupling in cells, and in most cases it acts as the immediate source of energy that powers cellular work.

(a) An open hydroelectric system. Water flowing through a turbine keeps driving the generator because intake and outflow of water keep the system from reaching equilibrium.

(b) A multistep open hydroelectric system. Cellular respiration is analogous to this system: Glucose is broken down in a series of exergonic reactions that power the work of the cell. The product of each reaction is used as the reactant for the next, so no reaction reaches equilibrium.

▲ Figure 8.8 **Equilibrium and work in open systems.**

The Structure and Hydrolysis of ATP

ATP (adenosine triphosphate) was introduced when we discussed the phosphate group as a functional group (see Concept 4.3). ATP contains the sugar ribose, with the nitrogenous base adenine and a chain of three phosphate groups (the triphosphate group) bonded to it (Figure 8.9a). In addition to its role in energy coupling, ATP is also one of the nucleoside triphosphates used to make RNA (see Figure 5.24).

The bonds between the phosphate groups of ATP can be broken by hydrolysis. When the terminal phosphate bond is broken by addition of a water molecule, a molecule of inorganic phosphate ($HOPO_3^{2-}$, abbreviated (P)$_i$ throughout this book) leaves the ATP, which becomes adenosine diphosphate, or ADP (Figure 8.9b). The reaction is exergonic and releases 30.5 kJ of energy per mole of ATP hydrolyzed:

$$ATP + H_2O \rightarrow ADP + \text{(P)}_i$$
$$\Delta G = -30.5 \text{ kJ/mol}$$

(a) **The structure of ATP.** In the cell, most hydroxyl groups of phosphates are ionized (—O⁻).

(b) **The hydrolysis of ATP.** The reaction of ATP and water yields inorganic phosphate ((P)$_i$) and ADP and releases energy.

▲ Figure 8.9 **The structure and hydrolysis of adenosine triphosphate (ATP).** Throughout this text, the chemical structure of the triphosphate group seen in **(a)** will be represented by the three joined yellow circles shown in **(b)**.

This is the free-energy change measured under standard conditions. In the cell, conditions do not conform to standard conditions, primarily because reactant and product concentrations differ from 1 *M*. For example, when ATP hydrolysis occurs under cellular conditions, the actual ΔG is about −54.4 kJ/mol, 78% greater than the energy released by ATP hydrolysis under standard conditions.

Because their hydrolysis releases energy, the phosphate bonds of ATP are sometimes referred to as high-energy phosphate bonds, but the term is misleading. The phosphate bonds of ATP are not unusually strong bonds, as "high-energy" may imply; rather, the reactants (ATP and water) themselves have high energy relative to the energy of the products (ADP and (P)$_i$). The release of energy during the hydrolysis of ATP comes from the chemical change to a state of lower free energy, not from the phosphate bonds themselves.

ATP is useful to the cell because the energy it releases on losing a phosphate group is somewhat greater than the energy most other molecules could deliver. But why does this hydrolysis release so much energy? If we reexamine the ATP molecule in Figure 8.9a, we can see that all three phosphate groups are negatively charged. These like charges are crowded together, and their mutual repulsion contributes to the instability of this region of the ATP molecule. The triphosphate tail of ATP is the chemical equivalent of a compressed spring.

How the Hydrolysis of ATP Performs Work

When ATP is hydrolyzed in a test tube, the release of free energy merely heats the surrounding water. In an organism, this same generation of heat can sometimes be beneficial. For instance, the process of shivering uses ATP hydrolysis during muscle contraction to warm the body. In most cases in the cell, however, the generation of heat alone would be an inefficient (and potentially dangerous) use of a valuable energy resource. Instead, the cell's proteins harness the energy released during ATP hydrolysis in several ways to perform the three types of cellular work—chemical, transport, and mechanical.

For example, with the help of specific enzymes, the cell is able to use the energy released by ATP hydrolysis directly to drive chemical reactions that, by themselves, are endergonic. If the ΔG of an endergonic reaction is less than the amount of energy released by ATP hydrolysis, then the two reactions can be coupled so that, overall, the coupled reactions are exergonic (Figure 8.10). This usually involves phosphorylation, the transfer of a phosphate group from ATP to some other molecule, such as the reactant. The recipient molecule with the phosphate group covalently bonded to it is then called a **phosphorylated intermediate**. The key to coupling exergonic and endergonic reactions is the formation of this phosphorylated

(a) Glutamic acid conversion to glutamine.
Glutamine synthesis from glutamic acid
(Glu) by itself is endergonic (ΔG is positive),
so it is not spontaneous.

$\Delta G_{Glu} = +14.2$ kJ/mol

**(b) Conversion reaction coupled with ATP
hydrolysis.** In the cell, glutamine synthesis
occurs in two steps, coupled by a phosphorylated intermediate. ❶ ATP phosphorylates
glutamic acid, making it less stable.
❷ Ammonia displaces the phosphate group,
forming glutamine.

**(c) Free-energy change for coupled
reaction.** ΔG for the glutamic acid
conversion to glutamine (+14.2 kJ/mol)
plus ΔG for ATP hydrolysis (–30.5 kJ/mol)
gives the free-energy change for the
overall reaction (–16.3 kJ/mol). Because
the overall process is exergonic (net ΔG is
negative), it occurs spontaneously.

$\Delta G_{Glu} = +14.2$ kJ/mol
$+ \Delta G_{ATP} = -30.5$ kJ/mol

Net $\Delta G = -16.3$ kJ/mol

▲ **Figure 8.10   How ATP drives chemical work: Energy coupling using ATP hydrolysis.** In this
example, the exergonic process of ATP hydrolysis is used to drive an endergonic process—the cellular
synthesis of the amino acid glutamine from glutamic acid and ammonia.

MAKE CONNECTIONS   *Referring to Figure 5.14, explain why glutamine (Gln) is diagrammed as
a glutamic acid (Glu) with an amino group attached.*

intermediate, which is more reactive (less stable) than the
original unphosphorylated molecule.

Transport and mechanical work in the cell are also
nearly always powered by the hydrolysis of ATP. In these
cases, ATP hydrolysis leads to a change in a protein's shape
and often its ability to bind another molecule. Sometimes
this occurs via a phosphorylated intermediate, as seen for
the transport protein in **Figure 8.11a**. In most instances
of mechanical work involving motor proteins "walking"

along cytoskeletal elements (**Figure 8.11b**), a cycle occurs
in which ATP is first bound noncovalently to the motor
protein. Next, ATP is hydrolyzed, releasing ADP and Ⓟᵢ.
Another ATP molecule can then bind. At each stage, the
motor protein changes its shape and ability to bind the
cytoskeleton, resulting in movement of the protein along
the cytoskeletal track. Phosphorylation and dephosphorylation promote crucial protein shape changes during many
other important cellular processes as well.

(a) Transport work: ATP phosphorylates transport proteins.

(b) Mechanical work: ATP binds noncovalently to motor proteins
and then is hydrolyzed.

▲ **Figure 8.11   How ATP drives transport and mechanical work.** ATP hydrolysis causes changes in the shapes and binding affinities of proteins.
This can occur either **(a)** directly, by phosphorylation, as shown for a membrane protein carrying out active transport of a solute (see also Figure 7.15),
or **(b)** indirectly, via noncovalent binding of ATP and its hydrolytic products, as is the case for motor proteins that move vesicles (and other organelles)
along cytoskeletal "tracks" in the cell (see also Figure 6.21).

ATP synthesis from ADP + Ⓟ$_i$ requires energy.

ATP hydrolysis to ADP + Ⓟ$_i$ yields energy.

Energy from catabolism (exergonic, energy-releasing processes)

Energy for cellular work (endergonic, energy-consuming processes)

▲ **Figure 8.12** **The ATP cycle.** Energy released by breakdown reactions (catabolism) in the cell is used to phosphorylate ADP, regenerating ATP. Chemical potential energy stored in ATP drives most cellular work.

The Regeneration of ATP

An organism at work uses ATP continuously, but ATP is a renewable resource that can be regenerated by the addition of phosphate to ADP (Figure 8.12). The free energy required to phosphorylate ADP comes from exergonic breakdown reactions (catabolism) in the cell. This shuttling of inorganic phosphate and energy is called the ATP cycle, and it couples the cell's energy-yielding (exergonic) processes to the energy-consuming (endergonic) ones. The ATP cycle proceeds at an astonishing pace. For example, a working muscle cell recycles its entire pool of ATP in less than a minute. That turnover represents 10 million molecules of ATP consumed and regenerated per second per cell. If ATP could not be regenerated by the phosphorylation of ADP, humans would use up nearly their body weight in ATP each day.

Because both directions of a reversible process cannot be downhill, the regeneration of ATP from ADP and Ⓟ$_i$ is necessarily endergonic:

$$ADP + Ⓟ_i \rightarrow ATP + H_2O$$

$$\Delta G = +30.5 \text{ kJ/mol (standard conditions)}$$

Since ATP formation from ADP and Ⓟ$_i$ is not spontaneous, free energy must be spent to make it occur. Catabolic (exergonic) pathways, especially cellular respiration, provide the energy for the endergonic process of making ATP. Plants also use light energy to produce ATP. Thus, the ATP cycle is a revolving door through which energy passes during its transfer from catabolic to anabolic pathways.

CONCEPT CHECK 8.3

1. How does ATP typically transfer energy from exergonic to endergonic reactions in the cell?

2. Which of the following combinations has more free energy: glutamic acid + ammonia + ATP, or glutamine + ADP + Ⓟ$_i$? Explain your answer.

3. **MAKE CONNECTIONS** Does Figure 8.11a show passive or active transport? Explain. (See Concepts 7.3 and 7.4.)

For suggested answers, see Appendix A.

Enzymes speed up metabolic reactions by lowering energy barriers

The laws of thermodynamics tell us what will and will not happen under given conditions but say nothing about the rate of these processes. A spontaneous chemical reaction occurs without any requirement for outside energy, but it may occur so slowly that it is imperceptible. For example, even though the hydrolysis of sucrose (table sugar) to glucose and fructose is exergonic, occurring spontaneously with a release of free energy ($\Delta G = -29.3$ kJ/mol), a solution of sucrose dissolved in sterile water will sit for years at room temperature with no appreciable hydrolysis. However, if we add a small amount of the enzyme sucrase to the solution, then all the sucrose may be hydrolyzed within seconds, as shown below:

Sucrase

Sucrose ($C_{12}H_{22}O_{11}$) + H_2O → Glucose ($C_6H_{12}O_6$) + Fructose ($C_6H_{12}O_6$)

How does the enzyme do this?

An **enzyme** is a macromolecule that acts as a **catalyst**, a chemical agent that speeds up a reaction without being consumed by the reaction. In this chapter, we are focusing on enzymes that are proteins. (Some RNA molecules, called ribozymes, can function as enzymes; these will be discussed in Chapters 17 and 25.) Without regulation by enzymes, chemical traffic through the pathways of metabolism would become terribly congested because many chemical reactions would take such a long time. In the next two sections, we will see why spontaneous reactions can be slow and how an enzyme changes the situation.

The Activation Energy Barrier

Every chemical reaction between molecules involves both bond breaking and bond forming. For example, the hydrolysis of sucrose involves breaking the bond between glucose and fructose and one of the bonds of a water molecule and then forming two new bonds, as shown above. Changing one molecule into another generally involves contorting the starting molecule into a highly unstable state before the reaction can proceed. This contortion can be compared to the bending of a metal key ring when you pry it open to add a new key. The key ring is highly unstable in its opened form but returns to a stable state once the key is threaded all the way onto the ring. To reach the contorted state where bonds can change, reactant molecules must absorb energy from their surroundings. When the new bonds of the product molecules form, energy is released as heat, and the molecules return to stable shapes with lower energy than the contorted state.

The initial investment of energy for starting a reaction—the energy required to contort the reactant molecules so the bonds can break—is known as the *free energy of activation*, or **activation energy**, abbreviated E_A in this book. We can think of activation energy as the amount of energy needed to push the reactants to the top of an energy barrier, or uphill, so that the "downhill" part of the reaction can begin. Activation energy is often supplied by heat in the form of thermal energy that the reactant molecules absorb from the surroundings. The absorption of thermal energy accelerates the reactant molecules, so they collide more often and more forcefully. It also agitates the atoms within the molecules, making the breakage of bonds more likely. When the molecules have absorbed enough energy for the bonds to break, the reactants are in an unstable condition known as the *transition state*.

Figure 8.13 graphs the energy changes for a hypothetical exergonic reaction that swaps portions of two reactant molecules:

$$AB + CD \rightarrow AC + BD$$
Reactants   Products

The activation of the reactants is represented by the uphill portion of the graph, in which the free-energy content of the reactant molecules is increasing. At the summit, when energy equivalent to E_A has been absorbed, the reactants are in the transition state: They are activated, and their bonds can be broken. As the atoms then settle into their new, more stable bonding arrangements, energy is released to the surroundings. This corresponds to the downhill part of the curve, which shows the loss of free energy by the molecules. The overall decrease in free energy means that E_A is repaid with dividends, as the formation of new bonds releases more energy than was invested in the breaking of old bonds.

The reaction shown in Figure 8.13 is exergonic and occurs spontaneously ($\Delta G < 0$). However, the activation energy provides a barrier that determines the rate of the reaction. The reactants must absorb enough energy to reach the top of the activation energy barrier before the reaction can occur. For some reactions, E_A is modest enough that even at room temperature there is sufficient thermal energy for many of the reactant molecules to reach the transition state in a short time. In most cases, however, E_A is so high and the transition state is reached so rarely that the reaction will hardly proceed at all. In these cases, the reaction will occur at a noticeable rate only if energy is provided, usually by heat. For example, the reaction of gasoline and oxygen is exergonic and will occur spontaneously, but energy is required for the molecules to reach the transition state and react. Only when the spark plugs fire in an automobile engine can there be the explosive release of energy that pushes the pistons. Without a spark, a mixture of gasoline hydrocarbons and oxygen will not react because the E_A barrier is too high.

How Enzymes Speed Up Reactions

Proteins, DNA, and other complex cellular molecules are rich in free energy and have the potential to decompose spontaneously; that is, the laws of thermodynamics favour their breakdown. These molecules persist only because at temperatures typical for cells, few molecules can make it over the hump of activation energy. The barriers for selected reactions must occasionally be surmounted, however, for cells to carry out the processes needed for life. Heat can increase the rate of a reaction by allowing reactants to attain the transition state more often, but this would not work well in biological systems. First, high temperature denatures proteins and kills cells. Second, heat would speed up *all* reactions, not just those that are needed. Instead of heat, organisms use catalysis to speed up reactions.

An enzyme catalyzes a reaction by lowering the E_A barrier **(Figure 8.14)**, enabling the reactant molecules to absorb enough

The reactants AB and CD must absorb enough energy from the surroundings to reach the unstable transition state, where bonds can break.

After bonds have broken, new bonds form, releasing energy to the surroundings.

Transition state

E_A

Reactants

Products

$\Delta G < 0$

Progress of the reaction →

Free energy →

▲ Figure 8.13 **Energy profile of an exergonic reaction.** The "molecules" are hypothetical, with A, B, C, and D representing portions of the molecules. Thermodynamically, this is an exergonic reaction, with a negative ΔG, and the reaction occurs spontaneously. However, the activation energy (E_A) provides a barrier that determines the rate of the reaction.

DRAW IT *Graph the progress of an endergonic reaction in which EF and GH form products EG and FH, assuming that the reactants must pass through a transition state.*

▲ **Figure 8.14** **The effect of an enzyme on activation energy.** Without affecting the free-energy change (ΔG) for a reaction, an enzyme speeds the reaction by reducing its activation energy (E$_A$).

energy to reach the transition state even at moderate temperatures, as we'll discuss shortly. An enzyme cannot change the ΔG for a reaction; it cannot make an endergonic reaction exergonic. Enzymes can only hasten reactions that would eventually occur anyway, but this enables the cell to have a dynamic metabolism, routing chemicals smoothly through metabolic pathways. Also, enzymes are very specific for the reactions they catalyze, so they determine which chemical processes will be going on in the cell at any given time.

Substrate Specificity of Enzymes

The reactant an enzyme acts on is referred to as the enzyme's **substrate**. The enzyme binds to its substrate (or substrates, when there are two or more reactants), forming an **enzyme-substrate complex**. While enzyme and substrate are joined, the catalytic action of the enzyme converts the substrate to the product (or products) of the reaction. The overall process can be summarized as follows:

$$\text{Enzyme} + \text{Substrate(s)} \rightleftharpoons \text{Enzyme-substrate complex} \rightleftharpoons \text{Enzyme} + \text{Product(s)}$$

For example, the enzyme sucrase (most enzyme names end in *-ase*) catalyzes the hydrolysis of the disaccharide sucrose into its two monosaccharides, glucose and fructose (see p. 164):

$$\text{Sucrase} + \text{Sucrose} + \text{H}_2\text{O} \rightleftharpoons \text{Sucrase-sucrose-H}_2\text{O complex} \rightleftharpoons \text{Sucrase} + \text{Glucose} + \text{Fructose}$$

The reaction catalyzed by each enzyme is very specific; an enzyme can recognize its specific substrate even among closely related compounds. For instance, sucrase will act only on sucrose and will not bind to other disaccharides, such as maltose. What accounts for this molecular recognition? Recall that most enzymes are proteins, and proteins are macromolecules with unique three-dimensional configurations. The specificity of an enzyme results from its shape, which is a consequence of its amino acid sequence.

Only a restricted region of the enzyme molecule actually binds to the substrate. This region, called the **active site**, is typically a pocket or groove on the surface of the enzyme where catalysis occurs (**Figure 8.15a**). Usually, the active site is formed by only a few of the enzyme's amino acids, with the rest of the protein molecule providing a framework that determines the shape of the active site. The specificity of an enzyme is attributed to a complementary fit between the shape of its active site and the shape of the substrate, as well as a complementary match between the charged amino acids found in the active site and charged regions of the substrate.

An enzyme is not a stiff structure locked into a given shape. In fact, recent work by biochemists has shown clearly that enzymes (and other proteins as well) seem to "dance" between subtly different shapes in a dynamic equilibrium, with slight differences in free energy for each "pose." The shape that best fits the substrate isn't necessarily the one with the lowest energy, but during the very short time the enzyme takes on this shape, its active site can bind to the substrate. It has been known for more than 50 years that the active site itself is also not a rigid receptacle for the substrate. As the substrate enters the active site, the enzyme changes shape slightly due to interactions between the substrate's chemical groups

Enzyme

Enzyme-substrate complex

(a) In this space-filling model of the enzyme hexokinase (blue), the active site forms a groove on the surface. The enzyme's substrate is glucose (red).

(b) When the substrate enters the active site, it forms weak bonds with the enzyme, inducing a change in the shape of the protein. This change allows additional weak bonds to form, causing the active site to enfold the substrate and hold it in place.

▲ **Figure 8.15** **Induced fit between an enzyme and its substrate.**

and chemical groups on the side chains of the amino acids that form the active site. This shape change makes the active site fit even more snugly around the substrate (Figure 8.15b). The process is like a clasping handshake, with binding between enzyme and substrate becoming tighter after the initial contact. This so-called **induced fit** brings chemical groups of the active site into positions that enhance their ability to catalyze the chemical reaction.

Catalysis in the Enzyme's Active Site

In most enzymatic reactions, the substrate is held in the active site by so-called weak interactions, such as hydrogen bonds and ionic bonds. R groups of a few of the amino acids that make up the active site catalyze the conversion of substrate to product, and the product departs from the active site. The enzyme is then free to take another substrate molecule into its active site. The entire cycle happens so fast that a single enzyme molecule typically acts on about a thousand substrate molecules per second, and some enzymes are even faster. Enzymes, like other catalysts, emerge from the reaction in their original form. Therefore, very small amounts of enzyme can have a huge metabolic impact by functioning over and over again in catalytic cycles. Figure 8.16 shows a catalytic cycle involving two substrates and two products.

1 Substrates enter active site; enzyme changes shape such that its active site enfolds the substrates (induced fit).

2 Substrates are held in active site by weak interactions, such as hydrogen bonds and ionic bonds.

Substrates

Enzyme-substrate complex

5 Active site is available for two new substrate molecules.

Enzyme

4 Products are released.

Products

3 Substrates are converted to products.

▲ Figure 8.16 **The active site and catalytic cycle of an enzyme.** An enzyme can convert one or more reactant molecules to one or more product molecules. The enzyme shown here converts two substrate molecules to two product molecules.

DRAW IT *The enzyme-substrate complex passes through a transition state (see Figure 8.13). Label the part of the cycle where the transition state occurs.*

Most metabolic reactions are reversible, and an enzyme can catalyze either the forward or the reverse reaction, depending on which direction has a negative ΔG. This in turn depends mainly on the relative concentrations of reactants and products. The net effect is always in the direction of equilibrium.

Enzymes use a variety of mechanisms that lower activation energy and speed up a reaction (see Figure 8.16, step **3**):

- When there are two or more reactants, the active site provides a template on which the substrates can come together in the proper orientation for a reaction to occur between them.
- As the active site of an enzyme clutches the bound substrates, the enzyme may stretch the substrate molecules toward their transition-state form, stressing and bending critical chemical bonds that must be broken during the reaction. Because E_A is proportional to the difficulty of breaking the bonds, distorting the substrate helps it approach the transition state and thus reduces the amount of free energy that must be absorbed to achieve that state.
- The active site may also provide a microenvironment that is more conducive to a particular type of reaction than the solution itself would be without the enzyme. For example, if the active site has amino acids with acidic R groups, the active site may be a pocket of low pH in an otherwise neutral cell. In such cases, an acidic amino acid may facilitate H^+ transfer to the substrate as a key step in catalyzing the reaction.
- Amino acids in the active site directly participate in the chemical reaction. Sometimes this process even involves brief covalent bonding between the substrate and the side chain of an amino acid of the enzyme. Subsequent steps of the reaction restore the side chains to their original states, so that the active site is the same after the reaction as it was before.

The rate at which a particular amount of enzyme converts substrate to product is partly a function of the initial concentration of the substrate: The more substrate molecules that are available, the more frequently they access the active sites of the enzyme molecules. However, there is a limit to how fast the reaction can be pushed by adding more substrate to a fixed concentration of enzyme. At some point, the concentration of substrate will be high enough that all enzyme molecules have their active sites engaged. As soon as the product exits an active site, another substrate molecule enters. At this substrate concentration, the enzyme is said to be *saturated*, and the rate of the reaction is determined by the speed at which the active site converts substrate to product. When an enzyme population is saturated, the only way to increase the rate of product formation is to add more enzyme. Cells often increase the rate of a reaction by producing more enzyme molecules. You can graph the overall progress of an enzymatic reaction in the Scientific Skills Exercise.

Making a Line Graph and Calculating a Slope

Does the Rate of Glucose 6-Phosphatase Activity Change over Time in Isolated Liver Cells? Glucose 6-phosphatase, which is found in mammalian liver cells, is a key enzyme in control of blood glucose levels. The enzyme catalyzes the breakdown of glucose 6-phosphate into glucose and inorganic phosphate ($(P)_i$). These products are transported out of liver cells into the blood, increasing blood glucose levels. In this exercise, you will graph data from a time-course experiment that measured $(P)_i$ concentration in the buffer outside isolated liver cells, thus indirectly measuring glucose 6-phosphatase activity inside the cells.

How the Experiment Was Done Isolated rat liver cells were placed in a dish with buffer at physiological conditions (pH 7.4, 37°C). Glucose 6-phosphate (the substrate) was added to the dish, where it was taken up by the cells. Then a sample of buffer was removed every five minutes and the concentration of $(P)_i$ determined.

Data from the Experiment

Time (min)	Concentration of $(P)_i$ (µmol/mL)
0	0
5	10
10	90
15	180
20	270
25	330
30	355
35	355
40	355

Interpret the Data

1. To see patterns in the data from a time-course experiment like this, it is helpful to graph the data. First, determine which set of data goes on each axis. (a) What did the researchers intentionally vary in the experiment? This is the independent variable, which goes on the x-axis. (b) What are the units (abbreviated) for the independent variable? Explain in words what the abbreviation stands for. (c) What was measured by the researchers? This is the dependent variable, which goes on the y-axis. (d) What does the units abbreviation stand for? Label each axis, including the units.

2. Next, you'll want to mark off the axes with just enough evenly spaced tick marks to accommodate the full set of data. Determine the range of data values for each axis. (a) What is the largest value to go on the x-axis? What is a reasonable spacing for the tick marks, and what should be the highest one? (b) What is the largest value to go on the y-axis? What is a reasonable spacing for the tick marks, and what should be the highest one?

3. Plot the data points on your graph. Match each x-value with its partner y-value and place a point on the graph at that coordinate. Draw a line that connects the points. (For additional information about graphs, see the Scientific Skills Review in Appendix E and in the Study Area in MasteringBiology.)

4. Examine your graph and look for patterns in the data. (a) Does the concentration of $(P)_i$ increase evenly through the course of the experiment? To answer this question, describe the pattern you see in the graph. (b) What part of the graph shows the highest rate of enzyme activity? Consider that the rate of enzyme activity is related to the slope of the line, $\Delta y/\Delta x$ (the "rise" over the "run"), in µmol/mL · min, with the steepest slope indicating the highest rate of enzyme activity. Calculate the rate of enzyme activity (slope) where the graph is steepest. (c) Can you think of a biological explanation for the pattern you see?

5. If your blood sugar level is low from skipping lunch, what reaction (discussed in this exercise) will occur in your liver cells? Write out the reaction and put the name of the enzyme over the reaction arrow. How will this reaction affect your blood sugar level?

Fer Gregory/Shutterstock

Data from "Diets Enriched in Sucrose or Fat Increase Gluconeogenesis and G-6-Pase but Not Basal Glucose Production in Rats" by S. R. Commerford et al., from *American Journal of Physiology–Endocrinology and Metabolism*, September 2002, Volume 283(3). © Jane B Reece.

Effects of Local Conditions on Enzyme Activity

The activity of an enzyme—how efficiently the enzyme functions—is affected by general environmental factors, such as temperature and pH. It can also be affected by chemicals that specifically influence that enzyme. In fact, researchers have learned much about enzyme function by employing such chemicals.

Effects of Temperature and pH

Recall from Chapter 5 that the three-dimensional structures of proteins are sensitive to their environment. As a consequence, each enzyme works better under some conditions than under other conditions, because these *optimal conditions* favour the most active shape for the enzyme molecule.

Temperature and pH are environmental factors important in the activity of an enzyme. Up to a point, the rate of an enzymatic reaction increases with increasing temperature, partly because substrates collide with active sites more frequently when the molecules move rapidly. Above that temperature, however, the speed of the enzymatic reaction drops sharply. The thermal agitation of the enzyme molecule disrupts the hydrogen bonds, ionic bonds, and other weak interactions that stabilize the active shape of the enzyme, and the protein molecule eventually denatures. Each enzyme has an optimal temperature at which its reaction rate is greatest. Without denaturing the enzyme, this temperature allows the greatest number of molecular collisions and the fastest conversion of the reactants to product molecules. Most human enzymes have optimal temperatures of about 35–40°C (close to human body temperature). The thermophilic bacteria that live in hot springs contain enzymes with optimal temperatures of 70°C or higher **(Figure 8.17a)**.

Just as each enzyme has an optimal temperature, it also has a pH at which it is most active. The optimal pH values for most enzymes fall in the range of pH 6–8, but there are

(a) Optimal temperature for two enzymes

(b) Optimal pH for two enzymes

▲ **Figure 8.17 Environmental factors affecting enzyme activity.** Each enzyme has an optimal **(a)** temperature and **(b)** pH that favour the most active shape of the protein molecule.

DRAW IT *Given that a mature lysosome has an internal pH of around 4.5, draw a curve in (b) showing what you would predict for a lysosomal enzyme, labelling its optimal pH.*

exceptions. For example, pepsin, a digestive enzyme in the human stomach, works best at pH 2. Such an acidic environment denatures most enzymes, but pepsin is adapted to maintain its functional three-dimensional structure in the acidic environment of the stomach. In contrast, trypsin, a digestive enzyme residing in the alkaline environment of the human intestine, has an optimal pH of 8 and would be denatured in the stomach (**Figure 8.17b**).

Cofactors

Many enzymes require nonprotein helpers for catalytic activity. These adjuncts, called **cofactors**, may be bound tightly to the enzyme as permanent residents, or they may bind loosely and reversibly along with the substrate. The cofactors of some enzymes are inorganic, such as the metal atoms zinc, iron, and copper in ionic form. If the cofactor is an organic molecule, it is referred to, more specifically, as a **coenzyme**. Most vitamins are important in nutrition because they act as coenzymes or raw materials from which coenzymes are made.

Enzyme Inhibitors

Certain chemicals selectively inhibit the action of specific enzymes. Sometimes, the inhibitor attaches to the enzyme

by covalent bonds, in which case the inhibition is usually irreversible. Many enzyme inhibitors, however, bind to the enzyme by weak interactions, and when this occurs the inhibition is reversible. Some reversible inhibitors resemble the normal substrate molecule and compete for admission into the active site (**Figure 8.18a and b**). These mimics, called **competitive inhibitors**, reduce the productivity of enzymes by blocking substrates from entering active sites. This kind of inhibition can be overcome by increasing the concentration of substrate so that as active sites become available, more substrate molecules than inhibitor molecules are around to gain entry to the sites.

In contrast, **noncompetitive inhibitors** do not directly compete with the substrate to bind to the enzyme at the active site (**Figure 8.18c**). Instead, they impede enzymatic reactions by binding to another part of the enzyme. This interaction causes the enzyme molecule to change its shape in such a way that the active site becomes less effective at catalyzing the conversion of substrate to product.

Toxins and poisons are often irreversible enzyme inhibitors. An example is sarin, a nerve gas. Sarin was

▼ Figure 8.18 **Inhibition of enzyme activity.**

(a) Normal binding

A substrate can bind normally to the active site of an enzyme.

Substrate
Active site
Enzyme

(b) Competitive inhibition

A competitive inhibitor mimics the substrate, competing for the active site.

Competitive inhibitor

(c) Noncompetitive inhibition

A noncompetitive inhibitor binds to the enzyme away from the active site, altering the shape of the enzyme so that even if the substrate can bind, the active site functions less effectively, if it all.

Noncompetitive inhibitor

released by terrorists in the Tokyo subway in 1995, causing the death of several people and injury to many others. This small molecule binds covalently to the R group on the amino acid serine, which is found in the active site of acetylcholinesterase, an enzyme important in the nervous system. Other examples include the pesticides DDT and parathion, inhibitors of key enzymes in the nervous system. Finally, many antibiotics are inhibitors of specific enzymes in bacteria. For instance, penicillin blocks the active site of an enzyme that many bacteria use to make their cell walls.

The Evolution of Enzymes

EVOLUTION Thus far, biochemists have discovered and named more than 4000 different enzymes in various species, most likely a very small fraction of all enzymes. How did this grand profusion of enzymes arise? Recall that most enzymes are proteins, and proteins are encoded by genes. A permanent change in a gene, known as a *mutation*, can result in a protein with one or more changed amino acids. In the case of an enzyme, if the changed amino acids are in the active site or some other crucial region, the altered enzyme might have a novel activity or might bind to a different substrate. Under environmental conditions where the new function benefits the organism, natural selection would tend to favour the mutated form of the gene, causing it to persist in the population. This simplified model is generally accepted as the main way in which the multitude of different enzymes arose over the past few billion years of life's history.

Data supporting this model have been collected by researchers using a lab procedure that mimics evolution in natural populations. One group tested whether the function of an enzyme called β-galactosidase could change over time in populations of the bacterium *Escherichia coli* (*E. coli*). β-galactosidase breaks down the disaccharide lactose into the simple sugars glucose and galactose. Using molecular techniques, the researchers introduced random mutations into *E. coli* genes and then tested the bacteria for their ability to break down a slightly different disaccharide (one that has the sugar fucose in place of galactose). They selected the mutant bacteria that could do this best and exposed them to another round of mutation and selection. At the end of the experiment the "evolved" enzyme bound the new substrate several hundred times more strongly, and broke it down 10 to 20 times more quickly, than did the original enzyme.

The researchers found that six amino acids had changed in the enzyme altered in this experiment. Two of these changed amino acids were in the active site, two were nearby, and two were on the surface of the protein (Figure 8.19). This experiment and others like it strengthen the notion that a few changes can indeed alter enzyme function.

Two changed amino acids were found near the active site.

Active site

Two changed amino acids were found in the active site.

Two changed amino acids were found on the surface.

▲ **Figure 8.19 Mimicking evolution of an enzyme with a new function.** After seven rounds of mutation and selection in a lab, the enzyme β-galactosidase evolved into an enzyme specialized for breaking down a sugar different from lactose. This ribbon model shows one subunit of the altered enzyme; six amino acids were different.

Source: Protein Data Bank ID 3e1f: "Direct and Indirect Roles of His-418 in Metal Binding and in the Activity of Beta-Galactosidase (E. coli)" by Douglas H. Juers et al., from *Protein Science,* June 2009, Volume 18(6).

CONCEPT CHECK 8.4

1. Many spontaneous reactions occur very slowly. Why don't all spontaneous reactions occur instantly?

2. Why do enzymes act only on very specific substrates?

3. WHAT IF? Malonate is an inhibitor of the enzyme succinate dehydrogenase. How would you determine whether malonate is a competitive or noncompetitive inhibitor?

4. MAKE CONNECTIONS In nature, what conditions could lead to natural selection favouring bacteria with enzymes that could break down the fucose-containing disaccharide discussed above? See the discussion of natural selection in Concept 1.2.

For suggested answers, see Appendix A.

CONCEPT 8.5

Regulation of enzyme activity helps control metabolism

Chemical chaos would result if all of a cell's metabolic pathways were operating simultaneously. Intrinsic to life's processes is a cell's ability to tightly regulate its metabolic pathways by controlling when and where its various enzymes are active. It does this either by switching on and off the genes that encode specific enzymes (as we will discuss in Unit Three) or, as we discuss here, by regulating the activity of enzymes once they are made.

Allosteric Regulation of Enzymes

In many cases, the molecules that naturally regulate enzyme activity in a cell behave something like reversible noncompetitive inhibitors (see Figure 8.18c): These regulatory molecules change an enzyme's shape and the functioning of its active site by binding to a site elsewhere on the molecule, via noncovalent interactions. **Allosteric regulation** is the term used to describe any case in which a protein's function at one site is affected by the binding of a regulatory molecule to a separate site. It may result in either inhibition or stimulation of an enzyme's activity.

Allosteric Activation and Inhibition

Most enzymes known to be allosterically regulated are constructed from two or more subunits, each composed of a polypeptide chain with its own active site. The entire complex oscillates between two different shapes, one catalytically active and the other inactive (Figure 8.20a). In the simplest kind of allosteric regulation, an activating or inhibiting regulatory molecule binds to a regulatory site (sometimes called an allosteric site), often located where subunits join. The binding of an *activator* to a regulatory site stabilizes the shape that has functional active sites, whereas the binding of an *inhibitor* stabilizes the inactive form of the enzyme. The subunits of an allosteric enzyme fit together in such a way that a shape change in one subunit is transmitted to all others. Through this interaction of subunits, a single activator or inhibitor molecule that binds to one regulatory site will affect the active sites of all subunits.

Fluctuating concentrations of regulators can cause a sophisticated pattern of response in the activity of cellular enzymes. The products of ATP hydrolysis (ADP and P_i), for example, play a complex role in balancing the flow of traffic between anabolic and catabolic pathways by their effects on key enzymes. ATP binds to several catabolic enzymes allosterically, lowering their affinity for substrate and thus inhibiting their activity. ADP, however, functions as an activator of the same enzymes. This is logical because catabolism functions in regenerating ATP. If ATP production lags behind its use, ADP accumulates and activates the enzymes that speed up catabolism, producing more ATP. If the supply of ATP exceeds demand, then catabolism slows down as ATP molecules accumulate and bind to the same enzymes, inhibiting them. (You'll see specific examples of this type of regulation when you learn about cellular respiration in the next chapter.) ATP, ADP, and other related molecules also affect key enzymes in anabolic pathways. In this way, allosteric enzymes control the rates of important reactions in both sorts of metabolic pathways.

In another kind of allosteric activation, a *substrate* molecule binding to one active site in a multisubunit enzyme triggers a shape change in all the subunits, thereby increasing catalytic activity at the other active sites (Figure 8.20b). Called **cooperativity**, this mechanism amplifies the response of enzymes to substrates: One substrate molecule primes an enzyme to act on additional substrate molecules more readily. Cooperativity is considered "allosteric" regulation because binding of the substrate to one active site affects catalysis in another active site.

▼ Figure 8.20 **Allosteric regulation of enzyme activity.**

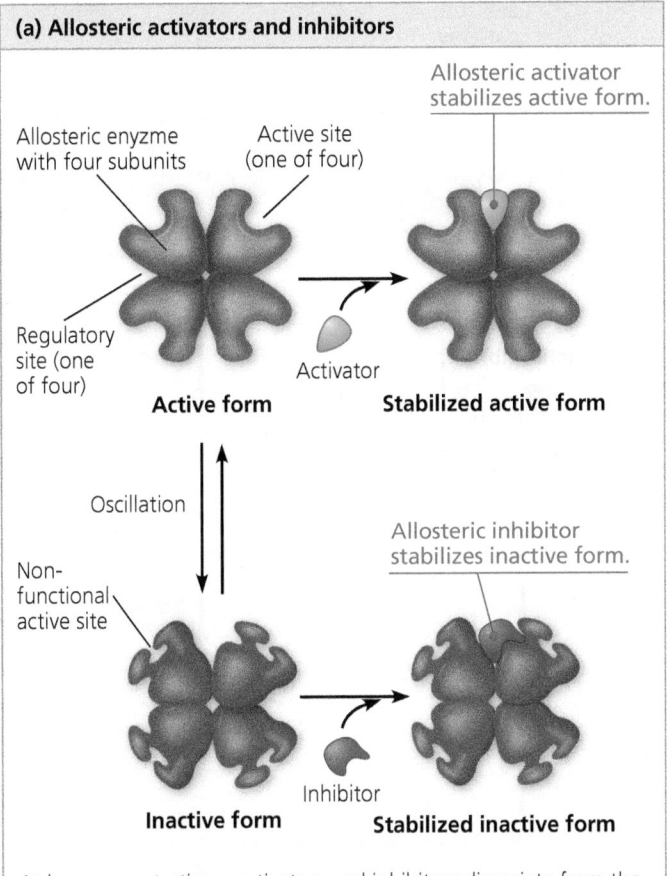

(a) Allosteric activators and inhibitors

Allosteric enzyme with four subunits

Active site (one of four)

Allosteric activator stabilizes active form.

Regulatory site (one of four)

Activator

Active form

Stabilized active form

Oscillation

Non-functional active site

Allosteric inhibitor stabilizes inactive form.

Inhibitor

Inactive form

Stabilized inactive form

At low concentrations, activators and inhibitors dissociate from the enzyme. The enzyme can then oscillate again.

(b) Cooperativity: another type of allosteric activation

Binding of one substrate molecule to active site of one subunit locks all subunits in active conformation.

Substrate

Inactive form

Stabilized active form

The inactive form shown on the left oscillates with the active form when the active form is not stabilized by substrate.

Source: Protein Data Bank ID 1MDYO: "Crystal Structure of MyoD bHLH Domain-DNA Complex: Perspectives on DNA Recognition and Implications for Transcriptional Activation" from *Cell*, May 1994, Volume 77(3).

Although hemoglobin is not an enzyme, classic studies of hemoglobin have elucidated the principle of cooperativity. Hemoglobin is made up of four subunits, each with an oxygen-binding site (see Figure 5.18). The binding of an oxygen molecule to one binding site increases the affinity for oxygen of the remaining binding sites. Thus, where

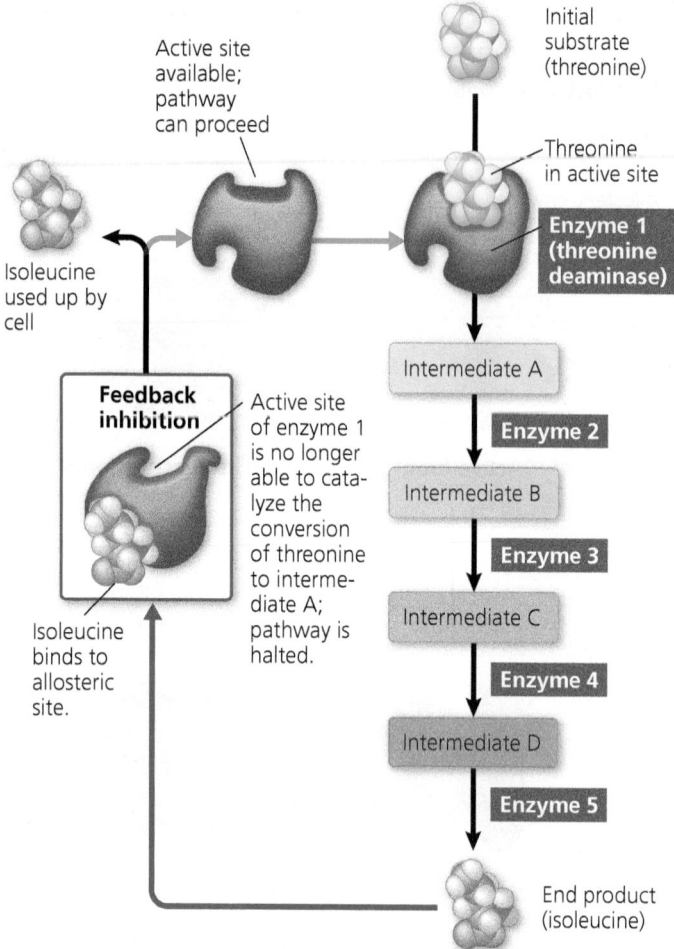

Active site available; pathway can proceed

Isoleucine used up by cell

Feedback inhibition

Active site of enzyme 1 is no longer able to catalyze the conversion of threonine to intermediate A; pathway is halted.

Isoleucine binds to allosteric site.

Initial substrate (threonine)

Threonine in active site

Enzyme 1 (threonine deaminase)

Intermediate A

Enzyme 2

Intermediate B

Enzyme 3

Intermediate C

Enzyme 4

Intermediate D

Enzyme 5

End product (isoleucine)

▲ **Figure 8.21** **Feedback inhibition in isoleucine synthesis.**

oxygen is at high levels, such as in the lungs or gills, hemoglobin's affinity for oxygen increases as more binding sites are filled. In oxygen-deprived tissues, however, the release of each oxygen molecule decreases the oxygen affinity of the other binding sites, resulting in the release of oxygen where it is most needed. Cooperativity works similarly in multisubunit enzymes that have been studied.

Feedback Inhibition

When ATP allosterically inhibits an enzyme in an ATP-generating pathway, as we discussed earlier, the result is feedback inhibition, a common mode of metabolic control. In **feedback inhibition**, a metabolic pathway is halted by the inhibitory binding of its end product to an enzyme that acts early in the pathway. Figure 8.21 shows an example of feedback inhibition operating on an anabolic pathway. Some cells use this five-step pathway to synthesize the amino acid isoleucine from threonine, another amino acid. As isoleucine accumulates, it slows down its own synthesis by allosterically inhibiting the enzyme for the first step of the pathway. Feedback inhibition thereby prevents the cell from wasting chemical resources by making more isoleucine than is necessary.

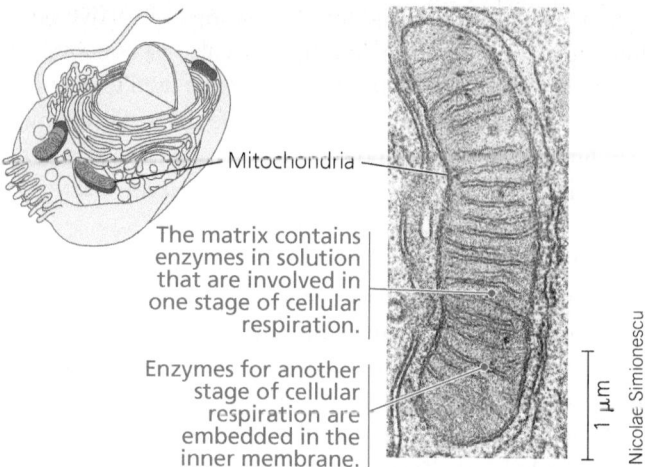

Mitochondria

The matrix contains enzymes in solution that are involved in one stage of cellular respiration.

Enzymes for another stage of cellular respiration are embedded in the inner membrane.

1 μm

Nicolae Simionescu

▲ **Figure 8.22** **Organelles and structural order in metabolism.** Organelles such as the mitochondrion (TEM) contain enzymes that carry out specific functions, in this case cellular respiration.

Source: Adaptation of figure 3.2 from *Human Anatomy and Physiology*, 8th Edition, by Elaine N. Marieb and Katja N. Hoehn, 2010. Copyright © 2010 by Pearson Education, Inc. Reprinted and electronically reproduced by permission of Pearson Education, Inc. Upper Saddle River, New Jersey.

Localization of Enzymes within the Cell

The cell is not just a bag of chemicals with thousands of different kinds of enzymes and substrates in a random mix. The cell is compartmentalized, and cellular structures help bring order to metabolic pathways. In some cases, a team of enzymes for several steps of a metabolic pathway are assembled into a multienzyme complex. The arrangement facilitates the sequence of reactions, with the product from the first enzyme becoming the substrate for an adjacent enzyme in the complex, and so on, until the end product is released. Some enzymes and enzyme complexes have fixed locations within the cell and act as structural components of particular membranes. Others are in solution within particular membrane-enclosed eukaryotic organelles, each with its own internal chemical environment. For example, in eukaryotic cells, the enzymes for cellular respiration reside in specific locations within mitochondria (Figure 8.22).

In this chapter, you have learned that metabolism, the intersecting set of chemical pathways characteristic of life, is a choreographed interplay of thousands of different kinds of cellular molecules. In the next chapter, we explore cellular respiration, the major catabolic pathway that breaks down organic molecules, releasing energy for the crucial processes of life.

CONCEPT CHECK 8.5

1. How do an activator and an inhibitor have different effects on an allosterically regulated enzyme?

2. **WHAT IF?** Regulation of isoleucine synthesis is an example of feedback inhibition of an anabolic pathway. With that in mind, explain how ATP might be involved in feedback inhibition of a catabolic pathway.

For suggested answers, see Appendix A.

8 Chapter Review

Go to **MasteringBiology**® for Assignments, the eText, and the Study Area with Animations, Activities, Vocab Self-Quiz, and Practice Tests.

SUMMARY OF KEY CONCEPTS

CONCEPT 8.1

An organism's metabolism transforms matter and energy, subject to the laws of thermodynamics (pp. 155–158)

- **Metabolism** is the collection of chemical reactions that occur in an organism. **Enzymes** catalyze reactions in intersecting **metabolic pathways**, which may be **catabolic** (breaking down molecules, releasing energy) or **anabolic** (building molecules, consuming energy).
- **Energy** is the capacity to cause change; some forms of energy do work by moving matter. **Kinetic energy** is associated with motion and includes **thermal energy** associated with random motion of atoms or molecules. **Heat** is thermal energy in transfer from one object to another. **Potential energy** is related to the location or structure of matter and includes **chemical energy** possessed by a molecule due to its structure.
- The **first law of thermodynamics**, conservation of energy, states that energy cannot be created or destroyed, only transferred or transformed. The **second law of thermodynamics** states that **spontaneous processes**, those requiring no outside input of energy, increase the **entropy** (disorder) of the universe.

> **?** *Explain how the highly ordered structure of a cell does not conflict with the second law of thermodynamics.*

CONCEPT 8.2

The free-energy change of a reaction tells us whether or not the reaction occurs spontaneously (pp. 158–161)

- A living system's **free energy** is energy that can do work under cellular conditions. The change in free energy (ΔG) during a biological process is related directly to enthalpy change (ΔH) and to the change in entropy (ΔS): $\Delta G = \Delta H - T\Delta S$. Organisms live at the expense of free energy. A spontaneous process occurs with no energy input; during such a process, free energy decreases and the stability of a system increases. At maximum stability, the system is at equilibrium and can do no work.
- In an **exergonic** (spontaneous) chemical reaction, the products have less free energy than the reactants ($-\Delta G$). **Endergonic** (nonspontaneous) reactions require an input of energy ($+\Delta G$). The addition of starting materials and the removal of end products prevent metabolism from reaching equilibrium.

> **?** *Explain the meaning of each component in the equation for the change in free energy of a spontaneous chemical reaction. Why are spontaneous reactions important in the metabolism of a cell?*

CONCEPT 8.3

ATP powers cellular work by coupling exergonic reactions to endergonic reactions (pp. 161–164)

- **ATP** is the cell's energy shuttle. Hydrolysis of its terminal phosphate yields ADP and ⓟᵢ and releases free energy.
- Through **energy coupling**, the exergonic process of ATP hydrolysis drives endergonic reactions by transfer of a phosphate group to specific reactants, forming a **phosphorylated intermediate** that is more reactive. ATP hydrolysis (sometimes with protein

phosphorylation) also causes changes in the shape and binding affinities of transport and motor proteins.
- Catabolic pathways drive regeneration of ATP from ADP + ⓟᵢ

> **?** *Describe the ATP cycle: How is ATP used and regenerated in a cell?*

CONCEPT 8.4

Enzymes speed up metabolic reactions by lowering energy barriers (pp. 164–170)

- In a chemical reaction, the energy necessary to break the bonds of the reactants is the **activation energy**, E_A.
- **Enzymes** lower the E_A barrier:

- Each enzyme has a unique **active site** that binds one or more **substrate(s)**, the reactants on which it acts. It then changes shape, binding the substrate(s) more tightly (**induced fit**).
- The active site can lower an E_A barrier by orienting substrates correctly, straining their bonds, providing a favourable microenvironment, or even covalently bonding with the substrate.
- Each enzyme has an optimal temperature and pH. Inhibitors reduce enzyme function. A **competitive inhibitor** binds to the active site, whereas a **noncompetitive inhibitor** binds to a different site on the enzyme.
- Natural selection, acting on organisms with variant enzymes, is responsible for the diversity of enzymes found in organisms.

> **?** *How do both activation energy barriers and enzymes help maintain the structural and metabolic order of life?*

CONCEPT 8.5

Regulation of enzyme activity helps control metabolism (pp. 170–172)

- Many enzymes are subject to **allosteric regulation**: Regulatory molecules, either activators or inhibitors, bind to specific regulatory sites, affecting the shape and function of the enzyme. In **cooperativity**, binding of one substrate molecule can stimulate binding or activity at other active sites. In **feedback inhibition**, the end product of a metabolic pathway allosterically inhibits the enzyme for a previous step in the pathway.
- Some enzymes are grouped into complexes, some are incorporated into membranes, and some are contained inside organelles, increasing the efficiency of metabolic processes.

> **?** *What roles do allosteric regulation and feedback inhibition play in the metabolism of a cell?*

TEST YOUR UNDERSTANDING

LEVEL 1: KNOWLEDGE/COMPREHENSION

1. Choose the pair of terms that correctly completes this sentence: Catabolism is to anabolism as _____ is to _____.
   a. exergonic; spontaneous
   b. exergonic; endergonic
   c. free energy; entropy
   d. work; energy

2. Most cells cannot harness heat to perform work because
   a. heat does not involve a transfer of energy.
   b. cells do not have much thermal energy; they are relatively cool.
   c. temperature is usually uniform throughout a cell.
   d. heat can never be used to do work.

3. Which of the following metabolic processes can occur without a net influx of energy from some other process?
   a. $ADP + \textcircled{P}_i \rightarrow ATP + H_2O$
   b. $C_6H_{12}O_6 + 6\ O_2 \rightarrow 6\ CO_2 + 6\ H_2O$
   c. $6\ CO_2 + 6\ H_2O \rightarrow C_6H_{12}O_6 + 6\ O_2$
   d. amino acids $\rightarrow$ protein

4. If an enzyme in solution is saturated with substrate, the most effective way to obtain a faster yield of products is to
   a. add more of the enzyme.
   b. heat the solution to 90°C.
   c. add more substrate.
   d. add a noncompetitive inhibitor.

5. Some bacteria are metabolically active in hot springs because
   a. they are able to maintain a lower internal temperature.
   b. high temperatures make catalysis unnecessary.
   c. their enzymes have high optimal temperatures.
   d. their enzymes are completely insensitive to temperature.

LEVEL 2: APPLICATION/ANALYSIS

6. If an enzyme is added to a solution where its substrate and product are in equilibrium, what will occur?
   a. Additional substrate will be formed.
   b. The reaction will change from endergonic to exergonic.
   c. The free energy of the system will change.
   d. Nothing; the reaction will stay at equilibrium.

LEVEL 3: SYNTHESIS/EVALUATION

7. **DRAW IT** Using a series of arrows, draw the branched metabolic reaction pathway described by the following statements, and then answer the question at the end. Use red arrows and minus signs to indicate inhibition.

   L can form either M or N.
   M can form O.
   O can form either P or R.
   P can form Q.
   R can form S.
   O inhibits the reaction of L to form M.
   Q inhibits the reaction of O to form P.
   S inhibits the reaction of O to form R.

   Which reaction would prevail if both Q and S were present in the cell in high concentrations?
   a. $L \rightarrow M$
   b. $M \rightarrow O$
   c. $L \rightarrow N$
   d. $O \rightarrow P$

8. **EVOLUTION CONNECTION**
   A recent revival of the antievolutionary "intelligent design" argument holds that biochemical pathways are too complex to have evolved, because all intermediate steps in a given pathway must be present to produce the final product. Critique this argument. How could you use the diversity of metabolic pathways that produce the same or similar products to support your case?

9. **SCIENTIFIC INQUIRY**
   DRAW IT A researcher has developed an assay to measure the activity of an important enzyme present in liver cells growing in culture. She adds the enzyme's substrate to a dish of cells and then measures the appearance of reaction products. The results are graphed as the amount of product on the y-axis versus time on the x-axis. The researcher notes four sections of the graph. For a short period of time, no products appear (section A). Then (section B) the reaction rate is quite high (the slope of the line is steep). Next, the reaction gradually slows down (section C). Finally, the graph line becomes flat (section D). Draw and label the graph, and propose a model to explain the molecular events occurring at each stage of this reaction profile.

10. **WRITE ABOUT A THEME: ENERGY AND MATTER**
    Life requires energy. In a short essay (100–150 words), describe the basic principles of bioenergetics in an animal cell. How is the flow and transformation of energy different in a photosynthesizing cell? Include the role of ATP and enzymes in your discussion.

11. **SYNTHESIZE YOUR KNOWLEDGE**

PayPal/Moment Select/Getty Images

Explain what is happening in this photo in terms of kinetic energy and potential energy. Include the energy conversions that occur when the penguins eat fish and climb back up on the glacier. Describe the role of ATP and enzymes in the underlying molecular processes, including what happens to the free energy of some of the molecules involved.

For selected answers, see Appendix A.

9

Cellular Respiration and Fermentation

Thomas & Pat Leeson/Science Source

▲ Figure 9.1 **How does eating plants power the work of life for this muskox?**

KEY CONCEPTS

9.1 Catabolic pathways yield energy by oxidizing organic fuels

9.2 Glycolysis harvests chemical energy by oxidizing glucose to pyruvate

9.3 After pyruvate is oxidized, the citric acid cycle completes the energy-yielding oxidation of organic molecules

9.4 During oxidative phosphorylation, chemiosmosis couples electron transport to ATP synthesis

9.5 Fermentation and anaerobic respiration enable cells to produce ATP without the use of oxygen

9.6 Glycolysis and the citric acid cycle connect to many other metabolic pathways

Life Is Work

Living cells require transfusions of energy from outside sources to perform their many tasks—for example, assembling polymers, pumping substances across membranes, moving, and reproducing. The muskox in **Figure 9.1** is obtaining energy for its cells by eating plants; some other animals obtain energy by feeding on other organisms that eat plants. The energy stored in the organic molecules of food ultimately comes from the sun. Energy flows into an eco-system as sunlight and exits as heat; in contrast, the chemical elements essential to life are recycled (**Figure 9.2**). Photosynthesis generates oxygen and organic molecules that are used by the mitochondria of eukaryotes (including plants and algae) as fuel for cellular respiration. Respiration breaks this fuel down, gener-ating ATP. The waste products of this type of respiration, carbon dioxide and water, are the raw materials for photosynthesis.

In this chapter, we consider how cells harvest the chemical energy stored in organic molecules and use it to generate ATP, the molecule that drives most cellular work. After presenting some basics about respiration, we'll focus on three key path-ways of respiration: glycolysis, the citric acid cycle, and oxidative phosphorylation. We'll also consider fermentation, a somewhat simpler pathway coupled to glycolysis that has deep evolutionary roots.

Photosynthesis
in chloroplasts

Cellular respiration
in mitochondria

Light
energy

ECOSYSTEM

$CO_2 + H_2O$

Organic
molecules $+ O_2$

ATP

**ATP powers
most cellular work**

Heat
energy

▲ **Figure 9.2 Energy flow and chemical recycling in ecosystems.** Energy flows into an ecosystem as sunlight and ultimately leaves as heat, while the chemical elements essential to life are recycled.

ANIMATION

BioFlix Visit the Study Area in **MasteringBiology** for the Bioflix® 3-D Animation on The Carbon Cycle.

Carl Johnson/Design Pics Inc/Alamy Stock Photo

CONCEPT 9.1

Catabolic pathways yield energy by oxidizing organic fuels

Metabolic pathways that release stored energy by breaking down complex molecules are called catabolic pathways (see Chapter 8). Electron transfer plays a major role in these pathways. In this section, we consider these processes, which are central to cellular respiration.

Catabolic Pathways and Production of ATP

Organic compounds possess potential energy as a result of the arrangement of electrons in the bonds between their atoms. Compounds that can participate in exergonic reactions can act as fuels. Through the activity of enzymes, a cell systematically degrades complex organic molecules that are rich in potential energy to simpler waste products that have less energy. Some of the energy taken out of chemical storage can be used to do work; the rest is dissipated as heat.

One catabolic process, **fermentation**, is a partial degradation of sugars or other organic fuel that occurs without the use of oxygen. However, the most efficient catabolic pathway is **aerobic respiration**, in which oxygen is consumed as a reactant along with the organic fuel (*aerobic* is

from the Greek *aer*, air, and *bios*, life). The cells of most eukaryotic and many prokaryotic organisms can carry out aerobic respiration. Some prokaryotes use substances other than oxygen as reactants in a similar process that harvests chemical energy without oxygen; this process is called *anaerobic respiration* (the prefix *an-* means "without"). Technically, the term **cellular respiration** includes both aerobic and anaerobic processes. However, it originated as a synonym for aerobic respiration because of the relationship of that process to organismal respiration, in which an animal breathes in oxygen. Thus, *cellular respiration* is often used to refer to the aerobic process, a practice we follow in most of this chapter.

Although very different in mechanism, aerobic respiration is in principle similar to the combustion of gasoline in an automobile engine after oxygen is mixed with the fuel (hydrocarbons). Food provides the fuel for respiration, and the exhaust is carbon dioxide and water. The overall process can be summarized as follows:

$$\text{Organic compounds} + \text{Oxygen} \rightarrow \text{Carbon dioxide} + \text{Water} + \text{Energy}$$

Carbohydrates, fats, and protein molecules from food can all be processed and consumed as fuel, as we will discuss later in the chapter. In animal diets, a major source of carbohydrates is starch, a storage polysaccharide that can be broken down into glucose ($C_6H_{12}O_6$) subunits. Here, we will learn the steps of cellular respiration by tracking the degradation of the sugar glucose:

$$C_6H_{12}O_6 + 6\,O_2 \rightarrow 6\,CO_2 + 6\,H_2O + \text{Energy (ATP + heat)}$$

This breakdown of glucose is exergonic, having a free-energy change of 2870 kilojoules per mole of glucose decomposed ($\Delta G = -2870$ kJ/mol). Recall that a negative ΔG indicates that the products of the chemical process store less energy than the reactants and that the reaction can happen spontaneously—in other words, without an input of energy.

Catabolic pathways do not directly move flagella, pump solutes across membranes, polymerize monomers, or perform other cellular work. Catabolism is linked to work by a chemical drive shaft—ATP (see Chapter 8). To keep working, the cell must regenerate its supply of ATP from ADP and Ⓟi (see Figure 8.12). To understand how cellular respiration accomplishes this, let's examine the fundamental chemical processes known as oxidation and reduction.

Redox Reactions: Oxidation and Reduction

How do the catabolic pathways that decompose glucose and other organic fuels yield energy? The answer is based on the transfer of electrons during the chemical reactions. The relocation of electrons releases energy stored in organic molecules, and this energy ultimately is used to synthesize ATP.

The Principle of Redox

In many chemical reactions, there is a transfer of one or more electrons (e^-) from one reactant to another. These electron transfers are called oxidation-reduction reactions, or **redox reactions** for short. In a redox reaction, the loss of electrons from one substance is called **oxidation**, and the addition of electrons to another substance is known as **reduction**. (Note that *adding* electrons is called *reduction*; adding negatively charged electrons to an atom *reduces* the amount of positive charge of that atom.) To take a simple, nonbiological example, consider the reaction between the elements sodium (Na) and chlorine (Cl) that forms table salt:

$$\overset{\text{becomes oxidized (loses electron)}}{\text{Na} + \text{Cl}} \longrightarrow \overset{}{\text{Na}^+ + \underset{\text{becomes reduced (gains electron)}}{\text{Cl}^-}}$$

We could generalize a redox reaction this way:

$$\overset{\text{becomes oxidized}}{Xe^- + Y} \longrightarrow X + \underset{\text{becomes reduced}}{Ye^-}$$

In the generalized reaction, substance Xe^-, the electron donor, is called the **reducing agent**; it reduces Y, which accepts the donated electron. Substance Y, the electron acceptor, is the **oxidizing agent**; it oxidizes Xe^- by removing its electron. Because an electron transfer requires both a donor and an acceptor, oxidation and reduction always go hand in hand.

Not all redox reactions involve the complete transfer of electrons from one substance to another; some change the degree of electron sharing in covalent bonds. Methane combustion, shown in **Figure 9.3**, is an example. The covalent electrons in methane are shared nearly equally between the bonded atoms because carbon and hydrogen have

▲ **Figure 9.3 Methane combustion as an energy-yielding redox reaction.** The reaction releases energy to the surroundings because the electrons lose potential energy when they end up being shared unequally, spending more time near electronegative atoms such as oxygen.

about the same affinity for valence electrons; they are about equally electronegative (see Chapter 2). But when methane reacts with oxygen, forming carbon dioxide, electrons end up shared less equally between the carbon atom and its new covalent partners, the oxygen atoms, which are very electronegative. In effect, the carbon atom has partially "lost" its shared electrons; thus, methane has been oxidized.

Now let's examine the fate of the reactant O_2. The two atoms of the oxygen molecule (O_2) share their electrons equally. But when oxygen reacts with the hydrogen from methane, forming water, the electrons of the covalent bonds spend more time near the oxygen (see Figure 9.3). In effect, each oxygen atom has partially "gained" electrons, so the oxygen molecule has been reduced. Because oxygen is so electronegative, it is one of the most potent of all oxidizing agents.

Energy must be added to pull an electron away from an atom, just as energy is required to push a ball uphill. The more electronegative the atom (the stronger its pull on electrons), the more energy is required to take an electron away from it. An electron loses potential energy when it shifts from a less electronegative atom toward a more electronegative one, just as a ball loses potential energy when it rolls downhill. A redox reaction that moves electrons closer to oxygen, such as the burning (oxidation) of methane, therefore releases chemical energy that can be put to work.

Oxidation of Organic Fuel Molecules During Cellular Respiration

The oxidation of methane by oxygen is the main combustion reaction that occurs at the burner of a gas stove. The combustion of gasoline in an automobile engine is also a redox reaction; the energy released pushes the pistons. But the energy-yielding redox process of greatest interest to biologists is respiration: the oxidation of glucose and other molecules in food. Examine again the summary equation for cellular respiration, but this time think of it as a redox process:

$$\overset{\text{becomes oxidized}}{C_6H_{12}O_6 + 6\,O_2} \longrightarrow 6\,CO_2 + \underset{\text{becomes reduced}}{6\,H_2O} + \text{Energy}$$

As in the combustion of methane or gasoline, the fuel (glucose) is oxidized and oxygen is reduced. The electrons lose potential energy along the way, and energy is released.

In general, organic molecules that have an abundance of hydrogen are excellent fuels because their bonds are a source of "hilltop" electrons, whose energy may be released as these electrons "fall" down an energy gradient when they are transferred to oxygen. The summary equation for respiration indicates that hydrogen is transferred from glucose to oxygen. But the important point, not visible in the summary equation, is that the energy state of the electron changes as hydrogen (with its electron) is transferred to oxygen. In respiration, the oxidation of glucose transfers electrons to a lower energy state, liberating energy that becomes available for ATP synthesis.

The main energy-yielding foods—carbohydrates and fats—are reservoirs of electrons associated with hydrogen. Only the barrier of activation energy holds back the flood of electrons to a lower energy state (see Figure 8.13). Without this barrier, a food substance like glucose would combine almost instantaneously with O_2. If we supply the activation energy by igniting glucose, it burns in air, releasing 2870 kJ of heat per mole of glucose (about 180 g). Body temperature is not high enough to initiate burning, of course. Instead, if you swallow some glucose, enzymes in your cells will lower the barrier of activation energy, allowing the sugar to be oxidized in a series of steps.

Stepwise Energy Harvest via NAD$^+$ and the Electron Transport Chain

If energy is released from a fuel all at once, it cannot be harnessed efficiently for constructive work. For example, if a gasoline tank explodes, it cannot drive a car very far. Cellular respiration does not oxidize glucose (or any other organic fuel) in a single explosive step either. Rather, glucose is broken down in a series of steps, each one catalyzed by an enzyme. At key steps, electrons are stripped from the glucose. As is often the case in oxidation reactions, each electron travels with a proton—thus, as a hydrogen atom. The hydrogen atoms are not transferred directly to oxygen, but instead are usually passed first to an electron carrier, a coenzyme called **NAD$^+$** (nicotinamide adenine

dinucleotide, a derivative of the vitamin niacin). NAD$^+$ is well suited as an electron carrier because it can cycle easily between oxidized (NAD$^+$) and reduced (NADH) states. As an electron acceptor, NAD$^+$ functions as an oxidizing agent during respiration.

How does NAD$^+$ trap electrons from glucose and the other organic molecules in food? Enzymes called dehydrogenases remove a pair of hydrogen atoms (2 electrons and 2 protons) from the substrate (glucose, in the above example), thereby oxidizing it. The enzyme delivers the 2 electrons along with 1 proton to its coenzyme, NAD$^+$ **(Figure 9.4)**. The other proton is released as a hydrogen ion (H$^+$) into the surrounding solution:

$$\text{H}-\overset{|}{\underset{|}{\text{C}}}-\text{OH} + \text{NAD}^+ \xrightarrow{\text{Dehydrogenase}} \overset{|}{\text{C}}=\text{O} + \text{NADH} + \text{H}^+$$

By receiving 2 negatively charged electrons but only 1 positively charged proton, the nicotinamide portion of NAD$^+$ has its charge neutralized when NAD$^+$ is reduced to NADH. The name NADH shows the hydrogen that has been received in the reaction. NAD$^+$ is the most versatile electron acceptor in cellular respiration and functions in several of the redox steps during the breakdown of glucose.

Electrons lose very little of their potential energy when they are transferred from glucose to NAD$^+$. Each NADH molecule formed during respiration represents stored energy that can be tapped to make ATP when the electrons complete their "fall" down an energy gradient from NADH to oxygen.

How do electrons that are extracted from glucose and stored as potential energy in NADH finally reach oxygen?

▲ **Figure 9.4 NAD$^+$ as an electron shuttle.** The full name for NAD$^+$, nicotinamide adenine dinucleotide, describes its structure—the molecule consists of two nucleotides joined together at their phosphate groups (shown in yellow). (Nicotinamide is a nitrogenous base, although not one that is present in DNA or RNA; see Figure 5.24.) The enzymatic transfer of 2 electrons and 1 proton (H$^+$) from an organic molecule in food to NAD$^+$ reduces the NAD$^+$ to NADH. Most of the electrons removed from food are transferred initially to NAD$^+$.

? *Describe the structural differences between the oxidized form and the reduced form of nicotinamide.*

(a) Uncontrolled reaction

(b) Cellular respiration

▲ **Figure 9.5 An introduction to electron transport chains. (a)** The one-step exergonic reaction of hydrogen with oxygen to form water releases a large amount of energy in the form of heat and light: an explosion. **(b)** In cellular respiration, the same reaction occurs in stages: An electron transport chain breaks the "fall" of electrons in this reaction into a series of smaller steps and stores some of the released energy in a form that can be used to make ATP. (The rest of the energy is released as heat.)

Source: Adaptation of figure 2.69 from *Molecular Biology of the Cell*, 4th Edition, by Bruce Alberts et al. Copyright © 2002 by Garland Science/Taylor & Francis LLC. Reprinted with permission.

It will help to compare the redox chemistry of cellular respiration to a much simpler reaction: the reaction between hydrogen and oxygen to form water **(Figure 9.5a)**. Mix H_2 and O_2, provide a spark for activation energy, and the gases combine explosively. In fact, combustion of liquid H_2 and O_2 is harnessed to help power the main engines of a space shuttle, boosting it into orbit. The explosion represents a release of energy as the electrons of hydrogen "fall" closer to the electronegative oxygen atoms. Cellular respiration also brings hydrogen and oxygen together to form water, but there are two important differences. First, in cellular respiration, the hydrogen that reacts with oxygen is derived from organic molecules rather than H_2. Second, instead of occurring in one explosive reaction, respiration uses an electron transport chain to break the fall of electrons to oxygen into several energy-releasing steps **(Figure 9.5b)**. An **electron transport chain** consists of a number of molecules, mostly proteins, built into the inner membrane of the mitochondria of eukaryotic cells and the plasma membrane of respiring prokaryotes. Electrons removed from glucose are shuttled by NADH to the "top," higher-energy end of the chain. At the "bottom," lower-energy end, O_2 captures these electrons along with hydrogen nuclei (H^+), forming water. (Anaerobically respiring prokaryotes have an electron acceptor at the end of the chain that is different from O_2.)

Electron transfer from NADH to oxygen is an exergonic reaction with a free-energy change of −222 kJ/mol. Instead of this energy being released and wasted in a single explosive step, electrons cascade down the chain from one carrier molecule to the next in a series of redox reactions, losing a small amount of energy with each step until they finally reach oxygen, the terminal electron acceptor, which has a very great affinity for electrons. Each "downhill" carrier is more electronegative than, and thus capable of oxidizing, its "uphill" neighbour, with oxygen at the bottom of the chain. Therefore, the electrons transferred from glucose to NAD^+, which is thus reduced to NADH, fall down an energy gradient in the electron transport chain to a far more stable location in the electronegative oxygen atom. Put another way, oxygen pulls electrons down the chain in an energy-yielding tumble analogous to gravity pulling objects downhill.

In summary, during cellular respiration, most electrons travel the following "downhill" route: glucose → NADH → electron transport chain → oxygen. Later in this chapter, you will learn more about how the cell uses the energy released from this exergonic electron fall to regenerate its supply of ATP. For now, having covered the basic redox mechanisms of cellular respiration, let's look at the entire process by which energy is harvested from organic fuels.

The Stages of Cellular Respiration: *A Preview*

The harvesting of energy from glucose by cellular respiration is a cumulative function of three metabolic stages. We list them here along with a colour-coding scheme we will use throughout the chapter to help you keep track of the big picture:

1. Glycolysis (colour-coded blue throughout the chapter)
2. Pyruvate oxidation and the citric acid cycle (colour-coded orange)
3. Oxidative phosphorylation: electron transport and chemiosmosis (colour-coded purple)

Biochemists usually reserve the term *cellular respiration* for stages 2 and 3 together. In this text, however, we include glycolysis as part of cellular respiration, because most respiring cells deriving energy from glucose use glycolysis to produce the starting material for the citric acid cycle.

◀ Figure 9.6 **An overview of cellular respiration.** During glycolysis, each glucose molecule is broken down into two molecules of the compound pyruvate. In eukaryotic cells, as shown here, the pyruvate enters the mitochondrion. There it is oxidized to acetyl CoA, which is further oxidized to CO_2 in the citric acid cycle. NADH and a similar electron carrier, a coenzyme called $FADH_2$, transfer electrons derived from glucose to electron transport chains, which are built into the inner mitochondrial membrane. (In prokaryotes, the electron transport chains are located in the plasma membrane.) During oxidative phosphorylation, electron transport chains convert the chemical energy to a form used for ATP synthesis in the process called chemiosmosis.

ANIMATION   **BioFlix** Visit the Study Area in **MasteringBiology** for the BioFlix® 3-D Animation on Cellular Respiration.

As diagrammed in **Figure 9.6**, glycolysis and pyruvate oxidation followed by the citric acid cycle are the catabolic pathways that break down glucose and other organic fuels. **Glycolysis**, which occurs in the cytosol, begins the degradation process by breaking glucose into two molecules of a compound called pyruvate. In eukaryotes, pyruvate enters the mitochondrion and is oxidized to a compound called acetyl CoA, which enters the **citric acid cycle**. There, the breakdown of glucose to carbon dioxide is completed. (In prokaryotes, these processes take place in the cytosol.) Thus, the carbon dioxide produced by respiration represents fragments of oxidized organic molecules.

Some of the steps of glycolysis and the citric acid cycle are redox reactions in which dehydrogenases transfer electrons from substrates to NAD^+, forming NADH. In the third stage of respiration, the electron transport chain accepts electrons (most often via NADH) from the breakdown products of the first two stages and passes these electrons from one molecule to another. At the end of the chain, the electrons are combined with molecular oxygen and hydrogen ions (H^+), forming water (see Figure 9.5b). The energy released at each step of the chain is stored in a form the mitochondrion (or prokaryotic cell) can use to make ATP from ADP. This mode of ATP synthesis is called **oxidative phosphorylation** because it is powered by the redox reactions of the electron transport chain.

In eukaryotic cells, the inner membrane of the mitochondrion is the site of electron transport and chemiosmosis, the processes that together constitute oxidative phosphorylation. (In prokaryotes, these processes take place in the plasma membrane.) Oxidative phosphorylation accounts for almost 90% of the ATP generated by respiration. A smaller amount of ATP is formed directly in a few

reactions of glycolysis and the citric acid cycle by a mechanism called **substrate-level phosphorylation** (Figure 9.7). This mode of ATP synthesis occurs when an enzyme transfers a phosphate group from a substrate molecule to ADP, rather than adding an inorganic phosphate to ADP as in oxidative phosphorylation. "Substrate molecule" here refers to an organic molecule generated as an intermediate during the catabolism of glucose. You'll see examples of substrate-level phosphorylation later in the chapter, in both glycolysis and the citric acid cycle.

When you withdraw a relatively large sum of money from an ATM machine, it is not delivered to you in a single bill of a large denomination. Instead, a number of smaller-denomination bills are dispensed that you can spend more easily. This is analogous to ATP production during cellular respiration. For each molecule of glucose degraded to carbon dioxide and water by respiration, the cell makes up to about 32 molecules of ATP, each with 30.5 kJ/mol of free energy. Respiration cashes in the large

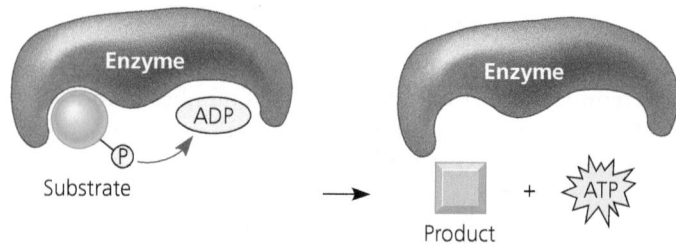

▲ Figure 9.7 **Substrate-level phosphorylation.** Some ATP is made by direct transfer of a phosphate group from an organic substrate to ADP by an enzyme. (For examples in glycolysis, see Figure 9.9, steps 7 and 10.)

MAKE CONNECTIONS *Review Figure 8.9. Do you think the potential energy is higher for the reactants or the products in the reaction shown above? Explain.*

denomination of energy banked in a single molecule of glucose (2870 kJ/mol) for the small change of many molecules of ATP, which is more practical for the cell to spend on its work.

This preview has introduced you to how glycolysis, the citric acid cycle, and oxidative phosphorylation fit into the process of cellular respiration. We are now ready to take a closer look at each of these three stages of respiration.

CONCEPT CHECK 9.1

1. Compare and contrast aerobic and anaerobic respiration.
2. **WHAT IF?** If the following redox reaction occurred, which compound would be oxidized? Which reduced?

$$C_4H_6O_5 + NAD^+ \rightarrow C_4H_4O_5 + NADH + H^+$$

For suggested answers, see Appendix A.

CONCEPT 9.2

Glycolysis harvests chemical energy by oxidizing glucose to pyruvate

The word *glycolysis* means "sugar splitting," and that is exactly what happens during this pathway. Glucose, a six-carbon sugar, is split into two three-carbon sugars. These smaller sugars are then oxidized and their remaining atoms rearranged to form two molecules of pyruvate. (Pyruvate is the ionized form of pyruvic acid.)

As summarized in **Figure 9.8**, glycolysis can be divided into two phases: the energy investment phase and the energy payoff phase. During the energy investment phase, the cell actually spends ATP. This investment is repaid with interest during the energy payoff phase, when ATP is produced by substrate-level phosphorylation and NAD$^+$ is reduced to NADH by electrons released from the oxidation of glucose. The net energy yield from glycolysis, per glucose molecule, is 2 ATP plus 2 NADH. The 10 steps of the glycolytic pathway are shown in **Figure 9.9**.

All of the carbon originally present in glucose is accounted for in the two molecules of pyruvate; no carbon is released as CO_2 during glycolysis. Glycolysis occurs whether or not O_2 is present. However, if O_2 *is* present, the chemical energy stored in pyruvate and NADH can be extracted by pyruvate oxidation, the citric acid cycle, and oxidative phosphorylation.

CONCEPT CHECK 9.2

1. During the redox reaction in glycolysis (step 6 in Figure 9.9), which molecule acts as the oxidizing agent? The reducing agent?

For suggested answers, see Appendix A.

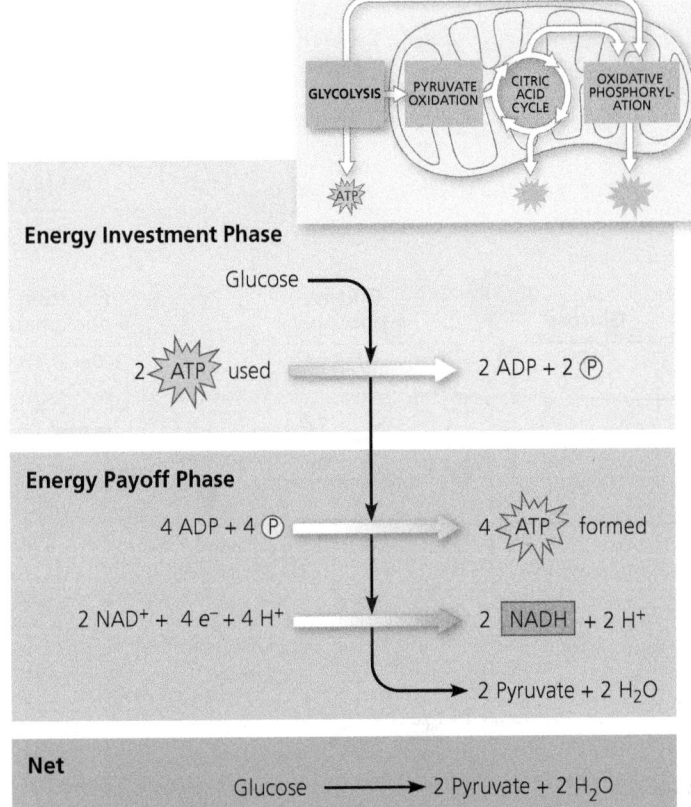

▲ Figure 9.8 **The energy input and output of glycolysis.**

CONCEPT 9.3

After pyruvate is oxidized, the citric acid cycle completes the energy-yielding oxidation of organic molecules

Glycolysis releases less than a quarter of the chemical energy in glucose that can be harvested by cells; most of the energy remains stockpiled in the two molecules of pyruvate. When O_2 is present, the pyruvate in eukaryotic cells enters a mitochondrion, where the oxidation of glucose is completed. In aerobically respiring prokaryotic cells, this process occurs in the cytosol. (Later in the chapter, we'll discuss what happens to pyruvate when O_2 is unavailable or in a prokaryote that is unable to use O_2.)

Oxidation of Pyruvate to Acetyl CoA

Upon entering the mitochondrion via active transport, pyruvate is first converted to a compound called acetyl coenzyme A, or **acetyl CoA** (Figure 9.10). This step, linking glycolysis and the citric acid cycle, is carried out by a multienzyme complex that catalyzes three reactions: ❶ Pyruvate's carboxyl group ($—COO^-$), which is already fully oxidized and thus

▼ Figure 9.9 **A closer look at glycolysis.** Note that glycolysis is a source of ATP and NADH.

GLYCOLYSIS: Energy Investment Phase

WHAT IF? *What would happen if you removed the dihydroxyacetone phosphate generated in step ④ as fast as it was produced?*

Source: Figure adapted from *Biochemistry*, 4th Edition, by Christopher K. Mathews et al. Copyright 2013 by Pearson Education, Inc. Adapted and electronically reproduced by permission of Pearson Education, Inc., Upper Saddle River, New Jersey.

has little chemical energy, is removed and given off as a molecule of CO_2. This is the first step in which CO_2 is released during respiration. ② The remaining two-carbon fragment is

▲ **Figure 9.10 Oxidation of pyruvate to acetyl CoA, the step before the citric acid cycle.** Pyruvate is a charged molecule, so in eukaryotic cells it must enter the mitochondrion via active transport, with the help of a transport protein. Next, a complex of several enzymes (the pyruvate dehydrogenase complex) catalyzes the three numbered steps, which are described in the text. The acetyl group of acetyl CoA will enter the citric acid cycle. The CO_2 molecule will diffuse out of the cell. By convention, coenzyme A is abbreviated S-CoA when it is attached to a molecule, emphasizing the sulphur atom (S).

oxidized, forming acetate (CH_3COO^-, the ionized form of acetic acid). The extracted electrons are transferred to NAD^+, storing energy in the form of NADH. ③ Finally, coenzyme A (CoA), a sulphur-containing compound derived from a B vitamin, is attached via its sulphur atom to the acetate, forming acetyl CoA, which has a high potential energy; in other words, the reaction of acetyl CoA to yield lower-energy products is highly exergonic. This molecule will now feed its acetyl group into the citric acid cycle for further oxidation.

The Citric Acid Cycle

The citric acid cycle functions as a metabolic furnace that oxidizes organic fuel derived from pyruvate. **Figure 9.11** summarizes the inputs and outputs as pyruvate is broken down to three CO_2 molecules, including the molecule of CO_2 released during the conversion of pyruvate to acetyl CoA. The cycle generates one ATP per turn by substrate-level phosphorylation, but most of the chemical energy is transferred to NAD^+ and a related electron carrier, the coenzyme FAD (flavin adenine dinucleotide, derived from riboflavin, a B vitamin), during the redox reactions. The reduced coenzymes, NADH and $FADH_2$, shuttle their cargo of high-energy electrons into the electron transport chain. The citric acid cycle is also called the tricarboxylic acid cycle or the Krebs cycle, the latter honouring Hans Krebs, the German-British scientist who was largely responsible for working out the pathway in the 1930s.

Now let's look at the citric acid cycle in more detail. The cycle has eight steps, each catalyzed by a specific enzyme.

The energy payoff phase occurs after glucose is split into two three-carbon sugars. Thus, the coefficient 2 precedes all molecules in this phase.

GLYCOLYSIS: Energy Payoff Phase

6 Two sequential reactions: (1) The sugar is oxidized by the transfer of electrons to NAD$^+$, forming NADH. (2) Using energy from this exergonic redox reaction, a phosphate group is attached to the oxidized substrate, making a high-energy product.

7 The phosphate group is transferred to ADP (substrate-level phosphorylation) in an exergonic reaction. The carbonyl group of G3P has been oxidized to the carboxyl group (—COO$^-$) of an organic acid (3-phosphoglycerate).

8 This enzyme relocates the remaining phosphate group.

9 Enolase causes a double bond to form in the substrate by extracting a water molecule, yielding phosphoenolpyruvate (PEP), a compound with a very high potential energy.

10 The phosphate group is transferred from PEP to ADP (a second example of substrate-level phosphorylation), forming pyruvate.

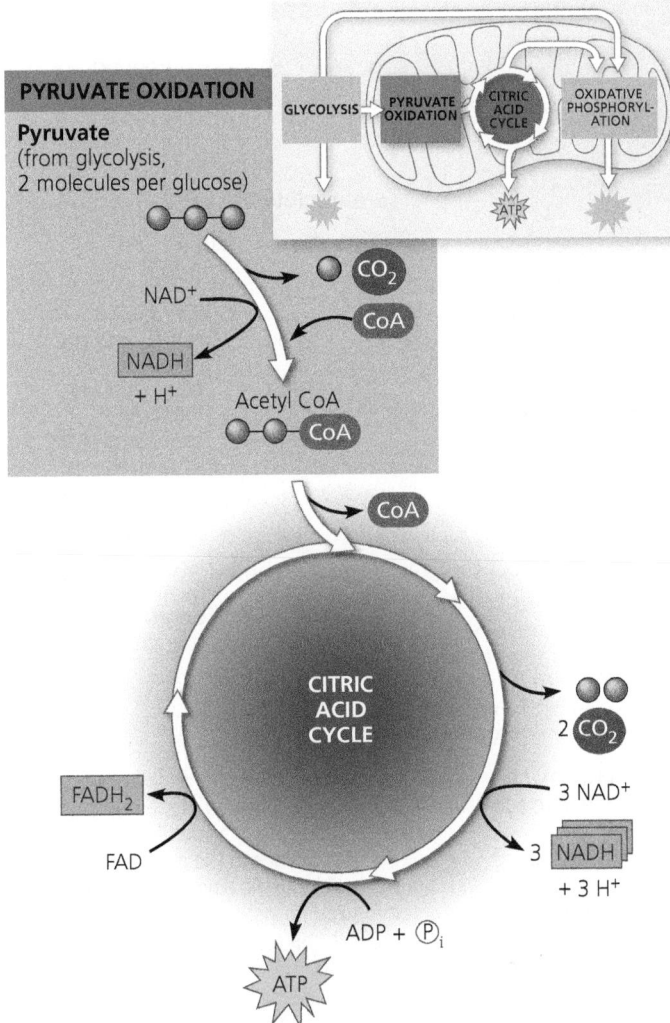

You can see in **Figure 9.12** that for each turn of the citric acid cycle, two carbons (red) enter in the relatively reduced form of an acetyl group (step **1**), and two different carbons (blue) leave in the completely oxidized form of CO_2 molecules (steps **3** and **4**). The acetyl group of acetyl CoA joins the cycle by combining with the compound oxaloacetate, forming citrate (step **1**). Citrate is the ionized form of citric acid, for which the cycle is named. The next seven steps decompose the citrate back to oxaloacetate. It is this regeneration of oxaloacetate that makes the process a *cycle*.

We can refer to Figure 9.12 in order to tally the energy-rich molecules produced by the citric acid cycle. For each acetyl group entering the cycle, 3 NAD$^+$ are reduced to NADH (steps **3**, **4**, and **8**). In step **6**, electrons are transferred not to NAD$^+$, but to FAD, which accepts 2 electrons and 2 protons to become FADH$_2$. In many animal tissue cells the reaction in step 5 produces a guanosine triphosphate (GTP) molecule by substrate-level phosphorylation. GTP is a molecule similar to ATP in its structure and cellular function. This GTP may be used to make an ATP molecule (as shown) or directly power work in the cell. In the cells of plants, bacteria, and some animal tissues, step **5** forms an ATP molecule directly by substrate-level phosphorylation. The output from step **5** represents the only ATP generated during the citric acid cycle. Recall

◄ **Figure 9.11 An overview of pyruvate oxidation and the citric acid cycle.** The inputs and outputs per pyruvate molecule are shown. To calculate on a per-glucose basis, multiply by 2, because each glucose molecule is split during glycolysis into two pyruvate molecules.

CHAPTER 9 Cellular Respiration and Fermentation 183

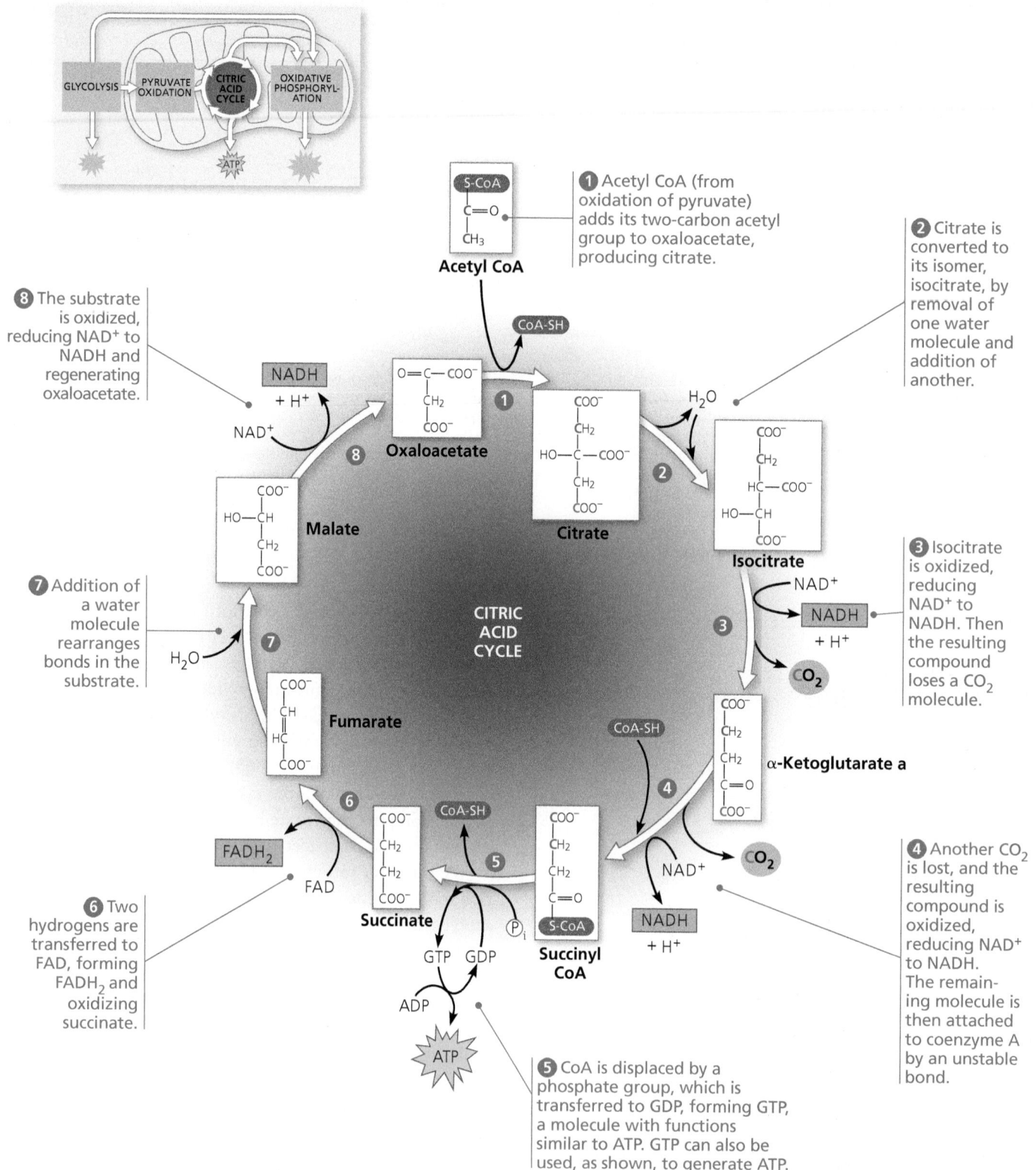

1 Acetyl CoA (from oxidation of pyruvate) adds its two-carbon acetyl group to oxaloacetate, producing citrate.

2 Citrate is converted to its isomer, isocitrate, by removal of one water molecule and addition of another.

8 The substrate is oxidized, reducing NAD⁺ to NADH and regenerating oxaloacetate.

3 Isocitrate is oxidized, reducing NAD⁺ to NADH. Then the resulting compound loses a CO_2 molecule.

7 Addition of a water molecule rearranges bonds in the substrate.

4 Another CO_2 is lost, and the resulting compound is oxidized, reducing NAD⁺ to NADH. The remaining molecule is then attached to coenzyme A by an unstable bond.

6 Two hydrogens are transferred to FAD, forming $FADH_2$ and oxidizing succinate.

5 CoA is displaced by a phosphate group, which is transferred to GDP, forming GTP, a molecule with functions similar to ATP. GTP can also be used, as shown, to generate ATP.

CITRIC ACID CYCLE

Oxaloacetate · Citrate · Isocitrate · α-Ketoglutarate a · Succinyl CoA · Succinate · Fumarate · Malate · Acetyl CoA

▲ **Figure 9.12 A closer look at the citric acid cycle.** In the chemical structures, red type traces the fate of the two carbon atoms that enter the cycle via acetyl CoA (step 1), and blue type indicates the two carbons that exit the cycle as CO_2 in steps 3 and 4. (The red type goes only through step 5 because the succinate molecule is symmetrical; the two ends cannot be distinguished from each other.) Notice that the carbon atoms that enter the cycle from acetyl CoA do not leave the cycle in the same turn. They remain in the cycle, occupying a different location in the molecules on their next turn, after another acetyl group is added. Therefore, the oxaloacetate that is regenerated at step 8 is made up of different carbon atoms each time around. In eukaryotic cells, all the citric acid cycle enzymes are located in the mitochondrial matrix except for the enzyme that catalyzes step 6, which resides in the inner mitochondrial membrane. Carboxylic acids are represented in their ionized forms, as —COO⁻, because the ionized forms prevail at the pH within the mitochondrion.

that each glucose gives rise to two acetyl CoAs that enter the cycle. Because the numbers noted earlier are obtained from a single acetyl group entering the pathway, the total yield per glucose from the citric acid cycle is 6 NADHs, 2 $FADH_2$s, and the equivalent of 2 ATPs.

Most of the ATP produced by respiration results from oxidative phosphorylation, when the NADH and $FADH_2$ produced by the citric acid cycle relay the electrons extracted from food to the electron transport chain. In the process, they supply the necessary energy for the phosphorylation of ADP to ATP. We will explore this process in the next section.

CONCEPT CHECK 9.3

1. Name the molecules that conserve most of the energy from the redox reactions of the citric acid cycle (see Figure 9.12). How is this energy converted to a form that can be used to make ATP?

2. What processes in your cells produce the CO_2 that you exhale?

3. **WHAT IF?** The conversions shown in Figure 9.10 and step 4 of Figure 9.12 are each catalyzed by a large multienzyme complex. What similarities are there in the reactions that occur in these two cases?

For suggested answers, see Appendix A.

CONCEPT **9.4**

During oxidative phosphorylation, chemiosmosis couples electron transport to ATP synthesis

Our main objective in this chapter is to learn how cells harvest the energy of glucose and other nutrients in food to make ATP. But the metabolic components of respiration we have dissected so far, glycolysis and the citric acid cycle, produce only 4 ATP molecules per glucose molecule, all by substrate-level phosphorylation: 2 net ATP from glycolysis and 2 ATP from the citric acid cycle. At this point, molecules of NADH (and $FADH_2$) account for most of the energy extracted from each glucose molecule. These electron escorts link glycolysis and the citric acid cycle to the machinery of oxidative phosphorylation, which uses energy released by the electron transport chain to power ATP synthesis. In this section, you will learn first how the electron transport chain works and then how electron flow down the chain is coupled to ATP synthesis.

The Pathway of Electron Transport

The electron transport chain is a collection of molecules embedded in the inner membrane of the mitochondrion in eukaryotic cells. (In prokaryotes, these molecules reside in the plasma membrane.) The folding of the inner membrane to form cristae increases its surface area, providing space for thousands of copies of the electron transport chain in each mitochondrion. Once again, we see that structure fits

function—the infolded membrane with its placement of electron carrier molecules in a row, one after the other, is well-suited for the series of sequential redox reactions that take place along the electron transport chain. Most components of the chain are proteins, which exist in multiprotein complexes numbered I through IV. Tightly bound to these proteins are *prosthetic groups*, nonprotein components essential for the catalytic functions of certain enzymes.

Figure 9.13 shows the sequence of electron carriers in the electron transport chain and the drop in free energy as

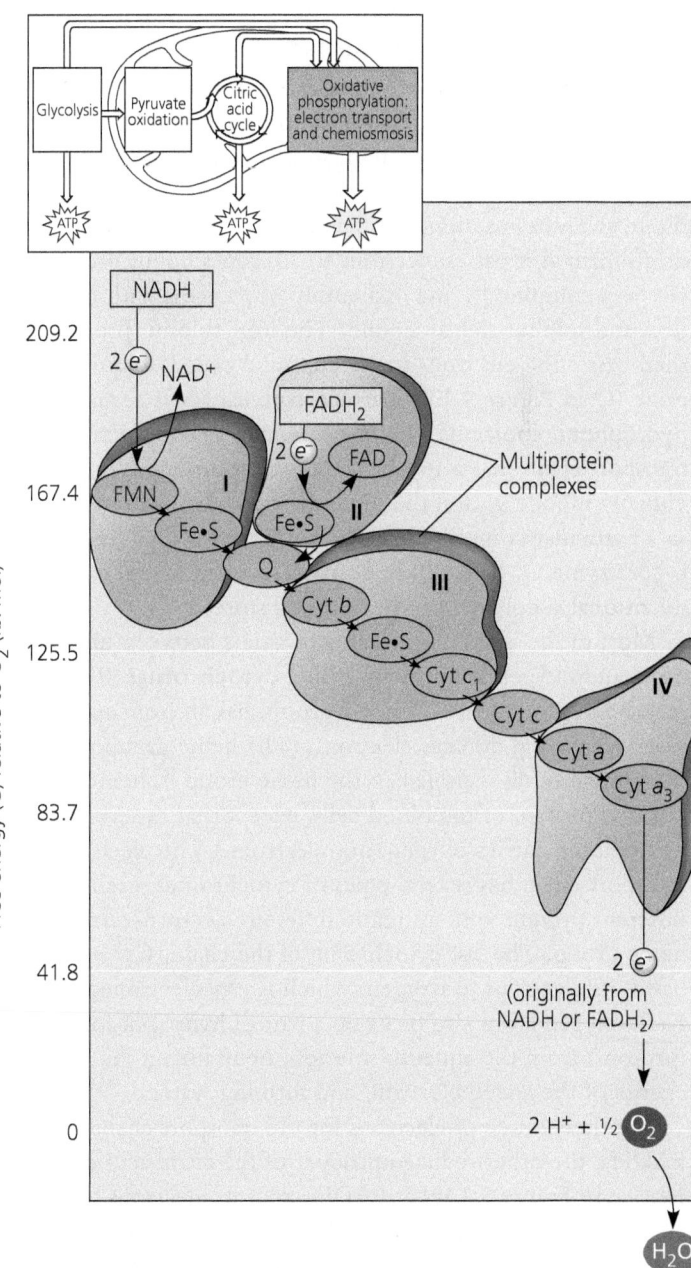

▲ **Figure 9.13 Free-energy change during electron transport.** The overall energy drop (ΔG) for electrons travelling from NADH to oxygen is 221.8 kJ/mol, but this "fall" is broken up into a series of smaller steps by the electron transport chain. (An oxygen atom is represented here as ½ O_2 to emphasize that the electron transport chain reduces molecular oxygen, O_2, not individual oxygen atoms.)

electrons travel down the chain. During electron transport along the chain, electron carriers alternate between reduced and oxidized states as they accept and then donate electrons. Each component of the chain becomes reduced when it accepts electrons from its "uphill" neighbour, which has a lower affinity for electrons (in other words, is less electro-negative). It then returns to its oxidized form as it passes electrons to its "downhill," more electronegative, neighbour.

Now let's take a closer look at the electron transport chain in Figure 9.13. We'll first describe the passage of electrons through complex I in some detail, as an illustra-tion of the general principles involved in electron transport. Electrons acquired from glucose by NAD^+ during glycolysis and the citric acid cycle are transferred from NADH to the first molecule of the electron transport chain in complex I. This molecule is a flavoprotein, so named because it has a prosthetic group called flavin mononucleotide (FMN). In the next redox reaction, the flavoprotein returns to its oxi-dized form as it passes electrons to an iron-sulphur protein (Fe·S in complex I), one of a family of proteins with both iron and sulphur tightly bound. The iron-sulphur protein then passes the electrons to a compound called ubiqui-none (Q in Figure 9.13). This electron carrier is a small hydrophobic molecule, the only member of the electron transport chain that is not a protein. Ubiquinone is indi-vidually mobile within the membrane rather than residing in a particular complex. (Another name for ubiquinone is coenzyme Q, or CoQ; you may have seen it sold as a nutritional supplement in health food stores.)

Most of the remaining electron carriers between ubiqui-none and oxygen are proteins called **cytochromes**. Their prosthetic group, called a heme group, has an iron atom that accepts and donates electrons. (The heme group in the cytochromes is similar to the heme group in hemoglo-bin, the protein of red blood cells, except that the iron in hemoglobin carries oxygen, not electrons.) The electron transport chain has several types of cytochromes, each a different protein with a slightly different electron-carrying heme group. The last cytochrome of the chain, Cyt a_3, passes its electrons to oxygen, which is *very* electronegative. Each oxygen atom also picks up a pair of hydrogen ions (protons) from the aqueous solution, neutralizing the -2 charge of the added electrons and forming water.

Another source of electrons for the transport chain is $FADH_2$, the other reduced product of the citric acid cycle. Notice in Figure 9.13 that $FADH_2$ adds its electrons to the electron transport chain from within complex II, at a lower energy level than NADH does. Consequently, although NADH and $FADH_2$ each donate an equivalent number of electrons (2) for oxygen reduction, the electron transport chain provides about one-third less energy for ATP synthe-sis when the electron donor is $FADH_2$ rather than NADH. We'll see why in the next section.

The electron transport chain makes no ATP directly. Instead, it eases the fall of electrons from food to oxygen, breaking a large free-energy drop into a series of smaller steps that release energy in manageable amounts, step by step. The importance of the role of the electron transport chain in cellular respiration is highlighted by the fact that defects in the complexes of the electron transport chain lead to human disease (Figure 9.14). How does the mito-chondrion (or the prokaryotic plasma membrane, in the case of prokaryotes) couple this electron transport and energy release to ATP synthesis? The answer is a mecha-nism called chemiosmosis.

▼ Figure 9.14 | **Impact**

What Happens When One of the Proteins Involved in Oxidative Phosphorylation Doesn't Function Properly?

The products of many mitochondrial genes (see Concept 15.5) are components of the complexes of the electron transport chain and ATP synthase. Mutations in one or more of these genes, and subsequent defects in the protein, can decrease the amount of ATP the cell can make. These mutations cause rare mitochondrial diseases, such as Leber's Hereditary Optic Neuropathy (LHON), which causes sudden blindness in young adults. Several LHON-causing mutations have been identified that disrupt complex I of the electron transport chain. Eric Shoubridge, a researcher from McGill University, has identified numer-ous mutations causing mitochondrial disease and showed that a single LHON-causing mutation predominantly affects patients of French-Canadian ancestry due to a founder effect (see Concept 23.3).

Healthy Vision   LHON Vision

Kevin Dodge/Blend Images/Alamy Stock Photo

Why It Matters In addition to causing a number of debilitating human diseases, mutations in mitochondrial DNA have been associated with the aging process. These mutations have enabled researchers to learn more about the process of oxidative phosphorylation and the role mitochondria play in aging. Unfortunately, treatment options for human mitochondrial disease are relatively limited.

Further Reading C. B. Park and N.-G. Larsson, Mitochondrial DNA mutations in disease and aging, *Journal of Cell Biology* 193:809–818 (2011). R. W. Taylor and D. M. Turnbull, Mitochondrial DNA mutations in human disease, *Nature Reviews Genetics* 6:389–402 (2005).

MAKE CONNECTIONS *Why do most mitochondrial diseases primarily affect muscles and the nervous system? (See Chapter 49.)*

Chemiosmosis: The Energy-Coupling Mechanism

Populating the inner membrane of the mitochondrion or the prokaryotic plasma membrane are many copies of a protein complex called **ATP synthase**, the enzyme that actually makes ATP from ADP and inorganic phosphate. ATP synthase works like an ion pump running in reverse. Ion pumps usually use ATP as an energy source to transport ions against their gradients. (In fact, the proton pump shown in Figure 7.17 is an ATP synthase.) Enzymes can catalyze a reaction in either direction, depending on the ΔG for the reaction, which is affected by the local concentrations of reactants and products (see Chapter 8). Rather than hydrolyzing ATP to pump protons against their concentration gradient, under the conditions of cellular respiration ATP synthase uses the energy of an existing ion gradient to power ATP synthesis. The power source for the ATP synthase is a difference in the concentration of H^+ on opposite sides of the inner mitochondrial membrane. (We can also think of this gradient as a difference in pH, since pH is a measure of H^+ concentration.) This process, in which energy stored in the form of a hydrogen ion gradient across a membrane is used to drive cellular work such as the synthesis of ATP, is called **chemiosmosis** (from the Greek *osmos*, push). We have previously used the word *osmosis* in discussing water transport, but here it refers to the flow of H^+ across a membrane.

From studying the structure of ATP synthase, scientists have learned how the flow of H^+ through this large enzyme powers ATP generation. ATP synthase is a multisubunit complex with four main parts, each made up of multiple polypeptides. Protons move one by one into binding sites on one of the parts (the rotor), causing it to spin in a way that catalyzes ATP production from ADP and inorganic phosphate (**Figure 9.15**). The flow of protons thus behaves somewhat like a rushing stream that turns a waterwheel. ATP synthase is the smallest molecular rotary motor known in nature.

How does the inner mitochondrial membrane or the prokaryotic plasma membrane generate and maintain the H^+ gradient that drives ATP synthesis by the ATP synthase protein complex? Establishing the H^+ gradient is a major function of the electron transport chain, which is shown in its mitochondrial location in **Figure 9.16**. The chain is an energy converter that uses the exergonic flow of electrons from NADH and $FADH_2$ to pump H^+ across the membrane, from the mitochondrial matrix into the intermembrane space. The H^+ has a tendency to move back across the membrane, diffusing down its gradient. And the ATP synthases are the only sites that provide a route through the membrane for H^+. As we described previously, the passage of H^+ through ATP synthase uses the exergonic flow of H^+ to drive the phosphorylation of ADP. Thus, the energy stored in an H^+ gradient across a membrane couples the redox reactions of the electron transport chain to ATP synthesis, an example of chemiosmosis.

At this point, you may be wondering how the electron transport chain pumps hydrogen ions. Researchers have found that certain members of the electron transport chain accept and release protons (H^+) along with electrons. (The aqueous solutions inside and surrounding the cell are a ready source of H^+.) At certain steps along the chain, electron transfers cause H^+ to be taken up and released into the surrounding solution. In eukaryotic cells, the electron carriers are spatially arranged in the inner mitochondrial membrane in such a way that H^+ is accepted from the mitochondrial matrix and deposited in the intermembrane space (see Figure 9.16). The H^+ gradient that results is referred to as a **proton-motive force**, emphasizing the capacity of the gradient to perform work. The force drives H^+ back across the membrane through the H^+ channels provided by ATP synthases.

In general terms, *chemiosmosis is an energy-coupling mechanism that uses energy stored in the form of an H^+ gradient across*

INTERMEMBRANE SPACE

H^+

Stator

Rotor

Internal rod

Catalytic knob

ADP + P_i

ATP

MITOCHONDRIAL MATRIX

1 H^+ ions flowing down their gradient enter a channel in a stator, which is anchored in the membrane.

2 H^+ ions enter binding sites within a rotor, changing the shape of each subunit so that the rotor spins within the membrane.

3 Each H^+ ion makes one complete turn before leaving the rotor and passing through a second channel in the stator into the mitochondrial matrix.

4 Spinning of the rotor causes an internal rod to spin as well. This rod extends like a stalk into the knob below it, which is held stationary by part of the stator.

5 Turning of the rod activates catalytic sites in the knob that produce ATP from ADP and P_i.

▲ **Figure 9.15 ATP synthase, a molecular mill.** The ATP synthase protein complex functions as a mill, powered by the flow of hydrogen ions. Multiple ATP synthases reside in eukaryotic mitochondrial and chloroplast membranes and in prokaryotic plasma membranes. Each part of the complex consists of a number of polypeptide subunits. ATP synthase is the smallest molecular rotary motor known in nature.

Intermembrane space

Inner mitochondrial membrane

Mitochondrial matrix

Protein complex of electron carriers

NADH (carrying electrons from food)

NAD⁺

$FADH_2$ → FAD

$2 H^+ + \frac{1}{2}O_2$ → H_2O

ADP + P_i → ATP

Inner mitochondrial membrane

ATP synthase

❶ Electron transport chain
Electron transport and pumping of protons (H^+), which create an H^+ gradient across the membrane

❷ Chemiosmosis
ATP synthesis powered by the flow of H^+ back across the membrane

Oxidative phosphorylation

▲ Figure 9.16 **Chemiosmosis couples the electron transport chain to ATP synthesis.** ❶ NADH and $FADH_2$ shuttle high-energy electrons extracted from food during glycolysis and the citric acid cycle into an electron transport chain built into the inner mitochondrial membrane. The gold arrows trace the transport of electrons, which are finally passed to a terminal acceptor (O_2, in the case of aerobic respiration) at the "downhill" end of the chain, forming water. Most of the electron carriers of the chain are grouped into four complexes (I–IV). Two

mobile carriers, ubiquinone (Q) and cytochrome c (Cyt c), move rapidly, ferrying electrons between the large complexes. As the complexes shuttle electrons, they pump protons from the mitochondrial matrix into the intermembrane space. $FADH_2$ deposits its electrons via complex II—at a lower energy level than complex I, where NADH deposits its electrons—and so results in fewer protons being pumped into the intermembrane space than occurs with NADH. Chemical energy that was originally harvested from food is transformed into a proton-motive

force, a gradient of H^+ across the membrane. ❷ During chemiosmosis, the protons flow back down their gradient via ATP synthase, which is built into the membrane nearby. The ATP synthase harnesses the proton-motive force to phosphorylate ADP, forming ATP. Together, electron transport and chemiosmosis make up oxidative phosphorylation.

WHAT IF? *If complex IV were nonfunctional, could chemiosmosis produce any ATP, and if so, how would the rate of synthesis differ?*

a membrane to drive cellular work. In mitochondria, the energy for gradient formation comes from exergonic redox reactions, and ATP synthesis is the work performed. But chemiosmosis also occurs elsewhere and in other variations. Chloroplasts use chemiosmosis to generate ATP during photosynthesis; in these organelles, light (rather than chemical energy) drives both electron flow down an electron transport chain and the resulting H^+ gradient formation. Prokaryotes, as already mentioned, generate H^+ gradients across their plasma membranes. They then tap the proton-motive force not only to make ATP inside the cell but also to rotate their flagella and to pump nutrients and waste products across the membrane. Because of its

central importance to energy conversions in prokaryotes and eukaryotes, chemiosmosis has helped unify the study of bioenergetics. Peter Mitchell was awarded the Nobel Prize in 1978 for originally proposing the chemiosmotic model.

An Accounting of ATP Production by Cellular Respiration

In the last few sections, we have looked rather closely at the key processes of cellular respiration. Now let's take a step back and remind ourselves of its overall function: harvesting the energy of glucose for ATP synthesis.

During respiration, most energy flows in this sequence: glucose → NADH → electron transport chain → proton-motive force → ATP. We can do some bookkeeping to calculate the ATP profit when cellular respiration oxidizes a molecule of glucose to six molecules of carbon dioxide. The three main departments of this metabolic enterprise are glycolysis, pyruvate oxidation and the citric acid cycle, along with the electron transport chain, which drives oxidative phosphorylation. **Figure 9.17** gives a detailed accounting of the ATP yield per glucose molecule oxidized. The tally adds the 4 ATP produced directly by substrate-level phosphorylation during glycolysis and the citric acid cycle to the many more molecules of ATP generated by oxidative phosphorylation. Each NADH that transfers a pair of electrons from glucose to the electron transport chain contributes enough to the proton-motive force to generate a maximum of 3 ATP.

Why are the numbers in Figure 9.17 inexact? There are three reasons we cannot state an exact number of ATP molecules generated by the breakdown of one molecule of glucose. First, phosphorylation and the redox reactions are not directly coupled to each other, so the ratio of the number of NADH molecules to the number of ATP molecules is not a whole number. We know that 1 NADH results in 10 H^+ being transported out across the inner mitochondrial membrane, but the exact number of H^+ that must reenter the mitochondrial matrix via ATP synthase to generate 1 ATP has long been debated. Based on experimental data,

however, most biochemists now agree that the most accurate number is 4 H^+. Therefore, a single molecule of NADH generates enough proton-motive force for the synthesis of 2.5 ATP. The citric acid cycle also supplies electrons to the electron transport chain via $FADH_2$, but since its electrons enter later in the chain, each molecule of this electron carrier is responsible for transport of only enough H^+ for the synthesis of 1.5 ATP. These numbers also take into account the slight energetic cost of moving the ATP formed in the mitochondrion out into the cytosol, where it will be used.

Second, the ATP yield varies slightly depending on the type of shuttle used to transport electrons from the cytosol into the mitochondrion. The mitochondrial inner membrane is impermeable to NADH, so NADH in the cytosol is segregated from the machinery of oxidative phosphorylation. The 2 electrons of NADH captured in glycolysis must be conveyed into the mitochondrion by one of several electron shuttle systems. Depending on the kind of shuttle in a particular cell type, the electrons are passed either to NAD^+ or to FAD in the mitochondrial matrix (see Figure 9.17). If the electrons are passed to FAD, as in brain cells, only about 1.5 ATP can result from each NADH that was originally generated in the cytosol. If the electrons are passed to mitochondrial NAD^+, as in liver cells and heart cells, the yield is about 2.5 ATP per NADH.

A third variable that reduces the yield of ATP is the use of the proton-motive force generated by the redox reactions

▲ **Figure 9.17 ATP yield per molecule of glucose at each stage of cellular respiration.**

? *Explain exactly how the total of 26 or 28 ATP (see the yellow bar in the figure) was calculated.*

Making a Bar Graph and Evaluating a Hypothesis

Does Thyroid Hormone Level Affect Oxygen Consumption in Cells? Some animals, such as mammals and birds, maintain a relatively constant body temperature, above that of their environment, by using heat produced as a by-product of metabolism. When the core temperature of these animals drops below an internal set point, their cells are triggered to reduce the efficiency of ATP production by the electron transport chains in mitochondria. At lower efficiency, extra fuel must be consumed to produce the same number of ATPs, generating additional heat. Because this response is moderated by the endocrine system, researchers hypothesized that thyroid hormone might trigger this cellular response. In this exercise, you will use a bar graph to visualize data from an experiment that compared the metabolic rate (by measuring oxygen consumption) in mitochondria of cells from animals with different levels of thyroid hormone.

Kitchin and Hurst/All Canada Photos/AGE Fotostock America Inc.

How the Experiment Was Done Liver cells were isolated from sibling rats that had low, normal, or elevated thyroid hormone levels. The oxygen consumption rate due to activity of the mitochondrial electron transport chains of each type of cell was measured under controlled conditions.

Data from the Experiment

Thyroid Hormone Level	Oxygen Consumption Rate (nmol O_2/min · mg cells)
Low	4.3
Normal	4.8
Elevated	8.7

Interpret the Data

1. To visualize any differences in oxygen consumption between cell types, it will be useful to graph the data in a bar graph. First, set up the axes. (a) What is the independent variable (intentionally varied by the researchers), which goes on the *x*-axis? List the categories along the *x*-axis; because they are discrete rather than continuous, you can list them in any order. (b) What is the dependent variable (measured by the researchers), which goes on the *y*-axis? (c) What units (abbreviated) should go on the *y*-axis? Label the *y*-axis, including the units specified in the data table. Determine the range of values of the data that will need to go on the *y*-axis. What is the largest

value? Draw evenly spaced tick marks and label them, starting with 0 at the bottom.

2. Graph the data for each sample. Match each *x*-value with its *y*-value and place a mark on the graph at that coordinate, then draw a bar from the *x*-axis up to the correct height for each sample. Why is a bar graph more appropriate than a scatter plot or line graph? (For additional information about graphs, see the Scientific Skills Review in Appendix E and in the Study Area in MasteringBiology.)

3. Examine your graph and look for a pattern in the data. (a) Which cell type had the highest rate of oxygen consumption, and which had the lowest? (b) Does this support the researchers' hypothesis? Explain. (c) Based on what you know about mitochondrial electron transport and heat production, predict which rats had the highest, and which had the lowest, body temperature.

Data from "The Quantitative Contributions of Mitochondrial Proton Leak and ATP Turnover Reactions to the Changed Respiration Rates of Hepatocytes from Rats of Different Thyroid Status" by Mary-Ellen Harper and Martin D. Brand, from *Journal of Biological Chemistry*, July 1993, Volume 268(20). © Jane B Reece.

---

of respiration to drive other kinds of work. For example, the proton-motive force powers the mitochondrion's uptake of pyruvate from the cytosol. However, if *all* the proton-motive force generated by the electron transport chain were used to drive ATP synthesis, one glucose molecule could generate a maximum of 28 ATP produced by oxidative phosphorylation plus 4 ATP (net) from substrate-level phosphorylation to give a total yield of about 32 ATP (or only about 30 ATP if the less efficient shuttle were functioning).

We can now roughly estimate the efficiency of respiration—that is, the percentage of chemical energy in glucose that has been transferred to ATP. Recall that the complete oxidation of a mole of glucose releases 2870 kJ of energy under standard conditions ($\Delta G = -2870$ kJ/mol). Phosphorylation of ADP to form ATP stores at least 30.5 kJ per mole of ATP. Therefore, the efficiency of respiration is

30.5 kJ per mole of ATP times 32 moles of ATP per mole of glucose divided by 2870 kJ per mole of glucose, which equals 0.34. Thus, about 34% of the potential chemical energy in glucose has been transferred to ATP; the actual percentage is bound to vary as ΔG varies under different cellular conditions. Cellular respiration is remarkably efficient in its energy conversion. By comparison, even the most efficient automobile converts only about 25% of the energy stored in gasoline to energy that moves the car.

The rest of the energy stored in glucose is lost as heat. We humans use some of this heat to maintain our relatively high body temperature (37°C), and we dissipate the rest through sweating and other cooling mechanisms.

Surprisingly, perhaps it may be beneficial under certain conditions to reduce the efficiency of cellular respiration. A remarkable adaptation is shown by hibernating mammals, which overwinter in a state of inactivity and lowered metabolism. Although their internal body temperature is lower than normal, it still must be kept significantly higher than the external air temperature. One type of tissue, called brown fat, is made up of cells packed full of mitochondria. The inner mitochondrial membrane contains a channel protein called the uncoupling protein, which allows protons to flow back down their concentration gradient without generating ATP. Activation of these proteins in hibernating mammals results in ongoing oxidation of stored fuel stores (fats), generating heat without any ATP production. In the absence of such an adaptation, the build-up of ATP would eventually cause cellular respiration to be shut down by regulatory mechanisms that will be discussed later. In the Scientific Skills Exercise, you can work with data in a related but different case where a decrease in metabolic efficiency in cells is used to generate heat.

CONCEPT CHECK 9.4

1. What effect would an absence of O_2 have on the process shown in Figure 9.16?

2. **WHAT IF?** In the absence of O_2, as in question 1, what do you think would happen if you decreased the pH of the intermembrane space of the mitochondrion? Explain your answer.

3. **MAKE CONNECTIONS** Membranes must be fluid to function properly (as you learned in Concept 7.1). How does the operation of the electron transport chain support that assertion?

For suggested answers, see Appendix A.

CONCEPT 9.5

Fermentation and anaerobic respiration enable cells to produce ATP without the use of oxygen

Because most of the ATP generated by cellular respiration is due to the work of oxidative phosphorylation, our estimate of ATP yield from aerobic respiration is contingent on an adequate supply of oxygen to the cell. Without the electronegative oxygen to pull electrons down the transport chain, oxidative phosphorylation eventually ceases. However, there are two general mechanisms by which certain cells can oxidize organic fuel and generate ATP *without* the use of oxygen: anaerobic respiration and fermentation. The distinction between these two is that an electron transport chain is used in anaerobic respiration but not in fermentation. (The electron transport chain is also called the respiratory chain because of its role in both types of cellular respiration.)

We have already mentioned anaerobic respiration, which takes place in certain prokaryotic organisms that live in environments without oxygen. These organisms have an electron transport chain but do not use oxygen as a final electron acceptor at the end of the chain. Oxygen performs this function very well because it is extremely electronegative, but other less electronegative substances can also serve as final electron acceptors. Some "sulphate-reducing" marine bacteria, for instance, use the sulphate ion (SO_4^{2-}) at the end of their respiratory chain. Operation of the chain builds up a proton-motive force used to produce ATP, but H_2S (hydrogen sulphide) is made as a by-product rather than water. The rotten-egg odour you may have smelled while walking through a salt marsh or a mudflat signals the presence of sulphate-reducing bacteria.

Fermentation is a way of harvesting chemical energy without using either oxygen or any electron transport chain—in other words, without cellular respiration. How can food be oxidized without cellular respiration? Remember, oxidation simply refers to the loss of electrons to an electron acceptor, so it does not need to involve oxygen. Glycolysis oxidizes glucose to two molecules of pyruvate. The oxidizing agent of glycolysis is NAD^+, and neither oxygen nor any electron transfer chain is involved. Overall, glycolysis is exergonic, and some of the energy made available is used to produce 2 ATP (net) by substrate-level phosphorylation. If oxygen *is* present, then additional ATP is made by oxidative phosphorylation when NADH passes electrons removed from glucose to the electron transport chain. But glycolysis generates 2 ATP whether oxygen is present or not—that is, whether conditions are aerobic or anaerobic.

As an alternative to respiratory oxidation of organic nutrients, fermentation is an extension of glycolysis that allows continuous generation of ATP by the substrate-level phosphorylation of glycolysis. For this to occur, there must be a sufficient supply of NAD^+ to accept electrons during the oxidation step of glycolysis. Without some mechanism to recycle NAD^+ from NADH, glycolysis would soon deplete the cell's pool of NAD^+ by reducing it all to NADH and would shut itself down for lack of an oxidizing agent. Under aerobic conditions, NAD^+ is recycled from NADH by the transfer of electrons to the electron transport chain. An anaerobic alternative is to transfer electrons from NADH to pyruvate, the end product of glycolysis.

Types of Fermentation

Fermentation consists of glycolysis plus reactions that regenerate NAD^+ by transferring electrons from NADH to pyruvate or derivatives of pyruvate. The NAD^+ can then be reused to oxidize sugar by glycolysis, which nets two molecules of ATP by substrate-level phosphorylation. There are many types of fermentation, differing in the end products formed from pyruvate. Two types commonly harnessed by humans for food and industrial production are alcohol fermentation and lactic acid fermentation.

In **alcohol fermentation** (Figure 9.18a), pyruvate is converted to ethanol (ethyl alcohol) in two steps. The first step releases carbon dioxide from the pyruvate, which is converted to the two-carbon compound acetaldehyde. In the second step, acetaldehyde is reduced by NADH to ethanol. This regenerates the supply of NAD^+ needed for the continuation of glycolysis. Many bacteria carry out alcohol fermentation under anaerobic conditions. Yeast (a fungus) also carries out alcohol fermentation. For thousands of years, humans have used yeast in brewing, winemaking, and baking. The CO_2 bubbles generated by baker's yeast during alcohol fermentation allow bread to rise.

During **lactic acid fermentation** (Figure 9.18b), pyruvate is reduced directly by NADH to form lactate as an end product, with no release of CO_2. (Lactate is the ionized form of lactic acid.) Lactic acid fermentation by certain fungi and bacteria is used in the dairy industry to make cheese and yogurt.

Human muscle cells make ATP by lactic acid fermentation when oxygen is scarce. This occurs during strenuous exercise, when sugar catabolism for ATP production outpaces the muscle's supply of oxygen from the blood. Under these conditions, the cells switch from aerobic respiration to fermentation. The lactate that accumulates was previously thought to cause muscle fatigue and pain, but recent research suggests instead that increased levels of potassium ions (K^+) may be to blame, while lactate appears to enhance muscle performance. In any case, the excess lactate is gradually carried away by the blood to the liver, where it is converted back to pyruvate by liver cells. Because oxygen is available, this pyruvate can then enter the mitochondria in liver cells and complete cellular respiration.

Comparing Fermentation with Anaerobic and Aerobic Respiration

Fermentation, anaerobic respiration, and aerobic respiration are three alternative cellular pathways for producing ATP by harvesting the chemical energy of food. All three use glycolysis to oxidize glucose and other organic fuels to pyruvate, with a net production of 2 ATP by substrate-level phosphorylation. And in all three pathways, NAD^+ is the oxidizing agent that accepts electrons from food during glycolysis.

A key difference is the contrasting mechanisms for oxidizing NADH back to NAD^+, which is required to sustain glycolysis. In fermentation, the final electron acceptor is an organic molecule such as pyruvate (lactic acid fermentation) or acetaldehyde (alcohol fermentation). In cellular respiration, by contrast, electrons carried by NADH are transferred to an electron transport chain, which regenerates the NAD^+ required for glycolysis.

Another major difference is the amount of ATP produced. Fermentation yields 2 molecules of ATP, produced by substrate-level phosphorylation. In the absence of an

(a) Alcohol fermentation

(b) Lactic acid fermentation

▲ Figure 9.18 **Fermentation.** In the absence of oxygen, many cells use fermentation to produce ATP by substrate-level phosphorylation. Pyruvate, the end product of glycolysis, serves as an electron acceptor for oxidizing NADH back to NAD^+, which can then be reused in glycolysis. Two of the common end products formed from fermentation are **(a)** ethanol and **(b)** lactate, the ionized form of lactic acid.

electron transport chain, the energy stored in pyruvate is unavailable. In cellular respiration, however, pyruvate is completely oxidized in the mitochondrion. Most of the chemical energy from this process is shuttled by NADH and $FADH_2$ in the form of electrons to the electron transport chain. There, the electrons move stepwise down a series of redox reactions to a final electron acceptor. (In aerobic respiration, the final electron acceptor is oxygen; in anaerobic respiration, the final acceptor is another molecule that is electronegative, although less so than oxygen.) Stepwise electron transport drives oxidative phosphorylation, yielding ATPs. Thus, cellular respiration harvests much more energy from each sugar molecule than fermentation can. In fact, aerobic respiration yields up to 32 molecules of ATP per glucose molecule—up to 16 times as much as does fermentation.

Some organisms, called **obligate anaerobes**, carry out only fermentation or anaerobic respiration. In fact, these organisms cannot survive in the presence of oxygen, some forms of which can actually be toxic if protective systems are not present in the cell. A few cell types, such as cells of the vertebrate brain, can carry out only aerobic oxidation of pyruvate, not fermentation. Other organisms, including yeasts and many bacteria, can make enough ATP to survive using either fermentation or respiration. Such species are called **facultative anaerobes**. On the cellular level, our muscle cells behave as facultative anaerobes. In such cells, pyruvate is a fork in the metabolic road that leads to two alternative catabolic routes (Figure 9.19). Under aerobic conditions, pyruvate can be converted to acetyl CoA, and oxidation continues in the citric acid cycle via aerobic respiration. Under anaerobic conditions, lactic acid fermentation occurs: Pyruvate is diverted from the citric acid cycle, serving instead as an electron acceptor to recycle NAD^+. To make the same amount of ATP, a facultative anaerobe has to consume sugar at a much faster rate when fermenting than when respiring.

The Evolutionary Significance of Glycolysis

EVOLUTION   The role of glycolysis in both fermentation and respiration has an evolutionary basis. Ancient prokaryotes are thought to have used glycolysis to make ATP long before oxygen was present in Earth's atmosphere. The oldest known fossils of bacteria date back 3.5 billion years, but appreciable quantities of oxygen probably did not begin to accumulate in the atmosphere until about 2.7 billion years ago. Cyanobacteria produced this O_2 as a by-product of photosynthesis. Therefore, early prokaryotes may have generated ATP exclusively from glycolysis. The fact that glycolysis is today the most widespread metabolic pathway among Earth's organisms suggests that it evolved very early in the history of life. The cytosolic location of glycolysis also implies great antiquity; the pathway does not require any of the membrane-enclosed organelles of the eukaryotic cell, which evolved approximately 1 billion years after the first prokaryotic cell. Glycolysis is a metabolic heirloom from early cells that continues to function in fermentation and as the first stage in the breakdown of organic molecules by respiration.

CONCEPT CHECK 9.5

1. Consider the NADH formed during glycolysis. What is the final acceptor for its electrons during fermentation? What is the final acceptor for its electrons during aerobic respiration?

2. WHAT IF?   A glucose-fed yeast cell is moved from an aerobic environment to an anaerobic one. How would its rate of glucose consumption change if ATP were to be generated at the same rate?

For suggested answers, see Appendix A.

▲ Figure 9.19 **Pyruvate as a key juncture in catabolism.** Glycolysis is common to fermentation and cellular respiration. The end product of glycolysis, pyruvate, represents a fork in the catabolic pathways of glucose oxidation. In a facultative anaerobe or a muscle cell, which are capable of both aerobic cellular respiration and fermentation, pyruvate is committed to one of those two pathways, usually depending on whether or not oxygen is present.

CONCEPT 9.6

Glycolysis and the citric acid cycle connect to many other metabolic pathways

So far, we have treated the oxidative breakdown of glucose in isolation from the cell's overall metabolic economy. In this section, you will learn that glycolysis and the citric acid cycle are major intersections of the cell's catabolic (breakdown) and anabolic (biosynthetic) pathways.

The Versatility of Catabolism

Throughout this chapter, we have used glucose as an example of a fuel for cellular respiration. But free glucose molecules are not common in the diets of humans and other animals. We obtain most of our energy in the form of fats, proteins, sucrose and other disaccharides, and starch, a polysaccharide. All these organic molecules in food can be used by cellular respiration to make ATP (Figure 9.20).

Glycolysis can accept a wide range of carbohydrates for catabolism. In the digestive tract, starch is hydrolyzed to glucose, which can then be broken down in the cells by glycolysis and the citric acid cycle. Similarly, glycogen, the polysaccharide that humans and many other animals store in their liver and muscle cells, can be hydrolyzed to glucose between meals as fuel for respiration. The digestion of

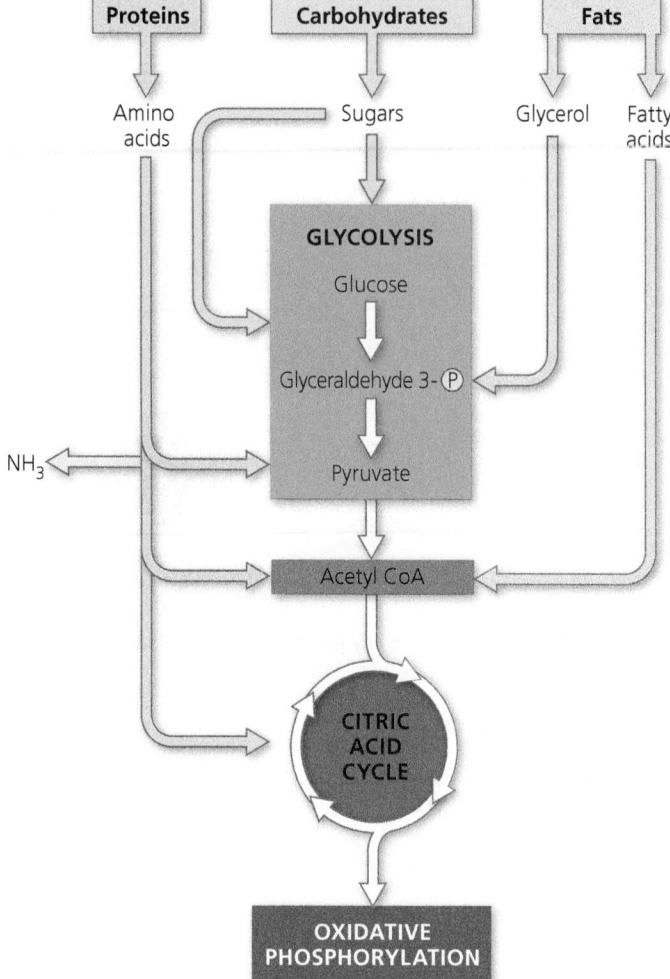

▲ Figure 9.20 The catabolism of various molecules from food. Carbohydrates, fats, and proteins can all be used as fuel for cellular respiration. Monomers of these molecules enter glycolysis or the citric acid cycle at various points. Glycolysis and the citric acid cycle are catabolic funnels through which electrons from all kinds of organic molecules flow on their exergonic fall to oxygen.

disaccharides, including sucrose, provides glucose and other monosaccharides as fuel for respiration.

Proteins can also be used for fuel, but first they must be digested to their constituent amino acids. Many of the amino acids are used by the organism to build new proteins. Amino acids present in excess are converted by enzymes to intermediates of glycolysis and the citric acid cycle. Before amino acids can feed into glycolysis or the citric acid cycle, their amino groups must be removed, a process called *deamination*. The nitrogenous refuse is excreted from the animal in the form of ammonia (NH_3), urea, or other waste products.

Catabolism can also harvest energy stored in fats obtained either from food or from storage cells in the body. After fats are digested to glycerol and fatty acids, the glycerol is converted to glyceraldehyde 3-phosphate,

an intermediate of glycolysis. Most of the energy of a fat is stored in the fatty acids. A metabolic sequence called **beta oxidation** breaks the fatty acids down to two-carbon fragments, which enter the citric acid cycle as acetyl CoA. NADH and $FADH_2$ are also generated during beta oxidation; they can enter the electron transport chain, leading to further ATP production. Fats make excellent fuels, in large part due to their chemical structure and the high energy level of their electrons (equally shared between carbon and hydrogen) compared to those of carbohydrates. A gram of fat oxidized by respiration produces more than twice as much ATP as a gram of carbohydrate. Unfortunately, this also means that a person trying to lose weight must work hard to use up fat stored in the body because so many kilojoules are stockpiled in each gram of fat.

Biosynthesis (Anabolic Pathways)

Cells need substance as well as energy. Not all the organic molecules of food are destined to be oxidized as fuel to make ATP. In addition to kilojoules, food must also provide the carbon skeletons that cells require to make their own molecules. Some organic monomers obtained from digestion can be used directly. For example, as previously mentioned, amino acids from the hydrolysis of proteins in food can be incorporated into the organism's own proteins. Often, however, the body needs specific molecules that are not present as such in food. Compounds formed as intermediates of glycolysis and the citric acid cycle can be diverted into anabolic pathways as precursors from which the cell can synthesize the molecules it requires. For example, humans can make about half of the 20 amino acids in proteins by modifying compounds siphoned away from the citric acid cycle; the rest are "essential amino acids" that must be obtained in the diet. Also, glucose can be made from pyruvate, and fatty acids can be synthesized from acetyl CoA. Of course, these anabolic, or biosynthetic, pathways do not generate ATP, but instead consume it.

In addition, glycolysis and the citric acid cycle function as metabolic interchanges that enable our cells to convert some kinds of molecules to others as we need them. For example, an intermediate compound generated during glycolysis, dihydroxyacetone phosphate (see Figure 9.9, step 5), can be converted to one of the major precursors of fats. If we eat more food than we need, we store fat even if our diet is fat-free. Metabolism is remarkably versatile and adaptable.

Regulation of Cellular Respiration via Feedback Mechanisms

Basic principles of supply and demand regulate the metabolic economy. The cell does not waste energy making more of a particular substance than it needs. If there is a glut of a certain amino acid, for example, the anabolic pathway that synthesizes that amino acid from an intermediate of the citric acid cycle is switched off. The most common mechanism for this control is feedback inhibition: The end product of the anabolic pathway inhibits the enzyme that catalyzes an early step of the pathway (see Figure 8.21). This prevents the needless diversion of key metabolic intermediates from uses that are more urgent.

The cell also controls its catabolism. If the cell is working hard and its ATP concentration begins to drop, respiration speeds up. When there is plenty of ATP to meet demand, respiration slows down, sparing valuable organic molecules for other functions. Again, control is based mainly on regulating the activity of enzymes at strategic points in the catabolic pathway. As shown in **Figure 9.21**, one important switch is phosphofructokinase, the enzyme that catalyzes step 3 of glycolysis (see Figure 9.9). That is the first step that commits the substrate irreversibly to the glycolytic pathway. By controlling the rate of this step, the cell can speed up or slow down the entire catabolic process. Phosphofructokinase can thus be considered the pacemaker of respiration.

Phosphofructokinase is an allosteric enzyme with receptor sites for specific inhibitors and activators. It is inhibited by ATP and stimulated by AMP (adenosine monophosphate), which the cell derives from ADP. As ATP accumulates, inhibition of the enzyme slows down glycolysis. The enzyme becomes active again as cellular work converts ATP to ADP (and AMP) faster than ATP is being regenerated. Phosphofructokinase is also sensitive to citrate, the first product of the citric acid cycle. If citrate accumulates in mitochondria, some of it passes into the cytosol and inhibits phosphofructokinase. This mechanism helps synchronize the rates of glycolysis and the citric acid cycle. As citrate accumulates, glycolysis slows down, and the supply of acetyl groups to the citric acid cycle decreases. If citrate consumption increases, either because of a demand for more ATP or because anabolic pathways are draining off intermediates of the citric acid cycle, glycolysis accelerates and meets the demand. Metabolic balance is augmented by the control of enzymes that catalyze other key steps of glycolysis and the citric acid cycle. Cells are thrifty, expedient, and responsive in their metabolism.

Cellular respiration and metabolic pathways play a role of central importance in organisms. Examine Figure 9.2 again to put cellular respiration into the broader context of energy flow and chemical cycling in ecosystems. The energy that keeps us alive is *released*, not *produced*, by cellular respiration. We are tapping energy that was stored in food by photosynthesis. In the next chapter, you will learn how photosynthesis captures light and converts it to chemical energy.

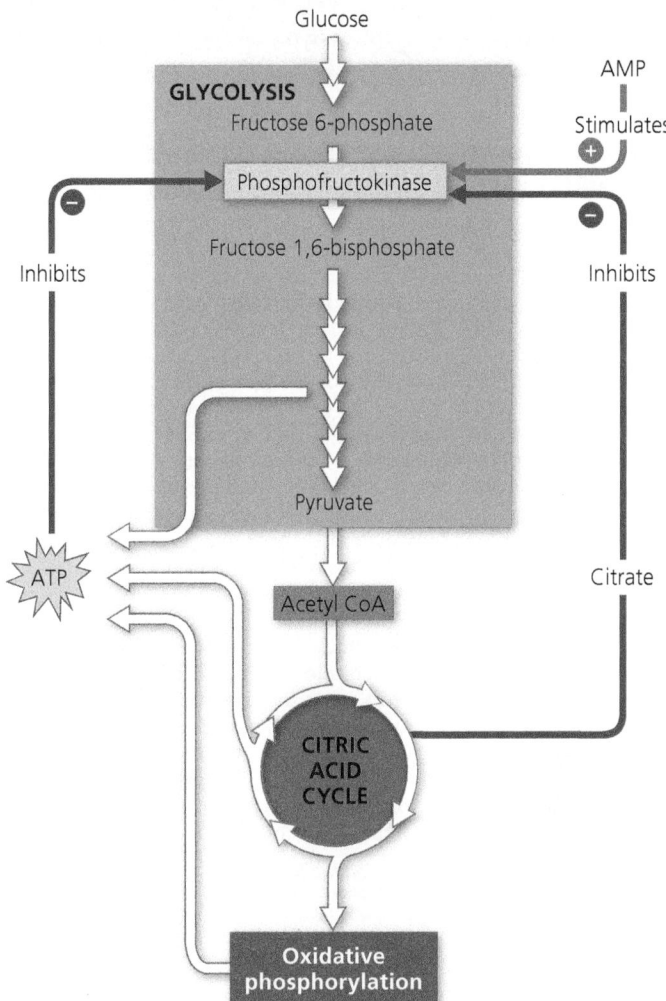

▲ Figure 9.21 **The control of cellular respiration.** Allosteric enzymes at certain points in the respiratory pathway respond to inhibitors and activators that help set the pace of glycolysis and the citric acid cycle. Phosphofructokinase, which catalyzes an early step in glycolysis (see Figure 9.9), is one such enzyme. It is stimulated by AMP (derived from ADP) but is inhibited by ATP and by citrate. This feedback regulation adjusts the rate of respiration as the cell's catabolic and anabolic demands change.

CONCEPT CHECK 9.6

1. MAKE CONNECTIONS Compare the structure of a fat (see Figure 5.9) with that of a carbohydrate (see Figure 5.3). What features of their structures make fat a much better fuel?

2. Under what circumstances might your body synthesize fat molecules?

3. WHAT IF? What will happen in a muscle cell that has used up its supply of oxygen and ATP? (Review Figures 9.19 and 9.21.)

4. WHAT IF? During intense exercise, can a muscle cell use fat as a concentrated source of chemical energy? Explain. (Review Figures 9.19 and 9.20.)

For suggested answers, see Appendix A.

9 Chapter Review

Go to **MasteringBiology**® for Assignments, the eText, and the Study Area with Animations, Activities, Vocab Self-Quiz, and Practice Tests.

SUMMARY OF KEY CONCEPTS

CONCEPT 9.1

Catabolic pathways yield energy by oxidizing organic fuels (pp. 176–181)

- Cells break down glucose and other organic fuels to yield chemical energy in the form of ATP. **Fermentation** is a process that results in the partial degradation of glucose without the use of oxygen. **Cellular respiration** is a more complete breakdown of glucose; in **aerobic respiration**, oxygen is used as a reactant. The cell taps the energy stored in food molecules through **redox reactions**, in which one substance partially or totally shifts electrons to another. **Oxidation** is the loss of electrons from one substance, while **reduction** is the addition of electrons to the other.
- During aerobic respiration, glucose ($C_6H_{12}O_6$) is oxidized to CO_2, and O_2 is reduced to H_2O. Electrons lose potential energy during their transfer from glucose or other organic compounds to oxygen. Electrons are usually passed first to NAD^+, reducing it to NADH, and then from NADH to an **electron transport chain**, which conducts them to O_2 in energy-releasing steps. The energy is used to make ATP.
- Aerobic respiration occurs in three stages: (1) **glycolysis**, (2) pyruvate oxidation and the **citric acid cycle**, and (3) **oxidative phosphorylation** (electron transport and chemiosmosis).

? *Describe the difference between the two processes in cellular respiration that produce ATP: oxidative phosphorylation and substrate-level phosphorylation.*

CONCEPT 9.2

Glycolysis harvests chemical energy by oxidizing glucose to pyruvate (p. 181)

- Glycolysis ("splitting of sugar") is a series of reactions that break down glucose into two pyruvate molecules, which may go on to enter the citric acid cycle, and nets 2 ATP and 2 NADH per glucose molecule.

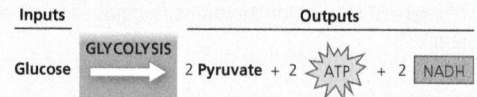

Inputs / Outputs

Glucose → GLYCOLYSIS → 2 Pyruvate + 2 ATP + 2 NADH

? *Which reactions in glycolysis are the source of energy for the formation of ATP and NADH?*

CONCEPT 9.3

After pyruvate is oxidized, the citric acid cycle completes the energy-yielding oxidation of organic molecules (pp. 181–185)

- In eukaryotic cells, pyruvate enters the mitochondrion and is oxidized to **acetyl CoA**, which is further oxidized in the citric acid cycle.

Inputs / Outputs

2 Pyruvate → 2 Acetyl CoA
2 Oxaloacetate
CITRIC ACID CYCLE
2 ATP   8 NADH
6 CO₂   2 FADH₂

? *What molecular products indicate the complete oxidation of glucose during cellular respiration?*

CONCEPT 9.4

During oxidative phosphorylation, chemiosmosis couples electron transport to ATP synthesis (pp. 185–191)

- NADH and $FADH_2$ transfer electrons to the electron transport chain. Electrons move down the chain, losing energy in several energy-releasing steps. Finally, electrons are passed to O_2, reducing it to H_2O.

- At certain steps along the electron transport chain, electron transfer causes protein complexes to move H^+ from the mitochondrial matrix (in eukaryotes) to the intermembrane space, storing energy as a **proton-motive force** (H^+ gradient). As H^+ diffuses back into the matrix through **ATP synthase**, its passage drives the phosphorylation of ADP to form ATP, a process called **chemiosmosis**.
- About 34% of the energy stored in a glucose molecule is transferred to ATP during cellular respiration, producing a maximum of about 32 ATP.

? *Briefly explain the mechanism by which ATP synthase produces ATP. List three locations in which ATP synthases are found.*

CONCEPT 9.5

Fermentation and anaerobic respiration enable cells to produce ATP without the use of oxygen (pp. 191–193)

- Glycolysis nets 2 ATP by substrate-level phosphorylation, whether oxygen is present or not. Under anaerobic conditions, either anaerobic respiration or fermentation can take place. In anaerobic respiration, an electron transport chain is present with a final electron acceptor other than oxygen. In fermentation, the electrons from NADH are passed to pyruvate or a derivative of pyruvate, regenerating the NAD^+ required to oxidize more glucose. Two common types of fermentation are **alcohol fermentation** and **lactic acid fermentation**.
- Fermentation and anaerobic or aerobic respiration all use glycolysis to oxidize glucose, but they differ in their final electron acceptor and whether an electron transport chain is used (respiration) or not (fermentation). Respiration yields more ATP; aerobic respiration, with O_2 as the final electron acceptor, yields about 16 times as much ATP as does fermentation.

- Glycolysis occurs in nearly all organisms and is thought to have evolved in ancient prokaryotes before there was O_2 in the atmosphere.

? *Which process yields more ATP, fermentation or anaerobic respiration? Explain.*

CONCEPT 9.6

Glycolysis and the citric acid cycle connect to many other metabolic pathways (pp. 193–195)

- Catabolic pathways funnel electrons from many kinds of organic molecules into cellular respiration. Many carbohydrates can enter glycolysis, most often after conversion to glucose. Amino acids of proteins must be deaminated before being oxidized. The fatty acids of fats undergo **beta oxidation** to two-carbon fragments and then enter the citric acid cycle as acetyl CoA. Anabolic pathways can use small molecules from food directly or build other substances using intermediates of glycolysis or the citric acid cycle.
- Cellular respiration is controlled by allosteric enzymes at key points in glycolysis and the citric acid cycle.

? *Describe how the catabolic pathways of glycolysis and the citric acid cycle intersect with anabolic pathways in the metabolism of a cell.*

TEST YOUR UNDERSTANDING

LEVEL 1: KNOWLEDGE/COMPREHENSION

1. The *immediate* energy source that drives ATP synthesis by ATP synthase during oxidative phosphorylation is the
   a. oxidation of glucose and other organic compounds.
   b. flow of electrons down the electron transport chain.
   c. H^+ concentration gradient across the membrane holding ATP synthase.
   d. transfer of phosphate to ADP.

2. Which metabolic pathway is common to both fermentation and cellular respiration of a glucose molecule?
   a. the citric acid cycle
   b. the electron transport chain
   c. glycolysis
   d. reduction of pyruvate to lactate

3. In mitochondria, exergonic redox reactions
   a. are the source of energy driving prokaryotic ATP synthesis.
   b. provide the energy that establishes the proton gradient.
   c. reduce carbon atoms to carbon dioxide.
   d. are coupled via phosphorylated intermediates to endergonic processes.

4. The final electron acceptor of the electron transport chain that functions in aerobic oxidative phosphorylation is
   a. oxygen.   b. water.   c. NAD^+.   d. pyruvate.

LEVEL 2: APPLICATION/ANALYSIS

5. What is the oxidizing agent in the following reaction?
   $$Pyruvate + NADH + H^+ \rightarrow Lactate + NAD^+$$
   a. oxygen   b. NADH   c. lactate   d. pyruvate

6. When electrons flow along the electron transport chains of mitochondria, which of the following changes occurs?
   a. The pH of the matrix increases.
   b. ATP synthase pumps protons by active transport.
   c. The electrons gain free energy.
   d. NAD^+ is oxidized.

7. Most CO_2 from catabolism is released during
   a. glycolysis.   b. the citric acid cycle.
   c. lactate fermentation.   d. electron transport.

8. Step 3 in Figure 9.9 is a major point of regulation of glycolysis. The enzyme phosphofructokinase is allosterically regulated by ATP and

related molecules (see Concept 8.5). Considering the overall result of glycolysis, would you expect ATP to inhibit or stimulate activity of this enzyme? Explain. (*Hint:* Make sure you consider the role of ATP as an allosteric regulator, not as a substrate of the enzyme.)

9. The proton pump shown in Figure 7.17 is depicted as a simplified oval purple shape, but it is, in fact, an ATP synthase (see Figure 9.15). Compare the processes shown in the two figures, and say whether they are involved in active or passive transport (see Concepts 7.3 and 7.4).

LEVEL 3: SYNTHESIS/EVALUATION

10. **INTERPRET THE DATA** Phosphofructokinase is an enzyme that acts on fructose 6-phosphate at an early step in glucose breakdown. Regulation of this enzyme controls whether the sugar will continue on in the glycolytic pathway. Considering this graph, under which condition is phosphofructokinase more active? Given what you know about glycolysis and regulation of metabolism by this enzyme, explain the mechanism by which phosphofructokinase activity differs depending on ATP concentration.

11. **DRAW IT** The graph here shows the pH difference across the inner mitochondrial membrane over time in an actively respiring cell. At the time indicated by the vertical arrow, a metabolic poison is added that specifically and completely inhibits all function of mitochondrial ATP synthase. Draw what you would expect to see for the rest of the graphed line.

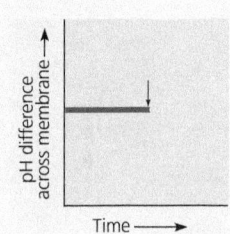

12. **EVOLUTION CONNECTION**
    ATP synthases are found in the prokaryotic plasma membrane and in mitochondria and chloroplasts. What does this suggest about the evolutionary relationship of these eukaryotic organelles to prokaryotes? How might the amino acid sequences of the ATP synthases from the different sources support or refute your hypothesis?

13. **SCIENTIFIC INQUIRY**
    In the 1930s, some physicians prescribed low doses of a compound called dinitrophenol (DNP) to help patients lose weight. This unsafe method was abandoned after some patients died. DNP uncouples the chemiosmotic machinery by making the lipid bilayer of the inner mitochondrial membrane leaky to H^+. Explain how this could cause weight loss and death.

14. **WRITE ABOUT A THEME: ORGANIZATION**
    In a short essay (100–150 words), explain how oxidative phosphorylation—the production of ATP using energy derived from the redox reactions of a spatially organized electron transport chain followed by chemiosmosis—is an example of how new properties emerge at each level of the biological hierarchy.

15. **SYNTHESIZE YOUR KNOWLEDGE**

Coenzyme Q (CoQ) is sold as a nutritional supplement. One company uses this marketing slogan for CoQ: "Give your heart the fuel it craves most." Considering the role of coenzyme Q, how do you think this product might function as a nutritional supplement to benefit the heart? Is CoQ used as a "fuel" during cellular respiration?

Michael Neelon(misc)/Alamy Stock Photo

For selected answers, see Appendix A.

10

Photosynthesis

KEY CONCEPTS

10.1 Photosynthesis converts light energy to the chemical energy of food

10.2 The light reactions convert solar energy to the chemical energy of ATP and NADPH

10.3 The Calvin cycle uses the chemical energy of ATP and NADPH to reduce CO_2 to sugar

10.4 Alternative mechanisms of carbon fixation have evolved in hot, arid climates

▲ Other organisms also benefit from photosynthesis.

Lenz Photography

▲ **Figure 10.1 How does sunlight help build the trees, ferns, and moss in this photo from Clayoquot Sound on Vancouver Island?**

The Process That Feeds the Biosphere

Life on Earth is solar powered. The chloroplasts in plants and other photosynthetic organisms capture light energy that has travelled 150 million kilometres from the sun and convert it to chemical energy that is stored in sugar and other organic molecules. This conversion process is called **photosynthesis**. Let's begin by placing photosynthesis in its ecological context.

Photosynthesis nourishes almost the entire living world directly or indirectly. An organism acquires the organic compounds it uses for energy and carbon skeletons by one of two major modes: autotrophic nutrition or heterotrophic nutrition. **Autotrophs** are "self-feeders" (*auto-* means "self," and *trophos* means "feeder"); they sustain themselves without eating anything derived from other living beings. Autotrophs produce their organic molecules from CO_2 and other inorganic raw materials obtained from the environment. They are the ultimate sources of organic compounds for all nonautotrophic organisms, and for this reason, biologists refer to autotrophs as the *producers* of the biosphere.

Almost all plants are autotrophs; the only nutrients they require are water and minerals from the soil and carbon dioxide from the air. Specifically, plants are *photoautotrophs*, organisms that use light as a source of energy to synthesize organic substances (Figure 10.1). Photosynthesis also occurs in algae, certain other unicellular eukaryotes, and some prokaryotes (Figure 10.2). In this chapter, we will touch

Martha Marks/Shutterstock

(a) Plants

(b) Multicellular alga

(c) Unicellular protists

(d) Cyanobacteria 40 μm

(e) Purple sulphur bacteria

▲ **Figure 10.2 Photoautotrophs.** These organisms use light energy to drive the synthesis of organic molecules from carbon dioxide and (in most cases) water. They feed themselves and the entire living world. **(a)** On land, plants are the predominant producers of food. In aquatic environments, photoautotrophs include unicellular and **(b)** multicellular algae, such as this kelp; **(c)** some non-algal unicellular eukaryotes, such as *Euglena*; **(d)** the prokaryotes called cyanobacteria; and **(e)** other photosynthetic prokaryotes, such as these purple sulphur bacteria, which produce sulphur (the yellow globules within the cells) (c–e, LMs).

on these other groups in passing, but our emphasis will be on plants. Variations in autotrophic nutrition that occur in prokaryotes and algae will be described in Chapters 27 and 28.

Heterotrophs obtain organic material by the second major mode of nutrition. Unable to make their own food, they live on compounds produced by other organisms (*hetero-* means "other"). Heterotrophs are the biosphere's *consumers*. The most obvious "other-feeding" occurs when an animal eats plants or other animals. But heterotrophic nutrition may be more subtle. Some heterotrophs consume the remains of dead organisms by decomposing and feeding on organic litter such as carcasses, feces, and fallen leaves; these types of organisms are known as decomposers. Most fungi and many types of prokaryotes get their nourishment this way. Almost all heterotrophs, including humans, are completely dependent, either directly or indirectly, on photoautotrophs for food—and also for oxygen, a by-product of photosynthesis.

The Earth's supply of fossil fuels was formed from remains of organisms that died hundreds of millions of years ago. In a sense, then, fossil fuels represent stores of the sun's energy from the distant past. Because these resources are being used at a much higher rate than they are replenished, researchers are exploring methods of capitalizing on the photosynthetic process to provide alternative fuels **(Figure 10.3)**.

▼ Figure 10.3 | **Impact**

Alternative Fuels from Plants and Algae

Biofuels from crops such as corn, soybeans, and canola have been proposed as a supplement or even replacement for fossil fuels. To produce "bioethanol," the starch made naturally by the plants is simply converted to glucose and then fermented to ethanol by microorganisms. Alternatively, a simple chemical process can yield "biodiesel" from plant oils. Either product can be mixed with gasoline or used alone to power vehicles. Some species of unicellular algae are especially prolific oil producers, and they can be easily cultured in containers such as the National Research Council's photobioreactor (aka *Biofence*) shown below. Note, however, that the current yield of biodiesel from algae is not high enough to replace conventional fossil fuel use, and efforts are underway to increase the quantity of biodiesel that can be obtained from algal farms.

Why It Matters The rate of fossil fuel use by humans far outpaces its formation in the Earth: Fossil fuels are a nonrenewable source of energy. If the power of sunlight can be efficiently tapped, then a sustainable alternative to fossil fuels could be generated. It is generally agreed that using algae is preferable to growing crops for this purpose because this use of cropland diminishes the food supply and drives up food prices.

Further Reading A. L. Haag, Algae bloom again, *Nature* 447:520–521 (2007); J. M. Galazka and J. H. L. Cate, Improving the bioconversion of plant biomass to biofuels: A multidisciplinary approach, *Energy and Environmental Science* 4:3329–3333 (2011).

WHAT IF? *The main product of fossil fuel combustion is CO_2, and this combustion is the source of the increase in atmospheric CO_2 concentration. Scientists have proposed strategically situating containers of these algae near industrial plants or near highly congested city streets. Considering the process of photosynthesis, how does this arrangement make sense?*

In this chapter, you'll learn how photosynthesis works. After discussing general principles of photosynthesis, we'll consider the two stages of photosynthesis: the light reactions, which capture solar energy and transform it into chemical energy; and the Calvin cycle, which uses that chemical energy to make the organic molecules of food. Finally, we will consider some aspects of photosynthesis from an evolutionary perspective.

CONCEPT 10.1

Photosynthesis converts light energy to the chemical energy of food

The remarkable ability of an organism to harness light energy and use it to drive the synthesis of organic compounds emerges from structural organization in the cell: Photosynthetic enzymes and other molecules are grouped together in a biological membrane, enabling the necessary series of chemical reactions to be carried out efficiently. The process of photosynthesis most likely originated in a group of bacteria that had infolded regions of the plasma membrane containing clusters of such molecules. In existing photosynthetic bacteria, infolded photosynthetic membranes function similarly to the internal membranes of the chloroplast, a eukaryotic organelle. According to what has come to be known as the endosymbiont theory, the original chloroplast was a photosynthetic prokaryote that lived inside an ancestor of eukaryotic cells. (You learned about this theory in Chapter 6 and it will be described more fully in Chapter 25.) Chloroplasts are present in a variety of photosynthesizing organisms (see some examples in Figure 10.2), but here we focus on chloroplasts in plants.

Chloroplasts: The Sites of Photosynthesis in Plants

All green parts of a plant, including green stems and unripened fruit, have chloroplasts, but the leaves are the major sites of photosynthesis in most plants (Figure 10.4). There are about half a million chloroplasts in a chunk of leaf with a top surface area of 1 mm². Chloroplasts are found mainly in the cells of the **mesophyll**, the tissue in the interior of the leaf. Carbon dioxide enters the leaf, and oxygen exits, by way of microscopic pores called **stomata** (singular, *stoma*; from the Greek, meaning "mouth"). Water absorbed by the roots is delivered to the leaves in veins. Leaves also use veins to export sugar to roots and other nonphotosynthetic parts of the plant.

A typical mesophyll cell has about 30–40 chloroplasts, each organelle measuring about 2–4 μm by 4–7 μm. A chloroplast has an envelope of two membranes surrounding

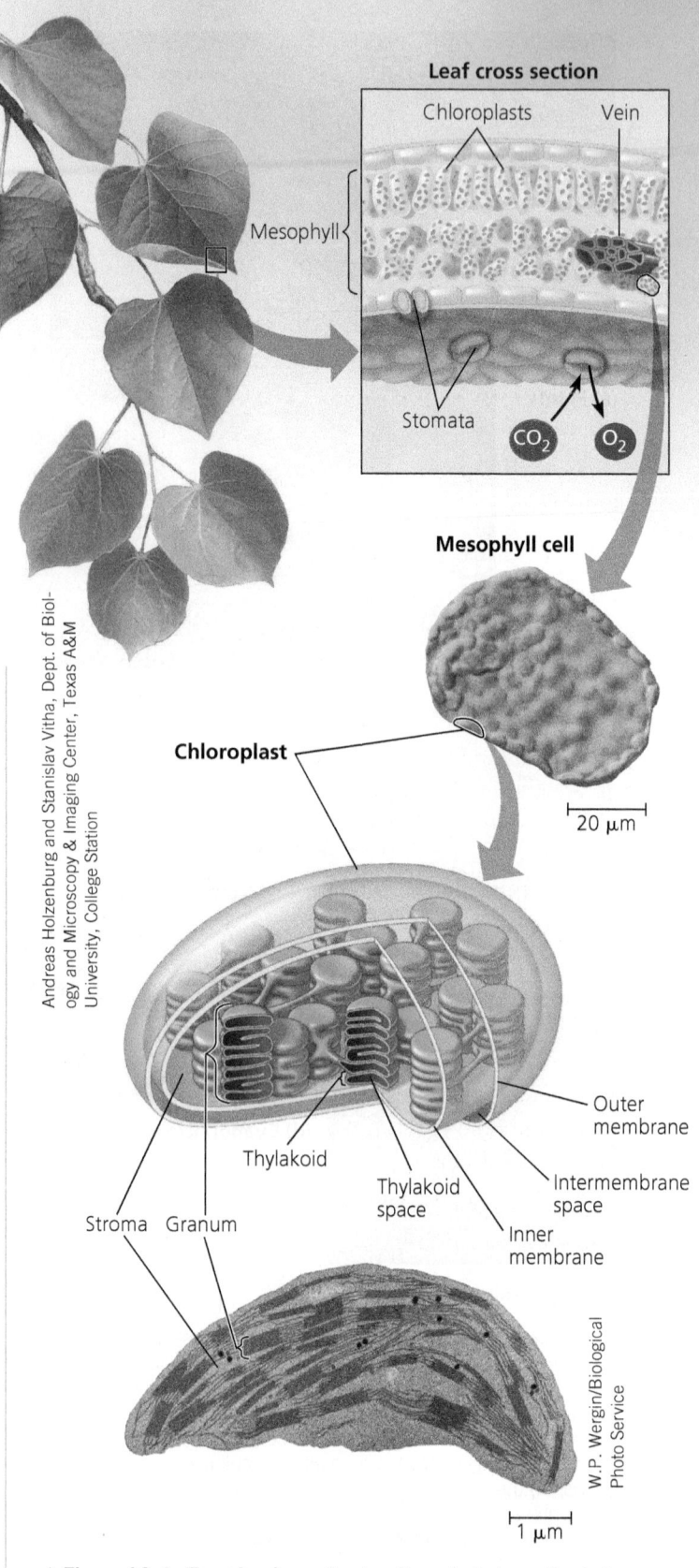

▲ Figure 10.4 **Zooming in on the location of photosynthesis in a plant.** Leaves are the major organs of photosynthesis in plants. These pictures take you into a leaf, then into a cell, and finally into a chloroplast, the organelle where photosynthesis occurs (middle, LM; bottom, TEM).

a dense fluid called the **stroma**. Suspended within the stroma is a third membrane system, made up of sacs called **thylakoids**, which segregates the stroma from the *thylakoid space* inside these sacs. In some places, thylakoid sacs are stacked in columns called *grana* (singular, *granum*). **Chlorophyll**, the green pigment that gives leaves their colour, resides in the thylakoid membranes of the chloroplast. (The internal photosynthetic membranes of some prokaryotes are also called thylakoid membranes; see Figure 27.8b.) It is the light energy absorbed by chlorophyll that drives the synthesis of organic molecules in the chloroplast. Now that we have looked at the sites of photosynthesis in plants, we are ready to look more closely at the process of photosynthesis.

Tracking Atoms Through Photosynthesis: *Scientific Inquiry*

Scientists have tried for centuries to piece together the process by which plants make food. Although some of the steps are still not completely understood, the overall photosynthetic equation has been known since the 1800s: In the presence of light, the green parts of plants produce organic compounds and oxygen from carbon dioxide and water. Using molecular formulas, we can summarize the complex series of chemical reactions in photosynthesis with this chemical equation:

$$6\ CO_2 + 12\ H_2O + \text{Light energy} \rightarrow C_6H_{12}O_6 + 6\ O_2 + 6\ H_2O$$

We use glucose ($C_6H_{12}O_6$) here to simplify the relationship between photosynthesis and respiration, but the direct product of photosynthesis is actually a three-carbon sugar that can be used to make glucose. Water appears on both sides of the equation because 12 molecules are consumed and 6 molecules are newly formed during photosynthesis. We can simplify the equation by indicating only the net consumption of water:

$$6\ CO_2 + 6\ H_2O + \text{Light energy} \rightarrow C_6H_{12}O_6 + 6\ O_2$$

Writing the equation in this form, we can see that the overall chemical change during photosynthesis is the reverse of the one that occurs during cellular respiration (see Concept 9.1). Both of these metabolic processes occur in plant cells. However, as you will soon learn, chloroplasts do not synthesize sugars by simply reversing the steps of respiration.

Now let's divide the photosynthetic equation by 6 to put it in its simplest possible form:

$$CO_2 + H_2O \rightarrow [CH_2O] + O_2$$

Here, the brackets indicate that CH_2O is not an actual sugar but represents the general formula for a carbohydrate (see Concept 5.2). In other words, we are imagining the synthesis of a sugar molecule one carbon at a time. Six repetitions would theoretically produce a glucose molecule, as shown by its molecular formula $C_6H_{12}O_6$. Let's now use this simplified formula to see how researchers tracked the elements C, H, and O from the reactants of photosynthesis to the products.

The Splitting of Water

One of the first clues to the mechanism of photosynthesis came from the discovery that the O_2 given off by plants is derived from H_2O and not from CO_2. The chloroplast splits water into hydrogen and oxygen. Before this discovery, the prevailing hypothesis was that photosynthesis split carbon dioxide ($CO_2 \rightarrow C + O_2$) and then added water to the carbon ($C + H_2O \rightarrow [CH_2O]$). This hypothesis predicted that the O_2 released during photosynthesis came from CO_2. This idea was challenged in the 1930s by C. B. van Niel, of Stanford University. Van Niel was investigating photosynthesis in bacteria that make their carbohydrate from CO_2 but do not release O_2. He concluded that, at least in these bacteria, CO_2 is not split into carbon and oxygen. One group of bacteria used hydrogen sulphide (H_2S) rather than water for photosynthesis, forming yellow globules of sulphur as a waste product (these globules are visible in Figure 10.2e). Here is the chemical equation for photosynthesis in these sulphur bacteria:

$$CO_2 + 2\ H_2S \rightarrow [CH_2O] + H_2O + 2\ S$$

Van Niel reasoned that the bacteria split H_2S and used the hydrogen atoms to make sugar. He then generalized that idea, proposing that all photosynthetic organisms require a hydrogen source but that the source varies:

$$\text{Sulphur bacteria: } CO_2 + 2\ H_2S \rightarrow [CH_2O] + H_2O + 2\ S$$
$$\text{Plants: } CO_2 + 2\ H_2O \rightarrow [CH_2O] + H_2O + O_2$$
$$\text{General: } CO_2 + 2\ H_2X \rightarrow [CH_2O] + H_2O + 2\ X$$

Thus, van Niel hypothesized that plants split H_2O as a source of electrons from hydrogen atoms, releasing O_2 as a by-product.

Nearly 20 years later, scientists confirmed van Niel's hypothesis by using oxygen-18 (^{18}O), a heavy isotope, as a tracer to follow the fate of oxygen atoms during photosynthesis. The experiments showed that the O_2 from plants was labelled with ^{18}O *only* if water was the source of the tracer (experiment 1). If the ^{18}O was introduced to the plant in the form of CO_2, the label did not turn up in the released O_2 (experiment 2). In the following summary, red denotes labelled atoms of oxygen (^{18}O):

$$\text{Experiment 1: } CO_2 + 2\ H_2O \rightarrow [CH_2O] + H_2O + O_2$$
$$\text{Experiment 1: } CO_2 + 2\ H_2O \rightarrow [CH_2O] + H_2O + O_2$$

A significant result of the shuffling of atoms during photosynthesis is the extraction of hydrogen from water and its

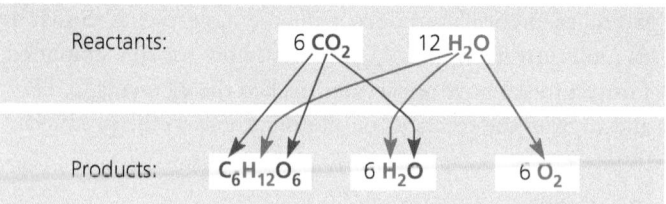

Reactants:	6 CO_2	12 H_2O	
Products:	$C_6H_{12}O_6$	6 H_2O	6 O_2

▲ Figure 10.5 **Tracking atoms through photosynthesis.** The atoms from CO_2 are shown in magenta, and the atoms from H_2O are shown in blue.

incorporation into sugar. The waste product of photosynthesis, O_2, is released to the atmosphere. **Figure 10.5** shows the fates of all atoms in photosynthesis.

Photosynthesis as a Redox Process

Let's briefly compare photosynthesis with cellular respiration. Both processes involve redox reactions. During cellular respiration, energy is released from sugar when electrons associated with hydrogen are transported by carriers to oxygen, forming water as a by-product. The electrons lose potential energy as they "fall" down the electron transport chain toward electronegative oxygen, and the mitochondrion harnesses that energy to synthesize ATP (see Figure 9.16). Photosynthesis reverses the direction of electron flow. Water is split, and electrons are transferred along with hydrogen ions from the water to carbon dioxide, reducing it to sugar.

$$\text{Energy} + 6\,CO_2 + 6\,H_2O \longrightarrow C_6H_{12}O_6 + 6\,O_2$$

becomes reduced

becomes oxidized

Because the electrons increase in potential energy as they move from water to sugar, this process requires energy—in other words, it is endergonic. This energy boost that occurs during photosynthesis is provided by light.

The Two Stages of Photosynthesis: *A Preview*

The equation for photosynthesis is a deceptively simple summary of a very complex process. Actually, photosynthesis is not a single process but two processes, each with multiple steps. These two stages of photosynthesis are known as the **light reactions** (the *photo* part of photosynthesis) and the **Calvin cycle** (the *synthesis* part) **(Figure 10.6)**.

The light reactions are the steps of photosynthesis that convert solar energy to chemical energy. Water is split, providing a source of electrons and protons (hydrogen ions, H^+) and giving off O_2 as a by-product. Light absorbed by chlorophyll drives a transfer of the electrons and hydrogen ions from water to an acceptor called **NADP+** (nicotinamide adenine dinucleotide phosphate), where they are temporarily stored. The electron acceptor NADP+ is first cousin to NAD+, which functions as an electron carrier in cellular respiration; the two molecules differ only by the presence of an extra phosphate group in the NADP+ molecule. The light reactions use solar power to reduce NADP+ to NADPH by adding a pair of electrons along with an H^+. The light reactions also generate ATP, using chemiosmosis to power the addition of a phosphate group to ADP, a process called **photophosphorylation**. Thus, light energy is initially converted to chemical energy in the form of two

▶ Figure 10.6 **An overview of photosynthesis: cooperation of the light reactions and the Calvin cycle.** In the chloroplast, the thylakoid membranes (green) are the sites of the light reactions, whereas the Calvin cycle occurs in the stroma (grey). The light reactions use solar energy to make ATP and NADPH, which supply chemical energy and reducing power, respectively, to the Calvin cycle. The Calvin cycle incorporates CO_2 into organic molecules, which are converted to sugar. (Recall that most simple sugars have formulas that are some multiple of CH_2O.)

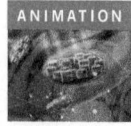

compounds: NADPH and ATP. NADPH, a source of electrons, acts as "reducing power" that can be passed along to an electron acceptor, reducing it, while ATP is the versatile energy currency of cells. Notice that the light reactions produce no sugar; that happens in the second stage of photosynthesis, the Calvin cycle.

The Calvin cycle is named for Melvin Calvin, who, along with his colleagues James Bassham and Andrew Benson, began to elucidate its steps in the late 1940s. The cycle begins by incorporating CO_2 from the air into organic molecules already present in the chloroplast. This initial incorporation of carbon into organic compounds is known as **carbon fixation**. The Calvin cycle then reduces the fixed carbon to carbohydrate by the addition of electrons. The reducing power is provided by NADPH, which acquired its cargo of electrons in the light reactions. To convert CO_2 to carbohydrate, the Calvin cycle also requires chemical energy in the form of ATP, which is also generated by the light reactions. Thus, it is the Calvin cycle that makes sugar, but it can do so only with the help of the NADPH and ATP produced by the light reactions. The metabolic steps of the Calvin cycle are sometimes referred to as the dark reactions, or light-independent reactions, because none of the steps requires light *directly*. Nevertheless, the Calvin cycle in most plants occurs during daylight, for only then can the light reactions provide the NADPH and ATP that the Calvin cycle requires. In essence, the chloroplast uses light energy to make sugar by coordinating the two stages of photosynthesis.

As Figure 10.6 indicates, the thylakoids of the chloroplast are the sites of the light reactions, while the Calvin cycle occurs in the stroma. On the outside of the thylakoids, molecules of $NADP^+$ and ADP pick up electrons and phosphate, respectively, and NADPH and ATP are then released to the stroma, where they play crucial roles in the Calvin cycle. The two stages of photosynthesis are treated in this figure as metabolic modules that take in ingredients and crank out products. In the next two sections, we'll look more closely at how the two stages work, beginning with the light reactions.

CONCEPT CHECK 10.1

1. How do the reactant molecules of photosynthesis reach the chloroplasts in leaves?

2. How did the use of an oxygen isotope help elucidate the chemistry of photosynthesis?

3. **WHAT IF?** The Calvin cycle requires ATP and NADPH, products of the light reactions. If a classmate asserted that the light reactions don't depend on the Calvin cycle and, with continual light, could just keep on producing ATP and NADPH, how would you respond?

For suggested answers, see Appendix A.

CONCEPT 10.2

The light reactions convert solar energy to the chemical energy of ATP and NADPH

Chloroplasts are chemical factories powered by the sun. Their thylakoids transform light energy into the chemical energy of ATP and NADPH, which will be used to synthesize glucose and other molecules that can be used as energy sources. To better understand the conversion of light to chemical energy, we need to know about some important properties of light.

The Nature of Sunlight

Light is a form of energy known as electromagnetic energy, also called electromagnetic radiation. Electromagnetic energy travels in rhythmic waves analogous to those created by dropping a pebble into a pond. Electromagnetic waves, however, are disturbances of electric and magnetic fields rather than disturbances of a material medium such as water.

The distance between the crests of electromagnetic waves is called the **wavelength**. Wavelengths range from less than a nanometre (for gamma rays) to more than a kilometre (for radio waves). This entire range of radiation is known as the **electromagnetic spectrum** (Figure 10.7). The segment most important to life is the narrow band from about 380 nm to 750 nm in wavelength. This radiation is known as **visible light** because it can be detected as various colours by the human eye.

The model of light as waves explains many of light's properties, but in certain respects light behaves as though it consists of discrete particles, called **photons**. Photons are

▲ Figure 10.7 **The electromagnetic spectrum.** White light is a mixture of all wavelengths of visible light. A prism can sort white light into its component colours by bending light of different wavelengths at different angles. (Droplets of water in the atmosphere can act as prisms, causing a rainbow to form.) Visible light drives photosynthesis.

not tangible objects, but they act like objects in that each of them has a fixed quantity of energy. The amount of energy is inversely related to the wavelength of the light: the shorter the wavelength, the greater the energy of each photon of that light. Thus, a photon of violet light packs nearly twice as much energy as a photon of red light (see Figure 10.7).

Although the sun radiates the full spectrum of electromagnetic energy, the atmosphere acts like a selective window, allowing visible light to pass through while screening out a substantial fraction of other radiation. The part of the spectrum we can see—visible light—is also the radiation that drives photosynthesis.

Photosynthetic Pigments: The Light Receptors

When light meets matter, it may be reflected, transmitted, or absorbed. Substances that absorb visible light are known as *pigments*. Different pigments absorb light of different wavelengths, and the wavelengths that are absorbed disappear. If a pigment is illuminated with white light, the colour we see is the colour most reflected or transmitted by the pigment. (If a pigment absorbs all wavelengths, it appears black.) We see green when we look at a leaf because chlorophyll absorbs violet-blue and red light while transmitting and reflecting green light (Figure 10.8). The ability of a pigment to absorb various wavelengths of light can be measured with an instrument called a **spectrophotometer**. This machine directs beams of light of different wavelengths through a solution of the pigment and measures the fraction of the light transmitted at each wavelength. A graph

plotting a pigment's light absorption versus wavelength is called an **absorption spectrum** (Figure 10.9).

The absorption spectra of chloroplast pigments provide clues to the relative effectiveness of different wavelengths for driving photosynthesis, since light can perform work in chloroplasts only if it is absorbed. Figure 10.10a shows the absorption spectra of three types of pigments in chloroplasts: **chlorophyll *a***, the key light-capturing pigment that participates directly in the light reactions; the accessory pigment **chlorophyll *b***, which works in conjunction with chlorophyll *a*; and a separate group of accessory pigments called carotenoids. The spectrum of chlorophyll *a* suggests

▼ Figure 10.9 | **Research Method**

Determining an Absorption Spectrum

Application An absorption spectrum is a visual representation of how well a particular pigment absorbs different wavelengths of visible light. Absorption spectra of various chloroplast pigments help scientists decipher the role of each pigment in a plant.

Technique A spectrophotometer measures the relative amounts of light of different wavelengths absorbed and transmitted by a pigment solution.

① White light is separated into colours (wavelengths) by a prism.

② One by one, the different colours of light are passed through the sample (chlorophyll in this example). Green light and blue light are shown here.

③ The transmitted light strikes a photoelectric tube, which converts the light energy to electricity.

④ The electric current is measured by a galvanometer. The meter indicates the fraction of light transmitted through the sample, from which we can determine the amount of light absorbed.

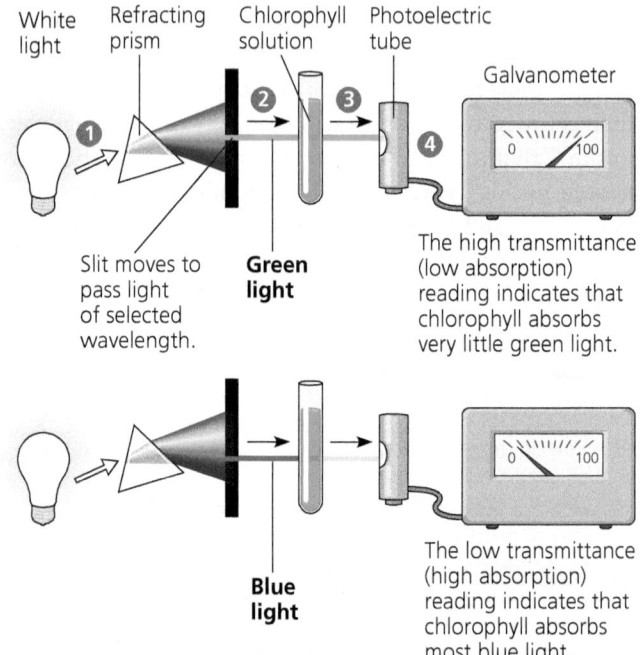

The high transmittance (low absorption) reading indicates that chlorophyll absorbs very little green light.

The low transmittance (high absorption) reading indicates that chlorophyll absorbs most blue light.

Results See Figure 10.10a for absorption spectra of three types of chloroplast pigments.

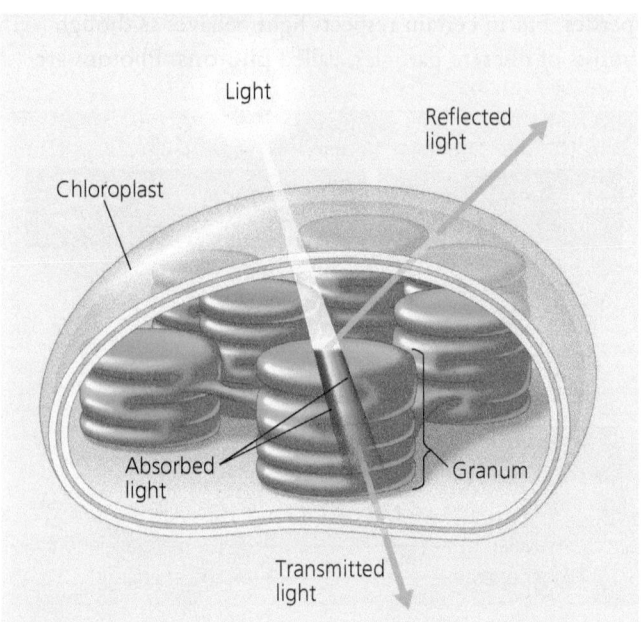

▲ Figure 10.8 **Why leaves are green: interaction of light with chloroplasts.** The chlorophyll molecules of chloroplasts absorb violet-blue and red light (the colours most effective in driving photosynthesis) and reflect or transmit green light. This is why leaves appear green.

Inquiry

Which wavelengths of light are most effective in driving photosynthesis?

Experiment Absorption and action spectra, along with a classic experiment by Theodor W. Engelmann, reveal which wavelengths of light are photosynthetically important.

Results

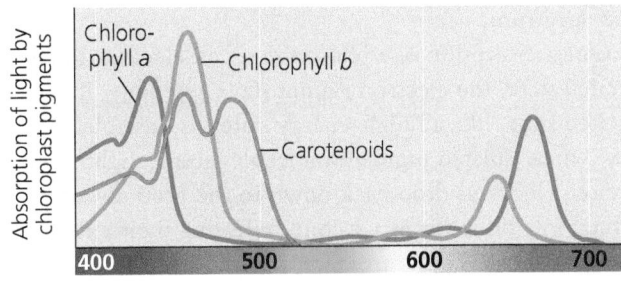

(a) Absorption spectra. The three curves show the wavelengths of light best absorbed by three types of chloroplast pigments.

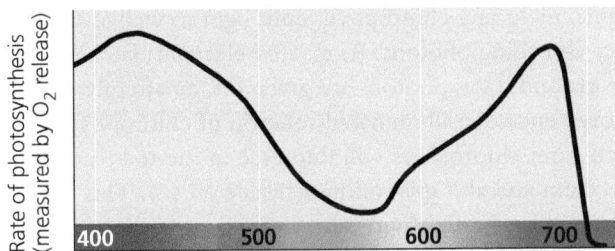

(b) Action spectrum. This graph plots the rate of photosynthesis versus wavelength. The resulting action spectrum resembles the absorption spectrum for chlorophyll *a* but does not match exactly (see part a). This is partly due to the absorption of light by accessory pigments such as chlorophyll *b* and carotenoids.

(c) Engelmann's experiment. In 1883, Theodor W. Engelmann illuminated a filamentous alga with light that had been passed through a prism, exposing different segments of the alga to different wavelengths. He used aerobic bacteria, which concentrate near an oxygen source, to determine which segments of the alga were releasing the most O_2 and thus photosynthesizing most. Bacteria congregated in greatest numbers around the parts of the alga illuminated with violet-blue or red light.

Conclusion Light in the violet-blue and red portions of the spectrum is most effective in driving photosynthesis.

Source: Based on "Bacterium photometricum. Ein Beitrag zur vergteiehenden Physiologie des Licht- und Farbensinnes" by Theodore W. Engelmann, from Archive Für Die Gesamte Physiologie Des Menschen Und Der Tiere, 1883, Volume 30(1). © Jane B Reece.

INTERPRET THE DATA *What wavelengths of light drive the highest rates of photosynthesis?*

---

that violet-blue and orange-red light work best for photosynthesis, since they are absorbed, while green is the least effective colour. This is confirmed by an **action spectrum** for photosynthesis (**Figure 10.10b**), which profiles the relative effectiveness of different wavelengths of radiation in driving the process. An action spectrum is prepared by illuminating chloroplasts with light of different colours and then plotting wavelength against some measure of photosynthetic rate, such as CO_2 consumption or O_2 release. The action spectrum for photosynthesis was first demonstrated by Theodor W. Engelmann, a German botanist, in 1883. Before equipment for measuring O_2 levels had even been invented, Engelmann performed a clever experiment in which he used bacteria to measure rates of photosynthesis in filamentous algae (**Figure 10.10c**). His results are a striking match to the modern action spectrum shown in Figure 10.10b.

Notice by comparing Figures 10.10a and 10.10b that the action spectrum for photosynthesis is much broader than the absorption spectrum of chlorophyll *a*. The absorption spectrum of chlorophyll *a* alone underestimates the effectiveness of certain wavelengths in driving photosynthesis. This is partly because accessory pigments with different absorption spectra are also present in chloroplasts—including chlorophyll *b* and carotenoids—broadening the spectrum of colours that can be used for photosynthesis. **Figure 10.11** shows the structure

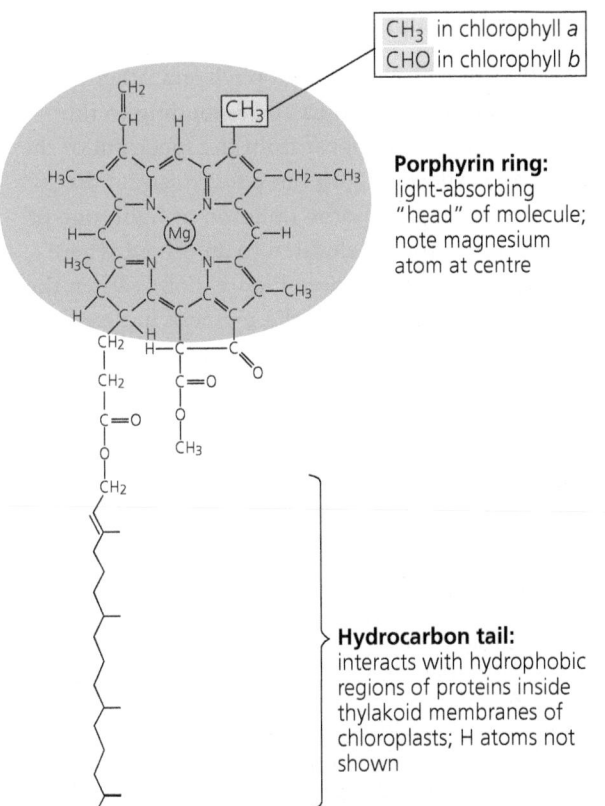

▲ **Figure 10.11 Structure of chlorophyll molecules in chloroplasts of plants.** Chlorophyll *a* and chlorophyll *b* differ only in one of the functional groups bonded to the porphyrin ring. (Also see the space-filling model of chlorophyll in Figure 1.4.)

of chlorophyll *a* compared with that of chlorophyll *b*. A slight structural difference between them is enough to cause the two pigments to absorb at slightly different wavelengths in the red and blue parts of the spectrum (see Figure 10.10a). As a result, chlorophyll *a* appears blue green and chlorophyll *b* appears olive green under visible light.

Other accessory pigments include **carotenoids**, hydrocarbons that are various shades of yellow and orange because they absorb violet and blue-green light (see Figure 10.10a). Carotenoids may broaden the spectrum of colours that can drive photosynthesis. However, a more important function of at least some carotenoids seems to be *photoprotection*: These compounds absorb and dissipate excessive light energy that would otherwise damage chlorophyll or interact with oxygen, forming reactive oxidative molecules that are dangerous to the cell. Interestingly, carotenoids similar to the photoprotective ones in chloroplasts have a photoprotective role in the human eye. These and related molecules are, of course, found naturally in many vegetables and fruits. They are also often advertised in health food products as "phytochemicals" (from the Greek *phyton*, plant), some of which have antioxidant properties. Plants can synthesize all the antioxidants they require, but humans and other animals must obtain some of them from their diets.

Excitation of Chlorophyll by Light

What exactly happens when chlorophyll and other pigments absorb light? The colours corresponding to the absorbed wavelengths disappear from the spectrum of the transmitted and reflected light, but energy cannot disappear. When a molecule absorbs a photon of light, one of the molecule's electrons is elevated to an orbital where it has more potential energy (see Figure 2.6b). When the electron is in its normal orbital, the pigment molecule is said to be in its ground state. Absorption of a photon boosts an electron to an orbital of higher energy, and the pigment molecule is then said to be in an excited state. The only photons absorbed are those whose energy is exactly equal to the energy difference between the ground state and an excited state, and this energy difference varies from one kind of molecule to another. Thus, a particular compound absorbs only photons corresponding to specific wavelengths, which is why each pigment has a unique absorption spectrum.

Once absorption of a photon raises an electron to an excited state, the electron cannot stay there long. The excited state, like all high-energy states, is unstable. Generally, when isolated pigment molecules absorb light, their excited electrons drop back down to the ground-state orbital in a billionth of a second, releasing their excess energy as heat. This conversion of light energy to heat is what makes the top of an automobile so hot on a sunny day. (White cars are coolest because their paint reflects all wavelengths of visible light.) In isolation, some pigments, including chlorophyll, emit light as well as heat after absorbing photons. As excited electrons fall back to the ground state, photons are given off, an afterglow called fluorescence. An illuminated solution of chlorophyll isolated from chloroplasts will fluoresce in the red part of the spectrum and also give off heat (**Figure 10.12**). This is best seen by illuminating with ultraviolet light, which chlorophyll can also absorb (see Figures 10.7 and 10.10a). Viewed under visible light, the fluorescence would be harder to see against the green of the solution.

A Photosystem: A Reaction-Centre Complex Associated with Light-Harvesting Complexes

Chlorophyll molecules excited by the absorption of light energy produce very different results in an intact chloroplast

▶ Figure 10.12 **Excitation of isolated chlorophyll by light. (a)** Absorption of a photon causes a transition of the chlorophyll molecule from its ground state to its excited state. The photon boosts an electron to an orbital where it has more potential energy. If the illuminated molecule exists in isolation, its excited electron immediately drops back down to the ground-state orbital, and its excess energy is given off as heat and fluorescence (light). **(b)** A chlorophyll solution excited with ultraviolet light fluoresces with a red-orange glow.

WHAT IF? *If a leaf containing a similar concentration of chlorophyll as the solution were exposed to the same ultraviolet light, no fluorescence would be seen. Propose an explanation for the difference in fluorescence emission between the solution and the leaf.*

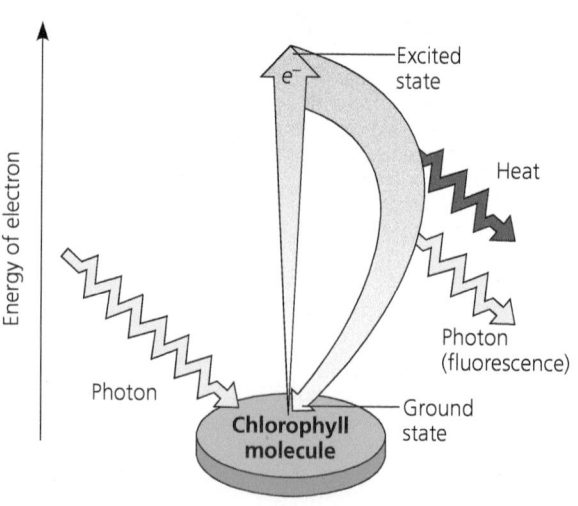

(a) Excitation of isolated chlorophyll molecule

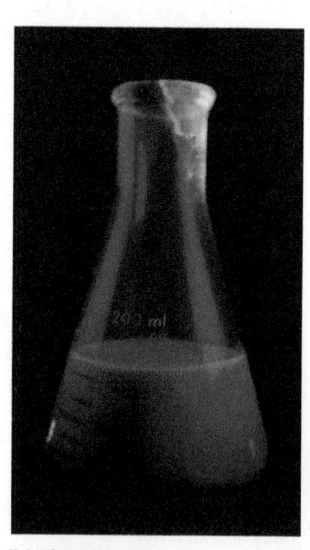

Christine Case

(b) Fluorescence

than they do in isolation (see Figure 10.12). In their native environment of the thylakoid membrane, chlorophyll molecules are organized along with other small organic molecules and proteins into complexes called photosystems.

A **photosystem** is composed of a **reaction-centre complex** surrounded by several light-harvesting complexes (**Figure 10.13**). The reaction-centre complex is an organized association of proteins holding a special pair of chlorophyll *a* molecules. Each **light-harvesting complex** consists of various pigment molecules (which may include chlorophyll *a*, chlorophyll *b*, and multiple carotenoids) bound to proteins. The number and variety of pigment molecules enable a photosystem to harvest light over a larger surface area and a larger portion of the spectrum than could any single pigment molecule alone. Together, these light-harvesting complexes act as an antenna for the reaction-centre complex. When a pigment molecule absorbs a photon, the energy is transferred from pigment molecule to pigment molecule within a light-harvesting complex, somewhat like a human "wave" at a sports arena, until it is passed into the reaction-centre complex. The reaction-centre complex also contains a molecule capable of accepting electrons and becoming reduced; this is called the **primary electron acceptor**. The pair of chlorophyll *a* molecules in the reaction-centre complex are special because their molecular environment—their location and the other molecules with which they are associated—enables them to use the energy from light not only to boost one of their electrons to a higher energy level, but also to transfer it to a different molecule—the primary electron acceptor.

The solar-powered transfer of an electron from the reaction-centre chlorophyll *a* pair to the primary electron acceptor is the first step of the light reactions. As soon as the chlorophyll electron is excited to a higher energy level, the primary electron acceptor captures it; this is a redox reaction. In the flask shown in Figure 10.12, isolated chlorophyll fluoresces because there is no electron acceptor, so electrons of photoexcited chlorophyll drop right back to the ground state. In the structured environment of a chloroplast, however, an electron acceptor is readily available, and the potential energy represented by the excited electron is not dissipated as light and heat. Thus, each photosystem—a reaction-centre complex surrounded by light-harvesting complexes—functions in the chloroplast as a unit. It converts light energy to chemical energy, which will ultimately be used for the synthesis of sugar.

The thylakoid membrane is populated by two types of photosystems that cooperate in the light reactions of photosynthesis. They are called **photosystem II (PS II)** and **photosystem I (PS I)**. (They were named in order of their discovery, but photosystem II functions first in the light reactions.) Each has a characteristic reaction-centre complex—a particular kind of primary electron acceptor

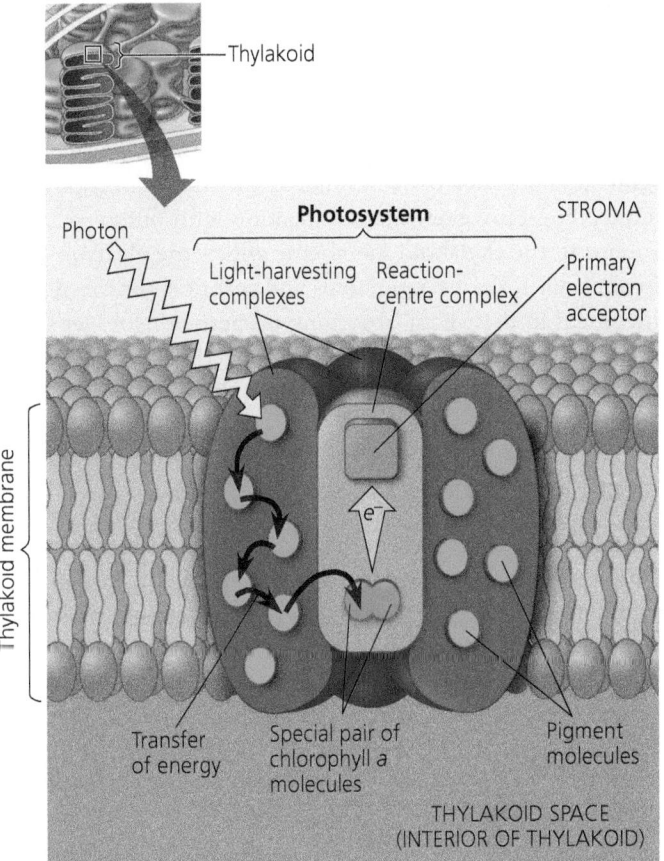

(a) How a photosystem harvests light. When a photon strikes a pigment molecule in a light-harvesting complex, the energy is passed from molecule to molecule until it reaches the reaction-centre complex. Here, an excited electron from the special pair of chlorophyll *a* molecules is transferred to the primary electron acceptor.

(b) Structure of a photosystem. This computer model, based on X-ray crystallography, shows two photosystem complexes side by side. Chlorophyll molecules (small green ball-and-stick models) are interspersed with protein subunits (cylinders and ribbons). For simplicity, this photosystem will be shown as a single complex in the rest of the chapter.

▲ **Figure 10.13** **The structure and function of a photosystem.**

Source: Adaptation of figure 1a from "Architecture of the Photosynthetic Oxygen-Evolving Center" by Kristina N. Ferreira et al., from Science, March 2004, Volume 303(5665). Copyright © 2004 by AAAS. Reprinted with permission.

next to a special pair of chlorophyll *a* molecules associated with specific proteins. The reaction-centre chlorophyll *a* of photosystem II is known as P680 because this pigment is best at absorbing light having a wavelength of 680 nm (in the red part of the spectrum). The chlorophyll *a* at the reaction-centre complex of photosystem I is called P700 because it most effectively absorbs light of wavelength 700 nm (in the far-red part of the spectrum). These two pigments, P680 and P700, are nearly identical chlorophyll *a* molecules. However, their association with different proteins in the thylakoid membrane affects the electron distribution in the two pigments and accounts for the slight differences in their light-absorbing properties. Now let's see how the two photosystems work together in using light energy to generate ATP and NADPH, the two main products of the light reactions.

Linear Electron Flow

Light drives the synthesis of ATP and NADPH by energizing the two photosystems embedded in the thylakoid membranes of chloroplasts. The key to this energy transformation is a flow of electrons through the photosystems and other molecular components built into the thylakoid membrane. This is called **linear electron flow**, and it occurs

during the light reactions of photosynthesis, as shown in **Figure 10.14**. The numbered steps in the text correspond to the numbered steps in the figure.

1 A photon of light strikes one of the pigment molecules in a light-harvesting complex of PS II, boosting one of its electrons to a higher energy level. As this electron falls back to its ground state, an electron in a nearby pigment molecule is simultaneously raised to an excited state. The process continues, with the energy being relayed to other pigment molecules until it reaches the P680 pair of chlorophyll *a* molecules in the PS II reaction-centre complex. It excites an electron in this pair of chlorophylls to a higher energy state.

2 This electron is transferred from the excited P680 to the primary electron acceptor. We can refer to the resulting form of P680, missing an electron, as $P680^+$.

3 An enzyme catalyzes the splitting of a water molecule into two electrons, two hydrogen ions (H^+), and an oxygen atom. The electrons are supplied one by one to the $P680^+$ pair, each electron replacing one transferred to the primary electron acceptor. ($P680^+$ is the

▼ Figure 10.14 **How linear electron flow during the light reactions generates ATP and NADPH.** The gold arrows trace the flow of light-driven electrons from water to NADPH. The black arrows trace the transfer of energy from pigment molecule to pigment molecule.

strongest biological oxidizing agent known; its electron "hole" must be filled. This greatly facilitates the transfer of electrons from the split water molecule.) The H^+ are released into the thylakoid space. The oxygen atom immediately combines with an oxygen atom generated by the splitting of another water molecule, forming O_2.

4 Each photoexcited electron passes from the primary electron acceptor of PS II to PS I via an electron transport chain, the components of which are similar to those of the electron transport chain that functions in cellular respiration. The electron transport chain between PS II and PS I is made up of the electron carrier plastoquinone (Pq), a cytochrome complex, and a protein called plastocyanin (Pc).

5 The exergonic "fall" of electrons to a lower energy level provides energy for the synthesis of ATP. As electrons pass through the cytochrome complex, H^+ are pumped into the thylakoid space, contributing to the proton gradient that is subsequently used in chemiosmosis.

6 Meanwhile, light energy has been transferred via light-harvesting complex pigments to the PS I reaction-centre complex, exciting an electron of the P700 pair of chlorophyll *a* molecules located there. The photoexcited electron is then transferred to PS I's primary electron acceptor, creating an electron "hole" in the P700—which we now can call $P700^+$. In other words, $P700^+$ can now act as an electron acceptor, accepting an electron that reaches the bottom of the electron transport chain from PS II.

7 Photoexcited electrons are passed in a series of redox reactions from the primary electron acceptor of PS I down a second electron transport chain through the protein ferredoxin (Fd). (This chain does not create a proton gradient and thus does not produce ATP.)

8 The enzyme $NADP^+$ reductase catalyzes the transfer of electrons from Fd to $NADP^+$. Two electrons are required for its reduction to NADPH. This molecule is at a higher energy level than water, and its electrons are more readily available for the reactions of the

▲ Figure 10.15 **A mechanical analogy for linear electron flow during the light reactions.**

Source: Adaptation of Figure 4.1 from Energy, Plants, and Man, by Richard Walker and David Alan Walker. Copyright © 1992 by Richard Walker and David Alan Walker. Reprinted with permission of Richard Walker.

Calvin cycle than were those of water. This process also removes an H^+ from the stroma.

The energy changes of electrons during their linear flow through the light reactions are shown in a mechanical analogy in **Figure 10.15**. Although the scheme shown in Figures 10.14 and 10.15 may seem complicated, do not lose track of the big picture. The light reactions use solar power to generate ATP and NADPH, which provide chemical energy and reducing power, respectively, to the carbohydrate-synthesizing reactions of the Calvin cycle.

Cyclic Electron Flow

In certain cases, photoexcited electrons can take an alternative path called **cyclic electron flow**, which uses photosystem I but not photosystem II. You can see in **Figure 10.16** that cyclic flow is a short circuit: The electrons cycle back

◀ Figure 10.16 **Cyclic electron flow.** Photoexcited electrons from PS I are occasionally shunted back from ferredoxin (Fd) to chlorophyll via the cytochrome complex and plastocyanin (Pc). This electron shunt supplements the supply of ATP (via chemiosmosis) but produces no NADPH. The "shadow" of linear electron flow is included in the diagram for comparison with the cyclic route. The two ferredoxin molecules in this diagram are actually one and the same—the final electron carrier in the electron transport chain of PS I—although it is depicted between the photosystems twice to clearly show its role in two parts of the process.

? *Look at Figure 10.15, and explain how you would alter it to show a mechanical analogy for cyclic electron flow.*

from ferredoxin (Fd) to the cytochrome complex and from there continue on to a P700 chlorophyll in the PS I reaction-centre complex. There is no production of NADPH and no release of oxygen that results from this process. On the other hand, cyclic flow does generate ATP.

Rather than having both PS II and PS I, several of the currently existing groups of photosynthetic bacteria are known to have a single photosystem related to either PS II or PS I. For these species, which include the purple sulphur bacteria (see Figure 10.2e), cyclic electron flow is the one and only means of generating ATP during the process of photosynthesis. Evolutionary biologists hypothesize that these bacterial groups are descendants of ancestral bacteria in which photosynthesis first evolved, in a form similar to cyclic electron flow.

Cyclic electron flow can also occur in photosynthetic species that possess both photosystems; this includes some prokaryotes, such as the cyanobacteria shown in Figure 10.2d, as well as the eukaryotic photosynthetic species that have been tested thus far. Although the process is probably in part an "evolutionary leftover," research suggests it plays at least one beneficial role for these organisms. Mutant plants that are not able to carry out cyclic electron flow are capable of growing well in low light, but do not grow well where light is intense. This is evidence for the idea that cyclic electron flow may be photoprotective. Later you'll learn more about cyclic electron flow as it relates to a particular adaptation of photosynthesis (C$_4$ plants; see Concept 10.4).

Whether ATP synthesis is driven by linear or cyclic electron flow, the actual mechanism is the same. Before we move on to consider the Calvin cycle, let's review chemiosmosis, the process that uses membranes to couple redox reactions to ATP production.

A Comparison of Chemiosmosis in Chloroplasts and Mitochondria

Chloroplasts and mitochondria generate ATP by the same basic mechanism: chemiosmosis. An electron transport chain assembled in a membrane pumps protons across the membrane as electrons are passed through a series of carriers that are progressively more electronegative. In this way, electron transport chains transform redox energy to a proton-motive force, potential energy stored in the form of an H$^+$ gradient across a membrane. An ATP synthase complex in the same

membrane couples the diffusion of hydrogen ions down their gradient to the phosphorylation of ADP, forming ATP.

Some of the electron carriers, including the iron-containing proteins called cytochromes, are very similar in chloroplasts and mitochondria. The ATP synthase complexes of the two organelles are quite similar. But there are noteworthy differences between photophosphorylation in chloroplasts and oxidative phosphorylation in mitochondria. In chloroplasts, the high-energy electrons dropped down the transport chain come from water, while in mitochondria they are extracted from organic molecules (which are thus oxidized). Chloroplasts do not need molecules from food to make ATP; their photosystems capture light energy and use it to drive the electrons from water to the top of the transport chain. In other words, mitochondria use chemiosmosis to transfer chemical energy from food molecules to ATP, whereas chloroplasts transform light energy into chemical energy in ATP.

Although the spatial organization of chemiosmosis differs slightly between chloroplasts and mitochondria, it is easy to see similarities in the two (Figure 10.17). The inner membrane of the mitochondrion pumps protons from the mitochondrial matrix out to the intermembrane space, which then serves as a reservoir of hydrogen ions. The thylakoid membrane of the chloroplast pumps protons from

▲ Figure 10.17 **Comparison of chemiosmosis in mitochondria and chloroplasts.** In both kinds of organelles, electron transport chains pump protons (H$^+$) across a membrane from a region of low H$^+$ concentration (light grey in this diagram) to one of high H$^+$ concentration (dark grey). The protons then diffuse back across the membrane through ATP synthase, driving the synthesis of ATP.

the stroma into the thylakoid space (interior of the thylakoid), which functions as the H$^+$ reservoir. If you imagine the cristae of mitochondria pinching off from the inner membrane, this may help you see how the thylakoid space and the intermembrane space are comparable spaces in the two organelles, while the mitochondrial matrix is analogous to the stroma of the chloroplast.

In the mitochondrion, protons diffuse down their concentration gradient from the intermembrane space through ATP synthase to the matrix, driving ATP synthesis. In the chloroplast, ATP is synthesized as the hydrogen ions diffuse from the thylakoid space back to the stroma through ATP synthase complexes, whose catalytic knobs are on the stroma side of the membrane (**Figure 10.18**). Thus, ATP forms in the stroma, where it is used to help drive sugar synthesis during the Calvin cycle.

The proton (H$^+$) gradient, or pH gradient, across the thylakoid membrane is substantial. When chloroplasts in

▲ **Figure 10.18 The light reactions and chemiosmosis: current model of the organization of the thylakoid membrane.** The gold arrows track the linear electron flow outlined in Figure 10.14. At least three steps in the light reactions contribute to the H$^+$ gradient by increasing H$^+$ concentration in the thylakoid space: ❶ Water is split by photosystem II on the side of the membrane facing the thylakoid space; ❷ as plastoquinone (Pq) transfers electrons to the cytochrome complex, four protons are translocated across the membrane into the thylakoid space; and ❸ a hydrogen ion is removed from the stroma when it is taken up by NADP$^+$. Notice that in step 2, hydrogen ions are being pumped from the stroma into the thylakoid space, as in Figure 10.17. The diffusion of H$^+$ from the thylakoid space back to the stroma (along the H$^+$ concentration gradient) powers the ATP synthase. These light-driven reactions store chemical energy in NADPH and ATP, which shuttle the energy to the carbohydrate-producing Calvin cycle.

an experimental setting are illuminated, the pH in the thylakoid space drops to about 5 (the H^+ concentration increases), and the pH in the stroma increases to about 8 (the H^+ concentration decreases). This gradient of three pH units corresponds to a thousandfold difference in H^+ concentration. If the lights are then turned off, the pH gradient is abolished, but it can quickly be restored by turning the lights back on. Experiments such as this provided strong evidence in support of the chemiosmotic model.

The currently accepted model for the organization of the light-reaction "machinery" within the thylakoid membrane is based on several research studies. Each of the molecules and molecular complexes in the figure is present in numerous copies in each thylakoid. Notice that NADPH, like ATP, is produced on the side of the membrane facing the stroma, where the Calvin cycle reactions take place.

Let's summarize the light reactions. Electron flow pushes electrons from water, where they are at a low state of potential energy, ultimately to NADPH, where they are stored at a high state of potential energy. The light-driven electron flow also generates ATP. Thus, the equipment of the thylakoid membrane converts light energy to chemical energy stored in ATP and NADPH. (Oxygen is a by-product.) Let's now see how the Calvin cycle uses the products of the light reactions to synthesize sugar from CO_2.

CONCEPT CHECK 10.2

1. What colour of light is *least* effective in driving photosynthesis? Explain.

2. Compared to a solution of isolated chlorophyll, why do intact chloroplasts release less heat and fluorescence when illuminated?

3. In the light reactions, what is the initial electron donor? Where do the electrons finally end up?

4. WHAT IF? In an experiment, isolated chloroplasts placed in an illuminated solution with the appropriate chemicals can carry out ATP synthesis. Predict what would happen to the rate of synthesis if a compound is added to the solution that makes membranes freely permeable to hydrogen ions.

For suggested answers, see Appendix A.

CONCEPT 10.3

The Calvin cycle uses the chemical energy of ATP and NADPH to reduce CO_2 to sugar

The Calvin cycle is similar to the citric acid cycle in that a starting material is regenerated after some molecules enter the cycle and others exit the cycle. However, the citric acid cycle is catabolic, oxidizing acetyl CoA and using the energy to synthesize ATP. In contrast, the Calvin cycle is anabolic, building carbohydrates from smaller molecules and consuming energy. Carbon enters the Calvin cycle in the form of CO_2 and leaves in the form of sugar. The cycle spends ATP as an energy source and consumes NADPH as reducing power for adding high-energy electrons to make the sugar.

As we mentioned previously (in Concept 10.1), the carbohydrate produced directly from the Calvin cycle is actually not glucose, but a three-carbon sugar; the name of this sugar is **glyceraldehyde 3-phosphate (G3P)**. For the net synthesis of one molecule of G3P, the cycle must take place three times, fixing three molecules of CO_2—one per turn of the cycle. (Recall that the term *carbon fixation* refers to the initial incorporation of CO_2 into organic material.) As we trace the steps of the cycle, it's important to keep in mind that we are following three molecules of CO_2 through the reactions. Figure 10.19 divides the Calvin cycle into three phases: carbon fixation, reduction, and regeneration of the CO_2 acceptor.

Phase 1: Carbon fixation. The Calvin cycle incorporates each CO_2 molecule, one at a time, by attaching it to a five-carbon sugar named ribulose bisphosphate (abbreviated RuBP). The enzyme that catalyzes this first step is RuBP carboxylase-oxygenase, or **rubisco**. (This is the most abundant protein in chloroplasts and is also thought to be the most abundant protein on Earth.) The product of the reaction is a six-carbon intermediate that is short-lived because it is so energetically unstable that it immediately splits in half, forming two molecules of 3-phosphoglycerate (for each CO_2 fixed).

Phase 2: Reduction. Each molecule of 3-phosphoglycerate receives an additional phosphate group from ATP, becoming 1,3-bisphosphoglycerate. Next, a pair of electrons donated from NADPH reduces 1,3-bisphosphoglycerate, which also loses a phosphate group in the process, becoming glyceraldehyde 3-phosphate (G3P). Specifically, the electrons from NADPH reduce a carboxyl group on 1,3-bisphosphoglycerate to the aldehyde group of G3P, which stores more potential energy. G3P is a sugar—the same three-carbon sugar formed in glycolysis by the splitting of glucose (see Figure 9.9). Notice in Figure 10.19 that for every *three* molecules of CO_2 that enter the cycle, there are *six* molecules of G3P formed. But only one molecule of this three-carbon sugar can be counted as a net gain of carbohydrate, because the rest are required to complete the cycle. The cycle began with 15 carbons' worth of carbohydrate in the form of three molecules of the five-carbon sugar RuBP. Now there are 18 carbons' worth of carbohydrate in the form of six molecules of G3P. One molecule exits the cycle to be used by the plant cell, but the

Input

3

CO_2, entering one per cycle

Phase 1: Carbon fixation

Rubisco

3 ℗ Short-lived intermediate

3 ℗ Ribulose bisphosphate (RuBP)

6 ℗ 3-Phosphoglycerate

6 ATP

6 ADP

Calvin Cycle

6 ℗ ℗ 1,3-Bisphosphoglycerate

6 NADPH

6 NADP⁺

6 ℗ᵢ

3 ADP

3 ATP

Phase 3: Regeneration of the CO_2 acceptor (RuBP)

5 ℗ G3P

6 ℗ Glyceraldehyde 3-phosphate (G3P)

Phase 2: Reduction

1 ℗ G3P (a sugar)

Output

Glucose and other organic compounds

▲ **Figure 10.19 The Calvin cycle.** This diagram summarizes three turns of the cycle, tracking carbon atoms (grey balls). The three phases of the cycle correspond to the phases discussed in the text. For every three molecules of CO_2 that enter the cycle, the net output is one molecule of glyceraldehyde 3-phosphate (G3P), a three-carbon sugar. The light reactions sustain the Calvin cycle by regenerating the required ATP and NADPH.

other five molecules must be recycled to regenerate the three molecules of RuBP.

Phase 3: Regeneration of the CO_2 acceptor (RuBP). In a complex series of reactions, the carbon skeletons of five molecules of G3P are rearranged by the last steps of the Calvin cycle into three molecules of RuBP. To accomplish this, the cycle spends three more molecules of ATP. The RuBP is now prepared to receive CO_2 again, and the cycle continues.

For the net synthesis of one G3P molecule, the Calvin cycle consumes a total of nine molecules of ATP and six molecules of NADPH. The light reactions regenerate the ATP and NADPH. The G3P spun off from the Calvin cycle becomes the starting material for metabolic pathways that synthesize other organic compounds, including glucose (formed by combining two molecules of G3P), the disaccharide sucrose, and other carbohydrates. Neither the light reactions nor the Calvin cycle alone can make sugar from CO_2. Photosynthesis is an emergent property

of the intact chloroplast, which integrates the two stages of photosynthesis.

CONCEPT CHECK 10.3

1. To synthesize one glucose molecule, the Calvin cycle uses _____ molecules of CO_2, _____ molecules of ATP, and _____ molecules of NADPH.

2. Explain why the large numbers of ATP and NADPH molecules used during the Calvin cycle are consistent with the high value of glucose as an energy source.

3. **WHAT IF?** Explain why a poison that inhibits an enzyme of the Calvin cycle will also inhibit the light reactions.

4. **DRAW IT** Redraw this cycle using numerals to indicate the numbers of carbons instead of grey balls, multiplying at each step to ensure that you have accounted for all carbons. In what forms do the carbon atoms enter and leave the cycle?

5. **MAKE CONNECTIONS** Review Figures 9.9 and 10.19. Discuss the roles of intermediate and product played by glyceraldehyde 3-phosphate (G3P) in the two processes shown in these figures.

For suggested answers, see Appendix A.

CONCEPT 10.4

Alternative mechanisms of carbon fixation have evolved in hot, arid climates

EVOLUTION Ever since plants first moved onto land about 475 million years ago, they have been adapting to the problems of terrestrial life, particularly the problem of dehydration. In Chapters 29 and 36, we will consider anatomical adaptations that help plants conserve water, while in this chapter we are concerned with metabolic adaptations. The solutions often involve trade-offs. An important example is the compromise between photosynthesis and the prevention of excessive water loss from the plant. The CO_2 required for photosynthesis enters a leaf (and the resulting O_2 exits) via stomata, the pores on the leaf surface (see Figure 10.4). However, stomata are also the main avenues of transpiration, the evaporative loss of water from leaves. On a hot, dry day, most plants close their stomata, a response that conserves water. This response also reduces photosynthetic yield by limiting access to CO_2. With stomata even partially closed, CO_2 concentrations begin to decrease in the air spaces within the leaf, and the concentration of O_2 released from the light reactions begins to increase. These conditions within the leaf favour an apparently wasteful process called photorespiration.

Photorespiration: An Evolutionary Relic?

In most plants, initial fixation of carbon occurs via rubisco, the Calvin cycle enzyme that adds CO_2 to ribulose bisphosphate. Such plants are called **C_3 plants** because the first organic product of carbon fixation is a three-carbon compound, 3-phosphoglycerate (see Figure 10.19). Rice, wheat, and soybeans are C_3 plants that are important in agriculture. When their stomata partially close on hot, dry days, C_3 plants produce less sugar because the declining level of CO_2 in the leaf starves the Calvin cycle. In addition, rubisco is capable of binding O_2 in place of CO_2. As CO_2 becomes scarce within the air spaces of the leaf and O_2 builds up, rubisco adds O_2 to the Calvin cycle instead of CO_2. The product splits, and a two-carbon compound leaves the chloroplast. Peroxisomes and mitochondria within the plant cell rearrange and split this compound, releasing CO_2. This process was discovered by Gleb Krotov and colleagues at Queen's University in the 1960s. Dr. Krotov named this process **photorespiration** because it occurs in the light (*photo*) and consumes O_2 while producing CO_2 (*respiration*). However, unlike normal cellular respiration, photorespiration uses ATP rather than generating it. And unlike photosynthesis, photorespiration produces no sugar. In fact, photorespiration *decreases* photosynthetic output by siphoning organic material from the Calvin cycle and releasing CO_2 that would otherwise be fixed. This CO_2 can eventually be fixed if it is still in the leaf once the CO_2 concentration is high enough. In the meantime, though, the process is energetically costly, much like a hamster running on its wheel.

How can we explain the existence of a metabolic process that seems to be counterproductive for the plant? According to one hypothesis, photorespiration is evolutionary baggage—a metabolic relic from a much earlier time when the atmosphere had less O_2 and more CO_2 than it does today. In the ancient atmosphere that prevailed when rubisco first evolved, the inability of the enzyme's active site to exclude O_2 would have made little difference. The hypothesis suggests that modern rubisco retains some of its chance affinity for O_2, which is now so concentrated in the atmosphere that a certain amount of photorespiration is inevitable.

We now know that, at least in some cases, photorespiration plays a protective role in plants. Plants that are impaired in their ability to carry out photorespiration (due to defective genes) are more susceptible to damage induced by excess light. Researchers consider this clear evidence that photorespiration acts to neutralize the otherwise damaging products of the light reactions, which build up when a low CO_2 concentration limits the progress of the Calvin cycle. Whether there are other benefits of photorespiration is still unknown. In many types of plants—including a significant number of crop plants—photorespiration drains away as much as 50% of the carbon fixed by the Calvin cycle. As heterotrophs that depend on carbon fixation in chloroplasts for our food, we naturally view photorespiration as wasteful. Indeed, if photorespiration could be reduced in certain plant species without otherwise affecting photosynthetic productivity, crop yields and food supplies might increase.

In some plant species, alternate modes of carbon fixation have evolved that minimize photorespiration and optimize the Calvin cycle—even in hot, arid climates. The two most important of these photosynthetic adaptations are C_4 photosynthesis and crassulacean acid metabolism (CAM).

C_4 Plants

The **C_4 plants** are so named because they preface the Calvin cycle with an alternate mode of carbon fixation that forms a four-carbon compound as its first product. The C_4 pathway is believed to have evolved independently at least 45 separate times and is used by several thousand species in at least 19 plant families. Among the C_4 plants important to agriculture are sugarcane and corn, members of the grass family.

The anatomy of a C_4 leaf is correlated with the mechanism of C_4 photosynthesis. In C_4 plants, there are two distinct types of photosynthetic cells: bundle-sheath cells and mesophyll cells. **Bundle-sheath cells** are arranged into tightly packed sheaths around the veins of the leaf (Figure 10.20). Between the bundle sheath and the leaf surface are the more loosely arranged mesophyll cells which, in C_4 leaves, are closely associated and never more than two to three cells away from the bundle-sheath cells. The Calvin cycle is confined to the chloroplasts of the bundle-sheath cells. However, the Calvin cycle is preceded by incorporation of CO_2 into organic compounds in the mesophyll cells. See the numbered steps in Figure 10.20, which are also described here:

❶ The first step is carried out by an enzyme present only in mesophyll cells called **PEP carboxylase**. This enzyme adds CO_2 to phosphoenolpyruvate (PEP), forming the four-carbon product oxaloacetate. PEP carboxylase has a much higher affinity for CO_2 than does rubisco and no affinity for O_2. Therefore, PEP carboxylase can fix carbon efficiently when rubisco cannot— that is, when it is hot and dry and stomata are partially closed, causing CO_2 concentration in the leaf to be lower and O_2 concentration to be relatively higher.

❷ After the C_4 plant fixes carbon from CO_2, the mesophyll cells export their four-carbon products (malate in the example shown in Figure 10.20) to bundle-sheath cells through plasmodesmata (see Figure 6.29).

❸ Within the bundle-sheath cells, the four-carbon compounds release CO_2, which is reassimilated into organic material by rubisco and the Calvin cycle. The same reaction regenerates pyruvate, which is transported to mesophyll cells. There, ATP is used to convert pyruvate to PEP, allowing the reaction cycle to continue;

this ATP can be thought of, in a sense, as the "price" of concentrating CO_2 in the bundle-sheath cells. To generate this extra ATP, bundle-sheath cells carry out cyclic electron flow, the process described earlier in this chapter (see Figure 10.16). In fact, these cells contain PS I but no PS II, so cyclic electron flow is their only photosynthetic mode of generating ATP.

In effect, the mesophyll cells of a C_4 plant pump CO_2 into the bundle sheath, keeping the CO_2 concentration in the bundle-sheath cells high enough for rubisco to bind CO_2 rather than O_2. The cyclic series of reactions involving PEP carboxylase and the regeneration of PEP can be thought of as a CO_2-concentrating pump that is powered by ATP. In this way, C_4 photosynthesis spends ATP energy to minimize photorespiration and enhance sugar production. This adaptation is especially advantageous in hot regions with intense sunlight, where stomata partially close during the day, and it is in such environments that C_4 plants evolved and thrive today.

The concentration of CO_2 in the atmosphere has drastically increased since the Industrial Revolution began in the 1800s, and it continues to rise today due to human activities such as the burning of fossil fuels. The resulting global climate change, including an increase in average temperatures around the planet, may have far-reaching effects on plant species. Scientists are concerned that increasing CO_2 concentration and temperature may affect C_3 and C_4 plants differently, thus changing the relative abundance of these species in a given plant community.

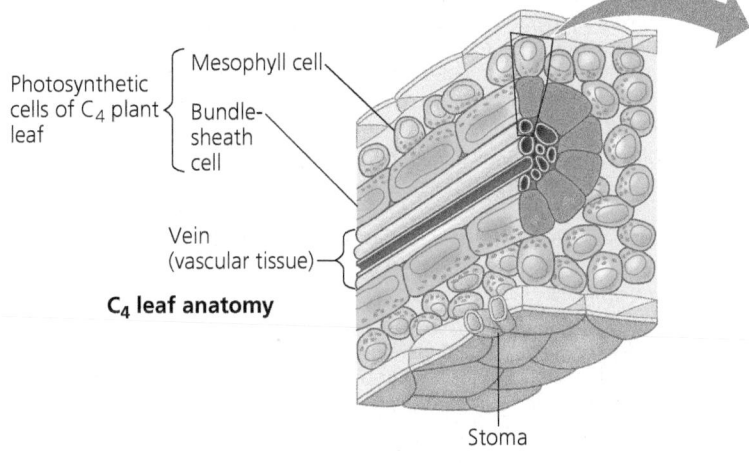

Photosynthetic cells of C_4 plant leaf
{ Mesophyll cell
Bundle-sheath cell }

Vein (vascular tissue)

C_4 leaf anatomy

Stoma

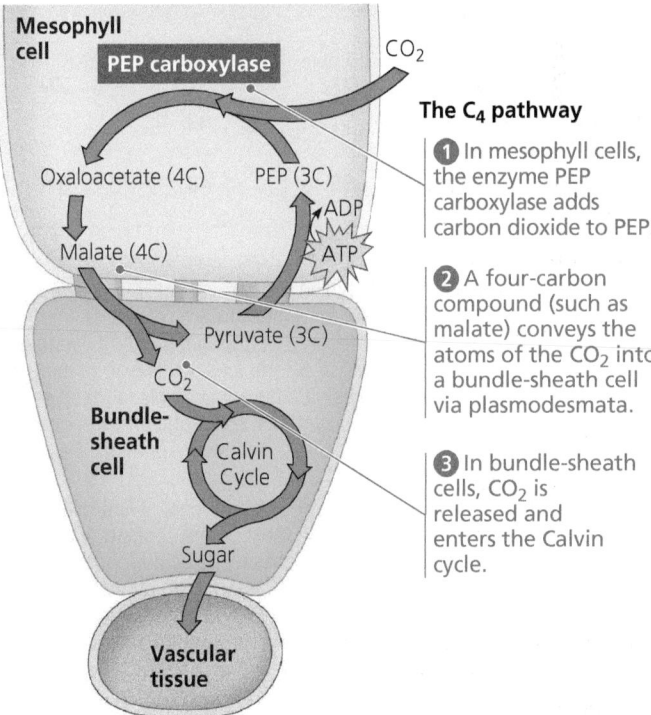

Mesophyll cell

PEP carboxylase

CO_2

Oxaloacetate (4C)   PEP (3C)

ADP
ATP

Malate (4C)

Pyruvate (3C)

CO_2

Bundle-sheath cell

Calvin Cycle

Sugar

Vascular tissue

The C_4 pathway

❶ In mesophyll cells, the enzyme PEP carboxylase adds carbon dioxide to PEP.

❷ A four-carbon compound (such as malate) conveys the atoms of the CO_2 into a bundle-sheath cell via plasmodesmata.

❸ In bundle-sheath cells, CO_2 is released and enters the Calvin cycle.

▲ Figure 10.20 **C_4 leaf anatomy and the C_4 pathway.** The structure and biochemical functions of the leaves of C_4 plants are an evolutionary adaptation to hot, dry climates. This adaptation maintains a CO_2 concentration in the bundle sheath that favours photosynthesis over photorespiration.

Which type of plant would stand to gain more from increasing CO_2 levels? Recall that in C_3 plants, the binding of O_2 rather than CO_2 by rubisco leads to photorespiration, lowering the efficiency of photosynthesis. C_4 plants overcome this problem by concentrating CO_2 in the bundle-sheath cells at the cost of ATP. Rising CO_2 levels should benefit C_3 plants by lowering the amount of photorespiration that occurs. At the same time, rising temperatures have the opposite effect, increasing photorespiration. (Other factors such as water availability may also come into play.) In contrast, many C_4 plants could be largely unaffected by increasing CO_2 levels or temperature. Researchers have investigated aspects of this question in several studies; you can work with data from one such experiment in the Scientific Skills Exercise. In different

regions, the particular combination of these two factors is likely to alter the balance of C_3 and C_4 plants in varying ways. The effects of such a widespread and variable change in community structure are unpredictable and thus a cause of legitimate concern.

CAM Plants

A second photosynthetic adaptation to arid conditions has evolved in many succulent (water-storing) plants, numerous cacti, pineapples, and representatives of several other plant families including the "hens and chicks" plants that are commonly seen in rock gardens throughout Canada. These plants open their stomata during the night and close them during the day, just the reverse of how other plants behave. Closing stomata during the day helps desert plants conserve water, but it also prevents CO_2 from entering the leaves. During the night, when their stomata are open, these plants take up CO_2 and incorporate it into a variety of organic acids. This mode of carbon fixation is called **crassulacean acid metabolism**, or **CAM**, after the plant family Crassulaceae, the succulents in which the process was first discovered. The mesophyll cells of **CAM plants** store the organic acids they make during the night in their vacuoles until morning, when the stomata close. During the day, when the light reactions can supply ATP and NADPH for the Calvin cycle, CO_2 is released from the organic acids made the night before to become incorporated into sugar in the chloroplasts.

Notice in **Figure 10.21** that the CAM pathway is similar to the C_4 pathway in that carbon dioxide is first incorporated into organic intermediates before it enters the Calvin cycle. The difference is that in C_4 plants, the initial steps of carbon fixation are separated structurally from the Calvin cycle, whereas in CAM plants, the two steps occur at separate times but within the same cell. (Keep in mind that CAM, C_4, and C_3 plants all eventually use the Calvin cycle to make sugar from carbon dioxide.)

Corn

Hen and chicks

C_4

CAM

(a) Spatial separation of steps. In C4 plants, carbon fixation and the Calvin cycle occur in different types of cells.

(b) Temporal separation of steps. In CAM plants, carbon fixation and the Calvin cycle occur in the same cells at different times.

▲ Figure 10.21 **C_4 and CAM photosynthesis compared.** Both adaptations are characterized by ❶ preliminary incorporation of CO_2 into organic acids, followed by ❷ transfer of CO_2 to the Calvin cycle. The C_4 and CAM pathways are two evolutionary solutions to the problem of maintaining photosynthesis with stomata partially or completely closed on hot, dry days.

CONCEPT CHECK 10.4

1. Describe how photorespiration lowers photosynthetic output for plants.

2. The presence of only PS I, not PS II, in the bundle-sheath cells of C_4 plants has an effect on O_2 concentration. What is that effect, and how might that benefit the plant?

3. **MAKE CONNECTIONS** Refer to the discussion of ocean acidification in Concept 3.3. Ocean acidification and changes in the distribution of C_3 and C_4 plants may seem to be two very different problems, but what do they have in common? Explain.

4. **WHAT IF?** How would you expect the relative abundance of C_3 versus C_4 and CAM species to change in a geographic region whose climate becomes much hotter and drier, with no change in CO_2 concentration?

For suggested answers, see Appendix A.

The Importance of Photosynthesis: *A Review*

In this chapter, we have followed photosynthesis from photons to food. The light reactions capture solar energy and use it to make ATP and transfer electrons from water to $NADP^+$, forming NADPH. The Calvin cycle uses the ATP and NADPH to produce sugar from carbon dioxide. The energy that enters the chloroplasts as sunlight becomes stored as chemical energy in organic compounds. The entire process is reviewed visually in **Figure 10.22**, where photosynthesis is also put in its natural context.

As for the fates of photosynthetic products, enzymes in the chloroplast and cytosol convert the G3P made in the Calvin cycle to many other organic compounds. In fact, the sugar made in the chloroplasts supplies the entire plant with chemical energy and carbon skeletons for the synthesis of all the major organic molecules of plant cells. About 50% of the organic material made by photosynthesis is consumed as fuel for cellular respiration in plant cell mitochondria.

Technically, green cells are the only autotrophic parts of the plant. The rest of the plant depends on organic molecules exported from leaves via veins (see Figure 10.22, top). In most plants, carbohydrate is transported out of the leaves to the rest of the plant in the form of sucrose, a disaccharide. After arriving at nonphotosynthetic cells, the sucrose provides raw material for cellular respiration and a multitude of anabolic pathways that synthesize proteins, lipids, and other products. A considerable amount of sugar in the form of glucose is linked together to make the polysaccharide cellulose (see Figure 5.6c), especially in plant cells that are still growing and maturing. Cellulose, the main ingredient of cell walls, is the most abundant organic molecule in the plant—and probably on the surface of the planet.

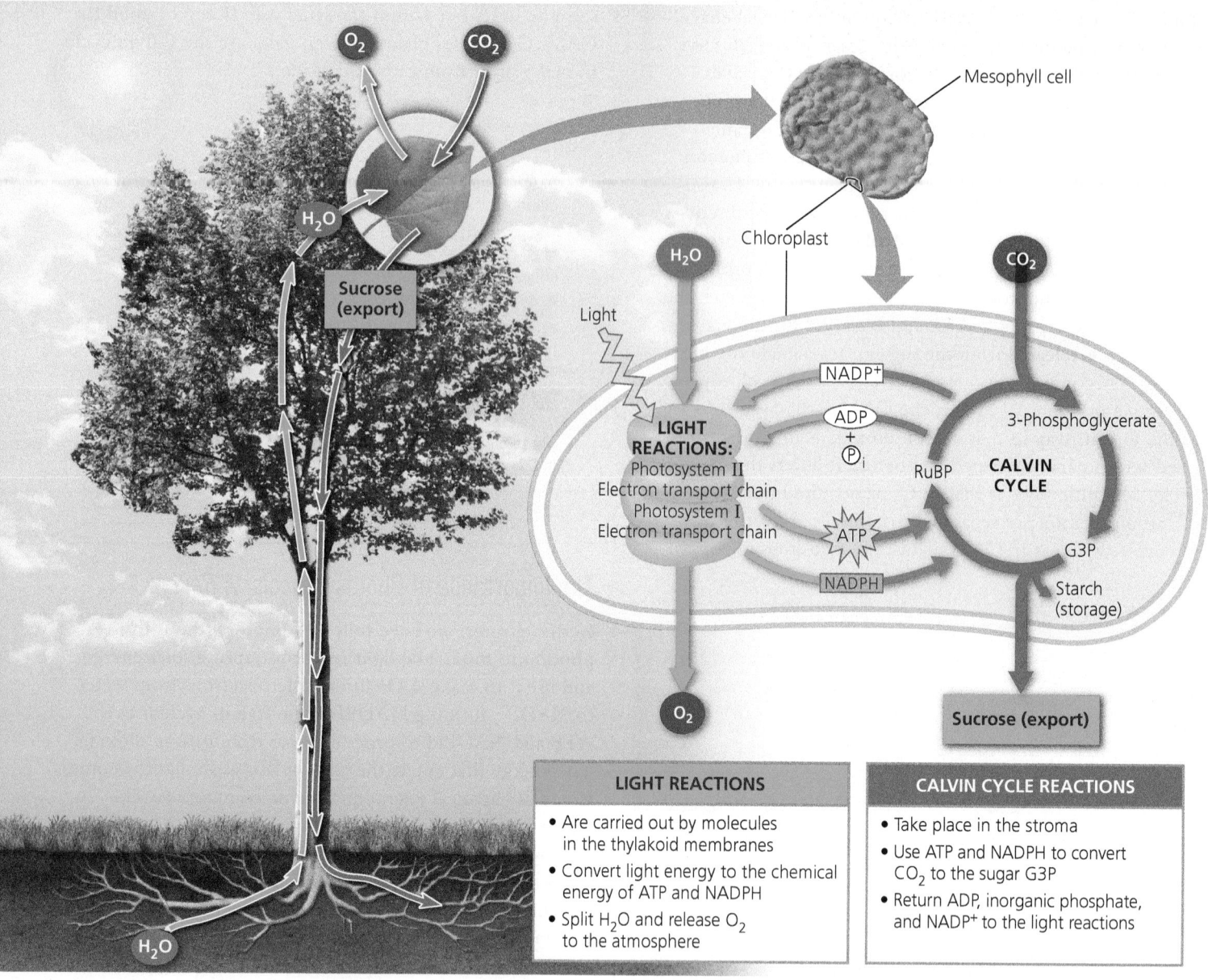

LIGHT REACTIONS

- Are carried out by molecules in the thylakoid membranes
- Convert light energy to the chemical energy of ATP and NADPH
- Split H_2O and release O_2 to the atmosphere

CALVIN CYCLE REACTIONS

- Take place in the stroma
- Use ATP and NADPH to convert CO_2 to the sugar G3P
- Return ADP, inorganic phosphate, and NADP⁺ to the light reactions

▲ **Figure 10.22 A review of photosynthesis.** This diagram outlines the main reactants and products of the light reactions and the Calvin cycle as they occur in the chloroplasts of plant cells. The entire ordered operation depends on the structural integrity of the chloroplast and its membranes. Enzymes in the chloroplast and cytosol convert glyceraldehyde 3-phosphate (G3P), the direct product of the Calvin cycle, to many other organic compounds.

MAKE CONNECTIONS *Can plants use the sugar they produce during photosynthesis to directly power the work of the cell? Explain. (See Figures 8.10, 8.11, and 9.6.)*

Most plants and other photosynthesizers make more organic material each day than they need to use as respiratory fuel and precursors for biosynthesis. They stockpile the extra sugar by synthesizing starch, storing some in the chloroplasts themselves and some in storage cells of roots, tubers, seeds, and fruits. In accounting for the consumption of the food molecules produced by photosynthesis, let's not forget that most plants lose leaves, roots, stems, fruits, and sometimes their entire bodies to heterotrophs, including humans.

On a global scale, photosynthesis is the process responsible for the presence of oxygen in our atmosphere.

Furthermore, while each chloroplast is miniscule, their collective productivity in terms of food production is prodigious: Photosynthesis makes an estimated 150 billion metric tonnes of carbohydrate per year (a metric tonne is 1000 kg). That's organic matter equivalent in mass to a stack of about 60 trillion biology textbooks—17 stacks of books reaching from Earth to the sun! No other chemical process on the planet can match the output of photosynthesis. And as we mentioned earlier, researchers are seeking ways to capitalize on photosynthetic production to produce alternative fuels. No chemical process is more important than photosynthesis to the welfare of life on Earth.

10 Chapter Review

Go to **MasteringBiology**® for Assignments, the eText, and the Study Area with Animations, Activities, Vocab Self-Quiz, and Practice Tests.

SUMMARY OF KEY CONCEPTS

CONCEPT 10.1

Photosynthesis converts light energy to the chemical energy of food (pp. 200–203)

- In **autotrophic** eukaryotes, photosynthesis occurs in **chloroplasts**, organelles containing **thylakoids**. Stacks of thylakoids form grana. **Photosynthesis** is summarized as

$$6\ CO_2 + 12\ H_2O + Light\ energy \rightarrow C_6H_{12}O_6 + 6\ O_2 + 6\ H_2O$$

Chloroplasts split water into hydrogen and oxygen, incorporating the electrons of hydrogen into sugar molecules. Photosynthesis is a redox process: H_2O is oxidized, and CO_2 is reduced. The **light reactions** in the thylakoid membranes split water, releasing O_2, producing ATP, and forming **NADPH**. The **Calvin cycle** in the **stroma** forms sugar from CO_2, using ATP for energy and NADPH for reducing power.

> **?** Compare and describe the roles of CO_2 and H_2O in respiration and photosynthesis.

CONCEPT 10.2

The light reactions convert solar energy to the chemical energy of ATP and NADPH (pp. 203–212)

- Light is a form of electromagnetic energy. The colours we see as **visible light** include those **wavelengths** that drive photosynthesis. A pigment absorbs light of specific wavelengths; **chlorophyll *a*** is the main photosynthetic pigment in plants. Other accessory pigments absorb different wavelengths of light and pass the energy on to chlorophyll *a*.
- A pigment goes from a ground state to an excited state when a **photon** of light boosts one of the pigment's electrons to a higher-energy orbital. This excited state is unstable. Electrons from isolated pigments tend to fall back to the ground state, giving off heat and/or light.
- A **photosystem** is composed of a **reaction-centre complex** surrounded by **light-harvesting complexes** that funnel the energy of photons to the reaction-centre complex. When a special pair of reaction-centre chlorophyll *a* molecules absorbs energy, one of its electrons is boosted to a higher energy level and transferred to the **primary electron acceptor**. **Photosystem II** contains P680 chlorophyll *a* molecules in the reaction-centre complex; **photosystem I** contains P700 molecules.
- **Linear electron flow** during the light reactions uses both photosystems and produces NADPH, ATP, and oxygen:

- **Cyclic electron flow** employs only photosystem I, producing ATP but no NADPH or O_2.
- During chemiosmosis in both mitochondria and chloroplasts, electron transport chains generate an H^+ gradient across a membrane. ATP synthase uses this proton-motive force to make ATP.

> **?** The absorption spectrum of chlorophyll *a* differs from the action spectrum of photosynthesis. Explain this observation.

CONCEPT 10.3

The Calvin cycle uses the chemical energy of ATP and NADPH to reduce CO_2 to sugar (pp. 212–213)

- The Calvin cycle occurs in the stroma, using electrons from NADPH and energy from ATP. One molecule of **G3P** exits the cycle per three CO_2 molecules fixed and is converted to glucose and other organic molecules.

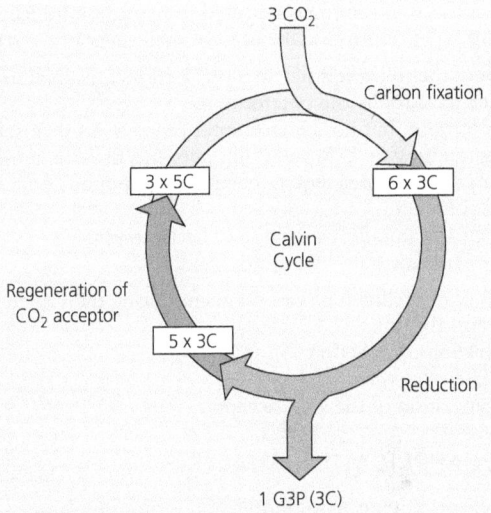

> **DRAW IT** On the diagram above, draw where ATP and NADPH are used and where rubisco functions. Describe these steps.

CONCEPT 10.4

Alternative mechanisms of carbon fixation have evolved in hot, arid climates (pp. 214–218)

- On dry, hot days, **C$_3$ plants** close their stomata, conserving water. Oxygen from the light reactions builds up. In **photorespiration**, O_2 substitutes for CO_2 in the active site of rubisco. This process consumes organic fuel and releases CO_2 without producing ATP or carbohydrate. Photorespiration may be an evolutionary relic, and it may play a photoprotective role.
- **C$_4$ plants** minimize the cost of photorespiration by incorporating CO_2 into four-carbon compounds in mesophyll cells. These compounds are exported to **bundle-sheath cells**, where they release carbon dioxide for use in the Calvin cycle.
- **CAM plants** open their stomata at night, incorporating CO_2 into organic acids, which are stored in mesophyll cells. During the day, the stomata close, and the CO_2 is released from the organic acids for use in the Calvin cycle.
- Organic compounds produced by photosynthesis provide the energy and building material for Earth's ecosystems.

? *Why are C_4 and CAM photosynthesis more energetically expensive than C_3 photosynthesis? What climate conditions would favour C_4 and CAM plants?*

TEST YOUR UNDERSTANDING

LEVEL 1: KNOWLEDGE/COMPREHENSION

1. The light reactions of photosynthesis supply the Calvin cycle with
   a. light energy.
   b. CO_2 and ATP.
   c. H_2O and NADPH.
   d. ATP and NADPH.

2. Which of the following sequences correctly represents the flow of electrons during photosynthesis?
   a. NADPH $\rightarrow$ O_2CO_2
   b. H_2O $\rightarrow$ NADPH $\rightarrow$ Calvin cycle
   c. H_2O $\rightarrow$ photosystem I $\rightarrow$ photosystem II
   d. NADPH $\rightarrow$ electron transport chain $\rightarrow$ O_2

3. How is photosynthesis similar in C_4 plants and CAM plants?
   a. In both cases, only photosystem I is used.
   b. Both types of plants make sugar without the Calvin cycle.
   c. In both cases, rubisco is not used to fix carbon initially.
   d. Both types of plants make most of their sugar in the dark.

4. Which of the following statements is a correct distinction between autotrophs and heterotrophs?
   a. Autotrophs, but not heterotrophs, can nourish themselves, beginning with CO_2 and other nutrients that are inorganic.
   b. Only heterotrophs require chemical compounds from the environment.
   c. Cellular respiration is unique to heterotrophs.
   d. Only heterotrophs have mitochondria.

5. Which of the following does *not* occur during the Calvin cycle?
   a. carbon fixation
   b. oxidation of NADPH
   c. release of oxygen
   d. regeneration of the CO_2 acceptor

LEVEL 2: APPLICATION/ANALYSIS

6. In mechanism, photophosphorylation is most similar to
   a. substrate-level phosphorylation in glycolysis.
   b. oxidative phosphorylation in cellular respiration.
   c. carbon fixation.
   d. reduction of NADP$^+$.

7. Which process is most directly driven by light energy?
   a. creation of a pH gradient by pumping protons across the thylakoid membrane
   b. reduction of NADP$^+$ molecules
   c. removal of electrons from chlorophyll molecules
   d. ATP synthesis

LEVEL 3: SYNTHESIS/EVALUATION

8. **SCIENCE, TECHNOLOGY, AND SOCIETY**
   Scientific evidence indicates that the CO_2 added to the air by the burning of wood and fossil fuels is contributing to global warming, a rise in global temperature. Tropical rain forests are estimated to be responsible for approximately 20% of global photosynthesis, yet the consumption of large amounts of CO_2 by living trees is thought to make little or *no* net contribution to reduction of global warming. Why might this be? (*Hint*: What processes in both living and dead trees produce CO_2?)

9. **EVOLUTION CONNECTION**
   Photorespiration can decrease soybeans' photosynthetic output by about 50%. Would you expect this figure to be higher or lower in wild relatives of soybeans? Why?

10. **SCIENTIFIC INQUIRY**
    MAKE CONNECTIONS The following diagram represents an experiment with isolated thylakoids. The thylakoids were first made acidic by soaking them in a solution at pH 4. After the thylakoid space reached pH 4, the thylakoids were transferred to a basic solution at pH 8. The thylakoids then made ATP in the dark. (See Concept 3.3 to review pH).

    Draw an enlargement of part of the thylakoid membrane in the beaker with the solution at pH 8. Draw ATP synthase. Label the areas of high H$^+$ concentration and low H$^+$ concentration. Show the direction protons flow through the enzyme, and show the reaction where ATP is synthesized. Would ATP end up in the thylakoid or outside of it? Explain why the thylakoids in the experiment were able to make ATP in the dark.

11. **WRITE ABOUT A THEME: ENERGY AND MATTER**
    Life is solar powered. Almost all the producers of the biosphere depend on energy from the sun to produce the organic molecules that supply the energy and carbon skeletons needed for life. In a short essay (100–150 words), describe how the process of photosynthesis in the chloroplasts of plants transforms the energy of sunlight into the chemical energy of sugar molecules.

12. **SYNTHESIZE YOUR KNOWLEDGE**

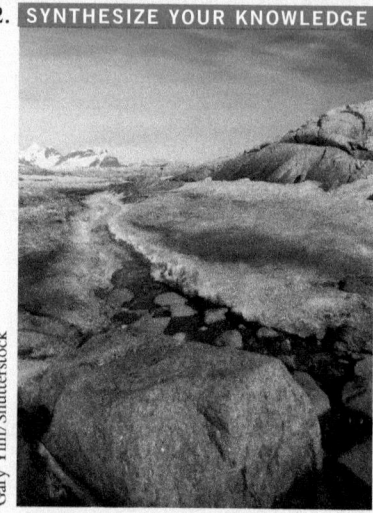

The photo shows "watermelon snow" in Antarctica, caused by a species of photosynthetic green algae that thrives in subzero temperatures (*Chlamydomonas nivalis*). These algae are also found in high-altitude year-round snowfields. In both locations, UV light levels tend to be high. Based on what you learned in this chapter, propose an explanation for why this photosynthetic alga appears reddish-pink.

Gary Yim/Shutterstock

For selected answers, see Appendix A.

11

Cell Communication

KEY CONCEPTS

11.1 External signals are converted to responses within the cell

11.2 Reception: A signalling molecule binds to a receptor protein, causing it to change shape

11.3 Transduction: Cascades of molecular interactions relay signals from receptors to target molecules in the cell

11.4 Response: Cell signalling leads to regulation of transcription or cytoplasmic activities

11.5 Apoptosis integrates multiple cell-signalling pathways

Tom & Pat Leeson/Science Source

▲ Figure 11.1 **How does cell signalling trigger the desperate flight of this snowshoe hare?**

Cellular Messaging

The showshoe hare in **Figure 11.1** flees for its life, racing and leaping to escape the predatory Canadian lynx nipping at its heals. The hare's heart is pounding and it's muscles are pumping as it hops furiously. These physiological functions are all part of the hare's "fight-or-flight" response, driven by hormones released from its adrenal glands at times of stress—in this case, upon sensing the lynx. What systems of cell-to-cell communication allow the trillions of cells in the hare to "talk" to each other, coordinating their activities?

Cells can signal to each other and interpret the signals they receive from other cells and the environment. The signals may include light and touch, but are most often chemicals. The flight response shown here is triggered by a signalling molecule called epinephrine (also called adrenaline; see the model to the left). Studying cell communication, biologists have discovered ample evidence for the evolutionary relatedness of all life. The same small set of cell-signalling mechanisms shows up again and again in diverse species, in processes ranging from bacterial signalling to embryonic development to cancer. In this chapter, we focus on the main mechanisms by which cells receive, process, and respond to chemical signals sent from other cells. We will also consider *apoptosis*, a type of programmed cell death that integrates input from multiple signalling pathways.

▶ **Epinephrine**

221

External signals are converted to responses within the cell

What does a "talking" cell say to a "listening" cell, and how does the latter cell respond to the message? Let's approach these questions by first looking at communication among microorganisms.

Evolution of Cell Signalling

EVOLUTION One topic of cell "conversation" is sex. Cells of the yeast *Saccharomyces cerevisiae*—which are used to make bread, wine, and beer—identify their mates by chemical signalling. There are two sexes, or mating types, called **a** and **α** (Figure 11.2). Each type secretes a specific factor that binds to receptors only on the other type of cell. When exposed to each other's mating factors, a pair of cells of opposite type change shape, grow toward each other, and fuse (mate). The new **a/α** cell contains all the genes of both original cells, a combination of genetic resources that provides advantages to the cell's descendants, which arise by subsequent cell divisions.

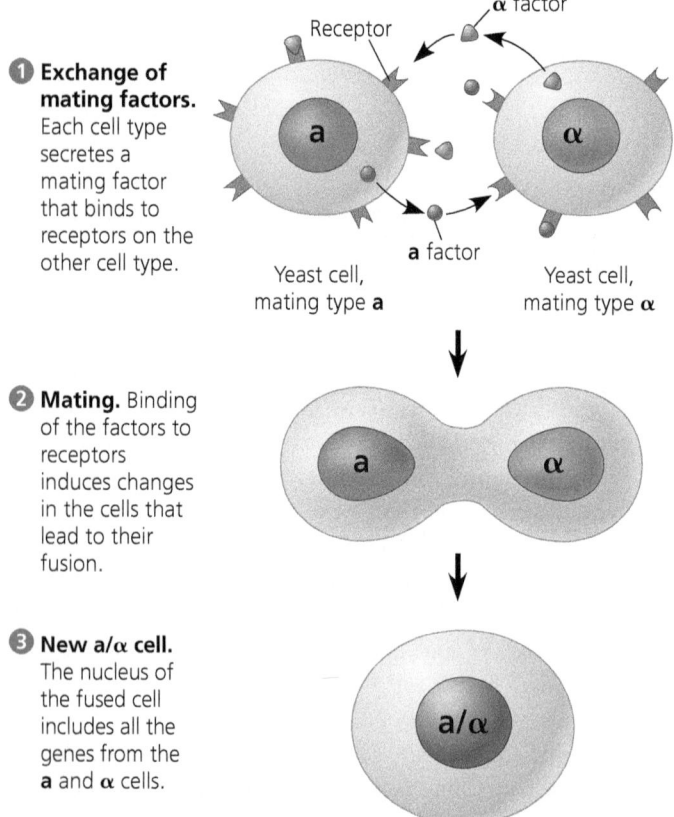

1 Exchange of mating factors. Each cell type secretes a mating factor that binds to receptors on the other cell type.

Receptor

α factor

a factor

Yeast cell, mating type **a**

Yeast cell, mating type **α**

2 Mating. Binding of the factors to receptors induces changes in the cells that lead to their fusion.

3 New a/α cell. The nucleus of the fused cell includes all the genes from the **a** and **α** cells.

▲ Figure 11.2 **Communication between mating yeast cells.** *Saccharomyces cerevisiae* cells use chemical signalling to identify cells of opposite mating type and initiate the mating process. The two mating types and their corresponding chemical signalling molecules, or mating factors, are called **a** and **α**.

Once received by the yeast cell surface receptor, a mating signal is changed, or *transduced*, into a form that brings about the cellular response of mating. This occurs in a series of steps called a *signal transduction pathway*. Many such pathways exist in both yeast and animal cells. In fact, the molecular details of signal transduction in yeasts and mammals are strikingly similar, even though their last common ancestor lived over a billion years ago. This suggests that early versions of cell-signalling mechanisms evolved well before the first multicellular creatures appeared on Earth.

Scientists think that signalling mechanisms first evolved in ancient prokaryotes and single-celled eukaryotes and then were adopted for new uses by their multicellular descendants. Cell signalling is critical in the microbial world (Figure 11.3). Bacterial cells secrete molecules that can be detected by other bacterial cells. Sensing the concentration of such signalling molecules allows bacteria to monitor the local density of cells, a phenomenon called *quorum sensing*. Quorum sensing allows bacterial populations to

1 Individual rod-shaped cells

0.5 mm

2 Aggregation in progress

2.5 mm

3 Spore-forming structure (fruiting body)

Fruiting bodies

▲ Figure 11.3 **Communication among bacteria.** Soil-dwelling bacteria called myxobacteria ("slime bacteria") use chemical signals to share information about nutrient availability. When food is scarce, starving cells secrete a molecule that stimulates neighbouring cells to aggregate. The cells form a structure, called a fruiting body, that produces thick-walled spores capable of surviving until the environment improves. The bacteria shown here are *Myxococcus xanthus* (steps 1–3, SEMs; lower photo, LM).

coordinate their behaviours in activities that require a given number of cells acting synchronously. One example is formation of a *biofilm*, an aggregation of bacterial cells adhered to a surface. The cells in the biofilm generally derive nutrition from the surface they are on. You have probably encountered biofilms many times, perhaps without realizing it. The slimy coating on a fallen log or on leaves lying on a forest path, and even the film on your teeth each morning, are examples of bacterial biofilms. (In fact, tooth-brushing disrupts biofilms that would otherwise cause cavities.) The formation of biofilms requires a sophisticated communication system, the basis of which is cell signalling.

Local and Long-Distance Signalling

Like bacteria or yeast cells, cells in a multicellular organism usually communicate via signalling molecules targeted for cells that may or may not be immediately adjacent. As we saw in Chapters 6 and 7, eukaryotic cells may communicate by direct contact (**Figure 11.4**), one type of local signalling. Both animals and plants have cell junctions that, where present, directly connect the cytoplasms of adjacent cells (**Figure 11.4a**). In these cases, signalling substances dissolved in the cytosol can pass freely between adjacent cells. Moreover, animal cells may communicate via direct contact between membrane-bound cell-surface molecules in a process called cell-cell recognition (**Figure 11.4b**). This sort of local signalling is especially important in embryonic development and the immune response.

In many other cases of local signalling, messenger molecules are secreted by the signalling cell. Some of these travel only short distances; such **local regulators** influence cells in

(a) Cell junctions. Both animals and plants have cell junctions that allow molecules to pass readily between adjacent cells without crossing plasma membranes.

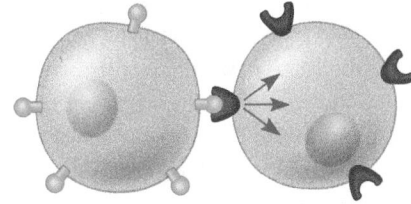

(b) Cell-cell recognition. Two cells in an animal may communicate by interaction between molecules protruding from their surfaces.

▲ Figure 11.4 **Communication by direct contact between cells.**

the vicinity. One class of local regulators in animals, *growth factors*, are compounds that stimulate nearby target cells to grow and divide. Numerous cells can simultaneously receive and respond to the molecules of growth factor produced by a single cell in their vicinity. This type of local signalling in animals is called *paracrine signalling* (**Figure 11.5a**).

(a) Paracrine signalling. A secreting cell acts on nearby target cells by secreting molecules of a local regulator (a growth factor, for example).

(b) Synaptic signalling. A nerve cell releases neurotransmitter molecules into a synapse, stimulating the target cell, such as a muscle or nerve cell.

(c) Endocrine (hormonal) signalling. Specialized endocrine cells secrete hormones into body fluids, often blood. Hormones reach virtually all body cells, but are bound only by some cells.

▲ Figure 11.5 **Local and long-distance cell signalling by secreted molecules in animals.** In both local and long-distance signalling, only specific target cells that can recognize a given signalling molecule will respond to it.

Another, more specialized type of local signalling called *synaptic signalling* occurs in the animal nervous system (Figure 11.5b). An electrical signal along a nerve cell triggers the secretion of neurotransmitter molecules. These molecules act as chemicals, diffusing across the synapse—the narrow space between the nerve cell and its target cell—triggering a response in the target cell.

Beyond communication through plasmodesmata (plant cell junctions), local signalling in plants is not as well understood. Because of their cell walls, plants use mechanisms somewhat different from those operating locally in animals.

Both animals and plants use chemicals called **hormones** for long-distance signalling. In hormonal signalling in animals, also known as *endocrine signalling*, specialized cells release hormone molecules, which travel via the circulatory system to other parts of the body where they reach target cells that can recognize and respond to the hormones (Figure 11.5c). Plant hormones (often called *plant growth regulators*) sometimes travel in vessels but more often reach their targets by moving through cells or by diffusing through the air as a gas (see Chapter 39). Hormones vary widely in size and type, as do local regulators. For instance, the plant hormone ethylene, a gas that promotes fruit ripening and helps regulate growth, is a hydrocarbon of only six atoms (C_2H_4), small enough to pass through cell walls. In contrast, the mammalian hormone insulin, which regulates sugar levels in the blood, is a protein with thousands of atoms.

What happens when a cell encounters a secreted signalling molecule? The ability of a cell to respond is determined by whether it has a specific receptor molecule that can bind to the signalling molecule. The information conveyed by this binding, the signal, must then be changed into another form—transduced—inside the cell before the cell can respond. The remainder of the chapter discusses this process, primarily as it occurs in animal cells.

The Three Stages of Cell Signalling: *A Preview*

Our current understanding of how chemical messengers act via signal transduction pathways had its origins in the pioneering work of Earl W. Sutherland, whose research led to a Nobel Prize in 1971. Sutherland and his colleagues at Vanderbilt University were investigating how the animal hormone epinephrine (adrenaline) stimulates the breakdown of the storage polysaccharide glycogen within liver cells and skeletal muscle cells. Glycogen breakdown releases the sugar glucose 1-phosphate, which the cell converts to glucose 6-phosphate. The liver or muscle cell can then use this compound, an early intermediate in glycolysis, for energy production. Alternatively, the compound can be stripped of phosphate and released from the cell into the blood as glucose, which can fuel cells throughout the body. Thus, one effect of epinephrine is the mobilization of fuel reserves, which can be used by the animal to either defend itself (fight) or escape whatever elicited a scare (flight). (The snowshoe hare in Figure 11.1 is obviously engaged in the latter.)

Sutherland's research team discovered that epinephrine stimulates glycogen breakdown by somehow activating a cytosolic enzyme, glycogen phosphorylase. However, when epinephrine was added to a test-tube mixture containing the enzyme and its substrate, glycogen, no breakdown occurred. Glycogen phosphorylase could be activated by epinephrine only when the hormone was added to *intact* cells in a solution. This result told Sutherland two things. First, epinephrine does not interact directly with the enzyme responsible for glycogen breakdown; an intermediate step or series of steps must be occurring inside the cell. Second, the plasma membrane itself is necessary for transmission of the signal to take place.

Sutherland's early work suggested that the process going on at the receiving end of a cellular conversation can be dissected into three stages: reception, transduction, and response (Figure 11.6):

1 Reception. Reception is the target cell's detection of a signalling molecule coming from outside the cell. A chemical signal is "detected" when the signalling molecule binds to a receptor protein located at the cell's surface or inside the cell.

▶ Figure 11.6 **Overview of cell signalling.** From the perspective of the cell receiving the message, cell signalling can be divided into three stages: signal reception, signal transduction, and cellular response. When reception occurs at the plasma membrane, as shown here, the transduction stage is usually a pathway of several steps, with each relay molecule in the pathway bringing about a change in the next molecule. The final molecule in the pathway triggers the cell's response. The three stages are explained in more detail in the text.

? *How does the epinephrine in Sutherland's experiment fit into this diagram of cell signalling?*

2 Transduction. The binding of the signalling molecule changes the receptor protein in some way, initiating the process of transduction. The transduction stage converts the signal to a form that can bring about a specific cellular response. In Sutherland's system, the binding of epinephrine to a receptor protein in a liver cell's plasma membrane leads to activation of glycogen phosphorylase. Transduction sometimes occurs in a single step but more often requires a sequence of changes in a series of different molecules—a **signal transduction pathway**. The molecules in the pathway are often called relay molecules.

3 Response. In the third stage of cell signalling, the transduced signal finally triggers a specific cellular response. The response may be almost any imaginable cellular activity—such as catalysis by an enzyme (for example, glycogen phosphorylase), rearrangement of the cytoskeleton, or activation of specific genes in the nucleus. The cell-signalling process helps ensure that crucial activities like these occur in the right cells, at the right time, and in proper coordination with the activities of other cells of the organism. We'll now explore the mechanisms of cell signalling in more detail, including a discussion of regulation and termination of the process.

CONCEPT CHECK 11.1

1. Explain how signalling is involved in ensuring that yeast cells fuse only with cells of the opposite mating type.

2. Explain how nerve cells provide examples of both local and long-distance signalling.

3. **WHAT IF?** When epinephrine is mixed with glycogen phosphorylase and glycogen in a test tube, is glucose 1-phosphate generated? Why or why not?

4. In liver cells, glycogen phosphorylase acts in which of the three stages of the signalling pathway associated with an epinephrine-initiated signal?

For suggested answers, see Appendix A.

CONCEPT 11.2

Reception: A signalling molecule binds to a receptor protein, causing it to change shape

A radio station broadcasts its signal indiscriminately, but it can be picked up only by radios tuned to the right frequency: Reception of the signal depends on the receiver. Similarly, the signals emitted by an **a** yeast cell are "heard" only by its prospective mates, **α** cells. In the case of the epinephrine circulating throughout the bloodstream of the snowshoe hare in Figure 11.1, the hormone encounters many types of cells, but only certain target cells detect and

react to the hormone molecule. A receptor protein on or in the target cell allows the cell to "hear" the signal and respond to it. The signalling molecule is complementary in shape to a specific site on the receptor and attaches there, like a key in a lock. The signalling molecule acts as a **ligand**, the term for a molecule that specifically binds to another molecule, often a larger one. Ligand binding generally causes a receptor protein to undergo a change in shape. For many receptors, this shape change directly activates the receptor, enabling it to interact with other cellular molecules. For other kinds of receptors, the immediate effect of ligand binding is to cause the aggregation of two or more receptor molecules, which leads to further molecular events inside the cell. Most signal receptors are plasma membrane proteins, but others are located inside the cell. We discuss both of these types next.

Receptors in the Plasma Membrane

Cell-surface receptor proteins play crucial roles in the biological systems of animals. The largest family of human cell surface receptors are the nearly 1000 G protein-coupled receptors (GPCRs); an example is shown in **Figure 11.7**.

Most water-soluble signalling molecules bind to specific sites on transmembrane receptor proteins that transmit information from the extracellular environment to the inside of the cell. We can see how cell-surface transmembrane receptors work by looking at three major types: G protein-coupled receptors (GPCRs), receptor tyrosine kinases, and ion channel receptors. These receptors are discussed and illustrated in **Figure 11.8**; study this figure before going on.

Given the many important functions of cell-surface receptors, it is not surprising that their malfunctions are associated with many human diseases, including cancer, heart disease, and asthma. To better understand and treat these conditions, a major focus of both university research

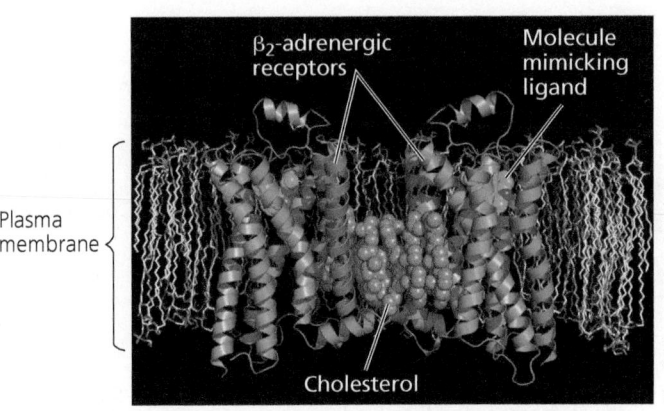

▲ **Figure 11.7 The structure of a G protein-coupled receptor (GPCR).** Shown here is a model of the human β₂-adrenergic receptor in the presence of a molecule mimicking the natural ligand (green in the model) and cholesterol (orange). Two receptor molecules (blue) are shown as ribbon models in a side view within the plasma membrane.

Exploring Cell-Surface Transmembrane Receptors

G Protein-Coupled Receptors

Signalling molecule binding site

Segment that interacts with G proteins

G protein-coupled receptor

A **G protein-coupled receptor (GPCR)** is a cell-surface transmembrane receptor that works with the help of a **G protein**, a protein that binds the energy-rich molecule GTP. Many different signalling molecules—including yeast mating factors, epinephrine (adrenaline) and many other hormones, as well as neurotransmitters—use GPCRs. These receptors vary in the binding sites for their signalling molecules (often referred to as their ligands) and also for different types of G proteins inside the cell. Nevertheless, GPCR proteins are all remarkably similar in structure. In fact, they make up a large family of eukaryotic receptor proteins with a secondary structure in which the single polypeptide, represented here in a ribbon model, has seven transmembrane α helices, outlined with cylinders and depicted in a row for clarity. Specific loops between the helices (here, the loops on the right) form binding sites for signalling molecules (outside the cell) and G proteins (on the cytoplasmic side).

GPCR-based signalling systems are extremely widespread and diverse in their functions, including roles in embryonic development and sensory reception. In humans, for example, vision, smell, and taste depend on GPCRs. Similarities in structure in G proteins and GPCRs in diverse organisms suggest that G proteins and their associated receptors evolved very early among eukaryotes.

Malfunctions of the associated G proteins themselves are involved in many human diseases, including bacterial infections. The bacteria that cause cholera, pertussis (whooping cough), and botulism, among others, make their victims ill by producing toxins that interfere with G protein function. Pharmacologists now realize that up to 60% of all medicines used today exert their effects by influencing G protein pathways.

① Loosely attached to the cytoplasmic side of the membrane, the G protein functions as a molecular switch that is either on or off, depending on which of two guanine nucleotides is attached, GDP or GTP—hence the term *G protein*. (GTP, or guanosine triphosphate, is similar to ATP.) When GDP is bound to the G protein, as shown above, the G protein is inactive. The receptor and G protein work together with another protein, usually an enzyme.

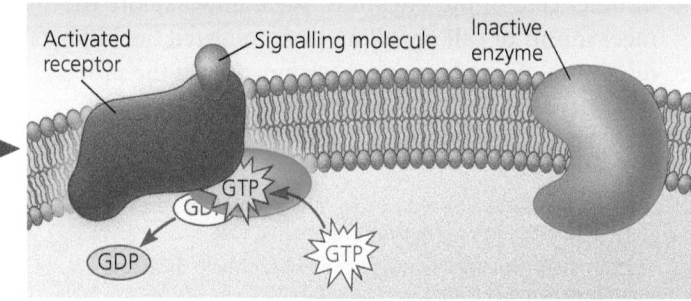

② When the appropriate signalling molecule binds to the extracellular side of the receptor, the receptor is activated and changes shape. Its cytoplasmic side then binds an inactive G protein, causing a GTP to displace the GDP. This activates the G protein.

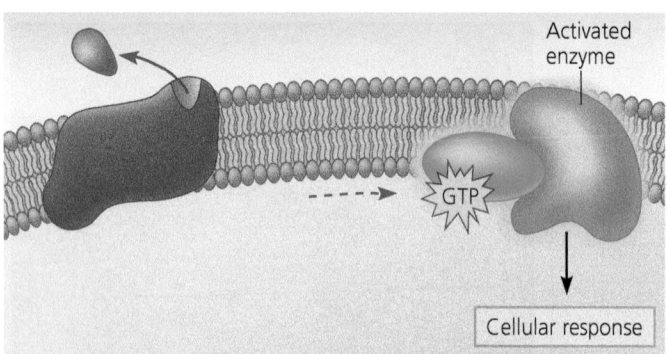

③ The activated G protein dissociates from the receptor, diffuses along the membrane, and then binds to an enzyme, altering the enzyme's shape and activity. Once activated, the enzyme can trigger the next step leading to a cellular response. Binding of signalling molecules is reversible: Like other ligands, they bind and dissociate many times. The ligand concentration outside the cell determines how often a ligand is bound and causes signalling.

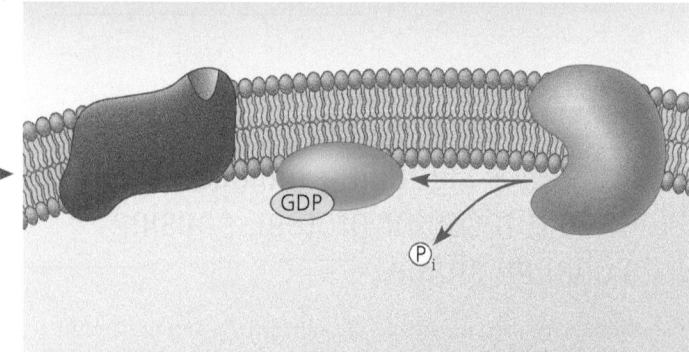

④ The changes in the enzyme and G protein are only temporary because the G protein also functions as a GTPase enzyme—in other words, it then hydrolyzes its bound GTP to GDP and ℗ᵢ. Now inactive again, the G protein leaves the enzyme, which returns to its original state. The G protein is now available for reuse. The GTPase function of the G protein allows the pathway to shut down rapidly when the signalling molecule is no longer present.

Receptor Tyrosine Kinases

Receptor tyrosine kinases (RTKs) belong to a major class of plasma membrane receptors characterized by having enzymatic activity. A kinase is any enzyme that catalyzes the transfer of phosphate groups. The part of the receptor protein extending into the cytoplasm functions more specifically as a tyrosine kinase, an enzyme that catalyzes the transfer of a phosphate group from ATP to the amino acid tyrosine on a substrate protein. Thus, RTKs are membrane receptors that attach phosphates to tyrosines.

One RTK may activate 10 or more different transduction pathways and cellular responses. Often, more than one signal transduction pathway can be triggered at once, helping the cell regulate and coordinate many aspects of cell growth and cell reproduction. The ability of a single ligand-binding event to trigger so many pathways is a key difference between RTKs and GPCRs, which activate a single transduction pathway. Abnormal RTKs that function even in the absence of signalling molecules are associated with many kinds of cancer.

❶ Many receptor tyrosine kinases have the structure depicted schematically here. Before the signalling molecule binds, the receptors exist as individual units referred to as monomers. Notice that each has an extracellular ligand-binding site, an α helix spanning the membrane, and an intracellular tail containing multiple tyrosines.

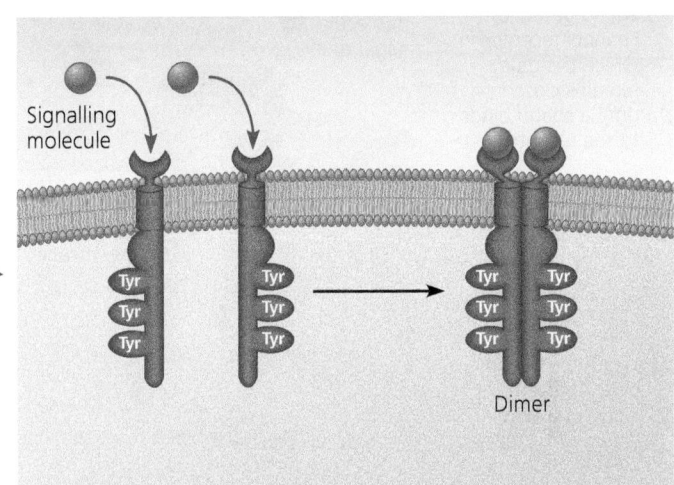

❷ The binding of a signalling molecule (such as a growth factor) causes two receptor monomers to associate closely with each other, forming a complex known as a dimer in a process called dimerization. (In some cases, larger clusters form. The details of monomer association are a focus of current research.)

❸ Dimerization activates the tyrosine kinase region of each monomer; each tyrosine kinase adds a phosphate from an ATP molecule to a tyrosine on the tail of the other monomer.

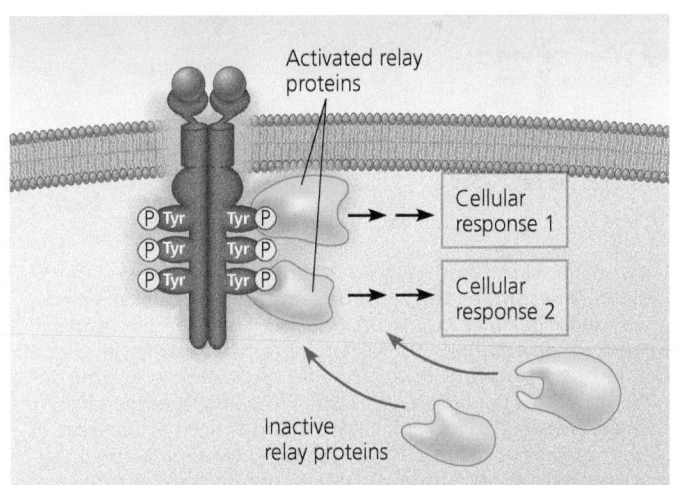

❹ Now that the receptor is fully activated, it is recognized by specific relay proteins inside the cell. Each such protein binds to a specific phosphorylated tyrosine, undergoing a resulting structural change that activates the bound protein. Each activated protein triggers a transduction pathway, leading to a cellular response.

Continued on next page

Exploring Cell-Surface Transmembrane Receptors

Ion Channel Receptors

A **ligand-gated ion channel** is a type of membrane receptor containing a region that can act as a "gate" when the receptor changes shape. When a signalling molecule binds as a ligand to the receptor protein, the gate opens or closes, allowing or blocking the flow of specific ions, such as Na^+ or Ca^{2+}, through a channel in the receptor. Like the other receptors we have discussed, these proteins bind the ligand at a specific site on their extracellular sides.

① Here we show a ligand-gated ion channel receptor in which the gate remains closed until a ligand binds to the receptor.

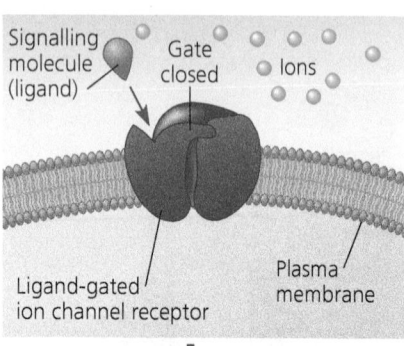

Signalling molecule (ligand)   Gate closed   Ions

Ligand-gated ion channel receptor

Plasma membrane

② When the ligand binds to the receptor and the gate opens, specific ions can flow through the channel and rapidly change the concentration of that particular ion inside the cell. This change may directly affect the activity of the cell in some way.

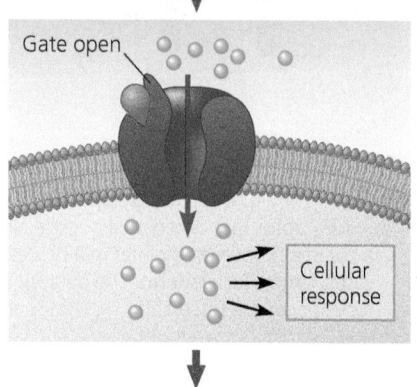

Gate open

Cellular response

③ When the ligand dissociates from this receptor, the gate closes and ions no longer enter the cell.

Gate closed

Ligand-gated ion channels are very important in the nervous system. For example, the neurotransmitter molecules released at a synapse between two nerve cells (see Figure 11.5b) bind as ligands to ion channels on the receiving cell, causing the channels to open. Ions flow in (or, in some cases, out), triggering an electrical signal that propagates down the length of the receiving cell. Some gated ion channels are controlled by electrical signals instead of ligands; these voltage-gated ion channels are also crucial to the functioning of the nervous system, as we will discuss in Chapter 48. Some ion channels are present on membranes of organelles, such as the ER.

Source: The World of the Cell, 3rd Edition, by Wayne M. Becker, Jane B. Reece, and Martin F. Poenie. Copyright © 1996 by Pearson Education. Reprinted and electronically reproduced by permission of Pearson Education, Inc., Upper Saddle River, New Jersey.

MAKE CONNECTIONS *Is the flow of ions through a ligand-gated channel an example of active or passive transport? (Review Concepts 7.3 and 7.4.)*

teams and the pharmaceutical industry has been to analyze the structure of these receptors.

Although cell-surface receptors represent 30% of all human proteins, determining their structures has proved challenging: They make up only 1% of the proteins whose structures have been determined by X-ray crystallography (see Figure 5.22). For one thing, cell-surface receptors tend to be flexible and inherently unstable, thus difficult to crystallize. It took years of persistent efforts for researchers to determine the first few of these structures, such as the GPCR shown in Figure 11.7. In that case, the β-adrenergic receptor was stable enough to be crystallized while it was among membrane molecules, in the presence of its ligand.

Abnormal functioning of receptor tyrosine kinases (RTKs) is associated with many types of cancers. For example, breast cancer patients have a poor prognosis if their tumour cells harbour excessive levels of a receptor tyrosine kinase called HER2 (see Concept 12.3 and Figure 18.27). Using molecular biological techniques, researchers have developed a protein called Herceptin that binds to HER2 on cells and inhibits cell division, thus thwarting further tumour development. In some clinical studies, treatment with Herceptin improved patient survival rates by more than one-third. One goal of ongoing research into these cell-surface receptors and other cell-signalling proteins is development of additional successful treatments.

Intracellular Receptors

Intracellular receptor proteins are found in either the cytoplasm or nucleus of target cells. To reach such a receptor, a signalling molecule passes through the target cell's plasma membrane. A number of important signalling molecules can do this because they are either hydrophobic enough or small enough to cross the hydrophobic interior of the membrane. These hydrophobic chemical messengers include the steroid hormones and thyroid hormones of animals. Another chemical signalling molecule with an intracellular receptor is nitric oxide (NO), a gas; its very small molecules readily pass between the membrane phospholipids.

Once a hormone has entered a cell, it may bind to an intracellular receptor in the cytoplasm or the nucleus. The binding changes the receptor into a hormone-receptor complex that is able to cause a response—in many cases, the turning on or off of particular genes.

The behaviour of aldosterone is a representative example of how steroid hormones work. This hormone is secreted by cells of the adrenal gland, a gland that sits above the kidney. Aldosterone then travels through the blood and enters cells all over the body. However, a response occurs only in kidney cells, which contain receptor molecules for this hormone. In these cells, the hormone binds to the receptor protein, activating it. With aldosterone attached, the active form of the receptor protein then enters the nucleus and turns on specific genes that control water and sodium flow in kidney cells, ultimately affecting blood volume (Figure 11.9).

How does the activated hormone-receptor complex turn on genes? Recall that the genes in a cell's DNA function by being transcribed and processed into messenger RNA (mRNA), which leaves the nucleus and is translated into a specific protein by ribosomes in the cytoplasm (see Figure 5.23). Special proteins called *transcription factors* control which genes are turned on—that is, which genes are transcribed into mRNA—in a particular cell at a particular time. When the aldosterone receptor is activated, it acts as a transcription factor that turns on specific genes. (You'll learn more about transcription factors in Chapters 17 and 18.)

By acting as a transcription factor, the aldosterone receptor itself carries out the transduction part of the signalling pathway. Most other intracellular receptors function in the same way, although many of them, such as the thyroid hormone receptor, are already in the nucleus before the signalling molecule reaches them. Interestingly, many of these intracellular receptor proteins are structurally similar, suggesting an evolutionary kinship.

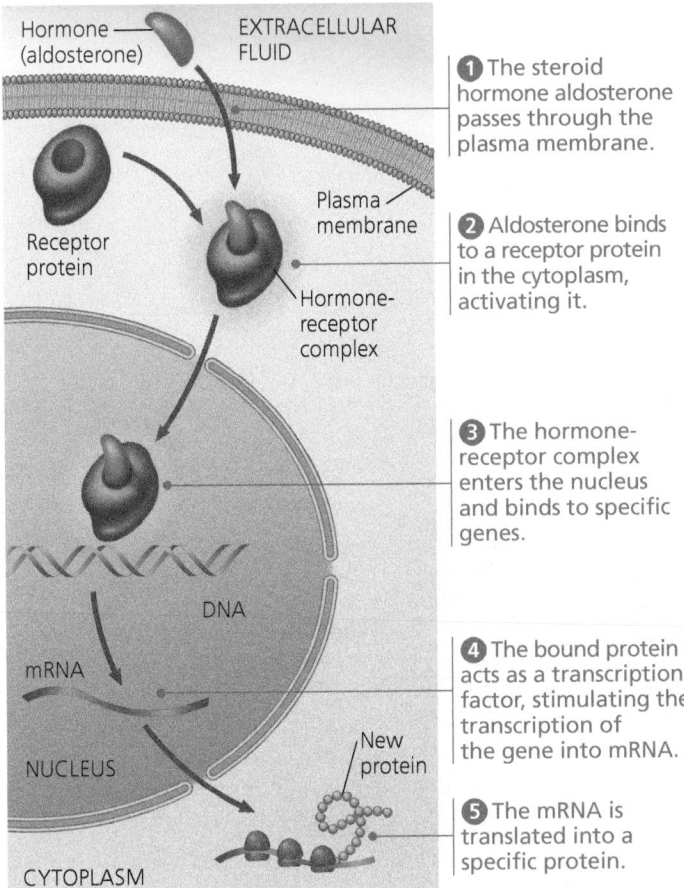

① The steroid hormone aldosterone passes through the plasma membrane.

② Aldosterone binds to a receptor protein in the cytoplasm, activating it.

③ The hormone-receptor complex enters the nucleus and binds to specific genes.

④ The bound protein acts as a transcription factor, stimulating the transcription of the gene into mRNA.

⑤ The mRNA is translated into a specific protein.

▲ Figure 11.9 **Steroid hormone interacting with an intracellular receptor.**

? *Why is a cell-surface receptor protein not required for this steroid hormone to enter the cell?*

CONCEPT CHECK 11.2

1. Nerve growth factor (NGF) is a water-soluble signalling molecule. Would you expect the receptor for NGF to be intracellular or in the plasma membrane? Why?

2. **WHAT IF?** What would the effect be if a cell made defective receptor tyrosine kinase proteins that were unable to dimerize?

3. **MAKE CONNECTIONS** How is ligand binding similar to the process of allosteric regulation of enzymes? See Figure 8.20.

4. **WHAT IF?** The model shown in Figure 11.7 represents the receptor in an inactive state, not bound to a G protein. Can you suggest an approach for crystallizing the protein that would reveal the structure of the receptor while it is actively signalling?

For suggested answers, see Appendix A.

CONCEPT 11.3

Transduction: Cascades of molecular interactions relay signals from receptors to target molecules in the cell

When receptors for signalling molecules are plasma membrane proteins, like most of those we have discussed, the transduction stage of cell signalling is usually a multistep pathway involving many molecules. Steps often include activation of proteins by addition or removal of phosphate groups or release of other small molecules or ions that act as messengers. One benefit of multiple steps is the possibility of greatly amplifying a signal. If each molecule in a pathway transmits the signal to numerous molecules at the next step in the series, the result is a geometric increase in the number of activated molecules by the end of the pathway. Moreover, multistep pathways provide more opportunities for coordination and control than do simpler systems. This allows regulation of the response, as we'll discuss later in the chapter.

Signal Transduction Pathways

The binding of a specific signalling molecule to a receptor in the plasma membrane triggers the first step in the chain of molecular interactions—the signal transduction pathway—that leads to a particular response within the cell. Like falling dominoes, the signal-activated receptor activates another molecule, which activates yet another molecule, and so on, until the protein that produces the final cellular response is activated. The molecules that relay a signal from receptor to response, which we call relay molecules in this book, are often proteins. The interaction of proteins is a major theme of cell signalling. Indeed, protein interaction is a unifying theme of all cellular activities.

Keep in mind that the original signalling molecule is not physically passed along a signalling pathway; in most cases, it never even enters the cell. When we say that the signal is relayed along a pathway, we mean that certain information is passed on. At each step, the signal is transduced into a different form, commonly a shape change in the next protein. Very often, the shape change is brought about by phosphorylation.

Protein Phosphorylation and Dephosphorylation

Previous chapters introduced the concept of activating a protein by adding one or more phosphate groups to it (see Figure 8.11a). In Figure 11.8, you have already seen how phosphorylation is involved in the activation of receptor tyrosine kinases. In fact, the phosphorylation and dephosphorylation of proteins is a widespread cellular mechanism for regulating protein activity. An enzyme that transfers phosphate groups from ATP to a protein is generally known as a **protein kinase**. Recall that a receptor tyrosine kinase is a specific kind of protein kinase that phosphorylates tyrosines on the other receptor tyrosine kinase in a dimer. Most cytoplasmic protein kinases, however, act on proteins different from themselves. Another distinction is that most cytoplasmic protein kinases phosphorylate either of two other amino acids, serine or threonine, rather than tyrosine. Serine/threonine kinases are widely involved in signalling pathways in animals, plants, and fungi.

Many of the relay molecules in signal transduction pathways are protein kinases, and they often act on other protein kinases in the pathway. Figure 11.10 depicts a hypothetical pathway containing three different protein

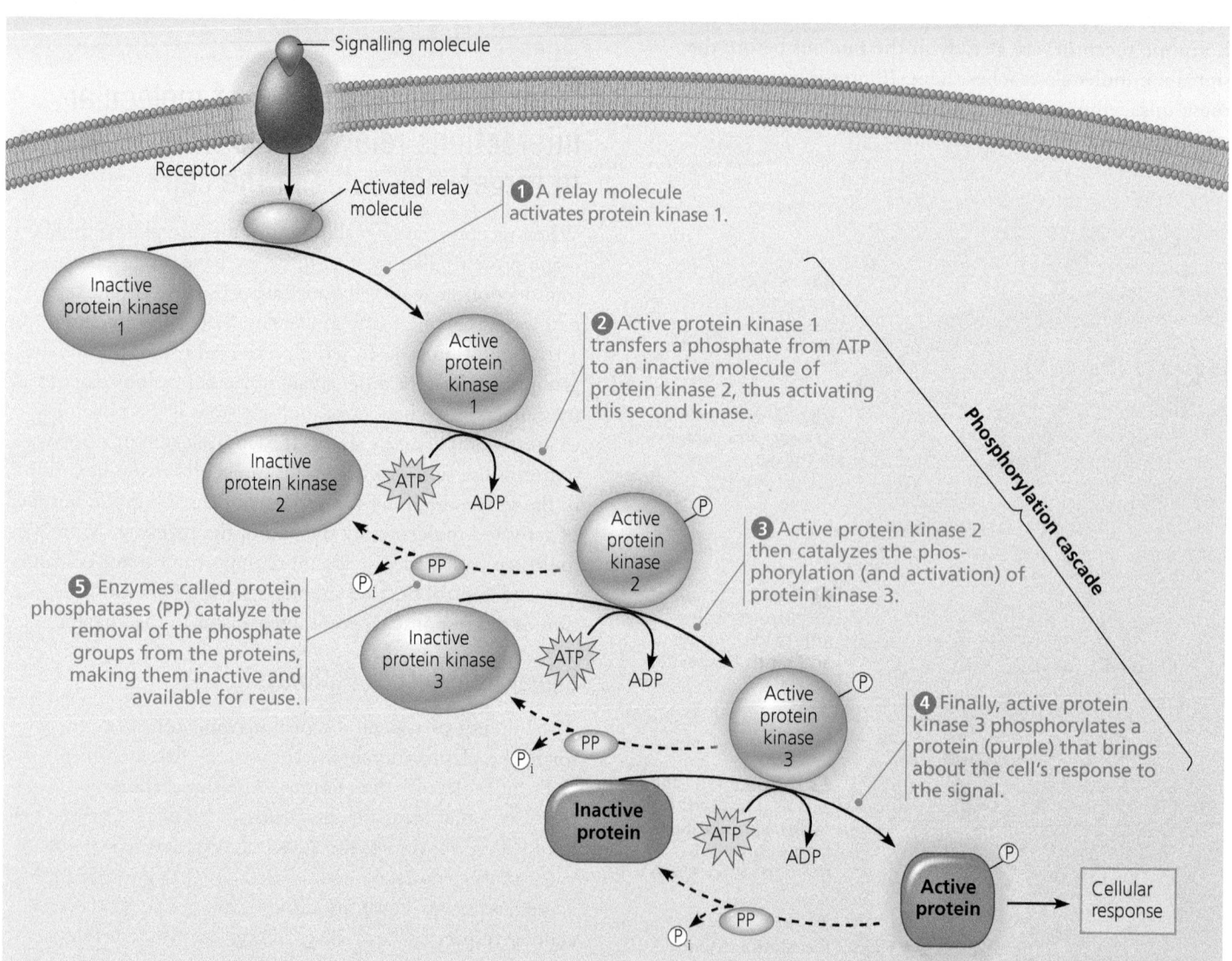

▲ Figure 11.10 **A phosphorylation cascade.** In a phosphorylation cascade, a series of different proteins in a pathway are phosphorylated in turn, each protein adding a phosphate group to the next one in line. Here, phosphorylation activates each protein, and dephosphorylation returns it to its inactive form. The active and inactive forms of each protein are represented by different shapes to remind you that activation is usually associated with a change in molecular shape.

WHAT IF? *What would happen if a mutation in protein kinase 3 made it incapable of being phosphorylated?*

kinases that create a "phosphorylation cascade." The sequence of steps shown in the figure is similar to many known pathways, including those triggered in yeast by mating factors and in animal cells by many growth factors. The signal is transmitted by a cascade of protein phosphorylations, each causing a shape change because of the interaction of the newly added phosphate groups with charged or polar amino acids on the protein being phosphorylated (see Figure 5.14). The change in shape alters the function of the protein, most often activating it. In some cases, though, phosphorylation *decreases* the activity of the protein.

The importance of protein kinases can hardly be overstated. About 2% of our own genes are thought to code for protein kinases. A single cell may have hundreds of different kinds, each specific for a different substrate protein. Together, they probably regulate the activity of a large proportion of the thousands of proteins in a cell. Among these are most of the proteins that, in turn, regulate cell division. Abnormal activity of such a kinase can cause abnormal cell division and contribute to the development of cancer.

Equally important in the phosphorylation cascade are the **protein phosphatases**, enzymes that can rapidly remove phosphate groups from proteins, a process called dephosphorylation. By dephosphorylating and thus inactivating protein kinases, phosphatases provide the mechanism for turning off the signal transduction pathway when the initial signal is no longer present. Phosphatases also make the protein kinases available for reuse, enabling the cell to respond again to an extracellular signal. The phosphorylation-dephosphorylation system acts as a molecular switch in the cell, turning activities on or off, or up or down, as required. At any given moment, the activity of a protein regulated by phosphorylation depends on the balance in the cell between active kinase molecules and active phosphatase molecules.

Small Molecules and Ions as Second Messengers

Not all components of signal transduction pathways are proteins. Many signalling pathways also involve small, nonprotein, water-soluble molecules or ions called **second messengers**. (This term is used because the pathway's "first messenger" is considered to be the extracellular signalling molecule—the ligand—that binds to the membrane receptor.) Because second messengers are small and also water soluble, they can readily spread throughout the cell by diffusion. For example, as we'll see shortly, a second messenger called cyclic AMP carries the signal initiated by epinephrine from the plasma membrane of a liver or muscle cell into the cell's interior, where the signal eventually brings about glycogen breakdown. Second messengers participate in pathways that are initiated by both G protein-coupled receptors and receptor tyrosine kinases. The two most widely used second messengers are cyclic AMP and calcium ions, Ca^{2+}. A large variety of relay proteins are sensitive to the cytosolic concentration of one or the other of these second messengers.

Cyclic AMP

As discussed previously, Earl Sutherland established that epinephrine somehow causes glycogen breakdown without passing through the plasma membrane. This discovery prompted him to search for a second messenger that transmits the signal from the plasma membrane to the metabolic machinery in the cytoplasm.

Sutherland found that the binding of epinephrine to the plasma membrane of a liver cell elevates the cytosolic concentration of a compound called cyclic adenosine monophosphate, abbreviated as either **cyclic AMP** or **cAMP** (Figure 11.11). An enzyme embedded in the plasma membrane, **adenylyl cyclase**, converts ATP to cAMP in response to an extracellular signal—in this case, provided

▲ Figure 11.11 **Cyclic AMP.** The second messenger cyclic AMP (cAMP) is made from ATP by adenylyl cyclase, an enzyme embedded in the plasma membrane. Note that the phosphate group in cAMP is attached to both the 5′ and the 3′ carbons; this cyclic arrangement is the basis for the molecule's name. Cyclic AMP is inactivated by phosphodiesterase, an enzyme that converts it to AMP.

WHAT IF? *What would happen if a molecule that inactivated phosphodiesterase were introduced into the cell?*

by epinephrine. But epinephrine doesn't stimulate adenylyl cyclase directly. When epinephrine outside the cell binds to a specific receptor protein, the protein activates adenylyl cyclase, which in turn can catalyze the synthesis of many molecules of cAMP. In this way, the normal cellular concentration of cAMP can be boosted 20-fold in a matter of seconds. The cAMP broadcasts the signal to the cytoplasm. It does not persist for long in the absence of the hormone because another enzyme, called phosphodiesterase, converts cAMP to AMP. Another surge of epinephrine is needed to boost the cytosolic concentration of cAMP again.

Subsequent research has revealed that epinephrine is only one of many hormones and other signalling molecules that trigger the formation of cAMP. It has also brought to light the other components of cAMP pathways, including G proteins, G protein-coupled receptors, and protein kinases (**Figure 11.12**). The immediate effect of an elevation in cAMP levels is usually the activation of a serine/threonine kinase called *protein kinase A*. The activated protein kinase A then phosphorylates various other proteins, depending on the cell type. (The complete pathway for epinephrine's stimulation of glycogen breakdown is shown later, in Figure 11.16.)

Further regulation of cell metabolism is provided by other G protein systems that *inhibit* adenylyl cyclase. In these systems, a different signalling molecule activates a different receptor, which in turn activates an *inhibitory* G protein that blocks the activation of adenylyl cyclase.

Now that we know about the role of cAMP in G protein signalling pathways, we can explain in molecular detail how certain microbes cause disease. Consider cholera, a disease that is frequently epidemic in places where the water supply is contaminated with human feces. People acquire the cholera bacterium, *Vibrio cholerae*, by drinking contaminated water. The bacteria form a biofilm on the lining of the small intestine and produce a toxin. The cholera toxin is an enzyme that chemically modifies a G protein involved in regulating salt and water secretion. Because the modified G protein is unable to hydrolyze GTP to GDP, it remains stuck in its active form, continuously stimulating adenylyl cyclase to make cAMP. The resulting high concentration of cAMP causes the intestinal cells to secrete large amounts of salts into the intestines, with water following by osmosis. An infected person quickly develops profuse diarrhea and if left untreated can soon die from the loss of water and salts.

Our understanding of signalling pathways involving cyclic AMP or related messengers has allowed us to develop treatments for certain conditions in humans. In one pathway, *cyclic GMP*, or *cGMP*, acts as a signalling molecule whose effects include relaxation of smooth muscle cells in artery walls. A compound that inhibits the hydrolysis of cGMP to GMP, thus prolonging the signal, was originally prescribed for chest pains because it increased blood flow to the heart muscle. Under the trade name Viagra, this compound is now widely used as a treatment for erectile dysfunction in human males. Because Viagra leads to dilation of blood vessels, it also allows increased blood flow to the penis, optimizing physiological conditions for penile erections.

Calcium Ions and Inositol Trisphosphate (IP₃)

Many of the signalling molecules that function in animals—including neurotransmitters, growth factors, and some hormones—induce responses in their target cells via signal transduction pathways that increase the cytosolic concentration of calcium ions (Ca^{2+}). Calcium is even more widely used than cAMP as a second messenger. Increasing the cytosolic concentration of Ca^{2+} causes many responses in animal cells, including muscle cell contraction, secretion of certain substances, and cell division. In plant cells, a wide range of hormonal and environmental stimuli can cause brief increases in cytosolic Ca^{2+} concentration, triggering various signalling pathways, such as the pathway for greening in response to light (see Figure 39.4). Cells use Ca^{2+} as a second messenger in pathways triggered by both G protein-coupled receptors and receptor tyrosine kinases.

Although cells always contain some Ca^{2+}, this ion can function as a second messenger because its concentration

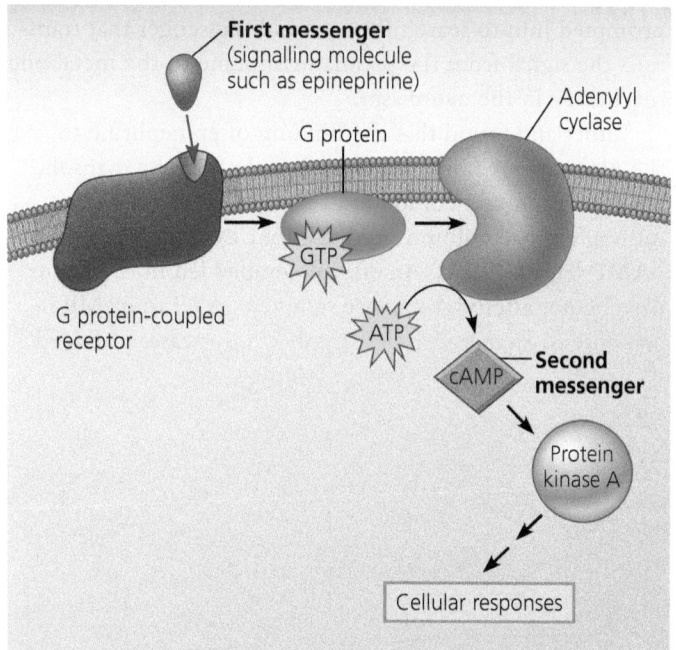

▲ **Figure 11.12 cAMP as a second messenger in a G protein signalling pathway.** The first messenger activates a G protein-coupled receptor, which activates a specific G protein. In turn, the G protein activates adenylyl cyclase, which catalyzes the conversion of ATP to cAMP. The cAMP then acts as a second messenger and activates another protein, usually protein kinase A, leading to cellular responses.

Source: Figure adapted from The World of the Cell, 3rd Edition, by Wayne M. Becker, Jane B. Reece, and Martin F. Poenie. Copyright © 1996 by Pearson Education, Inc. Adapted and electronically reproduced by permission of Pearson Education, Inc., Upper Saddle River, New Jersey.

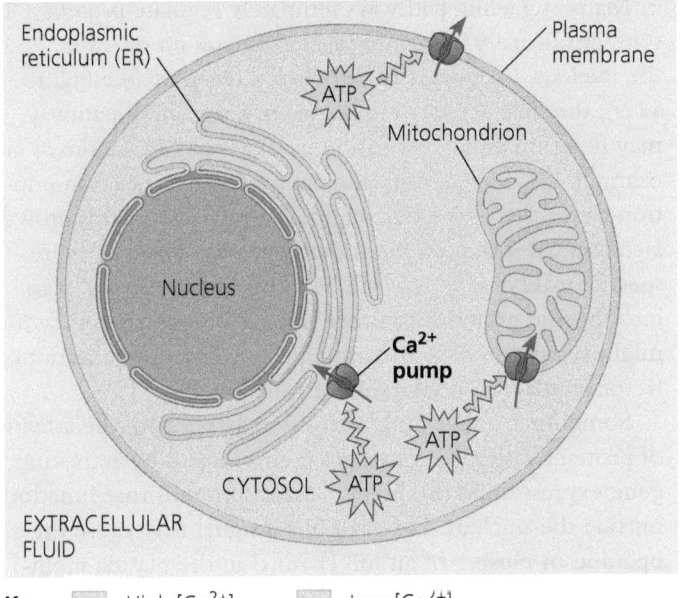

Key ▢ High [Ca²⁺] ▢ Low [Ca²⁺]

▲ Figure 11.13 **The maintenance of calcium ion concentrations in an animal cell.** The Ca^{2+} concentration in the cytosol is usually much lower (beige) than in the extracellular fluid and ER (blue). Protein pumps in the plasma membrane and the ER membrane, driven by ATP, move Ca^{2+} from the cytosol into the extracellular fluid and into the lumen of the ER. Mitochondrial pumps, driven by chemiosmosis (see Chapter 9), move Ca^{2+} into mitochondria when the calcium level in the cytosol rises significantly.

trisphosphate (IP₃) and **diacylglycerol (DAG)**. These two messengers are produced by cleavage of a certain kind of phospholipid in the plasma membrane. **Figure 11.14** shows the complete picture of how a signal causes IP_3 to stimulate the release of calcium from the ER. Because IP_3 acts before calcium in these pathways, calcium could be considered a "*third* messenger." However, scientists use the term *second messenger* for all small, nonprotein components of signal transduction pathways.

CONCEPT CHECK 11.3

1. What is a protein kinase, and what is its role in a signal transduction pathway?

2. When a signal transduction pathway involves a phosphorylation cascade, how does the cell's response get turned off?

3. What is the actual "signal" that is being transduced in any signal transduction pathway, such as those shown in Figures 11.6 and 11.10? In what way is this information being passed from the exterior to the interior of the cell?

4. **WHAT IF?** Upon activation of phospholipase C by the binding of a ligand to a receptor, what effect does the IP_3-gated calcium channel have on Ca^{2+} concentration in the cytosol?

For suggested answers, see Appendix A.

in the cytosol is normally much lower than the concentration outside the cell (**Figure 11.13**). In fact, the level of Ca^{2+} in the blood and extracellular fluid of an animal is often more than 10 000 times higher than that in the cytosol. Calcium ions are actively transported out of the cell and are actively imported from the cytosol into the endoplasmic reticulum (ER) (and, under some conditions, into mitochondria and chloroplasts) by various protein pumps. As a result, the calcium concentration in the ER is usually much higher than that in the cytosol. Because the cytosolic calcium level is low, a small change in absolute numbers of ions represents a relatively large percentage change in calcium concentration.

In response to a signal relayed by a signal transduction pathway, the cytosolic calcium level may rise, usually by a mechanism that releases Ca^{2+} from the cell's ER. The pathways leading to calcium release involves two other second messengers, **inositol**

1 A signalling molecule binds to a receptor, leading to activation of phospholipase C.

2 Phospholipase C cleaves a plasma membrane phospholipid called PIP_2 into DAG and IP_3.

3 DAG functions as a second messenger in other pathways.

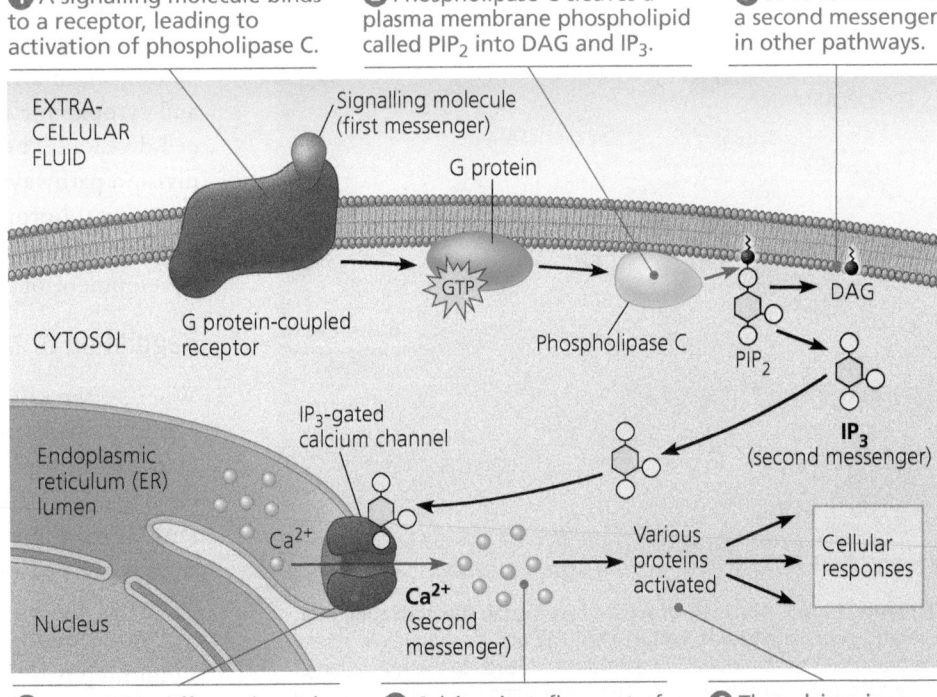

4 IP_3 quickly diffuses through the cytosol and binds to an IP_3-gated calcium channel in the ER membrane, causing it to open.

5 Calcium ions flow out of the ER (down their concentration gradient), raising the Ca^{2+} level in the cytosol.

6 The calcium ions activate the next protein in one or more signalling pathways.

▲ Figure 11.14 **Calcium and IP_3 in signalling pathways.** Calcium ions (Ca^{2+}) and inositol trisphosphate (IP_3) function as second messengers in many signal transduction pathways. In this figure, the process is initiated by the binding of a signalling molecule to a G protein-coupled receptor. A receptor tyrosine kinase could also initiate this pathway by activating phospholipase C.

CONCEPT 11.4

Response: Cell signalling leads to regulation of transcription or cytoplasmic activities

We now take a closer look at the cell's subsequent response to an extracellular signal—what some researchers call the "output response." What is the nature of the final step in a signalling pathway?

Nuclear and Cytoplasmic Responses

Ultimately, a signal transduction pathway leads to the regulation of one or more cellular activities. The response at the end of the pathway may occur in the nucleus of the cell or in the cytoplasm.

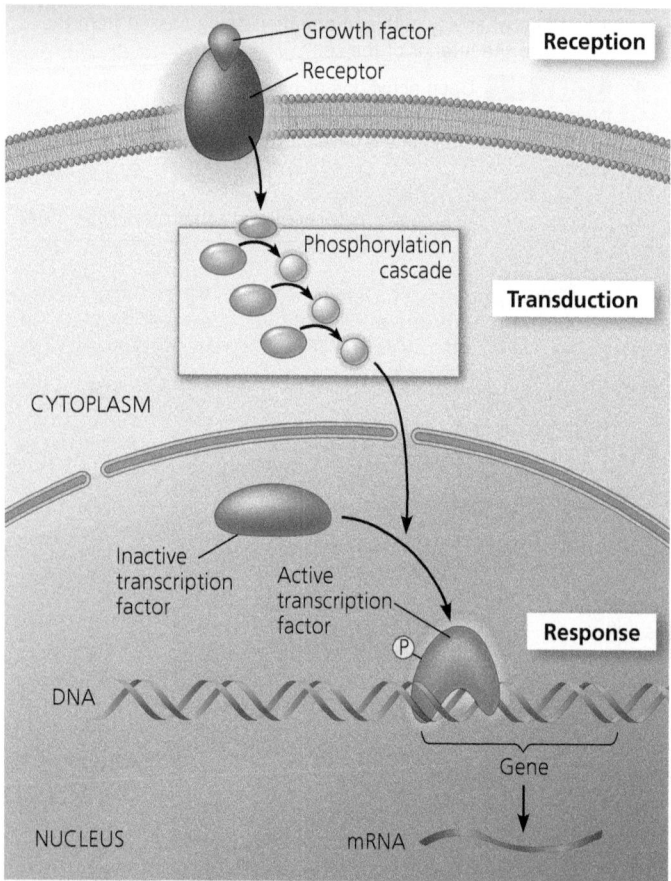

▲ Figure 11.15 **Nuclear responses to a signal: the activation of a specific gene by a growth factor.** This diagram is a simplified representation of a typical signalling pathway that leads to the regulation of gene activity in the cell nucleus. The initial signalling molecule, a local regulator called a growth factor, triggers a phosphorylation cascade, as in Figure 11.10. (The ATP molecules and phosphate groups are not shown here.) Once phosphorylated, the last kinase in the sequence enters the nucleus and there activates a gene-regulating protein, a transcription factor. This protein stimulates transcription of a specific gene (or genes). The mRNAs then direct the synthesis of a particular protein in the cytoplasm.

Many signalling pathways ultimately regulate protein synthesis, usually by turning specific genes on or off in the nucleus. Like an activated steroid receptor (see Figure 11.9), the final activated molecule in a signalling pathway may function as a transcription factor. Figure 11.15 shows an example in which a signalling pathway activates a transcription factor that turns a gene on: The response to this growth factor signal is transcription, the synthesis of one or more specific mRNAs, which will be translated in the cytoplasm into specific proteins. In other cases, the transcription factor might regulate a gene by turning it off. Often a transcription factor regulates several different genes.

Sometimes a signalling pathway may regulate the *activity* of proteins rather than causing their *synthesis* by activating gene expression. This directly affects proteins that function outside the nucleus. For example, a signal may cause the opening or closing of an ion channel in the plasma membrane or a change in cell metabolism. As we have seen, the response of liver cells to the hormone epinephrine helps regulate cellular energy metabolism by affecting the activity of an enzyme. The final step in the signalling pathway that begins with epinephrine binding activates the enzyme that catalyzes the breakdown of glycogen. Figure 11.16 shows the complete pathway leading to the release of glucose 1-phosphate molecules from glycogen. Notice that as each molecule is activated, the response is amplified, a subject we'll return to shortly.

Signal receptors, relay molecules, and second messengers participate in a variety of pathways, leading to both nuclear and cytoplasmic responses. Some of these pathways lead to cell division. The molecular messengers that initiate cell division pathways include growth factors and certain plant and animal hormones. Malfunctioning of growth factor pathways like the one in Figure 11.15 can contribute to the development of cancer, as we'll see in Chapter 18.

Regulation of the Response

Whether the response occurs in the nucleus or in the cytoplasm, it is not simply turned "on" or "off." Rather, the extent and specificity of the response are regulated in multiple ways. Here we'll consider four aspects of this regulation. First, as mentioned earlier, signalling pathways generally amplify the cell's response to a single signalling event. The degree of amplification depends on the function of the specific molecules in the pathway. Second, the many steps in a multistep pathway provide control points at which the cell's response can be further regulated, contributing to the specificity of the response and allowing coordination with other signalling pathways. Third, the overall efficiency of the response is enhanced by the presence of proteins known as scaffolding proteins. Finally, a crucial point in regulating the response is the termination of the signal.

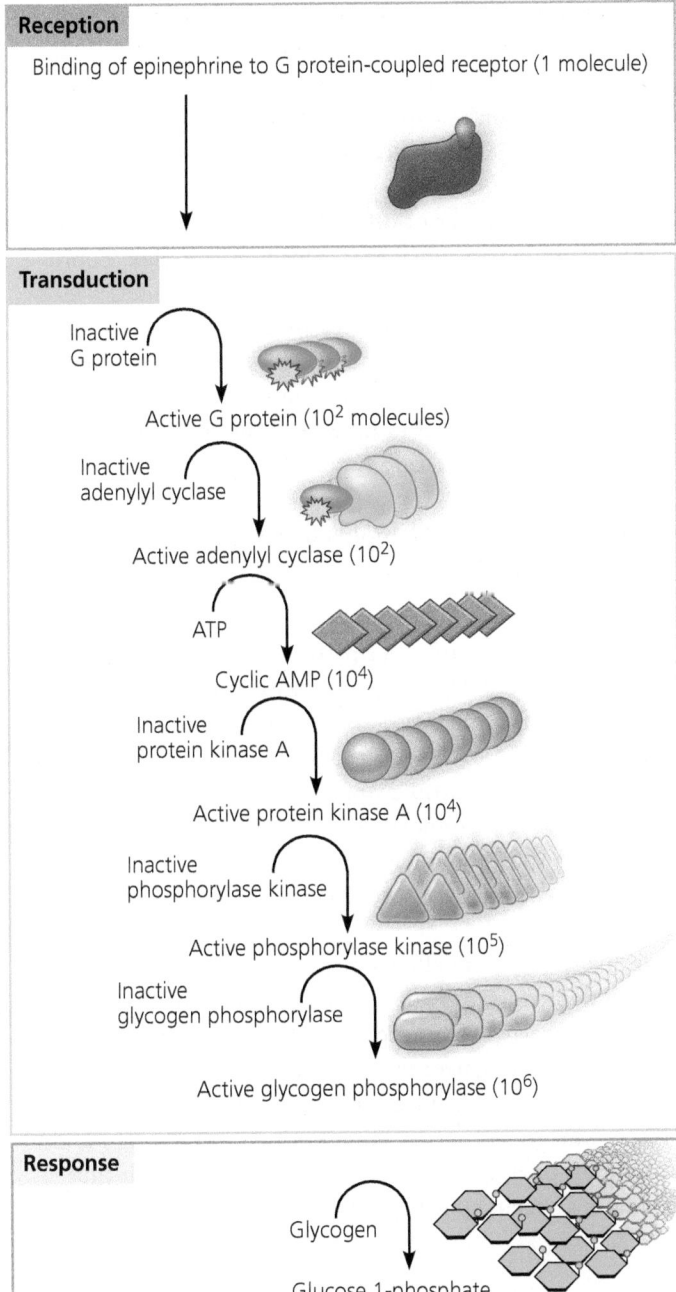

Reception

Binding of epinephrine to G protein-coupled receptor (1 molecule)

Transduction

Inactive G protein

Active G protein (10^2 molecules)

Inactive adenylyl cyclase

Active adenylyl cyclase (10^2)

ATP

Cyclic AMP (10^4)

Inactive protein kinase A

Active protein kinase A (10^4)

Inactive phosphorylase kinase

Active phosphorylase kinase (10^5)

Inactive glycogen phosphorylase

Active glycogen phosphorylase (10^6)

Response

Glycogen

Glucose 1-phosphate (10^8 molecules)

▲ Figure 11.16 **Cytoplasmic response to a signal: the stimulation of glycogen breakdown by epinephrine.** In this signalling system, the hormone epinephrine acts through a G protein-coupled receptor to activate a succession of relay molecules, including cAMP and two protein kinases (see also Figure 11.12). The final protein activated is the enzyme glycogen phosphorylase, which uses inorganic phosphate to release glucose monomers from glycogen in the form of glucose 1-phosphate molecules. This pathway amplifies the hormonal signal: One receptor protein can activate about 100 molecules of G protein, and each enzyme in the pathway, once activated, can act on many molecules of its substrate, the next molecule in the cascade. The number of activated molecules given for each step is approximate.

? *In the figure, how many glucose molecules are released in response to one signalling molecule? Calculate the factor by which the response is amplified in going from each step to the next.*

Signal Amplification

Elaborate enzyme cascades amplify the cell's response to a signal. At each catalytic step in the cascade, the number of activated products can be much greater than in the preceding step. For example, in the epinephrine-triggered pathway in Figure 11.16, each adenylyl cyclase molecule catalyzes the formation of 100 or so cAMP molecules, each molecule of protein kinase A phosphorylates about 10 molecules of the next kinase in the pathway, and so on. The amplification effect stems from the fact that these proteins persist in the active form long enough to process multiple molecules of substrate before they become inactive again. As a result of the signal's amplification, a small number of epinephrine molecules binding to receptors on the surface of a liver cell or muscle cell can lead to the release of hundreds of millions of glucose molecules from glycogen.

The Specificity of Cell Signalling and Coordination of the Response

Consider two different cells in your body—a liver cell and a heart muscle cell, for example. Both are in contact with your bloodstream and are therefore constantly exposed to many different hormone molecules, as well as to local regulators secreted by nearby cells. Yet the liver cell responds to some signals but ignores others, and the same is true for the heart cell. And some kinds of signals trigger responses in both cells—but different responses. For instance, epinephrine stimulates the liver cell to break down glycogen, but the main response of the heart cell to epinephrine is contraction, leading to a more rapid heartbeat. How do we account for this difference?

The explanation for the specificity exhibited in cellular responses to signals is the same as the basic explanation for virtually all differences between cells: Because different kinds of cells turn on different sets of genes, *different kinds of cells have different collections of proteins* (Figure 11.17). The response of a particular cell to a signal depends on its particular collection of signal receptor proteins, relay proteins, and proteins needed to carry out the response. A liver cell, for example, is poised to respond appropriately to epinephrine by having the proteins listed in Figure 11.16 as well as those needed to manufacture glycogen.

Thus, two cells that respond differently to the same signal differ in one or more of the proteins that handle and respond to the signal. Notice in Figure 11.17 that different pathways may have some molecules in common. For example, cells A, B, and C all use the same receptor protein for the red signalling molecule; differences in other proteins account for their differing responses. In cell D, a different receptor protein is used for the same signalling molecule, leading to yet another response. In cell B, a pathway that is

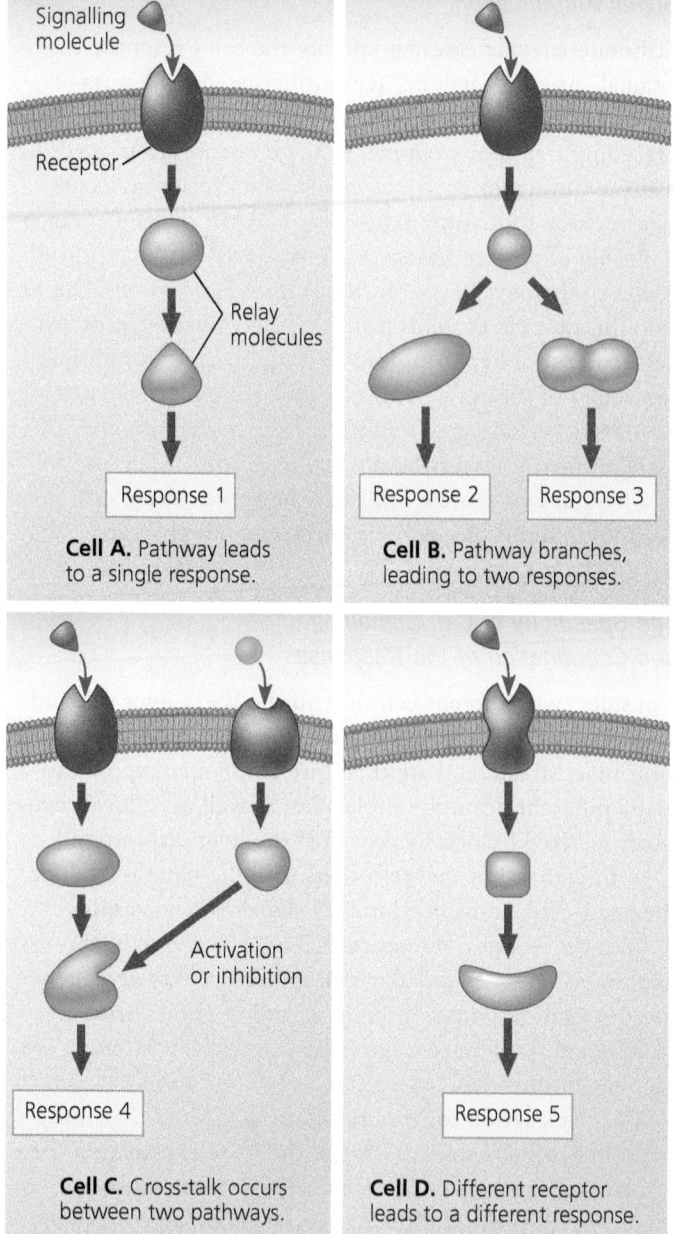

Cell A. Pathway leads to a single response.

Cell B. Pathway branches, leading to two responses.

Signalling molecule

Receptor

Relay molecules

Response 1

Response 2   Response 3

Activation or inhibition

Response 4

Response 5

Cell C. Cross-talk occurs between two pathways.

Cell D. Different receptor leads to a different response.

▲ **Figure 11.17 The specificity of cell signalling.** The particular proteins a cell possesses determine what signalling molecules it responds to and the nature of the response. The four cells in these diagrams respond to the same signalling molecule (red) in different ways because each has a different set of proteins (purple and teal). Note, however, that the same kinds of molecules can participate in more than one pathway.

MAKE CONNECTIONS *Study the signalling pathway shown in Figure 11.14 and explain how the situation pictured for cell B above could apply to that pathway.*

triggered by a single kind of signal diverges to produce two responses; such branched pathways often involve receptor tyrosine kinases (which can activate multiple relay proteins) or second messengers (which can regulate numerous proteins). In cell C, two pathways triggered by separate signals converge to modulate a single response. Branching

of pathways and "cross-talk" (interaction) between pathways are important in regulating and coordinating a cell's responses to information coming in from different sources in the body. (You'll learn more about this coordination in Concept 11.5.) Moreover, the use of some of the same proteins in more than one pathway allows the cell to economize on the number of different proteins it must make.

An example of a signal that leads to a complex, coordinated cellular response can be found in the processes leading to the mating of yeast cells described earlier (see Figure 11.2). In the Scientific Skills Exercise, you can work with data from experiments investigating the cellular response of a yeast cell to the signal initiated by a mating factor from a cell of the opposite mating type.

Signalling Efficiency: Scaffolding Proteins and Signalling Complexes

The illustrations of signalling pathways in Figure 11.17 (as well as diagrams of other pathways in this chapter) are greatly simplified. The diagrams show only a few relay molecules and, for clarity's sake, display these molecules spread out in the cytosol. If this were true in the cell, signalling pathways would operate very inefficiently because most relay molecules are proteins, and proteins are too large to diffuse quickly through the viscous cytosol. How does a particular protein kinase, for instance, find its substrate?

In many cases, the efficiency of signal transduction is apparently increased by the presence of **scaffolding proteins**, large relay proteins to which several other relay proteins are simultaneously attached. For example, one scaffolding protein isolated from mouse brain cells holds three protein kinases and carries these kinases with it when it binds to an appropriately activated membrane receptor; it thus facilitates a specific phosphorylation cascade (**Figure 11.18**).

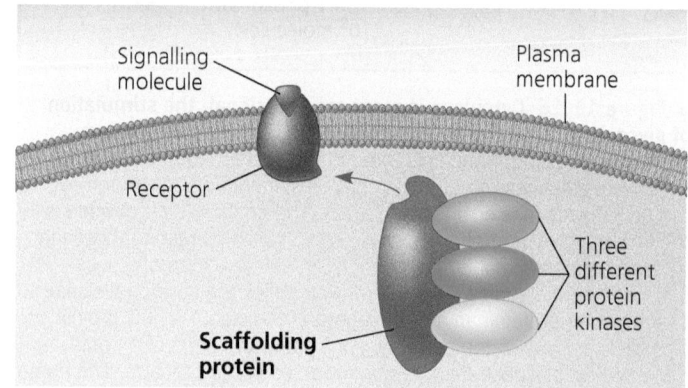

Signalling molecule

Plasma membrane

Receptor

Three different protein kinases

Scaffolding protein

▲ Figure 11.18 **A scaffolding protein.** The scaffolding protein shown here (orange) simultaneously binds to a specific activated membrane receptor and three different protein kinases. This physical arrangement facilitates signal transduction by these molecules and may directly activate relay molecules in some cases.

Using Experiments to Test a Model

① Mating factor activates receptor.

Mating factor

G protein-coupled receptor

Shmoo projection forming

Formin

② G protein binds GTP and becomes activated.

GDP

GTP

Phosphoryl-ation cascade

Fus3

Formin

Formin

P

Actin subunit

Fus3

P

④ Fus3 phos-phorylates formin, activating it.

Microfilament

Fus3

P

③ Phosphorylation cascade activates Fus3, which moves to plasma membrane.

⑤ Formin initiates growth of microfilaments that form the shmoo projections.

Are Both Fus3 Kinase and Formin Required for Directional Cell Growth During Mating in Yeast? When a yeast cell binds mating factor molecules from a cell of the opposite mating type, a signalling pathway causes it to grow a projection toward the potential mate. The cell with the projection is called a "shmoo" (because it resembles a 1950s cartoon character by that name). Researchers sought to determine how mating factor signalling leads to growth of this cell projection on one side of the cell—in other words, to asymmetric cell growth. Previous work had shown that activation of Fus3, one of the kinases in the signalling cascade, caused it to move to the membrane near where the mating factor bound its receptor. The researchers' first experiment identified one of the phosphorylation targets of Fus3 kinase as formin, a protein directing microfilament construction. Based on this information, the researchers developed the working model shown here for the signalling pathway that leads to the formation of shmoo projections in yeast cells.

How the Experiment Was Done To determine if Fus3 and formin were required for shmoo formation, the researchers generated two mutant yeast strains: one that lacked the gene for making Fus3 kinase (a strain called ΔFus3) and one that lacked the gene for making formin (Δformin). To observe the effects of these mutations on shmoo formation after cells' exposure to mating factor, the symmetry of growth was investigated. First, the existing cell walls of each strain were stained with a green fluorescent dye. These green-stained cells were then exposed to mating factor and stained with a red fluorescent dye that labels only new cell wall growth. Growth of the cell on all sides (symmetric growth) is indicated by a uniform yellow colour, resulting from merged green and red stains. (This occurs normally in wild-type cells that have not been exposed to mating factor, which are not shown.)

Data from the Experiment The micrographs above, right, were taken of wild-type, ΔFus3, and Δformin cells after they were stained green, exposed to mating factor, and then stained red. The wild-type cells expressed both Fus3 and formin.

Interpret the Data

1. A model helps scientists form a testable hypothesis. The diagram shows the working model of shmoo formation developed by the

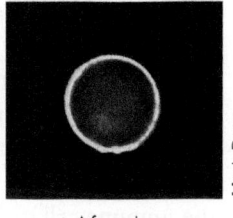

Wild type   ΔFus3   Δformin

Mark Rose

researchers. (a) What hypothesis from the model was being tested with the ΔFus3 strain? (b) With the Δformin strain? (c) What is the purpose of including wild-type yeast cells in the experiment?

2. When designing an experiment, scientists make predictions about what results will occur if their hypothesis is correct. (a) If the hypothesis about the role of Fus3 kinase activity in shmoo production is correct, what result should be observed in the ΔFus3 strain? If it is incorrect, what result is expected? (b) If the hypothesis about the role of formin in shmoo production is correct, what result should be observed in the Δformin strain? If it is incorrect, what result is expected?

3. For each micrograph, describe the shape of the cells and the pattern of cell wall staining. Explain the significance of your observations. Which strain(s) of yeast cells formed shmoos?

4. (a) Do the data support the hypothesis about the role of Fus3 kinase in shmoo production? (b) Do the data support the hypothesis about the role of formin in shmoo production? (c) Do the data support the working model (the working hypothesis) in the diagram?

5. Fus3 kinase and formin proteins are generally distributed evenly throughout a yeast cell. Based on the model in the diagram, explain why the projection would emerge on the same side of the cell that bound the mating factor.

6. What do you predict would happen if the yeast had a mutation that prevented the G protein from binding GTP?

Data from D. Matheos et al., Pheromone-induced polarization is dependent on the Fus3p MAPK acting through the formin Bni1p, *Journal of Cell Biology* 165:99–109 (2004).

Researchers have found scaffolding proteins in brain cells that *permanently* hold together networks of signalling pathway proteins at synapses. This hardwiring enhances the speed and accuracy of signal transfer between cells, because the rate of protein-protein interaction is not limited by diffusion. Furthermore, in some cases the scaffolding proteins themselves may directly activate relay proteins.

When signalling pathways were first discovered, they were thought to be linear, independent pathways. Our understanding of cellular communication has benefited from the realization that signalling-pathway components interact with each other in various ways. As seen in Figure 11.17, some proteins may participate in more than one pathway, either in different cell types or in the same cell at different times or under different conditions. These observations underscore the importance of transient—or, in some cases, permanent—protein complexes in the process of cell signalling.

The importance of the relay proteins that serve as points of branching or intersection in signalling pathways is highlighted by the problems arising when these proteins are defective or missing. For instance, in an inherited disorder called Wiskott-Aldrich syndrome (WAS), the absence of a single relay protein leads to such diverse effects as abnormal bleeding, eczema, and a predisposition to infections and leukemia. These symptoms are thought to arise primarily from the absence of the protein in cells of the immune system. By studying normal cells, scientists found that the WAS protein is located just beneath the immune cell surface. The protein interacts both with microfilaments of the cytoskeleton and with several different components of signalling pathways that relay information from the cell surface, including pathways regulating immune cell proliferation. This multifunctional relay protein is thus both a branch point and an important intersection point in a complex signal transduction network that controls immune cell behaviour. When the WAS protein is absent, the cytoskeleton is not properly organized and signalling pathways are disrupted, leading to the WAS symptoms.

Termination of the Signal

To keep Figure 11.17 simple, we did not indicate the *inactivation* mechanisms that are an essential aspect of any cell signalling pathway. For a cell of a multicellular organism to remain capable of responding to incoming signals, each molecular change in its signalling pathways must last only a short time. As we saw in the cholera example, if a signalling pathway component becomes locked into one state, whether active or inactive, consequences for the organism can be dire.

The ability of a cell to receive new signals depends on reversibility of the changes produced by prior signals. The binding of signalling molecules to receptors is reversible. As the external concentration of signalling molecules falls, fewer receptors are bound at any given moment, and the unbound receptors revert to their inactive form. The

cellular response occurs only when the concentration of receptors with bound signalling molecules is above a certain threshold. When the number of active receptors falls below that threshold, the cellular response ceases. Then, by a variety of means, the relay molecules return to their inactive forms: The GTPase activity intrinsic to a G protein hydrolyzes its bound GTP; the enzyme phosphodiesterase converts cAMP to AMP; protein phosphatases inactivate phosphorylated kinases and other proteins; and so forth. As a result, the cell is soon ready to respond to a fresh signal.

In this section, we explored the complexity of signalling initiation and termination in a single pathway, and we saw the potential for pathways to intersect with each other. In the next section, we'll consider one especially important network of interacting pathways in the cell.

CONCEPT CHECK 11.4

1. How can a target cell's response to a single hormone molecule result in a response that affects a million other molecules?

2. **WHAT IF?** If two cells have different scaffolding proteins, explain how they might behave differently in response to the same signalling molecule.

3. **MAKE CONNECTIONS** Review the discussion of protein phosphatases on page 231 and see Figure 11.10. Some human diseases are associated with malfunctioning protein phosphatases. How would such proteins affect signalling pathways?

For suggested answers, see Appendix A.

CONCEPT 11.5

Apoptosis integrates multiple cell-signalling pathways

To be or not to be? One of the most elaborate networks of signalling pathways in the cell seems to ask and answer this question, originally posed by Hamlet. Cells that are infected, are damaged, or have reached the end of their functional life span often undergo "programmed cell death" (Figure 11.19). The best-understood type of this controlled cell suicide is **apoptosis** (from the Greek, meaning "falling off," and used in a classic Greek poem to refer to leaves falling from a tree). During this process, cellular agents chop up the DNA and fragment the organelles and other cytoplasmic components. The cell shrinks and becomes lobed (a change called "blebbing"), and the cell's parts are packaged up in vesicles that are engulfed and digested by specialized scavenger cells, leaving no trace. Apoptosis protects neighbouring cells from damage that they would otherwise suffer if a dying cell merely leaked out all its contents, including its many digestive enzymes.

▲ Figure 11.19 **Apoptosis of a human white blood cell.** We can compare a normal white blood cell (left) with a white blood cell undergoing apoptosis (right). The apoptotic cell is shrinking and forming lobes ("blebs"), which eventually are shed as membrane-bounded cell fragments (colourized SEMs).

The signal that triggers apoptosis can come from either outside or inside the cell. Outside the cell, signalling molecules released from other cells can initiate a signal transduction pathway that activates the genes and proteins responsible for carrying out cell death (e.g., due to pathogen infection). Within a cell whose DNA has been irretrievably damaged, a series of protein-protein interactions can pass along a signal that similarly triggers cell death. Considering some examples of apoptosis can help us to see how signalling pathways are integrated in cells.

Apoptosis in the Soil Worm *Caenorhabditis elegans*

The molecular mechanisms of apoptosis were worked out by researchers studying embryonic development of a small soil worm, a nematode called *Caenorhabditis elegans*. Because the adult worm has only about 1000 cells, the researchers were able to work out the entire ancestry of each cell. The timely suicide of cells occurs exactly 131 times during normal development of *C. elegans* at precisely the same points in the cell lineage of each worm. In worms and other species, apoptosis is triggered by signals that activate a cascade of "suicide" proteins in the cells destined to die.

Genetic research on *C. elegans* initially revealed two key apoptosis genes, called *ced-3* and *ced-4* (*ced* stands for "cell death"), which encode proteins essential for apoptosis. The proteins are called Ced-3 and Ced-4, respectively. These and most other proteins involved in apoptosis are continually present in cells, but in inactive form; thus, regulation in this case occurs at the level of protein activity rather than through gene activity and protein synthesis. In *C. elegans*, a protein in the outer mitochondrial membrane, called Ced-9 (the product of the *ced-9* gene), serves as a master regulator of apoptosis, acting as a brake in the absence of a signal promoting apoptosis **(Figure 11.20).** When a death signal is received by the cell, signal transduction involves a change in Ced-9 that disables the brake,

(a) No death signal. As long as Ced-9, located in the outer mitochondrial membrane, is active, apoptosis is inhibited, and the cell remains alive.

(b) Death signal. When a cell receives a death signal, Ced-9 is inactivated, relieving its inhibition of Ced-3 and Ced-4. Active Ced-3, a protease, triggers a cascade of reactions leading to activation of nucleases and other proteases. The action of these enzymes causes the changes seen in apoptotic cells and eventual cell death.

▲ Figure 11.20 **Molecular basis of apoptosis in *C. elegans*.** Three proteins, Ced-3, Ced-4, and Ced-9, are critical to apoptosis and its regulation in the nematode. Apoptosis is more complicated in mammals but involves proteins similar to those in the nematode.

and the apoptotic pathway activates proteases and nucleases, enzymes that cut up the proteins and DNA of the cell. The main proteases of apoptosis are called *caspases*; in the nematode, the chief caspase is the Ced-3 protein.

Apoptotic Pathways and the Signals That Trigger Them

In humans and other mammals, several different pathways, involving about 15 different caspases, can carry out apoptosis. The pathway that is used depends on the type of cell and on the particular signal that initiates apoptosis. One major pathway involves certain mitochondrial proteins that are triggered to form molecular pores in the mitochondrial outer membrane, causing it to leak and release other proteins that promote apoptosis. Perhaps surprisingly, these latter include cytochrome *c*, which functions in mitochondrial electron transport in healthy cells (see Figure 9.16) but acts as a cell death factor when released from mitochondria. The process of mitochondrial apoptosis in mammals uses proteins similar to the nematode proteins Ced-3, Ced-4, and Ced-9. These can be thought of as relay proteins capable of transducing the apoptotic signal.

At key gateways into the apoptotic program, relay proteins integrate signals from several different sources and can send a cell down an apoptotic pathway. Often, the signal originates outside the cell, like the death-signalling molecule depicted in Figure 11.20b, which presumably was released by a neighbouring cell. When a death-signalling ligand occupies a cell-surface receptor, this binding leads to activation of caspases and other enzymes that carry out apoptosis, without involving the mitochondrial pathway. This process of signal reception, transduction, and response is similar to what we have discussed throughout this chapter. In a twist on the classic scenario, two other types of alarm signals that can lead to apoptosis originate from *inside* the cell rather than from a cell-surface receptor. One signal comes from the nucleus, generated when the DNA has suffered irreparable damage, and a second comes from the endoplasmic reticulum when excessive protein misfolding occurs. Mammalian cells make life-or-death "decisions" by somehow integrating the death signals and life signals they receive from these external and internal sources.

A built-in cell suicide mechanism is essential to development and maintenance in all animals. The similarities between apoptosis genes in nematodes and mammals, as well as the observation that apoptosis occurs in multicellular fungi and even in single-celled yeasts, indicate that the basic mechanism evolved early in the evolution of eukaryotes. In vertebrates, apoptosis is essential for normal development of the nervous system, for normal operation of the immune system, and for normal morphogenesis of hands and feet in humans and paws in other mammals (Figure 11.21). The level of apoptosis between the developing digits is lower in the webbed feet of ducks and other water birds than in the nonwebbed feet of land birds, such as chickens. In the case of humans, the failure of appropriate apoptosis can result in webbed fingers and toes.

Significant evidence points to the involvement of apoptosis in certain degenerative diseases of the nervous system, such as Parkinson's disease and Alzheimer's disease. In Alzheimer's disease, an accumulation of aggregated proteins in neuronal cells activates an enzyme that triggers apoptosis, resulting in the loss of brain function seen in those patients. Furthermore, cancer can result from a failure of cell suicide; some cases of human melanoma, for example, have been linked to faulty forms of the human version of the *C. elegans* Ced-4 protein. It is not surprising, therefore, that the pathways feeding into apoptosis are quite elaborate. After all, the life-or-death question is the most fundamental one imaginable for a cell.

This chapter has introduced you to many of the general mechanisms of cell communication, such as ligand binding, protein-protein interactions and shape changes, cascades of interactions, and protein phosphorylation. Throughout your study of biology, you will encounter numerous examples of cell signalling.

CONCEPT CHECK 11.5

1. Give an example of apoptosis during embryonic development, and explain its function in the developing embryo.

2. **WHAT IF?** What types of protein defects could result in apoptosis occurring when it should not? What types could result in apoptosis not occurring when it should?

For suggested answers, see Appendix A.

Interdigital tissue

Cells undergoing apoptosis

1 mm

Space between digits

Will Wood

▲ Figure 11.21 **Effect of apoptosis during paw development in the mouse.** In mice, humans, other mammals, and land birds, the embryonic region that develops into feet or hands initially has a solid, platelike structure. Apoptosis eliminates the cells in the interdigital regions, thus forming the digits. The embryonic mouse paws shown in these fluorescence light micrographs are stained so that cells undergoing apoptosis appear a bright yellowish green. Apoptosis of cells begins at the margin of each interdigital region (left), peaks as the tissue in these regions is reduced (middle), and is no longer visible when the interdigital tissue has been eliminated (right).

11 Chapter Review

Go to **MasteringBiology**® for Assignments, the eText, and the Study Area with Animations, Activities, Vocab Self-Quiz, and Practice Tests.

SUMMARY OF KEY CONCEPTS

CONCEPT 11.1

External signals are converted to responses within the cell (pp. 222–225)

- **Signal transduction pathways** are crucial for many processes. Signalling during yeast cell mating has much in common with processes in multicellular organisms, suggesting an early evolutionary origin of signalling mechanisms. Bacterial cells can sense the local density of bacterial cells (quorum sensing).
- Local signalling by animal cells involves direct contact or the secretion of local regulators. For long-distance signalling, animal and plant cells use **hormones**; animals also pass signals electrically.
- Like other hormones that bind to membrane receptors, epinephrine triggers a three-stage cell-signalling pathway:

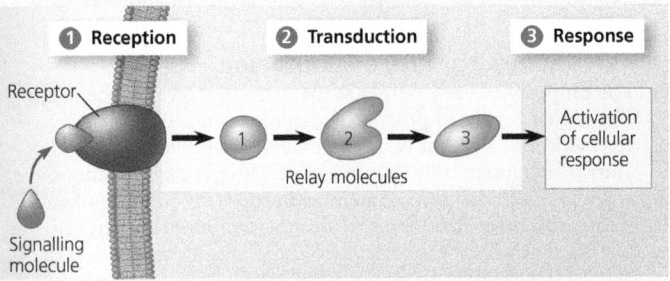

? *What determines whether a cell responds to a hormone such as epinephrine? What determines how a cell responds to such a hormone?*

CONCEPT 11.2

Reception: A signalling molecule binds to a receptor protein, causing it to change shape (pp. 225–229)

- The binding between signalling molecule (**ligand**) and receptor is highly specific. A specific shape change in a receptor is often the initial transduction of the signal.
- There are three major types of cell-surface transmembrane receptors: (1) **G protein-coupled receptors (GPCRs)** work with the help of cytoplasmic **G proteins**. Ligand binding activates the receptor, which then activates a specific G protein, which activates yet another protein, thus propagating the signal along a signal transduction pathway. (2) **Receptor tyrosine kinases (RTKs)** react to the binding of signalling molecules by forming dimers and then adding phosphate groups to tyrosines on the cytoplasmic part of the other monomer making up the dimer. Relay proteins in the cell can then be activated by binding to different phosphorylated tyrosines, allowing this receptor to trigger several pathways at once. (3) **Ligand-gated ion channels** open or close in response to binding by specific signalling molecules, regulating the flow of specific ions across the membrane.
- The activity of all three types of receptors is crucial to proper cell functioning, and abnormal GPCRs and RTKs are associated with many human diseases.
- Intracellular receptors are cytoplasmic or nuclear proteins. Signalling molecules that are hydrophobic or small enough to cross the plasma membrane bind to these receptors inside the cell.

? *How are the structures of a GPCR and an RTK similar? How does initiation of signal transduction differ for these two types of receptors?*

CONCEPT 11.3

Transduction: Cascades of molecular interactions relay signals from receptors to target molecules in the cell (pp. 229–233)

- At each step in a signal transduction pathway, the signal is transduced into a different form, which commonly involves a shape change in a protein. Many signal transduction pathways include phosphorylation cascades, in which a series of **protein kinases** each add a phosphate group to the next one in line, activating it. Enzymes called **protein phosphatases** remove the phosphate groups. The balance between phosphorylation and dephosphorylation regulates the activity of proteins involved in the sequential steps of a signal transduction pathway.
- **Second messengers**, such as the small molecule **cyclic AMP (cAMP)** and the ion Ca^{2+}, diffuse readily through the cytosol and thus help broadcast signals quickly. Many G proteins activate **adenylyl cyclase**, which makes cAMP from ATP. Cells use Ca^{2+} as a second messenger in both GPCR and RTK pathways. The tyrosine kinase pathways can also involve two other second messengers, **diacylglycerol (DAG)** and **inositol trisphosphate (IP$_3$)**. IP$_3$ can trigger a subsequent increase in Ca^{2+} levels.

? *What is the difference between a protein kinase and a second messenger? Can both types of molecules operate in the same signal transduction pathway?*

CONCEPT 11.4

Response: Cell signalling leads to regulation of transcription or cytoplasmic activities (pp. 234–238)

- Some pathways lead to a nuclear response: Specific genes are turned on or off by activated transcription factors. In others, the response involves cytoplasmic regulation.
- Cellular responses are not simply on or off; they are regulated at many steps. Each protein in a signalling pathway amplifies the signal by activating multiple copies of the next component; for long pathways, the total amplification may be over a millionfold. The combination of proteins in a cell confers specificity in the signals it detects and the responses it carries out. **Scaffolding proteins** increase signalling efficiency. Pathway branching further helps the cell coordinate signals and responses. Signal response is terminated quickly by the reversal of ligand binding.

? *What mechanisms in the cell terminate its response to a signal and maintain its ability to respond to new signals?*

CONCEPT 11.5

Apoptosis integrates multiple cell-signalling pathways (pp. 238–240)

- **Apoptosis** is a type of programmed cell death in which cell components are disposed of in an orderly fashion. Studies of the soil worm *Caenorhabditis elegans* clarified molecular details of the relevant signalling pathways. A death signal leads to activation of caspases and nucleases, the main enzymes involved in apoptosis.
- Several apoptotic signalling pathways exist in the cells of humans and other mammals, triggered in different ways. Signals eliciting apoptosis can originate from outside or inside the cell.

? *What is an explanation for the similarities between genes in yeasts, nematodes, and mammals that control apoptosis?*

TEST YOUR UNDERSTANDING

LEVEL 1: KNOWLEDGE/COMPREHENSION

1. Binding of a signalling molecule to which type of receptor leads directly to a change in the distribution of ions on opposite sides of the membrane?
   a. intracellular receptor
   b. G protein-coupled receptor
   c. phosphorylated receptor tyrosine kinase dimer
   d. ligand-gated ion channel

2. The activation of receptor tyrosine kinases is characterized by
   a. dimerization and phosphorylation.
   b. dimerization and IP_3 binding.
   c. a phosphorylation cascade.
   d. GTP hydrolysis.

3. Lipid-soluble signalling molecules, such as aldosterone, cross the membranes of all cells but affect only target cells because
   a. only target cells retain the appropriate DNA segments.
   b. intracellular receptors are present only in target cells.
   c. only target cells possess the cytosolic enzymes that transduce the aldosterone.
   d. only in target cells is aldosterone able to initiate the phosphorylation cascade leading to activated transcription factor.

4. Consider this pathway: epinephrine → G protein-coupled receptor → G protein → adenylyl cyclase → cAMP. Identify the second messenger.
   a. cAMP
   b. G protein
   c. GTP
   d. adenylyl cyclase

5. Apoptosis involves all but which of the following?
   a. fragmentation of the DNA
   b. cell-signalling pathways
   c. lysis of the cell
   d. digestion of cellular contents by scavenger cells

LEVEL 2: APPLICATION/ANALYSIS

6. Which observation suggested to Sutherland the involvement of a second messenger in epinephrine's effect on liver cells?
   a. Enzymatic activity was proportional to the amount of calcium added to a cell-free extract.
   b. Receptor studies indicated that epinephrine was a ligand.
   c. Glycogen breakdown was observed only when epinephrine was administered to intact cells.
   d. Glycogen breakdown was observed when epinephrine and glycogen phosphorylase were combined.

7. Protein phosphorylation is commonly involved with all of the following *except*
   a. activation of receptor tyrosine kinases.
   b. activation of protein kinase molecules.
   c. activation of G protein-coupled receptors.
   d. regulation of transcription by signalling molecules.

LEVEL 3: SYNTHESIS/EVALUATION

8. **DRAW IT** Draw the following apoptotic pathway, which operates in human immune cells. A death signal is received when a molecule called Fas binds to its cell-surface receptor. The binding of many Fas molecules to receptors causes receptor clustering. The intracellular regions of the receptors, when together, bind proteins called adaptor proteins. These in turn bind to inactive molecules of caspase-8, which become activated and then activate caspase-3. Once activated, caspase-3 initiates apoptosis.

9. **EVOLUTION CONNECTION**
   What evolutionary mechanisms might account for the origin and persistence of cell-to-cell signalling systems in unicellular prokaryotes?

10. **SCIENTIFIC INQUIRY**
    Epinephrine initiates a signal transduction pathway that involves production of cyclic AMP (cAMP) and leads to the breakdown of glycogen to glucose, a major energy source for cells. But glycogen breakdown is actually only part of the fight-or-flight response that epinephrine brings about; the overall effect on the body includes increased heart rate and alertness, as well as a burst of energy. Given that caffeine blocks the activity of cAMP phosphodiesterase, propose a mechanism by which caffeine ingestion leads to heightened alertness and sleeplessness.

11. **SCIENCE, TECHNOLOGY, AND SOCIETY**
    The aging process is thought to be initiated at the cellular level. Among the changes that can occur after a certain number of cell divisions is the loss of a cell's ability to respond to growth factors and other chemical signals. Much research into aging is aimed at understanding such losses, with the ultimate goal of significantly extending the human life span. Not everyone, however, agrees that this is a desirable goal. If life expectancy were greatly increased, what might be the social and ecological consequences?

12. **WRITE ABOUT A THEME ORGANIZATION**
    The property of life emerges at the biological level of the cell. The highly regulated process of apoptosis is not simply the destruction of a cell; it is also an emergent property. Write a short essay (about 100–150 words) that briefly explains the role of apoptosis in the development and proper functioning of an animal and then describes how this form of programmed cell death is a process that emerges from the orderly integration of signalling pathways.

13. **SYNTHESIZE YOUR KNOWLEDGE**

Maureen Spuhler

There are five basic tastes—sour, salty, sweet, bitter, and umami. Salt is detected when the concentration of salt outside of a taste bud cell is higher than that inside of it, and ion channels allow the passive leakage of Na^+ into the cell. The resulting change in membrane potential (see Concept 7.4) sends the "salty" signal to the brain. Umami is a savoury taste generated by glutamate (glutamic acid, found in monosodium glutamate, or MSG), which is used as a flavour enhancer in foods such as taco-flavoured tortilla chips. The glutamate receptor is a GPCR, which, when bound, initiates a signalling pathway that ends with a cellular response, perceived by you as "taste." If you eat a regular potato chip and then rinse your mouth, you will no longer taste salt. But if you eat a flavoured tortilla chip and then rinse, the taste persists. (Try it!) Propose a possible explanation for this difference.

For selected answers, see Appendix A.

12

The Cell Cycle

KEY CONCEPTS

12.1 Most cell division results in genetically identical daughter cells

12.2 The mitotic phase alternates with interphase in the cell cycle

12.3 The eukaryotic cell cycle is regulated by a molecular control system

National Center for Microscopy and Imaging Research/University of California, San Diego

▲ Figure 12.1 **How do dividing cells distribute chromosomes to daughter cells?**

The Key Roles of Cell Division

The ability of organisms to produce more of their own kind is the one characteristic that best distinguishes living things from nonliving matter. This unique capacity to procreate, like all biological functions, has a cellular basis. Rudolf Virchow, a German physician, put it this way in 1855: "Where a cell exists, there must have been a preexisting cell, just as the animal arises only from an animal and the plant only from a plant." He summarized this concept with the Latin axiom "*Omnis cellula e cellula*," meaning "Every cell from a cell." The continuity of life is based on the reproduction of cells, or **cell division**. The scanning electron micrograph in **Figure 12.1** shows a 3-D image of chromosomal movement as one cell divides into two.

Cell division plays several important roles in life. When a prokaryotic cell divides, it is actually reproducing, since the process gives rise to a new organism (another cell). The same is true of any unicellular eukaryote, such as the amoeba shown in **Figure 12.2a**. As for multicellular eukaryotes, cell division enables each of them to develop from a single cell—the fertilized egg. A two-celled embryo, the first stage in this process, is shown in **Figure 12.2b**. And cell division continues to function in renewal and repair in fully grown multicellular eukaryotes, replacing cells that die from normal wear and tear or accidents. For example,

Claire Walczak

▲ Chromosomes (blue) are moved by cell machinery (red) during division of a rat kangaroo cell.

100 μm

◀ **(a) Reproduction.** An amoeba, a single-celled eukaryote, is dividing into two cells. Each new cell will be an individual organism (LM).

50 μm

▶ **(b) Growth and development.** This micrograph shows a sand dollar embryo shortly after the fertilized egg divided, forming two cells (LM).

◀ **(c) Tissue renewal.** These dividing bone marrow cells will give rise to new blood cells (LM).

20 μm

▲ Figure 12.2 **The functions of cell division.**

dividing cells in your bone marrow continuously make new blood cells **(Figure 12.2c)**. The cell division process is an integral part of the **cell cycle**, the life of a cell from the time it is first formed during division of a parent cell until its own division into two daughter cells. (Our use of the words *daughter* or *sister* in relation to cells is the biological convention and is not meant to imply gender.) Passing identical genetic material to cellular offspring is a crucial function of cell division. In this chapter, you will learn how this process occurs. After studying the cellular mechanics of cell division in eukaryotes and bacteria, you will learn about the molecular control system that regulates progress through the eukaryotic cell cycle and what happens when the control system malfunctions. Because a breakdown in cell cycle control plays a major role in cancer development, this aspect of cell biology is an active area of research.

CONCEPT 12.1

Most cell division results in genetically identical daughter cells

The reproduction of a cell, with all of its complexity, cannot occur by a mere pinching in half; a cell is not like a soap bubble that simply enlarges and splits in two. In both prokaryotes and eukaryotes, most cell division involves the distribution of identical genetic material—DNA—to two daughter cells. (The exception is meiosis, the special type of eukaryotic cell division that can produce sperm and eggs.) What is most remarkable about cell division is the fidelity with which the DNA is passed along from one generation of cells to the next. A dividing cell replicates its DNA, allocates the two copies to opposite ends of the cell, and only then splits into daughter cells.

Cellular Organization of the Genetic Material

A cell's endowment of DNA, its genetic information, is called its **genome**. Although a prokaryotic genome is often a single DNA molecule, eukaryotic genomes usually consist of a number of DNA molecules. The overall length of DNA in a eukaryotic cell is enormous. A typical human cell, for example, has about 2 m of DNA—a length about 250 000 times greater than the cell's diameter. Before the cell can divide to form genetically identical daughter cells, all of this DNA must be copied, or replicated, and then the two copies must be separated so that each daughter cell ends up with a complete genome.

The replication and distribution of so much DNA is manageable because the DNA molecules are packaged into structures called **chromosomes**, so named because they take up certain dyes used in microscopy (from the Greek *chroma*, colour, and *soma*, body; **Figure 12.3**). Each eukaryotic chromosome consists of one very long, linear DNA molecule associated with many proteins (see Figure 6.9); the number of chromosomes varies depending upon the species. The DNA molecule carries several hundred to a few thousand genes, the units of information that specify an organism's inherited traits. The associated proteins maintain the structure of the chromosome and help control the activity of the genes. Together, the entire complex of DNA and proteins that is the building material of chromosomes is referred to as **chromatin**. As you will soon see,

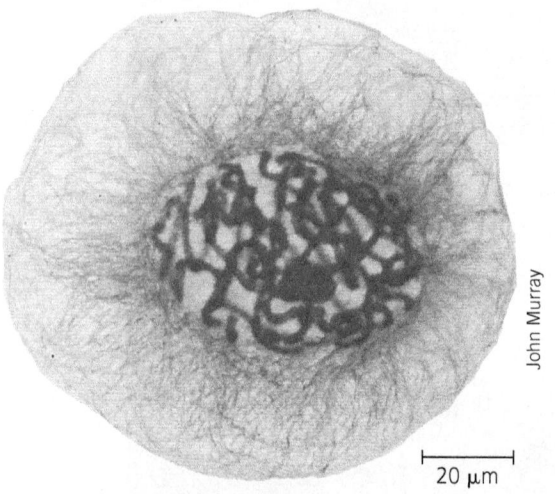

20 μm

▲ Figure 12.3 **Eukaryotic chromosomes.** Chromosomes (stained purple) are visible within the nucleus of this cell from an African blood lily. The thinner red threads in the surrounding cytoplasm are the cytoskeleton. The cell is preparing to divide (LM).

the chromatin of a chromosome varies in its degree of condensation during the process of cell division.

Every eukaryotic species has a characteristic number of chromosomes in each cell's nucleus. For example, the nuclei of human **somatic cells** (all body cells except the reproductive cells) each contain 46 chromosomes, made up of two sets of 23, one set inherited from each parent. Reproductive cells, or **gametes**—sperm and eggs—have one set, or half as many chromosomes as somatic cells; in our example, human gametes have one set of 23 chromosomes. The number of chromosomes in somatic cells varies widely among species: 18 in cabbage plants, 48 in chimpanzees, 56 in elephants, 90 in hedgehogs, and 148 in one species of alga. We'll now consider how these chromosomes behave during cell division.

Distribution of Chromosomes during Eukaryotic Cell Division

When a cell is not dividing, and even as it replicates its DNA in preparation for cell division, each chromosome is in the form of a long, thin chromatin fibre. After DNA replication, however, the chromosomes condense as a part of cell division: Each chromatin fibre becomes densely coiled and folded, making the chromosomes much shorter and so thick that we can see them with a light microscope.

Each duplicated chromosome has two **sister chromatids**, which are joined copies of the original chromosome (Figure 12.4). The two chromatids, each containing an identical DNA molecule, are initially attached all along their lengths by protein complexes called *cohesins*; this attachment is known as *sister chromatid cohesion*. Each sister chromatid has a **centromere**, a region of the chromosomal DNA where the chromatid is attached most closely to its sister chromatid. This attachment is mediated by proteins bound to the centromeric DNA; other bound proteins condense the DNA, giving the duplicated chromosome a narrow "waist." The portion of a chromatid to either side of the centromere is referred to as an *arm* of the chromatid. (An unduplicated chromosome has a single centromere, distinguished by the proteins that bind there, and two arms.)

Later in the cell division process, the two sister chromatids of each duplicated

Sister chromatids

Centromere   0.5 μm

Biophoto/Science Source

▲ **Figure 12.4 A highly condensed, duplicated human chromosome (SEM).**

DRAW IT *Circle one sister chromatid of the chromosome in this micrograph.*

chromosome separate and move into two new nuclei, one forming at each end of the cell. Once the sister chromatids separate, they are no longer called sister chromatids but are considered individual chromosomes; this step essentially doubles the number of chromosomes in the cell. Thus, each new nucleus receives a collection of chromosomes identical to that of the parent cell (Figure 12.5). **Mitosis**, the division of the genetic material in the nucleus, is usually

Chromosomes   **Chromosomal DNA molecules**

❶ One of the multiple chromosomes in a eukaryotic cell is represented here, not yet duplicated. Normally it would be a long, thin chromatin fibre containing one DNA molecule and associated proteins; here its condensed form is shown for illustration purposes only.

Centromere

Chromosome arm

Chromosome duplication (including DNA replication) and condensation

❷ Once duplicated, a chromosome consists of two sister chromatids connected along their entire lengths by sister chromatid cohesion. Each chromatid contains a copy of the DNA molecule.

Biophoto/Science Source

Sister chromatids

Separation of sister chromatids into two chromosomes

❸ Molecular and mechanical processes separate the sister chromatids into two chromosomes and distribute them to two daughter cells.

▲ **Figure 12.5 Chromosome duplication and distribution during cell division.**

? *How many chromatid arms does the chromosome in ❷ have?*

followed immediately by **cytokinesis**, the division of the cytoplasm. One cell has become two, each the genetic equivalent of the parent cell.

From a fertilized egg, mitosis and cytokinesis produced the 200 trillion somatic cells that now make up your body, and the same processes continue to generate new cells to replace dead and damaged ones. In contrast, you produce gametes—eggs or sperm—by a variation of cell division called *meiosis*, which yields daughter cells with only one set of chromosomes, half as many chromosomes as the parent cell. Meiosis in humans occurs only in special cells in the ovaries or testes (the gonads). Generating gametes, meiosis reduces the chromosome number from 46 (two sets) to 23 (one set). Fertilization fuses two gametes (egg and sperm) together and returns the chromosome number to 46 (two sets). Mitosis then conserves that number in every somatic cell nucleus of the new human individual. In Chapter 13, we will examine the role of meiosis in reproduction and inheritance in more detail. In the remainder of this chapter, we focus on mitosis and the rest of the cell cycle in eukaryotes.

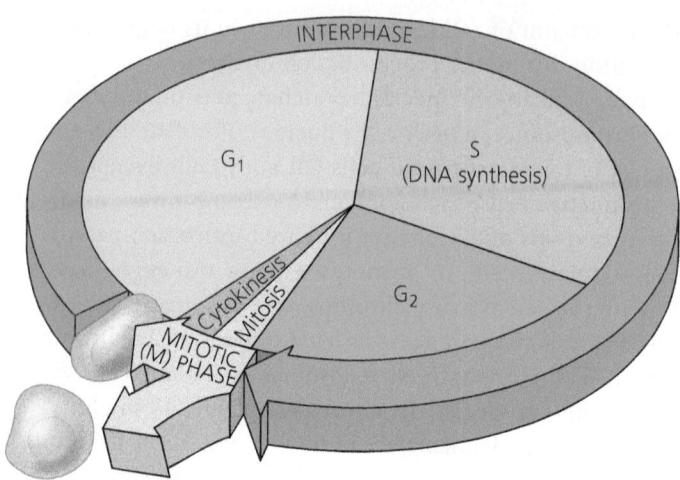

▲ Figure 12.6 **The cell cycle.** In a dividing cell, the mitotic (M) phase alternates with interphase, a growth period. The first part of interphase (G_1) is followed by the S phase, when the chromosomes duplicate; G_2 is the last part of interphase. In the M phase, mitosis distributes the daughter chromosomes to daughter nuclei, and cytokinesis divides the cytoplasm, producing two daughter cells. The relative durations of G_1, S, and G_2 may vary.

CONCEPT CHECK 12.1

1. How many chromosomes are drawn in each part of Figure 12.5? (Ignore the micrograph in part 2.)

2. **WHAT IF?** A chicken has 78 chromosomes in its somatic cells. How many chromosomes did the chicken inherit from each parent? How many chromosomes are in each of the chicken's gametes? How many chromosomes will be in each somatic cell of the chicken's offspring?

For suggested answers, see Appendix A.

CONCEPT 12.2

The mitotic phase alternates with interphase in the cell cycle

In 1882, a German anatomist named Walther Flemming developed dyes that allowed him to observe, for the first time, the behaviour of chromosomes during mitosis and cytokinesis. (In fact, Flemming coined the terms *mitosis* and *chromatin*.) During the period between one cell division and the next, it appeared to Flemming that the cell was simply growing larger. But we now know that many critical events occur during this stage in the life of a cell.

Phases of the Cell Cycle

Mitosis is just one part of the cell cycle (**Figure 12.6**). In fact, the **mitotic (M) phase**, which includes both mitosis and cytokinesis, is usually the shortest part of the cell cycle. The mitotic phase alternates with a much longer stage called **interphase**, which often accounts for about 90%

of the cycle. Interphase can be divided into subphases: the **G_1 phase** ("first gap"), the **S phase** ("synthesis"), and the **G_2 phase** ("second gap"). The G phases were misnamed as "gaps" when they were first observed because the cells appeared inactive, but we now know that intense metabolic activity and growth occur throughout interphase. During all three subphases of interphase, in fact, a cell grows by producing proteins and cytoplasmic organelles such as mitochondria and endoplasmic reticulum. Duplication of the chromosomes, crucial for eventual division of the cell, occurs entirely during the S phase. (We will discuss synthesis of DNA in Chapter 16.) Thus, a cell grows (G_1), continues to grow as it copies its chromosomes (S), grows more as it completes preparations for cell division (G_2), and divides (M). The daughter cells may then repeat the cycle.

A particular human cell might undergo one division in 24 hours. Of this time, the M phase would occupy less than 1 hour, while the S phase might occupy about 10–12 hours, or about half the cycle. The rest of the time would be apportioned between the G_1 and G_2 phases. The G_2 phase usually takes 4–6 hours; in our example, G_1 would occupy about 5–6 hours. G_1 is the most variable in length in different types of cells. Some cells in a multicellular organism divide very infrequently or not at all. These cells spend their time in G_1 (or a related phase called G_0) doing their job in the organism—a nerve cell carries impulses, for example.

Mitosis is conventionally broken down into five stages: **prophase**, **prometaphase**, **metaphase**, **anaphase**, and **telophase**. Overlapping with the latter stages of mitosis, cytokinesis completes the mitotic phase. **Figure 12.7**

Exploring Mitosis in an Animal Cell

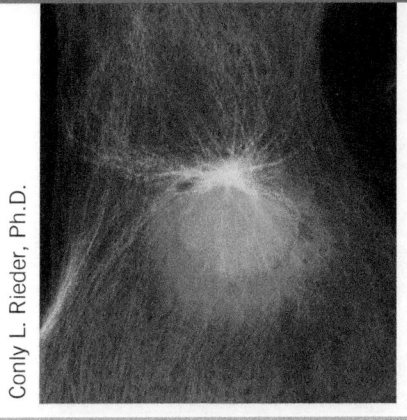

Conly L. Rieder, Ph.D.

G₂ of Interphase

Centrosomes
(with centriole pairs)

Chromosomes
(duplicated,
uncondensed)

Nucleolus

Nuclear
envelope

Plasma
membrane

Conly L. Rieder, Ph.D.

Prophase

Early mitotic
spindle

Aster

Centromere

Two sister chromatids
of one chromosome

Conly L. Rieder, Ph.D.

Prometaphase

Fragments
of nuclear
envelope

Nonkinetochore
microtubules

Kinetochore

Kinetochore
microtubule

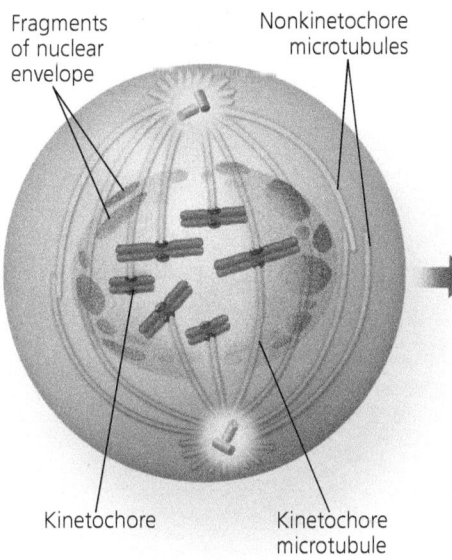

G₂ of Interphase

- A nuclear envelope encloses the nucleus.
- The nucleus contains one or more nucleoli (singular, *nucleolus*).
- Two centrosomes have formed by duplication of a single centrosome. Centrosomes are regions in animal cells that organize the microtubules of the spindle. Each centrosome contains two centrioles.
- Chromosomes, duplicated during S phase, cannot be seen individually because they have not yet condensed.

The fluorescence micrographs show dividing cells from a newt; this species has 22 chromosomes. Chromosomes appear blue, microtubules green, and intermediate filaments red. For simplicity, the drawings show only six chromosomes.

Prophase

- The chromatin fibres become more tightly coiled, condensing into discrete chromosomes observable with a light microscope.
- The nucleoli disappear.
- Each duplicated chromosome appears as two identical sister chromatids joined at their centromeres and, in some species, all along their arms by cohesins (sister chromatid cohesion).
- The mitotic spindle (named for its shape) begins to form. It is composed of the centrosomes and the microtubules that extend from them. The radial arrays of shorter microtubules that extend from the centrosomes are called asters ("stars").
- The centrosomes move away from each other, propelled partly by the lengthening microtubules between them.

Prometaphase

- The nuclear envelope fragments.
- The microtubules extending from each centrosome can now invade the nuclear area.
- The chromosomes have become even more condensed.
- Each of the two chromatids of each chromosome now has a kinetochore, a specialized protein structure at the centromere.
- Some of the microtubules attach to the kinetochores, becoming "kinetochore microtubules," which jerk the chromosomes back and forth.
- Nonkinetochore microtubules interact with those from the opposite pole of the spindle.

? *How many molecules of DNA are in the prometaphase drawing? How many molecules per chromosome? How many double helices are there per chromosome? Per chromatid?*

Continued on next page

Exploring Mitosis in an Animal Cell

Conly L. Rieder, Ph.D.

Metaphase

Conly L. Rieder, Ph.D.

Anaphase

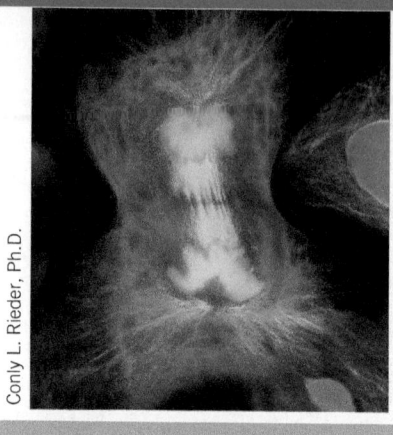

Conly L. Rieder, Ph.D.

10 μm

Telophase and Cytokinesis

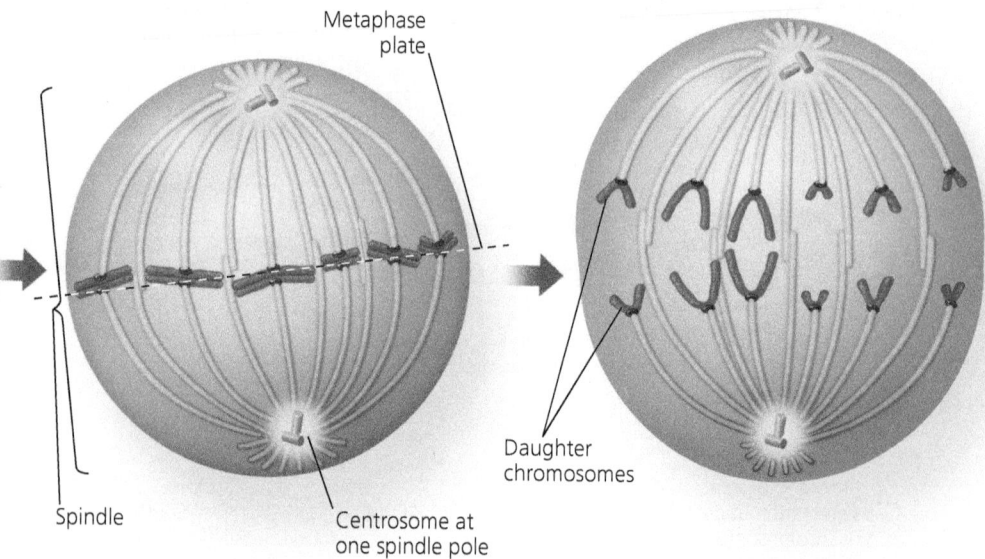

Metaphase plate

Spindle

Centrosome at one spindle pole

Daughter chromosomes

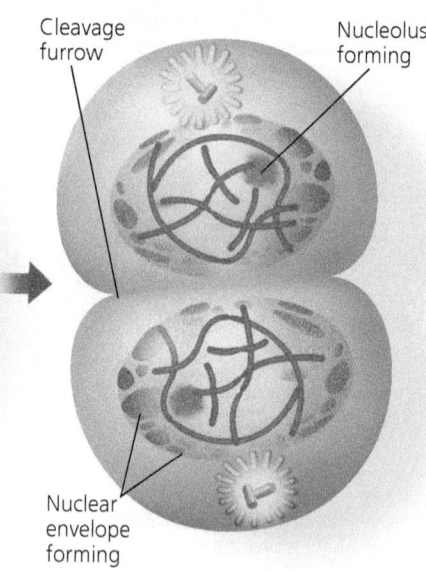

Cleavage furrow

Nucleolus forming

Nuclear envelope forming

Metaphase

- The centrosomes are now at opposite poles of the cell.

- The chromosomes have all arrived at the *metaphase plate*, a plane that is equidistant between the spindle's two poles. The chromosomes' centromeres lie at the metaphase plate.

- For each chromosome, the kinetochores of the sister chromatids are attached to kinetochore microtubules coming from opposite poles.

Anaphase

- Anaphase is the shortest stage of mitosis, often lasting only a few minutes.

- Anaphase begins when the cohesin proteins are cleaved. This allows the two sister chromatids of each pair to separate. Each chromatid thus becomes a distinct chromosome.

- The two liberated daughter chromosomes begin moving toward opposite ends of the cell as their kinetochore microtubules shorten. Because these microtubules are attached at the centromere region, the chromosomes move centromere first (at about 1 μm/min).

- The cell elongates as the nonkinetochore microtubules lengthen.

- By the end of anaphase, the two ends of the cell have equivalent—and complete—collections of chromosomes.

Telophase

- Two daughter nuclei form in the cell. Nuclear envelopes arise from the fragments of the parent cell's nuclear envelope and other portions of the endomembrane system.

- Nucleoli reappear.

- The chromosomes become less condensed.

- Any remaining spindle microtubules are depolymerized.

- Mitosis, the division of one nucleus into two genetically identical nuclei, is now complete.

Cytokinesis

- The division of the cytoplasm is usually well under way by late telophase, so the two daughter cells appear shortly after the end of mitosis.

- In animal cells, cytokinesis involves the formation of a cleavage furrow, which pinches the cell in two; in plant cells a cell plate forms.

ANIMATION

BioFlix Visit the Study Area in **MasteringBiology** for the BioFlix® 3-D Animation on Mitosis. BioFlix Tutorials can also be assigned in MasteringBiology.

describes these stages in an animal cell. Study this figure thoroughly before progressing to the next two sections, which examine mitosis and cytokinesis more closely.

The Mitotic Spindle: *A Closer Look*

Many of the events of mitosis depend on the **mitotic spindle**, which begins to form in the cytoplasm during prophase. This structure consists of fibres made of microtubules and associated proteins. While the mitotic spindle assembles, the other microtubules of the cytoskeleton partially disassemble, providing the material used to construct the spindle. The spindle microtubules elongate (polymerize) by incorporating more subunits of the protein tubulin (see Table 6.1) and shorten (depolymerize) by losing subunits.

In animal cells, the assembly of spindle microtubules starts at the **centrosome**, a subcellular region containing material that functions throughout the cell cycle to organize the cell's microtubules. (It is also a type of *microtubule-organizing centre*.) A pair of centrioles is located at the centre of the centrosome, but they are not essential for cell division: If the centrioles are destroyed with a laser microbeam, a spindle nevertheless forms during mitosis. In fact, centrioles are not even present in plant cells, which do form mitotic spindles.

During interphase in animal cells, the single centrosome duplicates, forming two centrosomes, which remain together near the nucleus. The two centrosomes move apart during prophase and prometaphase of mitosis as spindle microtubules grow out from them. By the end of prometaphase, the two centrosomes, one at each pole of the spindle, are at opposite ends of the cell. An **aster**, a radial array of short microtubules, extends from each centrosome. The spindle includes the centrosomes, the spindle microtubules, and the asters.

Each of the two sister chromatids of a duplicated chromosome has a **kinetochore**, a structure made up of proteins that have assembled on specific sections of DNA at each centromere. The chromosome's two kinetochores face in opposite directions. During prometaphase, some of the spindle microtubules attach to the kinetochores; these are called kinetochore microtubules. (The number of microtubules attached to a kinetochore varies among species, from one microtubule in yeast cells to 40 or so in some mammalian cells.) The kinetochore thus acts as a coupling device that allows the motor of the spindle to attach to its cargo, the chromosome. When one of a chromosome's kinetochores is "captured" by microtubules, the chromosome begins to move toward the pole from which those microtubules extend. However, this movement is checked as soon as microtubules from the opposite pole attach to the kinetochore on the other chromatid. What happens next is like a tug-of-war that ends in

a draw. The chromosome moves first in one direction, then the other, back and forth, finally settling midway between the two ends of the cell. At metaphase, the centromeres of all the duplicated chromosomes are on a plane midway between the spindle's two poles. This plane is called the **metaphase plate**, which is an imaginary plate rather than an actual cellular structure (Figure 12.8). Meanwhile, microtubules that do not attach to kinetochores have been elongating, and by

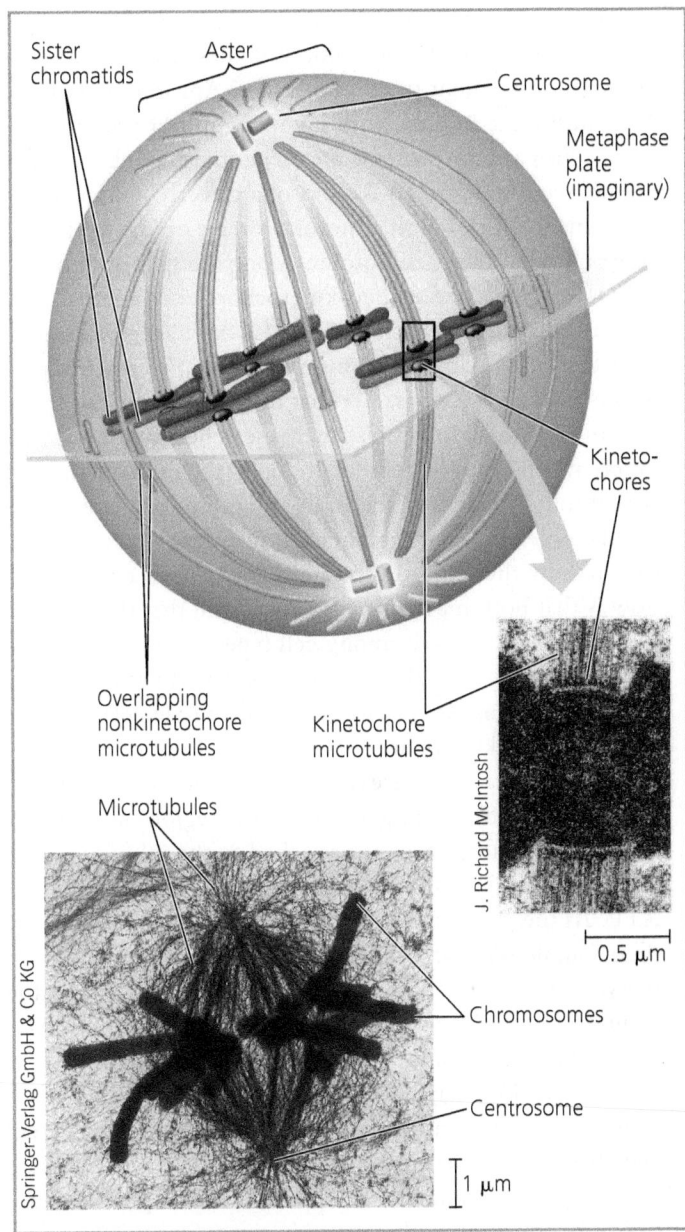

▲ Figure 12.8 **The mitotic spindle at metaphase.** The kinetochores of each chromosome's two sister chromatids face in opposite directions. Here, each kinetochore is attached to a *cluster* of kinetochore microtubules extending from the nearest centrosome. Nonkinetochore microtubules overlap at the metaphase plate (TEMs).

DRAW IT *On the lower micrograph, draw a line indicating the position of the metaphase plate. Circle an aster. Draw arrows indicating the directions of chromosome movement once anaphase begins.*

metaphase they overlap and interact with other nonkinetochore microtubules from the opposite pole of the spindle. By metaphase, the microtubules of the asters have also grown and are in contact with the plasma membrane. The spindle is now complete.

The structure of the spindle correlates well with its function during anaphase. Anaphase begins suddenly when the cohesins holding together the sister chromatids of each chromosome are cleaved by an enzyme called *separase*. Once separated, the chromatids become full-fledged chromosomes that move toward opposite ends of the cell.

How do the kinetochore microtubules function in this poleward movement of chromosomes? Apparently, two mechanisms are in play, both involving motor proteins. (To review how motor proteins move an object along a microtubule, see Figure 6.21.) Results of a cleverly designed experiment suggested that motor proteins on the kinetochores "walk" the chromosomes along the microtubules, which depolymerize at their kinetochore ends after the motor proteins have passed (**Figure 12.9**). (This is referred to as the "Pac-Man" mechanism because of its resemblance to the arcade game character that moves by eating all the dots in its path.) However, other researchers, working with different cell types or cells from other species, have shown that chromosomes are "reeled in" by motor proteins at the spindle poles and that the microtubules depolymerize after they pass by these motor proteins. The general consensus now is that both mechanisms are used and that their relative contributions vary among cell types.

In a dividing animal cell, the nonkinetochore microtubules are responsible for elongating the whole cell during anaphase. Nonkinetochore microtubules from opposite poles overlap each other extensively during metaphase (see Figure 12.8). During anaphase, the region of overlap is reduced as motor proteins attached to the microtubules walk them away from one another, using energy from ATP. As the microtubules push apart from each other, their spindle poles are pushed apart, elongating the cell. At the same time, the microtubules lengthen somewhat by the addition of tubulin subunits to their overlapping ends. As a result, the microtubules continue to overlap.

At the end of anaphase, duplicate groups of chromosomes have arrived at opposite ends of the elongated parent cell. Nuclei re-form during telophase. Cytokinesis generally begins during anaphase or telophase, and the spindle eventually disassembles by depolymerization of microtubules.

Cytokinesis: *A Closer Look*

In animal cells, cytokinesis occurs by a process known as **cleavage**. The first sign of cleavage is the appearance of a **cleavage furrow**, a shallow groove in the cell surface near the old metaphase plate (**Figure 12.10a**). On the cytoplasmic

---

▼ Figure 12.9   **Inquiry**

At which end do kinetochore microtubules shorten during anaphase?

Experiment Gary Borisy and colleagues at the University of Wisconsin wanted to determine whether kinetochore microtubules depolymerize at the kinetochore end or the pole end as chromosomes move toward the poles during mitosis. First they labelled the microtubules of a pig kidney cell in early anaphase with a yellow fluorescent dye.

Then they marked a region of the kinetochore microtubules between one spindle pole and the chromosomes by using a laser to eliminate the fluorescence from that region, while leaving the microtubules intact (see below). As anaphase proceeded, they monitored the changes in microtubule length on either side of the mark.

Results As the chromosomes moved poleward, the microtubule segments on the kinetochore side of the mark shortened, while those on the spindle pole side stayed the same length.

Conclusion During anaphase in this cell type, chromosome movement is correlated with kinetochore microtubules shortening at their kinetochore ends and not at their spindle pole ends. This experiment supports the hypothesis that during anaphase, a chromosome is walked along a microtubule as the microtubule depolymerizes at its kinetochore end, releasing tubulin subunits.

Source: Based on "Chromosomes Move Poleward in Anaphase along Stationary Microtubules That Coordinately Disassemble from Their Kinetochore Ends" by Gary J. Gorbsky et al., from *Journal of Cell Biology*, January 1987, Volume 104(1).

WHAT IF? *If this experiment had been done on a cell type in which "reeling in" at the poles was the main cause of chromosome movement, how would the mark have moved relative to the poles? How would the microtubule lengths have changed?*

▼ Figure 12.10 **Cytokinesis in animal and plant cells.**

(a) Cleavage of an animal cell (SEM)

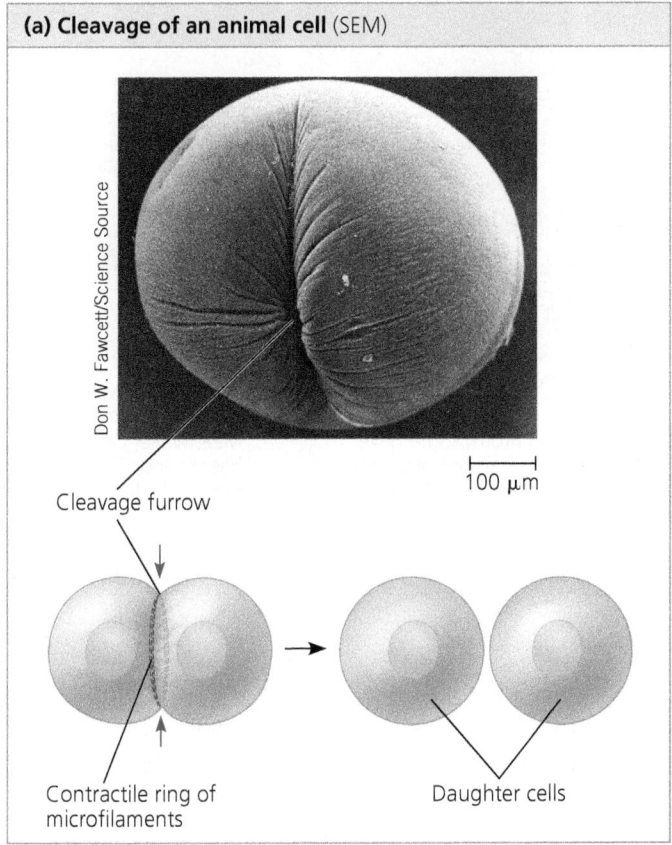

Cleavage furrow

100 μm

Contractile ring of microfilaments

Daughter cells

(b) Cell plate formation in a plant cell (TEM)

Vesicles forming cell plate

Wall of parent cell

Cell plate

New cell wall

1 μm

Daughter cells

side of the furrow is a contractile ring of actin microfilaments associated with molecules of the protein myosin. The actin microfilaments interact with the myosin molecules, causing the ring to contract. The contraction of the dividing cell's ring of microfilaments is like the pulling of a drawstring. The cleavage furrow deepens until the parent cell is pinched in two, producing two completely separated cells, each with its own nucleus and its own share of cytosol, organelles, and other subcellular structures.

Cytokinesis in plant cells, which have cell walls, is markedly different. There is no cleavage furrow. Instead, during telophase, vesicles derived from the Golgi apparatus move along microtubules to the middle of the cell, where they coalesce, producing a **cell plate** (Figure 12.10b). Cell wall materials carried in the vesicles collect inside the cell plate as it grows. The cell plate enlarges until its surrounding membrane fuses with the plasma membrane along the perimeter of the cell. Two daughter cells result, each with its own plasma membrane. Meanwhile, a new cell wall arising from the contents of the cell plate has formed between the daughter cells.

Figure 12.11 is a series of micrographs of a dividing plant cell. Examining this figure will help you review mitosis and cytokinesis.

Binary Fission in Bacteria

Prokaryotes (bacteria and archaea) can undergo a type of reproduction in which the cell grows to roughly double its size and then divides to form two cells. The term **binary fission**, meaning "division in half," refers to this process and to the asexual reproduction of single-celled eukaryotes, such as the amoeba in Figure 12.2a. However, the process in eukaryotes involves mitosis, while that in prokaryotes does not.

In bacteria, most genes are carried on a single bacterial chromosome that consists of a circular DNA molecule and associated proteins. Although bacteria are smaller and simpler than eukaryotic cells, the challenge of replicating their genomes in an orderly fashion and distributing the copies equally to two daughter cells is still formidable. The chromosome of the bacterium *Escherichia coli*, for example, when it is fully stretched out, is about 500 times as long as the cell. For such a long chromosome to fit within the cell requires that it be highly coiled and folded.

In *E. coli*, the process of cell division is initiated when the DNA of the bacterial chromosome begins to replicate at a specific place on the chromosome called the **origin of replication**, producing two origins. As the chromosome continues to replicate, one origin moves rapidly toward the opposite end of the cell (Figure 12.12). While the chromosome is replicating, the cell elongates. When replication is complete and the bacterium has reached about twice its initial size, its plasma membrane pinches inward, dividing

Nucleus
Nucleolus
Chromosomes condensing
Chromosomes
Cell plate
10 μm

Pearson Education

1 **Prophase.** The chromosomes are condensing and the nucleolus is beginning to disappear. Although not yet visible in the micrograph, the mitotic spindle is starting to form.

2 **Prometaphase.** Discrete chromosomes are now visible; each consists of two aligned, identical sister chromatids. Later in prometaphase, the nuclear envelope will fragment.

3 **Metaphase.** The spindle is complete, and the chromosomes, attached to microtubules at their kinetochores, are all at the metaphase plate.

4 **Anaphase.** The chromatids of each chromosome have separated, and the daughter chromosomes are moving to the ends of the cell as their kinetochore microtubules shorten.

5 **Telophase.** Daughter nuclei are forming. Meanwhile, cytokinesis has started: The cell plate, which will divide the cytoplasm in two, is growing toward the perimeter of the parent cell.

▲ Figure 12.11 **Mitosis in a plant cell.** These light micrographs show mitosis in cells of an onion root.

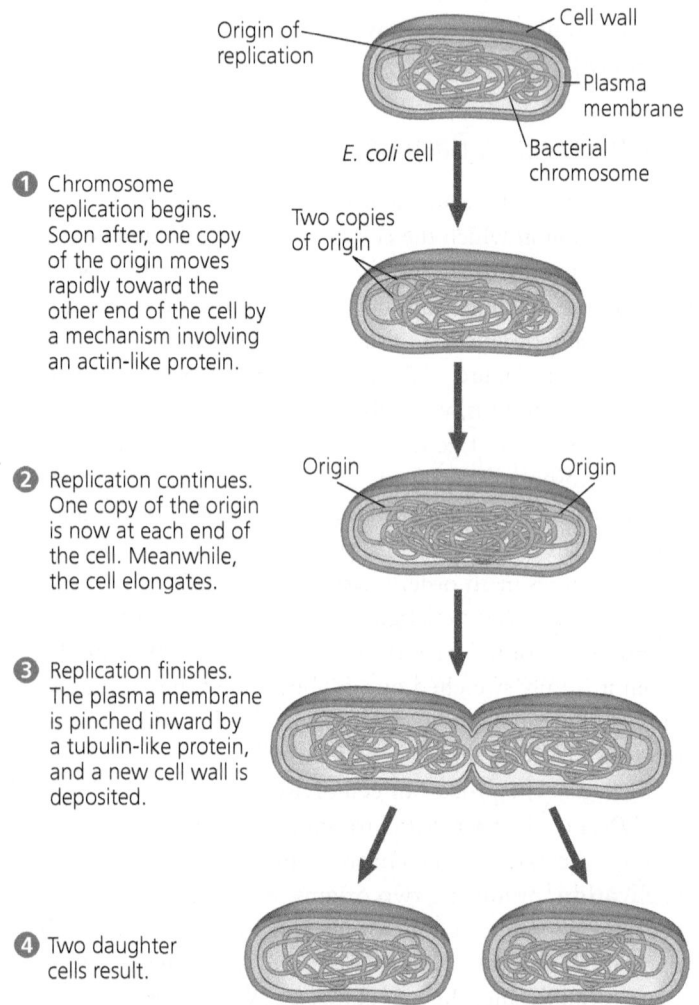

Origin of replication
Cell wall
Plasma membrane
Bacterial chromosome
E. coli cell

1 Chromosome replication begins. Soon after, one copy of the origin moves rapidly toward the other end of the cell by a mechanism involving an actin-like protein.

Two copies of origin

2 Replication continues. One copy of the origin is now at each end of the cell. Meanwhile, the cell elongates.

Origin   Origin

3 Replication finishes. The plasma membrane is pinched inward by a tubulin-like protein, and a new cell wall is deposited.

4 Two daughter cells result.

▲ Figure 12.12 **Bacterial cell division by binary fission.** The bacterium *E. coli*, shown here, has a single, circular chromosome.

the parent *E. coli* cell into two daughter cells. In this way, each cell inherits a complete genome.

Using the techniques of modern DNA technology to tag the origins of replication with molecules that glow green in fluorescence microscopy (see Figure 6.3), researchers have directly observed the movement of bacterial chromosomes. This movement is reminiscent of the poleward movements of the centromere regions of eukaryotic chromosomes during anaphase of mitosis, but bacteria don't have visible mitotic spindles or even microtubules. In most bacterial species studied, the two origins of replication end up at opposite ends of the cell or in some other very specific location, possibly anchored there by one or more proteins. How bacterial chromosomes move and how their specific location is established and maintained are active areas of research. Several proteins have been identified that play important roles. Polymerization of one protein resembling eukaryotic actin apparently functions in bacterial chromosome movement during cell division, and another protein that is related to tubulin helps pinch the plasma membrane inward, separating the two bacterial daughter cells.

The Evolution of Mitosis

EVOLUTION Given that prokaryotes preceded eukaryotes on Earth by more than a billion years (as we will discuss further in Chapter 25), we might hypothesize that mitosis evolved from simpler prokaryotic mechanisms of cell reproduction. The fact that some of the proteins involved in bacterial binary fission are related to eukaryotic proteins that function in mitosis supports that hypothesis.

(a) Bacteria. During binary fission in bacteria, the origins of the daughter chromosomes move to opposite ends of the cell. The mechanism involves polymerization of actin-like molecules, and possibly proteins that anchor the daughter chromosomes to specific sites on the plasma membrane.

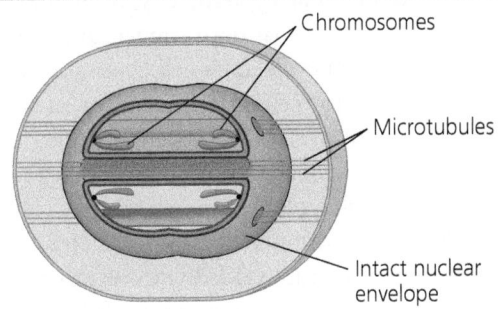

Chromosomes

Microtubules

Intact nuclear envelope

(b) Dinoflagellates. In unicellular protists called dinoflagellates, the chromosomes attach to the nuclear envelope, which remains intact during cell division. Microtubules pass through the nucleus inside cytoplasmic tunnels, reinforcing the spatial orientation of the nucleus, which then divides in a process reminiscent of bacterial binary fission.

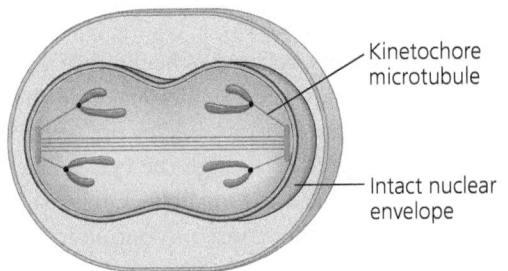

Kinetochore microtubule

Intact nuclear envelope

(c) Diatoms and some yeasts. In these two groups of unicellular eukaryotes, the nuclear envelope also remains intact during cell division. In these organisms, the microtubules form a spindle within the nucleus. Microtubules separate the chromosomes, and the nucleus splits into two daughter nuclei.

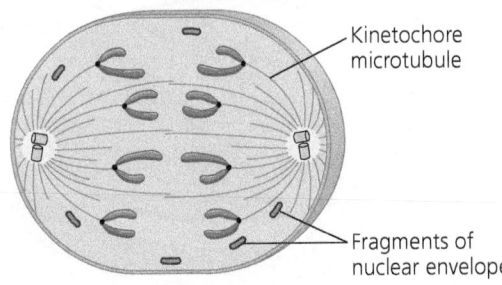

Kinetochore microtubule

Fragments of nuclear envelope

(d) Most eukaryotes. In most other eukaryotes, including plants and animals, the spindle forms outside the nucleus, and the nuclear envelope breaks down during mitosis. Microtubules separate the chromosomes, and two nuclear envelopes then form.

▲ **Figure 12.13 Mechanisms of cell division in several groups of organisms.** Some unicellular eukaryotes existing today have mechanisms of cell division that may resemble intermediate steps in the evolution of mitosis. Except for (a), these schematic diagrams do not show cell walls.

Source: Adaptation of figure 18.41 from *Molecular Biology of the Cell*, 4th Edition, by Bruce Alberts et al. Copyright © 2002 by Garland Science/Taylor & Francis LLC. Reprinted with permission.

As eukaryotes with nuclear envelopes and larger genomes evolved, the ancestral process of binary fission, seen today in bacteria, somehow gave rise to mitosis. Variations on cell division exist in different groups of organisms. These variant processes may be similar to mechanisms used by ancestral species and thus may resemble steps in the evolution of mitosis from a binary fission-like process presumably carried out by very early bacteria. Possible intermediate stages are suggested by two unusual types of nuclear division found today in certain unicellular eukaryotes—dinoflagellates, diatoms, and some yeasts (Figure 12.13). These two modes of nuclear division are thought to be cases where ancestral mechanisms have remained relatively unchanged over evolutionary time. In both types, the nuclear envelope remains intact, in contrast to what happens in most eukaryotic cells.

CONCEPT CHECK 12.2

1. How many chromosomes are drawn in Figure 12.8? Are they duplicated? How many chromatids are shown?
2. Compare cytokinesis in animal cells and plant cells.
3. During which stages of the cell cycle does a chromosome consist of two identical chromatids?
4. Compare the roles of tubulin and actin during eukaryotic cell division with the roles of tubulin-like and actin-like proteins during bacterial binary fission.
5. A kinetochore has been compared to a coupling device that connects a motor to the cargo that it moves. Explain.
6. **MAKE CONNECTIONS** What other functions do actin and tubulin carry out? Name the proteins they interact with to do so. (Review Figures 6.21a and 6.26a.)

For suggested answers, see Appendix A.

CONCEPT **12.3**

The eukaryotic cell cycle is regulated by a molecular control system

The timing and rate of cell division in different parts of a plant or animal are crucial to normal growth, development, and maintenance. The frequency of cell division varies with the type of cell. For example, human skin cells divide frequently throughout life, whereas liver cells maintain the ability to divide but keep it in reserve until an appropriate need arises—say, to repair a wound. Some of the most specialized cells, such as fully formed nerve cells and muscle cells, do not divide at all in a mature human. These cell cycle differences result from regulation at the molecular level. The mechanisms of this regulation are of great interest, not only to understand the life cycles of normal cells but also to learn how cancer cells manage to escape the usual controls.

The Cell Cycle Control System

What controls the cell cycle? In the early 1970s, a variety of experiments led to the hypothesis that the cell cycle is driven by specific signalling molecules present in the cytoplasm. Some of the first strong evidence for this hypothesis came from experiments with mammalian cells grown in culture. In these experiments, two cells in different phases of the cell cycle were fused to form a single cell with two nuclei (Figure 12.14). If one of the original cells was in the S phase and the other was in G_1, the G_1 nucleus immediately entered the S phase, as though stimulated by signalling

▼ **Figure 12.14** **Inquiry**

Do molecular signals in the cytoplasm regulate the cell cycle?

Experiment Researchers at the University of Colorado wondered whether a cell's progression through the cell cycle is controlled by cytoplasmic molecules. To investigate this, they selected cultured mammalian cells that were at different phases of the cell cycle and induced them to fuse. Two such experiments are shown here.

Experiment 1　　**Experiment 2**

| S | G_1 |
| M | G_1 |

Results

| S | S |
| M | M |

When a cell in the S phase was fused with a cell in G_1, the G_1 nucleus immediately entered the S phase—DNA was synthesized.

When a cell in the M phase was fused with a cell in G_1, the G_1 nucleus immediately began mitosis—a spindle formed and the chromosomes condensed, even though the chromosomes had not been duplicated.

Conclusion The results of fusing a G_1 cell with a cell in the S or M phase of the cell cycle suggest that molecules present in the cytoplasm during the S or M phase control the progression to those phases.

Source: Based on "Mammalian Cell Fusion: Induction of Premature Chromosome Condensation in Interphase Nuclei" by R. T. Johnson and P. N. Rao, from *Nature*, May 1970, Volume 226(5247). © Jane B Reece.

WHAT IF? *If the progression of phases did not depend on cytoplasmic molecules and, instead, each phase began when the previous one was complete, how would the results have differed?*

molecules present in the cytoplasm of the first cell. Similarly, if a cell undergoing mitosis (M phase) was fused with another cell in any stage of its cell cycle, even G_1, the second nucleus immediately entered mitosis, with condensation of the chromatin and formation of a mitotic spindle.

The experiment shown in Figure 12.14 and other experiments on animal cells and yeasts demonstrated that the sequential events of the cell cycle are directed by a distinct **cell cycle control system**, a cyclically operating set of molecules in the cell that both triggers and coordinates key events in the cell cycle. The cell cycle control system has been compared to the control device of an automatic washing machine (Figure 12.15). Like the washer's timing device, the cell cycle control system proceeds on its own, according to a built-in clock. However, just as a washer's cycle is subject to both internal control (such as the sensor that detects when the tub is filled with water) and external adjustment (such as starting or stopping the machine), the cell cycle is regulated at certain checkpoints by both internal and external signals that stop or restart the machine. A **checkpoint** is a control point in the cell cycle where stop and go-ahead signals can regulate the cycle. Three important checkpoints are found in the G_1, G_2, and M phases (the red gates in Figure 12.15).

To understand how cell cycle checkpoints work, we first need to see what kinds of molecules make up the cell cycle control system (the molecular basis for the cell cycle clock) and how a cell progresses through the cycle. Then we will consider the internal and external checkpoint signals that can make the clock either pause or continue.

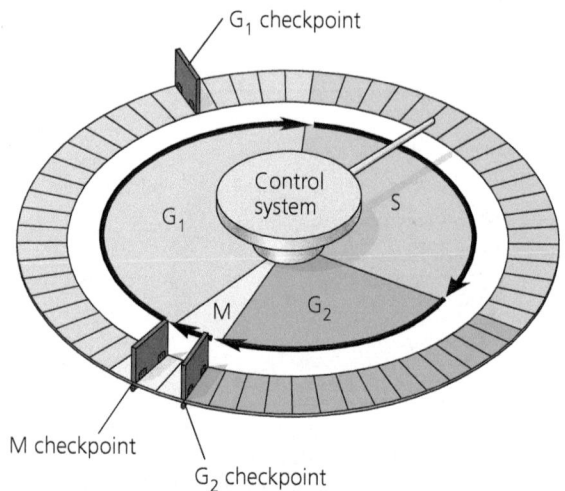

▲ **Figure 12.15 Mechanical analogy for the cell cycle control system.** In this diagram of the cell cycle, the flat "stepping stones" around the perimeter represent sequential events. Like the control device of an automatic washer, the cell cycle control system proceeds on its own, driven by a built-in clock. However, the system is subject to internal and external regulation at various checkpoints; three important checkpoints are shown (red).

The Cell Cycle Clock: Cyclins and Cyclin-Dependent Kinases

Rhythmic fluctuations in the abundance and activity of cell cycle control molecules pace the sequential events of the cell cycle. These regulatory molecules are mainly proteins of two types: protein kinases and cyclins. Protein kinases are enzymes that activate or inactivate other proteins by phosphorylating them (see Chapter 11).

Many of the kinases that drive the cell cycle are actually present at a constant concentration in the growing cell, but much of the time they are in an inactive form. To be active, such a kinase must be attached to a **cyclin**, a protein that gets its name from its cyclically fluctuating concentration in the cell. Because of this requirement, these kinases are called **cyclin-dependent kinases**, or **Cdks**. The activity of a Cdk rises and falls with changes in the concentration of its cyclin partner. **Figure 12.16a**, shows the fluctuating activity of **MPF** (maturation promoting factor), the cyclin-Cdk complex that was discovered first (in frog eggs). Note that the peaks of MPF activity correspond to the peaks of cyclin concentration. The cyclin level rises during the S and G_2 phases and then falls abruptly during M phase.

The initials MPF stand for "maturation-promoting factor," but we can think of MPF as "M-phase-promoting factor" because it triggers the cell's passage past the G_2 checkpoint into M phase (**Figure 12.16b**). When cyclins that accumulate during G_2 associate with Cdk molecules, the resulting MPF complex phosphorylates a variety of proteins, initiating mitosis. MPF acts both directly as a kinase and indirectly by activating other kinases. For example, MPF causes phosphorylation of various proteins of the nuclear lamina (see Figure 6.9), which promotes fragmentation of the nuclear envelope during prometaphase of mitosis. There is also evidence that MPF contributes to molecular events required for chromosome condensation and spindle formation during prophase.

During anaphase, MPF helps switch itself off by initiating a process that leads to the destruction of its own cyclin. The noncyclin part of MPF, the Cdk, persists in the cell, inactive until it becomes part of MPF again by associating with new cyclin molecules synthesized during the S and G_2 phases of the next round of the cycle.

The fluctuating activities of different cyclin-Cdk complexes are of major importance in controlling all the stages of the cell cycle and give the go-ahead signals at some checkpoints as well. As mentioned above, MPF controls the cell's passage through the G_2 checkpoint. Cell behaviour at the G_1 checkpoint is also regulated by the activity of cyclin-Cdk protein complexes. Animal cells appear to have at least three Cdk proteins and several different cyclins that operate at this checkpoint. Next, let's consider checkpoints in more detail.

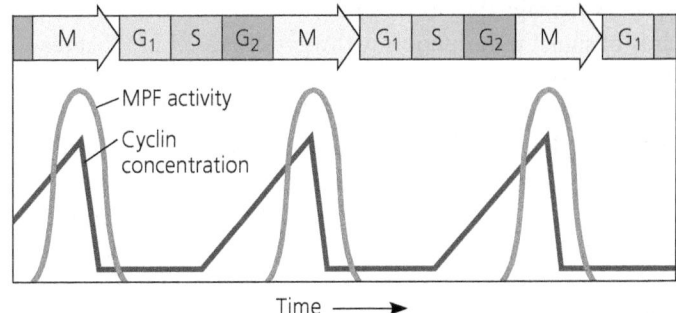

(a) Fluctuation of MPF activity and cyclin concentration during the cell cycle

❶ Synthesis of cyclin begins in late S phase and continues through G_2. Because cyclin is protected from degradation during this stage, it accumulates.

❺ During G_1, the degradation of cyclin continues, and the Cdk component of MPF is recycled.

❹ During anaphase, the cyclin component of MPF is degraded, terminating the M phase. The cell enters the G_1 phase.

❸ MPF promotes mitosis by phosphorylating various proteins. MPF's activity peaks during metaphase.

❷ Cyclin combines with Cdk, producing MPF. When enough MPF molecules accumulate, the cell passes the G_2 checkpoint and begins mitosis.

(b) Molecular mechanisms that help regulate the cell cycle

▲ **Figure 12.16 Molecular control of the cell cycle at the G_2 checkpoint.** The steps of the cell cycle are timed by rhythmic fluctuations in the activity of cyclin-dependent kinases (Cdks). Here we focus on a cyclin-Cdk complex in animal cells called MPF, which acts at the G_2 checkpoint as a go-ahead signal, triggering the events of mitosis.

? *Explain how the events in the diagram in (b) are related to the "Time" axis of the graph in (a).*

Stop and Go Signs: Internal and External Signals at the Checkpoints

Animal cells generally have built-in stop signals that halt the cell cycle at checkpoints until overridden by go-ahead signals. (The signals are transmitted within the cell by the kinds of signal transduction pathways discussed in Chapter 11.) Many signals registered at checkpoints come from cellular surveillance mechanisms inside the cell. These signals report whether crucial cellular processes that should have occurred by that point have in fact been completed correctly and thus whether or not the cell cycle should proceed. Checkpoints also register signals from outside the cell. Three important checkpoints are those in G_1, G_2, and M phases, shown in Figure 12.15.

For many cells, the G_1 checkpoint—dubbed the "restriction point" in mammalian cells—seems to be the most important. If a cell receives a go-ahead signal at the G_1 checkpoint, it will usually complete the G_1, S, G_2, and M phases and divide. If it does not receive a go-ahead signal at that point, it may exit the cycle, switching into a nondividing state called the **G_0 phase** (Figure 12.17a). Most cells of the human body are actually in the G_0 phase. As mentioned earlier, mature nerve cells and muscle cells never divide. Other cells, such as liver cells, can be "called back" from the G_0 phase to the cell cycle by external cues, such as growth factors released during injury.

Biologists are currently working out the pathways that link signals originating inside and outside the cell with the responses by cyclin-dependent kinases and other proteins. An example of an internal signal occurs at the third important checkpoint, the M phase checkpoint (Figure 12.17b). Anaphase, the separation of sister chromatids, does not begin until all the chromosomes are properly attached to the spindle at the metaphase plate. Researchers have

learned that as long as some kinetochores are unattached to spindle microtubules, the sister chromatids remain together, delaying anaphase. Only when the kinetochores of all the chromosomes are properly attached to the spindle does the appropriate regulatory protein complex become activated. (In this case, the regulatory molecule is not a cyclin-Cdk complex but, instead, a different complex made up of several proteins.) Once activated, the complex sets off a chain of molecular events that activates the enzyme separase, which cleaves the cohesins, allowing the sister chromatids to separate. This mechanism ensures that daughter cells do not end up with missing or extra chromosomes.

Studies using animal cells in culture have led to the identification of many external factors, both chemical and physical, that can influence cell division. For example, cells fail to divide if an essential nutrient is lacking in the culture medium. (This is analogous to trying to run a washing machine without the water supply hooked up; an internal sensor won't allow the machine to continue past the point where water is needed.) And even if all other conditions are favourable, most types of mammalian cells divide in culture only if the growth medium includes specific

▶ Figure 12.17 **Two important checkpoints.** At certain checkpoints in the cell cycle (red gates), cells do different things depending on the signals they receive. Events of the **(a)** G_1 and **(b)** M checkpoints are shown. In **(b)**, the G_2 checkpoint has already been passed by the cell.

WHAT IF? What might be the result if the cell ignored either checkpoint and progressed through the cell cycle?

In the absence of a go-ahead signal, a cell exits the cell cycle and enters G_0, a nondividing state.

(a) G_1 checkpoint

If a cell receives a go-ahead signal, the cell continues on in the cell cycle.

Prometaphase

A cell in mitosis receives a stop signal when any of its chromosomes are not attached to spindle fibres.

(b) M checkpoint

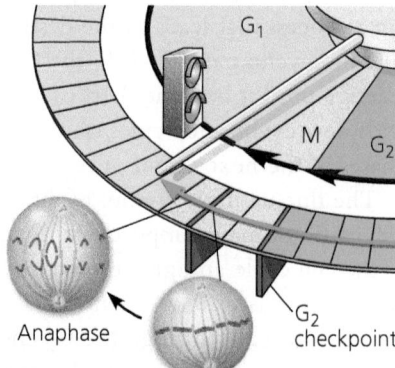

Metaphase

When all chromosomes are attached to spindle fibres from both poles, a go-ahead signal allows the cell to proceed into anaphase.

growth factors. As mentioned in Chapter 11, a **growth factor** is a protein released by certain cells that stimulates other cells to divide. Researchers have discovered more than 50 growth factors. Different cell types respond specifically to different growth factors or combinations of growth factors.

Consider, for example, *platelet-derived growth factor (PDGF)*, which is made by blood cell fragments called platelets. The experiment illustrated in **Figure 12.18** demonstrates that PDGF is required for the division of cultured fibroblasts, a type of connective tissue cell. Fibroblasts have PDGF receptors on their plasma membranes. The binding of PDGF molecules to these receptors (which are receptor tyrosine kinases; see Chapter 11) triggers a signal transduction pathway that allows the cells to pass the G_1 checkpoint and divide. PDGF stimulates fibroblast division not only in the artificial conditions of cell culture, but also in an animal's body. When an injury occurs, platelets release PDGF

in the vicinity. The resulting proliferation of fibroblasts helps heal the wound.

The effect of an external physical factor on cell division is clearly seen in **density-dependent inhibition**, a phenomenon in which crowded cells stop dividing (**Figure 12.19a**). As first observed many years ago, cultured cells normally divide until they form a single layer of cells on the inner surface of the culture flask, at which point the cells stop dividing. If some cells are removed, those bordering the open space begin dividing again and continue until the vacancy is filled. Follow-up studies revealed that the binding of a cell-surface protein to its counterpart on an adjoining cell sends a cell division-inhibiting signal to both cells, preventing them from moving forward in the cell cycle, even in the presence of growth factors.

◀ Figure 12.18 **The effect of platelet-derived growth factor (PDGF) on cell division.**

❶ A sample of human connective tissue is cut up into small pieces.

Scalpels

Petri dish

❷ Enzymes are used to digest the extracellular matrix in the tissue pieces, resulting in a suspension of free fibroblasts.

❸ Cells are transferred to culture vessels containing a basic growth medium consisting of glucose, amino acids, salts, and antibiotics (to prevent bacterial growth).

❹ PDGF is added to half the vessels. The culture vessels are incubated at 37°C for 24 hours.

Without PDGF

In the basic growth medium without PDGF (the control), the cells fail to divide.

With PDGF

In the basic growth medium plus PDGF, the cells proliferate. The SEM shows cultured fibroblasts.

Guenter Albrecht-Buehler, Ph.D

10 μm

MAKE CONNECTIONS

PDGF signals cells by binding to a cell-surface receptor tyrosine kinase. If you added a chemical that blocked phosphorylation, how would the results differ? (See Figure 11.8.)

Cells anchor to dish surface and divide (anchorage dependence).

When cells have formed a complete single layer, they stop dividing (density-dependent inhibition).

If some cells are scraped away, the remaining cells divide to fill the gap and then stop once they contact each other (density-dependent inhibition).

20 μm

Lan Bo Chen

(a) Normal mammalian cells. Contact with neighbouring cells and the availability of nutrients, growth factors, and a substratum for attachment limit cell density to a single layer.

20 μm

Lan Bo Chen

(b) Cancer cells. Cancer cells usually continue to divide well beyond a single layer, forming a clump of overlapping cells. They do not exhibit anchorage dependence or density-dependent inhibition.

▲ Figure 12.19 **Density-dependent inhibition and anchorage dependence of cell division.** Individual cells are shown disproportionately large in the drawings.

Most animal cells also exhibit **anchorage dependence** (see Figure 12.19a). To divide, they must be attached to a substratum, such as the inside of a culture flask or the extracellular matrix of a tissue. Experiments suggest that, like cell density, anchorage is signalled to the cell cycle control system via pathways involving plasma membrane proteins and elements of the cytoskeleton linked to them.

Density-dependent inhibition and anchorage dependence appear to function not only in cell culture but also in the body's tissues, checking the growth of cells at some optimal density and location during embryonic development and throughout an organism's life. Cancer cells, which we discuss next, exhibit neither density-dependent inhibition nor anchorage dependence (Figure 12.19b).

Loss of Cell Cycle Controls in Cancer Cells

Cancer cells do not heed the normal signals that regulate the cell cycle. In culture, they do not stop dividing when growth factors are depleted. A logical hypothesis is that cancer cells do not need growth factors in their culture medium to grow and divide. They may make a required growth factor themselves, or they may have an abnormality in the signalling pathway that conveys the growth factor's signal to the cell cycle control system even in the absence of that factor. Another possibility is an abnormal cell cycle control system. In these scenarios, the underlying basis of the abnormality is almost always a change in one or more genes (for example, a mutation) that alters the function of their protein products, resulting in faulty cell cycle control.

There are other important differences between normal cells and cancer cells that reflect derangements of the cell cycle. If and when they stop dividing, cancer cells do so at random points in the cycle, rather than at the normal checkpoints. Moreover, cancer cells can go on dividing indefinitely in culture if they are given a continual supply of nutrients; in essence, they are "immortal." A striking example is a cell line that has been reproducing in culture since 1951. Cells of this line are called HeLa cells because their original source was a tumour removed from a woman named Henrietta Lacks. Cells in culture that acquire the ability to divide indefinitely are said to have undergone **transformation**, the process that causes them to behave like cancer cells. By contrast, nearly all normal, nontransformed mammalian cells growing in culture divide only about 20 to 50 times before they stop dividing, and die. Finally, cancer cells evade the normal controls that trigger a cell to undergo apoptosis when something is wrong—for example, when an irreparable mistake has occurred during DNA replication preceding mitosis.

The abnormal behaviour of cancer cells can be catastrophic when it occurs in the body. The problem begins when a single cell in a tissue undergoes the first changes of the multistep process that converts a normal cell to a cancer cell. Because such a cell often has altered proteins on its surface, the body's immune system normally recognizes the cell as "non-self"—an abnormality—and destroys it. However, if the cell evades destruction, it may proliferate and form a tumour, a mass of abnormal cells within otherwise normal tissue. The abnormal cells may remain at the original site if they have too few genetic and cellular changes to survive at another site. In that case, the tumour is called a **benign tumour**. Most benign tumours do not cause serious problems and can be completely removed by surgery. In contrast, a **malignant tumour** includes cells whose genetic and cellular changes enable them to spread to new tissues and impair the functions of one or more organs; these cells are also considered *transformed* cells. An individual with a malignant tumour is said to have cancer; Figure 12.20 shows the development of breast cancer, as well as a typical breast cancer cell.

The changes that have occurred in cells of malignant tumours show up in many ways besides excessive

▼ Figure 12.20 **The growth and metastasis of a malignant breast tumour.** A series of genetic and cellular changes contribute to a tumour becoming malignant (cancerous). The cells of malignant (cancerous) tumours grow in an uncontrolled way and can spread to neighbouring tissues and, via lymph and blood vessels, to other parts of the body. The spread of cancer cells beyond their original site is called metastasis.

Breast cancer cell (colourized SEM)

Wellcome Images

❶ A tumour grows from a single cancer cell.

❷ Cancer cells invade neighbouring tissue.

❸ Cancer cells spread through lymph and blood vessels to other parts of the body.

❹ A small percentage of cancer cells may metastasize to another part of the body.

proliferation. These cells may have unusual numbers of chromosomes, though whether this is a cause or an effect of transformation is a topic of debate. Their metabolism may be altered, and they may cease to function in any constructive way. Abnormal changes on the cell surface cause cancer cells to lose attachments to neighbouring cells and the extracellular matrix, allowing them to spread into nearby tissues. Cancer cells may also secrete signalling molecules that cause blood vessels to grow toward the tumour. A few tumour cells may separate from the original tumour, enter blood vessels and lymph vessels, and travel to other parts of the body. There, they may proliferate and form a new tumour. This spread of cancer cells to locations distant from their original site is called **metastasis** (see Figure 12.20).

A tumour that appears to be localized may be treated with high-energy radiation, which damages DNA in cancer cells much more than it does in normal cells, apparently because the majority of cancer cells have lost the ability to repair such damage. To treat known or suspected metastatic tumours, chemotherapy is used, in which drugs that are toxic to actively dividing cells are administered through the circulatory system. As you might expect, chemotherapeutic drugs interfere with specific steps in the cell cycle. For example, the drug Taxol freezes the mitotic spindle by preventing microtubule depolymerization, which stops actively dividing cells from proceeding past metaphase and leads to their destruction. The side effects of chemotherapy are due to the drugs' effects on normal cells that divide often, due to the functioning of that cell type in the organism. For example, nausea results from chemotherapy's effects on intestinal cells, hair loss from effects on hair follicle cells, and susceptibility to infection from effects on immune system cells. You'll work with data from an experiment involving a potential chemotherapeutic agent in the Scientific Skills Exercise.

SCIENTIFIC SKILLS EXERCISE

Interpreting Histograms

Michael W. Davidson

At What Phase Is the Cell Cycle Arrested by an Inhibitor? Many medical treatments are aimed at stopping cancer cell proliferation by blocking the cell cycle of cancerous tumour cells. One potential treatment is a cell cycle inhibitor derived from human umbilical cord stem cells. In this exercise, you will compare two histograms to determine where in the cell cycle the inhibitor blocks the division of cancer cells.

How the Experiment Was Done In the treated sample, human glioblastoma (brain cancer) cells were grown in tissue culture in the presence of the inhibitor, while control sample cells were grown in its absence. After 72 hours of growth, the two cell samples were harvested. To get a "snapshot" of the phase of the cell cycle each cell was in at that time, the samples were treated with a fluorescent chemical that binds to DNA and then run through a flow cytometer, an instrument that records the fluorescence level of each cell. Computer software then graphed the number of cells in each sample with a particular fluorescence level, as shown below.

Data from the Experiment

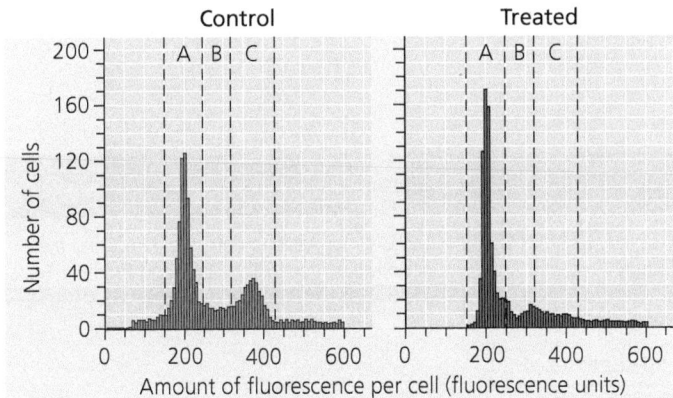

The data are plotted in a type of graph called a histogram (above), which groups values for a numeric variable on the x-axis into intervals. A histogram allows you to see how all the experimental subjects (cells, in this case) are distributed along a continuous variable (amount of

fluorescence). In these histograms, the bars are so narrow that the data appear to follow a curve for which you can detect peaks and dips. Each narrow bar represents the number of cells observed to have a level of fluorescence in the range of that interval. This in turn indicates the relative amount of DNA in those cells. Overall, comparing the two histograms allows you to see how the DNA content of this cell population is altered by the treatment.

Interpret the Data

1. Familiarize yourself with the data shown in the histograms. (a) Which axis indirectly shows the relative amount of DNA per cell? Explain your answer. (b) In the control sample, compare the first peak in the histogram (in region A) to the second peak (in region C). Which peak shows the population of cells with the higher amount of DNA per cell? Explain. (For additional information about graphs, see the Scientific Skills Review in Appendix E and in the Study Area in MasteringBiology.)

2. (a) In the control sample histogram, identify the phase of the cell cycle (G_1, S, or G_2) of the population of cells in each region delineated by vertical lines. Label the histogram with these phases and explain your answer. (b) Does the S phase population of cells show a distinct peak in the histogram? Why or why not?

3. The histogram representing the treated sample shows the effect of growing the cancer cells alongside human umbilical cord stem cells that produce the potential inhibitor. (a) Label the histogram with the cell cycle phases. Which phase of the cell cycle has the greatest number of cells in the treated sample? Explain. (b) Compare the distribution of cells among G_1, S, and G_2 phases in the control and treated samples. What does this tell you about the cells in the treated sample? (c) Based on what you learned in Concept 12.3, propose a mechanism by which the stem cell-derived inhibitor might arrest the cancer cell cycle at this stage. (More than one answer is possible.)

Based on "Regulation of Glioblastoma Progression by Cord Blood Stem Cells Is Mediated by Downregulation of Cyclin D1" by Kiran K. Velpula et al., from *PLoS ONE*, March 24, 2011, Volume 6(3). © Jane B Reece.

▼ Figure 12.21

Impact

The International Cancer Genome Consortium (ICGC)

The International Cancer Genome Consortium was co-founded by Thomas Hudson, the scientific director of the Ontario Institute of Cancer Research. The Consortium, which consists of researchers from 13 different countries, has a primary objective of producing a detailed registry of genomic changes that are found in different types of tumours. As of 2016, data had been gathered from over 15 000 cancer donors, revealing more than 42 million somatic mutations. (You'll learn more about the exact types of genomic changes, including somatic mutations and epigenetic modifications, in Chapter 18.)

Martin Krzywinski / Science Source

Why It Matters The identification of tumour-specific mutations will allow for treatment specifically tailored to the patient's cancer, leading to personalized medicine. (See Figure 21.6 for more examples of Canadian genomics research.)

MAKE CONNECTIONS *Based on what you learned in Chapters 11 and 12, what genes do you think would most likely lead to a cancer phenotype if the function of their protein products were disrupted?*

Over the past several decades, researchers have produced a flood of valuable information about cell-signalling pathways and how their malfunction contributes to the development of cancer through effects on the cell cycle. Coupled with new molecular techniques, such as the

ability to rapidly sequence the DNA of cells in a particular tumour, medical treatments for cancer are beginning to become more "personalized" to a particular patient's tumour (see Figure 18.27). For example, the cells of roughly 20% of breast cancer tumours show abnormally high amounts of a cell-surface receptor tyrosine kinase called HER2, and many show an increase in the number of estrogen receptor (ER) molecules, intracellular receptors that can trigger cell division. Based on lab findings, a physician can prescribe chemotherapy with a molecule that blocks the function of the specific protein (Herceptin for HER2 and tamoxifen for ERs). Treatment using these agents, when appropriate, has led to increased survival rates and fewer cancer recurrences.

Currently, scientists are interested in identifying the entire genomes of different types of cancer, in the hopes of further enhancing therapy based on a cancer subtype's specific genetic changes (Figure 12.21).

One of the big lessons we've learned about the development of cancer, though, is how very complex the process is. There are many areas that remain to be explored. Perhaps the reason we have so many unanswered questions about cancer cells is that there is still so much to learn about how normal cells function. The cell, life's basic unit of structure and function, holds enough secrets to engage researchers well into the future.

CONCEPT CHECK 12.3

1. In Figure 12.14, why do the nuclei resulting from experiment 2 contain different amounts of DNA?

2. How does MPF allow a cell to pass the G_2 phase checkpoint and enter mitosis? (See Figure 12.16.)

3. Explain in general how receptor tyrosine kinases and intracellular receptors might function in triggering cell division. (Review Figures 11.8 and 11.9 and Chapter 11.)

For suggested answers, see Appendix A.

12 Chapter Review

Go to **MasteringBiology**® for Assignments, the eText, and the Study Area with Animations, Activities, Vocab Self-Quiz, and Practice Tests.

SUMMARY OF KEY CONCEPTS

- Unicellular organisms reproduce by **cell division**; multicellular organisms depend on cell division for their development from a fertilized egg and for growth and repair. Cell division is part of the **cell cycle**, an ordered sequence of events in the life of a cell from its origin until it divides into daughter cells.

CONCEPT 12.1

Most cell division results in genetically identical daughter cells (pp. 244–246)

- The genetic material (DNA) of a cell—its **genome**—is partitioned among **chromosomes**. Each eukaryotic chromosome consists of one DNA molecule associated with many proteins that maintain chromosome structure and help control the activity of genes. Together, the complex of DNA and associated proteins is called **chromatin**. The chromatin of a chromosome exists in different states of condensation at different times. In animals, **gametes** have one set of chromosomes and **somatic cells** have two sets.

- Cells replicate their genetic material before they divide, each daughter cell receiving a copy of the DNA. Prior to cell division, chromosomes are duplicated. Each one then consists of two identical **sister chromatids** joined along their lengths by sister chromatid cohesion and held most tightly together at a constricted region at the **centromeres** of the chromatids. When this cohesion is broken, the chromatids separate during cell division, becoming the chromosomes of the new daughter cells. Eukaryotic cell division consists of **mitosis** (division of the nucleus) and **cytokinesis** (division of the cytoplasm).

? *Differentiate between these terms: chromosome, chromatin, and chromatid.*

CONCEPT 12.2

The mitotic phase alternates with interphase in the cell cycle (pp. 246–253)

- Between divisions, a cell is in **interphase**: the G_1, S, and G_2 phases. The cell grows throughout interphase, with DNA being replicated only during the synthesis (S) phase. Mitosis and cytokinesis make up the **mitotic (M) phase** of the cell cycle.

- The **mitotic spindle**, made up of microtubules, controls chromosome movement during mitosis. In animal cells, it arises from the **centrosomes** and includes spindle microtubules and **asters**. Some spindle microtubules attach to the **kinetochores** of chromosomes and move the chromosomes to the **metaphase plate**. After sister chromatids separate; motor proteins move them along kinetochore microtubules toward opposite ends of the cell. The cell elongates when motor proteins push nonkinetochore microtubules from opposite poles away from each other.
- Mitosis is usually followed by cytokinesis. Animal cells carry out cytokinesis by **cleavage**, and plant cells form a **cell plate**.
- During **binary fission** in bacteria, the chromosome replicates and the two daughter chromosomes actively move apart. Some of the proteins involved in bacterial binary fission are related to eukaryotic actin and tubulin.
- Since prokaryotes preceded eukaryotes by more than a billion years, it is likely that mitosis evolved from prokaryotic cell division. Certain unicellular eukaryotes exhibit mechanisms of cell division that may be similar to those of ancestors of existing eukaryotes. Such

mechanisms might represent intermediate steps in the evolution of mitosis.

? *In which of the three subphases of interphase and the stages of mitosis do chromosomes exist as single DNA molecules?*

CONCEPT 12.3

The eukaryotic cell cycle is regulated by a molecular control system (pp. 253–260)

- Signalling molecules present in the cytoplasm regulate progress through the cell cycle.
- The **cell cycle control system** is molecularly based. Cyclic changes in regulatory proteins work as a cell cycle clock. The key molecules are **cyclins** and **cyclin-dependent kinases (Cdks)**. The clock has specific **checkpoints** where the cell cycle stops until a go-ahead signal is received; important checkpoints occur in G_1, G_2, and M phases. Cell culture has enabled researchers to study the molecular details of cell division. Both internal signals and external signals control the cell cycle checkpoints via signal transduction pathways. Most cells exhibit **density-dependent inhibition** of cell division as well as **anchorage dependence**.
- Cancer cells elude normal cell cycle regulation and divide out of control, forming tumours. **Malignant tumours** invade surrounding tissues and can undergo **metastasis**, exporting cancer cells to other parts of the body, where they may form secondary tumours. Recent advances in understanding the cell cycle and cell signalling, as well as techniques for sequencing DNA, have led to improved cancer treatments.

? *Explain the significance of the G_1, G_2, and M checkpoints and the go-ahead signals involved in the cell cycle control system.*

TEST YOUR UNDERSTANDING

LEVEL 1: KNOWLEDGE/COMPREHENSION

1. Through a microscope, you can see a cell plate beginning to develop across the middle of a cell and nuclei forming on either side of the cell plate. This cell is most likely
   a. an animal cell in the process of cytokinesis.
   b. a plant cell in the process of cytokinesis.
   c. a bacterial cell dividing.
   d. a plant cell in metaphase.

2. Vinblastine is a standard chemotherapeutic drug used to treat cancer. Because it interferes with the assembly of microtubules, its effectiveness must be related to
   a. disruption of mitotic spindle formation.
   b. suppression of cyclin production.
   c. myosin denaturation and inhibition of cleavage furrow formation.
   d. inhibition of DNA synthesis.

3. One difference between cancer cells and normal cells is that cancer cells
   a. are unable to synthesize DNA.
   b. are arrested at the S phase of the cell cycle.
   c. continue to divide even when they are tightly packed together.
   d. cannot function properly because they are affected by density-dependent inhibition.

4. The decline of MPF activity at the end of mitosis is due to
   a. the destruction of the protein kinase Cdk.
   b. decreased synthesis of Cdk.
   c. the degradation of cyclin.
   d. the accumulation of cyclin.

5. In the cells of some organisms, mitosis occurs without cytokinesis. This will result in
   a. cells with more than one nucleus.
   b. cells that are unusually small.
   c. cells lacking nuclei.
   d. cell cycles lacking an S phase.

6. Which of the following does *not* occur during mitosis?
   a. condensation of the chromosomes
   b. replication of the DNA
   c. separation of sister chromatids
   d. spindle formation

LEVEL 2: APPLICATION/ANALYSIS

7. A particular cell has half as much DNA as some other cells in a mitotically active tissue. The cell in question is most likely in
   a. G_1.
   b. G_2.
   c. prophase.
   d. metaphase.

8. The drug cytochalasin B blocks the function of actin. Which of the following aspects of the animal cell cycle would be most disrupted by cytochalasin B?
   a. spindle formation
   b. spindle attachment to kinetochores
   c. cell elongation during anaphase
   d. cleavage furrow formation and cytokinesis

9. In the light micrograph below of dividing cells near the tip of an onion root, identify a cell in each of the following stages: prophase, prometaphase, metaphase, anaphase, and telophase. Describe the major events occurring at each stage.

USDA/ARS/Agricultural Research Service

10. **DRAW IT** Draw one eukaryotic chromosome as it would appear during interphase, during each of the stages of mitosis, and during cytokinesis. Also draw and label the nuclear envelope and any microtubules attached to the chromosome(s).

LEVEL 3: SYNTHESIS/EVALUATION

11. **EVOLUTION CONNECTION**
   The result of mitosis is that the daughter cells end up with the same number of chromosomes that the parent cell had. Another way to maintain the number of chromosomes would be to carry out cell division first and then duplicate the chromosomes in each daughter cell. Do you think this would be an equally good way of organizing the cell cycle? Why do you suppose that evolution has not led to this alternative?

12. **SCIENTIFIC INQUIRY**
   Although both ends of a microtubule can gain or lose subunits, one end (called the plus end) polymerizes and depolymerizes at a higher rate than the other end (the minus end). For spindle microtubules, the plus ends are in the centre of the spindle, and the minus ends are at the poles. Motor proteins that move along microtubules specialize in walking either toward the plus end or toward the minus end; the two types are called plus end–directed and minus end–directed motor proteins, respectively. Given what you know about chromosome movement and spindle changes during anaphase, predict which type of motor proteins would be present on (a) kinetochore microtubules and (b) nonkinetochore microtubules.

13. **WRITE ABOUT A THEME: INFORMATION**
   The continuity of life is based on heritable information in the form of DNA. In a short essay (100–150 words), explain how the process of mitosis faithfully parcels out exact copies of this heritable information in the production of genetically identical daughter cells.

14. **SYNTHESIZE YOUR KNOWLEDGE**

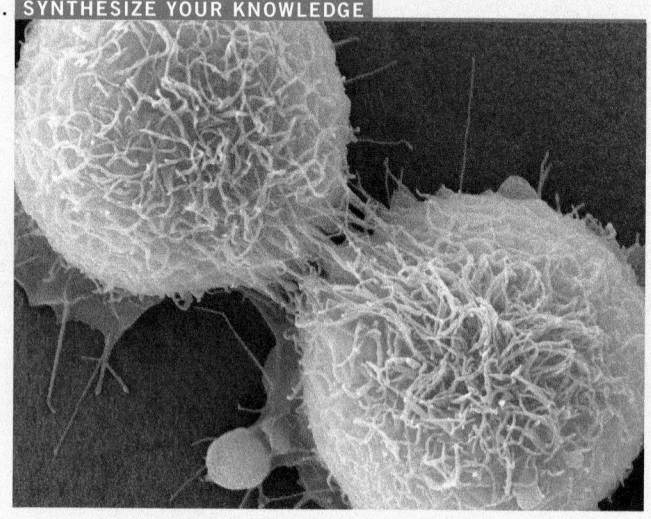

Steve Gschmeissner/Science Source

Shown here are two HeLa cancer cells that are just completing cytokinesis. Explain how the cell division of cancer cells like these is misregulated. What genetic and other changes might have caused these cells to escape normal cell cycle regulation?

For selected answers, see Appendix A.,

UNIT 3 GENETICS

AN INTERVIEW WITH
Charlie Boone

Charlie Boone did his undergraduate degree at Queen's University and his Ph.D. at McGill University. He is currently a Professor at the University of Toronto and studies systems biology and functional genomics. His research is funded by numerous grants, including those from CIHR, NSERC, Genome Canada, and the Howard Hughes Medical Institute.

> " I think it's our duty as scientists to do the most innovative and informative science possible, to move the field forward, and the most efficient way to do that is through serious collaborations with other experts and their labs. "

Used with permission from Charlie Boone/Boone Lab

▲ A correlation-based network that connects genes with genetic interaction profiles in yeast.

How did you first become interested in science?

It is the idea of being able to explore the unknown—I just like the idea of going into a place of knowledge that no one has gone before.

What are the main questions you are trying to answer in your research?

We study genetic interactions—in other words, we look at how variations in gene function combine with one another, and how mutations in two different genes can control the genotype-to-phenotype relationship. To explore this, we worked with yeast and, through collaboration, generated mutants in every single gene in the genome. Then we combined these mutants together to make all possible double mutants. For 6000 yeast genes, that is 18 million double mutants. We then score the phenotype of these double mutants for things such as additive effects or extreme negative reductions in fitness. Through this, we can produce a "global map" of all the genetic interactions in yeast.

What is the relevance of your research for students learning about genomics?

If two genes show a genetic interaction, then we know that they are functionally related to one and other, so we have learned something about what these genes do.

Genes in general will show 30–50 genetic interactions, and this gives us a nice measured pattern of their function that we can use as a way to quantify the function of a specific gene. And then you can compare all genes to other genes, and when you do that you end up creating a functional map of the cell. So it is a way of modelling cellular function and a way of modelling gene function.

What is the key "take-home" message for students about your research?

If you do systematic unbiased studies, then you can get a global picture of what is going on. If you do studies to completion, and cover the whole genome using all-by-all analysis in an unbiased fashion, you end up generating a model of the cell. We can do this for a model system like yeast, which has relatively simple genetics and a simple genome, and we could try and extrapolate that to humans. Yeast studies are basically showing us the path toward understanding life in more complex organisms.

Can you please comment on the value of collaboration between scientists?

Collaboration allows you to share ideas and expertise and thus work at a much higher level than you would be able to on your own. I think it's our duty as scientists to do the most innovative and informative science possible, to move the field forward, and the most efficient way to do that is through serious collaborations with other experts and their labs.

What do you enjoy most about life as a scientist?

I think it is really just an interesting way of life. It isn't a job. Every day we wake up and there is something happening that is novel and is interesting. So it is just a cool and unbelievably fun way to live—and you get paid for it.

What advice would you give to a biology student just starting out at university?

I think biology is one of the most exciting sciences of this century because this will be the time that we will figure out the functional wiring diagrams of all organisms, including humans. Right now we know almost nothing, but we are on the cusp of knowing everything. And if students participate in that, they will really enjoy their scientific career because they will watch everything unfold in front of them and understand it in incredible detail.

Source: Interview with Charlie Boone. Used with permission from Charlie Boone.

MAKE CONNECTIONS

Mutations and Inheritance of Cystic Fibrosis

In Unit 3 we explore the chromosomal basis and molecular basis of inheritance. How are genes passed on from parent to offspring? How do mutations occur, and how do those mutations cause disease?

Chromatid
(700 nm)

Replicated
chromosome
(1400 nm)

300-nm fibre

Loops

Scaffold

30-nm fibre

H1

Nucleosome
(10 nm in diameter)

Histone tail

Histones

DNA
double helix
(2 nm in diameter)

Chromosome 7

Chromosome 7 contains the gene responsible for cystic fibrosis. This gene encodes the cystic fibrosis transmembrane conductance regulator (or CFTR), a chloride channel.

— 7p22.3

p

— 7p11.2
— 7q11.22

q   *CFTR*
            7q31.2

— 7q36.3

The CFTR gene

The CFTR gene is about 189 kilobases long, and contains 27 exons. More than 1600 mutations can cause cystic fibrosis, but the most common mutation is a 3 base pair deletion, which results in the loss of phenylalanine at position 508 (delta F508). A database of all cystic fibrosis mutations found to date is maintained at the Hospital for Sick Children in Toronto, Ontario. The specific type and location of the mutation impacts the severity of the disease. (See Figure 17.27)

Simon Fraser/Science Source

Cystic Fibrosis (CF)

Cystic Fibrosis (CF) is the most common lethal genetic disease in Canada and affects one out of every 2500 people of European descent. If the CFTR protein doesn't function properly, then the build-up of chloride ions inside the cell leads to an electrolyte imbalance that causes thick and sticky mucus to accumulate outside the cell, leading to chronic bronchitis, recurrent bacterial infections (as seen in this X-ray), and poor nutrient absorption in the intestines. Untreated cystic fibrosis can lead to death before age 5, but with current treatment, more than half of CF patients in Canada survive into their 30s and beyond. (See Concept 14.4)

Cystic Fibrosis Treatment

Cystic fibrosis treatment includes antibiotics to prevent infection, gentle pounding on the chest to clear mucus from clogged airways, and lung transplantation if other treatments have not worked.

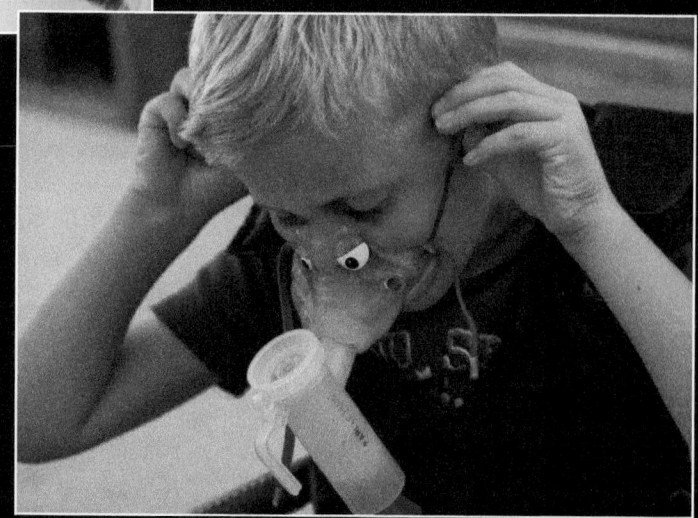

Paul Ro/Alamy Stock Photo

The CFTR protein

The CFTR protein acts as a chloride channel in cell membranes. It is found in cells that line passageways in the lungs, liver, intestines, reproductive tracts, pancreas, and skin. Mutations can cause the protein to misfold and not insert properly into the membrane. This can disrupt epithelial ion transport by causing decreased chloride secretion into the extracellular fluid, which also lowers the passive transport of sodium ions and water out of the cell. This results in the extracellular build-up of thick and sticky mucus.

Genetics of Cystic Fibrosis Transmission

Cystic fibrosis is an autosomal recessive disorder, which means that two mutated alleles are needed in order for an individual to show the disease. If a mother and father do not have cystic fibrosis, but are carriers, then they have a ¼ chance of having a child affected with cystic fibrosis. (See Concept 14.2)

Both parents are carriers of a mutated CF-allele

Phenotypically normal child; non-carrier of CF

Phenotypically normal child; carrier of CF

Child affected with CF

	Parents Normal *Aa* × Normal *Aa*	
	Sperm (A)	(a)
Eggs (A)	*AA* Normal	*Aa* Normal (carrier)
(a)	*Aa* Normal (carrier)	*aa* Cystic fibrosis

Phenotypically normal child; non-carrier of CF

A non-carrier of the CF mutation possesses two normal versions of the allele. All CFTR proteins that are produced are normal, and a functioning chloride channel is able to transport chloride across the plasma membrane.

Phenotypically normal child; carrier of CF
A carrier of the CF mutation possesses a normal version of the allele as well as a mutated version. Half of the proteins made are normal, and half contain the mutation. The normal proteins perform enough chloride transport such that symptoms are not usually seen.

Child affected with CF

An affected individual possesses two mutant versions of the allele. All proteins made are abnormal. If the mutation is a severe mutation, such as the delta F508 mutation, the protein does not get transported to the plasma membrane and instead gets targeted for degradation (not shown).

13

Meiosis and Sexual Life Cycles

KEY CONCEPTS

13.1 Offspring acquire genes from parents by inheriting chromosomes

13.2 Fertilization and meiosis alternate in sexual life cycles

13.3 Meiosis reduces the number of chromosome sets from diploid to haploid

13.4 Genetic variation produced in sexual life cycles contributes to evolution

Don W. Fawcett/Science Source

Canadian Press Images

▲ **Figure 13.1 What accounts for family resemblance?**

Variations on a Theme

We all know that offspring resemble their parents more than they do unrelated individuals. If you examine Canadian actor Eugene Levy and his son Dan shown in **Figure 13.1**, you can pick out some similar features between them. The transmission of traits from one generation to the next is called inheritance, or **heredity** (from the Latin *heres*, heir). However, sons and daughters are not identical copies of either parent or of their siblings. Along with inherited similarity, there is also **variation**. What are the biological mechanisms leading to the "family resemblance" evident between the father and son in the photo above? The answer to this question eluded biologists until the advance of genetics in the 20th century.

Genetics is the scientific study of heredity and hereditary variation. In this unit, you'll learn about genetics at multiple levels, from organisms to cells to molecules. We begin by examining how chromosomes pass from parents to offspring in sexually reproducing organisms. The processes of meiosis (a special type of cell division) and fertilization (the fusion of sperm and egg, as seen in the photo at the left) maintain a species' chromosome count during the sexual life cycle. We will describe the cellular mechanics of meiosis and explain how this process differs from mitosis. Finally, we will consider how both meiosis and fertilization contribute to genetic variation, such as the variation obvious in the father and son shown in Figure 13.1.

CONCEPT 13.1

Offspring acquire genes from parents by inheriting chromosomes

Family friends may tell you that you have your mother's freckles or your father's eyes. Of course, parents do not, in any literal sense, give their children freckles, eyes, hair, or any other traits. What, then, *is* actually inherited?

Inheritance of Genes

Parents endow their offspring with coded information in the form of hereditary units called **genes**. The genes we inherit from our mothers and fathers are our genetic link to our parents, and they account for family resemblances such as shared eye colour or freckles. Our genes program the specific traits that emerge as we develop from fertilized eggs into adults.

The genetic program is written in the language of DNA, the polymer of four different nucleotides you learned about in Concepts 1.1 and 5.5. Inherited information is passed on in the form of each gene's specific sequence of DNA nucleotides, much as printed information is communicated in the form of meaningful sequences of letters. In both cases, the language is symbolic. Just as your brain translates the word *apple* into a mental image of the fruit, cells translate genes into freckles and other features. Most genes program cells to synthesize specific enzymes and other proteins, whose cumulative action produces an organism's inherited traits. The programming of these traits in the form of DNA is one of the unifying themes of biology.

The transmission of hereditary traits has its molecular basis in the replication of DNA, which produces copies of genes that can be passed from parents to offspring. In animals and plants, reproductive cells called **gametes** are the vehicles that transmit genes from one generation to the next. During fertilization, male and female gametes (sperm and eggs) unite, passing on genes of both parents to their offspring.

Except for small amounts of DNA in mitochondria and chloroplasts, the DNA of a eukaryotic cell is packaged into chromosomes within the nucleus. Every species has a characteristic number of chromosomes. For example, humans have 46 chromosomes in their **somatic cells**—all cells of the body except the gametes and their precursors. Each chromosome consists of a single long DNA molecule elaborately coiled in association with various proteins. One chromosome includes several hundred to a few thousand genes, each of which is a specific sequence of nucleotides within the DNA molecule. A gene's specific location along the length of a chromosome is called the gene's **locus** (plural, *loci*; from the Latin, meaning "place"). Our genetic endowment (our genome) consists of the genes and other DNA that make up the chromosomes we inherited from our parents.

Comparison of Asexual and Sexual Reproduction

Only organisms that reproduce asexually have offspring that are exact genetic copies of themselves. In **asexual reproduction**, a single individual is the sole parent and passes copies of all its genes to its offspring without the fusion of gametes. For example, single-celled eukaryotic organisms can reproduce asexually by mitotic cell division, in which DNA is copied and allocated equally to two daughter cells. The genomes of the offspring are virtually exact copies of the parent's genome. Some multicellular organisms are also capable of reproducing asexually (Figure 13.2). Because the cells of the offspring are derived by mitosis in the parent, the "chip off the old block" is usually genetically identical to its parent. An individual that reproduces asexually gives rise to a **clone**, a group of genetically identical individuals. Genetic differences occasionally arise in asexually reproducing organisms as a result of changes in the DNA called mutations, which we will discuss in Chapter 17.

In **sexual reproduction**, two parents give rise to offspring that have unique combinations of genes inherited from the two parents. In contrast to a clone, offspring of sexual reproduction vary genetically from their siblings and both parents: They are variations on a common theme of family resemblance, not exact replicas. Genetic variation like that shown in Figure 13.1 is an important consequence of sexual reproduction. What mechanisms generate this genetic variation? The key is the behaviour of chromosomes during the sexual life cycle.

(a) Hydra   (b) Redwoods

▲ **Figure 13.2 Asexual reproduction in two multicellular organisms.** **(a)** This relatively simple animal, a hydra, reproduces by budding. The bud, a localized mass of mitotically dividing cells, develops into a small hydra, which detaches from the parent (LM). **(b)** All the trees in this circle of redwoods arose asexually from a single parent tree, whose stump is in the centre of the circle.

1. **MAKE CONNECTIONS** Using what you know about gene expression in a cell, explain what causes the traits of parents (such as hair colour) to show up in their offspring. (See Concept 5.5.)

2. How do asexually reproducing eukaryotic organisms produce offspring that are genetically identical to each other and to their parents?

3. **WHAT IF?** A horticulturalist breeds orchids, trying to obtain a plant with a unique combination of desirable traits. After many years, she finally succeeds. To produce more plants like this one, should she cross-breed it with another plant or clone it? Why?

For suggested answers, see Appendix A.

CONCEPT 13.2

Fertilization and meiosis alternate in sexual life cycles

A **life cycle** is the generation-to-generation sequence of stages in the reproductive history of an organism, from conception to production of its own offspring. In this section, we use humans as an example to track the behaviour of chromosomes through the sexual life cycle. We begin by considering the chromosome count in human somatic cells and gametes. We will then explore how the behaviour of chromosomes relates to the human life cycle and other types of sexual life cycles.

Sets of Chromosomes in Human Cells

In humans, each somatic cell has 46 chromosomes. During mitosis, the chromosomes become condensed enough to be visible under a light microscope. At this point, they can be distinguished from one another by their size, the positions of their centromeres, and the pattern of coloured bands produced by certain chromatin-binding stains.

Careful examination of a micrograph of the 46 human chromosomes from a single cell in mitosis reveals that there are two chromosomes of each of 23 types. This becomes clear when images of the chromosomes are arranged in pairs, starting with the longest chromosomes. The resulting ordered display is called a **karyotype** (Figure 13.3). The two chromosomes of a pair have the same length, centromere position, and staining pattern: These are called **homologous chromosomes**, or homologues. Both chromosomes of each pair carry genes controlling the same inherited characters. For example, if a gene for eye colour is situated at a particular locus on a certain chromosome, then the homologue of that chromosome will also have a version of the same gene specifying eye colour at the equivalent locus.

The two distinct chromosomes referred to as X and Y are an important exception to the general pattern of homologous chromosomes in human somatic cells. Human females have a homologous pair of X chromosomes (XX),

▼ Figure 13.3 | **Research Method**

Preparing a Karyotype

Application A karyotype is a display of condensed chromosomes arranged in pairs. Karyotyping can be used to screen for defective chromosomes or abnormal numbers of chromosomes associated with certain congenital disorders, such as trisomy 21 (Down syndrome).

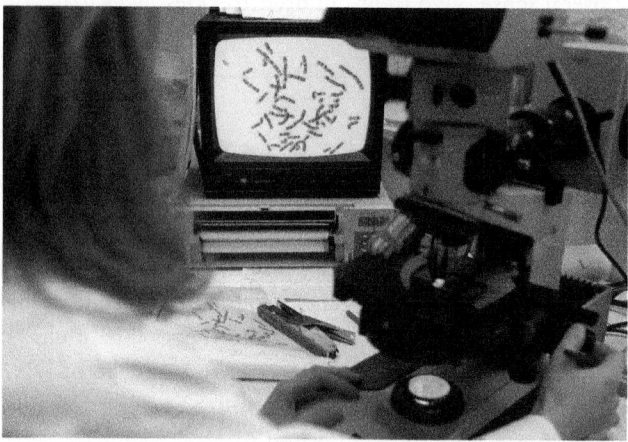

Véronique Burger/Science Source

Technique Karyotypes are prepared from isolated somatic cells, which are treated with a drug to stimulate mitosis and then grown in culture for several days. Cells arrested in metaphase, when chromosomes are most highly condensed, are stained and then viewed with a microscope equipped with a digital camera. A photograph of the chromosomes is displayed on a computer monitor, and digital software is used to arrange them in pairs according to their appearance.

CNRI/Science Source

Results This karyotype shows the chromosomes from a normal human male, digitally coloured to emphasize their banding patterns. The size of the chromosome, position of the centromere, and pattern of stained bands help identify specific chromosomes. Although difficult to discern in the karyotype, each metaphase chromosome consists of two closely attached sister chromatids (see the diagram of a pair of homologous duplicated chromosomes).

but males have one X and one Y chromosome (XY). Only small parts of the X and Y are homologous. Most of the genes carried on the X chromosome do not have counterparts on the tiny Y, and the Y chromosome has genes lacking on the X. Because they determine an individual's sex, the X and Y chromosomes are called **sex chromosomes**. The other chromosomes are called **autosomes**.

The pairs of homologous chromosomes in each human somatic cell are a consequence of our sexual origins. We inherit one chromosome of each pair from each parent. Thus, the 46 chromosomes in our somatic cells are actually two sets of 23 chromosomes—a maternal set (from our mother) and a paternal set (from our father). The number of chromosomes in a single set is represented by n. Any cell with two chromosome sets is called a **diploid cell** and has a diploid number of chromosomes, abbreviated $2n$. For humans, the diploid number is 46 ($2n = 46$), the number of chromosomes in our somatic cells. In a cell in which DNA synthesis has occurred, all the chromosomes are duplicated, and therefore each consists of two identical sister chromatids, associated closely at the centromere and along the arms. (Even though the chromosomes are duplicated, we still say the cell is diploid ($2n$) because it has only two sets of information.) **Figure 13.4** helps clarify the various terms that we use to describe duplicated chromosomes in a diploid cell.

Unlike somatic cells, gametes contain a single set of chromosomes. Such cells are called **haploid cells**, and each has a haploid number of chromosomes (n). For humans, the

haploid number is 23 ($n = 23$). The set of 23 consists of the 22 autosomes plus a single sex chromosome. An unfertilized egg contains an X chromosome, but a sperm may contain an X or a Y chromosome.

Each sexually reproducing species has a characteristic diploid number and haploid number. For example, the fruit fly, *Drosophila melanogaster*, has a diploid number ($2n$) of 8 and a haploid number (n) of 4, while for dogs, $2n$ is 78 and n is 39. Now let's consider chromosome behaviour during sexual life cycles. We'll use the human life cycle as an example.

Behaviour of Chromosome Sets in the Human Life Cycle

The human life cycle begins when a haploid sperm from the father fuses with a haploid egg from the mother (**Figure 13.5**). This union of gametes, culminating in fusion of their nuclei, is called **fertilization**. The resulting fertilized egg, or **zygote**, is diploid because it contains two haploid sets of chromosomes bearing genes representing the maternal and paternal family lines.

▲ **Figure 13.4 Describing chromosomes.** A cell from an organism with a diploid number of 6 ($2n = 6$) is depicted here following chromosome duplication and condensation. Each of the six duplicated chromosomes consists of two sister chromatids associated closely along their lengths. Each homologous pair is composed of one chromosome from the maternal set (red) and one from the paternal set (blue). Each set is made up of three chromosomes in this example (long, medium, and short). Together, one maternal and one paternal chromatid in a pair of homologous chromosomes are called nonsister chromatids.

[?] *How many sets of chromosomes are present in this diagram? How many pairs of homologous chromosomes are present?*

▲ **Figure 13.5 The human life cycle.** In each generation, the number of chromosome sets doubles at fertilization but is halved during meiosis. For humans, the number of chromosomes in a haploid cell is 23, consisting of one set ($n = 23$); the number of chromosomes in the diploid zygote and all somatic cells arising from it is 46, consisting of two sets ($2n = 46$).

This figure introduces a colour code that will be used for other life cycles later in this book. The aqua arrows identify haploid stages of a life cycle, and the tan arrows identify diploid stages.

As a human develops into a sexually mature adult, mitosis of the zygote and its descendant cells generates all the somatic cells of the body. Both chromosome sets in the zygote and all the genes they carry are passed with precision to the somatic cells.

The only cells of the human body not produced by mitosis are the gametes, which develop from specialized cells called *germ cells* in the gonads—ovaries in females and testes in males. Imagine what would happen if human gametes were made by mitosis: They would be diploid like the somatic cells. At the next round of fertilization, when two gametes fused, the normal chromosome number of 46 would double to 92, and each subsequent generation would double the number of chromosomes yet again. This does not happen, however, because in sexually reproducing organisms, gamete formation involves a type of cell division called **meiosis**. This type of cell division reduces the number of sets of chromosomes from two to one in the gametes, counterbalancing the doubling that occurs at fertilization. As a result of meiosis, each human sperm and egg is haploid ($n = 23$). Fertilization restores the diploid condition by combining two haploid sets of chromosomes, and the human life cycle is repeated, generation after generation (see Figure 13.5).

In general, the steps of the human life cycle are typical of many sexually reproducing animals. Indeed, the processes of fertilization and meiosis are the hallmarks of sexual reproduction in plants, fungi, and protists as well as in animals. Fertilization and meiosis alternate in sexual life cycles, maintaining a constant number of chromosomes in each species from one generation to the next.

The Variety of Sexual Life Cycles

Although the alternation of meiosis and fertilization is common to all organisms that reproduce sexually, the timing of these two events in the life cycle varies, depending on the species. These variations can be grouped into three main types of life cycles. In the type that occurs in humans and most other animals, gametes are the only haploid cells (Figure 13.6a). Meiosis occurs in germ cells during the production of gametes, which undergo no further cell division prior to fertilization. After fertilization, the diploid zygote divides by mitosis, producing a multicellular organism that is diploid.

Plants and some species of algae exhibit a second type of life cycle called **alternation of generations** (Figure 13.6b). This type includes both diploid and haploid stages that are multicellular. The multicellular diploid stage is called the *sporophyte*. Meiosis in the sporophyte produces haploid cells called *spores*. Unlike a gamete, a haploid spore doesn't fuse with another cell but divides mitotically, generating a multicellular haploid stage called the *gametophyte*. Cells of the gametophyte give rise to gametes by mitosis. Fusion of two haploid gametes at fertilization results in a diploid zygote, which develops into the next sporophyte generation. Therefore, in this type of life cycle, the sporophyte generation produces a gametophyte as its offspring, and the gametophyte generation produces the next sporophyte generation (see Figure 13.6b). Clearly, the term *alternation of generations* is a fitting name for this type of life cycle.

▲ Figure 13.6 **Three types of sexual life cycles.** The common feature of all three cycles is the alternation of meiosis and fertilization, key events that contribute to genetic variation among offspring. The cycles differ in the timing of these two key events.

A third type of life cycle occurs in most fungi and some protists, including some algae (Figure 13.6c). After gametes fuse and form a diploid zygote, meiosis occurs without a multicellular diploid offspring developing. Meiosis produces not gametes but haploid cells that then divide by mitosis and give rise to either unicellular descendants or a haploid multicellular adult organism. Subsequently, the haploid organism carries out further mitoses, producing the cells that develop into gametes. The only diploid stage found in these species is the single-celled zygote.

Note that *either* haploid or diploid cells can divide by mitosis, depending on the type of life cycle. Only diploid cells, however, can undergo meiosis because haploid cells have only a single set of chromosomes that cannot be further reduced. Though the three types of sexual life cycles differ in the timing of meiosis and fertilization, they share a fundamental result: genetic variation among offspring.

CONCEPT CHECK 13.2

1. **MAKE CONNECTIONS** In Figure 13.4, how many DNA molecules (double helices) are present (see Figure 12.5)? What is the haploid number of this cell? Is a set of chromosomes haploid or diploid?

2. In the karyotype shown in Figure 13.3, how many pairs of chromosomes are present? How many sets?

3. **WHAT IF?** A certain eukaryote lives as a unicellular organism, but during environmental stress it produces gametes. The gametes fuse, and the resulting zygote undergoes meiosis, generating new single cells. What type of organism could this be?

For suggested answers, see Appendix A.

CONCEPT 13.3

Meiosis reduces the number of chromosome sets from diploid to haploid

Many of the steps of meiosis closely resemble corresponding steps in mitosis. Meiosis, like mitosis, is preceded by the duplication of chromosomes. However, this single duplication is followed by not one but two consecutive cell divisions, called **meiosis I** and **meiosis II**. These two divisions result in four daughter cells (rather than the two daughter cells of mitosis), each with only half as many chromosomes as the parent cell—one set, rather than two.

The Stages of Meiosis

The overview of meiosis in **Figure 13.7** shows, for a single pair of homologous chromosomes in a diploid cell, that both members of the pair are duplicated and the copies sorted into four haploid daughter cells. Recall that sister chromatids are two copies of *one* chromosome, closely associated all along their lengths; this association is called *sister chromatid cohesion*. Together, the sister chromatids make up

▲ Figure 13.7 **Overview of meiosis: how meiosis reduces chromosome number.** After the chromosomes duplicate in interphase, the diploid cell divides twice, yielding four haploid daughter cells. This overview tracks just one pair of homologous chromosomes, which for the sake of simplicity are drawn in the condensed state throughout.

DRAW IT *Redraw the cells in this figure using a simple double helix to represent each DNA molecule.*

one duplicated chromosome (see Figure 13.4). In contrast, the two chromosomes of a homologous pair are individual chromosomes that were inherited from different parents. Homologues appear alike in the microscope, but they may have different versions of genes, each called an *allele*, at corresponding loci. Homologues are not associated with each other in any obvious way except during meiosis, as you will soon see.

Figure 13.8 describes in detail the two divisions of meiosis for an animal cell whose diploid number is 6. Study this figure thoroughly before going on.

Exploring Meiosis in an Animal Cell

MEIOSIS I: Separates homologous chromosomes

Prophase I	Metaphase I	Anaphase I	Telophase I and Cytokinesis

Centrosome (with centriole pair)

Sister chromatids

Chiasmata

Spindle

Homologous chromosomes

Fragments of nuclear envelope

Duplicated homologous chromosomes (red and blue) pair and exchange segments; 2n = 6 in this example.

Centromere (with kinetochore)

Metaphase plate

Microtubules attached to kinetochore

Chromosomes line up by homologous pairs.

Sister chromatids remain attached

Homologous chromosomes separate

Each pair of homologous chromosomes separates.

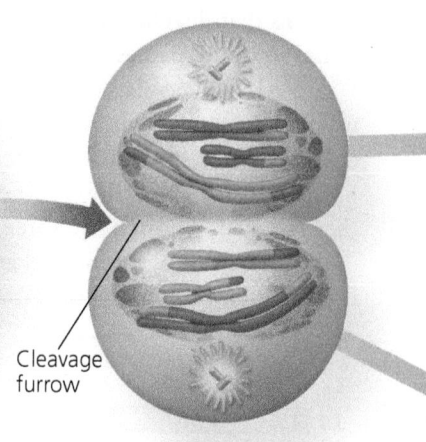

Cleavage furrow

Two haploid cells form; each chromosome still consists of two sister chromatids.

Prophase I

- Centrosome movement, spindle formation, and nuclear envelope breakdown occur as in mitosis. Chromosomes condense progressively throughout prophase I.

- During early prophase I, before the stage shown above, each chromosome pairs with its homolog, aligned gene by gene, and **crossing over** occurs: The DNA molecules of nonsister chromatids are broken (by proteins) and are rejoined to each other.

- At the stage shown above, each homologous pair has one or more X-shaped regions called **chiasmata** (singular, *chiasma*), where crossovers have occurred.

- Later in prophase I, after the stage shown above, microtubules from one pole or the other will attach to the two kinetochores, one at the centromere of each homologue. (The two kinetochores of a homologue, not yet visible above, act as a single kinetochore.) The homologous pairs will then move toward the metaphase plate.

Metaphase I

- Pairs of homologous chromosomes are now arranged at the metaphase plate, with one chromosome in each pair facing each pole.

- Both chromatids of one homologue are attached to kinetochore microtubules from one pole; those of the other homologue are attached to microtubules from the opposite pole.

Anaphase I

- Breakdown of proteins that are responsible for sister chromatid cohesion along chromatid arms allows homologues to separate.

- The homologues move toward opposite poles, guided by the spindle apparatus.

- Sister chromatid cohesion persists at the centromere, causing chromatids to move as a unit toward the same pole.

Telophase I and Cytokinesis

- When telophase I begins, each half of the cell has a complete haploid set of duplicated chromosomes. Each chromosome is composed of two sister chromatids; one or both chromatids include regions of nonsister chromatid DNA.

- Cytokinesis (division of the cytoplasm) usually occurs simultaneously with telophase I, forming two haploid daughter cells.

- In animal cells like these, a cleavage furrow forms. (In plant cells, a cell plate forms.)

- In some species, chromosomes decondense and nuclear envelopes form.

- No chromosome duplication occurs between meiosis I and meiosis II.

MEIOSIS II: Separates sister chromatids

Prophase II	Metaphase II	Anaphase II	Telophase II and Cytokinesis

During another round of cell division, the sister chromatids finally separate; four haploid daughter cells result, containing unduplicated chromosomes.

Sister chromatids separate

Haploid daughter cells forming

Prophase II

- A spindle apparatus forms.

- In late prophase II (not shown here), chromosomes, each still composed of two chromatids associated at the centromere, move toward the metaphase II plate.

Metaphase II

- The chromosomes are positioned at the metaphase plate as in mitosis.

- Because of crossing over in meiosis I, the two sister chromatids of each chromosome are *not* genetically identical.

- The kinetochores of sister chromatids are attached to microtubules extending from opposite poles.

Anaphase II

- Breakdown of proteins holding the sister chromatids together at the centromere allows the chromatids to separate. The chromatids move toward opposite poles as individual chromosomes.

Telophase II and Cytokinesis

- Nuclei form, the chromosomes begin decondensing, and cytokinesis occurs.

- The meiotic division of one parent cell produces four daughter cells, each with a haploid set of (unduplicated) chromosomes.

- The four daughter cells are genetically distinct from one another and from the parent cell.

MAKE CONNECTIONS *Look at Figure 12.7 and imagine the two daughter cells undergoing another round of mitosis, yielding four cells. Compare the number of chromosomes in each of those four cells, after mitosis, with the number in each cell in Figure 13.8, after meiosis. What is it about the process of meiosis that accounts for this difference, even though meiosis also includes two cell divisions?*

ANIMATION **BioFlix** Visit the Study Area in **MasteringBiology** for the BioFlix® 3-D Animation on Meiosis.

Crossing Over and Synapsis During Prophase I

Prophase I of meiosis is a very busy time. The prophase I cell shown in Figure 13.8 is at a point fairly late in prophase I, when homologous pairing, crossing over, and chromosome condensation have already taken place. The sequence of events leading up to that point is shown in more detail in **Figure 13.9**.

After interphase, the chromosomes have been duplicated and the sister chromatids are held together by proteins called *cohesins*. Early in prophase I, the two members of a homologous pair associate loosely along their length. Each gene on one homologue is aligned precisely with the corresponding gene on the other homologue. The DNA of two nonsister chromatids—one maternal and one paternal—is broken by specific proteins at precisely corresponding points. Next, the formation of a zipperlike structure called the *synaptonemal complex* holds one homologue tightly to the other. During this association, called *synapsis*, the DNA breaks are closed up so that each broken end is joined to the corresponding segment of the nonsister chromatid. Thus, a paternal chromatid is joined to a piece of maternal chromatid beyond the crossover point, and vice versa.

These points of crossing over become visible as chiasmata (singular, chiasma) after the synaptonemal complex disassembles and the homologues move slightly apart from each other. The homologues remain attached because sister chromatids are still held together by sister chromatid cohesion, even though some of the DNA may no longer be attached to its original chromosome. At least one crossover per chromosome must occur in order for the homologous pair to stay together as it moves to the metaphase I plate.

A Comparison of Mitosis and Meiosis

Figure 13.10 summarizes the key differences between meiosis and mitosis in diploid cells. Basically, meiosis reduces the number of chromosome sets from two (diploid) to one (haploid), whereas mitosis conserves the number of chromosome sets. Therefore, meiosis produces cells that differ genetically from their parent cell and from each other, whereas mitosis produces daughter cells that are genetically identical to their parent cell and to each other.

Three events unique to meiosis occur during meiosis I:

1. **Synapsis and crossing over.** During prophase I, duplicated homologues pair up, and the formation of the synaptonemal complex between them holds them in **synapsis**. Crossing over also occurs, as described above. Synapsis and crossing over normally do not occur during prophase of mitosis.

2. **Homologous pairs at the metaphase plate.** At metaphase I of meiosis, chromosomes are positioned at the metaphase plate as pairs of homologues rather than individual chromosomes, as in metaphase of mitosis.

1 After interphase, the chromosomes have been duplicated and sister chromatids are held together by proteins called cohesins (purple). Each pair of homologues associate along their length. The DNA molecules of two nonsister chromatids are broken at precisely corresponding points. The chromatin of the chromosomes is beginning to condense.

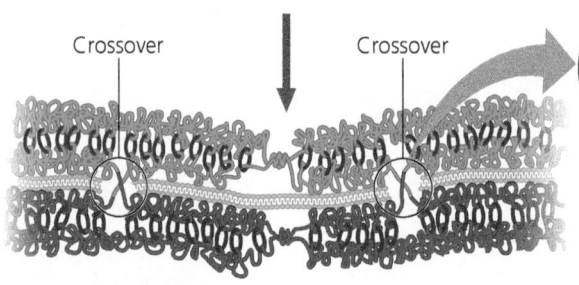

2 A zipperlike protein complex, the synaptonemal complex (green), begins to form, attaching one homologue to the other. The chromatin continues to condense.

3 The synaptonemal complex is fully formed; the two homologues are said to be in synapsis. During synapsis, the DNA breaks are closed up when each broken end is joined to the corresponding segment of the nonsister chromatid, producing crossovers.

4 After the synaptonemal complex disassembles, the homologues move slightly apart from each other but remain attached because of sister chromatid cohesion, even though some of the DNA may no longer be attached to its original chromosome. The points of attachment where crossovers have occurred show up as chiasmata. The chromosomes continue to condense as they move toward the metaphase plate.

▲ **Figure 13.9 Crossing over and synapsis in prophase I: a closer look.** For simplicity, the four chromatids of the homologous pair shown here are depicted side by side, but in reality, the blue chromosome would be right on top of the red one (see the top cell in Figure 13.12).

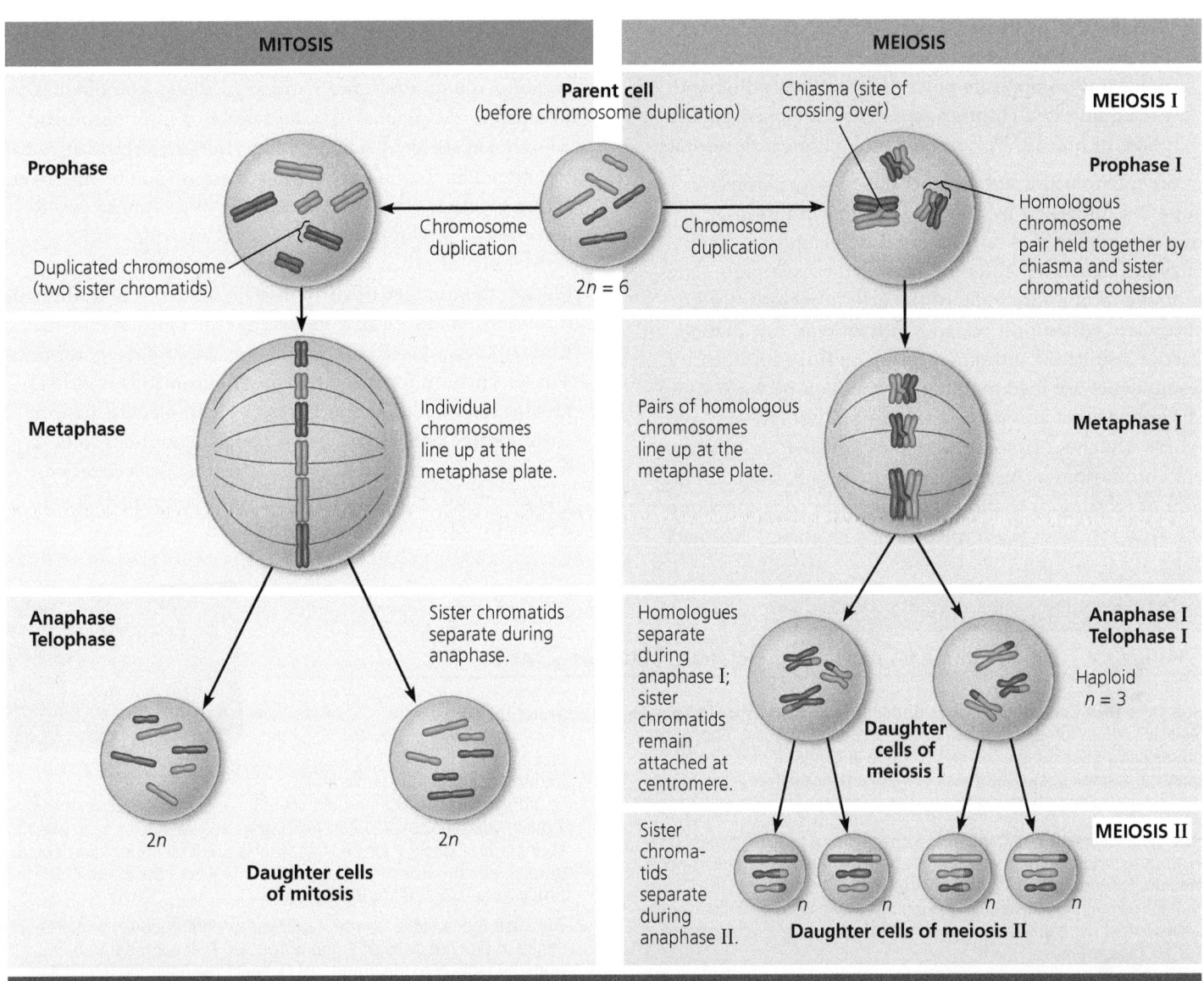

MITOSIS	MEIOSIS

Parent cell
(before chromosome duplication)

Chiasma (site of crossing over)

MEIOSIS I

Prophase

Duplicated chromosome (two sister chromatids)

Chromosome duplication

Chromosome duplication

$2n = 6$

Prophase I

Homologous chromosome pair held together by chiasma and sister chromatid cohesion

Metaphase

Individual chromosomes line up at the metaphase plate.

Pairs of homologous chromosomes line up at the metaphase plate.

Metaphase I

Anaphase
Telophase

Sister chromatids separate during anaphase.

Homologues separate during anaphase I; sister chromatids remain attached at centromere.

Anaphase I
Telophase I

Haploid $n = 3$

Daughter cells of meiosis I

$2n$ $2n$

Daughter cells of mitosis

Sister chromatids separate during anaphase II.

MEIOSIS II

n n n n

Daughter cells of meiosis II

SUMMARY

Property	Mitosis (occurs in both diploid and haploid cells)	Meiosis (can only occur in diploid cells)
DNA replication	Occurs during interphase before mitosis begins	Occurs during interphase before meiosis I begins
Number of divisions	One, including prophase, prometaphase, metaphase, anaphase, and telophase	Two, each including prophase, metaphase, anaphase, and telophase
Synapsis of homologous chromosomes	Does not occur	Occurs during prophase I along with crossing over between nonsister chromatids; resulting chiasmata hold pairs together due to sister chromatid cohesion
Number of daughter cells and genetic composition	Two, each genetically identical to the parent cell, with the same number of chromosomes	Four, each haploid (n); genetically different from the parent cell and from each other
Role in the animal or plant body	Enables multicellular animal or plant (gametophyte or sporophyte) to arise from a single cell; produces cells for growth, repair, and, in some species, asexual reproduction; produces gametes in the gametophyte plant	Produces gametes (in animals) or spores (in the sporophyte plant); reduces number of chromosome sets by half and introduces genetic variability among the gametes or spores

▲ Figure 13.10 **A comparison of mitosis and meiosis in diploid cells.**

DRAW IT *Could any other combinations of chromosomes be generated during meiosis II from the specific cells shown in telophase I? Explain. (Hint: Draw the cells as they would appear in metaphase II.)*

3. **Separation of homologues.** At anaphase I of meiosis, the duplicated chromosomes of each homologous pair move toward opposite poles, but the sister chromatids of each duplicated chromosome remain attached. In anaphase of mitosis, by contrast, sister chromatids separate.

Sister chromatids stay together due to sister chromatid cohesion, mediated by cohesin proteins. In mitosis, this attachment lasts until the end of metaphase, when enzymes cleave the cohesins, freeing the sister chromatids to move to opposite poles of the cell. In meiosis, sister chromatid cohesion is released in two steps, one at the start of anaphase I and one at anaphase II. In metaphase I, homologues are held together by cohesion between sister chromatid arms in regions beyond points of crossing over, where stretches of sister chromatids now belong to different chromosomes. As shown in Figure 13.8, the combination of crossing over and sister chromatid cohesion along the arms results in the formation of a chiasma. Chiasmata

hold homologues together as the spindle forms for the first meiotic division. At the onset of anaphase I, the release of cohesion along sister chromatid arms allows homologues to separate. At anaphase II, the release of sister chromatid cohesion at the centromeres allows the sister chromatids to separate. Thus, sister chromatid cohesion and crossing over, acting together, play an essential role in the lining up of chromosomes by homologous pairs at metaphase I.

Meiosis I is called the *reductional division* because it reduces the number of chromosome sets from two (diploid) to one (haploid). During meiosis II (the *equational division*), sister chromatids separate, producing haploid daughter cells. The mechanism for separating sister chromatids is virtually identical in meiosis II and mitosis. The molecular basis of chromosome behaviour during meiosis continues to be a focus of intense research. In the Scientific Skills Exercise, you can work with data tracking the amount of DNA in cells as they progress through meiosis.

SCIENTIFIC SKILLS EXERCISE

Making a Line Graph and Converting Between Units of Data

How Does DNA Content Change as Budding Yeast Cells Proceed Through Meiosis? When nutrients are low, cells of the budding yeast (*Saccharomyces cerevisiae*) exit the mitotic cell cycle and enter meiosis. In this exercise, you will track the DNA content of a population of yeast cells as they progress through meiosis.

How the Experiment Was Done Researchers grew a culture of yeast cells in a nutrient-rich medium and then transferred them to a nutrient-poor medium to induce meiosis. At different times after induction, the DNA content per cell was measured in a sample of the cells, and the average DNA content per cell was recorded in femtograms (fg; 1 femtogram = 1×10^{-15} gram).

Data from the Experiment

Time After Induction (hours)	Average Amount of DNA per Cell (fg)
0.0	24.0
1.0	24.0
2.0	40.0
3.0	47.0
4.0	47.5
5.0	48.0
6.0	48.0
7.0	47.5
7.5	25.0
8.0	24.0
9.0	23.5
9.5	14.0
10.0	13.0
11.0	12.5
12.0	12.0
13.0	12.5
14.0	12.0

Interpret the Data

1. First, set up your graph. (a) Place the labels for the independent variable and the dependent variable on the appropriate axes, followed by units of measurement in parentheses. Explain your choices. (b) Add tick marks and values for each axis in your graph. Explain your choices. (For additional information about graphs, see the Scientific Skills Review in Appendix E and in the Study Area in MasteringBiology.)

SCIMAT/Science Source

2. Because the variable on the *x*-axis varies continuously, it makes sense to plot the data on a line graph. (a) Plot each data point from the table onto the graph. (b) Connect the data points with line segments.

3. Most of the yeast cells in the culture were in G_1 of the cell cycle before being moved to the nutrient-poor medium. (a) How many femtograms of DNA are there in each yeast cell in G_1? Estimate this value from the data in your graph. (b) How many femtograms of DNA should be present in each cell in G_2? (See Concept 12.2 and Figure 12.6.) At the end of meiosis I (MI)? At the end of meiosis II (MII)? (See Figure 13.7.) (c) Using these values as a guideline, distinguish the different phases by inserting vertical dashed lines in the graph between phases and label each phase (G_1, S, G_2, MI, MII). You can figure out where to put the dividing lines based on what you know about the DNA content of each phase (see Figure 13.7). (d) Think carefully about the point where the line at the highest value begins to slope downward. What specific point of meiosis does this "corner" represent? What stage(s) correspond to the downward sloping line?

4. Given the fact that 1 fg of DNA = 9.78×10^5 base pairs (on average), you can convert the amount of DNA per cell to the length of DNA in numbers of base pairs. (a) Calculate the number of base pairs of DNA in the haploid yeast genome. Express your answer in millions of base pairs (Mb), a standard unit for expressing genome size. Show your work. (b) How many base pairs per minute were synthesized during the S phase of these yeast cells?

Further Reading G. Simchen, Commitment to meiosis: What determines the mode of division in budding yeast? *BioEssays* 31:169–177 (2009).

1. **MAKE CONNECTIONS** Compare the chromosomes in a cell at metaphase of mitosis with those in a cell at metaphase II. (See Figures 12.7 and 13.8.)

2. **WHAT IF?** After the synaptonemal complex disappears, how would the two homologues be associated if crossing over did not occur? What effect might this ultimately have on gamete formation?

For suggested answers, see Appendix A.

CONCEPT 13.4

Genetic variation produced in sexual life cycles contributes to evolution

How do we account for the genetic variation illustrated in Figure 13.1? As you will learn in later chapters, mutations are the original source of genetic diversity. These changes in an organism's DNA create the different versions of genes known as *alleles*. Once these differences arise, reshuffling of the alleles during sexual reproduction produces the variation that results in each member of a sexually reproducing population having a unique combination of traits.

Origins of Genetic Variation Among Offspring

In species that reproduce sexually, the behaviour of chromosomes during meiosis and fertilization is responsible for most of the variation that arises in each generation. Three mechanisms contribute to the genetic variation arising from sexual reproduction: independent assortment of chromosomes, crossing over, and random fertilization.

Independent Assortment of Chromosomes

One aspect of sexual reproduction that generates genetic variation is the random orientation of pairs of homologous chromosomes at metaphase of meiosis I. At metaphase I, the homologous pairs, each consisting of one maternal and one paternal chromosome, are situated at the metaphase plate. (Note that the terms *maternal* and *paternal* refer, respectively, to the mother and father of the individual whose cells are undergoing meiosis.) Each pair may orient with either its maternal or paternal homologue closer to a given pole—its orientation is as random as the flip of a coin. Thus, there is a 50% chance that a particular daughter cell of meiosis I will get the maternal chromosome of a certain homologous pair and a 50% chance that it will get the paternal chromosome.

Because each pair of homologous chromosomes is positioned independently of the other pairs at metaphase I, the first meiotic division results in each pair sorting its maternal and paternal homologues into daughter cells independently of every other pair. This is called *independent assortment*. Each daughter cell represents one outcome of all possible combinations of maternal and paternal chromosomes. As shown in **Figure 13.11**, the number of combinations possible for daughter cells formed by meiosis of a diploid cell with $n = 2$ (two pairs of homologous chromosomes) is four: two possible arrangements for the first pair times two possible arrangements for the second pair. Note that only two of the four combinations of daughter cells shown in the figure would result from meiosis of a *single* diploid cell, because a single parent cell would have one or the other possible chromosomal arrangement at metaphase I, but not both. However, the population of daughter cells resulting from meiosis of a large number of diploid cells contains all four types in approximately equal numbers. In the case of $n = 3$, eight combinations of chromosomes are possible for daughter cells. More generally, the number of possible combinations when chromosomes sort independently during meiosis is 2^n, where n is the haploid number of the organism.

In the case of humans ($n = 23$), the number of possible combinations of maternal and paternal chromosomes in the resulting gametes is 2^{23}, or about 8.4 million. Each gamete that you produce in your lifetime contains one of roughly 8.4 million possible combinations of chromosomes.

Crossing Over

As a consequence of the independent assortment of chromosomes during meiosis, each of us produces a collection of gametes differing greatly in their combinations of the chromosomes we inherited from our two parents.

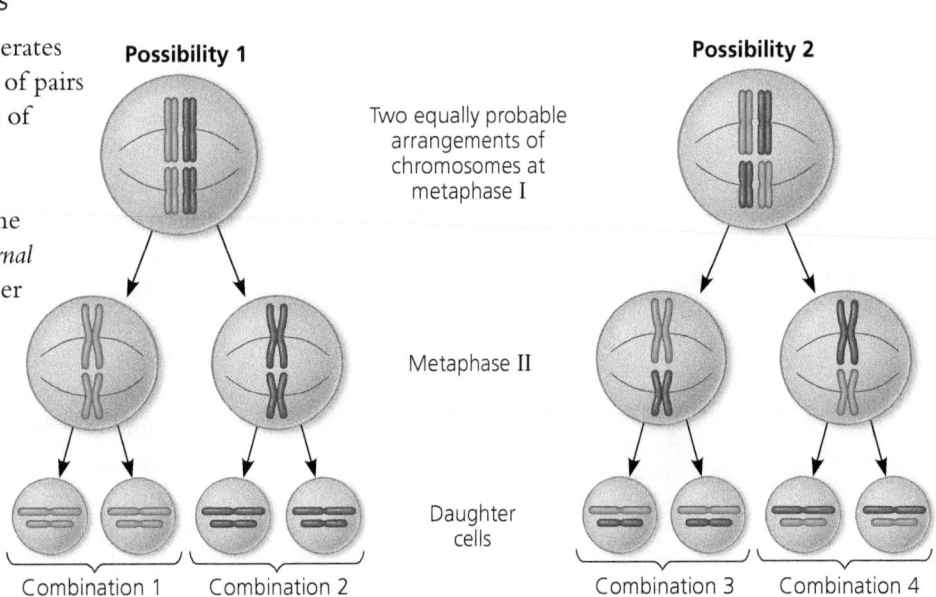

Possibility 1   **Possibility 2**

Two equally probable arrangements of chromosomes at metaphase I

Metaphase II

Daughter cells

Combination 1   Combination 2   Combination 3   Combination 4

▲ Figure 13.11 **The independent assortment of homologous chromosomes in meiosis.**

Figure 13.11 suggests that each chromosome in a gamete is exclusively maternal or paternal in origin. In fact, this is *not* the case, because crossing over produces **recombinant chromosomes**, individual chromosomes that carry genes (DNA) derived from two different parents (**Figure 13.12**). In meiosis in humans, an average of one to three crossover events occur per chromosome pair, depending on the size of the chromosomes and the position of their centromeres.

As you learned in Figure 13.9, crossing over produces chromosomes with new combinations of maternal and paternal alleles. At metaphase II, chromosomes that contain one or more recombinant chromatids can be oriented in two alternative, nonequivalent ways with respect to other chromosomes, because their sister chromatids are no longer identical (see Figure 13.12). The different possible arrangements of nonidentical sister chromatids during meiosis II further increase the number of genetic types of daughter cells that can result from meiosis.

You will learn more about crossing over in Chapter 15. The important point for now is that crossing over, by combining DNA inherited from two parents into a single chromosome, is an important source of genetic variation in sexual life cycles.

Random Fertilization

The random nature of fertilization adds to the genetic variation arising from meiosis. In humans, each male and female gamete represents one of about 8.4 million (2^{23}) possible chromosome combinations due to independent assortment. The fusion of a male gamete with a female gamete during fertilization will produce a zygote with any of about 70 trillion ($2^{23} \times 2^{23}$) diploid combinations. If we factor in the variation brought about by crossing over, the number of possibilities is truly astronomical. It may sound trite, but you really *are* unique.

The Evolutionary Significance of Genetic Variation Within Populations

EVOLUTION Now that you've learned how new combinations of genes arise among offspring in a sexually reproducing population, let's see how the genetic variation in a population relates to evolution. Darwin recognized that a population evolves through the differential reproductive success of its variant members. On average, those individuals best suited to the local environment leave the most offspring, thereby transmitting their genes. Thus, natural selection results in the accumulation of genetic variations favoured by the environment. As the environment changes, the population may survive if, in each generation, at least some of its members can cope effectively with the new conditions. Mutations are the original source of different alleles, which are then mixed and matched during meiosis. New and different combinations of alleles may work better than those that previously prevailed. In a stable environment, though, sexual reproduction seems as if it would be less advantageous than asexual reproduction, which ensures perpetuation of successful combinations of alleles. Furthermore, sexual reproduction is more expensive energetically than asexual reproduction. In spite of these apparent disadvantages, sexual reproduction is almost universal among animals. Why is this?

The ability of sexual reproduction to generate genetic diversity is the most commonly proposed explanation for the evolutionary persistence of this process. Consider the rare case of the bdelloid rotifer (**Figure 13.13**). This group has apparently not reproduced sexually throughout the 40 million years of its evolutionary history. Does this mean that genetic diversity is not advantageous in this species? It turns out that bdelloid rotifers are an exception that proves the rule: This group has mechanisms other than sexual reproduction for generating genetic diversity. For example, they live in environments that can dry up for long periods of time, during which they can enter a state of suspended animation. In this state, their cell membranes may crack in places, allowing entry of DNA from other rotifers and even other

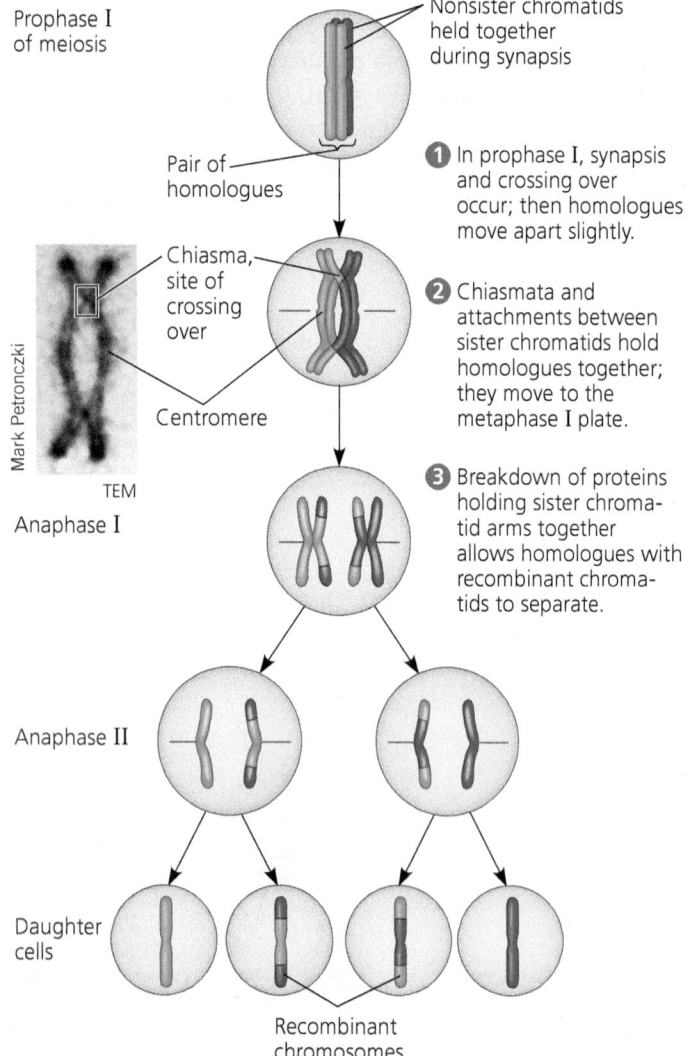

Prophase I of meiosis

Nonsister chromatids held together during synapsis

Pair of homologues

Chiasma, site of crossing over

Centromere

Mark Petronczki

TEM

Anaphase I

Anaphase II

Daughter cells

Recombinant chromosomes

❶ In prophase I, synapsis and crossing over occur; then homologues move apart slightly.

❷ Chiasmata and attachments between sister chromatids hold homologues together; they move to the metaphase I plate.

❸ Breakdown of proteins holding sister chromatid arms together allows homologues with recombinant chromatids to separate.

▲ Figure 13.12 **The results of crossing over during meiosis.**

▲ Figure 13.13 **A bdelloid rotifer, an animal that reproduces only asexually.**

species. Evidence suggests that this DNA can become incorporated into the genome of the rotifer, leading to increased genetic diversity. This supports the idea that genetic diversity is advantageous, and that sexual reproduction has persisted because it generates such diversity.

In this chapter, we have seen how sexual reproduction greatly increases the genetic variation present in a population.

Although Darwin realized that heritable variation is what makes evolution possible, he could not explain why offspring resemble—but are not identical to—their parents. Ironically, Gregor Mendel, a contemporary of Darwin, published a theory of inheritance that helps explain genetic variation, but his discoveries had no impact on biologists until 1900, more than 15 years after Darwin (1809–1882) and Mendel (1822–1884) had died. In the next chapter, you'll learn how Mendel discovered the basic rules governing the inheritance of specific traits.

CONCEPT CHECK 13.4

1. What is the original source of variation among the different alleles of a gene?
2. The diploid number for fruit flies is 8, and the diploid number for grasshoppers is 46. If no crossing over took place, would the genetic variation among offspring from a given pair of parents be greater in fruit flies or grasshoppers? Explain.
3. **WHAT IF?** If maternal and paternal chromatids have the same two alleles for every gene, will crossing over lead to genetic variation?

For suggested answers, see Appendix A.

13 Chapter Review

Go to **MasteringBiology**® for Assignments, the eText, and the Study Area with Animations, Activities, Vocab Self-Quiz, and Practice Tests.

SUMMARY OF KEY CONCEPTS

CONCEPT 13.1

Offspring acquire genes from parents by inheriting chromosomes (pp. 267–268)

- Each **gene** in an organism's DNA exists at a specific **locus** on a certain chromosome.
- In **asexual reproduction**, a single parent produces genetically identical offspring by mitosis. **Sexual reproduction** combines sets of genes from two parents, leading to genetically diverse offspring.

? *Explain why human offspring resemble their parents but are not identical to them.*

CONCEPT 13.2

Fertilization and meiosis alternate in sexual life cycles (pp. 268–271)

- Normal human **somatic cells** are **diploid**. They have 46 chromosomes made up of two sets of 23—one set from each parent. In human diploid cells, there are 22 **homologous** pairs of **autosomes**, each with a maternal and a paternal homologue. The 23rd pair, the **sex chromosomes**, determines whether the person is female (XX) or male (XY).
- In humans, ovaries and testes produce **haploid gametes** by **meiosis**, each gamete containing a single set of 23 chromosomes ($n = 23$). During **fertilization**, an egg and sperm unite, forming a diploid ($2n = 46$) single-celled **zygote**, which develops into a multicellular organism by mitosis.

- Sexual life cycles differ in the timing of meiosis relative to fertilization and in the point(s) of the cycle at which a multicellular organism is produced by mitosis.

? *Compare the life cycles of animals and plants, mentioning their similarities and differences.*

CONCEPT 13.3

Meiosis reduces the number of chromosome sets from diploid to haploid (pp. 271–277)

- The two cell divisions of meiosis, **meiosis I** and **meiosis II**, produce four haploid daughter cells. The number of chromosome sets is reduced from two (diploid) to one (haploid) during meiosis I, the reductional division.
- Meiosis is distinguished from mitosis by three events of meiosis I:

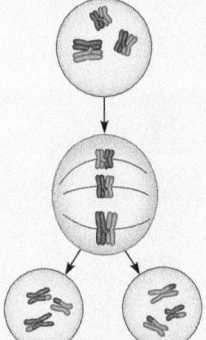

Prophase I: Each homologous pair undergoes **synapsis** and **crossing over** between nonsister chromatids with the subsequent appearance of **chiasmata**.

Metaphase I: Chromosomes line up as homologous pairs on the metaphase plate.

Anaphase I: Homologues separate from each other; sister chromatids remain joined at the centromere.

Meiosis II separates the sister chromatids.

Sister chromatid cohesion and crossing over allow chiasmata to hold homologues together until anaphase I. Cohesins are cleaved along the chromatid arms at anaphase I, allowing the homologues to separate, and at the centromeres in anaphase II, releasing sister chromatids.

? *During prophase I, homologous chromosomes pair up and undergo synapsis and crossing over. Explain why this cannot also occur during prophase II.*

CONCEPT 13.4

Genetic variation produced in sexual life cycles contributes to evolution (pp. 277–279)

- Three events in sexual reproduction contribute to genetic variation in a population: independent assortment of chromosomes during meiosis I, crossing over during meiosis I, and random fertilization of egg cells by sperm. During crossing over, DNA of nonsister chromatids in a homologous pair is broken and rejoined.
- Genetic variation is the raw material for evolution by natural selection. Mutations are the original source of this variation; recombination of variant genes in sexual reproduction generates additional genetic diversity.

? *Explain how three processes unique to meiosis generate a great deal of genetic variation.*

TEST YOUR UNDERSTANDING

LEVEL 1: KNOWLEDGE/COMPREHENSION

1. A human cell containing 22 autosomes and a Y chromosome is
   a. a sperm.
   b. an egg.
   c. a zygote.
   d. a somatic cell of a male.

2. Homologous chromosomes move toward opposite poles of a dividing cell during
   a. mitosis.
   b. meiosis I.
   c. meiosis II.
   d. fertilization.

LEVEL 2: APPLICATION/ANALYSIS

3. Meiosis II is similar to mitosis in that
   a. sister chromatids separate during anaphase.
   b. DNA replicates before the division.
   c. the daughter cells are diploid.
   d. homologous chromosomes synapse.

4. If the DNA content of a diploid cell in the G_1 phase of the cell cycle is x, then the DNA content of the same cell at metaphase of meiosis I would be
   a. $0.25x$.
   b. $0.5x$.
   c. x.
   d. $2x$.

5. If we continued to follow the cell lineage from question 4, then the DNA content of a single cell at metaphase of meiosis II would be
   a. $0.25x$.
   b. $0.5x$.
   c. x.
   d. $2x$.

6. **DRAW IT** The diagram at right shows a cell in meiosis.
   a. Copy the drawing to a separate sheet of paper and label appropriate structures with these terms, drawing lines or brackets as needed: chromosome (label as duplicated or unduplicated), centromere, kinetochore, sister chromatids, nonsister chromatids,

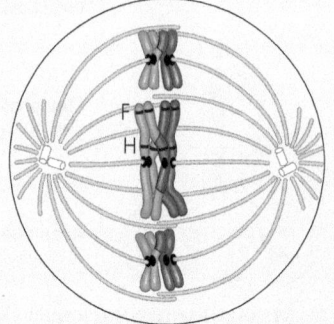

homologous pair, homologues, chiasma, sister chromatid cohesion.
   b. Describe the makeup of a haploid set and a diploid set.
   c. Identify the stage of meiosis shown.

LEVEL 3: SYNTHESIS/EVALUATION

7. How can you tell the cell in question 6 is undergoing meiosis, not mitosis?

8. **EVOLUTION CONNECTION**
   Many species can reproduce either asexually or sexually. What might be the evolutionary significance of the switch from asexual to sexual reproduction that occurs in some organisms when the environment becomes unfavourable?

9. **SCIENTIFIC INQUIRY**
   The diagram in question 6 represents a meiotic cell in a certain individual. A previous study has shown that the freckles gene is located at the locus marked F, and the hair-colour gene is located at the locus marked H, both on the long chromosome. The individual from whom this cell was taken has inherited different alleles for each gene ("freckles" and "black hair" from one parent, and "no freckles" and "blond hair" from the other). Predict allele combinations in the gametes resulting from this meiotic event. (It will help if you draw out the rest of meiosis, labelling alleles by name.) List other possible combinations of these alleles in this individual's gametes.

10. **WRITE ABOUT A THEME: INFORMATION**
    The continuity of life is based on heritable information in the form of DNA. In a short essay (100–150 words), explain how chromosome behaviour during sexual reproduction in animals ensures perpetuation of parental traits in offspring and, at the same time, genetic variation among offspring.

11. **SYNTHESIZE YOUR KNOWLEDGE**

Randy Ploetz

The Cavendish banana is the most popular fruit in the world, but is currently threatened by extinction due to a fungal agent (see the photo). This banana variety is "triploid" (3n, with three sets of chromosomes) and can only reproduce through cloning by cultivators. Given what you know about meiosis, explain how the banana's triploid number accounts for its seedless condition. Considering genetic diversity, discuss how the absence of sexual reproduction might contribute to the vulnerability of this domesticated species to infectious agents.

For selected answers, see Appendix A.

14

Mendel and the Gene Idea

KEY CONCEPTS

14.1 Mendel used the scientific approach to identify two laws of inheritance

14.2 Probability laws govern Mendelian inheritance

14.3 Inheritance patterns are often more complex than predicted by simple Mendelian genetics

14.4 Many human traits follow Mendelian patterns of inheritance

▲ Figure 14.1 **What principles of inheritance did Gregor Mendel discover by breeding garden pea plants?**

Drawing from the Deck of Genes

The crowd at a hockey or soccer match attests to the marvellous variety and diversity of humankind. Brown, blue, or grey eyes; black, brown, or blond hair—these are just a few examples of heritable variations that we may observe. What principles account for the transmission of such traits from parents to offspring?

The explanation of heredity most widely in favour during the 1800s was the "blending" hypothesis, the idea that genetic material contributed by the two parents mixes just as blue and yellow paints blend to make green. This hypothesis predicts that over many generations, a freely mating population will give rise to a uniform population of individuals, something we don't see. The blending hypothesis also fails to explain the reappearance of traits after they've skipped a generation.

An alternative to the blending model is a "particulate" hypothesis of inheritance: the gene idea. In this model, parents pass on discrete heritable units—genes—that retain their separate identities in offspring. An organism's collection of genes is more like a deck of cards than a pail of paint. Like playing cards, genes can be shuffled and passed along, generation after generation, in undiluted form.

Modern genetics had its genesis in an abbey garden, where a monk named Gregor Mendel documented a particulate mechanism for inheritance using pea plants (Figure 14.1). Mendel developed his theory of inheritance several

Mendel Museum, Augustinian Abbey Brno

◄ **Mendel (third from right, holding a sprig of fuchsia) with his fellow monks.**

decades before chromosomes were observed under the microscope and the significance of their behaviour was understood. In this chapter, we'll step into Mendel's garden to re-create his experiments and explain how he arrived at his theory of inheritance. We'll also explore inheritance patterns more complex than those observed by Mendel in garden peas. Finally, we will see how the Mendelian model applies to the inheritance of human variations, including hereditary disorders such as sickle-cell disease.

Mendel used the scientific approach to identify two laws of inheritance

Mendel discovered the basic principles of heredity by breeding garden peas in carefully planned experiments. As we retrace his work, you will recognize the key elements of the scientific process that were introduced in Chapter 1.

Mendel's Experimental, Quantitative Approach

Mendel grew up on his parents' small farm in a region of Austria that is now part of the Czech Republic. In this agricultural area, Mendel and the other children received agricultural training in school along with their basic education. As an adolescent, Mendel overcame financial hardship and illness to excel in high school and, later, at the Olmutz Philosophical Institute.

In 1843, at the age of 21, Mendel entered an Augustinian monastery, a reasonable choice at that time for someone who valued the life of the mind. He considered becoming a teacher but failed the necessary examination. In 1851, he left the monastery to pursue two years of study in physics and chemistry at the University of Vienna. These were very important years for Mendel's development as a scientist, in large part due to the strong influence of two professors. One was the physicist Christian Doppler, who encouraged his students to learn science through experimentation and trained Mendel to use mathematics to help explain natural phenomena. The other was a botanist named Franz Unger, who aroused Mendel's interest in the causes of variation in plants.

After attending the university, Mendel returned to the monastery and was assigned to teach at a local school, where several other instructors were enthusiastic about scientific research. In addition, his fellow monks shared a long-standing fascination with the breeding of plants. Around 1857, Mendel began breeding garden peas in the abbey garden to study inheritance. Although the question of heredity had long been a focus of curiosity at the monastery, Mendel's fresh approach allowed him to deduce principles that had remained elusive to others.

One reason Mendel probably chose to work with peas is that there are many varieties. For example, one variety has purple flowers, while another variety has white flowers. A heritable feature that varies among individuals, such as flower colour, is called a **character**. Each variant for a character, such as purple or white colour for flowers, is called a **trait**.

Other advantages of using peas are their short generation time and the large number of offspring from each mating. Furthermore, Mendel could strictly control mating between plants (Figure 14.2). The reproductive organs of a pea plant are in its flowers, and each pea flower has both pollen-producing organs (stamens) and an egg-bearing

▼ Figure 14.2 | **Research Method**

Crossing Pea Plants

Application By crossing (mating) two true-breeding varieties of an organism, scientists can study patterns of inheritance. In this example, Mendel crossed pea plants that varied in flower colour.

Technique

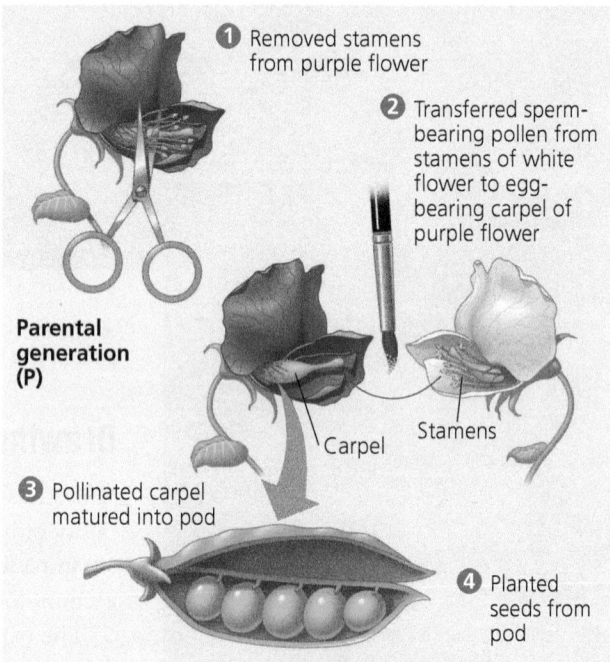

1. Removed stamens from purple flower
2. Transferred sperm-bearing pollen from stamens of white flower to egg-bearing carpel of purple flower

Parental generation (P)

Carpel

Stamens

3. Pollinated carpel matured into pod
4. Planted seeds from pod

Results When pollen from a white flower was transferred to a purple flower, the first-generation hybrids all had purple flowers. The result was the same for the reciprocal cross, which involved the transfer of pollen from purple flowers to white flowers.

First filial generation offspring (F₁)

5. Examined offspring: all purple flowers

organ (carpel). In nature, pea plants usually self-fertilize: Pollen grains from the stamens land on the carpel of the same flower, and sperm released from the pollen grains fertilize eggs present in the carpel.* To achieve cross-pollination of two plants, Mendel removed the immature stamens of a plant before they produced pollen and then dusted pollen from another plant onto the altered flowers (see Figure 14.2). Each resulting zygote then developed into a plant embryo encased in a seed (pea). His method allowed Mendel to always be sure of the parentage of new seeds.

Mendel chose to track only those characters that occurred in two distinct, alternative forms, such as purple or white flower colour. He also made sure that he started his experiments with varieties that were **true-breeding**—that is, over many generations of self-pollination, these plants had produced only the same variety as the parent plant. For example, a plant with purple flowers is true-breeding if the seeds produced by self-pollination in successive generations all give rise to plants that also have purple flowers.

In a typical breeding experiment, Mendel cross-pollinated two contrasting, true-breeding pea varieties—for example, purple-flowered plants and white-flowered plants (see Figure 14.2). This mating, or *crossing*, of two true-breeding varieties is called **hybridization**. The true-breeding parents are referred to as the **P generation** (parental generation), and their hybrid offspring are the **F₁ generation** (first filial generation, the word *filial* from the Latin word for "son"). Allowing these F₁ hybrids to self-pollinate (or to cross-pollinate with other F₁ hybrids) produces an **F₂ generation** (second filial generation). Mendel usually followed traits for at least the P, F₁, and F₂ generations. Had Mendel stopped his experiments with the F₁ generation, the basic patterns of inheritance would have eluded him. Mendel's quantitative analysis of the F₂ plants from thousands of genetic crosses like these allowed him to deduce two fundamental principles of heredity, now called the *law of segregation* and the *law of independent assortment*.

The Law of Segregation

If the blending model of inheritance were correct, the F₁ hybrids from a cross between purple-flowered and white-flowered pea plants would have pale purple flowers, a trait intermediate between those of the P generation. Notice in Figure 14.2 that the experiment produced a very different result: All the F₁ offspring had flowers of the same colour as the purple-flowered parents. What happened to the white-flowered plants' genetic contribution to the hybrids? If it were lost, then the F₁ plants could produce only purple-flowered

offspring in the F₂ generation. But when Mendel allowed the F₁ plants to self-pollinate and planted their seeds, the white-flower trait reappeared in the F₂ generation.

Mendel used very large sample sizes and kept accurate records of his results: 705 of the F₂ plants had purple flowers, and 224 had white flowers. These data fit a ratio of approximately three purple to one white (Figure 14.3). Mendel reasoned that the heritable factor for white flowers did not disappear in the F₁ plants, but was somehow hidden, or

▼ 14.3 Figure | **Inquiry**

When F₁ hybrid pea plants self- or cross-pollinate, which traits appear in the F₂ generation?

Experiment Around 1860, in a monastery garden in Brünn, Austria, Gregor Mendel used the character of flower colour in pea plants to follow traits through two generations. He crossed true-breeding purple-flowered plants and white-flowered plants (crosses are symbolized by ×). The resulting F₁ hybrids were allowed to self-pollinate or were cross-pollinated with other F₁ hybrids. The F₂ generation plants were then observed for flower colour.

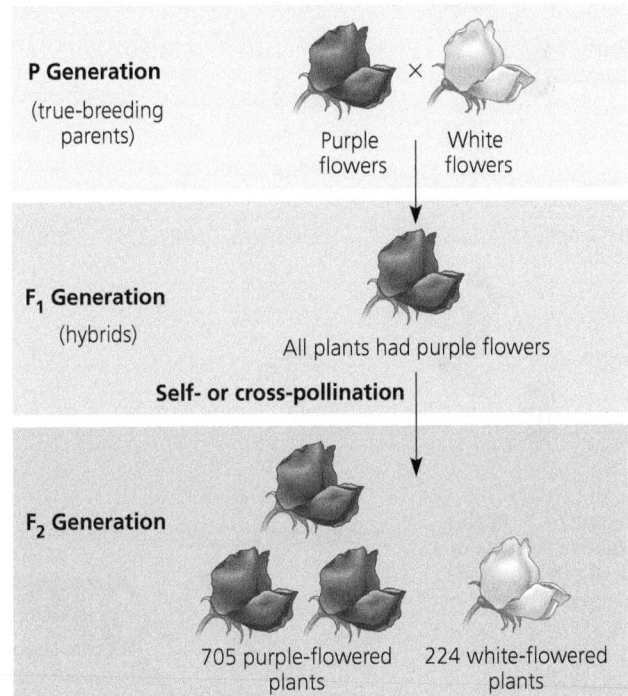

Results Both purple-flowered and white-flowered plants appeared in the F₂ generation, in a ratio of approximately 3:1.

Conclusion The "heritable factor" for the recessive trait (white flowers) had not been destroyed, deleted, or "blended" in the F₁ generation but was merely masked by the presence of the factor for purple flowers, which is the dominant trait.

Source: Based on "Experiments in Plant Hybridization" by Gregor Mendel, *from Proceedings of the Natural History Society of Brunn*, 1866, Volume 4. © Jane B Reece.

WHAT IF? *If you mated two purple-flowered plants from the P generation, what ratio of traits would you expect to observe in the offspring? Explain.*

---

*As you learned in Figure 13.6b, meiosis in plants produces spores, not gametes. In flowering plants like the pea, each spore develops into a microscopic haploid gametophyte that contains only a few cells and is located on the parent plant. The gametophyte produces sperm in pollen grains and eggs in the carpel. For simplicity, we will not include the gametophyte stage in our discussion of fertilization in plants.

Character	Dominant Trait	×	Recessive Trait	F₂ Generation Dominant: Recessive	Ratio
Flower colour	Purple	×	White	705:224	3.15:1
Seed colour	Yellow	×	Green	6022:2001	3.01:1
Seed shape	Round	×	Wrinkled	5474:1850	2.96:1
Pod shape	Inflated	×	Constricted	882:299	2.95:1
Pod colour	Green	×	Yellow	428:152	2.82:1
Flower position	Axial	×	Terminal	651:207	3.14:1
Stem length	Tall	×	Dwarf	787:277	2.84:1

Table 14.1 The Results of Mendel's F_1 Crosses for Seven Characters in Pea Plants

masked, when the purple-flower factor was present. In Mendel's terminology, purple flower colour is a *dominant* trait, and white flower colour is a *recessive* trait. The reappearance of white-flowered plants in the F_2 generation was evidence that the heritable factor causing white flowers had not been diluted or destroyed by coexisting with the purple-flower factor in the F_1 hybrids. Instead, it had been hidden when in the presence of the purple-flower factor.

Mendel observed the same pattern of inheritance in six other characters, each represented by two distinctly different traits (Table 14.1). For example, when Mendel crossed a true-breeding variety that produced smooth, round pea seeds with one that produced wrinkled seeds, all the F_1 hybrids produced round seeds; this is the dominant trait for seed shape. In the F_2 generation, approximately 75% of the seeds were round and 25% were wrinkled—a 3:1 ratio, as in Figure 14.3. Now let's see how Mendel deduced the law of segregation from his experimental results. In the discussion that follows, we will use modern terms instead of some of the terms used by Mendel. (For example, we'll use "gene" instead of Mendel's "heritable factor.")

Mendel's Model

Mendel developed a model to explain the 3:1 inheritance pattern that he consistently observed among the F_2 offspring in his pea experiments. We describe four related concepts making up this model, the fourth of which is the law of segregation.

First, *alternative versions of genes account for variations in inherited characters*. The gene for flower colour in pea plants, for example, exists in two versions, one for purple flowers and the other for white flowers. These alternative versions of a gene are called **alleles**. Today, we can relate this concept to chromosomes and DNA. As shown in Figure 14.4, each gene is a sequence of nucleotides at a specific place,

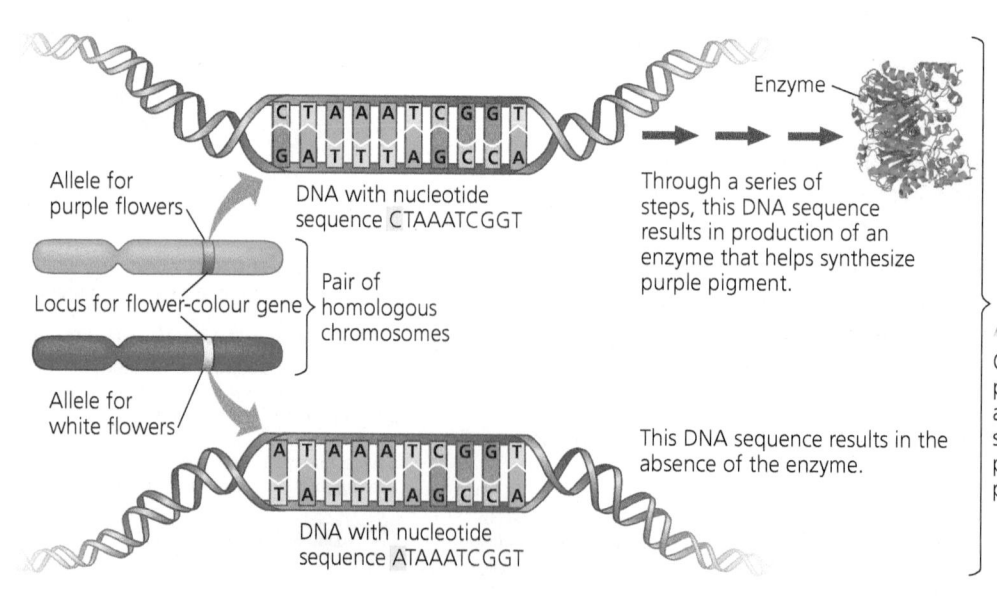

▶ Figure 14.4 **Alleles, alternative versions of a gene.** A somatic cell has two copies of each chromosome (forming a homologous pair) and thus two copies of each gene; the alleles may be identical or different. This figure depicts a pair of homologous chromosomes in an F_1 hybrid pea plant. The paternally inherited chromosome (blue), which was present in the sperm within a pollen grain, has an allele for purple flowers, and the maternally inherited chromosome (red), which was present in an egg within a carpel, has an allele for white flowers.

Allele for purple flowers

Locus for flower-colour gene

Allele for white flowers

Pair of homologous chromosomes

DNA with nucleotide sequence CTAAATCGGT

DNA with nucleotide sequence ATAAATCGGT

Enzyme

Through a series of steps, this DNA sequence results in production of an enzyme that helps synthesize purple pigment.

This DNA sequence results in the absence of the enzyme.

One purple-flower allele results in sufficient pigment for purple flowers.

or locus, along a particular chromosome. The DNA at that locus, however, can vary slightly in its nucleotide sequence. This variation in information content can affect the function of the encoded protein and thus an inherited character of the organism. The purple-flower allele and the white-flower allele are two DNA sequence variations possible at the flower-colour locus on one of a pea plant's chromosomes. The purple-flower allele sequence allows synthesis of purple pigment, and the white-flower allele sequence does not.

Second, *for each character, an organism inherits two copies* (that is, two alleles) *of a gene, one from each parent.* Remarkably, Mendel made this deduction without knowing about the role, or even the existence, of chromosomes. Each somatic cell in a diploid organism has two sets of chromosomes, one set inherited from each parent (see Figure 13.4). Thus, a genetic locus is actually represented twice in a diploid cell, once on each homologue of a specific pair of chromosomes. The two alleles at a particular locus may be identical, as in the true-breeding plants of Mendel's P generation. Or the alleles may differ, as in the F_1 hybrids (see Figure 14.4).

Third, *if the two alleles at a locus differ, then one, the* **dominant allele,** *determines the organism's appearance; the other, the* **recessive allele,** *has no noticeable effect on the organism's appearance.* Accordingly, Mendel's F_1 plants had purple flowers because the allele for that trait is dominant and the allele for white flowers is recessive.

The fourth and final part of Mendel's model, the **law of segregation,** states that *the two alleles for a heritable character segregate (separate from each other) during gamete formation and end up in different gametes.* Thus, an egg or a sperm gets only one of the two alleles that are present in the somatic cells of the organism making the gamete. In terms of chromosomes, this segregation corresponds to the distribution of copies of the two members of a pair of homologous chromosomes to different gametes in meiosis (see Figure 13.7). Note that if an organism has identical alleles for a particular character, then that allele is present in all gametes. Because it is the only allele that can be passed on to offspring, the offspring always look like their parents; this explains why these

plants are true-breeding. But if different alleles are present, as in the F_1 hybrids, then 50% of the gametes receive the dominant allele and 50% receive the recessive allele.

Does Mendel's segregation model account for the 3:1 ratio he observed in the F_2 generation of his numerous crosses? For the flower-colour character, the model predicts that the two different alleles present in an F_1 individual will segregate into gametes such that half the gametes will have the purple-flower allele and half will have the white-flower allele. During self-pollination, gametes of each class unite randomly. An egg with a purple-flower allele has an equal chance of being fertilized by a sperm with a purple-flower allele or one with a white-flower allele. Since the same is true for an egg with a white-flower allele, there are four equally likely combinations of sperm and egg. Figure 14.5 illustrates these combinations using a **Punnett square,** a

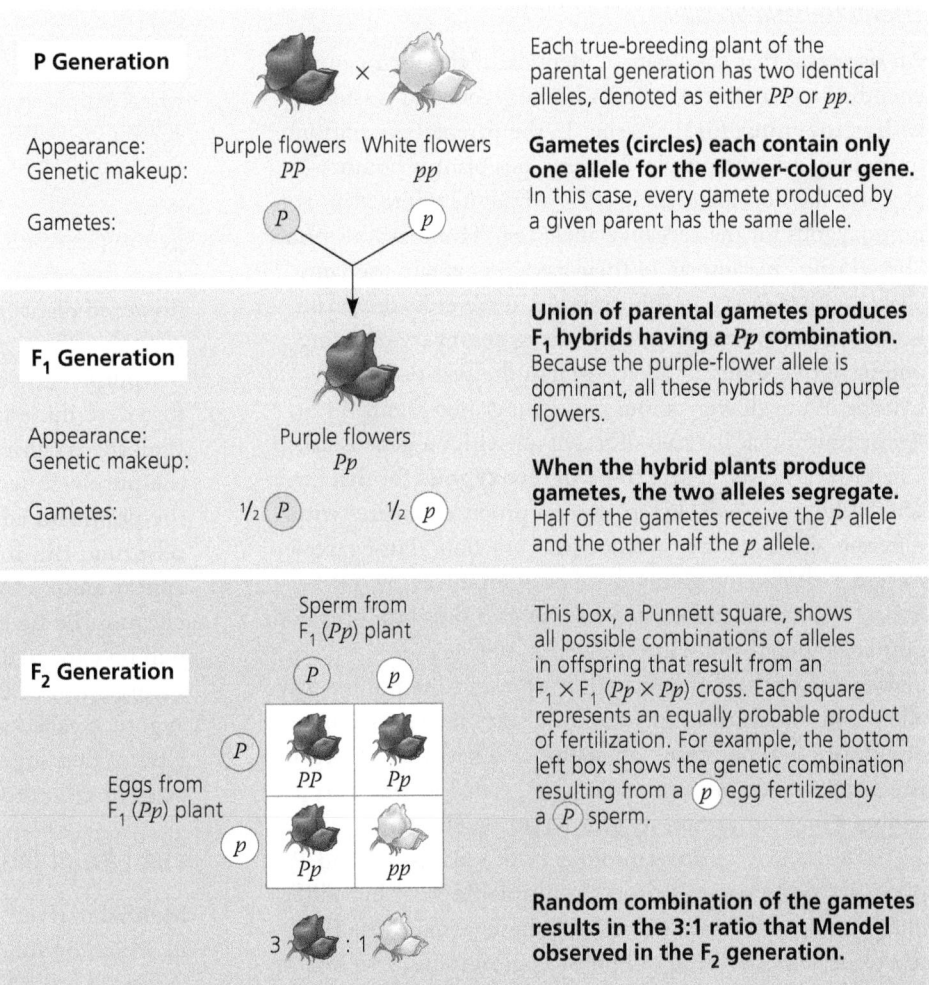

P Generation

Appearance: Purple flowers White flowers
Genetic makeup: *PP* *pp*
Gametes:

Each true-breeding plant of the parental generation has two identical alleles, denoted as either *PP* or *pp*.

Gametes (circles) each contain only one allele for the flower-colour gene. In this case, every gamete produced by a given parent has the same allele.

F_1 Generation

Appearance: Purple flowers
Genetic makeup: *Pp*
Gametes: ½ *P* ½ *p*

Union of parental gametes produces F_1 hybrids having a *Pp* combination. Because the purple-flower allele is dominant, all these hybrids have purple flowers.

When the hybrid plants produce gametes, the two alleles segregate. Half of the gametes receive the *P* allele and the other half the *p* allele.

F_2 Generation

Sperm from F_1 (*Pp*) plant
P *p*

Eggs from F_1 (*Pp*) plant
P   *PP* *Pp*
p   *Pp* *pp*

3 : 1

This box, a Punnett square, shows all possible combinations of alleles in offspring that result from an $F_1 \times F_1$ (*Pp* × *Pp*) cross. Each square represents an equally probable product of fertilization. For example, the bottom left box shows the genetic combination resulting from a *p* egg fertilized by a *P* sperm.

Random combination of the gametes results in the 3:1 ratio that Mendel observed in the F_2 generation.

▲ Figure 14.5 **Mendel's law of segregation.** This diagram shows the genetic makeup of the generations in Figure 14.3. It illustrates Mendel's model for inheritance of the alleles of a single gene. Each plant has two alleles for the gene controlling flower colour, one allele inherited from each of the plant's parents. To construct a Punnett square that predicts the F_2 generation offspring, we list all the possible gametes from one parent (here, the F_1 female) along the left side of the square and all the possible gametes from the other parent (here, the F_1 male) along the top. The boxes represent the offspring resulting from all the possible unions of male and female gametes.

handy diagrammatic device for predicting the allele composition of offspring from a cross between individuals of known genetic makeup. Notice that we use a capital letter to symbolize a dominant allele and a lowercase letter for a recessive allele. In our example, P is the purple-flower allele, and p is the white-flower allele; it is often useful as well to be able to refer to the gene itself as the P/p gene.

In the F_2 offspring, what colour will the flowers be? One-fourth of the plants have inherited two purple-flower alleles; clearly, these plants will have purple flowers. One-half of the F_2 offspring have inherited one purple-flower allele and one white-flower allele; these plants will also have purple flowers, the dominant trait. Finally, one-fourth of the F_2 plants have inherited two white-flower alleles and will express the recessive trait. Thus, Mendel's model accounts for the 3:1 ratio of traits that he observed in the F_2 generation.

Useful Genetic Vocabulary

An organism that has a pair of identical alleles for a gene encoding a character is called a homozygote and is said to be **homozygous** for that gene. In the parental generation in Figure 14.5, the purple-flowered pea plant is homozygous for the dominant allele (PP), while the white plant is homozygous for the recessive allele (pp). Homozygous plants "breed true" because all of their gametes contain the same allele—either P or p in this example. If we cross dominant homozygotes with recessive homozygotes, every offspring will have two different alleles—Pp in the case of the F_1 hybrids of our flower-colour experiment (see Figure 14.5). An organism that has two different alleles for a gene is called a heterozygote and is said to be **heterozygous** for that gene. Unlike homozygotes, heterozygotes produce gametes with different alleles, so they are not true-breeding. For example, P- and p-containing gametes are both produced by our F_1 hybrids. Self-pollination of the F_1 hybrids thus produces both purple-flowered and white-flowered offspring.

Because of the different effects of dominant and recessive alleles, an organism's traits do not always reveal its genetic composition. Therefore, we distinguish between an organism's appearance or observable traits, called its **phenotype**, and its genetic makeup, its **genotype**. As shown in Figure 14.5 for the case of flower colour in pea plants, PP and Pp plants have the same phenotype (purple flowers) but different genotypes. Figure 14.6 reviews these terms. Note that the term *phenotype* refers to physiological traits as well as traits that relate directly to appearance. For example, one pea variety lacks the normal ability to self-pollinate, which is a phenotypic trait (non-self-pollination).

The Testcross

Given a purple-flowered pea plant, we cannot tell if it is homozygous (PP) or heterozygous (Pp) because both

▲ Figure 14.6 **Phenotype versus genotype.** Grouping F_2 offspring from a cross for flower colour according to phenotype results in the typical 3:1 phenotypic ratio. In terms of genotype, however, there are actually two categories of purple-flowered plants, PP (homozygous) and Pp (heterozygous), giving a 1:2:1 genotypic ratio.

genotypes result in the same purple phenotype. To determine the genotype, we can cross this plant with a white-flowered plant (pp), which will make only gametes with the recessive allele (p). The allele in the gamete contributed by the purple-flowered plant of unknown genotype will therefore determine the appearance of the offspring (Figure 14.7). If all the offspring of the cross have purple flowers, then the purple-flowered mystery plant must be homozygous for the dominant allele, because a $PP \times pp$ cross produces all Pp offspring. But if both the purple and the white phenotypes appear among the offspring, then the purple-flowered parent must be heterozygous. The offspring of a $Pp \times pp$ cross will be expected to have a 1:1 phenotypic ratio. Breeding an organism of unknown genotype with a recessive homozygote is called a **testcross** because it can reveal the genotype of that organism. The testcross was devised by Mendel and continues to be used by geneticists.

The Law of Independent Assortment

Mendel derived the law of segregation from experiments in which he followed only a *single* character, such as flower colour. All the F_1 progeny produced in his crosses of true-breeding parents were **monohybrids**, meaning that they were heterozygous for the one particular character being followed in the cross. We refer to a cross between such heterozygotes as a **monohybrid cross**.

Mendel identified his second law of inheritance by following *two* characters at the same time, such as seed colour and seed shape. Seeds (peas) may be either yellow or green.

Research Method

The Testcross

Application An organism that exhibits a dominant trait, such as purple flowers in pea plants, can be either homozygous for the dominant allele or heterozygous. To determine the organism's genotype, geneticists can perform a testcross.

Technique In a testcross, the individual with the unknown genotype is crossed with a homozygous individual expressing the recessive trait (white flowers in this example), and Punnett squares are used to predict the possible outcomes.

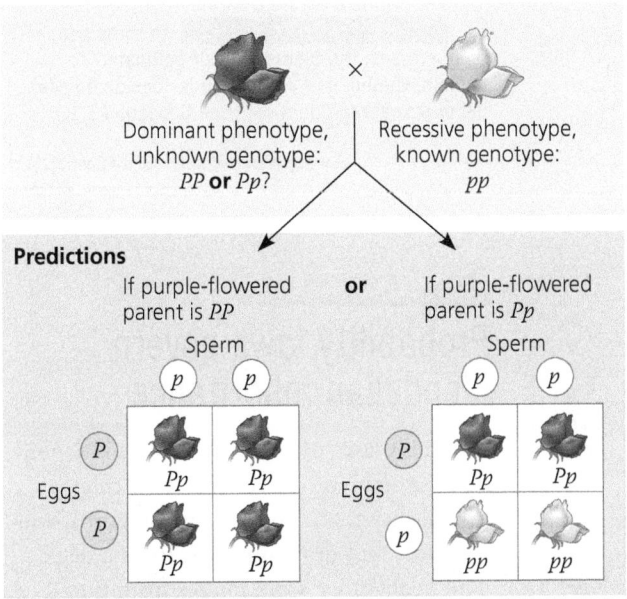

Results Matching the results to either prediction identifies the unknown parental genotype (either *PP* or *Pp* in this example). In this testcross, we transferred pollen from a white-flowered plant to the carpels of a purple-flowered plant; the opposite (reciprocal) cross would have led to the same results.

They also may be either round (smooth) or wrinkled. From single-character crosses, Mendel knew that the allele for yellow seeds is dominant (*Y*), and the allele for green seeds is recessive (*y*). For the seed-shape character, the allele for round is dominant (*R*), and the allele for wrinkled is recessive (*r*).

Imagine crossing two true-breeding pea varieties that differ in *both* of these characters—a cross between a plant with yellow-round seeds (*YYRR*) and a plant with green-wrinkled seeds (*yyrr*). The F_1 plants will be **dihybrids**, individuals heterozygous for the two characters being followed in the cross (*YyRr*). But are these two characters transmitted from parents to offspring as a package? That is, will

the *Y* and *R* alleles always stay together, generation after generation? Or are seed colour and seed shape inherited independently? **Figure 14.8** shows how a **dihybrid cross**, a cross between F_1 dihybrids, can determine which of these two hypotheses is correct.

The F_1 plants, of genotype *YyRr*, exhibit both dominant phenotypes, yellow seeds with round shapes, no matter which hypothesis is correct. The key step in the experiment is to see what happens when F_1 plants self-pollinate and produce F_2 offspring. If the hybrids must transmit their alleles in the same combinations in which the alleles were inherited from the P generation, then the F_1 hybrids will produce only two classes of gametes: *YR* and *yr*. This "dependent assortment" hypothesis predicts that the phenotypic ratio of the F_2 generation will be 3:1, just as in a monohybrid cross (see Figure 14.8, left side).

The alternative hypothesis is that the two pairs of alleles segregate independently of each other. In other words, genes are packaged into gametes in all possible allelic combinations, as long as each gamete has one allele for each gene (see Figure 13.11). In our example, an F_1 plant will produce four classes of gametes in equal quantities: *YR*, *Yr*, *yR*, and *yr*. If sperm of the four classes fertilize eggs of the four classes, there will be 16 (4 × 4) equally probable ways in which the alleles can combine in the F_2 generation, as shown in Figure 14.8, right side. These combinations result in four phenotypic categories with a ratio of 9:3:3:1 (nine yellow-round to three green-round to three yellow-wrinkled to one green-wrinkled). When Mendel did the experiment and classified the F_2 offspring, his results were close to the predicted 9:3:3:1 phenotypic ratio, supporting the hypothesis that the alleles for one gene—controlling seed colour, for example—segregate into gametes independently of the alleles of any other gene, such as seed shape.

Mendel tested his seven pea characters in various dihybrid combinations and always observed a 9:3:3:1 phenotypic ratio in the F_2 generation. Is this consistent with the 3:1 phenotypic ratio seen for the monohybrid cross shown in Figure 14.5? To explore this question, count the number of yellow and green peas, ignoring shape, and calculate the ratio. The results of Mendel's dihybrid experiments are the basis for what we now call the **law of independent assortment**, which states that two or more genes assort independently—that is, *each pair of alleles segregates independently of any other pair of alleles during gamete formation*.

This law applies only to genes (allele pairs) located on different chromosomes (that is, on chromosomes that are not homologous) or, alternatively, to genes that are very far apart on the same chromosome. (The latter case will be explained in Chapter 15, along with the more complex inheritance patterns of genes located near each other, which tend to be inherited together.) All the pea characters Mendel chose for analysis were controlled by genes on different chromosomes or were

Inquiry

Do the alleles for one character assort into gametes dependently or independently of the alleles for a different character?

Experiment Gregor Mendel followed the characters of seed colour and seed shape through the F_2 generation. He crossed a true-breeding plant with yellow-round seeds with a true-breeding plant with green-wrinkled seeds, producing dihybrid F_1 plants. Self-pollination of the F_1 dihybrids produced the F_2 generation. The two hypotheses (dependent and independent assortment) predict different phenotypic ratios.

Results

315 ⬤   108 ⬤   101 ▨   32 ▨   Phenotypic ratio approximately 9:3:3:1

Conclusion Only the hypothesis of independent assortment predicts the appearance of two of the observed phenotypes: green-round seeds and yellow-wrinkled seeds (see the right-hand Punnett square). The alleles for seed colour and seed shape sort into gametes independently of each other.

Source: Based on "Experiments in Plant Hybridization" by Gregor Mendel, from *Proceedings of the Natural History Society of Brunn*, 1866, Volume 4. © Jane B Reece.

WHAT IF? *Suppose Mendel had transferred pollen from an F_1 plant to the carpel of a plant that was homozygous recessive for both genes. Set up the cross and draw Punnett squares that predict the offspring for both hypotheses. Would this cross have supported the hypothesis of independent assortment equally well?*

far apart on the same chromosome; this situation greatly simplified interpretation of his multicharacter pea crosses. All the examples we consider in the rest of this chapter involve genes located on different chromosomes.

1. **DRAW IT** Pea plants heterozygous for flower position and stem length (*AaTt*) are allowed to self-pollinate, and 400 of the resulting seeds are planted. Draw a Punnett square for this cross. How many offspring would be predicted to have terminal flowers and be dwarf? (See Table 14.1.)

2. **WHAT IF?** List all gametes that could be made by a pea plant heterozygous for seed colour, seed shape, and pod shape (*YyRrIi*; see Table 14.1). How large a Punnett square would you need to draw to predict the offspring of a self-pollination of this "trihybrid"?

3. **MAKE CONNECTIONS** In some pea plant crosses, the plants are self-pollinated. Explain whether self-pollination is considered asexual or sexual reproduction. (See Concept 13.1.)

For suggested answers, see Appendix A.

CONCEPT 14.2

Probability laws govern Mendelian inheritance

Mendel's laws of segregation and independent assortment reflect the same rules of probability that apply to tossing coins, rolling dice, and drawing cards from a deck. The probability scale ranges from 0 to 1. An event that is certain to occur has a probability of 1, while an event that is certain *not* to occur has a probability of 0. With a coin that has heads on both sides, the probability of tossing heads is 1, and the probability of tossing tails is 0. With a normal coin, the chance of tossing heads is ½, and the chance of tossing tails is ½. The probability of drawing the ace of spades from a 52-card deck is $\frac{1}{52}$. The probabilities of all possible outcomes for an event must add up to 1. With a deck of cards, the chance of picking a card other than the ace of spades is $\frac{51}{52}$.

Tossing a coin illustrates an important lesson about probability. For every toss, the probability of heads is ½. The outcome of any particular toss is unaffected by what has happened on previous trials. We refer to phenomena such as coin tosses as independent events. Each toss of a coin, whether done sequentially with one coin or simultaneously with many, is independent of every other toss. And like two separate coin tosses, the alleles of one gene segregate into gametes independently of another gene's alleles (the law of independent assortment). We'll now look at two basic rules of probability that help us predict the outcome of the fusion of such gametes in simple monohybrid crosses and more complicated crosses.

The Multiplication and Addition Rules Applied to Monohybrid Crosses

How do we determine the probability that two or more independent events will occur together in some specific combination? For example, what is the chance that two coins tossed simultaneously will both land heads up? The **multiplication rule** states that to determine this probability, we multiply the probability of one event (one coin coming up heads) by the probability of the other event (the other coin coming up heads). By the multiplication rule, then, the probability that both coins will land heads up is $\frac{1}{2} \times \frac{1}{2} = \frac{1}{4}$.

We can apply the same reasoning to an F_1 monohybrid cross. With seed shape in pea plants as the heritable character, the genotype of F_1 plants is Rr. Segregation in a heterozygous plant is like flipping a coin in terms of calculating the probability of each outcome: Each egg produced has a $\frac{1}{2}$ chance of carrying the dominant allele (R) and a $\frac{1}{2}$ chance of carrying the recessive allele (r). The same odds apply to each sperm cell produced. For a particular F_2 plant to have wrinkled seeds, the recessive trait, both the egg and the sperm that come together must carry the r allele. The probability that an r allele will be present in both gametes at fertilization is found by multiplying $\frac{1}{2}$ (the probability that the egg will have an r) $\times$ $\frac{1}{2}$ (the probability that the sperm will have an r). Thus, the multiplication rule tells us that the probability of an F_2 plant having wrinkled seeds (rr) is $\frac{1}{4}$ **(Figure 14.9)**. Likewise, the probability of an F_2 plant carrying both dominant alleles for seed shape (RR) is $\frac{1}{4}$.

To figure out the probability that an F_2 plant from a monohybrid cross will be heterozygous rather than homozygous, we need to invoke a second rule. Notice in Figure 14.9 that the dominant allele can come from the egg and the recessive allele from the sperm, or vice versa. That is, F_1 gametes can combine to produce Rr offspring in two *mutually exclusive* ways: For any particular heterozygous F_2 plant, the dominant allele can come from the egg *or* the sperm, but not from both. According to the **addition rule**, the probability that any one of two or more mutually exclusive events will occur is calculated by adding their individual probabilities. As we have just seen, the multiplication rule gives us the individual probabilities that we will now add together. The probability for one possible way of obtaining an F_2 heterozygote—the dominant allele from the egg and the recessive allele from the sperm—is $\frac{1}{4}$. The probability for the other possible way—the recessive allele from the egg and the dominant allele from the sperm—is also $\frac{1}{4}$ (see Figure 14.9). Using the rule of

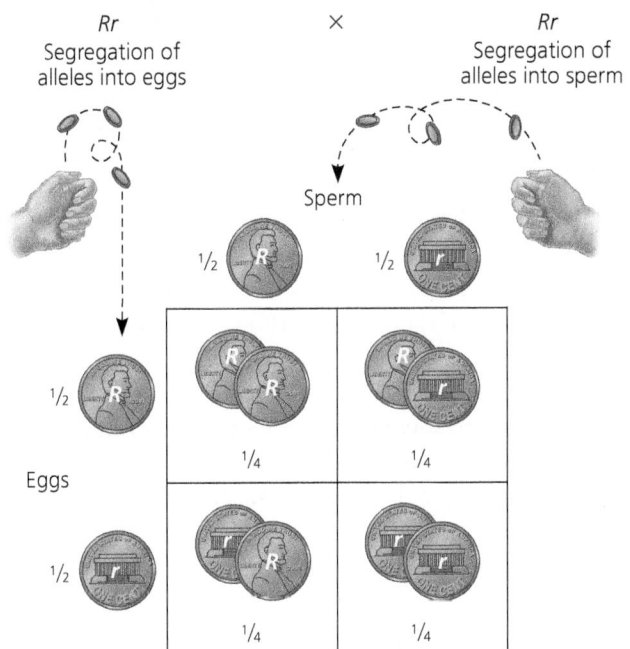

▲ **Figure 14.9 Segregation of alleles and fertilization as chance events.** When a heterozygote (Rr) forms gametes, whether a particular gamete ends up with an R or an r is like the toss of a coin. We can determine the probability for any genotype among the offspring of two heterozygotes by multiplying together the individual probabilities of an egg and sperm having a particular allele (R or r in this example).

addition, then, we can calculate the probability of an F_2 heterozygote as $\frac{1}{4} + \frac{1}{4} = \frac{1}{2}$.

Solving Complex Genetics Problems with the Rules of Probability

We can also apply the rules of probability to predict the outcome of crosses involving multiple characters. Recall that each allelic pair segregates independently during gamete formation (the law of independent assortment). Thus, a dihybrid or other multicharacter cross is equivalent to two or more independent monohybrid crosses occurring simultaneously. By applying what we have learned about monohybrid crosses, we can determine the probability of specific genotypes occurring in the F_2 generation without having to construct unwieldy Punnett squares.

Consider the dihybrid cross between $YyRr$ heterozygotes shown in Figure 14.8. We will focus first on the seed-colour character. For a monohybrid cross of Yy plants, we can use a simple Punnett square to determine that the probabilities of the offspring genotypes are $\frac{1}{4}$ for YY, $\frac{1}{2}$ for Yy, and $\frac{1}{4}$ for yy. We can draw a second Punnett square to determine that the same probabilities apply to the offspring genotypes for seed shape: $\frac{1}{4}$ RR, $\frac{1}{2}$ Rr, and $\frac{1}{4}$ rr. Knowing these probabilities, we can simply use the multiplication rule to determine the probability of each of the genotypes in the F_2 generation. To give two examples, the calculations for finding the probabilities of two of the possible F_2 genotypes (*YYRR* and *YyRR*) are shown below:

Probability of *YYRR* = ¼(probability of *YY*) × ¼(*RR*) = 1/16
Probability of *YyRR* = ½(*Yy*)	× ¼(*RR*) = ⅛

The *YYRR* genotype corresponds to the upper left box in the larger Punnett square in Figure 14.8 (one box = 1/16). Looking closely at the larger Punnett square in Figure 14.8, you will see that 2 of the 16 boxes (⅛) correspond to the *YyRR* genotype.

Now let's see how we can combine the multiplication and addition rules to solve even more complex problems in Mendelian genetics. Imagine a cross of two pea varieties in which we track the inheritance of three characters. Let's cross a trihybrid with purple flowers and yellow, round seeds (heterozygous for all three genes) with a plant with purple flowers and green, wrinkled seeds (heterozygous for flower colour but homozygous recessive for the other two characters). Using Mendelian symbols, our cross is *PpYyRr* × *Ppyyrr*. What fraction of offspring from this cross are predicted to exhibit the recessive phenotypes for *at least two* of the three characters?

To answer this question, we can start by listing all genotypes we could get that fulfill this condition: *ppyyRr*, *ppYyrr*, *Ppyyrr*, *PPyyrr*, and *ppyyrr*. (Because the condition is *at least two* recessive traits, it includes the last genotype, which shows all three recessive traits.) Next, we calculate the probability for each of these genotypes resulting from our *PpYyRr* × *Ppyyrr* cross by multiplying together the individual probabilities for the allele pairs, just as we did in our dihybrid example. Note that in a cross involving heterozygous and homozygous allele pairs (for example, *Yy* × *yy*), the probability of heterozygous offspring is ½ and the probability of homozygous offspring is ½. Finally, we use the addition rule to add the probabilities for all the different genotypes that fulfill the condition of at least two recessive traits resulting from our *PpYyRr* × *Ppyyrr* cross, as shown below:

ppyyRr ¼ (probability of *pp*) × ½ (*yy*) × ½ (*Rr*)	= 1/16
ppYyrr ¼ × ½ × ½	= 1/16
Ppyyrr ½ × ½ × ½	= 2/16
PPyyrr ¼ × ½ × ½	= 1/16
ppyyrr ¼ × ½ × ½	= 1/16
Chance of *at least two* recessive traits	= 6/16 or 3/8

In time, you'll be able to solve genetics problems faster by using the rules of probability than by filling in Punnett squares.

We cannot predict with certainty the exact numbers of progeny of different genotypes resulting from a genetic cross. But the rules of probability give us the *likelihood* of various outcomes. Usually, the larger the sample size, the closer the results will conform to our predictions. Mendel understood this statistical feature of inheritance and had a keen sense of the rules of chance. It was for this reason that he set up his experiments so as to generate, and then count, large numbers of offspring from his crosses.

CONCEPT CHECK 14.2

1. For any gene with a dominant allele *A* and recessive allele *a*, what proportions of the offspring from an *AA* × *Aa* cross are expected to be homozygous dominant, homozygous recessive, and heterozygous?

2. Two organisms, with genotypes *BbDD* and *BBDd*, are mated. Assuming independent assortment of the *B/b* and *D/d* genes, write the genotypes of all possible offspring from this cross and use the rules of probability to calculate the chance of each genotype occurring.

3. **WHAT IF?** Three characters (flower colour, seed colour, and pod shape) are considered in a cross between two pea plants (*PpYyIi* × *ppYyii*). What fraction of offspring is predicted to be homozygous recessive for at least two of the three characters?

For suggested answers, see Appendix A.

CONCEPT 14.3

Inheritance patterns are often more complex than predicted by simple Mendelian genetics

In the 20th century, geneticists extended Mendelian principles not only to diverse organisms, but also to patterns of inheritance more complex than those described by Mendel. For the work that led to his two laws of inheritance, Mendel chose pea plant characters that turn out to have a relatively simple genetic basis: Each character is determined by one gene, for which there are only two alleles, one completely dominant and the other completely recessive. (There is one exception: Mendel's pod-shape character is actually determined by two genes.) Not all heritable characters are determined so simply, and the relationship between genotype and phenotype is rarely so straightforward. Mendel himself realized that he could not explain the more complicated patterns he observed in crosses involving other pea characters or other plant species. This does not diminish the utility of Mendelian genetics, however, because the basic principles of segregation and independent assortment apply even to more complex patterns of inheritance. In this section, we will extend Mendelian genetics to hereditary patterns that were not reported by Mendel.

Extending Mendelian Genetics for a Single Gene

The inheritance of characters determined by a single gene deviates from simple Mendelian patterns when alleles are not completely dominant or recessive, when a particular gene has more than two alleles, or when a single gene produces multiple phenotypes. We will describe examples of each of these situations in this section.

Degrees of Dominance

Alleles can show different degrees of dominance and recessiveness in relation to each other. In Mendel's classic pea crosses, the F_1 offspring always looked like one of the two parental varieties because one allele in a pair showed **complete dominance** over the other. In such situations, the phenotypes of the heterozygote and the dominant homozygote are indistinguishable (see Figure 14.6).

For some genes, however, neither allele is completely dominant, and the F_1 hybrids have a phenotype somewhere between those of the two parental varieties. This phenomenon, called **incomplete dominance**, is seen when red snapdragons are crossed with white snapdragons: All the F_1 hybrids have pink flowers (**Figure 14.10**). This third, intermediate phenotype results from flowers of the heterozygotes having less red pigment than the red homozygotes. (This is unlike the case of Mendel's pea plants, where the *Pp* heterozygotes make enough pigment for the flowers to be purple, indistinguishable from those of *PP* plants.)

At first glance, incomplete dominance of either allele seems to provide evidence for the blending hypothesis of inheritance, which would predict that the red or white trait could never reappear among offspring of the pink hybrids. In fact, interbreeding F_1 hybrids produces F_2 offspring with a phenotypic ratio of one red to two pink to one white. (Because heterozygotes have a separate phenotype, the genotypic and phenotypic ratios for the F_2 generation are the same, 1:2:1.) The segregation of the red-flower and white-flower alleles in the gametes produced by the pink-flowered plants confirms that the alleles for flower colour are heritable factors that maintain their identity in the hybrids; that is, inheritance is particulate.

Another variation on dominance relationships between alleles is called **codominance**; in this variation, the two alleles each affect the phenotype in separate, distinguishable ways. For example, the human MN blood group is determined by codominant alleles for two specific molecules located on the surface of red blood cells, the M and N molecules. A single gene locus, at which two allelic variations are possible, determines the phenotype of this blood group. Individuals homozygous for the *M* allele (*MM*) have red blood cells with only M molecules; individuals homozygous for the *N* allele (*NN*) have red blood cells with only N molecules. But *both* M and N molecules are present on the red blood cells of individuals heterozygous for the *M* and *N* alleles (*MN*). Note that the MN phenotype is *not* intermediate between the M and N phenotypes, which

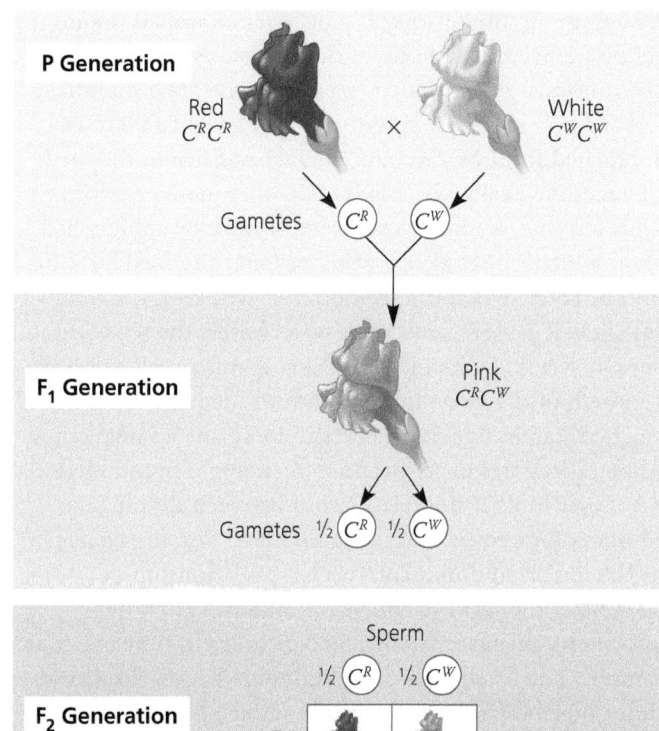

▲ **Figure 14.10 Incomplete dominance in snapdragon colour.** When red snapdragons are crossed with white ones, the F_1 hybrids have pink flowers. Segregation of alleles into gametes of the F_1 plants results in an F_2 generation with a 1:2:1 ratio for both genotype and phenotype. Neither allele is dominant, so rather than using upper- and lowercase letters, we use the letter *C* with a superscript to indicate an allele for flower colour: C^R for red and C^W for white.

? *Suppose a classmate argues that this figure supports the blending hypothesis for inheritance. What might your classmate say, and how would you respond?*

distinguishes codominance from incomplete dominance. Rather, *both* M and N phenotypes are exhibited by heterozygotes, since both molecules are present.

The Relationship Between Dominance and Phenotype

We've now seen that the relative effects of two alleles range from complete dominance of one allele, through incomplete dominance of either allele, to codominance of both alleles. It is important to understand that an allele is called *dominant* because it is seen in the phenotype, not because it somehow subdues a recessive allele. Alleles are simply variations in a gene's nucleotide sequence (see Figure 14.4). When a dominant allele coexists with a recessive allele in a heterozygote, they do not actually interact at all. It is in the pathway from genotype to phenotype that dominance and recessiveness come into play.

To illustrate the relationship between dominance and phenotype, we can use one of the characters Mendel studied—round versus wrinkled pea seed shape. The dominant allele (round) codes for an enzyme that helps convert an unbranched form of starch to a branched form in the seed. The recessive allele (wrinkled) codes for a defective form of this enzyme, leading to an accumulation of unbranched starch, which causes excess water to enter the seed by osmosis. Later, when the seed dries, it wrinkles. If a dominant allele is present, no excess water enters the seed and it does not wrinkle when it dries. One dominant allele results in enough of the enzyme to synthesize adequate amounts of branched starch, which means that dominant homozygotes and heterozygotes have the same phenotype: round seeds.

A closer look at the relationship between dominance and phenotype reveals an intriguing fact: For any character, the observed dominant/recessive relationship of alleles depends on the level at which we examine phenotype. **Tay-Sachs disease**, an inherited disorder in humans, is an example. The brain cells of a child with Tay-Sachs disease cannot metabolize certain lipids because a crucial enzyme does not work properly. As these lipids accumulate in brain cells, the child begins to suffer seizures, blindness, and degeneration of motor and mental performance and dies within a few years.

Only children who inherit two copies of the Tay-Sachs allele (homozygotes) have the disease. Thus, at the *organismal* level, the Tay-Sachs allele qualifies as recessive. However, the activity level of the lipid-metabolizing enzyme in heterozygotes is intermediate between the activity level in individuals homozygous for the normal allele and the activity level in individuals with Tay-Sachs disease. (The term *normal* is used in the genetic sense to refer to the allele coding for the enzyme that functions properly.) The intermediate phenotype observed at the *biochemical* level is characteristic of incomplete dominance of either allele. Fortunately, the heterozygote condition does not lead to disease symptoms, apparently because half the normal enzyme activity is sufficient to prevent lipid accumulation in the brain. Extending our analysis to yet another level, we find that heterozygous individuals produce equal numbers of normal and dysfunctional enzyme molecules. Thus, at the *molecular* level, the normal allele and the Tay-Sachs allele are codominant. As you can see, whether alleles appear to be completely dominant, incompletely dominant, or codominant depends on the level at which the phenotype is analyzed.

Frequency of Dominant Alleles Although you might assume that the dominant allele for a particular character would be more common than the recessive allele, this is not always the case. For an example of a rare dominant allele, about one baby out of 500 in Canada is born with extra fingers or toes, a condition known as polydactyly. Some cases are caused by the presence of a dominant allele. The low frequency of polydactyly indicates that the recessive allele, which results in five digits per appendage, is far more prevalent than the dominant allele in the population. In Chapter 23, you will learn how relative frequencies of alleles in a population are affected by natural selection.

Multiple Alleles

Only two alleles exist for the pea characters that Mendel studied, but most genes exist in more than two allelic forms. The ABO blood groups in humans, for instance, are determined by that person's two alleles of the blood group gene; there are three possible alleles: I^A, I^B, and i. A person's blood group may be one of four types: A, B, AB, or O. These letters refer to two carbohydrates—A and B—that may be found attached to specific cell-surface molecules on red blood cells. An individual's blood cells may have carbohydrate A (type A blood), carbohydrate B (type B), both (type AB), or neither (type O), as shown in **Figure 14.11**. Matching compatible blood groups is critical for safe blood transfusions (see Concept 43.3).

Pleiotropy

So far, we have treated Mendelian inheritance as though each gene affects only one phenotypic character. Most genes, however, have multiple phenotypic effects, a property called **pleiotropy** (from the Greek *pleion*, more). In humans, for example, pleiotropic alleles are responsible for the multiple symptoms associated with certain hereditary diseases, such

(a) The three alleles for the ABO blood groups and their carbohydrates. Each allele codes for an enzyme that may add a specific carbohydrate (designated by the superscript on the allele and shown as a triangle or circle) to red blood cells.

Allele	I^A	I^B	i
Carbohydrate	A △	B ○	none

(b) Blood group genotypes and phenotypes. There are six possible genotypes, resulting in four different phenotypes.

Genotype	I^AI^A or I^Ai	I^BI^B or I^Bi	I^AI^B	ii
Red blood cell appearance				
Phenotype (blood group)	A	B	AB	O

▲ Figure 14.11 **Multiple alleles for the ABO blood groups.** The four blood groups result from different combinations of three alleles.

? *Based on the surface carbohydrate phenotype in (b), what are the dominance relationships among the alleles?*

as cystic fibrosis and sickle-cell disease, discussed later in this chapter. In the garden pea, the gene that determines flower colour also affects the colour of the coating on the outer surface of the seed, which can be grey or white. Given the intricate molecular and cellular interactions responsible for an organism's development and physiology, it isn't surprising that a single gene can affect a number of characteristics.

Extending Mendelian Genetics for Two or More Genes

Dominance relationships, multiple alleles, and pleiotropy all have to do with the effects of the alleles of a single gene. We now consider two situations in which two or more genes are involved in determining a particular phenotype. In the first case, called epistasis, one gene affects the phenotype of another because the two gene products interact; in the second case, called *polygenic inheritance*, multiple genes independently affect a single trait.

Epistasis

In **epistasis** (from the Greek for "standing upon"), the phenotypic expression of a gene at one locus alters phenotypic expression of a gene at a second locus. An example will help clarify this concept. In Labrador retrievers (commonly called "Labs"), black coat colour is dominant to brown. Let's designate *B* and *b* as the two alleles for this character. For a Lab to have brown fur, its genotype must be *bb*; these dogs are called chocolate Labs. But there is more to the story. A second gene determines whether or not pigment will be deposited in the hair. The dominant allele, symbolized by *E*, results in the deposition of either black or brown pigment, depending on the genotype at the first locus. But if the Lab is homozygous recessive for the second locus (*ee*), then the coat is yellow (so-called golden Labs), regardless of the genotype at the black/brown locus. In this case, the gene for pigment deposition (*E/e*) is said to be epistatic to the gene that codes for black or brown pigment (*B/b*).

What happens if we mate black Labs that are heterozygous for both genes (*BbEe*)? Although the two genes affect the same phenotypic character (coat colour), they follow the law of independent assortment. Thus, our breeding experiment represents an F₁ dihybrid cross, like those that produced a 9:3:3:1 ratio in Mendel's experiments. We can use a Punnett square to represent the genotypes of the F₂ offspring (**Figure 14.12**). As a result of epistasis, the phenotypic ratio among the F₂ offspring is 9 black to 3 chocolate to 4 golden Labs. Other types of epistatic interactions produce different ratios, but all are modified versions of 9:3:3:1.

Polygenic Inheritance

Mendel studied characters that could be classified on an either-or basis, such as purple versus white flower colour.

▲ **Figure 14.12 An example of epistasis.** This Punnett square illustrates the genotypes and phenotypes predicted for offspring of matings between two black Labrador retrievers of genotype *BbEe*. The *E/e* gene, which is epistatic to the *B/b* gene coding for hair pigment, controls whether or not pigment of any colour will be deposited in the hair.

But many characters, such as human skin colour and height, are not one of two discrete characters, but instead vary in the population in gradations along a continuum. These are called **quantitative characters**. Quantitative variation usually indicates **polygenic inheritance**, an additive effect of two or more genes on a single phenotypic character. (In a way, this is the converse of pleiotropy, where a single gene affects several phenotypic characters.) Height is a good example of polygenic inheritance: A recent study using genomic methods identified at least 180 genes that affect height.

Skin pigmentation in humans is also controlled by many separately inherited genes. Here, we'll simplify the story in order to understand the concept of polygenic inheritance. Let's consider three genes, with a dark-skin allele for each gene (*A*, *B*, or *C*) contributing one "unit" of darkness (also a simplification) to the phenotype and being incompletely dominant to the other allele (*a*, *b*, or *c*). In our model, an *AABBCC* person would be very dark, while an *aabbcc* individual would be very light. An *AaBbCc* person would have skin of an intermediate shade. Because the alleles have a cumulative effect, the genotypes *AaBbCc* and *AABbcc* would make the same genetic contribution

Phenotypes: | 1/64 | 6/64 | 15/64 | 20/64 | 15/64 | 6/64 | 1/64 |

Number of dark-skin alleles: 0 1 2 3 4 5 6

◀ **Figure 14.13 A simplified model for polygenic inheritance of skin colour.** According to this model, three separately inherited genes affect the darkness of skin. The heterozygous individuals (*AaBbCc*) represented by the two rectangles at the top of this figure each carry three dark-skin alleles (black circles, which represent *A*, *B*, or *C*) and three light-skin alleles (white circles, which represent *a*, *b*, or *c*). The Punnett square shows all the possible genetic combinations in gametes and in offspring of a large number of hypothetical matings between these heterozygotes. The results are summarized by the phenotypic ratios under the Punnett square.

(three units) to skin darkness. There are seven skin-colour phenotypes that could result from a mating between *AaBbCc* heterozygotes, as shown in **Figure 14.13**. In a large number of such matings, the majority of offspring would be expected to have intermediate phenotypes (skin colour in the middle range). You can graph the predictions from the Punnett square in the Scientific Skills Exercise. Environmental factors, such as exposure to the sun, also affect the skin-colour phenotype.

Apomares/E+/Getty Images

SCIENTIFIC SKILLS EXERCISE

Making a Histogram and Analyzing a Distribution Pattern

What Is the Distribution of Phenotypes among Offspring of Two Parents Who Are Both Heterozygous for Three Additive Genes? Human skin colour is a polygenic trait that is determined by the additive effects of many different genes. In this exercise, you will work with a simplified model of skin-colour genetics where only three genes are assumed to affect the darkness of skin colour and where each gene has two alleles—dark or light (see Figure 14.13). In this model, each dark allele contributes equally to the darkness of skin colour, and each pair of alleles segregates independently of each other pair. Using a type of graph called a histogram, you will determine the distribution of phenotypes of offspring with different numbers of dark-skin alleles. (For additional information about graphs, see the Scientific Skills Review in Appendix E and in the Study Area in MasteringBiology.)

How This Model Is Analyzed To predict the phenotypes of the offspring of parents heterozygous for the three genes in our simplified model, we can use the Punnett square in Figure 14.13. The heterozygous individuals (*AaBbCc*) represented by the two rectangles at the top of this figure each carry three dark-skin alleles (black circles, which represent *A*, *B*, or *C*) and three light-skin alleles (white circles, which represent *a*, *b*, or *c*). The Punnett square shows all the possible genetic combinations in gametes and in offspring of a large number of hypothetical matings between these heterozygotes.

Predictions from the Punnett Square If we assume that each square in the Punnett square represents one offspring of the heterozygous *AaBbCc* parents, then the squares below show the frequencies of all seven possible phenotypes of offspring, with each phenotype having a specific number of dark-skin alleles:

Phenotypes: | 1/64 | 6/64 | 15/64 | 20/64 | 15/64 | 6/64 | 1/64 |

Number of dark-skin alleles: 0 1 2 3 4 5 6

Interpret the Data

1. A histogram is a bar graph that shows the distribution of numeric data (here, the number of dark-skin alleles). To make a histogram of the allele distribution, put skin colour (as the number of dark-skin alleles) along the *x*-axis and number of offspring (out of 64) with each phenotype on the *y*-axis. There are no gaps in our allele data, so draw the bars next to each other with no space in between.

2. You can see that the skin-colour phenotypes are not distributed uniformly. (a) Which phenotype has the highest frequency? Draw a vertical dashed line through that bar. (b) Distributions of values like this one tend to show one of several common patterns. Sketch a rough curve that approximates the values and look at its shape. Is it symmetrically distributed around a central peak value (a "normal distribution," sometimes called a bell curve); is it skewed to one end of the *x*-axis or the other (a "skewed distribution"); or does it show two apparent groups of frequencies (a "bimodal distribution")? Explain the reason for the curve's shape. (It will help to read the text description that supports Figure 14.13.)

3. If one of the three genes were lethal when homozygous recessive, what would happen to the distribution of phenotype frequencies? To determine this, use *bb* as an example of a lethal genotype. Using Figure 14.13, identify offspring where the centre circle (the *B/b* gene) in both the top and bottom rows of the square is white, representing the homozygous state *bb*. Because *bb* individuals would not survive, cross out those squares, then count the phenotype frequencies of the surviving offspring according to the number of dark-skin alleles (0–6) and graph the new data. What happens to the shape of the curve compared with the curve in question 2? What does this indicate about the distribution of phenotype frequencies?

Further Reading: R. A. Sturm, A golden age of human pigmentation genetics, *Trends in Genetics* 22:464–468 (2006).

Nature and Nurture: The Environmental Impact on Phenotype

Another departure from simple Mendelian genetics arises when the phenotype for a character depends on environment as well as genotype. A single tree, locked into its inherited genotype, has leaves that vary in size, shape, and greenness, depending on their exposure to wind and sun. For humans, nutrition influences height, exercise alters build, sun-tanning darkens the skin, and experience improves performance on intelligence tests. Even identical twins, who are genetic equals, accumulate phenotypic differences as a result of their unique experiences.

The autumn colours of sugar maple trees (*Acer sacchrum*) have a strong genetic basis, therefore sugar maple trees from Eastern Canada and the U.S. can be planted in different environments and still provide brilliant red-coloured leaves during the autumn. Environmental factors such as day length, temperature, and stress do have an effect on the timing, duration, and intensity of autumn colouration. Autumn colour change is due to temperature-sensitive chlorophyll breaking down and revealing yellow-orange carotenoids and the de novo synthesis of red anthocyanins in response to environmental cues. This can be a problem for visitors to Algonquin Provincial Park in Ontario who may miss peak autumn colour in the sugar maples because the timing varies from year to year, from as early as September 15th to as late as October 8th (see below).

Chris Hill/Shutterstock

Whether human characters are more influenced by genes or the environment—in everyday terms, nature versus nurture—is a debate that we will not attempt to settle here. We can say, however, that a genotype generally is not associated with a rigidly defined phenotype, but rather with a range of phenotypic possibilities due to environmental influences (Figure 14.14). For some characters, such as the ABO blood group system, the phenotypic range has no breadth whatsoever; that is, a given genotype mandates a very specific phenotype. Other characters, such as a person's blood count of red and white cells, vary quite a bit, depending on such

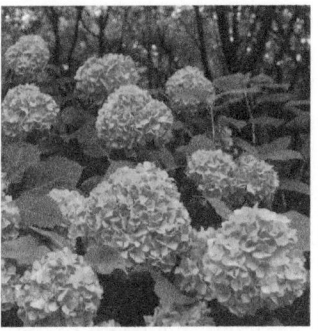

▲ **Figure 14.14 The effect of environment on phenotype.** The outcome of a genotype lies within its norm of reaction, a phenotypic range that depends on the environment in which the genotype is expressed. For example, hydrangea flowers of the same genetic variety range in colour from blue-violet to pink, with the shade and intensity of colour depending on the acidity and aluminum content of the soil.

factors as the altitude, the customary level of physical activity, and the presence of infectious agents.

Generally, the phenotypic range is broadest for polygenic characters. Environment contributes to the quantitative nature of these characters, as we have seen in the continuous variation of skin colour. Geneticists refer to such characters as **multifactorial**, meaning that many factors, both genetic and environmental, collectively influence phenotype.

A Mendelian View of Heredity and Variation

We have now broadened our view of Mendelian inheritance by exploring degrees of dominance as well as multiple alleles, pleiotropy, epistasis, polygenic inheritance, and the phenotypic impact of the environment. How can we integrate these refinements into a comprehensive theory of Mendelian genetics? The key is to make the transition from the reductionist emphasis on single genes and phenotypic characters to the emergent properties of the organism as a whole, one of the themes of this text.

The term *phenotype* can refer not only to specific characters, such as flower colour and blood group, but also to an organism in its entirety—*all* aspects of its physical appearance, internal anatomy, physiology, and behaviour. Similarly, the term *genotype* can refer to an organism's entire genetic makeup, not just its alleles for a single genetic locus. In most cases, a gene's impact on phenotype is affected by other genes and by the environment. In this integrated view of heredity and variation, an organism's phenotype reflects its overall genotype and unique environmental history.

Considering all that can occur in the pathway from genotype to phenotype, it is indeed impressive that Mendel could uncover the fundamental principles governing the transmission of individual genes from parents to offspring. Mendel's laws of segregation and of independent assortment explain heritable variations in terms of alternative forms of genes (hereditary "particles," now known as the alleles of genes) that are passed along, generation after generation, according to simple rules of probability. This theory of inheritance is equally valid for peas, flies, fishes, birds, and human beings—indeed, for any organism with a sexual life cycle. Furthermore, by extending the principles of segregation and independent assortment to help explain such hereditary patterns as epistasis and quantitative characters, we begin to see how broadly Mendelian genetics applies. From Mendel's abbey garden came a theory of particulate inheritance that anchors modern genetics. In the last section of this chapter, we will apply Mendelian genetics to human inheritance, with emphasis on the transmission of hereditary diseases.

CONCEPT CHECK 14.3

1. *Incomplete dominance* and *epistasis* are both terms that define genetic relationships. What is the most basic distinction between these terms?

2. If a man with type AB blood marries a woman with type O, what blood types would you expect in their children? What fraction would you expect of each type?

3. **WHAT IF?** A rooster with grey feathers and a hen of the same phenotype produce 15 grey, 6 black, and 8 white chicks. What is the simplest explanation for the inheritance of these colours in chickens? What phenotypes would you expect in the offspring of a cross between a grey rooster and a black hen?

For suggested answers, see Appendix A.

CONCEPT 14.4

Many human traits follow Mendelian patterns of inheritance

Peas are convenient subjects for genetic research, but humans are not. The human generation span is long—about 20 years—and human parents produce many fewer offspring than peas and most other species. Even more important, it wouldn't be ethical to ask pairs of humans to breed so that the phenotypes of their offspring could be analyzed! In spite of these constraints, the study of human genetics continues, spurred on by our desire to understand our own inheritance, and to develop treatments and cures for human and genetically based diseases. New molecular biological techniques have led to many breakthrough discoveries, as we will see in Chapter 20, but basic Mendelian genetics endures as the foundation of human genetics.

Pedigree Analysis

Unable to manipulate the mating patterns of people, geneticists instead analyze the results of matings that have already occurred. They do so by collecting information about a family's history for a particular trait and assembling this information into a family tree describing the traits of parents and children across the generations—a family **pedigree**.

Figure 14.15a shows a three-generation pedigree that traces the occurrence of a pointed contour of the hairline on the forehead. This trait, called a widow's peak, is due to a dominant allele, W. Because the widow's-peak allele is dominant, all individuals who lack a widow's peak must be homozygous recessive (ww). In this example, the two grandparents with widow's peaks must have the Ww genotype, since some of their offspring are homozygous recessive. The offspring in the second generation who *do* have widow's peaks must also be heterozygous, because they are the products of $Ww \times ww$ matings. The third generation in this pedigree consists of two sisters. The one who has a widow's peak could be either homozygous (WW) or heterozygous (Ww), given what we know about the genotypes of her parents (both Ww).

Figure 14.15b is a pedigree of the same family, but this time we focus on a recessive trait, the inability of individuals to taste a chemical called PTC (phenylthiocarbamide). Compounds similar to PTC are found in broccoli, Brussels sprouts, and related vegetables and account for the bitter taste some people report when eating these foods. We'll use t for the recessive allele and T for the dominant allele, which results in the ability to taste PTC. As you work your way through the pedigree, notice once again that you can apply what you have learned about Mendelian inheritance to understand the genotypes shown for the family members.

An important application of a pedigree is to help us calculate the probability that a future child will have a particular genotype and phenotype. Suppose that the couple represented in the second generation of Figure 14.15 decides to have one more child. What is the probability that the child will have a widow's peak? This is equivalent to a Mendelian F_1 monohybrid cross ($Ww \times Ww$), and thus the probability that a child will inherit a dominant allele and have a widow's peak is $\frac{3}{4}$ (derived from $\frac{1}{4}$ $WW + \frac{1}{2}$ Ww). What is the probability that the child will be unable to taste PTC? We can also treat this as a monohybrid cross ($Tt \times Tt$), but this time we want to know the chance that the offspring will be homozygous recessive (tt). That probability is $\frac{1}{4}$. Finally, what is the chance that the child will have a widow's peak *and* be unable to taste PTC? Assuming that the genes for these two characters are on different chromosomes, the two pairs of alleles will assort independently in this dihybrid cross ($WwTt \times WwTt$). Thus, we can use the multiplication rule: $\frac{3}{4}$ (chance of widow's peak) $\times \frac{1}{4}$ (chance of inability to taste PTC) $= \frac{3}{16}$ (chance of widow's peak and inability to taste PTC).

Pedigrees are a more serious matter when the alleles in question cause disabling or deadly diseases instead of

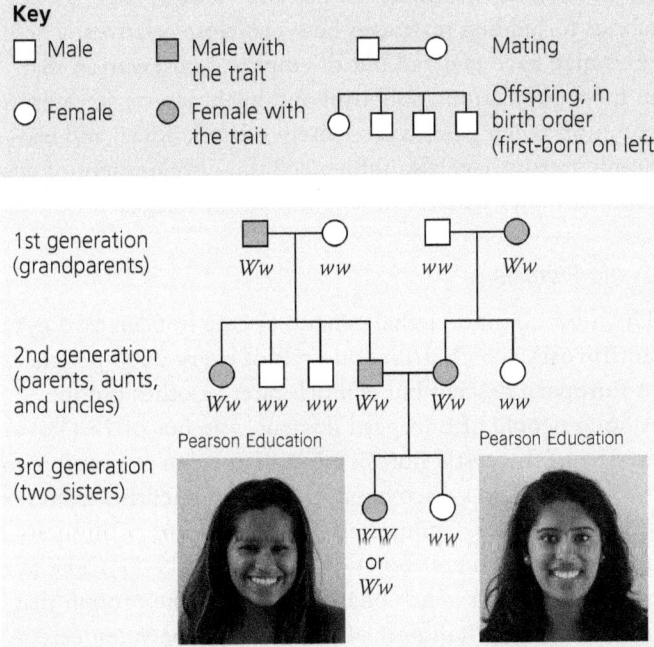

1st generation (grandparents)   *Ww*   *ww*   *ww*   *Ww*

2nd generation (parents, aunts, and uncles)   *Ww*   *ww*   *ww*   *Ww*   *Ww*   *ww*

Pearson Education   Pearson Education

3rd generation (two sisters)   *WW* or *Ww*   *ww*

Widow's peak   No widow's peak

(a) Is a widow's peak a dominant or recessive trait?

Tips for pedigree analysis: Notice in the third generation that the second-born daughter lacks a widow's peak, although both of her parents had the trait. Such a pattern indicates that the trait is due to a dominant allele. If it were due to a *recessive* allele, and both parents had the recessive phenotype (straight hairline), *all* of their offspring would also have the recessive phenotype.

1st generation (grandparents)   *Tt*   *Tt*   *tt*   *Tt*

2nd generation (parents, aunts, and uncles)   *TT* or *Tt*   *tt*   *tt*   *Tt*   *Tt*   *tt*

3rd generation (two sisters)   *tt*   *TT* or *Tt*

Pearson Education   Pearson Education

Cannot taste PTC   Can taste PTC

(b) Is the inability to taste a chemical called PTC a dominant or recessive trait?

Tips for pedigree analysis: Notice that the first-born daughter in the third generation has the trait (is unable to taste PTC), although both parents lack that trait (they *can* taste PTC). Such a pattern is explained if the non-taster phenotype is due to a recessive allele. (If it were due to a *dominant* allele, then at least one parent would also have had the trait.)

▲ **Figure 14.15 Pedigree analysis.** Each of these pedigrees traces a trait through three generations of the same family. The two traits have different inheritance patterns, as shown by the pedigrees.

innocuous human variations such as hairline or inability to taste an innocuous chemical. However, for disorders inherited as simple Mendelian traits, the same techniques of pedigree analysis apply.

Recessively Inherited Disorders

Thousands of genetic disorders are known to be inherited as simple recessive traits. These disorders range in severity from relatively mild, such as albinism (lack of pigmentation, which results in susceptibility to skin cancers and vision problems), to life-threatening, such as cystic fibrosis.

The Behaviour of Recessive Alleles

How can we account for the behaviour of alleles that cause recessively inherited disorders? Recall that genes code for proteins of specific function. An allele that causes a genetic disorder (let's call it allele *a*) codes for either a malfunctioning protein or no protein at all. In the case of disorders classified as recessive, heterozygotes (*Aa*) typically have the normal phenotype because one copy of the normal allele (*A*) produces a sufficient amount of the specific protein. Thus, a recessively inherited disorder shows up only in the homozygous individuals (*aa*) who inherit one recessive allele from each parent. Although phenotypically normal with regard to the disorder, heterozygotes may transmit the recessive allele to their offspring and thus are called **carriers**. **Figure 14.16** illustrates these ideas using albinism as an example.

Most people who have recessive disorders are born to parents who are carriers of the disorder but have a normal phenotype, as is the case shown in the Punnett square in

Parents

Normal   Normal
Aa   ×   *Aa*

Sperm

Ⓐ   ⓐ

Eggs

Ⓐ | *AA* Normal | *Aa* Normal (carrier)
ⓐ | *Aa* Normal (carrier) | *aa* Albino

Rick Guidotti/Positive Exposure

▲ **Figure 14.16 Albinism: a recessive trait.** One of the two sisters shown here has normal colouration; the other is albino. Most recessive homozygotes are born to parents who are carriers of the disorder but themselves have a normal phenotype, the case shown in the Punnett square.

? *What is the probability that the sister with normal colouration is a carrier of the albinism allele?*

Figure 14.16. A mating between two carriers corresponds to a Mendelian F₁ monohybrid cross, so the predicted genotypic ratio for the offspring is 1 *AA* : 2 *Aa* : 1 *aa*. Thus, each child has a ¼ chance of inheriting a double dose of the recessive allele; in the case of albinism, such a child will have albinism. From the genotypic ratio, we also can see that out of three offspring with the *normal* phenotype (one *AA* plus two *Aa*), two are predicted to be heterozygous carriers, a ⅔ chance. Recessive homozygotes could also result from *Aa* × *aa* and *aa* × *aa* matings, but if the disorder is lethal before reproductive age or results in sterility (neither of which is true for albinism), no *aa* individuals will reproduce. Even if recessive homozygotes are able to reproduce, such matings will occur relatively rarely because these individuals account for a much smaller percentage of the population than heterozygous carriers (for reasons we'll examine in Chapter 23).

In general, genetic disorders are not evenly distributed among all groups of people. For example, the incidence of Tay-Sachs disease, which we described earlier in this chapter, is disproportionately high among people of French Canadian heritage from eastern Quebec, and Ashkenazic Jews (Jewish people whose ancestors lived in central Europe).* In these populations, Tay-Sachs disease occurs in one out of 3600 births, an incidence about 100 times greater than that among the general population or Mediterranean (Sephardic) Jews. This uneven distribution results from the different genetic histories of the world's peoples during less technological times, when populations were more geographically (and hence genetically) isolated.

When a disease-causing recessive allele is rare, it is relatively unlikely that two carriers of the same harmful allele will meet and mate. However, if the man and woman are close relatives (for example, siblings or first cousins), the probability of passing on recessive traits increases greatly. These are called consanguineous ("same blood") matings, and they are indicated in pedigrees by double lines. Because people with recent common ancestors are more likely to carry the same recessive alleles than are unrelated people, it is more likely that a mating of close relatives will produce offspring homozygous for recessive traits—including harmful ones. Such effects can also be observed in many types of domesticated and zoo animals that have become inbred.

Although it is generally agreed that inbreeding causes an increase in autosomal recessive conditions compared to those resulting from matings between unrelated parents, there is debate among geneticists about exactly how much human consanguinity increases the risk of inherited diseases. For one thing, many harmful alleles have such severe effects that a homozygous embryo spontaneously aborts

long before birth. Most societies and cultures have laws or taboos forbidding marriages between close relatives. These rules may have evolved out of empirical observation that in most populations, stillbirths and birth defects are more common when parents are closely related. Social and economic factors have also influenced the development of customs and laws against consanguineous marriages.

Cystic Fibrosis

The most common lethal genetic disease in Canada is **cystic fibrosis**, which strikes one out of every 2500 people of European descent but is much rarer in other groups. Among people of European descent, one out of 25 (4%) are carriers of the cystic fibrosis allele. The gene responsible for cystic fibrosis was discovered in 1989 by scientists from the Hospital for Sick Children in Toronto as part of an international research collaboration (see Figure 17.27). The normal allele for this gene codes for a membrane protein that functions in the transport of chloride ions between certain cells and the extracellular fluid. These chloride transport channels are defective or absent in the plasma membranes of children who inherit two recessive alleles for cystic fibrosis. The result is an abnormally high concentration of intracellular chloride, which causes an uptake of water due to osmosis. This in turn causes the mucus that coats certain cells to become thicker and stickier than normal. The mucus builds up in the pancreas, lungs, digestive tract, and other organs, leading to multiple (pleiotropic) effects, including poor absorption of nutrients from the intestines, chronic bronchitis, and recurrent bacterial infections.

Untreated cystic fibrosis can cause death by the age of 5. Daily doses of antibiotics to prevent infection, gentle pounding on the chest to clear mucus from clogged airways, and other therapies can prolong life. In Canada, more than half of those with cystic fibrosis now survive into their 30s and beyond.

Sickle-Cell Disease: A Genetic Disorder with Evolutionary Implications

EVOLUTION The most common inherited disorder among people of African descent is **sickle-cell disease**, which affects one out of 400 African-Americans. Sickle-cell disease is caused by the substitution of a single amino acid in the hemoglobin protein of red blood cells; in homozygous individuals, all hemoglobin is of the sickle-cell (abnormal) variety. When the oxygen content of an affected individual's blood is low (at high altitudes or under physical stress, for instance), the sickle-cell hemoglobin proteins aggregate into long fibres that deform the red cells into a sickle shape (see Figure 5.19). Sickled cells may clump and clog small blood vessels, often leading to other symptoms throughout the body, including physical weakness, pain, organ damage,

---

*Note that although these two populations have a similar incidence rate of Tay-Sachs disease, the underlying causative mutation in each population is different.

and even stroke and paralysis. Regular blood transfusions can ward off brain damage in children with sickle-cell disease, and new drugs can help prevent or treat other problems. There is currently no widely available cure, but the disease is the target of ongoing gene therapy research.

Although two sickle-cell alleles are necessary for an individual to manifest full-blown sickle-cell disease and thus the condition is considered a recessive one, the presence of one sickle-cell allele can affect the phenotype. Thus, at the organismal level, the normal allele is incompletely dominant to the sickle-cell allele (Figure 14.17). At the molecular level, the two alleles are codominant; both normal and abnormal (sickle-cell) hemoglobins are made in heterozygotes (carriers), who are said to have *sickle-cell trait*. Heterozygotes are usually healthy but may suffer some symptoms during long periods of reduced blood oxygen.

About one out of ten African-Americans have sickle-cell trait, an unusually high frequency of heterozygotes for an allele with severe detrimental effects in homozygotes. Why haven't evolutionary processes resulted in the disappearance of the allele among this population? One explanation is that having a single copy of the sickle-cell allele reduces the frequency and severity of malaria attacks, especially among young children. The malaria parasite spends part of its life cycle in red blood cells (see Figure 28.16), and the presence of even heterozygous amounts of sickle-cell hemoglobin results in lower parasite densities and hence reduced malaria symptoms. Thus, in tropical Africa, where infection with the malaria parasite is common, the sickle-cell allele confers an advantage to heterozygotes even though it is harmful in the homozygous state. (The balance between these two effects will be discussed in Chapter 23. Also, see the Make Connections figure on pages 490–491.) The relatively high frequency of African-Americans with sickle-cell trait is a vestige of their African ancestry.

Dominantly Inherited Disorders

Although many harmful alleles are recessive, a number of human disorders are due to dominant alleles. One example is *achondroplasia*, a form of dwarfism that occurs in one of every 25 000 people. Heterozygous individuals have the dwarf phenotype (Figure 14.18). Therefore, all people who do not have achondroplasia—99.99% of the population— are homozygous for the recessive allele. Like the presence of extra fingers or toes mentioned earlier, achondroplasia is a trait for which the recessive allele is much more prevalent than the corresponding dominant allele.

Unlike achondroplasia, which is relatively harmless, some dominant alleles cause lethal diseases. Those that do are much less common than recessive alleles that have lethal effects. A lethal recessive allele is only lethal when homozygous; it can be passed from one generation to the next by heterozygous carriers because the carriers themselves have normal phenotypes. A lethal dominant allele, however, often causes the death of afflicted individuals before they can mature and reproduce, and in this case the allele is not passed on to future generations.

In cases of late-onset diseases, however, a lethal dominant allele may be passed on. If symptoms first appear after reproductive age, the individual may already have transmitted the allele to his or her children.

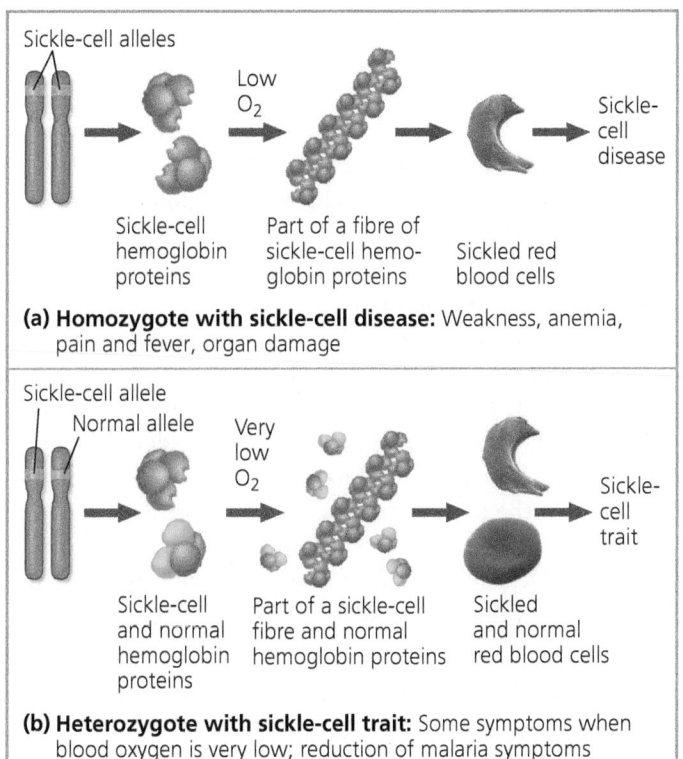

(a) **Homozygote with sickle-cell disease:** Weakness, anemia, pain and fever, organ damage

(b) **Heterozygote with sickle-cell trait:** Some symptoms when blood oxygen is very low; reduction of malaria symptoms

▲ Figure 14.17 **Sickle-cell disease and sickle-cell trait.**

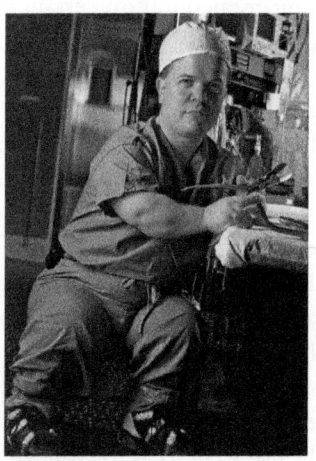

▲ Figure 14.18 **Achondroplasia: a dominant trait.** Dr. Michael C. Ain has achondroplasia, a form of dwarfism caused by a dominant allele. This has inspired his work: He is a specialist in the repair of bone defects caused by achondroplasia and other disorders. The dominant allele (*D*) might have arisen as a mutation in the egg or sperm of a parent or could have been inherited from an affected parent, as shown for an affected father in the Punnett square.

For example, **Huntington's disease**, a degenerative disease of the nervous system, is caused by a lethal dominant allele that has no obvious phenotypic effect until the individual is about 35 to 45 years old. Once the deterioration of the nervous system begins, it is irreversible and inevitably fatal. As with other dominant traits, a child born to a parent with the Huntington's disease allele has a 50% chance of inheriting the allele and the disorder (see the Punnett square in Figure 14.18). In Canada, this disease afflicts about one in 10 000 people.

At one time, the onset of symptoms was the only way to know if a person had inherited the Huntington's allele, but this is no longer the case. By analyzing DNA samples from a large family with a high incidence of the disorder, geneticists tracked the Huntington's allele to a locus near the tip of chromosome 4, and the gene was sequenced in 1993. This information led to the development of a test that could detect the presence of the Huntington's allele in an individual's genome. (The methods that make such tests possible are discussed in Chapter 20.) The availability of this test poses an agonizing dilemma for those with a family history of Huntington's disease. Some individuals may want to be tested for this disease before planning a family, whereas others may decide it would be too stressful to find out. Clearly, this is a highly personal decision.

Multifactorial Disorders

The hereditary diseases we have discussed so far are sometimes described as simple Mendelian disorders because they result from abnormality of one or both alleles at a single genetic locus. Many more people are susceptible to diseases that have a multifactorial basis—a genetic component plus a significant environmental influence. Heart disease, diabetes, cancer, alcoholism, certain mental illnesses such as schizophrenia and bipolar disorder, and many other diseases are multifactorial. In these cases, the hereditary component is polygenic. For example, many genes affect cardiovascular health, making some of us more prone than others to heart attacks and strokes. No matter what our genotype, however, our lifestyle has a tremendous effect on phenotype for cardiovascular health and other multifactorial characters. Exercise, a healthful diet, abstinence from smoking, and an ability to handle stressful situations all reduce our risk of heart disease and some types of cancer.

At present, so little is understood about the genetic contributions to most multifactorial diseases that the best public health strategy is to educate people about the importance of environmental factors and to promote healthful behaviour.

Genetic Testing and Counselling

Avoiding simple Mendelian disorders is possible when the risk of a particular genetic disorder can be assessed before

a child is conceived or during the early stages of the pregnancy. Many hospitals have genetic counsellors who can provide information to prospective parents concerned about a family history for a specific disease. Fetal and newborn testing can also reveal genetic disorders.

Counselling Based on Mendelian Genetics and Probability Rules

Consider the case of a hypothetical couple, John and Carol. Each had a brother who died from the same recessively inherited lethal disease. Before conceiving their first child, John and Carol seek genetic counselling to determine the risk of having a child with the disease. From the information about their brothers, we know that both parents of John and both parents of Carol must have been carriers of the recessive allele. Thus, John and Carol are both products of *Aa* × *Aa* crosses, where *a* symbolizes the allele that causes this particular disease. We also know that John and Carol are not homozygous recessive (*aa*), because they do not have the disease. Therefore, their genotypes are either *AA* or *Aa*.

Given a genotypic ratio of 1 *AA* : 2 *Aa* : 1 *aa* for offspring of an *Aa* × *Aa* cross, John and Carol each have a ⅔ chance of being carriers (*Aa*). According to the rule of multiplication, the overall probability of their firstborn having the disorder is ⅔ (the chance that John is a carrier) times ⅔ (the chance that Carol is a carrier) times ¼ (the chance of two carriers having a child with the disease), which equals ⅑. Suppose that Carol and John decide to have a child—after all, there is an ⅛ chance that their baby will not have the disorder. If, despite these odds, their child is born with the disease, then we would know that *both* John and Carol are, in fact, carriers (*Aa* genotype). If both John and Carol are carriers, there is a ¼ chance that any subsequent child this couple has will have the disease. The probability is higher for subsequent children because the diagnosis of the disease in the first child established that both parents are carriers, not because the genotype of the first child affects in any way that of future children.

When we use Mendel's laws to predict possible outcomes of matings, it is important to remember that each child represents an independent event in the sense that its genotype is unaffected by the genotypes of older siblings. Suppose that John and Carol have three more children, and *all three* have the hypothetical hereditary disease. There is only one chance in 64 (¼ × ¼ × ¼) that such an outcome will occur. Despite this run of misfortune, the chance that a fourth child of this couple will have the disease remains ¼.

Tests for Identifying Carriers

Most children with recessive disorders are born to parents with normal phenotypes. The key to accurately assessing the genetic risk for a particular disease is therefore to find out whether the prospective parents are heterozygous carriers of the recessive allele. For an increasing number of heritable disorders, tests are available that can distinguish individuals of normal phenotype who are dominant homozygotes from those who are heterozygous carriers (Figure 14.19). There are now tests that can identify carriers of the alleles for Tay-Sachs disease, sickle-cell disease, and the most common form of cystic fibrosis. A program testing for carriers of Tay-Sachs disease that began in the 1980s has successfully reduced the rate of babies born with this disease.

▼ Figure 14.19 **Impact**

Prenatal Genetic Testing

Since the sequencing of the human genome was completed in 2003, there has been an explosion in the number and kinds of DNA-based genetic tests. Currently, genetic testing for over 2000 different disease-causing alleles is available. Numerous hospitals and research centres across Canada offer prenatal genetic screening, including Mount Sinai Hospital in Toronto. Patients that undergo genetic testing and prenatal diagnosis at this hospital are teamed up with geneticists, genetic counsellors, and prenatal screening counsellors to assist them through the genetic screening process.

Eric Fahrner/Shutterstock

Why It Matters For prospective parents with a family history of a recessive or late-onset dominant disorder, deciding whether to have children can be a difficult decision. Genetic testing can eliminate some of the uncertainty and allow better predictions of the probabilities and risks involved.

Further Reading Andermann A., Blancquaert I., Genetic screening: A primer for primary care, *Canadian Family Physician* 56:333–339 (2010).

WHAT IF? *If one parent tests positive and the other tests negative for a recessive allele associated with a disorder, what is the probability that their first child will have the disorder? That their first child will be a carrier? That, if their first child is a carrier, the second will also be a carrier?*

MAKE CONNECTIONS *What other types of diseases, other than prenatal screening for inherited monogenic disorders, could genetic testing be used for?*

These tests for identifying carriers enable people with family histories of genetic disorders to make informed decisions about having children, including whether to do genetic testing of any potential fetus. The tests also raise other issues: Could carriers be denied life insurance even though they themselves are currently healthy? Current privacy legislation in Canada includes the *Human Reproductive and Genetic Technologies Act*, the *Personal Information Protection and Electronic Documents Act*, and the *Charter of Rights and Freedoms*. However, Canada currently does not have an Act that prevents discrimination due to genetic information. A question that remains is whether sufficient genetic counselling is available to help large numbers of individuals understand their genetic test results. Even when test results are clearly understood, affected individuals may still face difficult decisions. Advances in biotechnology offer the potential to reduce human suffering, but along with them come ethical issues that require conscientious deliberation.

Fetal Testing

Suppose a couple expecting a child learns that they are both carriers of the Tay-Sachs allele. In the 14th–16th week of pregnancy, tests performed along with a technique called **amniocentesis** can determine whether the developing fetus has Tay-Sachs disease (Figure 14.20a). In this procedure, a physician inserts a needle into the uterus and extracts about 10 mL of amniotic fluid, the liquid that bathes the fetus. Some genetic disorders can be detected from the presence of certain molecules in the amniotic fluid itself. Tests for other disorders, including Tay-Sachs disease, are performed on the DNA of cells cultured in the laboratory, descendants of fetal cells sloughed off into the amniotic fluid. A karyotype of these cultured cells can also identify certain chromosomal defects (see Figure 13.3).

In an alternative technique called **chorionic villus sampling (CVS)**, a physician inserts a narrow tube through the cervix into the uterus and suctions out a tiny sample of tissue from the placenta, the organ that transmits nutrients and fetal wastes between the fetus and the mother (Figure 14.20b). The cells of the chorionic villi of the placenta, the portion sampled, are derived from the fetus and have the same genotype and DNA sequence as the new individual. These cells are proliferating rapidly enough to allow karyotyping to be carried out immediately. This rapid analysis represents an advantage over amniocentesis, in which the cells must be cultured for several weeks before karyotyping. Another advantage of CVS is that it can be performed as early as the 8th–10th week of pregnancy.

Medical scientists have also developed methods for isolating fetal cells, or even fetal DNA, that have escaped into the mother's blood. Although very few are present, the cells can be cultured and tested, and the fetal DNA can be analyzed. In 2012, researchers were able to analyze the entire genome

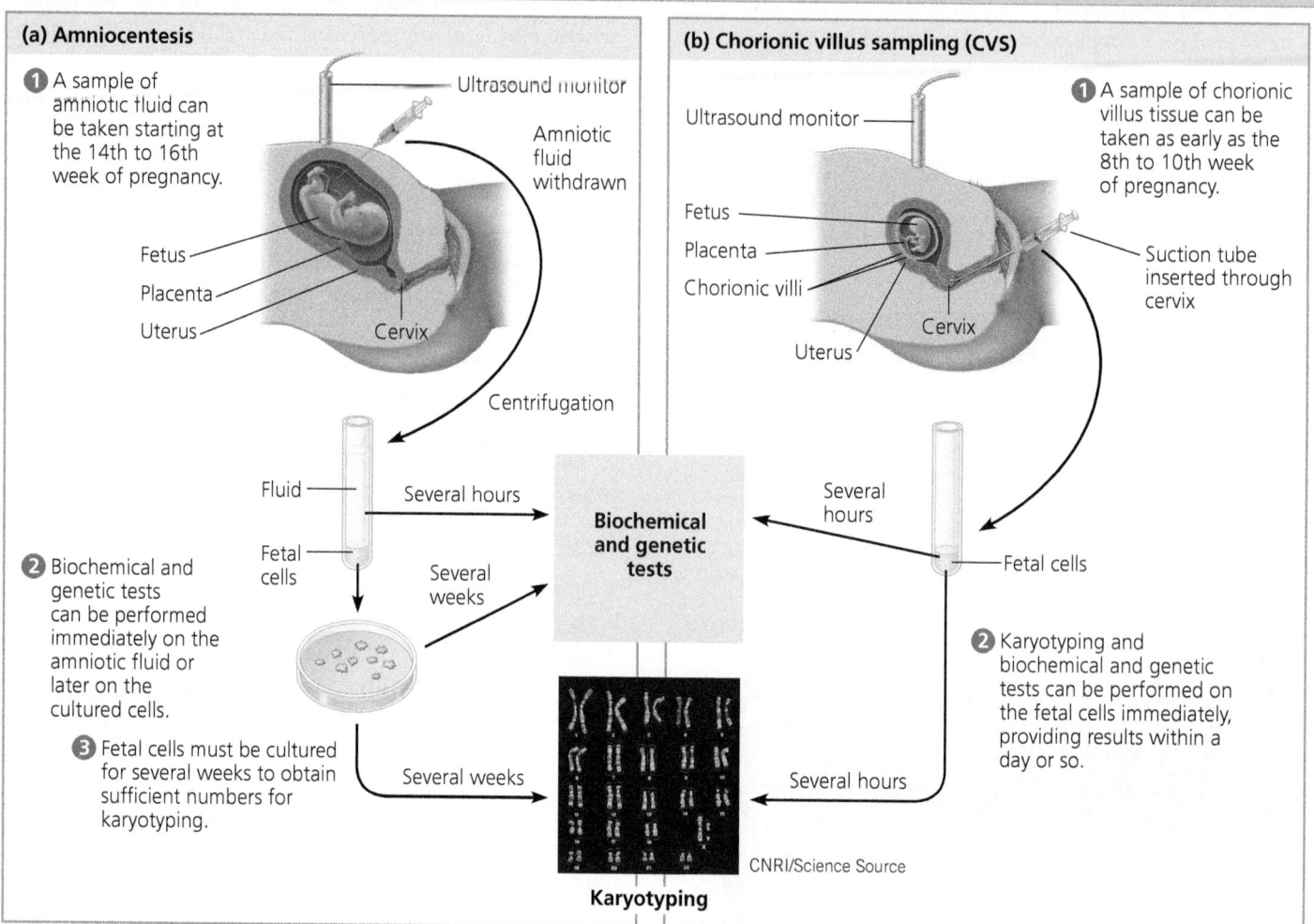

▼ Figure 14.20 **Testing a fetus for genetic disorders.** Biochemical tests may detect substances associated with particular disorders, and genetic testing can detect many genetic abnormalities. Karyotyping shows whether the chromosomes of the fetus are normal in number and appearance.

(a) Amniocentesis

❶ A sample of amniotic fluid can be taken starting at the 14th to 16th week of pregnancy.

Ultrasound monitor

Amniotic fluid withdrawn

Fetus

Placenta

Uterus

Cervix

Centrifugation

Fluid

Several hours

Fetal cells

❷ Biochemical and genetic tests can be performed immediately on the amniotic fluid or later on the cultured cells.

Several weeks

❸ Fetal cells must be cultured for several weeks to obtain sufficient numbers for karyotyping.

Several weeks

Biochemical and genetic tests

Karyotyping

CNRI/Science Source

(b) Chorionic villus sampling (CVS)

Ultrasound monitor

❶ A sample of chorionic villus tissue can be taken as early as the 8th to 10th week of pregnancy.

Fetus

Placenta

Chorionic villi

Cervix

Uterus

Suction tube inserted through cervix

Several hours

Fetal cells

❷ Karyotyping and biochemical and genetic tests can be performed on the fetal cells immediately, providing results within a day or so.

Several hours

of a fetus, comparing sequences of samples obtained from both parents and fetal DNA found in the mother's blood. This noninvasive method is rapidly becoming the method of choice in diagnosing most genetically based disorders.

Additionally, imaging techniques allow a physician to examine a fetus directly for major anatomical abnormalities that might not show up in genetic tests. In the *ultrasound* technique, reflected sound waves are used to produce an image of the fetus by a simple noninvasive procedure. In *fetoscopy*, a needle-thin tube containing a viewing scope and fibre optics (to transmit light) is inserted into the uterus.

Ultrasound and isolation of fetal cells or DNA from maternal blood pose no known risk to either mother or fetus, while the other procedures can cause complications in a small percentage of cases. Some provinces now offer maternal serum screening to women over age 35, due to their increased risk of bearing a child with Down syndrome, and may also be offered to younger women if there are known concerns. Maternal serum screening tests for proteins in the mother's blood that are indicative of chromosomal abnormalities in the fetus. If the results from the

serum screen are concerning, then amniocentesis or CVS is used for further diagnostic testing. If the fetal tests reveal a serious disorder, like Tay-Sachs, the parents face the difficult choice of either terminating the pregnancy or preparing to care for a child with a genetic disorder, one that might even be fatal. Parental and fetal screening for Tay-Sachs alleles done since 1980 has reduced the number of children born with this incurable disease by 90%.

Newborn Screening

Some genetic disorders can be detected at birth by simple biochemical tests that are now routinely performed across Canada. For example, babies born in Ontario are screened for 28 different disorders via the analysis of blood obtained from a heel prick in the first week of life. One common screening program is for phenylketonuria (PKU), a recessively inherited disorder that occurs in approximately one out of every 10 000–15 000 births in Canada. Children with this disease cannot properly metabolize the amino acid phenylalanine. This compound and its by-product, phenylpyruvate, can accumulate to toxic levels in the blood, causing severe intellectual disability (mental retardation). However, if PKU is detected in the newborn, a special diet low in phenylalanine will usually allow normal development. (Among many other substances, this diet excludes the artificial sweetener aspartame, which contains phenylalanine.) Unfortunately, few other genetic disorders are treatable at present.

Fetal and newborn screening for serious inherited diseases, tests for identifying carriers, and genetic counselling all rely on the Mendelian model of inheritance. We owe the "gene idea"—the concept of heritable factors transmitted according to simple rules of chance—to the elegant quantitative experiments of Gregor Mendel. The importance of his discoveries was overlooked by most biologists until early in the 20th century, decades after he reported his findings. In the next chapter, you will learn how Mendel's laws have their physical basis in the behaviour of chromosomes during sexual life cycles and how the synthesis of Mendelian genetics and a chromosome theory of inheritance catalyzed progress in genetics.

CONCEPT CHECK 14.4

1. Beth and Tom each have a sibling with cystic fibrosis, but neither Beth nor Tom nor any of their parents have the disease. Calculate the probability that if this couple has a child, the child will have cystic fibrosis. What would be the probability if a test revealed that Tom is a carrier but Beth is not? Explain your answers.

2. **MAKE CONNECTIONS** Review Figures 5.14, 5.18, and 5.19. Explain how the change of a single amino acid in hemoglobin leads to the aggregation of hemoglobin into long rods.

3. Joan was born with six toes on each foot, a dominant trait called polydactyly. Two of her five siblings and her mother, but not her father, also have extra digits. What is Joan's genotype for the number-of-digits character? Explain your answer. Use *D* and *d* to symbolize the alleles for this character.

4. **MAKE CONNECTIONS** In Table 14.1, note the phenotypic ratio of the dominant to recessive trait in the F_2 generation for the monohybrid cross involving flower colour. Then determine the phenotypic ratio for the offspring of the second-generation couple in Figure 14.15h. What accounts for the difference in the two ratios?

For suggested answers, see Appendix A.

14 Chapter Review

Go to **MasteringBiology®** for Assignments, the eText, and the Study Area with Animations, Activities, Vocab Self-Quiz, and Practice Tests.

SUMMARY OF KEY CONCEPTS

CONCEPT 14.1

Mendel used the scientific approach to identify two laws of inheritance (pp. 282–288)

- In the 1860s, Gregor Mendel formulated a theory of inheritance based on experiments with garden peas, proposing that parents pass on to their offspring discrete genes that retain their identity through generations. This theory includes two "laws."
- The **law of segregation** states that genes have alternative forms, or **alleles**. In a diploid organism, the two alleles of a gene segregate (separate) during meiosis and gamete formation; each sperm or egg carries only one allele of each pair. This law explains the 3:1 ratio of F_2 phenotypes observed when **monohybrids** self-pollinate. Each organism inherits one allele for each gene from each parent. In **heterozygotes**, the two alleles are different, and expression of one (the **dominant allele**) masks the phenotypic effect of the other (the **recessive allele**). **Homozygotes** have identical alleles of a given gene and are therefore **true-breeding**.
- The **law of independent assortment** states that the pair of alleles for a given gene segregates into gametes independently of the pair of alleles for any other gene. In a cross between **dihybrids** (individuals heterozygous for two genes), the offspring have four phenotypes in a 9:3:3:1 ratio.

? *When Mendel did crosses of true-breeding purple- and white-flowered pea plants, the white-flowered trait disappeared from the F_1 generation but reappeared in the F_2 generation. Use genetic terms to explain why that happened.*

CONCEPT 14.2

Probability laws govern Mendelian inheritance (pp. 288–290)

Rr
Segregation of alleles into sperm

Sperm

$1/2$ $1/2$

- The **multiplication rule** states that the probability of two or more events occurring together is equal to the product of the individual probabilities of the independent single events. The **addition rule** states that the probability of an event that can occur in two or more independent, mutually exclusive ways is the sum of the individual probabilities.
- The rules of probability can be used to solve complex genetics problems. A dihybrid or other multicharacter cross is equivalent to two or more independent monohybrid crosses occurring simultaneously. In calculating the chances of the various offspring genotypes from such crosses, each character is first considered separately and then the individual probabilities are multiplied.

DRAW IT *Redraw the Punnett square on the right side of Figure 14.8 as two smaller monohybrid Punnett squares, one for each gene. Below each square, list the fractions of each phenotype produced. Use the rule of multiplication to compute the overall fraction of each possible dihybrid phenotype. What is the phenotypic ratio?*

Inheritance patterns are often more complex than predicted by simple Mendelian genetics (pp. 290–296)

- Extensions of Mendelian genetics for a single gene:

Relationship Among Alleles of a Single Gene	Description	Example
Complete dominance of one allele	Heterozygous phenotype same as that of homozygous dominant	PP Pp
Incomplete dominance of either allele	Heterozygous phenotype intermediate between the two homozygous phenotypes	$C^R C^R$ $C^R C^W$ $C^W C^W$
Codominance	Both phenotypes expressed in heterozygotes	$I^A I^B$
Multiple alleles	In the whole population, some genes have more than two alleles	I^A, I^B, i
Pleiotropy	One gene is able to affect multiple phenotypic characters	Sickle-cell disease

- Extensions of Mendelian genetics for two or more genes:

Relationship Among Two or More Genes	Description	Example
Epistasis	The phenotypic expression of one gene affects that of another	$BbEe$ × $BbEe$ BE bE Be be ... 9 : 3 : 4
Polygenic inheritance	A single phenotypic character is affected by two or more genes	$AaBbCc$ × $AaBbCc$

- The expression of a genotype can be affected by environmental influences, resulting in a range of phenotypes. Polygenic characters that are also influenced by the environment are called **multifactorial** characters.
- An organism's overall phenotype, including its physical appearance, internal anatomy, physiology, and behaviour, reflects its overall genotype and unique environmental history. Even in more complex inheritance patterns, Mendel's fundamental laws of segregation and independent assortment still apply.

[?] *Which of the following are demonstrated by the inheritance patterns of the ABO blood group alleles: complete dominance, incomplete dominance, codominance, multiple alleles, pleiotropy, epistasis, and/or polygenic inheritance? Explain how, for each of your answers.*

Many human traits follow Mendelian patterns of inheritance (pp. 296–303)

- Analysis of family **pedigrees** can be used to deduce the possible genotypes of individuals and make predictions about future offspring. Such predictions are statistical probabilities rather than certainties.

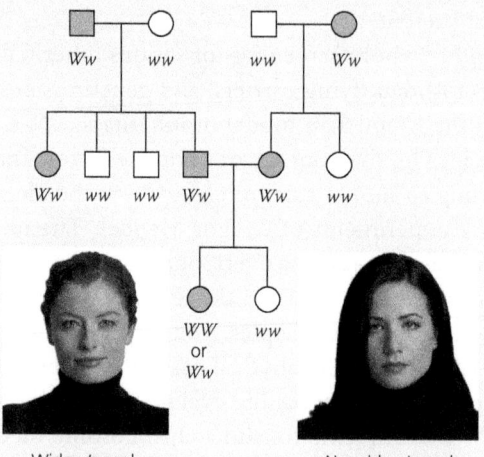

Widow's peak   No widow's peak

- Many genetic disorders are inherited as simple recessive traits. Most affected (homozygous recessive) individuals are children of phenotypically normal, heterozygous **carriers**.
- The sickle-cell allele has probably persisted for evolutionary reasons: Heterozygotes have an advantage because one copy of the sickle-cell allele reduces both the frequency and severity of malaria attacks.

Sickle-cell alleles → Sickle-cell hemoglobin proteins → Low O₂ → Part of a fibre of sickle-cell hemoglobin proteins → Sickled red blood cells → Sickle-cell disease

- Lethal dominant alleles are eliminated from the population if affected people die before reproducing. Nonlethal dominant alleles and lethal ones that strike relatively late in life can be inherited in a Mendelian way.
- Many human diseases are multifactorial—that is, they have both genetic and environmental components and do not follow simple Mendelian inheritance patterns.
- Using family histories, genetic counsellors help couples determine the probability that their children will have genetic disorders. Genetic testing of prospective parents to reveal whether they are carriers of recessive alleles associated with specific disorders has become widely available. **Maternal blood testing, amniocentesis**, and **chorionic villus sampling** can indicate whether a suspected genetic disorder is present in a fetus. Other genetic tests can be performed after birth.

[?] *Both members of a couple know that they are carriers of the cystic fibrosis allele. None of their three children has cystic fibrosis, but any one of them might be a carrier. They would like to have a fourth child but are worried that it would very likely have the disease, since the first three do not. What would you tell the couple? Would it remove some more uncertainty in their prediction if they could find out from genetic tests whether the three children are carriers?*

1. Write down symbols for the alleles. (These may be given in the problem.) When represented by single letters, the dominant allele is uppercase and the recessive is lowercase.

2. Write down the possible genotypes, as determined by the phenotype.
   a. If the phenotype is that of the dominant trait (for example, purple flowers), then the genotype is either homozygous dominant or heterozygous (*PP* or *Pp*, in this example).
   b. If the phenotype is that of the recessive trait, the genotype must be homozygous recessive (for example, *pp*).
   c. If the problem says "true-breeding," the genotype is homozygous.

3. Determine what the problem is asking for. If asked to do a cross, write it out in the form [Genotype] × [Genotype], using the alleles you've decided on.

4. To figure out the outcome of a cross, set up a Punnett square.
   a. Put the gametes of one parent at the top and those of the other on the left. To determine the allele(s) in each gamete for a given genotype, set up a systematic way to list all the possibilities. (Remember, each gamete has one allele of each gene.) Note that there are 2^n possible types of gametes, where *n* is the number of gene loci that are heterozygous. For example, an individual with genotype *AaBbCc* would produce $2^3 = 8$ types of gametes. Write the genotypes of the gametes in circles above the columns and to the left of the rows.
   b. Fill in the Punnett square as if each possible sperm were fertilizing each possible egg, making all of the possible offspring. In a cross of *AaBbCc* × *AaBbCc*, for example, the Punnett square would have 8 columns and 8 rows, so there are 64 different offspring; you would know the genotype of each and thus the phenotype. Count genotypes and phenotypes to obtain the genotypic and phenotypic ratios. Because the Punnett square is so large, this method is not the most efficient. Instead, see tip 5.

5. You can use the rules of probability if the Punnett square would be too big. (For example, see the question at the end of the summary for Concept 14.2 and question 7 on this page.) You can consider each gene separately (see pp. 289–290).

6. If, instead, the problem gives you the phenotypic ratios of offspring, but not the genotypes of the parents in a given cross, the phenotypes can help you deduce the parents' unknown genotypes.
   a. For example, if ½ of the offspring have the recessive phenotype and ½ the dominant, you know that the cross was between a heterozygote and a homozygous recessive.
   b. If the ratio is 3:1, the cross was between two heterozygotes.
   c. If two genes are involved and you see a 9:3:3:1 ratio in the offspring, you know that each parent is heterozygous for both genes. Caution: Don't assume that the reported numbers will exactly equal the predicted ratios. For example, if there are 13 offspring with the dominant trait and 11 with the recessive, assume that the ratio is one dominant to one recessive.

7. For pedigree problems, use the tips in Figure 14.15 and below to determine what kind of trait is involved:
   a. If parents without the trait have offspring with the trait, the trait must be recessive and the parents both carriers.
   b. If the trait is seen in every generation, it is most likely dominant (see the next possibility, though).
   c. If both parents have the trait, then in order for it to be recessive all offspring must show the trait.
   d. To determine the likely genotype of a certain individual in a pedigree, first label the genotypes of all the family members you can. Even if some of the genotypes are incomplete, label what you do know. For example, if an individual has the dominant phenotype, the genotype must be *AA* or *Aa*; you can write this as *A-*. Try different possibilities to see which fits the results. Use the rules of probability to calculate the probability of each possible genotype being the correct one.

TEST YOUR UNDERSTANDING

LEVEL 1: KNOWLEDGE/COMPREHENSION

1. **DRAW IT** Two pea plants heterozygous for the characters of pod colour and pod shape are crossed. Draw a Punnett square to determine the phenotypic ratios of the offspring.

2. A man with type A blood marries a woman with type B blood. Their child has type O blood. What are the genotypes of these three individuals? What genotypes, and in what frequencies, would you expect in future offspring from this marriage?

3. A man has six fingers on each hand and six toes on each foot. His wife and their daughter have the normal number of digits. Remember that extra digits is a dominant trait. What fraction of this couple's children would be expected to have extra digits?

4. **DRAW IT** A pea plant heterozygous for inflated pods (*Ii*) is crossed with a plant homozygous for constricted pods (*ii*). Draw a Punnett square for this cross to predict genotypic and phenotypic ratios. Assume that pollen comes from the *ii* plant.

LEVEL 2: APPLICATION/ANALYSIS

5. Flower position, stem length, and seed shape are three characters that Mendel studied. Each is controlled by an independently assorting gene and has dominant and recessive expression as indicated in Table 14.1. If a plant that is heterozygous for all three characters is allowed to self-fertilize, what proportion of the offspring would you expect to be as follows? (*Note*: Use the rules of probability instead of a huge Punnett square.)
   a. homozygous for the three dominant traits
   b. homozygous for the three recessive traits
   c. heterozygous for all three characters
   d. homozygous for axial and tall, heterozygous for seed shape

6. Phenylketonuria (PKU) is an inherited disease caused by a recessive allele. If a woman and her husband, who are both carriers, have three children, what is the probability of each of the following?
   a. All three children are of normal phenotype.
   b. One or more of the three children have the disease.
   c. All three children have the disease.
   d. At least one child is phenotypically normal.

(*Note:* It will help to remember that the probabilities of all possible outcomes always add up to 1.)

7. The genotype of F$_1$ individuals in a tetrahybrid cross is *AaBbCcDd*. Assuming independent assortment of these four genes, what are the probabilities that F$_2$ offspring will have the following genotypes?
   a. *aabbccdd*
   b. *AaBbCcDd*
   c. *AABBCCDD*
   d. *AaBBccDd*
   e. *AaBBCCdd*

8. What is the probability that each of the following pairs of parents will produce the indicated offspring? (Assume independent assortment of all gene pairs.)
   a. $AABBCC \times aabbcc \rightarrow AaBbCc$
   b. $AABbCc \times AaBbCc \rightarrow AAbbCC$
   c. $AaBbCc \times AaBbCc \rightarrow AaBbCc$
   d. $aaBbCC \times AABbcc \rightarrow AaBbCc$

9. Karen and Steve each have a sibling with sickle-cell disease. Neither Karen nor Steve nor any of their parents have the disease, and none of them has been tested to see if they have the sickle-cell trait. Based on this incomplete information, calculate the probability that if this couple has a child, the child will have sickle-cell disease.

10. In 1981, a stray black cat with unusual rounded, curled-back ears was adopted by a family in California. Hundreds of descendants of the cat have since been born, and cat fanciers hope to develop the curl cat into a show breed. Suppose you owned the first curl cat and wanted to develop a true-breeding variety. How would you determine whether the curl allele is dominant or recessive? How would you obtain true-breeding curl cats? How could you be sure they are true-breeding?

Norma Jubinville/Patricia Speciale

11. In tigers, a recessive allele of a particular gene causes both an absence of fur pigmentation (a white tiger) and a cross-eyed condition. If two phenotypically normal tigers that are heterozygous at this locus are mated, what percentage of their offspring will be cross-eyed? What percentage of cross-eyed tigers will be white?

12. In maize (corn) plants, a dominant allele I inhibits kernel colour, while the recessive allele i permits colour when homozygous. At a different locus, the dominant allele P causes purple kernel colour, while the homozygous recessive genotype pp causes red kernels. If plants heterozygous at both loci are crossed, what will be the phenotypic ratio of the offspring?

13. The pedigree below traces the inheritance of alkaptonuria, a biochemical disorder. Affected individuals, indicated here by the coloured circles and squares, are unable to metabolize a substance called alkapton, which colours the urine and stains body tissues. Does alkaptonuria appear to be caused by a dominant allele or by a recessive allele? Fill in the genotypes of the individuals whose genotypes can be deduced. What genotypes are possible for each of the other individuals?

George Arlene
Sandra Tom Sam Wilma Ann Michael
Daniel Alan Tina Carla
Christopher

14. Imagine that you are a genetic counsellor, and a couple planning to start a family comes to you for information. Charles was married once before, and he and his first wife had a child with cystic fibrosis. The brother of his current wife, Elaine, died of cystic fibrosis. What is the probability that Charles and Elaine will have a baby with cystic fibrosis? (Neither Charles, Elaine, nor their parents have cystic fibrosis.)

LEVEL 3: SYNTHESIS/EVALUATION

15. EVOLUTION CONNECTION

Over the past half century, there has been a trend in the United States and other developed countries for people to marry and start families later in life than did their parents and grandparents. What effects might this trend have on the incidence (frequency) of late-acting dominant lethal alleles in the population?

16. SCIENTIFIC INQUIRY

You are handed a mystery pea plant with tall stems and axial flowers and asked to determine its genotype as quickly as possible. You know that the allele for tall stems (T) is dominant to that for dwarf stems (t) and that the allele for axial flowers (A) is dominant to that for terminal flowers (a).
   a. What are *all* the possible genotypes for your mystery plant?
   b. Describe the *one* cross you would do, out in your garden, to determine the exact genotype of your mystery plant.
   c. While waiting for the results of your cross, you predict the results for each possible genotype listed in part a. How do you do this? Why is this not called "performing a cross"?
   d. Explain how the results of your cross and your predictions will help you learn the genotype of your mystery plant.

17. WRITE ABOUT A THEME: INFORMATION

The continuity of life is based on heritable information in the form of DNA. In a short essay (100–150 words), explain how the passage of genes from parents to offspring, in the form of particular alleles, ensures perpetuation of parental traits in offspring and, at the same time, genetic variation among offspring. Use genetic terms in your explanation.

18. SYNTHESIZE YOUR KNOWLEDGE

Rene Maltete/Gamma-Rapho/Getty Images

Just for fun, imagine that "shirt-striping" is a phenotypic character caused by a single gene. Make up a genetic explanation for the appearance of the family in the above photograph, consistent with their "shirt phenotypes." Include in your answer the presumed allele combinations for "shirt-striping" in each family member. What is the inheritance pattern shown by the child?

For selected answers, see Appendix A.

15

The Chromosomal Basis of Inheritance

KEY CONCEPTS

15.1 Morgan showed that Mendelian inheritance has its physical basis in the behaviour of chromosomes: *Scientific Inquiry*

15.2 Sex-linked genes exhibit unique patterns of inheritance

15.3 Linked genes tend to be inherited together because they are located near each other on the same chromosome

15.4 Alterations of chromosome number or structure cause some genetic disorders

15.5 Some inheritance patterns are exceptions to standard Mendelian inheritance

BiophotoAssociates /ScienceSource

▲ Figure 15.1 **Where are Mendel's hereditary factors located in the cell?**

Locating Genes Along Chromosomes

Today, we know that genes—Mendel's "factors"—are segments of DNA located along chromosomes. We can see the location of a particular gene by tagging chromosomes with a fluorescent dye that highlights that gene. For example, the two yellow spots in **Figure 15.1** mark a specific gene on human chromosome 6. (The chromosome has duplicated, so the allele on that chromosome is present as two copies, one per sister chromatid.) However, Gregor Mendel's "hereditary factors" were purely an abstract concept when he proposed their existence in 1860. At that time, no cellular structures had been identified that could house these imaginary units, and most biologists were sceptical about Mendel's proposed laws of inheritance.

Using improved techniques of microscopy, cytologists worked out the process of mitosis in 1875 (see the drawing at the lower left) and meiosis in the 1890s. Cytology and genetics converged as biologists began to see parallels between the behaviour of Mendel's proposed hereditary factors during sexual life cycles and the behaviour of chromosomes: As shown in **Figure 15.2**, chromosomes and genes are both present in pairs in diploid cells, and homologous chromosomes separate and alleles segregate during the process of meiosis. Furthermore, after meiosis, fertilization restores the paired condition for both chromosomes and genes.

John Hay Whitney Medical Library

307

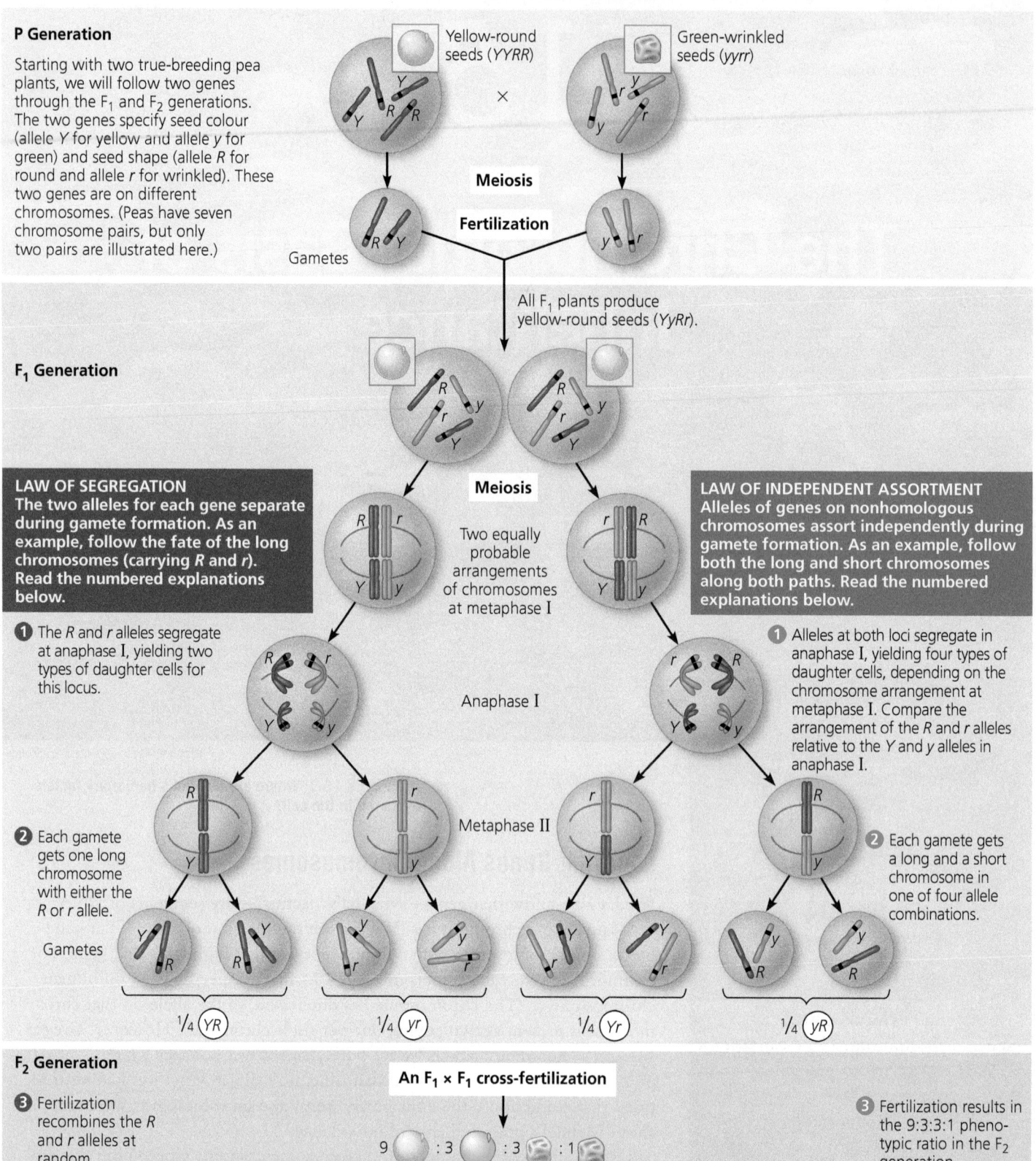

P Generation

Starting with two true-breeding pea plants, we will follow two genes through the F₁ and F₂ generations. The two genes specify seed colour (allele *Y* for yellow and allele *y* for green) and seed shape (allele *R* for round and allele *r* for wrinkled). These two genes are on different chromosomes. (Peas have seven chromosome pairs, but only two pairs are illustrated here.)

Yellow-round seeds (*YYRR*)

×

Green-wrinkled seeds (*yyrr*)

Meiosis

Fertilization

Gametes

All F₁ plants produce yellow-round seeds (*YyRr*).

F₁ Generation

LAW OF SEGREGATION
The two alleles for each gene separate during gamete formation. As an example, follow the fate of the long chromosomes (carrying *R* and *r*). Read the numbered explanations below.

Meiosis

Two equally probable arrangements of chromosomes at metaphase I

LAW OF INDEPENDENT ASSORTMENT
Alleles of genes on nonhomologous chromosomes assort independently during gamete formation. As an example, follow both the long and short chromosomes along both paths. Read the numbered explanations below.

❶ The *R* and *r* alleles segregate at anaphase I, yielding two types of daughter cells for this locus.

Anaphase I

❶ Alleles at both loci segregate in anaphase I, yielding four types of daughter cells, depending on the chromosome arrangement at metaphase I. Compare the arrangement of the *R* and *r* alleles relative to the *Y* and *y* alleles in anaphase I.

Metaphase II

❷ Each gamete gets one long chromosome with either the *R* or *r* allele.

Gametes

❷ Each gamete gets a long and a short chromosome in one of four allele combinations.

¼ *YR*   ¼ *yr*   ¼ *Yr*   ¼ *yR*

F₂ Generation

❸ Fertilization recombines the *R* and *r* alleles at random.

An F₁ × F₁ cross-fertilization

9 : 3 : 3 : 1

❸ Fertilization results in the 9:3:3:1 phenotypic ratio in the F₂ generation.

▲ **Figure 15.2 The chromosomal basis of Mendel's laws.** Here we correlate the results of one of Mendel's dihybrid crosses (see Figure 14.8) with the behaviour of chromosomes during meiosis (see Figure 13.8). The arrangement of chromosomes at metaphase I of meiosis and their movement during anaphase I account respectively for the independent assortment and segregation of the alleles for seed colour and shape. Each cell that undergoes meiosis in an F₁ plant produces two kinds of gametes. If we count the results for all cells, however, each F₁ plant produces equal numbers of all four kinds of gametes because the alternative chromosome arrangements at metaphase I are equally likely.

? *If you crossed an F₁ plant with a plant that was homozygous recessive for both genes* (**yyrr**), *how would the phenotypic ratio of the offspring compare with the 9:3:3:1 ratio seen here?*

Around 1902, Walter S. Sutton, Theodor Boveri, and others independently noted these parallels and began to develop the **chromosome theory of inheritance**. According to this theory, Mendelian genes have specific loci (positions) along chromosomes, and it is the chromosomes that undergo segregation and independent assortment. As you can see in Figure 15.2, the separation of homologues during anaphase I accounts for the segregation of the two alleles of a gene into separate gametes, and the random arrangement of chromosome pairs at metaphase I accounts for independent assortment of the alleles for two or more genes located on different homologue pairs. This figure traces the same dihybrid pea cross you learned about in Figure 14.8. By carefully studying Figure 15.2, you can see how the behaviour of chromosomes during meiosis in the F_1 generation and subsequent random fertilization give rise to the F_2 phenotypic ratio observed by Mendel.

In correlating the behaviour of chromosomes with that of genes, this chapter will extend what you learned in the past two chapters. First, we'll describe evidence from the fruit fly that strongly supported the chromosome theory. (Although this theory made a lot of sense, it still required experimental evidence.) Next, we'll explore the chromosomal basis for the transmission of genes from parents to offspring, including what happens when two genes are linked on the same chromosome. Finally, we will discuss some important exceptions to the standard mode of inheritance.

CONCEPT 15.1

Morgan showed that Mendelian inheritance has its physical basis in the behaviour of chromosomes: Scientific Inquiry

The first solid evidence associating a specific gene with a specific chromosome came early in the 1900s from the work of Thomas Hunt Morgan, an experimental embryologist at Columbia University. Although Morgan was initially sceptical about both Mendelian genetics and the chromosome theory, his early experiments provided convincing evidence that chromosomes are indeed the location of Mendel's heritable factors.

Morgan's Choice of Experimental Organism

Many times in the history of biology, important discoveries have come to those insightful or lucky enough to choose an experimental organism suitable for the research

problem being tackled. Mendel chose the garden pea because a number of distinct varieties were available. For his work, Morgan selected a species of fruit fly, *Drosophila melanogaster*, a common insect that feeds on the fungi growing on fruit. Fruit flies are prolific breeders; a single mating will produce hundreds of offspring, and a new generation can be bred every two weeks. Morgan's laboratory began using this convenient organism for genetic studies in 1907 and soon became known as "the fly room."

Another advantage of the fruit fly is that it has only four pairs of chromosomes, which are easily distinguishable with a light microscope. There are three pairs of autosomes and one pair of sex chromosomes. Female fruit flies have a pair of homologous X chromosomes, and males have one X chromosome and one Y chromosome.

While Mendel could readily obtain different pea varieties from seed suppliers, Morgan was probably the first person to want different varieties of the fruit fly. He faced the tedious task of carrying out many matings and then microscopically inspecting large numbers of offspring in search of naturally occurring variant individuals. After many months of this, he complained, "Two years' work wasted. I have been breeding those flies for all that time and I've got nothing out of it." Morgan persisted, however, and was finally rewarded with the discovery of a single male fly with white eyes instead of the usual red. The phenotype for a character most commonly observed in natural populations, such as red eyes in *Drosophila*, is called the **wild type** (Figure 15.3). Traits that are alternatives to the wild type, such as white eyes in *Drosophila*, are called *mutant phenotypes* because they are due to alleles assumed to have originated as changes, or mutations, in the wild-type allele.

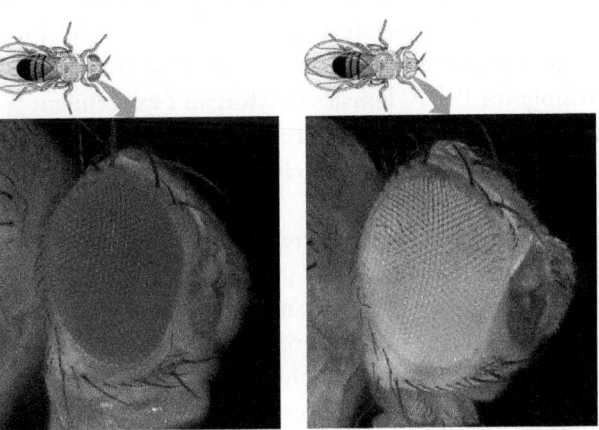

▲ Figure 15.3 **Morgan's first mutant.** Wild-type *Drosophila* flies have red eyes (left). Among his flies, Morgan discovered a mutant male with white eyes (right). This variation made it possible for Morgan to trace a gene for eye colour to a specific chromosome (LMs).

Morgan and his students invented a notation for symbolizing alleles in *Drosophila* that is still widely used for fruit flies. For a given character in flies, the gene takes its symbol from the first mutant (non–wild type) discovered. Thus, the allele for white eyes in *Drosophila* is symbolized by w. A superscript + identifies the allele for the wild-type trait: w^+ for the allele for red eyes, for example. Over the years, a variety of gene notation systems have been developed for different organisms. For example, human genes are usually written in all capitals, such as *HTT* for the gene involved in Huntington's disease. (Genes and alleles may be symbolized by more than one letter, as in this example.)

Correlating Behaviour of a Gene's Alleles with Behaviour of a Chromosome Pair

Morgan mated his white-eyed male fly with a red-eyed female. All the F_1 offspring had red eyes, suggesting that the wild-type allele is dominant. When Morgan bred the F_1 flies to each other, he observed the classical 3:1 phenotypic ratio among the F_2 offspring. However, there was a surprising additional result: The white-eye trait showed up only in males. All the F_2 females had red eyes, while half the males had red eyes and half had white eyes. Therefore, Morgan concluded that somehow a fly's eye colour was linked to its sex. (If the eye-colour gene were unrelated to sex, half of the white-eyed flies would have been female.)

Recall that a female fly has two X chromosomes (XX), while a male fly has an X and a Y (XY). The correlation between the trait of white eye colour and the male sex of the affected F_2 flies suggested to Morgan that the gene involved in his white-eyed mutant was located exclusively on the X chromosome, with no corresponding allele present on the Y chromosome. His reasoning can be followed in **Figure 15.4**. For a male, a single copy of the mutant allele would confer white eyes; since a male has only one X chromosome, there can be no wild-type allele (w^+) present to mask the recessive allele. However, a female could have white eyes only if both her X chromosomes carried the recessive mutant allele (w). This was impossible for the F_2 females in Morgan's experiment because all the F_1 fathers had red eyes, so each F_2 female received a w^+ allele on the X chromosome inherited from her father.

Morgan's finding of the correlation between a particular trait and an individual's sex provided support for the chromosome theory of inheritance: namely, that a specific gene is carried on a specific chromosome (in this case, an eye-colour gene on the X chromosome). In addition, Morgan's work indicated that genes located on a sex chromosome exhibit unique inheritance patterns, which we will discuss in the next section. Recognizing the importance of Morgan's early work, many bright students were attracted to his fly room.

▼ Figure 15.4　**Inquiry**

In a cross between a wild-type female fruit fly and a mutant white-eyed male, what colour eyes will the F_1 and F_2 offspring have?

Experiment Thomas Hunt Morgan wanted to analyze the behaviour of two alleles of a fruit fly eye-colour gene. In crosses similar to those done by Mendel with pea plants, Morgan and his colleagues mated a wild-type (red-eyed) female with a mutant white-eyed male.

Morgan then bred an F_1 red-eyed female to an F_1 red-eyed male to produce the F_2 generation.

Results The F_2 generation showed a typical Mendelian ratio of 3 red-eyed flies: 1 white-eyed fly. However, no females displayed the white-eye trait; all white-eyed flies were males.

Conclusion All F_1 offspring had red eyes, so the mutant white-eye trait (w) must be recessive to the wild-type red-eye trait (w^+). Since the recessive trait—white eyes—was expressed only in males in the F_2 generation, Morgan deduced that this eye-colour gene is located on the X chromosome and that there is no corresponding locus on the Y chromosome.

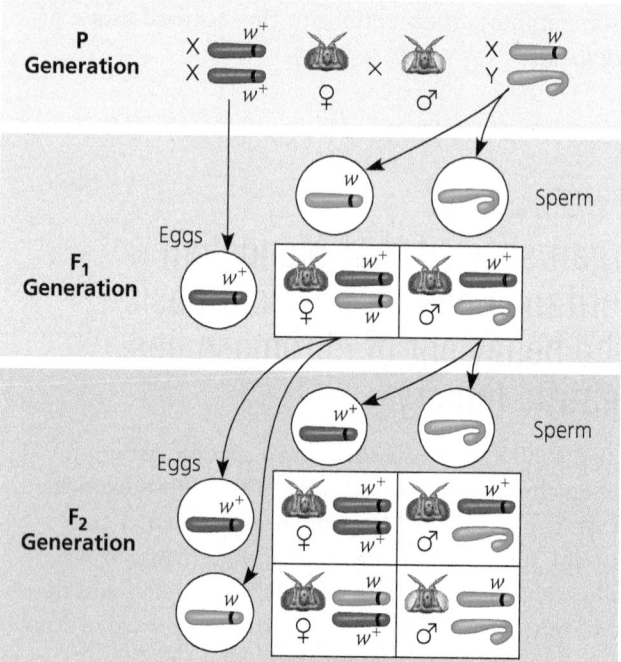

Source: Based on "Sex Limited Inheritance in Drosophila" by Thomas Hunt Morgan, from *Science*, New Series, July 1910, Volume 32(812). © Jane B Reece.

(MB) See the related Experimental Inquiry Tutorial in MasteringBiology.

WHAT IF? *Suppose this eye-colour gene were located on an autosome. Predict the phenotypes (including gender) of the F_2 flies in this hypothetical cross. (Hint: Draw a Punnett square.)*

1. Which one of Mendel's laws describes the inheritance of alleles for a single character? Which law relates to the inheritance of alleles for two characters in a dihybrid cross?

2. **MAKE CONNECTIONS** Review the description of meiosis (see Figure 13.8) and Mendel's laws of segregation and independent assortment (see Concept 14.1). What is the physical basis for each of Mendel's laws?

3. **WHAT IF?** Propose a possible reason that the first naturally occurring mutant fruit fly Morgan saw involved a gene on a sex chromosome.

For suggested answers, see Appendix A.

CONCEPT **15.2**

Sex-linked genes exhibit unique patterns of inheritance

As you just learned, Morgan's discovery of a trait (white eyes) that correlated with the sex of flies was a key episode in the development of the chromosome theory of inheritance. Because the identity of the sex chromosomes in an individual could be inferred by observing the sex of the fly, the behaviour of the two members of the pair of sex chromosomes could be correlated with the behaviour of the two alleles of the eye-colour gene. In this section, we'll take a closer look at the role of sex chromosomes in inheritance.

The Chromosomal Basis of Sex

Although the anatomical and physiological differences between women and men are numerous, the chromosomal basis for determining sex is rather simple. Humans and other mammals have two varieties of sex chromosomes, designated X and Y. The Y chromosome is much smaller than the X chromosome (**Figure 15.5**). A person who inherits two X chromosomes, one from each parent, usually develops as a female; a male inherits one X chromosome and one Y chromosome (**Figure 15.6a**). Short segments at either end of the Y chromosome are the only regions that are homologous with corresponding regions of the X. These homologous regions allow the X and Y chromosomes in males to

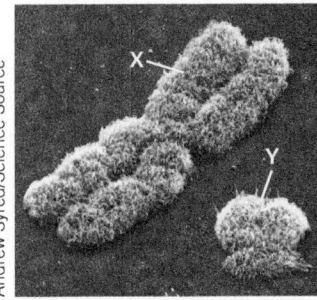

▲ Figure 15.5 **Human sex chromosomes.**

pair and behave like homologous chromosomes during meiosis in the testes. In mammalian testes and ovaries, the two sex chromosomes segregate during meiosis. Each egg contains one X chromosome. In contrast, sperm fall into two categories: Half the sperm cells a male produces receive an

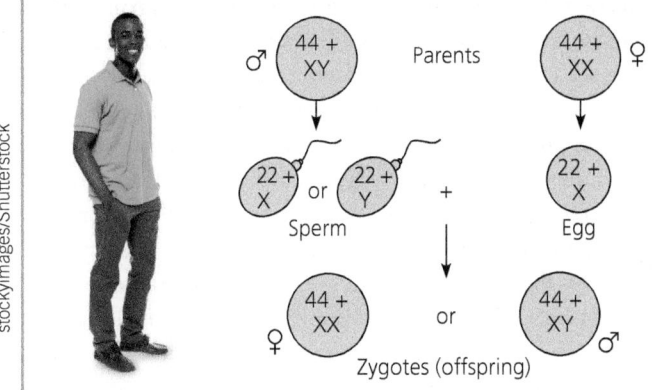

(a) The X-Y system. In mammals, the sex of an offspring depends on whether the sperm cell contains an X chromosome or a Y.

(b) The X-0 system. In grasshoppers, cockroaches, and some other insects, there is only one type of sex chromosome, the X. Females are XX; males have only one sex chromosome (X0). Sex of the offspring is determined by whether the sperm cell contains an X chromosome or no sex chromosome.

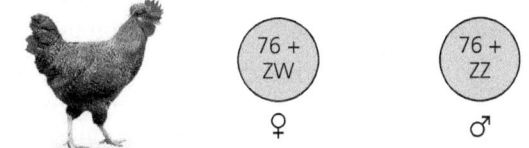

(c) The Z-W system. In birds, some fishes, and some insects, the sex chromosomes present in the egg (not the sperm) determine the sex of offspring. The sex chromosomes are designated Z and W. Females are ZW and males are ZZ.

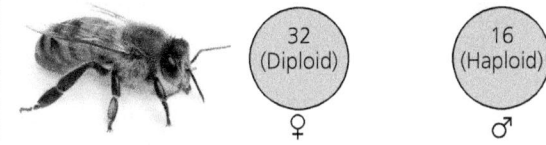

(d) The haplo-diploid system. There are no sex chromosomes in most species of bees and ants. Females develop from fertilized eggs and are thus diploid. Males develop from unfertilized eggs and are haploid; they have no fathers.

▲ Figure 15.6 **Some chromosomal systems of sex determination.** Numerals indicate the number of autosomes in the species pictured. In *Drosophila*, males are XY, but sex depends on the ratio between the number of X chromosomes and the number of autosome sets, not simply on the presence of a Y chromosome.

X chromosome, and half receive a Y chromosome. We can trace the sex of each offspring to the events of conception: If a sperm cell bearing an X chromosome happens to fertilize an egg, the zygote is XX, a female; if a sperm cell containing a Y chromosome fertilizes an egg, the zygote is XY, a male (see Figure 15.6a). Thus, sex determination is a matter of chance—a fifty-fifty chance. Note that the mammalian X-Y system isn't the only chromosomal system for determining sex. Figure 15.6b–d illustrates three other systems.

In humans, the anatomical signs of sex begin to emerge when the embryo is about two months old. Before then, the rudiments of the gonads are generic—they can develop into either testes or ovaries, depending on whether or not a Y chromosome is present and on what genes are active. A gene on the Y chromosome—called SRY, for sex-determining region of Y—is required for the development of testes. In the absence of SRY, the gonads develop into ovaries, even in an XY embryo.

A gene located on either sex chromosome is called a **sex-linked gene**. The human X chromosome contains approximately 1100 genes, which are called **X-linked genes**, while genes located on the Y chromosome are called *Y-linked genes*. Researchers have sequenced the human Y chromosome and have identified 78 genes that code for about 25 proteins (some genes are duplicates). About half of these genes are expressed only in the testes, and some are required for normal testicular functioning and the production of normal sperm. The Y chromosome is passed along virtually intact from a father to all his sons. Because there are so few Y-linked genes, very few disorders are transferred from father to son on the Y chromosome.

The development of female gonads requires a gene called *WNT4* (on chromosome 1, an autosome), which encodes a protein that promotes ovary development. An embryo that is XY but has extra copies of the *WNT4* gene can develop rudimentary female gonads. Overall, sex is determined by the interactions of a network of gene products like these.

The biochemical, physiological, and anatomical features that distinguish males and females are turning out to be more complex than previously thought, with many genes involved in their development. Because of the complexity of this process, many variations exist. Some individuals are born with intermediate sexual characteristics, or even with anatomical features that do not match their sense of their own gender. (The term *gender* refers to the state of being male, female, or otherwise, as experienced by the individual and by society, whereas an individual's sex is genetically determined.) Sex determination is an active area of research that should yield a more sophisticated understanding in years to come.

Inheritance of X-Linked Genes

The fact that males and females inherit a different number of X chromosomes leads to a pattern of inheritance different from that produced by genes located on autosomes. While there are very few Y-linked genes and many help determine sex, the X chromosomes have genes for many characters unrelated to sex. X-linked genes in humans follow the same pattern of inheritance that Morgan observed for the eye-colour locus he studied in *Drosophila* (see Figure 15.4). Fathers pass X-linked alleles to all of their daughters but to none of their sons. In contrast, mothers can pass X-linked alleles to both sons and daughters, as shown in Figure 15.7

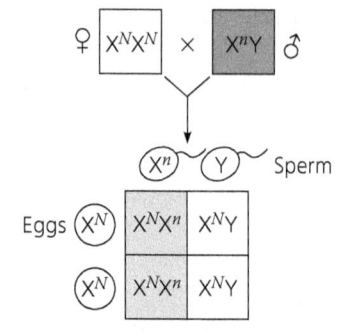

(a) A colour-blind father will transmit the mutant allele to all daughters but to no sons. When the mother is a dominant homozygote, the daughters will have the normal phenotype but will be carriers of the mutation.

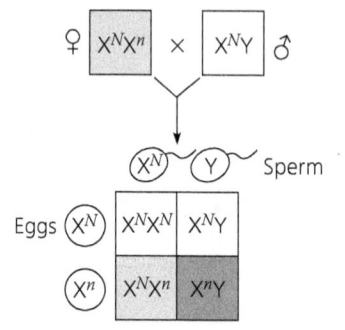

(b) If a carrier mates with a male who has normal colour vision, there is a 50% chance that each daughter will be a carrier like her mother and a 50% chance that each son will have the disorder.

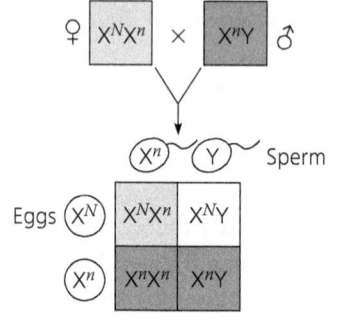

(c) If a carrier mates with a colour-blind male, there is a 50% chance that each child born to them will have the disorder, regardless of sex. Daughters who have normal colour vision will be carriers, whereas males who have normal colour vision will be free of the recessive allele.

▲ Figure 15.7 **The transmission of X-linked recessive traits.** In this diagram, colour blindness is used as an example. The superscript N represents the dominant allele for normal colour vision carried on the X chromosome, and the superscript n represents the recessive allele, which has a mutation causing colour blindness. White boxes indicate unaffected individuals, light orange boxes indicate carriers, and dark orange boxes indicate colour-blind individuals.

? If a colour-blind woman married a man who had normal colour vision, what would be the probable phenotypes of their children?

for the inheritance of a mild X-linked disorder, red-green colour blindness.

If an X-linked trait is due to a recessive allele, a female will express the phenotype only if she is homozygous for that allele. Because males have only one locus, the terms *homozygous* and *heterozygous* lack meaning for describing their X-linked genes; the term *hemizygous* is used in such cases. Any male receiving the recessive allele from his mother will express the trait. For this reason, far more males than females have X-linked recessive disorders. However, even though the chance of a female inheriting a double dose of the mutant allele is much less than the probability of a male inheriting a single dose, there *are* females with X-linked disorders. For instance, colour blindness is a mild disorder almost always inherited as an X-linked trait. A colour-blind daughter may be born to a colour-blind father whose mate is a carrier (see Figure 15.7c). Because the X-linked allele for colour blindness is relatively rare, though, the probability that such a man and woman will mate is low.

A number of human X-linked disorders are much more serious than colour blindness, such as **Duchenne muscular dystrophy**, which affects about one out of every 3500 males born worldwide. The disease is characterized by a progressive weakening of the muscles and loss of coordination. Affected individuals rarely live past their early 20s. Researchers have traced the disorder to the absence of a key muscle protein called dystrophin and have mapped the gene for this protein to a specific locus on the X chromosome.

Hemophilia is an X-linked recessive disorder defined by the absence of one or more of the proteins required for blood clotting. When a person with hemophilia is injured, bleeding is prolonged because a firm clot is slow to form. Small cuts in the skin are usually not a problem, but bleeding in the muscles or joints can be painful and can lead to serious damage. Currently, there are approximately 3000 people with hemophilia in Canada. In the 1800s, hemophilia was widespread among the royal families of Europe. Queen Victoria of England is known to have passed the allele to several of her descendants. Subsequent intermarriage with royal family members of other nations, such as Spain and Russia, further spread this X-linked trait, and its incidence is well documented in royal pedigrees. A few years ago, new genomic techniques allowed sequencing of tiny amounts of DNA isolated from the buried remains of royal family members. The genetic basis of the mutation, and how it resulted in a nonfunctional blood-clotting factor, is now understood. Today, people with hemophilia are treated as needed with intravenous injections of the protein that is missing.

X Inactivation in Female Mammals

Female mammals, including human females, inherit two X chromosomes—twice the number inherited by males—so you may wonder whether females make twice as much as males of the proteins encoded by X-linked genes. In fact, almost all of one X chromosome in each cell in female mammals becomes inactivated during early embryonic development. As a result, the cells of females and males have the same effective dose (one active copy) of most X-linked genes. The inactive X in each cell of a female condenses into a compact object called a **Barr body** (discovered by Canadian anatomist Murray Barr in 1948), which lies along the inside of the nuclear envelope. Most of the genes of the X chromosome that forms the Barr body are not expressed. In the ovaries, however, Barr-body chromosomes are reactivated in the cells that give rise to eggs, resulting in every female gamete (egg) having an active X after meiosis.

British geneticist Mary Lyon demonstrated that the selection of which X chromosome will form the Barr body occurs randomly and independently in each embryonic cell present at the time of X inactivation. As a consequence, females consist of a *mosaic* of two types of cells: those with the active X derived from the father and those with the active X derived from the mother. After an X chromosome is inactivated in a particular cell, all mitotic descendants of that cell have the same inactive X. Thus, if a female is heterozygous for a sex-linked trait, about half of her cells will express one allele, while the others will express the alternate allele. Figure 15.8 shows how this mosaicism results in the patchy colouration of a tortoiseshell cat. In humans, mosaicism can be observed in a recessive X-linked mutation that prevents the development of sweat glands. A woman who is heterozygous for this trait has patches of normal skin and patches of skin lacking sweat glands.

Inactivation of an X chromosome involves modification of the DNA and proteins bound to it called histones, including attachment of methyl groups ($-CH_3$) to DNA nucleotides. (The regulatory role of DNA methylation is discussed in Concept 18.2.) A particular region of each X chromosome contains several genes involved in the inactivation process. The two regions, one on each X chromosome, associate briefly with each other in each cell at an early stage of embryonic development. Then one of the genes, called *XIST* (for *X-i*nactive *s*pecific *t*ranscript) becomes active *only* on the chromosome that will become the Barr body. Multiple copies of the RNA product of this gene apparently attach to the X chromosome on which they are made,

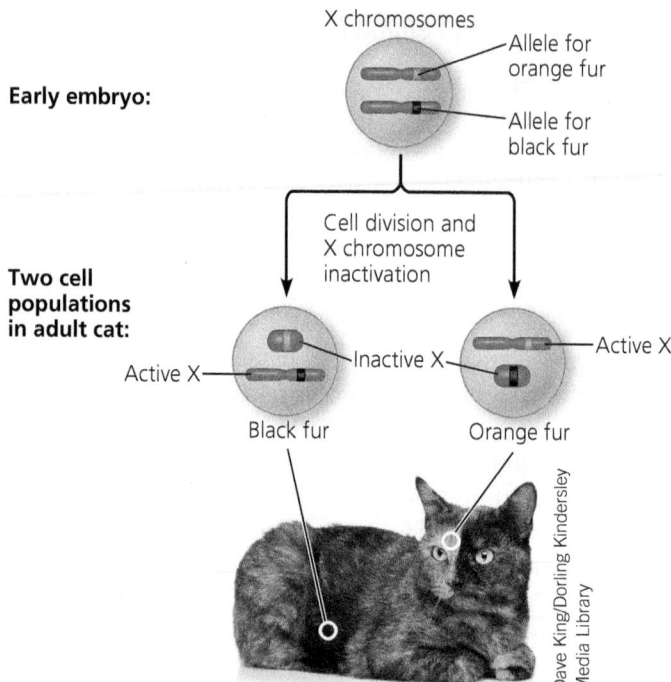

Early embryo:

X chromosomes

Allele for orange fur

Allele for black fur

Cell division and X chromosome inactivation

Two cell populations in adult cat:

Active X

Inactive X

Active X

Black fur

Orange fur

Dave King/Dorling Kindersley Media Library

▲ **Figure 15.8 X inactivation and the tortoiseshell cat.** The tortoiseshell gene is on the X chromosome, and the tortoiseshell phenotype requires the presence of two different alleles, one for orange fur and one for black fur. Normally, only females can have both alleles, because only they have two X chromosomes. If a female cat is heterozygous for the tortoiseshell gene, she is tortoiseshell. Orange patches are formed by populations of cells in which the X chromosome with the orange allele is active; black patches have cells in which the X chromosome with the black allele is active. ("Calico" cats also have white areas, which are determined by yet another gene.)

eventually almost covering it. Interaction of this RNA with the chromosome initiates X inactivation, and the RNA products of nearby genes help to regulate the process.

CONCEPT CHECK 15.2

1. A white-eyed female *Drosophila* is mated with a red-eyed (wild-type) male, the reciprocal cross of the one shown in Figure 15.4. What phenotypes and genotypes do you predict for the offspring?

2. Neither Tim nor Rhoda has Duchenne muscular dystrophy, but their firstborn son does. What is the probability that a second child will have the disease? What is the probability if the second child is a boy? A girl?

3. **MAKE CONNECTIONS** Consider what you learned about dominant and recessive alleles in Concept 14.1. If a disorder were caused by a dominant X-linked allele, how would the inheritance pattern differ from what we see for recessive X-linked disorders?

For suggested answers, see Appendix A.

Linked genes tend to be inherited together because they are located near each other on the same chromosome

The number of genes in a cell is far greater than the number of chromosomes; in fact, each chromosome (except the Y) has hundreds or thousands of genes. Genes located near each other on the same chromosome tend to be inherited together in genetic crosses; such genes are said to be genetically linked and are called **linked genes**. (Note the distinction between the terms *sex-linked gene*, referring to a single gene on a sex chromosome, and *linked genes*, referring to two or more genes on the same chromosome that tend to be inherited together.) When geneticists follow linked genes in breeding experiments, the results deviate from those expected from Mendel's law of independent assortment.

How Linkage Affects Inheritance

To see how linkage between genes affects the inheritance of two different characters, let's examine another of Morgan's *Drosophila* experiments. In this case, the characters are body colour and wing size, each with two different phenotypes. Wild-type flies have grey bodies and normal-sized wings. In addition to these flies, Morgan had managed to obtain, through breeding, doubly mutant flies with black bodies and wings much smaller than normal, called vestigial wings. The mutant alleles are recessive to the wild-type alleles, and neither gene is on a sex chromosome. In his investigation of these two genes, Morgan carried out the crosses shown in **Figure 15.9**. The first was a P generation cross to generate F_1 dihybrid flies, and the second was a testcross.

The resulting flies had a much higher proportion of the combinations of traits seen in the P generation flies (called parental phenotypes) than would be expected if the two genes assorted independently. Morgan thus concluded that body colour and wing size are usually inherited together in specific (parental) combinations because the genes for these characters are near each other on the same chromosome:

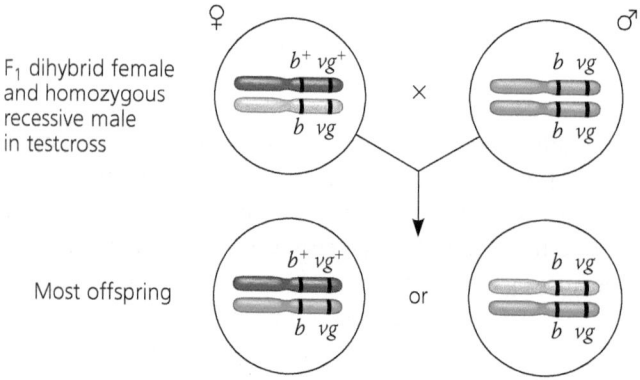

F_1 dihybrid female and homozygous recessive male in testcross

♀ $b^+\ vg^+$ $b\ vg$ ♂ $b\ vg$ $b\ vg$

×

Most offspring $b^+\ vg^+$ $b\ vg$ or $b\ vg$ $b\ vg$

Inquiry

How does linkage between two genes affect inheritance of characters?

Experiment Morgan wanted to know whether the genes for body colour and wing size were genetically linked and, if so, how this affected their inheritance. The alleles for body colour are b^+ (grey) and b (black), and those for wing size are vg^+ (normal) and vg (vestigial).

Morgan mated true-breeding P (parental) generation flies—wild-type flies with black, vestigial-winged flies—to produce heterozygous F_1 dihybrids ($b^+ b\ vg^+ vg$), all of which are wild-type in appearance.

He then mated wild-type F_1 dihybrid females with black, vestigial-winged males. This testcross will reveal the genotype of the eggs made by the dihybrid female.

The male's sperm contributes only recessive alleles, so the phenotype of the offspring reflects the genotype of the female's eggs.

Note: Although only females (with pointed abdomens) are shown, half the offspring in each class would be males (with rounded abdomens).

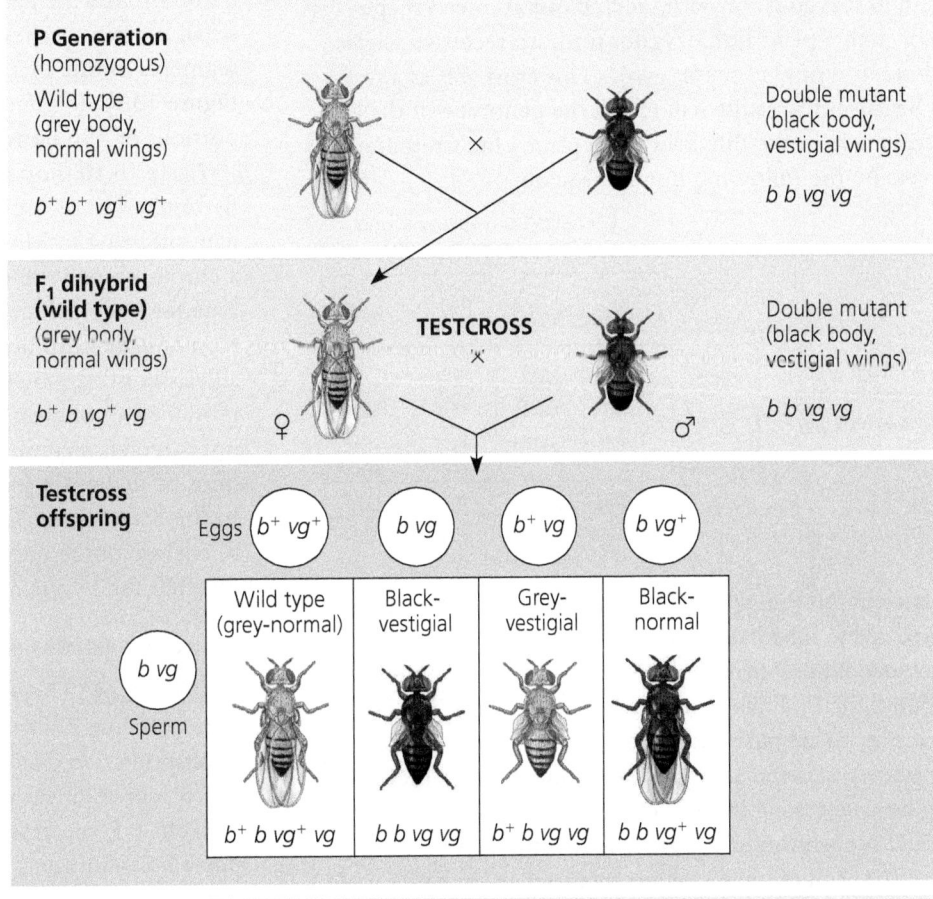

P Generation (homozygous)

Wild type (grey body, normal wings)

$b^+ b^+ vg^+ vg^+$

Double mutant (black body, vestigial wings)

$b b\ vg\ vg$

F_1 dihybrid (wild type) (grey body, normal wings)

$b^+ b\ vg^+ vg$ ♀

TESTCROSS

Double mutant (black body, vestigial wings)

$b b\ vg\ vg$ ♂

Testcross offspring

Eggs: $b^+ vg^+$ | $b\ vg$ | $b^+ vg$ | $b\ vg^+$

Sperm: $b\ vg$

Wild type (grey-normal)	Black-vestigial	Grey-vestigial	Black-normal
$b^+ b\ vg^+ vg$	$b b\ vg\ vg$	$b^+ b\ vg\ vg$	$b b\ vg^+ vg$

PREDICTED RATIOS

If genes are located on different chromosomes:	1	:	1	:	1	:	1
If genes are located on the same chromosome *and* parental alleles are always inherited together:	1	:	1	:	0	:	0

Results | 965 | : | 944 | : | 206 | : | 185 |

Conclusion Since most offspring had a parental (P generation) phenotype, Morgan concluded that the genes for body colour and wing size are genetically linked on the same chromosome. However, the production of a relatively small number of offspring with nonparental phenotypes indicated that some mechanism occasionally breaks the linkage between specific alleles of genes on the same chromosome.

Source: Based on "The Linkage of Two Factors in Drosophila That Are Not Sex-Linked" by Thomas Hunt Morgan and Clara J. Lynch, from *Biological Bulletin*, August 1912, Volume 23(3). © Jane B Reece.

WHAT IF? *If the parental (P generation) flies had been true-breeding for grey body with vestigial wings and black body with normal wings, which phenotypic class(es) would be largest among the testcross offspring?*

However, as Figure 15.9 shows, both of the combinations of traits not seen in the P generation (called nonparental phenotypes) were also produced in Morgan's experiments, suggesting that the body-colour and wing-size alleles are not always linked genetically. To understand this conclusion, we need to further explore **genetic recombination**, the production of offspring with combinations of traits that differ from those found in either P generation parent.

Genetic Recombination and Linkage

Meiosis and random fertilization generate genetic variation among offspring of sexually reproducing organisms due to independent assortment of chromosomes, crossing over in meiosis I, and the possibility of any sperm fertilizing any egg (see Concept 13.4). Here we'll examine the chromosomal basis of recombination of alleles in relation to the genetic findings of Mendel and Morgan.

Recombination of Unlinked Genes: Independent Assortment of Chromosomes

Mendel learned from crosses in which he followed two characters that some offspring have combinations of traits that do not match those of either parent. For example, consider a cross of a dihybrid pea plant with yellow round seeds, heterozygous for both seed colour and seed shape (*YyRr*), with a plant homozygous for both recessive alleles (with green wrinkled seeds, *yyrr*). (This cross acts as a test-cross because the results will reveal the genotype of the gametes made in the dihybrid *YyRr* plant.) Let's represent the cross by the following Punnett square:

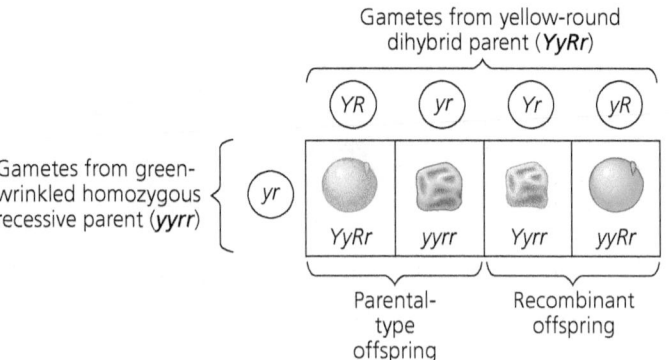

Gametes from yellow-round dihybrid parent (*YyRr*)

Gametes from green-wrinkled homozygous recessive parent (*yyrr*)

Parental-type offspring

Recombinant offspring

Notice in this Punnett square that one-half of the offspring are expected to inherit a phenotype that matches either of the phenotypes of the P (parental) generation, originally crossed to produce the F₁ dihybrid (see Figure 15.2). These matching offspring are called **parental types**. But two nonparental phenotypes are also found among the offspring. Because these offspring have new combinations of seed shape and colour, they are called **recombinant types**, or **recombinants** for short. When 50% of all offspring are recombinants, as in this example, geneticists say that there is a 50% frequency of recombination. The predicted phenotypic ratios among the offspring are similar to what Mendel actually found in his *YyRr* × *yyrr* crosses.

A 50% frequency of recombination in such testcrosses is observed for any two genes that are located on different chromosomes and thus cannot be linked. The physical basis of recombination between unlinked genes is the random orientation of homologous chromosomes at metaphase I of meiosis, which leads to the independent assortment of the two unlinked genes (see Figure 13.11 and the question in the Figure 15.2 legend).

Recombination of Linked Genes: Crossing Over

Now let's explain the results of the *Drosophila* testcross in Figure 15.9. Recall that most of the offspring from the testcross for body colour and wing size had parental phenotypes. That suggested that the two genes were on the same chromosome, since the occurrence of parental types with a frequency greater than 50% indicates that the genes are linked. About 17% of offspring, however, were recombinants.

Seeing these results, Morgan proposed that some process must occasionally break the physical connection between specific alleles of genes on the same chromosome. Later experiments showed that this process, now called **crossing over**, accounts for the recombination of linked genes. In crossing over, which occurs while replicated homologous chromosomes are paired during prophase of meiosis I, a set of proteins orchestrates an exchange of corresponding segments of one maternal and one paternal chromatid (see Figure 13.9). In effect, when a single crossover occurs, end portions of two nonsister chromatids trade places.

Figure 15.10 shows how crossing over in a dihybrid female fly resulted in recombinant eggs and ultimately recombinant offspring in Morgan's testcross. Most of the eggs had a chromosome with either the $b^+ vg^+$ or $b vg$ parental genotype for body colour and wing size, but some eggs had a recombinant chromosome ($b^+ vg$ or $b vg^+$). Fertilization of all classes of eggs by homozygous recessive sperm ($b vg$) produced an offspring population in which 17% exhibited a nonparental, recombinant phenotype, reflecting combinations of alleles not seen before in either P generation parent. In the Scientific Skills Exercise, you can use a statistical test to analyze the results from an F₁ dihybrid testcross and see whether the two genes assort independently or are linked.

New Combinations of Alleles: Variation for Natural Selection

EVOLUTION The physical behaviour of chromosomes during meiosis contributes to the generation of variation in offspring (see Concept 13.4). Each pair of homologous chromosomes lines up independently of other pairs during metaphase I, and crossing over prior to that, during prophase I, can mix and match parts of maternal and paternal homologues. Mendel's elegant experiments show that the behaviour of the abstract entities known as genes—or, more concretely, alleles of genes—also leads to variation in offspring (see Concept 14.1). Now, putting these different ideas together, you can see that the recombinant chromosomes resulting from crossing over may bring alleles together in new combinations, and the subsequent events of meiosis distribute to gametes the recombinant chromosomes in a multitude of combinations, such as the new variants seen in Figures 15.9 and 15.10. Random fertilization then increases even further the number of variant allele combinations that can be created.

This abundance of genetic variation provides the raw material on which natural selection works. If the traits conferred by particular combinations of alleles are better suited for a given environment, organisms possessing those genotypes will be expected to thrive and leave more offspring, ensuring the continuation of their genetic complement. In the next generation, of course, the alleles will be shuffled anew. Ultimately, the interplay between environment and phenotype (and thus genotype) will determine which genetic combinations persist over time.

► **Figure 15.10 Chromosomal basis for recombination of linked genes.** In these diagrams re-creating the testcross in Figure 15.9, we track chromosomes as well as genes. The maternal chromosomes are colour-coded red and pink to distinguish one homologue from the other before any meiotic crossing over has taken place. Because crossing over between the *b* and *vg* loci occurs in some, but not all, egg-producing cells, more eggs with parental-type chromosomes than with recombinant ones are produced in the mating females. Fertilization of the eggs by sperm of genotype *b vg* gives rise to some recombinant offspring. The recombination frequency is the percentage of recombinant flies in the total pool of offspring.

DRAW IT *Suppose, as in the question at the bottom of Figure 15.9, the parental (P generation) flies were true-breeding for grey body with vestigial wings and black body with normal wings. Draw the chromosomes in each of the four possible kinds of eggs from an F₁ female, and label each chromosome as "parental" or "recombinant."*

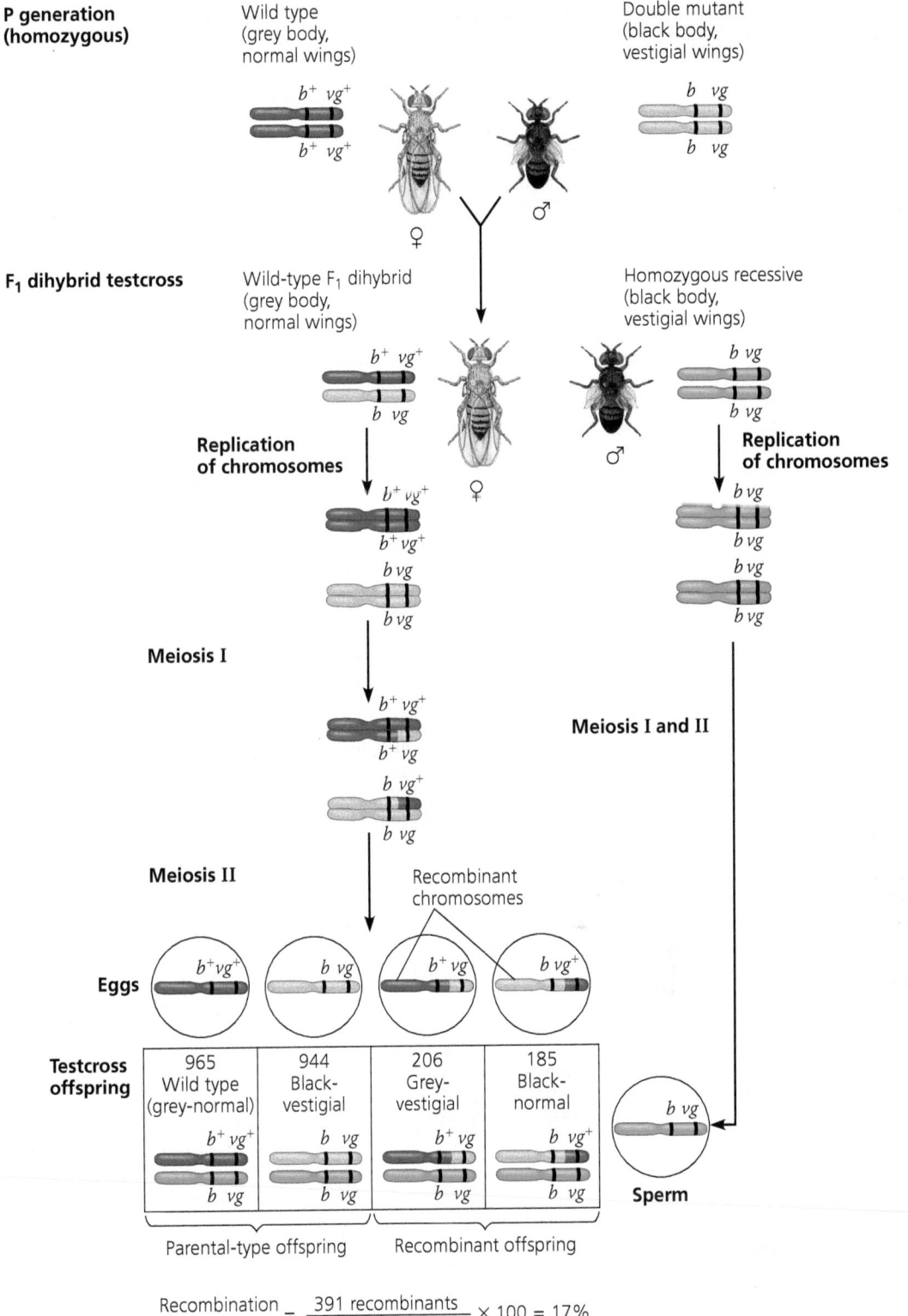

$$\text{Recombination frequency} = \frac{391 \text{ recombinants}}{2300 \text{ total offspring}} \times 100 = 17\%$$

Mapping the Distance Between Genes Using Recombination Data: *Scientific Inquiry*

The discovery of linked genes and recombination due to crossing over motivated one of Morgan's students, Alfred H. Sturtevant, to work out a method for constructing a **genetic map**, an ordered list of the genetic loci along a particular chromosome.

Sturtevant hypothesized that the percentage of recombinant offspring, the *recombination frequency*, calculated from experiments like the ones in Figures 15.9 and 15.10, depends on the distance between genes on a chromosome.

Using the Chi-Square Test

Are Two Genes Linked or Unlinked? Genes that are in close proximity on the same chromosome will result in the linked alleles being inherited together more often than not. But how can you tell if certain alleles are inherited together due to linkage or whether they just happen to assort together? In this exercise, you will use a simple statistical test, the chi-square (χ^2) test, to analyze phenotypes of F_1 testcross progeny in order to see whether two genes are linked or unlinked.

How These Experiments Are Done If genes are unlinked and assorting independently, the phenotypic ratio of offspring from an F_1 testcross is expected to be 1:1:1:1 (see Figure 15.9). If the two genes are linked, however, the observed phenotypic ratio of the offspring will not match that ratio. Given that random fluctuations in the data do occur, how much must the observed numbers deviate from the expected numbers for us to conclude that the genes are not assorting independently but may instead be linked? To answer this question, scientists use a statistical test. This test, called a chi-square test, compares an observed data set to an expected data set predicted by a hypothesis (here, that the genes are unlinked) and measures the discrepancy between the two, thus determining the "goodness of fit." If the discrepancy between the observed and expected data sets is so large that it is unlikely to have occurred by random fluctuation, we say there is statistically significant evidence against the hypothesis (or, more specifically, evidence for the genes being linked). If the discrepancy is small, then our observations are well explained by random variation alone. In this case, we say the observed data are consistent with our hypothesis, or that the discrepancy is statistically insignificant. Note, however, that consistency with our hypothesis is not the same as proof of our hypothesis. Also, the size of the experimental data set is important: With small data sets like this one, even if the genes are linked, discrepancies might be small by chance alone if the linkage is weak. For simplicity, we overlook the effect of sample size here.

Data from the Simulated Experiment In cosmos plants, purple stem (*A*) is dominant to green stem (*a*), and short petals (*B*) is dominant to long petals (*b*). In a simulated cross, *AABB* plants were crossed with *aabb* plants to generate F_1 dihybrids (*AaBb*), which were then testcrossed (*AaBb* × *aabb*). A total of 900 offspring plants were scored for stem colour and flower petal length.

Offspring from testcross of *AaBb* (F_1) × *aabb*	Purple stem/short petals (*A–B–*)	Green stem/short petals (*aaB–*)	Purple stem/long petals (*A–bb*)	Green stem/long petals (*aabb*)
Expected ratio if the genes are unlinked	1	1	1	1
Expected number of offspring (of 900)				
Observed number of offspring (of 900)	220	210	231	239

Interpret the Data

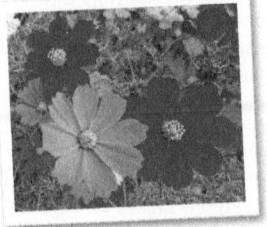

▲ Cosmos plants

1. The results in the data table are from a simulated F_1 dihybrid testcross. The hypothesis that the two genes are unlinked predicts the offspring phenotypic ratio will be 1:1:1:1. Using this ratio, calculate the expected number of each phenotype out of the 900 total offspring, and enter the values in the data table.

2. The goodness of fit is measured by χ^2. This statistic measures the amounts by which the observed values differ from their respective predictions to indicate how closely the two sets of values match. The formula for calculating this value is

$$\chi^2 = \sum \frac{(o - e)^2}{e}$$

where o = observed and e = expected. Calculate the χ^2 value for the data using the table below. Fill in the table, carrying out the operations indicated in the top row. Then add up the entries in the last column to find the χ^2 value.

Testcross Offspring	Expected (*e*)	Observed (*o*)	Deviation (*o* − *e*)	(*o* − *e*)^2	(*o* − *e*)^2/*e*
(*A–B–*)		220			
(*aaB–*)		210			
(*A–bb*)		231			
(*aabb*)		239			
				χ^2 = Sum	

3. The χ^2 value means nothing on its own—it is used to find the probability that, assuming the hypothesis is true, the observed data set could have resulted from random fluctuations. A low probability suggests that the observed data are not consistent with the hypothesis, and thus the hypothesis should be rejected. A standard cutoff point used by biologists is a probability of 0.05 (5%). If the probability corresponding to the χ^2 value is 0.05 or less, the differences between observed and expected values are considered statistically significant and the hypothesis (that the genes are unlinked) should be rejected. If the probability is above 0.05, the results are not statistically significant; the observed data are consistent with the hypothesis. To find the probability, locate your χ^2 value in the χ^2 Distribution Table in Appendix E. The "degrees of freedom" (df) of your data set is the number of categories (here, 4 phenotypes) minus 1, so df = 3. (a) Determine which values on the df = 3 line of the table your calculated χ^2 value lies between. (b) The column headings for these values show the probability range for your χ^2 number. Based on whether there are nonsignificant ($p > 0.05$) or significant ($p \leq 0.05$) differences between the observed and expected values, are the data consistent with the hypothesis that the two genes are unlinked and assorting independently, or is there enough evidence to reject this hypothesis?

He assumed that crossing over is a random event, with the chance of crossing over approximately equal at all points along a chromosome. Based on these assumptions, Sturtevant predicted that *the farther apart two genes are, the higher the probability that a crossover will occur between them and therefore the higher the recombination frequency.* His reasoning was simple: The greater the distance between two genes, the more points there are between them where crossing over can occur. Using recombination data from various fruit fly crosses, Sturtevant proceeded to assign relative positions to genes on the same chromosomes—that is, to *map* genes.

A genetic map based on recombination frequencies is called a **linkage map**. Figure 15.11 shows Sturtevant's linkage map of three genes: the body-colour (*b*) and wing-size (*vg*) genes depicted in Figure 15.10 and a third gene, called cinnabar (*cn*). Cinnabar is one of many *Drosophila* genes affecting eye colour. Cinnabar eyes, a mutant phenotype, are a brighter red than the wild-type colour. The recombination frequency between *cn* and *b* is 9%; that between *cn* and *vg*, 9.5%; and that between *b* and *vg*, 17%. In other words, crossovers between *cn* and *b* and between *cn* and *vg* are about half as frequent as crossovers between *b* and *vg*. Only a map that locates *cn* about midway between *b* and *vg* is consistent with these data, as you can prove to yourself by drawing alternative maps. Sturtevant expressed the distances between genes in **map units**, defining one map unit as equivalent to a 1% recombination frequency.

In practice, the interpretation of recombination data is more complicated than this example suggests. Some genes on a chromosome are so far from each other that a crossover between them is virtually certain. The observed frequency of recombination in crosses involving two such genes can have a maximum value of 50%, a result indistinguishable from that for genes on different chromosomes. In this case, the physical connection between genes on the same chromosome is not reflected in the results of genetic crosses. Despite being on the same chromosome and thus being *physically connected*, the genes are *genetically unlinked*; alleles of such genes assort independently, as if they were on different chromosomes. In fact, at least two of the genes for pea characters that Mendel studied are now known to be on the same chromosome, but the distance between them is so great that linkage is not observed in genetic crosses. Consequently, the two genes behaved as if they were on different chromosomes in Mendel's experiments. Genes located far apart on a chromosome are mapped by adding the recombination frequencies from crosses involving closer pairs of genes lying between the two distant genes.

Using recombination data, Sturtevant and his colleagues were able to map numerous *Drosophila* genes in linear arrays. They found that the genes clustered into four groups of linked genes (*linkage groups*). Light microscopy had revealed four pairs of chromosomes in *Drosophila*, so the linkage map provided additional evidence that genes are located on chromosomes. Each chromosome has a linear array of specific genes, each gene with its own locus (Figure 15.12).

▼ Figure 15.11 | **Research Method**

Constructing a Linkage Map

Application A linkage map shows the relative locations of genes along a chromosome.

Technique A linkage map is based on the assumption that the probability of a crossover between two genetic loci is proportional to the distance separating the loci. The recombination frequencies used to construct a linkage map for a particular chromosome are obtained from experimental crosses, such as the cross depicted in Figures 15.9 and 15.10. The distances between genes are expressed as map units, with one map unit equivalent to a 1% recombination frequency. Genes are arranged on the chromosome in the order that best fits the data.

Results In this example, the observed recombination frequencies between three *Drosophila* gene pairs (*b–cn* 9%, *cn–vg* 9.5%, and *b–vg* 17%) best fit a linear order in which *cn* is positioned about halfway between the other two genes:

The *b–vg* recombination frequency (17%) is slightly less than the sum of the *b–cn* and *cn–vg* frequencies (9 + 9.5 = 18.5%) because of the few times that one crossover occurs between *b* and *cn* and another crossover occurs between *cn* and *vg*. The second crossover would "cancel out" the first, reducing the observed *b–vg* recombination frequency while contributing to the frequency between each of the closer pairs of genes. The value of 18.5% (18.5 map units) is closer to the actual distance between the genes. In practice a geneticist would add the smaller distances in constructing a map.

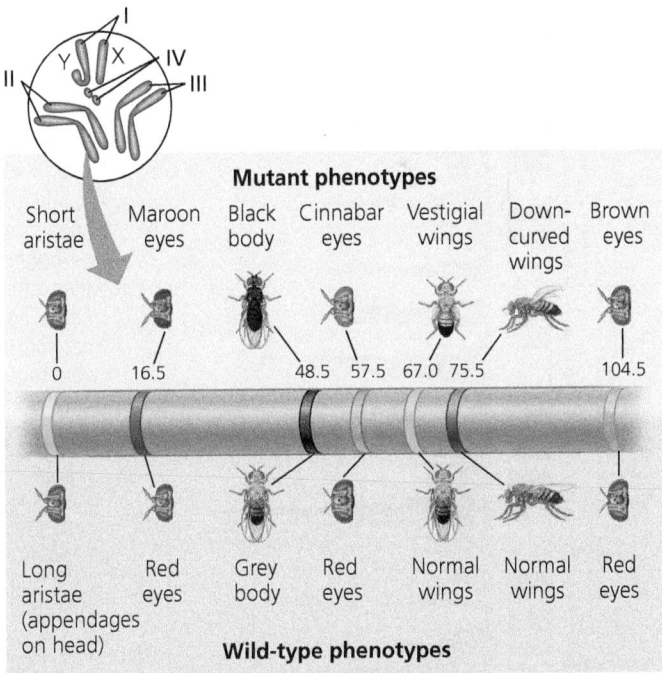

▲ **Figure 15.12 A partial genetic (linkage) map of a *Drosophila* chromosome.** This simplified map shows just a few of the genes that have been mapped on *Drosophila* chromosome II. The number at each gene locus indicates the number of map units between that locus and the locus for arista length (left). Notice that more than one gene can affect a given phenotypic characteristic, such as eye colour. Also, note that, in contrast to the homologous autosomes (II–IV), the X and Y sex chromosomes (I) have distinct shapes.

Because a linkage map is based strictly on recombination frequencies, it gives only an approximate picture of a chromosome. The frequency of crossing over is not actually uniform over the length of a chromosome, as Sturtevant assumed, and therefore map units do not correspond to actual physical distances (in nanometres, for instance). A linkage map does portray the order of genes along a chromosome, but it does not accurately portray the precise locations of those genes. Other methods enable geneticists to construct *cytogenetic maps* of chromosomes, which locate genes with respect to chromosomal features, such as stained bands, that can be seen in the microscope.

Chromosome maps of human chromosomes are particularly useful when they contain patient data and can inform us about medical disease while at the same time illustrating gene location. In 2003, a research team led by Dr. Stephen Scherer, from the Hospital for Sick Children in Toronto, decoded chromosome 7. Dr. Scherer's team produced a detailed annotated map of this chromosome and identified several candidate disease genes (**Figure 15.13**).

Technical advances over the last two decades have enormously increased the rate and affordability of DNA sequencing. Today, most researchers sequence whole genomes to map the locations of genes of a given species. The entire nucleotide sequence is the ultimate physical map of a chromosome, revealing the physical distances between gene loci in DNA nucleotides (see Concept 21.1). Comparing a linkage map with such a physical map or with a cytogenetic map of the same chromosome, we find that the linear order of genes is identical in all the maps, but the spacing between genes is not.

▼ Figure 15.13

Impact

Chromosome 7 Decoded

In 2003, an international research team led by Dr. Stephen Scherer, a Senior Scientist at the Hospital for Sick Children in Toronto, Ontario, produced a detailed annotated map and DNA sequence of human chromosome 7.

Gene Density

Disease: Cancer Examples	Chromosome 7 Abnormality
Acute lymphoblastic leukemia	Deletion 7q22
Acute myeloid leukemia	Deletion 7q22
Acute non-lymphoblastic leukemia	Monosomy 7
Bladder carcinoma	Trisomy 7
Brain tumours	Trisomy 7
Breast carcinoma	Deletion 7q11
Colorectal carcinoma	Trisomy 7
Lung adenocarcinoma	Deletion 7q22
Malignant melanoma	Deletion 7q
Non-Hodgkin's lymphoma	Deletion 7q22
Ovarian carcinoma	Deletion 7q31-q32
Primary lung carcinoma	Trisomy 7
Primary prostate carcinoma	Deletion 7q
Thyroid tumours	Trisomy 7

Why It Matters This achievement is significant because the annotated map incorporated patient data along with structural genetic features, such as chromosomal duplications (see Concept 15.4) and imprinted sites (see Concept 15.5). The researchers took raw DNA information and converted it into a medically useful tool that shows the identification of genes and mutations associated with many human diseases, including leukemia, obesity, and cystic fibrosis. This strategy also resulted in the discovery of candidate genes for autism and other developmental disorders.

Further Reading S.W. Scherer et al. Human chromosome 7: DNA sequence and biology, *Science* 300:767–772 (2003). Also, see www.chr7.org to search the database from the Chromosome 7 Annotation Project (click on "For Families" for general information on chromosome 7).

WHAT IF? *This study resulted in the identification of candidate genes for autism. If you were a researcher searching for genetic mutations associated with autism, what experiment would you conduct next based on the information contained in the chromosome 7 map? What other research could you also do that would help to elucidate the cause of autism?*

1. When two genes are located on the same chromosome, what is the physical basis for the production of recombinant offspring in a testcross between a dihybrid parent and a double-mutant (recessive) parent?

2. For each type of offspring of the testcross in Figure 15.9, explain the relationship between its phenotype and the alleles contributed by the female parent. (It will be useful to draw out the chromosomes of each fly and follow the alleles throughout the cross.)

3. **WHAT IF?** Genes *A*, *B*, and *C* are located on the same chromosome. Testcrosses show that the recombination frequency between *A* and *B* is 28% and between *A* and *C* is 12%. Can you determine the linear order of these genes? Explain.

For suggested answers, see Appendix A.

CONCEPT 15.4

Alterations of chromosome number or structure cause some genetic disorders

As you have learned so far in this chapter, the phenotype of an organism can be affected by small-scale changes involving individual genes. Random mutations are the source of all new alleles, which can lead to new phenotypic traits.

Large-scale chromosomal changes can also affect an organism's phenotype. Physical and chemical disturbances, as well as errors during meiosis, can damage chromosomes in major ways or alter their number in a cell. Large-scale chromosomal alterations in humans and other mammals often lead to spontaneous abortion (miscarriage) of a fetus, and individuals born with these types of genetic defects commonly exhibit various developmental disorders. Plants appear to tolerate such genetic defects better than animals do.

Abnormal Chromosome Number

Ideally, the meiotic spindle distributes chromosomes to daughter cells without error. But there is an occasional mishap, called a **nondisjunction**, in which the members of a pair of homologous chromosomes do not move apart properly during meiosis I or sister chromatids fail to separate during meiosis II (**Figure 15.14**). In nondisjunction, one gamete receives two of the same type of chromosome and another gamete receives no copy. The other chromosomes are usually distributed normally.

If either of the aberrant gametes unites with a normal one at fertilization, the zygote will also have an abnormal number of a particular chromosome, a condition known as **aneuploidy**. (Aneuploidy may involve more than one chromosome.) Fertilization involving a gamete that has no copy of a particular chromosome will lead to a missing chromosome in the zygote (so that the cell has $2n - 1$

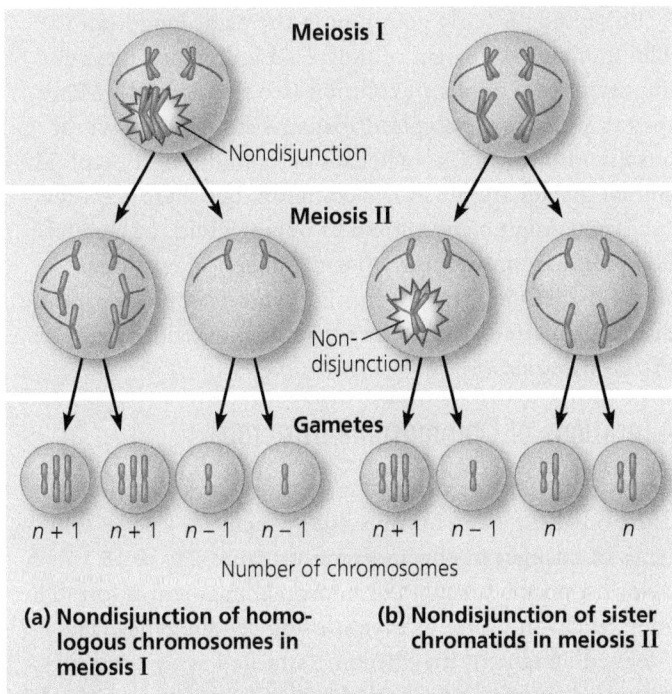

▲ **Figure 15.14 Meiotic nondisjunction.** Gametes with an abnormal chromosome number can arise by nondisjunction in either meiosis I or meiosis II. For simplicity, the figure does not show the spores formed by meiosis in plants. Ultimately, spores form gametes that have the defects shown. (See Figure 13.6.)

chromosomes); the aneuploid zygote is said to be **monosomic** for that chromosome. If a chromosome is present in triplicate in the zygote (so that the cell has $2n + 1$ chromosomes), the aneuploid cell is **trisomic** for that chromosome. Mitosis will subsequently transmit the anomaly to all embryonic cells. Monosomy and trisomy are estimated to occur in between 10% and 25% of human conceptions and are the main reason for pregnancy loss. If the organism survives, it usually has a set of traits caused by the abnormal dose of the genes associated with the extra or missing chromosome. Down syndrome is an example of trisomy in humans that will be discussed later. Nondisjunction can also occur during mitosis. If such an error takes place early in embryonic development, then the aneuploid condition is passed along by mitosis to a large number of cells and is likely to have a substantial effect on the organism.

Some organisms have more than two complete chromosome sets in all somatic cells. The general term for this chromosomal alteration is **polyploidy**; the specific terms *triploidy* (3n) and *tetraploidy* (4n) indicate three and four chromosomal sets, respectively. One way a triploid cell may arise is by the fertilization of an abnormal diploid egg produced by nondisjunction of all its chromosomes. Tetraploidy could result from the failure of a 2n zygote to divide after replicating its chromosomes. Subsequent normal mitotic divisions would then produce a 4n embryo.

Polyploidy is fairly common in the plant kingdom. The spontaneous origin of polyploid individuals plays an important role in plant evolution (see Chapter 24). Many species we eat are polyploid: Bananas are triploid, wheat hexaploid ($6n$), and strawberries octoploid ($8n$). Polyploid animal species are much less common, but there are a few fishes and amphibians known to be polyploid. In general, polyploids are more nearly normal in appearance than aneuploids. One extra (or missing) chromosome apparently disrupts genetic balance more than does an entire extra set of chromosomes.

Alterations of Chromosome Structure

Errors in meiosis or damaging agents such as radiation can cause breakage of a chromosome, which can lead to four types of changes in chromosome structure (Figure 15.15). A **deletion** occurs when a chromosomal fragment is lost. The affected chromosome is then missing certain genes. The "deleted" fragment may become attached as an extra segment to a sister or nonsister chromatid, producing a **duplication** of a portion of that chromosome. A chromosomal fragment may also reattach to the original chromosome but in the reverse orientation, producing an **inversion**. A fourth possible result of chromosomal breakage is for the fragment to join a nonhomologous chromosome, a rearrangement called a **translocation**.

Deletions and duplications are especially likely to occur during meiosis. In crossing over, nonsister chromatids sometimes exchange unequal-sized segments of DNA, so that one partner gives up more genes than it receives. The products of such an unequal crossover are one chromosome with a deletion and one chromosome with a duplication.

A diploid embryo that is homozygous for a large deletion (or has a single X chromosome with a large deletion, in a male) is usually missing a number of essential genes, a condition that is typically lethal. Duplications and translocations also tend to be harmful. In reciprocal translocations, in which segments are exchanged between nonhomologous chromosomes, and in inversions, the balance of genes is not abnormal—all genes are present in their normal doses. Nevertheless, translocations and inversions can alter phenotype because a gene's expression can be influenced by its location among neighbouring genes, which can have devastating effects.

Human Disorders Due to Chromosomal Alterations

Alterations of chromosome number and structure are associated with a number of serious human disorders. As described earlier, nondisjunction in meiosis results in aneuploidy in gametes and any resulting zygotes. Although the frequency of aneuploid zygotes may be quite high in humans, most of these chromosomal alterations are so

▼ Figure 15.15 **Alterations of chromosome structure.** Red arrows indicate breakage points. Dark purple highlights the chromosomal parts affected by the rearrangements.

(a) Deletion

A **deletion** removes a chromosomal segment.

(b) Duplication

A **duplication** repeats a segment.

(c) Inversion

An **inversion** reverses a segment within a chromosome.

(d) Translocation

A **translocation** moves a segment from one chromosome to a nonhomologous chromosome. In a reciprocal translocation, the most common type, nonhomologous chromosomes exchange fragments.

Less often, a nonreciprocal translocation occurs: A chromosome transfers a fragment but receives none in return (not shown).

disastrous to development that the affected embryos are spontaneously aborted long before birth. However, some types of aneuploidy appear to upset the genetic balance less than others, where individuals with certain aneuploid conditions can survive to birth and beyond. These individuals have a set of traits—a *syndrome*—characteristic of the type of aneuploidy. Genetic disorders caused by aneuploidy can be diagnosed before birth by fetal testing (see Figure 14.20).

Trisomy 21 (Down Syndrome)

One aneuploid condition, **Down syndrome**, affects approximately one out of every 740 children born in

Canada (**Figure 15.16**). Down syndrome is usually the result of an extra chromosome 21, so that each body cell has a total of 47 chromosomes. Because the cells are trisomic for chromosome 21, the scientific term for Down syndrome is *trisomy 21*. Trisomy 21 includes characteristic facial features, short stature, correctable heart defects, and developmental delays. Individuals with trisomy 21 have an increased chance of developing leukemia and Alzheimer's disease but have a lower rate of high blood pressure, atherosclerosis (hardening of the arteries), stroke, and many types of solid tumours. Although people with trisomy 21, on average, have a life span shorter than normal, most, with proper medical treatment, live to middle age and beyond. Many live independently or at home with their families, are employed, and are valuable contributors to their communities. Almost all males and about half of females with trisomy 21 are sexually underdeveloped and sterile.

The frequency of trisomy 21 increases with the age of the mother. While the disorder occurs in just 0.04% (4 out of 10 000 births) of children born to women under age 30, the risk climbs to 0.92% (92 out of 10 000) for mothers at age 40 and is even higher for older mothers. The correlation of trisomy 21 with maternal age has not yet been explained. Most cases result from nondisjunction during meiosis I, and some research points to an age-dependent abnormality in meiosis. Trisomies of some other chromosomes also increase in incidence with maternal age, although infants with other autosomal trisomies rarely survive for long. Due to its low risk and its potential for providing useful information, prenatal screening for trisomies in the embryo is now offered to all pregnant women in Canada.

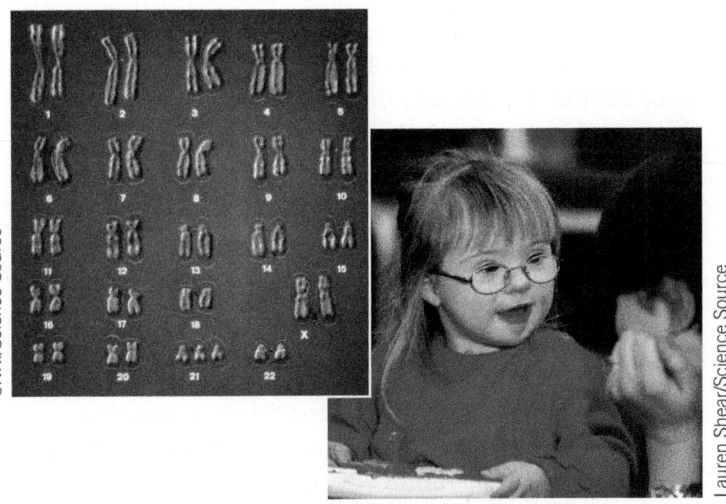

▲ **Figure 15.16 Trisomy 21 (Down syndrome).** The karyotype shows trisomy 21, the most common cause of Down syndrome. The child exhibits the facial features characteristic of this disorder.

CNRI/Science Source

Lauren Shear/Science Source

Aneuploidy of Sex Chromosomes

Aneuploid conditions involving sex chromosomes appear to upset the genetic balance less than those involving autosomes. This may be because the Y chromosome carries relatively few genes. Also, extra copies of the X chromosome become inactivated as Barr bodies.

An extra X chromosome in a male, producing XXY, occurs approximately once in every 500 to 1000 live male births. People with this disorder, called *Klinefelter syndrome*, have male sex organs, but the testes are abnormally small and the man is sterile. Even though the extra X is inactivated, some breast enlargement and other female body characteristics are common. Affected individuals may have subnormal intelligence. About 1 of every 1000 males is born with an extra Y chromosome (XYY). These males undergo normal sexual development and do not exhibit any well-defined syndrome but tend to be taller than average.

Females with trisomy X (XXX), which occurs once in approximately 1000 live female births, are healthy and have no unusual physical features other than being slightly taller than average. Triple-X females are at risk for learning disabilities but are fertile. Monosomy X, which is called *Turner syndrome*, occurs about once in every 2500 female births and is the only known viable monosomy in humans. Although these X0 individuals are phenotypically female, they are sterile because their sex organs do not mature. When provided with estrogen replacement therapy, girls with Turner syndrome do develop secondary sex characteristics. Most have normal intelligence.

Disorders Caused by Structurally Altered Chromosomes

Many deletions in human chromosomes, even in a heterozygous state, cause severe problems. One such syndrome, known as *cri du chat* ("cry of the cat"), results from a specific deletion in chromosome 5. A child born with this deletion is severely intellectually disabled, has a small head with unusual facial features, and has a cry that sounds like the mewing of a distressed cat. Such individuals usually die in infancy or early childhood.

Chromosomal translocations can also occur during mitosis; some have been implicated in certain cancers, including *chronic myelogenous leukemia (CML)*. This disease occurs when a reciprocal translocation happens during mitosis of pre-white blood cells. The exchange of a large portion of chromosome 22 with a small fragment from a tip of chromosome 9 produces a much shortened, easily recognized chromosome 22, called the *Philadelphia chromosome* (**Figure 15.17**). Such an exchange causes cancer by creating a new "fused" gene that leads to uncontrolled cell cycle progression. (The mechanism of gene activation will be discussed in Chapter 18.)

▲ **Figure 15.17 Translocation associated with chronic myelogenous leukemia (CML).** The cancerous cells in nearly all CML patients contain an abnormally short chromosome 22, the so-called Philadelphia chromosome, and an abnormally long chromosome 9. These altered chromosomes result from the reciprocal translocation shown here, which presumably occurred in a single white blood cell precursor undergoing mitosis and was then passed along to all descendant cells.

CONCEPT CHECK 15.4

1. About 5% of individuals with Down syndrome have a chromosomal translocation in which a third copy of chromosome 21 is attached to chromosome 14. If this translocation occurred in a parent's gonad, how could it lead to Down syndrome in a child?

2. **MAKE CONNECTIONS** The ABO blood type locus has been mapped to chromosome 9. A father who has type AB blood and a mother who has type O blood have a child with trisomy 9 and type A blood. Using this information, can you tell in which parent the nondisjunction occurred? Explain your answer. (See Figures 14.11 and 15.14.)

3. **MAKE CONNECTIONS** The gene that is activated on the Philadelphia chromosome codes for an intracellular tyrosine kinase. Review the discussion of cell cycle control in Concept 12.3, and explain how the activation of this gene could contribute to the development of cancer.

For suggested answers, see Appendix A.

CONCEPT 15.5

Some inheritance patterns are exceptions to standard Mendelian inheritance

In the previous section, you learned about deviations from the usual patterns of chromosomal inheritance due to abnormal events in meiosis and mitosis. We conclude this chapter by describing two normally occurring exceptions to Mendelian genetics, one involving genes located in the nucleus and the other involving genes located outside the nucleus. In both cases, the sex of the parent contributing an allele is a factor in the pattern of inheritance.

Genomic Imprinting

Throughout our discussions of Mendelian genetics and the chromosomal basis of inheritance, we have assumed that a given allele will have the same effect whether it was inherited from the mother or the father. This is probably a safe assumption most of the time. For example, when Mendel crossed purple-flowered pea plants with white-flowered pea plants, he observed the same results regardless of whether the purple-flowered parent supplied the eggs or the sperm. In recent years, however, geneticists have identified a number of traits in mammals that depend on which parent passed along the alleles for those traits. Such variation in phenotype depending on whether an allele is inherited from the male or female parent is called **genomic imprinting**. (Note that unlike sex-linked genes, most imprinted genes are on autosomes.) Using newer DNA sequence-based methods, over 60 imprinted genes have been identified, with hundreds more suspected.

Genomic imprinting occurs during gamete formation and results in the silencing of a particular allele of certain genes. Because these genes are imprinted differently in sperm and eggs, the offspring expresses only one allele of an imprinted gene, the one that has been inherited from a specific parent. The parent can be either the female or the male, depending on the particular gene. The imprints are then transmitted to all body cells during development. In each generation, the old imprints are "erased" in gamete-producing cells, and the chromosomes of the developing gametes are newly imprinted according to the sex of the individual forming the gametes. In a given species, the imprinted genes are always imprinted in the same way. For instance, a gene imprinted for maternal allele expression is always imprinted this way, generation after generation.

Consider, for example, the mouse gene for insulin-like growth factor 2 (*Igf2*), one of the first imprinted genes to be identified. Although this growth factor is required for normal prenatal growth, only the paternal allele is expressed (**Figure 15.18a**). Evidence that the *Igf2* gene is imprinted came initially from crosses between normal-sized (wild-type) mice and dwarf (mutant) mice homozygous for a recessive mutation in the *Igf2* gene. The phenotypes of heterozygous offspring (with one normal allele and one mutant) differed, depending on whether the mutant allele came from the mother or the father (**Figure 15.18b**).

What exactly is a genomic imprint? It turns out that imprinting can involve either silencing an allele in one type of gamete (egg or sperm) or activating it in the other. In many cases, the imprint seems to consist of methyl (—CH$_3$) groups that are added to cytosine nucleotides of one of the alleles. Such methylation may silence the allele, an effect

(a) Homozygote. A mouse homozygous for the wild-type *Igf2* allele is normal-sized. Only the paternal allele of this gene is expressed.

Mutant *Igf2* allele inherited from mother

Normal-sized mouse (wild type)

Normal *Igf2* allele is expressed.

Mutant *Igf2* allele is not expressed.

Mutant *Igf2* allele inherited from father

Dwarf mouse (mutant)

Mutant *Igf2* allele is expressed.

Normal *Igf2* allele is not expressed.

(b) Heterozygotes. Matings between wild-type mice and those homozygous for the recessive mutant *Igf2* allele produce heterozygous offspring. The dwarf (mutant) phenotype is seen only when the father contributed the mutant allele because the maternal allele is not expressed.

▲ **Figure 15.18 Genomic imprinting of the mouse *Igf2* gene.**

consistent with evidence that heavily methylated genes are usually inactive (see Concept 18.2). However, for a few genes, methylation has been shown to *activate* expression of the allele. This is the case for the *Igf2* gene: Methylation of certain cytosines on the paternal chromosome leads to expression of the paternal *Igf2* allele by an indirect mechanism involving chromatin condensation.

Genomic imprinting may affect only a small fraction of the genes in mammalian genomes, but most of the known imprinted genes are critical for embryonic development. In experiments with mice, embryos engineered to inherit both copies of certain chromosomes from the same parent usually die before birth, whether that parent is male or female. A few years ago, however, scientists in Japan combined the genetic material from two eggs in a zygote while allowing expression of the *Igf2* gene from only one of the egg nuclei. The zygote developed into an apparently healthy mouse. Normal development seems to require that embryonic cells have exactly one active copy—not zero, not two—of certain genes. The association of improper imprinting with abnormal development and certain cancers

has stimulated ongoing studies of how different genes are imprinted.

Inheritance of Organelle Genes

Although our focus in this chapter has been on the chromosomal basis of inheritance, we end with an important amendment: Not all of a eukaryotic cell's genes are located on nuclear chromosomes, or even in the nucleus; some genes are located in organelles in the cytoplasm. Because they are outside the nucleus, these genes are sometimes called *extranuclear genes* or *cytoplasmic genes*. Mitochondria, as well as chloroplasts and other plastids in plants, contain small circular DNA molecules that carry a number of genes. These organelles reproduce themselves and transmit their genes to daughter organelles. Genes on organelle DNA are not distributed to offspring according to the same rules that direct the distribution of nuclear chromosomes during meiosis, so they do not display Mendelian inheritance.

The first hint that extranuclear genes exist came from studies by the German scientist Karl Correns on the inheritance of yellow or white patches on the leaves of an otherwise green plant. In 1909, he observed that the colouration of the offspring was determined only by the maternal parent (the source of eggs) and not by the paternal parent (the source of sperm). Subsequent research showed that such colouration patterns, or variegation, are due to mutations in plastid genes that control pigmentation (**Figure 15.19**). In most plants, a zygote receives all its plastids from the cytoplasm of the egg and none from the sperm, which contributes little more than a haploid set of chromosomes. An egg may contain plastids with different alleles for a pigmentation gene. As the zygote develops, plastids containing wild-type or mutant pigmentation genes are distributed randomly to daughter cells. The pattern of leaf colouration

▶ **Figure 15.19 A painted nettle coleus plant.** The variegated (patterned) leaves on this coleus plant (*Solenostemon scutellarioides*) result from mutations that affect expression of pigment genes located in plastids, which generally are inherited from the maternal parent.

Geoff Kidd/Science Source

exhibited by a plant depends on the ratio of wild-type to mutant plastids in its various tissues.

Similar maternal inheritance is also the rule for mitochondrial genes in most animals and plants, because almost all the mitochondria passed on to a zygote come from the cytoplasm of the egg. (The few mitochondria contributed by the sperm appear to be destroyed in the egg by autophagy; see Figure 6.13.) The products of most mitochondrial genes help make up some of the protein complexes of the electron transport chain and ATP synthase (see Chapter 9). Defects in one or more of these proteins, therefore, reduce the amount of ATP the cell can make and have been shown to cause a number of rare human disorders in as many as 1 out of every 5000 births (see Figure 9.15). Because the parts of the body most susceptible to energy deprivation are the nervous system and the muscles, most mitochondrial diseases primarily affect these systems. For example, *mitochondrial myopathy* causes weakness, intolerance of exercise, and muscle deterioration. Another mitochondrial disorder is *Leber's hereditary optic neuropathy*, which can produce sudden blindness in people as young as their 20s or 30s. The four mutations found thus far to cause this disorder affect oxidative phosphorylation during cellular respiration, a crucial function for the cell (see Concept 9.4).

The fact that mitochondrial disorders are inherited only from the mother suggests a way to avoid passing along these disorders. The chromosomes from the egg of an affected mother could be transferred to an egg of a healthy donor which has had its own chromosomes removed. This "two-mother" egg could then be fertilized by a sperm from the prospective father and transplanted into the womb of the prospective mother, becoming an embryo with three parents. After optimizing conditions for this approach in monkeys, researchers reported in 2013 that they successfully carried out this procedure on human eggs. More research will be necessary to optimize experimental conditions for the health of the embryo, and eventual use of this procedure would require approval by the relevant federal agencies.

In addition to the rarer diseases clearly caused by defects in mitochondrial DNA, mitochondrial mutations inherited from a person's mother may contribute to at least some types of diabetes and heart disease, as well as to other disorders that commonly debilitate the elderly, such as Alzheimer's disease. In the course of a lifetime, new mutations gradually accumulate in our mitochondrial DNA, and some researchers think that these mutations play a role in the normal aging process.

Wherever genes are located in the cell—in the nucleus or in cytoplasmic organelles—their inheritance depends on the precise replication of DNA. In the next chapter, you will learn how this molecular reproduction occurs.

CONCEPT CHECK 15.5

1. Gene dosage—the number of copies of a gene that are actively being expressed—is important to proper development. Identify and describe two processes that establish the proper dosage of certain genes.

2. Reciprocal crosses between two primrose varieties, A and B, produced the following results: A female × B male → offspring with all green (nonvariegated) leaves; B female × A male → offspring with patterned (variegated) leaves. Explain these results.

3. **WHAT IF?** Mitochondrial genes are critical to the energy metabolism of cells, but mitochondrial disorders caused by mutations in these genes are generally not lethal. Why not?

For suggested answers, see Appendix A.

---

15 Chapter Review

Go to **MasteringBiology®** for Assignments, the eText, and the Study Area with Animations, Activities, Vocab Self-Quiz, and Practice Tests.

SUMMARY OF KEY CONCEPTS

CONCEPT 15.1

Morgan showed that Mendelian inheritance has its physical basis in the behaviour of chromosomes: *Scientific Inquiry* (pp. 309–311)

- Morgan's work with an eye-colour gene in *Drosophila* led to the **chromosome theory of inheritance**, which states that genes are located on chromosomes and that the behaviour of chromosomes during meiosis accounts for Mendel's laws.

? *What characteristic of the sex chromosomes allowed Morgan to correlate their behaviour with that of the alleles of the eye-colour gene?*

CONCEPT 15.2

Sex-linked genes exhibit unique patterns of inheritance (pp. 311–314)

- Sex is often chromosomally based. Humans and other mammals have an X-Y system in which sex is determined by whether a Y chromosome is present. Other systems are found in birds, fishes, and insects.

- The sex chromosomes carry **sex-linked genes**, virtually all of which are on the X chromosome (X-linked). Any male who inherits a recessive X-linked allele (from his mother) will express the trait, such as colour blindness.
- In mammalian females, one of the two X chromosomes in each cell is randomly inactivated during early embryonic development, becoming highly condensed into a **Barr body**.

? *Why are males affected much more often than females by X-linked disorders?*

CONCEPT 15.3

Linked genes tend to be inherited together because they are located near each other on the same chromosome (pp. 314–321)

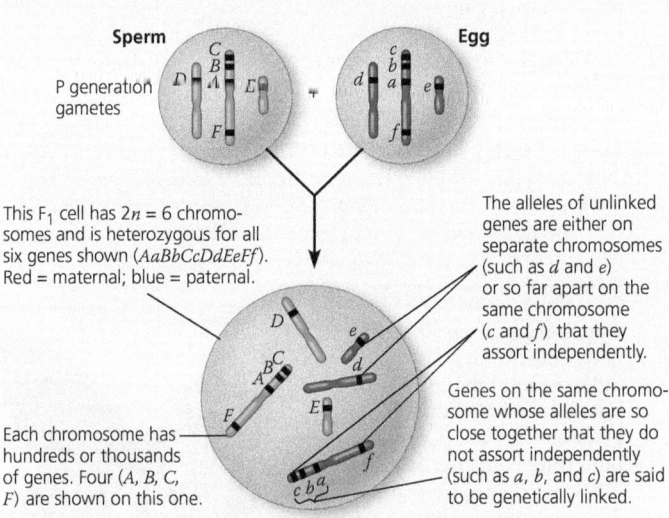

Sperm   Egg

P generation gametes

This F₁ cell has 2*n* = 6 chromosomes and is heterozygous for all six genes shown (*AaBbCcDdEeFf*). Red = maternal; blue = paternal.

Each chromosome has hundreds or thousands of genes. Four (*A, B, C, F*) are shown on this one.

The alleles of unlinked genes are either on separate chromosomes (such as *d* and *e*) or so far apart on the same chromosome (*c* and *f*) that they assort independently.

Genes on the same chromosome whose alleles are so close together that they do not assort independently (such as *a*, *b*, and *c*) are said to be genetically linked.

- Among offspring from an F₁ testcross, **parental types** have the same combination of traits as those in the P generation parents. **Recombinant types (recombinants)** exhibit new combinations of traits not seen in either P generation parent. Because of the independent assortment of chromosomes, unlinked genes exhibit a 50% frequency of recombination in the gametes. For genetically **linked genes**, **crossing over** between nonsister chromatids during meiosis I accounts for the observed recombinants, always less than 50%.
- The order of genes on a chromosome and the relative distances between them can be deduced from recombination frequencies observed in genetic crosses. These data allow construction of a **linkage map** (a type of **genetic map**). The farther apart genes are, the more likely their allele combinations will be recombined during crossing over.

? *Why are specific alleles of two distant genes more likely to show recombination than those of two closer genes?*

CONCEPT 15.4

Alterations of chromosome number or structure cause some genetic disorders (pp. 321–324)

- **Aneuploidy**, an abnormal chromosome number, can result from **nondisjunction** during meiosis. When a normal gamete unites with one containing two copies or no copies of a particular chromosome, the resulting zygote and its descendant cells either have one extra copy of that chromosome (**trisomy**, 2*n* + 1) or are missing a copy (**monosomy**, 2*n* − 1). **Polyploidy** (extra sets of chromosomes) can result from complete nondisjunction during gamete formation.

- Chromosome breakage can result in alterations of chromosome structure: **deletions**, **duplications**, **inversions**, and **translocations**. Translocations can be reciprocal or nonreciprocal.
- Changes in the number of chromosomes per cell or in the structure of individual chromosomes can affect the phenotype and, in some cases, lead to human disorders. Such alterations cause **Down syndrome** (usually due to trisomy of chromosome 21), certain cancers associated with chromosomal translocations that occur during mitosis, and various other human disorders.

? *Why are inversions and reciprocal translocations less likely to be lethal than are aneuploidy, duplications, deletions, and nonreciprocal translocations?*

CONCEPT 15.5

Some inheritance patterns are exceptions to standard Mendelian inheritance (pp. 324–326)

- In mammals, the phenotypic effects of a small number of particular genes depend on which allele is inherited from each parent, a phenomenon called **genomic imprinting**. Imprints are formed during gamete production, with the result that one allele (either maternal or paternal) is not expressed in offspring.
- The inheritance of traits controlled by the genes present in mitochondria and plastids depends solely on the maternal parent because the zygote's cytoplasm containing these organelles comes from the egg. Some diseases affecting the nervous and muscular systems are caused by defects in mitochondrial genes that prevent cells from making enough ATP.

? *Explain how genomic imprinting and inheritance of mitochondrial and chloroplast DNA are exceptions to standard Mendelian inheritance.*

TEST YOUR UNDERSTANDING

LEVEL 1: KNOWLEDGE/COMPREHENSION

1. A man with hemophilia (a recessive, sex-linked condition) has a daughter without the condition. She marries a man who does not have hemophilia. What is the probability that their daughter will have hemophilia? Their son? If they have four sons, what is the probability that all will be affected?

2. Pseudohypertrophic muscular dystrophy is an inherited disorder that causes gradual deterioration of the muscles. It is seen almost exclusively in boys born to apparently normal parents and usually results in death in the early teens. Is this disorder caused by a dominant or a recessive allele? Is its inheritance sex-linked or autosomal? How do you know? Explain why this disorder is almost never seen in girls.

3. A wild-type fruit fly (heterozygous for grey body colour and normal wings) is mated with a black fly with vestigial wings. The offspring have the following phenotypic distribution: wild-type, 778; black-vestigial, 785; black-normal, 158; grey-vestigial, 162. What is the recombination frequency between these genes for body colour and wing size?

4. A planet is inhabited by creatures that reproduce with the same hereditary patterns seen in humans. Three phenotypic characters are height (*T* = tall, *t* = dwarf), head appendages (*A* = antennae, *a* = no antennae), and nose morphology (*S* = upturned snout, *s* = downturned snout). Since the creatures are not "intelligent," Earth scientists are able to do some controlled breeding experiments using various heterozygotes in testcrosses. For tall heterozygotes with antennae, the offspring are tall-antennae, 46; dwarf-antennae, 7; dwarf-no antennae, 42; tall-no antennae,

5. For heterozygotes with antennae and an upturned snout, the

offspring are antennae-upturned snout, 47; antennae-downturned snout, 2; no antennae-downturned snout, 48; no antennae-upturned snout, 3. Calculate the recombination frequencies for both experiments.

LEVEL 2: APPLICATION/ANALYSIS

5. Using the information from question 4, scientists do a further testcross using a heterozygote for height and nose morphology. The offspring are tall-upturned snout, 40; dwarf-upturned snout, 9; dwarf-downturned snout, 42; tall-downturned snout, 9. Calculate the recombination frequency from these data; then use your answer from question 4 to determine the correct sequence of the three linked genes.

6. A wild-type fruit fly (heterozygous for grey body colour and red eyes) is mated with a black fruit fly with purple eyes. The offspring are wild-type, 721; black-purple, 751; grey-purple, 49; black-red, 45. What is the recombination frequency between these genes for body colour and eye colour? Using information from question 3, what fruit flies (genotypes and phenotypes) would you mate to determine the sequence of the body-colour, wing-size, and eye-colour genes on the chromosome?

7. Assume that genes A and B are on the same chromosome and are 50 map units apart. An animal heterozygous at both loci is crossed with one that is homozygous recessive at both loci. What percentage of the offspring will show recombinant phenotypes resulting from crossovers? Without knowing these genes are on the same chromosome, how would you interpret the results of this cross?

8. Two genes of a flower, one controlling blue (B) versus white (b) petals and the other controlling round (R) versus oval (r) stamens, are linked and are 10 map units apart. You cross a homozygous blue-oval plant with a homozygous white-round plant. The resulting F_1 progeny are crossed with homozygous white-oval plants, and 1000 F_2 progeny are obtained. How many F_2 plants of each of the four phenotypes do you expect?

9. You design *Drosophila* crosses to provide recombination data for gene a, which is located on the chromosome shown in Figure 15.12. Gene a has recombination frequencies of 14% with the vestigial-wing locus and 26% with the brown-eye locus. Approximately where is a located along the chromosome?

LEVEL 3: SYNTHESIS/EVALUATION

10. Banana plants, which are triploid, are seedless and therefore sterile. Propose a possible explanation.

11. **EVOLUTION CONNECTION**
Crossing over is thought to be evolutionarily advantageous because it continually shuffles genetic alleles into novel combinations, allowing evolutionary processes to occur. Until recently, it was thought that the genes on the Y chromosome might degenerate because they lack homologous genes on the X chromosome with which to recombine. However, when the Y chromosome was sequenced, eight large regions were found to be internally homologous to each other, and quite a few of the 78 genes represent duplicates. (Y chromosome researcher David Page has called it a "hall of mirrors.") What might be a benefit of these regions?

12. **SCIENTIFIC INQUIRY**
DRAW IT Assume you are mapping genes A, B, C, and D in *Drosophila*. You know that these genes are linked on the same chromosome, and you determine the recombination frequencies between each pair of genes to be as follows: *A–B*, 8%; *A–C*, 28%; *A–D*, 25%; *B–C*, 20%; *B–D*, 33%.
a. Describe how you determined the recombination frequencies for each pair of genes.
b. Draw a chromosome map based on your data.

13. **WRITE ABOUT A THEME: INFORMATION**
The continuity of life is based on heritable information in the form of DNA. In a short essay (100–150 words), relate the structure and behaviour of chromosomes to inheritance in both asexually and sexually reproducing species.

14. **SYNTHESIZE YOUR KNOWLEDGE**

James K. Adams

Butterflies have an X-Y sex determination system that is different from that of flies or humans. Female butterflies may be either XY or XO, while butterflies with two or more X chromosomes are males. This photograph shows a tiger swallowtail *gynandromorph*, an individual that is half male (left side) and half female (right side). Given that the first division of the zygote divides the embryo into the future right and left halves of the butterfly, propose a hypothesis that explains how nondisjunction during the first mitosis might have produced this unusual-looking butterfly.

For selected answers, see Appendix A.

16

The Molecular Basis of Inheritance

Science Picture Co/Science Source

▲ Figure 16.1 **What is the structure of DNA?**

KEY CONCEPTS

16.1 DNA is the genetic material

16.2 Many proteins work together in DNA replication and repair

16.3 A chromosome consists of a DNA molecule packed together with proteins

Life's Operating Instructions

The elegant double-helical structure of deoxyribonucleic acid, or DNA, has become an icon of modern biology (Figure 16.1). James Watson and Francis Crick shook the scientific world in April 1953 with their DNA model, which they constructed from sheet metal and wire, shown in the photo at the lower left. Gregor Mendel's heritable factors and Thomas Hunt Morgan's genes on chromosomes are, in fact, composed of DNA. Chemically speaking, your genetic endowment is the DNA you inherited from your parents. DNA, the substance of inheritance, is the most celebrated molecule of our time.

Of all nature's molecules, nucleic acids are unique in their ability to direct their own replication from monomers. Indeed, the resemblance of offspring to their parents has its basis in the accurate replication of DNA and its transmission from one generation to the next. Hereditary information in DNA directs the development of your biochemical, anatomical, physiological, and, to some extent, behavioural traits. In this chapter, you will discover how biologists deduced that DNA is the genetic material and how Watson and Crick worked out its structure. You will also learn how a molecule of DNA is copied during **DNA replication** and how cells repair their DNA. Finally, you will explore how a molecule of DNA is packaged together with proteins in a chromosome.

National Institute of Health

▲ **James Watson (left) and Francis Crick with their DNA model.**

CONCEPT 16.1

DNA is the genetic material

Today, even schoolchildren have heard of DNA, and scientists routinely manipulate DNA in the laboratory, often to change the heritable traits of cells in their experiments. Early in the 20th century, however, identifying the molecules of inheritance loomed as a major challenge to biologists.

The Search for the Genetic Material: *Scientific Inquiry*

Once T. H. Morgan's group showed that genes exist as parts of chromosomes (described in Concept 15.1), the two chemical components of chromosomes—DNA and protein—emerged as the leading candidates for the genetic material. Until the 1940s, the case for proteins seemed stronger. Biochemists had identified proteins as a class of macromolecules with great heterogeneity and specificity of function, essential requirements for the hereditary material. Moreover, little was known about nucleic acids, whose physical and chemical properties seemed far too uniform to account for the multitude of specific inherited traits exhibited by every organism. This view gradually changed as the role of DNA in heredity was first worked out in studies of bacteria and the viruses that infect them, systems far simpler than fruit flies or humans. Let's trace the search for the genetic material as a case study in scientific inquiry.

Evidence That DNA Can Transform Bacteria

In 1928, a British medical officer named Frederick Griffith was trying to develop a vaccine against pneumonia. He was studying *Streptococcus pneumoniae*, a bacterium that causes pneumonia in mammals. Griffith had two strains (varieties) of the bacterium, one pathogenic (disease-causing) and one nonpathogenic (harmless). He was surprised to find that when he killed the pathogenic bacteria with heat and then mixed the cell remains with living bacteria of the nonpathogenic strain, some of the living cells became pathogenic (Figure 16.2). Furthermore, this newly acquired trait of pathogenicity was inherited by all the descendants of the transformed bacteria. Apparently, some chemical component of the dead pathogenic cells caused this heritable change, although the identity of the substance was not known. Griffith called the phenomenon **transformation**, now defined as a change in genotype and phenotype due to the assimilation of external DNA by a cell.

Later work by Oswald Avery and his colleagues, American Maclyn McCarty, and Canadian Colin MacLeod, identified the transforming substance as DNA.

Scientists remained sceptical, however, since many still viewed proteins as better candidates for the genetic material. Also, many biologists were not convinced that bacterial genes would be similar in composition and function to those of more complex organisms. But the major reason for the continued doubt was that so little was known about DNA.

▼ Figure 16.2 | Inquiry

Can a genetic trait be transferred between different bacterial strains?

Experiment Frederick Griffith studied two strains of the bacterium *Streptococcus pneumoniae*. The S (smooth) strain can cause pneumonia in mice; it is pathogenic because the cells have an outer capsule that protects them from an animal's immune system. Cells of the R (rough) strain lack a capsule and are nonpathogenic. To test for the trait of pathogenicity, Griffith injected mice with the two strains:

Living S cells (pathogenic control)   Living R cells (nonpathogenic control)   Heat-killed S cells (nonpathogenic control)   Mixture of heat-killed S cells and living R cells

Results

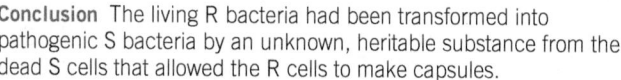

Mouse dies   **Mouse healthy**   **Mouse healthy**   **Mouse dies**

In blood sample, living S cells were found. They could reproduce, yielding more S cells.

Conclusion The living R bacteria had been transformed into pathogenic S bacteria by an unknown, heritable substance from the dead S cells that allowed the R cells to make capsules.

Source: Based on "The Significance of Pneumococcal Types" by Fred Griffith, from *Journal of Hygiene*, January 1928, Volume 27(2). © Jane B Reece.

WHAT IF? *How did this experiment rule out the possibility that the R cells simply used the dead S cells' capsules to become pathogenic?*

Evidence That Viral DNA Can Program Cells

Additional evidence that DNA was the genetic material came from studies of viruses that infect bacteria (Figure 16.3).

▲ Figure 16.3 **Viruses infecting a bacterial cell.** Phages called T2 attach to the host cell and inject their genetic material through the plasma membrane while the head and tail parts remain on the outer bacterial surface (colourized TEM).

Phage head
Tail sheath
Tail fibre
DNA
Bacterial cell
100 nm
88 Meckes/Science Source

These viruses are called **bacteriophages** (meaning "bacteria-eaters"), or **phages** for short. Viruses are much simpler than cells. A **virus** is little more than DNA (or sometimes RNA) enclosed by a protective coat, which is often simply protein. To produce more viruses, a virus must infect a cell and take over the cell's metabolic machinery.

Phages have been widely used as tools by researchers in molecular genetics. In 1952, Alfred Hershey and Martha Chase performed experiments showing that DNA is the genetic material of a phage known as T2. This is one of many phages that infect *Escherichia coli* (*E. coli*), a bacterium that normally lives in the intestines of mammals and is a model organism for molecular biologists. At that time, biologists already knew that T2, like many other phages, was composed almost entirely of DNA and protein. They also knew that the T2 phage could quickly turn an *E. coli* cell into a T2-producing factory that released many copies of new phages when the cell ruptured. Somehow, T2 could reprogram its host cell to produce viruses. But which viral component—protein or DNA—was responsible?

Hershey and Chase answered this question by devising an experiment showing that only one of the two components of T2 actually enters the *E. coli* cell during infection (Figure 16.4). In their experiment, they used a radioactive

▼ **Figure 16.4** | **Inquiry**

Is protein or DNA the genetic material of phage T2?

Experiment Alfred Hershey and Martha Chase used radioactive sulphur and phosphorus to trace the fates of protein and DNA, respectively, of T2 phages that infected bacterial cells. They wanted to see which of these molecules entered the cells and could reprogram them to make more phages.

Results When proteins were labelled (batch 1), radioactivity remained outside the cells; but when DNA was labelled (batch 2), radioactivity was found inside the cells. Bacterial cells with radioactive phage DNA released new phages with some radioactive phosphorus.

Conclusion Phage DNA entered bacterial cells, but phage proteins did not. Hershey and Chase concluded that DNA, not protein, functions as the genetic material of phage T2.

Source: Based on "Independent Functions of Viral Protein and Nucleic Acid in Growth of Bacteriophage" by Alfred D. Hershey and Martha Chase, from *Journal of General Physiology,* May 1952, Volume 36(1). © Jane B Reece.

WHAT IF? *How would the results have differed if proteins carried the genetic information?*

isotope of sulphur to tag protein in one batch of T2 and a radioactive isotope of phosphorus to tag DNA in a second batch. Because protein, but not DNA, contains sulphur, radioactive sulphur atoms were incorporated only into the protein of the phage. In a similar way, the atoms of radioactive phosphorus labelled only the DNA, not the protein, because nearly all the phage's phosphorus is in its DNA. In the experiment, separate samples of nonradioactive *E. coli* cells were infected with the protein-labelled and DNA-labelled batches of T2. The researchers then tested the two samples shortly after the onset of infection to see which type of molecule—protein or DNA—had entered the bacterial cells and would therefore be capable of reprogramming them.

Hershey and Chase found that the phage DNA entered the host cells but the phage protein did not. Moreover, when these bacteria were returned to a culture medium and the infection ran its course, the *E. coli* released phages that contained some radioactive phosphorus. This result further showed that the DNA inside the cell played an ongoing role during the infection process.

Hershey and Chase concluded that the DNA injected by the phage must be the molecule carrying the genetic information that makes the cells produce new viral DNA and proteins. The Hershey-Chase experiment was a landmark study because it provided powerful evidence that nucleic acids, rather than proteins, are the hereditary material, at least for certain viruses.

Additional Evidence That DNA Is the Genetic Material

Further evidence that DNA is the genetic material came from the laboratory of biochemist Erwin Chargaff. It was already known that DNA is a polymer of nucleotides, each consisting of three components: a nitrogenous (nitrogen-containing) base, a pentose sugar called deoxyribose, and a phosphate group (**Figure 16.5**). The base can be adenine (A), thymine (T), guanine (G), or cytosine (C). Chargaff analyzed the base composition of DNA from a number of different organisms. In 1950, he reported that the base composition of DNA varies from one species to another. For example, he found that 32.8% of sea urchin DNA nucleotides have the base A, whereas only 30.4% of human DNA nucleotides have the base A and only 24.7% of the DNA nucleotides from the bacterium *E. coli* have the base A. Chargaff's evidence of molecular diversity among species, which most scientists had presumed to be absent from DNA, made DNA a more credible candidate for the genetic material.

Chargaff also noticed a peculiar regularity in the ratios of nucleotide bases. In the DNA of each species he studied, the number of adenines approximately equalled the number of thymines, and the number of guanines

Sugar–phosphate backbone   **Nitrogenous bases**

5' end

Thymine (T)

Adenine (A)

Cytosine (C)

Guanine (G)

Phosphate

DNA nucleotide

Sugar (deoxyribose)

Nitrogenous base

3' end

▲ **Figure 16.5 The structure of a DNA strand.** Each DNA nucleotide monomer consists of a nitrogenous base (T, A, C, or G), the sugar deoxyribose (blue), and a phosphate group (yellow). The phosphate group of one nucleotide is attached to the sugar of the next, forming a "backbone" of alternating phosphates and sugars from which the bases project. The polynucleotide strand has directionality, from the 5' end (with the phosphate group) to the 3' end (with the —OH group of the sugar). 5' and 3' refer to the numbers assigned to the carbons in the sugar ring.

approximately equalled the number of cytosines. In sea urchin DNA, for example, Chargaff's analysis found the four bases in these percentages: A = 32.8% and T = 32.1%; G = 17.7% and C = 17.3%. (The percentages are not exactly the same because of limitations in Chargaff's techniques.)

These two findings became known as *Chargaff's rules*: (1) DNA base composition varies between species, and (2) for each species, the percentages of A and T bases are roughly equal, as are those of G and C bases. In the Scientific Skills Exercise, you can use Chargaff's rules to predict unknown percentages of nucleotide bases. The basis for these rules remained unexplained until the discovery of the double helix.

Working with Data in a Table

Given the Percentage Composition of One Nucleotide in a Genome, Can We Predict the Percentages of the Other Three Nucleotides? Even before the structure of DNA was elucidated, Erwin Chargaff and his coworkers noticed a pattern in the base composition of nucleotides from different organisms: The percentage of adenine (A) bases roughly equalled that of thymine (T) bases, and the percentage of cytosine (C) bases roughly equalled that of guanine (G) bases. Further, the percentage of each pair (A/T or C/G) varied from species to species. We now know that the 1:1 A/T and C/G ratios are due to complementary base pairing between A and T and between C and G in the DNA double helix, and interspecies differences are due to the unique sequences of bases along a DNA strand. In this exercise, you will apply Chargaff's rules to predict the composition of bases in a genome.

How the Experiments Were Done In Chargaff's experiments, DNA was extracted from the given organism, hydrolyzed to break apart the individual nucleotides, and then analyzed chemically. (These experiments provided approximate values for each type of nucleotide. Today, whole-genome sequencing allows base composition analysis to be done more precisely directly from the sequence data.)

Data from the Experiments Tables are useful for organizing sets of data representing a common set of values (here, percentages of A, G, C, and T) for a number of different samples (in this case, from different species). You can apply the patterns that you see in the known data to predict unknown values. In the table at the upper right, complete base distribution data are given for sea urchin DNA and salmon DNA; you will use Chargaff's rules to fill in the rest of the table with predicted values.

Source of DNA	Base Percentage			
	Adenine	Guanine	Cytosine	Thymine
Sea urchin	32.8	17.7	17.3	32.1
Salmon	29.7	20.8	20.4	29.1
Wheat	28.1	21.8	22.7	
E. coli	24.7	26.0		
Human	30.4			30.1
Ox	29.0			

Interpret the Data

1. Explain how the sea urchin and salmon data demonstrate both of Chargaff's rules.

2. Using Chargaff's rules, fill in the table with your predictions of the missing percentages of bases, starting with the wheat genome and proceeding through *E. coli*, human, and ox. Show how you arrived at your answers.

3. If Chargaff's rule—that the amount of A equals the amount of T and the amount of C equals the amount of G—is valid, then hypothetically we could extrapolate this to the combined DNA of all species on Earth (like one huge Earth genome). To see whether the data in the table support this hypothesis, calculate the average percentage for each base in your completed table by averaging the values in each column. Does Chargaff's equivalence rule still hold true?

Data from "Composition of the Desoxypentose Nucleic Acids of Four Genera of Sea-urchin" by Erwin Chargaff et al., *Biochemistry*, 1952, Volume 195. © Jane B Reece.

Building a Structural Model of DNA: *Scientific Inquiry*

Once most biologists were convinced that DNA was the genetic material, the challenge was to determine how the structure of DNA could account for its role in inheritance. By the early 1950s, the arrangement of covalent bonds in a nucleic acid polymer was well established (see Figure 16.5), and researchers focused on discovering the three-dimensional structure of DNA. Among the scientists working on the problem were American biochemist Linus Pauling, at the California Institute of Technology, and British physicist Maurice Wilkins and British biophysicist Rosalind Franklin, at King's College in London. First to come up with the complete answer, however, were two scientists who were relatively unknown at the time—the American James Watson and the Englishman Francis Crick.

The brief but celebrated partnership that solved the puzzle of DNA structure began soon after Watson journeyed to Cambridge University, where Crick was studying protein structure with a technique called X-ray crystallography (see Figure 5.22). While visiting the laboratory of Maurice Wilkins, Watson saw an X-ray diffraction image of DNA produced by Wilkins's accomplished colleague Rosalind Franklin (**Figure 16.6a**). Images produced by X-ray crystallography are not actually pictures of molecules. The spots and smudges in **Figure 16.6b** were produced by X-rays that were diffracted (deflected) as they passed through aligned fibres of purified DNA. Watson was familiar with the type of X-ray diffraction pattern that helical molecules produce, and an examination of the photo that Wilkins showed him confirmed that DNA was helical in shape. The

(a) Rosalind Franklin   **(b) Franklin's X-ray diffraction photograph of DNA**

▲ **Figure 16.6 Rosalind Franklin and her X-ray diffraction photo of DNA.** Franklin, a very accomplished X-ray crystallographer, conducted critical experiments resulting in the photograph that allowed Watson and Crick to deduce the double-helical structure of DNA.

photo also augmented earlier data obtained by Franklin and others suggesting the width of the helix and the spacing of the nitrogenous bases along it. The pattern in this photo implied that the helix was made up of two strands, contrary to a three-stranded model that Linus Pauling had proposed a short time earlier. The presence of two strands accounts for the now-familiar term **double helix** (Figure 16.7).

Watson and Crick began building models of a double helix that would conform to the X-ray measurements and what was then known about the chemistry of DNA, including Chargaff's rule of base equivalences. Having also read an unpublished annual report summarizing Franklin's work, they knew she had concluded that the sugar-phosphate backbones were on the outside of the DNA molecule, contrary to their working model. Franklin's arrangement was appealing because it put the negatively charged phosphate groups facing the aqueous surroundings, while the relatively hydrophobic nitrogenous bases were hidden in the interior. Watson constructed such a model, shown in the lower photo on the first page of this chapter. In this model, the two sugar-phosphate backbones are **antiparallel**—that is, their subunits run in opposite directions (see Figure 16.7). You can imagine the overall arrangement as a rope ladder with rigid rungs. The side ropes represent the sugar-phosphate backbones, and the rungs represent pairs of nitrogenous bases. Now imagine twisting the ladder to form a helix. Franklin's X-ray data indicated that the helix makes one full turn every 3.4 nm along its length. With the bases stacked just 0.34 nm apart, there are 10 layers of base pairs, or rungs of the ladder, in each full turn of the helix.

The nitrogenous bases of the double helix are paired in specific combinations: adenine (A) with thymine (T), and guanine (G) with cytosine (C). It was mainly by trial and error that Watson and Crick arrived at this key feature of DNA. At first, Watson imagined that the bases paired like with like—for example, A with A and C with C. But this model did not fit the X-ray data, which suggested that the double helix had a uniform diameter. Why is this requirement inconsistent with like-with-like pairing of bases? Adenine and guanine are purines, nitrogenous bases with two organic rings, while cytosine and thymine are nitrogenous bases called pyrimidines, which have a single ring. Thus, purines (A and G) are about twice as wide as pyrimidines (C and T). A purine-purine pair is too wide and a pyrimidine-pyrimidine pair too narrow to account for the 2-nm diameter of the double helix. Pairing a purine with

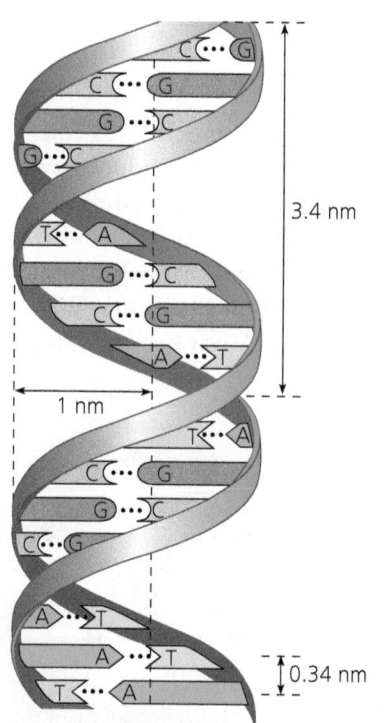

(a) Key features of DNA structure. The "ribbons" in this diagram represent the sugar-phosphate backbones of the two DNA strands. The helix is "right-handed," curving up to the right. The two strands are held together by hydrogen bonds (dotted lines) between the nitrogenous bases, which are paired in the interior of the double helix.

(b) Partial chemical structure. For clarity, the two DNA strands are shown untwisted in this partial chemical structure. Strong covalent bonds link the units of each strand, while weaker hydrogen bonds hold one strand to the other. Notice that the strands are antiparallel, meaning that they are oriented in opposite directions.

(c) Space-filling model. The tight stacking of the base pairs is clear in this computer model. Van der Waals interactions between the stacked pairs play a major role in holding the molecule together (see Chapter 2).

▲ Figure 16.7 **The double helix.**

a pyrimidine is the only combination that results in a uniform diameter for the double helix:

Purine + purine: too wide

Pyrimidine + pyrimidine: too narrow

Purine + pyrimidine: width consistent with X-ray data

Watson and Crick reasoned that there must be additional specificity of pairing dictated by the structure of the bases. Each base has chemical side groups that can form hydrogen bonds with its appropriate partner: Adenine can form two hydrogen bonds with thymine and only thymine; guanine forms three hydrogen bonds with cytosine and only cytosine. In shorthand, A pairs with T, and G pairs with C (Figure 16.8).

The Watson-Crick model took into account Chargaff's ratios and ultimately explained them. Wherever one strand of a DNA molecule has an A, the partner strand has a T. Similarly, a G in one strand is always paired with a C in the complementary strand. Therefore, in the DNA of any organism, the amount of adenine equals the amount of thymine, and the amount of guanine equals the amount of cytosine. (Modern DNA sequencing techniques have confirmed that the amounts are exactly equal.) Although the base-pairing rules dictate the combinations of nitrogenous bases that form the "rungs" of the double helix, they do not restrict the sequence of nucleotides *along* each DNA strand. The linear sequence of the four bases can be varied in countless ways, and each gene has a unique base sequence.

In April 1953, Watson and Crick surprised the scientific world with a succinct, one-page paper in the journal *Nature.*[*] The paper reported their molecular model for DNA: the double helix, which has since become the symbol of molecular biology. Watson and Crick, along with Maurice Wilkins, were awarded the Nobel Prize in 1962 for this work. (Sadly, Rosalind Franklin had died at the age of 37, in 1958, and was thus ineligible for the prize.) The beauty of the double helix model was that the structure of DNA suggested the basic mechanism of its replication.

CONCEPT CHECK 16.1

1. Given a polynucleotide sequence such as GAATTC, explain what further information you would need in order to identify which is the 5 end. (See Figure 16.5.)

2. **WHAT IF?** Griffith did not expect transformation to occur in his experiment. What results was he expecting? Explain.

For suggested answers, see Appendix A.

CONCEPT 16.2

Many proteins work together in DNA replication and repair

The relationship between structure and function is manifest in the double helix. The idea that there is specific pairing of nitrogenous bases in DNA was the flash of inspiration that led Watson and Crick to the double helix. At the same time, they saw the functional significance of the base-pairing rules. They ended their classic paper with this wry statement: "It has not escaped our notice that the specific pairing we have postulated immediately suggests a possible copying mechanism for the genetic material." In this section, you will learn about the basic principle of DNA replication, as well as some important details of the process.

The Basic Principle: Base Pairing to a Template Strand

In a second paper, Watson and Crick stated their hypothesis for how DNA replicates:

> Now our model for deoxyribonucleic acid is, in effect, a pair of templates, each of which is complementary to the other. We imagine that prior to duplication the hydrogen bonds are broken, and the two chains unwind and separate. Each chain then acts as a template for the formation on to itself of a new companion chain, so that eventually we shall have two pairs of chains, where we only had one before. Moreover, the sequence of the pairs of bases will have been duplicated exactly.[†]

Adenine (A)   Thymine (T)

Guanine (G)   Cytosine (C)

▲ **Figure 16.8 Base pairing in DNA.** The pairs of nitrogenous bases in a DNA double helix are held together by hydrogen bonds, shown here as black dotted lines.

---

[*] J. D. Watson and F. H. C. Crick, Molecular structure of nucleic acids: A structure for deoxyribose nucleic acids, *Nature* 171:737–738 (1953).

[†] J. D. Watson and F. H. C. Crick, Genetical implications of the structure of deoxyribonucleic acid, *Nature* 171:964–967 (1953).

(a) The parental molecule has two complementary strands of DNA. Each base is paired by hydrogen bonding with its specific partner, A with T and G with C.

(b) First, the two DNA strands are separated. Each parental strand can now serve as a template for a new, complementary strand.

(c) Nucleotides complementary to the parental (dark blue) strand are connected to form the sugar-phosphate backbones of the new "daughter" (light blue) strands.

▲ Figure 16.9 **A model for DNA replication: the basic concept.** In this simplified illustration, a short segment of DNA has been untwisted into a structure that resembles a ladder. The side rails of the ladder are the sugar-phosphate backbones of the two DNA strands; the rungs are the pairs of nitrogenous bases. Simple shapes symbolize the four kinds of bases. Dark blue represents DNA strands present in the parental molecule; light blue represents newly synthesized DNA.

Figure 16.9 illustrates Watson and Crick's basic idea. To make it easier to follow, we show only a short section of double helix in untwisted form. Notice that if you cover one of the two DNA strands of Figure 16.9a, you can still determine its linear sequence of nucleotides by referring to the uncovered strand and applying the base-pairing rules. The two strands are complementary; each stores the information necessary to reconstruct the other. When a cell copies a DNA molecule, each strand serves as a template for ordering nucleotides into a new, complementary strand. Nucleotides line up along the template strand according to the base-pairing rules and are linked to form the new strands. Where there was one double-stranded DNA molecule at the beginning of the process, there are soon two, each an exact replica of the "parental" molecule. The copying mechanism is analogous to using a photographic negative to make a positive image, which can in turn be used to make another negative, and so on.

This model of DNA replication remained untested for several years following publication of the DNA structure. The requisite experiments were simple in concept but difficult to perform. Watson and Crick's model predicts that when a double helix replicates, each of the two daughter molecules will have one old strand, from the parental molecule, and one newly made strand. This **semiconservative model** can be distinguished from a conservative model of replication, in which the two parental strands somehow come back together after the process (that is, the parental molecule is conserved). In yet a third model, called the dispersive model, all four strands of DNA following replication have a mixture of old and new DNA. These three models are shown in Figure 16.10. Although mechanisms for conservative or dispersive DNA replication are not easy to devise, these models remained possibilities until they could be ruled out. After two years of preliminary work at the California Institute

Parent cell	First replication	Second replication

(a) Conservative model. The two parental strands reassociate after acting as templates for new strands, thus restoring the parental double helix.

(b) Semiconservative model. The two strands of the parental molecule separate, and each functions as a template for synthesis of a new, complementary strand.

(c) Dispersive model. Each strand of *both* daughter molecules contains a mixture of old and newly synthesized DNA.

▲ Figure 16.10 **Three alternative models of DNA replication.** Each short segment of double helix symbolizes the DNA within a cell. Beginning with a parent cell, we follow the DNA for two more generations of cells—two rounds of DNA replication. Newly made DNA is light blue.

Does DNA replication follow the conservative, semiconservative, or dispersive model?

Experiment Matthew Meselson and Franklin Stahl cultured *E. coli* for several generations in a medium containing nucleotide precursors labelled with a heavy isotope of nitrogen, ^{15}N. They then transferred the bacteria to a medium with only ^{14}N, a lighter isotope. A sample was taken after the first DNA replication; another sample was taken after the second replication. They extracted DNA from the bacteria in the samples and then centrifuged each DNA sample to separate DNA of different densities.

❶ Bacteria cultured in medium with ^{15}N (heavy isotope)

❷ Bacteria transferred to medium with ^{14}N (lighter isotope)

Results

❸ DNA sample centrifuged after first replication

❹ DNA sample centrifuged after second replication

Less dense

More dense

Conclusion Meselson and Stahl compared their results to those predicted by each of the three models in Figure 16.10, as shown below. The first replication in the ^{14}N medium produced a band of hybrid (^{15}N-^{14}N) DNA. This result eliminated the conservative model. The second replication produced both light and hybrid DNA, a result that refuted the dispersive model and supported the semiconservative model. They therefore concluded that DNA replication is semiconservative.

Predictions:	First replication	Second replication
Conservative model		
Semiconservative model		
Dispersive model		

Source: Based on "The Replication of DNA in Escherichia coli" by Matthew Meselson and Franklin W. Stahl, from *PNAS*, July 1958, Volume 44(7). © Jane B Reece.

Inquiry in Action Read and analyze the original paper in *Inquiry in Action: Interpreting Scientific Papers.*

(MB) See the related Experimental Inquiry Tutorial in MasteringBiology.

WHAT IF? *If Meselson and Stahl had first grown the cells in ^{14}N-containing medium and then moved them into ^{15}N-containing medium before taking samples, what would have been the result?*

of Technology in the late 1950s, Matthew Meselson and Franklin Stahl devised a clever experiment that distinguished between the three models, described in detail in **Figure 16.11**. Their results supported the semiconservative model of DNA replication, as predicted by Watson and Crick, and their experiment is widely recognized among biologists as a classic example of elegant experimental design.

The basic principle of DNA replication is conceptually simple. However, the actual process involves some complicated biochemical gymnastics, as we will now see.

DNA Replication: *A Closer Look*

The bacterium *E. coli* has a single chromosome of about 4.6 million nucleotide pairs. In a favourable environment, an *E. coli* cell can copy all of this DNA and divide to form two genetically identical daughter cells in considerably less than an hour. Each of your somatic cells has 46 DNA molecules in its nucleus, one long double-helical molecule per chromosome. In all, that represents about 6 billion nucleotide pairs, or over a thousand times more DNA than is found in most bacterial cells. If we were to print the one-letter symbols for these bases (A, G, C, and T) the size of the type you are now reading, the 6 billion nucleotide pairs of information in a diploid human cell would fill about 1400 biology textbooks. Yet it takes one of your cells just a few hours to copy all of this DNA during S phase of interphase. This replication of an enormous amount of genetic information is achieved with very few errors—only about one per 10 billion nucleotides. The copying of DNA is remarkable in its speed and accuracy.

More than a dozen enzymes and other proteins participate in DNA replication. Much more is known about how this "replication machine" works in bacteria (such as *E. coli*) than in eukaryotes, and we will describe the basic steps of the process for *E. coli*, except where otherwise noted. What scientists have learned about eukaryotic DNA replication suggests, however, that most of the process is fundamentally similar for prokaryotes and eukaryotes.

Getting Started

The replication of chromosomal DNA begins at particular sites called **origins of replication**, short stretches of DNA that have a specific sequence of nucleotides. The *E. coli* chromosome, like many other bacterial chromosomes, is circular and has a single origin. Proteins that initiate DNA replication recognize this sequence and attach to the DNA, separating the two strands and opening up a replication "bubble" (**Figure 16.12a**). Replication of DNA then proceeds in both directions until the entire molecule is copied. In contrast to a bacterial chromosome, a eukaryotic chromosome may have hundreds or even a few thousand replication origins. Multiple replication bubbles form and eventually fuse, thus speeding up the copying of the very long DNA

(a) Origin of replication in an *E. coli* cell

(a) Origin of replication in an *E. coli* cell. In the circular chromosome of *E. coli* and many other bacteria, only one origin of replication is present. The parental strands separate at the origin, forming a replication bubble with two forks (red arrows). Replication proceeds in both directions until the forks meet on the other side, resulting in two daughter DNA molecules. The TEM shows a bacterial chromosome with a large replication bubble. New and old strands cannot be seen individually in the TEM.

(b) Origins of replication in a eukaryotic cell

(b) Origins of replication in a eukaryotic cell. In each linear chromosome of a eukaryote, DNA replication begins when replication bubbles form at many sites along the giant DNA molecule. The bubbles expand as replication proceeds in both directions (red arrows). Eventually, the bubbles fuse and synthesis of the daughter strands is complete. The TEM shows three replication bubbles along the DNA of a cultured Chinese hamster cell.

DRAW IT *In the TEM above, add arrows for the third bubble.*

molecules (**Figure 16.12b**). As in bacteria, eukaryotic DNA replication proceeds in both directions from each origin.

At each end of a replication bubble is a **replication fork**, a Y-shaped region where the parental strands of DNA are being unwound. Several kinds of proteins participate in the unwinding (**Figure 16.13**). **Helicases** are enzymes that untwist the double helix at the replication forks, separating the two parental strands and making them available as template strands. After the parental strands separate, **single-strand binding proteins** bind to the unpaired DNA strands, keeping them from re-pairing. The untwisting of the double helix causes tighter twisting and strain ahead of the replication fork. **Topoisomerase** is an enzyme that helps relieve this strain by breaking, swivelling, and rejoining DNA strands.

Synthesizing a New DNA Strand

The unwound sections of parental DNA strands are now available to serve as templates for the synthesis of new complementary DNA strands. However, the enzymes that synthesize DNA cannot *initiate* the synthesis of a polynucleotide; they can only add DNA nucleotides to the end of an already existing chain that is base-paired with the template strand. The initial nucleotide chain that is produced during DNA synthesis is actually a short stretch of RNA, not DNA. This RNA chain is called a **primer** and is synthesized by the enzyme **primase** (see Figure 16.13). Primase starts a complementary RNA chain with a single RNA nucleotide, and adds RNA nucleotides one at a time, using the parental DNA strand as a template. The completed primer, generally 5–10 nucleotides long,

Topoisomerase breaks, swivels, and rejoins the parental DNA ahead of the replication fork, relieving the strain caused by unwinding.

Primase synthesizes RNA primers, using the parental DNA as a template.

RNA primer

Helicase unwinds and separates the parental DNA strands.

Single-strand binding proteins stabilize the unwound parental strands.

▲ Figure 16.13 **Some of the proteins involved in the initiation of DNA replication.** The same proteins function at both replication forks in a replication bubble. For simplicity, only the left-hand fork is shown, and the DNA bases are drawn much larger in relation to the proteins than they are in reality.

is thus base-paired to the template strand. The new DNA strand will start from the 3′ end of the RNA primer.

Synthesizing a New DNA Strand

Enzymes called **DNA polymerases** catalyze the synthesis of new DNA by adding nucleotides to the 3′ end of a preexisting chain. In *E. coli*, there are several DNA polymerases, but two appear to play the major roles in DNA replication: DNA polymerase III and DNA polymerase I. The situation in eukaryotes is more complicated, with at least 11 different DNA polymerases discovered so far, although the general principles are the same.

Most DNA polymerases require a primer and a DNA template strand, along which complementary DNA nucleotides are lined up. In *E. coli*, DNA polymerase III (abbreviated DNA pol III) adds a DNA nucleotide to the RNA primer and then continues adding DNA nucleotides, complementary to the parental DNA template strand, to the growing end of the new DNA strand. The rate of elongation is about 500 nucleotides per second in bacteria and 50 per second in human cells.

Each nucleotide to be added to a growing DNA strand consists of a sugar attached to a base and to three phosphate groups. You have already encountered such a molecule—ATP (adenosine triphosphate; see Figure 8.9). The only difference between the ATP of energy metabolism and dATP, the adenine nucleotide used to make DNA, is the sugar component, which is deoxyribose in the building block of DNA but ribose in ATP. Like ATP, the nucleotides used for DNA synthesis are chemically reactive, partly because their triphosphate tails have an unstable cluster of negative charge. As DNA polymerase

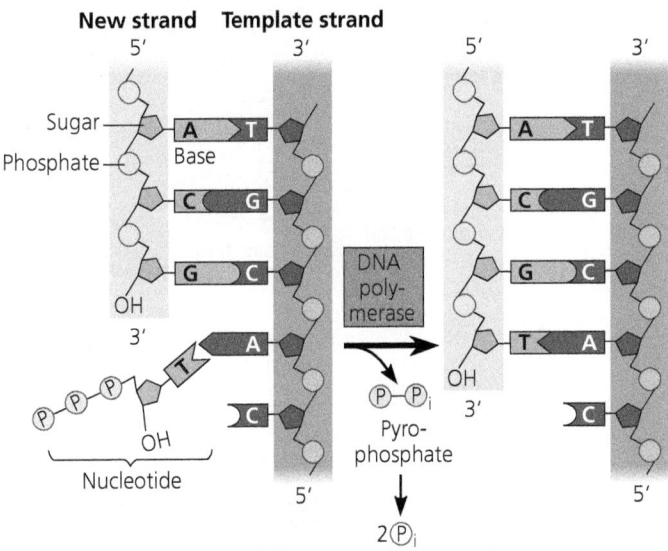

▲ Figure 16.14 **Incorporation of a nucleotide into a DNA strand.** DNA polymerase catalyzes the addition of a nucleoside triphosphate to the 3′ end of a growing DNA strand, with the release of two phosphates.

? *Use this diagram to explain what we mean when we say that each DNA strand has directionality.*

catalyzes each dehydration reaction (see Figure 5.2a) that joins a monomer to the growing end of a DNA strand, two phosphate groups are lost as a molecule of pyrophosphate (P—P_i). Subsequent hydrolysis of the pyrophosphate to two molecules of inorganic phosphate (P_i) is a coupled exergonic reaction that helps drive the polymerization reaction (**Figure 16.14**).

Antiparallel Elongation

As we have noted previously, the two ends of a DNA strand are different, giving each strand directionality, like a one-way street (see Figure 16.5). In addition, the two strands of DNA in a double helix are antiparallel, meaning that they are oriented in opposite directions to each other, like the two sides of a divided street (see Figure 16.7). Therefore, the two new strands formed during DNA replication must also be antiparallel to their template strands.

The antiparallel arrangement of the double helix, together with a key property of DNA polymerases, have an important effect on how replication occurs. Because of their structure, DNA polymerases can add nucleotides only to the free 3′ end of a primer or growing DNA strand, never to the 5′ end (see Figure 16.14). Thus, a new DNA strand can elongate only in the 5′ → 3′ direction. With this in mind, let's examine one of the two replication forks in a bubble (**Figure 16.15**). Along one template strand, DNA polymerase III can synthesize a complementary strand continuously by elongating the new DNA in the mandatory 5′ → 3′ direction. DNA pol III remains in the replication fork on that template strand and continuously adds nucleotides to the new complementary strand as the fork progresses. The DNA strand made by this mechanism is called the

Origin of replication
Leading strand
Lagging strand
Primer
Lagging strand
Leading strand
Overall directions of replication

1 After RNA primer is made, DNA pol III starts to synthesize the leading strand.

Origin of replication

3′
5′

RNA primer
Sliding clamp
DNA pol III

5′
3′
3′

Parental DNA
5′

3′
5′

5′
3′
3′

2 The leading strand is elongated continuously in the 5′ → 3′ direction as the fork progresses.

5′

▲ **Figure 16.15 Synthesis of the leading strand during DNA replication.** This diagram focuses on the left replication fork shown in the overview box. DNA polymerase III (DNA pol III), shaped like a cupped hand, is shown closely associated with a protein called the "sliding clamp" that encircles the newly synthesized double helix like a doughnut. The sliding clamp moves DNA pol III along the DNA template strand.

leading strand. Only one primer is required for DNA pol III to synthesize the entire leading strand (see Figure 16.15).

To elongate the other new strand of DNA in the mandatory 5′ → 3′ direction, DNA pol III must work along the other template strand in the direction *away from* the replication fork. The DNA strand elongating in this direction is called the **lagging strand**.[*] In contrast to the leading strand, which elongates continuously, the lagging strand is synthesized discontinuously, as a series of segments. These segments of the lagging strand are called **Okazaki fragments**, after Reiji Okazaki, the Japanese scientist who discovered them. The fragments are about 1000–2000 nucleotides long in *E. coli* and 100–200 nucleotides long in eukaryotes.

Figure 16.16 illustrates the steps in the synthesis of the lagging strand at one fork. Whereas only one primer is

[*]Synthesis of the leading strand and synthesis of the lagging strand occur concurrently and at the same rate. The lagging strand is so named because its synthesis is delayed slightly relative to synthesis of the leading strand; each new fragment of the lagging strand cannot be started until enough template has been exposed at the replication fork.

Origin of replication
Leading strand
Lagging strand
Lagging strand
Leading strand
Overall directions of replication

3′

1 Primase joins RNA nucleotides into a primer.

Origin of replication

Template strand
5′
3′
5′
3′
5′

2 DNA pol III adds DNA nucleotides to the primer, forming Okazaki fragment 1.

3′
RNA primer for fragment 1
5′
1
3′
5′
3′
5′

3 After reaching the next RNA primer to the right, DNA pol III detaches.

3′
Okazaki fragment 1
5′
1
3′
5′

RNA primer for fragment 2

4 Fragment 2 is primed. Then DNA pol III adds DNA nucleotides, detaching when it reaches the fragment 1 primer.

5′
3′
Okazaki fragment 2
2
1
3′
5′

5′
3′

5 DNA pol I replaces the RNA with DNA, adding nucleotides to the 3′ end of fragment 2 (and, earlier, of fragment 1).

2
1
3′
5′

6 DNA ligase forms a bond between the newest DNA and the DNA of fragment 1.

5′
3′

7 The lagging strand in this region is now complete.

2
1
3′
5′

← Overall direction of replication

▲ **Figure 16.16 Synthesis of the lagging strand.**

required on the leading strand, each Okazaki fragment on the lagging strand must be primed separately (steps ❶ and ❹). After DNA pol III forms an Okazaki fragment (steps ❷–❹), another DNA polymerase, DNA polymerase I (DNA pol I), replaces the RNA nucleotides of the adjacent primer with DNA nucleotides (step ❺). But DNA pol I cannot join the final nucleotide of this replacement DNA segment to the first DNA nucleotide of the adjacent Okazaki fragment. Another enzyme, **DNA ligase**, accomplishes this task, joining the sugar-phosphate backbones of all the Okazaki fragments into a continuous DNA strand (step ❻).

Figure 16.17 and Table 16.1 summarize DNA replication. Please study them carefully before proceeding.

The DNA Replication Complex

It is traditional—and convenient—to represent DNA polymerase molecules as locomotives moving along a DNA railroad track, but such a model is inaccurate in two important ways. First, the various proteins that participate in DNA replication actually form a single large complex, a "DNA replication machine." Many protein-protein interactions facilitate the efficiency of this complex. For example, by interacting with other proteins at the fork, primase

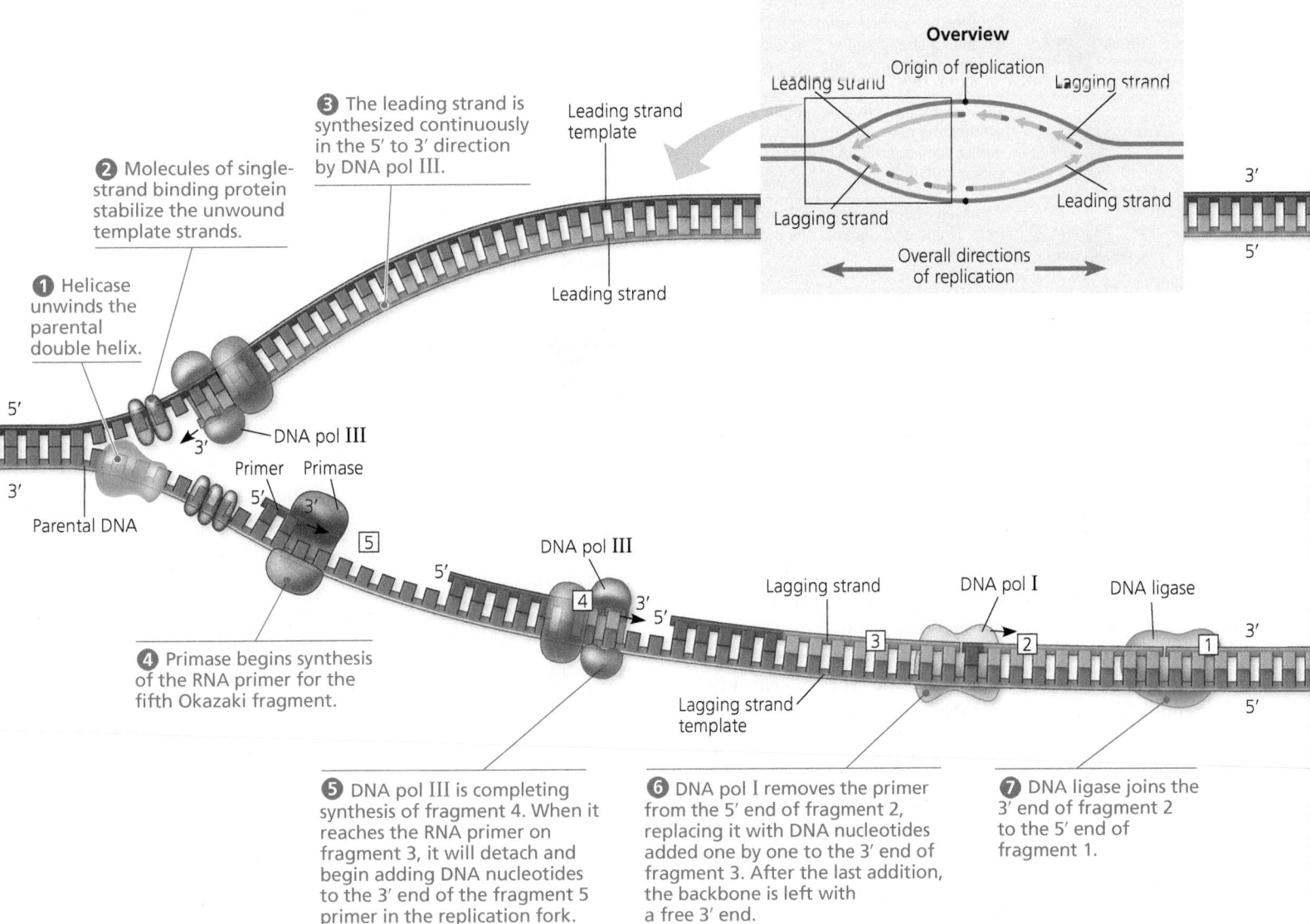

❶ Helicase unwinds the parental double helix.

❷ Molecules of single-strand binding protein stabilize the unwound template strands.

❸ The leading strand is synthesized continuously in the 5′ to 3′ direction by DNA pol III.

❹ Primase begins synthesis of the RNA primer for the fifth Okazaki fragment.

❺ DNA pol III is completing synthesis of fragment 4. When it reaches the RNA primer on fragment 3, it will detach and begin adding DNA nucleotides to the 3′ end of the fragment 5 primer in the replication fork.

❻ DNA pol I removes the primer from the 5′ end of fragment 2, replacing it with DNA nucleotides added one by one to the 3′ end of fragment 3. After the last addition, the backbone is left with a free 3′ end.

❼ DNA ligase joins the 3′ end of fragment 2 to the 5′ end of fragment 1.

▲ **Figure 16.17 A summary of bacterial DNA replication.** The detailed diagram shows the left-hand replication fork of the replication bubble in the overview (upper right). Viewing each daughter strand in its entirety in the overview, you can see that half of it is made continuously as the leading strand, while the other half (on the other side of the origin) is synthesized in fragments as the lagging strand.

DRAW IT *Draw a similar diagram showing the right-hand fork of this bubble, numbering the Okazaki fragments appropriately. Label all 5′ and 3′ ends.*

Table 16.1 Bacterial DNA Replication Proteins and Their Functions

Protein	Function
Helicase	Unwinds parental double helix at replication forks
Single-strand binding protein	Binds to and stabilizes single-stranded DNA until it is used as a template
Topoisomerase	Relieves overwinding strain ahead of replication forks by breaking, swivelling, and rejoining DNA strands
Primase	Synthesizes an RNA primer at 5′ end of leading strand and at 5′ end of each Okazaki fragment of lagging strand
DNA pol III	Using parental DNA as a template, synthesizes new DNA strand by adding nucleotides to an RNA primer or a pre-existing DNA strand
DNA pol I	Removes RNA nucleotides of primer from 5′ end and replaces them with DNA nucleotides
DNA ligase	Joins Okazaki fragments of lagging strand; on leading strand, joins 3′ end of DNA that replaces primer to rest of leading strand DNA

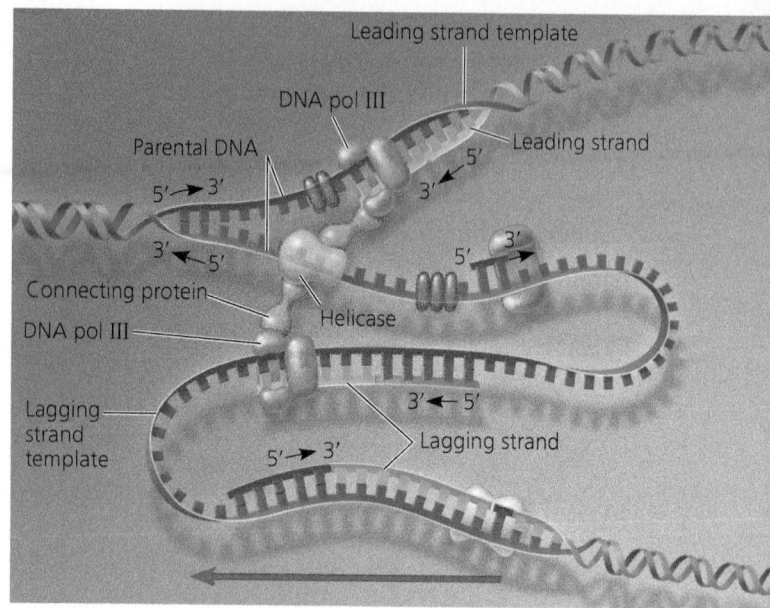

▲ Figure 16.18 A current model of the DNA replication complex. Two DNA polymerase III molecules work together in a complex, one on each template strand. The lagging strand template DNA loops through the complex, resembling the slide of a trombone. (This is often called the trombone model.)

DRAW IT Draw a line tracing the lagging strand template along the entire stretch of DNA shown here.

ANIMATION *BioFlix* Visit the Study Area in **MasteringBiology** for the BioFlix® 3-D Animation on DNA Replication.

apparently acts as a molecular brake, slowing progress of the replication fork and coordinating the placement of primers and the rates of replication on the leading and lagging strands. Second, the DNA replication complex may not move along the DNA; rather, the DNA may move through the complex during the replication process. In eukaryotic cells, multiple copies of the complex, perhaps grouped into "factories," may be anchored to the nuclear matrix, a framework of fibres extending through the interior of the nucleus. Experimental evidence in some types of cells supports a model in which two DNA polymerase molecules, one on each template strand, "reel in" the parental DNA and extrude newly made daughter DNA molecules. In this so-called trombone model, the lagging strand is looped back through the complex (Figure 16.18). Whether the complex moves along the DNA or whether the DNA moves through the complex, either anchored or not, are still open, unresolved questions that are under active investigation. It is also possible that the process varies among species.

Proofreading and Repairing DNA

We cannot attribute the accuracy of DNA replication solely to the specificity of base pairing. Initial pairing errors between incoming nucleotides and those in the template strand occur at a rate of one in 10^5 nucleotides. However, errors in the completed DNA molecule amount to only one in 10^{10} (10 billion) nucleotides, an error rate that is 100 000 times lower. This is because during DNA replication, many DNA polymerases proofread each nucleotide against its template as soon as it is covalently bonded to the growing strand. Upon finding an incorrectly paired nucleotide, the polymerase removes the nucleotide and then resumes synthesis. (This action is similar to fixing a texting error by deleting the wrong letter and then entering the correct one.)

Mismatched nucleotides sometimes evade proofreading by a DNA polymerase. In **mismatch repair**, other enzymes remove and replace incorrectly paired nucleotides that have resulted from replication errors. Researchers highlighted the importance of such repair enzymes when they found that a hereditary defect in one of them is associated with a form of colon cancer. Apparently, this defect allows cancer-causing errors to accumulate in the DNA faster than normal.

Incorrectly paired or altered nucleotides can also arise after replication. In fact, maintenance of the genetic information encoded in DNA requires frequent repair of various kinds of damage to existing DNA. DNA molecules are constantly subjected to potentially harmful chemical and physical agents, such as cigarette smoke and X-rays, as we'll discuss in Concept 17.5. In addition, DNA bases may undergo spontaneous chemical changes under normal cellular conditions. However, these changes in DNA are usually corrected before they become permanent changes—*mutations*—perpetuated through successive replications. Each cell continuously monitors and repairs its genetic material. Because repair of damaged DNA is so important to the survival of an organism, it is no surprise that many different DNA repair enzymes have evolved. Almost 100 are known in *E. coli*, and about 130 have been identified so far in humans.

Most cellular systems for repairing incorrectly paired nucleotides, whether they are due to DNA damage or to replication errors, use a mechanism that takes advantage of the base-paired structure of DNA. In many cases, a segment of the strand containing the damage is cut out (excised) by a DNA-cutting enzyme—a **nuclease**—and the resulting gap is then filled in with nucleotides, using the undamaged strand as a template. The enzymes involved in filling the gap are a DNA polymerase and DNA ligase. One such DNA repair system is called **nucleotide excision repair** (Figure 16.19).

An important function of the DNA repair enzymes in our skin cells is to repair genetic damage caused by the ultraviolet rays of sunlight. One type of damage, shown in Figure 16.19, is the covalent linking of thymine bases that are adjacent on a DNA strand. Such *thymine dimers* cause the DNA to buckle and interfere with DNA replication. The importance of repairing this kind of damage is underscored by a disorder called xeroderma pigmentosum (XP), which in most cases is caused by an inherited defect in a nucleotide excision repair enzyme. Individuals with XP are hypersensitive to sunlight; mutations in their skin cells caused by ultraviolet light are left uncorrected, often resulting in skin cancer. The effects are extreme: Without sun protection, children who have XP can develop skin cancer by age 10.

Evolutionary Significance of Altered DNA Nucleotides

EVOLUTION Faithful replication of the genome and repair of DNA damage are important for the functioning of the organism and for passing on a complete, accurate genome to the next generation. The error rate after proofreading and repair is extremely low, but rare mistakes do slip

1 Teams of enzymes detect and repair damaged DNA, such as this thymine dimer (often caused by ultraviolet radiation), which distorts the DNA molecule.

2 A nuclease enzyme cuts the damaged DNA strand at two points, and the damaged section is removed.

3 Repair synthesis by a DNA polymerase fills in the missing nucleotides.

4 DNA ligase seals the free end of the new DNA to the old DNA, making the strand complete.

▲ Figure 16.19 **Nucleotide excision repair of DNA damage.**

through. Once a mismatched nucleotide pair is replicated, the sequence change is permanent in the daughter molecule that has the incorrect nucleotide as well as in any subsequent copies. As we mentioned earlier, a permanent change in the DNA sequence is called a mutation.

Mutations can change the phenotype of an organism (as you'll learn in Concept 17.5). And if they occur in germ cells, which give rise to gametes, mutations can be passed on from generation to generation. The vast majority of such changes either have no effect or are harmful, but a very small percentage can be beneficial. In either case, mutations are the original source of the variation on which natural selection operates during evolution and are ultimately responsible for the appearance of new species. (You'll learn more about this process in Unit Four.) The balance between complete fidelity of DNA replication or repair and a low mutation rate has resulted in new proteins that contribute to different phenotypes. Ultimately, over long periods of time, this process leads to new species and thus to the rich diversity of life we see on Earth today.

Replicating the Ends of DNA Molecules

For linear DNA, such as the DNA of eukaryotic chromosomes, the usual replication machinery cannot complete the

5′ ends of daughter DNA strands. (This is another consequence of the fact that a DNA polymerase can add nucleotides only to the 3′ end of a preexisting polynucleotide.) Even if an Okazaki fragment can be started with an RNA primer hydrogen-bonded to the very end of the template strand, once that primer is removed, it cannot be replaced with DNA because there is no 3′ end available for nucleotide addition (Figure 16.20). As a result, repeated rounds of replication produce shorter and shorter DNA molecules with uneven ("staggered") ends.

Most prokaryotes have a circular chromosome, with no ends, so the shortening of DNA does not occur. But what protects the genes of linear eukaryotic chromosomes from being eroded away during successive rounds of DNA

Peter Lansdorp

⊢ 1 μm ⊣

▲ **Figure 16.21 Telomeres.** Eukaryotes have repetitive, noncoding sequences called telomeres at the ends of their DNA. Telomeres are stained orange in these mouse chromosomes (LM).

▲ **Figure 16.20 Shortening of the ends of linear DNA molecules.** Here we follow the end of one strand of a DNA molecule through two rounds of replication. After the first round, the new lagging strand is shorter than its template. After a second round, both the leading and lagging strands have become shorter than the original parental DNA. Although not shown here, the other ends of these DNA molecules also become shorter.

replication? It turns out that eukaryotic chromosomal DNA molecules have special nucleotide sequences called **telomeres** at their ends (Figure 16.21). Telomeres do not contain genes; instead, the DNA typically consists of multiple repetitions of one short nucleotide sequence. In each human telomere, for example, the six-nucleotide sequence TTAGGG is repeated between 100 and 1000 times.

Telomeres have two protective functions. First, specific proteins associated with telomeric DNA prevent the staggered ends of the daughter molecule from activating the cell's systems for monitoring DNA damage. (Staggered ends of a DNA molecule, which often result from double-strand breaks, can trigger signal transduction pathways leading to cell cycle arrest or cell death.) Second, telomeric DNA acts as a kind of buffer zone that provides some protection against the organism's genes shortening, somewhat like how the plastic-wrapped ends of a shoelace slow down its unravelling. Telomeres do not prevent the erosion of genes near the ends of chromosomes; they merely postpone it.

As shown in Figure 16.20, telomeres become shorter during every round of replication. Thus, as expected, telomeric DNA tends to be shorter in dividing somatic cells of older individuals and in cultured cells that have divided many times. It has been proposed that shortening of telomeres is somehow connected to the aging process of certain tissues and even to aging of the organism as a whole. The idea of a "telomere clock" acting as a cellular timekeeper of aging was first proposed by Canadian researcher Calvin Harley in 1990 (Figure 16.22).

But what about cells whose genome must persist virtually unchanged from an organism to its offspring over many generations? If the chromosomes of germ cells became shorter in every cell cycle, essential genes would eventually be missing from the gametes they produce. However, this does not occur: An enzyme called **telomerase** catalyzes the lengthening of telomeres in eukaryotic germ cells, thus restoring their original length and

▼ Figure 16.22 **Impact**

The Ticking Telomere Clock

As cells divide, telomeres get shorter and shorter. In 1990 Dr. Calvin Harley, then at McMaster University, proposed that this progressive telomere shortening acts as a biological "telomere clock" that directs the aging process.

Telomere length and aging

Telomere length (y-axis) vs Age (x-axis)

Health

Disease

——— Germ line cells
——— Somatic cells
——— Premature aging syndromes

Why It Matters Dr. Harley and colleagues showed that telomere function is closely linked with aging. As cells divide and telomeres get shorter, this can result in a loss of cell viability, which in turn can lead to the development of age-related diseases. Also, some premature aging syndromes are associated with decreased telomere length. Dr. Harley's hypothesis and subsequent studies on telomeres have inspired potential therapeutic strategies to treat age-associated human disease, such as heart failure, infertility, and decreased immune response to infection.

Further Reading M. A. Blasco, Telomeres and human disease: Ageing, cancer and beyond, *Nature Reviews Genetics* 6:611–622 (2005); C. B. Harley, A. B. Futcher, and C. W. Greider, Telomeres shorten during ageing of human fibroblasts, *Nature* 345:458–469 (1990).

MAKE CONNECTIONS *What cells would you expect to express high levels of telomerase?*

WHAT IF? *The absence of telomerase and the presence of excess telomerase can both impact the growth of tumours. Describe how both the absence or presence of this enzyme could contribute to tumour growth.*

compensating for the shortening that occurs during DNA replication. This enzyme contains its own RNA molecule that it uses as a template to artificially "extend" the leading strand, allowing the lagging strand to maintain a given length. Telomerase is not active in most human somatic cells, but its activity varies from tissue to tissue. The activity of telomerase in germ cells results in telomeres of maximum length in the zygote.

Normal shortening of telomeres may protect organisms from cancer by limiting the number of divisions that

somatic cells can undergo. Cells from large tumours often have unusually short telomeres, as we would expect for cells that have undergone many cell divisions. Further shortening would presumably lead to self-destruction of the tumour cells. Telomerase activity is abnormally high in cancerous somatic cells, suggesting that its ability to stabilize telomere length may allow these cancer cells to persist. Many cancer cells do seem capable of unlimited cell division, as do immortal strains of cultured cells (see Concept 12.3).

For several years, researchers have studied inhibition of telomerase as a possible cancer therapy. To date, while studies that inhibited telomerase in mice with tumours have led to the death of cancer cells, eventually the cells have restored the length of their telomeres by an alternative pathway. This is an area of ongoing research that may eventually yield useful cancer treatments.

Thus far in this chapter, you have learned about the structure and replication of a DNA molecule. In the next section, we'll take a step back and examine how DNA is packaged into chromosomes, the structures that carry the genetic information.

CONCEPT CHECK 16.2

1. What role does complementary base pairing play in the replication of DNA?

2. Make a table listing the functions of seven proteins involved in DNA replication in *E. coli*.

3. **MAKE CONNECTIONS** What is the relationship between DNA replication and the S phase of the cell cycle? See Figure 12.6.

4. **WHAT IF?** If the DNA pol I in a given cell were nonfunctional, how would that affect the synthesis of a *leading* strand? In the overview box in Figure 16.17, point out where DNA pol I would normally function on the top leading strand.

For suggested answers, see Appendix A.

CONCEPT 16.3

A chromosome consists of a DNA molecule packed together with proteins

Now that you have learned about the structure and replication of DNA, let's take a step back and examine how DNA is packaged into chromosomes, the structures that carry genetic information. The main component of the genome in most bacteria is one double-stranded, circular DNA molecule that is associated with a small amount of protein. Although we refer to this structure as the *bacterial chromosome*, it is very different from a eukaryotic chromosome, which consists of one linear DNA molecule associated with a large amount of protein. In *E. coli*, the chromosomal DNA consists of about 4.6 million nucleotide pairs, representing about 4400 genes. This is 100 times more DNA than is found in a typical virus, but only about one-thousandth as much DNA as in a human somatic cell. Still, that is a tremendous amount of DNA to be packaged in such a small container.

Stretched out, the DNA of an *E. coli* cell would measure about a millimetre in length, which is 500 times longer than the cell. Within a bacterium, however, certain proteins cause the chromosome to coil and "supercoil," densely packing it so that it fills only part of the cell. Unlike the nucleus of a eukaryotic cell, this dense region of DNA in a bacterium, called the **nucleoid**, is not bounded by membrane (see Figure 6.5).

▼ Figure 16.23

Exploring Chromatin Packing in a Eukaryotic Chromosome

This series of diagrams and transmission electron micrographs depicts a current model for the progressive levels of DNA coiling and folding. The illustration zooms out from a single molecule of DNA to a metaphase chromosome, which is large enough to be seen with a light microscope.

Stanley C. Holt/Biological Photo Service

Dr. Victoria E. Foe

DNA double helix (2 nm in diameter)

Nucleosome (10 nm in diameter)

Histones

Histone tail

H1

DNA, the double helix

Shown here is a ribbon model of DNA, with each ribbon representing one of the sugar-phosphate backbones. As you will recall from Figure 16.7, the phosphate groups along the backbone contribute a negative charge along the outside of each strand. The TEM shows a molecule of naked DNA; the double helix alone is 2 nm across.

Histones

Proteins called **histones** are responsible for the first level of DNA packing in chromatin. Although each histone is small—containing only about 100 amino acids—the total mass of histone in chromatin approximately equals the mass of DNA. More than a fifth of a histone's amino acids are positively charged (lysine or arginine) and therefore bind tightly to the negatively charged DNA.

Four types of histones are most common in chromatin: H2A, H2B, H3, and H4. The histones are very similar among eukaryotes; for example, all but two of the amino acids in cow H4 are identical to those in pea H4. The apparent conservation of histone genes during evolution probably reflects the important role of histones in organizing DNA within cells.

The four main types of histones are critical to the next level of DNA packing. (A fifth type of histone, called H1, is involved in a further stage of packing.)

Nucleosomes, or "beads on a string" (10-nm fibre)

In electron micrographs, unfolded chromatin is 10 nm in diameter (the *10-nm fibre*). Such chromatin resembles beads on a string (see the TEM). Each "bead" is a **nucleosome**, the basic unit of DNA packing; the "string" between beads is called *linker DNA*.

A nucleosome consists of DNA wound twice around a protein core composed of two molecules of each of the four main histone types. The amino end (N-terminus) of each histone (the *histone tail*) extends outward from the nucleosome.

In the cell cycle, the histones leave the DNA only briefly during DNA replication. Generally, they do the same during transcription, another process that requires access to the DNA by the cell's molecular machinery. Chapter 18 will discuss some recent findings about the role of histone tails and nucleosomes in the regulation of gene expression.

Each eukaryotic chromosome contains a single linear DNA double helix that, in humans, averages about 1.5×10^8 nucleotide pairs. This is an enormous amount of DNA relative to a chromosome's condensed length. If completely stretched out, such a DNA molecule would be about 4 cm long, thousands of times the diameter of a cell nucleus—and that's not even considering the DNA of the other 45 human chromosomes!

In the cell, eukaryotic DNA is precisely combined with a large amount of protein. Together, this complex of DNA and protein, called **chromatin**, fits into the nucleus through an elaborate, multilevel system of packing. Our current view of the successive levels of DNA packing in a chromosome is outlined in **Figure 16.23**. Study this figure carefully before reading further.

Chromatin undergoes striking changes in its degree of packing during the course of the cell cycle (see Figure 12.7).

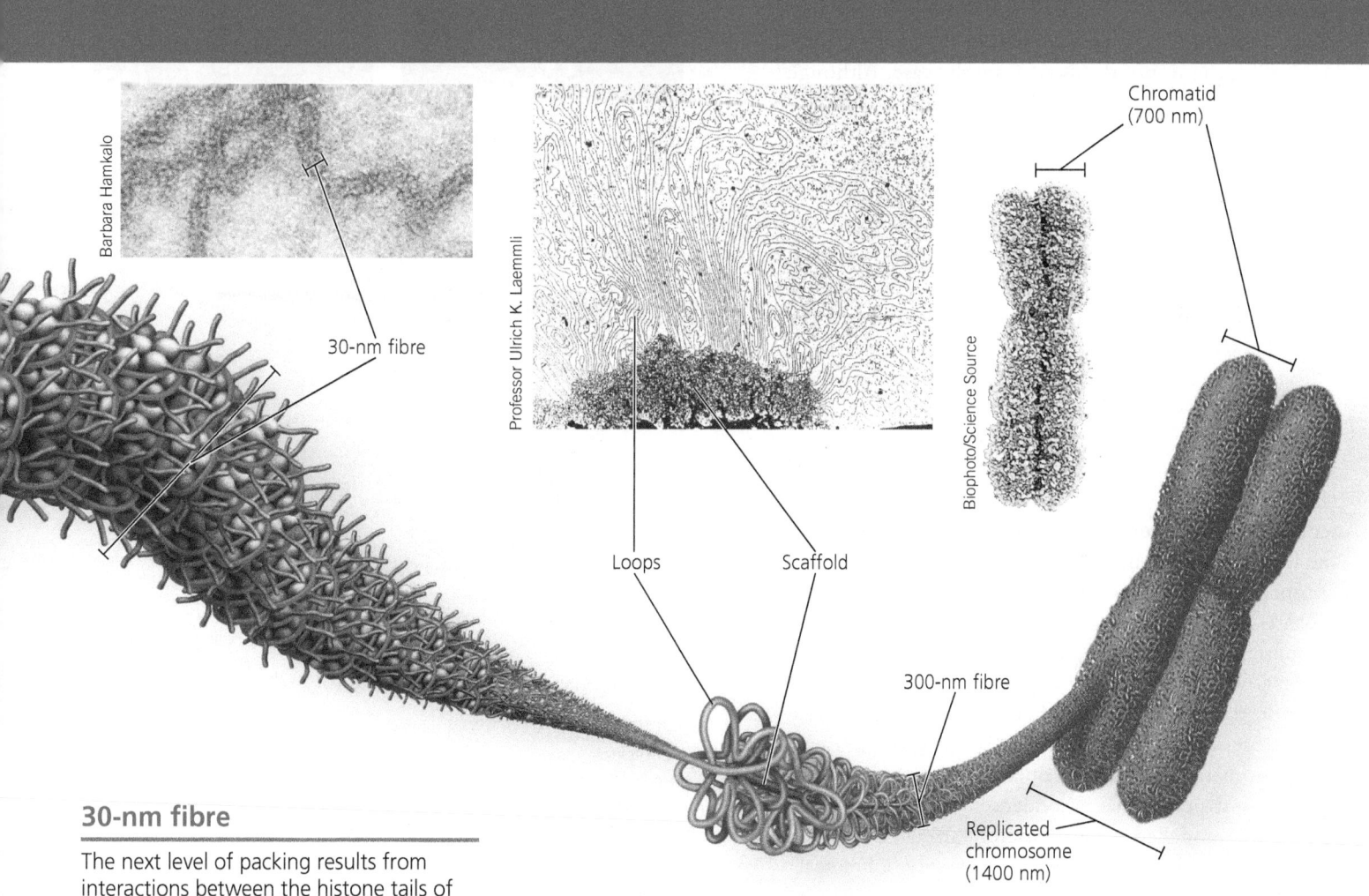

Barbara Hamkalo

Professor Ulrich K. Laemmli

Biophoto/Science Source

30-nm fibre

Loops   Scaffold

300-nm fibre

Chromatid (700 nm)

Replicated chromosome (1400 nm)

30-nm fibre

The next level of packing results from interactions between the histone tails of one nucleosome and the linker DNA and nucleosomes on either side. A fifth histone, H1, is involved at this level. These interactions cause the extended 10-nm fibre to coil or fold, forming a chromatin fibre roughly 30 nm in thickness, the *30-nm fibre* (see TEM). Although the 30-nm fibre is quite prevalent in the interphase nucleus, the packing arrangement of nucleosomes in this form of chromatin is still a matter of some debate.

Looped domains (300-nm fibre)

The 30-nm fibre, in turn, forms loops called *looped domains* attached to a chromosome scaffold made of proteins, making up a *300-nm* fibre (see TEM). The scaffold is rich in one type of topoisomerase, and H1 molecules also appear to be present.

Metaphase chromosome

In a mitotic chromosome, the looped domains themselves coil and fold in a manner not yet fully understood, further compacting all the chromatin to produce the characteristic metaphase chromosome shown in the micrograph above. The width of one chromatid is 700 nm. Particular genes always end up located at the same places in metaphase chromosomes, indicating that the packing steps are highly specific and precise.

In interphase cells stained for light microscopy, the chromatin usually appears as a diffuse mass within the nucleus, suggesting that the chromatin is highly extended. As a cell prepares for mitosis, its chromatin coils and folds up (condenses), eventually forming a characteristic number of short, thick metaphase chromosomes that are distinguishable from each other with the light microscope.

Though interphase chromatin is generally much less condensed than the chromatin of mitotic chromosomes, it shows several of the same levels of higher-order packing. Some of the chromatin comprising a chromosome seems to be present as a 10-nm fibre, but much is compacted into a 30-nm fibre, which in some regions is further folded into looped domains. Early on, biologists assumed that interphase chromatin was a tangled mass in the nucleus, like a bowl of spaghetti, but this is far from the case. Although an interphase chromosome lacks an obvious scaffold, its looped domains appear to be attached to the nuclear lamina, on the inside of the nuclear envelope, and perhaps also to fibres of the nuclear matrix. These attachments may help organize regions of chromatin where genes are active. The chromatin of each chromosome occupies a specific restricted area within the interphase nucleus, and the chromatin fibres of different chromosomes do not appear to be entangled (Figure 16.24).

Even during interphase, the centromeres and telomeres of chromosomes, as well as other chromosomal regions in some cells, exist in a highly condensed state similar to that seen in a metaphase chromosome. This type of interphase chromatin, visible as irregular clumps with a light microscope, is called **heterochromatin**, to distinguish it from the less compacted, more dispersed **euchromatin** ("true chromatin"). Because of its compaction, heterochromatic DNA is largely inaccessible to the machinery in the cell responsible for transcribing the genetic information coded in the DNA, a crucial early step in gene expression. In contrast, the looser packing of euchromatin makes its DNA accessible to this machinery, so the genes present in euchromatin can be transcribed. The chromosome is a dynamic structure that is condensed, loosened, modified, and remodelled as necessary for various cell processes, including mitosis, meiosis, and gene activity. Chemical modifications of histones affect the state of chromatin condensation and also have multiple effects on gene activity, as you'll see in Concept 18.2.

In this chapter, you have learned how DNA molecules are arranged in chromosomes and how DNA replication provides the copies of genes that parents pass to offspring. However, it is not enough that genes be copied and transmitted; the information they carry must be used by the cell. In other words, genes must also be expressed. In the next chapter, we will examine how the cell expresses the genetic information encoded in DNA.

▼ Figure 16.24   **Impact**

Painting Chromosomes

Using techniques you'll learn about in Chapter 20, researchers have been able to treat human chromosomes with special molecular tags, such that each chromosome pair can be seen as a different colour. Below on the left is a spread of chromosomes treated in this way; on the right they are organized into a karyotype.

National Institute of Health Genetics

Why It Matters The ability to visually distinguish among chromosomes has allowed researchers to see how the chromosomes are arranged in the interphase nucleus. As you can see in the interphase nucleus below, each chromosome appears to occupy a specific territory during interphase. In general, the two homologues of a pair are not located together.

Medical University of Graz

5 μm

Further Reading M. R. Speicher and N. P. Carter, The new cytogenetics: Blurring the boundaries with molecular biology, *Nature Reviews Genetics* 6:782–792 (2005); J. L. Marx, New methods for expanding the chromosomal paint kit, *Science* 273:430 (1996).

MAKE CONNECTIONS *If you arrested a human cell in metaphase I of meiosis and applied this technique, what would you observe? How would this differ from what you would see in metaphase of mitosis? Review Figure 13.8 and Figure 12.7.*

CONCEPT CHECK 16.3

1. Describe the structure of a nucleosome, the basic unit of DNA packing in eukaryotic cells.

2. What two properties, one structural and one functional, distinguish heterochromatin from euchromatin?

3. **MAKE CONNECTIONS** Interphase chromosomes appear to be attached to the nuclear lamina and perhaps also the nuclear matrix. Describe these two structures. See Figure 6.9 and the associated text.

For suggested answers, see Appendix A.

16 Chapter Review

SUMMARY OF KEY CONCEPTS

CONCEPT 16.1

DNA is the genetic material (pp. 330–335)

- Experiments with bacteria and with **phages** provided the first strong evidence that the genetic material is DNA.
- Watson and Crick deduced that DNA is a **double helix** and built a structural model. Two **antiparallel** sugar-phosphate chains wind around the outside of the molecule; the nitrogenous bases project into the interior, where they hydrogen-bond in specific pairs, A with T, G with C.

Sugar-phosphate backbone

Nitrogenous bases

Hydrogen bond

? *What does it mean when we say that the two DNA strands in the double helix are antiparallel? What would an end of the double helix look like if the strands were parallel?*

CONCEPT 16.2

Many proteins work together in DNA replication and repair (pp. 335–345)

- The Meselson-Stahl experiment showed that **DNA replication** is **semiconservative**: The parental molecule unwinds, and each strand then serves as a template for the synthesis of a new strand according to base-pairing rules.
- DNA replication at one **replication fork** is summarized here:

DNA pol III synthesizes **leading strand** continuously

Parental DNA

Helicase

DNA pol III starts DNA synthesis at 3' end of primer, continues in 5' → 3' direction

Primase synthesizes a short RNA **primer**

Lagging strand synthesized in short Okazaki fragments, later joined by **DNA ligase**

DNA pol I replaces the RNA primer with DNA nucleotides

Origin of replication

- DNA polymerases proofread new DNA, replacing incorrect nucleotides. In **mismatch repair**, enzymes correct errors that persist. **Nucleotide excision repair** is a general process by which **nucleases** and other enzymes replace damaged stretches of DNA.
- The ends of eukaryotic chromosomal DNA get shorter with each round of replication. The presence of **telomeres**, repetitive

sequences at the ends of linear DNA molecules, postpones the erosion of genes. **Telomerase** catalyzes the lengthening of telomeres in germ cells.

? *Compare DNA replication on the leading and lagging strands, including both similarities and differences.*

CONCEPT 16.3

A chromosome consists of a DNA molecule packed together with proteins (pp. 345–348)

- The chromosome of most bacterial species is a circular DNA molecule with some associated proteins, making up the **nucleoid** of the cell. The **chromatin** making up a eukaryotic chromosome is composed of DNA, **histones**, and other proteins. The histones bind to each other and to the DNA to form **nucleosomes**, the most basic units of DNA packing. Histone tails extend outward from each bead-like nucleosome core. Additional coiling and folding lead ultimately to the highly condensed chromatin of the metaphase chromosome. Chromosomes occupy restricted areas in the interphase nucleus. In interphase cells, most chromatin is less compacted (**euchromatin**), but some remains highly condensed (**heterochromatin**). Euchromatin, but not heterochromatin, is generally accessible for transcription of genes.

? *Describe the levels of chromatin packing you'd expect to see in an interphase nucleus.*

TEST YOUR UNDERSTANDING

LEVEL 1: KNOWLEDGE/COMPREHENSION

1. In his work with pneumonia-causing bacteria and mice, Griffith found that
   a. the protein coat from pathogenic cells was able to transform nonpathogenic cells.
   b. heat-killed pathogenic cells caused pneumonia.
   c. some substance from pathogenic cells was transferred to nonpathogenic cells, making them pathogenic.
   d. the polysaccharide coat of bacteria caused pneumonia.

2. What is the basis for the difference in how the leading and lagging strands of DNA molecules are synthesized?
   a. The origins of replication occur only at the 5' end.
   b. Helicases and single-strand binding proteins work at the 5' end.
   c. DNA polymerase can join new nucleotides only to the 3' end of a growing strand.
   d. DNA ligase works only in the 3' → 5' direction.

3. In analyzing the number of different bases in a DNA sample, which result would be consistent with the base-pairing rules?
   a. A = G
   b. A + G = C + T
   c. A + T = G + T
   d. A = C

4. The elongation of the leading strand during DNA synthesis
   a. progresses away from the replication fork.
   b. occurs in the 3' → 5' direction.
   c. does not require a template strand.
   d. depends on the action of DNA polymerase.

5. In a nucleosome, the DNA is wrapped around
   a. histones.
   b. ribosomes.
   c. polymerase molecules.
   d. a thymine dimer.

LEVEL 2: APPLICATION/ANALYSIS

6. *E. coli* cells grown on ^{15}N medium are transferred to ^{14}N medium and allowed to grow for two more generations (two rounds of DNA replication). DNA extracted from these cells is centrifuged. What density distribution of DNA would you expect in this experiment?
   a. one high-density and one low-density band
   b. one intermediate-density band
   c. one high-density and one intermediate-density band
   d. one low-density and one intermediate-density band

7. A biochemist isolates, purifies, and combines in a test tube a variety of molecules needed for DNA replication. When she adds some DNA to the mixture, replication occurs, but each DNA molecule consists of a normal strand paired with numerous segments of DNA a few hundred nucleotides long. What has she probably left out of the mixture?
   a. DNA polymerase
   b. DNA ligase
   c. Okazaki fragments
   d. primase

8. The spontaneous loss of amino groups from adenine in DNA results in hypoxanthine, an uncommon base, opposite thymine. What combination of proteins could repair such damage?
   a. nuclease, DNA polymerase, DNA ligase
   b. telomerase, primase, DNA polymerase
   c. telomerase, helicase, single-strand binding protein
   d. DNA ligase, replication fork proteins, adenylyl cyclase

9. **MAKE CONNECTIONS** Although the proteins that cause the *E. coli* chromosome to coil are not histones, what property would you expect them to share with histones, given their ability to bind to DNA (see Figure 5.14)?

LEVEL 3: SYNTHESIS/EVALUATION

10. **EVOLUTION CONNECTION**
    Some bacteria may be able to respond to environmental stress by increasing the rate at which mutations occur during cell division. How might this be accomplished? Might there be an evolutionary advantage of this ability? Explain.

11. **WRITE ABOUT A THEME: INFORMATION**
    The continuity of life is based on heritable information in the form of DNA, and structure and function are correlated at all levels of biological organization. In a short essay (100–150 words), describe how the structure of DNA is correlated with its role as the molecular basis of inheritance.

12. **SCIENTIFIC INQUIRY**

Barry Stoddard

DRAW IT Model building can be an important part of the scientific process. The illustration shown in the previous column is a computer-generated model of a DNA replication complex. The parental and newly synthesized DNA strands are colour-coded differently, as are each of the following three proteins: DNA pol III, the sliding clamp, and single-strand binding protein. Use what you've learned in this chapter to clarify this model by labelling each DNA strand and each protein and indicating the overall direction of DNA replication.

13. **SYNTHESIZE YOUR KNOWLEDGE**

This image shows DNA interacting with a computer-generated model of a TAL protein, one of a family of proteins found only in a species of the bacterium *Xanthomonas*. The bacterium uses proteins like this one to find particular gene sequences in cells of the organisms it infects, such as tomatoes, rice, and citrus fruits. Researchers are excited about working with this family of proteins. Their goal is to generate modified versions that can home in on specific gene sequences. Such proteins could then be used in an approach called gene therapy to "fix" mutated genes in individuals with genetic diseases. Given what you know about DNA structure and considering the image above, discuss how the TAL protein's structure suggests that it functions.

Thomas A. Steitz

For selected answers, see Appendix A.

17

Gene Expression: From Gene to Protein

KEY CONCEPTS

17.1 Genes specify proteins via transcription and translation

17.2 Transcription is the DNA-directed synthesis of RNA: *A closer look*

17.3 Eukaryotic cells modify RNA after transcription

17.4 Translation is the RNA-directed synthesis of a polypeptide: *A closer look*

17.5 Mutations of one or a few nucleotides can affect protein structure and function

Steven J.Kazlowski /AlamyStockPhoto

▲ Figure 17.1 **How does a single nucleotide mutation result in the dramatic difference in appearance between a Kermode bear and a black bear?**

The Flow of Genetic Information

On the northwestern coast and several islands off British Columbia, white Kermode, or "spirit bears," are found (Figure 17.1). The Kermode bear is a white phase subspecies (*kermodei*) of the American black bear (*Ursus americanus*). Although the Kermode bear is white, it is not considered an albino due to the fact that its skin and eyes are pigmented, and other than its fur colour, the Kermode bear is indistinguishable from the American black bear. What causes the striking phenotype of the Kermode bear? You learned in Chapter 14 that inherited traits are determined by genes. The information content of genes is in the form of specific sequences of nucleotides along strands of DNA, the genetic material. But how does this information determine an organism's traits? Put another way, what does a gene actually say? And how is its message translated by cells into a specific trait, such as brown hair, type A blood, or, in the case of the Kermode bear, white hair?

The mutation responsible for the white phase phenotype of the Kermode bear, which was identified by Kermit Ritland and colleagues at the University of British Columbia, is a single nucleotide mutation in the melanocortin 1 receptor gene (*MC1R*) that results in the substitution of a cysteine residue for a tyrosine residue at codon 298. The *MC1R* gene encodes a protein responsible

Peter Chadwick/Science Source

◄ **A Southern right whale female and her calf, an albino.**

351

for regulating skin and hair colour in mammals. Thus, the Kermode bear has a different phenotype than the American black bear due to a single nucleotide change that results in a modified protein product from the *MC1R* gene. Interestingly, mutations in the *MC1R* gene are also associated with coat colour in the domestic rabbit, yellow coat colour in Labrador retriever dogs, red hair in humans, and a predisposition for malignant melanoma in humans.

This example illustrates the main point of this chapter: The DNA inherited by an organism leads to specific traits by dictating the synthesis of proteins and of RNA molecules involved in protein synthesis. In other words, proteins are the link between genotype and phenotype. **Gene expression** is the process by which DNA directs the synthesis of proteins (or, in some cases, just RNAs). The expression of genes that code for proteins includes two stages: transcription and translation. This chapter describes the flow of information from gene to protein and explains how genetic mutations affect organisms through their proteins. Understanding the processes of gene expression, which are similar in all three domains of life, will allow us to revisit the concept of the gene in more detail at the end of the chapter.

CONCEPT 17.1

Genes specify proteins via transcription and translation

Before going into the details of how genes direct protein synthesis, let's step back and examine how the fundamental relationship between genes and proteins was discovered.

Evidence from the Study of Metabolic Defects

In 1902, British physician Archibald Garrod was the first to suggest that genes dictate phenotypes through enzymes, proteins that catalyze specific chemical reactions in the cell. He postulated that the symptoms of an inherited disease reflect an inability to make a particular enzyme. He later referred to such diseases as "inborn errors of metabolism." For example, people with a disease called alkaptonuria have black urine because it contains a chemical called alkapton, which darkens upon exposure to air. Garrod reasoned that most people have an enzyme that breaks down alkapton, whereas people with alkaptonuria have inherited an inability to make that enzyme, so alkapton is expelled in their urine.

Several decades later, research supported Garrod's hypothesis that a gene dictates the production of a specific enzyme, later named the *one gene–one enzyme hypothesis*. Biochemists learned that cells synthesize and degrade most organic molecules via metabolic pathways, in which each chemical reaction in a sequence is catalyzed by a specific enzyme (see Concept 8.1). Such metabolic pathways lead, for instance, to the synthesis of the pigments that give the black bear and Kermode bear in Figure 17.1 their fur colour or fruit flies (*Drosophila*) their eye colour (see Figure 15.3). In the 1930s, the American biochemist and geneticist George Beadle and his French colleague Boris Ephrussi speculated that in *Drosophila*, each mutation affecting eye colour blocks pigment synthesis at a specific step by preventing production of the enzyme that catalyzes that step. But neither the chemical reactions nor the enzymes that catalyze them were known at the time.

Nutritional Mutants in Neurospora: Scientific Inquiry

A breakthrough in demonstrating the relationship between genes and enzymes came a few years later at Stanford University, where Beadle and Edward Tatum began working with a bread mould, *Neurospora crassa*. Unlike the diploid organisms studied by Mendel (peas) and T. H. Morgan (fruit flies), *N. crassa* is a haploid species. In order to observe a change in a mutant's phenotype, Beadle and Tatum would need to disable just one allele (rather than two) of a protein-coding gene required for a specific metabolic activity. They bombarded *Neurospora* with X-rays, shown in the 1920s to cause genetic changes, and then looked among the survivors for mutants that differed in their nutritional needs from the wild-type bread mould.

Wild-type *Neurospora* has modest food requirements. It can grow in the laboratory on a simple solution containing minimal nutrients for growth—inorganic salts, glucose, and the vitamin biotin—incorporated into agar, a support medium. From this so-called *minimal medium*, wild-type mould cells use their metabolic pathways to produce all the other molecules they need to grow and divide repeatedly, forming visible colonies of cells. Beadle and Tatum identified mutants that could not survive on minimal medium, apparently because they were unable to synthesize certain essential molecules from the minimal ingredients. To ensure survival of these nutritional mutants, Beadle and Tatum allowed them to grow in parallel on *complete medium*, which consisted of minimal medium supplemented with all 20 amino acids and a few other nutrients. The complete growth medium could support any mutant that couldn't synthesize one of the supplements. Presumably, this inability was because a required enzyme no longer functioned after the gene encoding it had been disabled by the X-rays.

To characterize the metabolic defect in each nutritional mutant strain, Beadle and Tatum took samples from that mutant growing on complete medium and distributed them to a number of different vials. Each vial contained minimal medium plus only one additional nutrient. The particular supplement that allowed growth indicated the metabolic defect. For example, if the only supplemented vial that supported growth of the mutant was the one fortified with the amino acid arginine, the researchers could conclude that the mutant was defective in the biochemical pathway that wild-type cells use to synthesize arginine.

In fact, many such arginine-requiring mutants were obtained and studied by two colleagues of Beadle and Tatum, Adrian Srb and Norman Horowitz, who wanted to investigate the biochemical pathway for arginine synthesis in *Neurospora* (Figure 17.2). Srb and Horowitz pinned down each mutant's defect more specifically, using additional tests to distinguish among three classes of arginine-requiring mutants. Mutants in each class required a different set of compounds along the arginine-synthesizing pathway, which has three steps. These results, and those of many similar experiments done by Beadle and Tatum, suggested that each class was blocked at a different step in this pathway because mutants in that class lacked the enzyme that catalyzes the blocked step.

Because Beadle and Tatum set up their experimental conditions so that each mutant was defective in a single gene, the collected results, taken together, provided strong support for a working hypothesis they had proposed earlier. The *one gene–one enzyme hypothesis*, as they dubbed it, states that the function of a gene is to dictate the production of a specific enzyme. Further support for this hypothesis came from experiments that identified the specific enzymes lacking in the mutants. Beadle and Tatum shared a Nobel Prize in 1958 for "their discovery that genes act by regulating definite chemical events" (in the words of the Nobel committee).

The Products of Gene Expression: A Developing Story

As researchers learned more about proteins, they made revisions to the one gene–one enzyme hypothesis. First of all, not all proteins are enzymes. Keratin, the structural protein of animal hair, and the hormone insulin are two examples of nonenzymatic proteins. Because proteins that are not enzymes are nevertheless gene products, molecular biologists began to think in terms of one gene–one protein. However, many proteins are constructed from two or more different polypeptide chains, and each polypeptide is specified by its own gene. For example, hemoglobin, the oxygen-transporting protein of vertebrate red blood cells, contains two kinds of polypeptides, and thus two genes code for this protein (see Figure 5.18), one for each type of polypeptide. Beadle and Tatum's idea was therefore restated as the *one gene–one polypeptide hypothesis*. Even this description is not entirely accurate, though. First, many eukaryotic genes can each code for a set of closely related polypeptides via a process called *alternative splicing*, which you will learn about later in this chapter. Second, quite a few genes code for RNA molecules that have important functions in cells even though they are never translated into protein. For now, we will focus on genes that do code for polypeptides. (Note that it is common to refer to these gene products as proteins—a practice you will encounter in this text—rather than more precisely as polypeptides.)

Basic Principles of Transcription and Translation

Genes provide the instructions for making specific proteins. But a gene does not build a protein directly. The bridge between DNA and protein synthesis is the nucleic acid RNA. You learned in Chapter 5 that RNA is chemically similar to DNA except that it contains ribose instead of deoxyribose as its sugar and has the nitrogenous base uracil rather than thymine (see Figure 5.24). Thus, each nucleotide along a DNA strand has A, G, C, or T as its base, and each nucleotide along an RNA strand has A, G, C, or U as its base. An RNA molecule usually consists of a single strand.

It is customary to describe the flow of information from gene to protein in linguistic terms. Just as specific sequences of letters communicate information in a language such as English, both nucleic acids and proteins are polymers with specific sequences of monomers that convey information. In DNA or RNA, the monomers are the four types of nucleotides, which differ in their nitrogenous bases. Genes are typically hundreds or thousands of nucleotides long, each gene having a specific sequence of nucleotides. Each polypeptide of a protein also has monomers arranged in a particular linear order (the protein's primary structure), but its monomers are amino acids. Thus, nucleic acids and proteins contain information written in two different chemical languages. Getting from DNA to protein requires two major stages: transcription and translation.

Transcription is the synthesis of RNA using information in the DNA. The two nucleic acids are written in different forms of the same language, and the information is simply transcribed, or "rewritten," from DNA to RNA. Just as a DNA strand provides a template for making a new complementary strand during DNA replication, it also can serve as a template for assembling a complementary sequence of RNA nucleotides. For a protein-coding gene, the resulting RNA molecule is a faithful transcript of the gene's protein-building instructions. This type of RNA molecule is called **messenger RNA (mRNA)** because it carries a genetic message from the DNA to the protein-synthesizing machinery of the cell. (Transcription is the general term for the synthesis of *any* kind of RNA on a DNA template. Later, you will learn about some other types of RNA produced by transcription.)

Translation is the synthesis of a polypeptide using the information in the mRNA. During this stage, there is a

Inquiry

Do individual genes specify the enzymes that function in a biochemical pathway?

Experiment Working with the mould *Neurospora crassa*, Adrian Srb and Norman Horowitz, then at Stanford University, used Beadle and Tatum's experimental approach to isolate mutants that required arginine in their growth medium. The researchers showed that these mutants fell into three classes, each defective in a different gene. From studies by others on mammalian liver cells, they suspected that the metabolic pathway of arginine biosynthesis involved a precursor nutrient and the intermediate molecules ornithine and citrulline, as shown in the diagram on the right.

Their most famous experiment, shown here, tested both the *one gene–one enzyme hypothesis* and their postulated arginine-synthesizing pathway. In this experiment, they grew their three classes of mutants under the four different conditions shown in the Results Table below. They included minimal medium (MM) as a control, knowing that wild-type cells could grow on MM but mutant cells could not. (See test tubes below.)

Control: Minimal medium

Growth: Wild-type cells growing and dividing

No growth: Mutant cells cannot grow and divide

Results As shown in the table on the right, the wild-type strain was capable of growth under all experimental conditions, requiring only the minimal medium. The three classes of mutants each had a specific set of growth requirements. For example, class II mutants could not grow when ornithine alone was added but could grow when either citrulline or arginine was added.

Results Table	Classes of *Neurospora crassa*			
Condition		**Wild type**	**Class I mutants**	**Class II mutants**	**Class III mutants**
Minimal medium (MM) (control)					
MM + ornithine					
MM + citrulline					
MM + arginine (control)					
Summary of results		Can grow with or without any supplements	Can grow on ornithine, citrulline, or arginine	Can grow only on citrulline or arginine	Require arginine to grow

Conclusion From the growth requirements of the mutants, Srb and Horowitz deduced that each class of mutant was unable to carry out one step in the pathway for synthesizing arginine, presumably because it lacked the necessary enzyme, as shown in the table on the right. Because each of their mutants was mutated in a single gene, they concluded that each mutated gene must normally dictate the production of one enzyme. Their results supported the one gene–one enzyme hypothesis proposed by Beadle and Tatum and also confirmed that the arginine pathway described in the mammalian liver also operates in *Neurospora*. (Notice in the Results Table that a mutant can grow only if supplied with a compound made *after* the defective step because this bypasses the defect.)

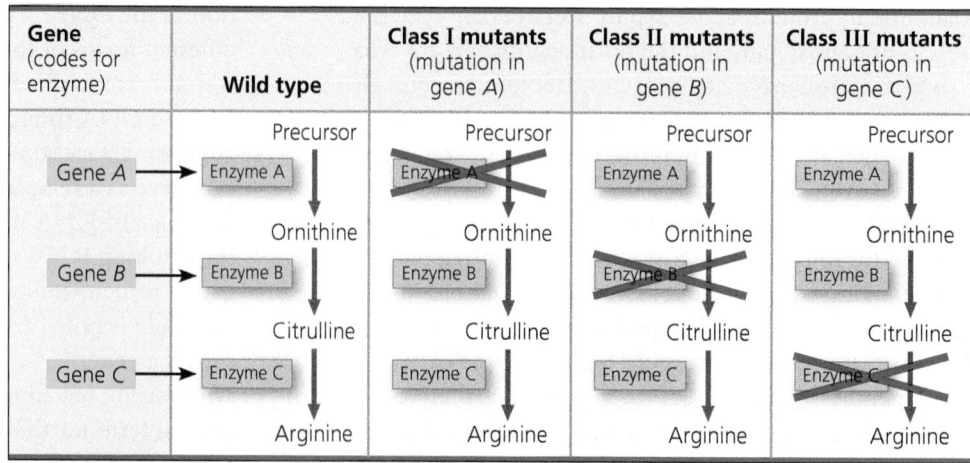

Source: Based on "The Ornithine Cycle in Neurospora and Its Genetic Control" by Adrian M. Srb and N. H. Horowitz, from *Biochemistry*, June 1944, Volume 154(1). © Jane B Reece.

WHAT IF? *Suppose the experiment had shown that class I mutants could grow only in MM supplemented by ornithine or arginine and that class II mutants could grow in MM supplemented by citrulline, ornithine, or arginine. What conclusions would the researchers have drawn from those results regarding the biochemical pathway and the defect in class I and class II mutants?*

change in language: The cell must translate the nucleotide sequence of an mRNA molecule into the amino acid sequence of a polypeptide. The sites of translation are **ribosomes**, complex particles that facilitate the orderly linking of amino acids into polypeptide chains.

Transcription and translation occur in all organisms, both those that lack a membrane-bounded nucleus (bacteria and archaea) and those that have one (eukaryotes). Because most studies of transcription and translation have used bacteria and eukaryotic cells, these are our main focus in this chapter. Our understanding of transcription and translation in archaea lags behind, but in the last section of the chapter we will discuss a few aspects of archaeal gene expression.

The basic mechanics of transcription and translation are similar for bacteria and eukaryotes, but there is an important difference in the flow of genetic information within the cells. Because bacteria do not have nuclei, their DNA is not separated by nuclear membranes from ribosomes and the other protein-synthesizing equipment (Figure 17.3a). As you will see later, this lack of compartmentalization allows translation of an mRNA to begin while its transcription is still in progress. In a eukaryotic cell, by contrast, the nuclear envelope separates transcription from translation in space and time (Figure 17.3b). Transcription occurs in the nucleus, and mRNA is then transported to the cytoplasm, where translation occurs. But before eukaryotic RNA transcripts from protein-coding genes can leave the nucleus, they are modified in various ways to produce the final, functional mRNA. The transcription of a protein-coding eukaryotic gene results in *pre-mRNA*, and further processing yields the finished mRNA. The initial RNA transcript from any gene, including those specifying RNA that is not translated into protein, is more generally called a **primary transcript**.

To summarize: Genes program protein synthesis via genetic messages in the form of messenger RNA. Put another way, cells are governed by a molecular chain of command with a directional flow of genetic information, shown here by arrows:

This concept was dubbed the *central dogma* by Francis Crick in 1956. How has the concept held up over time? In the 1970s, scientists were surprised to discover that some RNA molecules can act as templates for DNA synthesis, a process you'll read about in Chapter 19. However, these exceptions do not invalidate the idea that, in general, genetic information flows from DNA to RNA to protein. In the next section, we discuss how the instructions for assembling amino acids into a specific order are encoded in nucleic acids.

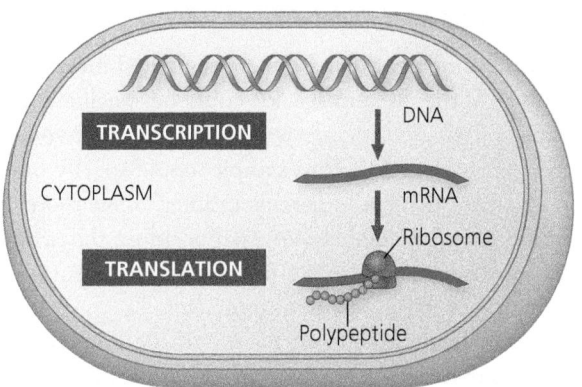

(a) Bacterial cell. In a bacterial cell, which lacks a nucleus, mRNA produced by transcription is immediately translated without additional processing.

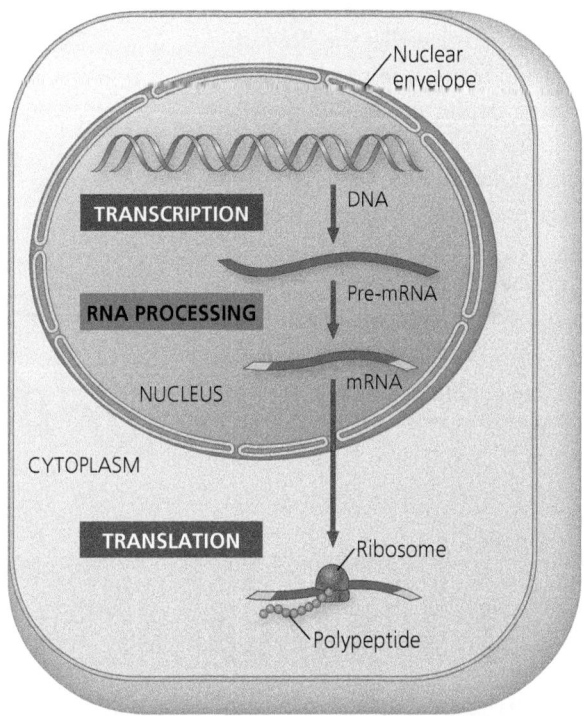

(b) Eukaryotic cell. The nucleus provides a separate compartment for transcription. The original RNA transcript, called pre-mRNA, is processed in various ways before leaving the nucleus as mRNA.

▲ Figure 17.3 **Overview: the roles of transcription and translation in the flow of genetic information.** In a cell, inherited information flows from DNA to RNA to protein. The two main stages of information flow are transcription and translation. A miniature version of part **(a)** or **(b)** accompanies several figures later in the chapter as an orientation diagram to help you see where a particular figure fits into the overall scheme.

The Genetic Code

When biologists began to suspect that the instructions for protein synthesis were encoded in DNA, they recognized a problem: There are only four nucleotide bases to specify 20 amino acids. Thus, the genetic code cannot be a language like Chinese, where each written symbol corresponds to a word. How many nucleotides, then, correspond to an amino acid?

Codons: Triplets of Nucleotides

If each kind of nucleotide base were translated into an amino acid, only 4 of the 20 amino acids could be specified. Would a language of two-letter code words suffice? The two-nucleotide sequence AG, for example, could specify one amino acid, and GT could specify another. Since there are four possible nucleotide bases in each position, this would give us 16 (that is 4 × 4, or 4^2) possible arrangements—still not enough to code for all 20 amino acids.

Triplets of nucleotide bases are the smallest units of uniform length that can code for all the amino acids. If each arrangement of three consecutive nucleotide bases specifies an amino acid, there can be 64 (that is, 4^3) possible code words—more than enough to specify all the amino acids. Experiments have verified that the flow of information from gene to protein is based on a **triplet code**: The genetic instructions for a polypeptide chain are written in the DNA as a series of nonoverlapping, three-nucleotide words. The series of words in a gene is transcribed into a complementary series of nonoverlapping, three-nucleotide words in mRNA, which is then translated into a chain of amino acids (**Figure 17.4**).

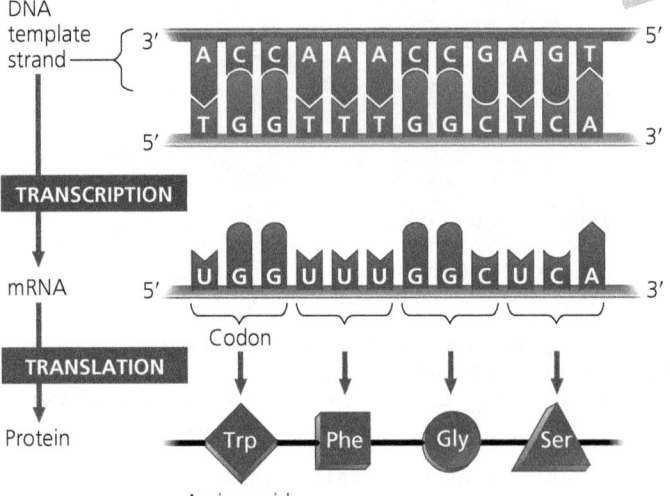

▲ **Figure 17.4 The triplet code.** For each gene, one DNA strand functions as a template for transcription of RNAs, such as mRNA. The base-pairing rules for DNA synthesis also guide transcription, except that uracil (U) takes the place of thymine (T) in RNA. During translation, the mRNA is read as a sequence of nucleotide triplets, called codons. Each codon specifies an amino acid to be added to the growing polypeptide chain. The mRNA is read in the 5′ → 3′ direction.

? *Write the sequence of the mRNA strand and the nontemplate DNA strand—in both cases reading from 5′ to 3′—and compare them.*

During transcription, the gene determines the sequence of nucleotide bases along the length of the RNA molecule that is being synthesized. For each gene, only one of the two DNA strands is transcribed. This strand is called the **template strand** because it provides the pattern, or template, for the sequence of nucleotides in an RNA transcript. For any given gene, the same strand is used as the template every time the gene is transcribed. However, farther along on the same chromosomal DNA molecule, the opposite strand may be the one that functions as the template for a different gene. The strand that is used as the template is determined by the orientation of the enzyme that transcribes the genes, which depends on particular DNA sequences associated with a given gene.

An mRNA molecule is complementary rather than identical to its DNA template because RNA nucleotides are assembled on the template according to base-pairing rules (see Figure 17.4). The pairs are similar to those that form during DNA replication, except that U, the RNA substitute for T, pairs with A and the mRNA nucleotides contain ribose instead of deoxyribose. Like a new strand of DNA, the RNA molecule is synthesized in an antiparallel direction to the template strand of DNA. (To review what is meant by "antiparallel" and the 5′ and 3′ ends of a nucleic acid chain, see Figure 16.7.) In the example in Figure 17.4, the nucleotide triplet ACC along the DNA (written as 3′-ACC-5′) provides a template for 5′-UGG-3′ in the mRNA molecule. The mRNA nucleotide triplets are called **codons**, and they are customarily written in the 5′ → 3′ direction. In our example, UGG is the codon for the amino acid tryptophan (abbreviated Trp). The term *codon* is also used for the DNA nucleotide triplets along the *nontemplate* strand. These codons are complementary to the template strand and thus identical in sequence to the mRNA, except that they have a T wherever there is a U in the mRNA. (For this reason, the nontemplate DNA strand is often called the *coding strand*; by convention, the sequence of the coding strand is used when a gene's sequence is reported.)

During translation, the sequence of codons along an mRNA molecule is decoded, or translated, into a sequence of amino acids making up a polypeptide chain. The codons are read by the translation machinery in the 5′ → 3′ direction along the mRNA. Each codon specifies which one of the 20 amino acids will be incorporated at the corresponding position along a polypeptide. Because codons are nucleotide triplets, the number of nucleotides making up a genetic message must be three times the number of amino acids in the protein product. For example, it takes 300 nucleotides along an mRNA strand to code for the amino acids in a polypeptide that is 100 amino acids long.

Cracking the Code

Molecular biologists cracked the genetic code of life in the early 1960s when a series of elegant experiments disclosed the amino acid translations of each of the RNA codons. The first codon was deciphered in 1961 by Marshall Nirenberg, of the National Institutes of Health, and his colleagues. Nirenberg synthesized an artificial mRNA by linking identical RNA nucleotides containing uracil as their base. No matter where this message started or stopped, it could contain only one codon in repetition: UUU. Nirenberg added this "poly-U" to a test-tube mixture containing amino acids, ribosomes, and the other components required for protein synthesis. His artificial system translated the poly-U into a polypeptide containing many units of the amino acid phenylalanine (Phe), strung together as a long polyphenylalanine chain. Thus, Nirenberg determined that the mRNA codon UUU specifies the amino acid phenylalanine. Soon, the amino acids specified by the codons AAA, GGG, and CCC were also determined.

Although more elaborate techniques were required to decode mixed triplets such as AUA and CGA, all 64 codons were deciphered by the mid-1960s. As **Figure 17.5**

Second mRNA base

	U	C	A	G	
U	UUU ⎤ Phe UUC ⎦ UUA ⎤ Leu UUG ⎦	UCU ⎤ UCC ⎥ Ser UCA ⎥ UCG ⎦	UAU ⎤ Tyr UAC ⎦ UAA Stop UAG Stop	UGU ⎤ Cys UGC ⎦ UGA Stop UGG Trp	U C A G
C	CUU ⎤ CUC ⎥ Leu CUA ⎥ CUG ⎦	CCU ⎤ CCC ⎥ Pro CCA ⎥ CCG ⎦	CAU ⎤ His CAC ⎦ CAA ⎤ Gln CAG ⎦	CGU ⎤ CGC ⎥ Arg CGA ⎥ CGG ⎦	U C A G
A	AUU ⎤ AUC ⎥ Ile AUA ⎦ AUG Met or start	ACU ⎤ ACC ⎥ Thr ACA ⎥ ACG ⎦	AAU ⎤ Asn AAC ⎦ AAA ⎤ Lys AAG ⎦	AGU ⎤ Ser AGC ⎦ AGA ⎤ Arg AGG ⎦	U C A G
G	GUU ⎤ GUC ⎥ Val GUA ⎥ GUG ⎦	GCU ⎤ GCC ⎥ Ala GCA ⎥ GCG ⎦	GAU ⎤ Asp GAC ⎦ GAA ⎤ Glu GAG ⎦	GGU ⎤ GGC ⎥ Gly GGA ⎥ GGG ⎦	U C A G

First mRNA base (5′ end of codon) — Third mRNA base (3′ end of codon)

▲ **Figure 17.5 The codon table for mRNA.** The three nucleotide bases of an mRNA codon are designated here as the first, second, and third bases, reading in the 5′ → 3′ direction along the mRNA. (Practise using this table by finding the codons in Figure 17.4.) The codon AUG not only stands for the amino acid methionine (Met) but also functions as a "start" signal for ribosomes to begin translating the mRNA at that point. Three of the 64 codons function as "stop" signals, marking where ribosomes end translation. See Figure 5.14 for a list of the full names of all the amino acids.

shows, 61 of the 64 triplets code for amino acids. The three codons that do not designate amino acids are "stop" signals, or termination codons, marking the end of translation. Notice that the codon AUG has a dual function: It codes for the amino acid methionine (Met) and also functions as a "start" signal, or initiation codon. Genetic messages usually begin with the mRNA codon AUG, which signals the protein-synthesizing machinery to begin translating the mRNA at that location. (Because AUG also stands for methionine, polypeptide chains begin with methionine when they are synthesized. However, an enzyme may subsequently remove this starter amino acid from the chain.)

Notice in Figure 17.5 that there is redundancy in the genetic code, but no ambiguity. For example, although codons GAA and GAG both specify glutamic acid (redundancy), neither of them ever specifies any other amino acid (no ambiguity). The redundancy in the code is not altogether random. In many cases, codons that are synonyms for a particular amino acid differ only in the third nucleotide base of the triplet. We will consider the significance of this redundancy later in the chapter.

Our ability to extract the intended message from a written language depends on reading the symbols in the correct groupings—that is, in the correct **reading frame**. Consider this statement: "The red dog ate the bug." Group the letters incorrectly by starting at the wrong point, and the result will probably be gibberish: for example, "her edd oga tet heb ug." The reading frame is also important in the molecular language of cells. The short stretch of polypeptide shown in Figure 17.4, for instance, will be made correctly only if the mRNA nucleotides are read from left to right (5′ → 3′) in the groups of three shown in the figure: UGG UUU GGC UCA. Although a genetic message is written with no spaces between the codons, the cell's protein-synthesizing machinery reads the message as a series of nonoverlapping three-letter words. The message is *not* read as a series of overlapping words—UGGUUU, and so on—which would convey a very different message.

Evolution of the Genetic Code

EVOLUTION The genetic code is nearly universal, shared by organisms from the simplest bacteria to the most complex plants and animals. The mRNA codon CCG, for instance, is translated as the amino acid proline in all organisms whose genetic code has been examined. In laboratory experiments, genes can be transcribed and translated after being transplanted from one species to another, sometimes with quite striking results, as shown in **Figure 17.6**! Bacteria can be programmed by the insertion of human genes to synthesize certain human proteins for medical use, such as insulin. Such applications have produced many exciting developments in the area of biotechnology (see Concept 20.4).

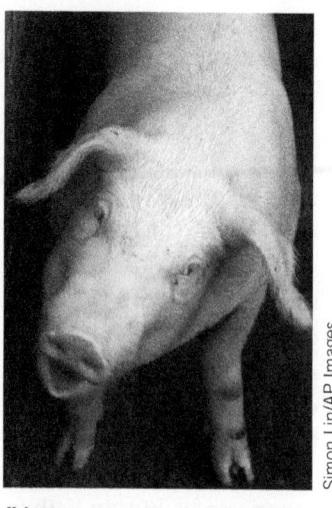

(a) Tobacco plant expressing a firefly gene. The yellow glow is produced by a chemical reaction catalyzed by the protein product of the firefly gene.

(b) Pig expressing a jellyfish gene. Researchers injected a jellyfish gene for a fluorescent protein into fertilized pig eggs. One developed into this fluorescent pig.

▲ **Figure 17.6 Expression of genes from different species.** Because diverse forms of life share a common genetic code, one species can be programmed to produce proteins characteristic of a different species by introducing the DNA from the different species into the first species.

Despite a small number of exceptions in which a few codons differ from the standard ones, the evolutionary significance of the code's *near* universality is clear. A language shared by all living things must have been operating very early in the history of life—early enough to be present in the common ancestor of all present-day organisms. A shared genetic vocabulary is a reminder of the kinship that bonds all life on Earth.

CONCEPT CHECK 17.1

1. **MAKE CONNECTIONS** In a research article about alkaptonuria published in 1902, Garrod suggested that humans inherit two "characters" (alleles) for a particular enzyme and that both parents must contribute a faulty version for the offspring to have the disorder. Today, would this disorder be called dominant or recessive? See Concept 14.4.

2. What polypeptide product would you expect from a poly-G mRNA that is 30 nucleotides long?

3. **DRAW IT** The template strand of a gene contains the sequence 3'-TTCAGTCGT-5'. Draw the nontemplate sequence and the mRNA sequence, indicating 5' and 3' ends of each. Compare the two sequences.

4. **DRAW IT** Suppose that the nontemplate sequence in question 3 was transcribed instead of the template sequence. Draw the mRNA sequence and translate it using Figure 17.5. (Be sure to pay attention to the 5' and 3' ends.) Predict how well the protein synthesized from the nontemplate strand would function, if at all.

For suggested answers, see Appendix A.

Transcription is the DNA-directed synthesis of RNA: *A closer look*

Now that we have considered the linguistic logic and evolutionary significance of the genetic code, we are ready to re-examine transcription, the first stage of gene expression, in more detail.

Molecular Components of Transcription

Messenger RNA, the carrier of information from DNA to the cell's protein-synthesizing machinery, is transcribed from the template strand of a gene. An enzyme called an **RNA polymerase** pries the two strands of DNA apart and joins together RNA nucleotides complementary to the DNA template strand, thus elongating the RNA polynucleotide (**Figure 17.7**). Like the DNA polymerases that function in DNA replication, RNA polymerases can assemble a polynucleotide only in its 5' → 3' direction, from a 3' → 5' template. Unlike DNA polymerases, however, RNA polymerases are able to start a chain from scratch; they don't need a primer.

Specific sequences of nucleotides along the DNA mark where transcription of a gene begins and ends. The DNA sequence where RNA polymerase attaches and initiates transcription is known as the **promoter**; in bacteria, the sequence that signals the end of transcription is called the **terminator**. (The termination mechanism is different in eukaryotes; we'll describe it later.) Molecular biologists refer to the direction of transcription as "downstream" and the other direction as "upstream." These terms are also used to describe the positions of nucleotide sequences within the DNA or RNA. Thus, the promoter sequence in DNA is said to be upstream from the terminator. The stretch of DNA downstream from the promoter that is transcribed into an RNA molecule is called a **transcription unit**.

Bacteria have a single type of RNA polymerase that synthesizes not only mRNA but also other types of RNA that function in protein synthesis, such as ribosomal RNA. In contrast, eukaryotes have at least three types of RNA polymerase in their nuclei. The one used for mRNA synthesis is called RNA polymerase II. The other RNA polymerases transcribe RNA molecules that are not translated into protein. In the discussion of transcription that follows, we start with the features of mRNA synthesis common to both bacteria and eukaryotes and then describe some key differences.

Synthesis of an RNA Transcript

The three stages of transcription, as shown in Figure 17.7 and described next, are initiation, elongation, and termination

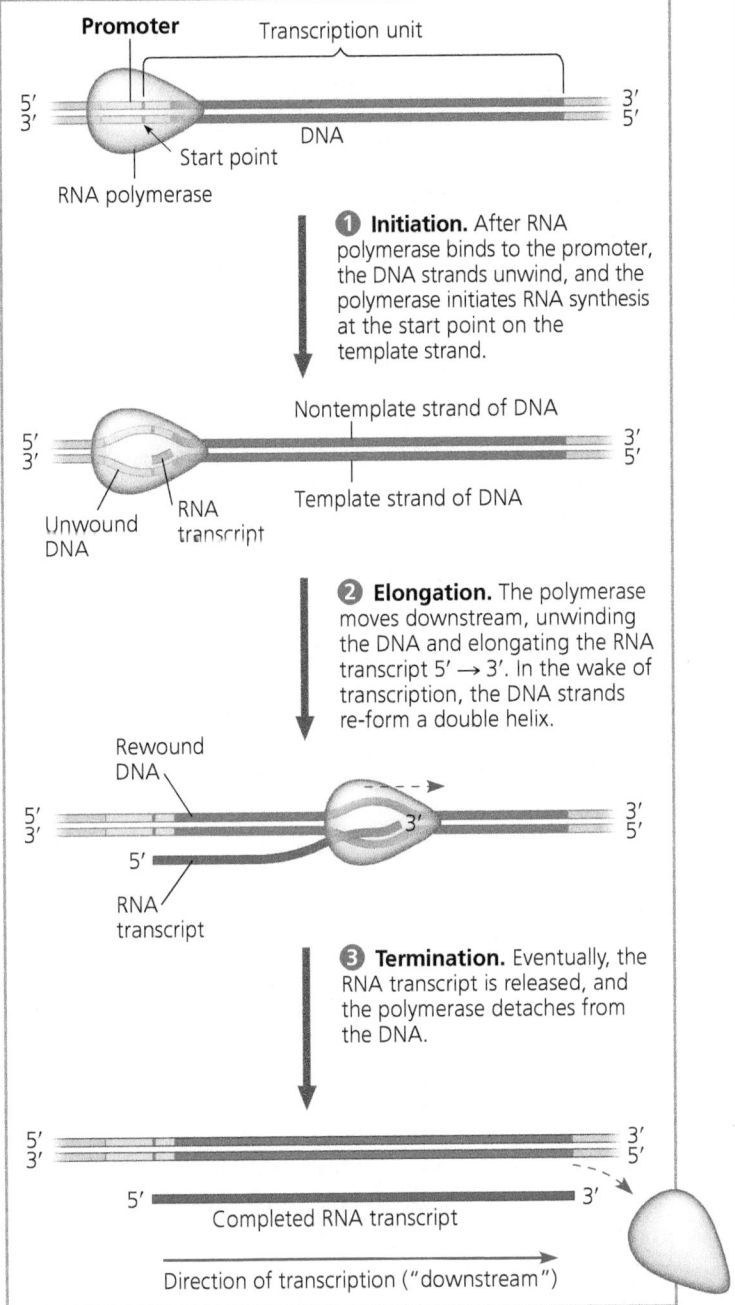

Promoter
Transcription unit

RNA polymerase

Start point

① **Initiation.** After RNA polymerase binds to the promoter, the DNA strands unwind, and the polymerase initiates RNA synthesis at the start point on the template strand.

Nontemplate strand of DNA

Unwound DNA

RNA transcript

Template strand of DNA

② **Elongation.** The polymerase moves downstream, unwinding the DNA and elongating the RNA transcript 5′ → 3′. In the wake of transcription, the DNA strands re-form a double helix.

Rewound DNA

RNA transcript

③ **Termination.** Eventually, the RNA transcript is released, and the polymerase detaches from the DNA.

Completed RNA transcript

Direction of transcription ("downstream")

▲ **Figure 17.7 The stages of transcription: initiation, elongation, and termination.** This general depiction of transcription applies to both bacteria and eukaryotes, but the details of termination differ, as described in the text. Also, in a bacterium, the RNA transcript is immediately usable as mRNA; in a eukaryote, the RNA transcript must first undergo processing.

MAKE CONNECTIONS *Compare the use of a template strand during transcription and replication. See Figure 16.17.*

of the RNA chain. Study Figure 17.7 to familiarize yourself with the stages and the terms used to describe them.

RNA Polymerase Binding and Initiation of Transcription

The promoter of a gene includes within it the transcription **start point** (the nucleotide where RNA synthesis

actually begins) and typically extends several dozen or more nucleotide pairs upstream from the start point. RNA polymerase binds in a precise location and orientation on the promoter, thereby determining where transcription starts and which of the two strands of the DNA helix is used as the template.

Certain sections of a promoter are especially important for binding RNA polymerase. In bacteria, part of the RNA polymerase itself specifically recognizes and binds to the promoter. In eukaryotes, a collection of proteins called **transcription factors** mediate the binding of RNA polymerase and the initiation of transcription. Only after transcription factors are attached to the promoter does RNA polymerase II bind to it. The whole complex of transcription factors and RNA polymerase II bound to the promoter is called a **transcription initiation complex**. Figure 17.8 shows the role of transcription factors and a crucial promoter DNA sequence called the **TATA box** in forming the initiation complex at a eukaryotic promoter.

The interaction between eukaryotic RNA polymerase II and transcription factors is an example of the importance of protein-protein interactions in controlling eukaryotic transcription. Once the appropriate transcription factors are firmly attached to the promoter DNA and the polymerase is bound in the correct orientation, the enzyme unwinds the two DNA strands and starts transcribing the template strand.

Elongation of the RNA Strand

As RNA polymerase moves along the DNA, it untwists the double helix, exposing about 10–20 DNA nucleotides at a time for pairing with RNA nucleotides (Figure 17.9). The enzyme adds nucleotides to the 3′ end of the growing RNA molecule as it continues along the double helix. In the wake of this advancing wave of RNA synthesis, the new RNA molecule peels away from its DNA template, and the DNA double helix re-forms. Transcription progresses at a rate of about 40 nucleotides per second in eukaryotes.

A single gene can be transcribed simultaneously by several molecules of RNA polymerase following each other like trucks in a convoy. A growing strand of RNA trails off from each polymerase, with the length of each new strand reflecting how far along the template the enzyme has travelled from the start point (see the mRNA molecules in Figure 17.23). The congregation of many polymerase molecules simultaneously transcribing a single gene increases the amount of mRNA transcribed from it, which helps the cell make the encoded protein in large amounts.

Termination of Transcription

The mechanism of termination differs between bacteria and eukaryotes. In bacteria, transcription proceeds through

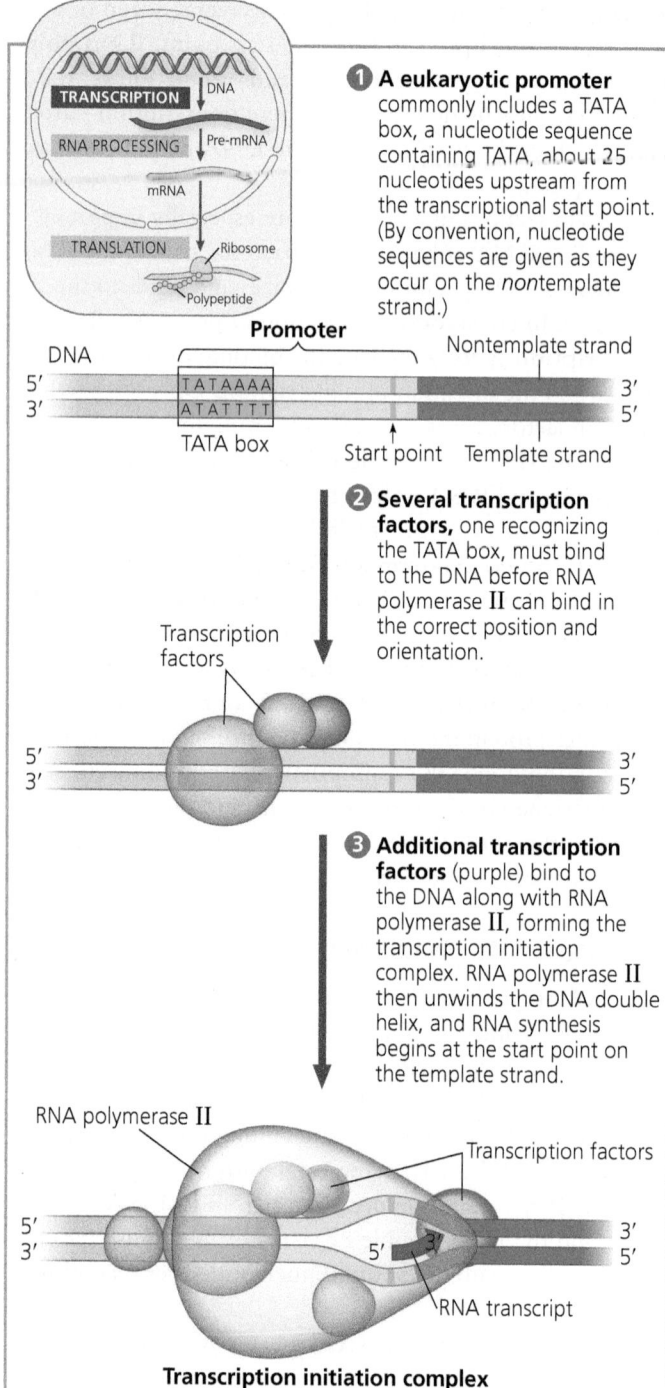

Promoter

DNA

5′ TATAAAA 3′
3′ ATATTTT 5′

TATA box

Nontemplate strand

Start point Template strand

① **A eukaryotic promoter** commonly includes a TATA box, a nucleotide sequence containing TATA, about 25 nucleotides upstream from the transcriptional start point. (By convention, nucleotide sequences are given as they occur on the *non*template strand.)

② **Several transcription factors,** one recognizing the TATA box, must bind to the DNA before RNA polymerase II can bind in the correct position and orientation.

Transcription factors

③ **Additional transcription factors** (purple) bind to the DNA along with RNA polymerase II, forming the transcription initiation complex. RNA polymerase II then unwinds the DNA double helix, and RNA synthesis begins at the start point on the template strand.

RNA polymerase II

Transcription factors

RNA transcript

Transcription initiation complex

▲ **Figure 17.8** **The initiation of transcription at a eukaryotic promoter.** In eukaryotic cells, proteins called transcription factors mediate the initiation of transcription by RNA polymerase II.

? *Explain how the interaction of RNA polymerase with the promoter would differ if the figure showed transcription initiation for bacteria.*

a terminator sequence in the DNA. The transcribed terminator (an RNA sequence) functions as the termination signal, causing the polymerase to detach from the DNA and release the transcript, which requires no further modification before translation. In eukaryotes, RNA polymerase II

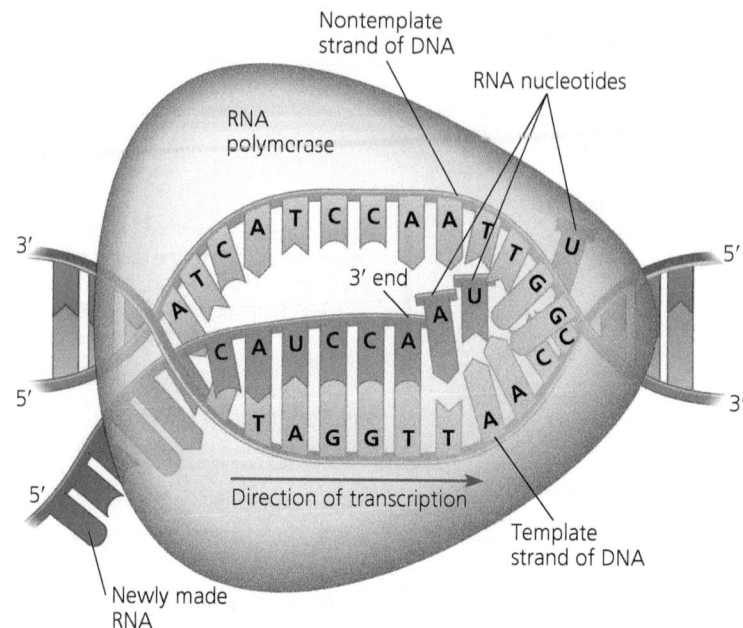

▲ **Figure 17.9** **Transcription elongation.** RNA polymerase moves along the DNA template strand, joining complementary RNA nucleotides to the 3′ end of the growing RNA transcript. Behind the polymerase, the new RNA peels away from the template strand, which re-forms a double helix with the nontemplate strand.

transcribes a sequence on the DNA called the polyadenylation signal sequence, which specifies a polyadenylation signal (AAUAAA) in the pre-mRNA. This is called a "signal" because once this stretch of six RNA nucleotides appears, it is immediately bound by certain proteins in the nucleus. Then, at a point about 10–35 nucleotides downstream from the AAUAAA, these proteins cut the RNA transcript free from the polymerase, releasing the pre-mRNA. The pre-mRNA then undergoes processing, the topic of the next section. Although that cleavage marks the end of the mRNA, the RNA polymerase II continues to transcribe. Enzymes begin to degrade the RNA starting at its newly exposed 5′ end. The polymerase continues transcribing, pursued by the enzymes, until they catch up to the polymerase and it dissociates from the DNA.

CONCEPT CHECK 17.2

1. What is a promoter, and is it located at the upstream or downstream end of a transcription unit?

2. What enables RNA polymerase to start transcribing a gene at the right place on the DNA in a bacterial cell? In a eukaryotic cell?

3. **WHAT IF?** Suppose X-rays caused a sequence change in the TATA box of a particular gene's promoter. How would that affect transcription of the gene? (See Figure 17.8.)

For suggested answers, see Appendix A.

CONCEPT 17.3

Eukaryotic cells modify RNA after transcription

Enzymes in the eukaryotic nucleus modify pre-mRNA in specific ways before the genetic message is dispatched to the cytoplasm. During this **RNA processing**, both ends of the primary transcript are altered. Also, in most cases, certain interior sections of the RNA molecule are cut out and the remaining parts spliced together. These modifications produce an mRNA molecule ready for translation.

Alteration of mRNA Ends

Each end of a pre-mRNA molecule is modified in a particular way (**Figure 17.10**). The 5′ end is synthesized first; it receives a **5′ cap**, a modified form of a guanine (G) nucleotide added onto the 5′ end after transcription of the first 20–40 nucleotides. The 3′ end of the pre-mRNA molecule is also modified before the mRNA exits the nucleus. Recall that the pre-mRNA is released soon after the polyadenylation signal, AAUAAA, is transcribed. At the 3′ end, an

enzyme adds 50–250 more adenine (A) nucleotides, forming a **poly-A tail**. The 5′ cap and poly-A tail share several important functions. First, they seem to facilitate the export of the mature mRNA from the nucleus. Second, they help protect the mRNA from degradation by hydrolytic enzymes. And third, they help ribosomes attach to the 5′ end of the mRNA once the mRNA reaches the cytoplasm. Figure 17.10 shows a diagram of a eukaryotic mRNA molecule with cap and tail. The figure also shows the untranslated regions (UTRs) at the 5′ and 3′ ends of the mRNA (referred to as the 5′ UTR and 3′ UTR). The UTRs are parts of the mRNA that will not be translated into protein, but they have other functions, such as ribosome binding.

Split Genes and RNA Splicing

A remarkable stage of RNA processing in the eukaryotic nucleus is the removal of large portions of the RNA molecule that is initially synthesized—a cut-and-paste job called **RNA splicing**, similar to editing a video (**Figure 17.11**). The average length of a transcription unit along a human DNA molecule is about 27 000 nucleotide pairs, so the primary RNA transcript is also that long. However, it takes

▲ **Figure 17.10 RNA processing: addition of the 5′ cap and poly-A tail.** Enzymes modify the two ends of a eukaryotic pre-mRNA molecule. The modified ends may promote the export of mRNA from the nucleus, and they help protect the mRNA from degradation. When the mRNA reaches the cytoplasm, the modified ends, in conjunction with certain cytoplasmic proteins, facilitate ribosome attachment. The 5′ cap and poly-A tail are not translated into protein, nor are the regions called the 5′ untranslated region (5′ UTR) and 3′ untranslated region (3′ UTR).

▲ **Figure 17.11 RNA processing: RNA splicing.** The RNA molecule shown here codes for β-globin, one of the polypeptides of hemoglobin. The numbers under the RNA refer to codons; β-globin is 146 amino acids long. The β-globin gene and its pre-mRNA transcript have three exons, corresponding to sequences that will leave the nucleus as mRNA. (The 5′ UTR and 3′ UTR are parts of exons because they are included in the mRNA; however, they do not code for protein.) During RNA processing, the introns are cut out and the exons spliced together. In many genes, the introns are much larger than the exons.

Source: The World of the Cell, 3rd Edition, by Wayne M. Becker, Jane B. Reece, and Martin F. Poenie. Copyright © 1996 by Pearson Education. Reprinted and electronically reproduced by permission of Pearson Education, Inc., Upper Saddle River, New Jersey.

only 1200 nucleotides in RNA to code for the average-sized protein of 400 amino acids. (Remember, each amino acid is encoded by a *triplet* of nucleotides.) This means that most eukaryotic genes and their RNA transcripts have long noncoding stretches of nucleotides, regions that are not translated. Even more surprising is that most of these noncoding sequences are interspersed between coding segments of the gene and thus between coding segments of the pre-mRNA. In other words, the sequence of DNA nucleotides that codes for a eukaryotic polypeptide is usually not continuous; it is split into segments. The noncoding segments of nucleic acid that lie between coding regions are called *in*tervening sequences, or **introns**. The other regions are called **exons**, because they are eventually *ex*pressed, usually by being translated into amino acid sequences. (Exceptions include the UTRs of the exons at the ends of the RNA, which make up part of the mRNA but are not translated into protein. Because of these exceptions, you may find it helpful to think of exons as sequences of RNA that *exit* the nucleus.) The terms *intron* and *exon* are used for both RNA sequences and the DNA sequences that encode them.

In making a primary transcript from a gene, RNA polymerase II transcribes both introns and exons from the DNA, but the mRNA molecule that enters the cytoplasm is an abridged version. The introns are cut out from the molecule and the exons joined together, forming an mRNA molecule with a continuous coding sequence. This is the process of RNA splicing.

How is pre-mRNA splicing carried out? The removal of introns is accomplished by a large complex made of proteins and small RNAs called a **spliceosome**. This complex binds to several short nucleotide sequences along an intron, including key sequences at each end **(Figure 17.12)**. The intron is then released (and rapidly degraded), and the spliceosome joins together the two exons that flanked the intron. It turns out that the small RNAs in the spliceosome not only participate in spliceosome assembly and splice site recognition, but also catalyze the splicing reaction.

Ribozymes

The idea of a catalytic role for RNAs in the spliceosome arose from the discovery of **ribozymes**, RNA molecules that function as enzymes. In some organisms, RNA splicing can occur without proteins or even additional RNA molecules: The intron RNA functions as a ribozyme and catalyzes its own excision! For example, in the ciliate protist *Tetrahymena*, self-splicing occurs in the production of ribosomal RNA (rRNA), a component of the organism's ribosomes. The pre-rRNA actually removes its own introns. The discovery of ribozymes rendered obsolete the idea that all biological catalysts are proteins.

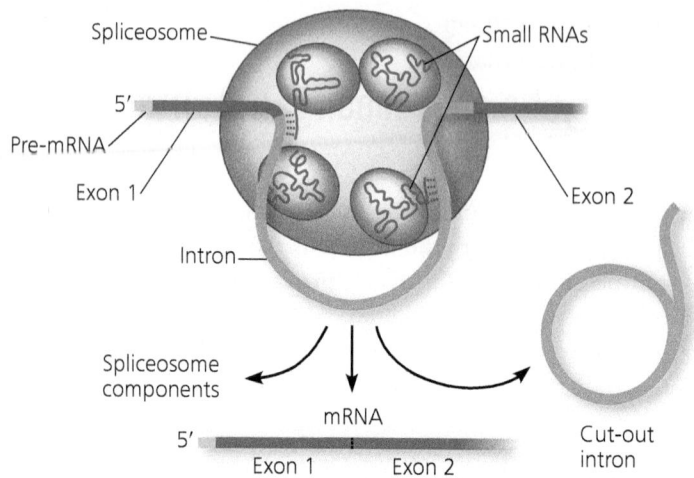

▲ **Figure 17.12 A spliceosome splicing a pre-mRNA.** The diagram shows a portion of a pre-mRNA transcript, with an intron (pink) flanked by two exons (red). Small RNAs within the spliceosome base-pair with nucleotides at specific sites along the intron. Next, the spliceosome catalyzes cutting of the pre-mRNA and the splicing together of the exons, releasing the intron for rapid degradation.

Three properties of RNA enable some RNA molecules to function as enzymes. First, because RNA is single-stranded, a region of an RNA molecule may base-pair with a complementary region elsewhere in the same molecule, which gives the molecule a particular three-dimensional structure. A specific structure is essential to the catalytic function of ribozymes, just as it is for enzymatic proteins. Second, like certain amino acids in an enzymatic protein, some of the bases in RNA contain functional groups that may participate in catalysis. Third, the ability of RNA to hydrogen-bond with other nucleic acid molecules (either RNA or DNA) adds specificity to its catalytic activity. For example, complementary base pairing between the RNA of the spliceosome and the RNA of a primary RNA transcript precisely locates the region where the ribozyme catalyzes splicing. Later in this chapter you will see how these properties of RNA also allow it to perform important noncatalytic roles in the cell, such as recognition of the three-nucleotide codons on mRNA.

The Functional and Evolutionary Importance of Introns

EVOLUTION Whether or not RNA splicing and the presence of introns have provided selective advantages during evolutionary history is a matter of some debate. In any case, it is informative to consider their possible adaptive benefits. Specific functions have not been identified for most introns, but at least some contain sequences that regulate gene expression, and many affect gene products.

One important consequence of the presence of introns in genes is that a single gene can encode more than one kind of polypeptide. Many genes are known to give rise to two or more different polypeptides, depending on which segments are treated as exons during RNA processing; this is called **alternative RNA splicing** (see Figure 18.13). For example, sex differences in fruit flies are largely due to differences in how males and females splice the RNA transcribed from certain genes. Results from the Human Genome Project (discussed in Concept 21.1) suggest that alternative RNA splicing is one reason humans can get along with about the same number of genes as a nematode (roundworm). Because of alternative splicing, the number of different protein products an organism produces can be much greater than its number of genes.

Proteins often have a modular architecture consisting of discrete structural and functional regions called **domains**. One domain of an enzyme, for example, might include the active site, while another might allow the enzyme to bind to a cellular membrane. In quite a few cases, different exons code for the different domains of a protein (Figure 17.13).

The presence of introns in a gene may facilitate the evolution of new and potentially beneficial proteins as a result of a process known as *exon shuffling* (see Figure 21.16). Introns increase the probability of crossing over between the exons of alleles of a gene—simply by providing more terrain for crossovers without interrupting coding sequences. This might result in new combinations of exons and proteins with altered structure and function. We can also imagine the occasional mixing and matching of exons between completely different (non-allelic) genes. Exon shuffling of either sort could lead to new proteins with novel combinations of functions. While most of the shuffling would result in nonbeneficial changes, occasionally a beneficial variant might arise.

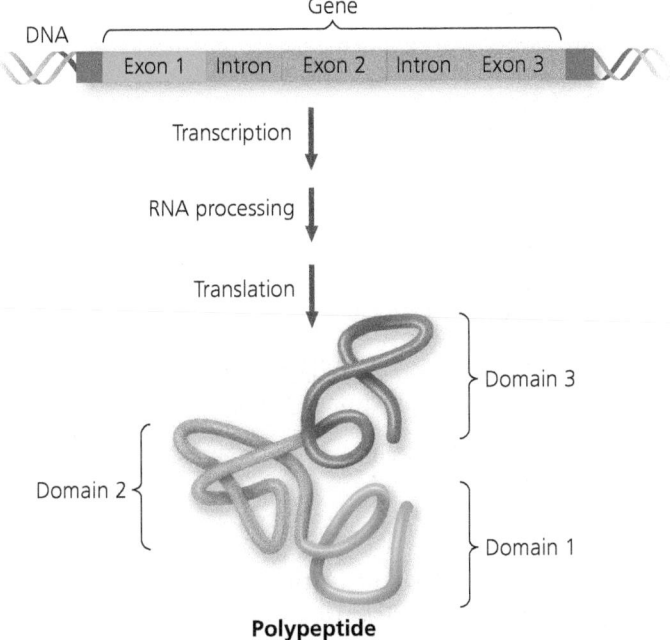

▲ **Figure 17.13 Correspondence between exons and protein domains.**

Source: Principles of Cell and Molecular Biology, 2nd Edition, by Lewis J. Kleinsmith and Valerie M. Kish. Copyright © 1995 by Pearson Education. Reprinted and electronically reproduced by permission of Pearson Education, Inc., Upper Saddle River, New Jersey.

CONCEPT 17.4

Translation is the RNA-directed synthesis of a polypeptide: *A closer look*

We will now examine in greater detail how genetic information flows from mRNA to protein—the process of translation. As we did for transcription, we'll concentrate on the basic steps of translation that occur in both bacteria and eukaryotes, while pointing out key differences.

Molecular Components of Translation

In the process of translation, a cell "reads" a genetic message and builds a polypeptide accordingly. The message is a series of codons along an mRNA molecule, and the translator is called **transfer RNA (tRNA)**. The function of tRNA is to transfer amino acids from the cytoplasmic pool of amino acids to a growing polypeptide in a ribosome. A cell keeps its cytoplasm stocked with all 20 amino acids, either by synthesizing them from other compounds or by taking them up from the surrounding solution. The ribosome, a structure made of proteins and RNAs, adds each amino acid brought to it by tRNA to the growing end of a polypeptide chain (Figure 17.14).

Translation is simple in principle but complex in its biochemistry and mechanics, especially in the eukaryotic cell. In dissecting translation, we'll concentrate on the slightly less complicated version of the process that occurs in bacteria. We'll begin by looking at the major players in this cellular process and then see how they act together in making a polypeptide.

The Structure and Function of Transfer RNA

The key to translating a genetic message into a specific amino acid sequence is the fact that each tRNA molecule enables translation of a given mRNA codon into a certain amino acid. This is possible because a tRNA bears a specific amino acid at one end of its three-dimensional structure, while at the other end is a nucleotide triplet that can base-pair with the complementary codon on mRNA.

(a) Two-dimensional structure. The four base-paired regions and three loops are characteristic of all tRNAs, as is the base sequence of the amino acid attachment site at the 3' end. The anticodon triplet is unique to each tRNA type, as are some sequences in the other two loops. (The asterisks mark bases that have been chemically modified, a characteristic of tRNA. The modified bases contribute to tRNA function in a way that is not yet understood.)

▲ **Figure 17.14 Translation: the basic concept.** As a molecule of mRNA is moved through a ribosome, codons are translated into amino acids, one by one. The interpreters are tRNA molecules, each type with a specific anticodon at one end and a corresponding amino acid at the other end. A tRNA adds its amino acid cargo to a growing polypeptide chain when the anticodon hydrogen-bonds to a complementary codon on the mRNA. The figures that follow show some of the details of translation in a bacterial cell.

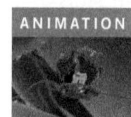

BioFlix Visit the Study Area in **MasteringBiology** for the BioFlix® 3-D Animation on Protein Synthesis.

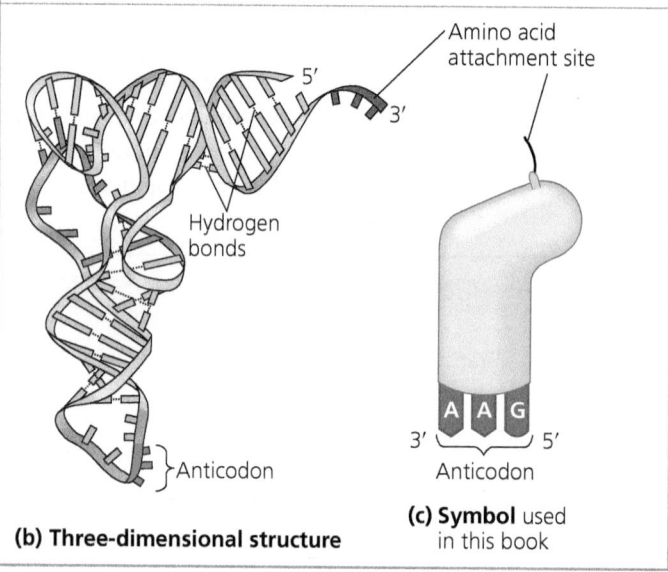

(b) Three-dimensional structure

(c) Symbol used in this book

▲ **Figure 17.15 The structure of transfer RNA (tRNA).** Anticodons are conventionally written 3' → 5' to align properly with codons written 5' → 3' (see Figure 17.14). For base pairing, RNA strands must be antiparallel, like DNA. For example, anticodon 3'-AAG-5' pairs with mRNA codon 5'-UUC-3'.

A tRNA molecule consists of a single RNA strand that is only about 80 nucleotides long (compared to hundreds of nucleotides for most mRNA molecules). Because of the presence of complementary stretches of nucleotide bases that can hydrogen-bond to each other, this single strand can fold back on itself and form a molecule with a three-dimensional structure. Flattened into one plane to clarify this base pairing, a tRNA molecule looks like a cloverleaf (**Figure 17.15a**). The tRNA actually twists and folds into a compact three-dimensional structure that is roughly L-shaped, with the 5' and 3' ends of the linear tRNA both located near one end of the structure (**Figure 17.15b**). The protruding 3' end acts as the attachment site for an amino acid. The loop extending from the other end of the L

includes the **anticodon**, the particular nucleotide triplet that base-pairs to a specific mRNA codon. Thus, the structure of a tRNA molecule fits its function.

Anticodons are conventionally written 3' → 5' to align properly with codons written 5' → 3' (see Figure 17.14). (For base pairing, RNA strands must be antiparallel, like DNA.)

As an example of how tRNAs work, consider the mRNA codon 5'-GGC-3', which is translated as the amino acid glycine. The tRNA that base-pairs with this codon by hydrogen bonding has 3'-CCG-5' as its anticodon and carries glycine at its other end (see the incoming tRNA approaching the ribosome in Figure 17.14). As an mRNA molecule is moved through a ribosome, glycine will be added to the polypeptide chain whenever the codon 5'-GGC-3' is presented for translation. Codon by codon, the genetic message is translated as tRNAs position each amino acid, in the order prescribed, and the ribosome adds that amino acid onto the growing polypeptide chain. The tRNA molecule is a translator in the sense that, in the context of the ribosome, it can read a nucleic acid word (the mRNA codon) and interpret it as a protein word (the amino acid).

Like mRNA and other types of cellular RNA, transfer RNA molecules are transcribed from DNA templates. In a eukaryotic cell, tRNA, like mRNA, is made in the nucleus and then travels from the nucleus to the cytoplasm, where it will participate in the process of translation. In both bacterial and eukaryotic cells, each tRNA molecule is used repeatedly, picking up its designated amino acid in the cytosol, depositing this cargo onto a polypeptide chain at the ribosome, and then leaving the ribosome, ready to pick up another of the same amino acid.

The accurate translation of a genetic message requires two instances of molecular recognition. First, a tRNA that binds to an mRNA codon specifying a particular amino acid must carry that amino acid, and no other, to the ribosome. The correct matching up of tRNA and amino acid is carried out by a family of related enzymes called **aminoacyl-tRNA synthetases** (Figure 17.16). The active site of each type of aminoacyl-tRNA synthetase fits only a specific combination of amino acid and tRNA. There are 20 different synthetases, one that joins each amino acid to an appropriate tRNA; each synthetase is able to bind to all the different tRNAs that code for its particular amino acid. The synthetase catalyzes the covalent attachment of the amino acid to its tRNA in a process driven by the hydrolysis of ATP. The resulting aminoacyl tRNA, also called a charged tRNA, is released from the enzyme and is then available to deliver its amino acid to a growing polypeptide chain on a ribosome.

The second instance of molecular recognition is the pairing of the tRNA anticodon with the appropriate mRNA codon. If one tRNA variety existed for each mRNA codon specifying an amino acid, there would be 61 tRNAs (see Figure 17.5). In fact, there are only about 45 bacterial tRNAs, signifying that some tRNAs must be able to bind to more than one codon. Such versatility is possible because the rules for base pairing between the third nucleotide base of a codon and the corresponding base of

1 The amino acid and the appropriate tRNA enter the active site of the specific synthetase.

Tyrosine (Tyr) (amino acid)

Tyrosyl-tRNA synthetase (enzyme), which can only bind tyrosine and Tyr-tRNA

Tyr-tRNA

Anticodon on tRNA complementary to the Tyr codon on mRNA

ATP

AMP + 2 (P)ᵢ

2 Using ATP, the synthetase catalyzes the covalent bonding of the amino acid to its specific tRNA.

Aminoacyl-tRNA synthetase

tRNA

Amino acid

3 The tRNA, charged with its amino acid, is released by the synthetase.

Computer model

▲ Figure 17.16 **An aminoacyl-tRNA synthetase joining a specific amino acid to a tRNA.** Linkage of the tRNA and amino acid is an endergonic process that occurs at the expense of ATP. The ATP loses two phosphate groups, becoming AMP (adenosine monophosphate).

a tRNA anticodon are relaxed compared to those at other codon positions. For example, the nucleotide base U at the 5' end of a tRNA anticodon can pair with either A or G in the third position (at the 3' end) of an mRNA codon. The flexible base pairing at this codon position is called **wobble**. Wobble explains why the synonymous codons for a given amino acid most often differ in their third nucleotide base, but not in the other bases. A case in point is that a tRNA with the anticodon 3'-UCU-5' can base-pair with either the mRNA codon 5'-AGA-3' or 5'-AGG-3', both of which code for arginine (see Figure 17.5).

Ribosomes

Ribosomes facilitate the specific coupling of tRNA anticodons with mRNA codons during protein synthesis. A ribosome consists of a large subunit and a small subunit, each made up of proteins and one or more

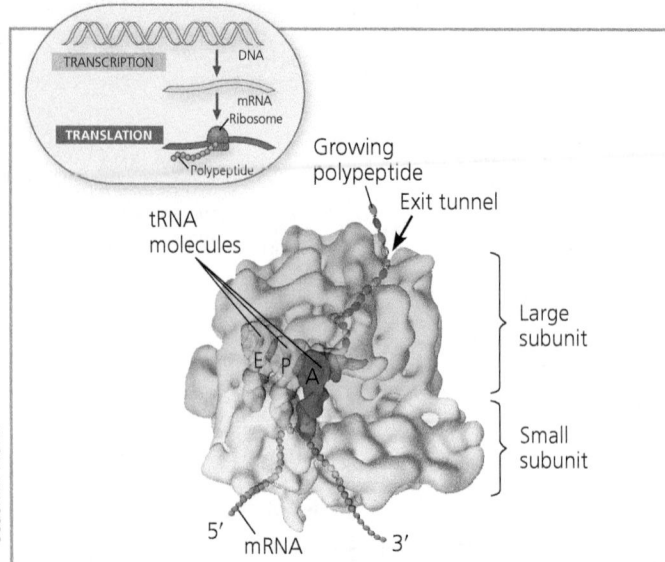

(a) Computer model of functioning ribosome. This is a model of a bacterial ribosome, showing its overall shape. The eukaryotic ribosome is roughly similar. A ribosomal subunit is a complex of ribosomal RNA molecules and proteins.

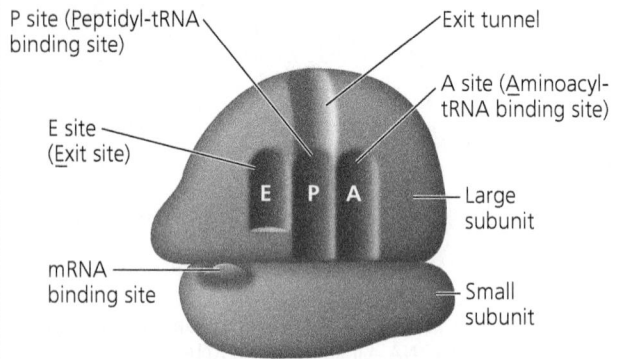

(b) Schematic model showing binding sites. A ribosome has an mRNA binding site and three tRNA binding sites, known as the A, P, and E sites. This schematic ribosome will appear in later diagrams.

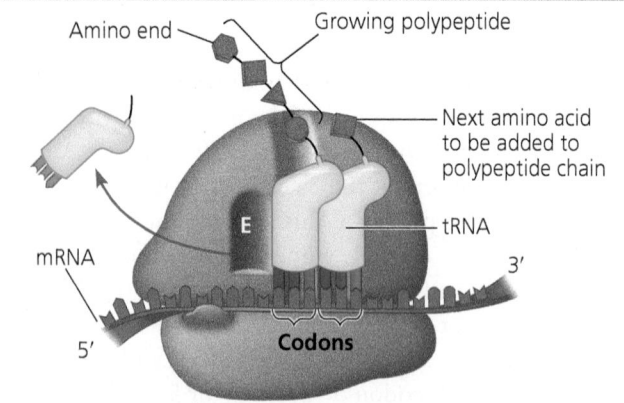

(c) Schematic model with mRNA and tRNA. A tRNA fits into a binding site when its anticodon base-pairs with an mRNA codon. The P site holds the tRNA attached to the growing polypeptide. The A site holds the tRNA carrying the next amino acid to be added to the polypeptide chain. Discharged tRNAs leave from the E site. The polypeptide grows at its carboxyl end.

▲ Figure 17.17 **The anatomy of a functioning ribosome.**

ribosomal RNAs (rRNAs) (Figure 17.17). In eukaryotes, the subunits are made in the nucleolus. Ribosomal RNA genes are transcribed, and the RNA is processed and assembled with proteins imported from the cytoplasm. Completed ribosomal subunits are then exported via nuclear pores to the cytoplasm. In both bacteria and eukaryotes, large and small subunits join to form a functional ribosome only when they attach to an mRNA molecule. About one-third of the mass of a ribosome is made up of proteins; the rest consists of rRNAs, either three molecules (in bacteria) or four (in eukaryotes). Because most cells contain thousands of ribosomes, rRNA is the most abundant type of cellular RNA.

Although the ribosomes of bacteria and eukaryotes are very similar in structure and function, eukaryotic ribosomes are slightly larger as well as differing somewhat from bacterial ribosomes in their molecular composition. The differences are medically significant. Certain antibiotic drugs can inactivate bacterial ribosomes without affecting eukaryotic ribosomes. These drugs, including tetracycline and streptomycin, are used to combat bacterial infections.

The structure of a ribosome reflects its function of bringing mRNA together with tRNAs carrying amino acids. In addition to a binding site for mRNA, each ribosome has three binding sites for tRNA, as described in Figure 17.17. The **P site** (**p**eptidyl-tRNA binding site) holds the tRNA carrying the growing polypeptide chain, while the **A site** (**a**minoacyl-tRNA binding site) holds the tRNA carrying the next amino acid to be added to the chain. Discharged tRNAs leave the ribosome from the **E site** (**e**xit site). The ribosome holds the tRNA and mRNA in close proximity and positions the new amino acid so that it can be added to the carboxyl end of the growing polypeptide. It then catalyzes the formation of the peptide bond. As the polypeptide becomes longer, it passes through an *exit tunnel* in the ribosome's large subunit. When the polypeptide is complete, it is released through the exit tunnel.

The widely accepted model is that rRNAs, rather than ribosomal proteins, are primarily responsible for both the structure and the function of the ribosome. The proteins, which are largely on the exterior, support the shape changes of the rRNA molecules as they carry out catalysis during translation. Ribosomal RNA is the main constituent of the interface between the two subunits and of the A and P sites, and it is the catalyst of peptide bond formation. Thus, a ribosome can be regarded as one colossal ribozyme!

Building a Polypeptide

We can divide translation, the synthesis of a polypeptide chain, into three stages (analogous to those of transcription): initiation, elongation, and termination. All three

1 A small ribosomal subunit binds to a molecule of mRNA. In a bacterial cell, the mRNA binding site on this subunit recognizes a specific nucleotide sequence on the mRNA just upstream of the start codon. An initiator tRNA, with the anticodon UAC, base-pairs with the start codon, AUG. This tRNA carries the amino acid methionine (Met).

2 The arrival of a large ribosomal subunit completes the initiation complex. Proteins called initiation factors (not shown) are required to bring all the translation components together. Hydrolysis of GTP provides the energy for the assembly. The initiator tRNA is in the P site; the A site is available to the tRNA bearing the next amino acid.

▲ Figure 17.18 **The initiation of translation.**

stages require protein "factors" that aid in the translation process. For certain aspects of chain initiation and elongation, energy is also required. It is provided by the hydrolysis of guanosine triphosphate (GTP), a molecule closely related to ATP.

Ribosome Association and Initiation of Translation

The initiation stage of translation brings together mRNA, a tRNA bearing the first amino acid of the polypeptide, and the two subunits of a ribosome (**Figure 17.18**). First, a small ribosomal subunit binds to both mRNA and a specific initiator tRNA, which carries the amino acid methionine. In bacteria, the small subunit can bind these two in either order; it binds the mRNA at a specific RNA sequence, just upstream of the start codon, AUG. In eukaryotes, the small subunit, with the initiator tRNA already bound, binds to the 5′ cap of the mRNA and then moves, or *scans*, downstream along the mRNA until it reaches the start codon; the initiator tRNA then hydrogen-bonds to the AUG start codon. In either bacteria or eukaryotes, the start codon signals the start of translation; this is important because it establishes the codon reading frame for the mRNA. In the Scientific Skills Exercise, you can work with DNA sequences encoding the ribosomal binding sites on the mRNAs of a group of *E. coli* genes.

The union of mRNA, initiator tRNA, and a small ribosomal subunit is followed by the attachment of a large ribosomal subunit, completing the *translation initiation complex*. Proteins called *initiation factors* are required to bring all these components together. The cell also expends energy

obtained by hydrolysis of a GTP molecule to form the initiation complex. At the completion of the initiation process, the initiator tRNA sits in the P site of the ribosome, and the vacant A site is ready for the next aminoacyl tRNA. Note that a polypeptide is always synthesized in one direction, from the initial methionine at the amino end, also called the N-terminus, toward the final amino acid at the carboxyl end, also called the C-terminus (see Figure 5.15).

Elongation of the Polypeptide Chain

In the elongation stage of translation, amino acids are added one by one to the previous amino acid at the C-terminus of the growing chain. Each addition involves the participation of several proteins called *elongation factors* and occurs in a three-step cycle described in **Figure 17.19**. Energy expenditure occurs in the first and third steps. Codon recognition requires hydrolysis of one molecule of GTP, which increases the accuracy and efficiency of this step. One more GTP is hydrolyzed to provide energy for the translocation step.

The mRNA is moved through the ribosome in one direction only, 5′ end first; this is equivalent to the ribosome moving 5′ → 3′ on the mRNA. The important point is that the ribosome and the mRNA move relative to each other, unidirectionally, codon by codon. The elongation cycle takes less than a tenth of a second in bacteria and is repeated as each amino acid is added to the chain until the polypeptide is completed. The empty tRNAs that are released from the E site return to the cytoplasm, where they will be reloaded with the appropriate amino acid (see Figure 17.16).

Termination of Translation

The final stage of translation is termination (**Figure 17.20** on p. 370). Elongation continues until a stop codon in the mRNA reaches the A site. The nucleotide base triplets UAG, UAA, and UGA (all written 5′ → 3′) do not code for amino acids but instead act as signals to stop translation. A *release factor*, a protein shaped like an aminoacyl tRNA, binds directly to a stop codon in the A site. The release factor causes the addition of a water molecule instead of an amino acid to the polypeptide chain. (Water molecules are abundant in the aqueous cellular environment.) This reaction breaks (hydrolyzes) the bond between the completed polypeptide and the tRNA in the P site, releasing the polypeptide through the exit tunnel of the ribosome's large subunit. The remainder of the translation assembly then

Interpreting a Sequence Logo

How Can a Sequence Logo Be Used to Identify Ribosome Binding Sites? When initiating translation, ribosomes bind to an mRNA at a ribosome binding site upstream of the AUG start codon. Because mRNAs from different genes all bind to a ribosome, the genes encoding these mRNAs are likely to have a similar base sequence where the ribosomes bind. Therefore, candidate ribosome binding sites on mRNA can be identified by comparing DNA sequences (and thus the mRNA sequences) of multiple genes in a species, searching the region upstream of the start codon for shared ("conserved") stretches of bases. In this exercise, you will analyze DNA sequences from multiple such genes, represented by a visual graphic called a sequence logo.

How the Experiment Was Done The DNA sequences of 149 genes from the *E. coli* genome were aligned using computer software. The aim was to identify similar base sequences—at the appropriate location in each gene—as potential ribosome binding sites. Rather than presenting the data as a series of 149 sequences aligned in a column (a sequence alignment), the researchers used a sequence logo.

Data from the Experiment To show how sequence logos are made, the potential ribosome binding regions from 10 *E. coli* genes are shown in a sequence alignment, followed by the sequence logo derived from the aligned sequences. Note that the DNA shown is the nontemplate (coding) strand, which is how DNA sequences are typically presented.

thrA	G G T A A C G A G G T A A C A A C C A T G C G A G T G
lacA	C A T A A C G G A G T G A T C G C A T T G A A C A T G
lacY	C G C G T A A G G A A A T C C A T T A T G T A C T A T
lacZ	T T C A C A C A G G A A A C A G C T A T G A C C A T G
lacI	C A A T T C A G G G T G G T G A A T G T G A A A C C A
recA	G G C A T G A C A G G A G T A A A A A T G G C T A T C
galR	A C C C A C T A A G G T A T T T T C A T G G C G A C C
metJ	A A G A G G A T T A A G T A T C T C A T G G C T G A A
lexA	A T A C A C C C A G G G G G G C G G A A T G A A A G C G
trpR	T A A C A A T G G C G A C A T A T T A T G G C C C A A

5′ ‑18 ‑17 ‑16 ‑15 ‑14 ‑13 ‑12 ‑11 ‑10 ‑9 ‑8 ‑7 ‑6 ‑5 ‑4 ‑3 ‑2 ‑1 0 1 2 3 4 5 6 7 8 3′

▲ **Sequence alignment**

▲ **Sequence logo**

Interpret the Data

1. In the sequence logo (bottom, left), the horizontal axis shows the primary sequence of the DNA by nucleotide position. Letters for each base are stacked on top of each other according to their relative frequency at that position among the aligned sequences, with the most common base as the largest letter at the top of the stack. The height of each letter represents the relative frequency of that base *at that position*. (a) In the sequence alignment, count the number of each base at position –9 and order them from most to least frequent. Compare this to the size and placement of each base at –9 in the logo. (b) Do the same for positions 0 and 1.

2. The height of a stack of letters in a logo indicates the predictive power of that stack (determined statistically). If the stack is tall, we can be more confident in predicting what base will be in that position if a new sequence is added to the logo. For example, at position 2, all 10 sequences have a G; the probability of finding a G there in a new sequence is very high, as is the stack. For short stacks, the bases all have about the same frequency, so it's hard to predict a base at those positions. (a) Which two positions have the most predictable bases? What bases do you predict would be at those positions in a newly sequenced gene? (b) Which 12 positions have the least predictable bases? How do you know? How does this reflect the relative frequencies of the bases shown in the 10 sequences? Use the two leftmost positions of the 12 as examples in your answer.

3. In the actual experiment, the researchers used 149 sequences to build their sequence logo, which is shown below. There is a stack at each position, even if short, because the sequence logo includes more data. (a) Which three positions in this sequence logo have the most predictable bases? Name the most frequent base at each. (b) Which positions have the least predictable bases? How can you tell?

4. A consensus sequence identifies the base occurring most often at each position in the set of sequences. (a) Write out the consensus sequence of this (the nontemplate) strand. In any position where the base can't be determined, put a dash. (b) Which provides more information—the consensus sequence or the sequence logo? What is lost in the less informative method?

5. (a) Based on the logo, what five adjacent base positions in the 5′ UTR region are most likely to be involved in ribosome binding? Explain. (b) What is represented by the bases in positions 0–2?

Material provided courtesy of Dr. Thomas Schneider, National Cancer Institute, National Institutes of Health, 2012.

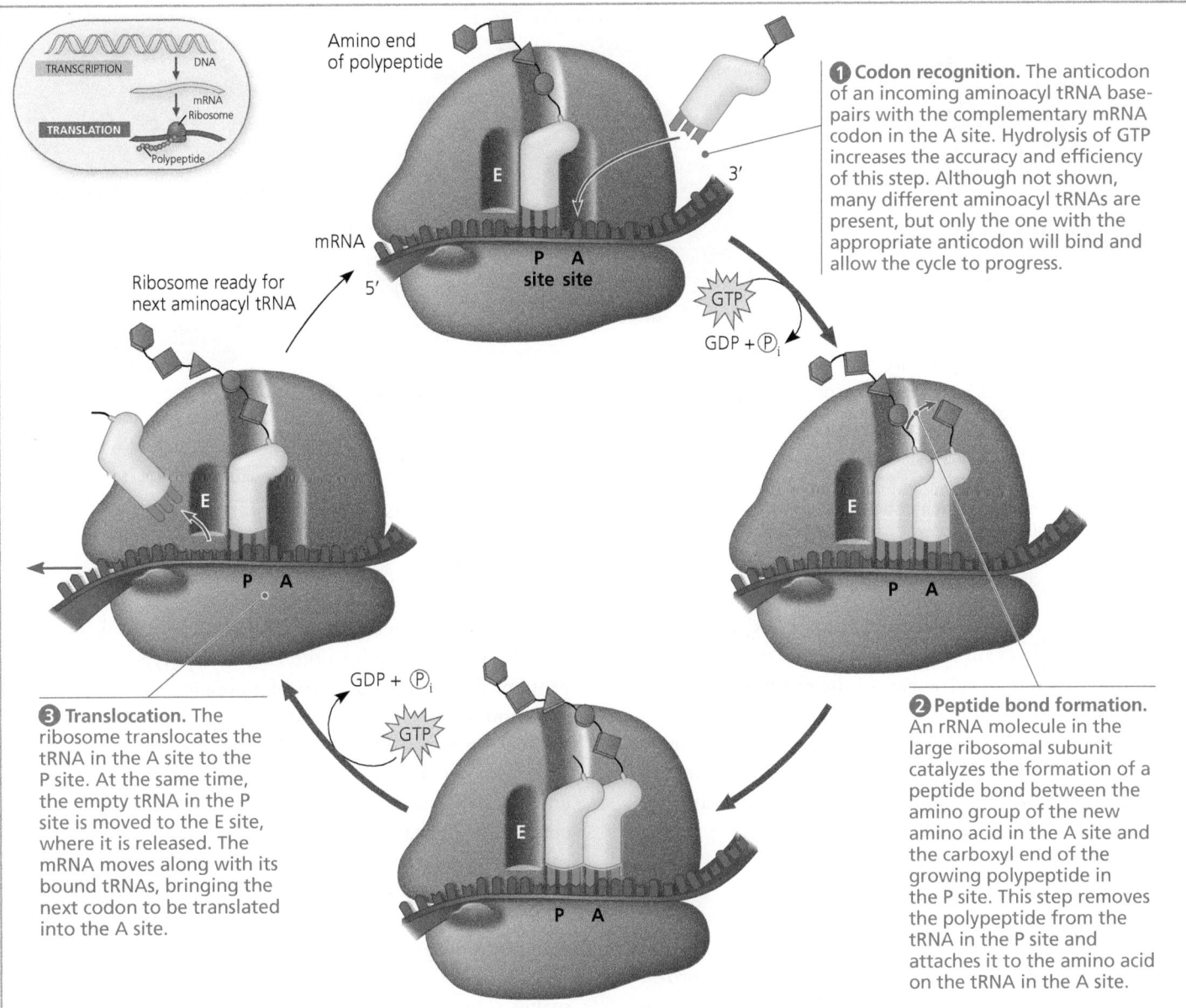

Amino end of polypeptide

mRNA

5'

3'

Ribosome ready for next aminoacyl tRNA

E

P A
site site

1 Codon recognition. The anticodon of an incoming aminoacyl tRNA base-pairs with the complementary mRNA codon in the A site. Hydrolysis of GTP increases the accuracy and efficiency of this step. Although not shown, many different aminoacyl tRNAs are present, but only the one with the appropriate anticodon will bind and allow the cycle to progress.

GTP

GDP + P_i

E

P A

2 Peptide bond formation. An rRNA molecule in the large ribosomal subunit catalyzes the formation of a peptide bond between the amino group of the new amino acid in the A site and the carboxyl end of the growing polypeptide in the P site. This step removes the polypeptide from the tRNA in the P site and attaches it to the amino acid on the tRNA in the A site.

E

P A

GDP + P_i

GTP

E

P A

3 Translocation. The ribosome translocates the tRNA in the A site to the P site. At the same time, the empty tRNA in the P site is moved to the E site, where it is released. The mRNA moves along with its bound tRNAs, bringing the next codon to be translated into the A site.

▲ **Figure 17.19 The elongation cycle of translation.** The hydrolysis of GTP plays an important role in the elongation process. Not shown are the proteins called elongation factors.

comes apart in a multistep process, aided by other protein factors. Breakdown of the translation assembly requires the hydrolysis of two more GTP molecules.

Completing and Targeting the Functional Protein

The process of translation is often not sufficient to make a functional protein. In this section, you will learn about modifications that polypeptide chains undergo after the translation process as well as some of the mechanisms used to target completed proteins to specific sites in the cell.

Protein Folding and Post-Translational Modifications

During its synthesis, a polypeptide chain begins to coil and fold spontaneously as a consequence of its amino acid

sequence (primary structure), forming a protein with a specific shape: a three-dimensional molecule with secondary and tertiary structure (see Figure 5.18). Thus, a gene determines primary structure, and primary structure in turn determines shape. In many cases, a chaperone protein (chaperonin) helps the polypeptide fold correctly (see Figure 5.21).

Additional steps—*post-translational modifications*—may be required before the protein can begin doing its particular job in the cell. Certain amino acids may be chemically modified by the attachment of sugars, lipids, phosphate groups, or other additions. Enzymes may remove one or more amino acids from the leading (amino) end of the polypeptide chain. In some cases, a polypeptide chain may be enzymatically cleaved into two or more pieces.

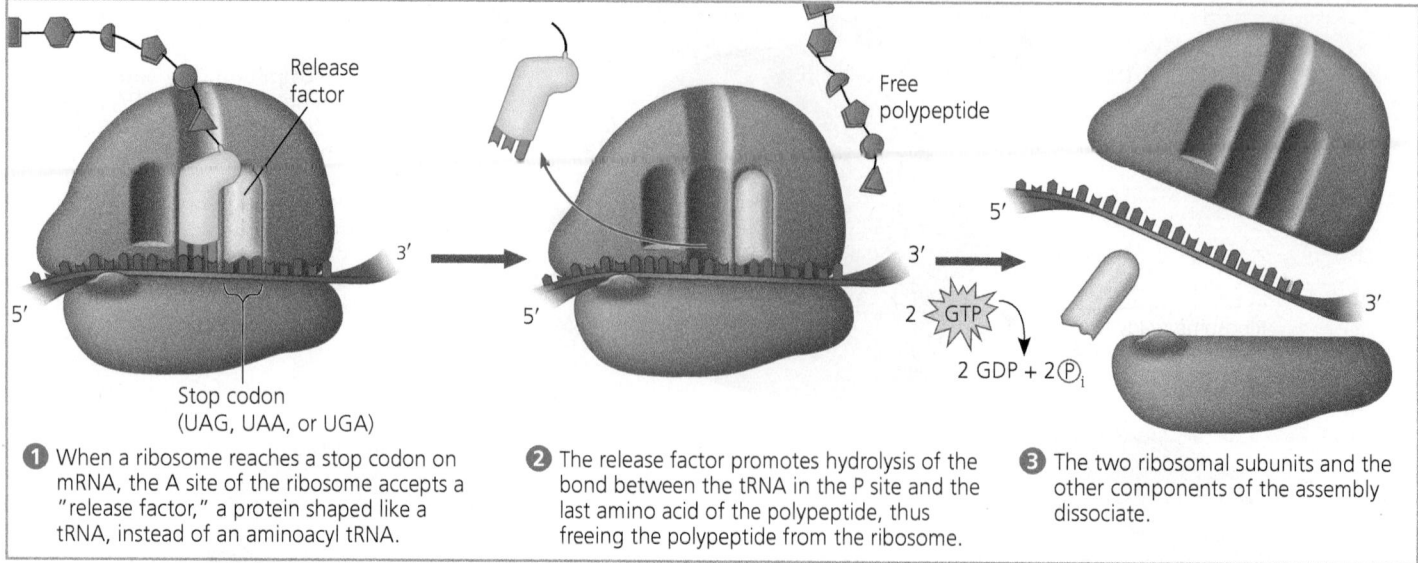

① When a ribosome reaches a stop codon on mRNA, the A site of the ribosome accepts a "release factor," a protein shaped like a tRNA, instead of an aminoacyl tRNA.

② The release factor promotes hydrolysis of the bond between the tRNA in the P site and the last amino acid of the polypeptide, thus freeing the polypeptide from the ribosome.

③ The two ribosomal subunits and the other components of the assembly dissociate.

▲ Figure 17.20 **The termination of translation.** Like elongation, termination requires GTP hydrolysis as well as additional protein factors, which are not shown here.

For example, the protein insulin is first synthesized as a single polypeptide chain but becomes active only after an enzyme cuts out a central part of the chain, leaving a protein made up of two polypeptide chains connected by disulfide bridges. In other cases, two or more polypeptides that are synthesized separately may come together, becoming the subunits of a protein that has quaternary structure. A familiar example is hemoglobin (see Figure 5.18).

Targeting Polypeptides to Specific Locations

In electron micrographs of eukaryotic cells active in protein synthesis, two populations of ribosomes (and polyribosomes) are evident: free and bound (see Figure 6.10). Free ribosomes are suspended in the cytosol and mostly synthesize proteins that stay in the cytosol and function there. In contrast, bound ribosomes are attached to the cytosolic side of the endoplasmic reticulum (ER) or to the nuclear envelope. Bound ribosomes make proteins of the endomembrane system (the nuclear envelope, ER, Golgi apparatus, lysosomes, vacuoles, and plasma membrane) as well as proteins secreted from the cell, such as insulin. It is important to note that the ribosomes themselves are identical and can alternate between being free ribosomes one time they are used and being bound ribosomes the next.

What determines whether a ribosome is free in the cytosol or bound to rough ER? Polypeptide synthesis always begins in the cytosol as a free ribosome starts to translate an mRNA molecule. There the process continues to completion—*unless* the growing polypeptide itself cues the ribosome to attach to the ER. The polypeptides of proteins destined for the endomembrane system or for secretion are marked by a **signal peptide**, which targets the protein to the ER (Figure 17.21). The signal peptide, a sequence of about 20 amino acids at or near the leading end (N-terminus) of the polypeptide, is recognized as it emerges from the ribosome by a protein-RNA complex called a **signal-recognition particle (SRP)**. This particle functions as an escort that brings the ribosome to a receptor protein built into the ER membrane. The receptor is part of a multiprotein translocation complex. Polypeptide synthesis continues there, and the growing polypeptide snakes across the membrane into the ER lumen via a protein pore. The signal peptide is usually removed by an enzyme. The rest of the completed polypeptide, if it is to be secreted from the cell, is released into solution within the ER lumen (as in Figure 17.21). Alternatively, if the polypeptide is to be a membrane protein, it remains partially embedded in the ER membrane. In either case, it travels in a transport vesicle from the ER to its destination (see, for example, Figure 7.9).

Other kinds of signal peptides are used to target polypeptides to mitochondria, chloroplasts, the interior of the nucleus, and other organelles that are not part of the endomembrane system. The critical difference in these cases is that translation is completed in the cytosol before the polypeptide is imported into the organelle. The mechanisms of translocation also vary, but in all cases studied to date, the "postal codes" that address proteins for secretion or to cellular locations are signal peptides of some sort. Bacteria

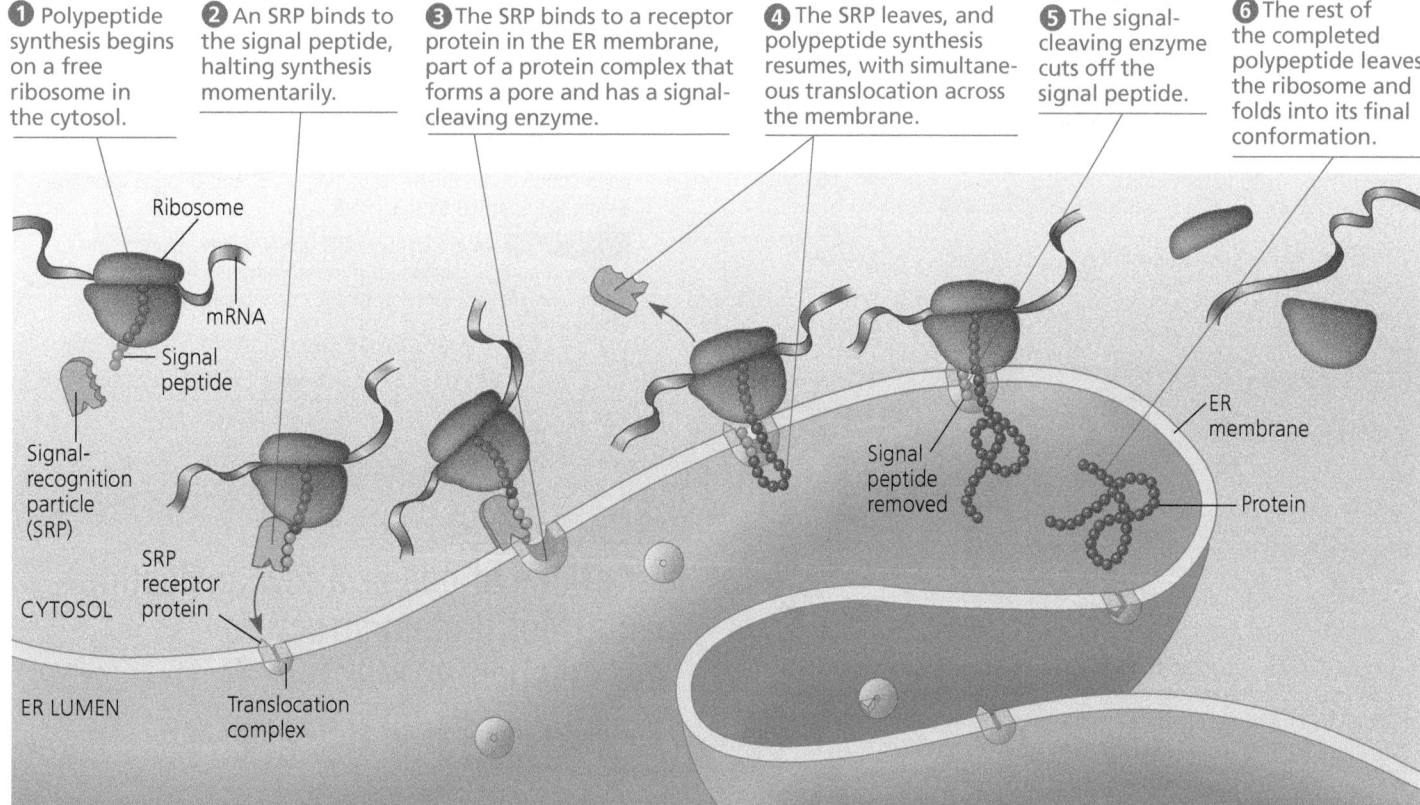

① Polypeptide synthesis begins on a free ribosome in the cytosol.

② An SRP binds to the signal peptide, halting synthesis momentarily.

③ The SRP binds to a receptor protein in the ER membrane, part of a protein complex that forms a pore and has a signal-cleaving enzyme.

④ The SRP leaves, and polypeptide synthesis resumes, with simultaneous translocation across the membrane.

⑤ The signal-cleaving enzyme cuts off the signal peptide.

⑥ The rest of the completed polypeptide leaves the ribosome and folds into its final conformation.

Ribosome

mRNA

Signal peptide

Signal-recognition particle (SRP)

SRP receptor protein

CYTOSOL

ER LUMEN

Translocation complex

Signal peptide removed

ER membrane

Protein

▲ Figure 17.21 **The signal mechanism for targeting proteins to the ER.**

MAKE CONNECTIONS *If this protein were destined for secretion, what would happen to it after its synthesis was completed? See Figure 7.9.*

also employ signal peptides to target proteins to the plasma membrane for secretion.

Making Multiple Polypeptides in Bacteria and Eukaryotes

In previous sections, you learned how a single polypeptide is synthesized using the information encoded in an mRNA molecule. When a polypeptide is required in a cell, though, the need is for many copies, not just one.

A single ribosome can make an average-sized polypeptide in less than a minute. In both bacteria and eukaryotes, however, multiple ribosomes translate an mRNA at the same time (Figure 17.22); that is, a single mRNA is used to make many copies of a polypeptide simultaneously. Once a ribosome is far enough past the start codon, a second ribosome can attach to the mRNA, eventually resulting in a number of ribosomes trailing along the mRNA. Such strings of ribosomes, called **polyribosomes** (or **polysomes**), can be seen with an electron microscope (see Figure 17.22). They enable a cell to make many copies of a polypeptide very quickly.

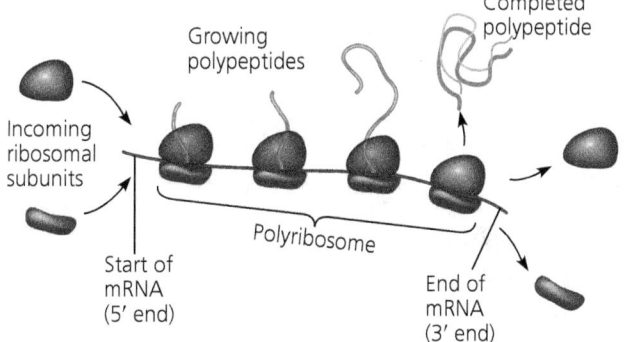

Incoming ribosomal subunits

Growing polypeptides

Completed polypeptide

Polyribosome

Start of mRNA (5' end)

End of mRNA (3' end)

(a) An mRNA molecule is generally translated simultaneously by several ribosomes in clusters called polyribosomes.

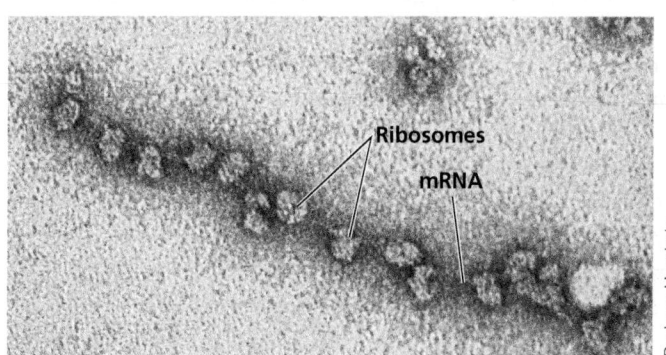

Ribosomes

mRNA

0.1 μm

Barbara Hamkalo

(b) This micrograph shows a large polyribosome in a bacterial cell. Growing polypeptides are not visible here (TEM).

▲ Figure 17.22 **Polyribosomes.**

▲ **Figure 17.23 Coupled transcription and translation in bacteria.** In bacterial cells, the translation of mRNA can begin as soon as the leading (5′) end of the mRNA molecule peels away from the DNA template. The micrograph (TEM) shows a strand of *E. coli* DNA being transcribed by RNA polymerase molecules. Attached to each RNA polymerase molecule is a growing strand of mRNA, which is already being translated by ribosomes. The newly synthesized polypeptides are not visible in the micrograph but are shown in the diagram.

? *Which one of the mRNA molecules started being transcribed first? On that mRNA, which ribosome started translating the mRNA first?*

Another way both bacteria and eukaryotes augment the number of copies of a polypeptide is by transcribing multiple mRNAs from the same gene, as we mentioned earlier. However, the coordination of the two processes—transcription and translation—differ in the two groups. The most important differences between bacteria and eukaryotes arise from the bacterial cell's lack of compartmental organization. Like a one-room workshop, a bacterial cell ensures a streamlined operation by coupling the two processes. In the absence of a nucleus, it can simultaneously transcribe and translate the same gene (**Figure 17.23**), and the newly made protein can quickly diffuse to its site of function.

In contrast, the eukaryotic cell's nuclear envelope segregates transcription from translation and provides a compartment for extensive RNA processing. This processing stage includes additional steps, discussed earlier, the regulation of which can help coordinate the eukaryotic cell's elaborate activities. **Figure 17.24** summarizes the path from gene to polypeptide in a eukaryotic cell.

CONCEPT CHECK 17.4

1. What two processes ensure that the correct amino acid is added to a growing polypeptide chain?

2. Discuss the ways in which rRNA structure likely contributes to ribosomal function.

3. Describe how a polypeptide to be secreted reaches the endomembrane system.

4. **WHAT IF?** **DRAW IT** Draw a tRNA with the anticodon 3′-CGU-5′. What two different codons could it bind to? Draw each codon on an mRNA, labelling all 5′ and 3′ ends. Add the amino acid carried by this tRNA.

5. **WHAT IF?** In eukaryotic cells, mRNAs have been found to have a circular arrangement in which proteins hold the poly-A-tail near the 5′ cap. How might this increase translation efficiency?

For suggested answers, see Appendix A.

CONCEPT 17.5

Mutations of one or a few nucleotides can affect protein structure and function

Now that you have explored the process of gene expression, you are ready to understand the effects of changes to the genetic information of a cell (or virus). These changes, called **mutations**, are responsible for the huge diversity of genes found among organisms because mutations are the ultimate source of new genes. Earlier, we considered chromosomal rearrangements that affect long segments of DNA (see Figure 15.15); these are considered large-scale mutations. Here we examine small-scale mutations of one or a few nucleotide pairs, including **point mutations**, changes in a single nucleotide pair of a gene.

If a point mutation occurs in a gamete or in a cell that gives rise to gametes, it may be transmitted to offspring and to future generations. If the mutation has an adverse effect on the phenotype of a person, the mutant condition is referred to as a genetic disorder or hereditary disease. For example, we can trace the genetic basis of sickle-cell disease to the mutation of a single nucleotide pair in the gene that encodes the β-globin polypeptide of hemoglobin. The change of a single nucleotide in the DNA's template strand leads to an altered mRNA and the production of an abnormal protein (**Figure 17.25** on p. 374; also see Figure 5.19). In individuals who are homozygous for the mutant allele, the sickling of red blood cells caused by the altered hemoglobin produces the multiple symptoms associated with sickle-cell disease (see Concept 14.4). Another disorder caused by a point mutation is a heart condition called familial cardiomyopathy that is responsible for some incidents of sudden death in young athletes and others. Point mutations in several genes encoding muscle proteins have been identified, any of which can lead to this disorder.

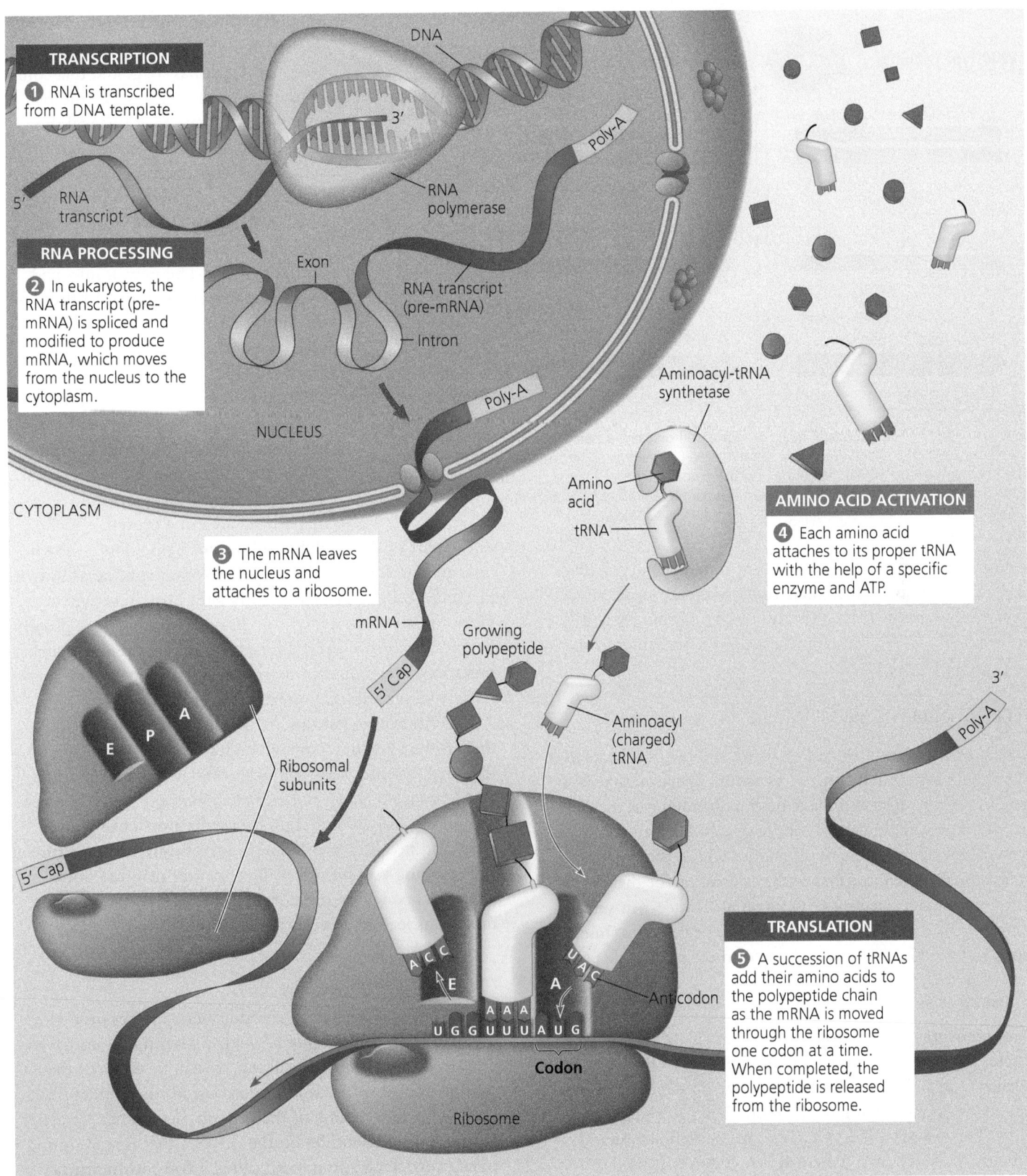

TRANSCRIPTION

① RNA is transcribed from a DNA template.

DNA

3'

RNA transcript

5'

RNA polymerase

Poly-A

RNA PROCESSING

② In eukaryotes, the RNA transcript (pre-mRNA) is spliced and modified to produce mRNA, which moves from the nucleus to the cytoplasm.

Exon

RNA transcript (pre-mRNA)

Intron

Poly-A

NUCLEUS

CYTOPLASM

Aminoacyl-tRNA synthetase

Amino acid

tRNA

AMINO ACID ACTIVATION

④ Each amino acid attaches to its proper tRNA with the help of a specific enzyme and ATP.

③ The mRNA leaves the nucleus and attaches to a ribosome.

mRNA

Growing polypeptide

5' Cap

Aminoacyl (charged) tRNA

3'

Poly-A

E P A

Ribosomal subunits

5' Cap

TRANSLATION

⑤ A succession of tRNAs add their amino acids to the polypeptide chain as the mRNA is moved through the ribosome one codon at a time. When completed, the polypeptide is released from the ribosome.

A C C

E

A A A

U A C

A

Anticodon

U G G U U U A U G

Codon

Ribosome

▲ Figure 17.24 **A summary of transcription and translation in a eukaryotic cell.** This diagram shows the path from one gene to one polypeptide. Keep in mind that each gene in the DNA can be transcribed repeatedly into many identical RNA molecules and that each mRNA can be translated repeatedly to yield many identical polypeptide molecules. (Also, remember that the final products of some genes are not polypeptides but RNA molecules, including tRNA and rRNA.) In general, the steps of transcription and translation are similar in bacterial, archaeal, and eukaryotic cells. The major difference is the occurrence of RNA processing in the eukaryotic nucleus. Other significant differences are found in the initiation stages of both transcription and translation and in the termination of transcription.

Wild-type β-globin	Sickle-cell β-globin	
Wild-type β-globin DNA	Mutant β-globin DNA	In the DNA, the mutant (sickle-cell) template strand (top) has an A where the wild-type template has a T.
3′ C T C 5′ 5′ G A G 3′	3′ C A C 5′ 5′ G T G 3′	
mRNA	mRNA	The mutant mRNA has a U instead of an A in one codon.
5′ G A G 3′	5′ G U G 3′	
Normal hemoglobin	Sickle-cell hemoglobin	The mutant β-globin has a valine (Val) instead of a glutamic acid (Glu).
Glu	Val	

▲ **Figure 17.25** **The molecular basis of sickle-cell disease: a point mutation.** The allele that causes sickle-cell disease differs from the wild-type (normal) allele by a single DNA nucleotide pair. The micrographs are SEMs of a normal red blood cell (on the left) and a sickled red blood cell (right) from individuals homozygous for either wild-type or mutant alleles, respectively.

Some diseases are caused by many different point mutations. For example, more than 1000 different mutations have been identified that can cause cystic fibrosis. Scientists are currently researching mutation-specifc treatments for this disease (Figure 17.26).

Types of Small-Scale Mutations

Let's now consider how small-scale mutations affect proteins. We should first note that many mutations occur outside of genes, and any effect they have on the phenotype of the organism may be subtle and hard to detect. For that reason, we will concentrate here on mutations within protein-coding genes. Small-scale mutations within a gene can be divided into two general categories: (1) single nucleotide-pair substitutions and (2) nucleotide-pair insertions or deletions. Insertions and deletions can involve one or more nucleotide pairs.

Substitutions

A **nucleotide-pair substitution** is the replacement of one nucleotide and its partner with another pair of nucleotides (Figure 17.27a). Some substitutions have no effect on the encoded protein, owing to the redundancy of the genetic code. For example, if 3′-CCG-5′ on the template strand mutated to 3′-CCA-5′, the mRNA codon that used to be GGC would become GGU, but a glycine would still be inserted at the proper location in the protein (see Figure 17.5). In other words, a change in a nucleotide pair may transform one codon into another that is translated into the same amino acid. Such a change is an example of a **silent mutation**, which has no observable effect on the

phenotype. (Silent mutations can occur outside genes as well.) Interestingly, recent research has suggested that some silent mutations may have an indirect effect on where or at what level the gene gets expressed, even though the actual protein is the same. Substitutions that change one amino acid to another one are called **missense mutations**. Such a mutation may have little effect on the protein: The new amino acid may have properties similar to those of the amino acid it replaces, or it may be in a region of the protein where the exact sequence of amino acids is not essential to the protein's function.

However, the nucleotide-pair substitutions of greatest interest are those that cause a major change in a protein. The alteration of a single amino acid in a crucial area of a protein—such as in the part of the β-globin subunit of hemoglobin shown in Figure 17.25 or in the active site of an enzyme as shown in Figure 8.19—can significantly alter protein activity. Occasionally, such a mutation leads to an improved protein or one with novel capabilities, but much more often such mutations are neutral or detrimental, leading to a useless or less active protein that impairs cellular function.

Substitution mutations are usually missense mutations; that is, the altered codon still codes for an amino acid and thus makes sense, although not necessarily the *right* sense. But a point mutation can also change a codon for an amino acid into a stop codon. This is called a **nonsense mutation**, and it causes translation to be terminated prematurely; the resulting polypeptide will be shorter than the polypeptide encoded by the normal gene. Nearly all nonsense mutations lead to nonfunctional proteins.

Insertions and Deletions

Insertions and **deletions** are additions or losses of nucleotide pairs in a gene (Figure 17.27b). These mutations have a disastrous effect on the resulting protein more often than substitutions do. Insertion or deletion of nucleotides may alter the reading frame of the genetic message, the triplet grouping of nucleotides on the mRNA that is read during translation. Such a mutation, called a **frameshift mutation**, occurs whenever the number of nucleotides inserted or deleted is not a multiple of three. All nucleotides downstream of the deletion or insertion will be improperly grouped into codons: The result will be extensive missense mutations, usually ending sooner or later in a nonsense mutation that leads to premature termination. Unless the

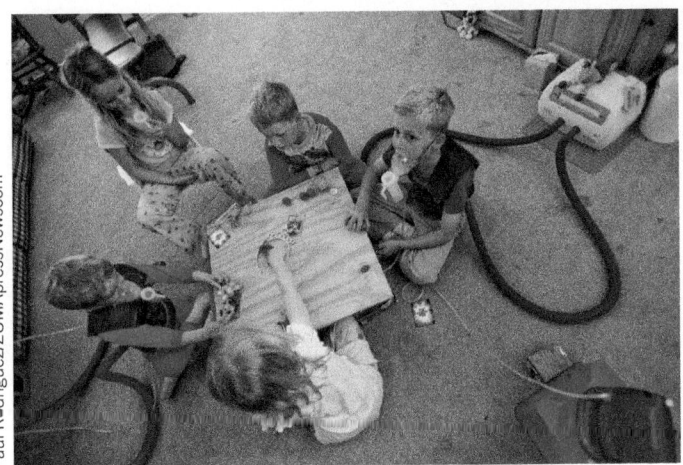

▼ Figure 17.26 | **Impact**

Mutation-Specific Disease Treatment

In 1989, a team including scientists from the Hospital for Sick Children in Toronto identified the gene responsible for cystic fibrosis (CF). This gene codes for the cystic fibrosis transmembrane regulator (CFTR), a membrane chloride channel. Since discovery of this gene, over 1600 CF-causing mutations have been identified and are recorded in the Cystic Fibrosis Mutation Database at the Hospital for Sick Children.

Recently, treatment modalities that are targeted to a patient's specific CF-causing mutation have been in development. One treatment increases CFTR function in the cell membrane, another treatment helps the CFTR protein to fold properly and insert into the membrane, and another treatment assists the translation process to read through an early stop codon.

Why It Matters Currently, cystic fibrosis affects approximately 1 in 3600 children born in Canada. Despite the discovery of the CF gene over 20 years ago, current therapies, such as mucus-thinning drugs and antibiotics, only treat the symptoms of the disease. The generation of mutation-specific therapies will allow treatment targeted to the underlying molecular basis of the disease and launch CF treatment as one of the frontrunners of personalized medicine.

Further Reading D. Sheppard, Cystic fibrosis: CFTR correctors to the rescue, *Chemistry & Biology* 18:145–147 (2011); E. Dolgin, Mutation-specific cystic fibrosis treatments on the verge of approval, *Nature* 7:396–397 (2011).

MAKE CONNECTIONS *Figure 5.26 introduced the idea of personalized medicine based on an individual's genome, and Chapter 14 introduced several inherited genetic diseases. Do you think some genetic diseases would be better candidates for personalized medicine compared with other genetic diseases? Why or why not?*

frameshift is very near the end of the gene, the protein is almost certain to be nonfunctional. Insertions and deletions also occur outside of coding regions; these are not called frameshift mutations, of course, but can have effects on the phenotype—for instance they can affect how a gene is expressed.

New Mutations and Mutagens

Mutations can arise in a number of ways. Errors during DNA replication or recombination can lead to nucleotide-pair substitutions, insertions, or deletions, as well as to mutations affecting longer stretches of DNA. If an incorrect nucleotide is added to a growing chain during replication, for example, the base on that nucleotide will then be mismatched with the nucleotide base on the other strand. In many cases, the error will be corrected by DNA proofreading and repair systems (see Concept 16.2). Otherwise, the incorrect base will be used as a template in the next round of replication, resulting in a mutation. Such mutations are called *spontaneous mutations*. It is difficult to calculate the rate at which such mutations occur. Rough estimates have been made of the rate of mutation during DNA replication for both *E. coli* and eukaryotes, and the numbers are similar: About one nucleotide in every 10^{10} is altered, and the change is passed on to the next generation of cells.

A number of physical and chemical agents, called **mutagens**, interact with DNA in ways that cause mutations. In the 1920s, Hermann Muller discovered that X-rays caused genetic changes in fruit flies, and he used X-rays to make *Drosophila* mutants for his genetic studies. But he also recognized an alarming implication of his discovery: X-rays and other forms of high-energy radiation pose hazards to the genetic material of people as well as laboratory organisms. Mutagenic radiation, a physical mutagen, includes ultraviolet (UV) light, which can cause disruptive thymine dimers in DNA (see Figure 16.19).

Chemical mutagens fall into several categories. Nucleotide analogues are chemicals similar to normal DNA nucleotides but that pair incorrectly during DNA replication. Other chemical mutagens interfere with correct DNA replication by inserting themselves into the DNA and distorting the double helix. Still other mutagens cause chemical changes in bases that change their pairing properties.

Researchers have developed a variety of methods to test the mutagenic activity of chemicals. A major application of these tests is the preliminary screening of chemicals to identify those that may cause cancer. This approach makes sense because most carcinogens (cancer-causing chemicals) are mutagenic, and conversely, most mutagens are carcinogenic.

How can you find information regarding the mutagenicity of a controlled product? The Workplace Hazardous Materials Information System (WHMIS), which operates through Health Canada, classifies products according to toxicological hazards and physical hazards. Mutagenicity and carcinogenicity are two of the 12 categories of toxicological hazards that are included in the WHMIS database.

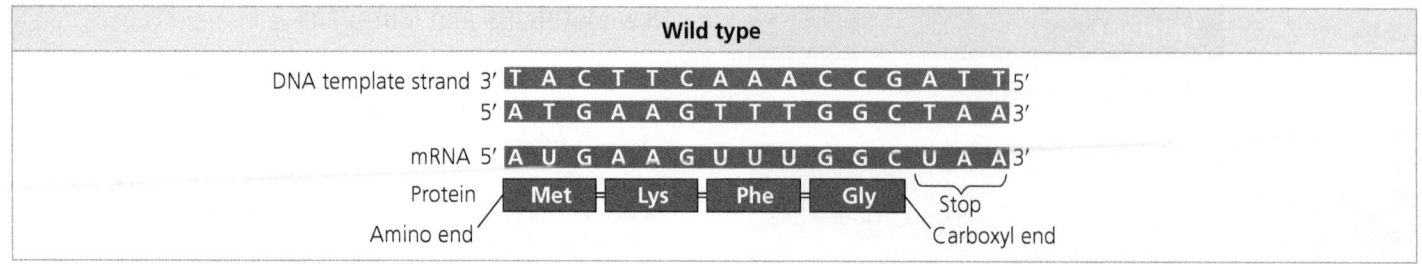

(a) Nucleotide-pair substitution	**(b) Nucleotide-pair insertion or deletion**

(a) Nucleotide-pair substitution

A instead of G

3' T A C T T C A A A C C A A T T 5'
5' A T G A A G T T T G G T T A A 3'

U instead of C

5' A U G A A G U U U G G U U A A 3'
Met | Lys | Phe | Gly | Stop

Silent (no effect on amino acid sequence)

T instead of C

3' T A C T T C A A A T C G A T T 5'
5' A T G A A G T T T A G C T A A 3'

A instead of G

5' A U G A A G U U U A G C U A A 3'
Met | Lys | Phe | Ser | Stop

Missense (a single nucleotide change causes a codon coding for Gly to become a codon coding for Ser)

A instead of T

3' T A C A T C A A A C C G A T T 5'
5' A T G T A G T T T G G C T A A 3'

U instead of A

5' A U G U A G U U U G G U U A A 3'
Met | Stop

Nonsense (a single nucleotide change causes a codon coding for Lys to become a stop codon)

(b) Nucleotide-pair insertion or deletion

Extra A

3' T A C A T T C A A A C C G A T T 5'
5' A T G T A A G T T T G G C T A A 3'

Extra U

5' A U G U A A G U U U U G G C U A A 3'
Met | Stop

Frameshift causing immediate nonsense **(1 nucleotide-pair insertion)**

A missing

3' T A C T T C A A C C G A T T 5'
5' A T G A A G T T G G C T A A 3'

U missing

5' A U G A A G U U G G C U A A ··· 3'
Met | Lys | Leu | Ala ···

Frameshift causing extensive missense **(1 nucleotide-pair deletion)**

T T C missing

3' T A C A A A C C G A T T 5'
5' A T G T T T G G C T A A 3'

A A G missing

5' A U G U U U G G C U A A 3'
Met | Phe | Gly | Stop

No frameshift, but one amino acid missing **(3 nucleotide-pair deletion)**. A 3 nucleotide-pair insertion (not shown) would lead to an extra amino acid.

▲ Figure 17.27 **Types of small-scale mutations that affect mRNA sequence.** All but one of the types shown here also affect the amino acid sequence of the encoded polypeptide.

What Is a Gene? *Revisiting the Question*

Our definition of a gene has evolved over the past few chapters, as it has through the history of genetics. We began with the Mendelian concept of a gene as a discrete unit of inheritance that affects a phenotypic character (Chapter 14). We saw that Morgan and his colleagues assigned such genes to specific loci on chromosomes (Chapter 15). We went on to view a gene as a region of specific nucleotide sequence along the length of the DNA molecule of a chromosome (Chapter 16). Finally, in this

chapter, we have considered a functional definition of a gene as a DNA sequence that codes for a specific polypeptide chain. All these definitions are useful, depending on the context in which genes are being studied.

We now realize that saying a gene codes for a polypeptide is an oversimplification. Most eukaryotic genes contain noncoding segments (such as introns), so large portions of these genes have no corresponding segments in polypeptides. Molecular biologists also often include promoters and certain other regulatory regions of DNA within the boundaries of a gene. These DNA sequences are not transcribed, but they can be considered part of the functional gene because they must be present for transcription to occur. Our definition of a gene must also be broad enough to include the DNA that is transcribed into rRNA, tRNA, and other RNAs that are not translated. These genes have no polypeptide products but play crucial roles in the cell. Thus, we arrive at the following definition: *A gene is a region of DNA that can be expressed to produce a final functional product that is either a polypeptide or an RNA molecule.*

When considering phenotypes, however, it is often useful to start by focusing on genes that code for polypeptides. In this chapter, you have learned in molecular terms how a typical gene is expressed—by transcription into RNA and then translation into a polypeptide that forms a protein of specific structure and function. Proteins, in turn, bring about an organism's observable phenotype.

A given type of cell expresses only a subset of its genes. This is an essential feature in multicellular organisms: You'd be in trouble if the lens cells in your eyes started expressing the genes for hair proteins, which are normally expressed only in hair follicle cells! Gene expression is precisely regulated, which we'll explore in the next chapter, beginning with the simpler case of bacteria and continuing with eukaryotes.

CONCEPT CHECK 17.5

1. What happens when one nucleotide pair is lost from the middle of the coding sequence of a gene?

2. **MAKE CONNECTIONS** Individuals heterozygous for the sickle-cell allele are generally healthy but show phenotypic effects of the allele under some circumstances; see Concept 14.4. Explain in terms of gene expression.

3. **WHAT IF?** **DRAW IT** The template strand of a gene includes this sequence:
   3'-TACTTGTCCGATATC-5'. It is mutated to
   3'-TACTTGTCCAATATC-5'. For both normal and mutant sequences, draw the double-stranded DNA, the resulting mRNA, and the amino acid sequence each encodes. What is the effect of the mutation on the amino acid sequence?

For suggested answers, see Appendix A.

---

17 Chapter Review

Go to **MasteringBiology®** for Assignments, the eText, and the Study Area with Animations, Activities, Vocab Self-Quiz, and Practice Tests.

SUMMARY OF KEY CONCEPTS

CONCEPT 17.1

Genes specify proteins via transcription and translation (pp. 352–358)

- Beadle and Tatum's studies of mutant strains of *Neurospora* led to the one gene–one polypeptide hypothesis. During **gene expression**, the information encoded in genes is used to make specific polypeptide chains (enzymes and other proteins) or RNA molecules.
- **Transcription** is the synthesis of RNA complementary to a **template strand** of DNA, providing a nucleotide-to-nucleotide transfer of information. **Translation** is the synthesis of a polypeptide whose amino acid sequence is specified by the nucleotide sequence in **mRNA**.
- Genetic information is encoded as a sequence of nonoverlapping nucleotide triplets, or **codons**. A codon in messenger RNA (mRNA) either is translated into an amino acid (61 of the 64 codons) or serves as a stop signal (3 codons). Codons must be read in the correct **reading frame**.

? *Describe the process of gene expression, by which a gene affects the phenotype of an organism.*

CONCEPT 17.2

Transcription is the DNA-directed synthesis of RNA: *A closer look* **(pp. 358–360)**

- RNA synthesis is catalyzed by **RNA polymerase**, which links together RNA nucleotides complementary to a DNA template strand. This process follows the same base-pairing rules as DNA replication, except that in RNA, uracil substitutes for thymine.

- The three stages of transcription are initiation, elongation, and termination. A **promoter**, often including a **TATA box** in eukaryotes, establishes where RNA synthesis is initiated. **Transcription factors** help eukaryotic RNA polymerase recognize promoter sequences, forming a **transcription initiation complex**. Termination differs in bacteria and eukaryotes.

? *What are the similarities and differences in the initiation of gene transcription in bacteria and eukaryotes?*

CONCEPT 17.3

Eukaryotic cells modify RNA after transcription (pp. 361–363)

- Eukaryotic mRNAs undergo **RNA processing**, which includes RNA splicing, the addition of a modified nucleotide 5' **cap** to the 5′ end and the addition of a **poly-A tail** to the 3′ end. The processed mRNA includes an untranslated region (5′ UTR or 3′ UTR) at each end of the coding segment.

Pre-mRNA / mRNA splicing diagram: 5′ Cap, 5′ Exon Intron Exon Intron Exon 3′, Poly-A tail → mRNA: 5′ UTR, Coding segment, 3′ UTR

- Most eukaryotic genes are split into segments: They have **introns** interspersed among the **exons** (the regions included in the mRNA). In **RNA splicing**, introns are removed and exons joined. RNA splicing is typically carried out by **spliceosomes**, but in some cases RNA alone catalyzes its own splicing. The catalytic ability of some RNA molecules, called **ribozymes**, derives from the inherent properties of RNA. The presence of introns allows for **alternative RNA splicing**.

? *What function do the 5′ cap and the poly-A tail serve on a eukaryotic mRNA?*

CONCEPT 17.4

Translation is the RNA-directed synthesis of a polypeptide: *A closer look* (pp. 363–372)

- A cell translates an mRNA message into protein using **transfer RNAs (tRNAs)**. After being bound to a specific amino acid by an **aminoacyl-tRNA synthetase**, a tRNA lines up via its **anticodon** at the complementary codon on mRNA. A **ribosome**, made up of **ribosomal RNAs (rRNAs)** and proteins, facilitates this coupling with binding sites for mRNA and tRNA.
- Ribosomes coordinate the three stages of translation: initiation, elongation, and termination. The formation of peptide bonds between amino acids is catalyzed by rRNAs as tRNAs move through the **A** and **P sites** and exit through the **E site**.
- After translation, modifications to proteins can affect their shape. Free ribosomes in the cytosol initiate synthesis of all proteins, but proteins with a **signal peptide** are synthesized on the ER.

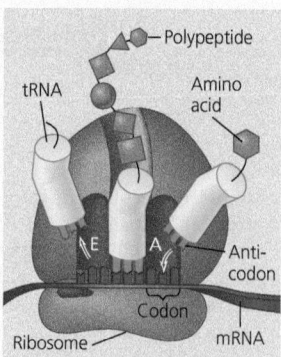

Ribosome/translation diagram labeled: Polypeptide, tRNA, Amino acid, E, P, A, Anticodon, Codon, Ribosome, mRNA

- A gene can be transcribed by multiple RNA polymerases simultaneously. Also, a single mRNA molecule can be translated simultaneously by a number of ribosomes, forming a **polyribosome**. In bacteria, these processes are coupled, but in eukaryotes they are separated in space and time by the nuclear membrane.

? *What function do tRNAs serve in the process of translation?*

CONCEPT 17.5

Mutations of one or a few nucleotides can affect protein structure and function (pp. 372–377)

- Small-scale **mutations** include **point mutations**, changes in one DNA nucleotide pair, which may lead to production of nonfunctional proteins. **Nucleotide-pair substitutions** can cause **missense** or **nonsense mutations**. Nucleotide-pair **insertions** or **deletions** may produce **frameshift mutations**.
- Spontaneous mutations can occur during DNA replication, recombination, or repair. Chemical and physical **mutagens** cause DNA damage that can alter genes.

? *What will be the results of chemically modifying one nucleotide base of a gene? What role is played by DNA repair systems in the cell?*

TEST YOUR UNDERSTANDING

LEVEL 1: KNOWLEDGE/COMPREHENSION

1. In eukaryotic cells, transcription cannot begin until
   a. the two DNA strands have completely separated and exposed the promoter.
   b. several transcription factors have bound to the promoter.
   c. the 5′ caps are removed from the mRNA.
   d. the DNA introns are removed from the template.

2. Which of the following is *not* true of a codon?
   a. It may code for the same amino acid as another codon.
   b. It never codes for more than one amino acid.
   c. It extends from one end of a tRNA molecule.
   d. It is the basic unit of the genetic code.

3. The anticodon of a particular tRNA molecule is
   a. complementary to the corresponding mRNA codon.
   b. complementary to the corresponding triplet in rRNA.
   c. the part of tRNA that bonds to a specific amino acid.
   d. catalytic, making the tRNA a ribozyme.

4. Which of the following is *not* true of RNA processing?
   a. Exons are cut out before mRNA leaves the nucleus.
   b. Nucleotides may be added at both ends of the RNA.
   c. Ribozymes may function in RNA splicing.
   d. RNA splicing can be catalyzed by spliceosomes.

5. Which component is *not* directly involved in translation?
   a. GTP
   b. DNA
   c. tRNA
   d. ribosomes

LEVEL 2: APPLICATION/ANALYSIS

6. Using Figure 17.5, identify a 5′ → 3′ sequence of nucleotides in the DNA template strand for an mRNA coding for the polypeptide sequence Phe-Pro-Lys.
   a. 5′-UUUGGGAAA-3′
   b. 5′-GAACCCCTT-3′
   c. 5′-CTTCGGGAA-3′
   d. 5′-AAACCCUUU-3′

7. Which of the following mutations would be *most* likely to have a harmful effect on an organism?
   a. a deletion of three nucleotides near the middle of a gene
   b. a single nucleotide deletion in the middle of an intron
   c. a single nucleotide deletion near the end of the coding sequence
   d. a single nucleotide insertion downstream of, and close to, the start of the coding sequence

8. Would the coupling of the processes shown in Figure 17.23 be found in a eukaryotic cell? Explain why or why not.

9. **DRAW IT** Fill in the following table:

Type of RNA	Functions
Messenger RNA (mRNA)	
Transfer RNA (tRNA)	
	Plays catalytic (ribozyme) roles and structural roles in ribosomes
Primary transcript	
Small nuclear RNA (snRNA)	

LEVEL 3: SYNTHESIS/EVALUATION

10. **EVOLUTION CONNECTION**
    Most amino acids are coded for by a set of similar codons (see Figure 17.5). What evolutionary explanations can you give for this pattern? (*Hint*: There is one explanation relating to ancestry, and some less obvious ones of a "form-fits-function" type.)

11. **SCIENTIFIC INQUIRY**
    Knowing that the genetic code is almost universal, a scientist uses molecular biological methods to insert the human β-globin gene (shown in Figure 17.11) into bacterial cells, hoping the cells will express it and synthesize functional β-globin protein. Instead, the protein produced is nonfunctional and is found to contain many fewer amino acids than does β-globin made by a eukaryotic cell. Explain why.

12. **WRITE ABOUT A THEME: INFORMATION**
    Evolution accounts for the unity and diversity of life, and the continuity of life is based on heritable information in the form of DNA. In a short essay (100–150 words), discuss how the fidelity with which DNA is inherited is related to the processes of evolution. (Review the discussion of proofreading and DNA repair in Concept 16.2.)

13. **SYNTHESIZE YOUR KNOWLEDGE**

Vasiliy Koval/Shutterstock

Some mutations result in proteins that function well at one temperature but are nonfunctional at a different (usually higher) temperature. Siamese cats have such a "temperature-sensitive" mutation in a gene encoding an enzyme that makes dark pigment in the fur. The mutation results in the breed's distinctive point markings and lighter body colour (see the photo). Using this information and what you learned in the chapter, explain the pattern of the cat's fur pigmentation.

For selected answers, see Appendix A.

18

Regulation of Gene Expression

▲ **Figure 18.1 How can this fish's eyes see equally well in both air and water?**

KEY CONCEPTS

18.1 Bacteria often respond to environmental change by regulating transcription

18.2 Eukaryotic gene expression is regulated at many stages

18.3 Noncoding RNAs play multiple roles in controlling gene expression

18.4 A program of differential gene expression leads to the different cell types in a multicellular organism

18.5 Cancer results from genetic changes that affect cell cycle control

Beauty in the Eye of the Beholder

The fish in **Figure 18.1** is keeping an eye out for predators—or, more precisely, both halves of each eye! *Anableps anableps*, commonly known as "cuatro ojos" ("four eyes"), glide through freshwater lakes and ponds in Central and South America with the upper half of each eye protruding from the water. The eye's upper half is particularly well-suited for aerial vision and the lower half for aquatic vision. The molecular basis of this specialization has recently been revealed: The cells of the two parts of the eye express a slightly different set of genes involved in vision, even though these two groups of cells are quite similar and contain identical genomes. What is the biological mechanism underlying the difference in gene expression that makes this remarkable feat possible?

A hallmark of prokaryotic and eukaryotic cells alike—from a bacterium to the cells of a fish—is their intricate and precise regulation of gene expression. In this chapter, we first explore how bacteria regulate expression of their genes in response to different environmental conditions. We then examine the general mechanisms by which eukaryotes regulate gene expression, including the many roles played by RNA molecules. In the final two sections, we explore the role of gene regulation in both embryonic development, as the ultimate example of proper gene regulation, and cancer, as an illustration of what happens when regulation goes awry. Orchestrating proper gene expression by all cells is crucial to the functions of life.

Bacteria often respond to environmental change by regulating transcription

Bacterial cells that can conserve resources and energy have a selective advantage over cells that are unable to do so. Thus, natural selection has favoured bacteria that express only the genes whose products are needed by the cell.

Consider, for instance, an individual *Escherichia coli* (*E. coli*) cell living in the erratic environment of a human colon, dependent for its nutrients on the whimsical eating habits of its host. If the environment is lacking in the amino acid tryptophan, which the bacterium needs to survive, the cell responds by activating a metabolic pathway that makes tryptophan from another compound. If the human host later eats a tryptophan-rich meal, the bacterial cell stops producing tryptophan, thus avoiding wasting resources to produce a substance readily available in prefabricated form from the surrounding solution.

A metabolic pathway can be controlled on two levels, as shown for the synthesis of tryptophan in Figure 18.2. First, cells can adjust the activity of enzymes already present. This is a fairly fast response, which relies on the sensitivity of many enzymes to chemical cues that increase or decrease their catalytic activity (see Concept 8.5). The activity of the first enzyme in the pathway is inhibited by tryptophan, the pathway's end product (Figure 18.2a). Thus, if tryptophan accumulates in a cell, it shuts down the synthesis of more tryptophan by inhibiting enzyme activity. Such *feedback inhibition*, typical of anabolic (biosynthetic) pathways, allows a cell to adapt to short-term fluctuations in the supply of a substance it needs.

Second, cells can adjust the production level of certain enzymes; that is, they can regulate the expression of the genes encoding the enzymes. If, in our example, the environment provides all the tryptophan the cell needs, the cell stops making the enzymes that catalyze the synthesis of tryptophan (Figure 18.2b). In this case, the control of enzyme production occurs at the level of transcription, the synthesis of messenger RNA from the genes that code for these enzymes.

Regulation of the tryptophan synthesis pathway is just one example of how bacteria tune their metabolism to changing environments. More generally, many genes of the bacterial genome are switched on or off by changes in the metabolic status of the cell. One basic mechanism for this control of gene expression in bacteria, described as the *operon model*, was discovered in 1961 by François Jacob and Jacques Monod at the Pasteur Institute in Paris. Let's see what an operon is and how it works.

Operons: The Basic Concept

E. coli synthesizes the amino acid tryptophan from a precursor molecule in the three-step pathway shown in Figure 18.2. Each reaction in the pathway is catalyzed by a specific enzyme, and the five genes that code for the subunits of these enzymes are clustered together on the bacterial chromosome. A single promoter serves all five genes, which together constitute a transcription unit. (Recall from Concept 17.2 that a promoter is a site where RNA polymerase can bind to DNA and begin transcription.) Thus, transcription gives rise to one long mRNA molecule that codes for the five polypeptides making up the enzymes in the tryptophan pathway. The cell can translate this one mRNA into five separate polypeptides because the mRNA is punctuated with start and stop codons that signal where the coding sequence for each polypeptide begins and ends.

A key advantage of grouping genes of related function into one transcription unit is that a single "on-off switch" can control the whole cluster of functionally related genes; in other words, these genes are *coordinately controlled*. When an *E. coli* cell must make tryptophan for itself because the nutrient medium lacks this amino acid, all the enzymes for the metabolic pathway are synthesized at the same time. The switch is a segment of DNA called an **operator**. Both its location and name suit its function: Positioned within

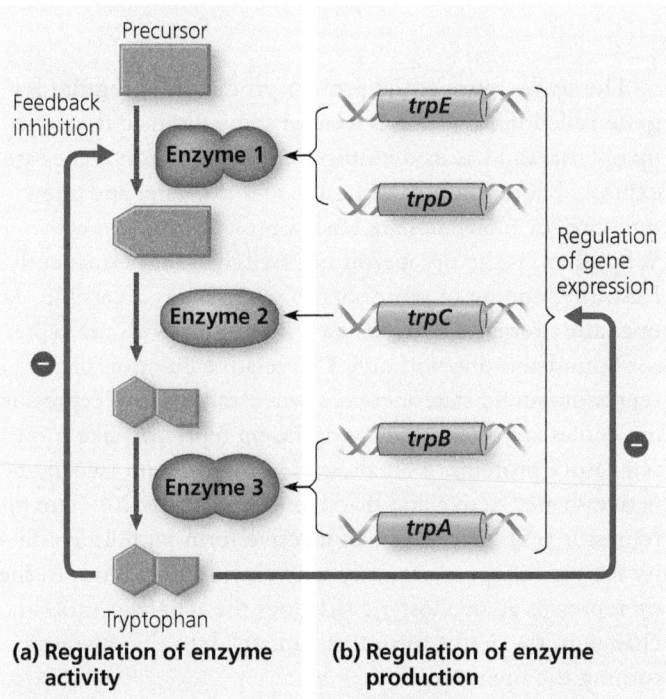

(a) Regulation of enzyme activity

(b) Regulation of enzyme production

▲ Figure 18.2 **Regulation of a metabolic pathway.** In the pathway for tryptophan synthesis, an abundance of tryptophan can both **(a)** inhibit the activity of the first enzyme in the pathway (feedback inhibition), a rapid response, and **(b)** repress expression of the genes encoding all subunits of the enzymes in the pathway, a longer-term response. Genes *trpE* and *trpD* encode the two subunits of enzyme 1, and genes *trpB* and *trpA* encode the two subunits of enzyme 3. (The genes were named before the order in which they functioned in the pathway was determined.) The symbol ⊖ stands for inhibition.

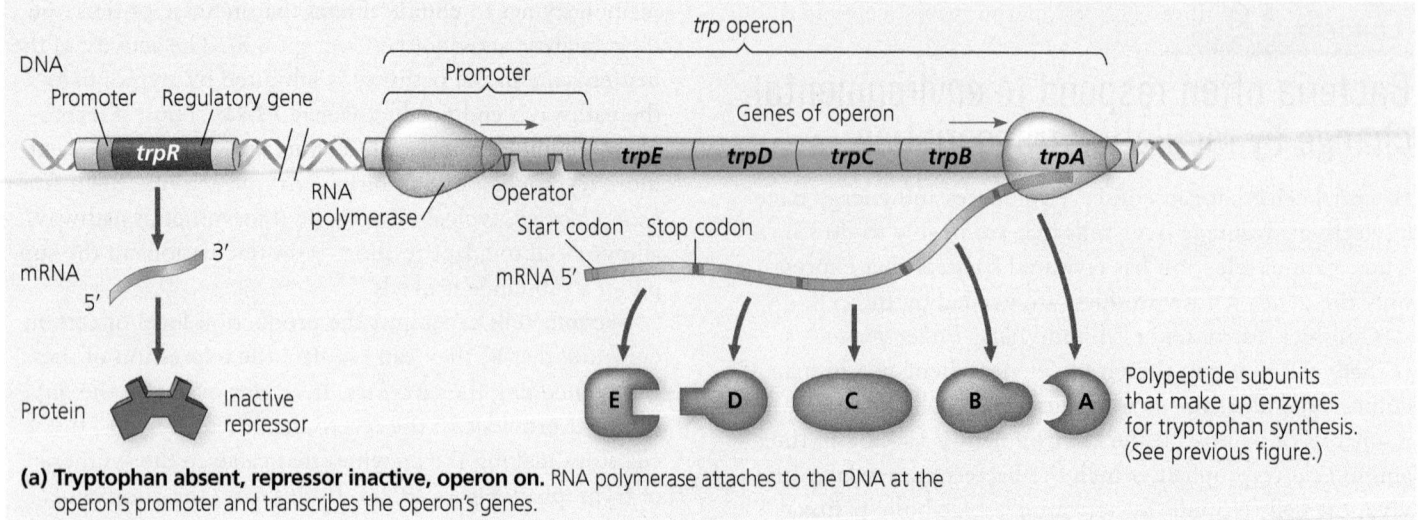

(a) **Tryptophan absent, repressor inactive, operon on.** RNA polymerase attaches to the DNA at the operon's promoter and transcribes the operon's genes.

(b) **Tryptophan present, repressor active, operon off.** As tryptophan accumulates, it inhibits its own production by activating the repressor protein, which binds to the operator, blocking transcription.

▲ **Figure 18.3 The *trp* operon in *E. coli*: regulated synthesis of repressible enzymes.** Tryptophan is an amino acid produced by an anabolic pathway catalyzed by repressible enzymes. **(a)** The five genes encoding the polypeptide subunits of the enzymes in this pathway (see Figure 18.2) are grouped, along with a promoter, into the *trp* operon. The *trp* operator (the repressor binding site) is located within the *trp* promoter (the RNA polymerase binding site). **(b)** Accumulation of tryptophan, the end product of the pathway, represses transcription of the *trp* operon, thus blocking synthesis of all the enzymes in the pathway and shutting down tryptophan production.

? *Describe what happens to the* trp *operon as the cell uses up its store of tryptophan.*

the promoter or, in some cases, between the promoter and the enzyme-coding genes, the operator controls the access of RNA polymerase to the genes. All together, the operator, the promoter, and the genes they control—the entire stretch of DNA required for enzyme production for the tryptophan pathway—constitute an **operon**. The *trp* operon (*trp* for tryptophan) is one of many operons in the *E. coli* genome (**Figure 18.3**).

If the operator is the operon's switch for controlling transcription, how does this switch work? By itself, the *trp* operon is turned on; that is, RNA polymerase can bind to the promoter and transcribe the genes of the operon. The operon can be switched off by a protein called the *trp* **repressor**. The repressor binds to the operator and blocks attachment of RNA polymerase to the promoter, preventing transcription of the genes. A repressor protein is specific for the operator of a particular operon. For example, the repressor that switches off the *trp* operon by binding to the *trp* operator has no effect on other operons in the *E. coli* genome.

The *trp* repressor is the protein product of a **regulatory gene** called *trpR*, which is located some distance from the *trp* operon and has its own promoter. Regulatory genes are expressed continuously, although at a low rate, and a few *trp* repressor molecules are always present in *E. coli* cells. Why, then, is the *trp* operon not switched off permanently? First, the binding of repressors to operators is reversible. An operator alternates between two states: one with the repressor bound and one without. The relative duration of the repressor-bound state increases when more active repressor molecules are present. Second, the *trp* repressor, like most regulatory proteins, is an allosteric protein, with two alternative shapes, active and inactive (see Figure 8.20). The *trp* repressor is synthesized in an inactive form with little affinity for the *trp* operator. Only when tryptophan binds to the *trp* repressor at an allosteric site does the repressor protein change to the active form that can attach to the operator, turning the operon off.

Tryptophan functions in this system as a **corepressor**, a small molecule that cooperates with a repressor protein to switch an operon off. As tryptophan accumulates, more tryptophan molecules associate with *trp* repressor molecules, which can then bind to the *trp* operator and shut down production of the tryptophan pathway enzymes. If the cell's tryptophan level drops, transcription of the operon's genes resumes. The *trp* operon is one example of how gene expression can respond to changes in the cell's internal and external environment.

Repressible and Inducible Operons: Two Types of Negative Gene Regulation

The *trp* operon is said to be a *repressible operon* because its transcription is usually on but can be inhibited (repressed) when a specific small molecule (in this case, tryptophan) binds allosterically to a regulatory protein. In contrast, an *inducible operon* is usually off but can be stimulated (induced) when a specific small molecule interacts with a regulatory protein. The classic example of an inducible operon is the *lac* operon (*lac* for lactose), which was the subject of Jacob and Monod's pioneering research.

The disaccharide lactose (milk sugar) is available to *E. coli* in the human colon if the host drinks milk. Lactose metabolism begins with hydrolysis of the disaccharide into its component monosaccharides (glucose and galactose), a reaction catalyzed by the enzyme β-galactosidase. Only a few molecules of this enzyme are present in an *E. coli* cell growing in the absence of lactose. If lactose is added to the bacterium's environment, however, the number of β-galactosidase molecules in the cell increases 1000-fold within about 15 minutes. How can a cell ramp up enzyme production this quickly?

The gene for β-galactosidase is part of the *lac* operon, which includes two other genes coding for enzymes that function in the use of lactose. The entire transcription unit is under the command of one main operator and promoter. The regulatory gene, *lacI*, located outside the operon, codes for an allosteric repressor protein that can switch off the *lac* operon by binding to the operator. So far, this sounds just like regulation of the *trp* operon, but there is one important difference. Recall that the *trp* repressor protein is inactive by itself and requires tryptophan as a corepressor in order to bind to the operator. The *lac* repressor, in contrast, is active by itself, binding to the operator and switching the *lac* operon off. In this case, a specific small molecule, called an **inducer**, *inactivates* the repressor.

For the *lac* operon, the inducer is allolactose, an isomer of lactose formed in small amounts from lactose that enters the cell. In the absence of lactose (and hence allolactose), the *lac* repressor is in its active configuration, and the genes of the *lac* operon are silenced (**Figure 18.4a**). If lactose is added to the cell's surroundings, allolactose binds to the *lac* repressor and alters its conformation, nullifying the repressor's ability to attach to the operator. Without the repressor bound, the *lac* operon is transcribed into mRNA for the lactose-utilizing enzymes (**Figure 18.4b**).

(a) Lactose absent, repressor active, operon off. The *lac* repressor is innately active, and in the absence of lactose it switches off the operon by binding to the operator.

(b) Lactose present, repressor inactive, operon on. Allolactose, an isomer of lactose, derepresses the operon by inactivating the repressor. In this way, the enzymes for lactose utilization are induced.

◀ Figure 18.4 **The *lac* operon in *E. coli*: regulated synthesis of inducible enzymes.** *E. coli* uses three enzymes to take up and metabolize lactose. The genes for these three enzymes are clustered in the *lac* operon. One gene, *lacZ*, codes for β-galactosidase, which hydrolyzes lactose to glucose and galactose. The second gene, *lacY*, codes for a permease, the membrane protein that transports lactose into the cell. The third gene, *lacA*, codes for an enzyme called transacetylase, whose function in lactose metabolism is still unclear. The gene for the *lac* repressor, *lacI*, happens to be adjacent to the *lac* operon, an unusual situation. The function of the teal region within the promoter will be revealed in Figure 18.5.

In the context of gene regulation, the enzymes of the lactose pathway are referred to as *inducible enzymes* because their synthesis is induced by a chemical signal (allolactose, in this case). Analogously, the enzymes for tryptophan synthesis are said to be repressible. *Repressible enzymes* generally function in anabolic pathways, which synthesize essential end products from raw materials (precursors). By suspending production of an end product when it is already present in sufficient quantity, the cell can allocate its organic precursors and energy for other uses. In contrast, inducible enzymes usually function in catabolic pathways, which break down a nutrient to simpler molecules. By producing the appropriate enzymes only when the nutrient is available, the cell avoids wasting energy and precursors making proteins that are not needed.

Regulation of both the *trp* and *lac* operons involves the *negative* control of genes, because the operons are switched off by the active form of the repressor protein. It may be easier to see this for the *trp* operon, but it is also true for the *lac* operon. Allolactose induces enzyme synthesis not by acting directly on the genome, but by freeing the *lac* operon from the negative effect of the repressor. Gene regulation is said to be *positive* only when a regulatory protein interacts directly with the genome to switch transcription on. Let's look at an example of the positive control of genes, again involving the *lac* operon.

Positive Gene Regulation

When glucose and lactose are both present in its environment, *E. coli* preferentially uses glucose. The enzymes for glucose breakdown in glycolysis (see Figure 9.9) are continually present. Only when lactose is present *and* glucose is in short supply does *E. coli* use lactose as an energy source, and only then does it synthesize appreciable quantities of the enzymes for lactose breakdown.

How does the *E. coli* cell sense the glucose concentration and relay this information to the *lac* operon? Again, the mechanism depends on the interaction of an allosteric regulatory protein with a small organic molecule, in this case **cyclic AMP (cAMP)**, which accumulates when glucose is scarce (see Figure 11.11 for the structure of cAMP). The regulatory protein, called *catabolite activator protein (CAP)*, is an **activator**, a protein that binds to DNA and stimulates transcription of a gene. When cAMP binds to this regulatory protein, CAP assumes its active shape and can attach to a specific site at the upstream end of the *lac* promoter (**Figure 18.5a**). This attachment increases the affinity of RNA polymerase for the promoter, which is actually rather low even when no repressor is bound to the operator. By facilitating the binding of RNA polymerase to the promoter and thereby increasing the rate of transcription, the attachment of CAP to the promoter directly stimulates

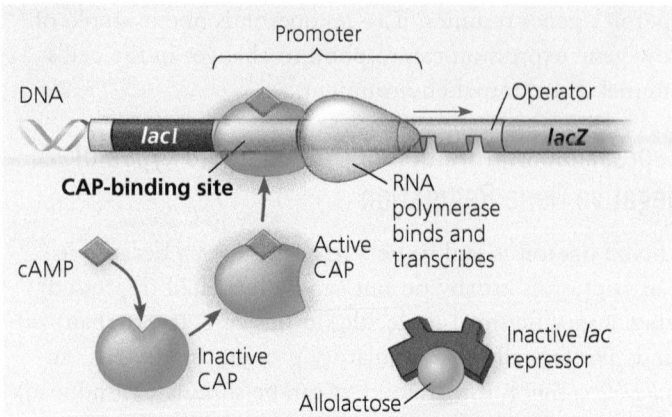

(a) Lactose present, glucose scarce (cAMP level high): abundant *lac* mRNA synthesized. If glucose is scarce, the high level of cAMP activates CAP, and the *lac* operon produces large amounts of mRNA coding for the enzymes in the lactose pathway.

(b) Lactose present, glucose present (cAMP level low): little *lac* mRNA synthesized. When glucose is present, cAMP is scarce, and CAP is unable to stimulate transcription at a significant rate, even though no repressor is bound.

▲ Figure 18.5 **Positive control of the *lac* operon by catabolite activator protein (CAP).** RNA polymerase has high affinity for the *lac* promoter only when catabolite activator protein (CAP) is bound to a DNA site at the upstream end of the promoter. CAP, in turn, attaches to its DNA site only when associated with cyclic AMP (cAMP), whose concentration in the cell rises when the glucose concentration falls. Thus, when glucose is present, even if lactose is also available, the cell preferentially catabolizes glucose and makes very little of the lactose-utilizing enzymes.

gene expression. Therefore, this mechanism qualifies as positive regulation.

If the amount of glucose in the cell increases, the cAMP concentration falls, and without cAMP, CAP detaches from the operon. Because CAP is inactive, RNA polymerase binds less efficiently to the promoter, and transcription of the *lac* operon proceeds at a low level, even in the presence of lactose (**Figure 18.5b**). Thus, the *lac* operon is under dual control: negative control by the *lac* repressor and positive control by CAP. The state of the *lac* repressor (with or without bound allolactose) determines whether or not transcription of the *lac* operon's genes occurs at all; the state of CAP (with or without bound cAMP) controls the *rate* of transcription if the operon is repressor-free. It is as though the operon has both an on-off switch and a volume control.

In addition to regulating the *lac* operon, CAP helps regulate other operons that encode enzymes used in catabolic pathways. All told, it may affect the expression of more than 100 genes in *E. coli*. When glucose is plentiful and CAP is inactive, the synthesis of enzymes that catabolize compounds other than glucose generally slows down. The ability to catabolize other compounds, such as lactose, enables a cell deprived of glucose to survive. The compounds present in the cell at the moment determine which operons are switched on—the result of simple interactions of activator and repressor proteins with the promoters of the genes in question.

CONCEPT CHECK 18.1

1. How does binding of the *trp* corepressor to the *trp* repressor alter repressor function and transcription? What about the binding of the *lac* inducer to the *lac* repressor?

2. Describe the binding of RNA polymerase, repressors, and activators to the *lac* operon when both lactose and glucose are scarce. What is the effect of these scarcities on transcription of the *lac* operon?

3. **WHAT IF?** A certain mutation in *E. coli* changes the *lac* operator so that the active repressor cannot bind. How would this affect the cell's production of β-galactosidase?

For suggested answers, see Appendix A.

CONCEPT 18.2

Eukaryotic gene expression is regulated at many stages

All organisms, whether prokaryotes or eukaryotes, must regulate which genes are expressed at any given time. Both unicellular organisms and the cells of multicellular organisms continually turn genes on and off in response to signals from their external and internal environments. Regulation of gene expression is also essential for cell specialization in multicellular organisms, which are made up of different types of cells. To perform its own distinct role, each cell type must maintain a specific program of gene expression in which certain genes are expressed and others are not.

Differential Gene Expression

A typical human cell might express about 20% of its protein-coding genes at any given time. Highly differentiated cells, such as muscle or nerve cells, express an even smaller fraction of their genes. Almost all the cells in a multicellular organism contain an identical genome. (Cells of the immune system are one exception, as you will see in Chapter 43.) However, the subset of genes expressed in the cells of each type is unique, allowing these cells to carry out their specific function. The differences between cell types, therefore, are due not to different genes being present, but to **differential gene expression**, the expression of different genes by cells with the same genome.

The function of any cell, whether a single-celled eukaryote or a particular cell type in a multicellular organism, depends on the appropriate set of genes being expressed. The transcription factors of a cell must locate the right genes at the right time, a task on a par with finding a needle in a haystack. When gene expression proceeds abnormally, serious imbalances and diseases, including cancer, can arise.

Figure 18.6 summarizes the process of gene expression in a eukaryotic cell, highlighting key stages in the expression of a protein-coding gene. Each stage depicted in Figure 18.6 is a potential control point at which gene expression can be turned on or off, accelerated, or slowed down.

Fifty or so years ago, an understanding of the mechanisms that control gene expression in eukaryotes seemed almost hopelessly out of reach. Since then, new research methods, notably advances in DNA technology (see Chapter 20), have enabled molecular biologists to uncover many details of eukaryotic gene regulation. In all organisms, gene expression is commonly controlled at transcription; regulation at this stage often occurs in response to signals coming from outside the cell, such as hormones or other signalling molecules. For this reason, the term *gene expression* is often equated with transcription for both bacteria and eukaryotes. While this may often be the case for bacteria, the greater complexity of eukaryotic cell structure and function provides opportunities for regulating gene expression at many additional stages (see Figure 18.6). In the remainder of this section, we'll examine some of the important control points of eukaryotic gene expression more closely.

Regulation of Chromatin Structure

Recall that the DNA of eukaryotic cells is packaged with proteins in an elaborate complex known as chromatin, the basic unit of which is the nucleosome (see Figure 16.23). The structural organization of chromatin not only packs a cell's DNA into a compact form that fits inside the nucleus, but also helps regulate gene expression in several ways. The location a gene's promoter, relative to both placement of nucleosomes and to the sites where the DNA attaches to the chromosome scaffold, can affect whether the gene is transcribed. In addition, genes within heterochromatin, which is highly condensed, are usually not expressed. Lastly, certain chemical modifications to chromatin—both to the histone proteins of the nucleosomes around which

Signal

Chromatin

Chromatin modification: DNA unpacking

DNA

Gene available for transcription

Transcription

RNA

Exon — Primary transcript
Intron

RNA processing

Tail
Cap — mRNA in nucleus

Transport to cytoplasm

NUCLEUS

CYTOPLASM

mRNA in cytoplasm

Degradation of mRNA

Translation

Polypeptide

Protein processing

Active protein

Degradation of protein

Transport to cellular destination

Cellular function (such as enzymatic activity or structural support)

▲ Figure 18.6 **Stages in gene expression that can be regulated in eukaryotic cells.** In this diagram, the coloured boxes indicate the processes most often regulated; each colour indicates the type of molecule that is affected (blue = DNA, orange = RNA, purple = protein). The nuclear envelope separating transcription from translation in eukaryotic cells offers an opportunity for post-transcriptional control in the form of RNA processing that is absent in prokaryotes. In addition, eukaryotes have a greater variety of control mechanisms operating before transcription and after translation. The expression of any given gene, however, does not necessarily involve every stage shown; for example, not every polypeptide is cleaved.

DNA is wrapped, and to the nucleotides that make up DNA—can influence both chromatin structure and gene expression. Here we examine the effects of these modifications, which are catalyzed by specific enzymes.

Histone Modifications and DNA Methylation

There is abundant evidence that chemical modifications to histones, the proteins around which the DNA is wrapped in nucleosomes, play a direct role in the regulation of gene transcription. The N-terminus of each histone molecule in a nucleosome protrudes outward from the nucleosome (**Figure 18.7a**). These histone tails are accessible to various modifying enzymes that catalyze the addition or removal of specific chemical groups, such as acetyl (—$COCH_3$), methyl, and phosphate groups. Generally, **histone acetylation** appears to promote transcription by opening up the chromatin structure (**Figure 18.7b**), while addition of methyl groups can lead to the condensation of chromatin and reduced transcription.

While some enzymes methylate the tails of histone proteins, a different set of enzymes can methylate certain bases in the DNA itself, usually cytosine. Such **DNA methylation** occurs in most plants, animals, and fungi. Long stretches of inactive DNA, such as that of inactivated mammalian X chromosomes (see Figure 15.8), are generally more methylated than regions of actively transcribed DNA, although there are exceptions. On a smaller scale, individual genes are usually more heavily methylated in cells in which they are not expressed. Removal of the extra methyl groups can turn on some of these genes.

Once methylated, genes usually stay that way through successive cell divisions in a given individual. At DNA sites where one strand is already methylated, enzymes methylate the correct daughter strand after each round of DNA replication. Methylation patterns are thus passed on, and cells forming specialized tissues keep a chemical record of what occurred during embryonic development. A methylation pattern maintained in this way also accounts for *genomic imprinting* in mammals, where methylation permanently regulates expression of either the maternal or paternal allele of particular genes at the start of development (see Figure 15.18).

Epigenetic Inheritance

The chromatin modifications that we just discussed do not change the DNA sequence, yet they still may be passed along to future generations of cells. Inheritance of traits transmitted by mechanisms not involving the nucleotide sequence itself is called **epigenetic inheritance**. Whereas mutations in the DNA are permanent changes, modifications to the chromatin can be reversed. For example, DNA methylation patterns are largely erased and reestablished during gamete formation.

(a) **Histone tails protrude outward from a nucleosome.** The amino acids in the histone tails are accessible for chemical modification.

(b) **Acetylation of histone tails promotes loose chromatin structure that permits transcription.** A region of chromatin in which nucleosomes are unacetylated forms a compact structure (left) in which the DNA is not transcribed. When nucleosomes are highly acetylated (right), the chromatin becomes less compact, and the DNA is accessible for transcription.

▲ Figure 18.7 **A simple model of histone tails and the effect of histone acetylation.** In addition to acetylation, histones can undergo several other types of modifications that also help determine the chromatin configuration in a region.

Researchers are amassing more and more evidence for the importance of epigenetic information in the regulation of gene expression. Epigenetic variations might help explain why one identical twin acquires a genetically based disease, such as schizophrenia, but the other does not, despite their identical genomes. Alterations in normal patterns of DNA methylation are seen in some cancers, where they are associated with inappropriate gene expression. Evidently, enzymes that modify chromatin structure are integral parts of the eukaryotic cell's machinery for regulating transcription.

Regulation of Transcription Initiation

Chromatin-modifying enzymes provide initial control of gene expression by making a region of DNA either more or less able to bind the transcription machinery. Once the chromatin of a gene is optimally modified for expression, the initiation of transcription is the next major step at which gene expression is regulated. As in bacteria, the regulation of transcription initiation in eukaryotes involves proteins that bind to DNA and either facilitate or inhibit binding of RNA polymerase. The process is more complicated in eukaryotes, however. Before looking at how eukaryotic cells control their transcription, let's review the structure of a typical eukaryotic gene and its transcript.

Organization of a Typical Eukaryotic Gene and Its Transcript

A eukaryotic gene and the DNA elements (segments) that control it are typically organized as shown in **Figure 18.8**, which extends what you learned about eukaryotic genes in Chapter 17. Recall that a cluster of proteins called a *transcription initiation complex* assembles on the promoter

sequence at the "upstream" end of the gene. One of these proteins, RNA polymerase II, then proceeds to transcribe the gene, synthesizing a primary RNA transcript (pre-mRNA). RNA processing includes enzymatic addition of a 5′ cap and a poly-A tail, as well as splicing out of introns, to yield a mature mRNA. Associated with most eukaryotic genes are multiple **control elements**, segments of noncoding DNA that serve as binding sites for the proteins called transcription factors, which in turn regulate transcription. Control elements and the transcription factors they bind are critical to the precise regulation of gene expression seen in different cell types.

The Roles of General and Specific Transcription Factors

Transcription factors are of two types: General transcription factors act at the promoter of all genes, while some genes require specific transcription factors that bind to control elements that may be close to or further away from the promoter.

General Transcription Factors at the Promoter To initiate transcription, eukaryotic RNA polymerase requires the assistance of transcription factors. Some transcription factors, such as those illustrated in Figure 17.8, are essential for the transcription of *all* protein-coding genes; therefore, they are often called *general transcription factors*. A few general transcription factors bind to a DNA sequence such as the TATA box within the promoter, but many bind to proteins, including other transcription factors and RNA polymerase II. Protein-protein interactions are crucial to the initiation of eukaryotic transcription. Only when the complete initiation complex has assembled can the polymerase begin to move along the DNA template strand, producing a complementary strand of RNA.

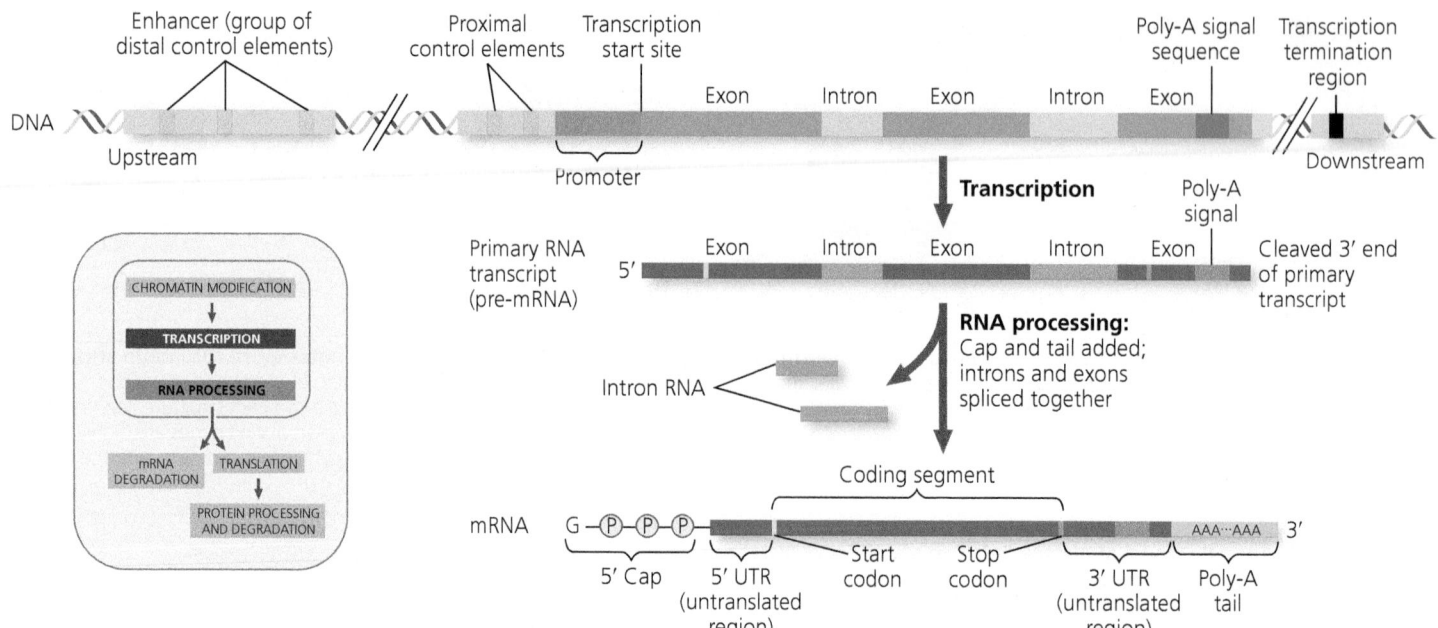

▲ Figure 18.8 A eukaryotic gene and its transcript. Each eukaryotic gene has a promoter, a DNA sequence where RNA polymerase binds and starts transcription, proceeding "downstream." A number of control elements (gold) are involved in regulating the initiation of transcription; these are DNA sequences located near (proximal to) or far from (distal to) the promoter. Distal control elements can be grouped together as enhancers, one of which is shown for this gene. A polyadenylation (poly-A) signal sequence in the last exon of the gene is transcribed into an RNA sequence that signals where the transcript is cleaved and the poly-A tail added. Transcription may continue for hundreds of nucleotides beyond the poly-A signal before terminating. RNA processing of the primary transcript into a functional mRNA involves three steps: addition of the 5′ cap, addition of the poly-A tail, and splicing. In the cell, the 5′ cap is added soon after transcription is initiated; splicing and poly-A tail addition may also occur while transcription is still under way (see Figure 17.10).

The interaction of general transcription factors and RNA polymerase II with a promoter usually leads to a low rate of initiation and production of few RNA transcripts from genes that are not expressed all the time, but instead are regulated. In eukaryotes, high levels of transcription of these particular genes at the appropriate time and place depend on the interaction of control elements with another set of proteins, which can be thought of as *specific transcription factors*.

Enhancers and Specific Transcription Factors As you can see in Figure 18.8, some control elements, named *proximal control elements*, are located close to the promoter. (Although some biologists consider proximal control elements part of the promoter, in this text we do not.) The more distant *distal control elements*, groupings of which are called **enhancers**, may be thousands of nucleotides upstream or downstream of a gene or even within an intron. A given gene may have multiple enhancers, each active at a different time or in a different cell type or location in the organism. Each enhancer, however, is generally associated with only that gene and no other.

In eukaryotes, the rate of gene expression can be strongly increased or decreased by the binding of specific transcription factors, either activators or repressors, to the control elements of enhancers. Hundreds of transcription activators have been discovered in eukaryotes; the structure of one example is shown in **Figure 18.9**. In a large number of activator proteins, researchers have identified two common structural domains: a DNA-binding domain—a part

▲ Figure 18.9 The structure of MyoD, a specific transcription factor that acts as an activator. The MyoD protein is made up of two subunits (purple and salmon) with extensive regions of α helix. Each subunit has a DNA-binding domain and an activation domain (indicated by brackets for the purple subunit). The activation domain includes binding sites for the other subunit as well as other proteins. MyoD is involved in muscle development in vertebrate embryos and will be discussed further in Concept 18.4.

of the protein's three-dimensional structure that binds to DNA—and one or more activation domains. Activation domains bind other regulatory proteins or components of the transcription machinery, facilitating a series of protein–protein interactions that result in enhanced transcription of a given gene.

Figure 18.10 shows the currently accepted model for how binding of activators to an enhancer located far from the promoter can influence transcription. Protein-mediated bending of the DNA is thought to bring the bound activators into contact with a group of *mediator proteins*, which in turn interact with proteins at the promoter. These protein-protein interactions help assemble and position the initiation complex on the promoter. Many studies support this model, including one showing that the proteins regulating a mouse globin gene contact both the gene's promoter and an enhancer located about 50 000 nucleotides upstream. Protein interactions allow these two regions in the DNA to come together in a very specific fashion, in spite of the large number of nucleotide pairs between them.

1 Activator proteins bind to distal control elements grouped as an enhancer in the DNA. This enhancer has three binding sites, each called a distal control element.

DNA

Activators

Enhancer

Distal control element

Promoter

Gene

TATA box

2 A DNA-bending protein brings the bound activators closer to the promoter. General transcription factors, mediator proteins, and RNA polymerase II are nearby.

DNA-bending protein

General transcription factors

Group of mediator proteins

RNA polymerase II

3 The activators bind to certain mediator proteins and general transcription factors, helping them form an active transcription initiation complex on the promoter.

RNA polymerase II

Transcription initiation complex

RNA synthesis

▲ Figure 18.10 **A model for the action of enhancers and transcription activators.** Bending of the DNA by a protein enables enhancers to influence a promoter hundreds or even thousands of nucleotides away. Specific transcription factors called activators bind to the enhancer DNA sequences and then to a group of mediator proteins, which in turn bind to general transcription factors, assembling the transcription initiation complex. These protein-protein interactions facilitate the correct positioning of the complex on the promoter and the initiation of RNA synthesis. Only one enhancer (with three orange control elements) is shown here, but a gene may have several enhancers that act at different times or in different cell types.

In the Scientific Skills Exercise, you can work with data from an experiment that identified the control elements in an enhancer of a particular human gene.

Specific transcription factors that function as repressors can inhibit gene expression in several different ways. Some repressors bind directly to control element DNA (in enhancers or elsewhere), blocking activator binding. Other repressors interfere with the activator itself so it can't bind the DNA.

In addition to influencing transcription directly, some activators and repressors act indirectly by affecting chromatin structure. Studies using yeast and mammalian cells show that some activators recruit proteins that acetylate histones near the promoters of specific genes, thus promoting transcription (see Figure 18.7). Similarly, some repressors recruit proteins that remove acetyl groups from histones, leading to reduced transcription, a phenomenon referred to as *silencing*. Indeed, recruitment of chromatin-modifying proteins seems to be the most common mechanism of repression in eukaryotic cells.

Combinatorial Control of Gene Activation In eukaryotes, the precise control of transcription depends largely on the

SCIENTIFIC SKILLS EXERCISE

Analyzing DNA Deletion Experiments

Getty Images

What Control Elements Regulate Expression of the *mPGES-1* Gene? The promoter of a gene includes the DNA immediately upstream of the transcription start site, but the control elements regulating the level at which the gene is transcribed may be thousands of base pairs upstream of the promoter, grouped in an enhancer. Because the distance and spacing of control elements make them difficult to identify, scientists begin by deleting possible control elements and measuring the effect on gene expression. In this exercise, you will analyze data obtained from DNA deletion experiments that tested possible control elements for the human gene *mPGES-1*. This gene codes for an enzyme that synthesizes a type of prostaglandin, a chemical made during inflammation.

How the Experiment Was Done The researchers hypothesized that there were three possible control elements in an enhancer region located 8–9 kilobases upstream of the *mPGES-1* gene. Control elements regulate whatever gene is in the appropriate downstream location. Thus, to test the activity of the possible elements, researchers first synthesized molecules of DNA ("constructs") with the intact enhancer region upstream of a "reporter gene," a gene whose mRNA product could be easily measured experimentally. Next, they synthesized three more DNA constructs but deleted one of the three proposed control elements in each (see left side of figure). The researchers then introduced each DNA construct into a separate human cell culture, where the cells took up the artificial DNA molecules. After 48 hours, the amount of reporter gene mRNA made by the cells was measured. Comparing these amounts allowed researchers to determine if any of the deletions had an effect on expression of the reporter gene, mimicking the effect that deletions would have had on *mPGES-1* gene expression. (The *mPGES-1* gene itself couldn't be used to measure expression levels because the cells express their own *mPGES-1* gene, mRNA which would otherwise confuse the results.)

Data from the Experiment The diagrams on the left side of the figure show the intact DNA sequence (top) and the three experimental DNA constructs. A red X is located on the possible control element (1, 2, or 3) that was deleted in each experimental DNA construct. The area between the slashes represents the approximately eight kilobases of DNA located between the promoter and the enhancer region. The horizontal bar graph on the right shows the amount of reporter gene mRNA that was present

© 2012 The Biochemical Society

in each cell culture after 48 hours relative to the amount that was in the culture containing the intact enhancer region (top bar = 100%).

Interpret the Data

1. (a) What is the independent variable in the graph (that is, what variable was manipulated by the scientists)? (b) What is the dependent variable (that is, what variable responded to the changes in the independent variable)? (c) What was the control treatment in this experiment? Label it on the diagram.

2. Do the data suggest that any of these possible control elements are actual control elements? Explain.

3. (a) Did deletion of any of the possible control elements cause a *reduction* in reporter gene expression? If so, which one(s), and how can you tell? (b) If loss of a control element causes a reduction in gene expression, what must be the normal role of that control element? Provide a biological explanation for how the loss of such a control element could lead to a reduction in gene expression.

4. (a) Did deletion of any of the possible control elements cause an *increase* in reporter gene expression relative to the control? If so, which one(s), and how can you tell? (b) If loss of a control element causes an increase in gene expression, what must be the normal role of that control element? Propose a biological explanation for how the loss of such a control element could lead to an increase in gene expression.

Based on "Regulation of Human Microsomal Prostaglandin E Synthase-1 by IL-1b Requires a Distal Enhancer Element with a Unique Role for C/EBPb" by Jewell N. Walters et al., from *Biochemical Journal*, April 15, 2012, Volume 443(2). © Jane B Reece.

binding of activators to DNA control elements. Considering the great number of genes that must be regulated in a typical animal or plant cell, the number of completely different nucleotide sequences found in control elements is surprisingly small. A dozen or so short nucleotide sequences appear again and again in the control elements for different genes. On average, each enhancer is composed of about 10 control elements, each of which can bind only one or two specific transcription factors. It is the particular *combination* of control elements in an enhancer associated with a gene, rather than the presence of a single unique control element, that is important in regulating transcription of the gene.

Even with only a dozen control element sequences available, a very large number of combinations are possible. Each combination of control elements will be able to activate transcription only when the appropriate activator proteins are present, which may occur at a precise time during development or in a particular cell type. **Figure 18.11** illustrates how the use of different combinations of just a few

control elements can allow differential regulation of transcription in two cell types. This can occur because each cell type contains a different group of activator proteins. How these groups came to differ during embryonic development will be explored in Concept 18.4.

Coordinately Controlled Genes in Eukaryotes

How does the eukaryotic cell deal with a group of genes of related function that need to be turned on or off at the same time? Earlier in this chapter, you learned that in bacteria such coordinately controlled genes are often clustered into an operon, which is regulated by a single promoter and transcribed into a single mRNA molecule. Thus, the genes are expressed together, and the encoded proteins are produced concurrently. With a few minor exceptions, operons that work in this way have *not* been found in eukaryotic cells.

Co-expressed eukaryotic genes, such as genes coding for the enzymes of a metabolic pathway, are typically scattered over different chromosomes. Here, coordinate gene

(a) Liver cell. The albumin gene is expressed, and the crystallin gene is not.

(b) Lens cell. The crystallin gene is expressed, and the albumin gene is not.

◄ **Figure 18.11 Cell type–specific transcription.** Both liver cells and lens cells have the genes for making the proteins albumin and crystallin, but only liver cells make albumin (a blood protein) and only lens cells make crystallin (the main protein of the lens of the eye). The specific transcription factors made in a cell determine which genes are expressed. In this example, the genes for albumin and crystallin are shown at the top, each with an enhancer made up of three different control elements. Although the enhancers for the two genes share one control element (grey), each enhancer has a unique combination of elements. All the activators required for high-level expression of the albumin gene are present only in liver cells **(a)**, whereas the activators needed for expression of the crystallin gene are present only in lens cells **(b)**. For simplicity, we consider only the role of activators here, although the presence or absence of repressors may also influence transcription in certain cell types.

? *Describe the enhancer for the albumin gene in each cell. How would the nucleotide sequence of this enhancer in the liver cell compare with that in the lens cell?*

expression depends on the association of a specific combination of control elements with every gene of a dispersed group. Activator proteins in the nucleus that recognize the control elements bind to them, promoting simultaneous transcription of the genes, no matter where they are in the genome.

Coordinate control of dispersed genes in a eukaryotic cell often occurs in response to chemical signals from outside the cell. A steroid hormone, for example, enters a cell and binds to a specific intracellular receptor protein, forming a hormone-receptor complex that serves as a transcription activator (see Figure 11.9). Every gene whose transcription is stimulated by a given steroid hormone, regardless of its chromosomal location, has a control element recognized by that hormone-receptor complex. This is how estrogen activates a group of genes that stimulate cell division in uterine cells, preparing the uterus for pregnancy.

Many signalling molecules, such as nonsteroid hormones and growth factors, bind to receptors on a cell's surface and never actually enter the cell. Such molecules can control gene expression indirectly by triggering signal transduction pathways that activate particular transcription factors (see Figure 11.15). Coordinate regulation in such pathways is the same as for steroid hormones: Genes with the same sets of control elements are activated by the same chemical signals. Because this system for coordinating gene regulation is so widespread, scientists think that it probably arose early in evolutionary history.

Nuclear Architecture and Gene Expression

You saw in Figure 16.24 that each chromosome in the interphase nucleus occupies a distinct territory. The chromosomes are not completely isolated, however. Recently, "chromosome conformation capture" techniques have been developed that allow researchers to cross-link and identify regions of chromosomes that associate with each other during interphase. These studies reveal that loops of chromatin extend from individual chromosomal territories into specific sites in the nucleus (Figure 18.12). Different loops from the same chromosome and loops from other chromosomes may congregate in such sites, some of which are rich in RNA polymerases and other transcription-associated proteins. Like a recreation centre that draws members from many different neighbourhoods, these so-called *transcription factories* are thought to be areas specialized for a common function.

The old view that the nuclear contents are like a bowl of amorphous chromosomal spaghetti has given way to a new model of a nucleus with a defined architecture and regulated movements of chromatin. Several lines of evidence suggest that genes that are not being expressed are located in the outer edges of the nucleus, while those that

▲ **Figure 18.12 Chromosomal interactions in the interphase nucleus.** Although each chromosome has its own territory (see Figure 16.24), loops of chromatin may extend into other sites in the nucleus. Some of these sites are transcription factories that are occupied by multiple chromatin loops from the same chromosome (blue loops) or other chromosomes (red and green loops).

are being expressed are found in its interior region. Relocation of particular genes from their chromosomal territories to transcription factories may be part of the process of readying genes for transcription. This is an exciting area of current research that raises many fascinating questions for consideration.

Mechanisms of Post-Transcriptional Regulation

Transcription alone does not constitute gene expression. The expression of a protein-coding gene is ultimately measured by the amount of functional protein a cell makes, and much happens between the synthesis of the RNA transcript and the activity of the protein in the cell. Many regulatory mechanisms operate at the various stages after transcription (see Figure 18.6). These mechanisms allow a cell to fine-tune gene expression rapidly in response to environmental changes without altering its transcription patterns. Here we discuss how cells can regulate gene expression once a gene has been transcribed.

RNA Processing

RNA processing in the nucleus and the export of mature RNA to the cytoplasm provide several opportunities for regulating gene expression that are not available in prokaryotes. One example of regulation at the RNA-processing level is **alternative RNA splicing**, in which different mRNA molecules are produced from the same primary transcript, depending on which RNA segments are treated as exons and which as introns. Regulatory proteins specific to a cell type control intron-exon choices by binding to regulatory sequences within the primary transcript.

A simple example of alternative RNA splicing is shown in Figure 18.13 for the troponin T gene, which encodes two different (though related) proteins. Other genes code for many more possible products. For instance, researchers have found a *Drosophila* gene with enough alternatively spliced exons to generate about 19 000 membrane proteins that have different extracellular domains. At least 17 500 (94%) of the alternative mRNAs are actually synthesized. Each developing nerve cell in the fly appears to synthesize a different form of the protein, which acts as a unique identifier on the cell surface and helps prevent excessive overlap of nerve cells during development of the nervous system.

It is clear that alternative RNA splicing can significantly expand the repertoire of a eukaryotic genome. In fact, alternative splicing was proposed as one explanation for the surprisingly low number of human genes counted

when the human genome was sequenced. The number of human genes was found to be similar to that of a soil worm (nematode), a mustard plant, or a sea anemone. This discovery prompted questions about what, if not the number of genes, accounts for the more complex morphology (external form) of humans. It turns out that more than 90% of human protein-coding genes probably undergo alternative splicing. Thus, the extent of alternative splicing greatly multiplies the number of possible human proteins, which may be better correlated with complexity of form.

Initiation of Translation and mRNA Degradation

Translation is another opportunity for regulating gene expression and occurs most commonly at the initiation stage (see Figure 17.18). For some mRNAs, the initiation of translation can be blocked by regulatory proteins that bind to specific sequences or structures within the untranslated region (UTR) at the 5′ or 3′ end, preventing the attachment of ribosomes. (Recall from Concept 17.3 that both the 5′ cap and the poly-A tail of an mRNA molecule are important for ribosome binding.)

Alternatively, translation of *all* the mRNAs in a cell may be regulated simultaneously. In a eukaryotic cell, such "global" control usually involves the activation or inactivation of one or more of the protein factors required to initiate translation. This mechanism plays a role in starting translation of mRNAs that are stored in eggs. Just after fertilization, translation is triggered by the sudden activation of translation initiation factors. The response is a burst of synthesis of the proteins encoded by the stored mRNAs. Some plants and algae store mRNAs during periods of darkness; light then triggers the reactivation of the translational apparatus.

The life span of mRNA molecules in the cytoplasm is important in determining the pattern of protein synthesis in a cell. Bacterial mRNA molecules typically are degraded by enzymes within a few minutes of their synthesis. This short life span of mRNAs is one reason bacteria can change their patterns of protein synthesis so quickly in response to environmental changes. In contrast, mRNAs in multicellular eukaryotes typically survive for hours, days, or even weeks. For instance, the mRNAs for the hemoglobin polypeptides (α-globin and β-globin) in developing red blood cells are unusually stable, and these long-lived mRNAs are translated repeatedly in red blood cells.

Nucleotide sequences that affect how long an mRNA remains intact are often found in the untranslated region (UTR) at the 3′ end of the molecule (see Figure 18.8). In one experiment, researchers transferred such a sequence from the short-lived mRNA for a growth factor to the 3′ end of a normally stable globin mRNA. The globin mRNA was quickly degraded.

During the past few years, other mechanisms that degrade or block expression of mRNA molecules have

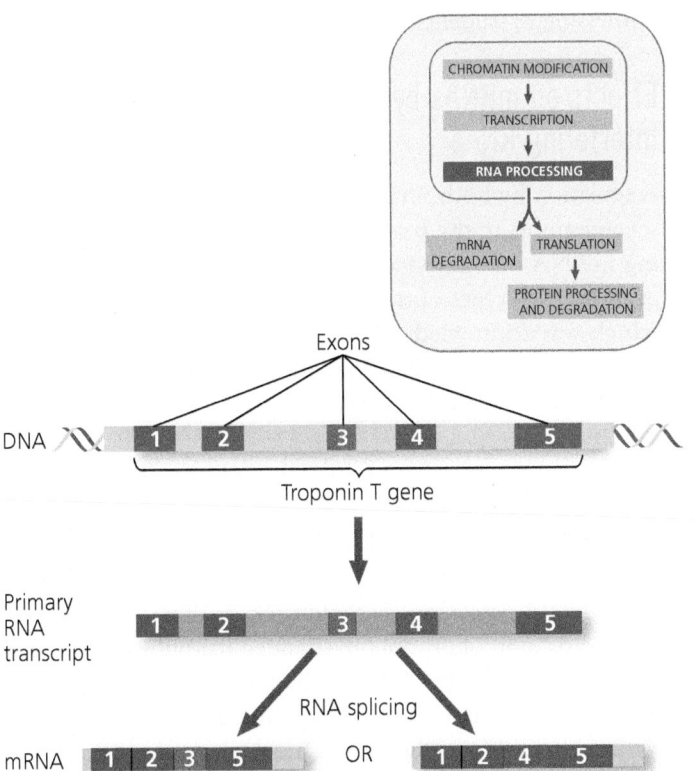

▲ Figure 18.13 **Alternative RNA splicing of the troponin T gene.** The primary transcript of this gene can be spliced in more than one way, generating different mRNA molecules. Notice that one mRNA molecule has ended up with exon 3 (green) and the other with exon 4 (purple). These two mRNAs are translated into different but related muscle proteins.

come to light. These mechanisms involve an important group of newly discovered RNA molecules that regulate gene expression at several levels, and we will discuss them later in this chapter.

Protein Processing and Degradation

The final opportunities for controlling gene expression occur after translation. Often, eukaryotic polypeptides must be processed to yield functional protein molecules. For instance, cleavage of the initial insulin polypeptide (pro-insulin) forms the active hormone. In addition, many proteins undergo chemical modifications that make them functional. Regulatory proteins are commonly activated or inactivated by the reversible addition of phosphate groups, and proteins destined for the surface of animal cells acquire sugars. Cell-surface proteins and many others must also be transported to target destinations in the cell in order to function. Regulation might occur at any of the steps involved in modifying or transporting a protein.

Finally, the length of time each protein functions in the cell is strictly regulated by selective degradation. Many proteins, such as the cyclins involved in regulating the cell cycle, must be relatively short-lived if the cell is to function appropriately (see Figure 12.16). To mark a protein for destruction, the cell commonly attaches molecules of a small protein called ubiquitin to the protein. Giant protein complexes called **proteasomes** then recognize the ubiquitin-tagged proteins and degrade them.

CONCEPT CHECK 18.2

1. In general, what are the effects of histone acetylation and DNA methylation on gene expression?

2. Compare the roles of general and specific transcription factors in regulating gene expression.

3. **WHAT IF?** Suppose you compared the nucleotide sequences of the distal control elements in the enhancers of three genes that are expressed only in muscle cells. What would you expect to find? Why?

4. Once mRNA encoding a particular protein reaches the cytoplasm, what are four mechanisms that can regulate the amount of the protein that is active in the cell?

For suggested answers, see Appendix A.

CONCEPT 18.3

Noncoding RNAs play multiple roles in controlling gene expression

Genome sequencing has revealed that protein-coding DNA accounts for only 1.5% of the human genome and a similarly small percentage of the genomes of many other multicellular eukaryotes. A very small fraction of the non-protein-coding DNA consists of genes for RNAs such as ribosomal RNA and transfer RNA. Scientists assumed until recently that most of the remaining DNA was not transcribed, thinking that since it didn't specify proteins or the few known types of RNA, such DNA didn't contain meaningful genetic information—in fact, it was called "junk DNA." However, a flood of recent data has contradicted this idea. For example, a massive study of the entire human genome showed that roughly 75% of the genome is transcribed at some point in any given cell. Introns account for only a fraction of this transcribed, nontranslated RNA. These and other results suggest that a significant amount of the genome may be transcribed into non-protein-coding RNAs—also called *noncoding RNAs*, or *ncRNAs*—including a variety of small RNAs. Researchers are uncovering more evidence of the biological roles of these ncRNAs every day.

Biologists are excited about these discoveries, which have revealed a large, diverse population of RNA molecules in the cell that play crucial roles in regulating gene expression—but have gone largely unnoticed until recently. Clearly, we must revise our long-standing view, that because mRNAs code for proteins they are the most important RNAs functioning in the cell. This represents a major shift in the thinking of biologists, one that you are witnessing as students entering this field of study.

Effects on mRNAs by MicroRNAs and Small Interfering RNAs

Regulation by both small and large ncRNAs occurs at several points in the pathway of gene expression, including mRNA translation and chromatin modification. We'll examine two types of small ncRNAs, the importance of which was acknowledged when their discovery was the focus of the 2006 Nobel Prize in Physiology or Medicine, which was awarded for work completed only eight years earlier.

Since 1993, a number of research studies have uncovered small single-stranded RNA molecules, called **microRNAs (miRNAs)**, that are capable of binding to complementary sequences in mRNA molecules. The miRNAs are made from longer RNA precursors that fold back on themselves, forming one or more short double-stranded hairpin structures, each held together by hydrogen bonds (Figure 18.14). After each hairpin is cut away from the precursor, it is trimmed by an enzyme (fittingly called Dicer) into a short double-stranded fragment of about 22 nucleotide pairs. One of the two strands is degraded, while the other strand, which is the miRNA, forms a complex with one or more proteins; the miRNA allows the complex to bind to any mRNA molecule with seven to eight nucleotides of complementary sequence. The miRNA-protein complex then either

① The miRNA binds to a target mRNA with at least seven complementary bases.

miRNA

miRNA-protein complex

mRNA degraded

OR

Translation blocked

② If miRNA and mRNA bases are complementary all along their length, the mRNA is degraded (left); if the match is less complete, translation is blocked (right).

▲ Figure 18.14 **Regulation of gene expression by miRNAs.** A 22-nucleotide miRNA, formed by enzymatic processing of an RNA precursor, associates with one or more proteins in a complex. The complex can then degrade or block translation of target mRNAs.

degrades the target mRNA or blocks its translation. It has been estimated that expression of at least one-half of all human genes may be regulated by miRNAs, a remarkable figure given that the existence of miRNAs was unknown 25 years ago.

Another class of small RNAs is called **small interfering RNAs (siRNAs)**. These are similar in size and function to miRNAs—both can associate with the same proteins, producing similar results. In fact, if siRNA precursor RNA molecules are injected into a cell, the cell's machinery can process them into siRNAs that turn off expression of genes with related sequences, similarly to how miRNAs function. The distinction between miRNAs and siRNAs is based on subtle differences in the structure of their precursors, which in both cases are RNA molecules that are mostly double-stranded. The blocking of gene expression by siRNAs is called **RNA interference (RNAi)**, and it is used in the laboratory as a means of disabling specific genes to investigate their function.

How did the RNAi pathway evolve? As you will learn in Concept 19.2, some viruses have double-stranded RNA

genomes. Given that the cellular RNAi pathway can process double-stranded RNAs into homing devices that lead to destruction of related RNAs, some scientists think that this pathway may have evolved as a natural defence against infection by such viruses. However, the fact that RNAi can also affect the expression of nonviral cellular genes may reflect a different evolutionary origin for the RNAi pathway. Moreover, many species, including mammals, apparently produce their own long, double-stranded RNA precursors to small RNAs such as siRNAs. Once produced, these RNAs can interfere with gene expression at stages other than translation, as we'll discuss next.

Chromatin Remodelling by ncRNAs

The pervasive function of noncoding RNAs in regulating gene expression is becoming increasingly obvious, and one more effect of ncRNAs is worth discussing here. In addition to regulating mRNAs, some ncRNAs act to bring about remodelling of chromatin structure. One example occurs during formation of heterochromatin at the centromere, as studied in a species of yeast.

In the S phase of the cell cycle, the centromeric regions of DNA must be loosened for chromosomal replication and then re-condensed into heterochromatin in preparation for mitosis. In some yeasts, siRNAs produced by the yeast cells themselves are required to re-form the heterochromatin at the centromeres. A model for how this happens is shown in **Figure 18.15**. Exactly how the process starts and the order of the steps are still being debated, but biologists all agree on the general idea: The siRNA system in yeast interacts with other noncoding RNAs and with chromatin-modifying enzymes to remodel chromatin structure at the centromere. In most mammalian cells, siRNAs are not known to occur, and the mechanism for centromere DNA condensation is not yet understood. However, it may turn out to involve other small ncRNAs.

A newly discovered class of small ncRNAs is called *piwi-interacting RNAs*, or *piRNAs*. These RNAs also induce formation of heterochromatin, blocking expression of some parasitic DNA elements in the genome known as transposons. (Transposons are discussed in Chapter 21.) Usually 24–31 nucleotides in length, piRNAs are processed from a longer, single-stranded RNA precursor. They play an indispensable role in the germ cells of many animal species, where they appear to help reestablish appropriate methylation patterns in the genome during gamete formation.

Finally, ncRNAs are responsible for X chromosome inactivation, which, in most female mammals, prevents expression of genes located on one of the X chromosomes (see Figure 15.8). In this case, transcripts of the *XIST* gene located on the chromosome to be inactivated bind

① RNA transcripts (red) are produced from centromeric DNA.

Centromeric DNA

RNA polymerase

Sister chromatids (two DNA molecules)

RNA transcript

② Each RNA transcript is used as a template by a yeast enzyme that synthesizes the complementary strand, forming double-stranded RNA.

③ The double-stranded RNA is processed into short, single-stranded siRNAs that associate with proteins, forming siRNA-protein complexes.

siRNA-protein complex

④ The siRNA-protein complexes bind the RNA transcripts being produced from the centromeric DNA and, in this way, are tethered to the centromere region.

⑤ Proteins in the siRNA-protein complexes recruit enzymes (green) that chemically modify the histones within the chromatin and initiate chromatin condensation.

Centromeric DNA

Chromatin-modifying enzymes

⑥ Ultimately, this process leads to formation of heterochromatin at the centromere.

Heterochromatin at the centromere region

▲ Figure 18.15 **Condensation of chromatin at the centromere.** In one type of yeast, siRNAs and longer noncoding RNAs cooperate in the pathway that leads to re-formation of highly condensed heterochromatin at the centromere of each chromatid after DNA replication.

back to and coat that chromosome, and this binding leads to condensation of the entire chromosome into heterochromatin. The cases we have just described involve chromatin remodelling in large regions of the chromosome. Because chromatin structure affects transcription and thus gene expression, RNA-based regulation of chromatin structure is likely to play an important role in gene regulation.

The Evolutionary Significance of Small ncRNAs

EVOLUTION Small ncRNAs can regulate gene expression at multiple steps and in many ways. While this section has focused on ncRNAs in eukaryotes, small ncRNAs are also used by bacteria as a defence system, called the CRISPR-Cas9 system, against viruses that infect them. (You'll learn more about this in Concept 19.2.) The use of ncRNAs thus evolved long ago, but we don't yet know how bacterial ncRNAs are related to those of eukaryotes.

What about the evolutionary significance of small eukaryotic ncRNAs? In general, extra levels of gene regulation might allow evolution of a higher degree of complexity of form. Therefore, the versatility of miRNA regulation has led some biologists to hypothesize that an increase in the number of different miRNAs specified by the genome of a given species has allowed morphological complexity to increase over evolutionary time. While this hypothesis is still being debated, it is logical to expand the discussion to include all small ncRNAs. Exciting new techniques for rapidly sequencing genomes are beginning to allow biologists to ask how many genes for ncRNAs are present in the genome of a given species. A survey of different species supports the notion that siRNAs evolved first, followed by miRNAs and later piRNAs, which are found only in animals. And while there are hundreds of types of miRNAs, there appear to be many thousands of types of piRNAs, allowing the potential for very sophisticated gene regulation by piRNAs.

Given the extensive functions of ncRNAs, it is not surprising that many of the ncRNAs characterized thus far play important roles in embryonic development—the topic we turn to in the next section. Embryonic development is perhaps the ultimate example of precisely regulated gene expression.

CONCEPT CHECK 18.3

1. Compare miRNAs and siRNAs, including their functions.

2. **WHAT IF?** Suppose the mRNA being degraded in Figure 18.14 coded for a protein that promotes cell division in a multicellular organism. What would happen if a mutation disabled the gene for the miRNA that triggers this degradation?

For suggested answers, see Appendix A.

CONCEPT 18.4

A program of differential gene expression leads to the different cell types in a multicellular organism

In the embryonic development of multicellular organisms, a fertilized egg (a zygote) gives rise to cells of many different types, each with a different structure and corresponding function. Typically, cells are organized into tissues, tissues into organs, organs into organ systems, and organ systems into the whole organism. Thus, any developmental program must produce cells of different types that form higher-level structures arranged in a particular way in three dimensions. The processes that occur during development in plants and animals are detailed in Chapters 35 and 47, respectively. In this chapter, we focus on the program of regulation of gene expression that orchestrates development, using a few animal species as examples.

A Genetic Program for Embryonic Development

The photos in **Figure 18.16** illustrate the dramatic difference between a frog zygote (fertilized egg) and the tadpole it becomes. This remarkable transformation results from three interrelated processes: cell division, cell differentiation, and morphogenesis. Through a succession of mitotic cell divisions, the zygote gives rise to a large number of cells. Cell division alone, however, would merely produce a great ball of identical cells, nothing like a tadpole. During embryonic development, cells not only increase in number, but also undergo cell **differentiation**, the process by which cells become specialized in structure and function. Moreover, the different kinds of cells are not randomly distributed but are organized into tissues and organs in a particular three-dimensional arrangement. The physical

(a) Fertilized eggs of a frog   **(b) Newly hatched tadpole**

▲ **Figure 18.16 From fertilized egg to animal: what a difference four days makes.** It takes just four days for cell division, differentiation, and morphogenesis to transform each of the fertilized frog eggs shown in **(a)** into a tadpole like the one in **(b)**.

processes that give an organism its shape constitute **morphogenesis**, the development of the form of an organism and its structures.

All three processes are rooted in cellular behaviour. Even morphogenesis, the shaping of the organism, can be traced back to changes in the shape, motility, and other characteristics of the cells that make up various regions of the embryo. As you have seen, the activities of a cell depend on the genes it expresses and the proteins it produces. Almost all cells in an organism have the same genome; therefore, differential gene expression results from the genes being regulated differently in each cell type.

In Figure 18.11, you saw a simplified view of how differential gene expression occurs in two cell types, a liver cell and a lens cell. Each of these fully differentiated cells has a particular mix of specific activators that turn on the collection of genes whose products are required in the cell. The fact that both cells arose through a series of mitoses from a common fertilized egg inevitably leads to a question: How do different sets of activators come to be present in the two cells?

It turns out that materials placed into the egg by the mother set up a sequential program of gene regulation that is carried out as cells divide, and this program coordinates cell differentiation during embryonic development. To understand how this works, we will consider two basic developmental processes: First, we'll explore how cells that arise from early embryonic mitoses develop the differences that start each cell along its own differentiation pathway. Second, we'll see how cellular differentiation leads to one particular cell type, using muscle development as an example.

Cytoplasmic Determinants and Inductive Signals

What generates the first differences among cells in an early embryo? And what controls the differentiation of all the various cell types as development proceeds? By this point in the chapter, you can probably deduce the answer: The specific genes expressed in any particular cell of a developing organism determine its path. Two sources of information, used to varying extents in different species, "tell" a cell which genes to express at any given time during embryonic development.

One important source of information early in development is the egg's cytoplasm, which contains both RNA and proteins encoded by the mother's DNA. The cytoplasm of an unfertilized egg is not homogeneous. Messenger RNA, proteins, other substances, and organelles are distributed unevenly in the unfertilized egg, and this unevenness has a profound impact on the development of the future embryo in many species. Maternal substances in the egg that influence the course of early development are called

cytoplasmic determinants (Figure 18.17a). After fertilization, early mitotic divisions distribute the zygote's cytoplasm into separate cells. The nuclei of these cells may thus be exposed to different cytoplasmic determinants, depending on which portions of the zygotic cytoplasm a cell received. The combination of cytoplasmic determinants in a cell helps determine its developmental fate by regulating expression of the cell's genes during the course of cell differentiation.

▼ **Figure 18.17** **Sources of developmental information for the early embryo.**

(a) Cytoplasmic determinants in the egg

The unfertilized egg has molecules in its cytoplasm, encoded by the mother's genes, that influence development. Many of these cytoplasmic determinants, like the two shown here, are unevenly distributed in the egg. After fertilization and mitotic division, the cell nuclei of the embryo are exposed to different sets of cytoplasmic determinants and, as a result, express different genes.

(b) Induction by nearby cells

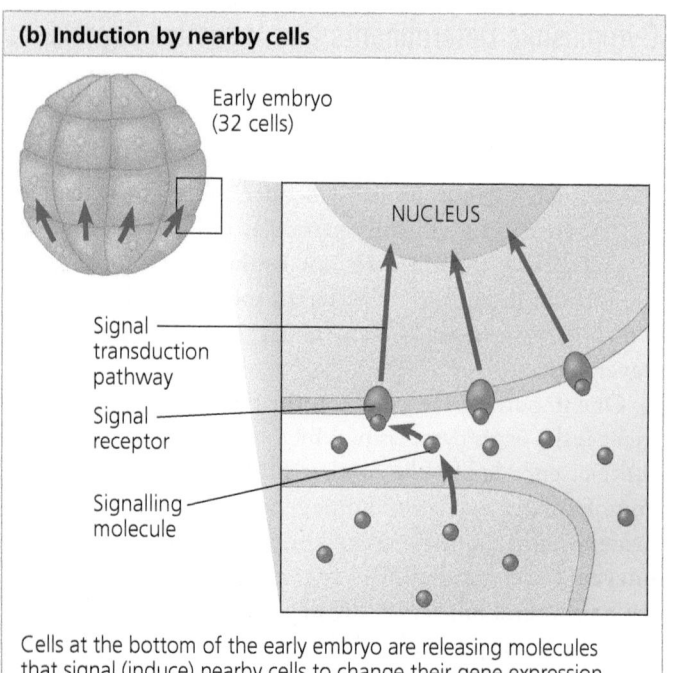

Cells at the bottom of the early embryo are releasing molecules that signal (induce) nearby cells to change their gene expression.

The other major source of developmental information, which becomes increasingly important as the number of embryonic cells increases, is the environment around a particular cell. Most influential are the signals conveyed to an embryonic cell from other embryonic cells in the vicinity, including contact with cell-surface molecules on neighbouring cells and the binding of growth factors secreted by neighbouring cells (see Concept 11.2). Such signals cause changes in the target cells, a process called **induction** (Figure 18.17b). The molecules passing along these signals within the target cell are cell-surface receptors and other signalling pathway proteins expressed by the embryo's own genes. In general, the signalling molecules send a cell down a specific developmental path by causing changes in its gene expression that eventually result in observable cellular changes. Thus, interactions between embryonic cells help induce differentiation into the many specialized cell types making up a new organism.

Sequential Regulation of Gene Expression During Cellular Differentiation

The earliest changes that set a cell on its path to specialization are subtle ones, showing up only at the molecular level. Before biologists knew much about the molecular changes occurring in embryos, they coined the term **determination** to refer to the point at which an embryonic cell is irreversibly committed to becoming a particular cell type. Once it has undergone determination, an embryonic cell can be experimentally placed in another location in the embryo and it will still differentiate into the cell type that is its normal fate. Differentiation, then, is the process by which a cell attains its determined fate. As the tissues and organs of an embryo develop and their cells differentiate, the cells become more noticeably different in structure and function.

Today we understand determination in terms of molecular changes. The outcome of determination, observable cell differentiation, is marked by the expression of genes for *tissue-specific proteins*. These proteins are found only in a specific cell type and give the cell its characteristic structure and function. The first evidence of differentiation is the appearance of mRNAs for these proteins. Eventually, differentiation is observable with a microscope as changes in cellular structure. On the molecular level, different sets of genes are sequentially expressed in a regulated manner as new cells arise from division of their precursors. A number of the steps in gene expression may be regulated during differentiation, with transcription being the most common. In the fully differentiated cell, transcription remains the principal regulatory point for maintaining appropriate gene expression.

Differentiated cells are specialists at making tissue-specific proteins. For example, as a result of transcriptional regulation, liver cells specialize in making albumin, and lens cells specialize in making crystallin (see Figure 18.11). Skeletal muscle cells in vertebrates are another instructive example. Each of these cells is a long fibre containing many nuclei within a single plasma membrane. Skeletal muscle cells have high concentrations of muscle-specific versions of the contractile proteins myosin and actin, as well as membrane receptor proteins that detect signals from nerve cells.

Muscle cells develop from embryonic precursor cells that have the potential to develop into a number of cell types, including cartilage cells and fat cells, but particular conditions commit them to becoming muscle cells. Although the committed cells appear unchanged under the microscope, determination has occurred, and they are now *myoblasts*. Eventually, myoblasts start to churn out large amounts of muscle-specific proteins and fuse to form mature, elongated, multinucleate skeletal muscle cells (Figure 18.18).

Researchers have worked out what happens at the molecular level during muscle cell determination by growing myoblasts in culture and analyzing them using molecular techniques you will learn about in Chapter 20. In a series of experiments, they isolated different genes, caused each to be expressed in a separate embryonic precursor cell, and then looked for differentiation into myoblasts and muscle cells. In this way, they identified several so-called "master regulatory genes" whose protein products commit the cells to becoming skeletal muscle. Thus, in the case of muscle cells, the molecular basis of determination is the expression of one or more of these master regulatory genes.

To understand more about how commitment occurs in muscle cell differentiation, let's focus on the master regulatory gene called *myoD* (see Figure 18.18). This gene encodes MyoD protein, a transcription factor that binds to specific control elements in the enhancers of various target genes and stimulates their expression (see Figure 18.9). Some target

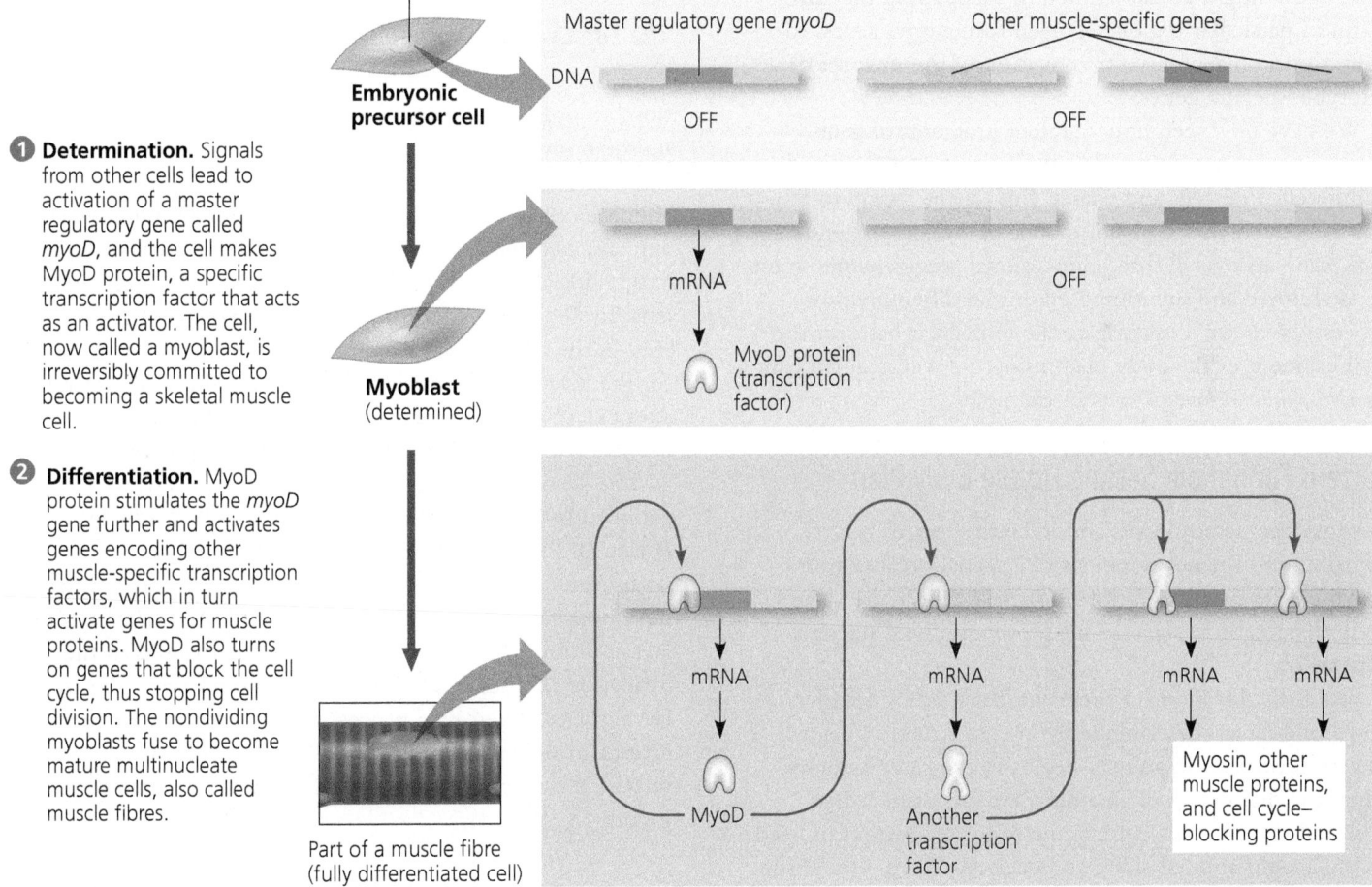

❶ **Determination.** Signals from other cells lead to activation of a master regulatory gene called *myoD*, and the cell makes MyoD protein, a specific transcription factor that acts as an activator. The cell, now called a myoblast, is irreversibly committed to becoming a skeletal muscle cell.

❷ **Differentiation.** MyoD protein stimulates the *myoD* gene further and activates genes encoding other muscle-specific transcription factors, which in turn activate genes for muscle proteins. MyoD also turns on genes that block the cell cycle, thus stopping cell division. The nondividing myoblasts fuse to become mature multinucleate muscle cells, also called muscle fibres.

▲ Figure 18.18 **Determination and differentiation of muscle cells.** Skeletal muscle cells arise from embryonic cells as a result of changes in gene expression. (In this depiction, the process of gene activation is greatly simplified.)

WHAT IF? *What would happen if a mutation in the* myoD *gene resulted in a MyoD protein that could not activate the* myoD *gene?*

genes for MyoD encode still other muscle-specific transcription factors. MyoD also stimulates expression of the *myoD* gene itself, an example of positive feedback that perpetuates MyoD's effect in maintaining the cell's differentiated state. Presumably, all the genes activated by MyoD have enhancer-control elements recognized by MyoD and are thus coordinately controlled. Finally, the secondary transcription factors activate the genes for proteins such as myosin and actin that confer the unique properties of skeletal muscle cells.

The *myoD* gene deserves its designation as a master regulatory gene. Researchers have shown that MyoD is capable of changing some kinds of fully differentiated non-muscle cells, such as fat cells and liver cells, into muscle cells. Why doesn't it work on *all* kinds of cells? One likely explanation is that activation of the muscle-specific genes is not solely dependent on MyoD but requires a particular *combination* of regulatory proteins, some of which are lacking in cells that do not respond to MyoD. The determination and differentiation of other kinds of tissues may play out in a similar fashion. A growing body of experimental evidence supports the idea that master regulatory proteins like MyoD might actually function by opening the chromatin in particular regions. This in turn allows access to transcription machinery for activation of the next set of cell type–specific genes.

We have now seen how different programs of gene expression that are activated in the fertilized egg can result in differentiated cells and tissues. But for the tissues to function effectively in the organism as a whole, the organism's *body plan*—its overall three-dimensional arrangement—must be established and superimposed on the differentiation process. Next we'll investigate the molecular basis for the establishment of the body plan, using the well-studied fruit fly *Drosophila melanogaster* as an example.

Pattern Formation: Setting Up the Body Plan

Cytoplasmic determinants and inductive signals both contribute to the development of a spatial organization in which the tissues and organs of an organism are all in their characteristic places. This process is called **pattern formation**.

Just as the locations of the front, back, and sides of a new building are determined before construction begins, pattern formation in animals begins in the early embryo, when the major axes of an animal are established. In a bilaterally symmetrical animal the relative positions of head and tail, right and left sides, and back and front—the three major body axes—are set up before the organs appear. The molecular cues that control pattern formation, collectively called **positional information**, are provided by cytoplasmic determinants and inductive signals (see Figure 18.17).

These cues tell a cell its location relative to the body axes and to neighbouring cells and determine how the cell and its descendants will respond to future molecular signals.

During the first half of the 20th century, classical embryologists made detailed anatomical observations of embryonic development in a number of species and performed experiments in which they manipulated embryonic tissues. Although this research laid the groundwork for understanding the mechanisms of development, it did not reveal the specific molecules that guide development or determine how patterns are established.

In the 1940s, scientists began using the genetic approach—the study of mutants—to investigate *Drosophila* development. That approach has had spectacular success. These studies have established that genes control development and have led to an understanding of the key roles that specific molecules play in defining position and directing differentiation. By combining anatomical, genetic, and biochemical approaches to the study of *Drosophila* development, researchers have discovered developmental principles common to many other species, including humans.

The Life Cycle of Drosophila

Fruit flies and other arthropods have a modular construction, an ordered series of segments. These segments make up the body's three major parts: the head, the thorax (the midbody, from which the wings and legs extend), and the abdomen (**Figure 18.19a**). Like other bilaterally symmetrical animals, *Drosophila* has an anterior-posterior (head-to-tail) axis, a dorsal-ventral (back-to-belly) axis, and a right-left axis. In *Drosophila*, cytoplasmic determinants that are localized in the unfertilized egg provide positional information for the placement of anterior-posterior and dorsal-ventral axes even before fertilization. We'll focus here on the molecules involved in establishing the anterior-posterior axis.

The *Drosophila* egg develops in the female's ovary, surrounded by ovarian cells called nurse cells and follicle cells (**Figure 18.19b**, top). These support cells supply the egg with nutrients, mRNAs, and other substances needed for development and make the eggshell. After fertilization and laying of the egg, embryonic development results in the formation of a segmented larva, which goes through three larval stages. Then, in a process much like that by which a caterpillar becomes a butterfly, the fly larva forms a cocoon in which it metamorphoses into the adult fly pictured in Figure 18.19a.

Genetic Analysis of Early Development: Scientific Inquiry

Edward B. Lewis was a visionary American biologist who, in the 1940s, first showed the value of the genetic approach to studying embryonic development in *Drosophila*. Lewis studied

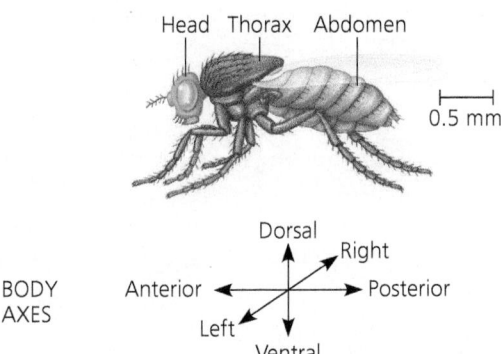

Head Thorax Abdomen

0.5 mm

BODY AXES

Dorsal
Right
Anterior ← → Posterior
Left
Ventral

(a) Adult. The adult fly is segmented, and multiple segments make up each of the three main body parts—head, thorax, and abdomen. The body axes are shown by arrows.

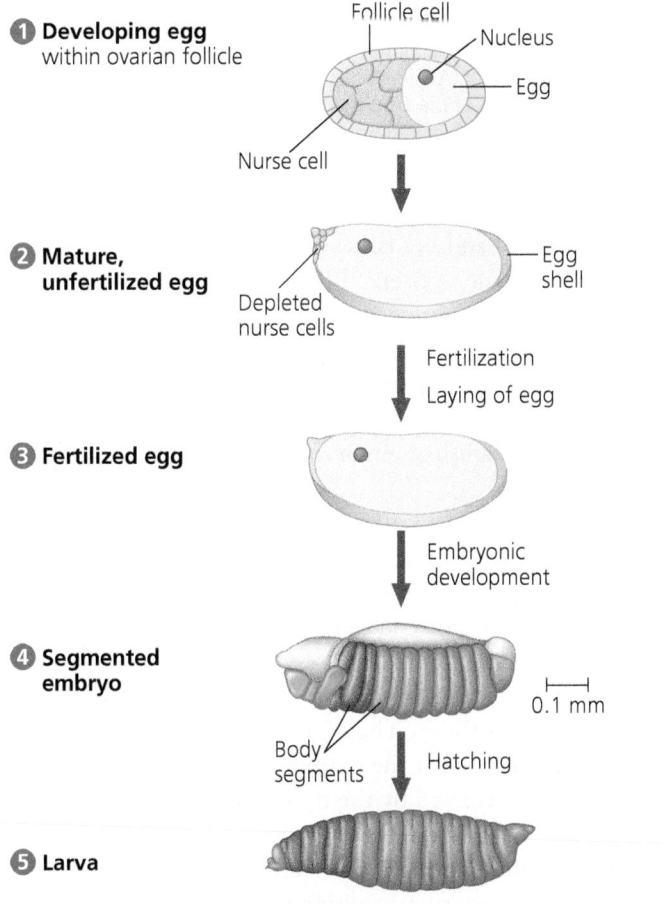

1 **Developing egg** within ovarian follicle

Follicle cell
Nucleus
Egg
Nurse cell

2 **Mature, unfertilized egg**

Egg shell
Depleted nurse cells

Fertilization
Laying of egg

3 **Fertilized egg**

Embryonic development

4 **Segmented embryo**

0.1 mm
Body segments
Hatching

5 **Larva**

(b) Development from egg to larva. **1** The egg (yellow) is surrounded by support cells (follicle cells) within one of the mother's ovaries. **2** The developing egg enlarges as nutrients and mRNAs are supplied to it by other support cells (nurse cells), which shrink. Eventually, the mature egg fills the egg shell that is secreted by the follicle cells. **3** The egg is fertilized within the mother and then laid. It develops into **4** a segmented embryo and then **5** a larva, which has three stages. The third stage forms a pupa (not shown), within which the larva metamorphoses into the adult shown in (a).

▲ Figure 18.19 **Key developmental events in the life cycle of *Drosophila*.**

bizarre mutant flies with developmental defects that led to extra wings or legs in the wrong place (Figure 18.20). He located the mutations on the fly's genetic map, thus connecting the developmental abnormalities to specific genes. This research supplied the first concrete evidence that genes somehow direct the developmental processes studied by embryologists. The genes Lewis discovered, called **homeotic genes**, control pattern formation in the late embryo, larva, and adult.

Further insight into pattern formation during early embryonic development did not come for another 30 years, when two researchers in Germany, Christiane Nüsslein-Volhard and Eric Wieschaus, set out to identify *all* the genes that affect segment formation in *Drosophila*. The project was daunting for three reasons. The first was the sheer number of *Drosophila* genes, now known to total about 14 000. The genes affecting segmentation might be just a few needles in a haystack or might be so numerous and varied that the scientists would be unable to make sense of them. Second, mutations affecting a process as fundamental as segmentation would surely be **embryonic lethals**, mutations with phenotypes causing death at the embryonic or larval stage. Because organisms with embryonic lethal mutations never reproduce, they cannot be bred for study. The researchers dealt with this problem by looking for recessive mutations, which can be propagated in heterozygous flies that act as genetic carriers. Third, cytoplasmic determinants in the egg were known to play a role in axis formation, so the researchers knew they would have to study the mother's genes as well as those of the embryo. It is the mother's genes that we will discuss further as we focus on how the anterior-posterior body axis is set up in the developing egg.

Nüsslein-Volhard and Wieschaus began their search for segmentation genes by exposing flies to a mutagenic chemical that affected the flies' gametes. They mated the

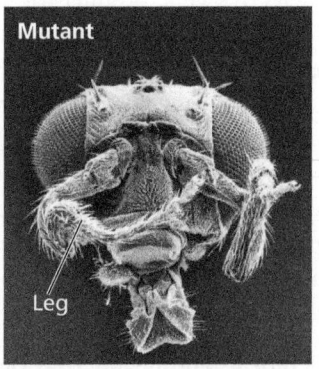

Wild type
Eye
Antenna

Mutant
Leg

F. Rudolf Turner

▲ Figure 18.20 **Abnormal pattern formation in *Drosophila*.** Mutations in certain regulatory genes, called homeotic genes, cause a misplacement of structures in an animal. These colourized scanning electron micrographs contrast the head of a wild-type fruit fly, bearing a pair of small antennae, with that of a homeotic mutant (a fly with a mutation in a single gene), bearing a pair of legs in place of antennae.

mutagenized flies and then scanned their descendants for dead embryos or larvae with abnormal segmentation or other defects. For example, to find genes that might set up the anterior-posterior axis, they looked for embryos or larvae with abnormal ends, such as two heads or two tails, predicting that such abnormalities would arise from mutations in maternal genes required for correctly setting up the offspring's head or tail end.

Using this approach, Nüsslein-Volhard and Wieschaus eventually identified about 1200 genes essential for pattern formation during embryonic development. Of these, about 120 were essential for normal segmentation. Over several years, the researchers were able to group these segmentation genes by general function, to map them, and to clone many of them for further study in the lab. The result was a detailed molecular understanding of the early steps in pattern formation in *Drosophila*.

When the results of Nüsslein-Volhard and Wieschaus were combined with Lewis's earlier work, a coherent picture of *Drosophila* development emerged. In recognition of their discoveries, the three researchers were awarded a Nobel Prize in 1995. Next, let's consider a specific example of the genes that Nüsslein-Volhard, Wieschaus, and coworkers found.

Axis Establishment

As we mentioned earlier, cytoplasmic determinants in the egg are the substances that initially establish the axes of the *Drosophila* body. These substances are encoded by genes of the mother, fittingly called maternal effect genes. A **maternal effect gene** is a gene that, when mutant in the mother, results in a mutant phenotype in the offspring, regardless of the offspring's own genotype. In fruit fly development, the mRNA or protein products of maternal effect genes are placed in the egg while it is still in the mother's ovary. When the mother has a mutation in such a gene, she makes a defective gene product (or none at all), and her eggs are defective; when these eggs are fertilized, they fail to develop properly.

Because they control the orientation (polarity) of the egg and consequently that of the fly, these maternal effect genes are also called **egg-polarity genes**. One group of these genes sets up the anterior-posterior axis of the embryo, while a second group establishes the dorsal-ventral axis. Like mutations in segmentation genes, mutations in maternal effect genes are generally embryonic lethals.

Bicoid: A Morphogen That Determines Head Structures

To see how maternal effect genes determine the body axes of the offspring, we will focus on one such gene, called *bicoid*, a term meaning "two-tailed." An embryo or larva whose mother has two mutant *bicoid* alleles lacks the front half of its body and has posterior structures at both ends (Figure 18.21). This phenotype suggested to

▲ Figure 18.21 **Effect of the *bicoid* gene on *Drosophila* development.** A wild-type fruit fly larva has a head, three thoracic (T) segments, eight abdominal (A) segments, and a tail. A larva whose mother has two mutant alleles of the *bicoid* gene has two tails and lacks all anterior structures (LMs).

Nüsslein-Volhard and her colleagues that the product of the mother's *bicoid* gene is essential for setting up the anterior end of the fly and might be concentrated at the future anterior end of the embryo. This hypothesis is an example of the *morphogen gradient hypothesis* first proposed by embryologists a century ago, in which gradients of substances called **morphogens** establish an embryo's axes and other features of its form.

DNA technology and other modern biochemical methods enabled the researchers to test whether the *bicoid* product, a protein called Bicoid, is in fact a morphogen that determines the anterior end of the fly. The first question they asked was whether the mRNA and protein products of this gene are located in the egg in a position consistent with the hypothesis. They found that *bicoid* mRNA is highly concentrated at the extreme anterior end of the mature egg, as predicted by the hypothesis (Figure 18.22). After the egg is fertilized, the mRNA is translated into protein. The Bicoid protein then diffuses from the anterior end toward the posterior, resulting in a gradient of protein within the early embryo, with the highest concentration at the anterior end. These results are consistent with the hypothesis that Bicoid protein specifies the fly's anterior end. To test the hypothesis more specifically, scientists injected pure *bicoid* mRNA into various regions of early embryos. The protein that resulted from its translation caused anterior structures to form at the injection sites.

The *bicoid* research was groundbreaking for several reasons. First, it led to the identification of a specific protein required for some of the earliest steps in pattern formation. It thus helped us understand how different regions of the

▼ Figure 18.22 Inquiry

Could Bicoid be a morphogen that determines the anterior end of a fruit fly?

Experiment Using a genetic approach to study *Drosophila* development, Christiane Nüsslein-Volhard and colleagues at the European Molecular Biology Laboratory in Heidelberg, Germany, analyzed expression of the *bicoid* gene. The researchers hypothesized that *bicoid* normally codes for a morphogen that specifies the head (anterior) end of the embryo. To test this hypothesis, they used molecular techniques to determine where the mRNA and protein encoded by this gene were found in the fertilized egg and early embryo of wild-type flies.

Results *Bicoid* mRNA (dark blue) was confined to the anterior end of the unfertilized egg. Later in development, Bicoid protein (dark orange) was seen to be concentrated in cells at the anterior end of the embryo.

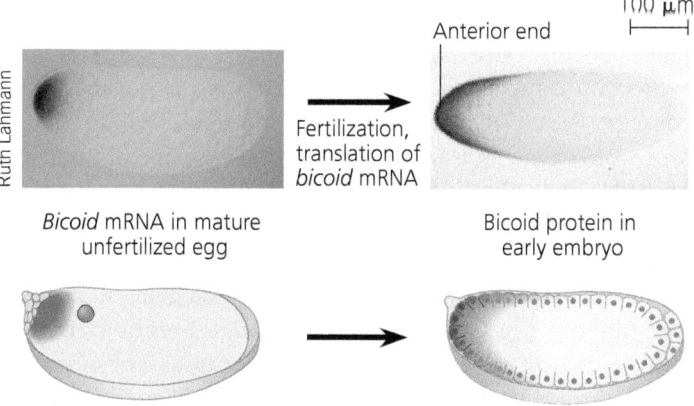

Bicoid mRNA in mature unfertilized egg

Bicoid protein in early embryo

Conclusion The location of *bicoid* mRNA and the diffuse gradient of Bicoid protein seen later support the hypothesis that Bicoid protein is a morphogen specifying formation of head-specific structures.

Source: Based on C. Nüsslein-Volhard et al., Determination of anteroposterior polarity in Drosophila, *Science* 238:1675–1681 (1987); W. Driever and C. Nüsslein-Volhard, A gradient of bicoid protein in Drosophila embryos, *Cell* 54:83–93 (1988); T. Berleth et al., The role of localization of bicoid RNA in organizing the anterior pattern of the Drosophila embryo, *EMBO Journal* 7:1749–1756 (1988). © Jane B Reece.

WHAT IF? *If the hypothesis is correct, predict what would happen if you injected* bicoid *mRNA into the anterior end of an egg from a female with a mutation disabling the* bicoid *gene.*

egg can give rise to cells that go down different developmental pathways. Second, it increased our understanding of the mother's critical role in the initial phases of embryonic development. Finally, the principle that a gradient of morphogens can determine polarity and position has proved to be a key developmental concept for a number of species, just as early embryologists had hypothesized.

Maternal mRNAs are crucial during development of many species. In *Drosophila*, gradients of specific proteins encoded by maternal mRNAs not only determine the posterior and anterior ends but also establish the dorsal-ventral axis. As the fly embryo grows, it reaches a point when the embryonic program of gene expression takes over, and the

maternal mRNAs must be destroyed. (This process involves miRNAs in *Drosophila* and other species.) Later, positional information encoded by the embryo's genes, operating on an ever finer scale, establishes a specific number of correctly oriented segments and triggers the formation of each segment's characteristic structures. When the genes operating in this final step are abnormal, the pattern of the adult is abnormal, as you saw in Figure 18.20.

Evolutionary Developmental Biology ("Evo-Devo")

EVOLUTION The fly with legs emerging from its head in Figure 18.20 is the result of a single mutation in one gene, a homeotic gene. The gene does not encode any antenna protein, however. Instead, it encodes a transcription factor that regulates other genes, and its malfunction leads to misplaced structures, such as legs instead of antennae. The observation that a change in gene regulation during development could lead to such a fantastic change in body form prompted some scientists to consider whether these types of mutations could contribute to evolution by generating novel body shapes. Ultimately this line of inquiry gave rise to the field of evolutionary developmental biology, so-called "evo-devo," which will be further discussed in Chapter 21.

In this section, we have seen how a carefully orchestrated program of sequential gene regulation controls the transformation of a fertilized egg into a multicellular organism. The program is carefully balanced between turning on the genes for differentiation in the right place and turning off other genes. Even when an organism is fully developed, gene expression is regulated in a similarly fine-tuned manner. In the final section of this chapter, we'll consider how fine this tuning is by looking at how specific changes in expression of just a few genes can lead to the development of cancer.

CONCEPT CHECK 18.4

1. **MAKE CONNECTIONS** As you learned in Chapter 12, mitosis gives rise to two daughter cells that are genetically identical to the parent cell. Yet you, the product of many mitotic divisions, are not composed of identical, zygote-like cells. Why?

2. **MAKE CONNECTIONS** Explain how the signalling molecules released by an embryonic cell can induce changes in a neighbouring cell without entering the cell. (See Figures 11.15 and 11.16.)

3. How do fruit fly maternal effect genes determine the polarity of the egg and embryo?

4. **WHAT IF?** In Figure 18.17b, the lower cell is synthesizing signalling molecules, whereas the upper cell is expressing receptors for these molecules. In terms of gene regulation, explain how these cells came to synthesize different molecules.

For suggested answers, see Appendix A.

CONCEPT 18.5

Cancer results from genetic changes that affect cell cycle control

In Concept 12.3, we considered cancer as a type of disease in which cells escape from the control mechanisms that normally limit their growth. Now that we have discussed the molecular basis of gene expression and its regulation, we are ready to look at cancer more closely. The gene regulation systems that go wrong during cancer turn out to be the very same systems that play important roles in embryonic development, the immune response, and many other biological processes. Thus, research into the molecular basis of cancer has both benefitted from and informed many other fields of biology.

Types of Genes Associated with Cancer

The genes that normally regulate cell growth and division during the cell cycle include genes for growth factors, their receptors, and the intracellular molecules of signalling pathways. (To review cell signalling, see Chapter 11; for the cell cycle, see Chapter 12.) Mutations that alter any of these genes in somatic cells can lead to cancer. The agent of such change can be random spontaneous mutation. However, it is likely that many cancer-causing mutations also result from environmental influences, such as chemical carcinogens, X-rays and other high-energy radiation, and some viruses.

Cancer research led to the discovery of cancer-causing genes called **oncogenes** (from the Greek *onco*, tumour) in certain types of viruses (see Chapter 19). Subsequently, close counterparts of viral oncogenes were found in the genomes of humans and other animals. The normal versions of the cellular genes, called **proto-oncogenes**, code for proteins that stimulate normal cell growth and division.

How might a proto-oncogene—a gene that has an essential function in normal cells—become an oncogene, a cancer-causing gene? In general, an oncogene arises from a genetic change that leads to an increase either in the amount of the proto-oncogene's protein product or in the intrinsic activity of each protein molecule. The genetic changes that convert proto-oncogenes to oncogenes fall into three main categories: movement of DNA within the genome, amplification of a proto-oncogene, and point mutations in a control element or in the proto-oncogene itself (Figure 18.23).

Cancer cells are frequently found to contain chromosomes that have broken and rejoined incorrectly, translocating fragments from one chromosome to another (see Figure 15.15). Now that you have learned how gene expression is regulated, you can understand the possible consequences of such translocations. If a translocated proto-oncogene ends up near an especially active promoter (or other control element), its transcription may increase, making it an oncogene. The second main type of genetic change, amplification, increases the number of copies of the proto-oncogene in the cell through repeated gene duplication (discussed in Concept 21.5). The third possibility is a point mutation either (1) in the promoter or an enhancer that controls a proto-oncogene, causing an increase in its expression, or (2) in the coding sequence of the proto-oncogene, changing the gene's product to a protein that is more active or more resistant to degradation than the normal protein. All these mechanisms can lead to abnormal stimulation of the cell cycle and put the cell on the path to becoming a cancer cell.

▲ Figure 18.23 **Genetic changes that can turn proto-oncogenes into oncogenes.**

In addition to genes whose products normally promote cell division, cells contain genes whose normal products *inhibit* cell division. Such genes are called **tumour-suppressor genes**, since the proteins they encode help prevent uncontrolled cell growth. Any mutation that decreases the normal activity of a tumour-suppressor protein may contribute to the onset of cancer, in effect stimulating growth through the absence of suppression.

The protein products of tumour-suppressor genes have various functions. Some tumour-suppressor proteins repair damaged DNA, a function that prevents the cell from accumulating cancer-causing mutations. Other tumour-suppressor proteins control the adhesion of cells to each other or to the extracellular matrix; proper cell anchorage is crucial in normal tissues—and is often absent in cancers. Still other tumour-suppressor proteins are components of cell-signalling pathways that inhibit the cell cycle.

Interference with Normal Cell-Signalling Pathways

The proteins encoded by many proto-oncogenes and tumour-suppressor genes are components of cell-signalling pathways. Let's take a closer look at how such proteins function in normal cells and what goes wrong with their function in cancer cells. We will focus on the products of two key genes, the *ras* proto-oncogene and the *p53* tumour-suppressor gene. Mutations in *ras* occur in about 30% of human cancers, and mutations in *p53* in more than 50%.

The Ras protein, encoded by the *ras* gene (named for *ra*t *s*arcoma, a connective tissue cancer), is a G protein that relays a signal from a growth factor receptor on the plasma membrane to a cascade of protein kinases (see Figure 11.8). The cellular response at the end of the pathway is the synthesis of a protein that stimulates the cell cycle (Figure 18.24a). Normally, such a pathway will not operate unless triggered by the appropriate growth factor. But certain mutations in the *ras* gene can lead to production of a hyperactive Ras protein that triggers the kinase cascade even in the absence of growth factor, resulting in increased cell division (Figure 18.24b). In fact, hyperactive versions or excess amounts of any of the pathway's components can have the same outcome: excessive cell division.

Figure 18.25a shows a pathway in which a signal leads to the synthesis of a protein that suppresses the cell cycle. In this case, the signal is damage to the cell's DNA, perhaps as the result of exposure to ultraviolet light. Operation of this signalling pathway blocks the cell cycle until the damage has been repaired. Otherwise, the damage might contribute to tumour formation by causing mutations or chromosomal abnormalities. Thus, the genes for the components of the pathway act as tumour-suppressor genes. The *p53* gene, named for the 53 000-dalton molecular weight of its protein product, is a tumour-suppressor gene. The protein it encodes is a specific transcription factor that promotes the synthesis of cell cycle–inhibiting proteins. That is why a mutation that knocks out the *p53* gene, like a mutation

(a) Normal cell cycle–stimulating pathway.

(b) Mutant cell cycle–stimulating pathway.

◀ **Figure 18.24 Normal and mutant cell cycle–stimulating pathway. (a)** The normal pathway is triggered by ❶ a growth factor that binds to ❷ its receptor in the plasma membrane. The signal is relayed to ❸ a G protein called Ras. Like all G proteins, Ras is active when GTP is bound to it. Ras passes the signal to ❹ a series of protein kinases. The last kinase activates ❺ a transcription factor (activator) that turns on one or more genes for ❻ a protein that stimulates the cell cycle. **(b)** If a mutation makes Ras or any other pathway component abnormally active, excessive cell division and cancer may result.

(a) Normal cell cycle–inhibiting pathway

(b) Mutant cell cycle–inhibiting pathway

◀ Figure 18.25 **Normal and mutant cell cycle–inhibiting pathway. (a)** In the normal pathway, ❶ DNA damage is an intracellular signal that is passed via ❷ protein kinases, leading to activation of ❸ p53. Activated p53 promotes ❹ transcription of the gene for ❺ a protein that inhibits the cell cycle. The resulting suppression of cell division ensures that the damaged DNA is not replicated. If the DNA damage is irreparable, then the p53 signal leads to programmed cell death (apoptosis). **(b)** Mutations causing deficiencies in any pathway component can contribute to the development of cancer.

? *Explain whether a cancer causing mutation in a tumour-suppressor gene, such as p53, is more likely to be a recessive or a dominant mutation.*

that leads to a hyperactive Ras protein, can lead to excessive cell growth and cancer **(Figure 18.25b)**.

The *p53* gene has been called the "guardian angel of the genome." Once the gene is activated—for example, by DNA damage—the p53 protein functions as an activator for several other genes. Often it activates a gene called *p21*, whose product halts the cell cycle by binding to cyclin-dependent kinases, allowing time for the cell to repair the DNA. Researchers recently showed that p53 also activates expression of a group of miRNAs, which in turn inhibit the cell cycle. In addition, the p53 protein can turn on genes directly involved in DNA repair. Finally, when DNA damage is irreparable, p53 activates "suicide" genes, whose protein products bring about programmed cell death (apoptosis; see Figure 11.20). Thus, p53 acts in several ways to prevent a cell from passing on mutations due to DNA damage. If mutations do accumulate and the cell survives through many divisions—as is more likely if the *p53* tumour-suppressor gene is defective or missing—cancer may ensue.

The many functions of p53 suggest a complex picture of regulation in normal cells, one that we do not yet fully understand. For the present, the diagram in Figure 18.24 is an accurate view of how mutations can contribute to cancer, but we still don't know exactly how a particular cell becomes a cancer cell. As we discover previously unknown aspects of gene regulation, it is informative to study their role in the onset of cancer. Such studies have shown, for instance, that DNA methylation and histone modification

patterns differ in normal and cancer cells and that miRNAs probably participate in cancer development. While we've learned a lot about cancer by studying cell-signalling pathways, there is still a lot left to learn.

The Multistep Model of Cancer Development

More than one somatic mutation is generally needed to produce all the changes characteristic of a full-fledged cancer cell. This may help explain why the incidence of cancer increases greatly with age. If cancer results from an accumulation of mutations and if mutations occur throughout life, then the longer we live, the more likely we are to develop cancer.

The model of a multistep path to cancer is well supported by studies of one of the best-understood types of human cancer, colorectal cancer. About 23 000 new cases of colorectal cancer are diagnosed each year in Canada, and the disease causes more than 9000 deaths annually. Like most cancers, colorectal cancer develops gradually **(Figure 18.26)**. The first sign is often a polyp, a small, benign growth in the colon lining. The cells of the polyp look normal, although they divide unusually frequently. The tumour grows and may eventually become malignant, invading other tissues. The development of a malignant tumour is parallelled by a gradual accumulation of mutations that convert proto-oncogenes to oncogenes and knock out tumour-suppressor genes. A *ras* oncogene and a mutated *p53* tumour-suppressor gene are often involved.

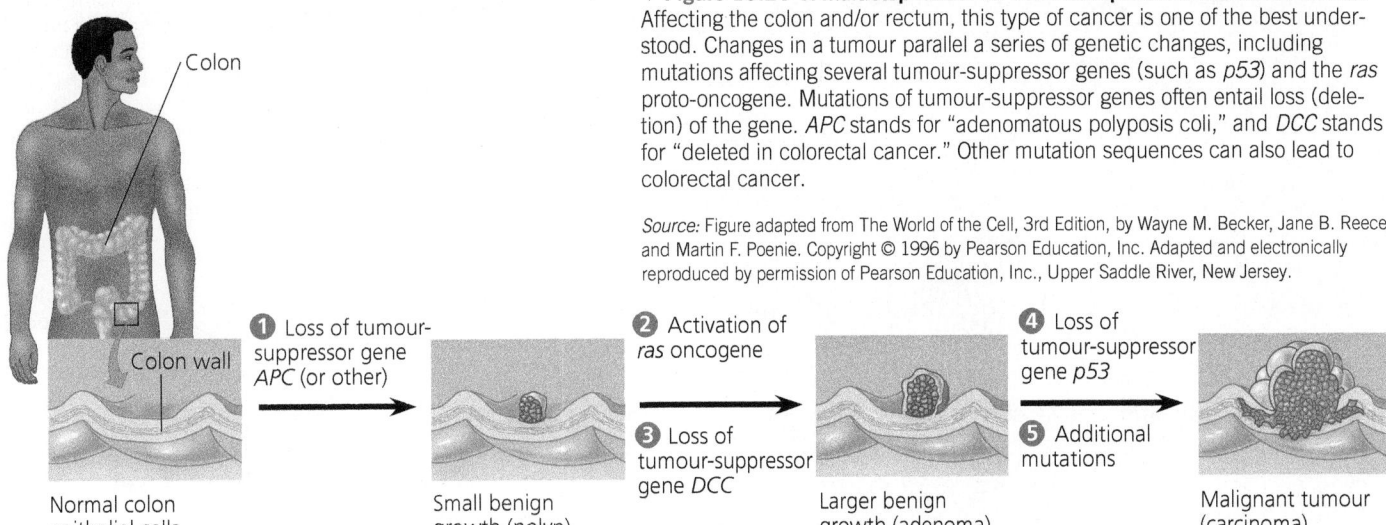

▼ **Figure 18.26 A multistep model for the development of colorectal cancer.** Affecting the colon and/or rectum, this type of cancer is one of the best understood. Changes in a tumour parallel a series of genetic changes, including mutations affecting several tumour-suppressor genes (such as *p53*) and the *ras* proto-oncogene. Mutations of tumour-suppressor genes often entail loss (deletion) of the gene. *APC* stands for "adenomatous polyposis coli," and *DCC* stands for "deleted in colorectal cancer." Other mutation sequences can also lead to colorectal cancer.

Source: Figure adapted from The World of the Cell, 3rd Edition, by Wayne M. Becker, Jane B. Reece, and Martin F. Poenie. Copyright © 1996 by Pearson Education, Inc. Adapted and electronically reproduced by permission of Pearson Education, Inc., Upper Saddle River, New Jersey.

About half a dozen changes must occur at the DNA level for a cell to become fully cancerous. These changes usually include the appearance of at least one active oncogene and the mutation or loss of several tumour-suppressor genes. Furthermore, since mutant tumour-suppressor alleles are usually recessive, in most cases mutations must knock out *both* alleles in a cell's genome to block tumour suppression. (Most oncogenes, on the other hand, behave as dominant alleles.) The order in which these changes must occur is still under investigation, as is the relative importance of different mutations.

Since we understand the progression of this type of cancer, routine screenings are recommended to identify and remove any suspicious polyps. The colorectal cancer mortality rate has been declining for the past 20 years, due in part to increased screening and in part to improved treatments. Treatments for other cancers have improved as well. Dramatic technical advances in the sequencing of DNA and mRNA have allowed medical researchers to compare the genes expressed by different types of tumours and by the same type in different individuals. These comparisons have led to personalized cancer treatments based on the molecular characteristics of an individual's tumour.

Breast cancer is the second most common form of cancer in Canada, and the first among women. Each year, this cancer strikes over 25 000 women (and some men) in Canada and kills 5000 (450 000 worldwide). A major problem with understanding breast cancer is its heterogeneity: Tumours differ in significant ways. Identifying differences between types of breast cancer is expected to improve treatment and decrease the mortality rate. In November 2012, The Cancer Genome Atlas Network, sponsored by the National Institutes of Health, published the results of a multi-team effort that used a genomics approach to profile subtypes of breast cancer based on their molecular signatures. Four major types of breast cancer were identified (Figure 18.27). Another recent study, led by scientists at the B.C. Cancer Agency, was able to identify the mutations that are associated with the deadliest form of breast cancer and to track the genomic evolution of these tumours (Figure 18.28). These findings help to explain why different patients often show different responses to treatment, and could be used to predict which treatments would likely be the most effective.

Inherited Predisposition and Environmental Factors Contributing to Cancer

The fact that multiple genetic changes are required to produce a cancer cell helps explain the observation that cancers can run in families. An individual inheriting an oncogene or a mutant allele of a tumour-suppressor gene is one step closer to accumulating the necessary mutations for cancer to develop than is an individual without any such mutations.

Geneticists are devoting significant effort to identifying inherited cancer alleles so that predisposition to certain cancers can be detected early in life. About 15% of colorectal cancers, for example, involve inherited mutations. Many of these affect the tumour-suppressor gene called *adenomatous polyposis coli*, or *APC* (see Figure 18.26). This gene has multiple functions in the cell, including regulation of cell migration and adhesion. Even in patients with no family history of the disease, the *APC* gene is mutated in 60% of colorectal cancers. In these individuals, new mutations must occur in both *APC* alleles before the gene's function is lost. Since only 15% of colorectal cancers are associated with known inherited mutations, researchers continue in their efforts to identify "markers" that could predict the risk of developing this type of cancer.

▼ Figure 18.27

Genomics, Cell Signalling, and Cancer

Modern medicine that melds genome-wide molecular studies with cell-signalling research is transforming the treatment of many diseases, such as breast cancer. Using micro-array analysis (*see Figure 20.13*) and other techniques, researchers measured the relative levels of mRNA transcripts for every gene in many different breast cancer tumour samples. They identified four major subtypes of breast cancer, shown below, that differ in their expression of three signal receptors involved in regulating cell growth and division (*see Figures 11.8 and 11.9*). Normal levels of these signal receptors (indicated by +) are represented in a normal breast cell at the right. The absence (–) or excess expression (++ or +++) of these receptors can cause aberrant cell signalling, leading in some cases to inappropriate cell division, which may contribute to cancer (*see Figure 18.24*). Breast cancer treatments are becoming more effective because they can be tailored to the specific cancer subtype.

Normal Breast Cells in a Milk Duct

- $ER\alpha^+$
- PR^+
- $HER2^+$

Duct interior

Estrogen receptor alpha ($ER\alpha$)

Progesterone receptor (PR)

HER2 (a receptor tyrosine kinase)

Support cell

Extracellular matrix

Breast Cancer Subtypes

Luminal A	Luminal B	HER2	Basal-like
• $ER\alpha^{+++}$	• $ER\alpha^{++}$	• $ER\alpha^-$	• $ER\alpha^-$
• PR^{++}	• PR^{++}	• PR^-	• PR^-
• $HER2^-$	• $HER2^-$ (shown); some $HER2^{++}$	• $HER2^{++}$	• $HER2^-$
• 40% of breast cancers	• 15–20% of breast cancers	• 10–15% of breast cancers	• 15–20% of breast cancers
• Best prognosis	• Poorer prognosis than luminal A subtype	• Poorer prognosis than luminal A subtype	• More aggressive; poorer prognosis than other subtypes

Both luminal subtypes overexpress $ER\alpha$ (luminal A more than luminal B) and PR, and usually lack expression of HER2. Both can be treated with drugs that target $ER\alpha$ and inactivate it, the most well-known drug being Tamoxifen. These subtypes can also be treated with drugs that inhibit estrogen synthesis.

The HER2 subtype overexpresses HER2. Because it does not express either $ER\alpha$ or PR at normal levels, the cells are unresponsive to therapies aimed against those two receptors. However, patients with the HER2 subtype can be treated with Herceptin, an antibody protein that inactivates the tyrosine kinase activity of HER2 (see Concept 12.3).

The basal-like subtype is "triple negative"—it does not express $ER\alpha$, PR, or HER2. It often has a mutation in the tumour-suppressor gene BRCA1 (*see Concept 18.5*). Treatments that target ER, PR, or HER2 are not effective, but new treatments are being developed. Currently, patients are treated with cytotoxic chemotherapy, which selectively kills fast-growing cells.

MAKE CONNECTIONS *When researchers compared gene expression in normal breast cells and cells from breast cancers, they found that the genes showing the most significant differences in expression encoded signal receptors, as shown here. Given what you learned in Chapters 11, 12, and this chapter, explain why this result is not surprising.*

Roy Kaltschmidt/Lawrence Berkeley National Laboratory

Impact

Analyzing the Genomic Evolution of Breast Cancer

Triple negative breast cancer (the basal-like subtype) is the deadliest subtype of breast cancer. In a study led by scientists from the B.C. Cancer Agency, tumour samples from 2000 women were analyzed, revealing that the tumours show a diverse spectrum of cellular mutations that contribute to cancer development. Genes associated with some cellular pathways contained mutations more frequently than others, as shown in the figure below. The analysis of these mutations allowed the researchers to identify 10 different subtypes of triple negative breast cancer and to track the genomic evolution of the tumour samples.

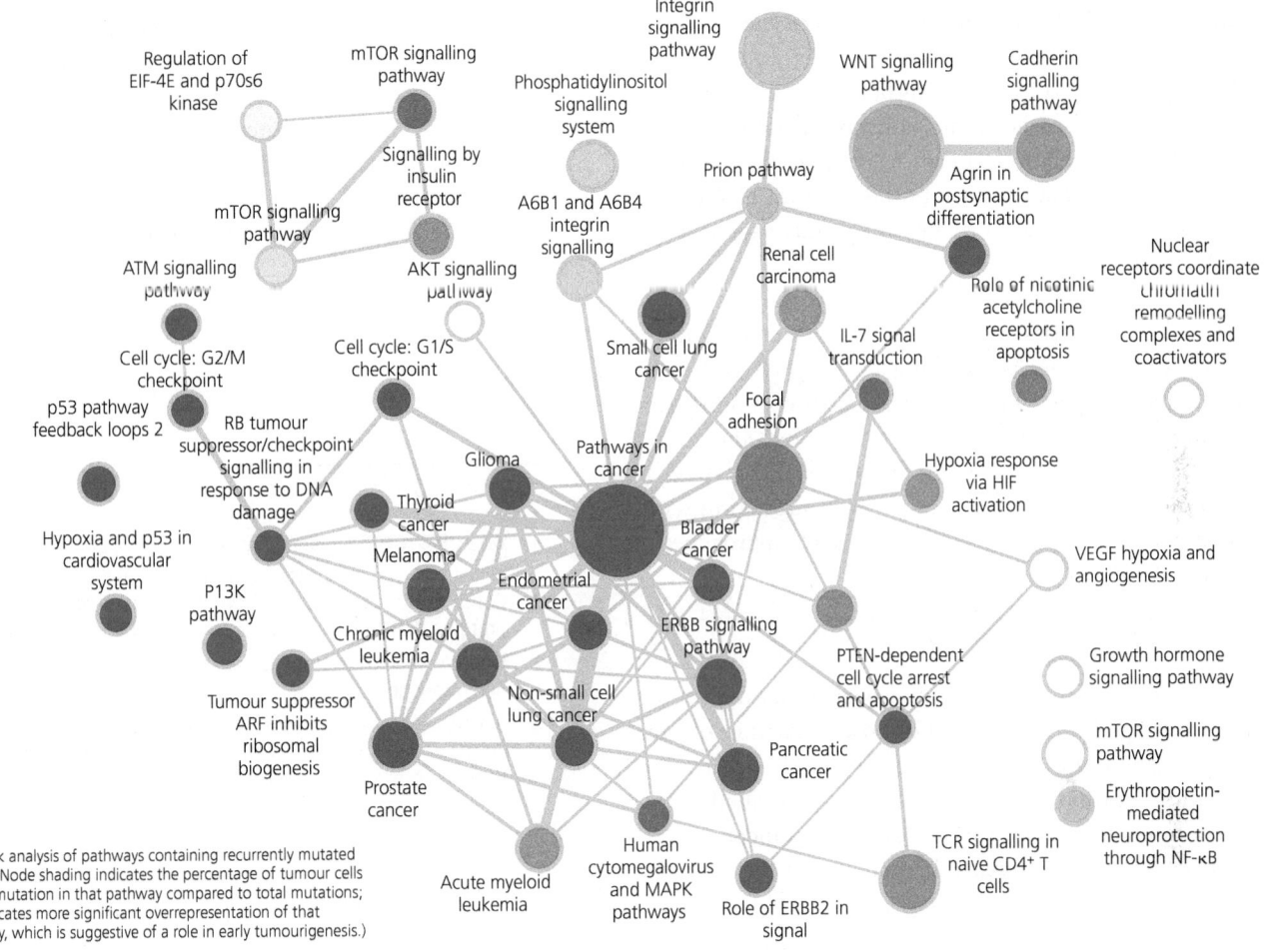

Network analysis of pathways containing recurrently mutated genes. (Node shading indicates the percentage of tumour cells with a mutation in that pathway compared to total mutations; red indicates more significant overrepresentation of that pathway, which is suggestive of a role in early tumourigenesis.)

Why It Matters By looking at the mutation profiles of the tumour samples, the researchers were able to identify which mutations likely occurred early versus late in the progression of the cancer. These findings help to explain why different patients often show different responses to treatment, and could be used to predict which treatments would likely be the most effective. Tumour sequencing and mutation analysis has the potential to completely change the way that breast cancer is treated.

Further Reading S.P. Shah et al., The clonal and mutational evolution spectrum of primary triple-negative breast cancers, *Nature* 486:395–399 (2012); S.P. Shah et al., Mutational evolution in a lobular breast tumour profiled at single nucleotide resolution, *Nature* 461:809–813 (2009).

WHAT IF? *You are analyzing mutation data that shows only a small proportion of clonal samples contain Mutation A, whereas another type of mutation (Mutation B) is common in the samples. What is a potential explanation for these results?*

Given the prevalence and significance of breast cancer, it is not surprising that it was one of the first cancers for which the role of inheritance was investigated. It turns out that for 5–10% of patients with breast cancer, there is evidence of a strong inherited predisposition. Geneticist Mary-Claire King began working on this problem in the mid-1970s. After 16 years of research, she convincingly demonstrated that mutations in one gene—*BRCA1*—were associated with increased susceptibility to breast cancer, a finding that flew in the face of medical opinion at the time. (*BRCA* stands for breast cancer.) Mutations in that gene or a gene called *BRCA2* are found in at least half of inherited breast cancers, and tests using DNA sequencing can detect these mutations. A woman who inherits one mutant *BRCA1* allele has a 60% probability of developing breast cancer before the age of 50, compared with only a 2% probability for an individual homozygous for the normal allele.

BRCA1 and *BRCA2* are considered tumour-suppressor genes because their wild-type alleles protect against breast cancer and their mutant alleles are recessive. (Note that mutations in *BRCA1* are commonly found in the genomes of cells from basal-like breast cancers; see Figure 18.27.) The BRCA1 and BRCA2 proteins both appear to function in the cell's DNA damage repair pathway. More is known about BRCA2, which, in association with another protein, helps repair breaks that occur in both strands of DNA; this repair function is crucial for maintaining undamaged DNA in a cell's nucleus.

Because DNA breakage can contribute to cancer, it makes sense that the risk of cancer can be lowered by minimizing exposure to DNA-damaging agents, such as the ultraviolet radiation in sunlight and chemicals found in cigarette smoke. Novel methods for early diagnosis and treatment of specific cancers are being developed that rely on new techniques for analyzing, and perhaps interfering with, gene expression in tumours. Ultimately, such approaches may lower the death rate from cancer.

The Role of Viruses in Cancer

The study of genes associated with cancer, inherited or not, increases our basic understanding of how disruption of normal gene regulation can result in this disease. In addition to the mutations and other genetic alterations described in this section, a number of *tumour viruses* can cause cancer in various animals, including humans. In fact, one of the earliest breakthroughs in understanding cancer came in 1911, when Peyton Rous, an American pathologist, discovered a virus that causes cancer in chickens. The Epstein-Barr virus, which causes infectious mononucleosis, has been linked to several types of cancer in humans, notably Burkitt's lymphoma. Papillomaviruses are associated with cancer of the cervix, and a virus called HTLV-1 causes a type of adult leukemia. Worldwide, viruses seem to play a role in about 15% of the cases of human cancer.

Viruses may at first seem very different from mutations as a cause of cancer. However, we now know that viruses can interfere with gene regulation in several ways if they integrate their genetic material into the DNA of a cell. Viral integration may donate an oncogene to the cell, disrupt a tumour-suppressor gene, or convert a proto-oncogene to an oncogene. In addition, some viruses produce proteins that inactivate p53 and other tumour-suppressor proteins, making the cell more prone to becoming cancerous. Viruses are powerful biological agents, and you'll learn more about their function in Chapter 19.

CONCEPT CHECK 18.5

1. **MAKE CONNECTIONS** The p53 protein can activate genes involved in apoptosis, or programmed cell death. Review Concept 11.5 and discuss how mutations in genes coding for proteins that function in apoptosis could contribute to cancer.

2. Under what circumstances is cancer considered to have a hereditary component?

3. Cancer-promoting mutations are likely to have different effects on the activity of proteins encoded by proto-oncogenes than they do on proteins encoded by tumour-suppressor genes. Explain.

For suggested answers, see Appendix A.

---

18 Chapter Review

Go to **MasteringBiology®** for Assignments, the eText, and the Study Area with Animations, Activities, Vocab Self-Quiz, and Practice Tests.

SUMMARY OF KEY CONCEPTS

CONCEPT 18.1

Bacteria often respond to environmental change by regulating transcription (pp. 381–385)

- Cells control metabolism by regulating enzyme activity or the expression of genes coding for enzymes. In bacteria, genes are often clustered into **operons**, with one promoter serving several adjacent genes. An **operator** site on the DNA switches the operon on or off, resulting in coordinated regulation of the genes.

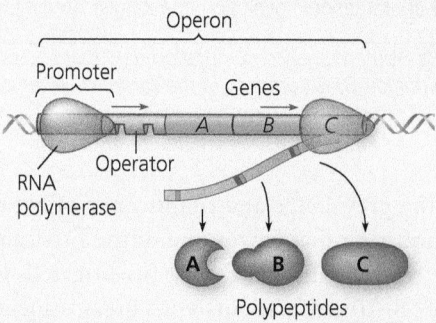

- Both repressible and inducible operons are examples of negative gene regulation. In either type of operon, binding of a specific

repressor protein to the operator shuts off transcription. (The repressor is encoded by a separate **regulatory gene**.) In a repressible operon, the repressor is active when bound to a **corepressor**, usually the end product of an anabolic pathway.

Repressible operon:

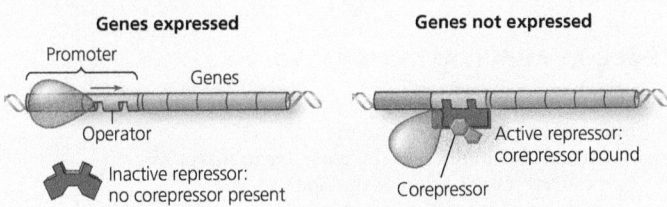

In an inducible operon, binding of an **inducer** to an innately active repressor inactivates the repressor and turns on transcription. Inducible enzymes usually function in catabolic pathways.

Inducible operon:

- Some operons are also subject to positive gene regulation via a stimulatory **activator** protein, such as catabolite activator protein (CAP), which, when activated by **cyclic AMP**, binds to a site within the promoter and stimulates transcription.

? *Compare and contrast the roles of a corepressor and an inducer in negative regulation of an operon.*

CONCEPT 18.2

Eukaryotic gene expression is regulated at many stages (pp. 385–394)

? *Describe what must happen for a cell type–specific gene to be transcribed in a cell of that type.*

CONCEPT 18.3

Noncoding RNAs play multiple roles in controlling gene expression (pp. 394–396)

? *Why are miRNAs called noncoding RNAs? Explain how they participate in gene regulation.*

CONCEPT 18.4

A program of differential gene expression leads to the different cell types in a multicellular organism (pp. 397–403)

- Embryonic cells undergo **differentiation**, becoming specialized in structure and function. **Morphogenesis** encompasses the processes that give shape to the organism and its various parts. Cells differ in structure and function not because they contain different genes but because they express different portions of a common genome.
- **Cytoplasmic determinants** in the unfertilized egg regulate the expression of genes in the zygote and embryo that affect the developmental fate of embryonic cells. In the process called **induction**, signalling molecules from embryonic cells cause transcriptional changes in nearby target cells.
- Differentiation is heralded by the appearance of tissue-specific proteins, which enable differentiated cells to carry out their specialized roles.
- In animals, **pattern formation**, the development of a spatial organization of tissues and organs, begins in the early embryo. **Positional information**, the molecular cues that control pattern formation, tells a cell its location relative to the body's axes and to other cells. In *Drosophila*, gradients of **morphogens** encoded by **maternal effect genes** determine the body axes. For example, the gradient of **Bicoid** protein determines the anterior-posterior axis.

? *Describe the two main processes that cause embryonic cells to head down different pathways to their final fates.*

CONCEPT 18.5

Cancer results from genetic changes that affect cell cycle control (pp. 404–410)

- The products of **proto-oncogenes** and **tumour-suppressor genes** control cell division. A DNA change that makes a proto-oncogene excessively active converts it to an **oncogene**, which may promote excessive cell division and cancer. A tumour-suppressor gene encodes a protein that inhibits abnormal cell division. A mutation in a tumour-suppressor gene that reduces the activity of its protein product may also lead to excessive cell division and possibly to cancer.

- Many proto-oncogenes and tumour-suppressor genes encode components of growth-stimulating and growth-inhibiting signalling pathways, respectively, and mutations in these genes can interfere with normal cell-signalling pathways. A hyperactive version of a protein in a stimulatory pathway, such as **Ras** (a G protein), functions as an oncogene protein. A defective version of a protein in an inhibitory pathway, such as **p53** (a transcription activator), fails to function as a tumour suppressor.

- In the multistep model of cancer development, normal cells are converted to cancer cells by the accumulation of mutations affecting proto-oncogenes and tumour-suppressor genes. Technical advances in DNA and mRNA sequencing are enabling cancer treatments that are more individually based.
- Genomics-based studies have resulted in researchers proposing four subtypes of breast cancer, based on expression of genes by tumour cells.
- Individuals who inherit a mutant allele of a proto-oncogene or tumour-suppressor gene have a predisposition to develop a particular cancer. Certain viruses promote cancer by integration of viral DNA into a cell's genome.

[?] *Compare the usual functions of proteins encoded by proto-oncogenes with the functions of proteins encoded by tumour-suppressor genes.*

TEST YOUR UNDERSTANDING

LEVEL 1: KNOWLEDGE/COMPREHENSION

1. If a particular operon encodes enzymes for making an essential amino acid and is regulated like the *trp* operon, then
   a. the amino acid inactivates the repressor.
   b. the repressor is active in the absence of the amino acid.
   c. the amino acid acts as a corepressor.
   d. the amino acid turns on transcription of the operon.

2. Muscle cells differ from nerve cells mainly because they
   a. express different genes.
   b. contain different genes.
   c. use different genetic codes.
   d. have unique ribosomes.

3. The functioning of enhancers is an example of
   a. a eukaryotic equivalent of prokaryotic promoter functioning.
   b. transcriptional control of gene expression.
   c. the stimulation of translation by initiation factors.
   d. post-translational control that activates certain proteins.

4. Cell differentiation always involves
   a. the production of tissue-specific proteins.
   b. the movement of cells.
   c. the transcription of the *myoD* gene.
   d. the selective loss of certain genes from the genome.

5. Which of the following is an example of post-transcriptional control of gene expression?
   a. the addition of methyl groups to cytosine bases of DNA
   b. the binding of transcription factors to a promoter
   c. the removal of introns and alternative splicing of exons
   d. gene amplification contributing to cancer

LEVEL 2: APPLICATION/ANALYSIS

6. What would occur if the repressor of an inducible operon were mutated so it could not bind the operator?
   a. irreversible binding of the repressor to the promoter
   b. reduced transcription of the operon's genes
   c. buildup of a substrate for the pathway controlled by the operon
   d. continuous transcription of the operon's genes

7. Absence of *bicoid* mRNA from a *Drosophila* egg leads to the absence of anterior larval body parts and mirror-image duplication of posterior parts. This is evidence that the product of the *bicoid* gene
   a. is transcribed in the early embryo.
   b. normally leads to formation of tail structures.
   c. normally leads to formation of head structures.
   d. is a protein present in all head structures.

8. Which of the following statements about the DNA in one of your brain cells is true?
   a. Most of the DNA codes for protein.
   b. The majority of genes are likely to be transcribed.
   c. Each gene lies immediately adjacent to an enhancer.
   d. It is the same as the DNA in one of your heart cells.

9. Within a cell, the amount of protein made using a given mRNA molecule depends partly on
   a. the degree of DNA methylation.
   b. the rate at which the mRNA is degraded.
   c. the number of introns present in the mRNA.
   d. the types of ribosomes present in the cytoplasm.

10. Proto-oncogenes can change into oncogenes that cause cancer. Which of the following best explains the presence of these potential time bombs in eukaryotic cells?
   a. Proto-oncogenes first arose from viral infections.
   b. Proto-oncogenes normally help regulate cell division.
   c. Proto-oncogenes are genetic "junk."
   d. Proto-oncogenes are mutant versions of normal genes.

LEVEL 3: SYNTHESIS/EVALUATION

11. **DRAW IT** The diagram below shows five genes, including their enhancers, from the genome of a certain species. Imagine that orange, blue, green, black, red, and purple activator proteins exist that can bind to the appropriately colour-coded control elements in the enhancers of these genes.

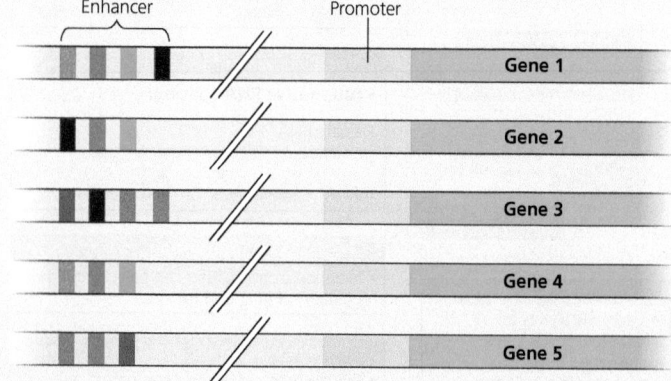

(a) Draw an X above enhancer elements (of all the genes) that would have activators bound in a cell in which only gene 5 is transcribed. Which coloured activators would be present?

(b) Draw a dot above all enhancer elements that would have activators bound in a cell in which the green, blue, and orange activators are present. Which gene(s) would be transcribed?

(c) Imagine that genes 1, 2, and 4 code for nerve-specific proteins, and genes 3 and 5 are skin specific. Which activators would have to be present in each cell type to ensure transcription of the appropriate genes?

12. EVOLUTION CONNECTION

DNA sequences can act as "tape measures of evolution" (see Chapter 5). Scientists analyzing the human genome sequence were surprised to find that some of the regions of the human genome that are most highly conserved (similar to comparable regions in other species) don't code for proteins. Propose a possible explanation for this observation.

13. SCIENTIFIC INQUIRY

Prostate cells usually require testosterone and other androgens to survive. But some prostate cancer cells thrive despite treatments that eliminate androgens. One hypothesis is that estrogen, often considered a female hormone, may be activating genes normally controlled by an androgen in these cancer cells. Describe one or more experiments to test this hypothesis. (See Figure 11.9 to review the action of these steroid hormones.)

14. SCIENCE, TECHNOLOGY, AND SOCIETY

Trace amounts of dioxin were present in Agent Orange, a defoliant sprayed on vegetation during the Vietnam War. Animal tests suggest that dioxin can cause birth defects, cancer, liver and thymus damage, and immune system suppression, sometimes leading to death. But the animal tests are equivocal; a hamster is not affected by a dose that can kill a guinea pig. Dioxin acts like a steroid hormone, entering a cell and binding to a cytoplasmic receptor that then binds the cell's DNA. How might this mechanism help explain the variety of dioxin's effects on different body systems and in different animals? How might you determine whether a type of illness is related to dioxin exposure? How might you determine whether a particular individual became ill as a result of exposure to dioxin? Which would be more difficult to demonstrate? Why?

15. WRITE ABOUT A THEME: INTERACTIONS

In a short essay (100–150 words), discuss how the processes shown in Figure 18.2 are examples of feedback mechanisms regulating biological systems.

16. SYNTHESIZE YOUR KNOWLEDGE

Peter Herring/Image Quest Marine

The flashlight fish has an organ under its eye that emits light, which serves to startle predators and attract prey, and allows the fish to communicate with other fish. Some species can rotate the organ inside and then out, so the light appears to flash on and off. The light is not actually emitted by the fish itself, however, but by bacteria that live in the organ in a mutualistic relationship with the fish. (While providing light for the fish, the bacteria receive nutrients from the fish and in fact are unable to survive anywhere else.) The bacteria must multiply until they reach a certain density in the organ (a *quorum*; see Concept 11.1), at which point they all begin emitting light at the same time. There is a group of six or so genes, called *lux* genes, whose gene products are necessary for light formation. Given that these bacterial genes are regulated together, propose a hypothesis for how the genes are organized and regulated.

For selected answers, see Appendix A.

19

Viruses

KEY CONCEPTS

19.1 A virus consists of a nucleic acid surrounded by a protein coat

19.2 Viruses replicate only in host cells

19.3 Viruses and prions are formidable pathogens in animals and plants

Science Source

▲ Figure 19.1 **Are the viruses (blue) budding from this infected cell (yellow-green) alive?**

A Borrowed Life

The image in **Figure 19.1** shows a remarkable event: a cell under siege, releasing scores more of its invaders, which will go on to infect other cells. By injecting its genetic information into a cell, a single virus hijacks a cell, recruiting cellular machinery to manufacture many new viruses and promote further infection. In the colourized scanning electron micrograph above, filamentous Ebola virus particles can be seen budding from an infected cell.

Compared to eukaryotic and even prokaryotic cells, viruses are much smaller and simpler in structure. Lacking the structures and metabolic machinery found in a cell, a **virus** is an infectious particle consisting of little more than genes packaged in a protein coat. The image to the left shows the attack of a bacterial cell by numerous structures that resemble miniature lollipops. These structures, a type of virus called T4 bacteriophage, are seen infecting a bacterial cell. The French-Canadian microbiologist Félix d'Hérelle discovered this virus in 1917 and named it bacteriophage, or bacteria-eater (from the Greek *phagein* meaning to eat).

Are viruses living or nonliving? Because viruses are capable of causing many diseases, researchers in the late 1800s saw a parallel with bacteria and proposed that viruses were the simplest of living forms. However, viruses cannot

Eye of Science/Science Source

reproduce or carry out metabolism outside of a host cell. Most biologists studying viruses today would likely agree that they are not alive but exist in a shady area between life-forms and chemicals. The simple phrase used recently by two researchers describes them aptly enough: Viruses lead "a kind of borrowed life," perhaps similar to obligate parasites.

To a large extent, molecular biology was born in the laboratories of biologists studying viruses that infect bacteria. Experiments with these viruses provided important evidence that genes are made of nucleic acids, and they were critical in working out the molecular mechanisms of the fundamental processes of DNA replication, transcription, and translation.

Beyond their value as experimental systems, viruses have unique genetic mechanisms that are interesting in their own right and that also help us understand how viruses cause disease. In addition, the study of viruses has led to the development of techniques that enable scientists to manipulate genes and transfer them from one organism to another. These techniques play an important role in basic research, biotechnology, and medical applications. For instance, viruses are used as agents of gene transfer in gene therapy (see Chapter 20).

There are an estimated 10^{31} viruses on earth, with the majority existing in the oceans. The colourized TEM in Figure 19.2, taken by Dr. Steven Short from the University of Toronto Mississauga, shows viral particles being released from algae upon cell lysis. Viruses that infect eukaryotic algae, known as algal viruses, are widespread and have tremendous genetic diversity.

In this chapter, we will explore the biology of viruses, beginning with their structure and then describing how they replicate. Next, we will discuss the role of viruses as disease-causing agents, or pathogens, and conclude by considering some even simpler infectious agents, such as prions.

CONCEPT 19.1

A virus consists of a nucleic acid surrounded by a protein coat

Scientists were able to detect viruses indirectly long before they were actually able to see them. The story of how viruses were discovered begins near the end of the 19th century.

The Discovery of Viruses: *Scientific Inquiry*

Tobacco mosaic disease stunts the growth of tobacco plants and gives their leaves a mottled, or mosaic, colouration. In 1883, Adolf Mayer, a German scientist, discovered that he could transmit the disease from plant to plant by rubbing sap extracted from diseased leaves onto healthy plants. After an unsuccessful search for an infectious microbe in the sap, Mayer suggested that the disease was caused by unusually small bacteria that were invisible under a microscope. This

John Wiley & Sons, Inc.

▲ Figure 19.2 **Algal viral particles can be seen leaving these algae upon cell lysis.**

hypothesis was tested a decade later by Dimitri Ivanowsky, a Russian biologist who passed sap from infected tobacco leaves through a filter designed to remove bacteria. After filtration, the sap still produced mosaic disease.

But Ivanowsky clung to the hypothesis that bacteria caused tobacco mosaic disease. Perhaps, he reasoned, the bacteria were small enough to pass through the filter or made a toxin that could do so. The second possibility was ruled out when the Dutch botanist Martinus Beijerinck carried out a classic series of experiments that showed that the infectious agent in the filtered sap could replicate (Figure 19.3).

In fact, the pathogen replicated only within the host it infected. In further experiments, Beijerinck showed that, unlike bacteria used in the lab at that time, the mysterious agent of mosaic disease could not be cultivated on nutrient media in test tubes or petri dishes. Beijerinck imagined a replicating particle much smaller and simpler than a bacterium, and he is generally credited with being the first scientist to voice the concept of a virus. His suspicions were confirmed in 1935 when the American scientist Wendell Stanley crystallized the infectious particle, now known as tobacco mosaic virus (TMV). Subsequently, TMV and many other viruses were actually seen with the help of the electron microscope.

Structure of Viruses

The tiniest viruses are only 20 nm in diameter—smaller than a ribosome. Millions could easily fit on a pinhead. Even the largest known virus, which has a diameter of 1500 nanometres (1.5 μm), is just barely visible under the light microscope. Stanley's discovery that some viruses could be crystallized was exciting and puzzling news. Not even the simplest of cells can aggregate into regular crystals. But if viruses are not cells, then what are they? Examining the structure of a virus more closely reveals that it is an infectious particle consisting of nucleic acid enclosed in a protein coat and, for some viruses, surrounded by a membranous envelope.

Viral Genomes

We usually think of genes as being made of double-stranded DNA, but many viruses defy this convention. Their genomes may consist of double-stranded DNA, single-stranded DNA, double-stranded RNA, or single-stranded RNA, depending on the type of virus. A virus is called a DNA virus or an RNA virus based on the kind of nucleic acid that makes up its genome. In either case, the genome is usually organized as a single linear or circular molecule of nucleic acid, although the genomes of some viruses consist of multiple molecules of nucleic acid. The smallest viruses known have only three genes in their genome, while the largest have several hundred to 2000. For comparison, bacterial genomes contain about 200 to a few thousand genes.

▼ Figure 19.3 **Inquiry**

What causes tobacco mosaic disease?

Experiment In the late 1800s, Martinus Beijerinck, of the Technical School in Delft, the Netherlands, investigated the properties of the agent that causes tobacco mosaic disease (then called spot disease).

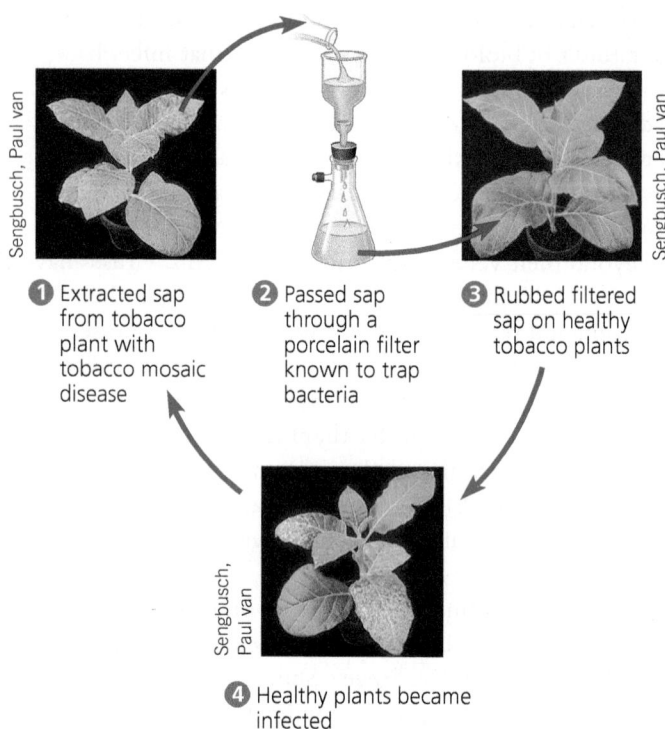

① Extracted sap from tobacco plant with tobacco mosaic disease

② Passed sap through a porcelain filter known to trap bacteria

③ Rubbed filtered sap on healthy tobacco plants

④ Healthy plants became infected

Results When the filtered sap was rubbed on healthy plants, they became infected. Their sap, when extracted and filtered, could then act as the source of infection for another group of plants. Each successive group of plants developed the disease to the same extent as earlier groups.

Conclusion The infectious agent was apparently not a bacterium because it could pass through a bacterium-trapping filter. The pathogen must have been replicating in the plants because its ability to cause disease was undiluted after several transfers from plant to plant.

Source: M. J. Beijerinck, Concerning a *contagium vivum fluidum* as cause of the spot disease of tobacco leaves, *Verhandelingen der Koninkyke akademie Wettenschappen te Amsterdam* 65:3–21 (1898). Translation published in English as *Phytopathological Classics* Number 7 (1942), American Phytopathological Society Press, St. Paul, MN. © Jane B Reece.

WHAT IF? *If Beijerinck had observed that the infection of each group was weaker than that of the previous group and that ultimately the sap could no longer cause disease, what might he have concluded?*

Capsids and Envelopes

The protein shell enclosing the viral genome is called a **capsid**. Depending on the type of virus, the capsid may be rod-shaped, polyhedral, or more complex in shape. Capsids are built from a large number of protein subunits called *capsomeres*, but the number of different *kinds* of proteins in a capsid is usually small. Tobacco mosaic virus has a rigid, rod-shaped capsid made from over a thousand molecules of a single type of protein arranged in a helix; rod-shaped viruses are commonly called *helical viruses* for this reason (Figure 19.4a). Adenoviruses, which infect the respiratory tracts of animals, have 252 identical protein molecules arranged in a polyhedral capsid with 20 triangular facets—an icosahedron; thus, these and other similarly shaped viruses are referred to as *icosahedral viruses* (Figure 19.4b).

Some viruses have accessory structures that help them infect their hosts. For instance, a membranous envelope surrounds the capsids of influenza viruses and many other viruses found in animals (Figure 19.4c). These **viral envelopes**, which are derived from the membranes of the host cell, contain host cell phospholipids and membrane proteins. They also contain proteins and glycoproteins of viral origin. (Glycoproteins are proteins with carbohydrates covalently attached.) Some viruses carry a few viral enzyme molecules within their capsids.

Many of the most complex capsids are found among the viruses that infect bacteria, called **bacteriophages**, or simply **phages**. The first phages studied included seven that infect *Escherichia coli*. These seven phages were named type 1 (T1), type 2 (T2), and so forth, in the order of their discovery. The three T-even phages (T2, T4, and T6) turned out to be very similar in structure. Their capsids have elongated icosahedral heads enclosing their DNA. Attached to the head is a protein tail piece with fibres by which the phages attach to a bacterial cell (Figure 19.4d). In the next section, we'll examine how these few viral parts function together with cellular components to produce large numbers of viral progeny.

CONCEPT CHECK 19.1

1. Compare the structures of tobacco mosaic virus (TMV) and influenza virus (see Figure 19.4).

2. **MAKE CONNECTIONS** Bacteriophages were used to provide evidence that DNA carries genetic information (see Figure 16.4). Briefly describe the experiment carried out by Hershey and Chase, including in your description why the researchers chose to use phages.

For suggested answers, see Appendix A.

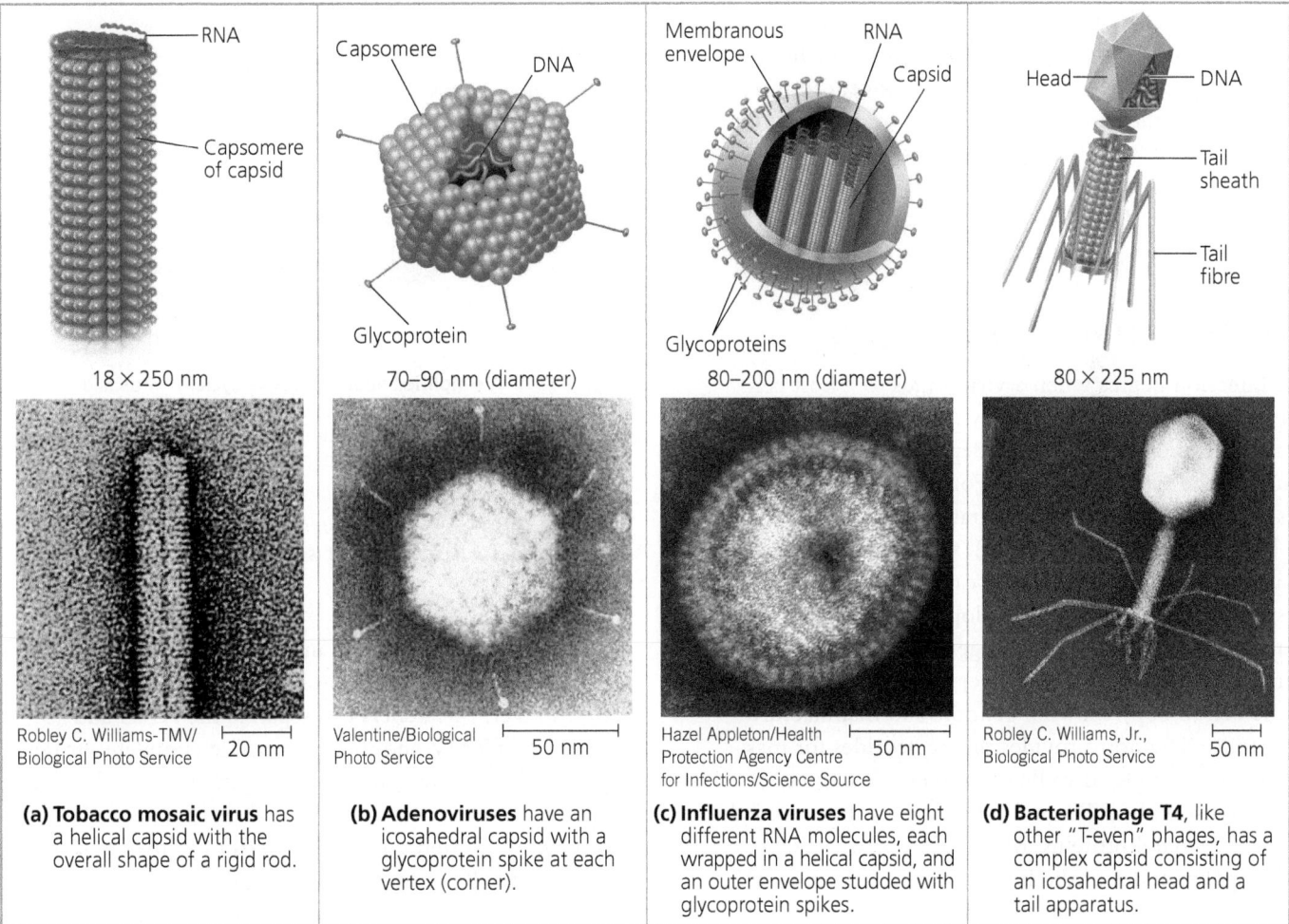

18 × 250 nm

70–90 nm (diameter)

80–200 nm (diameter)

80 × 225 nm

Robley C. Williams-TMV/Biological Photo Service — 20 nm

Valentine/Biological Photo Service — 50 nm

Hazel Appleton/Health Protection Agency Centre for Infections/Science Source — 50 nm

Robley C. Williams, Jr., Biological Photo Service — 50 nm

(a) Tobacco mosaic virus has a helical capsid with the overall shape of a rigid rod.

(b) Adenoviruses have an icosahedral capsid with a glycoprotein spike at each vertex (corner).

(c) Influenza viruses have eight different RNA molecules, each wrapped in a helical capsid, and an outer envelope studded with glycoprotein spikes.

(d) Bacteriophage T4, like other "T-even" phages, has a complex capsid consisting of an icosahedral head and a tail apparatus.

▲ Figure 19.4 **Viral structure.** Viruses are made up of nucleic acid (DNA or RNA) enclosed in a protein coat (the capsid) and sometimes further wrapped in a membranous envelope. The individual protein subunits making up the capsid are called capsomeres. Although diverse in size and shape, viruses have many common structural features. (All micrographs are colourized TEMs.)

CONCEPT 19.2

Viruses replicate only in host cells

Viruses lack metabolic enzymes and equipment for making proteins, such as ribosomes. They are obligate intracellular parasites; in other words, they can replicate only within a host cell. It is fair to say that viruses in isolation are merely packaged sets of genes in transit from one host cell to another.

Each particular virus can infect cells of only a limited number of host species, called the **host range** of the virus. This host specificity results from the evolution of recognition systems by the virus. Viruses usually identify host cells by a "lock-and-key" fit between viral surface proteins and specific receptor molecules on the outside of cells. According to one model, such receptor molecules originally carried out functions that benefitted the host cell but were co-opted later by viruses as portals of entry. Some viruses have broad host ranges. For example, West Nile virus and equine encephalitis virus are distinctly different viruses that can each infect mosquitoes, birds, horses, and humans. Other viruses have host ranges so narrow that they infect only a single species. Measles virus, for instance, can infect only humans. Furthermore, viral infection of multicellular eukaryotes is usually limited to particular tissues. Human cold viruses infect only the cells lining the upper respiratory tract, and the AIDS virus binds to receptors present only on certain types of immune cells.

General Features of Viral Replicative Cycles

A viral infection begins when a virus binds to a host cell and the viral genome makes its way inside **(Figure 19.5)**. The mechanism of genome entry depends on the type of virus and the type of host cell. For example, T-even phages use their elaborate tail apparatus to inject DNA into a bacterium (see Figure 19.4d). Other viruses are taken up by endocytosis or, in the case of enveloped viruses, by fusion of the viral envelope with the host's plasma membrane. Once the viral genome is inside, the proteins it encodes can commandeer the host, reprogramming the cell to copy the viral genome and manufacture viral proteins. The host provides the nucleotides for making viral nucleic acids, as well as enzymes, ribosomes, tRNAs, amino acids, ATP, and other components needed for making the viral proteins. Many DNA viruses use the DNA polymerases of the host cell to synthesize new genomes along the templates provided by the viral DNA. In contrast, to replicate their genomes, RNA viruses use virally encoded RNA polymerases that can use RNA as a template. (Uninfected cells generally make no enzymes for carrying out this process.)

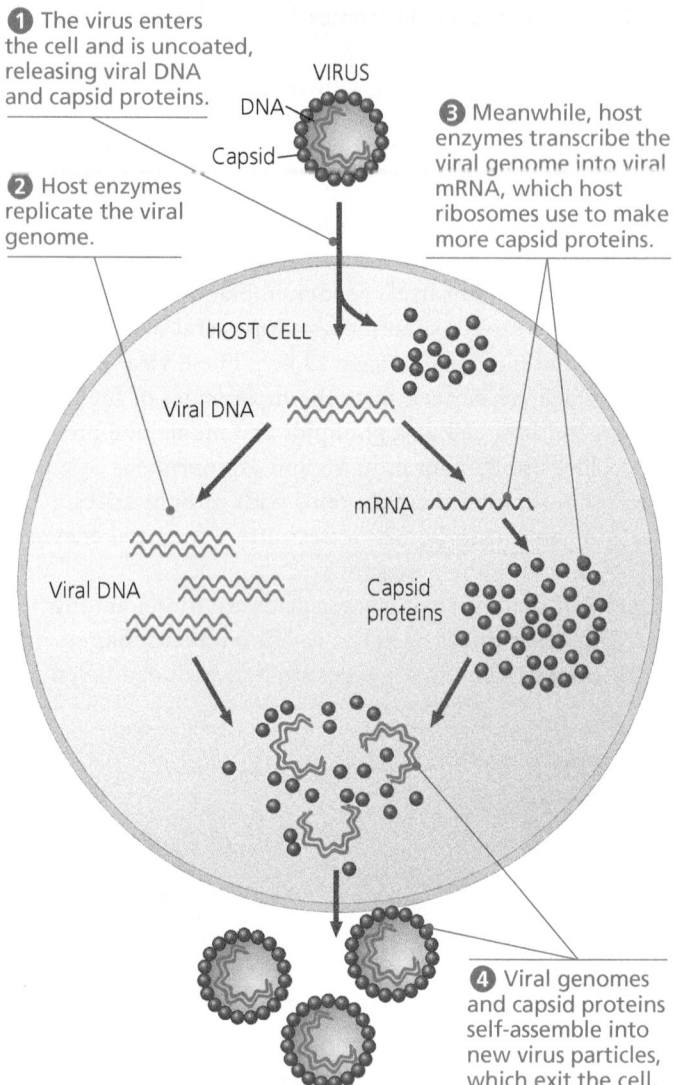

1 The virus enters the cell and is uncoated, releasing viral DNA and capsid proteins.

2 Host enzymes replicate the viral genome.

3 Meanwhile, host enzymes transcribe the viral genome into viral mRNA, which host ribosomes use to make more capsid proteins.

4 Viral genomes and capsid proteins self-assemble into new virus particles, which exit the cell.

▲ Figure 19.5 **A simplified viral replicative cycle.** A virus is an obligate intracellular parasite that uses the equipment and small molecules of its host cell to replicate. In this simplest of viral cycles, the parasite is a DNA virus with a capsid consisting of a single type of protein.

DRAW IT *Label each of the straight black arrows with one word representing the name of the process that is occurring. Review Figure 17.24.*

After the viral nucleic acid molecules and capsomeres are produced, they spontaneously self-assemble into new viruses. In fact, researchers can separate the RNA and capsomeres of TMV and then reassemble complete viruses simply by mixing the components together under the right conditions. The simplest type of viral replicative cycle ends with the exit of hundreds or thousands of viruses from the infected host cell, a process that often damages or destroys the cell. Such cellular damage and death, as well as the body's responses to this destruction, cause many of the symptoms associated with viral infections. The viral progeny that exit a cell have the potential to infect additional cells, spreading the viral infection.

► Figure 19.6 **The lytic cycle of phage T4, a virulent phage.** Phage T4 has almost 300 genes, which are transcribed and translated using the host cell's machinery. One of the first phage genes translated after the viral DNA enters the host cell codes for an enzyme that degrades the host cell's DNA (step 2); the phage DNA is protected from breakdown because it contains a modified form of cytosine that is not recognized by the enzyme. The entire lytic cycle, from the phage's first contact with the cell surface to cell lysis, takes only 20–30 minutes at 37°C.

1 **Attachment.** The T4 phage uses its tail fibres to bind to specific surface proteins on an *E. coli* cell that act as receptors.

2 **Entry of phage DNA and degradation of host DNA.** The sheath of the tail contracts, injecting the phage DNA into the cell and leaving an empty capsid outside. The cell's DNA is hydrolyzed.

5 **Release.** The phage directs production of an enzyme that damages the bacterial cell wall, allowing fluid to enter. The cell swells and finally bursts, releasing 100 to 200 phage particles.

Phage assembly

Head   Tail   Tail fibres

4 **Self-assembly.** Three separate sets of proteins self-assemble to form phage heads, tails, and tail fibres. The phage genome is packaged inside the capsid as the head forms.

3 **Synthesis of viral genomes and proteins.** The phage DNA directs production of phage proteins and copies of the phage genome by host and viral enzymes, using components within the cell.

There are many variations on the simplified viral replicative cycle we have just described. We will now take a look at some of these variations in bacterial viruses (phages) and animal viruses; later in the chapter, we will consider plant viruses.

Replicative Cycles of Phages

Phages are the best understood of all viruses, although some of them are also among the most complex. Research on phages led to the discovery that some double-stranded DNA viruses can replicate by two alternative mechanisms: the lytic cycle and the lysogenic cycle.

The Lytic Cycle

A phage replicative cycle that culminates in death of the host cell is known as a **lytic cycle**. The term refers to the last stage of infection, during which the bacterium lyses (breaks open) and releases the phages that were produced within the cell. Each of these phages can then infect a healthy cell, and a few successive lytic cycles can destroy an entire bacterial population in just a few hours. A phage that replicates only by a lytic cycle is a **virulent phage**.

Figure 19.6 illustrates the major steps in the lytic cycle of T4, a typical virulent phage.

The Lysogenic Cycle

Instead of lysing their host cells, many phages coexist with them in a state called lysogeny. In contrast to the lytic cycle, which kills the host cell, the **lysogenic cycle** allows replication of the phage genome without destroying the host. Phages capable of using both modes of replicating within a bacterium are called **temperate phages**. A temperate phage called lambda, written with the Greek letter λ, has been widely used in biological research. Phage λ resembles T4, but its tail has only one short tail fibre.

Infection of an *E. coli* cell by phage λ begins when the phage binds to the surface of the cell and injects its linear DNA genome (**Figure 19.7**). Within the host, the λ DNA molecule forms a circle. What happens next depends on the replicative mode: lytic cycle or lysogenic cycle. During a lytic cycle, the viral genes immediately turn the host cell into a λ-producing factory, and the cell soon lyses and releases its virus progeny. During a lysogenic cycle, however, the λ DNA molecule is incorporated into a specific site on the *E. coli* chromosome by viral proteins that

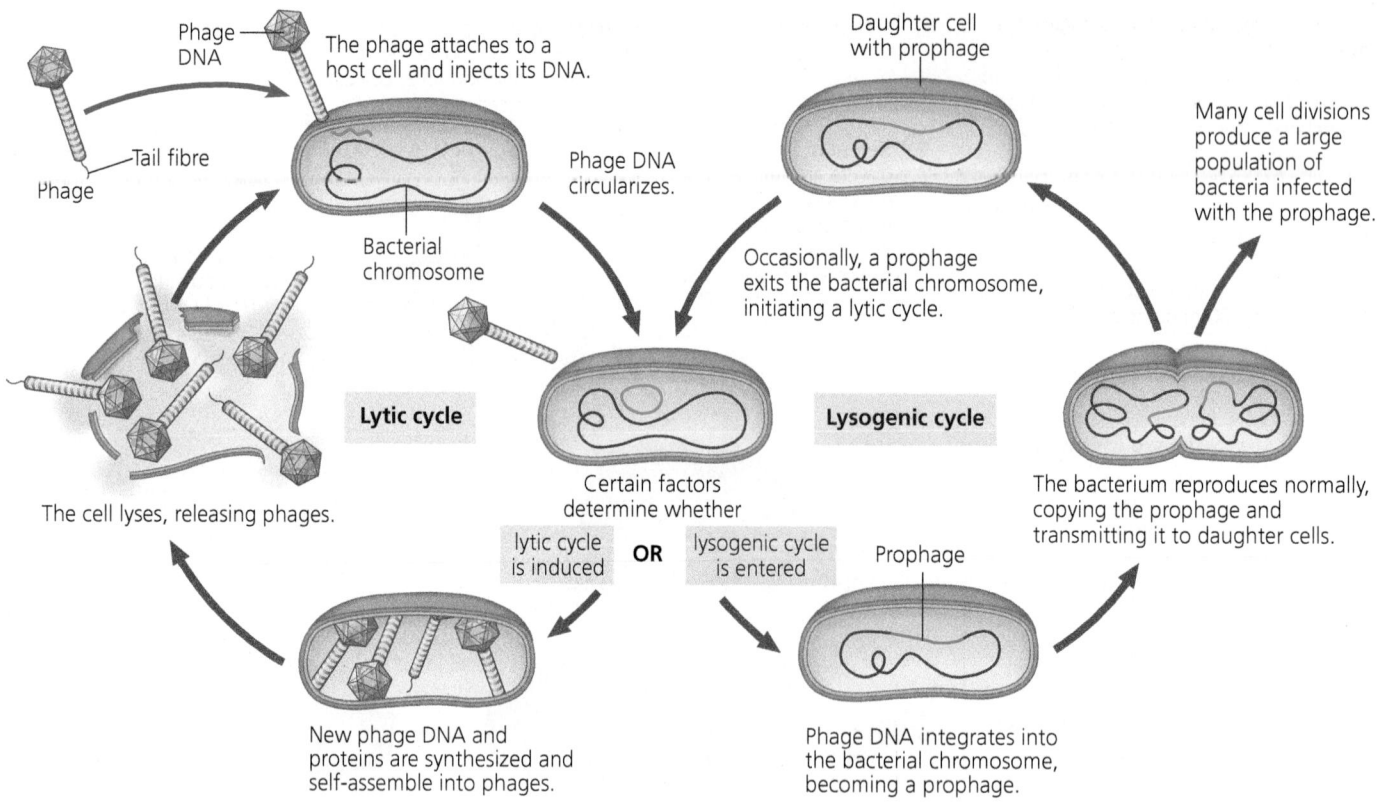

The phage attaches to a host cell and injects its DNA.

Phage DNA
Phage

Tail fibre

Phage DNA circularizes.

Bacterial chromosome

Lytic cycle

The cell lyses, releasing phages.

Certain factors determine whether

lytic cycle is induced **OR** lysogenic cycle is entered

New phage DNA and proteins are synthesized and self-assemble into phages.

Daughter cell with prophage

Many cell divisions produce a large population of bacteria infected with the prophage.

Occasionally, a prophage exits the bacterial chromosome, initiating a lytic cycle.

Lysogenic cycle

The bacterium reproduces normally, copying the prophage and transmitting it to daughter cells.

Prophage

Phage DNA integrates into the bacterial chromosome, becoming a prophage.

▲ **Figure 19.7 The lytic and lysogenic cycles of phage λ, a temperate phage.** After entering the bacterial cell and circularizing, the λ DNA can immediately initiate the production of a large number of progeny phages (lytic cycle) or integrate into the bacterial chromosome (lysogenic cycle). In most cases, phage λ follows the lytic pathway, which is similar to that detailed in Figure 19.5. However, once a lysogenic cycle begins, the prophage may be carried in the host cell's chromosome for many generations. Phage λ has one main tail fibre, which is short.

break both circular DNA molecules and join them to each other. When integrated into the bacterial chromosome in this way, the viral DNA is known as a **prophage**. One prophage gene codes for a protein that prevents transcription of most of the other prophage genes. Thus, the phage genome is mostly silent within the bacterium. Every time the *E. coli* cell prepares to divide, it replicates the phage DNA along with its own chromosome such that each daughter cell inherits a prophage. A single infected cell can quickly give rise to a large population of bacteria carrying the virus in prophage form. This mechanism enables viruses to propagate without killing the host cells on which they depend.

The term *lysogenic* signifies that prophages are capable of generating active phages that lyse their host cells. This occurs when the λ genome (or that of another temperate phage) is induced to exit the bacterial chromosome and initiate a lytic cycle. An environmental signal, such as a certain chemical or high-energy radiation, usually triggers the switchover from the lysogenic to the lytic mode.

In addition to the gene for the viral protein that prevents transcription, a few other prophage genes may be expressed during lysogeny. Expression of these genes may alter the host's phenotype, a phenomenon that can have important medical significance. For example, the three species of bacteria that cause the human diseases diphtheria, botulism, and scarlet fever would not be so harmful to humans without certain prophage genes that cause the host bacteria to make toxins. And the difference between the *E. coli* strain in our intestines and the O157:H7 strain that has caused several deaths by food poisoning appears to be the presence of toxin genes of prophages in the O157:H7 strain.

Bacterial Defences Against Phages

After reading about the lytic cycle, you may have wondered why phages haven't exterminated all bacteria. Lysogeny is one major reason why bacteria have been spared from extinction caused by phages. Bacteria also have their own defences against phages. First, natural selection favours bacterial mutants with surface proteins that are no longer recognized as receptors by a particular type of phage. Second, when phage DNA does enter a bacterium, the DNA often is identified as foreign and cut up by cellular enzymes called restriction enzymes, which are so named because they *restrict* a phage's ability to replicate within the bacterium. (Restriction enzymes are used in molecular biology and DNA cloning techniques; see Concept 20.1.) The bacterium's own DNA is methylated in a way that prevents attack by its own restriction enzymes. A third defence is a system present in both bacteria and archaea called the *CRISPR-Cas system.*

The CRISPR–Cas system was discovered during a study of repetitive DNA sequences present in the genomes of many prokaryotes. These sequences, which puzzled scientists, were named <u>c</u>lustered <u>r</u>egularly <u>i</u>nterspaced <u>s</u>hort <u>p</u>alindromic <u>r</u>epeats (CRISPRs) because each sequence read the same forward and backward (a palindrome), with different stretches of "spacer DNA" in between the repeats. At first, scientists assumed the spacer DNA sequences were random and meaningless, but analysis by several research groups showed that each spacer sequence corresponded to DNA from a particular phage that had infected the cell. Further studies revealed that particular nuclease proteins interact with the CRISPR region. These nucleases, called Cas (<u>C</u>RISPR-<u>as</u>sociated) proteins, can identify and cut phage DNA, thereby defending the bacterium against phage infection.

When a phage infects a bacterial cell that has the CRISPR-Cas system, the DNA of the invading phage is integrated into the genome between two repeat sequences. If the cell survives the infection, any further attempt by the same type of phage to infect this cell (or its offspring) triggers transcription of the CRISPR region into RNA molecules (**Figure 19.8**). These RNAs are cut into pieces and then bound by Cas proteins. A Cas protein uses a portion of the phage-related RNA as a homing device to identify the invading phage DNA and cut it, leading to its destruction. In Concept 20.1, you'll learn how this system is used in the laboratory to alter genes in other cells.

Just as natural selection favours bacteria that have receptors altered by mutation or that have enzymes that cut phage DNA, it also favours phage mutants that can bind to altered receptors or that are resistant to enzymes. Thus, the bacterium-phage relationship is in constant evolutionary flux.

Replicative Cycles of Animal Viruses

Everyone has suffered from viral infections, whether cold sores, influenza, or the common cold. Like all viruses, those that cause illness in humans and other animals can replicate only inside host cells. Many variations on the basic scheme of viral infection and replication are represented among the animal viruses. One key variable is the nature of the viral genome (double- or single-stranded DNA or

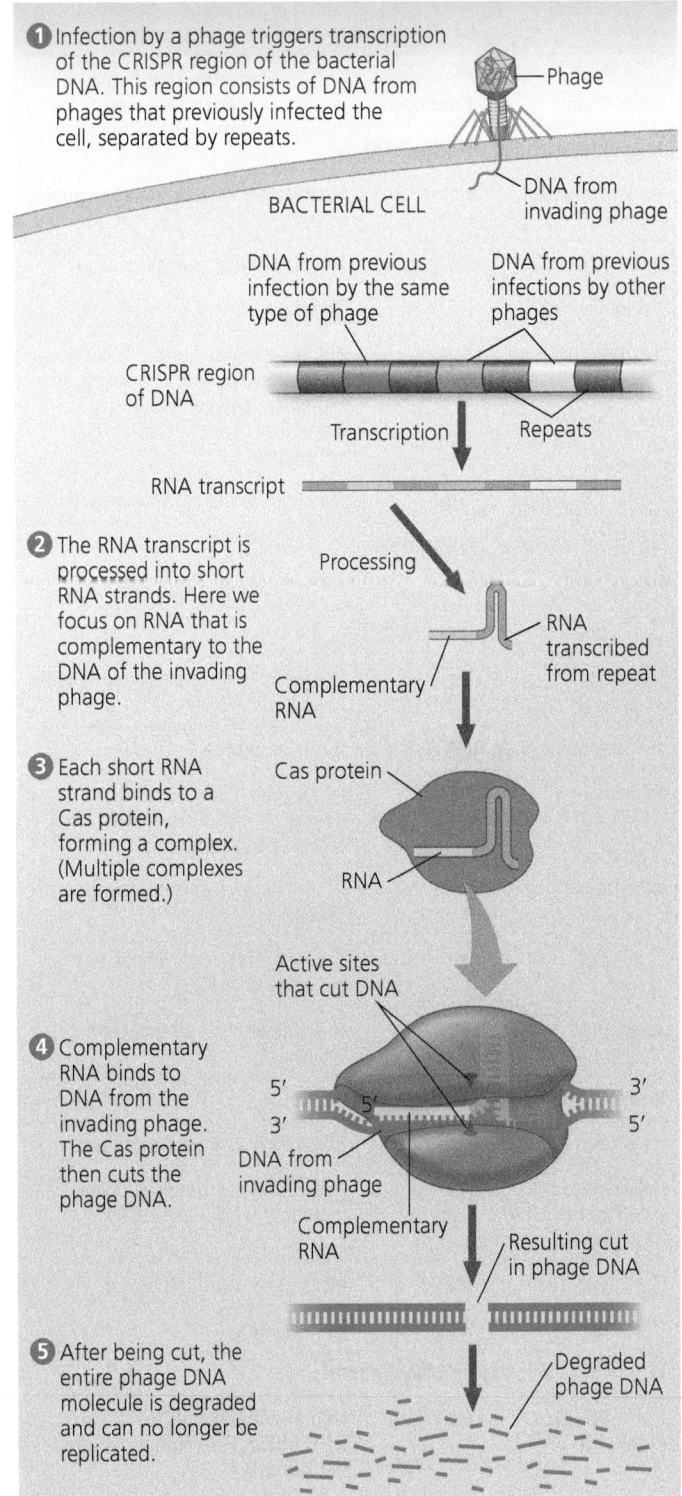

1 Infection by a phage triggers transcription of the CRISPR region of the bacterial DNA. This region consists of DNA from phages that previously infected the cell, separated by repeats.

2 The RNA transcript is processed into short RNA strands. Here we focus on RNA that is complementary to the DNA of the invading phage.

3 Each short RNA strand binds to a Cas protein, forming a complex. (Multiple complexes are formed.)

4 Complementary RNA binds to DNA from the invading phage. The Cas protein then cuts the phage DNA.

5 After being cut, the entire phage DNA molecule is degraded and can no longer be replicated.

▲ Figure 19.8 **The CRISPR-Cas system: a type of bacterial immune system.**

RNA), which is the basis for the common classification of viruses shown in **Table 19.1**. Single-stranded RNA viruses are further classified into three classes (IV–VI) according to how the RNA genome functions in a host cell.

Table 19.1 Classes of Animal Viruses

Class/Family	Envelope	Examples That Cause Human Diseases
I. Double-Stranded DNA (dsDNA)		
Adenovirus (see Figure 19.4b)	No	Respiratory viruses; tumour-causing viruses
Papillomavirus	No	Warts, cervical cancer
Polyomavirus	No	Tumours
Herpesvirus	Yes	Herpes simplex I and II (cold sores, genital sores); varicella zoster (shingles, chicken pox); Epstein-Barr virus (mononucleosis, Burkitt's lymphoma)
Poxvirus	Yes	Smallpox virus; cowpox virus
II. Single-Stranded DNA (ssDNA)		
Parvovirus	No	B19 parvovirus (mild rash)
III. Double-Stranded RNA (dsRNA)		
Reovirus	No	Rotavirus (diarrhea); Colorado tick fever virus
IV. Single-Stranded RNA (ssRNA); Serves as mRNA		
Picornavirus	No	Rhinovirus (common cold); poliovirus; hepatitis A virus; other enteric (intestinal) viruses
Coronavirus	Yes	Severe acute respiratory syndrome (SARS)
Flavivirus	Yes	Yellow fever virus; West Nile virus; hepatitis C virus
Togavirus	Yes	Rubella virus; equine encephalitis viruses
V. ssRNA; Template for mRNA Synthesis		
Filovirus	Yes	Ebola virus (hemorrhagic fever)
Orthomyxovirus (see Figures 19.4c and 19.12a)	Yes	Influenza virus (many subtypes, including H1N1 and H5N1)
Paramyxovirus	Yes	Measles virus; mumps virus
Rhabdovirus	Yes	Rabies virus
VI. ssRNA; Template for DNA Synthesis		
Retrovirus (see Figure 19.10)	Yes	Human immunodeficiency virus (HIV/AIDS); RNA tumour viruses (leukemia)

Another variable is the presence or absence of a membranous envelope. Whereas few bacteriophages have an envelope or RNA genome, many animal viruses have both. In fact, nearly all animal viruses with RNA genomes have an envelope, as do some with DNA genomes (see Table 19.1). Rather than consider all the mechanisms of viral infection and replication, we will focus first on the roles of viral envelopes and then on the functioning of RNA as the genetic material of many animal viruses.

Viral Envelopes

An animal virus equipped with an envelope—that is, a membraneous outer layer—uses it to enter the host cell. Protruding from the outer surface of this envelope are viral glycoproteins that bind to specific receptor molecules on the surface of a host cell. **Figure 19.9** outlines the events in the replicative cycle of an enveloped virus with an RNA genome. Ribosomes bound to the endoplasmic reticulum (ER) of the host cell make the protein parts of the envelope glycoproteins; cellular enzymes in the ER and Golgi apparatus then add the sugars. The resulting viral glycoproteins, embedded in membrane derived from the host cell are transported to the cell surface. In a process much like exocytosis, new viral capsids are wrapped in membrane as they bud from the cell. In other words, the viral envelope is usually derived from the host cell's plasma membrane, although all or most of the molecules of this membrane are specified by viral genes. The enveloped viruses are now free to infect other cells. This replicative cycle does not necessarily kill the host cell, in contrast to the lytic cycles of phages.

Some viruses have envelopes that are not derived from plasma membrane. Herpesviruses, for example, are temporarily cloaked in membrane derived from the nuclear envelope of the host; they then shed this membrane in the cytoplasm and acquire a new envelope made from membrane of the Golgi apparatus. These viruses have a double-stranded DNA genome and replicate within the host cell nucleus, using a combination of viral and cellular enzymes to replicate and transcribe their DNA. In the case of herpesviruses, copies of the viral DNA can remain behind as mini-chromosomes in the nuclei of certain nerve cells. There they remain latent until some sort of physical or emotional stress triggers a new round of active virus production. The infection of other cells by these new viruses causes the blisters characteristic of herpes, such as cold sores or genital sores. Once someone acquires a herpesvirus infection, flare-ups may recur throughout the person's life.

RNA as Viral Genetic Material

Although some phages and most plant viruses are RNA viruses, the broadest variety of RNA genomes is found among the viruses that infect animals. There are three types of single-stranded RNA genomes found in animal viruses. The genome of class IV viruses can directly serve as mRNA and thus can be translated into viral protein immediately after infection. Figure 19.9 shows a virus of class V, in which the RNA genome serves instead as a *template*

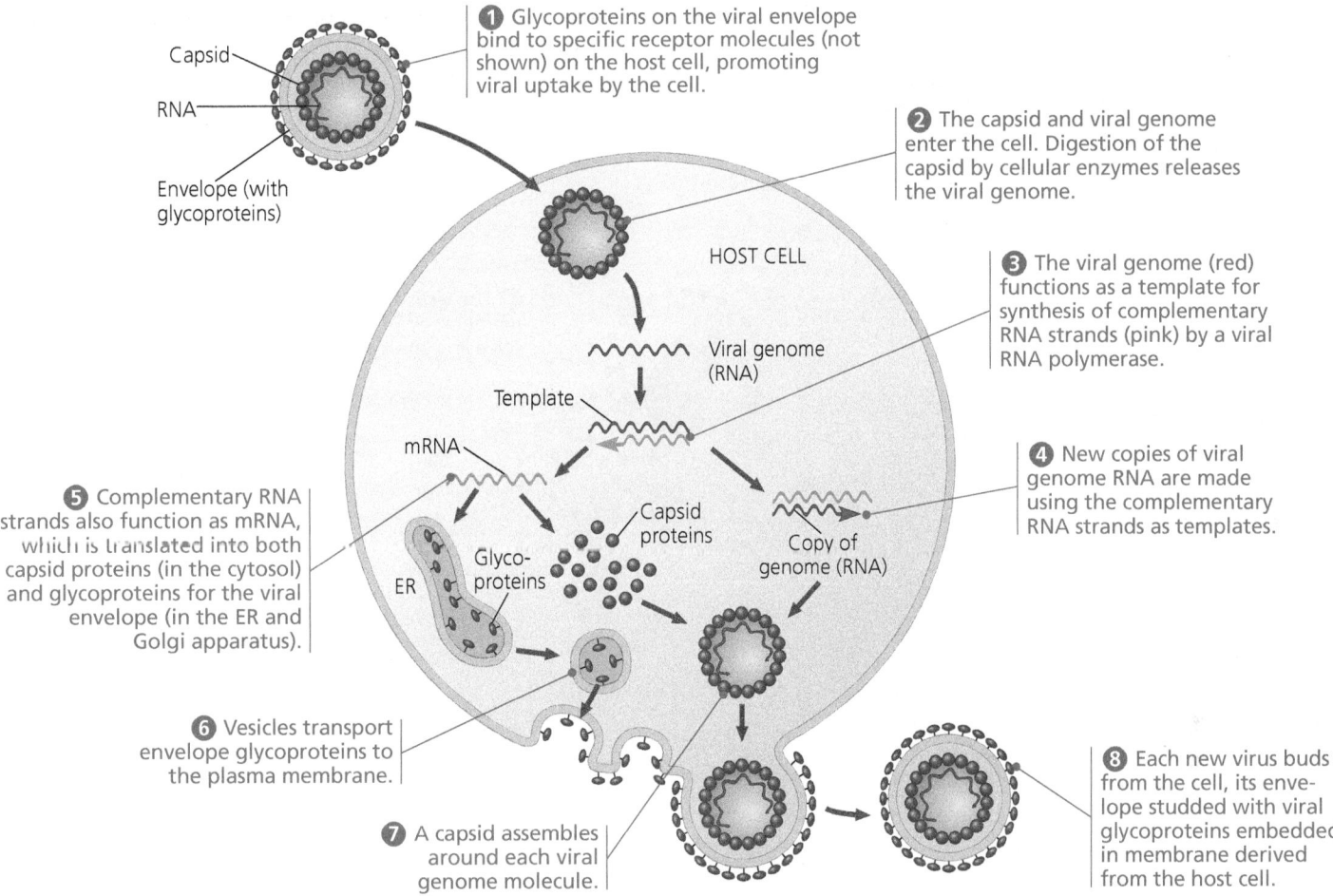

① Glycoproteins on the viral envelope bind to specific receptor molecules (not shown) on the host cell, promoting viral uptake by the cell.

Capsid

RNA

Envelope (with glycoproteins)

② The capsid and viral genome enter the cell. Digestion of the capsid by cellular enzymes releases the viral genome.

HOST CELL

Viral genome (RNA)

③ The viral genome (red) functions as a template for synthesis of complementary RNA strands (pink) by a viral RNA polymerase.

Template

mRNA

⑤ Complementary RNA strands also function as mRNA, which is translated into both capsid proteins (in the cytosol) and glycoproteins for the viral envelope (in the ER and Golgi apparatus).

Capsid proteins

Glyco-proteins

Copy of genome (RNA)

④ New copies of viral genome RNA are made using the complementary RNA strands as templates.

ER

⑥ Vesicles transport envelope glycoproteins to the plasma membrane.

⑦ A capsid assembles around each viral genome molecule.

⑧ Each new virus buds from the cell, its envelope studded with viral glycoproteins embedded in membrane derived from the host cell.

▲ Figure 19.9 The replicative cycle of an enveloped RNA virus. Shown here is a virus with a single-stranded RNA genome that functions as a template for synthesis of mRNA. Some enveloped viruses enter the host cell by fusion of the envelope with the cell's plasma membrane; others enter by endocytosis. For all enveloped RNA viruses, the formation of new envelopes for progeny viruses occurs by the mechanism depicted in this figure.

[?] *Name a virus that has infected you and has a replicative cycle matching this one. (Hint: See Table 19.1.)*

for mRNA synthesis. The RNA genome is transcribed into complementary RNA strands, which function both as mRNA and as templates for the synthesis of additional copies of genomic RNA. All viruses that use an RNA genome as a template for mRNA transcription require RNA → RNA synthesis. These viruses use a viral enzyme capable of carrying out this process; there are no such enzymes in most cells. The enzyme used in this process is encoded by the viral genome, and after its synthesis the protein is packaged during viral self-assembly with the genome inside the viral capsid.

The RNA animal viruses with the most complicated replicative cycles are the **retroviruses** (class VI). These viruses are equipped with an enzyme called **reverse transcriptase**, which transcribes an RNA template into DNA, providing an RNA → DNA information flow, the opposite of the usual direction. This unusual phenomenon is the source of the name retroviruses (*retro* means "backward"). Of particular medical importance is **HIV (human immunodeficiency virus)**, the retrovirus that causes **AIDS (acquired immunodeficiency syndrome)**. HIV and other retroviruses are enveloped viruses that contain two identical molecules of single-stranded RNA and two molecules of reverse transcriptase.

The HIV replicative cycle (traced in **Figure 19.10**) is typical of a retrovirus. After HIV enters a host cell, its reverse transcriptase molecules are released into the cytoplasm, where they catalyze synthesis of viral DNA. The newly made viral DNA then enters the cell's nucleus and integrates into the DNA of a chromosome. The integrated viral DNA, called a **provirus**, never leaves the host's genome, remaining a permanent resident of the cell. (Recall that a prophage, in contrast, leaves the host's genome at the start of a lytic cycle.) The RNA polymerase of the host transcribes the proviral DNA into RNA molecules, which can function both as mRNA for the synthesis of viral proteins and as genomes for the new viruses that will be assembled and released from the cell. In Concept 43.4, we

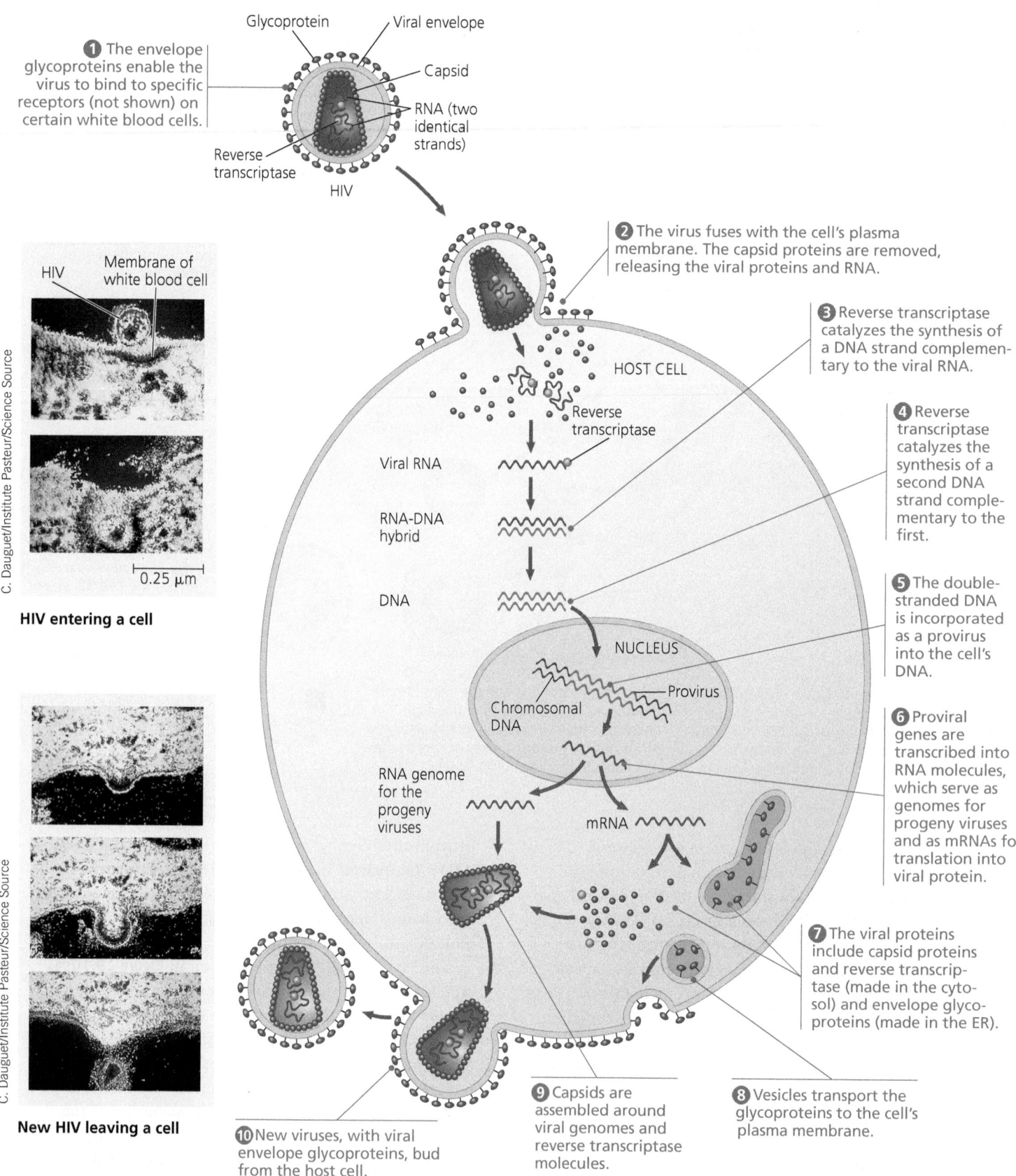

1 The envelope glycoproteins enable the virus to bind to specific receptors (not shown) on certain white blood cells.

Glycoprotein — Viral envelope

Capsid

RNA (two identical strands)

Reverse transcriptase

HIV

2 The virus fuses with the cell's plasma membrane. The capsid proteins are removed, releasing the viral proteins and RNA.

3 Reverse transcriptase catalyzes the synthesis of a DNA strand complementary to the viral RNA.

4 Reverse transcriptase catalyzes the synthesis of a second DNA strand complementary to the first.

5 The double-stranded DNA is incorporated as a provirus into the cell's DNA.

6 Proviral genes are transcribed into RNA molecules, which serve as genomes for progeny viruses and as mRNAs for translation into viral protein.

7 The viral proteins include capsid proteins and reverse transcriptase (made in the cytosol) and envelope glycoproteins (made in the ER).

8 Vesicles transport the glycoproteins to the cell's plasma membrane.

9 Capsids are assembled around viral genomes and reverse transcriptase molecules.

10 New viruses, with viral envelope glycoproteins, bud from the host cell.

HOST CELL

Reverse transcriptase

Viral RNA

RNA-DNA hybrid

DNA

NUCLEUS

Chromosomal DNA

Provirus

RNA genome for the progeny viruses

mRNA

HIV

Membrane of white blood cell

C. Dauguet/Institute Pasteur/Science Source

0.25 µm

HIV entering a cell

C. Dauguet/Institute Pasteur/Science Source

New HIV leaving a cell

▲ Figure 19.10 **The replicative cycle of HIV, the retrovirus that causes AIDS.** Note in step **5** that DNA synthesized from the viral RNA genome is integrated as a provirus into the host cell chromosomal DNA, a characteristic unique to retroviruses. For simplicity, the cell-surface proteins that act as receptors for HIV are not shown. The photos on the left (artificially coloured TEMs) show HIV entering and leaving a human white blood cell.

MAKE CONNECTIONS *Describe what is known about binding of HIV to immune system cells. (See Figure 7.8.) How was this discovered?*

describe how HIV causes the deterioration of the immune system that occurs in AIDS.

Evolution of Viruses

EVOLUTION We began this chapter by asking whether or not viruses are alive. Viruses do not really fit our definition of living organisms. An isolated virus is biologically inert, unable to replicate its genes or regenerate its own ATP. Yet it has a genetic program written in the universal language of life. Do we think of viruses as nature's most complex associations of molecules or as the simplest forms of life? Either way, we must bend our usual definitions. Although viruses cannot replicate or carry out metabolic activities independently, their use of the genetic code makes it hard to deny their evolutionary connection to the living world.

How did viruses originate? Viruses have been found that infect every form of life—not just bacteria, animals, and plants, but also archaea, fungi, and algae and other protists. Because they depend on cells for their own propagation, it seems likely that viruses are not the descendants of precellular forms of life but evolved—possibly multiple times—*after* the first cells appeared. Most molecular biologists favour the hypothesis that viruses originated from naked bits of cellular nucleic acids that moved from one cell to another, perhaps via injured cell surfaces. The evolution of genes coding for capsid proteins may have allowed viruses to bind cell membranes, thus facilitating the infection of uninjured cells.

Candidates for the original sources of viral genomes include plasmids and transposons. *Plasmids* are small, circular DNA molecules found in bacteria and in the unicellular eukaryotes called yeasts. Plasmids exist apart from and can replicate independently of the bacterial chromosome, and are occasionally transferred between cells. *Transposons* are DNA segments that can move from one location to another within a cell's genome. Thus, plasmids, transposons, and viruses all share an important feature: They are *mobile genetic elements*.

Consistent with this notion of pieces of DNA shuttling from cell to cell is the observation that a viral genome can have more in common with the genome of its host than with the genomes of viruses that infect other hosts. Indeed, some viral genes are essentially identical to genes of the host.

The debate about the origin of viruses was reinvigorated in 2003 by reports of one of the largest viruses yet discovered: Mimivirus is a double-stranded DNA (dsDNA) virus with an icosahedral capsid that is 400 nm in diameter, the size of a small bacterium. Its genome contains 1.2 million bases (Mb)—about 100 times as many as the influenza virus genome—and an estimated 1000 genes. Perhaps the most surprising aspect of mimivirus, however, was that its genome included genes previously found only in cellular genomes. Some of these genes code for proteins involved in translation, DNA repair, protein folding, and polysaccharide synthesis. Whether mimivirus evolved *before* the first cells and then developed an exploitative relationship with them, or evolved more recently and simply scavenged genes from its hosts is not yet settled. Since 2013 several even larger viruses have been discovered that cannot be classified with any existing known virus. One such virus is 1 μm (1000 nm) in diameter, with a dsDNA genome of around 2–2.5 Mb, larger than that of some small eukaryotes. What's more, over 90% of its 2000 or so genes are unrelated to cellular genes, inspiring the naming of this virus as pandoravirus. A second virus, called *Pithovirus sibericum*, with a diameter of 1.5 μm and 500 genes, was discovered in permanently frozen soil in Siberia. This virus, once thawed, was able to infect an amoeba after being frozen for 30 000 years! How these and all other viruses fit in the tree of life is an intriguing, unresolved question.

The ongoing evolutionary relationship between viruses and the genomes of their host cells is an association that continues to make viruses very useful experimental systems in molecular biology. Knowledge about viruses also allows many practical applications, since viruses have a tremendous impact on all organisms through their ability to cause disease.

CONCEPT CHECK 19.2

1. Compare the effect on the host cell of a lytic (virulent) phage and a lysogenic (temperate) phage.
2. **MAKE CONNECTIONS** Compare the CRISPR-Cas system to the miRNA system discussed in Concept 18.3, including their mechanism and their functions.
3. **MAKE CONNECTIONS** The RNA virus in Figure 19.9 has a viral RNA polymerase that functions in step 3 of the virus's replicative cycle. Compare this RNA polymerase to the one in Figure 17.9 in terms of template and overall function.
4. Why is HIV called a retrovirus?
5. **WHAT IF?** If you were a researcher trying to combat HIV infection, what molecular processes could you attempt to block? (See Figure 19.10.)

For suggested answers, see Appendix A.

CONCEPT 19.3

Viruses and prions are formidable pathogens in animals and plants

Diseases caused by viral infections afflict humans, agricultural crops, and livestock worldwide. Other smaller, less complex entities known as prions also cause disease in animals. We'll first discuss animal viruses.

Viral Diseases in Animals

A viral infection can produce symptoms by a number of different routes. Viruses may damage or kill cells by causing the release of hydrolytic enzymes from lysosomes. Some viruses cause infected cells to produce toxins that lead to disease symptoms, and some have molecular components that are toxic, such as envelope proteins. How much damage a virus causes depends partly on the ability of the infected tissue to regenerate by cell division. People usually recover completely from colds because the epithelium of the respiratory tract, which the viruses infect, can efficiently repair itself. In contrast, damage inflicted by poliovirus to mature nerve cells is permanent because these cells do not divide and usually cannot be replaced. Many of the temporary symptoms associated with viral infections, such as fever and body aches, actually result from the body's own efforts to defend itself against infection rather than from cell death caused by the virus.

The immune system is a complex and critical part of the body's natural defences (see Chapter 43). It is also the basis for the major medical tool for preventing viral infections—vaccines. A **vaccine** is a harmless variant or derivative of a pathogen that stimulates the immune system to mount defences against the harmful pathogen. Smallpox, a viral disease that was at one time a devastating scourge in many parts of the world, was eradicated by a vaccination program carried out by the World Health Organization (WHO). The very narrow host range of the smallpox virus—it infects only humans—was a critical factor in the success of this program. Similar worldwide vaccination campaigns are currently under way to eradicate polio and measles. Effective vaccines are also available to protect against rubella, mumps, hepatitis B, and a number of other viral diseases.

An effective vaccine against hepatitis C, which has infected 2–3% of the global population including 250 000 Canadians, has previously been elusive. However, Dr. Michael Houghton, who directed the research team that discovered the hepatitis C virus in the late 1980s, has recently developed a vaccine at the University of Alberta that has been shown to be effective in producing antibodies against several strains of the virus in early human clinical trials. Although more research is needed before this vaccine can be administered to the public, the initial results are cause for cautious optimism.

Although vaccines can prevent certain viral illnesses, medical technology can do little, at present, to cure most viral infections once they occur. The antibiotics that help us recover from bacterial infections are powerless against viruses. Antibiotics kill bacteria by inhibiting enzymes specific to bacteria but have no effect on eukaryotic or virally encoded enzymes. However, the few enzymes that are encoded only by viruses have provided targets for other drugs. Most antiviral drugs resemble nucleosides and as a result interfere with viral nucleic acid synthesis. One such drug is acyclovir, which impedes herpesvirus replication by inhibiting the viral polymerase that synthesizes viral DNA but not the eukaryotic one. Similarly, azidothymidine (AZT) curbs HIV replication by interfering with the synthesis of DNA by reverse transcriptase. In the past two decades, much effort has gone into developing drugs to treat HIV. Currently, multidrug treatments, sometimes called "cocktails," have been found to be most effective. Such treatments commonly include a combination of two nucleoside mimics and a protease inhibitor, which interferes with an enzyme required for assembly of the viruses. Another effective treatment involves a drug called maraviroc, which blocks a protein on the surface of human immune cells that helps bind the HIV virus (see Figure 7.8). This drug has also been used successfully to prevent infection in individuals who either have been exposed to, or are at risk of exposure to, HIV.

We now know viruses are also responsible for between 21–40% of human cancers. These viruses are called oncoviruses, and future research may show that they are linked to even more cancers. For example, human papillomavirus (HPV) is transmitted by contact, can infect skin or mucosal cells, and is considered to be one of the most common sexually transmitted diseases in the world. There are more than 100 different types of HPV, and some of these are responsible for genital warts and several types of cancer, including 70% of cervical cancer. Dr. Eduardo Franco and colleagues from McGill University have played a major role in HPV research, both in characterizing HPV and in testing and clinically validating the vaccine for HPV that is being used across Canada in preventing cervical cancer.

Emerging Viruses

Viruses that suddenly become apparent are often referred to as *emerging viruses*. HIV, the AIDS virus, is a classic example: This virus appeared in San Francisco in the early 1980s, seemingly out of nowhere, although later studies uncovered a case in the Belgian Congo in 1959. A number of other dangerous emerging viruses cause encephalitis, inflammation of the brain. One example is the West Nile virus, which was first detected in Canada in birds in August 2001, and in humans in 2002. The Public Health Agency of Canada produces weekly West Nile Virus MONITOR reports and maps during the West Nile virus season, which annually runs from May to October.

The deadly Ebola virus (see Figure 19.1), recognized initially in 1976 in central Africa, is one of several emerging viruses that cause *hemorrhagic fever*, an often fatal illness characterized by fever, vomiting, massive bleeding, and circulatory system collapse. In 2014, a widespread outbreak of Ebola virus in western Africa caused the World Health Organization to declare an international health emergency. By mid-2015 the outbreak, centred in Guinea, Sierra Leone, and Liberia, had caused over 27 000 illnesses and 11 000 deaths. Canada's National Microbiology Laboratory in Winnipeg has long been studying Ebola. One project, led by

---

▼ Figure 19.11 | **Impact**

Sequencing the SARS Genome

During the SARS outbreak, samples of the SARS virus were sent to Canada's Michael Smith Genome Sciences Centre, located in Vancouver, British Columbia. Because they had a rapid response emergency plan in place, this Centre was able to generate the first genome sequence of SARS in only six days. The SARS accelerated vaccine initiative (SAVI) was then established in April 2003, with a goal of developing a human SARS vaccine. Lead by Drs. Brett Finlay and Robert Brunham at the UBC Centre for Disease Control, SAVI developed three prototype SARS vaccines. However, due to the fact that SARS cases decreased in the summer of 2003, there were not enough affected patients to progress to Phase II/III clinical trials. Currently, SARS is not a worldwide threat. However, the vaccines are ready to be developed further should SARS re-emerge.

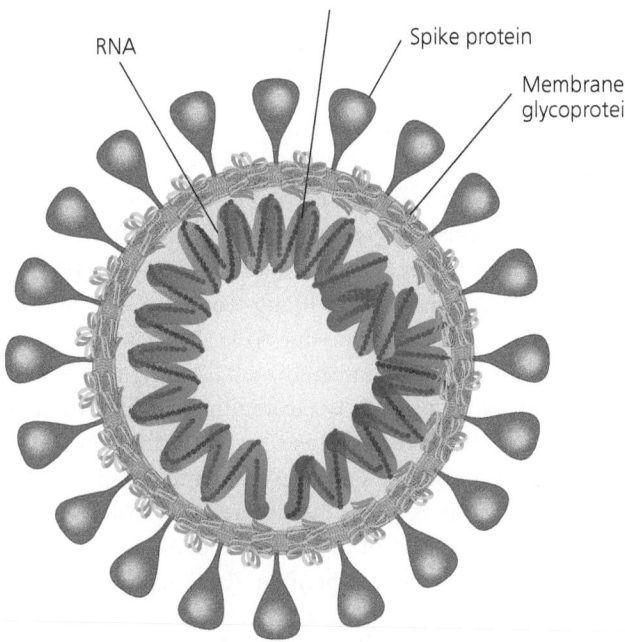

Why It Matters The rapid generation of the SARS genome, and the subsequent establishment of the vaccine development initiative, showed how modern science could be applied to combatting emerging infectious diseases, and also emphasized the importance of establishing rapid response emergency plans.

Further Reading B. B. Finlay et al., Rapid response research to emerging infectious disease: Lessons from SARS, *Nature Reviews Microbiology*, 2:602–607 (2004).

Source: Based on B.B. Finlay et al., Rapid response research to emerging infectious disease: lessons from SARS, *Nature Reviews Microbiology*, 2:602–607 (2004). © Jane B Reece.

MAKE CONNECTIONS *SARS is an RNA virus. What implication does this have on vaccine development, compared with DNA viruses?*

Dr. Gary Kobinger, identified and developed a cocktail of antibodies (proteins that recognize specific parts of the Ebola virus) that are part of a post-exposure drug treatment called ZMapp. Another project, led by Heinz Feldmann, produced a promising Ebola vaccine, which recently started undergoing clinical trials. The National Microbiology Laboratory also sent two mobile laboratory teams to West Africa to assist with rapid diagnosis during the recent outbreak.

In November 2002, the first severe acute respiratory syndrome (SARS) coronavirus outbreak, or **epidemic**, occurred in Guangdong province in China, and the first outbreak in Toronto followed in March 2003. Canada was the hardest-hit country outside of Asia with respect to SARS cases (438) and deaths (44), and a World Health Organization (WHO) Travel Health Advisory was issued stating that people should avoid travelling to Toronto. Because of an excellent rapid response emergency plan and collaboration, Canadian scientists were able to quickly sequence the genome of the SARS virus (**Figure 19.11**).

In 2009, a widespread outbreak of a flu-like illness appeared in Mexico and the United States. The infectious agent was quickly identified as an influenza virus related to viruses that cause the seasonal flu (**Figure 19.12a**). This particular virus was named H1N1 for reasons that will be explained shortly. The illness spread rapidly, prompting WHO to declare a global epidemic, or **pandemic**, shortly thereafter. Half a year later, the disease had reached 207 countries, including Canada. It had infected over 600 000 people, killing almost 8000. Public health agencies responded rapidly with guidelines for shutting down schools and other public places, and vaccine development and screening efforts were accelerated (**Figure 19.12b**).

In May 2009, the full genome of H1N1 flu samples from patients in Canada and Mexico was sequenced by a team of scientists led by Dr. Frank Plummer, who was at that time

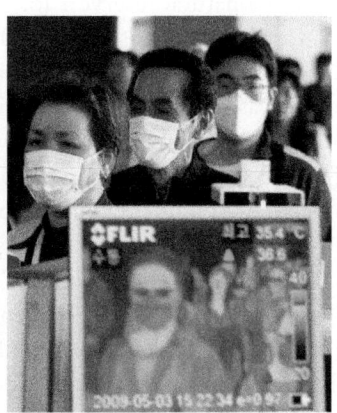

(a) 2009 pandemic H1N1 influenza A virus. Viruses (blue) are seen on an infected cell (green) in this colourized SEM.

(b) 2009 pandemic screening. At a South Korean airport, thermal scans were used to detect passengers with a fever who might have the H1N1 flu.

▲ Figure 19.12 **Influenza in humans.**

the Director General of the National Microbiology Laboratory in Winnipeg. Having the viral genome sequence contributes to understanding how the virus causes disease and helps with development of a vaccine.

How do such viruses burst on the human scene, giving rise to harmful diseases that were previously rare or even unknown? Three processes contribute to the emergence of viral diseases. The first, and perhaps most important, is the mutation of existing viruses. RNA viruses tend to have an unusually high rate of mutation because viral RNA polymerases do not proofread and correct errors in replicating their RNA genomes. Some mutations change existing viruses into new genetic varieties (strains) that can cause disease, even in individuals who are immune to the ancestral virus. For instance, seasonal flu epidemics are caused by new strains of influenza virus genetically different enough from earlier strains that people have little immunity to them. You'll see an example of this process in the Scientific Skills Exercise, where you'll analyze genetic changes in variants of the H1N1 flu virus and correlate them with spread of the disease.

A second process that can lead to the emergence of viral diseases is the dissemination of a viral disease from a small, isolated human population. For instance, AIDS went unnamed and virtually unnoticed for decades before it began to spread around the world. In this case, technological and social factors, including affordable international travel, blood transfusions, sexual promiscuity, and the abuse of intravenous drugs, allowed a previously rare human disease to become a global scourge.

A third source of new viral diseases in humans is the spread of existing viruses from other animals. Scientists estimate that about three-quarters of new human diseases originate in this way. Animals that harbour and can transmit a particular virus but are generally unaffected by it are said to act as a natural reservoir for that virus. For example, the H1N1 virus that caused the 2009 flu pandemic mentioned earlier was likely passed to humans from pigs; for this reason, it was originally called "swine flu."

In general, flu epidemics provide an instructive example of the effects of viruses moving between species. There are three types of influenza virus: types B and C, which infect only humans and have never caused an epidemic, and type A, which infects a wide range of animals, including birds, pigs, horses, and humans. Influenza A strains have caused four major flu epidemics among humans in the last 100 years. The worst was the first one, the "Spanish flu" pandemic of 1918–1919, which killed about 40–50 million people, including many World War I soldiers.

Different strains of influenza A are given standardized names; for example, both the strain that caused the 1918 flu and the one that caused the 2009 pandemic flu are called H1N1. The name identifies which forms of two viral surface proteins are present: hemagglutinin (H) and neuraminidase (N). There are 16 different types of hemagglutinin, a protein that helps the flu virus attach to host cells, and 9 types of neuraminidase, an enzyme that helps release new virus particles from infected cells. Waterbirds have been found that carry viruses with all possible combinations of H and N. Variations of the hemagglutinin protein are used each year to generate vaccines against the strains predicted most likely to occur the next year.

A likely scenario for the 1918 pandemic and others is that the virus mutated as it passed from one host species to another. When an animal like a pig or a bird is infected with more than one strain of flu virus, the different strains can undergo genetic recombination if the RNA molecules making up their genomes mix and match during viral assembly. Pigs were probably the main hosts for recombination that led to the 2009 flu virus, which turns out to contain sequences from bird, pig, and human flu viruses. Coupled with mutation, these reassortments can lead to the emergence of a viral strain capable of infecting human cells. People who have never been exposed to that particular strain before will lack immunity, and the recombinant virus has the potential to be highly pathogenic. If such a flu virus recombines with viruses that circulate widely among humans, it may acquire the ability to spread easily from person to person, dramatically increasing the potential for a major human outbreak.

The many avian flu viruses carried by wild and domestic birds pose a potential long-term threat. A case in point is an H5N1 virus; the first transmission of H5N1 from birds to humans was documented in Hong Kong in 1997. Since then, the overall mortality rate due to H5N1 has been greater than 50% of those infected—an alarming number. Also, the host range of H5N1 is expanding, which provides increasing chances for reassortment between different strains. If the H5N1 avian flu virus evolves so that it can spread easily from person to person, it could represent a major global health threat akin to that of the 1918 pandemic.

How easily could this happen? In 2011, scientists working with ferrets, small mammals that are animal models for human flu, found out that only a few mutations of the avian flu virus would allow infection of cells in the human nasal cavity and windpipe. Furthermore, when the scientists transferred nasal swabs serially from ferret to ferret, the virus became transmissible through the air. Reports of this startling discovery at a scientific conference ignited a firestorm of debate about whether to publish the results. The risks of doing this type of research (what if the new virus escapes or the procedure falls into the hands of bioterrorists?) must be considered in relation to the risks of not doing it—the possibility that we will be unable to combat new, more transmissible viruses because we lack an understanding of how they develop.

Analyzing a Sequence-Based Phylogenetic Tree to Understand Viral Evolution

How Can Sequence Data Be Used to Track Flu Virus Evolution During Pandemic Waves? In 2009, an influenza A H1N1 virus caused a pandemic, and the virus has continued to resurface in outbreaks across the world. Researchers in Taiwan were curious about why the virus kept appearing despite widespread flu vaccine initiatives. They hypothesized that newly evolved variant strains of the H1N1 virus were able to evade human immune system defences. To test this hypothesis, they needed to determine if each wave of the flu outbreak was caused by a different H1N1 variant strain.

How the Experiment Was Done Scientists obtained the genome sequences for 4703 virus isolates collected from patients with H1N1 flu in Taiwan. They compared the sequences in different strains for the viral hemagglutinin (HA) gene, and based on mutations that had occurred, arranged the isolates into a phylogenetic tree (see Figure 26.5 for information on how to read phylogenetic trees).

Dong Yanjun/Imaginechina/AP Images

▲ **H1N1 flu vaccination.**

Data from the Experiment The figure to the left shows a phylogenetic tree; each branch tip is one variant strain of the H1N1 virus with a unique HA gene sequence. The tree is a way to visualize a working hypothesis about the evolutionary relationships between H1N1 variants.

Interpret the Data

1. The phylogenetic tree shows the hypothesized evolutionary relationship between the variant strains of H1N1 virus. The more closely connected two variants are, the more alike they are in terms of HA gene sequence. Each fork in a branch, called a node, shows where two lineages separate due to different accumulated mutations. The length of the branches is a measure of how many sequence differences there are between the variants, indicating how distantly related they are. Referring to the phylogenetic tree, which variants are more closely related to each other: A/Taiwan/1018/2011 and A/Taiwan/552/2011 or A/Taiwan/1018/2011 and A/Taiwan/8542/2009? Explain your answer.

2. The scientists arranged the branches into groups made up of one ancestral variant and all of its descendant, mutated variants. They are colour-coded in the figure. Using Group 11 as an example, trace the lineage of its variants. (a) Do all of the nodes have the same number of branches or branch tips? (b) Are all of the branches in the group the same length? (c) What do these results indicate?

3. The graph at the lower left shows the number of isolates collected (each from an ill patient) on the y-axis and the month and year that the isolates were collected on the x-axis. Each group of variants is plotted separately with a line colour that matches the tree diagram. (a) Which group of variants was the earliest to cause the first wave of H1N1 flu in over 100 patients in Taiwan? (b) Once a group of variants had a peak number of infections, did members of that same group cause another (later) wave of infection? (c) One variant in Group 1 (green, uppermost branch) was used to make a vaccine that was distributed very early in the pandemic. Based on the graphed data, does it look like the vaccine was effective?

4. Groups 9, 10, and 11 all had H1N1 variants that caused a large number of infections at the same time in Taiwan. Does this mean that the scientists' hypothesis, that new variants cause new waves of infection, was incorrect? Explain your answer.

Source: New Variants and Age Shift to High Fatality Groups Contribute to Severe Successive Waves in the 2009 Influenza Pandemic in Taiwan by J.R. Yang et al., from *PLoS ONE*, November 30, 2011, Volume 6(11).

▲ Scientists graphed the number of isolates by the month and year of isolate collection to show the period in which each viral variant was actively causing illness in people.

Data from J.R. Yang et al., New variants and age shift to high fatality groups contribute to severe successive waves in the 2009 influenza pandemic in Taiwan, *PLoS ONE* 6(11): e28288 (2011).

As we have seen, emerging viruses are generally not new; rather, they are existing viruses that mutate, disseminate more widely in the current host species, or spread to new host species. Changes in host behaviour or environmental changes can increase the viral traffic responsible for emerging diseases. For instance, new roads built through remote areas can allow viruses to spread between previously isolated human populations. Also, the destruction of forests to expand cropland can bring humans into contact with other animals that may host viruses capable of infecting humans.

Recently, scientists have become concerned about the possible effects of climate change on worldwide viral transmission. A mosquito-borne virus called chikungunya, which causes an acute illness with fever, rashes, and long-term joint pain, has long been considered a tropical virus. In the mid-2000s, however, it appeared in northern Italy and more recently in southeastern France. Dengue fever, also carried by mosquitoes, has appeared as well in Florida and Portugal, regions where it had not been seen before. The possibility that global climate change has allowed mosquito species carrying these viruses to expand their range is troubling. This is an area of active research by scientists applying climate change models to what is known about the habitat requirements of mosquito species.

Viral Diseases in Plants

More than 2000 types of viral diseases of plants are known, and together they account for an estimated annual loss of $15 billion worldwide due to their destruction of agricultural and horticultural crops. Common signs of viral infection include bleached or brown spots on leaves and fruits, stunted growth, and damaged flowers or roots, all of which can diminish the yield and quality of crops.

Plant viruses have the same basic structure and mode of replication as animal viruses. Most plant viruses discovered thus far, including tobacco mosaic virus (TMV), have an RNA genome. Many have a helical capsid, like TMV, while others have an icosahedral capsid (see Figure 19.4).

Viral diseases of plants spread by two major routes. In the first route, called *horizontal transmission*, a plant is infected from an external source of the virus. Because the invading virus must get past the plant's outer protective layer of cells (the epidermis), a plant becomes more susceptible to viral infections if it has been damaged by wind, injury, or herbivores. Herbivores, especially insects, pose a double threat because they can also act as carriers of viruses, transmitting disease from plant to plant. Moreover, farmers and

gardeners may transmit plant viruses inadvertently on pruning shears and other tools. The other route of viral infection is *vertical transmission*, in which a plant inherits a viral infection from a parent. Vertical transmission can occur in asexual propagation (for example, through cuttings) or in sexual reproduction via infected seeds.

Once a virus enters a plant cell and begins replicating, viral genomes and associated proteins can spread throughout the plant by means of plasmodesmata, the cytoplasmic connections that penetrate the walls between adjacent plant cells (see Figure 36.19). The passage of viral macromolecules from cell to cell is facilitated by virally encoded proteins that cause enlargement of plasmodesmata. Scientists have not yet devised cures for most viral plant diseases. Consequently, research efforts are focused largely on reducing the transmission of such diseases and on breeding resistant varieties of crop plants.

Prions: Proteins as Infectious Agents

The viruses we have discussed in this chapter are infectious agents that spread diseases, and their genetic material is composed of nucleic acids, whose ability to be replicated is well known. Surprisingly, there are also *proteins* that are known to be infectious. Proteins called **prions** appear to cause a number of degenerative brain diseases in various animal species. These diseases include scrapie in sheep; mad cow disease, which has plagued the European beef industry in recent years; and variant Creutzfeldt-Jakob disease in humans, which has caused the death of some 175 people in the United Kingdom since 1996. Prions can be transmitted in food, as may occur when people eat prion-laden beef from cattle with mad cow disease. Kuru, another human disease caused by prions, was identified in the early 1900s among the South Fore natives of New Guinea. A kuru epidemic peaked there in the 1960s, puzzling scientists, who at first thought the disease had a genetic basis. Eventually, however, anthropological investigations ferreted out how the disease was spread: ritual cannibalism, a widespread practice among South Fore natives at that time.

Two characteristics of prions are especially alarming. First, prions act very slowly, with an incubation period of at least 10 years before symptoms develop. The lengthy incubation period prevents sources of infection from being identified until long after the first cases appear, allowing many more infections to occur. Second, prions are virtually indestructible; they are not destroyed or deactivated by heating to normal cooking temperatures. To date, there is no known cure for prion diseases, and the only hope for

Shutterstock

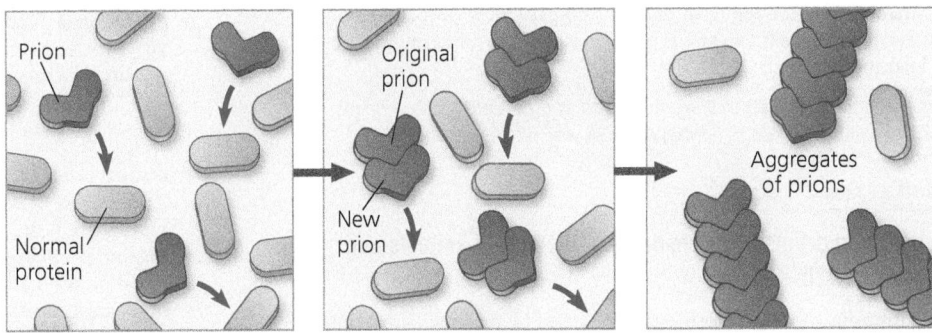

► **Figure 19.13 Model for how prions propagate.** Prions are misfolded versions of normal brain proteins. When a prion contacts a normally folded version of the same protein, it may induce the normal protein to assume the abnormal shape. The resulting chain reaction may continue until high levels of prion aggregation cause cellular malfunction and eventual degeneration of the brain.

developing effective treatments lies in understanding the process of infection.

How can a protein, which cannot replicate itself, be a transmissible pathogen? According to the leading model, a prion is a misfolded form of a protein normally present in brain cells. When the prion gets into a cell containing the normal form of the protein, the prion somehow converts normal protein molecules to the misfolded prion versions. Several prions then aggregate into a complex that can convert other normal proteins to prions, which join the chain (Figure 19.13). Prion aggregation interferes with normal cellular functions and causes disease symptoms. This model was greeted with much scepticism when it was first proposed by Stanley Prusiner in the early 1980s, but it is now widely accepted. Prusiner was awarded the Nobel Prize in 1997 for his work on prions. He has recently proposed that prions are also involved in neurodegenerative diseases such as Alzheimer's and Parkinson's disease. There are many outstanding questions about these small infectious agents.

CONCEPT CHECK 19.3

1. Describe two ways in which a preexisting virus can become an emerging virus.
2. Contrast horizontal and vertical transmission of viruses in plants.
3. **WHAT IF?** TMV has been isolated from virtually all commercial tobacco products. Why, then, is TMV infection not an additional hazard for smokers?

For suggested answers, see Appendix A.

19 Chapter Review

Go to **MasteringBiology®** for Assignments, the eText, and the Study Area with Animations, Activities, Vocab Self-Quiz, and Practice Tests.

SUMMARY OF KEY CONCEPTS

CONCEPT 19.1

A virus consists of a nucleic acid surrounded by a protein coat (pp. 415–417)

- Researchers discovered viruses in the late 1800s by studying a plant disease, tobacco mosaic disease.
- A **virus** is a small nucleic acid genome enclosed in a protein **capsid** and sometimes a membranous **viral envelope** containing viral proteins that help viruses enter cells. The genome may be single- or double-stranded DNA or RNA.

? *Are viruses generally considered living or nonliving? Explain.*

CONCEPT 19.2

Viruses replicate only in host cells (pp. 418–425)

- Viruses use enzymes, ribosomes, and small molecules of host cells to synthesize progeny viruses during replication. Each type of virus has a characteristic **host range**, affected by whether cell-surface proteins are present that viral surface proteins can bind to.

- **Phages** (viruses that infect bacteria) can replicate by two alternative mechanisms: the **lytic cycle** and the **lysogenic cycle**.

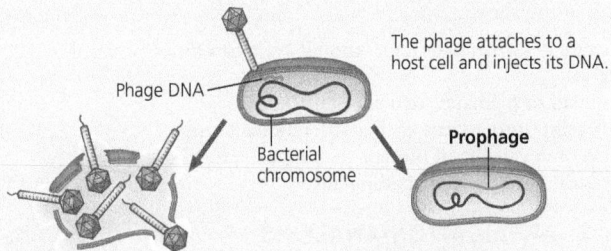

The phage attaches to a host cell and injects its DNA.

Phage DNA

Bacterial chromosome

Prophage

Lytic cycle
- **Virulent** or **temperate phage**
- Destruction of host DNA
- Production of new phages
- Lysis of host cell causes release of progeny phages

Lysogenic cycle
- **Temperate phage** only
- Genome integrates into bacterial chromosome as **prophage**, which (1) is replicated and passed on to daughter cells and (2) can be induced to leave the chromosome and initiate a lytic cycle

- Bacteria have various ways of defending themselves against phage infections, including the CRISPR system.
- Many animal viruses have an envelope. **Retroviruses** (such as **HIV**) use the enzyme **reverse transcriptase** to copy their RNA genome into DNA, which can be integrated into the host genome as a **provirus**.

- Since viruses can replicate only within cells, they probably evolved after the first cells appeared, perhaps as packaged fragments of cellular nucleic acid.

? *Describe enzymes that are not found in most cells but are necessary for the replication of certain types of viruses.*

CONCEPT 19.3

Viruses and prions are formidable pathogens in animals and plants (pp. 425–431)

- Symptoms of viral diseases may be caused by direct viral harm to cells or by the body's immune response. **Vaccines** stimulate the immune system to defend the host against specific viruses. An **epidemic**, a widespread outbreak of a disease, can become a **pandemic**, a global epidemic.
- Outbreaks of emerging viral diseases in humans are usually not new, but rather are caused by existing viruses that expand their host territory. The H1N1 2009 flu virus was a new combination of pig, human, and avian viral genes that caused a pandemic. The H5N1 avian flu virus has the potential to cause a high-mortality flu pandemic.
- Viruses enter plant cells through damaged cell walls (horizontal transmission) or are inherited from a parent (vertical transmission).
- **Prions** are slow-acting, virtually indestructible infectious proteins that cause brain diseases in mammals.

? *What aspect of an RNA virus makes it more likely than a DNA virus to become an emerging virus?*

TEST YOUR UNDERSTANDING

LEVEL 1: KNOWLEDGE/COMPREHENSION

1. Which of the following characteristics, structures, or processes is common to both bacteria and viruses?
   a. metabolism
   b. ribosomes
   c. genetic material composed of nucleic acid
   d. cell division

2. Emerging viruses arise by
   a. mutation of existing viruses.
   b. the spread of existing viruses to new host species.
   c. the spread of existing viruses more widely within their host species.
   d. all of the above.

3. To cause a human pandemic, the H5N1 avian flu virus would have to
   a. spread to primates such as chimpanzees.
   b. develop into a virus with a different host range.
   c. become capable of human-to-human transmission.
   d. become much more pathogenic.

LEVEL 2: APPLICATION/ANALYSIS

4. A bacterium is infected with an experimentally constructed bacteriophage composed of the T2 phage protein coat and T4 phage DNA. The new phages produced would have
   a. T2 protein and T4 DNA.
   b. T2 protein and T2 DNA.
   c. T4 protein and T4 DNA.
   d. T4 protein and T2 DNA.

5. RNA viruses require their own supply of certain enzymes because
   a. host cells rapidly destroy the viruses.
   b. host cells lack enzymes that can replicate the viral genome.
   c. these enzymes translate viral mRNA into proteins.
   d. these enzymes penetrate host cell membranes.

6. **DRAW IT** Redraw Figure 19.9 to show the replicative cycle of a virus with a single-stranded genome that can function as mRNA (a class IV virus).

LEVEL 3: SYNTHESIS/EVALUATION

7. **EVOLUTION CONNECTION**
   The success of some viruses lies in their ability to evolve rapidly within the host. Such a virus evades the host's defences by mutating and producing many altered progeny viruses before the body can mount an attack. Thus, the viruses present late in infection differ from those that initially infected the body. Discuss this as an example of evolution in microcosm. Which viral lineages tend to predominate?

8. **SCIENTIFIC INQUIRY**
   When bacteria infect an animal, the number of bacteria in the body increases in an exponential fashion (graph A). After infection by a virulent animal virus with a lytic replicative cycle, there is no evidence of infection for a while. Then the number of viruses rises suddenly and subsequently increases in a series of steps (graph B). Explain the difference in the curves.

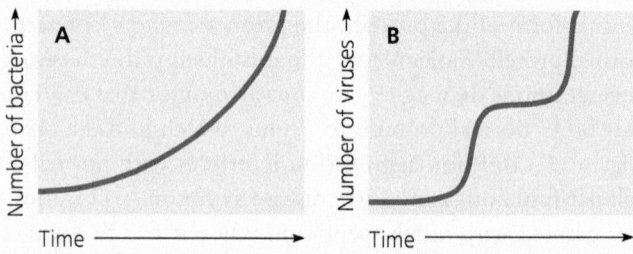

9. **WRITE ABOUT A THEME: ORGANIZATION**
   While viruses are considered by most scientists to be nonliving, they do show some characteristics of life, including the correlation of structure and function. In a short essay (100–150 words), discuss how the structure of a virus correlates with its function.

10. **SYNTHESIZE YOUR KNOWLEDGE**

Nelson Hale/Shutterstock

Oseltamivir (Tamiflu)—an antiviral drug prescribed for influenza—acts to inhibit the enzyme neuraminidase. Explain how this drug could prevent infection in someone exposed to the flu or could shorten the course of flu in an infected patient (the two reasons for which it is prescribed).

For selected answers, see Appendix A.

20
DNA Tools and Biotechnology

KEY CONCEPTS

20.1 DNA sequencing and DNA cloning are valuable tools for genetic engineering and biological inquiry

20.2 Biologists use DNA technology to study gene expression and function

20.3 Cloned organisms and stem cells are useful for basic research and other applications

20.4 The practical applications of DNA-based biotechnology affect our lives in many ways

Dr. Ian Derrington

▲ Figure 20.1 **How can the technique shown in this model advance our sequencing of genomes?**

The DNA Toolbox

The last decade or so has seen some extraordinary feats in biology, among them determination of the complete DNA sequences of several extinct species, including woolly mammoths (see below, left), Neanderthals, and a 700 000-year-old horse. Pivotal to those discoveries was the sequencing of the human genome, essentially completed in 2003. This endeavour marked a turning point in biology because it sparked remarkable technological advances in DNA sequencing.

The first human genome sequence took several years at a cost of 1 billion dollars; the time and cost of sequencing a genome have been in free fall since then. Figure 20.1 shows a model of a sequencing technique in which the nucleotides of a single strand of DNA are passed one by one through a tiny pore in a membrane, and the resulting tiny changes in an electrical current are used to determine the nucleotide sequence. Developers of this technique, which you will learn more about later in the chapter, claim that ultimately we will be able to sequence a human genome in about 6 hours on a $1200 device the size of a pack of gum.

In this chapter, we'll first describe the main techniques for sequencing and manipulating DNA—**DNA technology**—and for using these DNA tools to analyze gene expression. Next, we'll explore advances in cloning organisms and

John Elk III/Alamy Stock Photo

▲ Woolly mammoth, an extinct organism whose genome was sequenced using mummified remains producing stem cells, techniques that have both expanded our basic understanding of biology and enhanced our ability to apply that understanding to global problems. In the last section, we'll survey the practical applications of DNA-based **biotechnology**, the manipulation of organisms or their components to make useful products. Today, the applications of DNA technology affect everything from agriculture to criminal law to medical research. We will end by considering some of the important social and ethical issues that arise as biotechnology becomes more pervasive in our lives.

CONCEPT 20.1

DNA sequencing and DNA cloning are valuable tools for genetic engineering and biological inquiry

The discovery of the structure of the DNA molecule, and specifically the recognition that its two strands are complementary to each other, opened the door for the development of DNA sequencing and other techniques used in biological research today. Key to these techniques is **nucleic acid hybridization**, the base pairing of one strand of a nucleic acid to a complementary sequence on a strand from *another* nucleic acid molecule. In this section, we'll first describe DNA sequencing techniques. Then we'll explore other important methods used in **genetic engineering**, the direct manipulation of genes for practical purposes.

DNA Sequencing

Researchers can exploit the principle of complementary base pairing to determine the complete nucleotide sequence of a DNA molecule, a process called **DNA sequencing**. The DNA is first cut into fragments, and then each fragment is sequenced. Today, sequencing is carried out by machines (**Figure 20.2**). The first automated procedure used a technique called *dideoxyribonucleotide (or dideoxy) chain termination sequencing*. In this technique, one strand of a DNA fragment is used as a template for synthesis of a nested set of complementary fragments; these are further analyzed to yield the sequence, as shown in detail in **Figure 20.3**. Biochemist Frederick Sanger received the Nobel Prize in 1980 for developing this method. Dideoxy sequencing is still used today for routine small-scale sequencing jobs.

In the last 15 years, "next-generation sequencing" techniques have been developed that do not rely on chain termination. Instead, DNA fragments are amplified (copied) to yield an enormous number of identical fragments (**Figure 20.4** on page 436). A specific strand of each fragment is immobilized, and the complementary strand is synthesized, one nucleotide at a time. A chemical technique enables electronic monitors to identify in real time which of the four nucleotides is added; this method is thus called *sequencing by synthesis*. Thousands or hundreds of thousands of fragments, each about 300 nucleotides long, are sequenced in parallel, accounting for the high rate

1 Robots that prepare sequencing reactions and load samples into wells

2 Large –80°C freezers that store DNA

3 Robots that collect bacterial samples for sequencing

4 Thermocyclers used to heat and cool samples for sequencing reactions

5 Robotic sequencers

6 Dispensing robots that prepare reactions

GenomeSciencesCentre

▲ Figure 20.2 **The sequencing lab at Canada's Michael Smith Genome Sciences Centre in British Columbia.**

Research Method

Dideoxy Chain Termination Method for Sequencing DNA

Application The sequence of nucleotides in any DNA fragment of up to 800–1000 base pairs in length can be determined rapidly with machines that carry out sequencing reactions and separate the labelled reaction products by length.

Technique This method is based on synthesis of a nested set of DNA strands complementary to one strand of a DNA fragment. Each new strand starts with the same primer and ends with a dideoxyribonucleotide (ddNTP), a modified deoxyribonucleotide (dNTP). Incorporation of a ddNTP terminates a growing DNA strand because it lacks a 3'—OH group, the site for attachment of the next nucleotide (see Figure 16.14). In the set of new strands, each nucleotide position along the original sequence is represented by strands ending at that point with the complementary ddNTP. Because each type of ddNTP is tagged with a distinct fluorescent label, the identity of the ending nucleotides of the new strands, and ultimately the entire original sequence, can be determined.

1 The fragment of DNA to be sequenced is denatured into single strands and incubated in a test tube with the necessary ingredients for DNA synthesis: a primer designed to base-pair with the known 3' end of the template strand, DNA polymerase, the four dNTPs, and the four ddNTPs, each tagged with a specific fluorescent molecule.

2 Synthesis of each new strand starts at the 3' end of the primer and continues until a ddNTP happens to be inserted instead of the equivalent dNTP. The incorporated ddNTP prevents further elongation of the strand. Eventually, a set of labelled strands of every possible length is generated, with the colour of the tag representing the last nucleotide in the sequence.

3 The labelled strands in the mixture are separated by passage through a gel that allows shorter strands to move through more quickly than longer ones. For DNA sequencing, the gel is in a capillary tube, and its small diameter allows a fluorescence detector to sense the colour of each fluorescent tag as the strands come through. Strands differing in length by as little as one nucleotide can be distinguished from each other.

Results The colour of the fluorescent tag on each strand indicates the identity of the nucleotide at its 3' end. The results can be printed out as a spectrogram, and the sequence, which is complementary to the template strand, can then be read from bottom (shortest strand) to top (longest strand). (Notice that the sequence here begins after the primer.)

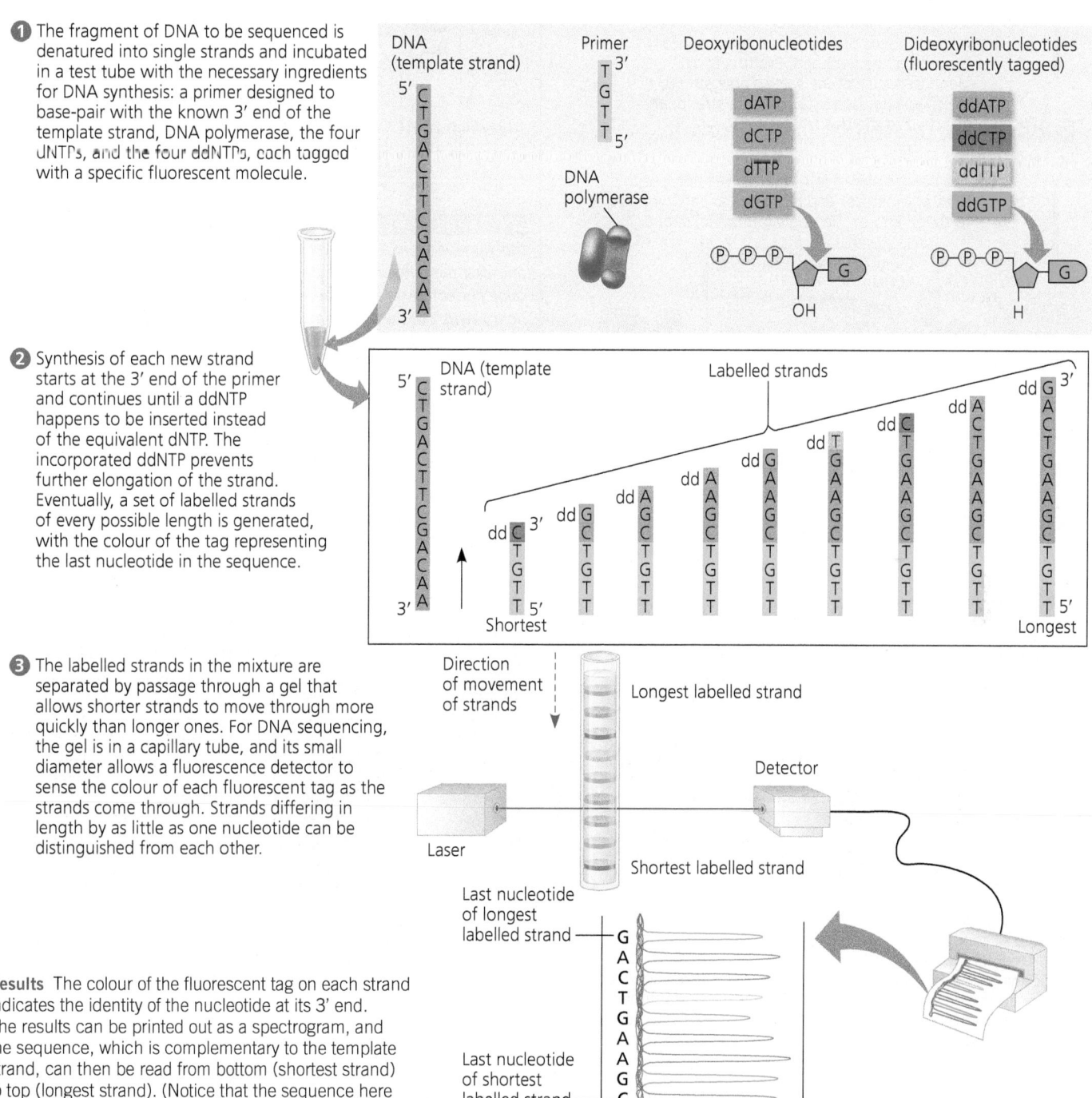

1 Genomic DNA is fragmented, and fragments of 300 base pairs are selected.

2 Each fragment is isolated with a bead in a droplet of aqueous solution.

3 The fragment is copied over and over by a technique called PCR (to be described later). All the 5′ ends of one strand are specifically "captured" by the bead. Eventually, 10^6 identical copies of the same single strand, which will be used as a template strand, are attached to the bead.

4 The bead is placed into a small well along with DNA polymerases and primers that can hybridize to the 3′ end of the single (template) strand.

DNA polymerase

Template strand of DNA

5′ 3′ 5′
Primer

A T G C

Application In current next-generation sequencing techniques, each fragment is 300 nucleotides long; by sequencing the fragments in parallel, about 2 billion nucleotides can be sequenced in 24 hours.

Technique See numbered steps and diagrams.

Results Each of the 2 000 000 wells in the multiwell plate, which holds a different fragment, yields a different sequence. The results for one fragment are shown below as a "flow-gram." The sequences of the entire set of fragments are analyzed using computer software, which "stitches" them together into a whole sequence—here, an entire genome.

4-mer ■ A
        □ T
3-mer ■ G
        □ C
2-mer

1-mer

TTCTGCGAA

INTERPRET THE DATA *If the template strand has two or more identical nucleotides in a row, their complementary nucleotides will be added one after the other in the same flow step. How are two or more of the same nucleotide (in a row) detected in the flow-gram? (See sample on the right.) Write out the sequence of the first 25 nucleotides in the flow-gram above, starting from the left. (Ignore the very short lines.)*

5 The well is one of 2 million on a multiwell plate, each containing a different DNA fragment to be sequenced. A solution of one of the four nucleotides is added to all wells and then washed off. This is done sequentially for all four nucleotides: dATP, dTTP, dGTP, and then dCTP. The entire process is then repeated.

6 In each well, if the next base on the template strand (T in this example) is complementary to the added nucleotide (A, here), the nucleotide is joined to the growing strand, releasing PP_i, which causes a flash of light that is recorded.

7 The nucleotide is washed off and a different nucleotide (dTTP, here) is added. If the nucleotide is not complementary to the next template base (G, here), it is not joined to the strand and there is no flash.

8 The process of adding and washing off the four nucleotides is repeated until every fragment has a complete complementary strand. The pattern of flashes reveals the sequence of the original fragment in each well.

▲ **Figure 20.4 Sequencing by synthesis: Next-generation sequencing.** The method shown starts with individual genomic DNA fragments, each of which is immobilized on a bead and amplified by PCR. The large number of copies is then sequenced using DNA polymerase to synthesize the identical single strands in parallel. In this technique, a flash of light is detected whenever the appropriate nucleotide base is added, determining the sequence base by base. In next-generation sequencing, each fragment is 300 nucleotides long but by sequencing the fragments in parallel, about 2 billion nucleotides can be sequenced in a 24-hour run.

of nucleotides sequenced per hour. This is an example of "high-throughput" DNA technology and is currently the method of choice for studies where massive numbers of DNA samples—even representing an entire genome—are being sequenced.

Next-generation sequencing is rapidly being complemented (or in some cases replaced) by "third-generation sequencing," with each new technique being faster and less expensive than the previous one. In some new methods, the DNA is neither cut into fragments nor amplified. Instead, a single, very long DNA molecule is sequenced on its own. Several groups have developed techniques that move a single strand of a DNA molecule through a very small pore (a *nanopore*) in a membrane, detecting the bases one by one by their interruption of an electrical current. One model of this concept is shown in Figure 20.1, in which the pore is a protein channel embedded in a lipid membrane. (Other researchers are using artificial membranes and nanopores.) The idea is that each type of base interrupts the current for a slightly different length of time. In 2015, after a year of use and review by scientists, the first nanopore sequencer went on the market; this device is the size of a small candy bar and plugs into a USB port. This is only one of many approaches to further increase the rate and cut the cost of sequencing.

Improved DNA sequencing techniques have transformed the way in which we can explore fundamental biological questions about evolution and how life works. Little more than 15 years after the human genome sequence was announced, researchers had completed sequencing thousands of genomes, with tens of thousands in progress. Complete genome sequences have been determined for cells from several cancers, for ancient humans, and for the many bacteria that live in the human intestine. In Chapter 21, you'll learn more about how this rapid acceleration of sequencing technology has revolutionized our study of the evolution of both species and the genome itself. Now, let's consider how individual genes are studied.

Making Multiple Copies of a Gene or Other DNA Segment

A molecular biologist studying a particular gene or group of genes faces a challenge. Naturally occurring DNA molecules are very long, and a single molecule usually carries hundreds or even thousands of genes. Moreover, in many eukaryotic genomes, protein-coding genes occupy only a small proportion of the chromosomal DNA, the rest being noncoding nucleotide sequences. A single human gene, for example, might constitute only 1/100 000 of a chromosomal DNA molecule. As a further complication, the distinctions between a gene and the surrounding DNA are subtle, consisting only of differences in nucleotide sequence. To work directly with specific genes, scientists have developed methods for preparing well-defined segments of DNA in multiple identical copies, a process called **DNA cloning**.

Most methods for cloning pieces of DNA in the laboratory share certain general features. One common approach uses bacteria, most often *Escherichia coli*. Recall from Figure 16.12 that the *E. coli* chromosome is a large circular molecule of DNA. In addition, *E. coli* and many other bacteria also have **plasmids**, small, circular DNA molecules that are replicated separately. A plasmid has only a small number of genes; these genes may be useful when the bacterium is in a particular environment but may not be required for survival or reproduction under most conditions.

To clone pieces of DNA using bacteria, researchers first obtain a plasmid (originally isolated from a bacterial cell and genetically engineered for efficient cloning) and insert DNA from another source ("foreign" DNA) into it (Figure 20.5). The resulting plasmid is now a **recombinant DNA molecule**, a molecule containing DNA from two different sources, very often different species. The plasmid is then returned to a bacterial cell, producing a *recombinant bacterium*. This single cell reproduces through repeated cell divisions to form a clone of cells, a population of genetically identical cells. Because the dividing bacteria replicate the recombinant plasmid and pass it on to their descendants, the foreign DNA and any genes it carries are cloned at the same time. The production of multiple copies of a single gene is a type of DNA cloning called **gene cloning**.

In our example in Figure 20.5, the plasmid acts as a **cloning vector**, a DNA molecule that can carry foreign DNA into a host cell and be replicated there. Bacterial plasmids are widely used as cloning vectors for several reasons they can be readily obtained from commercial suppliers; manipulated to form recombinant plasmids by insertion of foreign DNA in a test tube (referred to as *in vitro*, from the Latin meaning "in glass"), and then easily introduced into bacterial cells. Moreover, recombinant bacterial plasmids (and the foreign DNA they carry) multiply rapidly owing to the high reproductive rate of their host (bacterial) cells. The foreign DNA in Figure 20.5 is a gene from a eukaryotic cell; we will describe in more detail how the foreign DNA segment was obtained later in this section.

Gene cloning is useful for two basic purposes: to make many copies of, or *amplify*, a particular gene and to produce a protein product from it (see Figure 20.5). Researchers can isolate copies of a cloned gene from bacteria for use in basic research or to endow another organism with a new metabolic capability, such as pest resistance. For example, a resistance gene present in one crop species might be cloned and transferred into plants of another species. (Such organisms are called *genetically modified organisms,* or *GMOs*; they will be discussed later in the chapter.) Alternatively,

Bacterium

Bacterial chromosome

Plasmid

Cell containing gene of interest

1 Gene inserted into plasmid (a cloning vector)

Recombinant DNA (plasmid)

Gene of interest

DNA of chromosome ("foreign" DNA)

2 Plasmid put into bacterial cell

Recombinant bacterium

3 Host cell grown in culture to form a clone of cells containing the "cloned" gene of interest

Gene of interest

Protein expressed from gene of interest

Copies of gene

Protein harvested

4 Basic research and various applications

Gene for pest resistance inserted into plants

Human growth hormone treats stunted growth

Gene used to alter bacteria for cleaning up toxic waste

Protein dissolves blood clots in heart attack therapy

▲ **Figure 20.5 Gene cloning and some uses of cloned genes.** In this simplified diagram of gene cloning, we start with a plasmid (originally isolated from a bacterial cell) and a gene of interest from another organism. Only one plasmid and one copy of the gene of interest are shown at the top of the figure, but the starting materials would include many of each.

a protein with medical uses, such as human growth hormone, can be harvested in large quantities from cultures of bacteria carrying a cloned gene for the protein. (We'll describe the techniques for expressing cloned genes later.) Since one gene is only a very small part of the total DNA in a cell, the ability to amplify such rare DNA fragments is crucial for any application involving a single gene.

Using Restriction Enzymes to Make a Recombinant DNA Plasmid

Gene cloning and genetic engineering generally rely on the use of enzymes that cut DNA molecules at a limited number of specific locations. These enzymes, called restriction endonucleases, or **restriction enzymes**, were discovered in the late 1960s by biologists doing basic research on bacteria. Restriction enzymes protect the bacterial cell by cutting up foreign DNA from other organisms or phages (see Concept 19.2).

Hundreds of different restriction enzymes have been identified and isolated. Each restriction enzyme is very specific, recognizing a particular short DNA sequence, or **restriction site**, and cutting both DNA strands at precise points within this restriction site. The DNA of a bacterial cell is protected from the cell's own restriction enzymes by the addition of methyl groups ($-CH_3$) to adenines or cytosines within the sequences recognized by the enzymes.

Figure 20.6 shows how restriction enzymes are used to clone a foreign DNA fragment into a bacterial plasmid. At the top is a bacterial plasmid (like the one in Figure 20.5) that has a single restriction site recognized by a particular restriction enzyme from *E. coli*. As shown in Figure 20.6 most restriction sites are symmetrical. That is, the sequence of nucleotides is the same on both strands when read in the $5' \rightarrow 3'$ direction. The most commonly used restriction enzymes recognize sequences containing four to eight nucleotide pairs. Because any sequence this short usually occurs (by chance) many times in a long DNA molecule, a restriction enzyme will make many cuts in such a DNA molecule, yielding a set of **restriction fragments**. All copies of a given DNA molecule always yield the same set of restriction fragments when exposed to the same restriction enzyme.

The most useful restriction enzymes cleave the sugar-phosphate backbones in the two DNA strands in a staggered manner, as indicated in Figure 20.6. The resulting double-stranded restriction fragments have at least one single-stranded end, called a **sticky end**. These short extensions can form hydrogen-bonded base pairs with complementary sticky ends on any other DNA molecules cut with the same enzyme. The associations formed in this way are only temporary but can be made permanent by **DNA ligase**, which catalyzes the formation of covalent

1 Restriction enzyme cuts the sugar-phosphate backbones at each arrow.

Sticky end

2 DNA fragment from another source is added. Base pairing of sticky ends produces various combinations.

Fragment from different DNA molecule cut by the same restriction enzyme

One possible combination

3 DNA ligase seals the strands.

Recombinant DNA molecule

Recombinant plasmid

▲ **Figure 20.6 Using a restriction enzyme and DNA ligase to make recombinant DNA.** The restriction enzyme in this example (called *Eco*RI) recognizes a specific six-base-pair sequence, the restriction site, and makes staggered cuts in the sugar-phosphate backbones within this sequence, producing fragments with sticky ends. Any fragments with complementary sticky ends can base-pair, including the two original fragments. If the fragments come from different DNA molecules, the ligated product is recombinant DNA.

DRAW IT *The restriction enzyme* Hind*III recognizes the sequence 5'-AAGCTT-', cutting between the two A's. Draw the double-stranded sequence before and after the enzyme cuts it.*

bonds that close up the sugar–phosphate backbones of DNA strands (see Figure 16.16). You can see at the bottom of Figure 20.6 that the ligase-catalyzed joining of DNA from two different sources produces a stable recombinant DNA molecule.

To check the recombinant plasmids after they have been copied many times in host cells (see Figure 20.5), a researcher might cut the products again using the same restriction enzyme, expecting two DNA fragments, one the size of the plasmid and one the size of the inserted DNA. To separate and visualize the fragments, researchers carry out a technique called **gel electrophoresis**, which uses a gel made of a polymer as a molecular sieve to separate out a mixture of nucleic acid fragments by length (**Figure 20.7**).

(a) Each sample, a mixture of different DNA molecules, is placed in a separate well near one end of a thin slab of agarose gel. The gel is set into a small plastic support and immersed in an aqueous, buffered solution in a tray with electrodes at each end. The current is then turned on, causing the negatively charged DNA molecules to move toward the positive electrode.

(b) Shorter molecules are slowed down less than longer ones, so they move faster through the gel. After the current is turned off, a DNA-binding dye is added that fluoresces pink in UV light. Each pink band corresponds to many thousands of DNA molecules of the same length. The horizontal ladder of bands at the bottom of the gel is a set of restriction fragments of known sizes for comparison with samples of unknown length.

▲ **Figure 20.7 Gel electrophoresis.** A gel made of a polymer acts as a molecular sieve to separate nucleic acids or proteins differing in size, electrical charge, or other physical properties as they move in an electric field. In the example shown here, DNA molecules are separated by length in a gel made of a polysaccharide called agarose.

Gel electrophoresis is used in conjunction with many different techniques in molecular biology, including DNA sequencing.

Now that we have discussed the cloning vector in some detail, let's consider the foreign DNA to be inserted. The most common way to obtain many copies of the gene to be cloned is by PCR, described next.

Amplifying DNA: The Polymerase Chain Reaction (PCR) and Its Use in DNA Cloning

Today, most researchers have some information about the sequence of the gene or other DNA segment they want to clone. Using this information, they can start with the entire collection of genomic DNA from the particular species of interest and obtain many copies of the desired gene by using a technique called the **polymerase chain reaction**, or **PCR**. Figure 20.8 illustrates the steps in PCR. Within a few hours, this technique can make billions of copies of a specific target DNA segment in a sample, even if that segment makes up less than 0.001% of the total DNA in the sample.

In the PCR procedure, a three-step cycle brings about a chain reaction that produces an exponentially growing population of identical DNA molecules. During each cycle, the reaction mixture is heated to denature (separate) the strands of the double-stranded DNA and then cooled to allow annealing (hydrogen bonding) of short, single-stranded DNA primers complementary to sequences on opposite strands at each end of the target sequence; finally, a heat-stable DNA polymerase extends the primers in the $5' \rightarrow 3'$ direction. If a standard DNA polymerase were used, the protein would be denatured along with the DNA during the first heating step and would have to be replaced after each cycle. The key to automating PCR was the discovery of an unusual heat-stable DNA polymerase called *Taq* polymerase, named after the bacterial species from which it was first isolated. This bacterial species, *Thermus aquaticus*, lives in hot springs, and the stability of its DNA polymerase at high temperatures is an evolutionary adaptation that enables the enzyme to function at temperatures up to

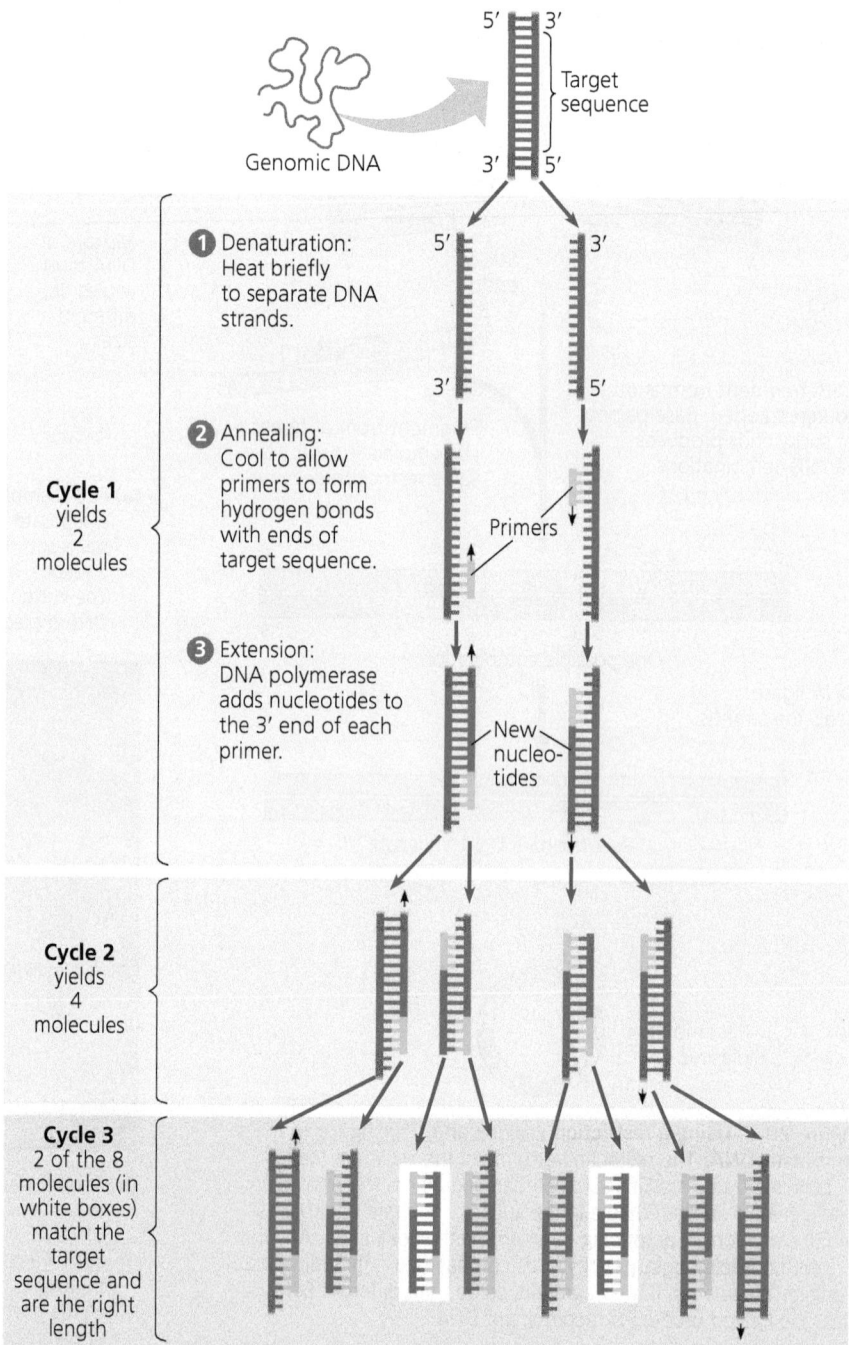

▼ Figure 20.8 **Research Method**

The Polymerase Chain Reaction (PCR)

Application With PCR, any specific segment—the target sequence—within a DNA sample can be copied many times (amplified) within a test tube.

Technique PCR requires double-stranded DNA containing the target sequence, a heat-resistant DNA polymerase, all four nucleotides, and two 15- to 20-nucleotide DNA strands that serve as primers. One primer is complementary to one end of the target sequence on one strand; the second primer is complementary to the other end of the sequence on the other strand.

Genomic DNA

Target sequence

Cycle 1 yields 2 molecules

1 Denaturation: Heat briefly to separate DNA strands.

2 Annealing: Cool to allow primers to form hydrogen bonds with ends of target sequence.

Primers

3 Extension: DNA polymerase adds nucleotides to the 3' end of each primer.

New nucleotides

Cycle 2 yields 4 molecules

Cycle 3 2 of the 8 molecules (in white boxes) match the target sequence and are the right length

Results After three cycles, two molecules match the target sequence exactly. After 30 more cycles, over 1 billion (10^9) molecules match the target sequence.

Source: Figure adapted from *The World Of The Cell,* 3rd Edition, by Wayne M. Becker, Jane B. Reece, and Martin F. Poenie. Copyright © 1996 by Pearson Education, Inc. Adapted and electronically reproduced by permission of Pearson Education, Inc., Upper Saddle River, New Jersey.

95°C. Today, researchers also use a DNA polymerase from the archaean species *Pyrococcus furiosus*. This enzyme, called *Pfu* polymerase, is more accurate and stable, but more expensive than *Taq* polymerase.

PCR is speedy and very specific. Only a minuscule amount of DNA need be present in the starting material, and this DNA can be partially degraded, as long as there are a few copies of the complete target sequence. The key to the high specificity is the pair of primers used for each PCR amplification. The primer sequences are chosen so they hybridize *only* to sequences at opposite ends of the target segment, one on the 3′ end of each strand. (For high specificity, the primers must be at least 15 or so nucleotides long.) With each successive cycle, the number of target segment molecules of the correct length doubles, so the number of molecules equals 2^n, where n is the number of cycles. After 30 or so cycles, about a billion copies of the target sequence are present!

Despite its speed and specificity, PCR amplification cannot substitute for gene cloning in cells to make large amounts of a gene. This is because occasional errors during PCR replication limit the number of good copies and the length of DNA fragments that can be copied. Instead, PCR is used to provide a supply of the specific DNA fragment for cloning. PCR primers are synthesized to include a restriction site at each end of the DNA fragment that matches the site in the cloning vector, and the fragment and vector are cut and ligated together (Figure 20.9). The resulting plasmids are sequenced so that those with error-free inserts can be selected.

Devised in 1985, PCR has had a major impact on biological research and genetic engineering. PCR has been used to amplify DNA from a wide variety of sources: a 40 000-year-old frozen woolly mammoth (see the photo on the first page of this chapter); fingerprints or tiny amounts of blood, tissue, or semen found at crime scenes; single embryonic cells for rapid prenatal diagnosis of genetic disorders (see Figure 14.19); and cells infected with viruses that are difficult to detect, such as HIV. (To test for HIV, viral genes are amplified.) We'll return to applications of PCR later in the chapter.

Expressing Cloned Eukaryotic Genes

Once a gene has been cloned in host cells, its protein product can be expressed in large amounts for research or for practical applications, which we'll explore in Concept 20.4. Cloned genes can be expressed in either bacterial or eukaryotic cells; each option has advantages and disadvantages.

Bacterial Expression Systems

Getting a cloned eukaryotic gene to function in bacterial host cells can be difficult because certain aspects of

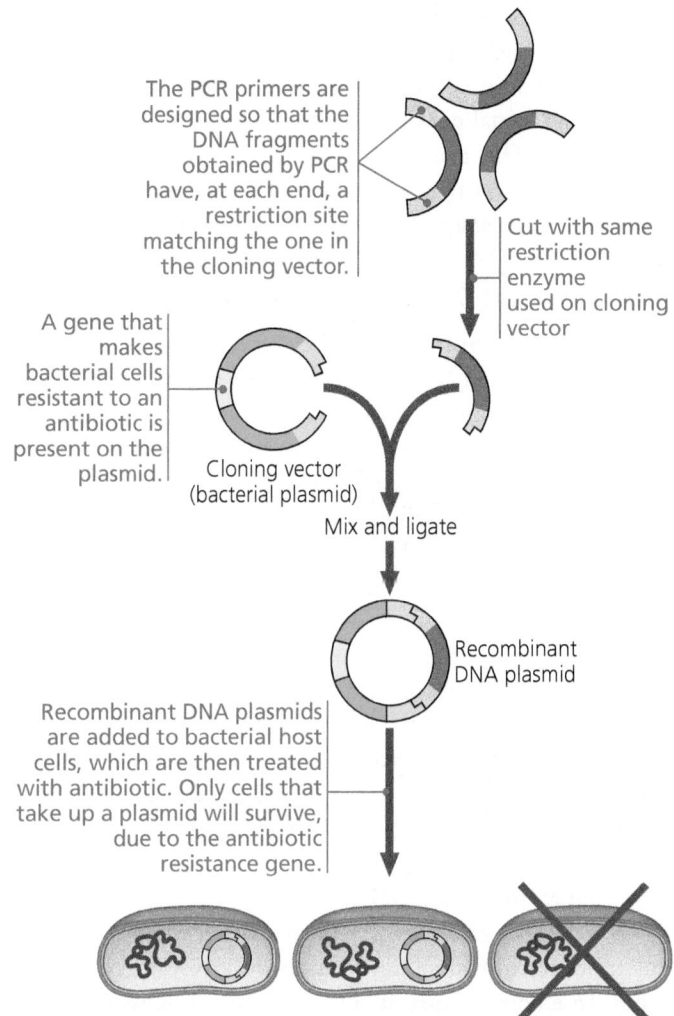

The PCR primers are designed so that the DNA fragments obtained by PCR have, at each end, a restriction site matching the one in the cloning vector.

Cut with same restriction enzyme used on cloning vector

A gene that makes bacterial cells resistant to an antibiotic is present on the plasmid.

Cloning vector (bacterial plasmid)

Mix and ligate

Recombinant DNA plasmid

Recombinant DNA plasmids are added to bacterial host cells, which are then treated with antibiotic. Only cells that take up a plasmid will survive, due to the antibiotic resistance gene.

▲ Figure 20.9 **Use of restriction enzymes and PCR in gene cloning.** This figure takes a closer look at the process shown at the top of Figure 20.5. PCR is used to produce multiple copies of the DNA fragment or gene of interest that will be ligated into a cloning vector, in this case a bacterial plasmid. Added on to the ends of each primer is the restriction site present in the cloning vector. Both the plasmid and the DNA fragments are cut with the same restriction enzyme, combined so the sticky ends can hybridize, ligated together, and introduced into bacterial host cells. The plasmid also contains an antibiotic resistance gene that allows only cells with a plasmid to survive when the antibiotic is present. Other genetic engineering techniques are used to ensure that cells with non recombinant plasmids can be eliminated.

gene expression are different in eukaryotes and bacteria. To overcome differences in promoters and other DNA control sequences, scientists usually employ an **expression vector**, a cloning vector that contains a highly active bacterial promoter just upstream of a restriction site where the eukaryotic gene can be inserted in the correct reading frame. The bacterial host cell will recognize the promoter and proceed to express the foreign gene now linked to that promoter. Such expression vectors allow the synthesis of many eukaryotic proteins in bacterial cells.

Another problem with expressing cloned eukaryotic genes in bacteria is the presence of noncoding regions (introns; see Concept 17.3) in most eukaryotic genes. Introns can make a eukaryotic gene very long and unwieldy, and they prevent correct expression of the gene by bacterial cells, which do not have RNA-splicing machinery. This problem can be surmounted by using a form of the gene that includes only the exons. (This is called *complementary DNA*, or *cDNA*; see Figure 20.11.)

Eukaryotic DNA Cloning and Expression Systems

Molecular biologists can avoid eukaryotic-bacterial incompatibility by using eukaryotic cells such as yeasts as hosts for cloning and expressing eukaryotic genes. Yeasts, single-celled fungi, are as easy to grow as bacteria, and they have plasmids, a rarity among eukaryotes.

In addition to enabling RNA splicing, eukaryotic host cells are advantageous because many eukaryotic proteins will not function unless they are modified after translation—for example, by the addition of carbohydrate groups (glycosylation) or lipid groups. Bacterial cells cannot carry out these modifications, and if the gene product requiring such processing is from a mammal, even yeast cells may not be able to modify the protein correctly. Several cultured cell types have proved successful as host cells for this purpose, including some mammalian cell lines and an insect cell line that can be infected by a virus (called baculovirus) carrying recombinant DNA.

Besides using vectors, scientists have developed other methods for introducing recombinant DNA into eukaryotic cells. In **electroporation**, a brief electrical pulse applied to a solution containing cells creates temporary holes in their plasma membranes, through which DNA can enter. (This technique is now commonly used for bacteria as well.) Alternatively, scientists can inject DNA directly into single eukaryotic cells using microscopically thin needles. Another way to get DNA into plant cells is by using the soil bacterium *Agrobacterium tumefaciens*, as we'll discuss later. Whatever the method, if the introduced DNA is incorporated into a cell's genome by genetic recombination, then it can be expressed by the cell. Expressing different versions of genes in cells allows researchers to study protein function, a topic we'll return to in Concept 20.2.

Cross-Species Gene Expression and Evolutionary Ancestry

EVOLUTION   The ability to express eukaryotic proteins in bacteria (even if the proteins aren't modified properly) is quite remarkable when we consider how different eukaryotic and bacterial cells are. In fact, examples abound of genes that are taken from one species and function perfectly well when transferred into another very different species (see Figure 17.6). These observations underscore the shared evolutionary ancestry of species living today.

One example involves a gene called *Pax-6*, which has been found in animals as diverse as vertebrates and fruit flies. The vertebrate *Pax-6* gene product (the PAX-6 protein) triggers a complex program of gene expression resulting in formation of the vertebrate eye, which has a single lens. Expression of the fly *Pax-6* gene leads to formation of the compound fly eye, which is quite different from the vertebrate eye. When the mouse *Pax-6* gene was cloned and introduced into a fly embryo so that it replaced the fly's own *Pax-6* gene, researchers were surprised to see that the mouse version of the gene led to formation of a compound fly eye (see Figure 50.17). Conversely, when the fly *Pax-6* gene was transferred into a vertebrate embryo—a frog, in this case—a frog eye formed. Although the genetic programs triggered in vertebrates and flies generate very different eyes, the two versions of the *Pax-6* gene can substitute for each other to trigger lens development, evidence of their evolution from a gene in a very ancient common ancestor. Because of their ancient evolutionary roots, all living organisms share the same basic mechanisms of gene expression. This commonality is the basis of many recombinant DNA techniques described in this chapter.

CONCEPT CHECK 20.1

1. MAKE CONNECTIONS   The restriction site for an enzyme called *Pvu*I is the following sequence:

   5'-C G A T C G-3'
   3'-G C T A G C-5'

   Staggered cuts are made between the T and C on each strand. What type of bonds are being cleaved? (See Concept 5.5.)

2. DRAW IT   One strand of a DNA molecule has the following sequence: 5'-CCTTGACGATCGTTACCG-3'. Draw the other strand. Will *Pvu*I (see question 1) cut this molecule? If so, draw the products.

3. What are some potential difficulties in using plasmid vectors and bacterial host cells to produce large quantities of proteins from cloned eukaryotic genes?

4. MAKE CONNECTIONS   Compare Figure 20.8 with Figure 16.20. How does replication of DNA ends during PCR proceed without shortening the fragments each time?

For suggested answers, see Appendix A.

CONCEPT 20.2

Biologists use DNA technology to study gene expression and function

To see how a biological system works, scientists seek to understand the functioning of the system's component parts. Analysis of when and where a gene or group of genes is expressed can provide important clues about their function.

Analyzing Gene Expression

Biologists driven to understand the assorted cell types of a multicellular organism, cancer cells, or the developing tissues of an embryo first try to discover which genes are expressed by the cells of interest. The most straightforward way to do this is usually to identify the mRNAs being made. We'll first examine techniques that look for patterns of expression of specific individual genes. Next, we'll explore ways to characterize groups of genes being expressed by cells or tissues of interest. As you will see, all of these procedures depend in some way on base pairing between complementary nucleotide sequences.

Studying the Expression of Single Genes

Suppose we have cloned a gene that we suspect plays an important role in the embryonic development of *Drosophila melanogaster* (the fruit fly). The first thing we might want to know is which embryonic cells express the gene—in other words, where in the embryo is the corresponding mRNA found? We can detect the mRNA by nucleic acid hybridization with molecules of complementary sequence that we can follow in some way. The complementary molecule, a short single-stranded nucleic acid that can be either RNA or DNA, is called a **nucleic acid probe**. Using our cloned gene as a template, we can synthesize a probe complementary to the mRNA. For example, if part of the sequence on the mRNA were

5′ ···CUCAUCACCGGC··· 3′

then we would synthesize this single-stranded DNA probe:

3′ GAGTAGTGGCCG 5′

Each probe molecule is labelled during synthesis with a fluorescent tag so we can follow it. A solution containing probe molecules is applied to *Drosophila* embryos, allowing the probe to hybridize specifically with any complementary sequences on the many mRNAs in embryonic cells in which the gene is being transcribed. Because this technique allows us to see the mRNA *in situ* (Latin for "in place") in the intact organism, this technique is called ***in situ* hybridization**. Different probes can be labelled with different fluorescent dyes, sometimes with strikingly beautiful results (Figure 20.10).

Other mRNA detection techniques may be preferable for comparing the amounts of a specific mRNA in several samples at the same time—for example, in different cell types or in embryos at different stages of development. One method that is widely used is called the **reverse transcriptase–polymerase chain reaction**, or **RT-PCR**.

RT-PCR begins by turning sample sets of mRNAs into double-stranded DNAs with the corresponding sequences.

The yellow probe hybridizes with mRNAs in cells that are expressing the *wingless* (*wg*) gene, which encodes a secreted signalling protein.

The blue probe hybridizes with mRNAs in cells that are expressing the *engrailed* (*en*) gene, which encodes a transcription factor.

▲ Figure 20.10 **Determining where genes are expressed by *in situ* hybridization analysis.** A *Drosophila* embryo was incubated in a solution containing probes for five different mRNAs, each probe labelled with a different fluorescently coloured tag. The embryo was then viewed from the belly (ventral) side using fluorescence microscopy; the resulting fluorescent micrograph is shown in the middle, above. Each colour marks where a specific gene is expressed as mRNA. The arrows from the groups of yellow and blue cells above the micrograph show a magnified view of nucleic acid hybridization of the appropriately coloured probe to the mRNA. Yellow cells (expressing the *wg* gene) interact with blue cells (expressing the *en* gene); their interaction helps establish the pattern in a body segment. The diagram at the bottom clarifies the eight segments visible in this view.

First, the enzyme reverse transcriptase (from a retrovirus; see Figure 19.10) is used to synthesize a complementary DNA copy of each mRNA in the sample, called a *reverse transcript* (Figure 20.11). Recall that the 3′ end of an mRNA has a stretch of adenine (A) nucleotides called a poly-A tail. This allows a short complementary strand of thymine deoxyribonucleotides (poly-dT) to be added and used as a primer for synthesis of this DNA strand. Following

❶ Reverse transcriptase is added to a test tube containing mRNA isolated from a sample of cells.

❷ Reverse transcriptase makes the first DNA strand using the mRNA as a template and a stretch of dT's as a DNA primer.

❸ mRNA is degraded by another enzyme.

❹ DNA polymerase synthesizes the second strand, using a primer in the reaction mixture. (Several options exist for primers.)

❺ The result is cDNA, which carries the complete coding sequence of the gene but no introns.

▲ **Figure 20.11 Making complementary DNA (cDNA) from eukaryotic genes.** Complementary DNA is DNA made *in vitro* using mRNA as a template for the first strand. Because the mRNA contains only exons, the resulting double-stranded cDNA carries the complete coding sequence of the gene but no introns. Although only one mRNA is shown here, the final collection of cDNAs would reflect all the mRNAs that were present in the cell sample. Figure 20.12 shows how the cDNA of interest is identified.

enzymatic degradation of the mRNA, a second DNA strand, complementary to the first, is synthesized by DNA polymerase. The resulting double-stranded DNA is called **complementary DNA (cDNA)**. (Made from mRNA, cDNA lacks introns and can be used for protein expression in bacteria, as mentioned earlier.). To analyze the timing of expression of the *Drosophila* gene of interest, for example, we would first isolate all the mRNAs from different stages of *Drosophila* embryos and then make cDNA from each stage (Figure 20.12).

Next in RT-PCR is the PCR step (see Figure 20.8). As you will recall, PCR is a way of rapidly making many copies of one specific stretch of double-stranded DNA, using primers that hybridize to the opposite ends of the segment of interest. In our case, we would add primers corresponding to a segment of our *Drosophila* gene, using the cDNA from each embryonic stage as a template for PCR amplification in separate samples. When the products are analyzed on a gel, copies of the amplified region will be observed as bands only in samples that originally contained mRNA

Research Method

RT-PCR Analysis of the Expression of Single Genes

Application RT-PCR uses the enzyme reverse transcriptase (RT) in combination with PCR and gel electrophoresis. RT-PCR can be used to compare gene expression between samples—for instance, in different embryonic stages, in different tissues, or in the same type of cell under different conditions.

Technique In this example, samples containing mRNAs from six embryonic stages of hummingbird were processed as shown below. (The mRNA from only one stage is shown.)

❶ **cDNA synthesis** is carried out by incubating the mRNAs with reverse transcriptase and other necessary components.

❷ **PCR amplification** of the sample is performed using primers specific to the *Drosophila* gene of interest.

❸ **Gel electrophoresis** will reveal amplified DNA products only in samples that contained mRNA transcribed from the specific *Drosophila* gene.

Results The mRNA for this gene first is expressed at stage 2 and continues to be expressed through stage 6. The size of the amplified fragment (shown by its position on the gel) depends on the distance between the primers that were used (not on the size of the mRNA).

from the gene of interest. A recent enhancement called *quantitative PCR* (or *real-time PCR*) uses a fluorescent dye that fluoresces only when bound to a double-stranded PCR product. The newer PCR machines can detect the light and measure the PCR product, thus avoiding the need for electrophoresis while also providing quantitative data, a distinct advantage. RT-PCR can also be carried out with mRNAs collected from different tissues at one time to discover which tissue is producing a specific mRNA.

In the Scientific Skills Exercise, you can work with data from an experiment that analyzed expression of a gene involved in paw formation in the mouse. The study investigated mRNA expression using two techniques. One of these methods was qualitative (*in situ* hybridization), whereas the other approach was quantitative (PCR).

Analyzing Quantitative and Spatial Gene Expression Data

How Is a Particular *Hox* Gene Regulated During Paw Development? *Hox* genes code for transcription factor proteins, which in turn control sets of genes important for animal development (see Concept 21.6 for more information on *Hox* genes). One group of *Hox* genes, the *Hoxd* genes, plays a role in establishing the pattern of the different digits (fingers and toes) at the end of a limb. Unlike the *mPGES-1* gene mentioned in the Chapter 18 Scientific Skills Exercise, *Hox* genes have very large, complicated regulatory regions, including control elements that may be hundreds of kilobases (kb; thousands of nucleotides) away from the gene.

In cases like this, how do biologists locate the DNA segments that contain important elements? They begin by removing (deleting) large segments of DNA and studying the effect on gene expression. In this exercise, you'll compare data from two different but complementary approaches that look at the expression of a specific *Hoxd* gene (*Hoxd13*). One approach quantifies overall expression; the other approach is less quantitative but gives important spatial localization information.

How the Experiment Was Done Researchers interested in the regulation of *Hoxd13* gene expression genetically engineered a set of mice (*transgenic* mice) that had different segments of DNA deleted upstream of the gene. They then compared levels and patterns of *Hoxd13* gene expression in the developing paws of 12.5-day-old transgenic mouse embryos (with the DNA deletions) with those seen in wild-type mouse embryos of the same age.

They used two different approaches: In some mice, they extracted the mRNA from the embryonic paws and quantified the overall level of *Hoxd13* mRNA in the whole paw using quantitative RT-PCR. In another set of the same transgenic mice, they used *in situ* hybridization to pinpoint exactly where in the paws the *Hoxd13* gene was expressed as mRNA. The particular technique that was used caused the *Hoxd13* mRNA to appear blue, or black for the highest mRNA levels.

Data from the Experiment The top-most diagram (upper right) depicts the very large regulatory region upstream of the *Hoxd13* gene. The area between the slashes represents the long stretch of DNA located between the promoter and the regulatory region.

The diagrams to the left of the bar graph show, first, the intact DNA (830 kb) and, next, the three altered DNA sequences. (Each is called a "deletion" because a particular section of DNA has been deleted from it.) A red X indicates the segment (A, B, and/or C) that was deleted in each experimental treatment.

The horizontal bar graph shows the amount of *Hoxd13* mRNA that was present in the digit-formation zone of each mutant 12.5-day-old embryo paw relative to the amount that was in the digit-formation zone of the mouse that had the intact regulatory region (top bar = 100%).

The images on the right are fluorescent micrographs of the embryo paws showing the location of the *Hoxd13* mRNA (stain appears blue or black). The white triangles show the location where the thumb will form.

Interpret the Data

1. The researchers hypothesized that all three regulatory segments (A, B, and C) were required for full expression of the *Hoxd13* gene. By

Blue = *Hoxd13* mRNA; white triangles = future thumb location

measuring the amount of *Hoxd13* mRNA in the embryo paw zones where digits develop, they could measure the effect of the regulatory segments singly and in combination. Refer to the graph to answer these questions, noting that the segments being tested are shown on the vertical axis and the relative amount of *Hoxd13* mRNA is shown on the horizontal axis. (a) Which of the four treatments was used as a control for the experiment? (b) The hypothesis is that all three segments together are required for highest expression of the *Hoxd13* gene. Is this supported by the results? Explain your answer.

2. (a) What is the effect on the amount of *Hoxd13* mRNA when segments B and C are both deleted, compared with the control? (b) Is this effect visible in the blue-stained regions of the *in situ* hybridizations? How would you describe the spatial pattern of gene expression in the embryo paws that lack segments B and C? (You'll need to look carefully at different regions of each paw and how they differ.)

3. (a) What is the effect on the amount of *Hoxd13* mRNA when just segment C is deleted, compared with the control? (b) Is this effect visible in the *in situ* hybridizations? How would you describe the spatial pattern of gene expression in embryo paws that lack just segment C, compared with the control and with the paws that lack segments B and C?

4. If the researchers had only measured the amount of *Hoxd13* mRNA and not done the *in situ* hybridizations, what important information about the role of the regulatory segments in *Hoxd13* gene expression during paw development would have been missed? Conversely, if the researchers had only done the *in situ* hybridizations, what information would have been inaccessible?

Data from "A Regulatory Archipelago Controls Hox Genes Transcription in Digits" by Thomas Montavon, et al., from *CELL*, November 23, 2011, Volume 147(5). © Jane B Reece.

Studying the Expression of Interacting Groups of Genes

A major goal of biologists is to learn how genes act together to produce and maintain a functioning organism. Now that the genomes of a number of species have been sequenced, it is possible to study the expression of large groups of genes—the so-called systems approach. Researchers use what is known about the whole genome to investigate which genes are transcribed in different tissues or at different stages of development. One aim is to identify networks of gene expression across an entire genome.

Genome-wide expression studies can be carried out using **DNA microarray assays**. A DNA microarray consists of tiny amounts of a large number of single-stranded DNA fragments representing different genes fixed to a glass slide in a tightly spaced array, or grid or dots. (The microarray is also called a *DNA chip* by analogy to a computer chip.) Ideally, these fragments represent all the genes of an organism.

The basic strategy in such studies is to isolate the mRNAs made in a cell of interest and use these molecules as templates for making the corresponding cDNAs by reverse transcription. In microarray assays (**Figure 20.13**), these cDNAs are labelled with fluorescent molecules and then allowed to hybridize to a DNA microarray. Most often, the cDNAs from two samples (for example, different tissues) are labelled with molecules that emit different colours and tested on the same microarray. DNA technology makes such studies possible; with automation, they are easily performed on a large scale. Scientists can now measure the expression of thousands of genes at one time.

Alternatively, with the advent of rapid, inexpensive DNA sequencing methods, researchers can now afford to simply sequence the cDNA samples from different tissues or different embryonic stages in order to discover which genes are expressed. This straightforward method is called *RNA sequencing* or *RNA-seq* (pronounced "RNA-seek"), even though it is the cDNA that is actually sequenced. As the price of DNA sequencing plummets, this method is growing more widespread for many applications. In most cases, however, expression of individual genes would still need to be confirmed by RT-PCR.

By uncovering gene interactions and providing clues to gene function, DNA microarray assays may contribute to a better understanding of diseases and suggest new diagnostic techniques or therapies. For instance, comparing patterns of gene expression in breast cancer tumours and noncancerous breast tissue has already resulted in more informed and effective treatment protocols. Ultimately, information from DNA microarray assays should provide a grander view of how ensembles of genes interact to form an organism and maintain its vital systems.

Determining Gene Function

Once they identify a gene of interest, how do scientists determine its function? A gene's sequence can be compared with sequences in other species. If the function of a similar gene in another species is known, one might suspect that the gene product in question performs a comparable task. Data about the location and timing of gene expression may reinforce the suggested function. To obtain stronger evidence, one approach is to disable the gene and then observe the consequences in the cell or organism.

Editing Genes and Genomes

Molecular biologists have long sought techniques for altering, or editing, the genetic material of cells or organisms in a predictable way. In one such technique, called *in vitro* **mutagenesis**, specific mutations are introduced into a cloned gene, and the mutated gene is returned to a cell in such a way that it disables ("knocks out") the normal cellular copies of the same gene. If the introduced mutations alter or destroy the function of the gene product, the phenotype of the mutant cell may help reveal the function of the missing normal protein. Using molecular and genetic techniques worked out in the 1980s, researchers can generate mice with any given gene disabled, in order to study the role of that gene in development and in the adult. Mario Capecchi, Martin Evans, and Oliver Smithies received the Nobel Prize in 2007 for developing this technique.

Over the past 10 years, biologists have developed a powerful new technique for gene editing in living cells and organisms, called the CRISPR-Cas9 system, which is taking the field of genetic engineering by storm. Cas9 is a bacterial protein that

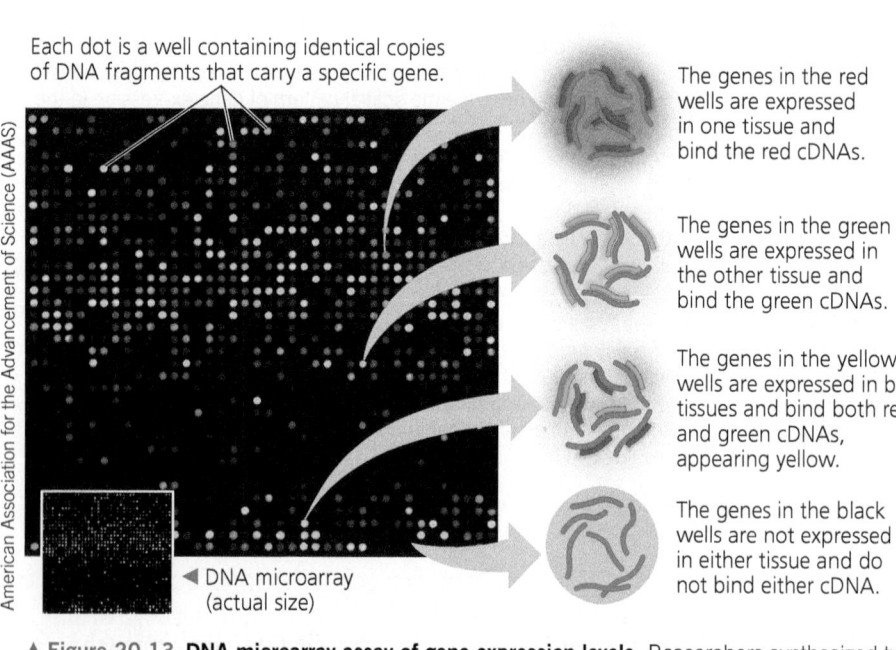

American Association for the Advancement of Science (AAAS)

Each dot is a well containing identical copies of DNA fragments that carry a specific gene.

The genes in the red wells are expressed in one tissue and bind the red cDNAs.

The genes in the green wells are expressed in the other tissue and bind the green cDNAs.

The genes in the yellow wells are expressed in both tissues and bind both red and green cDNAs, appearing yellow.

The genes in the black wells are not expressed in either tissue and do not bind either cDNA.

◄ DNA microarray (actual size)

▲ **Figure 20.13 DNA microarray assay of gene expression levels.** Researchers synthesized two sets of cDNAs, fluorescently labelled red or green, from mRNAs from two different human tissues. These cDNAs were hybridized with a microarray containing 5760 human genes (about 25% of human genes), resulting in the pattern shown here. The intensity of fluorescence at each spot is a measure of the relative expression in the two samples of the gene represented by that spot: Red indicates expression in one sample, green in the other, yellow in both, and black in neither.

helps defend bacteria against bacteriophage infections in a system worked out by Jennifer Doudna and Emmanuelle Charpentier. In bacterial cells, Cas9 acts together with a "guide RNA" made from the CRISPR region of the bacterial system (see Figure 19.8).

Similar to the restriction enzymes described earlier, Cas9 is a nuclease that cuts double-stranded DNA molecules. However, while a given restriction enzyme recognizes only one particular DNA sequence, the Cas9 protein will cut any sequence to which it is directed. Cas9 takes its marching orders from a guide RNA molecule that it binds and uses as a homing device, cutting both strands of any DNA sequence that is complementary to the guide RNA. Scientists have been able to exploit the function of Cas9 by introducing a Cas9-guide RNA complex into a cell they wish to alter (Figure 20.14). The guide RNA in the complex is engineered to be complementary to the "target" gene. Cas9 cuts both strands of the target DNA, and the resulting broken ends of DNA trigger a DNA repair system (similar to that shown in Figure 16.19). When there is no undamaged DNA for the enzymes of the repair system to use as a template, as shown at the bottom left of Figure 20.14a, the repair enzymes introduce or remove random nucleotides while rejoining the ends. Generally, this alters the DNA sequence so that the gene no longer works properly.

This technique is a highly effective way for researchers to knock out a given gene in order to study what that genes does, and has already been used in many organisms, including bacteria, fish, mice, insects, human cells, and various crop plants. Researchers have also modified the technique so that CRISPR-Cas9 can be used to repair a gene that has a mutation (see Figure 20.14b). They introduce a segment from the normal (functional) gene along with the CRISPR-Cas9 system. After Cas9 cuts the target DNA, repair enzymes can use the normal DNA as a template to repair the target DNA at the break point. This is used for gene therapy, which will be discussed later in the chapter.

In another application of CRISPR-Cas9, scientists are attempting to address the global problem of insect-borne diseases by altering genes in the insect so that, for example, it cannot transmit disease. An extra twist to this approach is engineering the new allele so that it is much more highly favoured for inheritance than is the wild-type allele. This is called a gene drive because the biased inheritance of the engineered gene during reproduction rapidly "drives" the new allele through the population.

Other Methods for Studying Gene Function

Another method for silencing expression of selected genes doesn't alter the genome; instead it exploits the phenomenon of **RNA interference (RNAi)**, described in Chapter 18. This experimental approach uses synthetic double-stranded RNA molecules matching the sequence of a particular gene

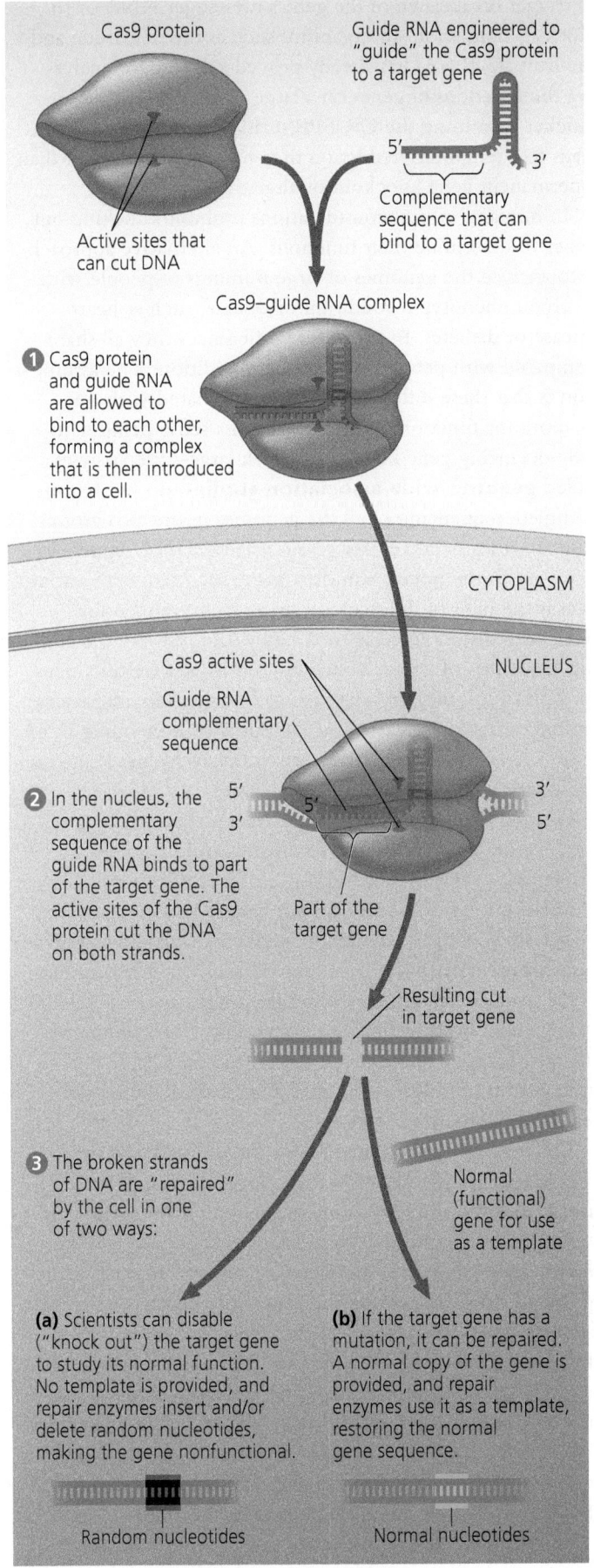

▲ Figure 20.14 **Gene editing using the CRISPR-Cas9 system**

to trigger breakdown of the gene's messenger RNA or to block its translation. In organisms such as the nematode and the fruit fly, RNAi has already proved valuable for analyzing the functions of genes on a large scale. This method is quicker than using the CRISPR-Cas9 system, but it only leads to a temporary reduction of gene expression rather than a permanent gene knockout or alteration.

In humans, ethical considerations prohibit knocking out genes to determine their functions. An alternative approach is to analyze the genomes of large numbers of people with a certain phenotypic condition or disease, such as heart disease or diabetes, to try to find differences they all share compared with people without that condition. The assumption is that these differences may be associated with one or more malfunctioning genes, thus in a sense being naturally occurring gene knockouts. Such large-scale analyses, called **genome-wide association studies**, do not require complete sequencing of all the genomes in the two groups. Instead, researchers test for *genetic markers*, DNA sequences that vary in the population. In a gene, such sequence variation is the basis of different alleles, as we have seen for sickle-cell disease (see Figure 17.25). And just like the coding sequences of genes, noncoding DNA at a specific locus on a chromosome may exhibit small nucleotide differences among individuals. Variations in coding or noncoding DNA sequence among a population are called *polymorphisms* (from the Greek for "many forms").

Among the most useful genetic markers in tracking down genes that contribute to diseases and disorders are single base-pair variations in the genomes of the human population. A single base-pair site where variation is found in at least 1% of the population is called a **single nucleotide polymorphism (SNP**, pronounced "snip"). A few million SNPs occur in the human genome, about once in 100–300 base pairs of both coding and noncoding DNA sequences. It isn't necessary to sequence the DNA of multiple individuals to find SNPs; today they can be detected by very sensitive microarray assays, or PCR.

Once a SNP is identified that is found in all affected people, researchers focus on that region and sequence it. In nearly all cases, the SNP itself does not contribute directly to the disease in question by altering the encoded protein; in fact, most SNPs are in noncoding regions. Instead, if the SNP and a disease-causing allele are close enough, scientists can take advantage of the fact that crossing over between the marker and the gene is very unlikely during gamete formation. Therefore, the marker and gene will almost always be inherited together, even though the marker is not part of the gene (Figure 20.15). SNPs have been found that correlate with diabetes, heart disease, and several types of cancer, and the search is on for genes that might be involved.

The experimental approaches you have learned about thus far focused on working with molecules, mainly DNA

▲ Figure 20.15 **Single nucleotide polymorphisms (SNPs) as genetic markers for disease-causing alleles.** This diagram depicts homologous segments of DNA from two groups of individuals, those in one group having a particular disease or condition with a genetic basis. Unaffected people have a T at a particular SNP locus, while affected people have a C at that locus. A SNP that varies in this way is likely to be closely linked to one or more alleles of genes that contribute to the disease in question.

MAKE CONNECTIONS   *What does it mean for a SNP to be "closely linked" to a disease-causing allele, and how does this allow the SNP to be used as a genetic marker? (See Concept 15.3.)*

and proteins. In a parallel line of inquiry, biologists have been developing powerful techniques for cloning whole multicellular organisms. One aim of this work is to obtain special types of cells, called stem cells, that can give rise to all types of tissues. Being able to manipulate stem cells would allow scientists to use the DNA-based methods previously discussed to alter stem cells for the treatment of diseases. Methods involving the cloning of organisms and production of stem cells are the subject of the next section.

CONCEPT CHECK 20.2

1. Describe the role of complementary base pairing during RT-PCR, DNA microarray analysis, and CRISPR-Cas9 editing.

2. **WHAT IF?** Consider the microarray in Figure 20.13. If a sample from normal tissue is labelled with a green fluorescent dye, and a sample from cancerous tissue is labelled red, what colour spots would represent genes you would be interested in if you were studying cancer? Explain.

For suggested answers, see Appendix A.

CONCEPT 20.3

Cloned organisms and stem cells are useful for basic research and other applications

Along with advances in DNA technology, scientists have been developing and refining methods for cloning whole multicellular organisms from single cells. In this context, cloning produces one or more organisms that are genetically identical to the "parent" that donated the single cell. This is often called *organismal cloning* to differentiate it from gene cloning and, more significantly, from cell cloning—the division of an asexually reproducing cell such as a bacterium into a group of genetically identical cells. (The common theme is that the product is genetically identical to the parent. In fact, the word *clone* comes from the Greek *klon*, meaning "twig.") The current interest in organismal cloning arises primarily from its ability to generate stem cells. A **stem cell** is a relatively unspecialized cell that can both reproduce itself indefinitely and, under appropriate conditions, differentiate into specialized cells of one or more types. Stem cells have great potential for regenerating damaged tissues.

The cloning of plants and animals was first attempted over 50 years ago in experiments designed to answer basic biological questions. For example, researchers wondered if all the cells of an organism have the same genes or whether cells lose genes during the process of differentiation (see Concept 18.4). One way to answer this question is to see whether a differentiated cell can generate a whole organism—in other words, whether cloning an organism is possible. Let's discuss these early experiments before we consider more recent progress in organismal cloning and procedures for producing stem cells.

Cloning Plants: Single-Cell Cultures

The successful cloning of whole plants from single differentiated cells was accomplished during the 1950s by F. C. Steward and his students at Cornell University, who worked with carrot plants. They found that differentiated cells taken from the root (the carrot) and incubated in culture medium could grow into normal adult plants, each genetically identical to the parent plant. These results showed that differentiation does not necessarily involve irreversible changes in the DNA. In plants, at least, mature cells can "dedifferentiate" and then give rise to all the specialized cell types of the organism. Any cell with this potential is said to be **totipotent**.

Plant cloning is used extensively in agriculture. For plants, such as orchids, cloning is the only commercially practical means of reproducing plants. In other cases, cloning has been used to reproduce a plant with valuable characteristics, such as resistance to plant pathogens. In fact, you yourself may be a plant cloner: If you have ever grown a new plant from a cutting, you have practised cloning!

Cloning Animals: Nuclear Transplantation

Differentiated cells from animals generally do not divide in culture, much less develop into the multiple cell types of a new organism. Therefore, early researchers had to use a different approach to answer the question of whether differentiated animal cells are totipotent. Their approach was to remove the nucleus of an egg (creating an *enucleated* egg) and replace it with the nucleus of a differentiated cell,

a procedure called *nuclear transplantation*, now more commonly called *somatic cell nuclear transfer*. If the nucleus from the differentiated donor cell retains its full genetic capability, then it should be able to direct development of the recipient cell into all the tissues and organs of an organism.

Such experiments were conducted on one species of frog (*Rana pipiens*) by Robert Briggs and Thomas King in the 1950s and on another frog species (*Xenopus laevis*) by John Gurdon in the 1970s (**Figure 20.16**). These researchers

▼ Figure 20.16 | Inquiry

Can the nucleus from a differentiated animal cell direct development of an organism?

Experiment John Gurdon and colleagues at Oxford University, in England, destroyed the nuclei of frog (*Xenopus laevis*) eggs by exposing the eggs to ultraviolet light. They then transplanted nuclei from cells of frog embryos and tadpoles into the enucleated eggs.

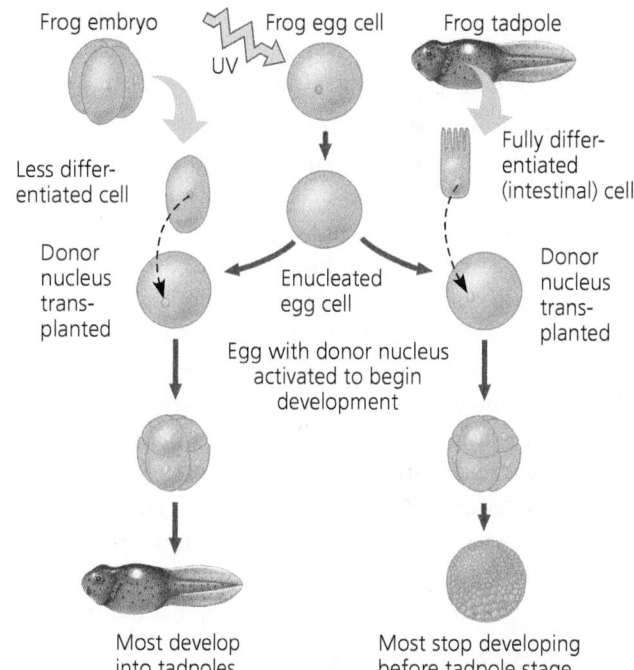

Frog embryo   Frog egg cell   Frog tadpole
UV

Less differentiated cell   Fully differentiated (intestinal) cell

Donor nucleus transplanted   Enucleated egg cell   Donor nucleus transplanted

Egg with donor nucleus activated to begin development

Most develop into tadpoles.   Most stop developing before tadpole stage.

Results When the transplanted nuclei came from an early embryo, whose cells are relatively undifferentiated, most of the recipient eggs developed into tadpoles. But when the nuclei came from the fully differentiated intestinal cells of a tadpole, fewer than 2% of the eggs developed into normal tadpoles, and most of the embryos stopped developing at a much earlier stage.

Conclusion The nucleus from a differentiated frog cell can direct development of a tadpole. However, its ability to do so decreases as the donor cell becomes more differentiated, presumably because of changes in the nucleus.

Source: Based on J. B. Gurdon et al., The developmental capacity of nuclei transplanted from keratinized cells of adult frogs, *Journal of Embryology and Experimental Morphology* 34:93–112 (1975). © Jane B Reece.

WHAT IF? *If each cell in a four-cell embryo were already so specialized that it was not totipotent, what results would you predict for the experiment on the left side of the figure?*

transplanted a nucleus from an embryonic or tadpole cell into an enucleated egg of the same species. In Gurdon's experiments, the transplanted nucleus was often able to support normal development of the egg into a tadpole. However, he found that the potential of a transplanted nucleus to direct normal development was inversely related to the age of the donor: the older the donor nucleus, the lower the percentage of normal tadpoles (see Figure 20.16).

From these results, Gurdon concluded that something in the nucleus *does* change as animal cells differentiate. In frogs and most other animals, nuclear potential tends to be restricted more and more as embryonic development and cell differentiation progress. These were foundational experiments that ultimately led to stem cell technology, and Gurdon received the 2012 Nobel Prize in Medicine for this work.

Reproductive Cloning of Mammals

In addition to cloning frogs, researchers were able to clone mammals using early embryonic cells as a source of donor nuclei. Until about 20 years ago, though, it was not known whether a nucleus from a fully differentiated cell could be reprogrammed successfully to act as a donor nucleus. In 1997, researchers in Scotland announced the birth of Dolly, a lamb cloned from an adult sheep by nuclear transfer from a differentiated mammary gland cell (Figure 20.17). Using a technique related to that in Figure 20.16, the researchers implanted early embryos into surrogate mothers. Out of several hundred embryos, one successfully completed normal development, and Dolly was born, a genetic clone of the nucleus donor. At the age of 6, Dolly suffered complications from a lung disease usually seen only in much older sheep and was euthanized. Dolly's premature death, as well as an arthritic condition, led to speculation that her cells were in some way not quite as healthy as those of a normal sheep, possibly reflecting incomplete reprogramming of the original transplanted nucleus. Reprogramming involves epigenetic changes that lead to changes in chromatin structure (see Concept 18.2), to be discussed shortly.

Since that time, researchers have cloned numerous other mammals, including mice, cats, cows, horses, pigs, dogs, and monkeys. In most cases, their goal has been the production of new individuals; this is known as *reproductive cloning*. We have already learned a lot from such experiments. For example, cloned animals of the same species do *not* always look or behave identically. In a herd of cows cloned from the same line of cultured cells, certain cows are dominant in behaviour and others are more submissive. Another example of nonidentity in clones is the first cloned cat, named CC for Carbon Copy (Figure 20.18). She has a calico coat, like her single female parent, but the colour and pattern are different because of random X chromosome inactivation, which is a normal occurrence during embryonic development (see Figure 15.8). And identical human twins, which are naturally occurring "clones," are always slightly different. Clearly, environmental influences and random phenomena play a significant role during development.

Faulty Gene Regulation in Cloned Animals Due to Epigenetic Differences

In most nuclear transplantation studies thus far, only a small percentage of cloned embryos develop normally to birth. And like Dolly, many cloned animals exhibit defects. Cloned mice, for instance, are prone to obesity, pneumonia, liver failure, and premature death. Scientists assert that even cloned animals that appear normal are likely to have subtle defects.

Researchers have uncovered some reasons for the low efficiency of cloning and the high incidence of abnormalities. In the nuclei of fully differentiated cells, a small subset of genes is turned on and expression of the rest of the genes is repressed. This regulation often is the result of epigenetic changes in chromatin, such as acetylation

▲ Figure 20.17 **Reproductive cloning of a mammal by nuclear transfer.** Dolly, shown here as a lamb, has a very different appearance from her surrogate mother, standing beside her.

▲ Figure 20.18 **CC, the first cloned cat, and her single parent.** Rainbow (left) donated the nucleus in a cloning procedure that resulted in CC (right). However, the two cats are not identical: Rainbow is a classic calico cat with orange patches on her fur and has a "reserved personality," while CC has a grey and white coat and is more playful.

of histones or methylation of DNA (see Figure 18.7). During the nuclear transfer procedure, many of these changes must be reversed in the later-stage nucleus from a donor animal for genes to be expressed or repressed appropriately in early stages of development. Researchers have found that the DNA in cells from cloned embryos, like that of differentiated cells, often has more methyl groups than does the DNA in equivalent cells from normal embryos of the same species. This finding suggests that the reprogramming of donor nuclei requires more accurate and complete chromatin restructuring than occurs during cloning procedures. Because DNA methylation helps regulate gene expression, misplaced or extra methyl groups in the DNA of donor nuclei may interfere with the pattern of gene expression necessary for normal embryonic development. In fact, the success of a cloning attempt may depend in large part on whether or not the chromatin in the donor nucleus can be artificially modified to resemble that of a newly fertilized egg.

▼ Figure 20.19 | **Impact**

Stem Cells: A Canadian Discovery

In Toronto in 1960, two Canadian scientists, Drs. James Till and Ernest McCulloch, made a discovery that held enormous potential: stem cells. While researching bone marrow cells and blood production, Drs. Till and McCulloch discovered a single cell that had the capacity to produce other types of cells while also self-replicating. This discovery laid the foundation for stem cell science in Canada, and was followed by the discovery of neural stem cells, cancer stem cells, and skin stem cells decades later.

Peter Foley/Corbis Images

Why It Matters Stem cells hold significant promise and may help in the treatment of a range of diseases, including arthritis, type 1 diabetes, muscular dystrophy, Parkinson's disease, and cancer. Drs. Till and McCulloch's discovery not only paved the way for new treatments, including bone marrow transplantation, but it also completely changed our perception of human development.

Further Reading J. Till and E. McCulloch, A direct measurement of the radiation sensitivity of normal mouse bone marrow cells, *Radiation Research* 14:1419–1430 (1961); A. Becker, E. McCulloch, and J. Till, Cytological demonstration of the clonal nature of spleen colonies derived from transplanted mouse marrow cells, *Nature* 197:452–454 (1963).

MAKE CONNECTIONS *Stem cells have the potential to differentiate into 200 different types of cells in the human body. What diseases, other than those listed above, do you think stem cells could provide a potential treatment for?*

① A stem cell can divide into another stem cell and a precursor cell (or into two stem cells or two precursor cells).

Stem cell

Cell division

Stem cell   and   Precursor cell

② A precursor cell can differentiate into one of several cell types, depending on external factors. This example is from a stem cell derived from bone marrow.

Fred Hossler/Corbis Images

SPL/Science Source

Mopic/Fotolia

Fat cells   or   Bone cells   or   White blood cells

▲ Figure 20.20 **How stem cells maintain their own population and generate differentiated cells.**

Stem Cells of Animals

Progress in cloning mammalian embryos, including primates, has heightened speculation about the cloning of humans, which has not yet been achieved past very early embryonic stages. The main reason researchers have been trying to clone human embryos is not for reproduction, but for the production of stem cells to treat human diseases. Stem cells were discovered in 1960 in Toronto, Ontario, by Drs. James Till and Ernest McCulloch (Figure 20.19). Recall that a stem cell is a relatively unspecialized cell that can both reproduce itself indefinitely and, under appropriate conditions, differentiate into specialized cells of one or more types (Figure 20.20). Thus, stem cells are able to both replenish their own population and generate cells that travel down specific differentiation pathways.

Embryonic and Adult Stem Cells

Many early animal embryos contain stem cells capable of giving rise to differentiated cells of any type. Stem cells can be isolated from early embryos at a stage called the blastula stage or its human equivalent, the blastocyst stage. In culture, these *embryonic stem (ES) cells* reproduce indefinitely; and depending on culture conditions, they can be made to differentiate into a wide variety of specialized cells (Figure 20.21), including even eggs and sperm.

The adult body also has stem cells, which serve to replace nonreproducing specialized cells as needed. In contrast to ES cells, *adult stem cells* are not able to give rise to all cell types in the organism, though they can generate multiple types. For example, one of the several types

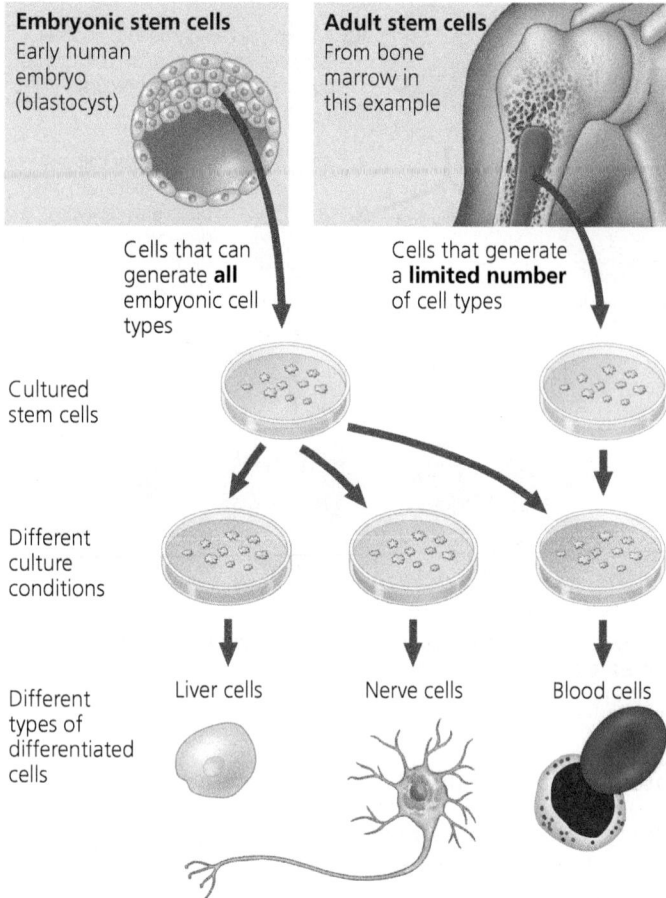

Embryonic stem cells
Early human embryo (blastocyst)

Adult stem cells
From bone marrow in this example

Cells that can generate **all** embryonic cell types

Cells that generate a **limited number** of cell types

Cultured stem cells

Different culture conditions

Different types of differentiated cells

Liver cells

Nerve cells

Blood cells

▲ **Figure 20.21** **Working with stem cells.** Animal stem cells, which can be isolated from early embryos or adult tissues and grown in culture, are self-perpetuating, relatively undifferentiated cells. Embryonic stem cells are easier to grow than adult stem cells and can theoretically give rise to *all* types of cells in an organism. The range of cell types that can arise from adult stem cells is not yet fully understood.

of stem cells in bone marrow can generate all the different kinds of blood cells (see Figure 20.21), and another type of bone marrow stem cell can differentiate into bone, cartilage, fat, muscle, and the linings of blood vessels. To the surprise of many, the adult brain has been found to contain stem cells that continue to produce certain kinds of nerve cells there. Researchers have also reported finding stem cells in skin, hair, eyes, and dental pulp. Although adult animals have only tiny numbers of stem cells, scientists are learning to identify and isolate these cells from various tissues and, in some cases, to grow them in culture. With the right culture conditions (for instance, the addition of specific growth factors), cultured stem cells from adult animals have been made to differentiate into multiple types of specialized cells, although none are as versatile as ES cells.

Research with embryonic or adult stem cells is a source of valuable data about differentiation and has enormous potential for medical applications. The ultimate aim is to

supply cells for the repair of damaged or diseased organs: for example, insulin-producing pancreatic cells for people with type 1 diabetes or certain kinds of brain cells for people with Parkinson's disease or Huntington's disease. Adult stem cells from bone marrow have long been used in bone marrow transplants as a source of immune system cells in patients whose own immune systems are nonfunctional because of genetic disorders or radiation treatments for cancer.

The developmental potential of adult stem cells is limited to certain tissues. ES cells hold more promise than adult stem cells for most medical applications because ES cells are **pluripotent**, capable of differentiating into many different cell types. In 2013, a research group reported that they had established ES cell lines from human blastocysts produced by transferring a nucleus from a differentiated cell into an enucleated egg. Prior to that report, cells were obtained only from embryos donated by patients undergoing infertility treatments or from long-term cell cultures originally established with cells isolated from donated embryos, which raises ethical and political issues. Although the techniques for cloning early human embryos are still being optimized, they represent a potential new source for ES cells that may be less controversial. Furthermore, with a donor nucleus from a person with a particular disease, researchers should be able to produce ES cells that match the patient and are thus not rejected by his or her immune system when used for treatment. When the main aim of cloning is to produce ES cells to treat disease, the process is called *therapeutic cloning*. Although most people believe that reproductive cloning of humans is unethical, opinions vary about the morality of therapeutic cloning.

Induced Pluripotent Stem (iPS) Cells

Resolving the debate now seems less urgent because researchers have learned to turn back the clock in fully differentiated cells, reprogramming them to act like ES cells. The accomplishment of this feat, which posed formidable obstacles, was announced in 2007, first by labs using mouse skin cells and then by additional groups using cells from human skin and other organs or tissues. In all these cases, researchers transformed the differentiated cells into a type of ES cell by using a retrovirus to introduce extra, cloned copies of four "stem cell" master regulatory genes. The "deprogrammed" cells are known as *induced pluripotent stem (iPS) cells* because, in using this fairly simple laboratory technique to return them to their undifferentiated state, pluripotency has been restored. The experiments that first transformed human differentiated cells into iPS cells are described in **Figure 20.22**. Shinya Yamanaka received the 2012 Nobel Prize in Medicine for this work, shared with John Gurdon, whose work you read about in Figure 20.16.

Inquiry

Can a fully differentiated human cell be "deprogrammed" to become a stem cell?

Experiment Shinya Yamanaka and colleagues at Kyoto University, in Japan, used a retroviral vector to introduce four genes into fully differentiated human skin fibroblast cells. The cells were then cultured in a medium that would support growth of stem cells.

Stem cell

Precursor cell

Oct3/4

Sox2

Four "stem cell" master regulator genes were introduced, using the retroviral cloning vector.

Klf4

c-Myc

Skin fibroblast cell

Induced pluripotent stem (iPS) cell

Results Two weeks later, the cells resembled embryonic stem cells in appearance and were actively dividing. Their gene expression patterns, gene methylation patterns, and other characteristics were also consistent with those of embryonic stem cells. The iPS cells were able to differentiate into heart muscle cells, as well as other cell types.

Conclusion The four genes induced differentiated skin cells to become pluripotent stem cells, with characteristics of embryonic stem cells.

Source: Based on K. Takahashi et al., Induction of pluripotent stem cells from adult human fibroblasts by defined factors, *Cell* 131:861–872 (2007). © Jane B Reece.

WHAT IF? *Patients with diseases such as heart disease, diabetes, or Alzheimer's could have their own skin cells reprogrammed to become iPS cells. Once procedures have been developed for converting iPS cells into heart, pancreatic, or nervous system cells, the patients' own iPS cells might be used to treat their disease. When organs are transplanted from a donor to a diseased recipient, the recipient's immune system may reject the transplant, a condition with serious and often fatal consequences. Would using iPS cells be expected to carry the same risk? Why or why not? Given that these cells are actively dividing, undifferentiated cells, what risks might this procedure carry?*

By many criteria, iPS cells can perform most of the functions of ES cells, but there are some differences in gene expression and other cellular functions, such as cell division. At least until these differences are fully understood, the study of ES cells will continue to make important contributions to the development of stem cell therapies. (In fact, it is likely that ES cells will always be a focus of basic research as well.) In the meantime, work is proceeding using the iPS cells that have been experimentally produced.

There are two major potential uses for human iPS cells. First, cells from patients suffering from diseases can be reprogrammed to become iPS cells, which can act as model cells for studying the disease and potential treatments. Human iPS cell lines have already been developed from individuals with type 1 diabetes, Parkinson's disease, Huntington's disease, Down syndrome, and many other diseases. Second, in the field of regenerative medicine, a patient's own cells could be reprogrammed into iPS cells and then used to replace nonfunctional tissues, such as insulin-producing cells of the pancreas.

In fact, in 2014 two research groups described successful methods for growing insulin-producing cells from both iPS cells and ES cells. Before using these in patients, however, they will have to develop a way to ensure these cells are not destroyed by the patients' immune system (the original cause of type 1 diabetes, where the immune system malfunctions).

In another surprising development, researchers have been able to identify genes that can directly reprogram a differentiated cell into another type of differentiated cell without passing through a pluripotent state. In the first reported example, one type of cell in the pancreas was transformed into another type. However, the two types of cells do not need to be very closely related: Another research group has been able to directly reprogram a skin fibroblast into a nerve cell. Development techniques that direct iPS cells or even fully differentiated cells to become specific cell types for regenerative medicine is an area of intense research, one that has already seen some success. The iPS cells created in this way could eventually provide tailor-made "replacement" cells for patients without using any human eggs or embryos, thus circumventing most ethical objections.

Alternatively, instead of creating "replacement" cells, new treatments may consist of activating one's own stem cells inside the body. Recently, success was achieved in this area when Dr. Michael Rudnicki and colleagues at the Ottawa Hospital Research Institute showed promise in treating a mouse model of Duchenne muscular dystrophy (see Concept 15.2) with a protein injection that stimulated stem cell proliferation (**Figure 20.23**).

▼ Figure 20.23 | **Impact**

Inducing stem cell growth to treat disease

Dr. Michael Rudnicki, a senior scientist at the Sprott Centre for Stem Cell Research at the Ottawa Hospital Research Institute, led the team that first discovered adult muscle stem cells, called satellite cells. Dr. Rudnicki and colleagues subsequently discovered that these cells are stimulated when they bind to a protein called Wnt7a. Recently, his team showed that injecting this protein into a mouse model of Duchenne muscular dystrophy (see Concept 15.2) resulted in an increase in muscle size and strength.

Normal muscle (left) and muscle from a patient with muscular dystrophy (right).

Why It Matters Duchenne muscular dystrophy affects one out of every 3500 newborn males and is characterized by a progressive weakening of the muscles and loss of coordination. Currently, no cure exists and most patients lose the ability to walk prior to age 12, with death occurring prior to age 25. Dr. Rudnicki's research could lead to a treatment for this disease, as well as other muscle-wasting diseases and muscle atrophy.

Further Reading J. Von Maltzahn, J. M. Renaud, G. Parisec, and M. A. Rudnicki, Wnt7a treatment ameliorates muscular dystrophy, *PNAS*, 109:20614–20619 (2012).

MAKE CONNECTIONS *How is the proposed treatment above, using a protein injection, different from an injection of human iPS cells? When organs are transplanted from a donor to a diseased recipient, the recipient's immune system may reject the transplant, a condition with serious and often fatal consequences. Would using a protein injection of Wnt7A or human iPS cells be expected to carry the same risk? Why or why not?*

CONCEPT CHECK 20.3

1. Based on current knowledge, how would you explain the difference in the percentage of tadpoles that developed from the two kinds of donor nuclei in Figure 20.16?

2. A few companies in China and South Korea provide a service for cloning dogs, using cells from their clients' pets to provide nuclei in procedures like that in Figure 20.16. Should their clients expect the clone to look identical to their original pet? Why or why not? What ethical questions does this bring up?

3. **MAKE CONNECTIONS** Based on what you know about muscle differentiation (see Figure 18.18) and genetic engineering, propose the first experiment you might try if you wanted to direct an embryonic stem cell or iPS cell to develop into a muscle cell.

For suggested answers, see Appendix A.

CONCEPT 20.4

The practical applications of DNA-based biotechnology affect our lives in many ways

DNA technology is in the news almost every day. Most often, the topic is a new and promising application in medicine, but this is just one of numerous fields benefitting from DNA technology and genetic engineering.

Medical Applications

One important use of DNA technology is the identification of human genes whose mutation plays a role in genetic diseases. These discoveries may lead to ways of diagnosing, treating, and even preventing such conditions. DNA technology is also contributing to our understanding of "nongenetic" diseases, from arthritis to AIDS, since a person's genes influence susceptibility to these diseases. Furthermore, diseases of all sorts involve changes in gene expression within the affected cells and often within the patient's immune system. By using DNA microarray assays (Figure 20.13) or other techniques to compare gene expression in healthy and diseased tissues, researchers are finding genes that are turned on or off in particular diseases. These genes and their products are potential targets for prevention or therapy.

Diagnosis and Treatment of Diseases

A new chapter in the diagnosis of infectious diseases has been opened by DNA technology, in particular the use of PCR and labelled nucleic acid probes to track down pathogens. For example, because the sequence of the RNA genome of HIV is known, RT-PCR can be used to amplify, and thus detect, HIV RNA in blood or tissue samples (see Figure 20.12). RT-PCR is often the best way to detect an otherwise elusive infective agent.

Medical scientists can now diagnose hundreds of human genetic disorders by using PCR with primers that target the genes associated with these disorders. The amplified DNA product is then sequenced to reveal the presence or absence of the disease-causing mutation. Among the genes for human diseases that have been identified are those for sickle-cell disease, hemophilia, cystic fibrosis, Huntington's disease, and Duchenne muscular dystrophy. Individuals afflicted with such diseases can often be identified before the onset of symptoms, even before birth (see Figure 14.19). PCR can also be used to identify symptomless carriers of potentially harmful recessive alleles.

As you learned earlier, genome-wide association studies have pinpointed SNPs (single nucleotide polymorphisms) that are linked to disease-causing alleles. Individuals can be tested by PCR and sequencing for a SNP that is correlated with the abnormal allele. The presence of particular SNPs is correlated with increased risk for conditions such as heart disease, Alzheimer's, and some types of cancer. Companies that offer individual genetic testing for risk factors like these are looking for previously identified, linked SNPs. It may be helpful for individuals to learn about their health risks, with the understanding that such genetic tests merely reflect correlations and do not make predictions.

The techniques described in this chapter have also prompted improvements in disease treatments. By analyzing the expression of many genes in breast cancer patients, researchers have been able to refine their understanding of the different subtypes of breast cancer (see Figure 18.27). Knowing the expression levels of particular genes can help physicians determine the likelihood that the cancer will recur, thus helping them design an appropriate treatment. Given that some low-risk patients have a 96% survival rate over a 10-year period with no treatment, gene expression analysis allows doctors and patients access to valuable information when they are considering treatment options.

Many envision a future of "personalized medicine" where each person's genetic profile can inform them about diseases or conditions for which they are especially at risk and help them make treatment choices. As we will discuss later in the chapter, a *genetic profile* is currently taken to mean a set of genetic markers such as SNPs. Ultimately, however, it will likely mean the complete DNA sequence of an individual—once sequencing becomes inexpensive enough. Our ability to sequence a person's genome rapidly and inexpensively is advancing faster than our development of appropriate treatments for the conditions we are characterizing. Still, the identification of genes involved in these conditions provides us with good targets for therapeutic interventions.

Human Gene Therapy and Gene Editing

Gene therapy—the introduction of genes into an afflicted individual for therapeutic purposes—holds great potential for treating the relatively small number of disorders traceable to a single defective gene. The aim of this approach is to insert a normal allele of the defective gene into the somatic cells of the tissue affected by the disorder.

For gene therapy of somatic cells to be permanent, the cells that have the normal allele must be cells that multiply throughout the patient's life. Bone marrow cells, which include the stem cells that give rise to all the cells of the blood and immune system, are prime candidates. Figure 20.24 outlines one procedure for gene therapy of an individual whose bone marrow cells do not produce a vital enzyme because of a single defective gene. One type of severe combined immunodeficiency (SCID) is caused

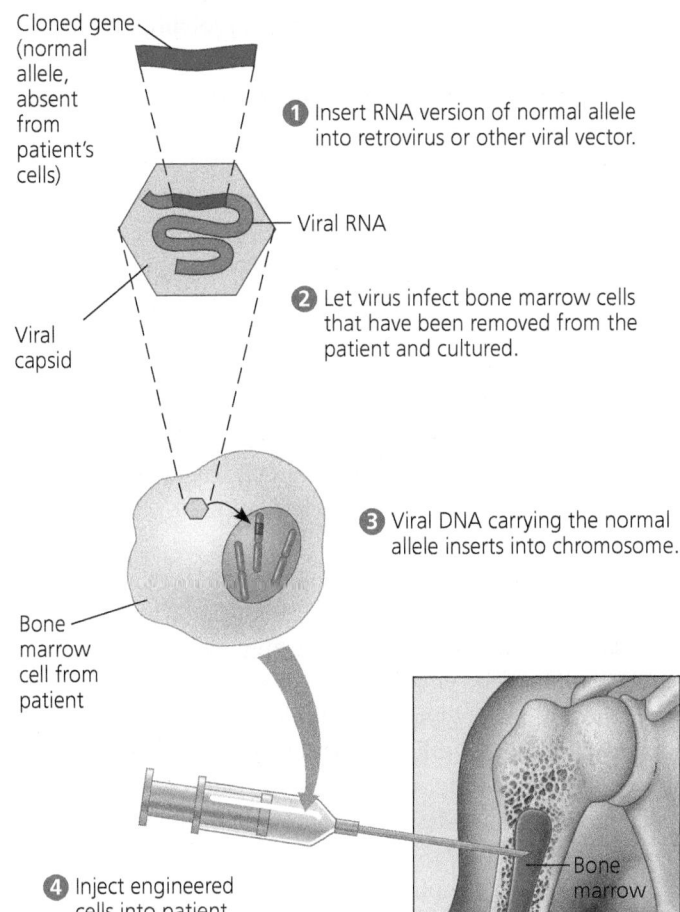

① Insert RNA version of normal allele into retrovirus or other viral vector.

Cloned gene (normal allele, absent from patient's cells)

Viral RNA

Viral capsid

② Let virus infect bone marrow cells that have been removed from the patient and cultured.

③ Viral DNA carrying the normal allele inserts into chromosome.

Bone marrow cell from patient

④ Inject engineered cells into patient.

Bone marrow

▲ **Figure 20.24 Gene therapy using a retroviral vector.** A retrovirus that has been rendered harmless is used as a vector in this procedure, which exploits the ability of a retrovirus to insert a DNA transcript of its RNA genome into the chromosomal DNA of its host cell (see Figure 19.10). If the foreign gene carried by the retroviral vector is expressed, the cell and its descendants will possess the gene product. Cells that reproduce throughout life, such as bone marrow cells, are ideal candidates for gene therapy.

by this kind of defect. If the treatment is successful, the patient's bone marrow cells will begin producing the missing protein, and the patient may be cured.

The procedure shown in Figure 20.24 was used in gene therapy trials for SCID in France in 2000. In that trial, 10 young children with SCID were treated by the same procedure. Nine of these patients showed significant, definitive improvement after two years, the first indisputable success of gene therapy. However, three of the patients subsequently developed leukemia, a type of blood cell cancer, and one of them died. Researchers have concluded it is likely that the insertion of the retroviral vector occurred near a gene that triggers the proliferation of blood cells. Using a viral vector that does not come from a retrovirus, clinical researchers have treated at least three other genetic diseases somewhat successfully with gene therapy: a type of progressive blindness; a degenerative disease of the nervous system; and a blood disorder involving the β-globin gene.

Gene therapy raises many technical issues. For example, how can the activity of the transferred gene be controlled so that cells make appropriate amounts of the gene product at the right time and in the right place? How can we be sure that the insertion of the therapeutic gene does not harm some other necessary cell function? As more is learned about DNA control elements and gene interactions, researchers may be able to answer such questions.

The development of the CRISPR-Cas9 system described earlier suggests a more direct approach that avoids the complications of using a viral vector in gene therapy: simply to edit the existing defective gene to correct the mutation. As shown in Figure 20.14b, the CRISPR-Cas9 system is capable of doing this.

In 2014, a group of researchers reported correcting a genetic defect in mice using CRISPR-Cas9 technology. The lab mice had been genetically engineered to have a mutation in a gene encoding a liver enzyme that metabolizes the amino acid tyrosine, mimicking a fatal genetic disorder in humans called tyrosinemia. A guide RNA molecule complementary to the mutated region of the gene was introduced into the mouse along with the Cas9 protein and a segment of DNA from the same region of the normal gene for use as a template. Subsequent analysis indicated that the faulty gene had been corrected in enough of the liver cells that the amount of functional enzyme made was sufficient to alleviate the disease symptoms. There are still hurdles to overcome before this approach can be used in clinical trials in humans, but the CRISPR technology is sparking widespread excitement among researchers and physicians alike.

In addition to technical challenges, gene therapy and gene editing provoke ethical questions. Some critics believe that tampering with human genes in any way is immoral or unethical. Other observers see no fundamental difference between the transplantation of genes into somatic cells and the transplantation of organs. You might wonder whether scientists are considering engineering human germ-line cells in the hope of correcting a defect in future generations. Such genetic engineering is now routinely done in laboratory mice, and, in fact, conditions that would allow genetic engineering of human embryos have been worked out.

The development of the CRISPR-Cas9 system has engendered much debate about the ethics of gene editing, related to applications both potential and real. In March of 2015, an editorial was published by leading scientists working with CRISPR-Cas9 calling for the research community to "strongly discourage" any experimental work on human eggs or embryos. A month later, however, scientists in China reported using CRISPR-Cas9 technology to edit a gene in human embryos. (They used "nonviable" fertilized eggs—zygotes—that would not develop all the way but could form blastocysts.) The researchers were attempting to edit the β-thalassemia gene, mutations in which cause a blood disease of the same name. They injected 86 zygotes, only four of which showed the gene to be edited properly. In many of the other embryos, there were effects on genes other than the β-thalassemia gene—at a much higher level than had been seen in mouse embryos or human cell lines. This study highlighted problems with the technique, at least in human embryos, and at the same time accelerated concern about ethical considerations. Under what circumstances, if any, should we alter the genomes of human germ lines? Would this inevitably lead to the practice of eugenics, a deliberate effort to control the genetic makeup of human populations? While we may not have to resolve these questions immediately due to technical issues, considering them is imperative because they will likely come to the fore at some point in the near future.

Pharmaceutical Products

The pharmaceutical industry derives significant benefit from advances in DNA technology and genetic research, applying them to the development of useful drugs to treat diseases. Pharmaceutical products are synthesized using methods of either organic chemistry or biotechnology, depending on the nature of the product.

Synthesis of Small Molecules for Use as Drugs Determining the sequence and structure of proteins crucial for tumour cell survival has led to the identification of small molecules that combat certain cancers by blocking the function of these proteins. One drug, imatinib (trade name Gleevec), is a small molecule that inhibits a specific tyrosine kinase (see Figure 11.8). The overexpression of this kinase, resulting from a chromosomal translocation, is instrumental in causing chronic myelogenous leukemia (CML; see Figure 15.17). Patients in the early stages of CML who are treated with imatinib have exhibited nearly complete, sustained remission from the cancer. Drugs that work in a similar way have also been used with success to treat a few types of lung and breast cancers. This approach is feasible only for cancers for which the molecular basis is fairly well understood.

In many cases of such drug-treated tumours, though, cells later arise that are resistant to the new drug. In one study, the whole genome of the tumour cells was sequenced both before and after the appearance of drug resistance. Comparison of the sequences showed genetic changes that allowed the tumour cells to "get around" the drug-inhibited protein. So we can see that cancer cells demonstrate the principles of evolution: Certain tumour cells have a random mutation that allows them to survive in the presence of a particular drug, and as a consequence of natural selection in the presence of the drug, these are the cells that survive and reproduce.

Protein Production in Cell Cultures Pharmaceutical products that are proteins are commonly synthesized on a large scale using cell cultures. You learned earlier in the chapter about DNA cloning and gene expression systems for producing large quantities of a chosen protein that is present naturally in only minute amounts. The host cells used in such expression systems can even be engineered to secrete a protein as it is made, thereby simplifying the task of purifying it by traditional biochemical methods.

Among the first pharmaceutical products manufactured in this way were human insulin and human growth hormone (hGH). More than 300 000 people with type 1 diabetes in Canada depend on insulin treatment to control their disease. Human growth hormone has been a boon to children born with a form of dwarfism caused by inadequate amounts of hGH, as well as helping AIDS patients gain weight. Another important pharmaceutical product produced by genetic engineering is tissue plasminogen activator (tPA). If administered shortly after a heart attack, tPA helps dissolve blood clots and reduces the risk of subsequent heart attacks.

Protein Production by "Pharm" Animals In some cases, instead of using cell systems to produce large quantities of protein products, pharmaceutical scientists can use whole animals. They can introduce a gene from an animal into the genome of another individual, often of a different species. This individual is then called a **transgenic** animal. To do this, they first remove eggs from a female of the recipient species and fertilize them *in vitro*. Meanwhile, they have cloned the desired gene from the donor organism. They then inject the cloned DNA directly into the nuclei of the fertilized eggs. Some of the cells integrate the foreign DNA, the *transgene*, into their genome and are able to express the foreign gene. The engineered embryos that arise from these zygotes are then surgically implanted in a surrogate mother. If an embryo develops successfully, the result is a transgenic animal that expresses its new, "foreign" gene.

Assuming that the introduced gene encodes a protein desired in large quantities, these transgenic animals can act as pharmaceutical "factories." For example, a transgene for a human blood protein such as antithrombin, which prevents blood clots, can be inserted into the genome of a goat in such a way that the transgene's product is secreted in the animal's milk (Figure 20.25). The protein is then purified from the milk (which is easier than purification from a cell culture).

▲ **Figure 20.25 Goats as "pharm" animals.** This transgenic goat carries a gene for a human blood protein, antithrombin, which she secretes in her milk. Patients with a rare hereditary disorder in which this protein is lacking suffer from formation of blood clots in their blood vessels. Easily purified from the goat's milk, the protein has been approved in Canada, the United States, and Europe for treating such patients.

Such proteins must be tested to ensure that they (or contaminants from the farm animals) will not cause allergic reactions or other adverse effects in patients who receive them.

Forensic Evidence and Genetic Profiles

In violent crimes, body fluids or small pieces of tissue may be left at the scene or on the clothes or other possessions of the victim or assailant. If enough blood, semen, or tissue is available, forensic laboratories can determine the blood type or tissue type by using antibodies to detect specific cell-surface proteins. However, such tests require fairly fresh samples in relatively large amounts. Also, because many people have the same blood or tissue type, this approach can only exclude a suspect; it cannot provide strong evidence of guilt.

DNA testing, on the other hand, can identify the guilty individual with a high degree of certainty, because the DNA sequence of every person is unique (except for identical twins). Genetic markers that vary in the population can be analyzed for a given person to determine that individual's unique set of genetic markers, or **genetic profile**. (This term is preferred over "DNA fingerprint" by forensic scientists, who want to emphasize the heritable aspect of these markers rather than the fact that they produce a pattern on a gel that, like a fingerprint, is visually recognizable.) The FBI started applying DNA technology to forensics in 1988, using a method involving gel electrophoresis and nucleic acid hybridization to detect similarities and differences in DNA samples. This method required much smaller samples of blood or tissue than earlier methods—only about 1000 cells.

Today, forensic scientists use an even more sensitive method that takes advantage of variations in length of genetic markers called **short tandem repeats (STRs)**. These are tandemly repeated units of two to five nucleotide sequences in specific regions of the genome. The number of repeats present in these regions is highly variable from person to person (polymorphic), and even for a single individual, the two alleles of an STR may differ from each other. For example, one individual may have the sequence ACAT repeated 30 times at one genome locus and 15 times at the same locus on the other homologue, whereas another individual may have 18 repeats at this locus on each homologue. (These two genotypes can be expressed by the two repeat numbers: 30,15 and 18,18.) PCR is used to amplify particular STRs, using sets of primers that are labelled with different-coloured fluorescent tags; the length of the region, and thus the number of repeats, can then be determined by electrophoresis. The PCR step allows use of this method even when the DNA is in poor condition or available only in minute quantities. A tissue sample containing as few as 20 cells can be sufficient for PCR amplification.

In a murder case, for example, this method can be used to compare DNA samples from the suspect, the victim, and a small amount of blood found at the crime scene. The forensic scientist tests only a few selected portions of the DNA—usually 13 STR markers. However, even this small set of markers can provide a forensically useful genetic profile because the probability that two people (who are not identical twins) would have exactly the same set of STR markers is vanishingly small. The Innocence Project, a nonprofit organization dedicated to overturning wrongful convictions, uses STR analysis of archived samples from crime scenes to revisit old cases. As of 2016, more than 340 innocent people had been released from prison as a result of forensic and legal work by this group (Figure 20.26).

Genetic profiles can also be useful for other purposes. A comparison of the DNA of a mother, her child, and the purported father can conclusively settle a question of paternity. Sometimes paternity is of historical interest: Genetic profiles provided strong evidence that Thomas Jefferson or one of his close male relatives fathered at least one of the children of his slave Sally Hemings. Genetic profiles can also identify victims of mass casualties. The largest such effort occurred after the attack on the World Trade Center in 2001; more than 10 000 samples of victims' remains were compared with DNA samples from personal items, such as toothbrushes, provided by families. Ultimately, forensic scientists succeeded in identifying almost 3000 victims using these methods.

Just how reliable is a genetic profile? The greater the number of markers examined in a DNA sample, the more likely it is that the profile is unique to one individual. In forensic cases using STR analysis with 13 markers, the probability of two people having identical DNA profiles is somewhere between one chance in 10 billion and one in

(a) In 1984, Earl Washington was convicted and sentenced to death for the 1982 rape and murder of Rebecca Williams. His sentence was commuted to life in prison in 1993 due to new doubts about the evidence. In 2000, STR analysis by forensic scientists associated with the Innocence Project showed conclusively that he was innocent. This photo shows Washington just before his release in 2001, after 17 years in prison.

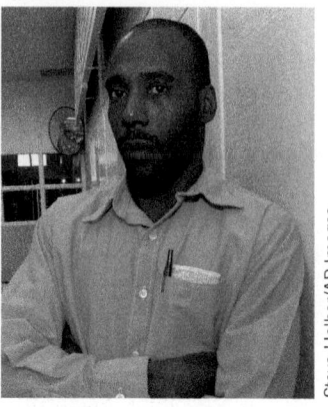

Steve Helber/AP Images

Source of sample	STR marker 1	STR marker 2	STR marker 3
Semen on victim	17,19	13,16	12,12
Earl Washington	16,18	14,15	11,12
Kenneth Tinsley	17,19	13,16	12,12

(b) In STR analysis, selected STR markers in a DNA sample are amplified by PCR, and the PCR products are separated by electrophoresis. The procedure reveals how many repeats are present for each STR locus in the sample. An individual has two alleles per STR locus, each with a certain number of repeats. This table shows the number of repeats for three STR markers in three samples: from semen found on the victim, from Washington, and from another man (Kenneth Tinsley), who was in prison because of an unrelated conviction. These and other STR data (not shown) exonerated Washington and led Tinsley to plead guilty to the murder.

▲ **Figure 20.26 STR analysis used to release an innocent man from prison.**

several trillion. (For comparison, the world's population is between 7 and 8 billion.) The exact probability depends on the frequency of those markers in the general population. Information on how common various markers are in different ethnic groups is critical because these marker frequencies may vary considerably among ethnic groups and between a particular ethnic group and the population as a whole. With the increasing availability of frequency data, forensic scientists can make extremely accurate statistical calculations. Thus, despite problems that can still arise from insufficient data, human error, or flawed evidence, genetic profiles are now accepted as compelling evidence by legal experts and scientists alike.

Environmental Cleanup

Increasingly, the remarkable ability of certain microorganisms to transform chemicals is being exploited for environmental cleanup. If the growth needs of such microbes make them unsuitable for direct use, scientists can now transfer the genes for their valuable metabolic capabilities into other microorganisms, which can then be used to treat environmental problems. For example, many bacteria can extract heavy metals, such as copper, lead, and nickel, from their environments and incorporate the metals into compounds such as copper sulphate or lead sulphate, which are readily recoverable. Genetically engineered microbes may become important in both mining (especially as ore reserves are depleted) and cleaning up highly toxic mining wastes. Biotechnologists are also trying to engineer microbes that can degrade chlorinated hydrocarbons and other harmful compounds. These microbes could be used in wastewater treatment plants or by manufacturers before the compounds are ever released into the environment. Scientists are hopeful that these engineered microbes will be able to facilitate the restoration of the oil sands region of northern Alberta, which will have 1 billion m^3 of contaminated water by 2025 in need of remediation.

Agricultural Applications

Scientists are working to learn more about the genomes of agriculturally important plants and animals. For a number of years, they have been using DNA technology in an effort to improve agricultural productivity. The selective breeding of both livestock (animal husbandry) and crops has exploited naturally occurring mutations and genetic recombination for thousands of years.

As we described earlier, DNA technology enables scientists to produce transgenic animals, which speeds up the selective breeding process. The goals of creating a transgenic animal are often the same as the goals of traditional breeding—for instance, to make a sheep with better quality wool, a pig with leaner meat, or a cow that will mature in a shorter time. Scientists might, for example, identify and clone a gene that causes the development of larger muscles (muscles make up most of the meat we eat) in one breed of cattle and transfer it to other cattle or even to sheep. However, problems such as low fertility or increased susceptibility to disease are not uncommon among farm animals carrying genes from other species. Animal health and welfare are important issues to consider when developing transgenic animals.

Agricultural scientists have already endowed a number of crop plants with genes for desirable traits, such as delayed ripening and resistance to spoilage and disease, as well as drought. Modifications can also add value to food crops, giving them a longer shelf life or improved flavour or nutritional value. For many plant species, a single tissue cell grown in culture can give rise to an adult plant. Thus, genetic manipulations can be performed on an ordinary somatic cell and the cell then used to generate an organism with new traits.

Genetic engineering is rapidly replacing traditional plant-breeding programs, especially for useful traits, such as herbicide or pest resistance, determined by one or a few

genes. Crops engineered with a bacterial gene making the plants resistant to an herbicide can grow while weeds are destroyed, and genetically engineered crops that can resist destructive insects reduce the need for chemical insecticides. In India, the insertion of a salinity resistance gene from a coastal mangrove plant into the genomes of several rice varieties has resulted in rice plants that can grow in water three times as salty as seawater. The research foundation that carried out this feat of genetic engineering estimates that one-third of all irrigated land has high salinity owing to overirrigation and intensive use of chemical fertilizers, representing a serious threat to the food supply. Thus, salinity-resistant crop plants would be enormously valuable worldwide.

Safety and Ethical Questions Raised by DNA Technology

Early concerns about potential dangers associated with recombinant DNA technology focused on the possibility that hazardous new pathogens might be created. What might happen, for instance, if in a research study cancer cell genes were transferred into bacteria or viruses? To guard against such rogue microbes, scientists developed a set of guidelines that were adopted as formal government regulations in Canada, the United States, and some other countries. One safety measure is a set of strict laboratory procedures designed to protect researchers from infection by engineered microbes and to prevent the microbes from accidentally leaving the laboratory. In addition, strains of microorganisms to be used in recombinant DNA experiments are genetically crippled to ensure that they cannot survive outside the laboratory. Finally, certain obviously dangerous experiments have been banned.

Today, most public concern about possible hazards centres not on recombinant microbes but on **genetically modified (GM) organisms** (GMOs) used as food. A GMO is an organism that has acquired by artificial means one or more genes from another species or even from another variety of the same species. Some salmon, for example, have been genetically modified by addition of a more active salmon growth hormone gene. However, the majority of the GM organisms that contribute to our food supply are not animals, but crop plants.

GM crops are widespread in Canada, the United States, Argentina, and Brazil; together these countries account for over 80% of the world's acreage devoted to such crops. In Canada, most corn, soybean, and canola crops are genetically modified, and GM products are not required to be labelled at present. However, the same foods are an ongoing subject of controversy in Europe, where the GM revolution has met with strong opposition. Many Europeans are concerned about the safety of GM foods and the possible environmental consequences of growing GM plants. Although a small number of GM crops have been grown on European soil, the European Union established a comprehensive legal framework regarding GMOs in 2015. Among other regulations, individual member states may ban either growing or importing of GM crops, which must be clearly labelled. The high degree of consumer distrust in Europe makes the future of GM crops there uncertain.

Advocates of a cautious approach toward GM crops fear that transgenic plants might pass their new genes to close relatives in nearby wild areas. We know that lawn and crop grasses, for example, commonly exchange genes with wild relatives via pollen transfer. If crop plants carrying genes for resistance to herbicides, diseases, or insect pests pollinated wild ones, the offspring might become "super weeds" that are very difficult to control. Another worry concerns possible risks to human health from GM foods. Some people fear that the protein products of transgenes might lead to allergic reactions. Although there is some evidence that this could happen, advocates claim that these proteins could be tested in advance to avoid producing ones that cause allergic reactions.

Today, governments and regulatory agencies throughout the world are grappling with how to facilitate the use of biotechnology in agriculture, industry, and medicine while ensuring that new products and procedures are safe. In Canada, such applications of biotechnology are evaluated for potential risks by various regulatory agencies, including Health Canada, Environment Canada, Agriculture and Agri-Food Canada, and the Canadian Food Inspection Agency. Meanwhile, these same agencies and the public must consider the ethical implications of biotechnology.

Advances in biotechnology have allowed us to obtain complete genome sequences for humans and many other species, providing a vast treasure trove of information about genes. We can ask how certain genes differ from species to species, as well as how genes and, ultimately, entire genomes have evolved. (These are the subjects of Chapter 21.) At the same time, the increasing speed and falling cost of sequencing the genomes of individuals are raising significant ethical questions. Who should have the right to examine someone else's genetic information? How should that information be used? Should a person's genome be a factor in determining eligibility for a job or insurance? Ethical considerations, as well as concerns about potential environmental and health hazards, will likely slow some applications of biotechnology. There is always a danger that too much regulation will stifle basic research and its potential benefits. However, the power of DNA technology and genetic engineering—our ability to profoundly and rapidly alter species that have been evolving for millennia—demands that we proceed with humility and caution.

CONCEPT CHECK 20.4

1. What is the advantage of using stem cells for gene therapy or gene editing?

2. List at least three different properties that have been acquired by crop plants via genetic engineering.

3. **WHAT IF?** As a physician, you have a patient with symptoms that suggest a hepatitis A infection, but you have not been able to detect viral proteins in the blood. Knowing that hepatitis A is an RNA virus, what lab tests could you perform to support your diagnosis? Explain the results that would support your hypothesis.

For suggested answers, see Appendix A.

---

20 Chapter Review

Go to **MasteringBiology**® for Assignments, the eText, and the Study Area with Animations, Activities, Vocab Self-Quiz, and Practice Tests.

SUMMARY OF KEY CONCEPTS

CONCEPT 20.1

DNA sequencing and DNA cloning are valuable tools for genetic engineering and biological inquiry (pp. 434–442)

- **Nucleic acid hybridization**, the base pairing of one strand of a nucleic acid to the complementary sequence on a strand from another nucleic acid molecule, is widely used in DNA technology.
- **DNA sequencing** can be carried out using the *dideoxy chain termination* method in automated sequencing machines.
- Next-generation (high-throughput) techniques for sequencing DNA are based on *sequencing by synthesis*: DNA polymerase is used

to synthesize a stretch of DNA from a single-stranded template, and the order in which nucleotides are added reveals the sequence.
- **Gene cloning** (or DNA cloning) produces multiple copies of a gene (or DNA segment) that can be used to manipulate and analyze DNA and to produce useful new products or organisms with beneficial traits.
- In **genetic engineering**, bacterial **restriction enzymes** are used to cut DNA molecules within short, specific nucleotide sequences (**restriction sites**), yielding a set of double-stranded restriction fragments with single-stranded **sticky ends**.

```
5'              3'        5'                3'
    |G|                   |AATTC|
    |CTTAA|               |    G|
3'              5'        3'                5'
                                 Sticky end
```

- The sticky ends on **restriction fragments** from one DNA source can base-pair with complementary sticky ends on fragments from other DNA molecules; sealing the base-paired fragments with **DNA ligase** produces **recombinant DNA** molecules.
- DNA restriction fragments of different lengths can be separated by **gel electrophoresis**.
- The **polymerase chain reaction (PCR)** can produce many copies of (amplify) a specific target segment of DNA *in vitro*, using primers that bracket the desired sequence and a heat-resistant DNA polymerase.
- To clone a eukaryotic gene:

Cloning vector (often a bacterial plasmid)

DNA fragments obtained by PCR or from another source (cut by same restriction enzyme used on cloning vector)

Mix and ligate

Recombinant DNA plasmids

Recombinant plasmids are returned to host cells, each of which divides to form a clone of cells.
- Several technical difficulties hinder the expression of cloned eukaryotic genes in bacterial host cells. The use of cultured eukaryotic cells as host cells, coupled with appropriate **expression vectors**, helps avoid these problems.

? *Describe how the process of gene cloning results in a cell clone containing a recombinant plasmid.*

CONCEPT 20.2

Biologists use DNA technology to study gene expression and function (pp. 442–448)

- Several techniques use hybridization of a **nucleic acid probe** to detect the presence of specific mRNAs.
- *In situ* **hybridization** and **RT-PCR** can detect the presence of a given mRNA in a tissue or an RNA sample, respectively.
- **DNA microarrays** are used to identify sets of genes co-expressed by a group of cells. Their cDNAs can also be sequenced (RNA-seq).
- For a gene of unknown function, experimental inactivation of the gene (a gene knockout) and observation of the resulting phenotypic effects can provide clues to its function. The CRISPR-Cas9 system allows researchers to edit genes in living cells in a specific, desired way, and its use is increasing. In humans, **genome-wide association studies** use **single nucleotide polymorphisms (SNPs)** as genetic markers for alleles that are associated with particular conditions.

? *What useful information is obtained by detecting expression of specific genes?*

CONCEPT 20.3

Cloned organisms and stem cells are useful for basic research and other applications (pp. 448–454)

- The question of whether all the cells in an organism have the same genome prompted the first attempts at organismal cloning.

- Single differentiated cells from plants are often **totipotent**: capable of generating all the tissues of a complete new plant.
- Transplantation of the nucleus from a differentiated animal cell into an enucleated egg can sometimes give rise to a new animal.
- Certain embryonic **stem cells** (ES cells) from animal embryos and particular adult stem cells from adult tissues can reproduce and differentiate both in the lab and in the organism, offering the potential for medical use. ES cells are **pluripotent** but difficult to acquire. Induced pluripotent stem (iPS) cells resemble ES cells in their capacity to differentiate; they can be generated by reprogramming differentiated cells. iPS cells hold promise for medical research and regenerative medicine.

? *Describe how a researcher could carry out (1) organismal cloning, (2) production of ES cells, and (3) generation of iPS cells, focusing on how the cells are reprogrammed and using mice as an example. (The procedures are basically the same in humans and mice.)*

CONCEPT 20.4

The practical applications of DNA-based biotechnology affect our lives in many ways (pp. 454–460)

- DNA technology, including the analysis of genetic markers such as SNPs, is increasingly being used in the diagnosis of genetic and other diseases and offers potential for better treatment of genetic disorders or even permanent cures through **gene therapy**, or gene editing with the CRISPR-Cas9 system. It also enables more informed cancer therapies. DNA technology is used with cell cultures in the large-scale production of protein hormones and other proteins with therapeutic uses. Some therapeutic proteins are being produced in **transgenic** "pharm" animals.
- Analysis of genetic markers such as **short tandem repeats (STRs)** in DNA isolated from tissue or body fluids found at crime scenes leads to a **genetic profile**. Use of genetic profiles can provide definitive evidence that a suspect is innocent or strong evidence of guilt. Such analysis is also useful in parenthood disputes and in identifying the remains of crime victims.
- Genetically engineered microorganisms can be used to extract minerals from the environment or degrade various types of toxic waste materials.
- The aims of developing transgenic plants and animals are to improve agricultural productivity and food quality.
- The potential benefits of genetic engineering must be carefully weighed against the potential for harm to humans or the environment.

? *What factors affect whether a given genetic disease would be a good candidate for successful gene therapy?*

TEST YOUR UNDERSTANDING

LEVEL 1: KNOWLEDGE/COMPREHENSION

1. In DNA technology, the term *vector* can refer to
   a. the enzyme that cuts DNA into restriction fragments.
   b. the sticky end of a DNA fragment.
   c. a SNP marker.
   d. a plasmid used to transfer DNA into a living cell.

2. Which of the following tools of DNA technology is incorrectly paired with its use?
   a. electrophoresis—separation of DNA fragments
   b. DNA ligase—cutting DNA, creating sticky ends of restriction fragments

c. DNA polymerase—polymerase chain reaction to amplify sections of DNA

d. reverse transcriptase—production of cDNA from mRNA

3. Plants are more readily manipulated by genetic engineering than are animals because
   a. plant genes do not contain introns.
   b. more vectors are available for transferring recombinant DNA into plant cells.
   c. a somatic plant cell can often give rise to a complete plant.
   d. plant cells have larger nuclei.

4. A paleontologist has recovered a bit of tissue from the 400-year-old preserved skin of an extinct dodo (a bird). To compare a specific region of the DNA from a sample with DNA from living birds, which of the following would be most useful for increasing the amount of dodo DNA available for testing?
   a. SNP analysis
   b. polymerase chain reaction (PCR)
   c. electroporation
   d. gel electrophoresis

5. DNA technology has many medical applications. Which of the following is *not* done routinely at present?
   a. production of hormones for treating diabetes and dwarfism
   b. production of microbes that can metabolize toxins
   c. introduction of genetically engineered genes into human gametes
   d. prenatal identification of genetic disease alleles

LEVEL 2: APPLICATION/ANALYSIS

6. Which of the following would *not* be true of cDNA produced using human brain tissue as the starting material?
   a. It could be amplified by the polymerase chain reaction.
   b. It was produced from pre-mRNA using reverse transcriptase.
   c. It could be labelled and used as a probe to detect genes expressed in the brain.
   d. It lacks the introns of the pre-mRNA.

7. Expression of a cloned eukaryotic gene in a bacterial cell involves many challenges. The use of mRNA and reverse transcriptase is part of a strategy to solve the problem of
   a. post-transcriptional processing.
   b. post-translational processing.
   c. nucleic acid hybridization.
   d. restriction fragment ligation.

8. Which of the following sequences in double-stranded DNA is most likely to be recognized as a cutting site for a restriction enzyme?
   a. AAGG   c. ACCA
      TTCC   TGGT
   b. GGCC   d. AAAA
      CCGG   TTTT

LEVEL 3: SYNTHESIS/EVALUATION

9. **MAKE CONNECTIONS** Imagine you want to study one of the human crystallins, proteins present in the lens of the eye (see Figure 1.9). To obtain a sufficient amount of the protein of interest, you decide to clone the gene that codes for it. Assume you know the sequence of this gene. How would you go about this?

10. **DRAW IT** You are cloning an aardvark gene, using a bacterial plasmid as a vector. The green diagram shows the plasmid, which contains the restriction site for the enzyme used in Figure 20.6. Above the plasmid is a segment of linear aardvark DNA that was synthesized using PCR. Diagram your cloning procedure, showing what would happen to these two molecules during each step. Use one colour for the aardvark DNA and its bases and another colour for those of the plasmid. Label each step and all 5′ and 3′ ends.

5′ GAATTCTAAAGCGCTTATGAATTC 3′
3′ CTTAAGATTTCGCGAATACTTAAG 5′

Aardvark DNA

GAATTC
CTTAAG

Plasmid

11. **EVOLUTION CONNECTION**
   Ethical considerations aside, if DNA-based technologies became widely used, how might they change the way evolution proceeds, as compared with the natural evolutionary mechanisms that have operated for the past 4 billion years?

12. **SCIENTIFIC INQUIRY**
   You hope to study a gene that codes for a neurotransmitter protein produced in human brain cells. You know the amino acid sequence of the protein. Explain how you might (a) identify what genes are expressed in a specific type of brain cell, (b) identify (and isolate) the neurotransmitter gene, (c) produce multiple copies of the gene for study, and (d) produce large quantities of the neurotransmitter for evaluation as a potential medication.

13. **WRITE ABOUT A THEME: INFORMATION**
   In a short essay (100–150 words), discuss how the genetic basis of life plays a central role in biotechnology.

14. **SYNTHESIZE YOUR KNOWLEDGE**

Galyna Andrushko/Shutterstock

The water in the Yellowstone National Park hot springs shown here is around 160°F (70°C). Biologists assumed that no species of organisms could live in water above about 130°F (55°C), so they were surprised to find several species of bacteria there, now called *thermophiles* ("heat-lovers"). You've learned in this chapter how an enzyme from one species, *Thermus aquaticus*, made feasible one of the most important DNA-based techniques used in labs today. What was the enzyme, and what was the value of its being isolated from a thermophile? Can you think of reasons other enzymes from this bacterium (or other thermophiles) might also be valuable?

For selected answers, see Appendix A.

21

Genomes and Their Evolution

KEY CONCEPTS

21.1 The Human Genome Project fostered development of faster, less expensive sequencing techniques

21.2 Scientists use bioinformatics to analyze genomes and their functions

21.3 Genomes vary in size, number of genes, and gene density

21.4 Multicellular eukaryotes have much noncoding DNA and many multigene families

21.5 Duplication, rearrangement, and mutation of DNA contribute to genome evolution

21.6 Comparing genome sequences provides clues to evolution and development

Karen Huntt/Corbis

▲ **Figure 21.1 What genomic information distinguishes a human from a chimpanzee?**

Reading the Leaves from the Tree of Life

The chimpanzee (*Pan troglodytes*) is our closest living relative on the evolutionary tree of life. The boy in **Figure 21.1** and his chimpanzee companion are intently studying the same leaf, but only one of them is able to speak about it. What accounts for this difference between two primates that share so much of their evolutionary history? With advances in sequencing technology, we are now addressing the genetic basis of such intriguing questions. Later in the chapter, you'll learn about the *FOXP2* gene, involved in speech, which differs between the two species.

The chimpanzee genome was sequenced two years after sequencing of the human genome. Now that we can compare our genome, base by base, with that of the chimpanzee, we can tackle the more general issue of what differences in genetic information account for the distinct characteristics of these two species of primates.

In addition to determining the sequences of the human and chimpanzee genomes, researchers have obtained complete genome sequences for *Escherichia coli* and numerous other prokaryotes, as well as many eukaryotes, including *Zea mays* (corn), *Drosophila melanogaster* (fruit fly), *Mus musculus* (house mouse), and *Pongo pygmaeus* (orangutan). In 2014, a high-quality sequence was announced for the genome of *Homo neanderthalensis,* an extinct species closely related to present-day humans. These whole and partial genomes are of great interest in their own right and are also providing important insights into evolution and other

Digital Zoo/Photodisc/Getty Images

biological processes. Broadening the human-chimpanzee comparison to the genomes of other primates and more distantly related animals should reveal the sets of genes that control group-defining characteristics. Beyond that, comparisons with the genomes of bacteria, archaea, fungi, protists, and plants should enlighten us about the long evolutionary history of shared ancient genes and their products.

With the genomes of many species fully sequenced, scientists can study whole sets of genes and their interactions, an approach called **genomics**. The sequencing efforts that feed this approach have generated, and continue to generate, enormous volumes of data. The need to deal with this ever-increasing flood of information has spawned the field of **bioinformatics**, the application of computational methods to store and analyze biological data.

We will begin this chapter by discussing two approaches to genome sequencing and some of the advances in bioinformatics and its applications. We will then summarize what has been learned from the genomes that have been sequenced thus far. Next, we will describe the composition of the human genome as a representative genome of a complex multicellular eukaryote. Finally, we will explore current ideas about how genomes evolve and about how the evolution of developmental mechanisms could have generated the great diversity of life on Earth today.

CONCEPT 21.1

The Human Genome Project fostered development of faster, less expensive sequencing techniques

Sequencing of the human genome, an ambitious undertaking, officially began as the **Human Genome Project** in 1990. Organized by an international, publicly funded consortium of scientists at universities and research institutes, the project involved 20 large sequencing centres in six countries plus a host of other labs working on smaller parts of the project.

After the human genome sequence was largely completed in 2003, the sequence of each chromosome was analyzed and described in a series of papers, the last of which covered chromosome 1 and was published in 2006. At this point, the sequencing was declared "virtually complete."

The ultimate goal in mapping any genome is to determine the complete nucleotide sequence of each chromosome. For the human genome, this was accomplished by sequencing machines, using the dideoxy chain termination method described in Figure 20.3. Even with automation, though, the sequencing of all 3 billion base pairs in a haploid set of human chromosomes presented a formidable challenge. In fact, a major thrust of the Human Genome Project was the development of technology for faster sequencing, as described in Chapter 20. Improvements

over the years chipped away at each time-consuming step, enabling the rate of sequencing to accelerate impressively: Whereas a productive lab could typically sequence 1000 base pairs a day in the 1980s, by the year 2000 each research centre working on the Human Genome Project was sequencing 1000 base pairs *per second*, 24 hours a day, seven days a week—and in 2014, automated machines could sequence about 2 billion nucleotides in 24 hours. Methods like this that analyze biological materials very rapidly and produce enormous volumes of data are said to be "high-throughput." Sequencing machines are an example of high-throughput devices.

Two approaches complemented each other in obtaining the complete sequence. The initial approach was a methodical one that built on an earlier storehouse of human genetic information. In 1998, however, molecular biologist J. Craig Venter set up a company (Celera Genomics) and declared his intention to sequence the entire human genome using an alternative strategy. The **whole-genome shotgun approach** starts with the cloning and sequencing of DNA fragments from randomly cut DNA. Powerful computer programs then assemble the resulting very large number of overlapping short sequences into a single continuous sequence (Figure 21.2).

❶ Cut the DNA from many copies of an entire chromosome into overlapping fragments short enough for sequencing.

❷ Clone the fragments in plasmid or other vectors.

❸ Sequence each fragment.

CGCCATCAGT   AGTCCGCTATACGA   ACGATACTGGT

CGCCATCAGT   ACGATACTGGT

❹ Order the sequences into one overall sequence with computer software.

AGTCCGCTATACGA

···CGCCATCAGTCCGCTATACGATACTGGT···

▲ Figure 21.2 **Whole-genome shotgun approach to sequencing.** In this approach, developed by Craig Venter and colleagues at Celera Genomics, random DNA fragments are sequenced and then ordered relative to each other.

? *The fragments in step 2 of this figure are depicted as scattered, rather than being in an ordered array. How does this depiction reflect the approach?*

Today, the whole-genome shotgun approach is still used, although newer "next-generation" sequencing techniques (see Figure 20.4), have resulted in massive increases in speed and decreases in the cost of sequencing entire genomes. In these new techniques, many very small DNA fragments (each about 300 base pairs long) are sequenced at the same time, and computer software rapidly assembles the complete sequence. Because of the sensitivity of these techniques, the fragments can be sequenced directly; the cloning step (❷ in Figure 21.2) is unnecessary. Whereas sequencing the first human genome took 13 years and cost $100 million, James Watson's genome was sequenced using next-generation techniques during four months in 2007 for about $1 million, and we are rapidly approaching the day when an individual's genome can be sequenced in a matter of hours for less than $1000.

These technological advances have also facilitated an approach called **metagenomics** (from the Greek *meta*, beyond), in which DNA from an entire community of species (a *metagenome*) is collected from an environmental sample and sequenced. Again, computer software sorts out the partial sequences and assembles them into the individual specific genomes. The ability to sequence the DNA of mixed microbial populations eliminates the need to culture each species separately in the lab, a difficulty that has limited the study of many microbial species.

So far, this approach has been applied to communities found in environments as diverse as the human intestine and ancient soils in the Arctic. A 2014 study of deep Arctic soils characterized dozens of species living together as a community as long as 50 000 years ago, including animals and plants as well as microbes.

At first glance, genome sequences of humans and other organisms are simply dry lists of nucleotide bases—millions of As, Ts, Cs, and Gs in mind-numbing succession. Making sense of this massive amount of data has called for new analytical approaches, which we discuss next.

CONCEPT CHECK 21.1

1. Describe the whole-genome shotgun approach.

For suggested answers, see Appendix A.

CONCEPT 21.2

Scientists use bioinformatics to analyze genomes and their functions

Each of the 20 or so sequencing centres around the world working on the Human Genome Project churned out voluminous amounts of DNA sequence day after day. As the data began to accumulate, the need to coordinate efforts to keep track of all the sequences became clear. Thanks to the foresight of research scientists and government officials

involved in the Human Genome Project, its goals included establishing centralized databases and refining analytical software, all to be made readily accessible on the Internet.

Centralized Resources for Analyzing Genome Sequences

Making bioinformatics resources available to researchers worldwide and speeding up the dissemination of information served to accelerate progress in DNA sequence analysis. For example, in preparation for the Human Genome Project in the United States, the National Library of Medicine and the National Institutes of Health (NIH) joined forces in 1988 to create the National Centre for Biotechnology Information (NCBI), which today maintains a website (www.ncbi.nlm.nih.gov) with extensive bioinformatics resources. On this site are links to databases, software, and a wealth of information about genomics and related topics. Similar websites have also been established by three genome centres with which the NCBI collaborates: the European Molecular Biology Laboratory, the DNA Data Bank of Japan, and BGI (formerly known as the Beijing Genome Institute) in Shenzhen, China. These large, comprehensive websites are complemented by others maintained by individual or small groups of laboratories. Smaller websites often provide databases and software designed for a narrower purpose, such as studying genetic and genomic changes in one particular type of cancer.

The NCBI database of sequences is called GenBank. As of October 2015, it included the sequences of 188 million fragments of genomic DNA, totalling 202 billion base pairs! GenBank is constantly updated, and the amount of data it contains increases rapidly. Any sequence in the database can be retrieved and analyzed using software from the NCBI website or elsewhere.

One very widely used software program available on the NCBI website called BLAST allows the visitor to compare a DNA sequence with every sequence in GenBank, base by base. A researcher might search for similar regions in other genes of the same species, or among the genes of other species. Another program allows comparison of protein sequences. Yet a third can search any protein sequence for conserved (common) stretches of amino acids (domains) for which a function is known or suspected, and it can show a three-dimensional model of the domain alongside other relevant information (Figure 21.3). There is even a software program that can align and compare a collection of sequences, either nucleic acids or polypeptides, and diagram them in the form of an evolutionary tree based on the sequence relationships. (One such diagram is shown in Figure 21.17.)

Two research institutions, Rutgers University and the University of California, San Diego, also maintain a worldwide Protein Data Bank, a database of all three-dimensional

1 In this window, a partial amino acid sequence from an unknown muskmelon protein ("Query") is aligned with sequences from other proteins that the computer program found to be similar. Each sequence represents a domain called WD40.

2 Four hallmarks of the WD40 domain are highlighted in yellow. (Sequence similarity is based on chemical aspects of the amino acids, so the amino acids in each hallmark region are not always identical.)

3 The Cn3D program displays a three-dimensional ribbon model of cow transducin (the protein highlighted in purple in the Sequence Alignment Viewer). This protein is the only one of those shown for which a structure has been determined. The sequence similarity of the other proteins to cow transducin suggests that their structures are likely to be similar.

4 Cow transducin contains seven WD40 domains, one of which is highlighted here in grey.

5 The yellow segments correspond to the WD40 hallmarks highlighted in yellow in the window above.

6 This window displays information about the WD40 domain from the Conserved Domain Database.

WD40 - Sequence Alignment Viewer

```
                Query  ~~~ktGGIRL~RHfksVSAVEWHRk~~gDYLSTlvLreSRAVLIHQlsk
          Cow [transducin]  ~nvrvSRELA~GHtgyLSCCRFLDd~~nQIVTs~~Sg~DTTCALWDie~
      Mustard weed [transducin]  gtvpvSRMLT~GHrgyVSCCQYVPnedaHLITs~~Sg~DQTCILWDvtt
            Corn [GNB protein]  gnmpvSRILT~GHkgyVSSCQYVPdgetRLITS~~Sg~DQTCVLWDvt~
          Human [PAFA protein]  ~~~ecIRTMH~GHdhnVSSVAIMPng~dHIVSA~~Sr~DKTIKMWEvg~
    Nematode [unknown protein #1]  ~~~rcVKTLK~GHtnyVFCCCFNPs~~gTLIAS~~GsfDETIRIWCar~
    Nematode [unknown protein #2]  ~~~rmTKTLK~GHnnyVFCCNFNPq~~sSLVVS~~GsfDESVRIWDvk~
        Fission yeast [FWDR protein]  ~~~seCISILhGHtdsVLCLTFDS~~~~TLLVS~~GsaDCTVKLWHfs~
```

CDD Descriptive Items

Name: WD40

WD40 domain, found in a number of eukaryotic proteins that cover a wide variety of functions including adaptor/regulatory modules in signal transduction, pre-mRNA processing and cytoskeleton assembly; typically contains a GH dipeptide 11-24 residues from its N-terminus and the WD dipeptide at its C-terminus and is 40 residues long, hence the name WD40;

WD40 - Cn3D 4.1

▲ **Figure 21.3 Bioinformatics tools available on the Internet.** A website maintained by the National Centre for Biotechnology Information allows scientists and the public to access DNA and protein sequences and other stored data. The site includes a link to a protein structure database (Conserved Domain Database, CDD) that can find and describe similar domains in related proteins, as well as software (Cn3D, "See in 3D") that displays three-dimensional models of domains for which the structure has been determined. Some results are shown from a search for regions of proteins similar to an amino acid sequence in a muskmelon protein. The WD40 domain is one of the most abundant domains in proteins encoded by eukaryotic genomes. Within these proteins, it often plays a key role in molecular interactions during signal transduction in cells.

Source: Simulated screen shots based on Mac OS X and from data found at NCBI, U.S. National Library of Medicine using Conserved Domain Database, Sequence Alignment Viewer, and Cn3D. © Jane B Reece.

protein structures that have been experimentally determined. (The database is accessible at www.wwpdb.org.) These structures can be rotated by the viewer to show all sides of the protein. Throughout this text, you'll find images of protein structures that have been obtained from the Protein Data Bank.

There is a vast array of resources available for researchers anywhere in the world to use free of charge. Let us now consider the types of questions scientists can address using these resources.

Identifying Protein-Coding Genes and Understanding Their Functions

Using available DNA sequences, geneticists can study genes directly, rather than taking the classical genetic approach, which requires determining the function of an unknown gene from the phenotype. But this more recent approach poses a new challenge: What does the gene actually do? Given a long DNA sequence from a database such as Gen-Bank, scientists aim to identify all protein-coding genes in the sequence and ultimately their functions. This process is called **gene annotation**, and it involves three lines of evidence to identify a gene.

First, computers are used to search for patterns that indicate genes. The usual approach is to use software to scan the stored sequences for transcriptional and translational start and stop signals, for RNA-splicing sites, and for other telltale signs of protein-coding genes. The software also looks for certain short sequences that specify known mRNAs. Thousands of such sequences, called *expressed sequence tags*, or *ESTs*, have been collected from cDNA sequences and are catalogued in computer databases. This type of analysis identifies sequences that may be previously unknown protein-coding genes.

Although the identities of about half of the human genes were known before the Human Genome Project began, the other genes, previously unknown, were revealed by DNA sequence analysis. Once such suspected genes are identified, the second step is to obtain clues about their identities and functions by using software to compare their sequences with those of known genes from other organisms. Due to redundancy in the genetic code, the DNA sequence itself may vary more among species than the protein sequence does. Thus, scientists interested in proteins often compare the predicted amino acid sequence of a protein to that of other proteins. Third, the identities of these genes must then be confirmed by using RNA-seq or some other method to show that the relevant RNA is actually expressed from the proposed gene.

Sometimes a newly identified sequence will match, at least partially, the sequence of a gene or protein whose function is well known. For example, a plant researcher working on signalling pathways in the muskmelon would be excited to see that a partial amino acid sequence from a gene she had identified matched with sequences in other species encoding a so-called "WD40 domain" (see Figure 21.3). These WD40 domains are present in many eukaryotes and are known to function in signal transduction pathways. Alternatively, a new gene sequence might be similar to a previously encountered sequence whose function is still unknown. Another possibility is that the sequence is entirely unlike anything ever seen before. This was true for about a third of the genes of *E. coli* when its genome was sequenced. In the last case, protein function is usually deduced through a combination of biochemical and functional studies. The biochemical approach aims to determine the three-dimensional structure of the protein as well as other attributes, such as potential binding sites for other molecules. Functional studies usually involve *knocking out* (blocking or disabling) the gene in an organism to see how the phenotype is affected. The CRISPR-Cas 9 system, described in Concept 20.2, is an example of an experimental technique used to block gene function.

Understanding Genes and Gene Expression at the Systems Level

The impressive computational power provided by the tools of bioinformatics allows the study of whole sets of genes and their interactions, as well as the comparison of genomes from different species. Genomics is a rich source of new insights into fundamental questions about genome organization, regulation of gene expression, embryonic development, and evolution.

One informative approach has been taken by a recently completed research project called ENCODE (Encyclopedia of DNA Elements), which ran from 2003 to 2012. The aim of the project was to learn everything possible about the functionally important elements in the human genome using multiple experimental techniques on different types of cultured cells. Investigators sought to identify protein-coding genes and genes for noncoding RNAs, along with sequences that regulate gene expression, such as enhancers and promoters. In addition, they extensively characterized DNA and histone modifications and chromatin structure—features termed *epigenetic*, since they vary in significant ways without changing the sequence of nucleotide bases (see Concept 18.2). The second phase of the project,

involving more than 440 scientists in 32 research groups, culminated with the simultaneous publication of 30 papers in 2012 describing over 1600 large data sets. The power of this project is that it provides the opportunity to compare results from specific projects with each other, yielding a much richer picture of the whole genome.

Perhaps the most striking finding is that about 75% of the genome is transcribed at some point in at least one of the cell types studied, even though less than 2% codes for proteins. Furthermore, biochemical functions have been assigned to DNA elements making up at least 80% of the genome. To learn more about the different types of functional elements, parallel projects are analyzing, in a similar way, the genomes of two model organisms, the soil nematode *Caenorhabditis elegans* and the fruit fly *Drosophila melanogaster*. Because genetic and biochemical experiments using DNA technology can be performed on these species, testing the activities of potentially functional DNA elements in their genomes is expected to illuminate the workings of the human genome.

Because the ENCODE project analyzed cells in culture, its potential for clinical applications was limited. A related project called the Roadmap Epigenomics Project set out to characterize the *epigenome*—the epigenetic features of the genome—of hundreds of human cell types and tissues. The aim was to focus on the epigenomes of stem cells, normal tissues from mature adults, and relevant tissues from individuals with diseases such as cancer and neurodegenerative and autoimmune disorders. In 2015, a series of papers reported on the results from 111 tissues. One of the most useful findings was that the original tissue in which a cancer arose can be identified in cells of a secondary tumour based on characterization of their epigenomes.

Systems Biology

The scientific progress resulting from sequencing genomes and studying large sets of genes has encouraged scientists to attempt similar systematic studies of sets of proteins and their properties (such as their abundance, chemical modifications, and interactions), an approach called **proteomics**. (A **proteome** is the entire set of proteins expressed by a cell or group of cells.) Proteins, not the genes that encode them, carry out most of the activities of the cell. Therefore, we must study when and where proteins are produced in an organism, as well as how they interact in networks, if we are to understand the functioning of cells and organisms.

Genomics and proteomics enable molecular biologists to approach the study of life from an increasingly global perspective. Using the tools we have described, biologists have begun to compile catalogues of genes and proteins—listings of all the "parts" that contribute to the operation of cells, tissues, and organisms. With such catalogues in hand, researchers have shifted their attention from the individual parts to their functional integration in biological systems. As you may recall,

▲ **Figure 21.4 The systems biology approach to protein interactions.** This global protein interaction map, developed by Charles Boone and colleagues at the University of Toronto, shows the likely interactions (lines) among about 4500 gene products (circles) in the yeast *Saccharomyces cerevisiae*. Circles of the same colour represent gene products involved in one of the 13 cellular functions listed around the map. The white dots represent proteins that haven't been assigned to any colour-coded function. The expanded area shows additional details of one map region where the gene products (blue dots) carry out amino acid biosynthesis, uptake, and related functions.

Concept 1.1 discussed this approach, called systems biology, which aims to model the dynamic behaviour of whole biological systems based on the study of the interactions among the system's parts. Because of the vast amounts of data generated in these types of studies, advances in computer technology and bioinformatics are crucial to studying systems biology.

One important use of the systems biology approach is to define gene and protein interaction networks. To map the protein interaction network in the yeast *Saccharomyces cerevisiae*, for instance, researchers used sophisticated techniques to knock out (disable) pairs of genes, one pair at a time, creating doubly mutant cells. They then used computer software to build a graphic model by "mapping" the gene products to certain locations in the model, based on the similarity of their interactions. This resulted in the network-like "functional map" of protein interactions shown in **Figure 21.4**. Processing the vast number of protein-protein interactions generated by this experiment and integrating them into the completed map required powerful computers, mathematical tools, and newly developed software.

Application of Systems Biology to Medicine

The Cancer Genome Atlas is another example of systems biology in which a large group of interacting genes and gene products is analyzed together. This project, under the joint leadership of the National Cancer Institute and the NIH, aims to determine how changes in biological systems lead to cancer. A three-year pilot project ending in 2010 set out to find all the common mutations in three types of cancer—lung cancer,

ovarian cancer, and glioblastoma of the brain—by comparing gene sequences and patterns of gene expression in cancer cells with those in normal cells. Work on glioblastoma confirmed the role of several suspected genes and identified a few previously unknown ones, suggesting possible new targets for therapies. The approach proved so fruitful for these three types of cancer that it has been extended to 10 other types, chosen because they are common and often lethal in humans.

As high-throughput techniques become more rapid and less expensive, they are being increasingly applied to the problem of cancer, such as the Road Epigenomics Project described earlier. Rather than sequencing only protein-coding genes, sequencing the whole genomes of many tumours of a particular type allows scientists to uncover common chromosomal abnormalities, as well as any other consistent changes in these aberrant genomes.

In addition to whole genome sequencing, silicon and glass "chips" that hold a microarray of most of the known human genes are now used to analyze gene expression patterns in patients suffering from various cancers and other diseases (**Figure 21.5**). Analyzing which genes are over- or underexpressed in a particular cancer may allow physicians to tailor patients' treatment to their unique genetic makeup and the specifics of their cancers. This approach has been used to characterize subsets of particular cancers, enabling more refined treatments. Breast cancer is one example (see Figure 18.28).

Ultimately, medical records may include an individual's DNA sequence, a sort of genetic bar code, with regions highlighted that predispose the person to specific diseases. The use

◄ Figure 21.5 **A human gene microarray chip.** Tiny spots of DNA arranged in a grid on this silicon wafer represent almost all of the genes in the human genome. Using this chip, researchers can analyze expression patterns for all these genes at the same time.

Affymetrix

of such sequences for personalized medicine—disease prevention and treatment—has great potential.

Systems biology is a very efficient way to study emergent properties at the molecular level. Novel properties arise at each successive level of biological complexity as a result of the arrangement of building blocks at the underlying level (see Concept 1.1). The more we can learn about the arrangement and interactions of the components of genetic systems, the deeper will be our understanding of whole organisms. Canada is contributing to this understanding by conducting innovative genomics research. Through support from Genome Canada, many ongoing Canadian genomics research projects are producing tangible results that will have an impact on both Canadian communities and the global population. These projects span many different research topics, including forestry, fisheries, human health, and the development of new technologies (Figure 21.6).

CONCEPT CHECK 21.2

1. What role does the Internet play in current genomics and proteomics research?

2. Explain the advantage of the systems biology approach to studying cancer versus the approach of studying a single gene at a time.

3. **MAKE CONNECTIONS** The ENCODE pilot project found that at least 75% of the genome is transcribed into RNAs, far more than could be accounted for by protein-coding genes. Review Concept 18.3 and suggest some roles that these RNAs might play.

4. **MAKE CONNECTIONS** In Concept 20.2, you learned about genome-wide association studies. Explain how these studies use the systems biology approach.

For suggested answers, see Appendix A.

CONCEPT 21.3

Genomes vary in size, number of genes, and gene density

The sequences of thousands of genomes have been completed, with tens of thousands of genomes either in progress or considered permanent drafts (because they require more work than it would be worth to complete them). Among the sequences in progress are roughly 3400 metagenomes. In the completely

sequenced group, about 5000 are genomes of bacteria, and 242 are archaeal genomes. There are 283 completed eukaryotic species along with 2635 permanent drafts. Among these are vertebrates, invertebrates, protists, fungi, and plants. Next, we'll discuss what we've learned about genome size, number of genes, and gene density, focusing on general trends.

Genome Size

Comparing the three domains (Bacteria, Archaea, and Eukarya), we find a general difference in genome size between prokaryotes and eukaryotes (Table 21.1). While there are some exceptions, most bacterial genomes have between 1 and 6 million base pairs (Mb); the genome of *E. coli*, for instance, has 4.6 Mb. Genomes of archaea are, for the most part, within the size range of bacterial genomes. (Keep in mind, however, that many fewer archaeal genomes have been completely sequenced, so this picture may change.) Eukaryotic genomes tend to be larger: The genome of the single-celled yeast *Saccharomyces cerevisiae* (a fungus) has about 12 Mb, while most animals

Table 21.1 Genome Sizes and Estimated Numbers of Genes*			
Organism	**Haploid Genome Size (Mb)**	**Number of Genes**	**Genes per Mb**
Bacteria			
Haemophilus influenzae	1.8	1700	940
Escherichia coli	4.6	4400	950
Archaea			
Archaeoglobus fulgidus	2.2	2500	1130
Methanosarcina barkeri	4.8	3600	750
Eukaryotes			
Saccharomyces cerevisiae (yeast, a fungus)	12	6300	525
Caenorhabditis elegans (nematode)	100	20 100	200
Arabidopsis thaliana (mustard family plant)	120	27 000	225
Daphnia pulex (water flea)	200	31 000	155
Drosophila melanogaster (fruit fly)	165	14 000	85
Urticularia gibba (bladderwort)	82	28 500	348
Zea mays (corn)	2300	32 000	14
Mus musculus (house mouse)	2600	22 000	11
Ailuropoda melanoleuca (giant panda)	2400	21 000	9
Homo sapiens (human)	3000	<21 000	7
Paris japonica (Japanese canopy plant)	149 000	ND	ND

*Some values given here are likely to be revised as genome analysis continues.
MB = million base pairs. ND = not determined.

and plants, which are multicellular, have genomes of at least 100 Mb. There are 165 Mb in the fruit fly genome, while humans have 3000 Mb, about 500 to 3000 times as many as a typical bacterium.

Aside from this general difference between prokaryotes and eukaryotes, a comparison of genome sizes among eukaryotes fails to reveal any systematic relationship between genome size and the organism's phenotype. For instance, the genome of *Paris japonica*, the Japanese canopy plant, contains 149 billion base pairs (149 000 Mb), while that of another plant, *Utricularia gibba*, the bladderwort, contains only 82 Mb. Even more striking, there is a single-celled amoeba, *Polychaos dubium*, whose genome size has been estimated at 670 billion base pairs (670 000 Mb). (This genome has not yet been sequenced.) On a finer scale, comparing two insect species, the cricket (*Anabrus simplex*) genome turns out to have 11 times as many base pairs as the *Drosophila melanogaster* genome. There is a wide range of genome sizes within the groups of unicellular eukaryotes, insects, amphibians, and plants and less of a range within mammals and reptiles.

Number of Genes

The number of genes also varies between prokaryotes and eukaryotes: Bacteria and archaea, in general, have fewer genes than eukaryotes. Free-living bacteria and archaea have from 1500 to 7500 genes, while the number of genes in eukaryotes ranges from about 5000 for unicellular fungi (yeasts) to at least 40 000 for some multicellular eukaryotes.

Within the eukaryotes, the number of genes in a species is often lower than expected from considering simply the size of its genome. Looking at Table 21.1, you can see that the genome of the nematode *C. elegans* is 100 Mb in size and contains roughly 20 100 genes. The *Drosophila melanogaster* genome, in comparison, is much bigger (165 Mb) but has only about two-thirds the number of genes—only 14 000 genes.

Considering an example closer to home, we noted that the human genome contains 3000 Mb, well over 10 times the size of either the *D. melanogaster* or *C. elegans* genome. At the outset of the Human Genome Project, biologists expected somewhere between 50 000 and 100 000 genes to be identified in the completed sequence, based on the

---

▼ Figure 21.6

Exploring Genomics Research in Canada

International Barcode of Life (iBOL)

◀ International Barcode of Life Network

Dr. Paul Hebert, at the University of Guelph, is leading an international consortium that is developing a comprehensive DNA barcode library for all species. This project is building a reference library of short (648 base pair) sequences from a standard segment of the mitochondrial DNA genome for all animal species. A similar library is being developed for plants based on two other gene regions. These reference libraries will create a DNA-based identification system (similar to scanning a barcode at the grocery store) that will allow anyone to quickly identify any species, anywhere. The potential applications of this tool are wide-ranging, including the identification of species in the field, the identification of smuggled endangered species, or the identification of disease-causing protists.

MonicaSchroeder/ScienceSource

DesignPicsInc/Alamy stock Photo

◀ GRASP: Genomics Research on Atlantic Salmon Project

Researchers William Davidson, from Simon Fraser University, and Ben Koop, from the University of Victoria, analyzed the genome of Atlantic salmon. The model of Atlantic salmon was chosen for this study due in part to its economic value (80% of all farmed salmon in British Columbia is Atlantic salmon). The researchers developed a microarray to analyze gene expression, and produced genetic maps. The data produced by this project has impacted the design of breeding programs, conservation strategies, and fisheries management. Currently, the data is being used to learn more about how Atlantic salmon fight pathogens.

▲ Genetics of Type 2 Diabetes Mellitus

Robert Sladek, of McGill University, is leading a team of Quebec scientists in a project that aims to identify genes that predispose people to developing type 2 diabetes mellitus. Currently, more than 2.5 million Canadians have this disorder. The identification of genes associated with type 2 diabetes may lead to the development of strategies that can prevent, treat, and even cure this disorder.

CNRI/ScienceSource

◀ Toward Single Cell Genomics

The cells in a multicellular organism can become specialized to have different functions. For example, in the human body neuronal cells have a different function than skin cells or liver cells or T cells. The exact way these cells become specialized is not well understood.

In order to analyze gene expression in a single cell, scientists need RNA; however, this is difficult to obtain given that cells are small (so small in fact that ~60 000 cells can fit on the head of a single pin). Carl Hansen and Marco Marra, scientists at the University of British Columbia, are trying to develop a new approach to analyze gene expression within a single cell. This new approach could lead to information on how cells become specialized or how cells become cancerous, resulting in the identification of gene targets and contributing to drug development.

number of known human proteins. As the project progressed, the estimate was revised downward several times, and the ENCODE project discussed above has established the number to be fewer than 21 000. This relatively low number, similar to the number of genes in the nematode *C. elegans*, surprised biologists, who had been expecting many more human genes.

What genetic attributes allow humans (and other vertebrates) to get by with no more genes than nematodes? An important factor is that vertebrate genomes "get more bang for the buck" from their coding sequences because of extensive alternative splicing of RNA transcripts. Recall that this process generates more than one polypeptide from a single gene (see Figure 18.13). A typical human gene contains about 10 exons, and an estimated 90% or more of these multi-exon genes are spliced in at least two different ways. Some genes are expressed in hundreds of alternatively spliced forms, others in just two. It is not yet possible to catalogue all of the different forms, but it is clear that the number of different proteins encoded in the human genome far exceeds the proposed number of genes.

Additional polypeptide diversity could result from post-translational modifications such as cleavage or the addition of carbohydrate groups in different cell types or at different developmental stages. Finally, the discovery of miRNAs and other small RNAs that play regulatory roles have added a new variable to the mix (see Concept 18.3). Some scientists think that this added level of regulation, when present, may contribute to greater organismal complexity for a given number of genes.

Gene Density and Noncoding DNA

We can take both genome size and number of genes into account by comparing gene density in different species. In other words, we can ask: How many genes there are in a given length of DNA? When we compare the genomes of bacteria, archaea, and eukaryotes, we see that eukaryotes generally have larger genomes but fewer genes in a given number of base pairs. Humans have hundreds or thousands of times as many base pairs in their genome as most bacteria, as we already noted, but only 5 to 15 times as many genes; thus, gene density is lower in humans (see Table 21.1). Even

▼ ARCTIC: Assessment of Risk for Colorectal Tumours in Canada

Colon/rectal cancer

Peter Gardiner/Science Source

- Transverse colon
- Tumour (colon)
- Ascending colon
- Descending colon
- Tumour (rectum)

Tom Hudson, a scientist at the Ontario Institute of Cancer Research, and Brent Zanke, from the Ottawa Health Research Institute, are leading a team of researchers in a project to identify genetic factors that can predict susceptibility to colon cancer. There are 16 000 cases of colon cancer every year in Canada, including 6000 deaths. Early detection of colon cancer is associated with better survival, and an increased understanding of colorectal cancer genetics will lead to the development of tests that can identify people at risk. Cancers of the colon and rectum are among the most common cancers in developed countries.

▶ The Tria Project: Mountain Pine Beetle System Genomics

A team of scientists led by Joerg Bohlmann at the University of British Columbia and by Steven Jones and Inanc Birol at Canada's Michael Smith Genome Sciences Centre recently decoded the genome of the mountain pine beetle. This insect has caused widespread damage to lodgepole pine forests across western Canada. Over 18 million hectares of lodgepole pine have been infested in BC alone (that is more than twice the size of New Brunswick and more than three times the size of Nova Scotia). Having a good understanding of this beetle's genome may lead to strategies that can assist with managing the current epidemic and with better prediction of future outbreaks. For example, genome variation between individual beetles may help the beetles to cope with different environments, changing climate, or new hosts. Also, the researchers have identified genes that help the beetle thrive: genes that encode enzymes to detoxify defence compounds produced by the pine trees, to degrade plant cells walls, and to produce beetle pheromones to coordinate mass attack. You'll learn more about the mountain pine beetle outbreak in Chapter 56.

All Canada Photos/Alamy stock Photos

◀ Stem Cell Genomics

SPL/Science Source

The Stem Cell Genomics Project was a collaboration of 25 Canadian scientists, led by University of Ottawa scientist Michael Rudnicki, that analyzed the gene expression patterns of stem cells from embryonic and adult tissues in humans and mice. An understanding of stem cells is key to the field of regenerative medicine and could lead to stem cell treatments for many diseases, including diabetes, stroke, Alzheimer's disease, and muscular dystrophy. Experimental data from the project, consisting of more than 1400 gene expression data sets, is available in StemBase (www.stembase.ca), a public database and analysis platform.

unicellular eukaryotes, such as yeasts, have fewer genes per million base pairs than bacteria and archaea. Among the genomes that have been sequenced completely, humans and other mammals have the lowest gene density.

In all bacterial genomes studied so far, most of the DNA consists of genes for protein, tRNA, or rRNA; the small amount remaining consists mainly of nontranscribed regulatory sequences, such as promoters. The sequence of nucleotides along a bacterial protein-coding gene is not interrupted by noncoding sequences (introns). In eukaryotic genomes, by contrast, most of the DNA neither encodes protein nor is transcribed into RNA molecules of known function, and the DNA includes more complex regulatory sequences. In fact, humans have 10 000 times as much noncoding DNA as bacteria. Some of this DNA in multicellular eukaryotes is present as introns within genes. Indeed, introns account for most of the difference in average length between human genes (27 000 base pairs) and bacterial genes (1000 base pairs).

In addition to introns, multicellular eukaryotes have a vast amount of non-protein-coding DNA between genes. In the next section, we will describe the composition and arrangement of these great stretches of DNA in the human genome.

CONCEPT CHECK 21.3

1. **MAKE CONNECTIONS** According to the best current estimate, the human genome contains fewer than 21 000 genes. However, there is evidence that human cells produce many more than 21 000 different polypeptides. What processes might account for this discrepancy? (See Concept 18.2.)

2. The Genomes Online Database (GOLD) website of the Joint Genome Institute has information about genome sequencing projects. Go to https://gold.jgi-psf.org/statistics, scroll through the page, and describe the information you find there. What percent of bacterial genome projects have medical relevance?

3. **WHAT IF?** What evolutionary processes might account for prokaryotes having smaller genomes than eukaryotes?

For suggested answers, see Appendix A.

CONCEPT 21.4

Multicellular eukaryotes have a lot of noncoding DNA and many multigene families

We have spent most of this chapter, and indeed this unit, focusing on genes that code for proteins. Yet the coding regions of these genes and noncoding RNA products such as rRNA, tRNA, and miRNA make up only a small portion of the genomes of most multicellular eukaryotes. For example, once the sequencing of the human genome was completed, it became clear that only a tiny part—about 1.5%—codes for proteins or is transcribed into rRNAs or tRNAs. **Figure 21.7** shows what is known about the makeup of the remaining 98.5% of the genome.

Gene-related regulatory sequences and introns account, respectively, for 5% and about 20% of the human genome.

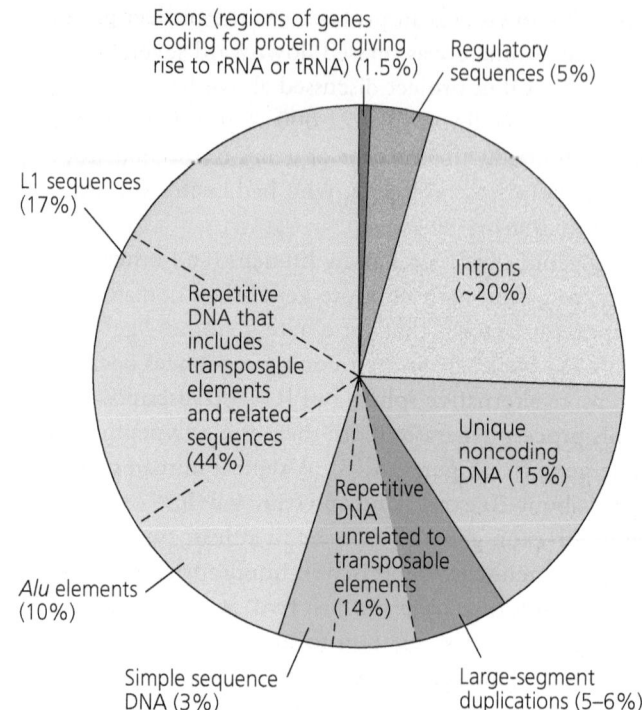

▲ Figure 21.7 **Types of DNA sequences in the human genome.** The gene sequences that code for proteins or are transcribed into rRNA or tRNA molecules make up only about 1.5% of the human genome (dark purple in the pie chart), while introns and regulatory sequences associated with genes (lighter purple) make up about a quarter. The vast majority of the human genome does not code for proteins or give rise to known RNAs, and much of it is repetitive DNA (dark and light green and teal). Because repetitive DNA is the most difficult to sequence and analyze, classification of some portions is tentative, and the percentages given here may shift slightly as genome analysis proceeds.

The rest, located between functional genes, includes some unique (single-copy) noncoding DNA, such as gene fragments and **pseudogenes**, former genes that have accumulated mutations over a long time and no longer produce functional proteins. (The genes that produce small noncoding RNAs are a tiny percentage of the genome, distributed between the 20% introns and the 15% unique noncoding DNA.) Most of the DNA between functional genes, however, is repetitive DNA, which consists of sequences that are present in multiple copies in the genome.

The bulk of many eukaryotic genomes consists of DNA sequences that neither code for proteins nor are transcribed to produce RNAs with known functions; this noncoding DNA was often described in the past as "junk DNA." However, genome comparisons over the past 10 years have revealed the persistence of this DNA in diverse genomes over many hundreds of generations. For example, the genomes of humans, rats, and mice contain almost 500 regions of noncoding DNA that are *identical* in sequence in all three species. This is a higher level of sequence conservation than is seen for protein-coding regions in these species, strongly suggesting that the noncoding regions have important functions. The results of the ENCODE project discussed earlier have underscored the key roles played by much of this noncoding DNA. In the next few pages, we examine how genes and noncoding DNA sequences are organized within genomes of multicellular eukaryotes, using the human genome as our main example. Genome organization tells us much about how genomes have evolved and continue to evolve, the subject of the next section in this chapter.

Transposable Elements and Related Sequences

Both prokaryotes and eukaryotes have stretches of DNA that can move from one location to another within the genome. These stretches are known as *transposable genetic elements*, or simply **transposable elements**. During the process called *transposition*, a transposable element moves from one site in a cell's DNA to a different target site by a type of recombination process. Transposable elements are sometimes called "jumping genes," but actually they never completely detach from the cell's DNA. Instead, the original and new DNA sites are brought very close together by enzymes and other proteins that bend the DNA. Surprisingly, about 75% of this repetitive DNA (44% of the entire human genome) is made up of transposable elements and sequences related to them.

The first evidence for wandering DNA segments came from American geneticist Barbara McClintock's breeding experiments with Indian corn (maize) in the 1940s and 1950s (Figure 21.8). As she tracked corn plants through multiple generations, McClintock identified changes in the colour of corn kernels that made sense only if she postulated the existence of genetic elements capable of moving from other locations in the genome into the genes for kernel colour, disrupting the genes so that the kernel colour was changed. McClintock's discovery was met with great scepticism and virtually discounted at the time. Her careful work and insightful ideas were finally validated many years later when transposable elements were found in bacteria. In 1983, at the age of 81, McClintock received the Nobel Prize for her pioneering research.

Movement of Transposons and Retrotransposons

Eukaryotic transposable elements are of two types. The first type are **transposons**, which move within a genome by means

AP Wide World Photos

Virginia Walbot

◀ Figure 21.8 **The effect of transposable elements on corn kernel colour.** Barbara McClintock first proposed the idea of mobile genetic elements after observing variegations in corn kernel colour (right).

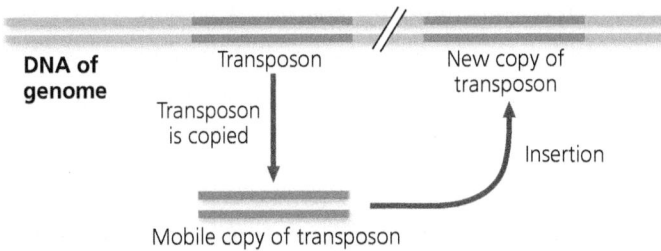

▲ Figure 21.9 **Transposon movement.** Movement of transposons by either the copy-and-paste mechanism (shown here) or the cut-and-paste mechanism involves a double-stranded DNA intermediate that is inserted into the genome.

Source: Figure adapted from THE WORLD OF THE CELL, 3rd Edition, by Wayne M. Becker, Jane B. Reece, and Martin F. Poenie. Copyright © 1996 by Pearson Education, Inc. Adapted and electronically reproduced by permission of Pearson Education, Inc., Upper Saddle River, New Jersey.

? *How would this figure differ if it showed the cut-and-paste mechanism?*

of a DNA intermediate. Transposons can move by a "cut-and-paste" mechanism, which removes the element from the original site, or by a "copy-and-paste" mechanism, which leaves a copy behind (Figure 21.9). Both mechanisms require an enzyme called *transposase*, which is generally encoded by the transposon.

Most transposable elements in eukaryotic genomes are of the second type, **retrotransposons**, which move by means of an RNA intermediate that is a transcript of the retrotransposon DNA. Thus, retrotransposons always leave a copy at the original site during transposition, since they are initially transcribed into an RNA intermediate (Figure 21.10). To insert at another site, the RNA intermediate is first converted back to DNA by reverse transcriptase, an enzyme encoded by the retrotransposon. (Reverse transcriptase is also encoded by retroviruses, as you learned in Concept 19.2. In fact, retroviruses may have evolved from retrotransposons.) Another cellular enzyme catalyzes insertion of the reverse-transcribed DNA at a new site.

▲ Figure 21.10 **Retrotransposon movement.** Movement begins with formation of a single-stranded RNA intermediate. The remaining steps are essentially identical to part of the retrovirus replicative cycle (see Figure 19.10).

Source: Figure adapted from *The World of the Cell*, 3rd Edition, by Wayne M. Becker, Jane B. Reece, and Martin F. Poenie. Copyright © 1996 by Pearson Education, Inc. Adapted and electronically reproduced by permission of Pearson Education, Inc., Upper Saddle River, New Jersey.

Sequences Related to Transposable Elements

Multiple copies of transposable elements and sequences related to them are scattered throughout eukaryotic genomes. A single unit is usually hundreds to thousands of base pairs long, and the dispersed copies are similar but usually not identical to each other. Some of these are transposable elements that can move; the enzymes required for this movement may be encoded by any transposable element, including the one that is moving. Others are related sequences that have lost the ability to move altogether. Transposable elements and related sequences make up 25–50% of most mammalian genomes (see Figure 21.7) and even higher percentages in amphibians and many plants. In fact, the very large size of some plant genomes is accounted for by extra transposable elements rather than by extra genes. For example, transposable elements make up 85% of the corn genome!

In humans and other primates, a large portion of transposable element–related DNA consists of a family of similar sequences called *Alu elements*. These sequences alone account for approximately 10% of the human genome. *Alu* elements are about 300 nucleotides long, much shorter than most functional transposable elements, and they do not code for any protein. However, many *Alu* elements are transcribed into RNA, and at least some of these RNAs are thought to help regulate gene expression.

An even larger percentage (17%) of the human genome is made up of a type of retrotransposon called *LINE-1*, or *L1*. These sequences are much longer than *Alu* elements—about 6500 base pairs—and typically have a very low rate of transposition. However, researchers working with rats have found *L1* retrotransposons to be more active in cells of the developing brain. They have proposed that different effects on gene expression of *L1* retrotransposition in developing neurons may contribute to the great diversity of neuronal cell types (see Concept 48.1).

Although many transposable elements encode proteins, these proteins do not carry out normal cellular functions. Therefore, transposable elements are usually included in the "noncoding" DNA category, along with other repetitive sequences.

Other Repetitive DNA, Including Simple Sequence DNA

Repetitive DNA that is not related to transposable elements probably arises due to mistakes during DNA replication or recombination. Such DNA accounts for about 14% of the human genome (see Figure 21.7). About a third of this (5–6% of the human genome) consists of duplications of long stretches of DNA, with each unit ranging from 10 000 to 300 000 base pairs. These long segments seem to have been copied from one chromosomal location to another site on the same or a different chromosome and probably include some functional genes.

In contrast to scattered copies of long sequences, **simple sequence DNA** contains many copies of tandemly repeated short sequences, as in the following example (showing one DNA strand only):

… GTTACGTTACGTTACGTTACGTTACGTTAC …

In this case, the repeated unit (GTTAC) consists of five nucleotides. Repeated units may contain as many as 500 nucleotides, but often contain fewer than 15 nucleotides, as in this example. When the unit contains two to five nucleotides, the series of repeats is called a **short tandem repeat**, or **STR**; we discussed the use of STR analysis in preparing genetic profiles in Concept 20.4. The number of copies of the repeated unit can vary from site to site within a given genome. There could be as many as several hundred thousand repetitions of the GTTAC unit at one site, but only half that number at another. STR analysis is performed on sites selected because they have relatively few repeats. The repeat number can vary from person to person, and since humans are diploid, each person has two alleles per site, which can differ. This diversity produces the variation represented in the genetic profiles that result from STR analysis. Altogether, simple sequence DNA makes up 3% of the human genome.

Much of a genome's simple sequence DNA is located at chromosomal telomeres and centromeres, suggesting that this DNA plays a structural role for chromosomes. The DNA at centromeres is essential for the separation of chromatids in cell division (see Concept 12.2). Centromeric DNA, along with simple sequence DNA located elsewhere, may also help organize the chromatin within the interphase nucleus. The simple sequence DNA located at telomeres, at the tips of chromosomes, prevents genes from being lost as the DNA shortens with each round of replication (see Concept 16.2). Telomeric DNA also binds proteins that protect the ends of a chromosome from degradation and from joining to other chromosomes.

Short repetitive sequences like those described here provide a challenge for whole genome shotgun sequencing, because the presence of many short repeats hinders accurate reassembly of fragment sequences by computers. Regions of simple sequence DNA account for much of the uncertainty present in estimates of whole genome sizes and are the reason some sequences are considered "permanent drafts."

Genes and Multigene Families

We finish our discussion of the various types of DNA sequences in eukaryotic genomes with a closer look at genes. Recall that DNA sequences that code for proteins or give rise to tRNA or rRNA compose a mere 1.5% of the human genome (see Figure 21.7). If we include introns and regulatory sequences associated with genes, the total amount of DNA that is gene-related—coding and noncoding—constitutes about 25% of the human genome. Put another way, only about 6% (1.5% out of 25%) of the length of the average gene is represented in the final gene product.

Like the genes of bacteria, many eukaryotic genes are present as unique sequences, with only one copy per haploid set of chromosomes. But in the human genome and the genomes of many other animals and plants, solitary genes make up less than half of the total gene-related DNA. The rest occur in **multigene families**, collections of two or more identical or very similar genes.

In multigene families that consist of *identical* DNA sequences, those sequences are usually clustered tandemly and, with the notable exception of the genes for histone proteins, have RNAs as their final products. An example is the family of identical DNA sequences that are the genes for the three largest rRNA molecules (Figure 21.11a). These rRNA molecules are transcribed from a single transcription unit that is repeated tandemly hundreds to thousands of times in one or several clusters in the genome of a multicellular eukaryote. The many copies of this rRNA transcription unit help cells to quickly make the millions of ribosomes needed for active protein synthesis. The primary transcript is cleaved to yield the three rRNA molecules, which combine with proteins and one other kind of rRNA (5S rRNA) to form ribosomal subunits.

The classic examples of multigene families of *nonidentical* genes are two related families of genes that encode globins, a group of proteins that include the α and β polypeptide subunits of hemoglobin. One family, located on chromosome 16 in humans, encodes various forms of α-globin; the other, on chromosome 11, encodes forms of β-globin (Figure 21.11b). The different forms of each globin subunit are expressed at different times in development, allowing hemoglobin to function effectively in the changing environment of the developing animal. In humans, for example, the embryonic and fetal forms of hemoglobin have a higher affinity for oxygen than the adult forms, ensuring the efficient transfer of oxygen from mother to fetus. Also found in the globin gene family clusters are several pseudogenes.

In Concept 21.5, we'll consider the evolution of these two globin gene families as we explore how arrangements of genes provide insight into the evolution of genomes. We'll also examine some processes that have shaped the genomes of different species over evolutionary time.

CONCEPT CHECK 21.4

1. Discuss the characteristics of mammalian genomes that make them larger than prokaryotic genomes.
2. Which of the three mechanisms described in Figures 21.9 and 21.10 result(s) in a copy remaining at the original site as well as a copy appearing in a new location?
3. Contrast the organizations of the rRNA gene family and the globin gene families. For each, explain how the existence of a family of genes benefits the organism.
4. **MAKE CONNECTIONS** Assign each DNA segment at the top of Figure 18.8 to a sector in the pie chart in Figure 21.7.

For suggested answers, see Appendix A.

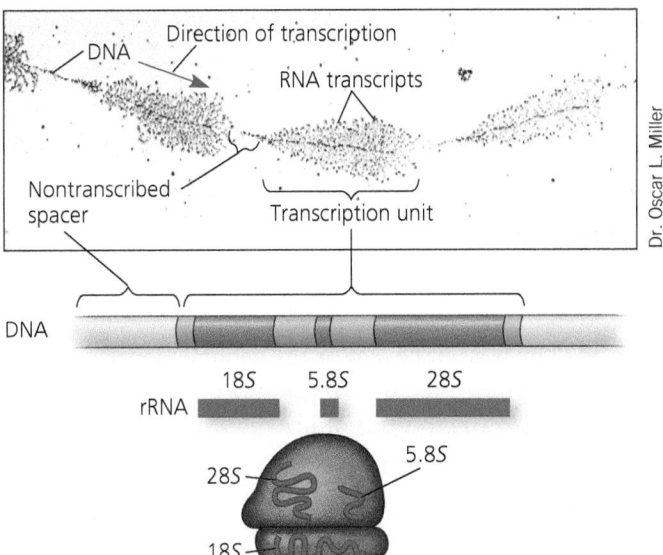

(a) Part of the ribosomal RNA gene family. The TEM at the top shows three of the hundreds of copies of rRNA transcription units in the rRNA gene family of a salamander genome. Each "feather" corresponds to a single unit being transcribed by about 100 molecules of RNA polymerase (dark dots along the DNA), moving left to right (red arrow). The growing RNA transcripts extend from the DNA, accounting for the feather-like appearance. In the diagram of a transcription unit below the TEM, the genes for three types of rRNA (darker blue) are adjacent to regions that are transcribed but later removed (medium blue). A single transcript is processed to yield one of each of the three rRNAs (red), key components of the ribosome.

(b) The human α-globin and β-globin gene families. Adult hemoglobin is composed of two α-globin and two β-globin polypeptide subunits, as shown in the molecular model. The genes (darker blue) encoding α- and β-globins are found in two families, organized as shown here. The noncoding DNA (light blue) separating the functional genes within each family includes pseudogenes (ψ; gold), versions of the functional genes that no longer encode functional polypeptides. Genes and pseudogenes are named with Greek letters, as you have seen previously for the α- and β-globins. Some genes are expressed only in the embryo or fetus.

▲ Figure 21.11 Gene families.

? In (a), how could you determine the direction of transcription if it wasn't indicated by the red arrow?

Duplication, rearrangement, and mutation of DNA contribute to genome evolution

EVOLUTION Now that we have explored the makeup of the human genome as an example, let's see what we can learn from the composition of the genome about how it evolved. The basis of change at the genomic level is mutation, which underlies much of genome evolution. It seems likely that the earliest forms of life had a minimal number of genes—those necessary for survival and reproduction. If this were indeed the case, one aspect of evolution must have been an increase in the size of the genome, with the extra genetic material providing the raw material for gene diversification. In this section, we will first describe how extra copies of all or part of a genome can arise and then consider subsequent processes that can lead to the evolution of proteins (or RNA products) with slightly different or entirely new functions.

Duplication of Entire Chromosome Sets

An accident in meiosis, such as failure to separate homologues during meiosis I, can result in one or more extra sets of chromosomes, a condition known as polyploidy. Although such accidents would most often be lethal, in rare cases they could facilitate the evolution of genes. In a polyploid organism, one set of genes can provide essential functions for the organism. The genes in the one or more extra sets can diverge by accumulating mutations; these variations may persist if the organism carrying them survives and reproduces. In this way, genes with novel functions can evolve. As long as one copy of an essential gene is expressed, the divergence of another copy can lead to its encoded protein acting in a novel way, thereby changing the organism's phenotype.

The outcome of this accumulation of mutations may eventually be the branching off of a new species. While polyploidy is rare among animals, it is relatively common among plants, especially flowering plants. Some botanists estimate that as many as 80% of the plant species that are alive today show evidence of polyploidy having occurred among their ancestral species. You'll learn more about how polyploidy leads to plant speciation in Concept 24.2.

Alterations of Chromosome Structure

With the recent explosion in genomic sequence information, we can now compare the chromosomal organizations of many different species in detail. This information allows us to make inferences about the evolutionary processes that shape chromosomes and may drive speciation. For example, scientists have long known that sometime in the last 6 million years, when the ancestors of humans and chimpanzees diverged as species, the fusion of two ancestral chromosomes in the human line led to different haploid numbers for humans ($n = 23$) and chimpanzees ($n = 24$). The banding patterns in stained chromosomes suggested that the ancestral versions of current chimpanzee chromosomes 12 and 13 fused end to end, forming chromosome 2 in an ancestor of the human lineage. With the recent explosion in genomic sequence information, we can now compare the chromosomal organizations of many different species on a much finer scale. This information allows us to make inferences about the evolutionary processes that shape chromosomes and may drive speciation. Sequencing and analysis of human chromosome 2 during the Human Genome Project provided very strong supporting evidence for the model we have just described (**Figure 21.12a**).

In another study of broader scope, researchers compared the DNA sequence of each human chromosome with the whole-genome sequence of the mouse. **Figure 21.12b** shows the results of this comparison for human chromosome 16: Large blocks of genes on this chromosome are found on four mouse chromosomes, indicating that the genes in each block stayed together during the evolution of the mouse and human lineages.

Performing the same comparative analysis between chromosomes of humans and six other mammalian species allowed the researchers to reconstruct the evolutionary history of chromosomal rearrangements in these eight species. They found many duplications and inversions of large portions of chromosomes, the result of errors during meiotic recombination in which the DNA broke and was rejoined incorrectly. The rate of these events seems to have accelerated about 100 million years ago, around the time large dinosaurs became extinct and the number of mammalian species increased rapidly. The apparent coincidence is interesting because chromosomal rearrangements are thought to contribute to the generation of new species. Although two individuals with different arrangements could still mate and produce offspring, the offspring would have two nonequivalent sets of chromosomes, making meiosis inefficient or even impossible. Thus, chromosomal rearrangements would lead to two populations that could not successfully mate with each other, a step on the way to their becoming two separate species. (You'll learn more about this in Concept 24.2.)

The same study also unearthed a pattern with medical relevance. Analysis of the chromosomal breakage points associated with the rearrangements showed that specific sites were used over and over again. A number of these recombination "hot spots" correspond to locations of chromosomal rearrangements within the human genome that are associated with congenital diseases (see Concept 15.4).

(a) Human and chimpanzee chromosomes. The positions of telomere-like and centromere-like sequences on human chromosome 2 (left) match those of telomeres on chimp chromosomes 12 and 13 and the centromere on chimp chromosome 13 (right). This suggests that chromosomes 12 and 13 in a human ancestor fused end to end to form human chromosome 2. The centromere from ancestral chromosome 12 remained functional on human chromosome 2, while the one from ancestral chromosome 13 did not.

(b) Human and mouse chromosomes. DNA sequences very similar to large blocks of human chromosome 16 (coloured areas in this diagram) are found on mouse chromosomes 7, 8, 16, and 17. This suggests that the DNA sequence in each block has stayed together in the mouse and human lineages since the time they diverged from a common ancestor.

▲ Figure 21.12 **Related chromosome sequences among mammals.**

Duplication and Divergence of Gene-Sized Regions of DNA

Errors during meiosis can also lead to the duplication of chromosomal regions that are smaller than the ones we've just discussed, including segments the length of individual genes. Unequal crossing over during prophase I of meiosis, for instance, can result in one chromosome with a deletion and another with a duplication of a particular gene. As illustrated in **Figure 21.13**, transposable elements can

▲ Figure 21.13 **Gene duplication due to unequal crossing over.** One mechanism by which a gene (or other DNA segment) can be duplicated is recombination during meiosis between copies of a transposable element flanking the gene. Such recombination between misaligned nonsister chromatids of homologous chromosomes produces one chromatid with two copies of the gene and one chromatid with no copy.

MAKE CONNECTIONS *Examine how crossing over occurs in Figure 13.12. In the middle panel above, draw a line through the portions that result in the upper chromatid in the bottom panel. Use a different colour to do the same for the other chromatid.*

provide homologous sites where nonsister chromatids can cross over, even when other chromatid regions are not correctly aligned.

Also, slippage can occur during DNA replication, such that the template shifts with respect to the new complementary strand, and a part of the template strand is either skipped by the replication machinery or used twice as a template. As a result, a segment of DNA is deleted or duplicated. It is easy to imagine how such errors could occur in regions of repeats. The variable number of repeated units of simple sequence DNA at a given site, used for STR analysis, is probably due to errors like these. Evidence that unequal crossing over and template slippage during DNA replication lead to duplication of genes is found in the existence of multigene families, such as the globin family.

Evolution of Genes with Related Functions: The Human Globin Genes

Figure 21.11b diagrams the organization of the α-globin and β-globin gene families. Now, let's consider how events such as duplications can lead to the evolution of genes with related functions like the globin genes. A comparison of gene sequences within a multigene family can suggest the order in which the genes arose. This approach to re-creating the evolutionary history of the globin genes indicates that they all evolved from one common ancestral globin gene that underwent duplication and divergence into the α-globin and β-globin ancestral genes about 450–500 million years ago (Figure 21.14). Each of these genes was later duplicated several times, and the copies then diverged from each other in sequence, yielding the current family members. In fact, the common ancestral globin gene also gave rise to the oxygen-binding muscle protein myoglobin and to the plant protein leghemoglobin. The latter two proteins function as monomers, and their genes are included in a "globin superfamily."

After the duplication events, the differences between the genes in the globin families undoubtedly arose from mutations that accumulated in the gene copies over many generations. The current model is that the necessary function provided by an α-globin protein, for example, was fulfilled by one gene, while other copies of the α-globin gene accumulated random mutations. Many mutations may have had an adverse effect on the organism and others may have had no effect, but a few mutations must have altered the function of the protein product in a way that was advantageous to the organism at a particular life stage without substantially changing the protein's oxygen-carrying function. Presumably, natural selection acted on these altered genes, maintaining them in the population.

In the Scientific Skills Exercise, you can compare amino acid sequences of the globin family members and see how such comparisons were used to generate the model for globin gene evolution shown in Figure 21.14. The existence of several pseudogenes among the functional globin genes provides additional evidence for this model: Random mutations in these "genes" over evolutionary time have destroyed their function.

Evolution of Genes with Novel Functions

In the evolution of the globin gene families, gene duplication and subsequent divergence produced family members whose protein products performed functions similar to each other (oxygen transport). However, an alternative scenario is that one copy of a duplicated gene can undergo alterations that lead to a completely new function for the protein product. The genes for lysozyme and α-lactalbumin are a good example.

Lysozyme is an enzyme that helps protect animals against bacterial infection by hydrolyzing bacterial cell walls; α-lactalbumin is a nonenzymatic protein that plays a role in milk production in mammals. The two proteins are quite similar in their amino acid sequences and three-dimensional structures (Figure 21.15 on p. 480). Both genes are found in mammals, but only the lysozyme gene is present in birds. These findings suggest that at some time after the lineages leading to mammals and birds had separated, the lysozyme gene was duplicated in the mammalian lineage but not in the avian lineage. Subsequently, one copy of the duplicated lysozyme gene evolved into a gene encoding α-lactalbumin, a protein with a completely different function affecting a key characteristic of mammals. In a recent study, evolutionary biologists searched vertebrate genomes for genes with similar sequences. There appear to be at least eight members of the lysozyme family, with related genes found in other mammalian species as well. The functions of all the encoded gene products are not yet known, but it will be exciting to discover whether they are as different as the functions of lysozyme and α-lactalbumin.

Besides the duplication and divergence of whole genes, rearrangement of existing DNA sequences within genes has also contributed to genome evolution. The presence of introns may have promoted the evolution of new proteins by facilitating the duplication or shuffling of exons, as we'll discuss next.

Rearrangements of Parts of Genes: Exon Duplication and Exon Shuffling

Recall from Concept 17.3 that an exon often codes for a protein domain, a distinct structural and functional region of a protein molecule. We've already seen that unequal crossing over during meiosis can lead to duplication of

▲ Figure 21.14 **A model for the evolution of the human α-globin and β-globin gene families from a single ancestral globin gene.**

? *The gold elements are pseudogenes. Explain how they could have arisen after gene duplication.*

Reading an Amino Acid Sequence Identity Table

How Have Amino Acid Sequences of Human Globin Genes Diverged During Their Evolution? To build a model of the evolutionary history of the globin genes (see Figure 21.14), researchers compared the amino acid sequences of the polypeptides they encode. In this exercise, you will analyze comparisons of the amino acid sequences of globin polypeptides to shed light on their evolutionary relationships.

How the Experiment Was Done Scientists obtained the DNA sequences for each of the eight globin genes and "translated" them into amino acid sequences. They then used a computer program to align the sequences (with dashes indicating gaps in one sequence) and calculate a percent identity value for each pair of globins. The percent identity reflects the number of positions with identical amino acids relative to the total number of amino acids in a globin polypeptide. The data were displayed in a table to show the pairwise comparisons.

Data from the Experiment The following table shows an example of a pairwise alignment—that of the α_1-globin (alpha-1 globin) and ζ-globin (zeta globin) amino acid sequences—using the standard single-letter symbols for amino acids. To the left of each line of amino acid sequence is the number of the first amino acid in that line. The percent identity value for the α_1- and ζ-globin amino acid sequences was calculated by

counting the number of matching amino acids (87, highlighted in yellow), dividing by the total number of amino acid positions (143), and then multiplying by 100. This resulted in a 61% identity value for the α_1-ζ pair, as shown in the amino acid identity table at the bottom of the page. The values for other globin pairs were calculated in the same way.

▲ Hemoglobin

Interpret the Data

1. Notice that in the alignment table, the data are arranged so each globin pair can be compared. (a) Notice that some cells in the table have dashed lines. Given the pairs that are being compared for these cells, what percent identity value is implied by the dashed lines? (b) Notice that the cells in the lower left half of the table are blank. Using the information already provided in the table, fill in the missing values. Why does it make sense that these cells were left blank?

2. The earlier that two genes arose from a duplicated gene, the more their nucleotide sequences can have diverged, which may result in amino acid differences in the protein products. (a) Based on that premise, identify which two genes are most divergent from each other. What is the percent amino acid identity between their polypeptides? (b) Using the same approach, identify which two globin genes are the most recently duplicated. What is the percent identity between them?

3. The model of globin gene evolution shown in Figure 21.14 suggests that an ancestral gene duplicated and mutated to become α- and β-globin genes, and then each one was further duplicated and mutated. What features of the data set support the model?

4. Make a list of all the percent identity values from the table, starting with 100% at the top. Next to each number write the globin pair(s) with that percent identity value. Use one colour for the globins from the α family and a different colour for the globins from the β family. (a) Compare the order of pairs on your list with their positions in the model shown in Figure 21.14. Does the order of pairs describe the same relative "closeness" of globin family members seen in the model? (b) Compare the percent identity values for pairs within the α or β group to the values for between-group pairs.

Data from NCBI database. © Jane B Reece. **Further Reading** R. C. Hardison, Globin genes on the move, *Journal of Biology* 7:35.1–35.5 (2008).

Globin	Alignment of Globin Amino Acid Sequences
α_1	1 MVLSPADKTNVKAAWGKVGAHAGEYGAEAL
ζ	1 MSLTKTERTIIVSMWAKISTQADTIGTETL
α_1	31 ERMFLSFPTTKTYFPHFDLSH-GSAQVKGH
ζ	31 ERLFLSHPQTKTYFPHFDL-HPGSAQLRAH
α_1	61 GKKVADALTNAVAHVDDMPNALSALSDLHA
ζ	61 GSKVVAAVGDAVKSIDDIGGALSKLSELHA
α_1	91 HKLRVDPVNFKLLSHCLLVTLAAHLPAEFT
ζ	91 YILRVDPVNFKLLSHCLLVTLAARFPADFT
α_1	121 PAVHASLDKFLASVSTVLTSKYR
ζ	121 AEAHAAWDKFLSVVSSVLTEKYR

Amino Acid Identity Table								
	α Family			**β Family**				
	α_1 (alpha 1)	α_2 (alpha 2)	ζ (zeta)	β (beta)	δ (delta)	ϵ (epsilon)	A_γ (gamma A)	G_γ (gamma G)
α Family α_1	-----	100	60	45	44	39	42	42
α_2		-----	60	45	44	39	42	42
ζ			-----	38	40	41	41	41
β Family β				-----	93	76	73	73
δ					-----	73	71	72
ϵ						-----	80	80
A_γ							-----	99
G_γ								-----

(a) Lysozyme

(b) α–lactalbumin

◀ Figure 21.15 **Comparison of lysozyme and α-lactalbumin proteins.** Computer-generated ribbon models of the similar structures of **(a)** lysozyme and **(b)** α-lactalbumin are shown, along with a comparison of the amino acid sequences of the two proteins. The amino acids are arranged in groups of 10 for ease of reading, and single-letter amino acid codes are used (see Figure 5.14). Identical amino acids are highlighted in yellow, and dashes indicate gaps in one sequence that have been introduced by the software to optimize the alignment.

| Lysozyme | 1 | KVFERCELAR | TLKRLGMDGY | RGISLANWMC | LAKWESGYNT | RATNYNAGDR |
| α–lactalbumin | 1 | KQFTKCELSQ | LLK--DIDGY | GGIALPELIC | TMFHTSGYDT | QAIVENN--E |

| Lysozyme | 51 | STDYGIFQIN | SRYWCNDGKT | PGAVNACHLS | CSALLQDNIA | DAVACAKRVV |
| α–lactalbumin | 51 | STEYGLFQIS | NKLWCKSSQV | PQSRNICDIS | CDKFLDDDIT | DDIMCAKKIL |

| Lysozyme | 101 | RDPQGIRAWV | AWRNRCQ-NR | DVRQYVQGCG | V | |
| α–lactalbumin | 101 | D-IKGIDYWL | AHKALCT--E | KLEQWLCEKL | – | |

(c) **Amino acid sequence alignments of lysozyme and α–lactalbumin**

a gene on one chromosome and its loss from the homologous chromosome (see Figure 21.13). By a similar process, a particular exon within a gene could be duplicated on one chromosome and deleted from the other. The gene with the duplicated exon would code for a protein containing a second copy of the encoded domain. This change in the protein's structure could augment its function by increasing its stability, enhancing its ability to bind a particular ligand, or altering some other property. Quite a few protein-coding genes have multiple copies of related exons, which presumably arose by duplication and then diverged. The gene encoding the extracellular matrix protein collagen is a good example. Collagen is a structural protein with a highly repetitive amino acid sequence, which reflects the repetitive pattern of exons in the collagen gene.

Alternatively, we can imagine the occasional mixing and matching of different exons either within a gene or between two different (nonallelic) genes owing to errors in meiotic recombination. This process, termed *exon shuffling*, could lead to new proteins with novel combinations of functions. As an example, let's consider the gene for tissue plasminogen activator (tPA). The tPA protein is an extracellular protein that helps control blood clotting. It has four domains of three types, each encoded by an exon; one exon is present in two copies. Because each type of exon is also found in other proteins, the current version of the gene for tPA is thought to have arisen by several instances of exon shuffling during errors in meiotic recombination and subsequent duplication **(Figure 21.16)**.

How Transposable Elements Contribute to Genome Evolution

The persistence of transposable elements as a large fraction of some eukaryotic genomes is consistent with the idea

▲ Figure 21.16 **Evolution of a new gene by exon shuffling.** Exon shuffling could have moved exons, each encoding a particular domain, from ancestral forms of the genes for epidermal growth factor, fibronectin, and plasminogen (left) into the evolving gene for tissue plasminogen activator, tPA (right). Duplication of the "kringle" exon from the plasminogen gene after its movement could account for the two copies of this exon in the tPA gene.

? *How could the presence of transposable elements within introns have facilitated the exon shuffling shown here?*

that they play an important role in shaping a genome over evolutionary time. These elements can contribute to the evolution of the genome in several ways. They can promote recombination, disrupt cellular genes or control elements, and carry entire genes or individual exons to new locations.

Transposable elements of similar sequence scattered throughout the genome facilitate recombination between different chromosomes by providing homologous regions for crossing over. Most such recombination events are probably detrimental, causing chromosomal translocations and other changes in the genome that may be lethal to the organism. But over the course of evolutionary time, an occasional recombination event of this sort may be advantageous to the organism. (For the change to be heritable, of course, it must happen in a cell that will give rise to a gamete.)

The movement of a transposable element can have a variety of consequences. For instance, if a transposable element "jumps" into the middle of a protein-coding sequence, it will prevent the production of a normal transcript of the gene. (Introns provide a sort of "safety zone" that does not affect the transcript, because the transposable element will be spliced out.) If a transposable element inserts within a regulatory sequence, the transposition may lead to increased or decreased production of one or more proteins. Transposition caused both types of effects on the genes coding for pigment-synthesizing enzymes in McClintock's corn kernels. Again, while such changes are usually harmful, in the long run some may provide a survival advantage. A possible example was mentioned earlier: At least some of the *Alu* transposable elements in the human genome are known to produce RNAs that regulate expression of human genes.

During transposition, a transposable element may carry along a gene or group of genes to a new position in the genome. This mechanism probably accounts for the location of the α-globin and β-globin gene families on different human chromosomes, as well as the dispersion of the genes of certain other gene families. By a similar tag-along process, an exon from one gene may be inserted into another gene in a mechanism similar to that of exon shuffling during recombination. For example, an exon may be inserted by transposition into the intron of a protein-coding gene. If the inserted exon is retained in the RNA transcript during RNA splicing, the protein that is synthesized will have an additional domain, which may confer a new function on the protein.

Most often, the processes discussed in this section produce harmful effects, which may be lethal, or no effect. In a few cases, however, small heritable changes may occur that are beneficial. Over many generations, the resulting genetic diversity provides valuable raw material for natural selection. Diversification of genes and their products is an important factor in the evolution of new species. Thus, the accumulation of changes in the genome of each species provides a record of its evolutionary history. To read this record, we must be able to identify genomic changes. Comparing the genomes of different species allows us to do that, increasing our understanding of how genomes evolve. You will learn more about these topics next.

CONCEPT CHECK 21.5

1. Describe three examples of errors in cellular processes that lead to DNA duplications.

2. Explain how multiple exons might have arisen in the ancestral EGF and fibronectin genes shown in Figure 21.16 (left).

3. What are three ways that transposable elements are thought to contribute to genome evolution?

4. **WHAT IF?** In 2005, Icelandic scientists reported finding a large chromosomal inversion present in 20% of northern Europeans, and they noted that Icelandic women with this inversion had significantly more children than women without it. What would you expect to happen to the frequency of this inversion in the Icelandic population in future generations?

For suggested answers, see Appendix A.

CONCEPT 21.6

Comparing genome sequences provides clues to evolution and development

EVOLUTION One researcher has likened the current state of biology to the Age of Exploration in the 1400s, which occurred soon after major improvements in navigation and ship design. In the last 30 years, we have seen rapid advances in genome sequencing and data collection, new techniques for assessing gene activity across the whole genome, and refined approaches for understanding how genes and their products work together in complex systems. We are truly poised on the brink of a new world.

Comparisons of genome sequences from different species reveal a lot about the evolutionary history of life, from very ancient to more recent. Similarly, comparative studies of the genetic programs that direct embryonic development in different species are beginning to clarify the mechanisms that generated the great diversity of life-forms present today. In this final section of the chapter, we will discuss what has been learned from these two approaches.

Comparing Genomes

The more similar in sequence the genes and genomes of two species are, the more closely related those species are in their evolutionary history—because not enough time has passed for mutations and other changes to accumulate.

Comparing genomes of closely related species sheds light on more recent evolutionary events, whereas comparing genomes of very distantly related species helps us understand ancient evolutionary history. In either case, learning about characteristics that are shared or divergent between groups enhances our picture of the evolution of organisms and biological processes. As you learned in Chapter 1, the evolutionary relationships between species can be represented by a diagram in the form of a tree (often turned sideways), where each branch point marks the divergence of two lineages. Figure 21.17 shows the evolutionary relationships of some groups and species we will discuss.

Comparing Distantly Related Species

Determining which genes have remained similar—that is, are *highly conserved*—in distantly related species can help clarify evolutionary relationships among species that diverged from each other long ago. Indeed, comparisons of the specific gene sequences of bacteria, archaea, and eukaryotes indicate that these three groups diverged between 2 and 4 billion years ago and strongly support the theory that they are the fundamental domains of life (see Figure 21.17).

In addition to their value in evolutionary biology, comparative genomic studies confirm the relevance of research on model organisms to our understanding of biology in general and human biology in particular. Very ancient genes can still be surprisingly similar in disparate species. A 2015 study

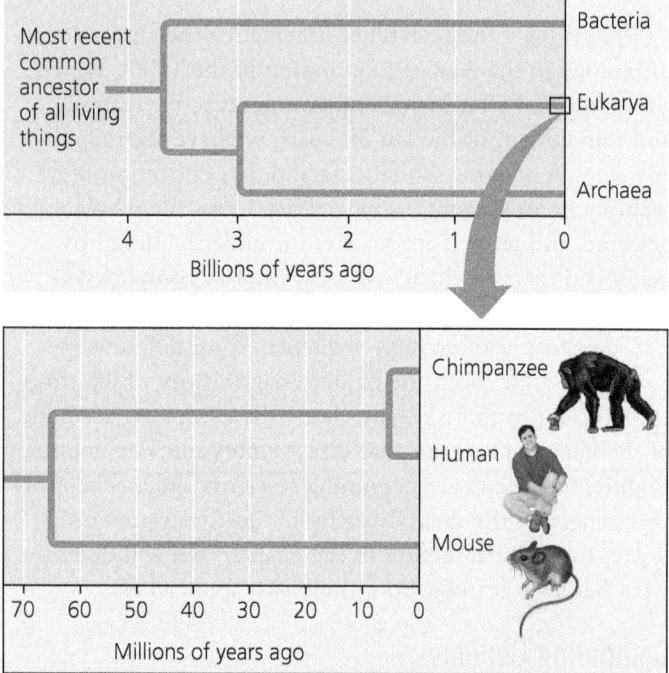

▲ Figure 21.17 **Evolutionary relationships of the three domains of life.** The tree diagram at the top shows the ancient divergence of bacteria, archaea, and eukaryotes. A portion of the eukaryote lineage is expanded in the inset to show the more recent divergence of three mammalian species discussed in this chapter.

focused on 414 important yeast genes, and tested the ability of the human version of each gene to function equivalently in yeast cells. Remarkably, the researchers concluded that 47% of these yeast genes could be replaced by the human gene. This striking result underscores the common origin of yeasts and humans—two distantly related species.

Comparing Closely Related Species

The genomes of two closely related species are likely to be organized similarly because of their relatively recent divergence. Their recently shared history also means that only a small number of gene differences are found when their genomes are compared. The particular genetic differences can therefore be more easily correlated with phenotypic differences between the two species. An exciting application of this type of analysis is seen as researchers compare the human genome with the genomes of the chimpanzee, mouse, rat, and other mammals. Identifying the genes shared by all of these species but not by nonmammals gives us clues about what it takes to make a mammal, while finding the genes shared by chimpanzees and humans but not by rodents tells us something about primates. And, of course, comparing the human genome with that of the chimpanzee helps us answer the tantalizing question we asked at the beginning of the chapter: What genomic information defines a human or a chimpanzee?

An analysis of the overall composition of the human and chimpanzee genomes, which are thought to have diverged only about 6 million years ago (see Figure 21.17), reveals some general differences. Considering single nucleotide substitutions, the two genomes differ by only 1.2%. When researchers looked at longer stretches of DNA, however, they were surprised to find a further 2.7% difference due to insertions or deletions of larger regions in the genome of one or the other species; many of the insertions were duplications or other repetitive DNA. In fact, a third of the human duplications are not present in the chimpanzee genome, and some of these duplications contain regions associated with human diseases. There are more *Alu* elements in the human genome than in the chimpanzee genome, and the latter contains many copies of a retroviral provirus not present in humans. All of these observations provide clues to the forces that might have swept the two genomes along different paths, but we don't have a complete picture yet.

Along with chimpanzees, bonobos are the other African ape species that are the closest living relatives to humans. The sequencing of the bonobo genome, completed in 2012, revealed that in some regions, human sequences were more closely related to either chimpanzee or bonobo sequences than chimpanzee or bonobo sequences were to each other. Such a fine-grained comparison of three closely related species allows even more detail to be worked out in reconstructing their related evolutionary history.

Life in View/Science Source

Infected mosquitos spread malaria when they bite people. See Figure 28.16.

mrfiza/Shutterstock

Evolution in Populations

- Homozygotes with two sickle-cell alleles are strongly selected against because of mortality caused by sickle-cell disease. In contrast, heterozygotes experience few harmful effects from sickling yet are more likely to survive malaria than are homozygotes.
- In regions where malaria is common, the net effect of these opposing selective forces is heterozygote advantage. This has caused evolutionary change in populations—the products of which are the areas of relatively high frequencies of the sickle-cell allele shown in the map below.

Effects on Individual Organisms

- The formation of sickled red blood cells causes homozygotes with two copies of the sickle-cell allele to have sickle-cell disease.
- Some sickling also occurs in heterozygotes, but not enough to cause the disease; they have sickle-cell trait. See Figure 14.17.

The sickled blood cells of a homozygote block small blood vessels, causing great pain and damage to organs such as the heart, kidney, and brain.

Normal red blood cells are flexible and are able to flow freely through small blood vessels.

Key
Frequencies of the sickle-cell allele

- 3.0–6.0%
- 6.0–9.0%
- 9.0–12.0%
- 12.0–15%
- >15.0%

Distribution of malaria caused by *Plasmodium falciparum* (a parasitic unicellular eukaryote)

MAKE CONNECTIONS   *In a region free of malaria, would individuals who are heterozygous for the sickle-cell allele be selected for or selected against? Explain.*

FOXP2 gene product regulates genes that function in vocalization in vertebrates. First, mutations in this gene can produce severe speech and language impairment in humans. Moreover, the *FOXP2* gene is expressed in the brains of zebra finches and canaries at the time when these songbirds are learning their songs. But perhaps the strongest evidence comes from a "knock-out" experiment in which researchers disrupted the *FOXP2* gene in mice and analyzed the resulting phenotype (see Figure 21.18). The homozygous mutant mice had malformed brains and failed to emit normal ultrasonic vocalizations, and mice with one faulty copy of the gene also showed significant problems with vocalization. These results support the idea that the *FOXP2* gene product turns on genes involved in vocalization.

Expanding on this analysis, another research group more recently replaced the *FOXP2* gene in mice with a "humanized" copy coding for the human versions of two amino acids that differ between human and chimp; these are the changes potentially responsible for a human's ability to speak. Although the mice were generally healthy, they had subtly different vocalizations and showed changes in brain cells in circuits associated with speech in human brains.

In 2010, the Neanderthal genome was sequenced from a very small amount of preserved genomic DNA, and a high-quality sequence was completed in 2014. Neanderthals (*Homo neanderthalensis*) are members of the same genus to which humans (*Homo sapiens*) belong (see Concept 34.7). A reconstruction of their evolutionary history based on genomic comparisons between the two species suggests that some groups of humans and Neanderthals coexisted and interbred for a period of time before Neanderthals became extinct about 30 000 years ago. While Neanderthals have sometimes been portrayed as primitive beings that could only grunt, their *FOXP2* gene sequence encodes a protein identical to that of humans. This suggests that Neanderthals may have been capable of speech of some type and, along with other observed genetic similarities, forces us to reevaluate our image of our recent extinct relatives.

The *FOXP2* story is an excellent example of how different approaches can complement each other in uncovering biological phenomena of widespread importance. The *FOXP2* experiments used mice as a model for humans because it would be unethical (as well as impractical) to carry out such experiments in humans. Mice and humans diverged about 65.5 million years ago (see Figure 21.17) and share about 85% of their genes. This genetic similarity can be exploited in studying human genetic disorders. If researchers know the organ or tissue that is affected by a particular genetic disorder, they can look for genes that are expressed in these locations in mice.

Even though more distantly related to humans, fruit flies have also been a useful model species for study of such human disorders as Parkinson's disease and alcoholism, while nematodes (soil worms) have yielded a wealth of information about aging.

Further research efforts are under way to extend genomic studies to many more microbial species, additional primates, and neglected species from diverse branches of the tree of life. These studies will advance our understanding of all aspects of biology, including health and ecology as well as evolution.

Comparing Genomes Within a Species

Another exciting consequence of our ability to analyze genomes is our growing understanding of the spectrum of genetic variation in humans. Because the history of the human species is so short—probably about 200 000 years—the amount of DNA variation among humans is small compared to that of many other species. Much of our diversity seems to be in the form of single nucleotide polymorphisms (SNPs). SNPs are single base-pair sites where variation is found in at least 1% of the population (see Concept 20.2); they are usually detected by DNA sequencing. In the human genome, SNPs occur on average about once in 100–300 base pairs. Scientists have already identified the location of several million SNP sites in the human genome and continue to find more. These are stored in databases around the world, one of which is run by the National Center for Biotechnology Information (NCBI) and can be accessed at http://www.ncbi.nlm.nih.gov/SNP/.

In the course of this search, they have also found other variations—including inversions, deletions, and duplications. The most surprising discovery has been the widespread occurrence of *copy-number variants* (CNVs), loci where some individuals have one or multiple copies of a particular gene or genetic region, rather than the standard two copies (one on each homologue). CNVs result from regions of the genome being duplicated or deleted inconsistently within the population. A recent study of 40 people found more than 8000 CNVs involving 13% of the genes in the genome, and these CNVs probably represent just a small subset of the total. Since these variants encompass much longer stretches of DNA than the single nucleotides of SNPs, CNVs are more likely to have phenotypic consequences and to play a role in complex diseases and disorders. At the very least, the high incidence of copy-number variation casts doubt on the meaning of the phrase "a normal human genome."

Copy-number variants, SNPs, and variations in repetitive DNA such as short tandem repeats (STRs) are useful genetic markers for studying human evolution. In one study, the genomes of two Africans from different communities were sequenced: Archbishop Desmond Tutu, the South African civil rights advocate and a member of the Bantu tribe, the majority population in southern Africa; and !Gubi, a hunter-gatherer from the Khoisan community in Namibia, a minority African population that is probably the human group with the oldest known lineage. The comparison revealed many differences, as you might expect. The analysis was then broadened to compare the protein-coding regions of !Gubi's genome with those of three other Khoisan community members (self-identified Bushmen) living nearby. Remarkably, the four African genomes differed more from each other than a European would from an Asian. These data highlight the extensive diversity among African genomes. Extending this approach will help us answer important questions about the differences between human populations and the migratory routes of human populations throughout history.

Widespread Conservation of Developmental Genes Among Animals

Biologists in the field of evolutionary developmental biology, or **evo-devo** as it is often called, compare developmental processes of different multicellular organisms. Their aim is to understand how these processes have evolved and how changes in them can modify existing organismal features or lead to new ones. With the advent of molecular techniques and the recent flood of genomic information, we are beginning to realize that the genomes of related species with strikingly different forms may have only minor differences in gene sequence or, perhaps more importantly, in gene regulation. Discovering the molecular basis of these differences in turn helps us understand the origins of the myriad diverse forms that cohabit this planet, thus informing our study of evolution.

In Chapter 18, you learned about the homeotic genes in *Drosophila melanogaster*, which encode transcription factors that regulate gene expression and specify the identity of body segments in the fruit fly (see Figure 18.19). Molecular analysis of the homeotic genes in *Drosophila* has shown that they all include a 180-nucleotide sequence called a **homeobox**, which codes for a 60–amino-acid *homeodomain* in the encoded proteins. An identical or very similar nucleotide sequence has been discovered in the homeotic genes of many invertebrates and vertebrates. In fact, the nucleotide sequences are so similar between humans and fruit flies that one researcher has whimsically referred to flies as "little people with wings." The resemblance even extends to the organization of these genes: The vertebrate genes homologous to the homeotic genes of fruit flies have kept the same chromosomal arrangement (Figure 21.19). Homeobox-containing sequences have also been found in regulatory genes of much more distantly related eukaryotes, including plants and yeasts. From these similarities, we can deduce that the homeobox DNA sequence evolved very early in the history of life and was sufficiently valuable to organisms to have been conserved in animals and plants virtually unchanged for hundreds of millions of years.

Homeotic genes in animals were named *Hox* genes, short for *homeobox*-containing genes, because homeotic genes were the first genes found to have this sequence. Other

▲ **Figure 21.19 Conservation of homeotic genes in a fruit fly and a mouse.** Homeotic genes that control the form of anterior and posterior structures of the body occur in the same linear sequence on chromosomes in *Drosophila* and mice. Each coloured band on the chromosomes shown here represents a homeotic gene. In fruit flies, all homeotic genes are found on one chromosome. The mouse and other mammals have the same or similar sets of genes on four chromosomes. The colour code indicates the parts of the embryos in which these genes are expressed and the adult body regions that result. All of these genes are essentially identical in flies and mice, except for those represented by black bands, which are less similar in the two animals.

homeobox-containing genes were later found that do not act as homeotic genes; that is, they do not directly control the identity of body parts. However, most of these genes, in animals at least, are associated with development, suggesting their ancient and fundamental importance in that process. In *Drosophila*, for example, homeoboxes are present not only in the homeotic genes but also in the egg-polarity gene *bicoid* (see Figures 18.21 and 18.22), in several of the segmentation genes, and in a master regulatory gene for eye development.

Researchers have discovered that the homeobox-encoded homeodomain is the part of a protein that binds to DNA when the protein functions as a transcription factor. Elsewhere in the protein, domains that are more variable interact with other transcription factors, allowing the homeodomain-containing protein to recognize specific enhancers and regulate the associated genes. Proteins with homeodomains probably regulate development by coordinating the transcription of batteries of developmental genes, switching them on or off. In embryos of *Drosophila* and other animal species, different combinations of homeobox genes are active in different parts of the embryo. This selective expression of regulatory genes, varying over time and space, is central to pattern formation.

Developmental biologists have found that in addition to homeotic genes, many other genes involved in development are highly conserved from species to species. These include numerous genes encoding components of signalling pathways. The extraordinary similarity among some developmental genes in different animal species raises a question: How can the same genes be involved in the development of animals whose forms are so very different from each other?

Ongoing studies are suggesting answers to this question. In some cases, small changes in regulatory sequences of particular genes cause changes in gene expression patterns that can lead to major changes in body form. For example, the differing patterns of expression of the *Hox* genes along the body axis in insects and crustaceans can explain the variation in number of leg-bearing segments among these segmented animals **(Figure 21.20)**. In other cases, similar genes direct different developmental processes in various organisms, resulting in diverse body shapes. Several *Hox* genes, for instance, are expressed in the embryonic and larval stages of the sea urchin, a nonsegmented animal that has a body plan quite different from those of insects and mice. Sea urchin adults make the pincushion-shaped shells you may have seen on the beach; two species of live sea urchins are shown in the photo below. Sea urchins are among the organisms long used in classical embryological studies (see Concept 47.1).

In this final chapter of the genetics unit, you have learned how studying genomic composition and comparing

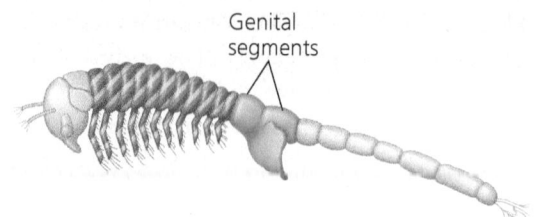

(a) Expression of four *Hox* genes in the brine shrimp *Artemia*

(b) Expression of the grasshopper versions of the same four *Hox* genes

© 1995 The Royal Society

▲ **Figure 21.20 Effect of differences in *Hox* gene expression in crustaceans and insects.** Changes in the expression patterns of *Hox* genes have occurred over evolutionary time. These changes account in part for the different body plans of the brine shrimp *Artemia*, a crustacean (top), and the grasshopper, an insect. Shown here are regions of the adult body colour-coded for expression of four *Hox* genes that determine formation of particular body parts during embryonic development. Each colour represents a specific *Hox* gene. Coloured stripes on the thorax of *Artemia* indicate co-expression of three *Hox* genes.

Source: Adaptation of figure 3 from "Hox Genes and the Evolution of Diverse Body Plans" by Michael Akam, from *Philosophical Transactions of the Royal Society B: Biological Sciences,* September 29, 1995, Volume 349(1329): 313–319. Copyright © 1995 by the Royal Society. Reprinted with permission.

the genomes of different species can disclose much about how genomes evolve. Further, comparing developmental programs, we can see that the unity of life is reflected in the similarity of molecular and cellular mechanisms used to establish body pattern, although the genes directing development may differ among organisms. The similarities between genomes reflect the common ancestry of life on Earth. But the differences are also crucial, for they have created the huge diversity of organisms that have evolved. In the remainder of the text, we expand our perspective beyond the level of molecules, cells, and genes to explore this diversity on the organismal level.

CONCEPT CHECK 21.6

1. Would you expect the genome of the macaque (a monkey) to be more similar to the mouse genome or the human genome? Why?

2. The DNA sequences called homeoboxes, which help homeotic genes in animals direct development, are common to flies and mice. Given this similarity, explain why these animals are so different.

3. **WHAT IF?** There are three times as many *Alu* elements in the human genome as in the chimpanzee genome. How do you think these extra *Alu* elements arose in the human genome? Propose a role they might have played in the divergence of these two species.

For suggested answers, see Appendix A.

WaterFrame/Alamy Stock Photo

21 Chapter Review

Go to **MasteringBiology**® for Assignments, the eText, and the Study Area with Animations, Activities, Vocab Self-Quiz, and Practice Tests.

SUMMARY OF KEY CONCEPTS

CONCEPT 21.1

The Human Genome Project fostered development of faster, less expensive sequencing techniques (pp. 464–465)

- The **Human Genome Project** was largely completed in 2003, aided by major advances in sequencing technology.
- In the **whole-genome shotgun approach**, the whole genome is cut into many small, overlapping fragments that are sequenced; computer software then assembles the genome sequence.

? *How did the Human Genome Project result in more rapid, less expensive DNA sequencing technology?*

CONCEPT 21.2

Scientists use bioinformatics to analyze genomes and their functions (pp. 465–469)

- Computer analysis of genome sequences aids **gene annotation**, the identification of protein-coding sequences. Methods to determine gene function include comparing sequences of newly discovered genes with those of known genes in other species and observing the effects of experimentally inactivating the genes.
- In systems biology, scientists use the computer-based tools of **bioinformatics** to compare genomes and study sets of genes and proteins as whole systems (**genomics** and **proteomics**). Studies include large-scale analyses of protein interactions, functional DNA elements, and genes contributing to medical conditions.

? *What has been the most significant finding of the ENCODE pilot project? Why was the project expanded to include nonhuman species?*

CONCEPT 21.3

Genomes vary in size, number of genes, and gene density (pp. 469–472)

	Bacteria	Archaea	Eukarya
Genome size	Most are 1–6 Mb		Most are 10–4000 Mb, but a few are much larger
Number of genes	1500–7500		5000–40 000
Gene density	Higher than in eukaryotes		Lower than in prokaryotes (Within eukaryotes, lower density is correlated with larger genomes.)
Introns	None in protein-coding genes	Present in some genes	Present in most genes of multicellular eukaryotes, but only in some genes of unicellular eukaryotes
Other noncoding DNA	Very little		Can exist in large amounts; generally more repetitive noncoding DNA in multicellular eukaryotes

? *Compare genome size, gene number, and gene density (a) in the three domains and (b) among eukaryotes.*

CONCEPT 21.4

Multicellular eukaryotes have much noncoding DNA and many multigene families (pp. 472–475)

- Only 1.5% of the human genome codes for proteins or gives rise to rRNAs or tRNAs; the rest is noncoding DNA, including **pseudogenes** and **repetitive DNA** of unknown function.
- The most abundant type of repetitive DNA in multicellular eukaryotes consists of **transposable elements** and related sequences. In eukaryotes, there are two types of transposable elements: **transposons**, which move via a DNA intermediate, and **retrotransposons**, which are more prevalent and move via an RNA intermediate.
- Other repetitive DNA includes short noncoding sequences that are tandemly repeated thousands of times (**simple sequence DNA**, which includes **STRs**); these sequences are especially prominent in centromeres and telomeres, where they probably play structural roles in the chromosome.
- Though many eukaryotic genes are present in one copy per haploid chromosome set, others (most, in some species) are members of a gene family, such as the human globin gene families:

? *Explain how the function of transposable elements might account for their prevalence in human noncoding DNA.*

CONCEPT 21.5

Duplication, rearrangement, and mutation of DNA contribute to genome evolution (pp. 476–481)

- Errors in cell division can lead to extra copies of all or part of entire chromosome sets, which may then diverge if one set accumulates sequence changes. Polyploidy occurs more often among plants than animals, and contributes to speciation.
- The chromosomal organization of genomes can be compared among species, providing information about evolutionary relationships. Within a given species, rearrangements of chromosomes are thought to contribute to the emergence of new species.
- The genes encoding the various related but different globin proteins evolved from one common ancestral globin gene, which duplicated and diverged into α-globin and β-globin ancestral genes. Subsequent duplication and random mutation gave rise to the present globin genes, all of which code for oxygen-binding proteins. The copies of some duplicated genes have diverged so much that the functions of their encoded proteins (such as lysozyme and α-lactalbumin) are now substantially different.
- Rearrangement of exons within and between genes during evolution has led to genes containing multiple copies of similar exons and/or several different exons derived from other genes.
- Movement of transposable elements or recombination between copies of the same element can generate new sequence combinations that are beneficial to the organism. These may alter the functions of genes or their patterns of expression and regulation.

? *How could chromosomal rearrangements lead to the emergence of new species?*

CONCEPT 21.6

Comparing genome sequences provides clues to evolution and development (pp. 481–486)

- Comparisons of genomes from widely divergent and closely related species provide valuable information about ancient and more recent evolutionary history, respectively. Human and chimpanzee sequences are about 4% different. Along with nucleotide variations in specific genes, these differences may account for the distinct characteristics of the two species. Analysis of single nucleotide polymorphisms (SNPs) and copy-number variants (CNVs) among individuals in a species can also shed light on the evolution of that species.

- Evolutionary developmental (**evo-devo**) biologists have shown that homeotic genes and some other genes associated with animal development contain a **homeobox** region whose sequence is highly conserved among diverse species. Related sequences are present in the genes of plants and yeasts.

? *What type of information can be obtained by comparing the genomes of closely related species? Of very distantly related species?*

TEST YOUR UNDERSTANDING

LEVEL 1: KNOWLEDGE/COMPREHENSION

1. Bioinformatics includes all of the following except
   a. using computer programs to align DNA sequences.
   b. using DNA technology to combine DNA from two different sources in a test tube.
   c. developing computer-based tools for genome analysis.
   d. using mathematical tools to make sense of biological systems.

2. Homeotic genes
   a. encode transcription factors that control the expression of genes responsible for specific anatomical structures.
   b. are found only in *Drosophila* and other arthropods.
   c. are the only genes that contain the homeobox domain.
   d. encode proteins that form anatomical structures in the fly.

LEVEL 2: APPLICATION/ANALYSIS

3. Two eukaryotic proteins have one domain in common but are otherwise very different. Which of the following processes is most likely to have contributed to this similarity?
   a. gene duplication
   b. RNA splicing
   c. exon shuffling
   d. random point mutations

4. Below are the amino acid sequences (using the single-letter code; see Figure 5.14) of four short segments of the *FOXP2* protein from six species: chimpanzee (C), orangutan (O), gorilla (G), rhesus macaque (R), mouse (M), and human (H). These segments contain all of the amino acid differences between the *FOXP2* proteins of these species.

   1. ATETI...PKSSD...TSSTT...NARRD
   2. ATETI...PKSSE...TSSTT...NARRD
   3. ATETI...PKSSD...TSSTT...NARRD
   4. ATETI...PKSSD...TSSNT...SARRD
   5. ATETI...PKSSD...TSSTT...NARRD
   6. VTETI...PKSSD...TSSTT...NARRD

   Use a highlighter to colour any amino acid that varies among the species. (Colour that amino acid in all sequences.)
   a. The C, G, R sequences are identical. Which lines correspond to those sequences?

   b. The H sequence differs from that of the C, G, R species at two amino acids. Underline the two differences in the H sequence.
   c. The O sequence differs from the C, G, R sequences at one amino acid (having V instead of A) and from the H sequence at three amino acids. Which line is the O sequence?
   d. In the M sequence, circle the amino acid(s) that differ from the C, G, R sequences, and draw a square around those that differ from the H sequence.
   e. Primates and rodents diverged between 60 and 100 million years ago, and chimpanzees and humans about 6 million years ago. What can you conclude by comparing the amino acid differences between the mouse and the C, G, R species with those between the human and the C, G, R species?

LEVEL 3: SYNTHESIS/EVALUATION

5. **EVOLUTION CONNECTION**
   Genes important in the embryonic development of animals, such as homeobox-containing genes, have been relatively well conserved during evolution; that is, they are more similar among different species than are many other genes. Why is this?

6. **SCIENTIFIC INQUIRY**
   The scientists mapping the SNPs in the human genome noticed that groups of SNPs tended to be inherited together, in blocks known as haplotypes, ranging in length from 5000 to 200 000 base pairs. There are as few as four or five commonly occurring combinations of SNPs per haplotype. Integrating what you've learned throughout this chapter and this unit, propose an explanation for this observation.

7. **WRITE ABOUT A THEME: INFORMATION**
   The continuity of life is based on heritable information in the form of DNA. In a short essay (100–150 words), explain how mutations in protein-coding genes and regulatory DNA contribute to evolution.

8. **SYNTHESIZE YOUR KNOWLEDGE**

Patrick Landmann/Science Source

Insects have three thoracic (trunk) segments. While researchers have found insect fossils with pairs of wings on all three segments, modern insects have wings or related structures on only the second and third segment. It turns out that in modern insects, *Hox* gene products act to inhibit wing formation on the first segment. The treehopper insect (above) is somewhat of an exception. In addition to having wings on its second segment, the treehopper's first segment has an ornate helmet that resembles a set of thorns, which a recent study has found to be a modified, fused pair of "wings." The thorn-like structure helps to camouflage the treehopper in tree branches, thus reducing its risk of predation. Explain how changes in gene regulation could have led to the evolution of such a structure.

For selected answers, see Appendix A.

AN INTERVIEW WITH
Hans Larsson

Hans Larsson was born in Edmonton, did his undergraduate degree in Evolutionary Biology at McGill University, and his Ph.D. at the University of Chicago in Organismal Biology and Anatomy. He is currently an Associate Professor and Director of the Redpath Museum at McGill University, and is the Curator of Vertebrate Paleontology at the Redpath Museum.

How did you become interested in science?

Easily. Since I was 5 years old I was just fascinated with dinosaurs, and when my parents moved to Ontario I would go to the Royal Ontario Museum, and also the Canadian Museum of Nature in Ottawa.

> " I am always in a situation where I feel like I'm in over my head—everything is a bit strange and unpredictable. And that, I think, is the most fun part of science. "

McGill University

Polypterus, a "walking fish"

Can you tell us about your research?

My research is very broad. The best term to describe the focus would be macroevolution. A subfield of evolution, macroevolution includes the big, broad scale changes over time. Some of our research has included finding new species of dinosaurs. For example, we found six new species of dinosaurs and six new crocodiles in the Sahara in Africa, new records for fossil plants and marine reptiles in the Canadian high Arctic, dinosaurs from Argentina, and crocodiles from Brazil.

On the more experimental side, we have been working a lot with skeletal development and patterning—trying to describe how the skeleton develops in key living taxa (like birds) and addressing how development plays into large-scale evolutionary transitions—like the dinosaur to bird transition, and the fish to tetrapod transition. In one paper that we published in *Nature*, we described how we took fish very closely related to lobe-finned fishes and raised them on land for a year. We looked at their behaviour and walking mechanics, and their musculoskeletal anatomy. We used high-resolution microCT scanning to measure how the bones had changed, and we identified trends in how they modified their skeleton that were similar to trends we see in the fossil record 400 mya.★ This is exciting for two reasons. First, we could actually link behaviour changes in fish to anatomical changes and thus we could propose behavioural changes that might have been changing 400 mya. Secondly, we could show the mechanisms of phenotypic plasticity—mechanisms that allow individuals to transform parts of their phenotype in a novel, and sometimes very extreme, environment (in this case fish living on land). We were able to show that phenotypic plasticity may be a major facilitator for major evolutionary changes—and that was the first experiment to show that.

What questions are you trying to answer right now?

We have a smorgasbord of questions, such as:, How do genomic to developmental changes influence large-scale evolutionary transformations? For this question, we are looking at series of embryos and are developing gene expression profiles, then looking at the dynamics of developmental changes and comparing that to the historical patterns that we see in skeletal evolution. We can then check to see if we can find a correspondence between what we see in the lab and what we see in the fossil record. In brief, we are looking for developmental switch points that allow birds to become birds, rather than staying in a more ancestral dinosaurian state.

What is the main thing you want students to take away from your research?

I really want to impress that we have so much more to discover. What is written in textbooks is just the tip of the iceberg.

What do you enjoy most about life as a scientist?

It is really fun to discover, and I live for the discovery, be it expedition discovery and going around the high Arctic in a helicopter or around Africa in a Land Rover—or in the lab dissecting embryos and experimenting—that is all very discovery oriented. I am always in a situation where I feel like I'm in over my head—everything is a bit strange and unpredictable. And that, I think, is the most fun part of science.

What advice do you have for introductory biology students just starting out at university?

Think broad and outside the box. And if you are interested in an academic career or research, then do it right away. Get involved with a lab early on—even if it is just dishwashing at first. Become a part of research as soon as you can.

★mya = million years ago

Source: Interview with Hans Larsson. Used with permission from Hans Larsson.

MAKE CONNECTIONS

The Sickle-Cell Allele

This child has sickle-cell disease, a genetic disorder that strikes individuals that have two copies of the sickle-cell allele. This allele causes an abnormality in the structure and function of hemoglobin, the oxygen-carrying protein in red blood cells. Although sickle-cell disease is lethal if not treated, in some regions the sickle-cell allele can reach frequencies as high as 15–20%. How can such a harmful allele be so common?

MedicImage/Alamy

Events at the Molecular Level

- Due to a point mutation, the sickle-cell allele differs from the wild-type allele by a single nucleotide. See Figure 17.25.
- The resulting change in one amino acid leads to hydrophobic interactions between the sickle-cell hemoglobin proteins under low-oxygen conditions.
- As a result, the sickle-cell proteins bind to each other in chains that together form a fibre.

Consequences for Cells

- The abnormal hemoglobin fibres distort the red blood cell into a sickle shape under low-oxygen conditions, such as those found in blood vessels returning to the heart.

Template strand

Sickle-cell allele on chromosome

An adenine replaces a thymine in the template strand of the sickle-cell allele, changing one codon in the mRNA produced during transcription. This change causes an amino-acid change in sickle-cell hemoglobin: A valine replaces a glutamic acid at one position. See Figure 5.19.

Sickle-cell hemoglobin

Low-oxygen conditions

Fibre

Sickled red blood cell

Wild-type allele

Normal hemoglobin (does not aggregate into fibres)

Normal red blood cell

Life in View/Science Source

Infected mosquitos spread malaria when they bite people. See Figure 28.16.

mrfiza/Shutterstock

Evolution in Populations

- Homozygotes with two sickle-cell alleles are strongly selected against because of mortality caused by sickle-cell disease. In contrast, heterozygotes experience few harmful effects from sickling yet are more likely to survive malaria than are homozygotes.
- In regions where malaria is common, the net effect of these opposing selective forces is heterozygote advantage. This has caused evolutionary change in populations—the products of which are the areas of relatively high frequencies of the sickle-cell allele shown in the map below.

Effects on Individual Organisms

- The formation of sickled red blood cells causes homozygotes with two copies of the sickle-cell allele to have sickle-cell disease.
- Some sickling also occurs in heterozygotes, but not enough to cause the disease; they have sickle-cell trait. See Figure 14.17.

The sickled blood cells of a homozygote block small blood vessels, causing great pain and damage to organs such as the heart, kidney, and brain.

Normal red blood cells are flexible and are able to flow freely through small blood vessels.

Key

Frequencies of the sickle-cell allele

- 3.0–6.0%
- 6.0–9.0%
- 9.0–12.0%
- 12.0–15%
- >15.0%

Distribution of malaria caused by *Plasmodium falciparum* (a parasitic unicellular eukaryote)

 MAKE CONNECTIONS   *In a region free of malaria, would individuals who are heterozygous for the sickle-cell allele be selected for or selected against? Explain.*

22

Descent with Modification: A Darwinian View of Life

▲ Figure 22.1 **How does this beetle defend itself against predators?**

KEY CONCEPTS

22.1 The Darwinian revolution challenged traditional views of a young Earth inhabited by unchanging species

22.2 Descent with modification by natural selection explains the adaptations of organisms and the unity and diversity of life

22.3 Evolution is supported by an overwhelming amount of scientific evidence

"Endless Forms Most Beautiful"—*Charles Darwin*

On a leafy forest floor in New Brunswick, a wolf spider attacks a type of bombardier beetle. However, instead of a juicy beetle meal, the predator is blasted with a hot burst of chemical spray (Figure 22.1). How does the beetle achieve this? In its abdomen, the beetle stores hydroquinones, hydrogen peroxide, catalase, and peroxidases in two special glands. When these secretions are mixed within a reaction centre, a complex chemical reaction occurs and produces an audible "popping" explosion of 100°C noxious spray. Bombardier beetles can revolve their abdomen tip and aim their spray with great accuracy, resulting in a distinct and effective defence mechanism.

Interesting in its own right, this type of bombardier beetle is also a member of an astonishingly diverse group: the more than 380 000 species of beetles. In fact, nearly one in every five known species is a beetle. These beetles all share similar features, such as three pairs of legs, a hard outer surface, and two pairs of wings. But they also differ from one another. How did there come to be so many beetles, and what causes their similarities and differences?

The bombardier beetle and its many close relatives illustrate three key observations about life:

• the striking ways in which organisms are suited for life in their environments*

▲ Mountain pine beetle (*Dendroctonus ponderosae*)

*Here and throughout this text, the term *environment* refers to other organisms as well as to the physical aspects of an organism's surroundings.

- the many shared characteristics (unity) of life
- the rich diversity of life

Over 150 years ago, Charles Darwin was inspired to develop a scientific explanation for these three broad observations. When he published his hypothesis in *The Origin of Species*, Darwin ushered in a scientific revolution—the era of evolutionary biology.

For now, we will define **evolution** as *descent with modification*, a phrase Darwin used in proposing that Earth's many species are descendants of ancestral species that were different from the present-day species. Evolution can also be defined more narrowly as a change in the genetic composition of a population from generation to generation, as discussed further in Chapter 23.

We can also view evolution in two related but different ways: as a pattern and as a process. The *pattern* of evolutionary change is revealed by data from a range of scientific disciplines, including biology, geology, physics, and chemistry. These data are facts—they are observations about the natural world. The *process* of evolution consists of the mechanisms that produce the observed pattern of change. These mechanisms represent natural causes of the natural phenomena we observe. Indeed, the power of evolution as a unifying theory is its ability to explain and connect a vast array of observations about the living world.

As with all general theories in science, we continue to test our understanding of evolution by examining whether it can account for new observations and experimental results. In this and the following chapters, we will examine how ongoing discoveries shape what we know about the pattern and process of evolution. To set the stage, we will first retrace Darwin's quest to explain the adaptations, unity, and diversity of what he called life's "endless forms most beautiful."

CONCEPT 22.1

The Darwinian revolution challenged traditional views of a young Earth inhabited by unchanging species

What impelled Darwin to challenge the prevailing views about Earth and its life? Darwin's revolutionary proposal developed over time, influenced by the work of others and by his travels (Figure 22.2). As we will see, his ideas also had deep historical roots.

1809 Lamarck publishes his hypothesis of evolution.

1798 Malthus publishes "Essay on the Principle of Population."

1795 Hutton proposes his principle of gradualism.

1812 Cuvier publishes his extensive studies of vertebrate fossils.

1830 Lyell publishes *Principles of Geology*.

The Natural History Museum / Alamy Stock Photo

Sketch of a flying frog by Wallace

1858 While studying species in the Malay Archipelago, Wallace (shown above in 1848) sends Darwin his hypothesis of natural selection.

Charles Darwin

1809 Charles Darwin is born.

1831–1836 Darwin travels around the world on HMS *Beagle*.

1844 Darwin writes his essay on descent with modification.

1859 *On the Origin of Species* is published.

Marine iguana in the Galápagos Islands

Wayne Lynch/AGE Fotostock

ON THE ORIGIN OF SPECIES

BY MEANS OF NATURAL SELECTION,

PRESERVATION OF FAVOURED RACES IN THE STRUGGLE FOR LIFE.

By CHARLES DARWIN, M.A.

LONDON: JOHN MURRAY, ALBEMARLE STREET. 1859.

American Museum of Natural History

▲ **Figure 22.2 The intellectual context of Darwin's ideas.**

Scala Naturae and Classification of Species

Long before Darwin was born, several Greek philosophers suggested that life might have changed gradually over time. But one philosopher who greatly influenced early Western science, Aristotle (384–322 BCE), viewed species as fixed (unchanging). Through his observations of nature, Aristotle recognized certain "affinities" among organisms. He concluded that life-forms could be arranged on a ladder, or scale, of increasing complexity, later called the *scala naturae* ("scale of nature"). Each form of life, perfect and permanent, had its allotted rung on this ladder.

These ideas were generally consistent with the Old Testament account of creation, which holds that species were individually designed by God and therefore perfect. In the 1700s, many scientists interpreted the often remarkable match of organisms to their environment as evidence that the Creator had designed each species for a particular purpose.

One such scientist was Carolus Linnaeus (1707–1778), a Swedish physician and botanist who sought to classify life's diversity, in his words, "for the greater glory of God." Linnaeus developed the two-part, or *binomial*, format for naming species (such as *Homo sapiens* for humans) that is still used today. In contrast to the linear hierarchy of the *scala naturae*, Linnaeus adopted a nested classification system, grouping similar species into increasingly general categories. For example, similar species are grouped in the same genus, similar genera (plural of genus) are grouped in the same family, and so on (see Figure 1.15).

Linnaeus did not ascribe the resemblances among species to evolutionary kinship, but rather to the pattern of their creation. A century later, however, Darwin argued that classification should be based on evolutionary relationships. He also noted that scientists using the Linnaean system often grouped organisms in ways that reflected those relationships.

Ideas about Change over Time

Among other sources of information, Darwin drew from the work of scientists studying **fossils**, the remains or traces of organisms from the past. All fossils are found in sedimentary rocks formed from the sand and mud that settle to the bottom of seas, lakes, swamps, and other aquatic habitats (Figure 22.3). New layers of sediment cover older ones and compress them into superimposed layers of rock called **strata** (singular, *stratum*). The fossils in a particular stratum provide a glimpse of some of the organisms that populated Earth at the time that layer formed. Later, erosion may carve through upper (younger) strata, revealing deeper (older) strata that had been buried.

Paleontology, the study of fossils, was developed in large part by French scientist Georges Cuvier (1769–1832). In examining strata near Paris, Cuvier noted that the older the stratum, the more dissimilar its fossils were to current

❶ Rivers carry sediment into aquatic habitats such as seas and swamps. Over time, sedimentary rock layers (strata) form under water. Some strata contain fossils.

❷ As water levels change and the bottom surface is pushed upward, the strata and their fossils are exposed.

Younger stratum with more recent fossils

Older stratum with older fossils

▲ Figure 22.3 **Formation of sedimentary strata with fossils.**

life-forms. He also observed that, from one layer to the next, some new species appeared while others disappeared. He inferred that extinctions must have been a common occurrence, but he staunchly opposed the idea of evolution. Cuvier speculated that each boundary between strata represented a sudden catastrophic event, such as a flood, that had destroyed many of the species living in that area. Such regions, he reasoned, were later repopulated by different species immigrating from other areas.

In contrast, other scientists suggested that profound change could take place through the cumulative effect of slow but continuous processes. In 1795, Scottish geologist James Hutton (1726–1797) proposed that Earth's geologic features could be explained by gradual mechanisms such as valleys being formed by rivers. The leading geologist of Darwin's time, Charles Lyell (1797–1875), incorporated Hutton's thinking into his proposal that the same geologic processes are operating today as in the past, and at the same rate.

Hutton and Lyell's ideas strongly influenced Darwin's thinking. Darwin agreed that if geologic change results from slow, continuous actions rather than from sudden events, then Earth must be much older than the widely accepted age of a few thousand years. It would, for example, take a very long time for a river to carve a canyon by erosion. He later reasoned that perhaps similarly slow and subtle processes could produce substantial biological change. Darwin was not the first to apply the idea of gradual change to biological evolution, however.

Lamarck's Hypothesis of Evolution

Although some 18th-century naturalists suggested that life evolves as environments change, only one proposed a mechanism for *how* life changes over time: French biologist Jean-Baptiste de Lamarck (1744–1829). Alas, Lamarck is primarily remembered today *not* for his visionary recognition that evolutionary change explains patterns in fossils and the match of organisms to their environments, but for the incorrect mechanism he proposed.

Lamarck published his hypothesis in 1809, the year Darwin was born. By comparing living species with fossil forms, Lamarck had found what appeared to be several lines of descent, each a chronological series of older to younger fossils leading to a living species. He explained his findings using two principles that were widely accepted at the time. The first was *use and disuse*, the idea that parts of the body that are used extensively become larger and stronger, while those that are not used deteriorate. Among many examples, he cited a giraffe stretching its neck to reach leaves on high branches. The second principle, *inheritance of acquired characteristics*, stated that an organism could pass these modifications to its offspring. Lamarck reasoned that the long, muscular neck of the living giraffe had evolved over many generations as giraffes stretched their necks ever higher.

Lamarck also thought that evolution happens because organisms have an innate drive to become more complex. Darwin rejected this idea, but he, too, thought that variation was introduced into the evolutionary process in part through inheritance of acquired characteristics. Today, however, our understanding of genetics refutes this mechanism: Experiments show that traits acquired by use during an individual's life are not inherited in the way proposed by Lamarck (Figure 22.4).

Lamarck was vilified in his own time, especially by Cuvier, who denied that species ever evolve. In retrospect, however, Lamarck did recognize that the match of organisms to their environments can be

▲ Figure 22.4 **Acquired traits cannot be inherited.** This bonsai tree was "trained" to grow as a dwarf by pruning and shaping. However, seeds from this tree would produce offspring of normal size.

explained by gradual evolutionary change, and he did propose a testable explanation for how this change occurs.

CONCEPT CHECK 22.1

1. How did Hutton's and Lyell's ideas influence Darwin's thinking about evolution?

2. **MAKE CONNECTIONS** Scientific hypotheses must be testable (see Concept 1.3). Applying this criterion, are Cuvier's explanation of the fossil record and Lamarck's hypothesis of evolution scientific? Explain your answer in each case.

For suggested answers, see Appendix A.

CONCEPT 22.2

Descent with modification by natural selection explains the adaptations of organisms and the unity and diversity of life

As the 19th century dawned, it was generally thought that species had remained unchanged since their creation. A few clouds of doubt about the permanence of species were beginning to gather, but no one could have forecast the thundering storm just beyond the horizon. How did Charles Darwin become the lightning rod for a revolutionary view of life?

Darwin's Research

Charles Darwin (1809–1882) was born in Shrewsbury, in western England. Even as a boy, he had a consuming interest in nature. When he was not reading nature books, he was fishing, hunting, riding, and collecting insects. Darwin's father, a physician, could see no future for his son as a naturalist and sent him to medical school in Edinburgh. But Charles found medicine boring and surgery before the days of anesthesia horrifying. He quit medical school and enrolled at Cambridge University, intending to become a clergyman. (At that time many scholars of science belonged to the clergy.)

At Cambridge, Darwin became the protégé of John Henslow, a botany professor. Soon after Darwin graduated, Henslow recommended him to Captain Robert FitzRoy, who was preparing the survey ship HMS *Beagle* for a long voyage around the world. Darwin would pay his own way and serve as a conversation partner to the young captain. FitzRoy, who was himself an accomplished scientist, accepted Darwin because he was a skilled naturalist and because they were of similar age and social class.

The Voyage of the Beagle

Darwin embarked from England on the *Beagle* in December 1831. The primary mission of the voyage was to chart poorly known stretches of the South American coastline. Darwin, however, spent most of his time on shore, observing and collecting thousands of plants and animals. He described features of organisms that made them well suited to such diverse environments as the humid jungles of Brazil, the expansive grasslands of Argentina, and the towering peaks of the Andes.

Darwin observed that the plants and animals in temperate regions of South America more closely resembled species living in the South American tropics than species living in temperate regions of Europe. Furthermore, the fossils he found, though clearly different from living species, distinctly resembled the living organisms of South America.

Darwin also spent much time thinking about geology. Despite repeated bouts of seasickness, he read Lyell's *Principles of Geology* during the voyage. He experienced geologic change firsthand when a violent earthquake shook the coast of Chile, and he observed afterward that rocks along the coast had been thrust upward by several feet. Finding fossils of ocean organisms high in the Andes, Darwin inferred that the rocks containing the fossils must have been raised there by many similar earthquakes. These observations reinforced what he had learned from Lyell: Physical evidence did not support the traditional view that Earth was only a few thousand years old.

Darwin's interest in the species (or fossils) found in an area was further stimulated by the *Beagle*'s stop at the Galápagos, a group of volcanic islands located near the equator about 900 km west of Ecuador (Figure 22.5). Darwin was fascinated by the unusual organisms there. The birds he collected included several kinds of mockingbirds. These mockingbirds, though similar to each other, were different species.

Some were unique to individual islands, while others lived on two or more adjacent islands. Furthermore, although the animals on the Galápagos resembled species living on the South American mainland, most of the Galápagos species were not known from anywhere else in the world. Darwin hypothesized that the Galápagos had been colonized by organisms that had strayed from South America and then diversified, giving rise to new species on the various islands.

Darwin's Focus on Adaptation

During the voyage of the *Beagle*, Darwin observed many examples of **adaptations**, inherited characteristics of organisms that enhance their survival and reproduction in specific environments. Later, as he reassessed his observations, he began to perceive adaptation to the environment and the origin of new species as closely related processes. Could a new species arise from an ancestral form by the gradual accumulation of adaptations to a different environment? From studies made years after Darwin's voyage, biologists have concluded that this is indeed what happened to the diverse group of Galápagos finches (see Figure 1.23). The finches' various beaks and behaviours are adapted to the specific foods available on their home islands (Figure 22.6). Darwin realized that explaining such adaptations was essential to understanding evolution. His explanation of how adaptations arise centred on **natural selection**, a process in which individuals that have certain inherited traits tend to survive and reproduce at higher rates than other individuals *because of* those traits.

By the early 1840s, Darwin had worked out the major features of his hypothesis. He set these ideas on paper in 1844,

▲ Figure 22.5 **The voyage of HMS *Beagle* (December 1831-October 1836).**

(a) Cactus-eater. The long, sharp beak of the cactus ground finch (*Geospiza scandens*) helps it tear and eat cactus flowers and pulp.

(b) Insect-eater. The green warbler finch (*Certhidea olivacea*) uses its narrow, pointed beak to grasp insects.

(c) Seed-eater. The large ground finch (*Geospiza magnirostris*) has a large beak adapted for cracking seeds that fall from plants to the ground.

▲ **Figure 22.6 Three examples of beak variation in Galápagos finches.** The Galápagos Islands are home to more than a dozen species of closely related finches, some found only on a single island. The most striking differences among them are their beaks, which are adapted for specific diets.

MAKE CONNECTIONS *Review Figure 1.23. To which of the other two species shown above is the cactus-eater more closely related (that is, with which does it share a more recent common ancestor)?*

when he wrote a long essay on descent with modification and its underlying mechanism, natural selection. Yet he was still reluctant to publish his ideas, in part because he anticipated the uproar they would cause. During this time, Darwin continued to compile evidence in support of his hypothesis. By the mid-1850s, he had described his ideas to Lyell and a few others. Lyell, who was not yet convinced of evolution, nevertheless urged Darwin to publish on the subject before someone else came to the same conclusions and published first.

In June 1858, Lyell's prediction came true. Darwin received a manuscript from Alfred Russel Wallace (1823–1913), a British naturalist working in the South Pacific islands of the Malay Archipelago (see Figure 22.5). Wallace had developed a hypothesis of natural selection nearly identical to Darwin's. He asked Darwin to evaluate his paper and forward it to Lyell if it merited publication. Darwin complied, writing to Lyell: "Your words have come true with a vengeance.... I never saw a more striking coincidence ... so all my originality, whatever it may amount to, will be smashed." On July 1, 1858, Lyell and a colleague presented Wallace's paper, along with extracts from Darwin's unpublished 1844 essay, to the Linnean Society of London. Darwin quickly finished his book, titled *On the Origin of Species by Means of Natural Selection* (commonly referred to as *The Origin of Species*), and published it the next year. Although Wallace had submitted his ideas for publication first, he admired Darwin and thought that Darwin had developed the idea of natural selection so extensively that he should be known as its main architect.

Within a decade, Darwin's book and its proponents had convinced most scientists that life's diversity is the product of evolution. Darwin succeeded where previous evolutionists had failed, mainly by presenting a plausible scientific mechanism with immaculate logic and an avalanche of evidence.

The Origin of Species

In his book, Darwin amassed evidence that the three broad observations about nature listed at the beginning of this chapter—the unity of life, the diversity of life, and the match between organisms and their environments—resulted from descent with modification by natural selection.

Descent with Modification

In the first edition of *The Origin of Species*, Darwin never used the word *evolution* (although the final word of the book is "evolved"). Rather, he discussed *descent with modification*, a phrase that summarized his view of life. Organisms share many characteristics, leading Darwin to perceive unity in life. He attributed the unity of life to the descent of all organisms from an ancestor that lived in the remote past. He also thought that as the descendants of that ancestral organism lived in various habitats, they gradually accumulated diverse modifications, or adaptations, that fit them to specific ways of life. Darwin reasoned that, over a long period of time, descent with modification eventually led to the rich diversity of life we see today.

Darwin viewed the history of life as a tree, with multiple branchings from a common trunk out to the tips of the youngest twigs (Figure 22.7). In this diagram, the tips of the twigs that are labelled A–D represent several groups of organisms living in the present day, while the unlabelled branches represent groups that are extinct. Each fork of the tree represents the most recent common ancestor of all the lines of evolution that subsequently branch from that point. Darwin reasoned that such a branching process, along with past extinction events, could explain the large morphological gaps that sometimes exist in between related groups of organisms.

As an example, consider the three living species of elephants: the Asian elephant (*Elephas maximus*) and two species

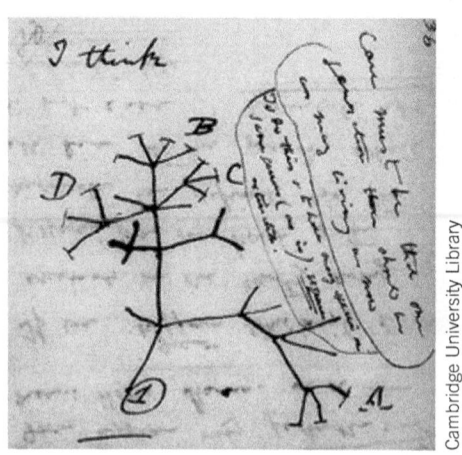

Cambridge University Library

of African elephants (*Loxodonta africana* and *L. cyclotis*). These closely related species are very similar because they shared the same line of descent until a relatively recent split from their common ancestor, as shown in the tree diagram in **Figure 22.8**. Note that seven lineages related to elephants have become extinct over the past 32 million years. As a result, there are no living species that fill the morphological gap between the elephants and their nearest relatives today, the hyraxes and manatees. Such extinctions are not uncommon. In fact, many evolutionary branches, even some major ones, are dead ends: Scientists estimate that over 99% of all species that have ever lived are now extinct. As in Figure 22.8, fossils of extinct species can document the divergence of present-day groups by "filling in" gaps between them.

Artificial Selection, Natural Selection, and Adaptation

Darwin proposed the mechanism of natural selection to explain the observable patterns of evolution. He crafted his argument carefully, hoping to persuade even the most sceptical readers. First he discussed familiar examples of selective breeding of domesticated plants and animals. Humans have modified other species over many generations by selecting and breeding individuals that possess desired traits, a process called **artificial selection** (Figure 22.9). As a result of artificial selection, crops, livestock animals, and pets often bear little resemblance to their wild ancestors.

Darwin then argued that a similar process occurs in nature. He based his argument on two observations, from which he drew two inferences:

Observation #1: Members of a population often vary in their inherited traits (Figure 22.10).

Observation #2: All species can produce more offspring than their environment can support (Figure 22.11), and many of these offspring fail to survive and reproduce.

Inference #1: Individuals whose inherited traits give them a higher probability of surviving and reproducing in a given environment tend to leave more offspring than other individuals.

Hyracoidea (Hyraxes)

Sirenia (Manatees and relatives)

†*Moeritherium*

†*Barytherium*

†*Deinotherium*

†*Mammut*

†*Platybelodon*

†*Stegodon*

†*Mammuthus*

Elephas maximus (Asia)

Loxodonta africana (Africa)

Loxodonta cyclotis (Africa)

60   34   24   5.5 2 10⁴ 0

Millions of years ago   Years ago

▲ Figure 22.8 **Descent with modification.** This evolutionary tree of elephants and their relatives is based mainly on fossils—their anatomy, order of appearance in strata, and geographic distribution. Note that most branches of descent ended in extinction (denoted by the dagger symbol †). (Time line not to scale.)

Source: Figure adapted from artwork by Utako Kikutani (as appeared in "What Can Make a Four-Ton Mammal a Most Sensitive Beast?" by Jeheskel Shoshani, from *Natural History*, November 1997, Volume 106(1), 36–45). Copyright © 1997 by Utako Kikutani. Reprinted with permission of the artist.

? *Based on the tree shown here, approximately when did the most recent ancestor shared by* Mammuthus *(woolly mammoths), Asian elephants, and African elephants live?*

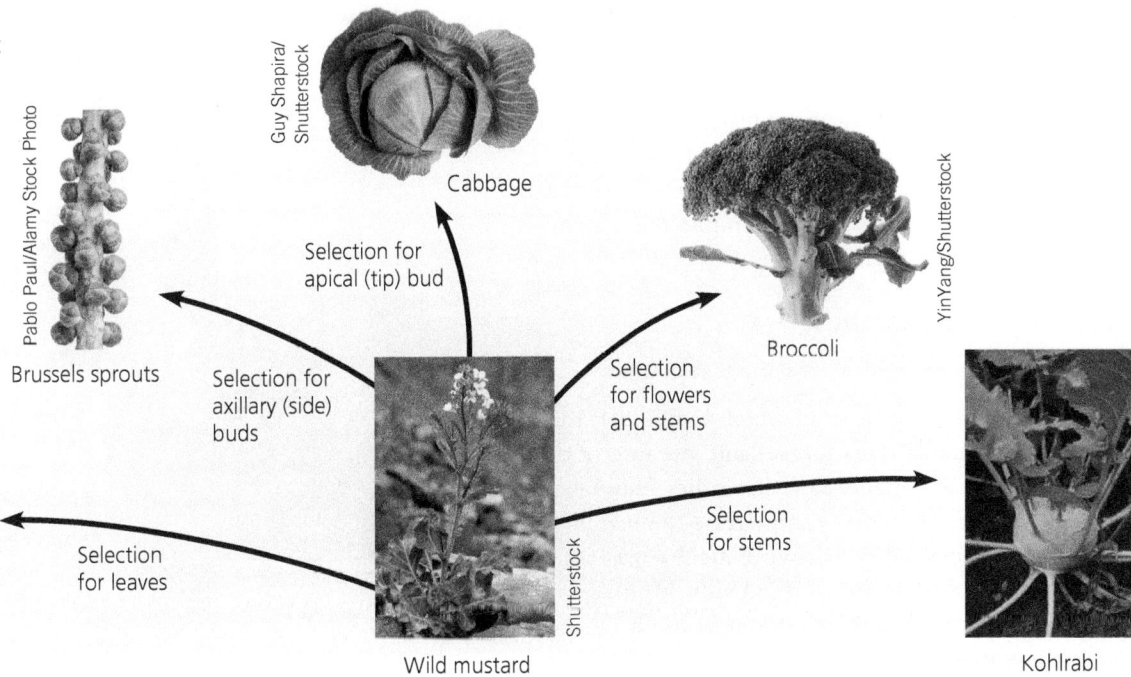

▶ Figure 22.9 **Artificial selection.** These different vegetables have all been selected from one species of wild mustard. By selecting variations in different parts of the plant, breeders have obtained these divergent results.

Cabbage

Guy Shapira/Shutterstock

Selection for apical (tip) bud

Pablo Paul/Alamy Stock Photo

Brussels sprouts

Selection for axillary (side) buds

YinYang/Shutterstock

Broccoli

Selection for flowers and stems

Peter Turner Photography/Shutterstock

Selection for leaves

Selection for stems

Shutterstock

nercisa/Shutterstock

Kale

Wild mustard

Kohlrabi

Inference #2: This unequal ability of individuals to survive and reproduce will lead to the accumulation of favourable traits in the population over generations.

As inferences #1 and #2 suggest, Darwin saw an important connection between natural selection and the capacity of organisms to "overreproduce." He began to make this connection after reading an essay by economist Thomas Malthus, who contended that much of human suffering—disease, famine, and war—resulted from the human population's potential to increase faster than food supplies and other resources. Similarly, Darwin realized that the capacity to overreproduce was characteristic of all species. Of the many eggs laid, young born, and seeds spread, only a tiny fraction complete their development and leave offspring of their own. The rest are eaten, starved, diseased, unmated, or unable to tolerate environmental conditions such as salinity or temperature.

An organism's heritable traits can influence not only its own performance, but also how well its offspring cope with environmental challenges. For example, an organism might have a trait that gives its offspring an advantage in escaping predators, obtaining food, or tolerating environmental conditions. When such advantages increase the number of offspring that survive and reproduce, the traits that are favoured will likely appear at a greater frequency in the next generation. Thus, over time, natural selection resulting from factors such as predators, lack of food, or adverse physical conditions can lead to an increase in the proportion of favourable traits in a population.

How rapidly do such changes occur? Darwin reasoned that if artificial selection can bring about dramatic change in a relatively short period of time, then natural selection

Laura Jesse

▲ Figure 22.10 **Variation in a population.** Individuals in this population of Asian ladybird beetles vary in colour and spot pattern. Natural selection may act on these variations only if (1) they are heritable and (2) they affect the beetles' ability to survive and reproduce.

▶ Figure 22.11 **Overproduction of offspring.** A single puffball fungus can produce billions of offspring. If all of these offspring and their descendants survived to maturity, they would carpet the surrounding land surface.

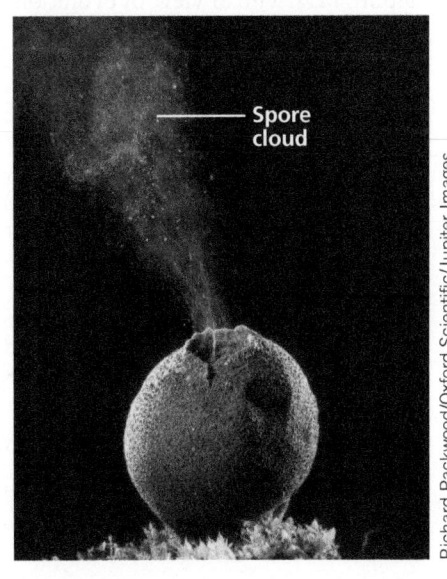

Spore cloud

Richard Packwood/Oxford Scientific/Jupiter Images

should be capable of substantial modification of species over many hundreds of generations. Even if the advantages of some heritable traits over others are slight, the advantageous variations will gradually accumulate in the population, and less favourable variations will diminish. Over time, this process will increase the frequency of individuals with favourable adaptations and hence refine the match between organisms and their environment.

Natural Selection: A Summary

Let's now recap the main ideas of natural selection:

- Natural selection is a process in which individuals that have certain heritable traits survive and, because of those traits, reproduce at a higher rate than other individuals.
- Over time, natural selection can increase the match between organisms and their environment (Figure 22.12).
- If an environment changes, or if individuals move to a new environment, natural selection may result in adaptation to these new conditions, sometimes giving rise to new species.

One subtle but important point is that although natural selection occurs through interactions between individual organisms and their environment, *individuals do not evolve*. Rather, it is the population that evolves over time.

A second key point is that natural selection can amplify or diminish only those heritable traits that differ among the individuals in a population. Thus, even if a trait is heritable, if all the individuals in a population are genetically identical for that trait, evolution by natural selection cannot occur.

Third, remember that environmental factors vary from place to place and over time. A trait that is favourable in one place or time may be useless—or even detrimental—in other places or times. Natural selection is always operating, but which traits are favoured depends on the context in which a species lives and mates.

Next, we will survey the wide range of observations that support a Darwinian view of evolution by natural selection.

CONCEPT CHECK 22.2

1. How does the concept of descent with modification explain both the unity and diversity of life?
2. **WHAT IF?** If you discovered a fossil of an extinct mammal that lived high in the Andes, would you predict that it would more closely resemble present-day mammals from South American jungles or present-day mammals that live high in African mountains? Explain.
3. **MAKE CONNECTIONS** Review Figures 14.6 and 14.7 on the relationship between genotype and phenotype. In a particular pea population, suppose that flowers with the white phenotype are favoured by natural selection. Predict what would happen over time to the frequency of the *p* allele in the population, and explain your reasoning.

For suggested answers, see Appendix A.

A flower mantid in Malaysia

A flower-eyed mantid in South Africa

A leaf mantid in Borneo

▲ Figure 22.12 **Camouflage as an example of evolutionary adaptation.** Related species of the insects called mantids have diverse shapes and colours that evolved in different environments.

? *Explain how these mantids demonstrate the three key observations about life introduced at the beginning of this chapter: the match between organisms and their environments, unity, and diversity.*

CONCEPT 22.3

Evolution is supported by an overwhelming amount of scientific evidence

In *The Origin of Species*, Darwin marshalled a broad range of evidence to support the concept of descent with modification. Still—as he readily acknowledged—there were instances in which key evidence was lacking. For example, Darwin referred to the origin of flowering plants as an "abominable mystery," and he lamented the lack of fossils showing how earlier groups of organisms gave rise to new groups.

In the last 150 years, new discoveries have filled many of the gaps that Darwin identified. The origin of flowering plants, for example, is much better understood (see Chapter 30), and many fossils have been discovered that signify the origin of new groups of organisms (see Chapter 25). In this section, we will consider four types of data that document the pattern of evolution and illuminate how it occurs: direct observations of evolution, homology, the fossil record, and biogeography.

Direct Observations of Evolutionary Change

Biologists have documented evolutionary change in thousands of scientific studies. We will examine many such studies throughout this unit, but let's look at two examples here.

Natural Selection in Response to Introduced Plant Species

Animals that eat plants, called herbivores, often have adaptations that help them feed efficiently on their primary food sources. What happens when herbivores begin to feed on a plant species with different characteristics than their usual food source?

An opportunity to study this question in nature is provided by soapberry bugs, which use their "beak," a hollow, needlelike mouthpart, to feed on seeds located within the fruits of various plants. In southern Florida, the soapberry bug *Jadera haematoloma* feeds on the seeds of a native plant, the balloon vine (*Cardiospermum corindum*). In central Florida, however, balloon vines have become rare. Instead, soapberry bugs in that region now feed on goldenrain tree (*Koelreuteria elegans*), a species recently introduced from Asia.

Soapberry bugs feed most effectively when their beak length closely matches the depth at which seeds are found within a fruit. Goldenrain tree fruit consists of three flat lobes, and its seeds are much closer to the fruit surface than are the seeds of the plump, round fruit of the native balloon vine. These differences led researchers to predict that in populations that feed on goldenrain tree, natural selection would result in beaks that are *shorter* than those in populations that feed on balloon vine (Figure 22.13). Indeed, beak lengths are shorter in the populations that feed on goldenrain tree.

Researchers have also studied beak length evolution in soapberry bug populations that feed on plants introduced to Louisiana, Oklahoma, and Australia. In each of these locations, the fruit of the introduced plants is larger than the fruit of the native plant. Thus, in populations feeding on introduced species in these regions, researchers predicted that natural selection would result in the evolution of *longer* beak length. Again, data collected in field studies upheld this prediction.

The adaptation observed in these soapberry bug populations had important consequences: In Australia, for example, the increase in beak length nearly doubled the success with which soapberry bugs could eat the seeds of the introduced species. Furthermore, since historical data show that the goldenrain tree reached central Florida just 35 years before the scientific studies were initiated, the results demonstrate that natural selection can cause rapid evolution in a wild population.

The Evolution of Drug-Resistant Bacteria

An example of ongoing natural selection that dramatically affects humans is the evolution of drug-resistant pathogens (disease-causing organisms and viruses). This is a particular problem with bacteria and viruses because resistant strains of these pathogens can proliferate very quickly.

▼ Figure 22.13 | Inquiry

Can a change in a population's food source result in evolution by natural selection?

Field Study Soapberry bugs (*Jadera haematoloma*) feed most effectively when the length of their "beak" closely matches the depth within the fruits of the seeds they eat. Scott Carroll and his colleagues measured beak lengths in soapberry bug populations in southern Florida feeding on the native balloon vine. They also measured beak lengths in populations in central Florida feeding on the introduced goldenrain tree, which has a flatter fruit shape than the balloon vine. The researchers then compared the measurements to those of museum specimens collected in the two areas before the goldenrain tree was introduced.

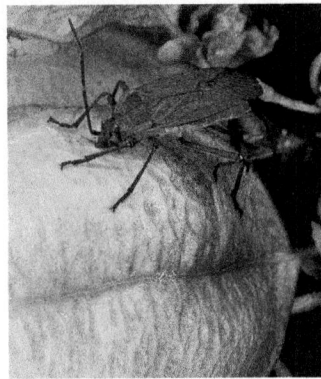

Soapberry bug with beak inserted in balloon vine fruit

Scott P. Carroll

Results Beak lengths were shorter in populations feeding on the introduced species than in populations feeding on the native species, in which the seeds are buried more deeply. The average beak length in museum specimens from each population (indicated by red arrows) was similar to beak lengths in populations feeding on native species.

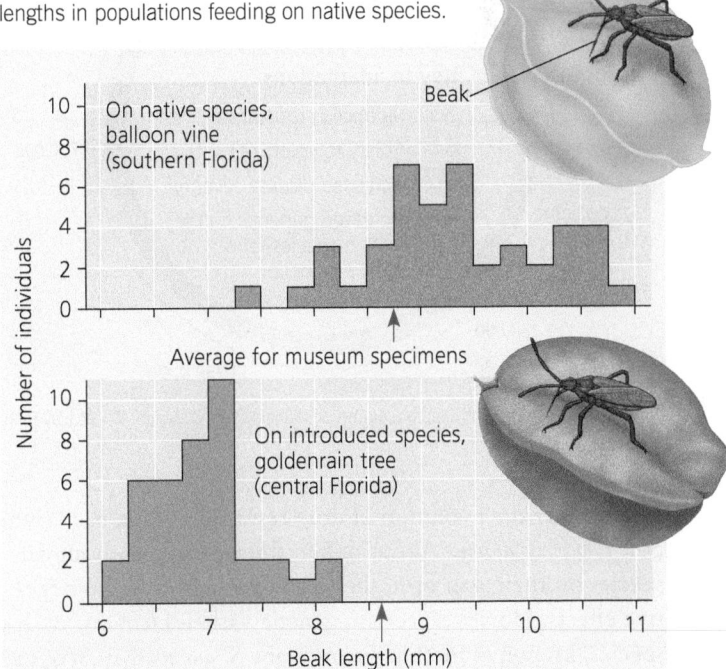

Conclusion Museum specimens and contemporary data suggest that a change in the size of the soapberry bug's food source can result in evolution by natural selection for matching beak size.

Source: Adaptation of Figure 4 from "Host Race Radiation in the Soapberry Bug: Natural History with the History" by Scott P. Carroll and Christin Boyd, from *Evolution*, 1992, Volume 46(4). Copyright © 1992 by Society for the Study of Evolution. Reprinted with permission of John Wiley & Sons Ltd; Adaptation of Figure 6.11 from Ecology by Michael L. Cain et al. Copyright © 2008 by Sinauer Associates, Inc. Reprinted with permission.

WHAT IF? *When soapberry bug eggs from a population fed on balloon vine fruits were reared on goldenrain tree fruits (or vice versa), the beak lengths of the adult insects matched those in the population from which the eggs were obtained. Interpret these results.*

Impact

The Rise of MRSA

Most methicillin-resistant *Staphylococcus aureus* (MRSA) infections are caused by recently appearing strains such as clone USA300. Resistant to multiple antibiotics and highly contagious, this strain and its close relatives can cause lethal infections of the skin, lungs, and blood. Researchers have identified key areas of the USA300 genome that code for its particularly virulent properties.

Why It Matters MRSA infections have proliferated dramatically in the past few decades, and the annual death toll in Canada is in the thousands. There is grave concern about the continuing evolution of drug resistance and the resulting difficulty of treating MRSA infections. Ongoing studies of how MRSA strains colonize their hosts and cause disease may help scientists develop drugs to combat MRSA.

The circular chromosome of clone USA300 has been sequenced and contains 2 872 769 base pairs of DNA.

The highlighted regions contain genes that increase the strain's virulence (see the key).

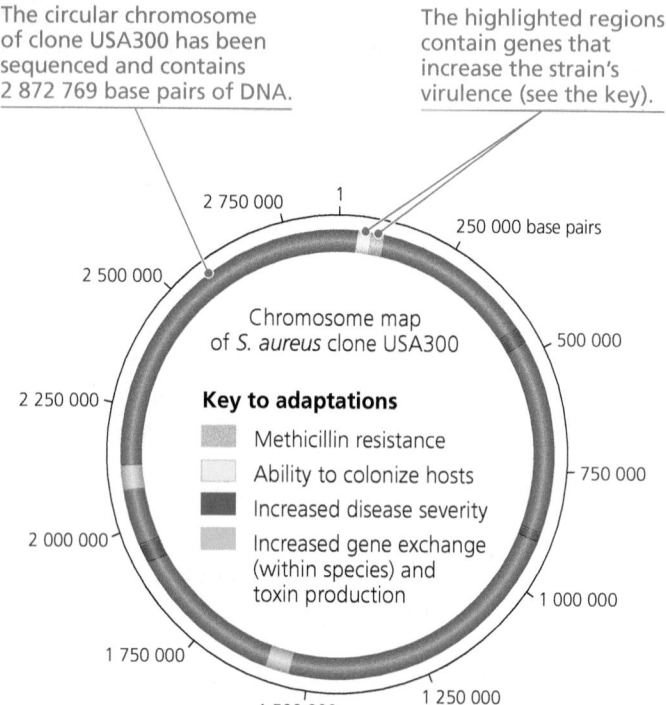

Key to adaptations

- Methicillin resistance
- Ability to colonize hosts
- Increased disease severity
- Increased gene exchange (within species) and toxin production

Figure created by Dr. Binh Diep on request of Michael Cain. Copyright © 2011 by Binh Diep. Reprinted with permission.

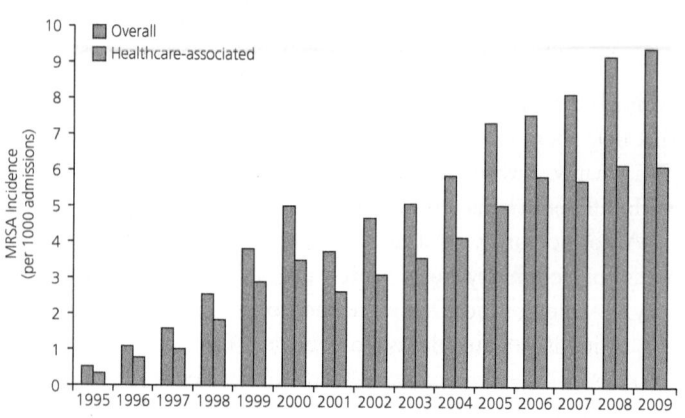

MRSA infections severe enough to result in hospitalization have proliferated greatly in recent years. Healthcare settings are associated with the majority of cases in all years surveyed.

Source of information: http://www.phac-aspc.gc.ca/nois-sinp/projects/res2009/ld/f8a-eng.php

Further Reading General information about MRSA can be found on the Public Health Agency of Canada website (www.phac-aspc.gc.ca/id-mi/mrsa-eng.php) and in G. Taubes, The bacteria fight back, *Science* 321:356–361 (2008).

WHAT IF? *Efforts are underway to develop drugs that target* S. aureus *specifically and to develop drugs that slow the growth of MRSA but do not kill it. Based on how natural selection works and on the fact that bacterial species can exchange genes, explain why each of these strategies might be effective.*

Consider the evolution of drug resistance in the bacterium *Staphylococcus aureus*. About one in three people harbour this species on their skin or in their nasal passages with no negative effects. However, certain genetic varieties (strains) of this species, known as methicillin-resistant *S. aureus* (MRSA), are formidable pathogens. The past decade has seen an alarming increase in virulent forms of MRSA such as clone USA300, a strain that can cause "flesh-eating disease" and potentially fatal infections, many of which are acquired from healthcare settings (Figure 22.14). How did clone USA300 and other strains of MRSA become so dangerous?

The story begins in 1943, when penicillin became the first widely used antibiotic. Since then, penicillin and other antibiotics have saved millions of lives. However, by 1945, more than 20% of the *S. aureus* strains seen in hospitals were already resistant to penicillin. These bacteria had an enzyme,

penicillinase, that could destroy penicillin. Researchers responded by developing antibiotics that were not destroyed by penicillinase, but some *S. aureus* populations developed resistance to each new drug within a few years.

Then, in 1959, doctors began using the powerful antibiotic methicillin—within two years, methicillin-resistant strains of *S. aureus* appeared. How did these resistant strains emerge? Methicillin works by deactivating a protein that bacteria use to synthesize their cell walls. However, *S. aureus* populations exhibited variations in how strongly their members were affected by the drug. In particular, some individuals were able to synthesize their cell walls using a different protein that was not affected by methicillin. These individuals survived the methicillin treatments and reproduced at higher rates than did other individuals. Over time, these resistant individuals became increasingly common, leading to the spread of MRSA.

Initially, MRSA could be controlled by antibiotics that work differently from the way methicillin works. But this has become increasingly difficult because some MRSA strains are resistant to multiple antibiotics—probably because bacteria can exchange genes with members of their own and other species (see Figure 27.13). Thus, the multidrug-resistant strains of today may have emerged over time as MRSA strains that were resistant to different antibiotics exchanged genes.

The *S. aureus* and soapberry bug examples highlight two key points about natural selection. First, natural selection is a process of editing, not a creative mechanism. A drug does not *create* resistant pathogens; it *selects for* resistant individuals that are already present in the population. Second, natural selection depends on time and place. It favours those characteristics in a genetically variable population that provide an advantage in the current, local environment. What is beneficial in one situation may be useless or even harmful in another. Beak lengths arise that match the size of the typical fruit eaten by a particular soapberry bug population. However, a beak length suitable for fruit of one size can be disadvantageous when the bug is feeding on fruit of another size.

Homology

A second type of evidence for evolution comes from analyzing similarities among different organisms. As we've discussed, evolution is a process of descent with modification: characteristics present in an ancestral organism are altered (by natural selection) in its descendants over time as they face different environmental conditions. As a result, related species can have characteristics that have an underlying similarity yet function differently. Similarity resulting from common ancestry is known as **homology**. Although homologies may have a similar underlying structure that evolved from a common origin, they may actually look quite different as the examples in the next section will illustrate. As this section will explain, an understanding of homology can be used to make testable predictions and explain observations that are otherwise puzzling.

Anatomical and Molecular Homologies

The view of evolution as a remodelling process leads to the prediction that closely related species should share similar features—and they do. Of course, closely related species share the features used to determine their relationship, but they also share many other features. Some of these shared features make little sense except in the context of evolution. For

Humerus
Radius
Ulna
Carpals
Metacarpals
Phalanges

Human   Cat   Whale   Bat

▲ **Figure 22.15 Mammalian forelimbs: homologous structures.** Even though they have become adapted for different functions, the forelimbs of all mammals are constructed from the same basic skeletal elements: one large bone (purple), attached to two smaller bones (orange and tan), attached to several small bones (gold), attached to several digits composed of metacarpals (green) attached to phalanges (blue).

example, the forelimbs of all mammals, including humans, cats, whales, and bats, show the same arrangement of bones from the shoulder to the tips of the digits, even though these appendages have very different functions: lifting, walking, swimming, and flying (Figure 22.15). Such striking anatomical resemblances would be highly unlikely if these structures had arisen anew in each species. Rather, the underlying skeletons of the arms, forelegs, flippers, and wings of different mammals are **homologous structures** that represent variations on a structural theme that was present in their common ancestor.

Comparing early stages of development in different animal species reveals additional anatomical homologies not visible in adult organisms. For example, at some point in their development, all vertebrate embryos have a tail located posterior to (behind) the anus, as well as structures called pharyngeal (throat) arches (Figure 22.16). These homologous arches ultimately develop into structures with

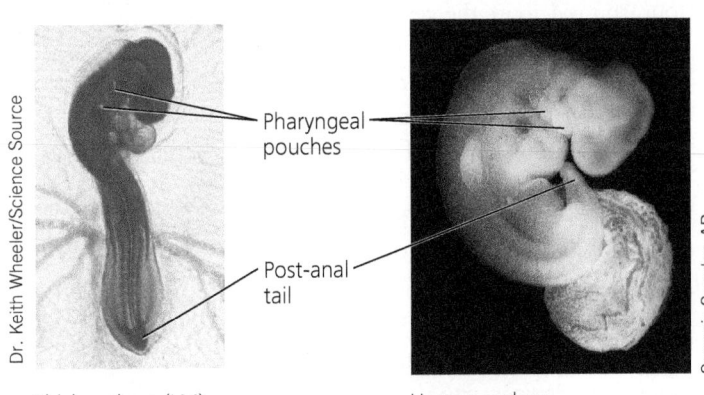

Pharyngeal pouches

Post-anal tail

Chick embryo (LM)   Human embryo

▲ **Figure 22.16 Anatomical similarities in vertebrate embryos.** At some stage in their embryonic development, all vertebrates have a tail located posterior to the anus (referred to as a post-anal tail), as well as pharyngeal (throat) pouches. Descent from a common ancestor can explain such similarities.

very different functions, such as gills in fishes and parts of the ears and throat in humans and other mammals.

Some of the most intriguing homologies concern "leftover" structures of marginal, if any, importance to the organism. These **vestigial structures** are remnants of features that served a function in the organism's ancestors. For instance, the skeletons of some snakes retain vestiges of the pelvis and leg bones of walking ancestors. Another example is provided by eye remnants that are buried under scales in blind species of cave fishes. We would not expect to see these vestigial structures if snakes and blind cave fishes had origins separate from other vertebrate animals.

Biologists also observe similarities among organisms at the molecular level. All forms of life use the same genetic language of DNA and RNA, and the genetic code is essentially universal. Thus, it is likely that all species descended from common ancestors that used this code. But molecular homologies go beyond a shared code. For example, organisms as dissimilar as humans and bacteria share genes inherited from a very distant common ancestor. Some of these homologous genes have acquired new functions, while others, such as those coding for the ribosomal subunits used in protein synthesis (see Figure 17.17), have retained their original functions. It is also common for organisms to have genes that have lost their function, even though the homologous genes in related species may be fully functional. Like vestigial structures, it appears that such inactive "pseudogenes" may be present simply because a common ancestor had them.

Homologies and "Tree Thinking"

Some homologous characteristics, such as the genetic code, are shared by all species because they date to the deep ancestral past. In contrast, homologous characteristics that evolved more recently are shared only within smaller groups of organisms. Consider the *tetrapods* (from the Greek *tetra*, four, and *pod*, foot), the vertebrate group that consists of amphibians, mammals, and reptiles (including birds—see Figure 22.17). All tetrapods have limbs with digits (see Figure 22.15), whereas other vertebrates do not. Thus, homologous characteristics form a nested pattern: All life shares the deepest layer, and each successive smaller group adds its own homologies to those it shares with larger groups. This nested pattern is exactly what we would expect to result from descent with modification from a common ancestor.

Biologists often represent the pattern of descent from common ancestors with an **evolutionary tree**, a diagram that reflects evolutionary relationships among groups of organisms. We will explore in detail how evolutionary trees are constructed in Chapter 26, but for now, let's consider how we can interpret and use such trees.

Figure 22.17 is an evolutionary tree of tetrapods and their closest living relatives, the lungfishes. In this diagram, each branch point represents the common ancestor of all species that descended from it. For example, lungfishes and all tetrapods descended from ancestor ❶, whereas mammals, lizards and snakes, crocodiles, and birds all descended from ancestor ❸. As expected, the three homologies shown on the tree—limbs with digits, the amnion (a protective embryonic membrane), and feathers—form a nested pattern. Limbs with digits were present in common ancestor ❷ and hence are found in all of the descendants of that ancestor (the tetrapods). The amnion was present only in ancestor ❸ and hence is shared only by some tetrapods (mammals and reptiles). Feathers were present only in common ancestor ❻ and hence are found only in birds.

To explore "tree thinking" further, note that in Figure 22.17, mammals are positioned closer to amphibians than to birds. As a result, you might conclude that mammals are more closely related to amphibians than they are to birds. However, mammals are actually more closely related to birds than to amphibians because mammals and birds share a more recent common ancestor (ancestor ❸) than do mammals and amphibians (ancestor ❷). Ancestor ❷ is also the most recent common ancestor of birds and amphibians,

Each branch point represents the common ancestor of the lineages beginning there and to the right of it.

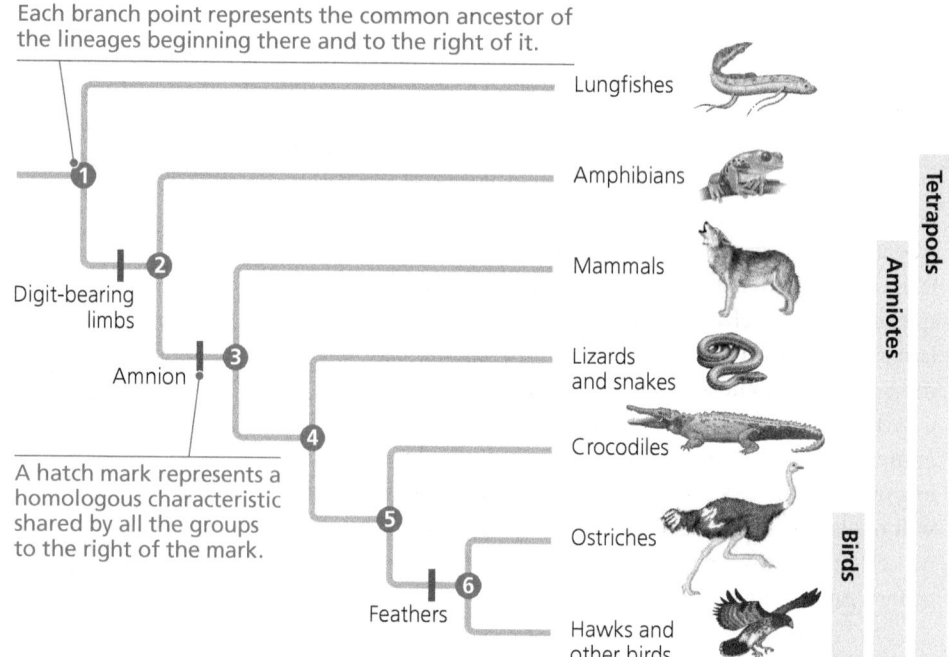

A hatch mark represents a homologous characteristic shared by all the groups to the right of the mark.

▲ Figure 22.17 **Tree thinking: information provided in an evolutionary tree.** This evolutionary tree for tetrapods and their closest living relatives, the lungfishes, is based on anatomical and DNA sequence data. The purple bars indicate the origin of three important homologies, each of which evolved only once. Birds are nested within and evolved from reptiles; hence, the group of organisms called "reptiles" technically includes birds.

? *Are crocodiles more closely related to lizards or birds? Explain your answer.*

making mammals and birds equally related to amphibians. Finally, note that the tree in Figure 22.17 shows the relative timing of evolutionary events but not their actual dates. Thus, we can conclude that ancestor ❷ lived before ancestor ❸, but we do not know when that was.

Evolutionary trees are hypotheses that summarize our current understanding of patterns of descent. Our confidence in these relationships, as with any hypothesis, depends on the strength of the supporting data. In the case of Figure 22.17, the tree is supported by a variety of independent data sets, including both anatomical, developmental, and DNA sequence data. As a result, biologists feel confident that it accurately reflects evolutionary history. As you will read in Chapter 26, scientists can use such well-supported evolutionary trees to make specific and sometimes surprising predictions about organisms.

A Different Cause of Resemblance: Convergent Evolution

Although organisms that are closely related share characteristics because of common descent, distantly related organisms can resemble one another for a different reason: **convergent evolution**, the independent evolution of similar features in different lineages. Consider marsupial mammals, many of which live in Australia. Marsupials are distinct from another group of mammals—the eutherians—few of which live in Australia. (Eutherians complete their embryonic development in the uterus, whereas marsupials are born as embryos and complete their development in an external pouch.) Some Australian marsupials have eutherian look-alikes with superficially similar adaptations. For instance, a forest-dwelling Australian marsupial called the sugar glider is superficially very similar to flying squirrels, gliding eutherians that live in North American forests (Figure 22.18). But the sugar glider has many other characteristics that make it a marsupial, much more closely related to kangaroos and other Australian marsupials than to flying squirrels or other eutherians. Once again, our understanding of evolution can explain these observations. Although they evolved independently from different ancestors, these two mammals have adapted to similar environments in similar ways. In such examples in which species share features because of convergent evolution, the resemblance is said to be **analogous**, not homologous. Analogous features share similar function, but not common ancestry, while homologous features share common ancestry, but not necessarily similar function.

The Fossil Record

A third type of evidence for evolution comes from fossils. The fossil record documents the pattern of evolution, showing that past organisms differed from present-day organisms and that many species have become extinct. Fossils also show the evolutionary changes that have occurred in various groups of organisms. To give one of hundreds of

▲ **Figure 22.18 Convergent evolution.** The ability to glide through the air evolved independently in these two distantly related mammals.

Steve Bloom Images/Alamy Stock Photo

possible examples, researchers found that the pelvic bone in fossil stickleback fish became greatly reduced in size over time in a number of different lakes. The consistent nature of this change suggests that the reduction in the size of the pelvic bone may have been driven by natural selection.

Fossils can also shed light on the origins of new groups of organisms. An example is the fossil record of cetaceans, the mammalian order that includes whales, dolphins, and porpoises. Some of these fossils provided an unexpected line of support for a hypothesis based on DNA sequence data: that cetaceans are closely related to even-toed ungulates, a group that includes deer, pigs, camels, and cows (Figure 22.19). What else can fossils tell us about cetacean origins? The earliest cetaceans lived 50–60 million years ago. The fossil record indicates that prior to that time, most mammals were terrestrial. Although scientists had long realized that whales and other cetaceans originated from land mammals, few fossils had been found that revealed how cetacean limb structure had changed over time, leading eventually to the loss of hind limbs and the development of flippers and tail flukes. In the past few decades, however, a series of remarkable fossils have been discovered in Pakistan, Egypt, and North America. These fossils document steps in the transition from life on land to life in the sea, filling in some of the gaps between ancestral and living cetaceans (Figure 22.20).

Collectively, the recent fossil discoveries document the origin of a major new group of mammals, the cetaceans. These discoveries also show that cetaceans and their close living relatives

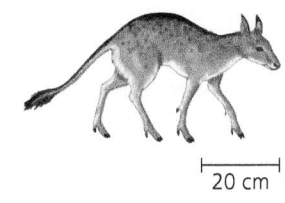

20 cm

▲ *Diacodexis*, an early even-toed ungulate

(hippopotamuses, pigs, deer, and other even-toed ungulates) are much more different from each other than were *Pakicetus* and early even-toed ungulates, such as *Diacodexis*. Similar patterns are seen in fossils documenting the origins of other major new groups of organisms, including mammals (see Chapter 25), flowering plants (see Chapter 30), and tetrapods (see Chapter 34). In each of these cases, the fossil record shows that, over time, descent with modification produced increasingly large differences among related groups of organisms, ultimately resulting in the diversity of life we see today.

Biogeography

A fourth type of evidence for evolution comes from **biogeography**, the scientific study of the geographic distributions of species. The geographic distributions of organisms are influenced by many factors, including *plate tectonics*, the slow movement of Earth's continents over time. About 250 million years ago, these movements united all of Earth's landmasses into a single large continent called **Pangaea** (see Figure 25.16). Roughly 200 million years ago, Pangaea began to break apart; by 20 million years ago, the continents we know today were within a few hundred kilometres of their present locations.

We can use our understanding of evolution and continental drift to predict where fossils of different groups of organisms might be found. For example, scientists have constructed evolutionary trees for horses based on anatomical data. These trees and the ages of fossils of horse ancestors suggest that present-day horse species originated 5 million years ago in North America. At that time, North and South America were close to their present locations, but they were not yet connected, making it difficult for horses to travel between them. Thus, we would predict that the oldest horse fossils should be found only on the continent on which horses

Most mammals

(a) *Canis* (dog)

Cetaceans and even-toed ungulates

(b) *Pakicetus*   (c) *Sus* (pig)   (d) *Odocoileus* (deer)

Northeastern Ohio Universities College of Medicine

▲ Figure 22.19 **Ankle bones: one piece of the puzzle.** Comparing fossils and present-day examples of the astragalus (a type of ankle bone) provides one line of evidence that cetaceans are closely related to even-toed ungulates. **(a)** In most mammals, the astragalus is shaped like that of a dog, with a double hump on one end (indicated by the red arrows) but not at the opposite end (blue arrow). **(b)** Fossils show that the early cetacean *Pakicetus* had an astragalus with double humps at both ends, a unique shape that is otherwise found only in even-toed ungulates, as shown here for **(c)** a pig and **(d)** a deer.

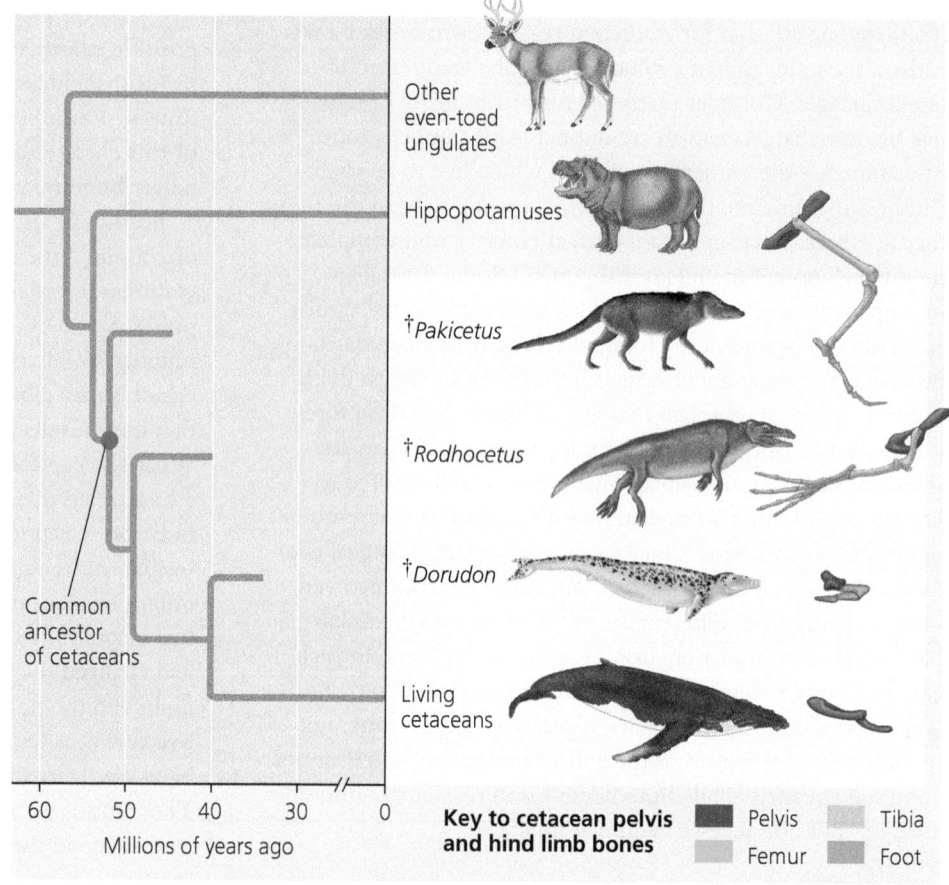

Other even-toed ungulates

Hippopotamuses

†*Pakicetus*

†*Rodhocetus*

†*Dorudon*

Living cetaceans

Common ancestor of cetaceans

60   50   40   30   0
Millions of years ago

Key to cetacean pelvis and hind limb bones

Pelvis   Tibia
Femur   Foot

▲ Figure 22.20 **The transition to life in the sea.** Multiple lines of evidence support the hypothesis that cetaceans evolved from terrestrial mammals. Fossils document the reduction over time in the pelvis and hind limb bones of extinct cetacean ancestors, including *Pakicetus*, *Rodhocetus*, and *Dorudon*. DNA sequence data support the hypothesis that cetaceans are most closely related to hippopotamuses and the other even-toed ungulates.

? *Which happened first during the evolution of cetaceans: changes in hind limb structure or the origin of tail flukes?*

originated—North America. This prediction and others like it for different groups of organisms have been upheld, providing more evidence for evolution.

We can also use our understanding of evolution to explain biogeographic data. For example, islands generally have many plant and animal species that are **endemic**, (found nowhere else in the world). Yet, as Darwin described in *The Origin of Species*, most island species are closely related to species from the nearest mainland or a neighbouring island. He explained this observation by suggesting that islands are colonized by species from the nearest mainland. These colonists eventually give rise to new species as they adapt to their new environments. Such a process also explains why two islands with similar environments in distant parts of the world tend to be populated not by species that are closely related to each other, but rather by species related to those of the nearest mainland, where the environment is often quite different.

What Is Theoretical About Darwin's View of Life?

Some people dismiss Darwin's ideas as "just a theory." However, as we have seen, the *pattern* of evolution—the observation that life has evolved over time—has been documented directly and is supported by a vast amount of evidence. In addition, Darwin's explanation of the *process* of evolution—that natural selection is the primary cause of the observed pattern of evolutionary change—makes sense of massive amounts of data. The effects of natural selection also can be observed and tested in nature. One such experiment is described in the Scientific Skills Exercise.

What, then, is theoretical about evolution? Recall from Chapter 1 that the scientific meaning of the term *theory* is very different from its meaning in everyday use. The colloquial use of the word *theory* comes close to what scientists mean by a hypothesis. In science, a theory is more comprehensive than a hypothesis. A theory, such as the theory

---

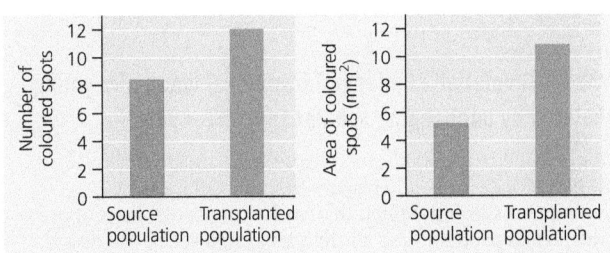

of evolution by natural selection, accounts for many observations and explains and integrates a great variety of phenomena. Such a unifying theory does not become widely accepted unless its predictions stand up to thorough and continual testing by experiment and additional observation. As the rest of this unit demonstrates, this has certainly been the case with the theory of evolution by natural selection.

The scepticism of scientists as they continue to test theories prevents these ideas from becoming dogma. For example, although Darwin thought that evolution was a very slow process, we now know that this isn't always true. New species can form in relatively short periods of time (a few thousand years or less; see Chapter 24). Furthermore, as we will explore throughout this unit, evolutionary biologists now recognize that natural selection is not the only mechanism responsible for evolution. Indeed, the study of evolution today is livelier than ever as scientists use a wide range of experimental approaches and genetic analyses to test predictions based on natural selection and other evolutionary mechanisms.

As we continue to explore this unit, remember that evolution, the core theme of biology, is what accounts for the unity and diversity of life. As Darwin wrote in the final sentence of *The Origin of Species*, "There is grandeur in this view of life ... [in which] endless forms most beautiful and most wonderful have been, and are being, evolved."

CONCEPT CHECK 22.3

1. Explain how the following statement is inaccurate: "Antibiotics have created drug resistance in MRSA."
2. How does evolution account for (a) the similar mammalian forelimbs with different functions shown in Figure 22.15 and (b) the similar forms of the two distantly related mammals shown in Figure 22.18?
3. **WHAT IF?** Dinosaurs originated 250–200 million years ago. Would you expect the geographic distribution of early dinosaur fossils to be broad (on many continents) or narrow (on one or a few continents only)? Explain.

For suggested answers, see Appendix A.

22 Chapter Review

Go to **MasteringBiology**® for Assignments, the eText, and the Study Area with Animations, Activities, Vocab Self-Quiz, and Practice Tests.

SUMMARY OF KEY CONCEPTS

CONCEPT 22.1

The Darwinian revolution challenged traditional views of a young Earth inhabited by unchanging species (pp. 493–495)

- Darwin proposed that life's diversity arose from ancestral species through natural selection, a departure from prevailing views.
- Cuvier studied fossils but denied that evolution occurs; he proposed that sudden catastrophic events in the past caused species to disappear from an area.
- Hutton and Lyell thought that geologic change could result from gradual mechanisms that operated in the past in the same manner as they do today.
- Lamarck hypothesized that species evolve, but the underlying mechanisms he proposed are not supported by evidence.

? *Why was the age of Earth important for Darwin's ideas about evolution?*

CONCEPT 22.2

Descent with modification by natural selection explains the adaptations of organisms and the unity and diversity of life (pp. 495–500)

- Darwin's experiences during the voyage of the *Beagle* gave rise to his idea that new species originate from ancestral forms through the accumulation of **adaptations**. He refined his theory for many years and finally published it in 1859 after learning that Wallace had come to the same idea.
- In *The Origin of Species*, Darwin proposed that evolution occurs by **natural selection**.

Observations

Individuals in a population vary in their heritable characteristics.	Organisms produce more offspring than the environment can support.

Inferences

Individuals that are well suited to their environment tend to leave more offspring than other individuals.

and

Over time, favourable traits accumulate in the population.

? *Describe how overreproduction and heritable variation relate to evolution by natural selection.*

CONCEPT 22.3

Evolution is supported by an overwhelming amount of scientific evidence (pp. 500–508)

- Researchers have directly observed natural selection leading to adaptive evolution in many studies, including research on soapberry bug populations and on MRSA.
- Organisms share characteristics because of common descent (**homologous**) or because natural selection affects independently evolving species in similar environments in similar ways (**convergent evolution; analogous**).

- Fossils show that past organisms differed from living organisms, that many species have become extinct, and that species have evolved over long periods of time; fossils also document the origin of major new groups of organisms.
- Evolutionary theory can explain biogeographic patterns.

? *Summarize the different lines of evidence supporting the hypothesis that cetaceans descended from land mammals and are closely related to even-toed ungulates.*

TEST YOUR UNDERSTANDING

LEVEL 1: KNOWLEDGE/COMPREHENSION

1. Which of the following is *not* an observation or inference on which natural selection is based?
   a. There is heritable variation among individuals.
   b. Poorly adapted individuals never produce offspring.
   c. Species produce more offspring than the environment can support.
   d. Only a fraction of an individual's offspring may survive.

2. Which of the following observations helped Darwin shape his concept of descent with modification?
   a. Species diversity is lower farther from the equator.
   b. Fewer species live on islands than on the nearest continents.
   c. Birds live on islands located farther from the mainland than the birds' maximum nonstop flight distance.
   d. South American temperate plants are more similar to the tropical plants of South America than to the temperate plants of Europe.

LEVEL 2: APPLICATION/ANALYSIS

3. Within six months of effectively using methicillin to treat *S. aureus* infections in a community, all new infections were caused by MRSA. How can this result best be explained?
   a. *S. aureus* can resist vaccines.
   b. A patient must have become infected with MRSA from another community.
   c. In response to the drug, *S. aureus* began making drug-resistant versions of the protein targeted by the drug.
   d. Some drug-resistant bacteria were present at the start of treatment, and natural selection increased their frequency.

4. The upper forelimbs of humans and bats have fairly similar skeletal structures, whereas the corresponding bones in whales have very different shapes and proportions. However, genetic data suggest that all three kinds of organisms diverged from a common ancestor at about the same time. Which of the following is the most likely explanation for these data?
   a. Forelimb evolution was adaptive in people and bats, but not in whales.
   b. Natural selection in an aquatic environment resulted in significant changes to whale forelimb anatomy.
   c. Genes mutate faster in whales than in humans or bats.
   d. Whales are not properly classified as mammals.

5. DNA sequences in many human genes are very similar to the sequences of corresponding genes in chimpanzees. The most likely explanation for this result is that

   a. humans and chimpanzees share a relatively recent common ancestor.
   b. humans evolved from chimpanzees.
   c. chimpanzees evolved from humans.
   d. convergent evolution led to the DNA similarities.

LEVEL 3: SYNTHESIS/EVALUATION

6. **EVOLUTION CONNECTION**
   Explain why anatomical and molecular features often fit a similar nested pattern. In addition, describe a process that can cause this not to be the case.

7. **SCIENTIFIC INQUIRY**
   DRAW IT Mosquitoes resistant to the pesticide DDT first appeared in India in 1959, but now are found throughout the world. (a) Graph the data in the table below. (b) Examining the graph, hypothesize why the percentage of mosquitoes resistant to DDT rose rapidly. (c) Suggest an explanation for the global spread of DDT resistance.

Month	0	8	12
Mosquitoes Resistant* to DDT	4%	45%	77%

Source: C. F. Curtis et al., Selection for and against insecticide resistance and possible methods of inhibiting the evolution of resistance in mosquitoes, *Ecological Entomology* 3:273–287 (1978).

*Mosquitoes were considered resistant if they were not killed within 1 hour of receiving a dose of 4% DDT.

8. **WRITE ABOUT A THEME: INTERACTIONS**
   Write a short essay (about 100–150 words) evaluating whether changes to an organism's physical environment are likely to result in evolutionary change. Use an example to support your reasoning.

9. **SYNTHESIZE YOUR KNOWLEDGE**

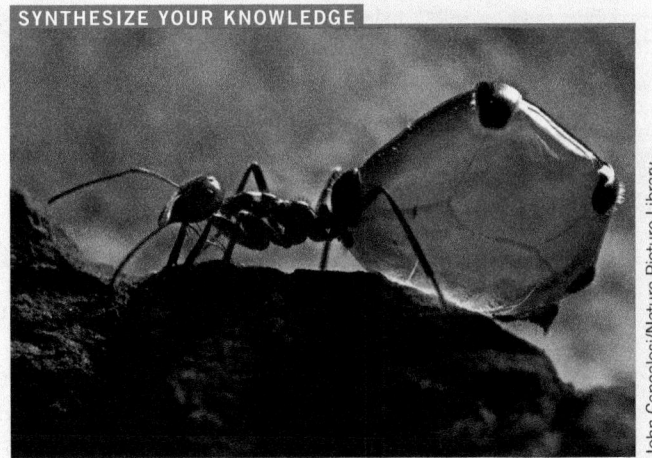

John Cancalosi/Nature Picture Library

This honeypot ant (genus *Myrmecocystus*) can store liquid food inside its expandable abdomen. Consider other ants you are familiar with, and explain how a honeypot ant exemplifies three key features of life: adaptation, unity, and diversity.

For selected answers, see Appendix A.

23

The Evolution of Populations

PiLensPhoto/Fotolia

KEY CONCEPTS

23.1 Genetic variation makes evolution possible

23.2 The Hardy-Weinberg equation can be used to test whether a population is evolving

23.3 Natural selection, genetic drift, and gene flow can alter allele frequencies in a population

23.4 Natural selection is the only mechanism that consistently causes adaptive evolution

PiLensPhoto/Fotolia

▲ Figure 23.1 **Are red squirrel populations evolving in response to climate change?**

The Smallest Unit of Evolution

One common misconception about evolution is that individual organisms evolve. It is true that natural selection acts on individuals: Each organism's traits affect its own survival and reproductive success compared with other individuals. But the evolutionary impact of natural selection is only apparent in the changes in a *population* of organisms over time.

Consider the red squirrel (*Tamiasciurus hudsonicus*) in **Figure 23.1**, from Kluane National Park and Reserve in the Yukon. These squirrels are small, diurnal mammals with an average life span of just three years. Dr. Stan Boutin from the University of Alberta and colleagues have been conducting long-term research on these squirrels. Since they began their study in 1987, they have recorded that female squirrels now give birth 18 days earlier in the spring than they did 10 years ago. Is this change in behaviour due to the warmer climate in the area or is it due to evolution? Their analysis has revealed that offspring are more likely to survive when born to mothers with a genetic propensity for giving birth earlier in the season. The offspring that are born earlier tend to be larger and better able to be independent when winter approaches later in the year. The result is that earlier-born squirrels have higher survival rates and are therefore more likely to be successful in breeding the next year. The Kluane red squirrel population has evolved by natural selection; however, individual squirrels did not evolve. Each female squirrel has the genetic propensity to give birth at a particular time, but the proportion of squirrels giving birth early in the spring increased from generation to generation.

Focusing on evolutionary change in populations, we can define evolution on its smallest scale, called **microevolution**, as change in allele frequencies in a population over generations. As we will see in this chapter, natural selection is not the only cause of microevolution. In fact, there are three main mechanisms that can cause allele frequency change: natural selection, genetic drift (chance events that alter allele frequencies), and gene flow (the transfer of alleles between populations). Each of these mechanisms has distinctive effects on the genetic composition of populations. However, only natural selection consistently improves the match between organisms and their environment. Before we examine natural selection and adaptation more closely, let's revisit a prerequisite for these processes in a population: genetic variation.

CONCEPT 23.1

Genetic variation makes evolution possible

In *The Origin of Species*, Darwin provided abundant evidence that life on Earth has evolved over time, and he proposed natural selection as the primary mechanism for that change. He observed that individuals differed in their inherited traits and that selection acted on such differences, leading to evolutionary change. Thus, Darwin realized that variation in heritable traits was a prerequisite for evolution, but he did not know precisely how organisms pass heritable traits to their offspring.

Just a few years after Darwin published *The Origin of Species*, Gregor Mendel wrote a groundbreaking paper on inheritance in pea plants (see Chapter 14). In that paper, Mendel proposed a particulate model of inheritance in which organisms transmit discrete heritable units (now called genes) to their offspring. Although Darwin did not know about genes, Mendel's paper set the stage for understanding the genetic differences on which evolution is based. Here we'll examine such genetic differences and how they are produced.

Genetic Variation

You probably have no trouble recognizing your friends in a crowd. Each person is unique, exhibiting differences in their facial features, height, and voice. Indeed, individual variation occurs in all species. In addition to the differences that we can see or hear, individuals vary extensively at the molecular level. For example, you cannot identify a person's blood group (A, B, AB, or O) from his or her appearance, but this and many other molecular traits vary among individuals.

Such phenotypic variations often reflect **genetic variation**, differences among individuals in the composition of their genes or other DNA sequences. Some heritable phenotypic differences occur on an "either-or" basis, such as the flower colours of Mendel's pea plants: Each plant had flowers that were either purple or white (see Figure 14.3). Characters that vary in this way are typically determined by a single gene locus, with different alleles producing distinct phenotypes. In contrast, other phenotypic differences vary in gradations along a continuum. Such variation usually results from the influence of two or more genes on a single phenotypic character. In fact, many phenotypic characters are influenced by multiple genes, including coat colour in horses (Figure 23.2), seed number in maize (corn), and height in humans.

How much do genes and other DNA sequences vary from one individual to another? Genetic variation at the whole-gene level (*gene variability*) can be quantified as the average percentage of loci that are heterozygous. (Recall that a heterozygous individual has two different alleles for a given locus, whereas a homozygous individual has two identical alleles for that locus.) As an example, on average the fruit fly (*Drosophila melanogaster*) is heterozygous for only 1920 of its 13 700 loci (14%) and homozygous for all the rest.

Considerable genetic variation can also be measured at the molecular level of DNA (*nucleotide variability*). But little of this variation results in phenotypic variation. The reason is that many of the differences occur within *introns*, non-coding segments of DNA lying between exons, the regions retained in mRNA after RNA processing (see Figure 17.11). And of the variations that occur within exons, most do not cause a change in the amino acid sequence of the protein encoded by the gene. For example, in the sequence

▲ **Figure 23.2 Phenotypic variation in horses.** In horses, coat colour varies along a continuum and is influenced by multiple genes.

Base-pair substitutions are shown in orange.

A red arrow indicates an insertion site.

The substitution at this site results in the translation of a different amino acid.

A deletion of 26 base pairs occurred here.

1   500   1,000   1,500   2,000   2,500

Exon   Intron

▲ Figure 23.3 **Extensive genetic variation at the molecular level.** This diagram summarizes data from a study comparing the DNA sequence of the alcohol dehydrogenase (*Adh*) gene in several fruit flies (*Drosophila melanogaster*). The *Adh* gene has four exons (dark blue) separated by introns (light blue); the exons include the coding regions that are ultimately translated into the amino acids of the *Adh* enzyme. Only one substitution has a phenotypic effect, producing a different form of the *Adh* enzyme.

Source: Data from figure 9.14 of *Evolution*, 1st edition, by Douglas J. Futuyma. Sinauer Associates, 2006; and "Nucleotide Polymorphism at the Alcohol Dehydrogenase Locus of Drosophila melanogaster" by Martin Kreitman, from *Nature*, August 1983, Volume 304(5925). ©Jane B Reece.

MAKE CONNECTIONS *Review Figures 17.5 and 17.10. Explain how a base-pair substitution that alters a coding region of the Adh locus could have no effect on amino acid sequence. Then explain how an insertion in an exon could have no effect on the protein produced.*

comparison of the gene for alcohol dehydrogenase (*Adh*) shown in **Figure 23.3**, there are 43 nucleotide sites with variable base pairs (where substitutions have occurred), as well as several sites where insertions or deletions have occurred. Although 18 variable sites occur within the four exons of the *Adh* gene, only one of these variations (at site 1490) results in an amino acid change. Note, however, that this single variable site is enough to cause genetic variation at the level of the gene—and hence two different forms of the *Adh* enzyme are produced.

It is important to bear in mind that some phenotypic variation does not result from genetic differences among individuals (**Figure 23.4** shows a striking example in a caterpillar of the southwestern United States). Phenotype is the product of an inherited genotype and many environmental influences (see Concept 14.3). In a human example, bodybuilders alter their phenotypes dramatically but do not pass their huge muscles on to the next generation. In general, only the genetically determined part of phenotypic variation can have evolutionary consequences. As such, genetic variation provides the raw material for evolutionary change: Without genetic variation, evolution cannot occur.

Sources of Genetic Variation

The genetic variation on which evolution depends originates when mutation, gene duplication, or other processes produce new alleles and new genes. Many new genetic variants can be produced in short periods of time in organisms that reproduce rapidly. Sexual reproduction can also result in genetic variation as existing genes are arranged in new ways.

Formation of New Alleles

As described in Chapters 17 and 21, new alleles can arise by *mutation*, a change in the nucleotide sequence of an organism's DNA. A mutation is like a shot in the dark—one cannot predict accurately which segments of DNA will be altered or in what way. In multicellular organisms, only mutations in cell lines that produce gametes can be passed to offspring. In plants and fungi, this is not as limiting as it may sound, since many different cell lines can produce gametes (see Figures 30.5 and 31.16). But in most animals, the majority of mutations occur in somatic cells and cannot be passed to offspring.

A change of as little as one base in a gene—a "point mutation"—can have a significant impact on phenotype, as in sickle-cell disease (see Figure 17.25). Organisms reflect thousands of generations of past selection, and hence most new mutations are at least slightly harmful. In some cases, natural selection quickly removes such harmful alleles. In diploid organisms, however, harmful alleles that are recessive can be hidden from selection. Indeed, a harmful recessive allele can persist for generations by propagation in heterozygous individuals (where its harmful effects are masked by the more favourable dominant allele). Such "heterozygote protection" maintains a huge pool of alleles that might not be favoured under present conditions, but that could be beneficial if the environment changes.

Erick Greene

▲ Figure 23.4 **Nonheritable variation.** These caterpillars of the moth *Nemoria arizonaria* owe their different appearances to chemicals in their diets, not to differences in their genotypes. **(a)** Caterpillars raised on a diet of oak flowers resemble the flowers, whereas **(b)** their siblings raised on oak leaves resemble oak twigs.

While many mutations are harmful, many others are not. Recall that much of the DNA in eukaryotic genomes does not encode proteins (see Figure 21.7). Point mutations in these noncoding regions generally result in **neutral variation**, differences in DNA sequence that do not confer a selective advantage or disadvantage. The redundancy in the genetic code is another source of neutral variation: Even a point mutation in a gene that encodes a protein will have no effect on the protein's function if its amino acid sequence is not changed. And even where there is an amino acid change, it may not affect the protein's shape and function. Finally, as you will see later in this chapter, a mutant allele may on rare occasions actually make its bearer better suited to the environment, enhancing reproductive success.

Altering Gene Number or Position

Chromosomal changes that delete, disrupt, or rearrange many loci at once are usually harmful. However, when such large-scale changes leave genes intact, they may not affect the organism's phenotype. In rare cases, chromosomal rearrangements may even be beneficial. For example, the translocation of part of one chromosome to a different chromosome could link DNA segments in a way that results in a positive effect.

A key potential source of variation is the duplication of genes due to errors in meiosis (such as unequal crossing over), slippage during DNA replication, or the activities of transposable elements (see Chapters 15 and 21). Duplications of large chromosome segments, like other chromosomal aberrations, are often harmful, but the duplication of smaller pieces of DNA may not be. Gene duplications that do not have severe effects can persist over generations, allowing mutations to accumulate. The result is an expanded genome with new genes that may take on new functions.

Such beneficial increases in gene number appear to have played a major role in evolution. For example, the remote ancestors of mammals had a single gene for detecting odours that has since been duplicated many times. As a result, humans today have about 850 olfactory receptor genes, and mice have 1300. This dramatic proliferation of olfactory genes probably helped early mammals, enabling them to detect faint odours and to distinguish among many different smells. More recently, about 60% of these olfactory receptor genes have been inactivated by mutations in humans, whereas mice have lost only 20% of theirs. Since mutation rates in humans and mice are similar, this difference is likely due to strong selection against mice with mutations that inactivate their olfactory genes. A versatile sense of smell appears to be much more important to mice than to humans!

Rapid Reproduction

Mutation rates tend to be low in plants and animals, averaging about one mutation in every 100 000 genes per generation, and they are often even lower in prokaryotes. But prokaryotes have many more generations per unit of time, so mutations can quickly generate genetic variation in populations of these organisms. The same is true of viruses. For instance, HIV has a generation span of about two days. It also has an RNA genome, which has a much higher mutation rate than a typical DNA genome because of the lack of RNA repair mechanisms in host cells (see Chapter 19). For this reason, it is unlikely that a single-drug treatment would ever be effective against HIV; mutant forms of the virus that are resistant to a particular drug would no doubt proliferate in relatively short order. The most effective AIDS treatments to date have been drug "cocktails" that combine several medications. It is less likely that multiple mutations conferring resistance to *all* the drugs will occur in a short time period.

Sexual Reproduction

In organisms that reproduce sexually, most of the genetic variation in a population results from the unique combination of alleles that each individual receives from its parents. Of course, at the nucleotide level, all the differences among these alleles have originated from past mutations and other processes that can produce new alleles. But it is the mechanism of sexual reproduction that shuffles existing alleles and deals them at random to produce individual genotypes.

As described in Chapter 13, three mechanisms contribute to this shuffling: crossing over, independent assortment of chromosomes, and fertilization. During meiosis, homologous chromosomes, one inherited from each parent, trade some of their alleles by crossing over. These homologous chromosomes and the alleles they carry are then distributed at random into gametes. Then, because myriad possible mating combinations exist in a population, fertilization brings together gametes that are likely to have different genetic backgrounds. The combined effects of these three mechanisms ensure that sexual reproduction rearranges existing alleles into fresh combinations each generation, providing much of the genetic variation that makes evolution possible.

CONCEPT CHECK 23.1

1. (a) Explain why genetic variation within a population is a prerequisite for evolution. (b) What factors can produce genetic differences between populations?
2. Of all the mutations that occur in a population, why do only a small fraction become widespread?
3. **MAKE CONNECTIONS** If a population stopped reproducing sexually (but still reproduced asexually), how would its genetic variation be affected over time? Explain. (See Concept 13.4)

For suggested answers, see Appendix A.

The Hardy-Weinberg equation can be used to test whether a population is evolving

Although the individuals in a population must differ genetically for evolution to occur, the presence of genetic variation does not guarantee that a population will evolve. For that to happen, one of the factors that causes evolution must be at work. In this section, we'll explore one way to test whether evolution is occurring in a population. The first step in this process is to clarify what we mean by a population.

Gene Pools and Allele Frequencies

A **population** is a group of individuals of the same species that live in the same area and interbreed. Different populations of a single species may be isolated geographically from one another, thus exchanging genetic material only rarely. Such isolation is common for species that live on widely separated islands or in different lakes. But not all populations are isolated, nor must populations have sharp boundaries (Figure 23.5). Still, members of a population typically breed with one another and thus, on average, are more closely related to each other than to members of other populations.

We can characterize a population's genetic makeup by describing its **gene pool**, which consists of all copies of every type of allele at every locus in all members of the population. If only one allele exists for a particular locus in a population, that allele is said to be *fixed* in the gene pool, and all individuals are homozygous for that allele. But if there are two or more alleles for a particular locus in a population, individuals may be either homozygous or heterozygous.

Each allele has a frequency (proportion) in the population. For example, imagine a population of 500 wildflower plants with two alleles, C^R and C^W, for a locus that codes for flower pigment. These alleles show incomplete dominance (see Figure 14.10); thus, each genotype has a distinct phenotype. Plants homozygous for the C^R allele ($C^R C^R$) produce red pigment and have red flowers; plants homozygous for the C^W allele ($C^W C^W$) produce no red pigment and have white flowers; and heterozygotes ($C^R C^W$) produce some red pigment and have pink flowers.

In our population, suppose there are 320 plants with red flowers, 160 with pink flowers, and 20 with white flowers. Because these are diploid organisms, there are a total of 1000 copies of the gene for flower colour in the population of 500 individuals. The C^R allele accounts for 800 of these copies ($320 \times 2 = 640$ for $C^R C^R$ plants, plus $160 \times 1 = 160$ for $C^R C^W$ plants).

When studying a locus with two alleles, the convention is to use p to represent the frequency of one allele and q to represent the frequency of the other allele. Thus, p, the frequency of the C^R allele in the gene pool of this population, is $800/1000 = 0.8 = 80\%$. And because there are only two alleles for this gene, the frequency of the C^W allele, represented by q, must be $200/1000 = 0.2 = 20\%$. For loci that have more than two alleles, the sum of all allele frequencies must still equal 1 (100%).

Next we'll see how allele and genotype frequencies can be used to test whether evolution is occurring in a population.

The Hardy-Weinberg Equation

One way to assess whether natural selection or other factors are causing evolution at a particular locus is to determine what the genetic makeup of a population would be if it were *not* evolving at that locus. We can then compare that scenario with data from a real population. If there are

▲ **Figure 23.5 One species, two populations.** These two caribou populations in the Yukon are not totally isolated; they sometimes share the same area. Still, members of either population are most likely to breed within their own population.

Gary Schultz/Photoshot Holdings Ltd.

Porcupine herd

Fortymile herd

James L. Davis/ProWildlife

no differences, we can conclude that the real population is not evolving. If there are differences, this suggests that the real population may be evolving—and then we can try to figure out why.

Hardy-Weinberg Equilibrium

In a population that is not evolving, allele and genotype frequencies will remain constant from generation to generation, provided that only Mendelian segregation and recombination of alleles are at work. Such a population is said to be in **Hardy-Weinberg equilibrium**, named for the British mathematician and German physician, respectively, who independently developed this idea in 1908.

To use the Hardy-Weinberg principle, it is helpful to think about genetic crosses in a new way. Previously, we used Punnett squares to determine the genotypes of offspring in a genetic cross (see Figure 14.5). Here, instead of considering the possible allele combinations from one cross, consider the combination of alleles in *all* of the crosses in a population.

Imagine that all the alleles for a given locus from all the individuals in a population were placed in a large bin (Figure 23.6). We can think of this bin as holding the population's gene pool for that locus. "Reproduction" occurs by

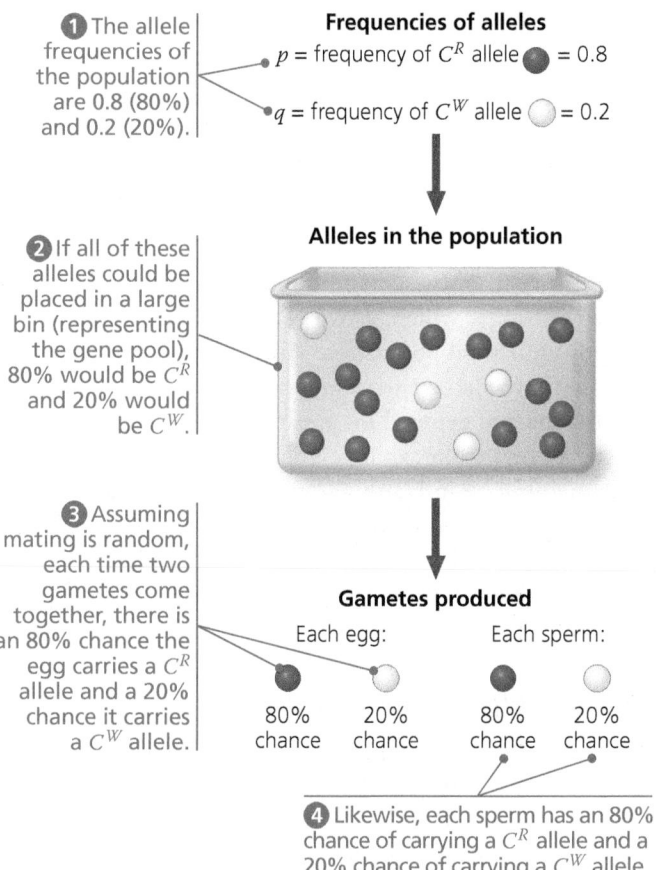

① The allele frequencies of the population are 0.8 (80%) and 0.2 (20%).

Frequencies of alleles

p = frequency of C^R allele ● = 0.8

q = frequency of C^W allele ○ = 0.2

② If all of these alleles could be placed in a large bin (representing the gene pool), 80% would be C^R and 20% would be C^W.

Alleles in the population

③ Assuming mating is random, each time two gametes come together, there is an 80% chance the egg carries a C^R allele and a 20% chance it carries a C^W allele.

Gametes produced

Each egg: Each sperm:

80% chance 20% chance 80% chance 20% chance

④ Likewise, each sperm has an 80% chance of carrying a C^R allele and a 20% chance of carrying a C^W allele.

▲ Figure 23.6 **Selecting alleles at random from a gene pool.**

selecting alleles at random from the bin; somewhat similar events occur in nature when fish release sperm and eggs into the water or when pollen (containing plant sperm) is blown about by the wind. By viewing reproduction as a process of randomly selecting and combining alleles from the bin (the gene pool), we are in effect assuming that mating occurs at random—that is, that all male-female matings are equally likely.

Let's apply the bin analogy to the hypothetical wild-flower population discussed earlier. In that population of 500 flowers, the frequency of the allele for red flowers (C^R) is $p = 0.8$, and the frequency of the allele for white flowers (C^W) is $q = 0.2$. Thus, a bin holding all 1000 copies of the flower-colour gene in the population contains 800 C^R alleles and 200 C^W alleles. Assuming that gametes are formed by selecting alleles at random from the bin, the probability that an egg or sperm contains a C^R or C^W allele is equal to the frequency of these alleles in the bin. Thus, as shown in Figure 23.7, each egg has an 80% chance of containing a C^R allele and a 20% chance of containing a C^W allele; the same is true for each sperm.

Using the rule of multiplication (see Figure 14.9), we can now calculate the frequencies of the three possible genotypes, assuming random unions of sperm and eggs. The probability that two C^R alleles will come together is $p \times p = p^2 = 0.8 \times 0.8 = 0.64$. Thus, about 64% of the plants in the next generation will have the genotype $C^R C^R$. The frequency of $C^W C^W$ individuals is expected to be about $q \times q = q^2 = 0.2 \times 0.2 = 0.04$, or 4%. $C^R C^W$ heterozygotes can arise in two different ways. If the sperm provides the C^R allele and the egg provides the C^W allele, the resulting heterozygotes will be $p \times q = 0.8 \times 0.2 = 0.16$, or 16% of the total. If the sperm provides the C^W allele and the egg the C^R allele, the heterozygous offspring will make up $q \times p = 0.2 \times 0.8 = 0.16$, or 16%. The frequency of heterozygotes is thus the sum of these possibilities: $pq + qp = 2pq = 0.16 + 0.16 = 0.32$, or 32%.

As shown in Figure 23.7, the genotype frequencies in the next generation must add up to 1 (100%). Thus, the equation for Hardy-Weinberg equilibrium states that at a locus with two alleles, the three genotypes will appear in the following proportions:

$$\underset{\substack{\text{Expected} \\ \text{frequency} \\ \text{of genotype} \\ C^R C^R}}{p^2} + \underset{\substack{\text{Expected} \\ \text{frequency} \\ \text{of genotype} \\ C^R C^W}}{2pq} + \underset{\substack{\text{Expected} \\ \text{frequency} \\ \text{of genotype} \\ C^W C^W}}{q^2} = 1$$

Note that for a locus with two alleles, only three genotypes are possible (in this case, $C^R C^R$, $C^R C^W$, and $C^W C^W$). As a result, the sum of the frequencies of the three genotypes must equal 1 (100%) in *any* population—regardless of whether the population is in Hardy-Weinberg equilibrium.

Gametes for each generation are drawn at random from the gene pool of the previous generation, as in Figure 23.6:

80% C^R ($p = 0.8$)　　20% C^W ($q = 0.2$)

Sperm
C^R (80%)　　C^W (20%)

Eggs
C^R (80%)

C^W (20%)

64% (p^2) $C^R C^R$　　16% (pq) $C^R C^W$

16% (qp) $C^R C^W$　　4% (q^2) $C^W C^W$

If the gametes come together at random, the genotype frequencies of this generation are in Hardy-Weinberg equilibrium:

64% $C^R C^R$, 32% $C^R C^W$, and 4% $C^W C^W$

Gametes of this generation:

64% C^R (from $C^R C^R$ plants) + 16% C^R (from $C^R C^W$ plants) = 80% C^R = 0.8 = p

4% C^W (from $C^W C^W$ plants) + 16% C^W (from $C^R C^W$ plants) = 20% C^W = 0.2 = q

With random mating, these gametes will result in the same mix of genotypes in the next generation:

64% $C^R C^R$, 32% $C^R C^W$, and 4% $C^W C^W$ plants

▲ **Figure 23.7 The Hardy-Weinberg principle.** In our wildflower population, the gene pool remains constant from one generation to the next. Mendelian processes alone do not alter frequencies of alleles or genotypes.

? *If the frequency of the C^R allele is 60%, predict the frequencies of the $C^R C^R$, $C^R C^W$, and $C^W C^W$ genotypes.*

A population is in Hardy-Weinberg equilibrium only if the genotype frequencies are such that the actual frequency of one homozygote is p^2, the actual frequency of the other homozygote is q^2, and the actual frequency of heterozygotes is $2pq$. Finally, as suggested by Figure 23.7, if a population such as our wildflowers is in Hardy-Weinberg equilibrium and its members continue to mate randomly generation after generation, allele and genotype frequencies will remain constant. The system operates somewhat

like a deck of cards: No matter how many times the deck is reshuffled to deal out new hands, the deck itself remains the same; aces do not grow more numerous than jacks. And the repeated shuffling of a population's gene pool over the generations cannot, in itself, change the frequency of one allele relative to another.

Conditions for Hardy-Weinberg Equilibrium

The Hardy-Weinberg principle describes a hypothetical population that is not evolving. But in real populations, the allele and genotype frequencies often *do* change over time. Such changes can occur when at least one of the following five conditions of Hardy-Weinberg equilibrium is not met:

1. **No mutations.** The gene pool is modified if mutations alter alleles or if entire genes are deleted or duplicated.
2. **Random mating.** If individuals mate preferentially within a subset of the population, such as their close relatives (inbreeding), random mixing of gametes does not occur, and genotype frequencies change.
3. **No natural selection.** Differences in the survival and reproductive success of individuals carrying different genotypes can alter allele frequencies.
4. **Extremely large population size.** The smaller the population, the more likely it is that allele frequencies will fluctuate by chance from one generation to the next (a process called genetic drift).
5. **No gene flow.** By moving alleles into or out of populations, gene flow can alter allele frequencies.

Departure from these conditions usually results in evolutionary change, which, as we've already described, is common in natural populations. But it is also common for natural populations to be in Hardy-Weinberg equilibrium for specific genes. This apparent contradiction occurs because a population can be evolving at some loci, yet simultaneously be in Hardy-Weinberg equilibrium at other loci. In addition, some populations evolve so slowly that the changes in their allele and genotype frequencies are difficult to distinguish from those predicted for a nonevolving population.

Applying the Hardy-Weinberg Equation

The Hardy-Weinberg equation is often used as an initial test of whether evolution is occurring at a specific locus in a population (you'll encounter an example in Concept Check 23.2, question 3). The equation also has medical applications, such as estimating the percentage of a population carrying the allele for an inherited disease. For example, consider phenylketonuria (PKU), a metabolic disorder that results from homozygosity for a recessive allele and occurs in approximately one out of every 12 000 babies born in Canada. Left untreated, PKU results in mental disability and other problems. (Newborns are now tested for PKU, and symptoms can be largely avoided with a diet very low in phenylalanine. For this reason, products that contain phenylalanine, such as diet soft drinks, carry warning labels.)

To apply the Hardy-Weinberg equation, we must assume that no new PKU mutations are being introduced into the population (condition 1), and that people neither choose their mates on the basis of whether or not they carry this gene nor generally mate with close relatives (condition 2). We must also ignore any effects of differential survival and reproductive success among PKU genotypes (condition 3) and assume that there are no effects of genetic drift (condition 4) or of gene flow from other populations into Canada (condition 5). These assumptions are reasonable: The mutation rate for the PKU gene is low, inbreeding is not common in Canada, selection occurs only against the rare homozygotes (and then only if dietary restrictions are not followed), the Canadian population is large, and populations outside the country have PKU allele frequencies similar to those seen in Canada. If all these assumptions hold, then the frequency of individuals in the population born with PKU will correspond to q^2 in the Hardy-Weinberg equation (q^2 = frequency of homozygotes). Because the allele is recessive, we must estimate the number of heterozygotes rather than counting them directly as we did with the pink flowers. Since we know there is approximately one PKU occurrence per 12 000 births ($q^2 = 0.0000833$), the frequency of the recessive allele for PKU is

$$q = \sqrt{0.0000833} = 0.00913$$

and the frequency of the dominant allele is
$$p = 1 - q = 1 - 0.00913 = 0.99087$$
The frequency of carriers, heterozygous people who do not have PKU but may pass the PKU allele to offspring, is
$$2pq = 2 \times 0.99087 \times 0.00913 = 0.0181$$

(approximately 1.8% of the Canadian population)

Remember, the assumption of Hardy-Weinberg equilibrium yields an approximation; the real number of carriers may differ. Still, our calculations suggest that harmful recessive alleles at this and other loci can be concealed in a population because they are carried by healthy heterozygotes.

The Scientific Skills Exercise provides another opportunity for you to apply the Hardy-Weinberg equation to allele data.

---

1. A population has 700 individuals, 85 of genotype *AA*, 320 of genotype *Aa*, and 295 of genotype *aa*. What are the frequencies of alleles *A* and *a*?

2. The frequency of allele *a* is 0.45 for a population in Hardy-Weinberg equilibrium. What are the expected frequencies of genotypes *AA*, *Aa*, and *aa*?

3. **WHAT IF?** A locus that affects susceptibility to a degenerative brain disease has two alleles, *A* and *a*. In a population, 16 people have genotype *AA*, 92 have genotype *Aa*, and 12 have genotype *aa*. Is this population evolving? Explain.

For suggested answers, see Appendix A.

CONCEPT 23.3

Natural selection, genetic drift, and gene flow can alter allele frequencies in a population

Note again the five conditions required for a population to be in Hardy-Weinberg equilibrium. A deviation from any of these conditions is a potential cause of evolution. New mutations (violation of condition 1) can alter allele frequencies, but because mutations are rare, the change from one generation to the next is likely to be very small. Nevertheless, as we'll see, mutation ultimately can have a large effect on allele frequencies when it produces new alleles that strongly influence fitness in a positive or negative way. Nonrandom mating (violation of condition 2) can affect the frequencies of homozygous and heterozygous genotypes but by itself usually has no effect on allele frequencies in the gene pool. The three mechanisms that alter allele frequencies directly and cause most evolutionary change are natural selection, genetic drift, and gene flow (violations of conditions 3–5).

Natural Selection

As you read in Chapter 22, Darwin's concept of natural selection is based on differential success in survival and reproduction: Individuals in a population exhibit variations in their heritable traits, and those with traits that are better suited to their environment tend to produce more offspring than those with traits that are not as well suited.

In genetic terms, we now know that selection results in alleles being passed to the next generation in proportions that differ from those in the present generation. For example, the fruit fly *D. melanogaster* has an allele that confers resistance to several insecticides, including DDT. This allele has a frequency of 0% in laboratory strains of *D. melanogaster* established from flies collected in the wild in the early 1930s, prior to DDT use. However, in strains established from flies collected after 1960 (following 20 or more years of DDT use), the allele frequency is 37%. We can infer that this allele either arose by mutation between 1930 and 1960 or that it was present in 1930, but very rare. In any case, the rise in frequency of this allele most likely occurred because DDT is a powerful poison that is a strong selective force in exposed fly populations.

As the *D. melanogaster* example shows, an allele that confers insecticide resistance will increase in frequency in a population exposed to that insecticide. Such changes are not coincidental. By consistently favouring some alleles over others, natural selection can cause *adaptive evolution* (evolution that results in a better match between organisms and their environment). We'll explore this process in more detail a little later in this chapter.

Genetic Drift

If you flip a coin 1000 times, a result of 700 heads and 300 tails might make you suspicious about that coin. But if you flip a coin only 10 times, an outcome of 7 heads and 3 tails would not be surprising. The smaller the number of coin flips, the more likely it is that chance alone will cause a deviation from the predicted result. (In this case, the prediction is an equal number of heads and tails.) Chance events can also cause allele frequencies to fluctuate unpredictably from one generation to the next, especially in small populations—a process called **genetic drift**.

Figure 23.8 models how genetic drift might affect a small population of our wildflowers. In this example, an allele is lost from the gene pool, but it is a matter of chance that the C^W allele is lost and not the C^R allele. Such unpredictable changes in allele frequencies can be caused by chance events associated with survival and reproduction. Perhaps a large animal such as a moose stepped on the three $C^W C^W$ individuals in generation 2, killing them and increasing the chance that only the C^R allele would be passed to the next generation. Allele frequencies can also be affected by chance events that occur during fertilization. For example, suppose two individuals of genotype $C^R C^W$ had a small number of offspring. By chance alone, every egg and sperm pair that generated offspring could happen to have carried the C^R allele and not the C^W allele.

Certain circumstances can result in genetic drift having a significant impact on a population. Two examples are the founder effect and the bottleneck effect.

The Founder Effect

When a few individuals become isolated from a larger population, this smaller group may establish a new population whose gene pool differs from the source population; this is called the **founder effect**. The founder effect might occur, for example, when a few members of a population are blown by a storm to a new island. Genetic drift, in which chance

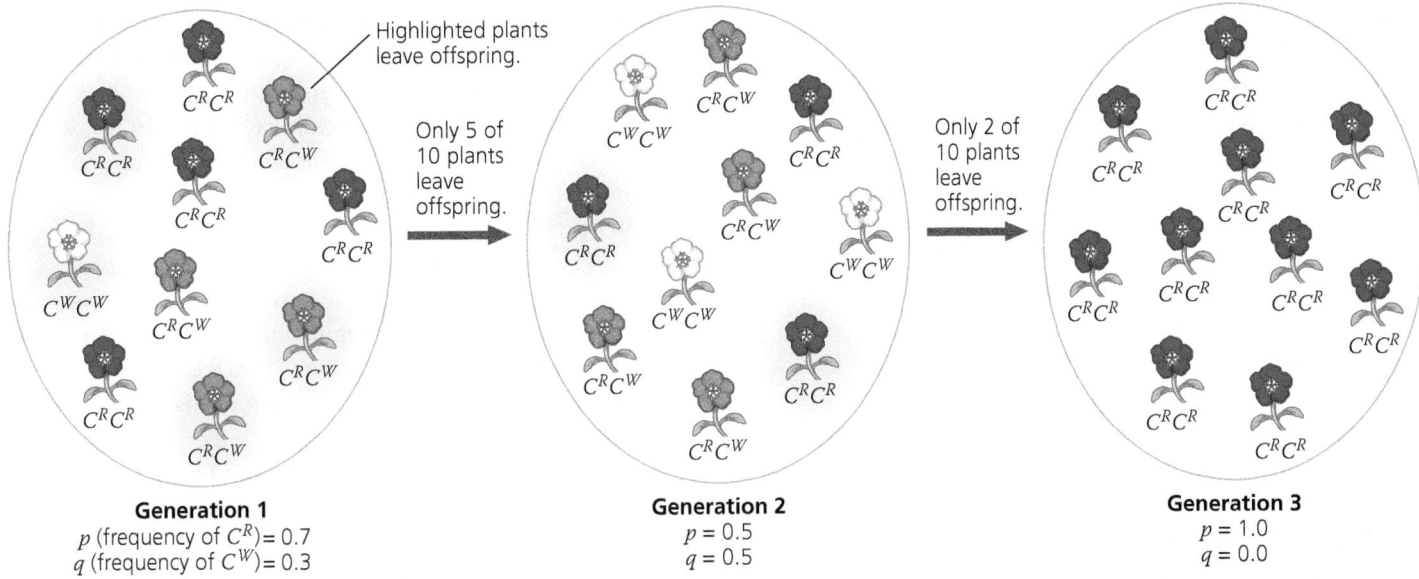

Generation 1
p (frequency of C^R) = 0.7
q (frequency of C^W) = 0.3

Highlighted plants leave offspring.

Only 5 of 10 plants leave offspring.

Generation 2
$p = 0.5$
$q = 0.5$

Only 2 of 10 plants leave offspring.

Generation 3
$p = 1.0$
$q = 0.0$

▲ **Figure 23.8 Genetic drift.** This small wildflower population has a stable size of 10 plants. Suppose that by chance only five plants of generation 1 (those highlighted in yellow) produce fertile offspring. (This could occur, for example, if only those plants happened to grow in a location that provided enough nutrients to support the production of offspring.) Again by chance, only two plants of generation 2 leave fertile offspring. As a result, by chance the frequency of the C^W allele first increases in generation 2, then falls to zero in generation 3.

ANIMATION *BioFlix* Visit the Study Area in **MasteringBiology** for the BioFlix® 3-D Animation on Mechanisms of Evolution

events alter allele frequencies, will occur in such a case if the storm indiscriminately transports some individuals (and their alleles), but not others, from the source population.

The founder effect probably accounts for the relatively high frequency of certain inherited disorders among isolated human populations. For example, in 1814, 15 British colonists founded a settlement on Tristan da Cunha, a group of small islands in the Atlantic Ocean midway between Africa and South America. Apparently, one of the colonists carried a recessive allele for retinitis pigmentosa, a progressive form of blindness that afflicts homozygous individuals. Of the founding colonists' 240 descendants on the island in the late 1960s, 4 had retinitis pigmentosa. The frequency of the allele that causes this disease is 10 times higher on Tristan da Cunha than in the populations from which the founders came.

The Bottleneck Effect

A sudden change in the environment, such as a fire or flood, may drastically reduce the size of a population. A severe drop in population size can cause the **bottleneck effect**, so named because the population has passed through a "bottleneck" that reduces its size **(Figure 23.9)**. By chance alone, certain alleles may be overrepresented among the survivors, others may be underrepresented, and some may be absent altogether. Ongoing genetic drift is likely to have substantial effects on the gene pool until the population becomes large enough that chance events have less impact.

But even if a population that has passed through a bottleneck ultimately recovers in size, it may have low levels of genetic variation for a long period of time—a legacy of the genetic drift that occurred when the population was small.

Human actions sometimes create severe bottlenecks for other species, as the following example shows.

Field Study: Impact of Genetic Drift on the Greater Prairie Chicken

Millions of greater prairie chickens (*Tympanuchus cupido*) once lived throughout the Canadian prairies and U.S. prairie

Original population

Bottlenecking event

Surviving population

▲ **Figure 23.9 The bottleneck effect.** Shaking just a few marbles through the narrow neck of a bottle is analogous to a drastic reduction in the size of a population. By chance, blue marbles are overrepresented in the surviving population and gold marbles are absent.

states. As these prairies were converted to farmland and other uses during the 19th and 20th centuries, the number of greater prairie chickens plummeted (Figure 23.10a). The Canadian Species at Risk Act (SARA) lists the greater prairie chicken as extirpated in Canada, but some populations of varying size remain through the U.S. prairie states. By 1993, only two Illinois populations remained, which together harboured fewer than 50 birds. The few surviving birds had low levels of genetic variation, and less than 50% of their eggs hatched, compared with much higher hatching rates of the larger populations in Kansas and Nebraska (Figure 23.10b).

These data suggest that genetic drift during the bottleneck may have led to a loss of genetic variation and an increase in the frequency of harmful alleles. To investigate

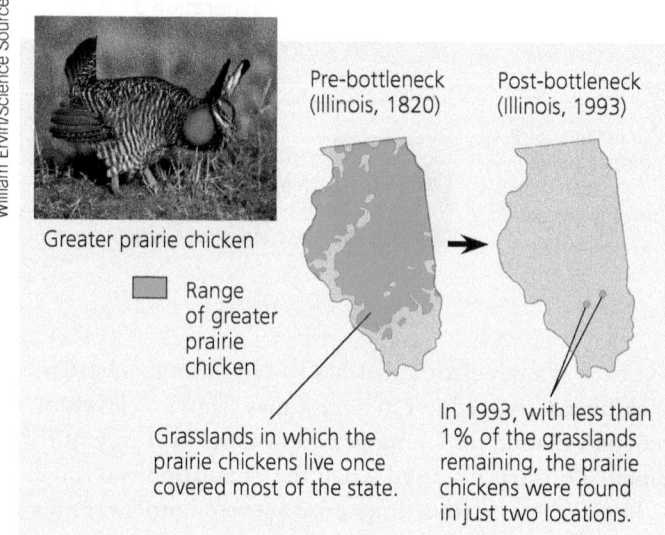

Greater prairie chicken

Pre-bottleneck (Illinois, 1820)   Post-bottleneck (Illinois, 1993)

Range of greater prairie chicken

Grasslands in which the prairie chickens live once covered most of the state.

In 1993, with less than 1% of the grasslands remaining, the prairie chickens were found in just two locations.

(a) The Illinois population of greater prairie chickens dropped from millions of birds in the 1800s to fewer than 50 birds in 1993.

Source: "Figure 20.6 (maps only)", from DISCOVER BIOLOGY, SECOND EDITION by Michael L. Cain, Hans Damman, Robert A. Lue & Carol Kaesuk Loon, Editors. Copyright © 2002 by Sinauer Associates, Inc. Used by permission of W. W. Norton & Company, Inc.

Location	Population size	Number of alleles per locus	Percentage of eggs hatched
Illinois			
1930–1960s	1000–25 000	5.2	93
1993	<50	3.7	<50
Kansas, 1998 (no bottleneck)	750 000	5.8	99
Nebraska, 1998 (no bottleneck)	75 000–200 000	5.8	96

(b) As a consequence of the drastic reduction in the size of the Illinois population, genetic drift resulted in a drop in the number of alleles per locus (averaged across six loci studied) and a decrease in the percentage of eggs that hatched.

▲ Figure 23.10 **Genetic drift and loss of genetic variation.**

this hypothesis, Juan Bouzat, of Bowling Green State University, Ohio, and his colleagues extracted DNA from 15 museum specimens of Illinois greater prairie chickens. Of the 15 birds, 10 had been collected in the 1930s, when there were 25 000 greater prairie chickens in Illinois, and 5 had been collected in the 1960s, when there were 1000 greater prairie chickens in Illinois. By studying the DNA of these specimens, the researchers were able to obtain a minimum, baseline estimate of how much genetic variation was present in the Illinois population *before* the population shrank to extremely low numbers. This baseline estimate is a key piece of information that is not usually available in cases of population bottlenecks.

The researchers surveyed six loci and found that the 1993 population had fewer alleles per locus than the pre-bottleneck Illinois or the current Kansas and Nebraska populations (see Figure 23.10b). Thus, as predicted, drift had reduced the genetic variation of the small 1993 population. Genetic drift may also have increased the frequency of harmful alleles, leading to the low egg-hatching rate. To counteract these negative effects, 271 birds from neighbouring states were added to the Illinois population over four years. This strategy succeeded: New alleles entered the population, and the egg-hatching rate improved to over 90%. Overall, studies on the Illinois greater prairie chicken illustrate the powerful effects of genetic drift in small populations and provide hope that in at least some populations, these effects can be reversed.

Effects of Genetic Drift: A Summary

The examples we've described highlight four key points:

1. **Genetic drift is significant in small populations.** Chance events can cause an allele to be disproportionately over- or underrepresented in the next generation. Although chance events occur in populations of all sizes, they tend to alter allele frequencies more substantially in small populations.

2. **Genetic drift can cause allele frequencies to change at random.** Because of genetic drift, an allele may increase in frequency one year, then decrease the next; the change from year to year is not predictable. Thus, unlike natural selection, which in a given environment consistently favours some alleles over others, genetic drift causes allele frequencies to change at random over time.

3. **Genetic drift can lead to a loss of genetic variation within populations.** By causing allele frequencies to fluctuate randomly over time, genetic drift can eliminate alleles from a population. Because evolution depends on genetic variation, such losses can influence how effectively a population can adapt to a change in the environment.

4. **Genetic drift can cause harmful alleles to become fixed.** Alleles that are neither harmful nor beneficial can be lost or become fixed entirely by chance through genetic drift. In very small populations, genetic drift can also cause alleles that are slightly harmful to become fixed. When this occurs, the population's survival can be threatened (as for the greater prairie chicken).

Gene Flow

Natural selection and genetic drift are not the only phenomena affecting allele frequencies. Allele frequencies can also change by **gene flow**, the transfer of alleles into or out of a population due to the movement of fertile individuals or their gametes. For example, suppose that near our original hypothetical wildflower population there is another population consisting primarily of white-flowered individuals ($C^W C^W$). Insects carrying pollen from these plants may fly to and pollinate plants in our original population. The introduced C^W alleles would modify our original population's allele frequencies in the next generation. Because alleles are exchanged between populations, gene flow tends to reduce the genetic differences between populations. In fact, if it is extensive enough, gene flow can result in two populations combining into a single population with a common gene pool.

Alleles transferred by gene flow can also affect how well populations are adapted to local environmental conditions. Researchers studying the songbird *Parus major* (Great tit) on the small Dutch island of Vlieland noted survival differences between two populations on the island. The survival rate of females born in the eastern population is twice that of those born in the central population, regardless of where the females eventually settle and raise offspring (**Figure 23.11**). This finding suggests that females born in the eastern population are better adapted to life on the island than females born in the central population. But extensive field studies also showed that the two populations are connected by high levels of gene flow (mating), which should reduce genetic differences between them. So how can the eastern population be better adapted to life on Vlieland than the central population?

The answer lies in the unequal amounts of gene flow from the mainland. In any given year, 43% of the first-time breeders in the central population are immigrants from the mainland, compared with only 13% in the eastern population. Birds with mainland genotypes survive and reproduce poorly on Vlieland, and in the eastern population, selection reduces the frequency of these genotypes. In the central population, however, gene flow from the mainland is so high that it overwhelms the effects of selection. As a result, females born in the central population have many immigrant genes, reducing the degree to which members of that population are adapted to life on the island. Researchers are

▲ Figure 23.11 **Gene flow and local adaptation.** In *Parus major* (Great tit) populations on Vlieland, the yearly survival rate of females born in the eastern population is higher than that of females born in the central population. Gene flow from the mainland to the central population is 3.3 times higher than it is to the eastern population, and birds from the mainland are selected against in both populations. These data suggest that gene flow from the mainland has prevented the central population from adapting fully to its local conditions.

Source: Figure adapted from "Gene Flow Maintains a Large Genetic Difference in Clutch Size at a Small Spatial Scale" by Erik Postma and Arie van Noordwijk, from *Nature*, January 6, 2005, Volume 433(7021). Copyright © 2005 by Macmillan Publishers Ltd. Reprinted with permission.

currently investigating why gene flow is so much higher in the central population and why birds with mainland genotypes have low fitness on Vlieland.

Gene flow can also transfer alleles that improve the ability of populations to adapt to local conditions. For example, gene flow has resulted in the worldwide spread of several insecticide-resistance alleles in the mosquito *Culex pipiens*, a vector of West Nile virus and other diseases. Each of these alleles has a unique genetic signature that allowed researchers to document that it arose by mutation in one or a few geographic locations. In their population of origin, these alleles increased because they provided insecticide resistance. These alleles were then transferred to new populations where, again, their frequencies increased as a result of natural selection.

Finally, gene flow has become an increasingly important agent of evolutionary change in human populations. Humans today move much more freely about the world than in the past. As a result, mating is more common between members of populations that previously had very little contact, leading to an exchange of alleles and fewer genetic differences between those populations.

CONCEPT CHECK 23.3

1. In what sense is natural selection more "predictable" than genetic drift?

2. Distinguish genetic drift from gene flow in terms of (a) how it occurs and (b) the implications for future genetic variation in a population.

3. **WHAT IF?** Suppose two plant populations exchange pollen and seeds. In one population, individuals of genotype *AA* are most common (9000 *AA*, 900 *Aa*, 100 *aa*), while the opposite is true in the other population (100 *AA*, 900 *Aa*, 9000 *aa*). If neither allele has a selective advantage, what will happen over time to the allele and genotype frequencies of these populations?

For suggested answers, see Appendix A.

CONCEPT 23.4

Natural selection is the only mechanism that consistently causes adaptive evolution

Evolution by natural selection is a blend of chance and "sorting": chance in the creation of new genetic variations (as in mutation) and sorting as natural selection favours some alleles over others. Because of this favouring process, the outcome of natural selection is *not* random. Instead, natural selection consistently increases the frequencies of alleles that provide reproductive advantage and thus leads to adaptive evolution.

Natural Selection: *A Closer Look*

In examining how natural selection brings about adaptive evolution, we'll begin with the concept of relative fitness and the different ways that an organism's phenotype is subject to natural selection.

Relative Fitness

The phrases "struggle for existence" and "survival of the fittest" are commonly used to describe natural selection, but these expressions are misleading if taken to mean direct competitive contests among individuals. There *are* animal species in which individuals, usually the males, lock horns or otherwise do combat to determine mating privilege. But reproductive success is generally more subtle and depends on many factors besides outright battle. For example, a barnacle that is more efficient at collecting food than its neighbours may have greater stores of energy and hence be able to produce a larger number of eggs. A moth may have more offspring than other moths in the same population because its body colours more effectively conceal it from predators, improving its chance of surviving long enough to produce more offspring. These examples illustrate how in a given environment, certain traits can lead to greater **relative fitness**: the contribution an individual makes to the gene pool of the next generation *relative to* the contributions of other individuals.

Although we often refer to the relative fitness of a genotype, remember that the entity that is subjected to natural selection is the whole organism, not the underlying genotype. Thus, selection acts more directly on the phenotype than on the genotype; it acts on the genotype indirectly, via how the genotype affects the phenotype.

Directional, Disruptive, and Stabilizing Selection

Natural selection can alter the frequency distribution of heritable traits in three ways, depending on which phenotypes in a population are favoured. These three modes of selection are called directional selection, disruptive selection, and stabilizing selection.

Directional selection occurs when conditions favour individuals exhibiting one extreme of a phenotypic range, thereby shifting a population's frequency curve for the phenotypic character in one direction or the other (**Figure 23.12a**). Directional selection is common when a population's environment changes or when members of a population migrate to a new (and different) habitat. For instance, researchers from the University of Alberta have shown that metabolic adaptations in the pine beetle are allowing it to survive in colder temperatures. Such adaptations have allowed the range of the pine beetle to expand northward and eastward, across the continental divide.

Disruptive selection (**Figure 23.12b**) occurs when conditions favour individuals at both extremes of a phenotypic range over individuals with intermediate phenotypes. One example is a population of black-bellied seedcracker finches in Cameroon whose members display two distinctly different beak sizes. Small-billed birds feed mainly on soft seeds, whereas large-billed birds specialize in cracking hard seeds. It appears that birds with intermediate-sized bills are relatively inefficient at cracking both types of seeds and thus have lower relative fitness.

Stabilizing selection (**Figure 23.12c**) acts against both extreme phenotypes and favours intermediate variants. This mode of selection reduces variation and tends to maintain the status quo for a particular phenotypic character. For example, the birth weights of most human babies lie in the range of 3–4 kg (6.6–8.8 pounds); babies who are either much smaller or much larger suffer higher rates of mortality.

▶ **Figure 23.12 Modes of selection.** These cases describe three ways in which a hypothetical deer mouse population with heritable variation in fur colouration from light to dark might evolve. The graphs show how the frequencies of individuals with different fur colours change over time. The large white arrows symbolize selective pressures against certain phenotypes.

MAKE CONNECTIONS *Review Figure 22.13. Which mode of selection has occurred in soapberry bug populations that feed on the introduced goldenrain tree? Explain.*

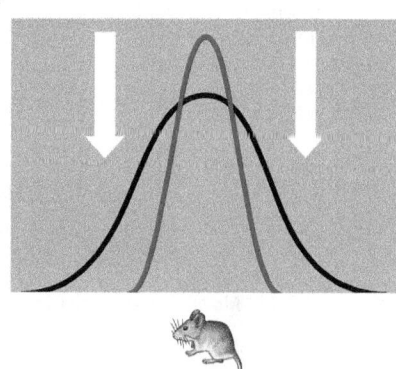

(a) Directional selection shifts the overall makeup of the population by favouring variants that are at one extreme of the distribution. In this case, lighter mice are selected against because they live among dark rocks, making it harder for them to hide from predators.

(b) Disruptive selection favours variants at both ends of the distribution. These mice have colonized a patchy habitat made up of light and dark rocks, with the result that mice of an intermediate colour are selected against.

(c) Stabilizing selection removes extreme variants from the population and preserves intermediate types. If the environment consists of rocks of an intermediate colour, both light and dark mice will be selected against.

Regardless of the mode of selection, however, the basic mechanism remains the same. Selection favours individuals whose heritable phenotypic traits provide higher reproductive success than do the traits of other individuals.

The Key Role of Natural Selection in Adaptive Evolution

The adaptations of organisms include many striking examples. Cuttlefish, for example, have the ability to change colour rapidly, enabling them to blend into different backgrounds. Another example is the remarkable jaws of snakes **(Figure 23.13)**, which allow them to swallow prey much larger than their own head (a feat analogous to a person swallowing a whole watermelon). Other adaptations, such as a version of an enzyme that shows improved function in cold environments, may be less visually dramatic but just as important for survival and reproduction.

Such adaptations can arise gradually over time as natural selection increases the frequencies of alleles that enhance survival and reproduction. As the proportion of individuals that have favourable traits increases, the match between a species and its environment improves; that is, adaptive evolution occurs. However, as we saw in Chapter 22, the physical and biological components of an organism's environment may change over time. As a result, what constitutes a "good match" between an organism and its environment can be a moving target, making adaptive evolution a continuous, dynamic process.

And what about the two other important mechanisms of evolutionary change in populations, genetic drift and gene flow? Both can, in fact, increase the frequencies of alleles that improve the match between organisms and their environment, but neither does so consistently. Genetic drift can cause the frequency of a slightly beneficial allele to increase, but it also can cause the frequency of such an allele to decrease. Similarly, gene flow may introduce

The bones of the upper jaw that are shown in green are movable.

Ligament

The skull bones of most terrestrial vertebrates are relatively rigidly attached to one another, limiting jaw movement. In contrast, most snakes have movable bones in their upper jaw, allowing them to swallow food much larger than their head.

Bruce Coleman/Photoshot Holdings Ltd.

▲ Figure 23.13 **Movable jaw bones in snakes.**

Source: Based on many sources including figure 11.3 from *Evolution* by Douglas J. Futuyma. Sinauer Associates 2005; and *Vertebrate Paleontology and Evolution* by Robert L. Carroll. W.H. Freeman & Co. 1988. © Jane B Reece.

alleles that are advantageous or ones that are disadvantageous. Natural selection is the only evolutionary mechanism that consistently leads to adaptive evolution.

Sexual Selection

Charles Darwin was the first to explore the implications of **sexual selection**, a form of selection in which individuals with certain inherited characteristics are more likely than other individuals to obtain mates. Sexual selection can result in **sexual dimorphism**, a difference between the two sexes in secondary sexual characteristics (**Figure 23.14**). These distinctions include differences in size, colour, ornamentation, and behaviour.

How does sexual selection operate? There are several ways. In **intrasexual selection**, meaning selection within the same sex, individuals of one sex compete directly for mates of the opposite sex. In many species, intrasexual selection occurs among males. For example, a single male may patrol a group of females and prevent other males from mating with them. The patrolling male may defend his status by defeating smaller, weaker, or less fierce males in combat. More often, this male is the psychological victor in ritualized displays that discourage would-be competitors but do not risk injury that would reduce his own fitness (see Figure 51.16). Intrasexual selection has also been observed among females in a variety of species, including ring-tailed lemurs and broad-nosed pipefish.

Dave Blackey/AGE Fotostock

▲ Figure 23.14 **Sexual dimorphism and sexual selection.** Peacocks (above left) and peahens (above right) show extreme sexual dimorphism. There is intrasexual selection between competing males, followed by intersexual selection when the females choose among the showiest males.

In **intersexual selection**, also called *mate choice*, individuals of one sex (usually the females) are choosy in selecting their mates from the other sex. In many cases, the female's choice depends on the showiness of the male's appearance or behaviour (see Figure 23.14). What intrigued Darwin about mate choice is that male showiness may not seem adaptive in any other way and may in fact pose some risk. For example, bright plumage may make male birds more visible to predators. But if such characteristics help a male gain a mate, and if this benefit outweighs the risk from predation, then both the bright plumage and the female preference for it will be reinforced because they enhance overall reproductive success.

How do female preferences for certain male characteristics evolve in the first place? One hypothesis is that females prefer male traits that are correlated with "good genes." If the trait preferred by females is indicative of a male's overall genetic quality, both the male trait and female preference for it should increase in frequency. Figure 23.15 describes one experiment testing this hypothesis in grey tree frogs (*Hyla versicolor*).

Other researchers have shown that in several bird species, the traits preferred by females are related to overall male health. Here, too, female preference appears to be based on traits that reflect "good genes," in this case alleles indicative of a robust immune system.

Balancing Selection

As we've seen, genetic variation is often found at loci affected by selection. What prevents natural selection from reducing the variation at those loci by culling all unfavourable alleles? As mentioned earlier, in diploid organisms, many unfavourable recessive alleles persist because they are

Do females select mates based on traits indicative of "good genes"?

Experiment Female grey tree frogs (*Hyla versicolor*) prefer to mate with males that give long mating calls. Allison Welch and colleagues, at the University of Missouri, tested whether the genetic makeup of long-calling (LC) males is superior to that of short-calling (SC) males. The researchers fertilized half the eggs of each female with sperm from an LC male and fertilized the remaining eggs with sperm from an SC male. The resulting half-sibling offspring were raised in a common environment, and several measures of their "performance" were tracked for two years.

Recording of SC male's call

Recording of LC male's call

SC male grey tree frog

Female grey tree frog

LC male grey tree frog

SC sperm × Eggs × LC sperm

Offspring of SC father

Offspring of LC father

Survival and growth of these half-sibling offspring compared

Results

Offspring Performance	1995	1996
Larval survival	LC better	NSD
Larval growth	NSD	LC better
Time to metamorphosis	LC better (shorter time to metamorphosis)	LC better (shorter time to metamorphosis)

NSD = no significant difference; LC better = offspring of LC males superior to offspring of SC males.

Conclusion Because offspring fathered by an LC male outperformed their half-siblings fathered by an SC male, the team concluded that the duration of a male's mating call is indicative of the male's overall genetic quality. This result supports the hypothesis that female mate choice can be based on a trait that indicates whether the male has "good genes."

Source: Based on A. M. Welch et al., Call duration as an indicator of genetic quality in male grey tree frogs, *Science* 280:1928–1930 (1998). © Jane B Reece.

Inquiry in Action Read and analyze the original paper in *Inquiry in Action: Interpreting Scientific Papers.*

WHAT IF? *Why did the researchers split each female frog's eggs into two batches for fertilization by different males? Why didn't they mate each female with a single male frog?*

hidden from selection when in heterozygous individuals. In addition, selection itself may preserve variation at some loci, thus maintaining two or more forms in a population. Known as **balancing selection**, this type of selection includes heterozygote advantage and frequency-dependent selection.

Heterozygote Advantage

If individuals who are heterozygous at a particular locus have greater fitness than do both kinds of homozygotes, they exhibit **heterozygote advantage**. In such a case, natural selection tends to maintain two or more alleles at that locus. Note that heterozygote advantage is defined in terms of *genotype*, not phenotype. Thus, whether heterozygote advantage represents stabilizing or directional selection depends on the relationship between the genotype and the phenotype. For example, if the phenotype of a heterozygote is intermediate to the phenotypes of both homozygotes, heterozygote advantage is a form of stabilizing selection.

An example of heterozygote advantage occurs at the locus in humans that codes for the β polypeptide subunit of hemoglobin, the oxygen-carrying protein of red blood cells. In homozygous individuals, a certain recessive allele at that locus causes sickle-cell disease. The red blood cells of people with sickle-cell disease become distorted in shape, or *sickled*, under low-oxygen conditions (see Figure 5.19), as occurs in the capillaries. These sickled cells can clump together and block the flow of blood in the capillaries, resulting in serious damage to organs such as the kidney, heart, and brain. Although some red blood cells become sickled in heterozygotes, not enough become sickled to cause sickle-cell disease.

Heterozygotes for the sickle-cell allele are protected against the most severe effects of malaria, a disease caused by a parasite that infects red blood cells (see Figure 28.16). This partial protection occurs because the body destroys sickled red blood cells rapidly, killing the parasites they harbour (but not affecting parasites inside normal red blood cells). Protection against malaria is important in tropical regions where the disease is a major killer. In such regions, selection favours heterozygotes over homozygous dominant individuals, who are more vulnerable to the effects of malaria, and also over homozygous recessive individuals, who develop sickle-cell disease. The frequency of the sickle-cell allele in Africa is generally highest in areas where the malaria parasite is most common (**Figure 23.16**). In some populations, it accounts for 20% of the hemoglobin alleles in the gene pool, a very high frequency for such a harmful allele.

Frequency-Dependent Selection

In **frequency-dependent selection**, the fitness of a phenotype depends on how common it is in the population.

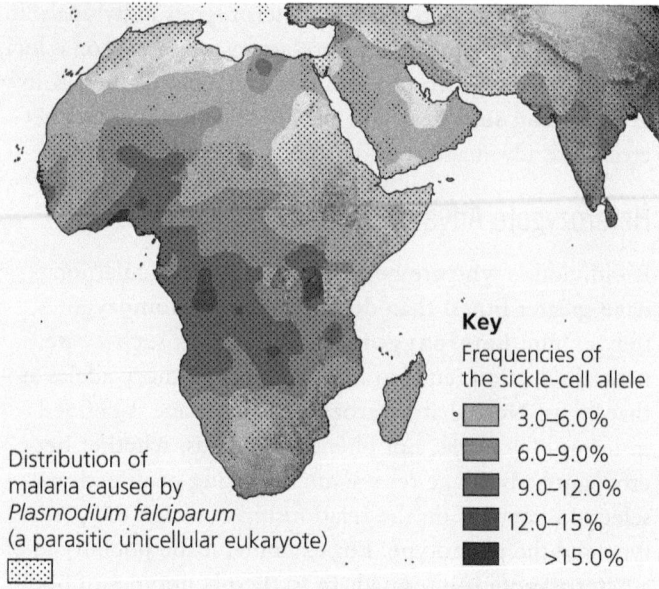

Distribution of
malaria caused by
Plasmodium falciparum
(a parasitic unicellular eukaryote)

Key
Frequencies of
the sickle-cell allele

	3.0–6.0%
	6.0–9.0%
	9.0–12.0%
	12.0–15%
	>15.0%

▲ Figure 23.16 **Mapping malaria and the sickle-cell allele.** The sickle-cell allele is most common in Africa, but it is not the only case of heterozygote advantage providing protection against malaria. Alleles at other loci (not shown on this map) are also favoured by heterozygote advantage in populations near the Mediterranean Sea and in southeast Asia where malaria is widespread.

Consider the scale-eating fish (*Perissodus microlepis*) of Lake Tanganyika, in Africa. These fish attack other fish from behind, darting in to remove a few scales from the flank of their prey. Of interest here is a peculiar feature of the scale-eating fish: Some are "left-mouthed" and some are "right-mouthed." Simple Mendelian inheritance determines these phenotypes, with the right-mouthed allele being dominant to the left-mouthed allele. Because their mouth twists to the left, left-mouthed fish always attack their prey's right flank (**Figure 23.17**). (To see why, twist your lower jaw and lips to the left and imagine trying to take a bite from the left side of a fish, approaching it from behind.) Similarly, right-mouthed fish always attack from the left. Prey species guard against attack from whatever phenotype of scale-eating fish is most common in the lake. Thus, from year to year, selection favours whichever mouth phenotype is least common. As a result, the frequency of left- and right-mouthed fish oscillates over time, and balancing selection (due to frequency dependence) keeps the frequency of each phenotype close to 50%.

Why Natural Selection Cannot Fashion Perfect Organisms

Though natural selection leads to adaptation, nature abounds with examples of organisms that are less than ideally "engineered" for their lifestyles. There are several reasons why.

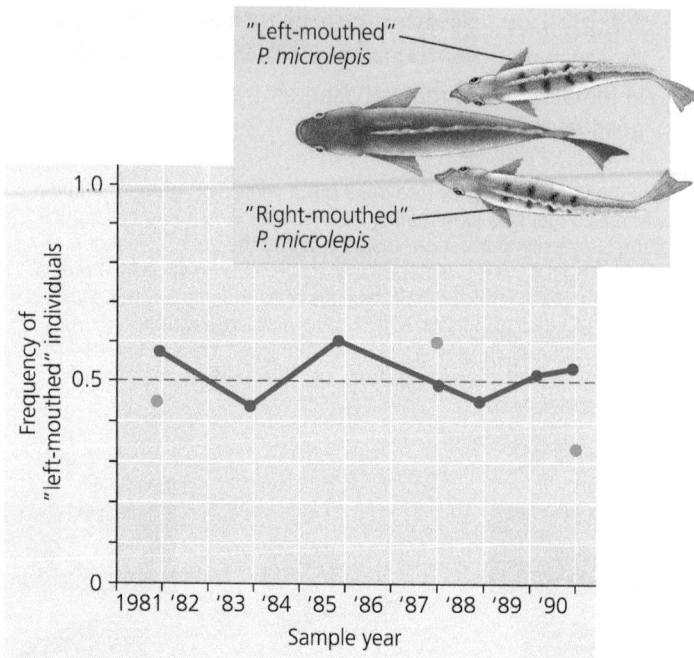

▲ Figure 23.17 **Frequency-dependent selection in scale-eating fish (*Perissodus microlepis*).** Michio Hori, of Kyoto University, Japan, noted that the frequency of left-mouthed individuals rises and falls in a regular manner. At each of three time periods when the phenotypes of breeding adults were assessed, adults that reproduced (represented by green dots) had the opposite phenotype of that which was most common in the population. Thus, it appeared that right-mouthed individuals were favoured by selection when left-mouthed individuals were more common, and vice versa.

Source: Based on the "Frequency-Dependent Natural Selection in the Handedness of Scale-Eating Cichlid Fish" by Michio Hori, from *Science*, April 1993, Volume 260(5105), AAAS. © Jane B Reece.

INTERPRET THE DATA *For 1981, 1987, and 1990, compare the frequency of left-mouthed individuals among breeding adults to the frequency of left-mouthed individuals in the entire population. What do the data suggest about when natural selection favours left-mouthed individuals over right-mouthed individuals (or vice versa)? Explain.*

1. **Selection can act only on existing variations.** Natural selection favours only the fittest phenotypes among those currently in the population, which may not be the ideal traits. New advantageous alleles do not arise on demand.

2. **Evolution is limited by historical constraints.** Each species has a legacy of descent with modification from ancestral forms. Evolution does not scrap the ancestral anatomy and build each new complex structure from scratch; rather, evolution co-opts existing structures and adapts them to new situations. We could imagine that if a terrestrial animal were to adapt to an environment in which flight would be advantageous, it might be best just to grow an extra pair of limbs that would serve as wings. However, evolution does not work this way; instead, it operates on the traits an organism already has. Thus, in birds and bats, an existing pair of limbs took on new functions for flight as these organisms evolved from nonflying ancestors.

3. **Adaptations are often compromises.** Each organism must do many different things. A seal spends part of its time on rocks; it could probably walk better if it had legs instead of flippers, but then it would not swim nearly as well. We humans owe much of our versatility and athleticism to our prehensile hands and flexible limbs, but these also make us prone to sprains, torn ligaments, and dislocations: Structural reinforcement has been compromised for agility.

4. **Chance, natural selection, and the environment interact.** Chance events can affect the subsequent evolutionary history of populations. For instance, when a storm blows insects or birds hundreds of kilometres over an ocean to an island, the wind does not necessarily transport those individuals that are best suited to the new environment. Thus, not all alleles present in the founding population's gene pool are better suited to the new environment than the alleles that are "left behind." In addition, the environment at a particular location may change unpredictably from year to year,

again limiting the extent to which adaptive evolution results in a close match between the organism and current environmental conditions.

With these four constraints, evolution does not tend to craft perfect organisms. Natural selection operates on a "better than" basis. We can, in fact, see evidence for evolution in the many imperfections of the organisms it produces.

CONCEPT CHECK 23.4

1. What is the relative fitness of a sterile mule? Explain.
2. Explain why natural selection is the only evolutionary mechanism that consistently leads to adaptive evolution.
3. **WHAT IF?** Consider a population in which heterozygotes at a certain locus have an extreme phenotype (such as being larger than homozygotes) that confers a selective advantage. Does such a situation represent directional, disruptive, or stabilizing selection? Explain your answer.

For suggested answers, see Appendix A.

---

23 Chapter Review

Go to **MasteringBiology**® for Assignments, the eText, and the Study Area with Animations, Activities, Vocab Self-Quiz, and Practice Tests.

SUMMARY OF KEY CONCEPTS

CONCEPT 23.1

Genetic variation makes evolution possible (pp. 511–513)

- **Genetic variation** refers to genetic differences among individuals within a population.
- The nucleotide differences that provide the basis of genetic variation arise by mutation and other processes that produce new alleles and new genes.
- New genetic variants are produced rapidly in organisms with short generation times. In sexually reproducing organisms, most of the genetic differences among individuals result from crossing over, the independent assortment of chromosomes, and fertilization.

    ? *Typically, most of the nucleotide variability that occurs within a genetic locus does not affect the phenotype. Explain why.*

CONCEPT 23.2

The Hardy-Weinberg equation can be used to test whether a population is evolving (pp. 514–518)

- A **population**, a localized group of organisms belonging to one species, is united by its **gene pool**, the aggregate of all the alleles in the population.

- For a population in **Hardy-Weinberg equilibrium**, the allele and genotype frequencies will remain constant if the population is large, mating is random, mutation is negligible, there is no gene flow, and there is no natural selection. For such a population, if p and q represent the frequencies of the only two possible alleles at a particular locus, then p^2 is the frequency of one kind of homozygote, q^2 is the frequency of the other kind of homozygote, and $2pq$ is the frequency of the heterozygous genotype.

    ? *Is it circular reasoning to calculate p and q from observed genotype frequencies and then use those values of p and q to test if the population is in Hardy-Weinberg equilibrium? Explain your answer. (Hint: Consider a specific case, such as a population with 195 individuals of genotype AA, 10 of genotype Aa, and 195 of genotype aa.)*

CONCEPT 23.3

Natural selection, genetic drift, and gene flow can alter allele frequencies in a population (pp. 518–522)

- In natural selection, individuals that have certain inherited traits tend to survive and reproduce at higher rates than other individuals *because of* those traits.
- In **genetic drift**, chance fluctuations in allele frequencies over generations tend to reduce genetic variation.
- **Gene flow**, the transfer of alleles between populations, tends to reduce genetic differences between populations over time.

    ? *Would two small, geographically isolated populations in very different environments be likely to evolve in similar ways? Explain.*

CONCEPT 23.4

Natural selection is the only mechanism that consistently causes adaptive evolution (pp. 522–527)

- One organism has greater **relative fitness** than a second organism if it leaves more fertile descendants than the second organism. The modes of natural selection differ in how selection acts on phenotype (the white arrows in the summary diagram below represent selective pressure on a population).

Original population   Evolved population

Directional selection   Disruptive selection   Stabilizing selection

- Unlike genetic drift and gene flow, natural selection consistently increases the frequencies of alleles that enhance survival and reproduction, thus improving the match between organisms and their environment.
- **Sexual selection** influences evolutionary change in secondary sex characteristics that can give individuals advantages in mating.
- Despite the winnowing effects of selection, populations have considerable genetic variation. Some of this variation represents **neutral variation**; additional variation can be maintained by diploidy and balancing selection.
- There are constraints to evolution: Natural selection can act only on available variation; structures result from modified ancestral anatomy; adaptations are often compromises; and chance, natural selection, and the environment interact.

? *How might secondary sex characteristics differ between males and females in a species in which females compete for mates?*

TEST YOUR UNDERSTANDING

LEVEL 1: KNOWLEDGE/COMPREHENSION

1. Natural selection changes allele frequencies because some _____ survive and reproduce more successfully than others.
   a. alleles   c. species
   b. loci   d. individuals

2. No two people are genetically identical, except for identical twins. The main source of genetic variation among human individuals is
   a. new mutations that occurred in the preceding generation.
   b. genetic drift.
   c. the reshuffling of alleles in sexual reproduction.
   d. environmental effects.

3. Sparrows with average-sized wings survive severe storms better than those with longer or shorter wings, illustrating
   a. the bottleneck effect.
   b. disruptive selection.
   c. neutral variation.
   d. stabilizing selection.

LEVEL 2: APPLICATION/ANALYSIS

4. If the nucleotide variability of a locus equals 0%, what is the gene variability and number of alleles at that locus?
   a. gene variability = 0%; number of alleles = 0
   b. gene variability = 0%; number of alleles = 1

c. gene variability = 0%; number of alleles = 2
d. gene variability > 0%; number of alleles = 2

5. There are 40 individuals in population 1, all with genotype *A1A1*, and there are 25 individuals in population 2, all with genotype *A2A2*. Assume that these populations are located far from each other and that their environmental conditions are very similar. Based on the information given here, the observed genetic variation is most likely an example of
   a. genetic drift.
   b. gene flow.
   c. nonrandom mating.
   d. directional selection.

6. A fruit fly population has a gene with two alleles, *A1* and *A2*. Tests show that 70% of the gametes produced in the population contain the *A1* allele. If the population is in Hardy-Weinberg equilibrium, what proportion of the flies carry both *A1* and *A2*?
   a. 0.7   c. 0.42
   b. 0.49   d. 0.21

LEVEL 3: SYNTHESIS/EVALUATION

7. **EVOLUTION CONNECTION**
   How is the process of evolution revealed by the imperfections of living organisms?

8. **SCIENTIFIC INQUIRY**
   INTERPRET THE DATA Richard Koehn, of the State University of New York, Stony Brook, and Thomas Hilbish, of the University of South Carolina, studied genetic variation in the marine mussel *Mytilus edulis* around Long Island, New York. They measured the frequency of a particular allele (*lap*^{94}) for an enzyme involved in regulating the mussel's internal saltwater balance. The researchers presented their data as a series of pie charts linked to sampling sites within Long Island Sound, where the salinity is highly variable, and along the coast of the open ocean, where salinity is constant:

Data from "The Adaptive Importance of Genetic Variance" by Richard K. Koehn and Thomas J. Hilbish, from *American Scientist*, March–April 1987, Volume 75(2).

Create a data table for the 11 sampling sites by estimating the frequency of *lap*^{94} from the pie charts. (*Hint:* Think of each pie chart as a clock face to help you estimate the proportion of the shaded area.) Then graph the frequencies for sites 1–8 to show how the frequency of this allele changes with increasing salinity in Long Island Sound (from southwest to northeast). How do the data from sites 9–11 compare with the data from the sites within the Sound?

Construct a hypothesis that explains the patterns you observe in the data and that accounts for the following observations: (1) The lap^{94} allele helps mussels maintain osmotic balance in water with a high salt concentration but is costly to use in less salty water; and (2) mussels produce larvae that can disperse long distances before they settle on rocks and grow into adults.

9. **WRITE ABOUT A THEME: ORGANIZATION**
Heterozygotes at the sickle-cell locus produce both normal and abnormal (sickle-cell) hemoglobin (see Concept 14.4). When hemoglobin molecules are packed into a heterozygote's red blood cells, some cells receive relatively large quantities of abnormal hemoglobin, making these cells prone to sickling. In a short essay (approximately 100–150 words), explain how these molecular and cellular events lead to emergent properties at the individual and population levels of biological organization.

10. **SYNTHESIZE YOUR KNOWLEDGE**

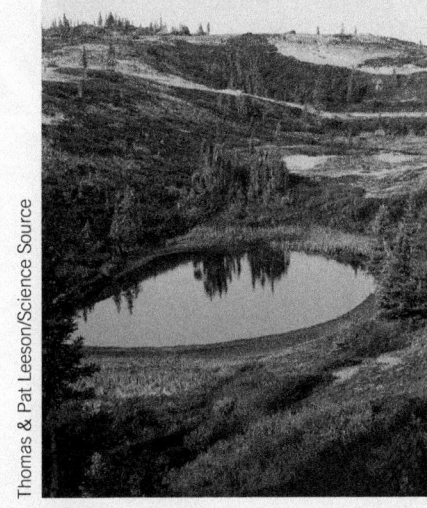

Thomas & Pat Leeson/Science Source

This kettle lake formed 14 000 years ago when a glacier that covered the surrounding area melted. Initially devoid of animal life, the lake was colonized by invertebrates and other animals over time. Hypothesize how mutation, natural selection, genetic drift, and gene flow may have affected populations that colonized the lake.

For selected answers, see Appendix A.

24

The Origin of Species

▲ Figure 24.1 **How did this flightless bird come to live on the isolated Galápagos Islands?**

KEY CONCEPTS

24.1 The biological species concept emphasizes reproductive isolation

24.2 Speciation can take place with or without geographic separation

24.3 Hybrid zones reveal factors that cause reproductive isolation

24.4 Speciation can occur rapidly or slowly and can result from changes in few or many genes

▲ **Galápagos tortoise**

That "Mystery of Mysteries"

Darwin came to the Galápagos Islands eager to explore landforms newly emerged from the sea. He noted that these volcanic islands, despite their geologic youth, were teeming with plants and animals found nowhere else in the world including the giant Galápagos tortoise and the flightless cormorant (Figure 24.1). Later he realized that these species, like the islands, were relatively new. He wrote in his diary: "Both in space and time, we seem to be brought somewhat near to that great fact—that mystery of mysteries—the first appearance of new beings on this Earth."

The "mystery of mysteries" that captivated Darwin is **speciation**, the process by which one species splits into two or more species. Speciation fascinated Darwin (and many biologists since) because it is responsible for the tremendous diversity of life, repeatedly yielding new species that differ from existing ones. Speciation explains not only differences between species, but also similarities between them (the unity of life). When one species splits into two, the species that result share many characteristics because they are descended from this common ancestral species. For example, DNA similarities indicate that the flightless cormorant (*Phalacrocorax harrisi*) in Figure 24.1 is closely related to flying cormorants found in the Americas. This suggests that the flightless cormorant may have originated from an ancestral cormorant species that migrated from the mainland to the Galápagos.

Speciation also forms a conceptual bridge between **microevolution**, changes over time in allele frequencies in a population, and **macroevolution**, the broad pattern of evolution above the species level. An example of macroevolutionary change is the origin of new groups of organisms, such as mammals or flowering plants, through a series of speciation events. We examined microevolutionary mechanisms (mutation, natural selection, genetic drift, and gene flow) in Chapter 23, and we'll turn to macroevolution in Chapter 25. In this chapter, we will explore the "bridge"—the mechanisms by which new species originate from existing ones. First, however, we need to establish what we actually mean when we talk about "species."

The biological species concept emphasizes reproductive isolation

The word *species* is Latin for "kind" or "appearance." In daily life, we commonly distinguish between various "kinds" of organisms—dogs and cats, for instance—from differences in their appearance. But are organisms truly divided into the discrete units we call species, or is this classification an arbitrary attempt to impose order on the natural world? To answer this question, biologists compare not only the morphology (body form) of different groups of organisms but also less obvious differences in physiology, biochemistry, and DNA sequences. The results generally confirm that morphologically distinct species are indeed discrete groups, differing in many ways besides their body forms.

The Biological Species Concept

The primary definition of species used in this textbook is the **biological species concept**. According to this concept, a **species** is a group of populations whose members have the potential to interbreed in nature and produce viable, fertile offspring—but do not produce viable, fertile offspring with members of other such groups **(Figure 24.2)**. Thus, the members of a biological species are united by being reproductively compatible, at least potentially. All human beings, for example, belong to the same species. A businesswoman in Manhattan may be unlikely to meet a dairy farmer in Mongolia, but if the two should happen to meet and mate, they could have viable babies that develop into fertile adults. In contrast, humans and chimpanzees remain distinct biological species even where they share territory, because many factors keep them from interbreeding and producing fertile offspring.

What holds the gene pool of a species together, causing its members to resemble each other more than they resemble

(a) Similarity between different species. The eastern meadowlark (*Sturnella magna*, left) and the western meadowlark (*Sturnella neglecta*, right) have similar body shapes and colourations. Nevertheless, they are distinct biological species because their songs and other behaviours are different enough to prevent interbreeding should they meet in the wild.

(b) Diversity within a species. As diverse as we may be in appearance, all humans belong to a single biological species (*Homo sapiens*), defined by our capacity to interbreed successfully.

▲ Figure 24.2 **The biological species concept is based on the potential to interbreed rather than on physical similarity.**

other species? To answer this question, we need to return to the evolutionary mechanism called *gene flow*, the transfer of alleles between populations (see Chapter 23). Typically, gene flow occurs between the different populations of a species. This ongoing exchange of alleles tends to hold the populations together genetically. As we'll explore in the following sections, the absence of gene flow plays a key role in the formation of new species, as well as in keeping them apart once their potential to interbreed has been reduced.

Reproductive Isolation

Because biological species are defined in terms of reproductive compatibility, the formation of a new species hinges on **reproductive isolation**—the existence of biological factors (barriers) that impede members of two species from interbreeding and producing viable, fertile offspring. Such

Exploring Reproductive Barriers

Prezygotic barriers impede mating or hinder fertilization if mating does occur

Habitat Isolation	Temporal Isolation	Behavioural Isolation	Mechanical Isolation

Individuals of different species

MATING ATTEMPT

Habitat Isolation

Two species that occupy different habitats within the same area may encounter each other rarely, if at all, even though they are not isolated by obvious physical barriers, such as mountain ranges.

Example: Two species of garter snakes in the genus *Thamnophis* occur in the same geographic areas, but one lives mainly in water (a) while the other is primarily terrestrial (b).

Temporal Isolation

Species that breed during different times of the day, different seasons, or different years cannot mix their gametes.

Example: In North America, the geographic ranges of the western spotted skunk (*Spilogale gracilis*) (c) and the eastern spotted skunk (*Spilogale putorius*) (d) overlap, but *S. gracilis* mates in late summer and *S. putorius* mates in late winter.

Behavioural Isolation

Courtship rituals that attract mates and other behaviours unique to a species are effective reproductive barriers, even between closely related species. Such behavioural rituals enable *mate recognition*—a way to identify potential mates of the same species.

Example: Blue-footed boobies mate only after a courtship display unique to their species. Part of the "script" calls for the male to high-step (e), a behaviour that calls the female's attention to his bright blue feet.

Mechanical Isolation

Mating is attempted, but morphological differences prevent its successful completion.

Example: The shells of two species of snails in the genus *Bradybaena* spiral in different directions: Moving inward to the centre, one spirals in a counterclockwise direction (f, left), the other in a clockwise direction (f, right). As a result, the snails' genital openings (indicated by arrows) are not aligned, and mating cannot be completed.

(a)
Joe McDonald/Photoshot

(b)
Joe McDonal/Photoshot

(c)
Hogle Zoo

(d)
APHIS Animal and Plant Health Inspection Service/USDA

(e)
Michael Dietrich/imageBROKER/Alamy

(f)
Takahiro Asami

Postzygotic barriers prevent a hybrid zygote from developing into a viable, fertile adult

| Gametic Isolation | Reduced Hybrid Viability | Reduced Hybrid Fertility | Hybrid Breakdown |

Gametic Isolation

Sperm of one species may not be able to fertilize the eggs of another species. For instance, sperm may not be able to survive in the reproductive tract of females of the other species, or biochemical mechanisms may prevent the sperm from penetrating the membrane surrounding the other species' eggs.

Example: Gametic isolation separates certain closely related species of aquatic animals, such as sea urchins (g). Sea urchins release their sperm and eggs into the surrounding water, where they fuse and form zygotes. It is difficult for gametes of different species, such as the red and purple urchins shown here, to fuse because proteins on the surfaces of the eggs and sperm bind very poorly to each other.

Reduced Hybrid Viability

The genes of different parent species may interact in ways that impair the hybrid's development or survival in its environment

Example: Some salamander subspecies of the genus *Ensatina* live in the same regions and habitats, where they may occasionally hybridize. But most of the hybrids do not complete development, and those that do are frail (h).

Reduced Hybrid Fertility

Even if hybrids are vigorous, they may be sterile. If the chromosomes of the two parent species differ in number or structure, meiosis in the hybrids may fail to produce normal gametes. Since the infertile hybrids cannot produce offspring when they mate with either parent species, genes cannot flow freely between the species.

Example: The hybrid offspring of a male donkey (i) and a female horse (j) is a mule (k), which is robust but sterile. A "hinny" (not shown), the offspring of a female donkey and a male horse, is also sterile.

EyeWire Collection/Getty Images

Hybrid Breakdown

Some first-generation hybrids are viable and fertile, but when they mate with one another or with either parent species, offspring of the next generation are feeble or sterile.

Example: Strains of cultivated rice have accumulated different mutant recessive alleles at two loci in the course of their divergence from a common ancestor. Hybrids between them are vigorous and fertile (l, left and right), but plants in the next generation that carry too many of these recessive alleles are small and sterile (l, centre). Although these rice strains are not yet considered different species, they have begun to be separated by postzygotic barriers.

William E. Ferguson

Charles W. Brown

Chase Swift/Corbis

Dawn YL/Fotolia

Kazutoshi Okuno

barriers block gene flow between the species and limit the formation of **hybrids**, offspring that result from an interspecific mating. Although a single barrier may not prevent all gene flow, a combination of several barriers can effectively isolate a species' gene pool.

Clearly, a fly cannot mate with a frog or a fern, but the reproductive barriers between more closely related species are not so obvious. These barriers can be classified according to whether they contribute to reproductive isolation before or after fertilization. **Prezygotic barriers** ("before the zygote") block fertilization from occurring. Such barriers typically act in one of three ways: by impeding members of different species from attempting to mate, by preventing an attempted mating from being completed successfully, or by hindering fertilization if mating is completed successfully. If a sperm cell from one species overcomes prezygotic barriers and fertilizes an ovum from another species, a variety of **postzygotic barriers** ("after the zygote") may contribute to reproductive isolation after the hybrid zygote is formed. For example, developmental errors may reduce survival among hybrid embryos. Or problems after birth may cause hybrids to be infertile or may decrease their chance of surviving long enough to reproduce. **Figure 24.3**, on the previous two pages, describes prezygotic and postzygotic barriers in more detail.

Limitations of the Biological Species Concept

One strength of the biological species concept is that it directs our attention to a way by which speciation can occur: by the evolution of reproductive isolation. However, the number of species to which this concept can be usefully applied is limited. There is, for example, no way to evaluate the reproductive isolation of fossils. The biological species concept also does not apply to organisms that reproduce asexually all or most of the time, such as prokaryotes. (Many prokaryotes do transfer genes among themselves, as we will discuss in Chapter 27, but this is not part of their reproductive process.) Furthermore, in the biological species concept, species are designated by the *absence* of gene flow. But there are many pairs of species that are morphologically and ecologically distinct, and yet gene flow occurs between them. An example is the grizzly bear (*Ursus arctos*) and polar bear (*Ursus maritimus*), whose hybrid offspring have been dubbed "grolar" or "nanulak" bears (**Figure 24.4**). Nanulak is a blend of the Inuit names for the polar bear (nanuk) and grizzly bear (aklak). As we'll discuss, natural selection can cause such species to remain distinct even though some gene flow occurs between them. This observation has led some researchers to argue that the biological species concept overemphasizes gene flow and downplays the role of natural selection. Because of the limitations to the biological species concept, alternative species concepts are useful in certain situations.

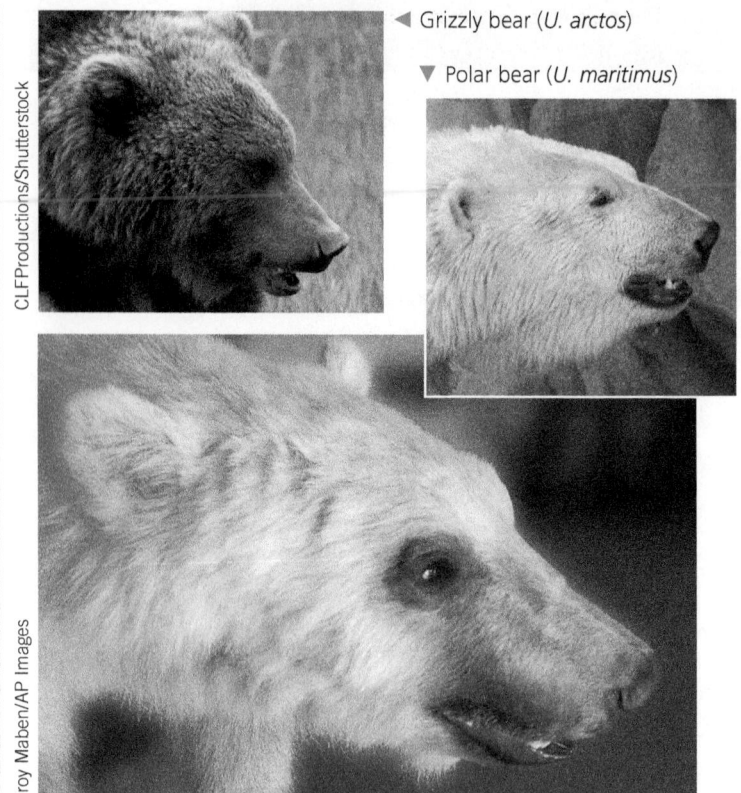

◄ Grizzly bear (*U. arctos*)

▼ Polar bear (*U. maritimus*)

▲ Hybrid "grolar" or "nanulak" bears

▲ **Figure 24.4 Hybridization between two species of bears in the genus *Ursus*.**

Other Definitions of Species

While the biological species concept emphasizes the *separateness* of species from one another due to reproductive barriers, several other definitions emphasize the *unity within* a species. For example, the **morphological species concept** characterizes a species by body shape and other structural features and suggests that each species is morphologically distinct. The morphological species concept can be applied to asexual and sexual organisms, and it can be useful even without information on the extent of gene flow. In practice, this is how scientists distinguish most species. One disadvantage, however, is that this definition relies on subjective criteria; researchers may disagree on which structural features distinguish a species.

The **ecological species concept** views a species in terms of its ecological niche, the sum of how members of the species interact with the nonliving and living parts of their environment (see Chapter 54). For example, two species of salamanders might be similar in appearance but differ in the foods they eat or in their ability to tolerate dry conditions. Unlike the biological species concept, the ecological species concept can accommodate asexual as well as sexual species. It also emphasizes the role of disruptive natural selection as organisms adapt to different environmental conditions.

The **phylogenetic species concept** defines a species as the smallest group of individuals that share a common ancestor, forming one branch on the tree of life. Biologists trace the phylogenetic history of a species by comparing its characteristics, such as morphology or molecular sequences, with those of other organisms. Such analyses can distinguish groups of individuals that are sufficiently different to be considered separate species. Of course, the difficulty with this species concept is determining the degree of difference required to indicate separate species.

In addition to those discussed here, more than 20 other species definitions have been proposed. The usefulness of each definition depends on the situation and the research questions being asked. For our purposes of studying how species originate, the biological species concept, with its focus on reproductive barriers, is particularly helpful.

CONCEPT CHECK 24.1

1. (a) Which species concept(s) could you apply to both asexual and sexual species? (b) Which would be most useful for identifying species in the field? Explain.

2. **WHAT IF?** Suppose you are studying two bird species that live in a forest and are not known to interbreed. One species feeds and mates in the treetops and the other on the ground. But in captivity, the birds can interbreed and produce viable, fertile offspring. What type of reproductive barrier most likely keeps these species separate in nature? Explain.

For suggested answers, see Appendix A.

CONCEPT 24.2

Speciation can take place with or without geographic separation

Now that we have a clearer sense of what constitutes a unique species, let's return to our discussion of the process by which such species arise from existing species. Speciation can occur in two main ways, depending on how gene flow is interrupted between populations of the existing species (Figure 24.5).

Allopatric ("Other Country") Speciation

In **allopatric speciation** (from the Greek *allos*, other, and *patra*, homeland), gene flow is interrupted when a population is divided into geographically isolated subpopulations. For example, the water level in a lake may subside, resulting in two or more smaller lakes that are now home to separated populations (see Figure 24.5a). Or a river may change course and divide a population of animals that cannot cross it. Allopatric speciation can also occur without geologic remodelling, such as when individuals colonize a remote area and their descendants become geographically isolated from the parent population. The flightless cormorant shown

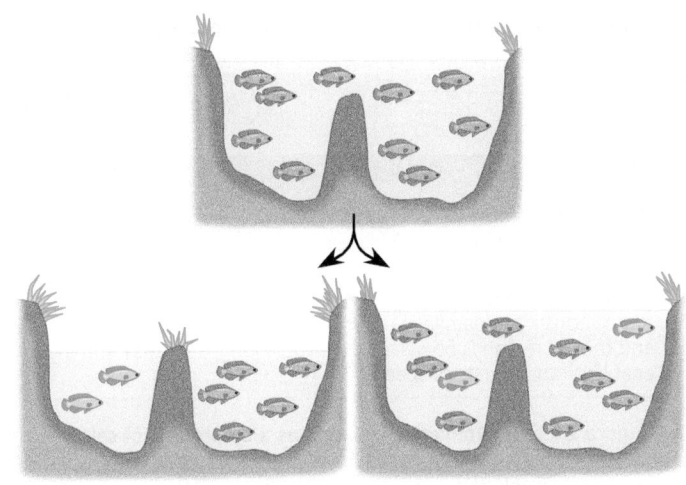

(a) Allopatric speciation. A population forms a new species while geographically isolated from its parent population.

(b) Sympatric speciation. A subset of a population forms a new species without geographic separation.

▲ Figure 24.5 **The geography of speciation.**

in Figure 24.1 most likely originated in this way from an ancestral flying species that reached the Galápagos Islands.

The Process of Allopatric Speciation

How formidable must a geographic barrier be to promote allopatric speciation? The answer depends on the ability of the organisms to move about. Birds, mountain lions, and coyotes can cross rivers and canyons—as can the wind-blown pollen of pine trees and the seeds of many flowering plants. In contrast, small rodents may find a wide river or deep canyon a formidable barrier.

Once geographic separation has occurred, the separated gene pools may diverge. Different mutations arise, and natural selection and genetic drift may alter allele frequencies in different ways in the separated populations. Reproductive isolation may then arise as a by-product of selection or drift having caused the populations to diverge genetically.

Figure 24.6 describes an example. On Andros Island, in the Bahamas, populations of the mosquitofish *Gambusia hubbsi* colonized a series of ponds that later became isolated from one another. Genetic analyses indicate that little or no gene flow currently occurs between the ponds. The environments of these ponds are very similar except that some contain many predatory fishes, while others do not. In the "high-predation" ponds, selection has favoured the evolution of a mosquitofish body shape that enables rapid bursts of speed (see Figure 24.6a). In ponds lacking predatory fishes, selection has favoured a different body shape, one that improves the ability to swim for long periods of time (see Figure 24.6b). How have these different selective pressures affected the evolution of reproductive barriers? Researchers answered this question by bringing together mosquitofish from the

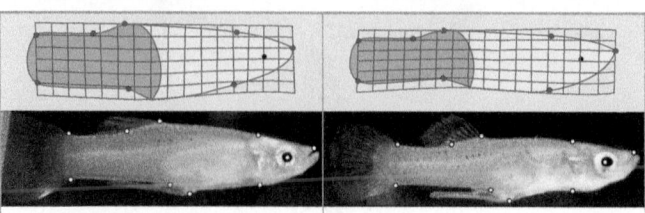

(a) Under high predation   **(b) Under low predation**

In ponds with predatory fishes, the head region of the mosquitofish is streamlined and the tail region is powerful, enabling rapid bursts of speed.	In ponds without predatory fishes, mosquitofish have a different body shape that favours long, steady swimming.

▲ **Figure 24.6 Reproductive isolation as a by-product of selection.** After bringing together mosquitofish from different ponds, researchers concluded that selection for traits that enable mosquitofish in high-predation ponds to avoid predators has isolated them reproductively from mosquitofish in low-predation ponds.

Source: Based on "Ecological Speciation in Gambusia Fishes" by R. B. Langerhans et al., from *Evolution*, September 2007, Volume 61(9), Society for the Study of Evolution. © Jane B Reece.

two types of ponds. They found that female mosquitofish prefer to mate with males whose body shape is similar to their own. This preference establishes a barrier to reproduction between mosquitofish from ponds with predators and those from ponds without predators. Thus, as a by-product of selection for avoiding predators, reproductive barriers have started to form in these allopatric populations.

Evidence of Allopatric Speciation

Many studies provide evidence that speciation can occur in allopatric populations. For example, laboratory studies show that reproductive barriers can develop when populations are isolated experimentally and subjected to different environmental conditions (**Figure 24.7**).

Field studies indicate that allopatric speciation also can occur in nature. Consider the 30 species of snapping shrimp in the genus *Alpheus* that live off the Isthmus of Panama, the land bridge that connects South and North America (**Figure 24.8**). Fifteen of these species live on the Atlantic side of the isthmus, while the other 15 live on the Pacific side. Before the isthmus formed, gene flow could occur between the Atlantic and Pacific populations of snapping shrimp. Did the species on different sides of the isthmus originate by allopatric speciation? Morphological and genetic data group these shrimp into 15 pairs of sister species, pairs whose member species are each other's closest relative. In each of these 15 pairs, one of the sister species lives on the Atlantic side of the isthmus, while the other lives on the Pacific side, strongly suggesting that the two species arose as a consequence of geographic separation. Furthermore, genetic analyses indicate that the *Alpheus* species originated from 9 to 3 million years ago, with the sister species that live in the deepest water diverging first. These divergence times are consistent with geologic evidence that the isthmus formed

Can divergence of allopatric populations lead to reproductive isolation?

Experiment Diane Dodd, then at Yale University, divided a laboratory population of the fruit fly *Drosophila pseudoobscura*, raising some flies on a starch medium and others on a maltose medium. After one year (about 40 generations), natural selection resulted in divergent evolution: Populations raised on starch digested starch more efficiently, while those raised on maltose digested maltose more efficiently. Dodd then put flies from the same or different populations in mating cages and measured mating frequencies. All flies used in the mating preference tests were reared for one generation on a standard cornmeal medium.

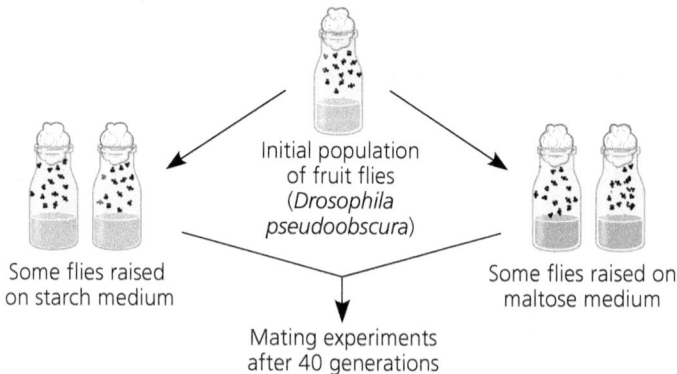

Initial population of fruit flies (*Drosophila pseudoobscura*)

Some flies raised on starch medium   Some flies raised on maltose medium

Mating experiments after 40 generations

Results Mating patterns among populations of flies raised on different media are shown below. When flies from "starch populations" were mixed with flies from "maltose populations," the flies tended to mate with like partners. But in the control group (shown on the right), flies from different populations adapted to starch were about as likely to mate with each other as with flies from their own population; similar results were obtained for control groups adapted to maltose.

		Female	
		Starch	Maltose
Male	Starch	22	9
	Maltose	8	20

Number of matings in experimental group

		Female	
		Starch population 1	Starch population 2
Male	Starch population 1	18	15
	Starch population 2	12	15

Number of matings in control group

Conclusion In the experimental group, the strong preference of "starch flies" and "maltose flies" to mate with like-adapted flies indicates that a reproductive barrier was forming between these fly populations. Although this reproductive barrier was not absolute (some mating between starch flies and maltose flies did occur), after 40 generations it appeared to be under way. This barrier may have been caused by differences in courtship behaviour that arose as an incidental by-product of differing selective pressures as these allopatric populations adapted to different sources of food.

Source: Based on D. M. B. Dodd, Reproductive isolation as a consequence of adaptive divergence in *Drosophila pseudoobscura*, *Evolution* 43:1308–1311 (1989). © Jane B Reece.

WHAT IF? *Why were all flies used in the mating preference tests reared on a standard medium (rather than on a starch or maltose medium)?*

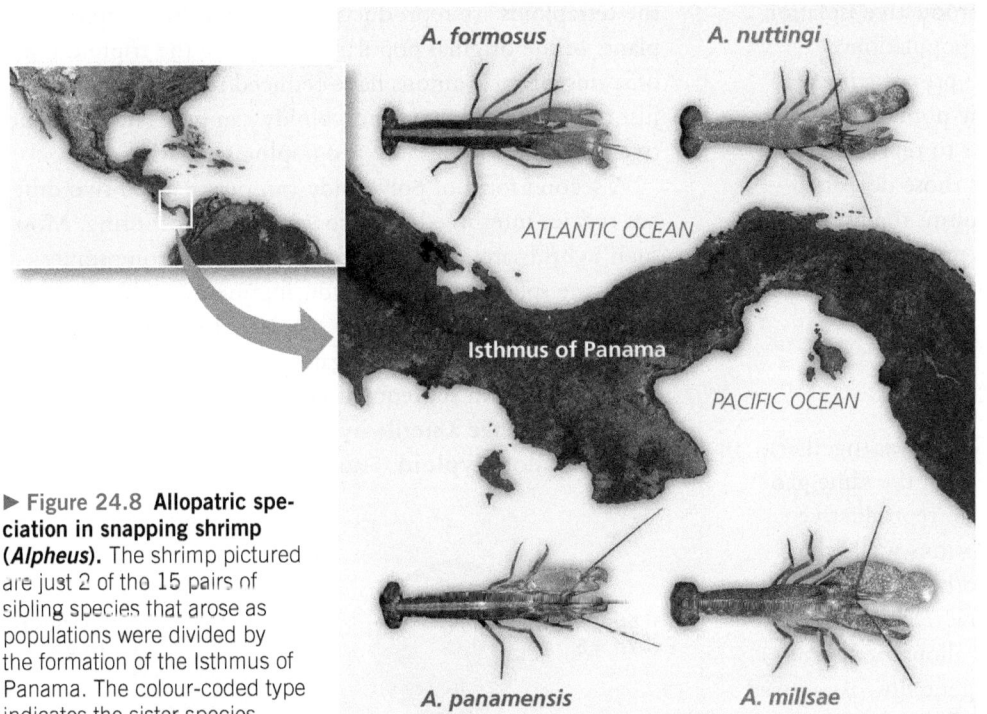

A. formosus

A. nuttingi

ATLANTIC OCEAN

Isthmus of Panama

PACIFIC OCEAN

A. panamensis

A. millsae

▶ Figure 24.8 **Allopatric speciation in snapping shrimp (Alpheus).** The shrimp pictured are just 2 of the 15 pairs of sibling species that arose as populations were divided by the formation of the Isthmus of Panama. The colour-coded type indicates the sister species.

Arthur Ankler/ Florida Museum of Natural History

gradually, starting 10 million years ago, and closing completely about 3 million years ago.

The importance of allopatric speciation is also suggested by the fact that regions that are isolated or highly subdivided by barriers typically have more species than do otherwise similar regions that lack such features. For example, many unique plants and animals are found on the geographically isolated Hawaiian Islands (we'll return to the origin of Hawaiian species in Chapter 25).

Field studies also show that reproductive isolation between two populations generally increases as the geographic distance between them increases, a finding consistent with allopatric speciation. In the Scientific Skills Exercise, you will analyze data

SCIENTIFIC SKILLS EXERCISE

Identifying Independent and Dependent Variables, Making a Scatter Plot, and Interpreting Data

Does Distance Between Salamander Populations Increase Their Reproductive Isolation? Allopatric speciation begins when populations become geographically isolated, preventing mating between individuals in different populations and thus stopping gene flow. It is logical that as distance between populations increases, so will their degree of reproductive isolation. To test this hypothesis, researchers studied populations of the dusky salamander (*Desmognathus ochrophaeus*) living on different mountain ranges in the southern Appalachians.

How the Experiment Was Done The researchers tested the reproductive isolation of pairs of salamander populations by leaving one male and one female together and later checking the females for the presence of sperm. Four mating combinations were tested for each pair of populations (A and B)—two *within* the same population (female A with male A and female B with male B) and two *between* populations (female A with male B and female B with male A).

Data from the Experiment The researchers used an index of reproductive isolation that ranged from a value of 0 (no isolation) to a value of 2 (full isolation). The proportion of successful matings for each mating combination was measured, with 100% success = 1 and no success = 0. The reproductive isolation value for two populations is the sum of the proportion of successful matings of each type within populations (AA + BB) minus the sum of the proportion of successful matings of each type between populations (AB + BA). The table provides distance and reproductive isolation data for 27 pairs of dusky salamander populations.

Interpret the Data

1. State the researchers' hypothesis, and identify the independent and dependent variables in this study. Explain why the researchers used four mating combinations for each pair of populations.

John Shaw/Photoshot License Limited

2. Calculate the value of the reproductive isolation index if (a) *all* of the matings within a population were successful, but *none* of the matings between populations were successful; (b) salamanders are equally successful in mating with members of their own population and members of another population.

3. Make a scatter plot to help you visualize any patterns that might indicate a relationship between the variables. Plot the independent variable on the x-axis and the dependent variable on the y-axis. (For additional information about graphs, see the Scientific Skills Review in Appendix E and the Study Area of MasteringBiology.)

4. Interpret your graph by (a) explaining in words any pattern indicating a possible relationship between the variables and (b) hypothesizing the possible cause of such a relationship.

Data from S. G. Tilley, A. Verrell, and S. J. Arnold, Correspondence between sexual isolation and allozyme differentiation: A test in the salamander *Desmognathus ochrophaeus*, *Proceedings of the National Academy of Sciences USA* 87:2715–2719 (1990). © Jane B Reece.

Geographic Distance (km)	15	32	40	47	42	62	63	81	86	107	107	115	137	147
Reproductive Isolation Value	0.32	0.54	0.50	0.50	0.82	0.37	0.67	0.53	1.15	0.73	0.82	0.81	0.87	0.87
Distance (continued)	137	150	165	189	219	239	247	53	55	62	105	179	169	
Isolation (continued)	0.50	0.57	0.91	0.93	1.5	1.22	0.82	0.99	0.21	0.56	0.41	0.72	1.15	

from one such study that examined reproductive isolation in geographically separated salamander populations.

Note that while geographic isolation prevents interbreeding between members of allopatric populations, physical separation is not a biological barrier to reproduction. Biological reproductive barriers such as those described in Figure 24.3 are intrinsic to the organisms themselves. Hence, it is biological barriers that can prevent interbreeding when members of different populations come into contact with one another.

Sympatric ("Same Country") Speciation

In **sympatric speciation** (from the Greek *syn*, together), speciation occurs in populations that live in the same geographic area (see Figure 24.5b). How can reproductive barriers form between sympatric populations while their members remain in contact with each other? Although such contact (and the ongoing gene flow that results) makes sympatric speciation less common than allopatric speciation, sympatric speciation can occur if gene flow is reduced by such factors as polyploidy, habitat differentiation, and sexual selection. (Note that these factors can also promote allopatric speciation.)

Polyploidy

A species may originate from an accident during cell division that results in extra sets of chromosomes, a condition called **polyploidy**. Polyploid speciation occasionally occurs in animals; for example, the grey tree frog *Hyla versicolor* (see Figure 23.15) is thought to have originated in this way. However, polyploidy is far more common in plants. Botanists estimate that more than 80% of the plant species alive today are descended from ancestors that formed by polyploid speciation.

Two distinct forms of polyploidy have been observed in plant (and a few animal) populations. An **autopolyploid** (from the Greek *autos*, self) is an individual that has more than two chromosome sets that are all derived from a single species. In plants, for example, a failure of cell division could double a cell's chromosome number from the diploid number (2*n*) to a tetraploid number (4*n*).

A tetraploid can produce fertile tetraploid offspring by self-pollinating or by mating with other tetraploids. In addition,

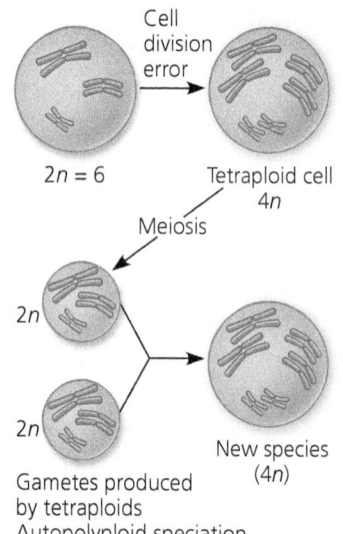

Cell division error

2*n* = 6   Tetraploid cell 4*n*

Meiosis

2*n*

2*n*

New species (4*n*)

Gametes produced by tetraploids
Autopolyploid speciation

the tetraploids are reproductively isolated from diploid plants of the original population, because the triploid (3*n*) offspring of such unions have reduced fertility. Thus, in just one generation, autopolyploidy can generate reproductive isolation without any geographic separation.

A second form of polyploidy can occur when two different species interbreed and produce hybrid offspring. Most such hybrids are sterile because the set of chromosomes from one species cannot pair during meiosis with the set of chromosomes from the other species. However, an infertile hybrid may be able to propagate itself asexually (as many plants can do). In subsequent generations, various mechanisms can change a sterile hybrid into a fertile polyploid called an **allopolyploid** (Figure 24.9). The allopolyploids are

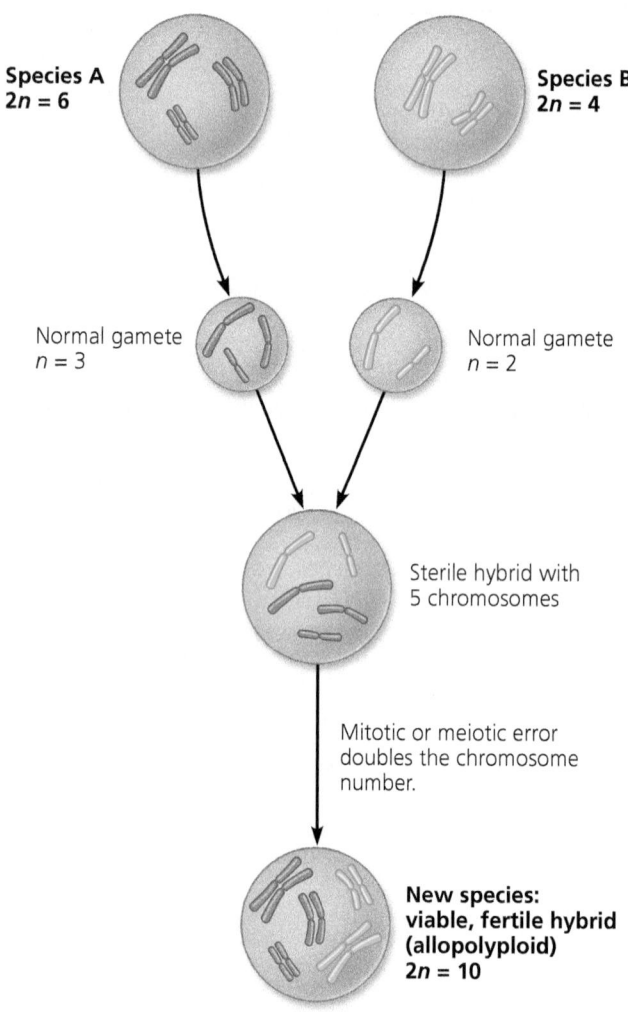

Species A
2*n* = 6

Species B
2*n* = 4

Normal gamete
n = 3

Normal gamete
n = 2

Sterile hybrid with 5 chromosomes

Mitotic or meiotic error doubles the chromosome number.

New species: viable, fertile hybrid (allopolyploid)
2*n* = 10

▲ **Figure 24.9 One mechanism for allopolyploid speciation in plants.** Most hybrids are sterile because their chromosomes are not homologous and cannot pair during meiosis. However, such a hybrid may be able to reproduce asexually. This diagram traces one mechanism that can produce fertile hybrids (allopolyploids) as new species. The new species has a diploid chromosome number equal to the sum of the diploid chromosome numbers of the two parent species.

fertile when mating with each other but cannot interbreed with either parent species; thus, they represent a new biological species.

Although polyploid speciation is relatively rare, even in plants, scientists have documented that at least five new plant species have originated in this way since 1850. One of these examples involves the origin of a new species of goatsbeard plant (genus *Tragopogon*) in the Pacific Northwest of the United States. *Tragopogon* first arrived in the region when humans introduced three European species in the early 1900s: *T. pratensis*, *T. dubius*, and *T. porrifolius*. These three species are now common weeds in abandoned parking lots and other urban sites. In 1950, a new *Tragopogon* species was discovered near the Idaho-Washington border, a region where all three European species also were found. Genetic analyses revealed that this new species, *Tragopogon miscellus*, is a tetraploid hybrid of two of the European species (**Figure 24.10**). Although the *T. miscellus* population grows mainly by reproduction of its own members, additional episodes of hybridization between the parent species continue to add new members to the *T. miscellus* population—just one of many examples in which scientists have observed speciation in progress.

Many important agricultural crops—such as oats, cotton, potatoes, tobacco, and wheat—are polyploids. The wheat used for bread, *Triticum aestivum*, is an allohexaploid (six sets of chromosomes, two sets from each of three different species). The first of the polyploidy events that eventually led to modern wheat probably occurred about 8000 years ago in the Middle East as a spontaneous hybrid of an early cultivated wheat species and a wild grass. Today, plant geneticists generate new polyploids in the laboratory by using chemicals that induce meiotic and mitotic errors. By harnessing the evolutionary process, researchers can produce new hybrid species with desired qualities, such as a hybrid that combines the high yield of wheat with the hardiness of rye.

Habitat Differentiation

Sympatric speciation can also occur when genetic factors enable a subpopulation to exploit a habitat or resource not used by the parent population. Such is the case with the North American apple maggot fly (*Rhagoletis pomonella*), a pest of apples. The fly's original habitat was the native hawthorn tree, but about 200 years ago, some populations colonized apple trees that had been introduced by European settlers. As apples mature more quickly than hawthorn fruit, natural selection has favoured apple-feeding flies with rapid development. These apple-feeding populations now show

▲ *R. pomonella* feeding on a hawthorn berry

temporal isolation from the hawthorn-feeding *R. pomonella*, providing a prezygotic restriction to gene flow between the two populations. Alleles that benefit the flies that use one host plant but harm the flies that use the other host plant have also been identified. As a result, natural selection operating on these alleles provides a postzygotic barrier to reproduction, further limiting gene flow. Altogether, although the two populations are still classified as subspecies rather than separate species, sympatric speciation appears to be well under way.

Sexual Selection

There is evidence that sympatric speciation can also be driven by sexual selection. Clues to how this can occur have been found in cichlid fish from one of Earth's hot spots of animal speciation, East Africa's Lake Victoria. This lake was once home to as many as 600 species of cichlids. Genetic data indicate that these species originated within the last 100 000 years from a small number of colonizing species that arrived from rivers and lakes located elsewhere. How did so many species—more than double the number of freshwater fish species known in all of Europe—originate within a single lake?

One hypothesis is that subgroups of the original cichlid populations adapted to different food sources and that the resulting genetic divergence contributed to speciation in Lake Victoria. But sexual selection, in which (typically) females select males based on their appearance (see Chapter 23),

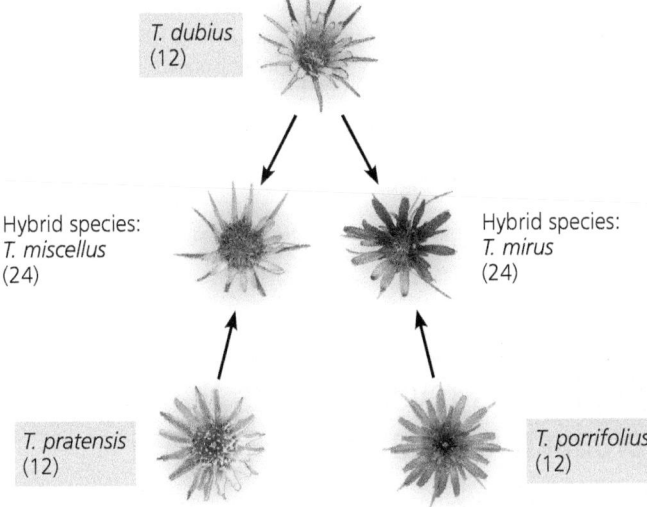

▲ **Figure 24.10 Allopolyploid speciation in *Tragopogon*.** The grey boxes indicate the three parent species. The diploid chromosome number of each species is shown in parentheses.

T. dubius (12)

Hybrid species: *T. miscellus* (24)

Hybrid species: *T. mirus* (24)

T. pratensis (12)

T. porrifolius (12)

may also have been a factor. Researchers have studied two closely related sympatric species of cichlids that differ mainly in the colouration of breeding males: Breeding *Pundamilia pundamilia* males have a blue-tinged back, whereas breeding *Pundamilia nyererei* males have a red-tinged back (Figure 24.11). Their results suggest that mate choice based on male breeding colouration is the main reproductive barrier that normally keeps the gene pools of these two species separate.

Allopatric and Sympatric Speciation: *A Review*

Now let's recap the two main modes by which new species form. In allopatric speciation, a new species forms in

---

▲ Figure 24.11 | **Inquiry**

Does sexual selection in cichlids result in reproductive isolation?

Experiment Ole Seehausen and Jacques van Alphen, then at the University of Leiden, placed males and females of *Pundamilia pundamilia* and *P. nyererei* together in two aquarium tanks, one with natural light and one with a monochromatic orange lamp. Under normal light, the two species are noticeably different in male breeding colouration; under monochromatic orange light, the two species are very similar in colour. The researchers then observed the mate choices of the females in each tank.

Normal light   **Monochromatic orange light**

P. pundamilia

P. nyererei

Results Under normal light, females of each species strongly preferred males of their own species. But under orange light, females of each species responded indiscriminately to males of both species. The resulting hybrids were viable and fertile.

Conclusion Seehausen and van Alphen concluded that mate choice by females based on male breeding colouration is the main reproductive barrier that normally keeps the gene pools of these two species separate. Since the species can still interbreed when this prezygotic behavioural barrier is breached in the laboratory, the genetic divergence between the species is likely to be small. This suggests that speciation in nature has occurred relatively recently.

Source: Based on O. Seehausen and J. J. M. van Alphen, The effect of male colouration on female mate choice in closely related Lake Victoria cichlids (*Haplochromis nyererei* complex), *Behavioral Ecology and Sociobiology* 42:1–8 (1998). © Jane B Reece.

WHAT IF? *Suppose that female cichlids living in the murky waters of a polluted lake could not distinguish colours well. In such waters, how might gene pools of these species change over time?*

---

geographic isolation from its parent population. Geographic isolation severely restricts gene flow. As a result, other reproductive barriers from the ancestral species may arise as a by-product of genetic changes that occur within the isolated population. Many different processes can produce such genetic changes, including natural selection under different environmental conditions, genetic drift, and sexual selection. Once formed, intrinsic reproductive barriers that arise in allopatric populations can prevent interbreeding with the parent population even if the populations come back into contact.

Sympatric speciation, in contrast, requires the emergence of a reproductive barrier that isolates a subset of a population from the remainder of the population in the same area. Though rarer than allopatric speciation, sympatric speciation can occur when gene flow to and from the isolated subpopulation is blocked. This can occur as a result of polyploidy, a condition in which an organism has extra sets of chromosomes. Sympatric speciation also can occur when a subset of a population becomes reproductively isolated because of natural selection that results from a switch to a habitat or food source not used by the parent population. Finally, sympatric speciation can result from sexual selection.

Having reviewed the geographic context in which species originate, we'll next explore in more detail what can happen when new or partially formed species come into contact.

CONCEPT CHECK 24.2

1. Summarize key differences between allopatric and sympatric speciation. Which type of speciation is more common, and why?
2. Describe two mechanisms that can decrease gene flow in sympatric populations, thereby making sympatric speciation more likely to occur.
3. **WHAT IF?** Is allopatric speciation more likely to occur on an island close to a mainland or on a more isolated island of the same size? Explain your prediction.
4. **MAKE CONNECTIONS** After reviewing the process of meiosis in Figure 13.8, describe how an error during meiosis could lead to polyploidy.

For suggested answers, see Appendix A.

CONCEPT 24.3

Hybrid zones reveal factors that cause reproductive isolation

What happens if species with incomplete reproductive barriers come into contact with one another? One possible outcome is the formation of a **hybrid zone**, a region in which members of different species meet and mate, producing at least some offspring of mixed ancestry. In this section, we'll explore hybrid zones and what they reveal about factors that cause the evolution of reproductive isolation.

Patterns Within Hybrid Zones

Some hybrid zones form as narrow bands, such as the one depicted in **Figure 24.12** for two species of toads in the genus *Bombina*, the yellow-bellied toad (*B. variegata*) and the fire-bellied toad (*B. bombina*). This hybrid zone, represented by the red line on the map, extends for 4000 km but is less than 10 km wide in most places. The hybrid zone occurs where the higher-altitude habitat of the yellow-bellied toad meets the lowland habitat of the fire-bellied toad. Across a given "slice" of the zone, the frequency of alleles specific to yellow-bellied toads typically decreases from close to 100% at the edge where only yellow-bellied

toads are found, to 50% in the central portion of the zone, to 0% at the edge where only fire-bellied toads are found.

What causes such a pattern of allele frequencies across a hybrid zone? We can infer that there is an obstacle to gene flow—otherwise, alleles from one parent species would also be common in the gene pool of the other parent species. Are geographic barriers reducing gene flow? Not in this case, since the toads can move throughout the hybrid zone. A more important factor is that hybrid toads have increased rates of embryonic mortality and a variety of morphological abnormalities, including ribs that are fused to the spine and malformed tadpole mouthparts. Because the hybrids have poor survival and reproduction, they produce few viable offspring with members of the parent species. As a result, hybrid individuals rarely serve as a stepping-stone from which alleles are passed from one species to the other. Outside the hybrid zone, additional obstacles to gene flow may

▲ **Figure 24.12 A narrow hybrid zone for *Bombina* toads in Europe.** The graph shows the pattern of species-specific allele frequencies across the width of the zone near Krakow, Poland. Individuals with frequencies close to 1.0 are yellow-bellied toads, individuals with frequencies close to 0.0 are fire-bellied toads, and individuals with intermediate frequencies are considered hybrids.

Source: Adaptation of figure 10.8 from *Hybrid Zone and the Evolutionary Process*, edited by Richard G. Harrison. Copyright © 1993 by Oxford University Press. Reprinted with permission.

? *Does the graph indicate that gene flow is spreading fire-bellied toad alleles into the range of the yellow-bellied toad? Explain.*

be provided by natural selection in the different environments in which the parent species live.

Hybrid zones typically are located wherever the habitats of the interbreeding species meet. Those regions often resemble a group of isolated patches scattered across the landscape—more like the complex pattern of spots on a Dalmatian than the continuous band shown in Figure 24.12. But regardless of whether they have complex or simple spatial patterns, hybrid zones form when two species lacking complete barriers to reproduction come into contact. Once formed, how does a hybrid zone change over time?

Hybrid Zones over Time

Studying a hybrid zone is like observing a natural experiment on speciation. Will the hybrids become reproductively isolated from their parents and form a new species, as occurred by polyploidy in the goatsbeard plant of the Pacific Northwest? If not, there are three possible outcomes for the hybrid zone over time: reinforcement of barriers, fusion of species, or stability (Figure 24.13). Let's examine what studies in the field suggest about these three possibilities.

Reinforcement: Strengthening Reproductive Barriers

Hybrids are often less fit than members of their parent species. In such cases, natural selection should strengthen prezygotic barriers to reproduction, reducing the formation of unfit hybrids. Because this process involves *reinforcing*

reproductive barriers, it is called **reinforcement**. If reinforcement is occurring, a logical prediction is that barriers to reproduction between species should be stronger for sympatric populations than for allopatric populations.

As an example, let's consider the evidence for reinforcement in two closely related species of European flycatcher, the pied flycatcher (*Ficedula hypoleuca*) and the collared flycatcher (*F. albicollis*). In allopatric populations of these birds, males of the two species closely resemble one another. But in sympatric populations, the males of the two species look very different: Male pied flycatchers are a dull brown, whereas male collared flycatchers have enlarged patches of white. Female pied and collared flycatchers do not select males of the other species when given a choice between males from sympatric populations, but they frequently do make mistakes when selecting between males from allopatric populations (Figure 24.14). Thus, barriers to reproduction appear to be stronger in birds from sympatric populations than in birds from allopatric populations, as you would predict if reinforcement is occurring. Similar results have been observed in a number of organisms, including fish, insects, plants, and other birds.

Fusion: Weakening Reproductive Barriers

Next let's consider the case in which two species contact one another in a hybrid zone, but the barriers to reproduction are not strong. So much gene flow may occur that reproductive barriers weaken further and the gene pools of the two species become increasingly alike. In effect,

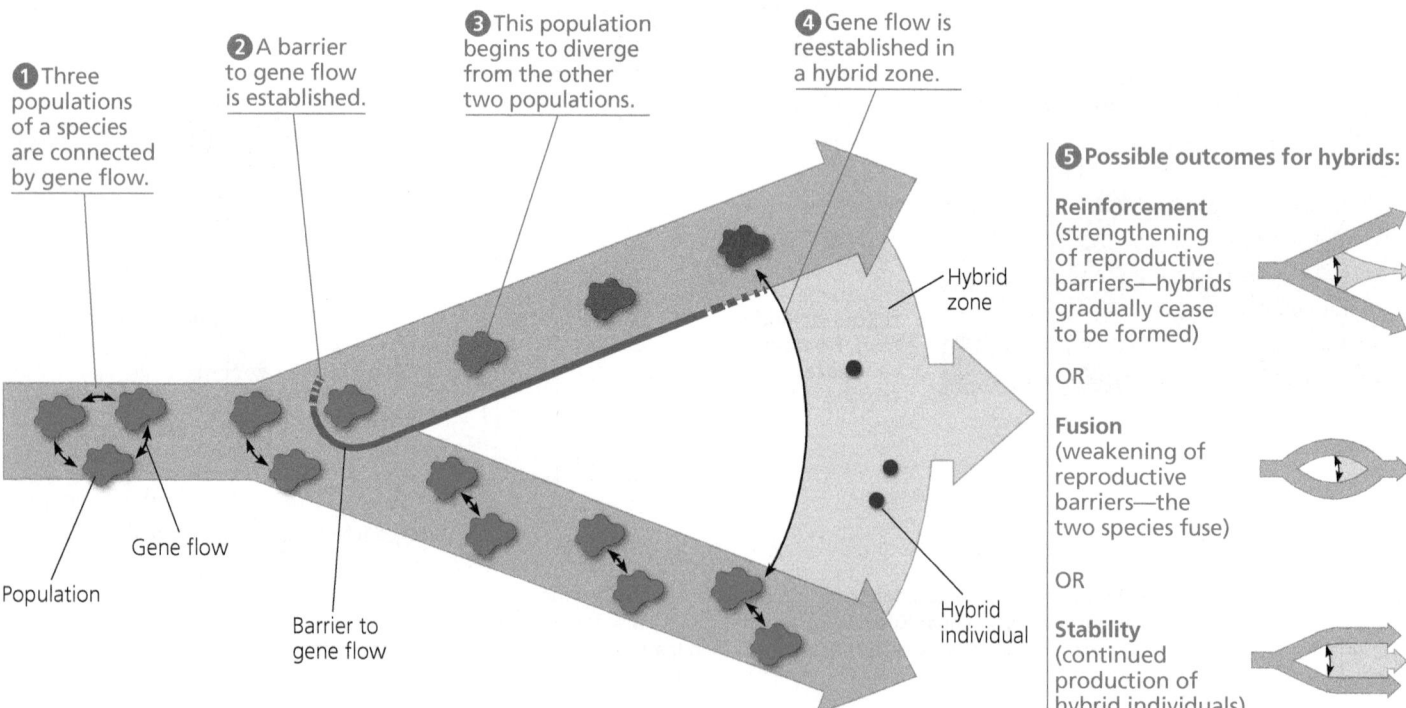

1 Three populations of a species are connected by gene flow.

2 A barrier to gene flow is established.

3 This population begins to diverge from the other two populations.

4 Gene flow is reestablished in a hybrid zone.

Gene flow

Population

Barrier to gene flow

Hybrid zone

Hybrid individual

5 Possible outcomes for hybrids:

Reinforcement (strengthening of reproductive barriers—hybrids gradually cease to be formed)

OR

Fusion (weakening of reproductive barriers—the two species fuse)

OR

Stability (continued production of hybrid individuals)

▲ Figure 24.13 **Formation of a hybrid zone and possible outcomes for hybrids over time.** The thick coloured arrows represent the passage of time.

WHAT IF? *Predict what might happen if gene flow were reestablished at step 3 in this process.*

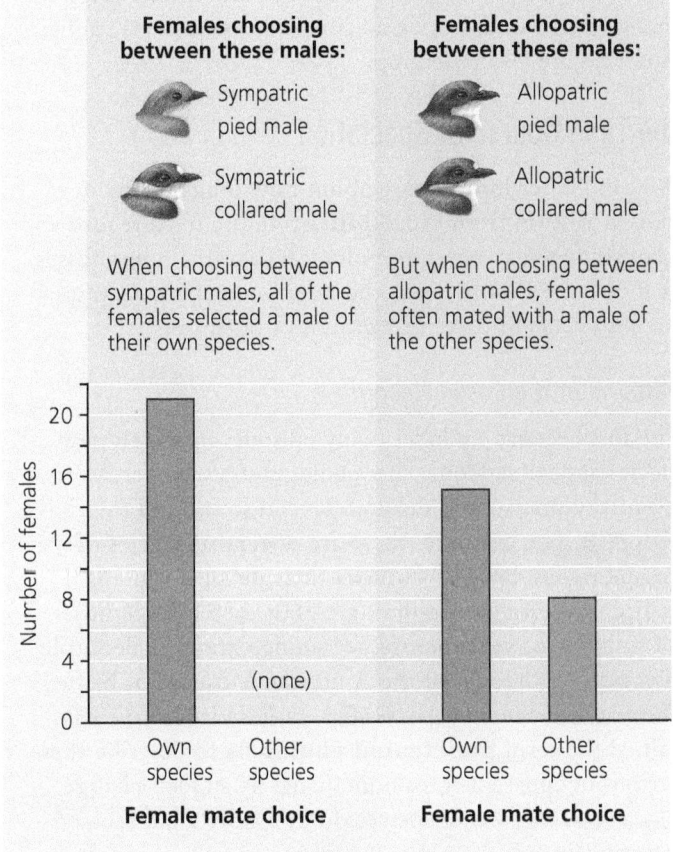

Females choosing
between these males:

Sympatric
pied male

Sympatric
collared male

When choosing between
sympatric males, all of the
females selected a male of
their own species.

Females choosing
between these males:

Allopatric
pied male

Allopatric
collared male

But when choosing between
allopatric males, females
often mated with a male of
the other species.

▲ Figure 24.14 Reinforcement of barriers to reproduction in closely
related species of European flycatchers.

Source: Adaptation of Figure 2 from "A Sexually Selected Character Displacement in
Flycatchers Reinforces Premating Isolation" by Glenn-Peter Saetre et al., from *Nature,*
June 1997, Volume 387(6633). Copyright © 1997 by Macmillan Publishers Ltd.
Reprinted with permission.

the speciation process reverses, eventually causing the two
hybridizing species to fuse into a single species.

Such a situation may be occurring among some of the Lake
Victoria cichlids we discussed earlier. In the past 30 years, about
200 of the former 600 species of Lake Victoria cichlids have
vanished. Some of these species were driven to extinction
by an introduced predator, the Nile perch. But many species not eaten by Nile perch also have disappeared—perhaps
in some cases by species fusion. Many pairs of ecologically
similar cichlid species are reproductively isolated because
the females of one species prefer to mate with males of
one colour, while females of the other species prefer to
mate with males of a different colour (see Figure 24.11).
Researchers think that murky waters caused by pollution
may have reduced the ability of females to use colour to
distinguish males of their own species from males of closely
related species. If further evidence supports this hypothesis,
it would seem that pollution in Lake Victoria has produced
a cascade of related effects. First, by decreasing the ability of
females to distinguish males of their own species, pollution
has increased the frequency of mating between members
of species that had been isolated reproductively from one

another. Second, as a result of these matings, many hybrids
have been produced, leading to fusion of the parent species'
gene pools and a loss of species (Figure 24.15).

Similar events may be affecting the polar bear (*Ursus
maritimus*). Fossils and genetic analyses indicate that polar
bears evolved from North American populations of grizzly
bears (*U. arctos*) between 100 000 and 200 000 years ago.
In recent decades, global warming has reduced the extent
of the Arctic Ocean ice packs from which polar bears hunt
for seals and other prey. At the same time, grizzly bears
have been documented moving farther into the Canadian
sub-arctic habitat, such as Wapusk National Park in Manitoba, in the Hudson Bay area. As the polar bear ice-pack
habitat disappears (placing them at risk of extinction), polar
bears are more likely to be found on land, where they may
encounter grizzly bears (Figure 24.4). Hybrid offspring of
polar bears and grizzly bears in the wild have been documented (see Figure 24.4). As ice-pack habitat continues to
disappear, increasing numbers of such hybrids may cause the
gene pool of these species to begin to fuse, thus contributing to the possible eventual extinction of the polar bear.

Stability: Continued Formation of Hybrid Individuals

Many hybrid zones are stable in the sense that hybrids continue to be produced. In some cases, this occurs because

▲ Figure 24.15 **Fusion: the breakdown of reproductive barriers.**
Increasingly cloudy water in Lake Victoria over the past 30 years may
have weakened reproductive barriers between *P. nyererei* and *P.
pundamilia.* In areas of cloudy water, the two species have hybridized
extensively, causing their gene pools to fuse.

the hybrids survive or reproduce better than members of either parent species, at least in certain habitats or years. But stable hybrid zones have also been observed in cases where the hybrids are selected *against*—an unexpected result.

For example, hybrids continue to form in the *Bombina* hybrid zone even though they are strongly selected against. One explanation relates to the narrowness of the *Bombina* hybrid zone (see Figure 24.12). Evidence suggests that members of both parent species migrate into the zone from the parent populations located outside the zone, thus leading to the continued production of hybrids. If the hybrid zone were wider, this would be less likely to occur, since the centre of the zone would receive little gene flow from distant parent populations located outside the hybrid zone.

Sometimes the outcomes in hybrid zones match our predictions (European flycatchers and cichlid fishes), and sometimes they don't (*Bombina*). But whether our predictions are upheld or not, events in hybrid zones can shed light on how barriers to reproduction between closely related species change over time. In the next section, we'll examine how interactions between hybridizing species can also provide a glimpse into the speed and genetic control of speciation.

CONCEPT CHECK 24.3

1. What are hybrid zones, and why can they be viewed as "natural laboratories" in which to study speciation?

2. **WHAT IF?** Consider two species that diverged while geographically separated but resumed contact before reproductive isolation was complete. Predict what would happen over time if the two species mated indiscriminately and (a) hybrid offspring survived and reproduced more poorly than offspring from intraspecific matings or (b) hybrid offspring survived and reproduced as well as offspring from intraspecific matings.

For suggested answers, see Appendix A.

CONCEPT 24.4

Speciation can occur rapidly or slowly and can result from changes in few or many genes

Darwin faced many unanswered questions when he began to ponder that "mystery of mysteries"—speciation. He found answers to some of those questions when he realized that evolution by natural selection helps explain both the diversity of life and the adaptations of organisms (see Concept 22.2). But biologists since Darwin have continued to ask fundamental questions about speciation. How long

does it take for new species to form? And how many genes change when one species splits into two? Answers to these questions are also emerging.

The Time Course of Speciation

We can gather information about how long it takes new species to form from broad patterns in the fossil record and from studies that use morphological data (including fossils) or molecular data to assess the time interval between speciation events in particular groups of organisms.

Patterns in the Fossil Record

The fossil record includes many episodes in which new species appear suddenly in a geologic stratum, persist essentially unchanged through several strata, and then disappear. For example, there are dozens of species of marine invertebrates that make their debut in the fossil record with novel morphologies, but then change little for millions of years before becoming extinct. Paleontologists Niles Eldredge, of the American Museum of Natural History, and Stephen Jay Gould, of Harvard University, coined the term **punctuated equilibria** to describe these periods of apparent stasis punctuated by sudden change (Figure 24.16a). Other species do not show a punctuated pattern; instead, they change more gradually over long periods of time (Figure 24.16b).

What do punctuated and gradual patterns tell us about how long it takes new species to form? Suppose that a species survived for 5 million years, but most of the morphological changes that caused it to be designated a new species occurred during the first 50 000 years of its existence—just 1% of its total lifetime. Time periods this short (in geologic terms) often cannot be distinguished in fossil strata, in part because the rate of sediment accumulation is too slow to separate layers this close in time. Thus, based on its fossils, the species would seem to have appeared suddenly and then lingered with little or no change before becoming extinct. Even though such a species may have originated more slowly than its fossils suggest (in this case taking 50 000 years), a punctuated pattern indicates that speciation occurred relatively rapidly. For species whose fossils changed much more gradually, we also cannot tell exactly when a new biological species formed, since information about reproductive isolation does not fossilize. However, it is likely that speciation in such groups occurred relatively slowly, perhaps taking millions of years.

Speciation Rates

The punctuated pattern suggests that once the process of speciation begins, it can be completed relatively rapidly—a suggestion supported by a growing number of studies.

(a) In a punctuated pattern, new species change most as they branch from a parent species and then change little for the rest of their existence.

Time

(b) Other species diverge from one another much more gradually over time.

▲ Figure 24.16 **Two models for the tempo of speciation.**

For example, rapid speciation produced the wild sunflower *Helianthus anomalus*. Genetic evidence indicates that this species originated by the hybridization of two other sunflower species, *H. annuus* and *H. petiolaris*. The hybrid species *H. anomalus* is ecologically distinct and reproductively isolated from both parent species **(Figure 24.17)**. Unlike the outcome of allopolyploid speciation, in which there is a change in chromosome number after hybridization, in these sunflowers the two parent species and the hybrid all have the same number of chromosomes ($2n = 34$). How, then, did speciation occur? To answer this question, researchers performed an experiment designed to mimic events in nature **(Figure 24.18)**. Their results indicated that natural selection

▲ Figure 24.17 **A hybrid sunflower species and its dry sand dune habitat.** The wild sunflower *Helianthus anomalus* originated via the hybridization of two other sunflowers, *H. annuus* and *H. petiolaris*, which live in nearby but moister environments.

could produce extensive genetic changes in hybrid populations over short periods of time. These changes appear to have caused the hybrids to diverge reproductively from their parents and form a new species, *H. anomalus*.

The sunflower example, along with the apple maggot fly, Lake Victoria cichlid, and fruit fly examples discussed earlier, suggests that new species can arise rapidly *once divergence begins*. But what is the total length of time between speciation events? This interval consists of the time that elapses before populations of a newly formed species start to diverge from one another plus the time it takes for speciation to be complete once divergence begins. It turns out that the total time between speciation events varies considerably. For example, in a survey of data from 84 groups of plants and animals, the interval between speciation events ranged from 4000 years (in cichlids of Lake Nabugabo, Uganda) to 40 million years (in some beetles). Overall, the time between speciation events averaged 6.5 million years and rarely took less than 500 000 years.

These data suggest that, on average, millions of years may pass before a newly formed species will itself give rise to another new species. As we'll see in Chapter 25, this result has implications for how long it takes life on Earth to recover from mass extinction events. Second, the extreme variability in the time it takes new species to form indicates that organisms do not have a "speciation clock" ticking inside them, causing them to produce new species at regular time intervals. Instead, speciation begins only after gene flow between populations is interrupted, perhaps by changing environmental conditions or by unpredictable events, such as a storm that transports a few individuals to an

Inquiry

How does hybridization lead to speciation in sunflowers?

Experiment At Indiana University, Loren Rieseberg and his colleagues crossed two parent sunflower species, *H. annuus* and *H. petiolaris*, to produce experimental hybrids in the laboratory (for each gamete, only two of the $n = 17$ chromosomes are shown).

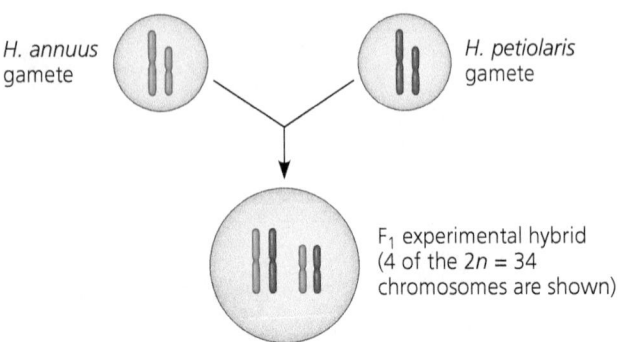

H. annuus gamete

H. petiolaris gamete

F_1 experimental hybrid (4 of the $2n = 34$ chromosomes are shown)

Note that in the first (F_1) generation, each chromosome of the experimental hybrids consisted entirely of DNA from one or the other parent species. The researchers then tested whether the F_1 and subsequent generations of experimental hybrids were fertile. They also used species-specific genetic markers to compare the chromosomes in the experimental hybrids with the chromosomes in the naturally occurring hybrid *H. anomalus*.

Results Although only 5% of the F_1 experimental hybrids were fertile, after just four more generations the hybrid fertility rose to more than 90%. The chromosomes of individuals from this fifth hybrid generation differed from those in the F_1 generation but were similar to those in *H. anomalus* individuals from natural populations:

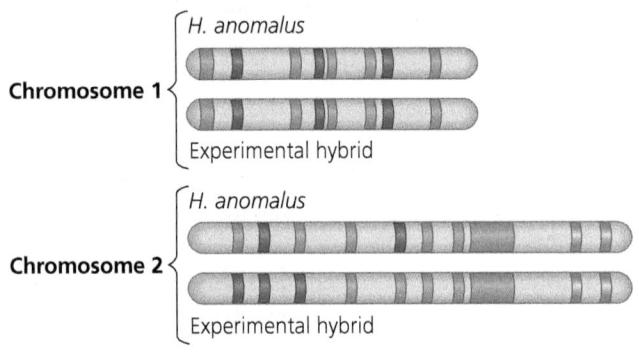

Chromosome 1 { *H. anomalus* / Experimental hybrid

Chromosome 2 { *H. anomalus* / Experimental hybrid

▨ Comparison region containing *H. annuus*-specific marker

▨ Comparison region containing *H. petiolaris*-specific marker

Conclusion Over time, the chromosomes in the population of experimental hybrids became similar to the chromosomes of *H. anomalus* individuals from natural populations. This suggests that the observed rise in the fertility of the experimental hybrids occurred as selection eliminated regions of DNA from the parent species that were not compatible with one another. Overall, it appeared that the initial steps of the speciation process occurred rapidly and could be mimicked in a laboratory experiment.

Source: Based on L. H. Rieseberg et al., Role of gene interactions in hybrid speciation: Evidence from ancient and experimental hybrids, *Science* 272:741–745 (1996). © Jane B Reece.

WHAT IF? *The increased fertility of the experimental hybrids could have resulted from natural selection for thriving under laboratory conditions. Evaluate this alternative explanation for the results.*

isolated area. Furthermore, once gene flow is interrupted, the populations must diverge genetically to such an extent that they become reproductively isolated—all before other events cause gene flow to resume, possibly reversing the speciation process (see Figure 24.15).

Studying the Genetics of Speciation

Studies of ongoing speciation (as in hybrid zones) can reveal traits that cause reproductive isolation. By identifying the genes that control those traits, scientists can explore a fundamental question of evolutionary biology: How many genes change when a new species forms?

In a few cases, the evolution of reproductive isolation is due to a change in a single gene. For example, in Japanese snails of the genus *Euhadra*, a change in a single gene can result in a mechanical barrier to reproduction. This gene controls the direction in which the shells spiral. When their shells spiral in different directions, the snails' genitalia are oriented in a manner that prevents mating (Figure 24.3f shows a similar example). Recent genetic analyses have uncovered other single genes that cause reproductive isolation in fruit flies or mice.

A major barrier to reproduction between two closely related species of monkey flower, *Mimulus cardinalis* and *M. lewisii*, also appears to be influenced by a relatively small number of genes. These two species are isolated by several prezygotic and postzygotic barriers. Of these, one prezygotic barrier, pollinator choice, accounts for most of the isolation: In a hybrid zone between *M. cardinalis* and *M. lewisii*, nearly 98% of pollinator visits were restricted to one species or the other.

The two monkey flower species are visited by different pollinators: Hummingbirds prefer the red-flowered *M. cardinalis*, and bumblebees prefer the pink-flowered *M. lewisii*. Pollinator choice is affected by at least two loci in the monkey flowers, one of which, the "yellow upper," or *yup*, locus, influences flower colour (Figure 24.19). By crossing the two parent species to produce F_1 hybrids and then performing repeated backcrosses of these F_1 hybrids to each parent species, Douglas Schemske and colleagues at Michigan State University succeeded in transferring the *M. cardinalis* allele at this locus into *M. lewisii*, and vice versa. In a field experiment, *M. lewisii* plants with the *M. cardinalis yup* allele received 68-fold more visits from hummingbirds than did wild-type *M. lewisii*. Similarly, *M. cardinalis* plants with the *M. lewisii yup* allele received 74-fold more visits from bumblebees than did wild-type *M. cardinalis*. Thus, a mutation at a single locus can influence pollinator preference and hence contribute to reproductive isolation in monkey flowers.

In other organisms, the speciation process is influenced by larger numbers of genes and gene interactions. For example, hybrid sterility between two subspecies of the

(a) Typical *Mimulus lewisii*

(b) *M. lewisii* **with an** *M. cardinalis* **flower-colour allele**

(c) Typical *Mimulus cardinalis*

(d) *M. cardinalis* **with an** *M. lewisii* **flower-colour allele**

▲ **Figure 24.19 A locus that influences pollinator choice.** Pollinator preferences provide a strong barrier to reproduction between *Mimulus lewisii* and *M. cardinalis*. After transferring the *M. lewisii* allele for a flower-colour locus into *M. cardinalis* and vice versa, researchers observed a shift in some pollinators' preferences.

WHAT IF? *If* M. cardinalis *individuals that had the* M. lewisii *yup allele were planted in an area that housed both monkey flower species, how might the production of hybrid offspring be affected?*

fruit fly *Drosophila pseudoobscura* results from gene interactions among at least four loci, and postzygotic isolation in the sunflower hybrid zone discussed earlier is influenced by at least 26 chromosome segments (and an unknown number of genes). Overall, studies suggest that few or many genes can influence the evolution of reproductive isolation and hence the emergence of a new species.

From Speciation to Macroevolution

As you've seen, speciation may begin with differences as seemingly small as the colour on a cichlid's back. However, as speciation occurs again and again, such differences can accumulate and become more pronounced, eventually leading to the formation of new groups of organisms that differ greatly from their ancestors (as in the origin of whales from land-dwelling mammals; see Figure 22.20). Furthermore, as one group of organisms increases in size by producing many new species, another group of organisms may shrink, losing species to extinction. The cumulative effects of many such speciation and extinction events have helped shape the sweeping evolutionary changes that are documented in the fossil record. In the next chapter, we turn to such large-scale evolutionary changes as we begin our study of macroevolution.

CONCEPT CHECK 24.4

1. Speciation can occur rapidly between diverging populations, yet the length of time between speciation events is often more than a million years. Explain this apparent contradiction.

2. Summarize evidence that the *yup* locus acts as a prezygotic barrier to reproduction in two species of monkey flowers. Do these results demonstrate that the *yup* locus alone controls barriers to reproduction between these species? Explain.

3. **MAKE CONNECTIONS** Compare Figure 13.12 with Figure 24.18. What cellular process could cause the hybrid chromosomes to contain DNA from both parent species? Explain.

For suggested answers, see Appendix A.

---

24 Chapter Review

SUMMARY OF KEY CONCEPTS

CONCEPT 24.1

The biological species concept emphasizes reproductive isolation (pp. 531–535)

* A biological **species** is a group of populations whose individuals have the potential to interbreed and produce viable, fertile offspring with each other but not with members of other species. The **biological species concept** emphasizes reproductive isolation through prezygotic and postzygotic barriers that separate gene pools.

* Although helpful in thinking about how speciation occurs, the biological species concept has limitations. For instance, it cannot be applied to organisms known only as fossils or to organisms that reproduce only asexually. Thus, scientists use other species concepts, such as the **morphological species concept**, in certain circumstances.

? *Explain the role of gene flow in the biological species concept.*

CONCEPT 24.2

Speciation can take place with or without geographic separation (pp. 535–540)

- In **allopatric speciation**, gene flow is reduced when two populations of one species become geographically separated from each other. One or both populations may undergo evolutionary change during the period of separation, resulting in the establishment of prezygotic or postzygotic barriers to reproduction.
- In **sympatric speciation**, a new species originates while remaining in the same geographic area as the parent species. Plant species (and, more rarely, animal species) have evolved sympatrically through polyploidy. Sympatric speciation can also result from habitat shifts and sexual selection.

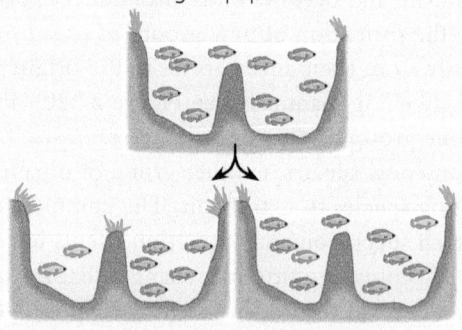

Original population

Allopatric speciation   Sympatric speciation

? *Can factors that cause sympatric speciation also cause allopatric speciation? Explain.*

CONCEPT 24.3

Hybrid zones reveal factors that cause reproductive isolation (pp. 540–544)

- Many groups of organisms form **hybrid zones** in which members of different species meet and mate, producing at least some offspring of mixed ancestry.
- Many hybrid zones are *stable* in that hybrid offspring continue to be produced over time. In others, **reinforcement** strengthens prezygotic barriers to reproduction, thus decreasing the formation of unfit hybrids. In still other hybrid zones, barriers to reproduction may weaken over time, resulting in the *fusion* of the species' gene pools (reversing the speciation process).

? *What factors can support the long-term stability of a hybrid zone if the parent species live in different environments?*

CONCEPT 24.4

Speciation can occur rapidly or slowly and can result from changes in few or many genes (pp. 544–547)

- New species can form rapidly once divergence begins—but it can take millions of years for that to happen. The time interval between speciation events varies considerably, from a few thousand years to tens of millions of years.
- New developments in genetics have enabled researchers to identify specific genes involved in some cases of speciation. Results show that speciation can be driven by few or many genes.

? *Is speciation something that happened only in the distant past, or are new species continuing to arise today? Explain.*

TEST YOUR UNDERSTANDING

LEVEL 1: KNOWLEDGE/COMPREHENSION

1. The *largest* unit within which gene flow can readily occur is a
   a. population.   c. genus.
   b. species.   d. hybrid.

2. Males of different species of the fruit fly *Drosophila* that live in the same parts of the Hawaiian Islands have different elaborate courtship rituals. These rituals involve fighting other males and making stylized movements that attract females. What type of reproductive isolation does this represent?
   a. habitat isolation
   b. temporal isolation
   c. behavioural isolation
   d. gametic isolation

3. According to the punctuated equilibria model,
   a. given enough time, most existing species will branch gradually into new species.
   b. most new species accumulate their unique features relatively rapidly as they come into existence, then change little for the rest of their duration as a species.
   c. most evolution occurs in sympatric populations.
   d. speciation is usually due to a single mutation.

LEVEL 2: APPLICATION/ANALYSIS

4. Bird guides once listed the myrtle warbler and Audubon's warbler as distinct species. Recently, these birds have been classified as eastern and western forms of a single species, the yellow-rumped warbler. Which of the following pieces of evidence, if true, would be cause for this reclassification?
   a. The two forms interbreed often in nature, and their offspring have good survival and reproduction.
   b. The two forms live in similar habitats and have similar food requirements.
   c. The two forms have many genes in common.
   d. The two forms have similar food requirements.

5. Which of the following factors would *not* contribute to allopatric speciation?
   a. The separated population is small, and genetic drift occurs.
   b. The isolated population is exposed to different selection pressures than the ancestral population.
   c. Different mutations begin to distinguish the gene pools of the separated populations.
   d. Gene flow between the two populations is extensive.

6. Plant species A has a diploid number of 12. Plant species B has a diploid number of 16. A new species, C, arises as an allopolyploid from A and B. The diploid number for species C would probably be
   a. 14.   b. 16.   c. 28.   d. 56.

LEVEL 3: SYNTHESIS/EVALUATION

7. Suppose that a group of male pied flycatchers migrated from a region where there were no collared flycatchers to a region where both species were present (see Figure 24.14). Assuming events like this are very rare, which of the following scenarios is *least* likely?
   a. The frequency of hybrid offspring would increase.
   b. Migrant pied males would produce fewer offspring than would resident pied males.
   c. Migrant males would mate with collared females more often than with pied females.
   d. The frequency of hybrid offspring would decrease.

8. **EVOLUTION CONNECTION**
   What is the biological basis for assigning all human populations to a single species? Can you think of a scenario by which a second human species could originate in the future?

9. **SCIENCE, TECHNOLOGY, AND SOCIETY**

In the United States, the rare red wolf (*Canis lupus*) has been known to hybridize with coyotes (*Canis latrans*), which are much more numerous. Although red wolves and coyotes differ in terms of morphology, DNA, and behaviour, genetic evidence suggests that living red wolf individuals are actually hybrids. Red wolves are designated as an endangered species and hence receive legal protection under the Endangered Species Act. Some people think that their endangered status should be withdrawn because the remaining red wolves are hybrids, not members of a "pure" species. Do you agree? Why or why not?

10. **SCIENTIFIC INQUIRY**

DRAW IT   In this chapter, you read that bread wheat (*Triticum aestivum*) is an allohexaploid, containing two sets of chromosomes from each of three different parent species. Genetic analysis suggests that the three species pictured following this question each contributed chromosome sets to *T. aestivum*. (The capital letters here represent sets of chromosomes rather than individual genes.) Evidence also indicates that the first polyploidy event was a spontaneous hybridization of the early cultivated wheat species *T. monococcum* and a wild *Triticum* grass species. Based on this information, draw a diagram of one possible chain of events that could have produced the allohexaploid *T. aestivum*.

Ancestral species:

AA — *Triticum monococcum* (2n = 14)

BB — Wild *Triticum* (2n = 14)

DD — Wild *T. tauschii* (2n = 14)

Product:

AA BB DD — *T. aestivum* (bread wheat) (2n = 42)

11. **WRITE ABOUT A THEME: INFORMATION**

In sexually reproducing species, each individual begins life with DNA inherited from both parent organisms. In a short essay (100–150 words), apply this idea to what occurs when organisms of two species that have homologous chromosomes mate and produce (F_1) hybrid offspring. What percentage of the DNA in the F_1 hybrids' chromosomes comes from each parent species? As the hybrids mate and produce F_2 and later-generation hybrid offspring, describe how recombination and natural selection may affect whether the DNA in hybrid chromosomes is derived from one parent species or the other.

12. **SYNTHESIZE YOUR KNOWLEDGE**

Rolf Nussbaumer Photography/Alamy Stock Photo

Suppose that females of one population of strawberry poison dart frogs (*Dendrobates pumilio*) prefer to mate with males that have a bright red and black colouration. In a different population, the females prefer males with yellow skin. Propose a hypothesis to explain how such differences could have arisen in allopatric versus sympatric populations.

For selected answers, see Appendix A.

25

The History of Life on Earth

KEY CONCEPTS

25.1 Conditions on early Earth made the origin of life possible

25.2 The fossil record documents the history of life

25.3 Key events in life's history include the origins of single-celled and multicelled organisms and the colonization of land

25.4 The rise and fall of groups of organisms reflect differences in speciation and extinction rates

25.5 Major changes in body form can result from changes in the sequences and regulation of developmental genes

25.6 Evolution is not goal oriented

Lu & Brusatte (2015) A large, short-armed, winged dromaeosaurid (Dinosauria: Theropoda) from the Early Cretaceous of China and its implications of feather evolution). *Scientific Reports*, 5, Figure 1

▲ **Figure 25.1** Did *Tyrannosaurus rex* have feathers similar to this dinosaur?

Dinosaurs of a Feather

What can we learn from fossils? The examination of fossilized skeletons of dinosaurs can reveal a great deal about their body shape. However, they provide little insight into their outward appearance. Fortunately, bones are not the only tissues that are fossilized, and under the right conditions, soft tissues and feathers can also be preserved (Figure 25.1). Rare finds of skin impressions give paleontologists the tools required to paint a better picture of what these "terrible lizards" may have looked like. Many of these creatures were not scaly as once thought, but covered with feathers—a characteristic exclusive to birds today. For example, the velociraptors of *Jurassic Park* fame were actually much smaller than depicted and covered in plumage, including a fringe of long, quill-like feathers on their arms. Recent research headed by Dr. Darla Zelenitsky from the University of Calgary has uncovered winged dinosaurs in the Badlands of Alberta. Her findings were the first feathered non-avian dinosaurs in North America. But did *Tyrannosaurus rex*, the king of the dinosaurs, have feathers? Many of its relatives are known to be feathered, lending to the speculation that so was *T. rex*. However, the impressions of *T. rex*'s skin have yet to be found, leaving this a matter of heated debate.

Fossils from around the globe continue to tell us interesting stories about now-extinct species. For example, early Antarctic explorers visited one of

Courtesy of Darla Zelenitsky

◀ **Dr. Darla Zelenitsky in the Badlands of Alberta**

Earth's harshest, most barren environments, a land of extreme cold and almost no liquid water. Antarctic life is sparse and small—the largest fully terrestrial animal is a fly 5 mm long. But some of these explorers made an astonishing discovery: fossil evidence that life once thrived where it now barely exists. Fossils reveal that 500 million years ago, the ocean around Antarctica was warm and teeming with tropical invertebrates. Later, the continent was covered in forests for hundreds of millions of years. At various times, diverse animals stalked through these forests, including 3-m-tall predatory "terror birds" and giant dinosaurs such as the voracious *Cryolophosaurus*, a 7-m-long relative of *T. rex*.

Fossils tell us that past organisms were very different from those presently living. The sweeping changes in life on Earth as revealed by fossils illustrate **macroevolution**, the broad pattern of evolution above the species level. Examples of macroevolutionary change include the emergence of terrestrial vertebrates through a series of speciation events, the impact of mass extinctions on the diversity of life, and the origin of key adaptations such as flight in birds.

Taken together, such changes provide a grand view of the evolutionary history of life on Earth. We'll examine that history in this chapter, beginning with hypotheses regarding the origin of life. The origin of life is the most speculative topic of the entire unit, for no fossil evidence of that seminal episode exists. We will then turn to evidence from the fossil record and what it tells us about major events in the history of life, paying particular attention to factors that have helped to shape the rise and fall of different groups of organisms over time.

CONCEPT 25.1

Conditions on early Earth made the origin of life possible

Direct evidence of life on early Earth comes from fossils of microorganisms that are about 3.5 billion years old. But when and how did the first living cells appear? Observations and experiments in chemistry, geology, and physics have led scientists to propose one scenario that we'll examine here. They hypothesize that chemical and physical processes on early Earth, aided by the emerging force of natural selection, could have produced very simple cells through a sequence of four main stages:

1. The abiotic (nonliving) synthesis of small organic molecules, such as amino acids and nitrogenous bases
2. The joining of these small molecules into macromolecules, such as proteins and nucleic acids
3. The packaging of these molecules into **protocells**, droplets with membranes that maintained an internal chemistry different from that of their surroundings

4. The origin of self-replicating molecules that eventually made inheritance possible

Though speculative, this scenario leads to predictions that can be tested in the laboratory. In this section, we will examine some of the evidence for each stage.

Synthesis of Organic Compounds on Early Earth

There is scientific evidence that Earth and the other planets of the solar system formed about 4.6 billion years ago, condensing from a vast cloud of dust and rocks that surrounded the young sun. For the first few hundred million years, life probably could not have originated or survived on Earth because the planet was still being bombarded by huge chunks of rock and ice left over from the formation of the solar system. The collisions generated enough heat to vapourize any available water and prevent seas from forming. This early phase likely ended about 4.2–3.9 billion years ago.

As the bombardment of early Earth slowed, conditions on the planet were extremely different from those of today. The first atmosphere was probably thick with water vapour, along with various compounds released by volcanic eruptions, including nitrogen and its oxides, carbon dioxide, methane, ammonia, hydrogen, and hydrogen sulphide. As Earth cooled, the water vapour condensed into oceans, and much of the hydrogen escaped into space.

During the 1920s, Russian chemist A. I. Oparin and British scientist J. B. S. Haldane independently hypothesized that Earth's early atmosphere was a reducing (electron-adding) environment, in which organic compounds could have formed from simpler molecules. The energy for this organic synthesis could have come from lightning and intense UV radiation. Haldane suggested that the early oceans were a solution of organic molecules, a "primordial soup" from which life arose.

During 1953, Stanley Miller, working under the guidance of Harold Urey at the University of Chicago, tested the Oparin-Haldane hypothesis by creating laboratory conditions comparable to those that scientists at the time thought existed on early Earth (see Figure 4.2). His apparatus yielded a variety of amino acids found in organisms today, along with other organic compounds. Many laboratories have since repeated Miller's classic experiment using different recipes for the atmosphere, some of which also produced organic compounds.

However, some evidence suggests that the early atmosphere was made up primarily of nitrogen and carbon dioxide and was neither reducing nor oxidizing (electron removing). Recent Miller-Urey-type experiments using such "neutral" atmospheres have also produced organic molecules. In addition, small pockets of the early atmosphere, such as those near the openings of volcanoes, may

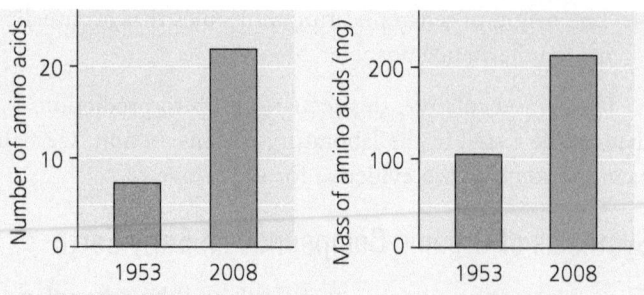

▲ **Figure 25.2 Amino acid synthesis in a simulated volcanic erup-tion.** In addition to his classic 1953 study, Miller also conducted an experiment simulating a volcanic eruption. In a 2008 reanalysis of those results, researchers found that far more amino acids were produced under simulated volcanic conditions than were produced in the conditions of the original 1953 experiment.

Source: Data from "The Miller Volcanic Spark Discharge Experiment" by Adam P. Johnson et al., from *Science,* October 2008, Volume 322(5900). © Jane B. Reece.

`MAKE CONNECTIONS` *How could more than 20 amino acids have been found in the 2008 experiment? (See Concept 5.4.)*

have been reducing. Perhaps the first organic compounds formed near volcanoes. In a 2008 test of this hypothesis, researchers used modern equipment to reanalyze molecules that Miller had saved from one of his experiments. The 2008 study found that numerous amino acids had formed under conditions that simulated a volcanic eruption (Figure 25.2).

Another hypothesis is that organic compounds were first produced in deep-sea hydrothermal vents, areas on the seafloor where heated water and minerals gush from Earth's interior into the ocean. Some of these vents, known as "black smokers," release water so hot (300–400°C) that organic compounds formed there may have been unstable. But other deep-sea vents, called alkaline vents, release water that has a high pH (9–11) and is warm (40–90°C) rather than hot, an environment that may have been more suitable for the origin of life (Figure 25.3).

Studies related to the volcanic–atmosphere and alkaline-vent hypotheses show that the abiotic synthesis of organic molecules is possible under various conditions. Another source of organic molecules may have been meteorites. For example, fragments of the Murchison meteorite, a 4.5-billion-year-old rock that landed in Australia in 1969, contain more than 80 amino acids, some in large amounts. These amino acids cannot be contaminants from Earth because they consist of an equal mix of D and L isomers (see Chapter 4). Organisms make and use only L isomers, with a few rare exceptions. Recent studies have shown that the Murchison meteorite also contained other key organic molecules, including lipids, simple sugars, and nitrogenous bases such as uracil.

Abiotic Synthesis of Macromolecules

The presence of small organic molecules, such as amino acids and nitrogenous bases, is not sufficient for the

◀ **Figure 25.3 Did life originate in deep-sea alkaline vents?** The first organic compounds—and indeed, the first cells—may have arisen in warm alkaline vents similar to this one from the 40 000-year-old "Lost City" vent field in the mid-Atlantic Ocean. These vents contain hydrocarbons and are full of tiny pores (inset) lined with iron and other catalytic minerals. Early oceans were acidic, and so a pH gradient would have formed between the interior of the vents and the surrounding ocean water. Energy for the synthesis of organic compounds could have been harnessed from this pH gradient.

emergence of life as we know it. Every cell has a vast assortment of macromolecules, including enzymes and other proteins and the nucleic acids that are essential for self-replication. Could such macromolecules have formed on early Earth? A 2009 study at the University of Manchester by John Sutherland demonstrated that one key step, the abiotic synthesis of RNA monomers, can occur spontaneously from simple precursor molecules. In addition, by dripping solutions of amino acids or RNA nucleotides onto hot sand, clay, or rock, researchers have produced polymers of these molecules. The polymers formed spontaneously, without the help of enzymes or ribosomes. Unlike proteins, the amino acid polymers are a complex mix of linked and cross-linked amino acids. Nevertheless, it is possible that such polymers may have acted as weak catalysts for a variety of chemical reactions on early Earth.

Protocells

All organisms must be able to carry out both reproduction and energy processing (metabolism). DNA molecules carry genetic information, including the instructions needed to replicate themselves accurately during reproduction. But DNA replication requires elaborate enzymatic machinery along with an abundant supply of nucleotide building blocks provided by the cell's metabolism. This suggests that self-replicating molecules and a metabolism-like source of building blocks may have appeared together in early protocells. The necessary conditions may have been met in vesicles, fluid-filled compartments enclosed by a

Source: Figure adapted from "Experimental Models of Primitive Cellular Compartments: Encapsulation, Growth, and Division" by Martin M. Hanczyc, Shelly M. Fuji-kawa, and Jack W. Szostak from *Science*, October 2003, Volume 302(5645). Copyright © 2003 by AAAS. Reprinted with permission.

(a) Self-assembly. The presence of montmorillonite clay greatly increases the rate of vesicle self-assembly.

(b) Reproduction. Vesicles can divide on their own, as in this vesicle "giving birth" to smaller vesicles (LM).

(c) Absorption of RNA. This vesicle has incorporated montmorillonite clay particles coated with RNA (orange).

▲ Figure 25.4 **Features of abiotically produced vesicles.**

membrane-like structure. Recent experiments show that abiotically produced vesicles can exhibit certain properties of life, including simple reproduction and metabolism, as well as the maintenance of an internal chemical environment different from that of their surroundings (**Figure 25.4**).

For example, vesicles can form spontaneously when lipids or other organic molecules are added to water. When this occurs, the hydrophobic molecules in the mixture organize into a bilayer similar to the lipid bilayer of a plasma membrane. Adding substances such as *montmorillonite*, a soft mineral clay produced by the weathering of volcanic ash, greatly increases the rate of vesicle self-assembly (**Figure 25.4a**). This clay, which is thought to have been common on early Earth, provides surfaces on which organic molecules become concentrated, increasing the likelihood that the molecules will react with each other and form vesicles. Abiotically produced vesicles can "reproduce" on their own (**Figure 25.4b**), and they can increase in size ("grow") without dilution of their contents. Vesicles also can absorb montmorillonite particles, including those on which RNA and other organic molecules have become attached (**Figure 25.4c**). Finally, experiments have shown

that some vesicles have a selectively permeable bilayer and can perform metabolic reactions using an external source of reagents—another important prerequisite for life.

Self-Replicating RNA

The first genetic material was most likely RNA, not DNA. RNA plays a central role in protein synthesis, can also carry out a number of enzyme-like catalytic functions. Thomas Cech, of the University of Colorado, called these RNA catalysts **ribozymes**. Some ribozymes can make complementary copies of short pieces of RNA, provided that they are supplied with nucleotide building blocks.

Natural selection on the molecular level has produced ribozymes capable of self-replication in the laboratory. How does this occur? Unlike double-stranded DNA, which takes the form of a uniform helix, single-stranded RNA molecules assume a variety of specific three-dimensional shapes mandated by their nucleotide sequences. In a particular environment, RNA molecules with certain base sequences are more stable and replicate faster and with fewer errors than other sequences. The RNA molecule whose sequence is best suited to the surrounding environment and has the greatest ability to replicate itself will leave the most descendant molecules. Occasionally, a copying error will result in a molecule that folds into a shape that is even more stable or more adept at self-replication than the ancestral sequence. Similar selection events may have occurred on early Earth. Thus, the molecular biology of today may have been preceded by an "RNA world," in which small RNA molecules that carried genetic information were able to replicate and to store information about the vesicles that carried them.

A vesicle with self-replicating, catalytic RNA would differ from its many neighbours that lacked such molecules. If that vesicle could grow, split, and pass its RNA molecules to its daughters, the daughters would be protocells. Although the first such protocells must have carried only limited amounts of genetic information, specifying only a few properties, their inherited characteristics could have been acted on by natural selection. The most successful of the early protocells would have increased in number because they could exploit their resources effectively and pass their abilities on to subsequent generations.

Once RNA sequences that carried genetic information appeared in protocells, many further changes would have been possible. For example, RNA could have provided the template on which DNA nucleotides were assembled. Double-stranded DNA is a more stable repository for genetic information than the more fragile RNA. DNA also can be replicated more accurately. Accurate replication was advantageous as genomes grew larger through gene duplication and other processes and as more properties of the protocells became coded in genetic information. Once DNA appeared, the stage was set for a blossoming of new forms of life—a change we see documented in the fossil record.

CONCEPT CHECK 25.1

1. What hypothesis did Miller test in his classic experiment?
2. How would the appearance of protocells have represented a key step in the origin of life?
3. **MAKE CONNECTIONS** In changing from an "RNA world" to today's "DNA world," genetic information must have flowed from RNA to DNA. After reviewing Figures 17.3 and 19.9, suggest how this could have occurred. Is such a flow a common occurrence today?

For suggested answers, see Appendix A.

CONCEPT 25.2

The fossil record documents the history of life

Starting with the earliest traces of life, the fossil record opens a window into the world of long ago and provides glimpses of the evolution of life over billions of years. In this section, we'll explore what the fossil record reveals about the major changes in the history of life—what those changes have been and how they may have occurred.

The Fossil Record

Sedimentary rocks are the richest source of fossils. As a result, the fossil record is based primarily on the sequence in which fossils have accumulated in sedimentary rock layers, called *strata* (see Figure 22.3). Useful information is also provided by other types of fossils, such as insects preserved in amber (fossilized tree sap) and mammals frozen in ice.

The fossil record shows that there have been great changes in the kinds of organisms on Earth at different points in time (Figure 25.5). Many past organisms were unlike today's organisms, and many organisms that once were common are now extinct. As we'll see later, fossils also document how new groups of organisms arose from previously existing ones.

As substantial and significant as the fossil record is, keep in mind that it is an incomplete chronicle of evolutionary change. Many of Earth's organisms did not die in the right place at the right time to be preserved as fossils. Of those fossils that were formed, many were destroyed by later geologic processes, and only a fraction of the others have been discovered. As a result, the known fossil record is biased in favour of species that existed for a long time, were abundant and widespread in certain kinds of environments, and had hard shells, skeletons, or other parts that facilitated

their fossilization. Even with its limitations; however, the fossil record is a remarkably detailed account of biological change over the vast scale of geologic time. Furthermore, as shown by the recently unearthed fossils of whale ancestors with hind limbs (see Figures 22.19 and 22.20), gaps in the fossil record continue to be filled by new discoveries.

Although some of these new discoveries are fortuitous, others illustrate the predictive nature of paleontology. For instance, researchers seeking to discover a close ancestor of early terrestrial vertebrates predicted that such a fossil would most likely be located in a river bed (which would have sedimentary rocks) containing rocks that were 375 million years old (an age based on previously known fossils). After digging for several years in one of the few such places on Earth, on Ellesmere Island in Nunavut, their predictions bore fruit with the discovery of *Tiktaalik*, an aquatic organism closely related to the first vertebrates to walk on land in 2006 (see Figures 25.5 and 34.20).

How Rocks and Fossils Are Dated

Fossils are valuable data for reconstructing the history of life, but only if we can determine where they fit in that unfolding story. While the order of fossils in rock strata tells us the sequence in which the fossils were laid down—their relative ages—it does not tell us their actual (absolute) ages. Examining the relative positions of fossils in strata is like peeling off layers of wallpaper in an old house. You can determine the sequence in which the layers were applied, but not the year each layer was added.

How can we determine the absolute age of a fossil? (Note that "absolute" dating does not mean errorless, but that an age is given in years rather than relative terms such as *before* and *after*.) One of the most common techniques is **radiometric dating**, which is based on the decay of radioactive isotopes (see Chapter 2). In this process, a radioactive "parent" isotope decays to a "daughter" isotope at a constant rate. The rate of decay is expressed by the **half-life**, the time required for 50% of the parent isotope to decay (Figure 25.6 on p. 556). Each type of radioactive isotope has a characteristic half-life, which is not affected by temperature, pressure, or other environmental variables. For example, carbon-14 decays relatively quickly; it has a half-life of 5730 years. Uranium-238 decays slowly; its half-life is 4.5 billion years.

Fossils contain isotopes of elements that accumulated in the organisms when they were alive. For example, a living organism contains the most common carbon isotope, carbon-12, as well as a radioactive isotope, carbon-14. When the organism dies, it stops accumulating carbon, and the amount of carbon-12 in its tissues does not change over time. However, the carbon-14 that it contains at the time of death slowly decays into another element, nitrogen-14. Thus, by measuring the ratio of carbon-14 to carbon-12

▼ **Figure 25.5 Documenting the history of life.** These fossils illustrate representative organisms from different points in time. Although prokaryotes and unicellular eukaryotes are only shown at the base of the diagram, these organisms continue to thrive today. In fact, most organisms on Earth are unicellular.

▼ *Rhomaleosaurus victor*, a plesiosaur. These large marine reptiles were important predators from 200 million to 65.5 million years ago.

Franz Xaver Schmidt

1 m

▼ *Dimetrodon*, the largest known carnivore of its day, was more closely related to mammals than to reptiles. The spectacular "sail" on its back probably functioned in temperature regulation.

Maureen Spuhler

0.5 m

▼ *Tiktaalik*, an extinct aquatic organism that is the closest known relative of the first vertebrates to walk on land

Ted Daeschler/The Academy of Natural Sciences

Present

100 million years ago

175

200

270

300

375

400

500

525

565

600

1500

3500

Roger Jones

4.5 cm

▲ *Coccosteus cuspidatus*, a placoderm (fishlike vertebrate) that had a bony shield covering its head and front end

► *Hallucigenia*, a member of a morphologically diverse group of animals found in the Burgess Shale fossil bed in the Canadian Rockies

1 cm

Chip Clark

◄ *Dickinsonia costata*, a member of the Ediacaran biota, an extinct group of soft-bodied organisms

2.5 cm

Museum of Paleontology

Biological Photo Service

▲ Some prokaryotes bind thin films of sediments together, producing layered rocks called stromatolites, such as these in Shark Bay, Australia.

Sinclair Stammers/Science Source

▲ A section through a fossilized stromatolite

► A unicellular eukaryote thought to be either an alga or a fungus

Andrew H. Knoll

▲ Figure 25.6 **Radiometric dating.** In this diagram, each division of the clock face represents a half-life.

Source: Figure adapted from *Geological Time,* 2nd Edition, by Don L. Eicher. Copyright © 1976 by Pearson Education, Inc. Adapted and electronically reproduced by permission of Pearson Education, Inc., Upper Saddle River, New Jersey.

DRAW IT *Relabel the x-axis of this graph in years to illustrate the radioactive decay of uranium-238 (half-life = 4.5 billion years).*

in a fossil, we can determine the fossil's age. This method works for fossils up to about 75 000 years old; fossils older than that contain too little carbon-14 to be detected with current techniques. Radioactive isotopes with longer half-lives are used to date older fossils.

Determining the age of these older fossils in sedimentary rocks is challenging. Organisms do not use radioisotopes with long half-lives, such as uranium-238, to build their bones or shells. Moreover, the sedimentary rocks themselves tend to consist of sediments of differing ages. Though we usually cannot date these old fossils directly, an indirect method can be used to infer the age of fossils that are sandwiched between two layers of volcanic rocks. As lava cools into volcanic rock, radioisotopes from the surrounding environment become trapped in the newly formed rock. Some of the trapped radioisotopes have long half-lives, allowing geologists to estimate the ages of ancient volcanic rocks. If two volcanic layers surrounding fossils are determined to be 525 million and 535 million years old, for example, then the fossils are roughly 530 million years old.

The Origin of New Groups of Organisms

Some fossils provide a detailed look at the origin of new groups of organisms. Such fossils are central to our understanding of evolution; they illustrate how new features arise and how long it takes for such changes to occur. We'll examine one such case here: the origin of mammals.

Along with amphibians and reptiles, mammals belong to the group of animals called *tetrapods* (from the Greek *tetra*, four, and *pod*, foot), named for having four limbs. Mammals

have a number of unique anatomical features that fossilize readily, allowing scientists to trace their origin. For example, the lower jaw is composed of one bone (the dentary) in mammals but several bones in other tetrapods. In addition, the lower and upper jaws hinge between a different set of bones in mammals than in other tetrapods. As we'll explore in Chapter 34, mammals also have a unique set of three bones that transmit sound in the middle ear (the hammer, anvil, and stirrup), whereas other tetrapods have only one such bone (the stirrup). Finally, the teeth of mammals are differentiated into incisors (for tearing), canines (for piercing), and the multipointed premolars and molars (for crushing and grinding). In contrast, the teeth of other tetrapods usually consist of a row of undifferentiated, single-pointed teeth.

As detailed in **Figure 25.7**, the fossil record shows that the unique features of mammalian jaws and teeth evolved gradually over time, in a series of steps. As you study, bear in mind that it includes just a few examples of the fossil skulls that document the origin of mammals. If all the known fossils in the sequence were arranged by shape and placed side by side, their features would blend smoothly from one group to the next. Some of these fossils would reflect how the features of a group that dominates life today, the mammals, gradually arose in a previously existing group, the cynodonts. Others would reveal side branches on the tree of life—groups of organisms that thrived for millions of years but ultimately left no descendants that survive today.

CONCEPT CHECK 25.2

1. Your measurements indicate that a fossilized skull you unearthed has a carbon-14/carbon-12 ratio about 1/16 that of the skulls of present-day animals. What is the approximate age of the fossilized skull?

2. Describe an example from the fossil record that shows how life has changed over time.

3. **WHAT IF?** Suppose researchers discover a fossil of an organism that lived 300 million years ago but had mammalian teeth and a mammalian jaw hinge. What inferences might you draw from this fossil about the origin of mammals and the evolution of novel skeletal structures? Explain.

For suggested answers, see Appendix A.

CONCEPT 25.3

Key events in life's history include the origins of single-celled and multicelled organisms and the colonization of land

The study of fossils has helped geologists establish a **geologic record** of Earth's history, which is divided into four eons (**Table 25.1** on page 558). The first three eons—the Hadean, Archaean, and the Proterozoic—together lasted about 4 billion years. The Phanerozoic eon, roughly the

▼ Figure 25.7
Exploring The Origin of Mammals

Over the course of 120 million years, mammals originated gradually from a group of tetrapods called synapsids. Shown here are a few of the many fossil organisms whose morphological features represent intermediate steps between living mammals and their synapsid ancestors. The evolutionary context of the origin of mammals is shown in the tree diagram at right (the dagger symbol † indicates extinct lineages).

Key to skull bones

- ▓ Articular
- ▓ Dentary
- ▓ Quadrate
- ▓ Squamosal

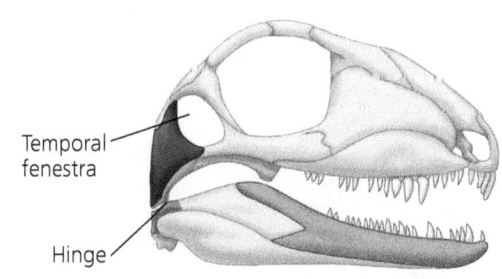

Synapsid (300 mya)

Synapsids had multiple bones in the lower jaw and single-pointed teeth. The jaw hinge was formed by the articular and quadrate bones. Synapsids also had an opening called the temporal fenestra behind the eye socket. Powerful cheek muscles for closing the jaws probably passed through the temporal fenestra. Over time, this opening enlarged and moved in front of the hinge between the lower and upper jaws, thereby increasing the power and precision with which the jaws could be closed (much as moving a doorknob away from the hinge makes a door easier to close).

Therapsid (280 mya)

Later, a group of synapsids called therapsids appeared. Therapsids had large dentary bones, long faces, and the first examples of specialized teeth, large canines. These trends continued in a group of therapsids called cynodonts.

Early cynodont (260 mya)

In early cynodont therapsids, the dentary was the largest bone in the lower jaw, the temporal fenestra was large and positioned forward of the jaw hinge, and teeth with several cusps first appeared (not visible in the diagram). As in earlier synapsids, the jaw had an articular-quadrate hinge.

Later cynodont (220 mya)

Later cynodonts had teeth with complex cusp patterns and their lower and upper jaws hinged in two locations: They retained the original articular-quadrate hinge and formed a new, second hinge between the dentary and squamosal bones. (The temporal fenestra is not visible in this or the below cynodont skull at the angles shown.)

Very late cynodont (195 mya)

In some very late (non-mammalian) cynodonts and early mammals, the original articular-quadrate hinge was lost, leaving the dentary-squamosal hinge as the only hinge between the lower and upper jaws, as in living mammals. The articular and quadrate bones migrated into the ear region (not shown), where they functioned in transmitting sound. In the mammal lineage, these two bones later evolved into the familiar hammer (malleus) and anvil (incus) shown in Figure 34.37.

Source: (300, 280, 260, 220 mya) Based on many sources, including figure 4.10 from *Evolution*, by Douglas J. Futuyma. Sinauer Associates 2005; and *Vertebrate Paleontology and Evolution* by Robert L. Carroll. W.H. Freeman & Co. 1988. © Jane B. Reece; (195 mya) Based on the source: "A New Mammaliaform from the Early Jurassic and Evolution of Mammalian Characteristics" by Zhe-Xi Luo, Alfred W. Crompton, and Ai-Lin Sun from *Science*, May 2001, Volume 292(5521). AAAS. © Jane B. Reece.

Table 25.1   The Geologic Record

Relative Duration of Eons	Era	Period	Epoch	Age (Millions of Years Ago)	Some Important Events in the History of Life
Phanerozoic	Cenozoic	Quaternary	Holocene		Historical time
				0.01	
			Pleistocene		Ice ages; origin of genus *Homo*
				2.6	
		Neogene	Pliocene		Appearance of bipedal human ancestors
				5.3	
			Miocene		Continued radiation of mammals and angiosperms; earliest direct human ancestors
				23	
		Paleogene	Oligocene		Origins of many primate groups
				33.9	
			Eocene		Angiosperm dominance increases; continued radiation of most present-day mammalian orders
				55.8	
			Paleocene		Major radiation of mammals, birds, and pollinating insects
				65.5	
Proterozoic	Mesozoic	Cretaceous			Flowering plants (angiosperms) appear and diversify; many groups of organisms, including most dinosaurs, become extinct at end of period
				145.5	
		Jurassic			Gymnosperms continue as dominant plants; dinosaurs abundant and diverse
				199.6	
		Triassic			Cone-bearing plants (gymnosperms) dominate landscape; dinosaurs evolve and radiate; origin of mammals
				251	
	Paleozoic	Permian			Radiation of reptiles; origin of most present-day groups of insects; extinction of many marine and terrestrial organisms at end of period
				299	
		Carboniferous			Extensive forests of vascular plants form; first seed plants appear; origin of reptiles; amphibians dominant
				359	
		Devonian			Diversification of bony fishes; first tetrapods and insects appear
				416	
		Silurian			Diversification of early vascular plants
				444	
		Ordovician			Marine algae abundant; colonization of land by diverse fungi, plants, and animals
				488	
		Cambrian			Sudden increase in diversity of many animal phyla (Cambrian explosion)
				542	
		Ediacaran			Diverse algae and soft-bodied invertebrate animals appear
				635	
Archaean				2100	Oldest fossils of eukaryotic cells appear
				2500	
				2700	Concentration of atmospheric oxygen begins to increase
				3500	Oldest fossils of cells (prokaryotes) appear
Hadean				3850	Oldest known rocks on Earth's surface
				Approx. 4600	Origin of Earth

last half billion years, encompasses most of the time that animals have existed on Earth. It is divided into three eras: the Paleozoic, Mesozoic, and Cenozoic. Each era represents a distinct age in the history of Earth and its life. For example, the Mesozoic era is sometimes called the "age of reptiles" because of its abundance of reptilian fossils, including those of dinosaurs. The boundaries between the eras correspond to major extinction events seen in the fossil record, when many forms of life disappeared and were replaced by forms that evolved from the survivors.

As we've seen, the fossil record provides a sweeping overview of the history of life over geologic time. Here we will focus on a few major events in that history, returning to study the details in Unit Five. **Figure 25.8** uses the analogy of a clock to place these events in the context of the geologic record. This clock will reappear at various points in this section as a quick visual reminder of when the events we are discussing took place.

The First Single-Celled Organisms

The earliest direct evidence of life, dating from 3.5 billion years ago, comes from fossilized stromatolites (see Figure 25.5). **Stromatolites** are layered rocks that form when certain prokaryotes bind thin films of sediment together. Present-day stromatolites are found in a few warm, shallow, salty bays. If microbial communities complex enough to form stromatolites existed 3.5 billion years ago, it is a reasonable hypothesis that single-celled organisms originated much earlier, perhaps as early as 3.9 billion years ago.

Early prokaryotes were Earth's sole inhabitants for more than 1.5 billion years. As we will see, these prokaryotes transformed life on our planet.

Photosynthesis and the Oxygen Revolution

Most atmospheric oxygen gas (O_2) is of biological origin, produced during the water-splitting step of photosynthesis. When oxygenic photosynthesis first evolved, the free O_2 it produced probably dissolved in the surrounding water until it reached a high enough concentration to react with dissolved iron. This would have caused the iron to precipitate as iron oxide, which accumulated as sediments. These sediments were compressed into banded iron formations, red layers of rock containing iron oxide that are a source of iron ore today. Once all of the dissolved iron had precipitated, additional

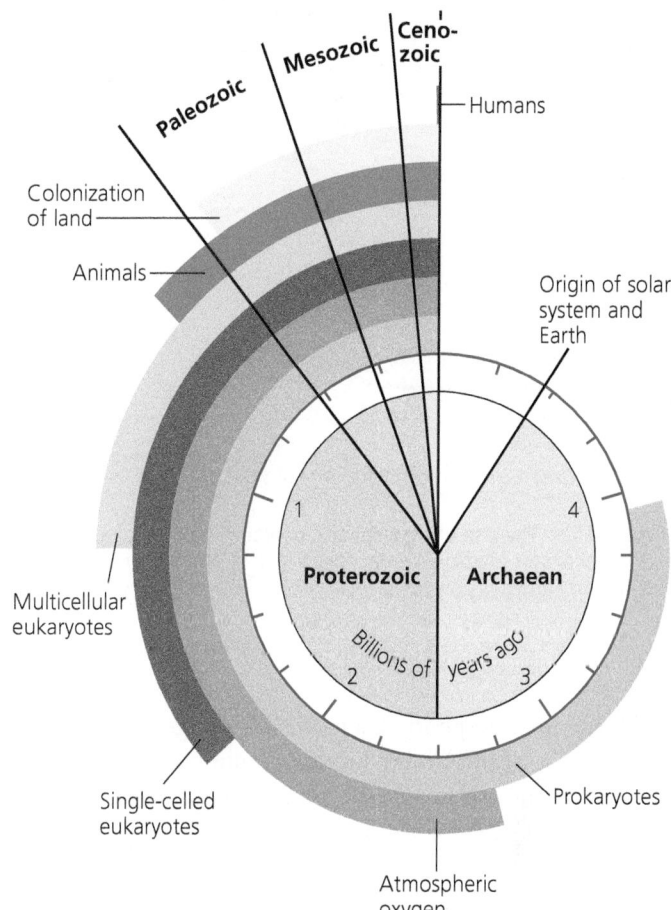

▲ Figure 25.8 **Clock analogy for some key events in Earth's history.** The clock ticks down from the origin of Earth 4.6 billion years ago to the present.

Source: Adapted from "When Did Photosynthesis Emerge on Earth?" by David J. Des Marais, from *Science*, September 2000, Volume 289(5485). © Jane B. Reece.

O_2 dissolved in the water until the seas and lakes became saturated with O_2. After this occurred, the O_2 finally began to "gas out" of the water and enter the atmosphere. This change left its mark in the rusting of iron-rich terrestrial rocks, a process that began about 2.7 billion years ago. This chronology implies that bacteria similar to today's cyanobacteria (oxygen-releasing, photosynthetic bacteria) originated well before 2.7 billion years ago.

The amount of atmospheric O_2 increased gradually from about 2.7 to 2.4 billion years ago, but then shot up relatively rapidly to between 1% and 10% of its present level (**Figure 25.9**). This "oxygen revolution" had an enormous impact on life. In certain of its chemical forms, oxygen attacks chemical bonds and can inhibit enzymes and damage cells. As a result, the rising concentration of atmospheric O_2 probably doomed many prokaryotic groups. Some species survived in habitats that remained anaerobic, where we find their descendants living today (see Chapter 27). Among other survivors, diverse adaptations to the changing atmosphere evolved, including cellular respiration, which uses O_2 in the process of harvesting the energy stored in organic molecules.

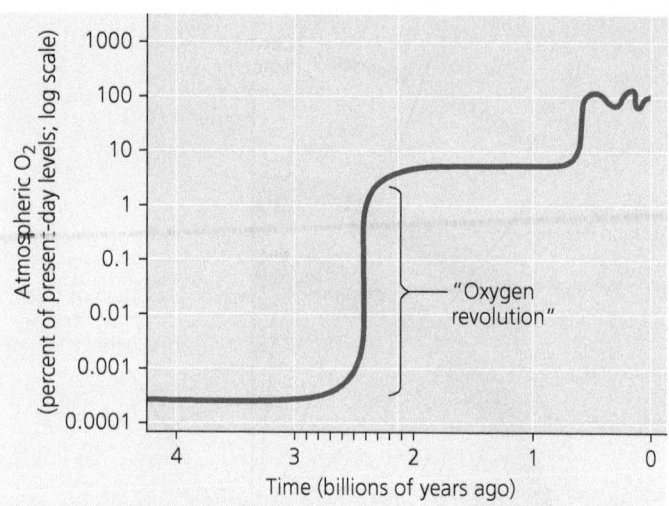

▲ **Figure 25.9 The rise of atmospheric oxygen.** Chemical analyses of ancient rocks have enabled this reconstruction of atmospheric oxygen levels during Earth's history.

Source: Adaptation of Figure 2 from "The Rise of Atmospheric Oxygen" by Lee R. Kump, from *Nature*, January 2008, Volume 451(7176). Copyright © 2008 by Macmillan Publishers Ltd. Reprinted with permission.

The rise in atmospheric O_2 levels left a huge imprint on the history of life. A few hundred million years later, another fundamental change occurred: the origin of the eukaryotic cell.

The First Eukaryotes

Single-celled eukaryotes

The oldest widely accepted fossils of eukaryotic organisms are 1.8 billion years old. Recall that eukaryotic cells have more complex organization than prokaryotic cells: Eukaryotic cells have a nuclear envelope, mitochondria, endoplasmic reticulum, and other internal structures that prokaryotes lack. Also, unlike prokaryotic cells, eukaryotic cells have a well-developed cytoskeleton, a feature that enables eukaryotic cells to change their shape and thereby surround and engulf other cells.

How did these eukaryotic features evolve from prokaryotic cells? Much evidence supports the **endosymbiont theory**, which posits that mitochondria and plastids (a general term for chloroplasts and related organelles) were formerly small prokaryotes that began living within larger cells. The term *endosymbiont* refers to a cell that lives within another cell, called the *host cell*. The prokaryotic ancestors of mitochondria and plastids probably gained entry to the host cell as undigested prey or internal parasites. Though such a process may seem unlikely, scientists have directly observed cases in which endosymbionts that began as prey or parasites came to have a mutually beneficial relationship with the host in as little as five years.

By whatever means the relationships began, we can hypothesize how the symbiosis could have become beneficial. For example, in a world that was becoming increasingly aerobic, a host that was itself an anaerobe would have benefited from endosymbionts that could make use of the oxygen. Over time, the host and endosymbionts would have become a single organism, its parts inseparable. Although all eukaryotes have mitochondria or remnants of these organelles, they do not all have plastids. Thus, the hypothesis of **serial endosymbiosis** supposes that mitochondria evolved before plastids through a sequence of endosymbiotic events (Figure 25.10).

A great deal of evidence supports the endosymbiotic origin of mitochondria and plastids:

- The inner membranes of both organelles have enzymes and transport systems that are homologous to those found in the plasma membranes of living prokaryotes.
- Mitochondria and plastids replicate by a splitting process that is similar to that of certain prokaryotes. In addition, each of these organelles contains circular DNA molecules that, like the chromosomes of bacteria, are not associated with histones or large amounts of other proteins.
- As might be expected of organelles descended from free-living organisms, mitochondria and plastids also have the cellular machinery (including ribosomes) needed to transcribe and translate their DNA into proteins.
- Finally, in terms of size, RNA sequences, and sensitivity to certain antibiotics, the ribosomes of mitochondria and plastids are more similar to prokaryotic ribosomes than they are to the cytoplasmic ribosomes of eukaryotic cells.

The Origin of Multicellularity

An orchestra can play a greater variety of musical compositions than a violin soloist can; the increased complexity of the orchestra makes more variations possible. Likewise, the appearance of structurally complex eukaryotic cells sparked the evolution of greater morphological diversity than was possible for the simpler prokaryotic cells. After the first eukaryotes appeared, a great range of unicellular forms evolved, giving rise to the diversity of single-celled eukaryotes that continue to flourish today. Another wave of diversification also occurred: Some single-celled eukaryotes gave rise to multicellular forms, whose descendants include a variety of algae, plants, fungi, and animals.

Multicellular eukaryotes

Early Multicellular Eukaryotes

The oldest known fossils of multicellular eukaryotes that can be resolved taxonomically are of

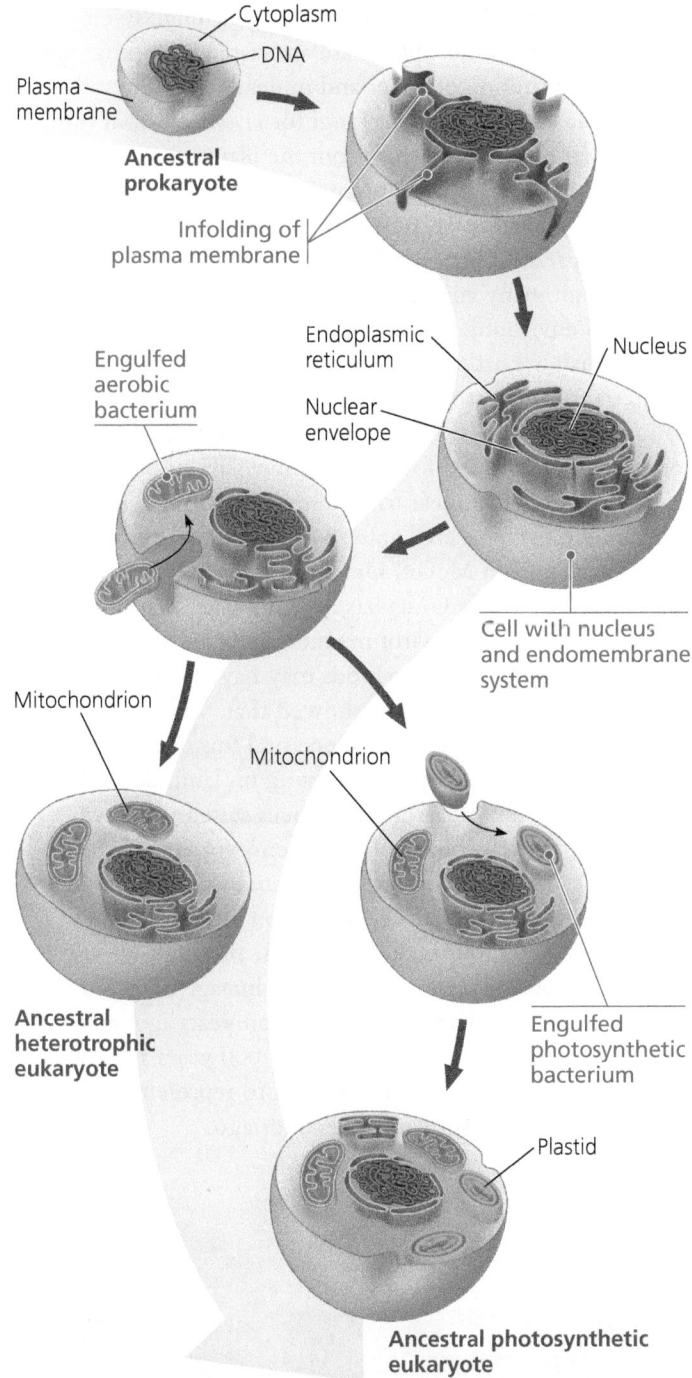

These fossils, referred to as the Ediacaran biota, were of soft-bodied organisms—some over 1 m long—that lived from 600 to 535 million years ago.

The rise of large eukaryotes in the Ediacaran period represents an enormous change in the history of life. Before that time, Earth was a microbial world; Its only inhabitants were single-celled prokaryotes and eukaryotes, along with an assortment of microscopic, multicellular eukaryotes. As the diversification of the Ediacaran biota came to a close about 535 million years ago, the stage was set for another, even more spectacular burst of evolutionary change.

The Cambrian Explosion

Many present-day animal phyla appear suddenly in fossils formed early in the Cambrian period (535–525 million years ago), a phenomenon referred to as the **Cambrian explosion**. Fossils of several animal groups—sponges, cnidarians (sea anemones and their relatives), and molluscs—appear in even older rocks dating from the late Proterozoic (Figure 25.11).

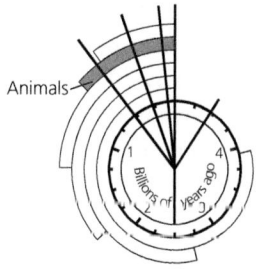

▲ Figure 25.10 **A hypothesis for the origin of eukaryotes through serial endosymbiosis.** The proposed ancestors of mitochondria were aerobic, heterotrophic prokaryotes (meaning they used oxygen to metabolize organic molecules obtained from other organisms). The proposed ancestors of plastids were photosynthetic prokaryotes. In this figure, the arrows represent change over evolutionary time.

relatively small red algae that lived 1.2 billion years ago; even older fossils, dating to 1.8 billion years ago, may also be of small, multicellular eukaryotes. Larger and more diverse multicellular eukaryotes do not appear in the fossil record until about 600 million years ago (see Figure 25.5).

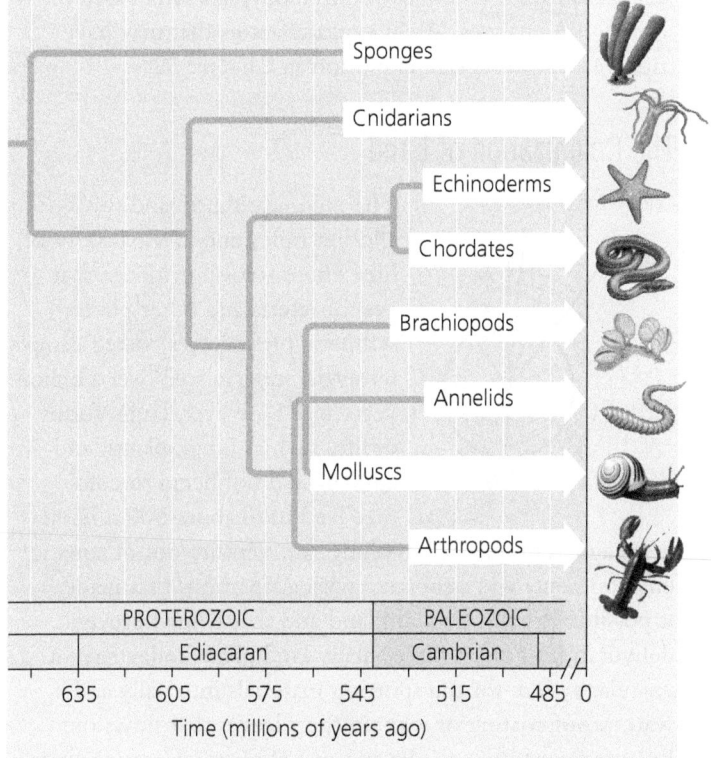

▲ Figure 25.11 **Appearance of selected animal groups.** The white bars indicate earliest appearances of these animal groups in the fossil record.

DRAW IT *Circle the branch point that represents the most recent common ancestor of chordates and annelids. What is a minimum estimate of that ancestor's age?*

Prior to the Cambrian explosion, all large animals were soft-bodied. The fossils of large pre-Cambrian animals reveal little evidence of predation. Instead, these animals appear to have been grazers (feeding on algae), suspension feeders, or scavengers, not hunters. The Cambrian explosion changed all of that. In a relatively short period of time (10 million years), predators over 1 m in length emerged that had claws and other features for capturing prey; simultaneously, new defensive adaptations, such as sharp spines and heavy body armour, appeared in their prey (see Figure 25.5).

Although the Cambrian explosion had an enormous impact on life on Earth, it is possible that many animal phyla originated long before that time. Recent DNA analyses suggest that sponges, an early-diverging animal group, had evolved by 700 million years ago; such analyses also indicate that the common ancestor of arthropods, chordates, and other animal phyla that radiated during the Cambrian explosion lived 670 million years ago. Researchers have unearthed 710-million-year-old fossils containing steroids indicative of a particular group of sponges—a finding that supports the molecular data. In contrast, the oldest fossil assigned to an extant animal phylum is that of the mollusc *Kimberella*, which lived 560 million years ago. Overall, molecular and fossil data indicate that the Cambrian explosion had a "long fuse"—at least 25 million years long based on the age of *Kimberella* fossils, and over 100 million years long based on some DNA analyses. We'll explore factors that may have triggered the Cambrian explosion in Chapter 32.

The Colonization of Land

Colonization of land

The colonization of land was another milestone in the history of life. There is fossil evidence that cyanobacteria and other photosynthetic prokaryotes coated damp terrestrial surfaces well over a billion years ago. However, larger forms of life, such as fungi, plants, and animals, did not begin to colonize land until about 500 million years ago. This gradual evolutionary venture out of aquatic environments was associated with adaptations that made it possible to reproduce on land and that helped prevent dehydration. For example, many land plants today have a vascular system for transporting materials internally and a waterproof coating of wax on their leaves that slows the loss of water to the air. Early signs of these adaptations were present 420 million years ago, at which time small plants (about 10 cm high) existed that had a vascular system but lacked true roots or leaves. By 40 million years later, plants had diversified greatly and included reeds and treelike plants with true roots and leaves.

Plants colonized land in the company of fungi. Even today, the roots of most plants are associated with fungi that aid in the absorption of water and minerals from the soil (see Chapter 31). These root fungi (or *mycorrhizae*), in turn, obtain their organic nutrients from the plants. Such mutually beneficial associations of plants and fungi are evident in some of the oldest fossilized plants, dating this relationship back to the early spread of life onto land (Figure 25.12).

Although many animal groups are now represented in terrestrial environments, the most widespread and diverse land animals are arthropods (particularly insects and spiders) and tetrapods. Arthropods were among the first animals to colonize land, roughly 450 million years ago. The earliest tetrapods found in the fossil record lived about 365 million years ago and appear to have evolved from a group of lobe-finned fishes (see Chapter 34). Recent work by Dr. Hans Larsson from McGill University (see the interview at the beginning of this Unit) has demonstrated that phenotypic plasticity—the environmentally induced variation of physical traits—in stem tetrapods may have facilitated their colonization of land. Larsson showed that, when reared in terrestrial environments, the pectoral fins of *Polyterus*, an extant fish species capable of living on land, developed biomechanical and physical differences suited for crawling. It may be that similar plastic phenotypes in stem tetrapods became heritable through *genetic assimilation*, when a phenotype is no longer dependent on environmental conditions. Tetrapods include humans, although we are late arrivals on the scene. The human lineage diverged from other primates around 6–7 million years ago, and our species originated only about 195 000 years ago. If the clock of Earth's history were rescaled to represent an hour, humans appeared less than 0.2 seconds ago.

Zone of arbuscule-containing cells

100 nm

Remy W, Taylor TN, Hass H, Kerp H./Proceedings of the National Academy of Sciences

▲ **Figure 25.12 An ancient symbiosis.** This 405-million-year-old fossil stem (cross section) documents mycorrhizae in the early land plant *Aglaophyton major*. The inset shows an enlarged view of a cell containing a branched fungal structure called an arbuscule; the fossil arbuscule resembles those seen in plant cells today.

1. The first appearance of free oxygen in the atmosphere likely triggered a massive wave of extinctions among the prokaryotes of the time. Why?

2. What evidence supports the hypothesis that mitochondria preceded plastids in the evolution of eukaryotic cells?

3. **WHAT IF?** What would a fossil record of life today look like?

For suggested answers, see Appendix A.

CONCEPT 25.4

The rise and fall of groups of organisms reflect differences in speciation and extinction rates

From its beginnings, life on Earth has seen the rise and fall of groups of organisms. Anaerobic prokaryotes originated, flourished, and then declined as the oxygen content of the atmosphere rose. Billions of years later, the first tetrapods emerged from the sea, giving rise to several major new groups of organisms. One of these, the amphibians, went on to dominate life on land for 100 million years, until other tetrapods (including dinosaurs and, later, mammals) replaced them as the dominant terrestrial vertebrates.

The rise and fall of these and other major groups of organisms have shaped the history of life. Narrowing our focus, we can also see that the rise or fall of any particular group is related to the speciation and extinction rates of its member species (Figure 25.13). Just as a population increases in size when there are more births than deaths, the rise of a group of organisms occurs when it produces more new species than are lost to extinction. The reverse occurs when a group is in decline. In the Scientific Skills Exercise, you will interpret data from the fossil record about changes in a snail species in the early Paleogene period. Such changes in the fates of groups of organisms have been influenced by large-scale processes such as plate tectonics, mass extinctions, and adaptive radiations.

Plate Tectonics

If photographs of Earth were taken from space every 10 000 years and spliced together to make a movie, it would show that the seemingly "rock solid" continents we live on move over time. Since the origin of multicellular eukaryotes roughly 1.5 billion years ago, there have been three occasions (1.1 billion, 600 million, and 250 million years ago) when most of the landmasses of Earth came together to form a supercontinent, then later broke apart. Each time they yielded a different configuration of continents. Looking into the future, some geologists have estimated that the continents will come together again and form a new supercontinent roughly 250 million years from now.

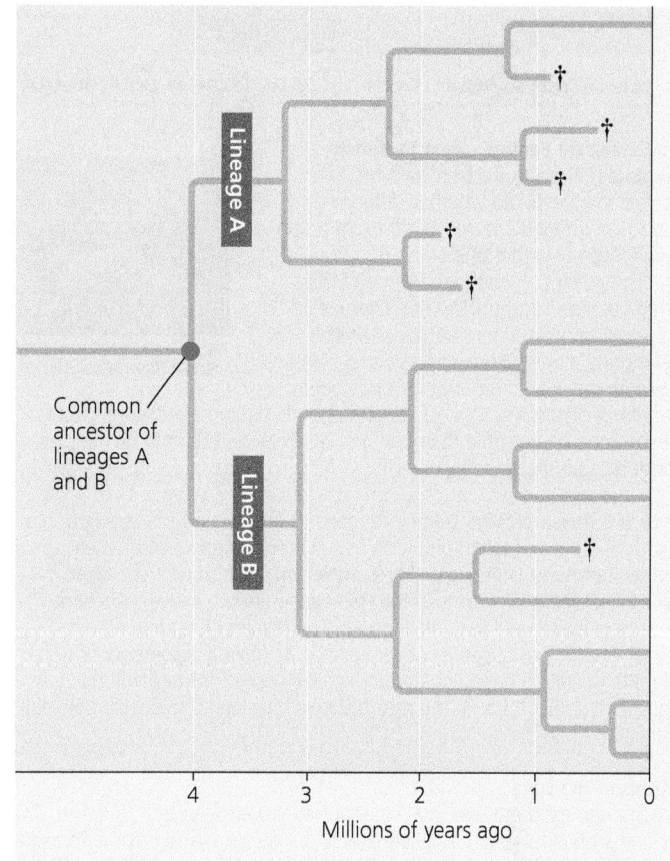

▲ Figure 25.13 **How speciation and extinction affect diversity.** The species diversity of an evolutionary lineage will increase when more new member species originate than are lost to extinction. In this hypothetical example, by 2 million years ago both lineage A and lineage B have given rise to four species, and no species have become extinct (denoted by a dagger symbol). By time 0, however, lineage A contains only one species while lineage B contains eight species.

INTERPRET THE DATA *Consider the period from 2 million years ago to time 0. For each lineage, determine how many speciation and extinction events occurred during that time.*

According to the theory of **plate tectonics**, the continents are part of great plates of Earth's crust that essentially float on the hot, underlying portion of the mantle (Figure 25.14). Movements in the mantle cause the plates to move over time in a process called *continental drift*. Geologists can measure the rate at which the plates are moving now, usually only a few centimetres per year. They can also infer the past locations of the continents using the magnetic signal recorded in rocks at the time of their formation.

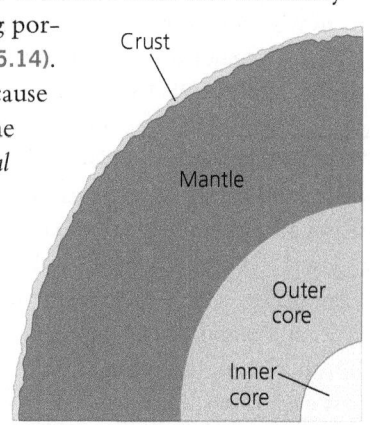

▲ Figure 25.14 **Cutaway view of Earth.** The thickness of the crust is exaggerated here.

Estimating Quantitative Data from a Graph and Developing Hypotheses

Do Ecological Factors Affect Evolutionary Rates? Researchers studied the fossil record to investigate whether differing modes of larval dispersal might explain species longevity within one taxon of marine snails, the family Volutidae. Some of the snail species had nonplanktonic larvae, developing directly into adults without a swimming stage. Other species had planktonic larvae that could swim and disperse very long distances. The adults of these planktonic species tended to have broad geographic distributions, whereas nonplanktonic species tended to be more isolated.

Biophoto Associates/Science Source

How the Research Was Done The researchers studied the stratigraphic distribution of volutes in outcrops of sedimentary rocks located along North America's Gulf coast. These rocks, which formed from 65 to 37 million years ago, early in the Paleogene period, are an excellent source of well-preserved snail fossils. The researchers were able to classify each fossil species of volute snail as having planktonic or nonplanktonic larvae based on features of the earliest formed whorls of the snail's shell. Each bar in the graph shows how long one species of snail persisted in the fossil record.

Interpret the Data

1. You can estimate quantitative data (fairly precisely) from a graph. The first step is to obtain a conversion factor by measuring along an axis that has a scale. In this case, 25 million years (my; from 65 to 40 million years ago (mya) on the *x*-axis) is represented by a distance of 7.0 cm. This yields a conversion factor (a ratio) of 25 my/7.0 cm = 3.6 my/cm. To estimate the time period represented by a horizontal bar on this graph, measure the length of that bar in centimetres and multiply that measurement by the conversion factor, 3.6 my/cm. For example, a bar that measures 1.1 cm on the graph represents a persistence time of 1.1 cm × 3.6 my/cm = 4 million years.

2. Calculate the mean (average) persistence times for species with planktonic larvae and species with nonplanktonic larvae.

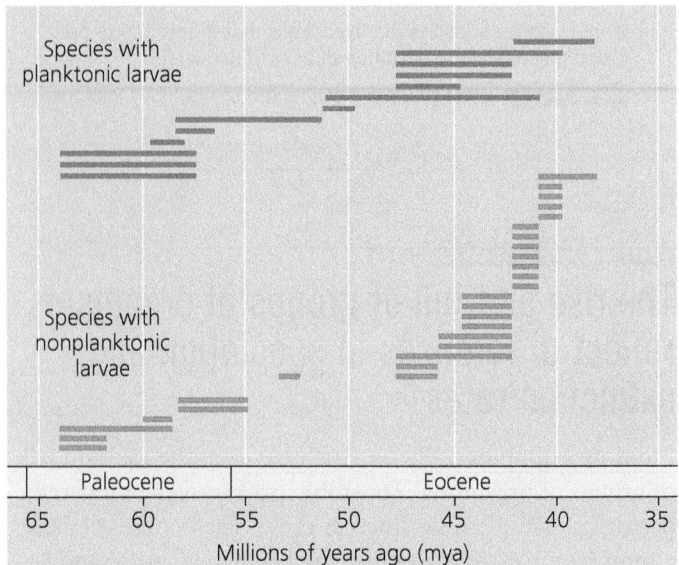

Adaptation of figure 1 from "Larval Dispersal and Species Longevity in Lower Tertiary Gastropods" by Thor A. Hansen, from *Science,* February 1978, Volume 199(4331). Copyright © 1978 by AAAS. Reprinted with permission.

3. Count the number of new species that form in each group beginning at 60 mya (the first three species in each group were present around 64 mya, the first time period sampled, so we don't know when those species first appear in the fossil record).

4. Propose a hypothesis to explain the differences in longevity of snail species with planktonic and nonplanktonic larvae.

Data from: T. A. Hansen, Larval dispersal and species longevity in Lower Tertiary gastropods, *Science* 199:885–887 (1978). Reprinted with permission from AAAS.

This method works because as a continent shifts its position over time, the direction of magnetic north recorded in its newly formed rocks also changes.

Earth's major tectonic plates are shown in **Figure 25.15**. Many important geologic processes, including the formation of mountains and islands, occur at plate boundaries. In some cases, two plates are moving away from each other, as are the North American and Eurasian plates, which are currently drifting apart at a rate of about 2 cm per year. In other cases, two plates are sliding past each other, forming regions where earthquakes are common. California's infamous San Andreas Fault is part of a border where two plates slide past each

▲ **Figure 25.15 Earth's major tectonic plates.** The arrows indicate direction of movement. The reddish orange dots represent zones of violent tectonic activity.

Source: Based on *Earthquake Information Bulletin,* December 1977, Volume 9(6), edited by Henry Spall.

other. In still other cases, two plates are colliding. Typically, oceanic plates (those found on the bottom of the ocean) are more dense than terrestrial plates. As a result, when an oceanic plate collides with a terrestrial plate, the oceanic plate usually sinks below the terrestrial plate. When two oceanic plates or two terrestrial plates collide with each other, violent upheavals occur and mountains form along the plate boundaries. One spectacular example of this occurred 45 million years ago, when the Indian plate crashed into the Eurasian plate, starting the formation of the Himalayan mountains.

Consequences of Continental Drift

Plate movements rearrange geography slowly, but their cumulative effects are dramatic. In addition to reshaping the physical features of our planet, continental drift also has a major impact on life on Earth.

One reason for its great impact on life is that continental drift alters the habitats in which organisms live. Consider the changes shown in Figure 25.16. About 250 million years ago, plate movements brought all the previously separated landmasses together into a supercontinent named **Pangaea**. Ocean basins became deeper, which lowered sea level and drained shallow coastal seas. At that time, as now, most marine species inhabited shallow waters, and the formation of Pangaea destroyed a considerable amount of that habitat. The interior of the vast continent was cold and dry, probably an even more severe environment than that of central Asia today. Overall, the formation of Pangaea had a tremendous impact on the physical environment and climate, which drove some species to extinction and provided new opportunities for groups of organisms that survived the crisis.

Organisms are also affected by the climate change that occurs when a continent changes location. The southern tip of Labrador, Canada, for example, once was located in the tropics but has moved 40° to the north over the last 200 million years. When faced with the changes in climate that such shifts in position entail, organisms adapt, move to a new location, or become extinct (this last outcome occurred for many organisms stranded on Antarctica).

Continental drift also promotes allopatric speciation on a grand scale. When supercontinents break apart, regions that once were connected become geographically isolated. As the continents drifted apart over the last 200 million years, each became a separate evolutionary arena, with lineages of plants and animals that diverged from those on other continents.

Finally, continental drift can help explain puzzles about the geographic distribution of extinct organisms, such as why fossils of the same species of Permian freshwater reptiles have been discovered in both Brazil and the West African nation of Ghana. These two parts of the world, now separated by 3000 km of ocean, were joined together when these reptiles were living. Continental drift also explains much about the current distributions of organisms,

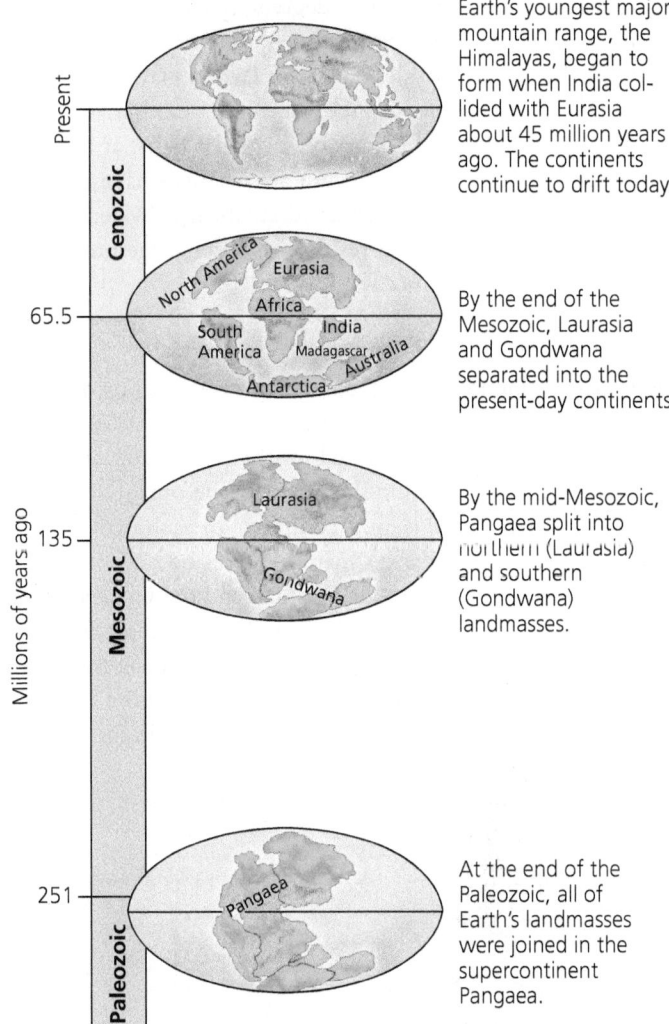

Earth's youngest major mountain range, the Himalayas, began to form when India collided with Eurasia about 45 million years ago. The continents continue to drift today.

By the end of the Mesozoic, Laurasia and Gondwana separated into the present-day continents.

By the mid-Mesozoic, Pangaea split into northern (Laurasia) and southern (Gondwana) landmasses.

At the end of the Paleozoic, all of Earth's landmasses were joined in the supercontinent Pangaea.

▲ Figure 25.16 **The history of continental drift during the Phanerozoic eon.**

such as why Australian fauna and flora contrast so sharply with those of the rest of the world. Marsupial mammals fill ecological roles in Australia analogous to those filled by eutherians (placental mammals) on other continents (see Figure 22.18). Fossil evidence suggests that marsupials originated in what is now Asia and reached Australia via South America and Antarctica while the continents were still joined. The subsequent breakup of the southern continents set Australia "afloat" like a giant raft of marsupials. In Australia, marsupials diversified, and the few eutherians that lived there became extinct; on other continents, most marsupials became extinct, and the eutherians diversified.

Mass Extinctions

The fossil record shows that the overwhelming majority of species that ever lived are now extinct. A species may become extinct for many reasons. Its habitat may have been destroyed, or its environment may have changed in a manner unfavourable to the species. For example, if ocean temperatures fall by even a few degrees, species that are otherwise well adapted may perish. Even if physical factors in the environment remain stable, biological factors may change—the origin of one species can spell doom for another.

Although extinction occurs on a regular basis, at certain times disruptive global environmental changes have caused the rate of extinction to increase dramatically. When this occurs, a **mass extinction** results, in which large numbers of species become extinct worldwide.

The "Big Five" Mass Extinction Events

Five mass extinctions are documented in the fossil record over the past 500 million years (Figure 25.17). These events are particularly well documented for the decimation of hard-bodied animals that lived in shallow seas, the organisms for which the fossil record is most complete. In each mass extinction, 50% or more of Earth's marine species became extinct.

Two mass extinctions—the Permian and the Cretaceous—have received the most attention. The Permian mass extinction, which defines the boundary between the Paleozoic and Mesozoic eras (251 million years ago), claimed about 96% of marine animal species and drastically altered life in the ocean.

Terrestrial life was also affected. For example, 8 out of 27 known orders of insects were wiped out. This mass extinction occurred in less than 200 000 years, with a majority of the extinctions occurring in just 20 000 years—an instant in the context of geologic time (Figure 25.18).

The Permian mass extinction occurred during the most extreme episode of volcanism in the past 500 million years. Geologic data indicate that 1.6 million km^2 (roughly half the size of western Europe) in Siberia was covered with lava hundreds of metres thick. Recently, Stephen Grasby and colleagues at the University of Calgary provided the first direct evidence of coal combustion correlated with the end-Permian mass extinction through analysis of volcanic ash detected in Permian-aged rocks in the Canadian arctic.

Besides spewing enormous amounts of lava and ash, the eruptions are thought to have produced enough carbon dioxide to warm the global climate by an estimated 6°C, harming many temperature-sensitive species. The rise in atmospheric CO_2 levels would also have led to ocean acidification, thereby reducing the availability of calcium carbonate, which is required by reef-building corals and many shell-building species. The explosions would also have added nutrients such as phosphorous to ecosystems, stimulating the growth of microorganisms. Upon their deaths, these microorganisms would have provided food for bacterial decomposers. Bacteria use oxygen as they decompose the bodies of dead organisms, thus causing oxygen concentrations to drop. This would have harmed oxygen-breathers and promoted the growth of anaerobic bacteria that emit a poisonous metabolic by-product, hydrogen sulphide (H_2S) gas. Overall, the volcanic eruptions appear to have triggered a series of catastrophic events that together resulted in the Permian mass extinction.

The Capitanian extinction 260 mya, 12 million years before the Permian extinction, has long been recognized by paleontologists as an event involving a significant loss of biodiversity in equatorial regions only. However, in 2015, an international team of scientists, including Stephen Grasby, uncovered a corresponding loss of biodiversity within northern boreal regions. This evidence suggests that the Capitanian extinction was pandemic and should be considered a mass extinction event. However, the inclusion of this event on the list of mass extinctions remains a topic of controversy and heated debate.

▲ Figure 25.17 **Mass extinction and the diversity of life.** The five generally recognized mass extinction events, indicated by red arrows, represent peaks in the extinction rate of marine animal families (red line and left vertical axis). These mass extinctions interrupted the overall increase in the number of marine animal families over time (blue line and right vertical axis).

Source: Adaptation of figures 1 and 2 from "Mass Extinctions in the Marine Fossil Record" by David M. Raup and J. John Sepkoski, Jr., from *Science*, March 1982, Volume 215(4539). Figure also based on: Figure 1 from "A Kinetic Model of Phanerozoic Taxonomic Diversity. III. Post-Paleozoic Families and Mass Extinctions" by J. John Sepkoski, Jr., from *Paleobiology*, Volume 10(2); and Figures 7.3a and 7.6 from *Evolution*, by Douglas J. Futuyma. Sinauer Associates, Inc., 2006.

INTERPRET THE DATA *Ninety-six percent of marine animal species became extinct in the Permian mass extinction. Explain why the blue curve shows only a 50% drop at that time.*

Figure 25.18 ▼ Impact

Pinpointing the End-Permian Mass Extinction

In 2011, an international team of scientists, including Charles Henderson from the University of Calgary, determined a precise date for the end-Permian mass extinction. Through the analysis of radioactive decay of uranium in zircon crystals (a mineral useful in radiometric dating) in volcanic ash beds in China, along with fossil counts of 1485 species, the researchers determined that the end-Permian mass extinction peaked 252.28 million years ago, during a period of less than 200 000 years (a blink of the eye in the geologic perspective). Dr. Henderson's role involved identifying features of conodonts (an extinct eel-like animal) and placing those features (and thus the fossils) in an extinction timeline. The research also showed that land animals and marine animals went extinct at the same time.

Charles Henderson

Why It Matters Prior to this study, scientists had only an approximate date for when the end-Permain mass extinction occurred. The knowledge of an exact date and some information on the progression of the extinction makes it easier to correctly identify the cause. The researchers determined that the extinction date is linked with an immense release of carbon dioxide and/or methane into the atmosphere, likely due to massive volcanic eruptions and widespread forest fires.

Further Reading S-Z Shen et al., Calibrating the end-Permian mass extinction, *Science* 334:1367–1372 (2011).

MAKE CONNECTIONS *Based on what you learned in Chapter 3, why would land and marine animals have gone extinct at the same time, as is indicated by this research?*

The Cretaceous mass extinction occurred about 65.5 million years ago and marks the boundary between the Mesozoic and Cenozoic eras. This event extinguished more than half of all marine species and eliminated many families of terrestrial plants and animals, including all dinosaurs (except birds, which are members of the same group; see Chapter 34). One clue to a possible cause of the Cretaceous mass extinction is a thin layer of clay enriched in iridium that separates sediments from the Mesozoic and Cenozoic eras. Iridium is an element that is very rare on Earth but common in many of the meteorites and other extraterrestrial objects that occasionally fall to Earth. Walter Alvarez and the late Luis Alvarez, of the University of California, Berkeley, and their colleagues proposed that this clay is fallout from a huge cloud of debris that billowed into the atmosphere when an asteroid or large comet collided with Earth. This cloud would have blocked sunlight and severely disturbed the global climate for several months.

Is there evidence of such an asteroid or comet? Research has focused on the Chicxulub crater, a 65-million-year-old scar beneath sediments off the Yucatán coast of Mexico (Figure 25.19). The impact, however, was not the only source of dust and debris blanketing the Earth. Paul Renne, also at UC Berkeley, demonstrated that the asteroid collision coincides with, and may have caused, an increase in volcanic activity around the globe. In India, where the largest known changes occurred, the eruption rate doubled, spewing tonnes of ash and CO_2 into the atmosphere and augmenting the effects of the impact. Moreover, the increased volcanism persisted for 500 000 years into the Triassic, prolonging the effects on the climate and delaying the recovery of biodiversity.

Is a Sixth Mass Extinction Under Way?

As we will explore in Chapter 56, human actions, such as habitat destruction, are modifying the global environment to such an extent that many species are threatened with extinction. Moreover, global climate change and the accompanying rise in temperatures are impacting species in nearly all habitats. More than a thousand species have become extinct in the last 400 years. Scientists estimate that this rate is 100 to 1000 times the typical background rate seen in the fossil record. Is a sixth mass extinction now in progress?

This question is difficult to answer, in part because it is hard to document the total number of extinctions occurring today. Tropical rain forests, for example, harbour many undiscovered species. As a result, destroying tropical forest may drive species to extinction before we even learn of their existence. Such uncertainties make it hard to assess the full extent of the current extinction crisis. Even so, it is clear that losses to date have not reached those of the "big five" mass extinctions, in which large percentages of Earth's species became extinct. This does not in any way discount the seriousness of today's situation. Many biologists have made scientific predictions of extinction rates due to climate change with some as high as 54% in the next 100 years—large enough to be considered a mass extinction event. Monitoring programs show that many species are declining at an alarming rate, and studies on polar bears, pine trees, and other species suggest that climate change may hasten some of these declines. Indeed, the fossil record indicates that over the last 500 million years, extinction

▼ **Figure 25.19 Trauma for Earth and Its Cretaceous life.** Beneath the Caribbean Sea, the 65-million-year-old Chicxulub impact crater measures 180 km across. The horseshoe shape of the crater and the pattern of debris in sedimentary rocks indicate that an asteroid or comet struck at a low angle from the southeast. This artist's interpretation represents the impact and its immediate effect: a cloud of hot vapour and debris that could have killed many of the plants and animals in North America within hours.

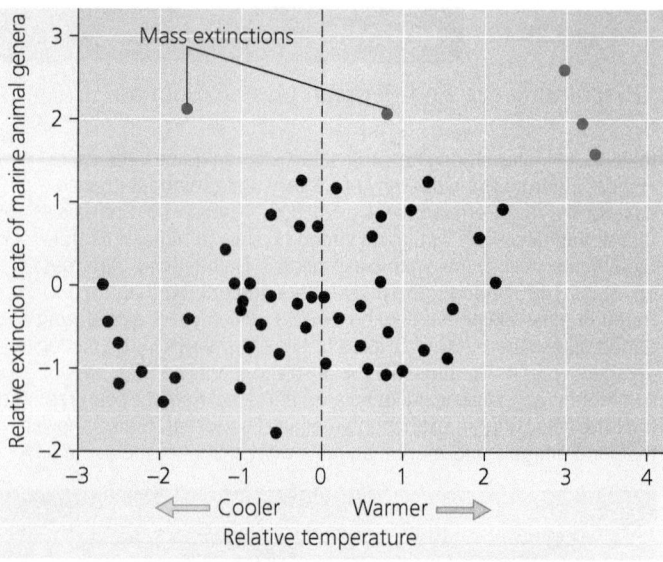

▲ **Figure 25.20 Fossil extinctions and temperature.** Extinction rates increased when global temperatures were high. Temperatures were estimated using ratios of oxygen isotopes and converted to an index in which 0 is the overall average temperature.

Source: Adaptation of Figure 3b from "A Long-Term Association between Global Temperature and Biodiversity, Origination and Extinction in the Fossil Record" by Peter J. Mayhew et al., from *Proceedings of the Royal Society B: Biological Sciences,* January 2008, Volume 275(1630): 47–53, The Royal Society. © Jane B. Reece.

rates have tended to increase when global temperatures were high **(Figure 25.20)**. Overall, present-day and fossil evidence both suggest that unless dramatic actions are taken, a sixth, human-caused mass extinction is likely to occur within the next few centuries or millennia.

Consequences of Mass Extinctions

Mass extinctions have significant and long-term effects. By eliminating large numbers of species, a mass extinction can reduce a thriving and complex ecological community to a pale shadow of its former self. And once an evolutionary lineage disappears, it cannot reappear. The course of evolution is changed forever. Consider what would have happened if the early primates living 66 million years ago had died out in the Cretaceous mass extinction. Humans would not exist, and life on Earth would differ greatly from what it is today.

The fossil record shows that it typically takes 5–10 million years for the diversity of life to recover to previous levels after a mass extinction. In some cases, it has taken much longer than that: It took about 100 million years for the number of marine families to recover after the Permian mass extinction (see Figure 25.17). These data have sobering implications. If

current trends continue and a sixth mass extinction occurs, it will take millions of years for life on Earth to recover.

Mass extinctions can also alter ecological communities by changing the types of organisms found in them. For example, after the Permian and Cretaceous mass extinctions, the percentage of marine organisms that were predators increased substantially **(Figure 25.21)**. A rise in the number of predator species can increase both the pressures faced by prey and the competition among predators for food. In addition, mass extinctions can curtail lineages with highly advantageous features. For example, in the late Triassic, a group of gastropods (snails and their relatives) arose that could drill through the shells of bivalves (such as clams) and feed on the animals inside. Although shell drilling provided access to a new and abundant source of food, this newly formed group was wiped out during the mass extinction at the end of the Triassic (about 200 million years ago). Another 120 million years passed before another group of gastropods (the oyster drills) exhibited the ability to drill through shells. As their predecessors might have done if they had not originated at an unfortunate time, oyster drills have since diversified into many new species. Finally, by eliminating so many species, mass extinctions can pave the way for adaptive radiations, in which new groups of organisms proliferate.

Adaptive Radiations

The fossil record indicates that the diversity of life has increased over the past 250 million years (see the blue line in Figure 25.17). This increase has been fuelled by **adaptive radiations**, periods of evolutionary change in which groups

The percentage of marine genera that were predators remained close to 15% for 200 million years.

After the Permian mass extinction, the percentage of predators rose sharply and then stabilized near 22% for 150 million years—until it was disrupted again by the Cretaceous mass extinction.

▲ Figure 25.21 **Mass extinctions and ecology.** The Permian and Cretaceous mass extinctions (indicated by red arrows) altered the ecology of the oceans by increasing the percentage of marine genera that were predators.

Source: Adaptation of Figure 3 from "Anatomical and Ecological Constraints on Phanerozoic Animal Diversity in the Marine Realm" by Richard K. Bambach et al., from *PNAS,* May 2002, Volume 99(10). Copyright © 2002 by National Academy of Sciences. Reprinted with permission.

of organisms form many new species whose adaptations allow them to fill different ecological roles, or niches, in their communities. Large-scale adaptive radiations occurred after each of the big five mass extinctions, when survivors became adapted to the many vacant ecological niches. Adaptive radiations have also occurred in groups of organisms that possessed major evolutionary innovations, such as seeds or armoured body coverings, or that colonized regions in which they faced little competition from other species.

Worldwide Adaptive Radiations

Fossil evidence indicates that mammals underwent a dramatic adaptive radiation after the extinction of terrestrial dinosaurs 65.5 million years ago (Figure 25.22). Although mammals originated about 180 million years ago, the mammal fossils older than 65.5 million years are mostly small and not morphologically diverse.

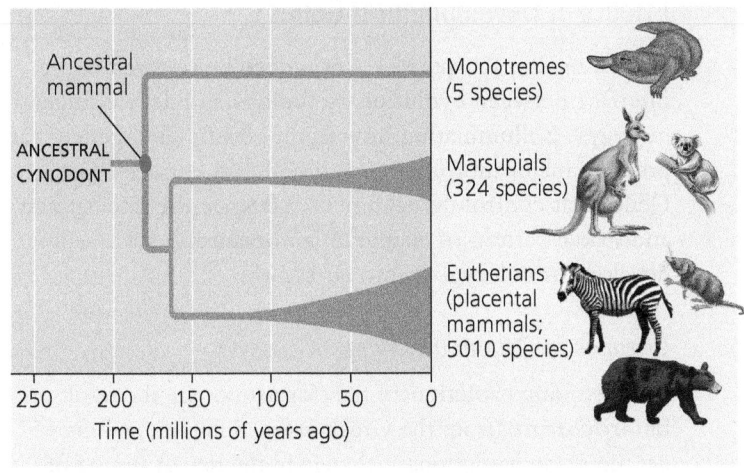

▲ Figure 25.22 **Adaptive radiation of mammals.**

Many species appear to have been nocturnal based on their large eye sockets, similar to those in living nocturnal mammals. A few early mammals were intermediate in size, such as *Repenomamus giganticus*, a 1-m-long predator that lived 130 million years ago—but none approached the size of many dinosaurs. Early mammals may have been restricted in size and diversity because they were eaten or outcompeted by the larger and more diverse dinosaurs. With the disappearance of the dinosaurs (except for birds), mammals expanded greatly in both diversity and size, filling the ecological roles once occupied by terrestrial dinosaurs.

The history of life has also been greatly altered by radiations in which groups of organisms increased in diversity as they came to play entirely new ecological roles in their communities. Examples include the rise of photosynthetic prokaryotes, the evolution of large predators in the Cambrian explosion, and the radiations following the colonization of land by plants, insects, and tetrapods. Each of these last three radiations was associated with major evolutionary innovations that facilitated life on land. The radiation of land plants, for example, was associated with key adaptations, such as stems that support plants against gravity and a waxy coat that protects leaves from water loss. Finally, organisms that arise in an adaptive radiation can serve as a new source of food for still other organisms. In fact, the diversification of land plants stimulated a series of adaptive radiations in insects that ate or pollinated plants, one reason that insects are the most diverse group of animals on Earth today.

Regional Adaptive Radiations

Striking adaptive radiations have also occurred over more limited geographic areas. Such radiations can be initiated when a few organisms make their way to a new, often distant location in which they face relatively little competition from other organisms. The Hawaiian archipelago is one of the world's great showcases of this type of adaptive radiation (Figure 25.23). Located about 3500 km from the nearest continent, the volcanic islands are progressively older as one follows the chain toward the northwest; the youngest island, Hawaii, is less than a million years old and still has active volcanoes. Each island was born "naked" and was gradually populated by stray organisms that rode the ocean currents and winds either from far-distant land areas or from older islands of the archipelago itself. The physical diversity of each island, including immense variation in elevation and rainfall, provides many opportunities for evolutionary divergence by natural selection. Multiple invasions followed by speciation events have ignited an explosion of adaptive radiation in Hawaii. Most of the thousands of species that inhabit the islands are found nowhere else on Earth.

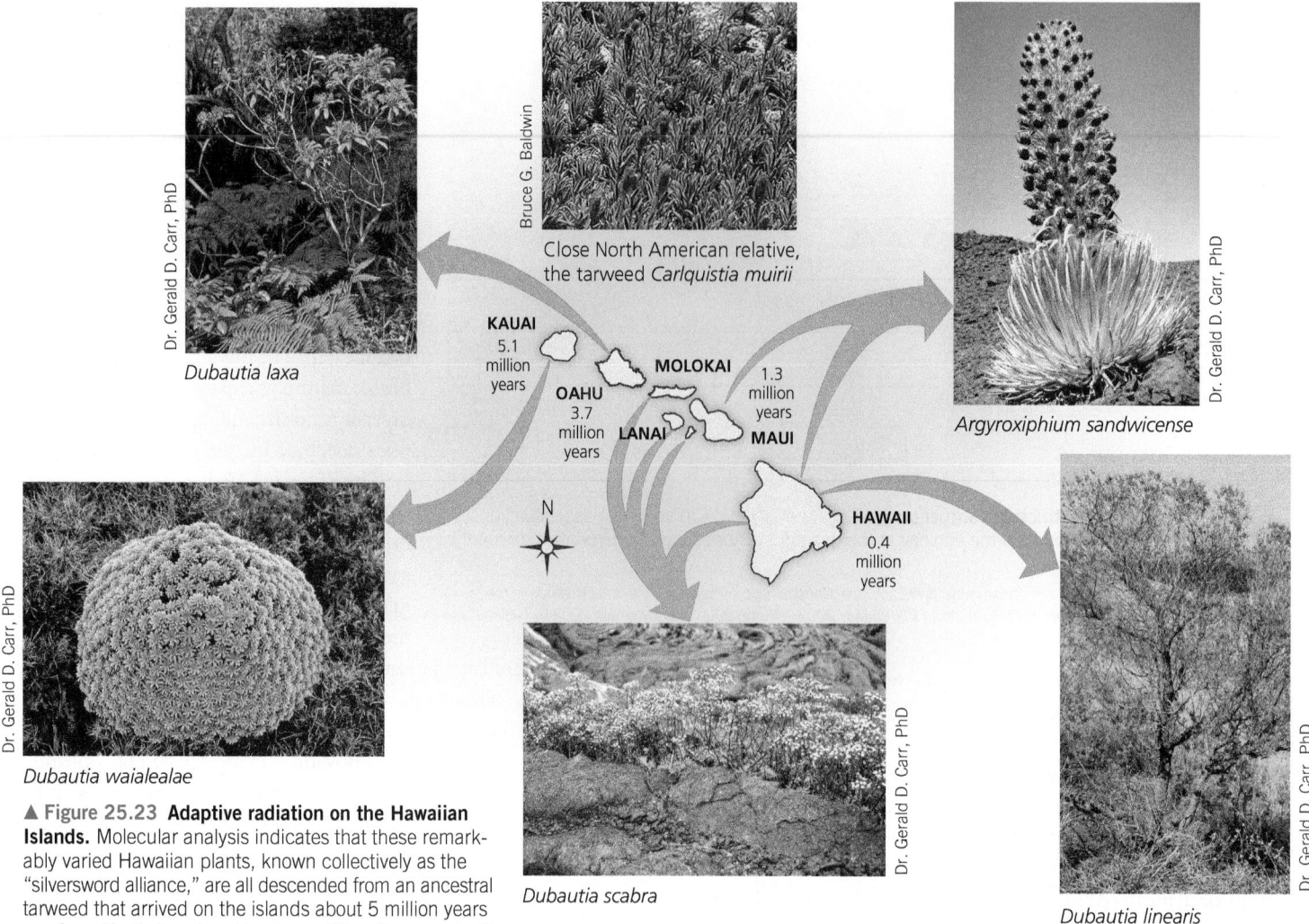

Dr. Gerald D. Carr, PhD

Dubautia laxa

Bruce G. Baldwin

Close North American relative, the tarweed *Carlquistia muirii*

KAUAI
5.1 million years

OAHU
3.7 million years

MOLOKAI

LANAI

MAUI
1.3 million years

N

HAWAII
0.4 million years

Dr. Gerald D. Carr, PhD

Argyroxiphium sandwicense

Dr. Gerald D. Carr, PhD

Dubautia waialealae

▲ **Figure 25.23 Adaptive radiation on the Hawaiian Islands.** Molecular analysis indicates that these remarkably varied Hawaiian plants, known collectively as the "silversword alliance," are all descended from an ancestral tarweed that arrived on the islands about 5 million years ago from North America. Members of the silversword alliance have since spread into different habitats and formed new species with strikingly different adaptations.

Dr. Gerald D. Carr, PhD

Dubautia scabra

Dr. Gerald D. Carr, PhD

Dubautia linearis

CONCEPT CHECK 25.4

1. Explain the consequences of continental drift for life on Earth.
2. What factors promote adaptive radiations?
3. **WHAT IF?** If a mass extinction were caused by a sudden catastrophic event, would dates of the last observation in the fossil record of species lost in the extinction differ for rare versus common species? Explain.

For suggested answers, see Appendix A.

CONCEPT 25.5

Major changes in body form can result from changes in the sequences and regulation of developmental genes

The fossil record tells us what the great changes in the history of life have been and when they occurred. Moreover, an understanding of plate tectonics, mass extinction, and adaptive radiation provides a picture of how those changes came about. But we can also seek to understand the intrinsic biological mechanisms that underlie changes seen in the fossil record. For this, we turn to genetic mechanisms of change, paying particular attention to genes that influence development.

Effects of Developmental Genes

As you read in Chapter 21, "evo-devo"—research at the interface between evolutionary biology and developmental biology—is illuminating how slight genetic divergences can produce major morphological differences between species. Genes that control development influence the rate, timing, and spatial pattern of change in an organism's form as it develops from a zygote into an adult.

Changes in Rate and Timing

Many striking evolutionary transformations are the result of **heterochrony** (from the Greek *hetero*, different, and *chronos*, time), an evolutionary change in the rate or timing of developmental events. For example, an organism's shape depends in part on the relative growth rates of different body parts during development. Changes to these rates can alter the adult form substantially, as seen in the contrasting shapes of human and chimpanzee skulls **(Figure 25.24)**. Other examples of the dramatic evolutionary effects of heterochrony include how increased growth rates of finger bones yielded the skeletal structure of wings in bats (see Figure 22.15) and how slowed growth of leg and pelvic bones led to the reduction and eventual loss of hind limbs in whales (see Figure 22.20).

Heterochrony can also alter the timing of reproductive development relative to the development of nonreproductive organs. If reproductive organ development accelerates compared to other organs, the sexually mature stage of a species may retain body features that were juvenile structures in an ancestral species, a condition called **paedomorphosis** (from the Greek *paedos*, of a child, and *morphosis*, formation). For example, most salamander species have aquatic larvae that undergo metamorphosis in becoming adults. But some species grow to adult size and

Chimpanzee infant   Chimpanzee adult

Jean Kern

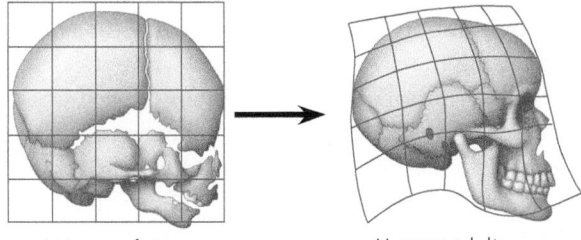

Chimpanzee fetus   Chimpanzee adult

Human fetus   Human adult

▲ **Figure 25.24 Relative skull growth rates.** In the human evolutionary lineage, mutations that slowed the growth of the jaw relative to other parts of the skull produced an adult whose head resembles that of a chimpanzee infant.

become sexually mature while retaining gills and other larval features **(Figure 25.25)**. Such an evolutionary alteration of developmental timing can produce animals that appear very different from their ancestors, even though the overall genetic change may be small. Indeed, recent evidence indicates that a change at a single locus was probably sufficient to bring about paedomorphosis in the axolotl salamander, although other genes may have contributed as well.

Changes in Spatial Pattern

Substantial evolutionary changes can also result from alterations in genes that control the placement and spatial organization of body parts. For example, master regulatory genes called **homeotic genes** (see Figure 18.20 and 21.19) determine such basic features as where a pair of wings and a pair of legs will develop on a bird or how a plant's flower parts are arranged.

The products of one class of homeotic genes, the *Hox* genes, provide positional information in an animal embryo. This information prompts cells to develop into structures appropriate for a particular location. Changes in *Hox* genes or in how they are expressed can have a profound impact on morphology. For example, among crustaceans, a change in the location where two *Hox* genes (*Ubx* and *Scr*) are expressed correlates with the conversion of a swimming appendage to a feeding appendage. Similarly, when comparing plant species, changes to the expression of homeotic genes known as *MADS-box* genes can produce flowers that differ dramatically in form (see Chapter 35).

The Evolution of Development

The 565-million-year-old fossils of Ediacaran animals in Figure 25.5 suggest that a set of genes sufficient to produce

Gills

Juniors Bildarchiv GmbH/Alamy

▲ **Figure 25.25 Paedomorphosis.** The adults of some species retain features that were juvenile in ancestors. This salamander is an axolotl, an aquatic species that grows to full size, becomes sexually mature, and reproduces while retaining certain larval (tadpole) characteristics, including gills.

complex animals existed at least 30 million years *before* the Cambrian explosion. If such genes have existed for so long, how can we explain the astonishing increases in diversity seen during and since the Cambrian explosion?

Adaptive evolution by natural selection provides one answer to this question. As we've seen throughout this unit, by sorting among differences in the sequences of protein-encoding genes, selection can improve adaptations rapidly. In addition, new genes (created by gene duplication events) can take on a wide range of new metabolic and structural functions. Thus, adaptive evolution of both new and existing genes may have played a key role in shaping the great diversity of life.

Examples in the previous section suggest that developmental genes may play a critical role. Next we'll examine how new morphological forms arise from changes in the nucleotide sequences or regulation of developmental genes.

Changes in Genes

New developmental genes arising after gene duplication events very likely facilitated the origin of novel morphological forms. But since other genetic changes also may have occurred at such times, it can be difficult to establish causal links between genetic and morphological changes that occurred in the past.

This difficulty was sidestepped in a recent study of developmental changes associated with the divergence of six-legged insects from crustacean-like ancestors that had more than six legs. In insects, such as *Drosophila*, the *Ubx* gene is expressed in the abdomen, while in crustaceans, such as *Artemia*, it is expressed in the main trunk of the body (**Figure 25.26**). When expressed, the *Ubx* gene

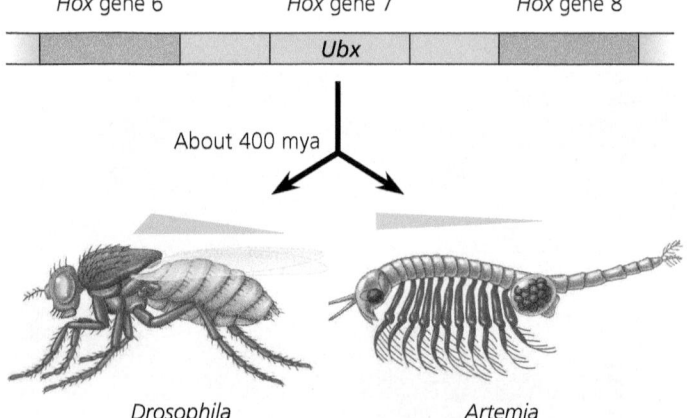

| Hox gene 6 | Hox gene 7 | Hox gene 8 |

Ubx

About 400 mya

Drosophila   Artemia

▲ Figure 25.26 **Origin of the insect body plan.** Expression of the *Hox* gene *Ubx* suppresses the formation of legs in fruit flies (*Drosophila*) but not in brine shrimp (*Artemia*), thus helping to build the insect body plan. Fruit fly and brine shrimp *Hox* genes have evolved independently for 400 million years. The green triangles indicate the relative amounts of *Ubx* expression in different body regions.

Source: Adaptation of Figure 1a from "Hox Protein Mutation and Macroevolution of the Insect Body Plan" by Matthew Ronshaugen et al., from c. Copyright © 2002 by Macmillan Publishers Ltd. Reprinted with permission.

suppresses leg formation in insects but not in crustaceans. To examine the workings of this gene, researchers cloned the *Ubx* gene from *Drosophila* and *Artemia*. Next, they genetically engineered fruit fly embryos to express either the *Drosophila Ubx* gene or the *Artemia Ubx* gene throughout their bodies. The *Drosophila* gene suppressed 100% of the limbs in the embryos, as expected, whereas the *Artemia* gene suppressed only 15%.

The researchers then sought to uncover key steps involved in the evolutionary transition from a crustacean *Ubx* gene to an insect *Ubx* gene. Their approach was to identify mutations that would cause the *Artemia Ubx* gene to suppress leg formation, thus making the crustacean gene act more like an insect *Ubx* gene. To do this, they constructed a series of "hybrid" *Ubx* genes, each of which contained known segments of the *Drosophila Ubx* gene and known segments of the *Artemia Ubx* gene. By inserting these hybrid genes into fruit fly embryos (one hybrid gene per embryo) and observing their effects on leg development, the researchers were able to pinpoint the exact amino acid changes responsible for the suppression of additional limbs in insects. In so doing, this study provided evidence linking a particular change in the nucleotide sequence of a developmental gene to a major evolutionary change: the origin of the six-legged insect body plan.

Changes in Gene Regulation

Changes in the nucleotide sequence or regulation of developmental genes can result in morphological changes that harm the organism (see Chapter 18). Moreover, a change in the nucleotide sequence of a gene may affect its function wherever the gene is expressed. In contrast, changes in the regulation of gene expression can be limited to a single cell type (see Chapter 18). Thus, a change in the regulation of a developmental gene may have fewer harmful side effects than a change to the sequence of the gene. This line of reasoning has prompted researchers to suggest that changes in the form of organisms may often be caused by mutations that affect the regulation of developmental genes—not their sequences.

This idea is supported by studies in a variety of species, including threespine stickleback fish. These fish live in the open ocean and in shallow, coastal waters. In western Canada, they also live in lakes formed when the coastline receded during the past 12 000 years. Marine stickleback fish have a pair of spines on their ventral (lower) surface, which deter some predators. These spines are often reduced or absent in stickleback fish living in lakes that lack predatory fishes and that are also low in calcium. Spines may have been lost because they are not advantageous in the absence of predators, and the limited calcium is needed for purposes other than constructing spines.

At the genetic level, the developmental gene, *Pitx1*, was known to influence whether stickleback fish have ventral spines. Was the reduction of spines in some lake populations due to changes in the *Pitx1* gene or to changes in how the gene is expressed (Figure 25.27)? The researchers' results indicate that the regulation of gene expression has changed, not the DNA sequence. Furthermore, lake stickleback fish do express the *Pitx1* gene in tissues not related to the production of spines (for example, the mouth),

illustrating how morphological change can be caused by altering the expression of a developmental gene in some parts of the body but not others. In a 2010 follow-up study, researchers showed that changes to the *Pel* enhancer, a noncoding DNA region that affects expression of the *Pitx1* gene, resulted in the reduction of ventral spines in lake sticklebacks.

▼ Figure 25.27 | **Inquiry**

What causes the loss of spines in lake stickleback fish?

Experiment Marine populations of the threespine stickleback fish (*Gasterosteus aculeatus*) have a set of protective spines on their lower (ventral) surface; however, these spines have been lost or reduced in some lake populations of this fish. Working at Stanford University, Michael Shapiro, David Kingsley, and colleagues performed genetic crosses and found that most of the reduction in spine size resulted from the effects of a single developmental gene, *Pitx1*. The researchers then tested two hypotheses about how *Pitx1* causes this morphological change.

Hypothesis A: A change in the DNA sequence of *Pitx1* had caused spine reduction in lake populations. To test this idea, the team used DNA sequencing to compare the coding sequence of the *Pitx1* gene between marine and lake stickleback populations.

Hypothesis B: A change in the regulation of the expression of *Pitx1* had caused spine reduction. To test this idea, the researchers monitored where in the developing embryo the *Pitx1* gene was expressed. They conducted whole-body *in situ* hybridization experiments (see Chapter 20) using *Pitx1* DNA as a probe to detect *Pitx1* mRNA in the fish.

Threespine stickleback
(*Gasterosteus aculeatus*)

David Horsley

Results

| **Test of Hypothesis A:** Are there differences in the coding sequence of the *Pitx1* gene in marine and lake stickleback fish? | **Result: No** → | The 283 amino acids of the *Pitx1* protein are identical in marine and lake stickleback populations. |

| **Test of Hypothesis B:** Are there any differences in the regulation of expression of *Pitx1*? | **Result: Yes** → | Red arrows (→) indicate regions of *Pitx1* gene expression in the photographs below. *Pitx1* is expressed in the ventral spine and mouth regions of developing marine stickleback fish but only in the mouth region of developing lake stickleback fish. |

Marine stickleback embryo **Lake stickleback embryo**

Close-up of mouth

Close-up of ventral surface

Mike Shapiro

Conclusion The loss or reduction of ventral spines in lake populations of threespine stickleback fish appears to have resulted primarily from a change in the regulation of *Pitx1* gene expression, not from a change in the gene's sequence.

Source: Based on M. D. Shapiro et al., Genetic and developmental basis of evolutionary pelvic reduction in three-spine sticklebacks, *Nature* 428:717–723 (2004). © Jane B. Reece.

WHAT IF? *Describe the set of results that would have led researchers to the conclusion that a change in the coding sequence of the* Pitx1 *gene was more important than a change in regulation of gene expression.*

1. How can heterochrony cause the evolution of different body forms?

2. Why is it likely that *Hox* genes have played a major role in the evolution of novel morphological forms?

3. **MAKE CONNECTIONS** Given that changes in morphology are often caused by changes in the regulation of gene expression, predict whether noncoding DNA is likely to be affected by natural selection. See Concept 18.3 to review noncoding DNA and regulation of gene expression.

For suggested answers, see Appendix A.

CONCEPT 25.6

Evolution is not goal oriented

What does our study of macroevolution tell us about how evolution works? One lesson is that, throughout the history of life, the origin of new species has been affected by both the small-scale factors described in Chapter 23 (such as natural selection operating in populations) and the large-scale factors described here (such as continental drift promoting bursts of speciation throughout the globe). Moreover, to paraphrase the Nobel Prize–winning geneticist François Jacob, evolution is like tinkering—a process in which new forms arise by the slight modification of existing developmental genes. Over time, such tinkering has led to three key features of the natural world described in Chapter 22: the striking ways in which organisms are suited for life in their environments; the many shared characteristics of life; and the rich diversity of life.

Evolutionary Novelties

François Jacob's view of evolution harkens back to Darwin's concept of descent with modification. As new species form, novel and complex structures can arise as gradual modifications of ancestral structures. In many cases, complex structures have evolved in increments from simpler versions that performed the same basic function. For example, consider the human eye, an intricate organ constructed from numerous parts that work together in forming an image and transmitting it to the brain. How could the human eye have evolved in gradual increments? Some argue that if the eye needs all of its components to function, a partial eye could not have been of use to our ancestors.

The flaw in this argument, as Darwin himself noted, lies in the assumption that only complicated eyes are useful. In fact, many animals depend on eyes that are far less complex than our own. The simplest eyes that we know of are patches of light-sensitive photoreceptor cells. These simple eyes appear to have had a single evolutionary origin and are now found in a variety of animals, including small molluscs called limpets. Such eyes have no equipment for focusing images, but they do enable the animal to distinguish light from dark. Limpets cling more tightly to their rock when a shadow falls on them, a behavioural adaptation that reduces the risk of being eaten (Figure 25.28).

▲ Figure 25.28 Limpets (*Patella vulgata*), molluscs that can sense light and dark with a simple patch of photoreceptor cells.

Limpets have had a long evolutionary history; we can conclude that their "simple" eyes are quite adequate to support their survival and reproduction.

In the animal kingdom, complex eyes have evolved independently from such basic structures many times (Figure 25.29). Some molluscs, such as squids and octopuses, have eyes as complex as those of humans and other vertebrates. Although complex mollusc eyes evolved independently of vertebrate eyes, both evolved from a simple cluster of photoreceptor cells present in a common ancestor. In each case, the complex eye evolved through a series of incremental modifications that benefitted the eyes' owners at every stage. Evidence of their independent evolution may also be found in their structure: Vertebrate eyes detect light at the back layer of the retina and conduct nerve impulses toward the front, while complex mollusc eyes do the reverse.

Throughout their evolutionary history, eyes retained their basic function of vision. But evolutionary novelties can also arise when structures that originally played one role gradually acquire a different one. For example, as cynodonts gave rise to early mammals, bones that formerly comprised the jaw hinge (the articular and quadrate; see Figure 25.7) were incorporated into the ear region of mammals, where they eventually took on a new function: the transmission of sound (see Chapter 34). Structures that evolve in one context but become co-opted for another function are sometimes called *exaptations* to distinguish them from the adaptive origin of the original structure. Note that the concept of exaptation does not imply that a structure somehow evolves in anticipation of future use. Natural selection cannot predict the future; it can only improve a structure in the context of its *current* utility. Novel features, such as the new jaw hinge and ear bones of early mammals, can arise gradually via a series of intermediate stages, each of which has some function in the organism's current context.

Sinclair Stammers/Science Source

▼ Figure 25.29 **A range of eye complexity among molluscs.**

(a) Patch of pigmented cells

The limpet *Patella* has a simple patch of photoreceptors.

(b) Eyecup

The slit shell mollusc *Pleurotomaria* has an eyecup.

(c) Pinhole camera-type eye

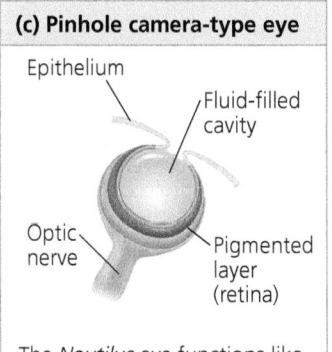

The *Nautilus* eye functions like a pinhole camera (an early type of camera lacking a lens).

(d) Eye with primitive lens

The marine snail *Murex* has a primitive lens consisting of a mass of crystal-like cells. The cornea is a transparent region of tissue that protects the eye and helps focus light.

(e) Complex camera lens-type eye

The squid *Loligo* has a complex eye with features (cornea, lens, and retina) similar to those of vertebrate eyes. However, the squid eye evolved independently from vertebrate eyes.

Source: Adaptations of figure 3-1(a–d, f) from *Evolution*, 3rd Edition, by Monroe W. Strickberger. Copyright © 2005 by Jones & Bartlett Learning, Burlington, MA. Adapted with permission.

Evolutionary Trends

What else can we learn from patterns of macroevolution? Consider evolutionary "trends" observed in the fossil record. For instance, some evolutionary lineages exhibit a trend toward larger or smaller body size. An example is the evolution of the present-day horse (genus *Equus*), a descendant of the 55-million-year-old *Hyracotherium* (**Figure 25.30**). About the size of a large dog, *Hyracotherium* had four toes on its front feet, three toes on its hind feet, and teeth adapted for browsing on bushes and trees. In comparison, present-day horses are larger, have only one toe on each foot, and possess teeth modified for grazing on grasses.

Extracting a single evolutionary progression from the fossil record can be misleading, however; it is like describing a bush as growing toward a single point by tracing only the branches that lead to that twig. For example, by selecting certain species from the available fossils, it is possible to arrange a succession of animals intermediate between *Hyracotherium* and living horses that shows a trend toward large, single-toed species (follow the yellow highlighting in Figure 25.30). However, if we consider *all* fossil horses known today, this apparent trend vanishes. The genus *Equus* did not evolve in a straight line; it is the only surviving twig of an evolutionary tree that is so branched that it is more like a bush. *Equus* actually descended through a series of speciation episodes that included several adaptive radiations, not all of which led to large, one-toed, grazing horses. In fact, phylogenetic analyses suggest that all lineages that include grazers are closely related to *Parahippus*; the many other horse lineages, all of which are now extinct, remained multi-toed browsers for 35 million years.

Branching evolution *can* result in a real evolutionary trend even if some species counter the trend. One model of long-term trends proposed by Steven Stanley, of Johns Hopkins University, views species as analogous to individuals: Speciation is their birth, extinction is their death, and new species that diverge from them are their offspring. In this model, Stanley suggests that just as populations of individual organisms undergo natural selection, species undergo *species selection*. The species that endure the longest and generate the most new offspring species determine the direction of major evolutionary trends. The species selection model suggests that "differential speciation success" plays a role in macroevolution similar to the role of differential reproductive success in microevolution. Evolutionary trends can also result directly from natural selection. For example, when horse ancestors invaded the grasslands that spread during the mid-Cenozoic, there was strong selection for grazers that could escape predators by running faster. This trend would not have occurred without open grasslands.

Whatever its cause, an evolutionary trend does not imply that there is some intrinsic drive toward a particular phenotype. Evolution is the result of the interactions between organisms and their current environments; if environmental conditions change, an evolutionary trend may cease or even reverse itself. The cumulative effect of these ongoing interactions between organisms and their environments is enormous: It is through them that the staggering diversity of life—Darwin's "endless forms most beautiful"—has arisen.

CONCEPT CHECK 25.6

1. How can the Darwinian concept of descent with modification explain the evolution of such complex structures as the vertebrate eye?

2. **WHAT IF?** The myxoma virus kills up to 99.8% of infected European rabbits in populations with no previous exposure to the virus. The virus is transmitted between living rabbits by mosquitoes. Describe an evolutionary trend (in either the rabbit or virus) that might occur after a rabbit population first encounters the virus.

For suggested answers, see Appendix A.

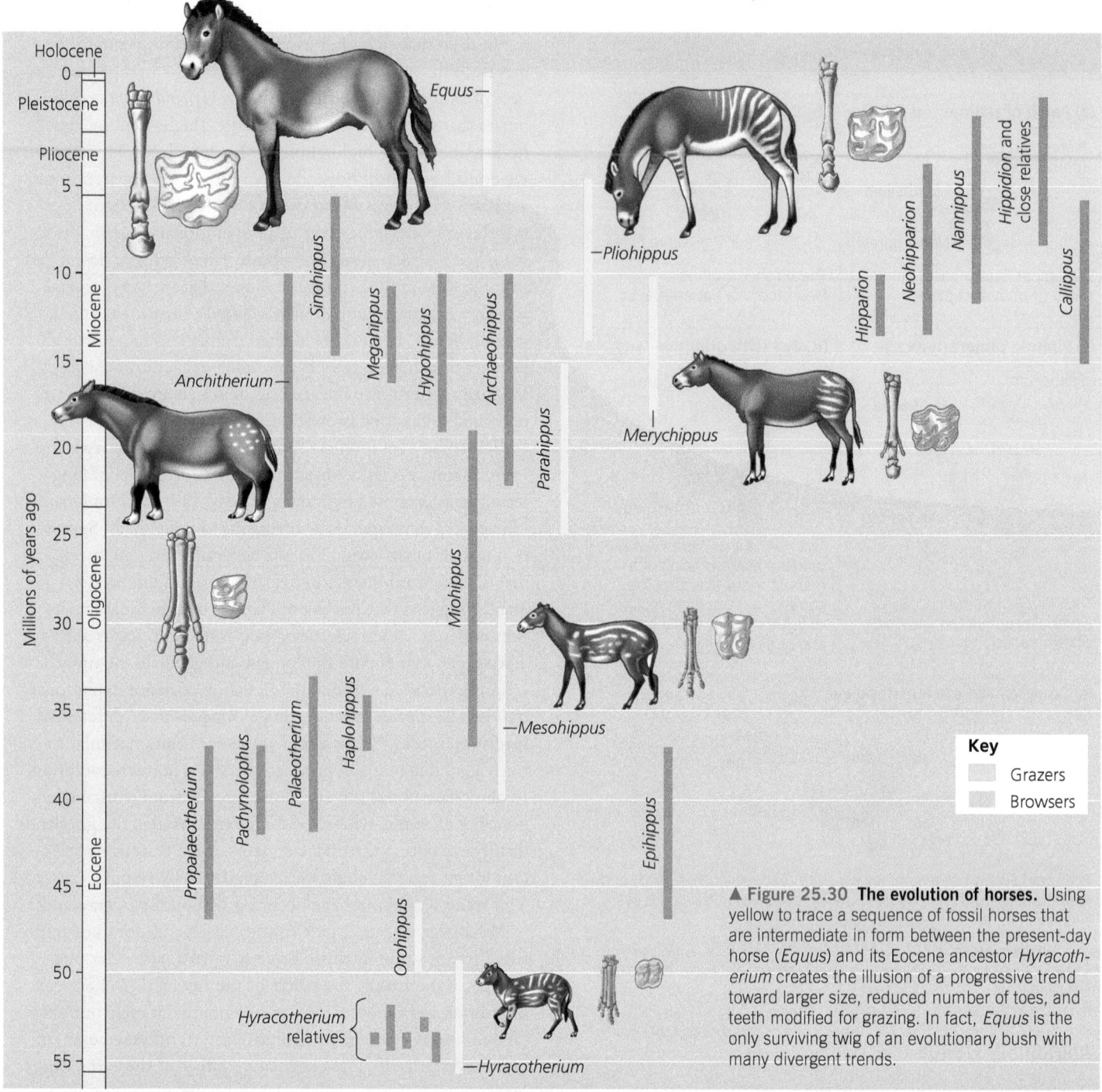

▲ Figure 25.30 **The evolution of horses.** Using yellow to trace a sequence of fossil horses that are intermediate in form between the present-day horse (*Equus*) and its Eocene ancestor *Hyracotherium* creates the illusion of a progressive trend toward larger size, reduced number of toes, and teeth modified for grazing. In fact, *Equus* is the only surviving twig of an evolutionary bush with many divergent trends.

Key
- Grazers
- Browsers

---

25 Chapter Review

SUMMARY OF KEY CONCEPTS

CONCEPT 25.1

Conditions on early Earth made the origin of life possible (pp. 551–554)

- Earth formed 4.6 billion years ago. Experiments simulating possible early atmospheres have produced organic molecules from inorganic precursors. Amino acids, lipids, sugars, and nitrogenous bases have also been found in meteorites.
- Amino acids and RNA nucleotides polymerize when dripped onto hot sand, clay, or rock. Organic compounds can spontaneously assemble into **protocells**, membrane-bounded droplets that have some properties of cells.
- The first genetic material may have been short pieces of RNA capable of guiding polypeptide synthesis and self-replication. Early protocells containing such RNA would have increased through natural selection.

? *Describe the roles that montmorillonite clay and vesicles may have played in the origin of life.*

CONCEPT 25.2

The fossil record documents the history of life (pp. 554–556)

- The fossil record, based largely on fossils found in sedimentary rocks, documents the rise and fall of different groups of organisms over time.
- Sedimentary strata reveal the relative ages of fossils. The absolute ages of fossils can be estimated by radiometric dating and other methods.
- The fossil record shows how new groups of organisms can arise via the gradual modification of preexisting organisms.

? *What are the challenges of estimating the absolute ages of old fossils? Explain how these challenges may be overcome in some circumstances.*

CONCEPT 25.3

Key events in life's history include the origins of single-celled and multicelled organisms and the colonization of land (pp. 556–563)

? *What is the "Cambrian explosion," and why is it significant?*

CONCEPT 25.4

The rise and fall of groups of organisms reflect differences in speciation and extinction rates (pp. 563–570)

- In **plate tectonics**, continental plates move gradually over time, altering the physical geography and climate of Earth. These changes lead to extinctions in some groups of organisms and bursts of speciation in others.
- Evolutionary history has been punctuated by five **mass extinctions** that radically altered the history of life. Some of these extinctions may have been caused by changes in continent positions, volcanic activity, or impacts from meteorites or comets.
- Large increases in the diversity of life have resulted from **adaptive radiations** that followed mass extinctions. Adaptive radiations have also occurred in groups of organisms that possessed major evolutionary innovations or that colonized new regions in which there was little competition from other organisms.

? *Explain how the broad evolutionary changes seen in the fossil record are the cumulative result of speciation and extinction events.*

CONCEPT 25.5

Major changes in body form can result from changes in the sequences and regulation of developmental genes (pp. 570–574)

- Developmental genes affect morphological differences between species by influencing the rate, timing, and spatial patterns of change in an organism's form as it develops into an adult.

- The evolution of new forms can be caused by changes in the nucleotide sequences or regulation of developmental genes.

? *How could changes in a single gene or DNA region ultimately lead to the origin of a new group of organisms?*

CONCEPT 25.6

Evolution is not goal oriented (pp. 574–576)

- Novel and complex biological structures can evolve through a series of incremental modifications, each of which benefits the organism that possesses it.
- Evolutionary trends can be caused by factors such as natural selection in a changing environment or species selection. Like all aspects of evolution, evolutionary trends result from interactions between organisms and their current environments.

? *Explain the reasoning behind the statement "Evolution is not goal oriented."*

TEST YOUR UNDERSTANDING

LEVEL 1: KNOWLEDGE/COMPREHENSION

1. Fossilized stromatolites
   a. formed around deep-sea vents.
   b. resemble structures formed by bacterial communities that are found today in some warm, shallow, salty bays.
   c. provide evidence that plants moved onto land in the company of fungi around 500 million years ago.
   d. contain the first undisputed fossils of eukaryotes and date from 2.1 billion years ago.

2. The oxygen revolution changed Earth's environment dramatically. Which of the following took advantage of the presence of free oxygen in the oceans and atmosphere?
   a. the evolution of cellular respiration, which used oxygen to help harvest energy from organic molecules
   b. the persistence of some animal groups in anaerobic habitats
   c. the evolution of photosynthetic pigments that protected early algae from the corrosive effects of oxygen
   d. the evolution of chloroplasts after early protists incorporated photosynthetic cyanobacteria

3. Which factor most likely caused animals and plants in India to differ greatly from species in nearby southeast Asia?
   a. The species became separated by convergent evolution.
   b. The climates of the two regions are similar.
   c. India is in the process of separating from the rest of Asia.
   d. India was a separate continent until 45 million years ago.

4. Adaptive radiations can be a direct consequence of three of the following four factors. Select the exception.
   a. vacant ecological niches
   b. genetic drift
   c. colonization of an isolated region that contains suitable habitat and few competitor species
   d. evolutionary innovation

5. Which of the following steps has *not* yet been accomplished by scientists studying the origin of life?
   a. synthesis of small RNA polymers by ribozymes
   b. formation of molecular aggregates with selectively permeable membranes
   c. formation of protocells that use DNA to direct the polymerization of amino acids
   d. abiotic synthesis of organic molecules

6. **DRAW IT** Use the unlabelled clock diagram on the next page to test your memory of the sequence of key events in the history of life described in this chapter by labelling the coloured bars. As a visual aid to help you study, add labels that represent other

significant events, including the Cambrian explosion, origin of mammals, and Permian and Cretaceous mass extinctions.

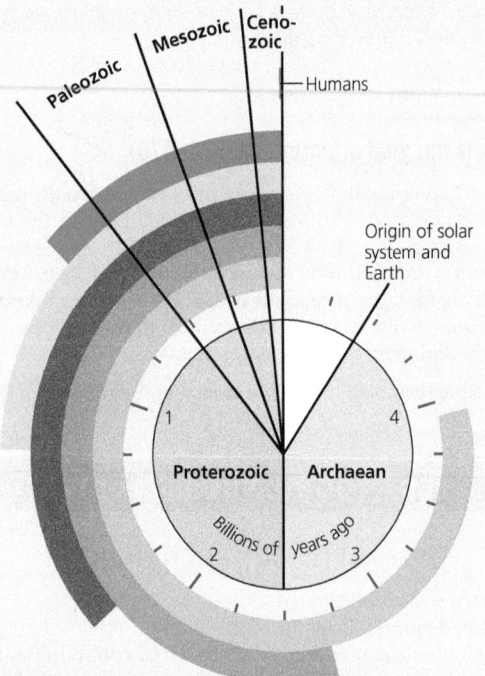

Source: Adapted from "When Did Photosynthesis Emerge on Earth?" by David J. Des Marais, from *Science,* September 2000, Volume 289(5485). © Jane B. Reece.

LEVEL 2: APPLICATION/ANALYSIS

7. A genetic change that caused a certain *Hox* gene to be expressed along the tip of a vertebrate limb bud instead of farther back helped make possible the evolution of the tetrapod limb. This type of change is illustrative of
   a. the influence of environment on development.
   b. paedomorphosis.
   c. a change in a developmental gene or in its regulation that altered the spatial organization of body parts.
   d. heterochrony.

8. A swim bladder is a gas-filled sac that helps fish maintain buoyancy. The evolution of the swim bladder from lungs of an ancestral fish is an example of
   a. exaptation.
   b. changes in *Hox* gene expression.
   c. paedomorphosis.
   d. adaptive radiation.

LEVEL 3: SYNTHESIS/EVALUATION

9. **EVOLUTION CONNECTION**
   Describe how gene flow, genetic drift, and natural selection all can influence macroevolution.

10. **SCIENTIFIC INQUIRY**
    Herbivory (plant eating) has evolved repeatedly in insects, typically from meat-eating or detritus-feeding ancestors (detritus is dead organic matter). Moths and butterflies, for example, eat plants, whereas their "sister group" (the insect group to which they are most closely related), the caddisflies, feed on animals, fungi, or detritus. As illustrated in the phylogenetic tree on the following page, the combined moth/butterfly and caddisfly group shares a common ancestor with flies and fleas. Like caddisflies, flies and fleas are thought to have evolved from ancestors that did not eat plants.

There are 140 000 species of moths and butterflies and 7000 species of caddisflies. State a hypothesis about the impact of herbivory on adaptive radiations in insects. How could this hypothesis be tested?

11. **SCIENCE, TECHNOLOGY, AND SOCIETY**
    Experts estimate that human activities cause the extinction of hundreds of species every year. In contrast, the natural rate of extinction is thought to average only a few species per year. If human actions continue to alter the global environment, especially by destroying tropical rain forests and changing Earth's climate, the likely result will be a wave of extinctions that could rival those at the end of the Cretaceous period. Considering that life has endured five mass extinctions, should we be concerned that we may cause a sixth mass extinction? How would such an extinction differ from previous extinctions? What might be some of the consequences?

12. **WRITE ABOUT A THEME: ORGANIZATION**
    You have seen many examples of how form fits function at all levels of the biological hierarchy. However, we can imagine forms that would function better than some forms actually found in nature. For example, if the wings of a bird were not formed from its forelimbs, such a hypothetical bird could fly yet also hold objects with its forelimbs. In a short essay (100–150 words), use the concept of "evolution as tinkering" to explain why there are limits to the functionality of forms in nature.

13. **SYNTHESIZE YOUR KNOWLEDGE**

In 2010, the Soufrière Hills volcano on the Caribbean island of Montserrat erupted violently, spewing huge clouds of ash and gases into the sky. Explain how the volcanic eruptions at the end of the Permian period and the formation of Pangaea, both of which occurred about 251 million years ago, set in motion events that altered evolutionary history.

For selected answers, see Appendix A.

UNIT 5

THE EVOLUTIONARY HISTORY OF BIOLOGICAL DIVERSITY

AN INTERVIEW WITH

Patrick Keeling

Patrick Keeling did his undergraduate degree at Western University in Genetics, completed his Ph.D. at Dalhousie University, and then did two post-doctoral positions in Australia and Indiana. His is currently a Professor in the Department of Botany at UBC.

What type of scientist are you?

I'm an evolutionary biologist and a microbiologist.

How did you become interested in evolutionary history?

In my second-year undergraduate biology class we were learning about the origin of mitochondria and plastids and the idea of endosymbiotic bacteria came up and the instructor indicated there was some debate about this topic—and that got me really interested.

What questions are you trying to answer right now in your research?

I'm interested in questions about the ancient, deep events in the evolution of complex cells, such as things that happen early on in eukaryotic evolution. I also like to focus on massive transitions, such as when two cells merge and become one cell, or when that cell becomes a parasite, or when microbial cells massively alter their evolutionary direction and start doing something else.

A specific example that we've worked on is the parasite that causes malaria, *Plasmodium falciparum*. It was discovered that this parasite has plastids (like chloroplast in plants, but not photosynthetic), and this set up some bizarre questions like: What is it doing with this plastid? Where did the plastid come from? Did an alga evolve into an intercellular parasite? My lab has been looking at these questions for 15 years. If an alga turned into an intercellular parasite, then how did it happen? To answer this question we use a combination of cell biology and genomics research. We go out and find new lineages that people didn't know about, and we also work a lot on organisms that are free-living relatives of parasites. We have learned that there is a link between how some of these parasites originated in coral. It was a symbiotic event based on photosynthesis and somewhere along the line that relationship soured and the endosymbiont became a parasite — then a million years of evolution later we have these parasites all over the animal kingdom.

What is the key take-home message for students about your research?

Biology and evolution have generated far more diversity than our model systems have led us to believe. Almost everything in biology has an exception somewhere. The amazing diversity of how life survives continues to astonish me everyday.

What's the most surprising thing you have found through your research?

We've found a lot of things that are pretty surprising, but for nostalgic reasons I would say it was a discovery during my Ph.D. that one of the organisms I worked on does not use the universal genetic code: that is the kind of thing you usually take for granted. We also made a phylogenetic link between the malarial parasite and its free-living relatives. This is a massive transition—to go from a photosynthetic free living algae, to being a nonphotosynthetic parasite. It seems like an impossible leap, but when you start breaking it down into its stages, it begins to make a lot more sense. So it was surprising at first, but it gets easier to understand the more we know about it.

What is the relevance of your research for first-year students studying diversity?

Several things. First, most of the diversity that is on the planet is microbial. Second, protists are really important, and along with bacteria and archaea, they form the foundation of every ecosystem on the planet. For a lot of the things we think of as being life-sustaining systems, it is the microbes that are really doing the hard work. Animals, plants, and fungi are beneficiaries of all that hard work. If animals, plants, and fungi just disappeared off the face of the earth, microbes would barely notice, but if microbes disappeared, everything else would die.

What advice would you give to a biology student just starting out at university?

You have to pay attention and think for yourself: Find the things that spark your own imagination and take the time to look into them deeper—because there is always more going on than what you are learning.

> " If animals, plants, and fungi just disappeared off the face of the earth, microbes would barely notice, but if microbes disappeared, everything else would die. "

Source: Interview with Patrick Keeling. Used with permission from Patrick Keeling.

MAKE CONNECTIONS

This unit explores the evolutionary history of biological diversity. The evolution of organelles via endosymbiosis is an example of one of the interesting concepts you'll learn about in this unit.

Evolution and Diversity of Life

Primary Endosymbiosis

Cyanobacterium (photosynthetic)   **Nonphotosynthetic eukaryote**

- Thylakoid membranes
- Flagellum
- Nucleus

Heterotrophic eukaryote feeds on cyanobacteria

- Phagocytosis (Figure 7.19)

**Chapter 27
Bacteria and Archaea**

Symbiosis (Concept 27.5) eventually established over time

- Symbiont
- Cyanobacteria inside host vacuole

Conversion to chloroplast over time. This is how the red and green algae (*Archaeplastida*) (Concept 28.4) evolved.

- Chloroplast

Domain Archaea — Crenarchaeotes, Euryarchaeotes, Korarchaeotes, Nanoarchaeotes

Proteobacteria, Chlamydias, Spirochetes, Gram positive bacteria, Cyanobacteria — Domain Bacteria

Endosymbiosis leading to mitochondria

Endosymbiosis leading to chloroplasts

Evolution of organelles through endosymbiosis has been a major innovation in the evolution of eukaryotic cells. Mitochondria evolved from endosymbiotic proteobacteria (red bubbles), while the chloroplast in the *Arachaeplastida* evolved from endosymbiotic cyanobacteria (green bubbles, left panel). (Concepts 25.3 and 28.1)

The three domains of life (Concept 26.6) and the major groups within them. Purple branches are prokaryotes, red/green are eukaryotes. Endosymbiosis has played a vital role in evolution of eukaryotes, and the major events in eukaryotic cell evolution involving endosymbiosis are indicated by red (mitochondrial origin) or green (chloroplast origin) bubbles. The direction of transfer being from small to large bubbles.

Secondary Endosymbiosis

The root of the eukaryotic tree is unknown, but see Figure 28.25 to see approaches for examining the possibilities.

Excavata

Chapter 28
Evolution of cell diversity: Excavata, SAR clade, *Archaeplastida*, and some unikonts

Secondary endosymbiotic origin of plastids

Stramenopile Alveolate Rhizaria (SAR)

Domain Eukarya

Archaeplastida

Primary endosymbiotic origin of plastid/ mitochondria

Chapters 29–30
Origin and evolution of land plants

Unikonta

Chapter 31
Fungi

Chapters 32–34
Origin and evolution of animals

Photosynthetic eukaryote

Nonphotosynthetic eukaryote

Chloroplast

Nucleus

Nonphotosynthetic eukaryote feeds on photosynthetic eukaryote. Over time, a symbiosis is established.

Symbiont inside host vacuole

Plasma membrane from symbiont

Over time, the endosymbiont is converted to a permanent organelle (plastid), resulting in a new photosynthetic lineage. See Concept 28.1.

Vestigial nucleus from endosymbiont, called a nucleomorph (if present)

Evolution of a plastid via secondary endosymbiosis is thought to have occurred on at least three separate occasions leading to the evolution of the SAR clade, some of the Excavata, and some lineages of the Rhizaria. Eukaryotic branches that are green indicate those that acquired photosynthesis via endosymbiosis. (See Concept 28.1)

MAKE CONNECTIONS *Locate the ciliates within the Alveolate clade in* Figure 28.2. *The ciliates are not photosynthetic and lack plastids yet are within a clade whose members frequently have plastids. Propose hypotheses to explain the lack of plastids in ciliates.*

26

Phylogeny and the Tree of Life

KEY CONCEPTS

26.1 Phylogenies show evolutionary relationships

26.2 Phylogenies are inferred from morphological and molecular data

26.3 Shared characters are used to construct phylogenetic trees

26.4 An organism's evolutionary history is documented in its genome

26.5 Molecular clocks help track evolutionary time

26.6 Our understanding of the tree of life continues to change based on new data

Ariadne Van Zandbergen/Alamy Stock Photo

▲ Figure 26.1 **Which is a descendent of dinosaurs—the Nile crocodile or the yellow-billed stork?**

Investigating the Tree of Life

Look closely at **Figure 26.1** that shows a Nile crocodile and a yellow-billed stork. Which of the two are more closely related to dinosaurs? Probably contrary to your initial impulse, most scientists now agree that birds and dinosaurs share a more recent common ancestor, and thus are more similar to one another than either is to crocodiles. If you are surprised, you are not alone. The superficial similarities of the crocodile and the now extinct dinosaur seem uncanny. All three are reptiles and share a number of common features. But how do scientists categorize organisms and ultimately determine these evolutionary relationships? First, they compare **morphological characteristics**. For instance, the closest *living* relatives of birds are crocodiles. Birds and crocodiles share a number of anatomical features, such as a mandibular fenestra (a hole in the lower jaw). Curiously, they also maintain some behavioural similarities. Crocodiles and birds both "sing" to defend territories and attract mates (although a crocodile's "song" is more like a bellow), and they build nests. A variety of morphological and molecular features, however, were used to

José Antonio Peñas/Science Source

◀ Artists depiction of *Anchiornis huxleyi*, an early feathered dinosaur.

combine birds and crocodiles in a taxonomic group—the **Archosauria** (see Figure 34.25)—with the reasoning that any feature shared by birds and crocodiles is likely to have been present in their common ancestor (denoted by the blue dot in Figure 26.3). Dinosaurs are extinct, so it can be a challenge to determine their evolutionary relationships; doing so depends upon the fossil record. Dinosaurs like the Albertasaurus share a number of anatomical features with birds such as fused clavicles (wishbone) and the shifting of the pubic bone toward the back. Some of the most convincing evidence linking birds and dinosaurs, to the exclusion of crocodiles, lies with the discovery of feathered dinosaur fossil specimens **(Figure 26.2a)**. The evolution of feathers is a significant event in dinosaur diversification, and a research group at the University of Alberta has discovered many transitional proto-feather forms preserved in amber (fossilized tree resin, **Figure 26.2b**) that allow for an examination of feather fine structure not possible with compressed fossil specimens.

Determining the classification of organisms is now heavily dependent on **molecular characteristics** that include specific DNA or protein sequences. Computer programs are then used to determine similarities among these molecular characters. While the morphological evidence linking crocodiles and birds is strong, getting sequence information from extinct organisms is a particular challenge! Amazingly, a group of scientists was able to extract connective tissue protein (collagen) from fossilized soft tissue, and the partial amino acid sequence of this protein supported the bird-dinosaur grouping, in agreement with the morphological evidence.

Lizards and snakes

Crocodilians

Ornithischian dinosaurs

Saurischian dinosaurs

Common ancestor of crocodilians, dinosaurs, and birds

▲ Fi... ...atives.

Phylogenies represent hypotheses of how different organisms relate to one another

Ultimately, these different characteristics are used to create a **phylogeny** (Figure 26.3), a hypothesis for the evolutionary history of a species or group of species. Phylogenies are represented as **evolutionary trees**, and in this chapter we will explore how these trees are constructed and what they mean. Importantly, these trees represent hypotheses of how different organisms relate to one another. Thinking of phylogenies as hypotheses also allows us to use them in a powerful way: We can make and test predictions based on the assumption that a phylogeny—our hypothesis—is correct. This is best illustrated in the case of an extinct group: the dinosaurs. For example, in an approach known as *phylogenetic bracketing,* we can predict that features shared by two groups of closely related organisms (birds and dinosaurs) are present in their common ancestor and all of its descendants unless independent data indicate otherwise. This approach has been used to make novel predictions about dinosaurs. For example, biologists predicted that dinosaurs had four-chambered hearts, sang, built nests, and exhibited brooding because both crocodiles and birds exhibit these features. Internal organs, such as the heart, rarely fossilize, and it is, of course, difficult to test whether dinosaurs sang to defend territories and attract mates. However, fossilized dinosaur eggs and nests have provided evidence supporting the prediction of brooding in dinosaurs. Finally, by supporting predictions based on the phylogenetic hypothesis shown in Figure 26.3, fossil discoveries of nests and brooding in dinosaurs provide independent data that suggest that the hypothesis is correct.

To construct phylogenies, biologists use **systematics**, a discipline focused on classifying organisms and determining their evolutionary relationships. Systematists use data ranging from fossils and anatomy to molecules and genes to infer evolutionary relationships. A phylogenetic hypothesis may be modified when new evidence compels systematists to revise their trees. This information is enabling biologists to construct a tree of all life, which will continue to be refined as additional data are collected.

NATURE, Xing Xu, Xiaoting Zheng, Hailu You, Exceptional dinosaur fossils show ontogenetic development of early feathers, April 29, 2010, vol 464, issue 7293, figure 1A. Copyright 2010, Reprinted by permission via Copyright Clearance Center.

Pascal Goetgheluck/ScienceSource

▲ **Figure 26.2 Early feathered dinosaur fossils. (a)** Fossil specimen of an oviraptorosaur *Similicaudipteryx* discovered in Northern China, showing the primitive feather structures. **(b)** Proto-feather preserved in amber from the late Cretaceous period (100–66 mya) discovered in southern Alberta by a group at the University of Alberta.

Phylogenies show evolutionary relationships

Organisms share many characteristics because of common ancestry (see Chapter 22). As a result, we can learn a great deal about a species if we know its evolutionary history. For example, an organism is likely to share many of its genes, metabolic pathways, and structural proteins with its close relatives. We'll consider practical applications of such information at the close of this section, but first we'll examine how organisms are named and classified, the scientific discipline of **taxonomy**. We'll also look at how we can interpret and use diagrams that represent evolutionary history.

Binomial Nomenclature

Common names for organisms—such as monkey, finch, and lilac—convey meaning in casual usage, but they can also cause confusion. Each of these names, for example, refers to more than one species. Moreover, some common names do not accurately reflect the kind of organism they signify. Consider these three "fishes": jellyfish (a cnidarian), crayfish (a small lobsterlike crustacean), and silverfish (an insect). And of course, a given organism has different names in different languages.

To avoid ambiguity when communicating about their research, biologists refer to organisms by Latin scientific names. The two-part format of the scientific name, commonly called a **binomial**, was instituted in the 18th century by Carolus Linnaeus (see Chapter 22). The first part of a binomial is the name of the **genus** (plural, *genera*) to which the species belongs. The second part, called the specific epithet, is unique for each species within the genus. An example of a binomial is *Castor canadensis*, the scientific name for the largest rodent in Canada, the North American beaver. Notice that the first letter of the genus is capitalized and the entire binomial is italicized. (Newly created scientific names are also "latinized": You can name an insect you discover after a friend, but you must add a Latin ending.) Many of the more than 11 000 binomials assigned by Linnaeus are still used today, including the optimistic name he gave our own species—*Homo sapiens*, meaning "wise man."

Hierarchical Classification

In addition to naming species, Linnaeus also grouped them into a hierarchy of increasingly inclusive categories. The first grouping is built into the binomial: Species that appear to be closely related are grouped into the same genus. For example, the North American beaver (*Castor canadensis*) belongs to a genus with only one other species, the Eurasian beaver (*Castor fiber*). Beyond genera, taxonomists employ

progressively more comprehensive categories of classification. The taxonomic system named after Linnaeus, the Linnaean system, places related genera in the same **family**, families into **orders**, orders into **classes**, classes into **phyla** (singular, *phylum*), phyla into **kingdoms**, and, more recently, kingdoms into **domains** (Figure 26.4). The resulting biological classification of a particular organism is somewhat like a postal address identifying a person in a particular apartment, in a building with many apartments, on a street with many apartment buildings, in a city with many streets, and so on.

The named taxonomic unit at any level of the hierarchy is called a **taxon** (plural, *taxa*). In the beaver example, *Castor* is a taxon at the genus level, and Rodentia is a taxon at the order level that includes all the many families of rodents, like those that include rats (Muroidea), squirrels (Sciuridae), and porcupines (Erethizontidae). Note that in the Linnaean system, taxa broader than the genus are not italicized, though they are capitalized.

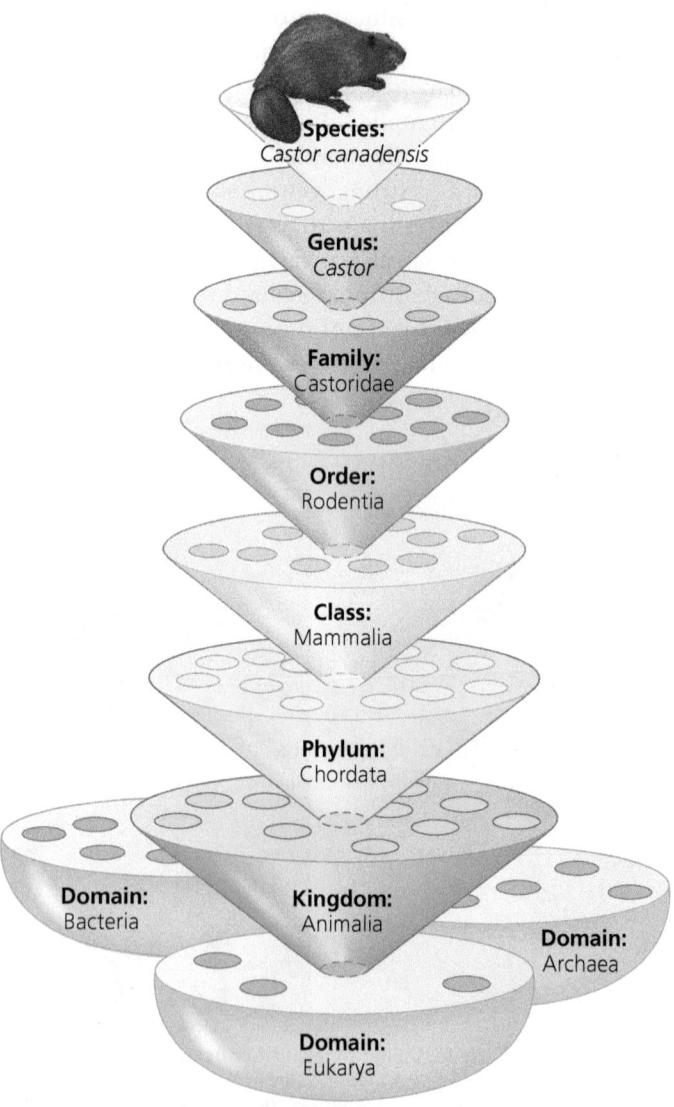

▲ Figure 26.4 **Linnaean classification.** At each level, or "rank," species are placed in groups within more inclusive groups.

Classifying species is a way to structure our human view of the world. We lump together various species of trees to which we give the common name of pines and distinguish them from other trees that we call firs. Taxonomists have decided that pines and firs are different enough to be placed in separate genera, yet similar enough to be grouped into the same family, Pinaceae. As with pines and firs, higher levels of classification are usually defined by particular characters chosen by taxonomists. However, characters that are useful for classifying one group of organisms may not be appropriate for other organisms. For this reason, the larger categories often are not comparable between lineages; that is, an order of snails does not exhibit the same degree of morphological or genetic diversity as an order of mammals. Furthermore, as we'll see, the placement of species into orders, classes, and so on, does not necessarily reflect evolutionary history.

Linking Classification and Phylogeny

The evolutionary history of a group of organisms can be represented in a branching diagram called a **phylogenetic tree**. As in **Figure 26.5**, the branching pattern often matches how taxonomists have classified groups of organisms nested within more inclusive groups. Sometimes, however, taxonomists have placed a species within a genus (or other group)

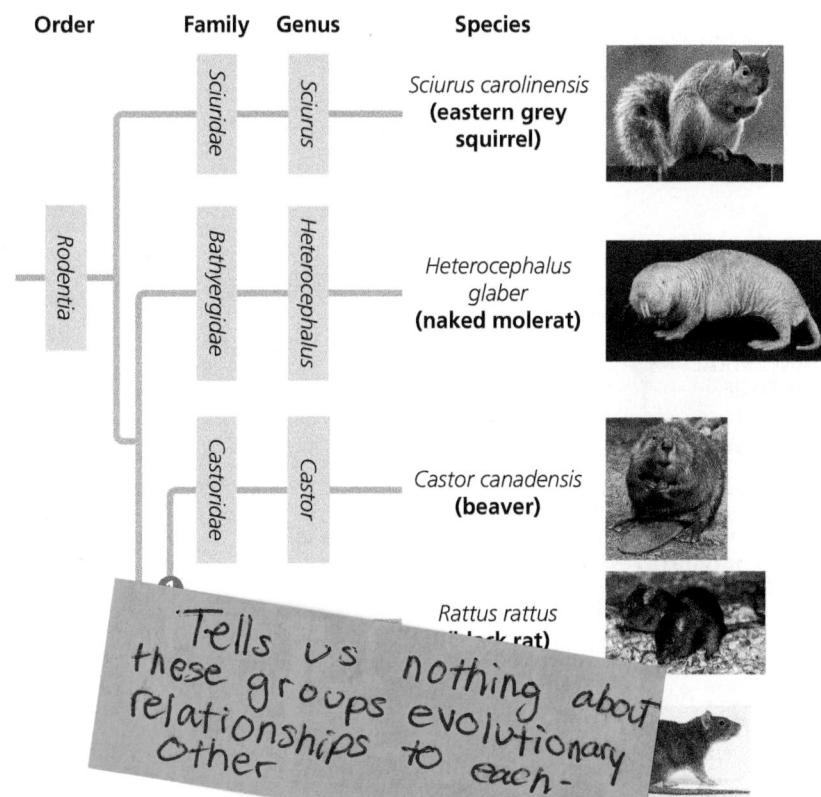

Tells us nothing about these groups evolutionary relationships to each-other [handwritten note]

▲ **Figure 26.5** **The connection between classification** [and phylogeny].
Hierarchical classification can reflect the branching patterns of phylogenetic trees. This tree traces possible evolutionary relationships between some of the taxa within order Rodentia, itself a branch of class Mammalia. The branch point ❶ represents the most recent common ancestor of all members of the mouse-rat-gerbil (Muroidea) and beaver (Castoridae) families. The branch point ❷ represents the most recent common ancestor of black rats and common sewer (brown) rats.

? *What does this phylogenetic tree indicate about the evolutionary relationships between the squirrel, the beaver, and the rat?*

these relationships often are depicted as a series of dichotomies, or two-way **branch points**. Each branch point (or internal node) represents the divergence of two evolutionary lineages from a common ancestor. In **Figure 26.6**, for example, branch point ❸ represents the common ancestor of taxa A, B, and C. The position of branch point ❹ to the right of ❸ indicates that taxa B and C diverged after their shared lineage split from that of taxon A. (Tree branches can be rotated around a branch point without changing their evolutionary relationships.)

In Figure 26.6, taxa B and C are **sister taxa**, groups of organisms that share an immediate common ancestor (branch point ❹) and hence are each other's closest relatives. Note also that this tree, like most of the phylogenetic trees in this book, is **rooted**, which means that a branch point within the tree (often drawn farthest to the left) represents the most recent common ancestor of all taxa in the tree. The term **basal taxon** refers to a lineage that diverges early in the history of a group and hence, like taxon G in Figure 26.6, lies on a branch that originates near the common ancestor of

[Handwritten margin notes, left side]:
The branching of phylogenetic tree → matches how taxonomists have classified groups of organisms nested within more inclusive groups

→ Sometimes taxonomists place a species with a genus that is not most closely related because a key feature could have lost a feature shared by close relatives

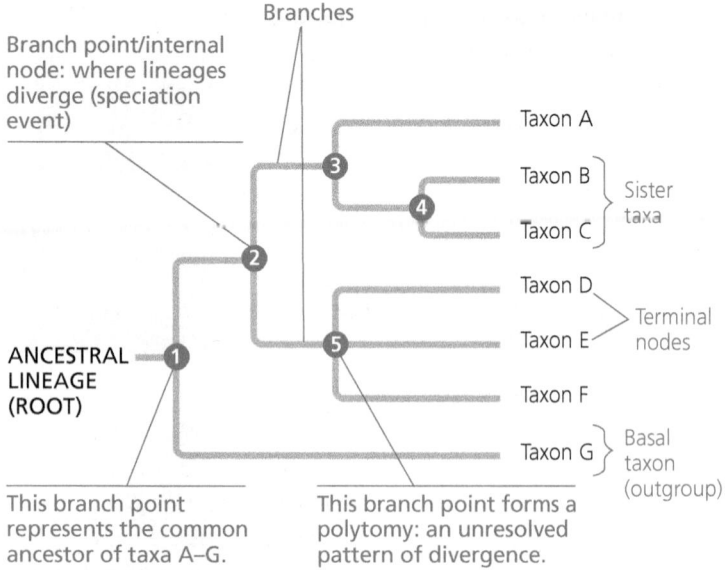

Branches

Branch point/internal node: where lineages diverge (speciation event)

Taxon A

Taxon B ⎫
Taxon C ⎬ Sister taxa

Taxon D
Taxon E ⎫ Terminal nodes

Taxon F

Taxon G ⎫ Basal taxon (outgroup)

ANCESTRAL LINEAGE (ROOT)

This branch point represents the common ancestor of taxa A–G.

This branch point forms a polytomy: an unresolved pattern of divergence.

▲ **Figure 26.6 Anatomy of a phylogenetic tree.**

DRAW IT *Redraw this tree, rotating the branches around branch points* ② *and* ③. *Does your new version tell a different story about the evolutionary relationships between the taxa? Explain.*

the group. Finally, the lineage leading to taxa D–F includes a **polytomy**, a branch point from which more than two descendant groups emerge. A polytomy signifies that evolutionary relationships among the taxa are not yet clear.

CONCEPT CHECK 26.1

1. Which levels of the classification in Figure 26.4 do humans share with beavers?

2. **WHAT IF?** Suppose new evidence indicates that taxon E in Figure 26.6 is the sister taxon of a group consisting of taxa D and F. Redraw the tree accordingly.

For suggested answers, see Appendix A.

CONCEPT 26.2

Phylogenies are inferred from morphological and molecular data

To infer phylogeny, systematists must gather as much information as possible about the morphology, genes, and biochemistry of the relevant organisms. It is important to focus on features that result from common ancestry, because only such features reflect evolutionary relationships.

Morphological and Molecular Homologies

Recall that phenotypic and genetic similarities due to shared ancestry are called *homologies*. For example, the similarity in the number and arrangement of bones in the forelimbs of mammals is due to their descent from a common ancestor

with the same bone structure; this is an example of a morphological homology (see Figure 22.15). In the same way, genes or other DNA sequences are homologous if they are descended from sequences carried by a common ancestor.

In general, organisms that share very similar morphologies or similar DNA sequences are likely to be more closely related than organisms with vastly different structures or sequences. In some cases, however, the morphological divergence between related species can be great and their genetic divergence small (or vice versa). Consider the Hawaiian silversword plants discussed in Chapter 25. These species vary dramatically in appearance throughout the islands. Some are tall, twiggy trees, and others are dense, ground-hugging shrubs (see Figure 25.23). But despite these striking phenotypic differences, the silverswords' genes are very similar. Based on these small molecular divergences, scientists estimate that the silversword group began to diverge 5 million years ago, which is also about the time when the oldest of the current islands formed. We'll discuss how scientists use molecular data to estimate such divergence times later in this chapter.

Sorting Homology from Analogy

A potential red herring in constructing a phylogeny is similarity due to convergent evolution—called **analogy**—rather than to shared ancestry (**homology**). As you read in Chapter 22, convergent evolution occurs when similar environmental pressures and natural selection produce similar (analogous) adaptations in organisms from different evolutionary lineages. For example, the two mole-like animals illustrated in **Figure 26.7** are very similar in their external appearance. However, their internal anatomy, physiology, and reproductive systems are very dissimilar. Australian "moles" are marsupials; their young complete their embryonic development in a pouch on the outside of the mother's body. North American moles, in contrast, are eutherians; their young complete their embryonic development in the uterus within the mother's body. Indeed, genetic comparisons and the fossil record provide evidence that the common ancestor of these moles lived 140 million years ago, about the time the marsupial and eutherian mammals diverged. This common ancestor and most of its descendants were not mole-like, but analogous

Australian marsupial "mole"

North American eutherian mole

▲ **Figure 26.7 Convergent evolution of analogous burrowing characteristics.** A long body, large front paws, small eyes, and a pad of thickened skin that protects the nose all evolved independently in these species.

characteristics evolved independently in these two mole lineages as they became adapted to similar lifestyles.

Distinguishing between homology and analogy is critical in reconstructing phylogenies. To see why, consider bats and birds, both of which have adaptations that enable flight. This superficial resemblance might imply that bats are more closely related to birds than they are to cats, which cannot fly. But a closer examination reveals that a bat's wing is far more similar to the forelimbs of cats and other mammals than to a bird's wing. Bats and birds descended from a common tetrapod ancestor that lived about 320 million years ago. This common ancestor could not fly. Thus, although the underlying skeletal systems of bats and birds are homologous, their *wings* are not. Flight is enabled in different ways—stretched membranes in the bat wing versus feathers in the bird wing. Fossil evidence also documents that bat wings and bird wings arose independently from the forelimbs of different tetrapod ancestors. Thus, with respect to flight, a bat's wing is *analogous*, not homologous, to a bird's wing. Analogous structures that arose independently are also called **homoplasies** (from the Greek, meaning "to mould in the same way").

Besides corroborative similarities and fossil evidence, another clue to distinguishing between homology and analogy is the complexity of the characters being compared. The more elements that are similar in two complex structures, the more likely it is that they evolved from a common ancestor. For instance, the skulls of an adult human and an adult chimpanzee both consist of many bones fused together. The compositions of the skulls match almost perfectly, bone for bone. It is highly improbable that such complex structures, matching in so many details, have separate origins. More likely, the genes involved in the development of both skulls were inherited from a common ancestor. The same argument applies to comparisons at the gene level. Genes are sequences of thousands of nucleotides, each of which represents an inherited character in the form of one of the four DNA bases: A (adenine), G (guanine), C (cytosine), or T (thymine). If genes in two organisms share many portions of their nucleotide sequences, it is likely that the genes are homologous.

Evaluating Molecular Homologies

Comparisons of DNA molecules often pose technical challenges for researchers. The first step after sequencing the molecules is to align comparable sequences from the species being studied. If the species are very closely related, the sequences probably differ at only one or a few sites. In contrast, comparable nucleic acid sequences in distantly related species usually have different bases at many sites and may have different lengths. This is because insertions and deletions accumulate over long periods of time.

Suppose, for example, that certain noncoding DNA sequences near a particular gene are very similar in two species, except that the first base of the sequence has been deleted in one of the species. The effect is that the remaining sequence shifts back one notch. A comparison of the two sequences that does not take this deletion into account would overlook what in fact is a very good match. To address such problems, researchers have developed computer programs that estimate the best way to align comparable DNA segments of differing lengths (Figure 26.8).

Such molecular comparisons reveal that many base substitutions and other differences have accumulated in the comparable genes of an Australian mole and a North American mole. The many differences indicate that their lineages have diverged greatly since their common ancestor; thus, we say that the living species are not closely related. In contrast, the high degree of gene sequence similarity among the silverswords indicates that they are all very closely related, in spite of their considerable morphological differences.

Just as with morphological characters, it is necessary to distinguish homology from analogy in evaluating molecular similarities for evolutionary studies. Two sequences that resemble each other at many points along their length most likely are homologous (see Figure 26.8). But in organisms that do not appear to be closely related, the bases that their otherwise very different sequences happen to share may simply be coincidental matches, called molecular homoplasies

① These homologous DNA sequences are identical as species 1 and species 2 begin to diverge from their common ancestor.

1 CCATCAGAGTCC
2 CCATCAGAGTCC

② Deletion and insertion mutations shift what had been matching sequences in the two species.

Deletion
1 CCATCA(G)AGTCC
2 CCAT CAGAGTCC
(G T A) Insertion

③ Of the regions of the species 2 sequence that match the species 1 sequence, those shaded orange no longer align because of these mutations.

1 CCAT CAAGTCC
2 CCATGTACAGAGTCC

④ The matching regions realign after a computer program adds gaps in sequence 1.

1 CCAT___CA_AGTCC
2 CCATGTACAGAGTCC

▲ Figure 26.8 **Aligning segments of DNA.** Systematists search for similar sequences along DNA segments from two species (only one DNA strand is shown for each species). In this example, 11 of the original 12 bases have not changed since the species diverged. Hence, those portions of the sequences still align once the length is adjusted.

```
ACGGATAGTCCACTAGGCACTA
TCACCGACAGGTCTTTGACTAG
```

▲ Figure 26.9 **A molecular homoplasy.**

(Figure 26.9). Scientists have developed statistical tools that can help distinguish "distant" homologies from such coincidental matches in extremely divergent sequences.

To date, researchers have sequenced more than 110 billion bases of DNA from thousands of species. This enormous collection of data has fuelled a boom in the study of phylogeny. The new data have supported earlier hypotheses regarding many evolutionary relationships, such as that between Australian and North American moles, and have clarified other relationships, such as those between the various silverswords. In the rest of this unit, you will see how our understanding of phylogeny has been transformed by **molecular systematics**, the discipline that uses data from DNA and other molecules to determine evolutionary relationships.

CONCEPT CHECK 26.2

1. Decide whether each of the following pairs of structures more likely represents analogy or homology, and explain your reasoning: (a) a porcupine's quills and a cactus's spines; (b) a cat's paw and a human's hand; (c) an owl's wing and a hornet's wing.

2. **WHAT IF?** Suppose that species A and species B have similar appearances but very divergent gene sequences and that species B and species C have very different appearances but similar gene sequences. Which pair of species is more likely to be closely related: A and B, or B and C? Explain.

For suggested answers, see Appendix A.

CONCEPT 26.3

Shared characters are used to construct phylogenetic trees

In reconstructing phylogenies, the first step is to distinguish homologous features from analogous ones (since only homology reflects evolutionary history). Next we must choose a method of inferring phylogeny from these homologous characters. A widely used set of methods is known as cladistics.

Cladistics

In the approach to systematics called **cladistics**, common ancestry is the primary criterion used to classify organisms. Using this methodology, biologists attempt to place species into groups called **clades**, each of which includes an ancestral species and all of its descendants (Figure 26.10a). Clades, like taxonomic categories of the Linnaean system, are nested within larger clades. In Figure 26.5, for example, the squirrel group (Sciuridae) represents a clade within a larger clade (Rodentia) that also includes the beaver group (Castoridae).

A taxon is equivalent to a clade only if it is **monophyletic** (from the Greek, meaning "single tribe"), signifying that it consists of an ancestral species and all of its descendants (see Figure 26.10a). Contrast this with a **paraphyletic** ("beside the tribe") group, which consists of an ancestral species and some, but not all, of its descendants (Figure 26.10b), or a **polyphyletic** ("many tribes") group, which includes distantly related species but not their most recent common ancestor (Figure 26.10c).

Note that in a paraphyletic group, the most recent common ancestor of all members of the group *is* part of the

▼ Figure 26.10 **Monophyletic, paraphyletic, and polyphyletic groups.**

(a) Monophyletic group (clade)

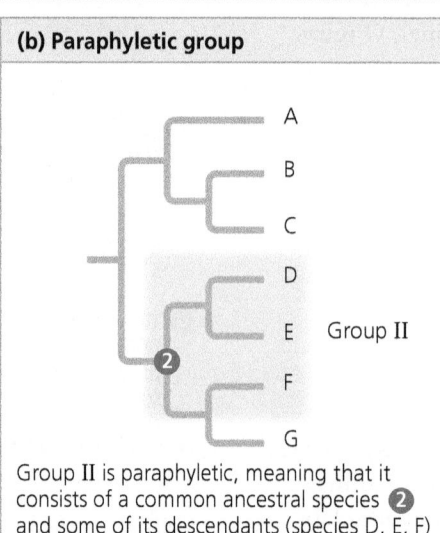

Group I, consisting of three species (A, B, C) and their common ancestor ❶, is a monophyletic group (clade), meaning that it consists of an ancestral species and *all* of its descendants.

(b) Paraphyletic group

Group II is paraphyletic, meaning that it consists of a common ancestral species ❷ and some of its descendants (species D, E, F) but not all of them (missing species G).

(c) Polyphyletic group

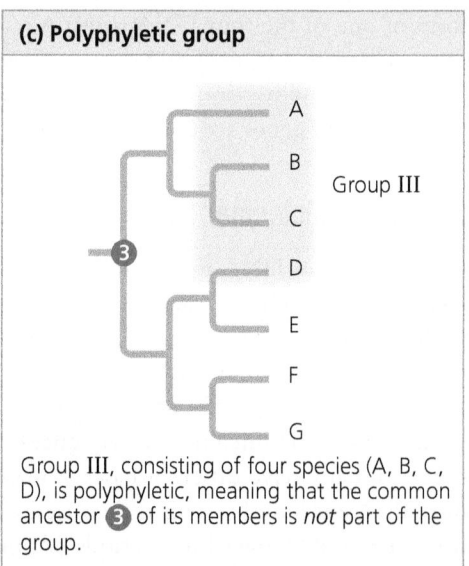

Group III, consisting of four species (A, B, C, D), is polyphyletic, meaning that the common ancestor ❸ of its members is *not* part of the group.

group, whereas in a polyphyletic group the most recent common ancestor *is not* part of the group. For example, a group consisting of even-toed ungulates (hippopotamuses, deer, and their relatives) and their common ancestor is paraphyletic because it includes the common ancestor but excludes cetaceans (whales, dolphins, and porpoises), which descended from that ancestor (Figure 26.11). In contrast, a group consisting of seals and cetaceans (based on their similar body forms) would be polyphyletic because it does not include the common ancestor of seals and cetaceans. Biologists avoid defining such polyphyletic groups; if new evidence indicates that an existing group is polyphyletic, organisms in that group are reclassified.

Shared Ancestral and Shared Derived Characters

As a result of descent with modification, organisms both share characteristics with their ancestors and differ from them. For example, all mammals have backbones, but a backbone does not distinguish mammals from other vertebrates because *all* vertebrates have backbones. The backbone predates the branching of mammals from other vertebrates. Thus for mammals, the backbone is a **shared ancestral character**, a character that originated in an ancestor of the taxon. In contrast, hair is a character shared by all mammals but *not* found in their ancestors. Thus, in mammals, hair is considered a **shared derived character**, an evolutionary novelty unique to a clade.

Note that it is a relative matter whether a particular character is considered ancestral or derived. A backbone can also qualify as a shared derived character, but only at a deeper branch point that distinguishes all vertebrates from other animals.

Inferring Phylogenies Using Derived Characters

Shared derived characters are unique to particular clades. Because all features of organisms arose at some point in the history of life, it should be possible to determine the clade in which each shared derived character first appeared and to use that information to infer evolutionary relationships.

To see how this analysis is done, consider the set of characters shown in Figure 26.12a for each of five vertebrates—a leopard, turtle, frog, bass, and lamprey (a jawless aquatic vertebrate). As a basis of comparison, we need to select an outgroup. An **outgroup** is a species or group of species from an evolutionary lineage that is known to have diverged before the lineage that includes the species we are studying (the **ingroup**). A suitable outgroup can be determined based on evidence from morphology, paleontology, embryonic development, and gene sequences. An appropriate outgroup for our example is the lancelet, a small animal that lives in mudflats and (like vertebrates) is a member of Chordata. Unlike the vertebrates, however, the lancelet does not have a backbone.

By comparing members of the ingroup with each other and with the outgroup, we can determine which characters were derived at the various branch points of vertebrate evolution. For example, *all* of the vertebrates in the ingroup have backbones: This character was present in the ancestral vertebrate, but not in the outgroup. Now note that hinged jaws are a character absent in lampreys but present in other members of the ingroup; this character helps us to identify an early branch point in the vertebrate clade. Proceeding in this way, we can translate the data in our table of characters into a phylogenetic tree that groups all the ingroup taxa into a hierarchy based on their shared derived characters (Figure 26.12b).

Maximum Parsimony and Maximum Likelihood

As the database of DNA sequences that enables us to study more species grows, the difficulty of building the phylogenetic tree that best describes their evolutionary history also grows. What if you are analyzing data for 50 species? There are 3×10^{76} different ways to arrange 50 species into a tree! And which tree in this huge forest reflects the

This group is paraphyletic because it does not include all the descendants of the common ancestor (it excludes cetaceans).

Common ancestor of even-toed ungulates

Other even-toed ungulates

Hippopotamuses

Cetaceans

Seals

Bears

Other carnivores

This group is polyphyletic because it does not include the most recent common ancestor of its members.

▲ Figure 26.11 **Examples of a paraphyletic and a polyphyletic group.**

? *Circle the branch point that represents the most recent common ancestor of cetaceans and seals. Explain why that ancestor would not be part of a cetacean–seal group defined by their similar body forms.*

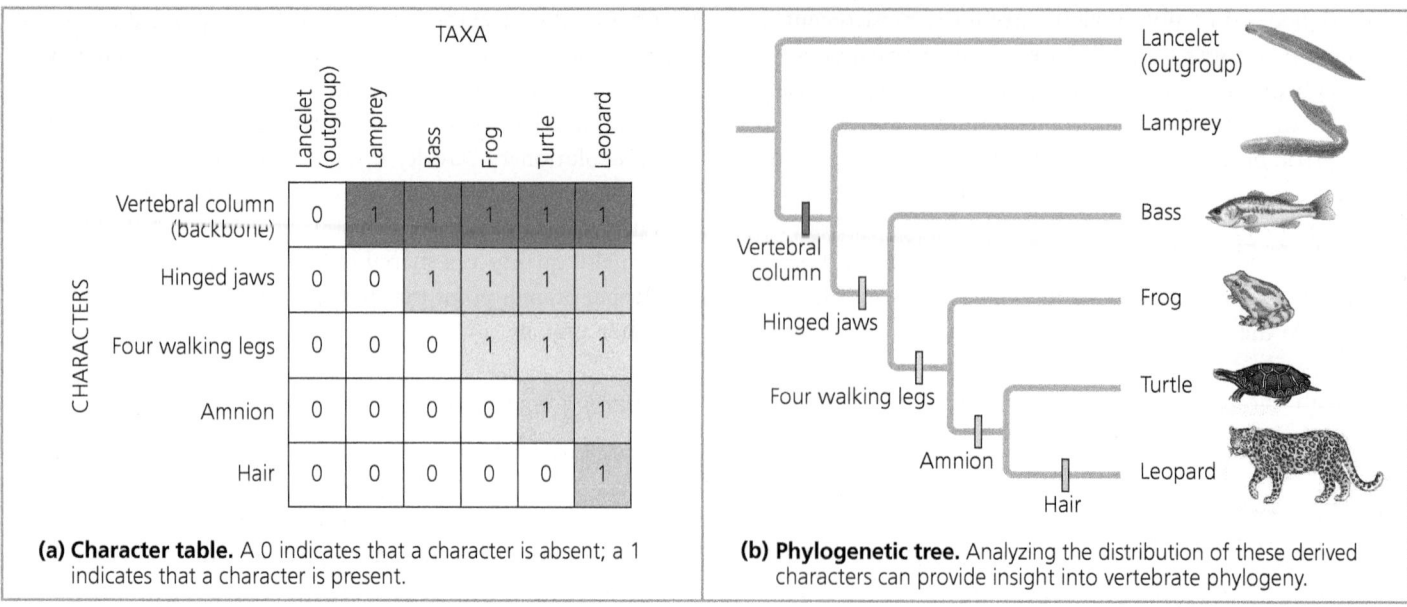

	TAXA					
CHARACTERS	Lancelet (outgroup)	Lamprey	Bass	Frog	Turtle	Leopard
Vertebral column (backbone)	0	1	1	1	1	1
Hinged jaws	0	0	1	1	1	1
Four walking legs	0	0	0	1	1	1
Amnion	0	0	0	0	1	1
Hair	0	0	0	0	0	1

(a) Character table. A 0 indicates that a character is absent; a 1 indicates that a character is present.

(b) Phylogenetic tree. Analyzing the distribution of these derived characters can provide insight into vertebrate phylogeny.

▲ Figure 26.12 **Constructing a phylogenetic tree.** The characters used here include the amnion, a membrane that encloses the embryo inside a fluid-filled sac (see Figure 34.26).

DRAW IT *In (b), circle the most inclusive clade for which a hinged jaw is a shared ancestral character.*

true phylogeny? Systematists can never be sure of finding the most accurate tree in such a large data set, but they can narrow the possibilities by applying the principles of maximum parsimony and maximum likelihood.

According to the principle of **maximum parsimony**, we should first investigate the simplest explanation that is consistent with the facts. (The parsimony principle is also called "Occam's razor" after William of Occam, a 14th-century English philosopher who advocated this minimalist problem-solving approach of "shaving away" unnecessary complications.) In the case of trees based on morphology, the most parsimonious tree requires the fewest evolutionary events, as measured by the origin of shared derived morphological characters. For phylogenies based on DNA, the most parsimonious tree requires the fewest base changes.

A **maximum likelihood** approach identifies the tree most likely to have produced a given set of DNA data, based on certain probability rules about how DNA sequences change over time. For example, the underlying probability rules could be based on the assumption that all nucleotide substitutions are equally likely. However, if evidence suggests that this assumption is not correct, more complex rules could be devised to account for different rates of change among different nucleotides or at different positions in a gene.

Scientists have developed many computer programs to search for trees that are parsimonious and likely. When a large amount of accurate data is available, the methods used in these programs usually yield similar trees. As an example

of one method, Figure 26.13 walks you through the process of identifying the most parsimonious molecular tree for a three-species problem. Computer programs use the principle of parsimony to estimate phylogenies in a similar way: They examine large numbers of possible trees and identify those that require the fewest evolutionary changes.

Interpreting Phylogenetic Trees

It's important to recognize that phylogentic trees are hypotheses about how the various organisms in the tree are related to one another. They are hypotheses not because any biologist disputes the validity of evolution, but because there are many different types of data used to create the tree, and phylogenetic usefulness of these different characteristics (morphological, biochemical, or molecular) is not always known. The best hypothesis is the one that best fits all the available data. A phylogenetic hypothesis may be modified when new evidence compels systematists to revise their trees. Indeed, while many older phylogenetic hypotheses have been supported by new morphological and molecular data, others have been changed or rejected. These trees allow scientists to make testable predictions about the biology of clade members, an example being the bird-crocodile-dinosaur relationships discussed at the beginning of the chapter.

Phylogenetic trees are also intended to show patterns of descent, not phenotypic similarity. Although closely related organisms often resemble one another due to their common ancestry, they may not if their lineages have evolved at

Research Method

Applying Parsimony to a Problem in Molecular Systematics

Application In considering possible phylogenies for a group of species, systematists compare molecular data for the species. An efficient way to begin is by identifying the most parsimonious hypothesis—the one that requires the fewest evolutionary events (molecular changes) to have occurred.

Technique Follow the numbered steps as we apply the principle of parsimony to a hypothetical phylogenetic problem involving three closely related bird species.

Species I   Species II   Species III

1 First, draw the three possible phylogenies for the species. (Although only 3 trees are possible when ordering 3 species, the number of possible trees increases rapidly with the number of species: There are 15 trees for 4 species and 34,459,425 trees for 10 species.)

Three phylogenetic hypotheses:

2 Tabulate the molecular data for the species. In this simplified example, the data represent a DNA sequence consisting of just four nucleotide bases. Data from several outgroup species (not shown) were used to infer the ancestral DNA sequence.

	Site 1	2	3	4
Species I	C	T	A	T
Species II	C	T	T	C
Species III	A	G	A	C
Ancestral sequence	A	G	T	T

3 Now focus on site 1 in the DNA sequence. In the tree on the left, a single base-change event, represented by the purple hatchmark on the branch leading to species I and II (and labelled 1/C, indicating a change at site 1 to nucleotide C), is sufficient to account for the site 1 data. In the other two trees, two base-change events are necessary.

4 Continuing the comparison of bases at sites 2, 3, and 4 reveals that each of the three trees requires a total of five additional base-change events (purple hatchmarks).

Results To identify the most parsimonious tree, we total all of the base-change events noted in steps 3 and 4. We conclude that the first tree is the most parsimonious of the three possible phylogenies. (In a real example, many more sites would be analyzed. Hence, the trees would often differ by more than one base-change event.)

6 events   7 events   7 events

different rates or faced very different environmental conditions. For example, even though crocodiles are more closely related to birds than to lizards (see Figure 22.17), they look more like lizards because morphology has changed dramatically in the bird lineage. In this example, gross morphology may suggest crocodiles and lizards are more closely related to each other than birds, but these traits were not phylogenetically useful. With other data (anatomical, biochemical, molecular, and so on), the closer relationship of birds and crocodiles was obvious and the hypothesis changed.

It's important to understand what exactly is being represented in a particular phylogenetic tree; to do that, you have to know something about how the tree was created. Two main types of trees are often shown: a **cladogram** and a **phylogram**. Most of the trees in this chapter are cladograms, meaning that they depict only the branching order, while the branch lengths and order of the terminal taxa convey no additional information. The chronology represented by the branching pattern of a cladogram is relative (earlier versus later). Cladograms can be displayed in a variety of different ways—with the taxa on the top, to the side, or in a radial pattern (**Figure 26.14**).

Regardless of their format, however, cladograms only depict the sequence in which different clades arose (from a series of common ancestors). The internal nodes can also be freely rotated without altering the interpretation of the tree (Figure 26.14b). No assumptions should be made about when particular species evolved or how much change occurred in each lineage. For example, the tree in Figure 26.5 does not indicate that the black rat evolved more recently than the beaver (compare branch lengths); rather, the tree shows only that the most recent common ancestor of the black rat and beaver (branch point ❶) lived before the most recent common ancestor of the black rat and brown rat ❷.

To determine when the different taxa evolved, you need additional data (see below). With cladograms (or phylograms), you should not assume that a taxon on a phylogenetic tree evolved from the taxon next to it. Though it is commonly said that humans evolved from chimpanzees, this is not the case. We can only say that chimpanzees and humans shared a common ancestor (Figure 26.14d). That ancestor, which is now extinct, was neither a human nor a chimpanzee. The ancestor's characteristics can only be gleaned from the fossil record or through phylogenetic bracketing to predict characteristics shared by the clade that includes both.

Phylograms are like cladograms in that they depict evolutionary patterns, but the branch lengths are proportional to the evolutionary change (**Figure 26.15a**) or to the times at which particular events occurred (**Figure 26.15b**). For phylograms where the branch lengths are proportional to genetic change, the branch length of the phylogenetic tree reflects the number of changes that have taken place in a particular DNA sequence in that lineage. In Figure 26.15a, for example, note that the total length of the horizontal lines from the base of the tree to the chimpanzee is less than that of the line leading to the outgroup species, the squirrel monkey. This implies that in the time since chimpanzees and squirrel monkeys diverged from a common ancestor, more genetic changes have occurred in the squirrel monkey lineage than in the chimpanzee lineage.

Even though the branches of a phylogenetic tree may have different lengths, among organisms alive today, all the different lineages that descend from a common ancestor have survived for the same number of years. To take an extreme example, humans and bacteria had a common ancestor that lived over 3 billion years ago. Fossils and genetic evidence indicate that this ancestor was a single-celled prokaryote. Even though bacteria have apparently changed little in their morphology since that common ancestor, there have nonetheless been 3 billion years of evolution in the bacterial lineage, just as there have been

(a) Rectangular cladogram

Squirrel Monkey
Baboon
Orangutan
Gorilla
Chimpanzee
Human

Many trees have an outgroup. Squirrel monkeys are the outgroup in this example because they are known to have diverged before the other primates on the tree.

(b) Rectangular cladogram-variant

Squirrel Monkey
Orangutan
Chimpanzee
Human
Gorilla
Baboon

Order of terminal taxa is unimportant. Evolutionary trees are like hanging mobiles that allow free rotation around the "nodes." Trees (a) and (b) are identical except the branches were rotated around the indicated node.

(c) Diagonal cladogram

Squirrel Monkey
Baboon
Orangutan
Gorilla
Chimpanzee
Human

Depiction of humans on the bottom does not mean they are "higher" or more evolved. There is no "higher" or "lower" in evolution.

(d) Radial cladogram

Baboon   Orangutan
Squirrel Monkey   Gorilla
Human   Chimpanzee

Chimpanzees and humans share a common ancestor. Humans did not evolve from chimpanzees.

▲ Figure 26.14 **Interpreting cladograms.** With cladograms, only the branching order is important. Branch length and the order of the terminal taxa are irrelevant. Trees (a) to (d) are different styles of cladograms, all depicting identical relationships.

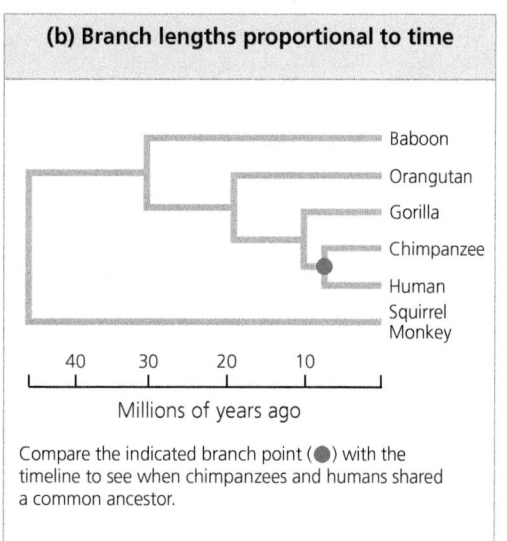

(a) Branch lengths proportional to genetic change

Squirrel Monkey
Baboon
Orangutan
Gorilla
Chimpanzee
Human

Trees constructed by estimating the genetic distance between pairs of sequences usually have a scale representing the number of changes. The longer the branch, the greater the divergence between sequences. This is the most commonly used type of tree.

(b) Branch lengths proportional to time

Baboon
Orangutan
Gorilla
Chimpanzee
Human
Squirrel Monkey

40   30   20   10
Millions of years ago

Compare the indicated branch point (●) with the timeline to see when chimpanzees and humans shared a common ancestor.

▲ **Figure 26.15 Interpreting phylograms.** Phylograms depict evolutionary patterns, but the branch lengths are proportional to an estimate of divergence between species. (a) Branch lengths are proportional to the degree of genetic divergence between pairs of taxa when DNA or protein sequences are compared. (b) Branch lengths are calibrated to time with nodes mapped to the dates based on the fossil evidence.

3 billion years of evolution in the eukaryotic lineage that includes humans. It is important to note that the absolute branch length depends on what genes/protein sequences you are comparing and how the comparisons are calculated. While you may predict that branch lengths would be the same when comparing different genes from the same organisms, it is not the case. Different genes evolve at different rates, and this can change branch lengths—but hopefully not the topology of the tree itself.

Other phylograms can have branch lengths that are proportional to time rather than genetic difference (Figure 26.15b), though these are less common and more difficult to construct. Figure 26.15b is based on the same molecular data as Figure 26.15a, but the branch points are mapped onto the geological time scale. To calibrate the branch lengths in these trees, you require fossil data to place branch points in the context of geological time. In this style of tree, it is obvious that all lineages have diverged from a common ancestor for the same amount of time.

Applying Phylogenies

Phylogenies offer a way to understand biological diversity by putting it in an evolutionary context, but understanding phylogeny can have practical applications. DNA evidence is used to detect illegal hunting, which continues to be a threat to a variety of vertebrate populations. In many cases of suspected poaching, the only evidence is the skin, bone or meat of a particular animal. DNA can be recovered from these samples, and following DNA sequencing, phylogenies can be constructed to determine what animal the sample

came from and, in some cases, which population. In Canada, we have the Wildlife DNA Forensic Laboratory located at Trent University that specializes in the DNA analysis of wildlife for scientific and forensic purposes and whose work has led to the conviction of poachers.

Constructing phylogenies with the sequence of a standardized gene is being used to facilitate species identification (**Figure 26.16**). In 2003, Dr. Paul Hebert from the University of Guelph proposed that the sequence of a mitochondrial gene could be used as a universal "DNA barcode" for species identification. The use of molecular sequence data for classification was not new, but Dr. Hebert proposed that the gene encoding cytochrome oxidase (CO1) could be a universal identification tool for animals. Use of the cytochrome oxidase I gene located on the mitochondrial genome has shown promise as a DNA barcode for identification of species in many eukaryotic groups. One goal of this approach is to make species identification faster, cheaper, and more routine for a nonspecialist, simply from collecting a small tissue sample from the organism of interest. Dr. Hebert is currently leading an international consortium that is developing a comprehensive DNA barcode library for all species (see Figure 21.6).

CONCEPT CHECK 26.3

1. To distinguish a particular clade of mammals within the larger clade that corresponds to class Mammalia, would hair be a useful character? Why or why not?

2. Which of the trees shown here depicts an evolutionary history different from the other two? Explain.

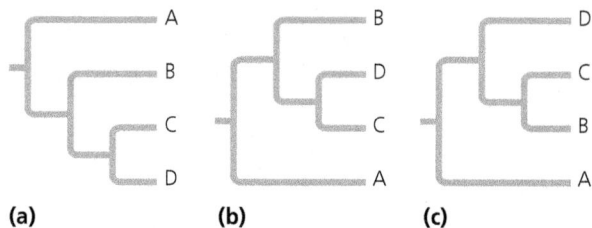

A
B
C
D
(a)

B
D
C
A
(b)

D
C
B
A
(c)

3. **WHAT IF?** Draw a phylogenetic tree that includes the relationships from both Figure 25.7 and Figure 26.3. Traditionally, all the taxa shown besides birds and mammals were classified as reptiles. Would a cladistic approach support that classification? Explain.

For suggested answers, see Appendix A.

Research Method

Using a Molecular Marker for Universal Species Identification

Application Identification of a species is often difficult, requiring a specialist with an understanding of taxonomic keys. In other cases, there may be insufficient phenotypic diversity to easily distinguish species, or the morphology may vary depending on conditions or life stage. Such challenges are obvious in the image of red algae collected at different sites on Canada's western coast. The larger specimen (left) was collected in a sheltered region while the smaller one (right) came from a site exposed to greater wave action. Note the differences in size, blade width, and branching morphology. To a nonspecialist, these may look like two different species.

Technique Cytochrome oxidase (CO1) is a component of the mitochondrial electron transport chain, present in all aerobic eukaryotes. The approach uses PCR (see Figure 20.8) to amplify a portion of the CO1 gene on the mitochondrial genome **1**. This DNA fragment is then sequenced **2** and compared to other CO1 sequences to determine the identity of the species in question.

Gary Saunders

Species identification using the CO1 sequence as a DNA barcode (partial sequence).

Results Within animals, the DNA barcode has been a successful marker for species-level identification. Currently, work is being done on the other eukaryotic groups to test the universality of the CO1 DNA barcode approach. Dr. Gary Saunders at the University of New Brunswick, for instance, has been successfully using the CO1 DNA barcode to differentiate red algal species like the ones shown above. Large databases of reference barcode sequences combined with appropriate morphological analyses should allow scientists to use simple DNA comparison programs to test samples of unknown species to quickly and accurately identify them. One such database is the Barcode of Life Data (BOLD) System.

The CO1 DNA barcode approach provides a cheap, easy, and unbiased method for identifying species. While there is unlikely to be a DNA barcode system to identify all eukaryotes, work is under way to develop other gene systems for targeted groups.

Source: Based on P. D. N. Hebert, A. Cywinska, S. L. Ball, & J. R. deWaard, Biological identifications through DNA barcodes. *Proceedings: Biological Sciences* 270(1512):313–321. doi:10.1098/rspb.2002.2218. © Jane B Reece.

CONCEPT 26.4

An organism's evolutionary history is documented in its genome

As you have seen in this chapter, molecular systematics—using comparisons of nucleic acids or other molecules to deduce relatedness—can reveal phylogenetic relationships that cannot be determined by nonmolecular methods such as comparative anatomy. For example, molecular systematics helps us uncover evolutionary relationships between groups that have little common ground for morphological comparison, such as animals and fungi. And molecular methods allow us to reconstruct phylogenies among groups of present-day organisms for which the fossil record is poor or lacking entirely.

Different genes can evolve at different rates, even in the same evolutionary lineage. As a result, molecular trees can represent short or long periods of time, depending on which genes are used. For example, the DNA that codes for ribosomal RNA (rRNA) changes relatively slowly. Therefore, comparisons of DNA sequences in these genes are useful for investigating relationships between taxa that diverged hundreds of millions of years ago. Studies of rRNA sequences indicate, for instance, that fungi are more closely related to animals than to green plants. In contrast, mitochondrial DNA (mtDNA) evolves relatively rapidly and can be used to explore recent evolutionary events. One research team has traced the relationships among Native American groups through their mtDNA sequences. The molecular findings corroborate other evidence that the Pima of Arizona, the Maya of Mexico, and the Yanomami of Venezuela are closely related, probably descending from the first of three waves of immigrants that crossed the Bering land bridge from Asia to the Americas about 15 000 years ago.

Gene Duplications and Gene Families

What does molecular systematics reveal about the evolutionary history of genome change? Consider gene duplication, which plays a particularly important role in evolution because it increases the number of genes in the genome, providing more opportunities for further evolutionary changes. Molecular techniques now allow us to trace the phylogenies of gene duplications and the influence of these duplications on genome evolution. These molecular phylogenies must account for repeated duplications that have resulted in *gene families*, groups of related genes within an organism's genome (see Figure 21.11).

Accounting for such duplications leads us to distinguish two types of homologous genes: orthologous genes and paralogous genes (see Figure 26.18). **Orthologous genes** (from the Greek *orthos*, exact) are those found in different species, and their divergence traces back to the speciation events that produced the species (Figure 26.17a). For example, the cytochrome *c* genes (which code for an electron transport chain protein) in humans and dogs are orthologous. In **paralogous genes** (from the Greek *para*, in parallel), the homology results from gene duplication; hence, multiple copies of these genes have diverged from one another within a species (Figure 26.17b). In Chapter 23, you encountered the example of olfactory receptor genes, which have undergone many gene duplications in vertebrates; humans have about 390 of these paralogous genes, while mice have more than 1000.

▼ Figure 26.17 **Two types of homologous genes.** Coloured bands mark regions of the genes where differences in base sequences have accumulated.

(a) Formation of orthologous genes: a product of speciation

Ancestral gene

Ancestral species

Speciation with divergence of gene

Orthologous genes

Species A   **Species B**

(b) Formation of paralogous genes: within a species

Ancestral gene

Species C

Gene duplication and divergence

Paralogous genes

Species C after many generations

Note that orthologous genes can only diverge after speciation has taken place, that is, after the genes are found in separate gene pools. For example, although the cytochrome *c* genes in humans and dogs serve the same function, the gene's sequence in humans has diverged from that in dogs in the time since these species last shared a common ancestor. Paralogous genes, on the other hand, can diverge within a species because they are present in more than one copy in the genome. The paralogous genes that make up the olfactory receptor gene family in mice have diverged from each other during their long evolutionary history. They now specify proteins that confer sensitivity to a wide variety of molecules, ranging from food odours to sex pheromones.

Genome Evolution

Now that we can compare the entire genomes of different organisms, including our own, two patterns have emerged. First, lineages that diverged long ago often share many orthologous genes. For example, though the human and mouse lineages diverged about 65 million years ago, 99% of the genes of humans and mice are orthologous. And 50% of human genes are orthologous with those of yeast, despite 1 billion years of divergent evolution. Such commonalities explain why disparate organisms nevertheless share many biochemical and developmental pathways. As a result of these shared pathways, the functioning of genes linked to diseases in humans can often be investigated by studying yeast and other organisms distantly related to humans.

Second, the number of genes a species has doesn't seem to increase through duplication at the same rate as perceived phenotypic complexity. Humans have only about four times as many genes as yeast, a single-celled eukaryote, even though—unlike yeast—we have a large, complex brain and a body with more than 200 different types of tissues. Evidence is emerging that many human genes are more versatile than those of yeast: A single human gene can encode multiple proteins that perform different tasks in various body tissues. Unravelling the mechanisms that cause this genomic versatility and phenotypic variation is an exciting challenge.

CONCEPT CHECK 26.4

1. Explain how comparing proteins of two species can yield data about the species' evolutionary relationship.

2. **WHAT IF?** Suppose gene A is orthologous in species 1 and species 2, and gene B is paralogous to gene A in species 1. Suggest a sequence of two evolutionary events that could result in the following: Gene A differs considerably between species, yet gene A and gene B show little divergence from each other.

3. **MAKE CONNECTIONS** Review Figure 18.13; then suggest how a particular gene could have different functions in different tissues within an organism.

For suggested answers, see Appendix A.

Molecular clocks help track evolutionary time

One goal of evolutionary biology is to understand the relationships among all organisms, including those for which there is no fossil record. However, if we attempt to determine the timing of molecular phylogenies that extend beyond the fossil record, we must rely on an assumption about how change occurs at the molecular level.

Molecular Clocks

We stated earlier that researchers have estimated that the common ancestor of Hawaiian silversword plants lived about 5 million years ago. How did they make this estimate? They relied on the concept of a **molecular clock**, a yardstick for measuring the absolute time of evolutionary change based on the observation that some genes and other regions of genomes appear to evolve at constant rates. The assumption underlying the molecular clock is that the number of nucleotide substitutions in orthologous genes is proportional to the time that has elapsed since the species branched from their common ancestor (divergence time). In the case of paralogous genes, the number of substitutions is proportional to the time since the ancestral gene was duplicated.

We can calibrate the molecular clock of a gene that has a reliable average rate of evolution by graphing the number of genetic differences—for example, nucleotide, codon, or amino acid differences—against the dates of evolutionary branch points that are known from the fossil record (Figure 26.18).

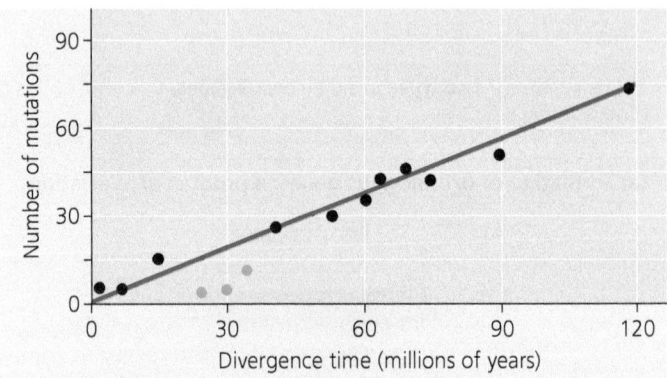

▲ **Figure 26.18 A molecular clock for mammals.** The number of accumulated mutations in seven proteins has increased over time in a consistent manner for most mammal species. The three green data points represent primate species, whose proteins appear to have evolved more slowly than those of other mammals. The divergence time for each data point was based on fossil evidence.

Source: Adaptation of figure 4.3C from Molecular Markers, Natural History, and Evolution, 2nd Edition, by John C. Avise. Copyright © 2004 by Sinauer Associates, Inc. Reprinted with permission.

INTERPRET THE DATA *Use the graph to estimate the divergence time for a mammal with a total of 30 mutations in the seven proteins.*

The average rates of genetic change inferred from such graphs can then be used to estimate the dates of events that cannot be discerned from the fossil record, such as the origin of the silverswords discussed earlier.

Of course, no gene marks time with complete precision. In fact, some portions of the genome appear to have evolved in irregular bursts that are not at all clocklike. And even those genes that seem to act as reliable molecular clocks are accurate only in the statistical sense of showing a fairly smooth *average* rate of change. Over time, there may still be deviations from that average rate. Furthermore, the same gene may evolve at different rates in different groups of organisms. And even among genes that are clocklike, the rate of the clock may vary greatly from one gene to another; some genes evolve a million times faster than others.

Differences in Clock Speed

What causes such differences in the speed at which clocklike genes evolve? The answer stems from the fact that some mutations are selectively neutral—neither beneficial nor detrimental. Of course, many new mutations are harmful and are removed quickly by selection. But if most of the rest are neutral and have little or no effect on fitness, then the rate of evolution of those neutral mutations should indeed be regular, like a clock. Differences in the clock rate for different genes are a function of how important a gene is. If the exact sequence of amino acids that a gene specifies is essential to survival, most of the mutational changes will be harmful and only a few will be neutral. As a result, such genes change only slowly. But if the exact sequence of amino acids is less critical, fewer of the new mutations will be harmful and more will be neutral. Such genes change more quickly.

Potential Problems with Molecular Clocks

In fact, molecular clocks do not run as smoothly as would be expected if the underlying mutations were selectively neutral. Many irregularities are likely to be the result of natural selection, with certain DNA changes favoured over others. Consequently, some scientists question the utility of molecular clocks for timing evolution. Their scepticism is part of a broader debate about the extent to which neutral genetic variation can account for some kinds of DNA diversity. Indeed, evidence suggests that almost half the amino acid differences in proteins of two *Drosophila* species, *D. simulans* and *D. yakuba*, are not neutral but have resulted from directional natural selection. But because the direction of natural selection may change repeatedly over long periods of time (and hence may average out), some genes experiencing selection can nevertheless serve as approximate markers of elapsed time.

Another question arises when researchers attempt to extend molecular clocks beyond the time span documented by the fossil record. Although some fossils are more than 3 billion years old, these are very rare. An abundant fossil record extends back only about 550 million years, but molecular clocks have been used to date evolutionary divergences that occurred a billion or more years ago. These estimates assume that the clocks have been constant for all that time. Such estimates are highly uncertain.

In some cases, problems may be avoided by calibrating molecular clocks with data on the rates at which genes have evolved in different taxa. In other cases, problems may be avoided by using many genes rather than the common approach of using just one or a few genes. By using many genes, fluctuations in evolutionary rate due to natural selection or other factors that vary over time may average out. For example, one group of researchers constructed molecular clocks of vertebrate evolution from published sequence data for 658 nuclear genes. Despite the broad period of time covered (nearly 600 million years) and the fact that natural selection probably affected some of these genes, their estimates of divergence times agreed closely with fossil-based estimates. As this example suggests, if used with care, molecular clocks can aid our understanding of evolutionary relationships.

Applying a Molecular Clock: The Origin of HIV

Researchers have used a molecular clock to date the origin of HIV infection in humans. Phylogenetic analysis shows that HIV, the virus that causes AIDS, is descended from viruses that infect chimpanzees and other primates. (Most of these viruses do not cause AIDS-like diseases in their native hosts.) When did HIV jump to humans? There is no simple answer, because the virus has spread to humans more than once. The multiple origins of HIV are reflected in the variety of strains (genetic types) of the virus. HIV's genetic material is made of RNA, and like other RNA viruses, it evolves quickly.

The most widespread strain in humans is HIV-1 M. To pinpoint the earliest HIV-1 M infection, researchers compared samples of the virus from various times during the epidemic, including a sample from 1959. A comparison of gene sequences showed that the virus has evolved in a clocklike fashion (Figure 26.19). Extrapolating backward in time using the molecular clock indicates that the HIV-1 M strain first spread to humans during the 1930s.

CONCEPT CHECK 26.5

1. What is a molecular clock? What assumption underlies the use of a molecular clock?

2. **MAKE CONNECTIONS** Review Concept 17.5. Explain how numerous base changes could occur in an organism's DNA yet have no effect on its fitness.

3. **WHAT IF?** Suppose a molecular clock dates the divergence of two taxa at 80 million years ago, but new fossil evidence shows that the taxa diverged at least 120 million years ago. Explain how this could happen.

For suggested answers, see Appendix A.

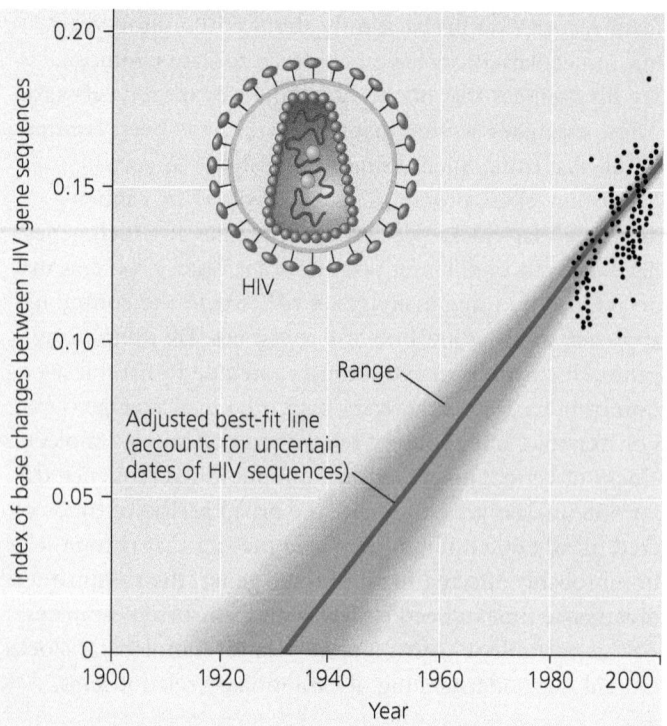

▲ **Figure 26.19 Dating the origin of HIV-1 M.** The black data points are based on DNA sequences of an HIV gene in blood samples collected from patients. (The dates when these individual HIV gene sequences arose are not known with certainty because a person can harbour the virus for years before symptoms occur.) Projecting the gene's rate of change backward in time suggests that the virus originated in the 1930s.

Source: Based on the source: "Timing the Ancestor of the HIV-1 Pandemic Strains" by B. Korber et al., from *Science,* June 2000, Volume 288(5472). © Jane B. Reece.

CONCEPT 26.6

Our understanding of the tree of life continues to change based on new data

In recent decades, we have gained insight into even the very deepest branches of the tree of life through molecular systematics.

From Two Kingdoms to Three Domains

Early taxonomists classified all known species into two kingdoms: plants and animals.

Classification schemes with more than two kingdoms gained broad acceptance in the late 1960s, when many biologists recognized five kingdoms: Monera (prokaryotes), Protista (a diverse kingdom consisting mostly of unicellular organisms), Plantae, Fungi, and Animalia. This system highlighted the two fundamentally different types of cells, prokaryotic and eukaryotic, and set the prokaryotes apart from all eukaryotes by placing them in their own kingdom, Monera.

However, phylogenies based on genetic data soon began to reveal a problem with this system: Some prokaryotes differ as much from each other as they do from eukaryotes. Such difficulties have led biologists to adopt a three-domain system. The three domains—Bacteria, Archaea, and Eukarya—are a

taxonomic level higher than the kingdom level. The validity of these domains is supported by many studies, including a recent study that analyzed nearly 100 completely sequenced genomes.

The domain Bacteria contains most of the currently known prokaryotes, including the bacteria closely related to chloroplasts and mitochondria. The second domain, Archaea, consists of a diverse group of prokaryotic organisms that inhabit a wide variety of environments. The third domain, Eukarya, consists of all the organisms that have cells containing true nuclei. This domain includes many groups of single-celled organisms, multicellular plants, fungi, and animals. **Figure 26.20** represents one possible

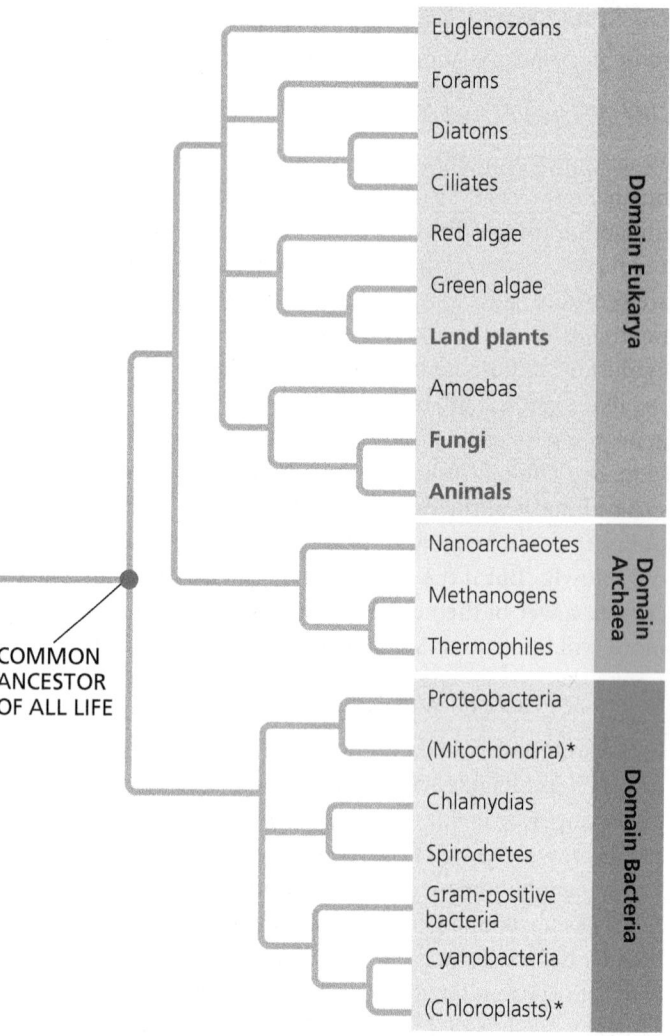

▲ **Figure 26.20 The three domains of life.** This phylogenetic tree is based on sequence data for rRNA and other genes. For simplicity, only some of the major branches in each domain are shown. Lineages within Eukarya that are dominated by multicellular organisms (land plants, fungi, and animals) are in blue type, while the two lineages denoted by an asterisk are based on DNA from cellular organelles. All other lineages consist solely or mainly of single-celled organisms.

MAKE CONNECTIONS *At the start of Unit Five, you were introduced to Dr. Keeling's research, which includes deciphering the endosymbiotic origin of organelles. After reviewing endosymbiont theory (see Figure 6.16), explain the specific positions of the mitochondrion and chloroplast lineages on this tree.*

phylogenetic tree for the three domains and the many lineages they encompass.

The three-domain system highlights the fact that much of the history of life has been about single-celled organisms. The two prokaryotic domains consist entirely of single-celled organisms, and even in Eukarya, only the branches shown in blue type (plants, fungi, and animals) are dominated by multicellular organisms. Of the five kingdoms previously recognized by taxonomists, most biologists continue to recognize Plantae, Fungi, and Animalia, but not Monera and Protista. The kingdom Monera is obsolete because it would have members in two different domains. The kingdom Protista has also crumbled because it includes members that are more closely related to plants, fungi, or animals than to other protists (see Chapter 28).

The Important Role of Horizontal Gene Transfer

In the phylogeny shown in Figure 26.20, the first major split in the history of life occurred when bacteria diverged from other organisms. If this tree is correct, eukaryotes and archaea are more closely related to each other than either is to bacteria.

This reconstruction of the tree of life is based in part on sequence comparisons of rRNA genes, which code for the RNA components of ribosomes. However, some other genes reveal a different set of relationships. For example, researchers have found that many of the genes that influence metabolism in yeast (a unicellular eukaryote) are more similar to genes in the domain Bacteria than they are to genes in the domain Archaea—a finding that suggests that the eukaryotes may share a more recent common ancestor with bacteria than with archaea.

What causes trees based on data from different genes to yield such different results? Comparisons of complete genomes from the three domains show that there have been substantial movements of genes between organisms in the different domains. These took place through **horizontal gene transfer**, a process in which genes are transferred from one genome to another through mechanisms such as exchange of transposable elements and plasmids, viral infection (see Chapter 19), and perhaps fusions of organisms (as when a host and its endosymbiont become a single organism). Recent research reinforces the view that horizontal gene transfer is important. For example, a 2008 analysis indicated that, on average, 80% of the genes in 181 prokaryotic genomes had moved between species at some point during the course of evolution. Because phylogenetic trees are based on the assumption that genes are passed vertically from one generation to the next, the occurrence of such horizontal transfer events

helps to explain why trees built using different genes can give inconsistent results.

Horizontal gene transfer can also occur between eukaryotes. For example, over 200 cases of the horizontal transfer of transposons have been reported in eukaryotes, including humans and other primates, plants, birds, and the gecko shown in **Figure 26.21**. Nuclear genes have also been transferred horizontally from one eukaryote to another. The Scientific Skills Exercise describes one such example, giving you the opportunity to interpret data on the transfer of a pigment gene to an aphid from another species.

Overall, horizontal gene transfer has played a key role throughout the evolutionary history of life and it continues to occur today. Some biologists have argued that horizontal gene transfer was so common that the early history of life should be represented not as a dichotomously branching tree like that in Figure 26.20, but rather as a tangled network of connected branches (**Figure 26.22**). Although scientists continue to debate whether early steps in the history of life are best represented as a tree or a tangled web, in recent decades there have been many exciting discoveries about evolutionary events that occurred over time. We'll explore such discoveries in the rest of this unit's chapters, beginning with Earth's earliest inhabitants, the prokaryotes.

▼ Figure 26.21 **A recipient of transferred genes: the Mediterranean house gecko (*Hemidactylus turcicus*).** Recent genetic evidence indicates that this gecko is one of 17 reptile species that acquired the transposon *SPIN* as a result of horizontal gene transfer. The transposon may have been transferred from one species to another by the feeding activities of blood-sucking insects.

Ilias Strachinis/Shutterstock

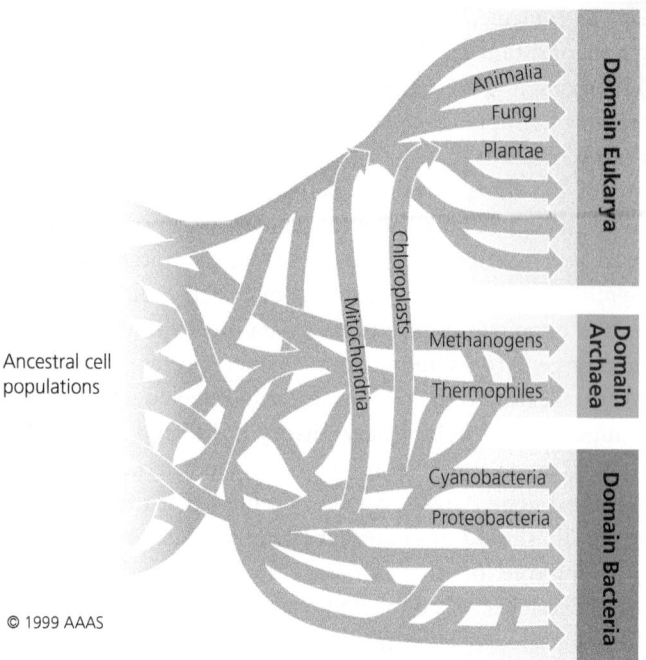

◀ **Figure 26.22 A tangled web of life.** Horizontal gene transfer may have been so common in the early history of life that the base of a "tree of life" might be more accurately portrayed as a tangled web.

Source: Adaptation of figure 3 from "Phylogenetic Classification and the Universal Tree" by W. Ford Doolittle, from *Science*, June 1999, Volume 284(5423). Copyright © 1999 by AAAS. Reprinted with permission.

CONCEPT CHECK 26.6

1. Why is the kingdom Monera no longer considered a valid taxon?

2. Explain why phylogenies based on different genes can yield different branching patterns for the tree of all life.

3. **WHAT IF?** Draw the three possible dichotomously branching trees showing evolutionary relationships for the domains Bacteria, Archaea, and Eukarya. Two of these trees have been supported by genetic data. Is it likely that the third tree might also receive such support? Explain your answer.

For suggested answers, see Appendix A.

SCIENTIFIC SKILLS EXERCISE

Using Protein Sequence Data to Test an Evolutionary Hypothesis

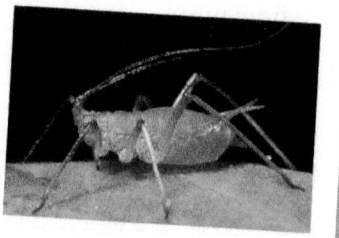

Nigel Cattlin/Alamy

Did Aphids Acquire Their Ability to Make Carotenoids Through Horizontal Gene Transfer? Carotenoids are coloured molecules that have diverse functions in many organisms, such as photosynthesis in plants and light detection in animals. Plants and many microorganisms can synthesize carotenoids from scratch, but animals generally cannot (they must obtain carotenoids from their diet). One exception is the pea aphid *Acyrthosiphon pisum*, a small plant-dwelling insect whose genome includes a full set of genes for the enzymes needed to make carotenoids. Because other animals lack these genes, it is unlikely that aphids inherited them from a single-celled common ancestor shared with microorganisms and plants. So where did they come from? Evolutionary biologists hypothesize that an aphid ancestor acquired these genes by horizontal gene transfer from distantly related organisms.

How the Experiment Was Done Scientists obtained the DNA sequences for the carotenoid-biosynthesis genes from several species, including aphids, fungi, bacteria, and plants. A computer "translated" these sequences into amino acid sequences of the encoded polypeptides and aligned the amino acid sequences. This allowed the team to compare the corresponding polypeptides in the different organisms.

Data from the Experiment The sequences below show the first 60 amino acids of one polypeptide of the carotenoid-biosynthesis enzymes in the plant *Arabidopsis thaliana* (bottom) and the corresponding amino acids in five nonplant species, using the one-letter abbreviations

for the amino acids (see Figure 5.14). A hyphen (-) indicates that a species lacks a particular amino acid found in the *Arabidopsis* sequence.

Interpret the Data

1. In the rows of data for the organisms being compared with the aphid, highlight the amino acids that are identical to the corresponding amino acids in the aphid.

2. Which organism has the most amino acids in common with the aphid? Rank the partial polypeptides from the other four organisms in degree of similarity to that of the aphid.

3. Do these data support the hypothesis that aphids acquired the gene for this polypeptide by horizontal gene transfer? Why or why not? If horizontal gene transfer did occur, what type of organism is likely to have been the source?

4. What additional sequence data would support your hypothesis?

5. How would you account for the similarities between the aphid sequence and the sequences for the bacteria and plant?

Data from Nancy A. Moran, Yale University. See N. A. Moran and T. Jarvik, Lateral transfer of genes from fungi underlies carotenoid production in aphids, *Science* 328:624–627 (2010). © Jane B. Reece.

Organism	Alignment of Amino Acid Sequences					
Acyrthosiphon (aphid)	IKIIIGSGV	GGTAAAARLS	KKGFQVEVYE	KNSYNGGRCS	IIR-HNGHRF	DQGPSL--YL
Ustilago (fungus)	KKVVIIGAGA	GGTALAARLG	RRGYSVTVLE	KNSFGGGRCS	LIH-HDGHRW	DQGPSL--YL
Gibberella (fungus)	KSVIVIGAGV	GGVSTAARLA	KAGFKVTILE	KNDFTGGRCS	LIH-NDGHRF	DQGPSL--LL
Staphylococcus (bacterium)	MKIAVIGAGV	TGLAAAARIA	SQGHEVTIFE	KNNNVGGRMN	QLK-KDGFTF	DMGPTI--VM
Pantoea (bacterium)	KRTFVIGAGF	GGLALAIRLQ	AAGIATTVLE	QHDKPGGRAY	VWQ-DQGFTF	DAGPTV--IT
Arabidopsis (plant)	WDAVVIGGGH	NGLTAAAYLA	RGGLSVAVLE	RRHVIGGAAV	TEEIVPGFKF	SRCSYLQGLL

SUMMARY OF KEY CONCEPTS

CONCEPT 26.1

Phylogenies show evolutionary relationships (pp. 584–586)

- Linnaeus's **binomial** classification system gives organisms two-part names: a **genus** plus a specific epithet.
- In the Linnaean system, species are grouped in increasingly broad taxa: Related genera are placed in the same family, families in orders, orders in classes, classes in phyla, phyla in kingdoms, and (more recently) kingdoms in domains.
- Systematists depict evolutionary relationships as branching **phylogenetic trees**. Many systematists propose that classification be based entirely on evolutionary relationships.

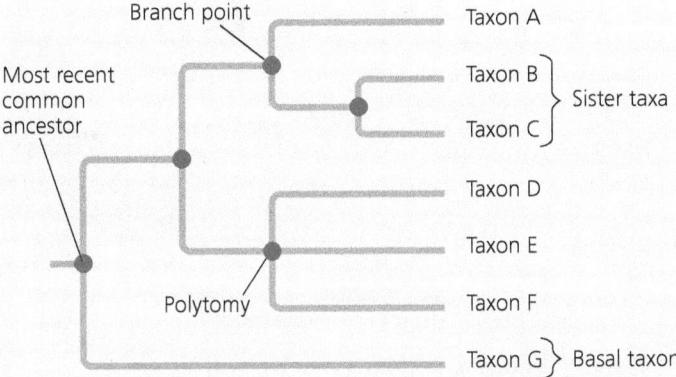

- Phylograms depict evolutionary relationships with branch lengths proportional to time or amount of genetic change; cladograms are phylogenetic trees where only the patterns of descent are meaningful.
- Much information can be learned about a species from its evolutionary history; hence, phylogenies are useful in a wide range of applications.

[?] *Humans and chimpanzees are sister species. Explain what that means.*

CONCEPT 26.2

Phylogenies are inferred from morphological and molecular data (pp. 586–588)

- Organisms with similar morphologies or DNA sequences are likely to be more closely related than organisms with very different structures and genetic sequences.
- To infer phylogeny, **homology** (similarity due to shared ancestry) must be distinguished from **analogy** (similarity due to convergent evolution).
- Computer programs are used to align comparable DNA sequences and to distinguish molecular homologies from coincidental matches between taxa that diverged long ago.

[?] *Why is it necessary to distinguish homology from analogy to infer phylogeny?*

CONCEPT 26.3

Shared characters are used to construct phylogenetic trees (pp. 588–594)

- A **clade** is a monophyletic grouping that includes an ancestral species and all of its descendants.
- Clades can be distinguished by their **shared derived characters**.

- Among phylogenies, the most parsimonious tree is the one that requires the fewest evolutionary changes. The most likely tree is the one based on the most likely pattern of changes.
- Well-supported phylogenetic hypotheses are consistent with a wide range of data.

[?] *Explain the logic of using shared derived characters to infer phylogeny.*

CONCEPT 26.4

An organism's evolutionary history is documented in its genome (pp. 595–596)

- **Orthologous genes** are homologous genes found in different species as a result of speciation. **Paralogous genes** are homologous genes within a species that result from gene duplication; such genes can diverge and potentially take on new functions.
- Distantly related species can have orthologous genes. The small variation in gene number in organisms of varying complexity suggests that genes are versatile and may have multiple functions.

[?] *When reconstructing phylogenies, is it better to compare orthologous or paralogous genes? Explain.*

CONCEPT 26.5

Molecular clocks help track evolutionary time (pp. 596–598)

- Some regions of DNA change at a rate consistent enough to serve as a **molecular clock**, in which the amount of genetic change is used to estimate the date of past evolutionary events. Other DNA regions change in a less predictable way.
- A molecular clock analysis suggests that the most common strain of HIV jumped from primates to humans in the 1930s.

[?] *Describe some assumptions and limitations of molecular clocks.*

CONCEPT 26.6

Our understanding of the tree of life continues to change based on new data (pp. 598–600)

- Past classification systems have given way to the current view of the tree of life, which consists of three great **domains**: Bacteria, Archaea, and Eukarya.
- Phylogenies based on rRNA genes suggest that eukaryotes are most closely related to archaea, while data from some other genes suggest a closer relationship to bacteria.
- Genetic analyses indicate that extensive horizontal gene transfer has occurred throughout the evolutionary history of life.

? *Why was the five-kingdom system abandoned for a three-domain system?*

TEST YOUR UNDERSTANDING

LEVEL 1: KNOWLEDGE/COMPREHENSION

1. In Figure 26.5, which similarly inclusive taxon descended from the same common ancestor as Muroidea?
   a. Sciuridae
   c. Rodentia
   b. Castoridae
   d. *Castor*

2. Three living species X, Y, and Z share a common ancestor T, as do extinct species U and V. A grouping that consists of species T, X, Y, and Z (but not U or V) makes up
   a. a monophyletic clade.
   b. an ingroup, with species U as the outgroup.
   c. a paraphyletic group.
   d. a polyphyletic group.

3. In a comparison of birds and mammals, having four limbs is
   a. a shared ancestral character.
   b. a shared derived character.
   c. a character useful for distinguishing birds from mammals.
   d. an example of analogy rather than homology.

LEVEL 2: APPLICATION/ANALYSIS

4. Based on this tree, which statement is *not* correct?

   - Salamander
   - Lizard
   - Goat
   - Human

   a. The salamander lineage is a basal taxon.
   b. Salamanders are a sister group to the group containing lizards, goats, and humans.
   c. Salamanders are as closely related to goats as to humans.
   d. Lizards are more closely related to salamanders than to humans.

5. If you were using cladistics to build a phylogenetic tree of cats, which of the following would be the best outgroup?
   a. lion
   c. wolf
   b. domestic cat
   d. leopard

6. The relative lengths of the squirrel monkey and gorilla branches in the phylogeny in Figure 26.15 indicate that
   a. squirrel monkeys evolved before gorillas.
   b. gorillas evolved before squirrel monkeys.

   c. the homologue has evolved more slowly in gorillas.
   d. the homologue has evolved more rapidly in gorillas.

LEVEL 3: SYNTHESIS/EVALUATION

7. **EVOLUTION CONNECTION**
   Darwin suggested looking at a species' close relatives to learn what its ancestors may have been like. How does his suggestion anticipate recent methods, such as phylogenetic bracketing and the use of outgroups in cladistic analysis?

8. **SCIENTIFIC INQUIRY**
   DRAW IT (a) Draw a phylogenetic tree based on the first five characters in the table below. Place hatch marks on the tree to indicate the origin(s) of each of the six characters. (b) Assume that tuna and dolphins are sister species and redraw the phylogenetic tree accordingly. Place hatch marks on the tree to indicate the origin(s) of each of the six characters. (c) How many evolutionary changes are required in each tree?

Character	Lancelet (outgroup)	Lamprey	Tuna	Salamander	Turtle	Leopard	Dolphin
Backbone	0	1	1	1	1	1	1
Hinged jaw	0	0	1	1	1	1	1
Four limbs	0	0	0	1	1	1	1*
Amnion	0	0	0	0	1	1	1
Milk	0	0	0	0	0	1	1
Dorsal fin	0	0	1	0	0	0	1

*Although adult dolphins have only two obvious limbs (their flippers), as embryos they have two hind-limb buds, for a total of four limbs.

9. **WRITE ABOUT A THEME: INFORMATION**
   In a short essay (100–150 words), explain how genetic information along with an understanding of the process of descent with modification enables scientists to reconstruct phylogenies that extend hundreds of millions of years back in time.

10. **SYNTHESIZE YOUR KNOWLEDGE**

David Fleetham/Nature Picture Library

This West Indian manatee (*Trichechus manatus*) is an aquatic mammal. Like amphibians and reptiles, mammals are tetrapods (vertebrates with four limbs). Explain why manatees are considered tetrapods even though they lack hind limbs, and suggest traits that manatees likely share with leopards and other mammals (see Figure 26.12b). How might early members of the manatee lineage have differed from today's manatees?

For selected answers, see Appendix A.

27

Bacteria and Archaea

KEY CONCEPTS

27.1 Structural and functional adaptations contribute to prokaryotic success

27.2 Rapid reproduction, mutation, and genetic recombination promote genetic diversity in prokaryotes

27.3 Diverse nutritional and metabolic adaptations have evolved in prokaryotes

27.4 Prokaryotes have radiated into a diverse set of lineages

27.5 Prokaryotes play crucial roles in the biosphere

27.6 Prokaryotes have both beneficial and harmful impacts on humans

David Nunuk/Science Source

▲ Figure 27.1 **Why is this tailings pond releasing methane?**

Masters of Adaptation

The oil sands in northern Alberta represent one of the largest oil reserves in the world with an estimated 170 billion barrels of oil embedded within the sandy-clay soil. Extracting this important resource requires more energy than traditional well reserves and is dependent on tremendous volumes of water, steam, and solvents. The waste from this process, called tailings, is contained in ponds like the one shown above **(Figure 27.1)**. The tailings composition varies depending on the extraction method and on the age and mineralogy of the oil-sands resource, but in general it is a mixture of sand, inorganic (heavy metals) and organic (benzene, toluene, and so on) contaminants, solvents, processing additives, and residual hydrocarbons, covered by an oily slick. This is a toxic environment for flora and fauna alike, but for many microbes, this mixture of chemicals represents a source of energy. The prokaryotes that make these tailings ponds their home can have significant impacts on toxicity and emissions. The presence of methanogens, prokaryotes that utilize organic carbon and release methane, have posed a particular problem. While estimates of the amount of methane released vary widely, the Mildred Lake Settling Basin (around 22 km^2) conservatively may emit over 16 billion litres of methane per year, equivalent to the methane released from 250 000 cattle! Since methane is a more potent greenhouse gas than carbon dioxide, under-standing the microbiology of tailings ponds is increasingly important. A Canadian research initiative, the Hydrocarbon Metagenome Project, centred at the Universities of Calgary and Alberta, is seeking to identify the microbial communities that inhabit tailings ponds through random sequencing DNA isolated from these environments. This may improve our understanding of the conditions that can lead to the microbial production of methane, carbon dioxide, or hydrogen sulphide. Ultimately, the ponds inhabitants may be used for biotechnological approaches to reduce emissions and help remediate these areas.

Prokaryotes are indeed masters of adaptation and live in the most unexpected places. The Great Salt Lake in Utah can reach salinities that are 32% higher than seawater, yet the abundance of prokaryotes, such as *Halobacterium*, can be so high that they colour the water pink. This ability to tolerate such high salt levels is due to compensatory activity of K^+ pumps, which helps balance the ionic concentration inside the cell so that the cells don't lose water through osmosis. Other prokaryotes can tolerate the cold temperatures under glaciers in the Canadian Arctic, thrive in hot springs above the boiling temperature of water, or, like *Picrophilus oshimae,* can grow at a pH of 0.03 (acidic enough to dissolve metal). Some have even been found living in rocks 3.2 km below Earth's surface. But perhaps the most impressive is *Deinococcus radiodurans,* which can survive 3 million rads of radiation (3000 times the dose fatal to humans). At this level of radiation, D. *radiodurans'* DNA is shattered into hundreds of pieces, an occurrence that would be fatal to most other organisms. However, this bacterium has an amazing ability to piece together the fragmented chromosome using a special repair and recombination mechanism.

Prokaryotic species are also very well adapted to more "normal" habitats—the lands and waters in which most other species are found. Their ability to adapt to a broad range of habitats helps explain why prokaryotes are the most abundant organisms on Earth: The number of prokaryotes in a handful of fertile soil is greater than the number of people who have ever lived. In this chapter, we'll examine the adaptations, diversity, and enormous ecological impact of these tiny organisms.

CONCEPT 27.1

Structural and functional adaptations contribute to prokaryotic success

The first organisms to inhabit Earth were prokaryotes that lived 3.5 billion years ago (Chapter 25). Throughout their long evolutionary history, prokaryotic populations have been (and continue to be) subjected to natural selection

in all kinds of environments, resulting in their enormous diversity today.

Prokaryotes have a variety of distinctive shapes (Figure 27.2) and are unicellular, though the cells of some species remain attached to each other after cell division. Prokaryotic cells typically have diameters of 0.5–5 μm, much smaller than the 10–100 μm diameter of many eukaryotic cells. (One notable exception, *Thiomargarita namibiensis*, can be 750 μm across—bigger than the dot on this i.) Finally, although they are unicellular and small, prokaryotes are well organized, achieving all of an organism's life functions within a single cell.

Cell-Surface Structures

A key feature of nearly all prokaryotic cells is the cell wall, which maintains cell shape, protects the cell, and prevents it from bursting in a hypotonic environment (see Chapter 7). In a hypertonic environment, most prokaryotes lose water and shrink away from their wall (plasmolyze). Such water losses can inhibit cell reproduction. Thus, salt can be used to preserve foods because it causes prokaryotes to lose water, preventing them from rapidly multiplying.

The cell walls of prokaryotes differ in structure from those of eukaryotes. In eukaryotes that have cell walls, such as plants and fungi, the walls are usually made of cellulose or chitin (see Chapter 5). In contrast, most bacterial cell walls contain **peptidoglycan**, a polymer composed of

(a) Spherical **(b) Rod-shaped** **(c) Spiral**

▲ Figure 27.2 **The most common shapes of prokaryotes. (a)** Cocci (singular, *coccus*) are spherical prokaryotes. They occur singly, in pairs (diplococci), in chains of many cells (streptococci), and in clusters resembling bunches of grapes (staphylococci). **(b)** Bacilli (singular, *bacillus*) are rod-shaped prokaryotes. They are usually solitary, but in some forms the rods are arranged in chains (streptobacilli). **(c)** Spiral prokaryotes include spirilla, which range from comma-like shapes to loose coils, and spirochetes (shown here), which are corkscrew-shaped (colourized SEMs).

(a) Gram-positive bacteria

Gram-positive bacteria

Cell wall — Peptido-glycan layer

Plasma membrane

10 μm

L. Brent Selinger/ Pearson Education

Gram-positive bacteria have a thick wall made of peptidoglycan. The crystal violet enters the cell, where it forms a complex with the iodine in the stain. Too large to pass through the thick cell wall, this complex is not removed by the alcohol rinse. Result: The crystal violet masks the red safranin dye.

(b) Gram-negative bacteria

Gram-negative bacteria

Carbohydrate portion of lipopolysaccharide

Cell wall — Outer membrane, Peptido-glycan layer

Plasma membrane

Gram-negative bacteria have a thin layer of peptidoglycan, which is located between the plasma membrane and an outer membrane. The crystal violet–iodine complex can pass through this thin cell wall and hence is removed by the alcohol rinse. Result: The safranin dye stains the cell pink or red.

modified sugars cross-linked by short polypeptides. This molecular fabric encloses the entire bacterium and anchors other molecules that extend from its surface. Archaeal cell walls contain a variety of polysaccharides and proteins but lack peptidoglycan.

Using a technique called the **Gram stain**, developed by the nineteenth-century Danish physician Hans Christian Gram, scientists can classify many bacterial species into two groups based on differences in cell wall composition. Samples are first stained with crystal violet dye and iodine, then rinsed in alcohol, and finally stained with a red dye such as safranin. The structure of a bacterium's cell wall determines the staining response (**Figure 27.3**). **Gram-positive** bacteria have simpler walls with a relatively large amount of peptidoglycan. **Gram-negative** bacteria have less peptidoglycan and are structurally more complex, with an outer membrane that contains lipopolysaccharides (carbohydrates bonded to lipids).

Gram staining is a valuable tool in medicine for quickly determining if a patient's infection is due to gram-negative or to gram-positive bacteria. This information has treatment implications. The lipid portions of the lipopolysaccharides in the walls of many gram-negative bacteria are toxic, causing fever or shock. Furthermore, the outer membrane of a gram-negative bacterium helps protect it from the body's defences. Gram-negative bacteria also tend to be more resistant than gram-positive species to antibiotics because the outer membrane impedes entry of the drugs. However, certain gram-positive species have

virulent strains that are resistant to one or more antibiotics. (Figure 22.14 discusses one example: multidrug-resistant *Staphylococcus aureus*, which can cause lethal skin infections.)

The effectiveness of certain antibiotics, such as penicillin, derives from their inhibition of peptidoglycan cross-linking. The resulting cell wall may not be functional, particularly in gram-positive bacteria. Such drugs destroy many species of pathogenic bacteria without adversely affecting human cells, which do not have peptidoglycan.

The cell wall of many prokaryotes is surrounded by a sticky layer of polysaccharide or protein. This layer is called a **capsule** if it is dense and well-defined (**Figure 27.4**) or a *slime layer* if it is less well organized. Both kinds of sticky

Bacterial cell wall

Bacterial capsule

Tonsil cell

200 nm

Dr. Immo Rantala/SPL\Science Source

▲ **Figure 27.4 Capsule.** The polysaccharide capsule around this *Streptococcus* bacterium enables the prokaryote to attach to cells in the respiratory tract—in this colourised TEM, a tonsil cell.

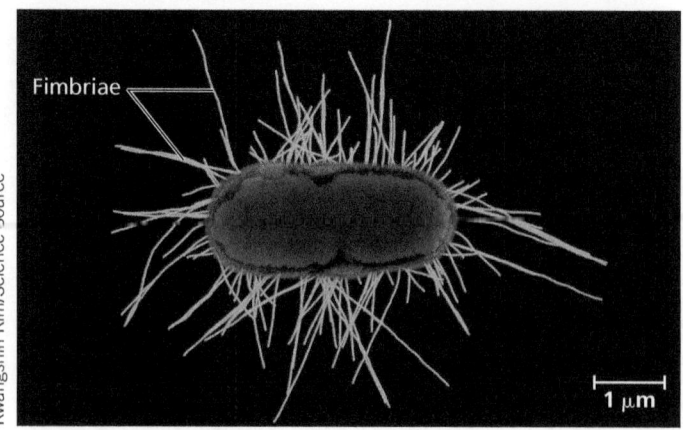

Kwangshin Kim/Science Source

▲ **Figure 27.5 Fimbriae.** These numerous protein-containing appendages enable some prokaryotes to attach to surfaces or to other cells (colourized TEM).

H.S. Pankratz, T.C. Beaman/Biological Photo Service

▲ **Figure 27.6 An endospore.** *Bacillus anthracis*, the bacterium that causes the disease anthrax, produces endospores (TEM). An endospore's protective, multilayered coat helps it survive in the soil for years.

outer layers enable prokaryotes to adhere to their substrate or to other individuals in a colony. Some capsules and slime layers protect against dehydration, and some shield pathogenic prokaryotes from attacks by their host's immune system.

Some prokaryotes stick to their substrate or to one another by means of hairlike appendages called **fimbriae** (singular, *fimbria*) (Figure 27.5). For example, the bacterium that causes gonorrhea, *Neisseria gonorrhoeae*, uses fimbriae to fasten itself to the mucous membranes of its host. Fimbriae are usually shorter and more numerous than **pili** (singular, *pilus*), appendages that pull two cells together prior to DNA transfer from one cell to the other (see Figure 27.12); pili are sometimes referred to as *sex pili*.

Endospores

The ability of some prokaryotes to withstand harsh conditions also contributes to their success. Some can live in harsh environments because of particular biochemical or structural adaptations; others use a strategy of creating a resistant form and waiting for conditions to improve. Certain bacteria develop resistant cells called **endospores** when they lack an essential nutrient (Figure 27.6). The original cell produces a copy of its chromosome and surrounds it with a tough multilayered structure, forming the endospore. Water is removed from the endospore, and its metabolism halts. The original cell then lyses, releasing the endospore. Most endospores are so durable that they can survive in boiling water; killing them requires heating lab equipment to 121°C under high pressure. In less hostile environments, endospores can remain dormant but viable for centuries, able to rehydrate and resume metabolism when their environment improves. *Bacillus anthracis* (Figure 27.6), which causes anthrax in livestock and humans, produces a resistant endospore that can remain dormant in the soil for decades and become reactive upon inhalation or ingestion. It is because

of this stability and the serious illness the bacterium causes that anthrax is a bioterrorism concern.

Motility

About half of all prokaryotes are capable of **taxis**, a directed movement toward or away from a stimulus (from the Greek *taxis*, to arrange). For example, prokaryotes that exhibit *chemotaxis* change their movement pattern in response to chemicals. They may move *toward* nutrients or oxygen (positive chemotaxis) or *away from* a toxic substance (negative chemotaxis). Some species can move at velocities exceeding 50 μm/sec—up to 50 times their body length per second. For perspective, consider that a person 1.7 m tall moving that fast would be running 306 km per hour!

Of the various structures that enable prokaryotes to move, the most common are flagella (Figure 27.7). Flagella (singular, *flagellum*) may be scattered over the entire surface of the cell or concentrated at one or both ends. Prokaryotic flagella differ greatly from eukaryotic flagella: They are one-tenth the width and are not covered by an extension of the plasma membrane (see Figure 6.24). The flagella of prokaryotes are also very different in their molecular composition and their mechanism of propulsion. Among prokaryotes, bacterial and archaeal flagella are similar in size and rotation mechanism, but they are composed of different proteins. Overall, these structural and molecular comparisons suggest that the flagella of bacteria, archaea, and eukaryotes arose independently. Since the flagella of organisms in the three domains perform similar functions but probably are not related by common descent, it is likely that they are analogous, not homologous, structures.

Evolutionary Origins of Bacterial Flagella

The bacterial flagellum shown in Figure 27.7 has three main parts (the motor, hook, and filament) that are themselves composed of 42 different kinds of proteins. How could such

Figure 27.7 **A prokaryotic flagellum.** The motor of a prokaryotic flagellum consists of a system of rings embedded in the cell wall and plasma membrane (TEM). ATP-driven pumps in the motor transport protons out of the cell. The diffusion of protons back into the cell provides the force that turns a curved hook and thereby causes the attached filament to rotate and propel the cell. (This diagram shows flagellar structures characteristic of gram-negative bacteria.)

Julius Adler

20 nm

a complex structure evolve? In fact, much evidence indicates that bacterial flagella originated as simpler structures that were modified in a stepwise fashion over time. As in the case of the human eye (see Concept 25.6), biologists asked whether a less complex version of the flagellum could still benefit its owner. Analyses of hundreds of bacterial genomes indicate that only half of the flagellum's protein components appear to be necessary for it to function; the others are inessential or not encoded in the genomes of some species. Of the 21 proteins required by all species studied to date, 19 are modified versions of proteins that perform other tasks in bacteria. For example, a set of 10 proteins in the motor are homologous to 10 similar proteins in a secretory system found in bacteria. (A secretory system is a protein complex that enables a cell to secrete certain macromolecules.) Two other proteins in the motor are homologous to proteins that function in ion transport. The proteins that comprise the rod, hook, and filament are all related to each other and are descended from an ancestral protein that formed a pilus-like tube. These findings suggest that the bacterial flagellum evolved as other proteins were added to an ancestral secretory system. This is an example of *exaptation*, the process in which existing structures take on new functions through descent with modification.

Internal Organization and DNA

The cells of prokaryotes are simpler than those of eukaryotes in both their internal structure and the physical

arrangement of their DNA (see Figure 6.5). Prokaryotic cells lack the complex compartmentalization found in eukaryotic cells. However, some prokaryotic cells do have specialized membranes that perform metabolic functions **(Figure 27.8)**. These membranes are usually infoldings of the plasma membrane.

The genome of a prokaryote is structurally different from a eukaryotic genome and in most cases has considerably less DNA. In the majority of prokaryotes, the genome consists of a circular chromosome with many fewer proteins than found in the linear chromosomes of eukaryotes **(Figure 27.9)**. Also unlike eukaryotes, prokaryotes lack a membrane-bounded nucleus; their chromosome is located in the **nucleoid**, a region of cytoplasm that appears lighter than the surrounding cytoplasm in electron micrographs. In addition to its single chromosome, a typical prokaryotic cell may also have much smaller rings of independently replicating DNA molecules called **plasmids** (see Figure 27.9), most carrying only a few genes.

As explained in Chapters 16 and 17, DNA replication, transcription, and translation are fundamentally similar processes in prokaryotes and eukaryotes, although there are some differences. For example, prokaryotic ribosomes are slightly smaller than eukaryotic ribosomes and differ in their protein and RNA content. These differences allow certain antibiotics, such as erythromycin and tetracycline, to bind to ribosomes and block protein synthesis in prokaryotes but not in eukaryotes. As a result, people can use

0.2 μm

Respiratory membrane

S.W. Watson/Copyright Clearance Center

(a) Aerobic prokaryote

1 μm

Thylakoid membranes

N.J. Lang/Biological Photo Service

(b) Photosynthetic prokaryote

▲ Figure 27.8 **Specialized membranes of prokaryotes. (a)** Infoldings of the plasma membrane, reminiscent of the cristae of mitochondria, function in cellular respiration in some aerobic prokaryotes (TEM). **(b)** Photosynthetic prokaryotes called cyanobacteria have thylakoid membranes, much like those in chloroplasts (TEM).

Chromosome

Plasmids

1 μm

Huntington Potter

▲ **Figure 27.9** **A prokaryotic chromosome and plasmids.** The thin, tangled loops surrounding this ruptured *E. coli* cell are parts of the cell's large, circular chromosome (colourized TEM). Two of the cell's plasmids, the much smaller rings of DNA, are also shown.

these antibiotics to kill or inhibit the growth of bacteria. However, this approach is not without side-effects since mitochondria have a translational system similar to that of prokaryotes, from which they evolved.

Reproduction

Prokaryotes are highly successful in part because of their potential to reproduce quickly in a favourable environment. By *binary fission* (see Figure 12.12), a single prokaryotic cell divides into 2 cells, which then divide into 4, 8, 16, and so on. Under optimal conditions, many prokaryotes can divide every 1–3 hours; some species can produce a new generation in only 20 minutes. If reproduction continued unchecked at this rate, a single prokaryotic cell could give rise to a colony outweighing Earth in only two days!

In reality, of course, prokaryotic reproduction is limited. The cells eventually exhaust their nutrient supply, poison themselves with metabolic wastes, face competition from other microorganisms, or are consumed by other organisms. For example, the well-studied bacterium *Escherichia coli* can divide every 20 minutes under ideal lab conditions, one reason it is used as a model organism in research. However, when growing in a human intestine, one of its natural environments, *E. coli* cells divide only once every 12–24 hours. But whether cell division occurs every 20 minutes or every few days, reproduction in prokaryotes draws attention to three key features of their biology: *They are small, they reproduce by binary fission, and they have short generation times.* As a result, prokaryotic populations can consist of many trillions of individuals—far more than populations of multicellular eukaryotes, such as plants and animals.

CONCEPT CHECK 27.1

1. Identify and explain at least two adaptations that enable prokaryotes to survive in environments too harsh for other organisms.

2. Contrast the cellular and DNA structures of prokaryotes and eukaryotes.

3. **MAKE CONNECTIONS** Suggest a hypothesis to explain why the thylakoid membranes of chloroplasts resemble those of cyanobacteria. Refer to Figure 6.18 and Figure 26.20.

For suggested answers, see Appendix A.

CONCEPT **27.2**

Rapid reproduction, mutation, and genetic recombination promote genetic diversity in prokaryotes

As we discussed in Unit Four, genetic variation is a prerequisite for natural selection to occur in a population. The diverse adaptations exhibited by prokaryotes suggest that their populations must have considerable genetic variation—and they do. For example, a ribosomal RNA gene can differ more between two strains of *E. coli* than it does between a human and a platypus. In this section, we'll examine three factors that give rise to high levels of genetic diversity in prokaryotes: rapid reproduction, mutation, and genetic recombination.

Rapid Reproduction and Mutation

In sexually reproducing species, the generation of a novel allele by a new mutation is rare for any particular gene. Instead, most of the genetic variation in sexual populations results from the way existing alleles are arranged in new combinations during meiosis and fertilization (see Chapter 13). Prokaryotes do not reproduce sexually, so at first glance their extensive genetic variation may seem puzzling. But in many species, this variation can result from a combination of rapid reproduction and mutation.

Consider the bacterium *Escherichia coli* as it reproduces by binary fission in a human intestine, one of its natural environments. After repeated rounds of division, most of the offspring cells are genetically identical to the original parent cell. However, if errors occur during DNA replication, some of the offspring cells may differ genetically. The probability of such a mutation occurring in a given *E. coli* gene is about one in 10 million (1×10^{-7}) per cell division. But among the 2×10^{10} new *E. coli* cells that arise each day in a person's intestine, there will be approximately ($2 \times 10^{10}) \times (1 \times 10^{-7}) = 2000$ bacteria that have a mutation in that gene. The total number of mutations when all 4300 *E. coli* genes are considered is about $4300 \times 2000 = 9$ million per day per human host.

The key point is that new mutations, though rare on a per gene basis, can increase genetic diversity quickly in species with short generation times and large populations. This diversity, in turn, can lead to rapid evolution: Individuals that are genetically better equipped for their environment tend to survive and reproduce at higher rates than other individuals (**Figure 27.10**). The ability of prokaryotes to adapt rapidly to new conditions highlights the point that although the structure of their cells is simpler than that of eukaryotic cells, prokaryotes are not "primitive" or "inferior" in an evolutionary sense. They are, in fact, highly evolved: For 3.5 billion years, prokaryotic populations have responded successfully to many types of environmental challenges.

Genetic Recombination

Although new mutations are a major source of variation in prokaryotic populations, additional diversity arises from *genetic recombination*, the combining of DNA from two sources. In eukaryotes, the sexual processes of meiosis and fertilization combine DNA from two individuals in a single zygote. But meiosis and fertilization do not occur in prokaryotes. Instead, three other mechanisms—transformation, transduction, and conjugation—can bring together prokaryotic DNA from different individuals (that is, cells). When the individuals are members of different species, this movement of genes from one organism to another is called *horizontal gene transfer* (in contrast to *vertical gene transfer,* the movement of genes from parent to offspring). Although scientists have found evidence that each of these mechanisms can transfer DNA within and between species in both domain Bacteria and domain Archaea, to date most of our knowledge comes from research on bacteria.

Transformation and Transduction

In **transformation**, the genotype and possibly phenotype of a prokaryotic cell are altered by the uptake of foreign DNA from its surroundings. For example, a harmless strain of *Streptococcus pneumoniae* can be transformed into pneumonia-causing cells if the cells are placed in a medium containing DNA from a pathogenic strain (see p. 330). This transformation occurs when a nonpathogenic cell takes up a piece of DNA carrying the allele for pathogenicity and replaces its own allele with the foreign allele, an exchange of homologous DNA segments. The cell is now a recombinant: Its chromosome contains DNA derived from two different cells.

For many years after transformation was discovered in laboratory cultures, most biologists thought the process to be too rare and haphazard to play an important role in natural bacterial populations. But researchers have since learned that many bacteria have cell-surface proteins that recognize

▼ Figure 27.10 | Inquiry

Can prokaryotes evolve rapidly in response to environmental change?

Experiment Vaughn Cooper and Richard Lenski, of Michigan State University, tested the ability of *E. coli* populations to adapt to a new environment. They established 12 populations, each founded by a single cell from an *E. coli* strain, and followed these populations for 20 000 generations (3000 days). To maintain a continual supply of resources, each day the researchers performed a *serial transfer*: They transferred 0.1 mL of each population to a new tube containing 9.9 mL of fresh growth medium. The growth medium used throughout the experiment provided a challenging environment that contained only low levels of glucose and other resources needed for growth.

Daily serial transfer

0.1 mL (population sample)

Old tube (discarded after transfer)

New tube (9.9 mL growth medium)

Samples were periodically removed from the 12 populations and grown in competition with the common ancestral strain in the experimental (low-glucose) environment.

Results The fitness of the experimental populations, as measured by the rate at which each population grew, increased rapidly for the first 5000 generations (two years) and more slowly for the next 15 000 generations. The graph below shows the averages for the 12 populations.

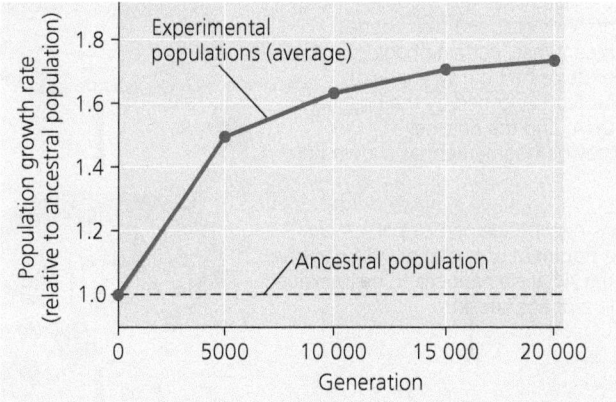

Source: Adaptation of Figure 1 from "The Population Genetics of Ecological Specialization in Evolving Escherichia Coli Populations" by Vaughn S. Cooper and Richard E. Lenski, from NATURE, October 12, 2000, Volume 407(679). Copyright © 2000 by Macmillan Publishers Ltd. Reprinted with permission.

Conclusion Populations of *E. coli* continued to accumulate beneficial mutations for 20 000 generations, allowing rapid evolution of improved performance in their new environment.

Source: Based on V. S. Cooper and R. E. Lenski, The population genetics of ecological specialization in evolving *Escherichia coli* populations, *Nature* 407:736–739 (2000). © Jane B Reece.

WHAT IF? *Suggest possible functions of the genes whose sequence or expression was altered as the experimental populations evolved in the low-glucose environment.*

DNA from closely related species and transport it into the cell. Once inside the cell, the foreign DNA can be incorporated into the genome by homologous DNA exchange.

In **transduction**, phages (from "bacteriophages," the viruses that infect bacteria) carry prokaryotic genes from one host cell to another. In most cases, transduction results from accidents that occur during the phage replicative cycle (**Figure 27.11**). A virus that carries prokaryotic DNA may not be able to replicate because it lacks some or all of its own genetic material. However, the virus can attach to another prokaryotic cell (a recipient) and inject prokaryotic DNA acquired from the first cell (the donor). If some of this DNA is then incorporated into the recipient cell's chromosome by DNA recombination, a recombinant cell is formed.

Conjugation and Plasmids

In a process called **conjugation**, DNA is transferred between two prokaryotic cells (usually of the same species)

❶ A phage infects a bacterial cell that carries the A^+ and B^+ alleles on its chromosome (brown). This bacterium will be the "donor" cell.

❷ The phage DNA is replicated, and the cell makes many copies of the proteins encoded by its genes. Meanwhile, certain phage proteins halt the synthesis of proteins encoded by the host cell's DNA, and the host cell's DNA may be fragmented, as shown here.

❸ As new phage particles assemble, a fragment of bacterial DNA carrying the A^+ allele happens to be packaged in a phage capsid.

❹ The phage carrying the A^+ allele from the donor cell infects a recipient cell with alleles A^- and B^-. Crossing over at two sites (dotted lines) allows donor DNA (brown) to be incorporated into recipient DNA (green).

❺ The genotype of the resulting recombinant cell (A^+B^-) differs from the genotypes of both the donor (A^+B^+) and the recipient (A^-B^-).

Phage DNA
Donor cell
Crossing over
Recipient cell
Recombinant cell
$A^+ B^+$
$A^+ B^+$
A^+
A^+
$A^- B^-$
$A^+ B^-$

▲ **Figure 27.11 Transduction.** Phages may carry pieces of a bacterial chromosome from one cell (the donor) to another (the recipient). If recombination occurs after the transfer, genes from the donor may be incorporated into the recipient's genome.

❓ *Under what circumstances would transduction result in horizontal gene transfer?*

Sex pilus
1 μm
Charles C. Brinton, Jr.

▲ **Figure 27.12 Bacterial conjugation.** The *E. coli* donor cell (left) extends a pilus that attaches to a recipient cell, a key first step in the transfer of DNA. The pilus is a flexible tube of protein subunits (TEM).

that are temporarily joined. In bacteria, the DNA transfer is always one way: One cell donates the DNA, and the other receives it. The best-understood mechanism is that used by *E. coli*, and we will focus on this organism for the rest of this section. In *E. coli*, a pilus of the donor cell attaches to the recipient (**Figure 27.12**). The pilus then retracts, pulling the two cells together, much like a grappling hook. The next step is thought to be the formation of a temporary "mating bridge" between the two cells, through which the donor may transfer DNA to the recipient. This is an unsettled issue, however, and recent evidence indicates that DNA may pass directly through the pilus, which is hollow.

In either case, the ability to form pili and donate DNA during conjugation results from the presence of a particular piece of DNA called the **F factor** (F for *f*ertility). The F factor of *E. coli* consists of about 25 genes, most required for the production of pili. The F factor can exist either as a plasmid or as a segment of DNA within the bacterial chromosome.

The F Factor as a Plasmid The F factor in its plasmid form is called the **F plasmid**. Cells containing the F plasmid, designated F^+ cells, function as DNA donors during conjugation. Cells lacking the F factor, designated F^-, function as DNA recipients during conjugation. The F^+ condition is transferrable in the sense that an F^+ cell converts an F^- cell to F^+ if a copy of the entire F plasmid is transferred (**Figure 27.13a**).

The F Factor in the Chromosome Chromosomal genes can be transferred during conjugation when the donor cell's F factor is integrated into the chromosome. A cell with the F factor built into its chromosome is called an *Hfr* cell (for *h*igh *f*requency of *r*ecombination). Like an F^+ cell, an Hfr cell functions as a donor during conjugation with an F^- cell

(Figure 27.13b). When chromosomal DNA from an Hfr cell enters an F⁻ cell, homologous regions of the Hfr and F⁻ chromosomes may align, allowing segments of their DNA to be exchanged. This results in the production of a recombinant bacterium that has genes derived from two different cells—a new genetic variant on which evolution can act.

R Plasmids and Antibiotic Resistance During the 1950s in Japan, physicians started noticing that some hospital patients with bacterial dysentery, which produces severe diarrhea, did not respond to antibiotics that had generally been effective in the past. Apparently, resistance to these antibiotics had evolved in certain strains of *Shigella*, the bacterium that causes the disease.

Eventually, researchers began to identify the specific genes that confer antibiotic resistance in *Shigella* and other pathogenic bacteria. Sometimes, mutation in a chromosomal gene of the pathogen can confer resistance. For example, a mutation in one gene may make it less likely that the pathogen will transport a particular antibiotic into its cell. Mutation in a different gene may alter the intracellular target protein for an antibiotic molecule, reducing its inhibitory effect. In other cases, bacteria have "resistance genes," which code for enzymes that specifically destroy or otherwise hinder the effectiveness of certain antibiotics, such as tetracycline or ampicillin. Such resistance genes are carried by plasmids known as **R plasmids** (R for *resistance*).

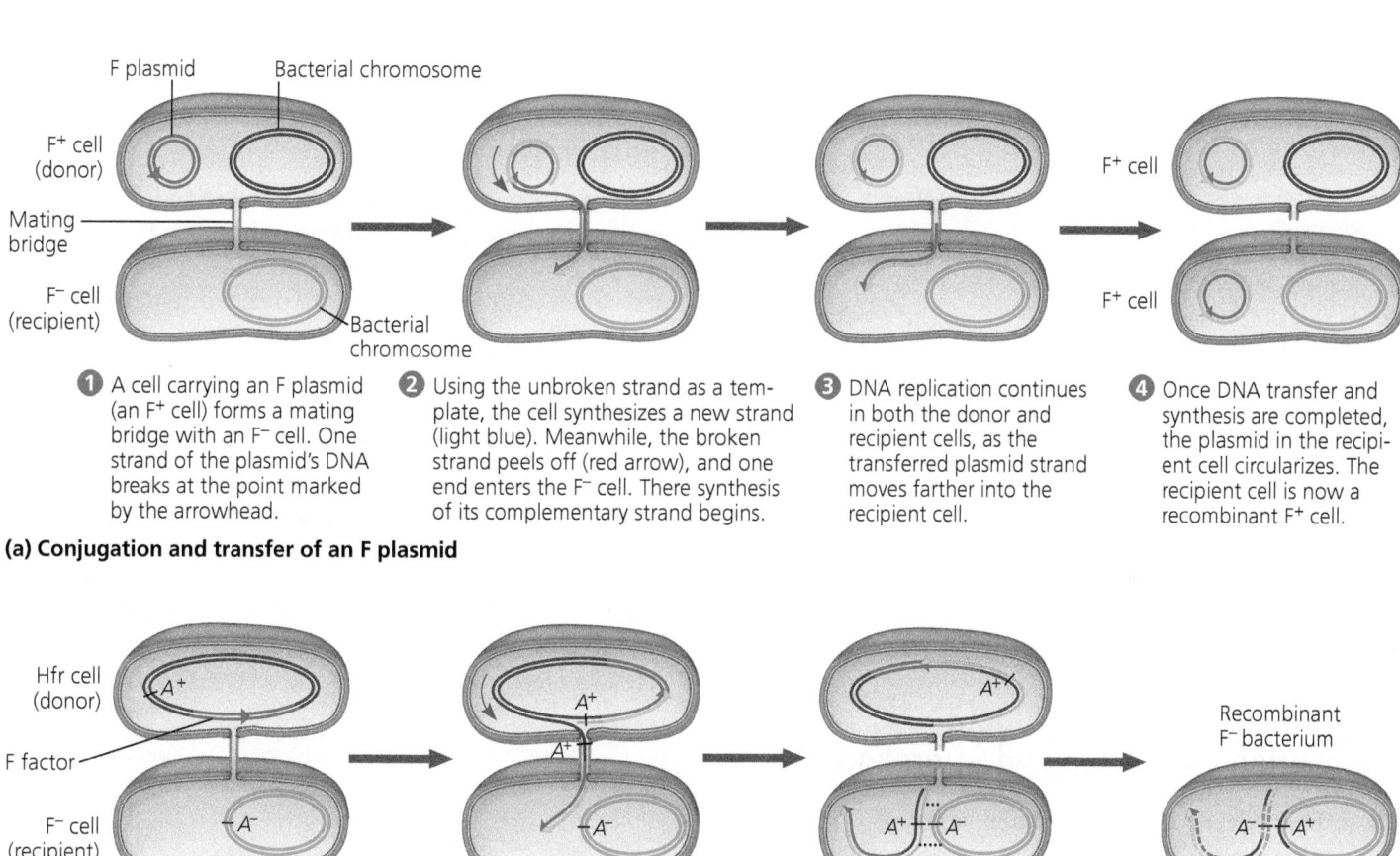

(a) Conjugation and transfer of an F plasmid

1 A cell carrying an F plasmid (an F⁺ cell) forms a mating bridge with an F⁻ cell. One strand of the plasmid's DNA breaks at the point marked by the arrowhead.

2 Using the unbroken strand as a template, the cell synthesizes a new strand (light blue). Meanwhile, the broken strand peels off (red arrow), and one end enters the F⁻ cell. There synthesis of its complementary strand begins.

3 DNA replication continues in both the donor and recipient cells, as the transferred plasmid strand moves farther into the recipient cell.

4 Once DNA transfer and synthesis are completed, the plasmid in the recipient cell circularizes. The recipient cell is now a recombinant F⁺ cell.

(b) Conjugation and transfer of part of an Hfr bacterial chromosome, resulting in recombination

1 In an Hfr cell, the F factor (dark blue) is integrated into the bacterial chromosome. Since an Hfr cell has all of the F factor genes, it can form a mating bridge with an F⁻ cell and transfer DNA.

2 A single strand of the F factor breaks and begins to move through the bridge. DNA replication occurs in both donor and recipient cells, resulting in double-stranded DNA (daughter strands shown in lighter colour).

3 The mating bridge usually breaks before the entire chromosome is transferred. Crossing over at two sites (dotted lines) can result in the exchange of homologous genes between the transferred DNA (brown) and the recipient's chromosome (green).

4 Cellular enzymes degrade any linear DNA not incorporated into the chromosome. The recipient cell, with a new combination of genes but no F factor, is now a recombinant F⁻ cell.

▲ **Figure 27.13 Conjugation and recombination in *E. coli*.** The DNA replication that accompanies transfer of an F plasmid or part of an Hfr bacterial chromosome is called *rolling circle replication*. In effect, the intact circular parental DNA strand "rolls" as its other strand peels off and a new complementary strand is synthesized.

Exposing a bacterial population to a specific antibiotic, whether in a laboratory culture or within a host organism, will kill antibiotic-sensitive bacteria but not those that happen to have R plasmids with genes that counter the antibiotic. Under these circumstances, we would predict that natural selection would cause the fraction of the bacterial population carrying genes for antibiotic resistance to increase, and that is exactly what happens. The medical consequences are also predictable: As you've read, resistant strains of pathogens are becoming more common, making the treatment of certain bacterial infections more difficult. The problem is compounded by the fact that many R plasmids, like F plasmids, have genes that encode pili and enable DNA transfer from one bacterial cell to another by conjugation. Making the problem still worse, some R plasmids carry as many as 10 genes for resistance to that many antibiotics.

CONCEPT CHECK 27.2

1. Although rare on a per gene basis, new mutations can add considerable genetic variation to prokaryotic populations in each generation. Explain how this occurs.

2. Distinguish between the three mechanisms of transferring DNA from one bacterial cell to another.

3. In a rapidly changing environment, which bacterial population would likely be more successful, one that includes individuals capable of conjugation or one that does not? Explain.

4. **WHAT IF?** If a nonpathogenic bacterium were to acquire resistance to antibiotics, could this strain pose a health risk to people? Explain. In general, how does DNA transfer among bacteria affect the spread of resistance genes?

For suggested answers, see Appendix A.

CONCEPT 27.3

Diverse nutritional and metabolic adaptations have evolved in prokaryotes

The extensive genetic variation found in prokaryotic populations is reflected in the diverse nutritional adaptations of prokaryotes. Like all organisms, prokaryotes can be categorized by how they obtain energy and the carbon used in building the organic molecules that make up cells. Every type of nutrition observed in eukaryotes is represented among prokaryotes, along with some nutritional modes unique to prokaryotes. In fact, prokaryotes have an astounding range of metabolic adaptations, much broader than that found in eukaryotes.

Organisms that obtain energy from light are called *phototrophs*, and those that obtain energy from chemicals are called *chemotrophs*. Organisms that need only CO_2 in some form as a carbon source are called *autotrophs*. In contrast,

heterotrophs require at least one organic nutrient, such as glucose, to make other organic compounds. Combining possible energy sources and carbon sources results in four major modes of nutrition, summarized in Table 27.1.

The Role of Oxygen in Metabolism

Prokaryotic metabolism also varies with respect to oxygen (O_2). **Obligate aerobes** must use O_2 for cellular respiration (see Chapter 9) and cannot grow without it. **Obligate anaerobes**, on the other hand, are poisoned by O_2. Some obligate anaerobes live exclusively by fermentation; others extract chemical energy by **anaerobic respiration**, in which substances other than O_2, such as nitrate ions (NO_3^-) or sulphate ions (SO_4^{2-}), accept electrons at the "downhill" end of electron transport chains. **Facultative anaerobes** use O_2 if it is present but can also carry out fermentation or anaerobic respiration in an anaerobic environment.

Nitrogen Metabolism

Nitrogen is essential for the production of amino acids and nucleic acids in all organisms. Whereas eukaryotes can obtain nitrogen from only a limited group of nitrogen compounds, prokaryotes can metabolize nitrogen in a wide variety of forms. For example, some cyanobacteria and some methanogens (a group of archaea) convert atmospheric nitrogen (N_2) to ammonia (NH_3), a process

Table 27.1	Major Nutritional Modes		
Mode	Energy Source	Carbon Source	Types of Organisms
AUTOTROPH			
Photoautotroph	Light	CO_2, HCO_3^-, or related compound	Photosynthetic prokaryotes (for example, cyanobacteria); plants; certain protists (for example, algae)
Chemoautotroph	Inorganic chemicals (such as H_2S, NH_3, or Fe^{2+})	CO_2, HCO_3^-, or related compound	Unique to certain prokaryotes (for example, *Sulfolobus*)
HETEROTROPH			
Photoheterotroph	Light	Organic compounds	Unique to certain aquatic and salt-loving prokaryotes (for example, *Rhodobacter*, *Chloroflexus*)
Chemoheterotroph	Organic compounds	Organic compounds	Many prokaryotes (for example, *Clostridium*) and protists; fungi; animals; some plants

called **nitrogen fixation**. The cells can then incorporate this "fixed" nitrogen into amino acids and other organic molecules. In terms of their nutrition, nitrogen-fixing cyanobacteria are some of the most self-sufficient organisms, since they need only light, CO_2, N_2, water, and some minerals to grow.

Nitrogen fixation by prokaryotes has a large impact on other organisms. For example, nitrogen-fixing prokaryotes can increase the nitrogen available to plants, which cannot use atmospheric nitrogen but can use the nitrogen compounds that the prokaryotes produce from ammonia. Some nitrogen-fixing bacteria can even live as symbionts in specialized tissue of certain plants (see Figure 37.11, for instance). Chapter 55 discusses this and other essential roles that prokaryotes play in the nitrogen cycles of ecosystems.

Metabolic Cooperation

Cooperation between prokaryotic cells allows them to use environmental resources they could not use as individual cells. In some cases, this cooperation takes place between specialized cells of a filament. For instance, the cyanobacterium *Anabaena* has genes that encode proteins for photosynthesis and for nitrogen fixation, but a single cell cannot carry out both processes at the same time. The reason is that photosynthesis produces O_2, which inactivates the enzymes involved in nitrogen fixation. Instead of living as isolated cells, *Anabaena* forms filamentous chains (Figure 27.14). Most cells in a filament carry out only photosynthesis, while a few specialized cells called **heterocysts** (sometimes called *heterocytes*) carry out only nitrogen fixation. Each heterocyst is surrounded by a thickened cell wall that restricts entry of O_2 produced by neighbouring photosynthetic cells. Intercellular connections allow heterocysts to transport fixed nitrogen to neighbouring cells and to receive carbohydrates.

Metabolic cooperation between different prokaryotic species often occurs in surface-coating colonies known as **biofilms**. Cells in a biofilm secrete signalling molecules that recruit nearby cells, causing the colonies to grow. The cells also produce polysaccharides and proteins that stick the cells to the substrate and to one another. Channels in the biofilm allow nutrients to reach cells in the interior and wastes to be expelled. Biofilms are common in nature, but they can cause problems by contaminating industrial products and medical equipment and contributing to tooth decay and more serious health problems. Altogether, damage caused by biofilms costs billions of dollars annually.

In another example of cooperation between prokaryotes, sulphate-consuming bacteria coexist with methane-consuming archaea in ball-shaped aggregates on the ocean floor. The bacteria appear to use the archaea's waste products, such as organic compounds and hydrogen. In turn, the bacteria produce sulphur compounds that the archaea use as oxidizing agents when they consume methane in the absence of oxygen. This partnership has global ramifications: Each year, these archaea consume an estimated 300 billion kilograms of methane, a major contributor to the greenhouse effect (see Chapter 56). Similar processes occur in tailings ponds associated with the oil sands in Alberta (Figure 27.1). Methane produced by anaerobic metabolism of hydrocarbons by methanogens in the lower, O_2-free zones of tailings ponds may be captured by *Methanotophic* prokaryotes, which use methane as an energy source and are often present in the upper, aerobic layers of the ponds. Understanding these interactions may be key to reducing emissions from such environments.

CONCEPT CHECK 27.3

1. Distinguish between the four major modes of nutrition, noting which are unique to prokaryotes.

2. A bacterium requires only the amino acid methionine as an organic nutrient and lives in lightless caves. What mode of nutrition does it employ? Explain.

3. **WHAT IF?** Describe what you might eat for a typical meal if humans, like cyanobacteria, could fix nitrogen.

For suggested answers, see Appendix A.

CONCEPT 27.4

Prokaryotes have radiated into a diverse set of lineages

Since their origin 3.5 billion years ago, prokaryotic populations have radiated extensively as a wide range of structural and metabolic adaptations have evolved in them. Collectively, these adaptations have enabled prokaryotes to inhabit every environment known to support life—if there are organisms in a particular place, some of those organisms are prokaryotes. In recent decades, advances in genomics are beginning to reveal the extent of prokaryotic diversity.

Susan M. Barns, Ph.D.

Photosynthetic cells

Heterocyst

20 μm

▲ **Figure 27.14 Metabolic cooperation in a prokaryote.** In the filamentous freshwater cyanobacterium *Anabaena*, heterocysts fix nitrogen, while the other cells carry out photosynthesis (LM).

An Overview of Prokaryotic Diversity

In the 1970s, microbiologists began using small-subunit ribosomal RNA as a marker for evolutionary relationships. Their results indicated that many prokaryotes once classified as bacteria are actually more closely related to eukaryotes and belong in a domain of their own: Archaea. Microbiologists have since analyzed larger amounts of genetic data—including more than 1700 entire genomes—and have concluded that a few traditional taxonomic groups, such as cyanobacteria, are monophyletic. However, other groups, such as gram-negative bacteria, are scattered throughout several lineages. **Figure 27.15** shows one phylogenetic hypothesis for some of the major taxa of prokaryotes based on molecular systematics.

One lesson from studying prokaryotic phylogeny is that the genetic diversity of prokaryotes is immense. When researchers began to sequence the genes of prokaryotes, they could investigate only the small fraction of species that could be cultured in the laboratory. In the 1980s, researchers began using the polymerase chain reaction (PCR; see Chapter 20) to analyze the genes of prokaryotes collected from the environment (such as from soil or water samples). Such "genetic prospecting" is now widely used; in fact, today entire prokaryotic genomes can be obtained from environmental samples using *metagenomics* (see Chapter 21). Each year these techniques add new branches to the tree of life. While only about 10 500 prokaryotic species have been assigned scientific names, a single handful of soil could contain 10 000 prokaryotic species by some estimates. Taking full stock of this diversity will require many years of research.

Another important lesson from molecular systematics is that horizontal gene transfer played a key role in the evolution of prokaryotes. Over hundreds of millions of years, prokaryotes have acquired genes from even distantly related species, and they continue to do so today. As a result, significant portions of the genomes of many prokaryotes are actually mosaics of genes imported from other species. As we saw in Chapter 26, such gene transfers can make it difficult to determine the root of the tree of life. Still, it is clear that for billions of years the prokaryotes have evolved in two separate lineages, the archaea and the bacteria (see Figure 27.15).

Bacteria

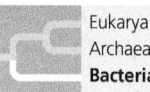

As surveyed in **Figure 27.16** on pages 616–617, bacteria include the vast majority of prokaryotic species familiar to most people, from the pathogenic species that cause strep throat and tuberculosis to the beneficial species used to make Swiss cheese and yogurt. Every major mode of nutrition and metabolism is represented among bacteria, and even a small taxonomic group of bacteria may contain species exhibiting many different nutritional modes. As we'll see, the diverse nutritional and metabolic capabilities of bacteria—and archaea—are behind the great impact of these tiny organisms on Earth and its life.

Archaea

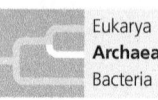

Archaea share certain traits with bacteria and other traits with eukaryotes (Table 27.2). However, archaea also have many unique characteristics, as we would expect in a taxon that has followed a separate evolutionary path for so long.

The first prokaryotes assigned to domain Archaea live in environments so extreme that few other organisms can survive there. Such organisms are called **extremophiles**, meaning "lovers" of extreme conditions (from the Greek *philos*, lover), and include extreme halophiles and extreme thermophiles.

Extreme halophiles (from the Greek *halo*, salt) live in highly saline environments, such as the Great Salt Lake and the Dead Sea. Some species merely tolerate salinity, while others require an environment that is several times saltier than sea water (which has a salinity of 3.5%). For example, the proteins and cell wall of *Halobacterium* have unusual features that improve function in extremely salty environments but render these organisms incapable of survival if the salinity drops below 9%.

▲ Figure 27.15 **A simplified phylogeny of prokaryotes.** This phylogenetic tree based on molecular data shows one of several debated hypotheses of the relationships between the major prokaryotic groups discussed in this chapter. Within Archaea, the placement of the korarchaeotes and nanoarchaeotes remains unclear.

? *Which domain is the sister group of Archaea?*

Table 27.2 A Comparison of the Three Domains of Life

CHARACTERISTIC	DOMAIN		
	Bacteria	Archaea	Eukarya
Nuclear envelope	Absent	Absent	Present
Membrane-enclosed organelles	Absent	Absent	Present
Peptidoglycan in cell wall	Present	Absent	Absent
Membrane lipids	Unbranched hydrocarbons	Some branched hydrocarbons	Unbranched hydrocarbons
RNA polymerase	One kind	Several kinds	Several kinds
Initiator amino acid for protein synthesis	Formyl-methionine	Methionine	Methionine
Introns in genes	Very rare	Present in some genes	Present in many genes
Response to the antibiotics streptomycin and chloramphenicol	Growth inhibited	Growth not inhibited	Growth not inhibited
Histones associated with DNA	Absent	Present in some species	Present
Circular chromosome	Present	Present	Absent
Growth at temperatures > 100°C	No	Some species	No

Extreme thermophiles (from the Greek *thermos*, hot) thrive in very hot environments (**Figure 27.17** on page 618). For example, archaea in the genus *Sulfolobus* live in sulphur-rich volcanic springs as hot as 90°C. At temperatures this high, the cells of most organisms die because, for example, their DNA does not remain in a double helix and many of their proteins denature. *Sulfolobus* and other extreme thermophiles avoid this fate because their DNA and proteins have adaptations that make them stable at high temperatures. One extreme thermophile that lives near deep-sea hot springs called *hydrothermal vents* is informally known as "strain 121," since it can reproduce even at 121°C. Another extreme thermophile, *Pyrococcus furiosus*, is used in biotechnology as a source of heat-stable DNA polymerase for the PCR technique (see Chapter 20).

Many other archaea live in more moderate environments. Consider the **methanogens**, archaea that release methane as a by-product of their unique ways of obtaining energy. Many methanogens use CO_2 to oxidize H_2, a process that produces both energy and methane waste. Among the strictest of anaerobes, methanogens are poisoned by O_2. Although some methanogens live in extreme environments, such as under kilometres of ice in Greenland, others live in swamps and marshes where other microorganisms have consumed all the O_2. The "marsh gas" found in such environments is the methane released by these archaea. Methanogens also produce methane in tailings ponds, as

discussed at the start of this chapter (Figure 27.1). Other species of methanogens inhabit the anaerobic environment within the guts of cattle, termites, and other herbivores, playing an essential role in the nutrition of these animals. Methanogens also have an important application as decomposers in sewage treatment facilities.

Many extreme halophiles and all known methanogens are archaea in the clade Euryarchaeota (from the Greek *eurys*, broad, a reference to the habitat range of these prokaryotes). The euryarchaeotes also include some extreme thermophiles, though most thermophilic species belong to a second clade, Crenarchaeota (*cren* means "spring," such as a hydrothermal spring). Recently, genetic prospecting has revealed many species of euryarchaeotes and crenarchaeotes that are not extremophiles. These archaea exist in habitats ranging from farm soils to lake sediments to the surface waters of the open ocean.

New findings continue to update the picture of archaeal phylogeny. Researchers sampling a hot spring in Yellowstone National Park discovered archaea that do not appear to belong to either Euryarchaeota or Crenarchaeota and placed them in a new clade, Korarchaeota (from the Greek *koron*, young man). In 2002, researchers exploring hydrothermal vents off the coast of Iceland discovered archaeal cells only 0.4 μm in diameter. The genome is one of the smallest known of any organism, containing only 500 000 base pairs. Genetic analysis indicates that this prokaryote belongs to a fourth archaeal clade, Nanoarchaeota (from the Greek *nanos*, dwarf). In 2015, a team sampling sediments from a hydrothermal vent at the Arctic Mid-Ocean Ridge identified a novel archaeal lineage using a metagenomic sequencing approach. This new lineage was named the "Lokiarchaeota" and it is significant because Lokiarchaeota are hypothesized to share a common ancestry with eukaryotes. Genetic analyses identified a number of proteins that are characteristic of eukaryotic cells in the Lokiarchaeota and phylogenetic analyses grouped them together, to the exclusion of other archaea. This discovery suggests that eukaryotes may have evolved from the archae and that continued genetic prospecting in unusual environments may provide more clues about the evolution of the eukaryotic cell.

CONCEPT CHECK 27.4

1. Explain how molecular systematics has contributed to our understanding of prokaryotic phylogeny.
2. How has genetic prospecting contributed to our understanding of prokaryotic diversity and phylogeny?
3. Some scientists and educators are recommending we stop using the word "prokaryote" when referring to Bacteria and Archaea. Look at Figure 27.15 and Table 27.2 and suggest why *prokaryote* may not be the best term to describe these groups.
4. **WHAT IF?** What would the discovery of a bacterial species that is a methanogen imply about the evolution of the methane-producing pathway?

For suggested answers, see Appendix A.

Exploring Selected Major Groups of Bacteria

Proteobacteria

This large and diverse clade of gram-negative bacteria includes photoautotrophs, chemoautotrophs, and heterotrophs. Some proteobacteria are anaerobic, while others are aerobic. Molecular systematists currently recognize five subgroups of proteobacteria; the phylogenetic tree at right shows their relationships based on molecular data.

Alpha
Beta
Gamma } Proteobacteria
Delta
Epsilon

Subgroup: Alpha Proteobacteria

Many of the species in this subgroup are closely associated with eukaryotic hosts. For example, *Rhizobium* species live in nodules within the roots of legumes (plants of the pea/bean family), where the bacteria convert atmospheric N_2 to compounds the host plant can use to make proteins. Species in the genus *Agrobacterium* produce tumours in plants; genetic engineers use these bacteria to carry foreign DNA into the genomes of crop plants. As explained in Chapter 25, scientists hypothesize that mitochondria evolved from aerobic alpha proteobacteria through endosymbiosis.

Rhizobium (arrows) inside a root cell of a legume (TEM)

L. Evans/Biological Photo Service

Subgroup: Beta Proteobacteria

This nutritionally diverse subgroup includes *Nitrosomonas*, a genus of soil bacteria that play an important role in nitrogen recycling by oxidizing ammonium (NH_4^+), producing nitrite (NO_2^-) as a waste product.

Nitrosomonas (colourized TEM)

Yuichi Sawa

Subgroup: Gamma Proteobacteria

This subgroup's autotrophic members include sulphur bacteria such as *Thiomargarita namibiensis* (see p. 604), which obtain energy by oxidizing H_2S, producing sulphur as a waste product (the small globules in the photograph at right). Some heterotrophic gamma proteobacteria are pathogens; for example, *Legionella* causes Legionnaires' disease, *Salmonella* is responsible for some cases of food poisoning, and *Vibrio cholerae* causes cholera. *Escherichia coli*, a common resident of the intestines of humans and other mammals, normally is not pathogenic.

Thiomargarita namibiensis containing sulphur wastes (LM)

National Library of Medicine

Subgroup: Delta Proteobacteria

This subgroup includes the slime-secreting myxobacteria. When the soil dries out or food is scarce, the cells congregate into a fruiting body that releases resistant "myxospores." These cells found new colonies in favourable environments. Another group of delta proteobacteria, the bdellovibrios, attack other bacteria, charging at up to 100 µm/sec (comparable to a human running 240 km/hr). The attack begins when a bdellovibrio attaches to specific molecules found on the outer covering of some bacterial species. The bdellovibrio then drills into its prey by using digestive enzymes and spinning at 100 revolutions per second.

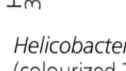

Fruiting bodies of *Chondromyces crocatus*, a myxobacterium (SEM)

Patricia Grilione

Subgroup: Epsilon Proteobacteria

Most species in this subgroup are pathogenic to humans or other animals. Epsilon proteobacteria include *Campylobacter*, which causes blood poisoning and intestinal inflammation, and *Helicobacter pylori*, which causes stomach ulcers.

Helicobacter pylori (colourized TEM)

Science Source

Chlamydias

These parasites can survive only within animal cells, depending on their hosts for resources as basic as ATP. The gram-negative walls of chlamydias are unusual in that they lack peptidoglycan. One species, *Chlamydia trachomatis*, is the most common cause of blindness in the world and also causes nongonococcal urethritis, the most common sexually transmitted disease in Canada and the United States.

Chlamydia (arrows) inside an animal cell (colourized TEM)

2.5 μm

Moredon Animal Health/SPL/Science Source

Spirochetes

These gram-negative heterotrophs spiral through their environment by means of rotating, internal, flagellum-like filaments. Many spirochetes are free-living, but others are notorious pathogenic parasites: *Treponema pallidum* causes syphilis, and *Borrelia burgdorferi* causes Lyme disease (see Figure 27.21).

Leptospira, a spirochete (colourized TEM)

5 μm

CNRI/SPL/Science Source

Cyanobacteria

These gram-negative photoautotrophs are the only prokaryotes with plantlike, oxygen-generating photosynthesis. (In fact, chloroplasts evolved from an endosymbiotic cyanobacterium.) Both solitary and filamentous cyanobacteria are abundant components of freshwater and marine *phytoplankton,* the collection of photosynthetic organisms that drift near the water's surface. Some filaments have cells specialized for nitrogen fixation, the process that incorporates atmospheric N_2 into inorganic compounds that can be used in the synthesis of amino acids and other organic molecules (see Figure 27.14).

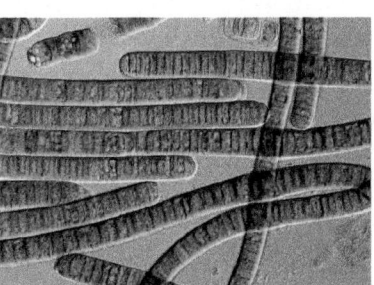

Oscillatoria, a filamentous cyanobacterium

40 μm

Institute of Botany Academy of Sciences

Gram-Positive Bacteria

Gram-positive bacteria rival the proteobacteria in diversity. Species in one subgroup, the actinomycetes (from the Greek *mykes,* fungus, for which these bacteria were once mistaken), form colonies containing branched chains of cells. Two species of actinomycetes cause tuberculosis and leprosy. However, most actinomycetes are free-living species that help decompose the organic matter in soil; their secretions are partly responsible for the "earthy" odour of rich soil. Soil-dwelling species in the genus *Streptomyces* (top) are cultured by pharmaceutical companies as a source of many antibiotics, including streptomycin.

Gram-positive bacteria include many solitary species, such as *Bacillus anthracis* (see Figure 27.6), which causes anthrax, and *Clostridium botulinum,* which causes botulism. The various species of *Staphylococcus* and *Streptococcus* are also gram-positive bacteria.

Mycoplasmas (bottom) are the only bacteria known to lack cell walls. They are also the tiniest known cells, with diameters as small as 0.1 μm, only about five times as large as a ribosome. Mycoplasmas have small genomes—*Mycoplasma genitalium* has only 517 genes, for example. Many mycoplasmas are free-living soil bacteria, but others are pathogens.

Streptomyces, the source of many antibiotics (SEM)

5 μm

Dr. Paul Alan Hoskisson

Hundreds of mycoplasmas covering a human fibroblast cell (colourized SEM)

2 μm

David M. Phillips/Science Source

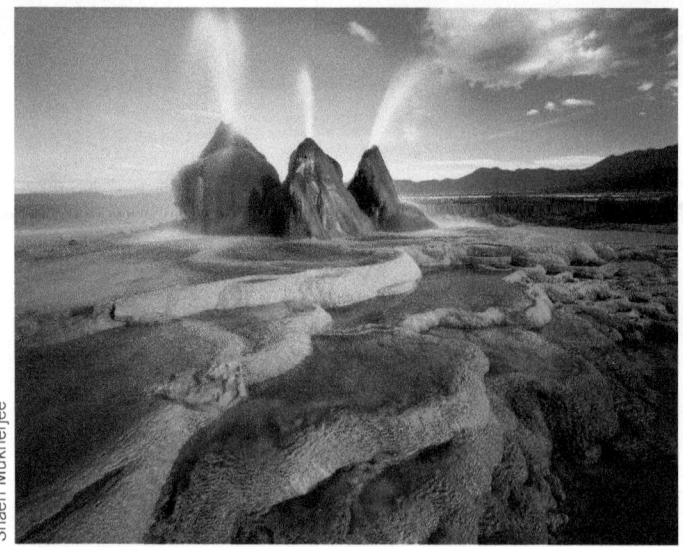

▲ Figure 27.17 **Extreme thermophiles.** Orange and yellow colonies of thermophilic prokaryotes grow in the hot water of a Nevada geyser.

Shaeri Mukherjee

MAKE CONNECTIONS *How might the enzymes of thermophiles differ from those of other organisms? (Review enzymes in Concept 8.4.)*

CONCEPT 27.5

Prokaryotes play crucial roles in the biosphere

If humans were to disappear from the planet tomorrow, life on Earth would change for many species, but few would be driven to extinction. In contrast, prokaryotes are so important to the biosphere that if they were to disappear, the prospects of survival for many other species would be dim.

Chemical Recycling

The atoms that make up the organic molecules in all living things were at one time part of inorganic substances in the soil, air, and water. Sooner or later, those atoms will return there. Ecosystems depend on the continual recycling of chemical elements between the living and nonliving components of the environment, and prokaryotes play a major role in this process. For example, chemoheterotrophic prokaryotes function as **decomposers**, breaking down dead organisms as well as waste products and thereby unlocking supplies of carbon, nitrogen, and other elements. Without the actions of prokaryotes and other decomposers such as fungi, all life would cease. (See Chapter 55 for a detailed discussion of chemical cycles.)

Prokaryotes also convert some molecules to forms that can be taken up by other organisms. Cyanobacteria and other autotrophic prokaryotes use CO_2 to make organic compounds such as sugars, which are then passed up through food chains. Cyanobacteria also produce atmospheric O_2, and a variety of prokaryotes fix atmospheric nitrogen (N_2)

into forms that other organisms can use to make the building blocks of proteins and nucleic acids. Under some conditions, prokaryotes can increase the availability of nutrients that plants require for growth, such as nitrogen, phosphorus, and potassium (**Figure 27.18**). Prokaryotes can also *decrease* the availability of key plant nutrients; this occurs when prokaryotes "immobilize" nutrients by using them to synthesize molecules that remain within their cells. Thus, prokaryotes can have complex effects on soil nutrient concentrations. In marine environments, a 2005 study found that an archaean from the clade Crenarchaeota can perform nitrification, a key step in the nitrogen cycle (see Figure 55.13). Crenarchaeotes dominate the oceans by numbers, comprising an estimated 10^{28} cells. The sheer abundance of these organisms suggests that they may have a large impact on the global nitrogen cycle; scientists are investigating this possibility.

Ecological Interactions

Prokaryotes play a central role in many ecological interactions. Consider **symbiosis** (from a Greek word meaning "living together"), an ecological relationship in which two species live in close contact with each other. Prokaryotes often form symbiotic associations with much larger organisms. In general, the larger organism in a symbiotic relationship is known as the **host**, and the smaller is known as the **symbiont**. There are many cases in which a prokaryote

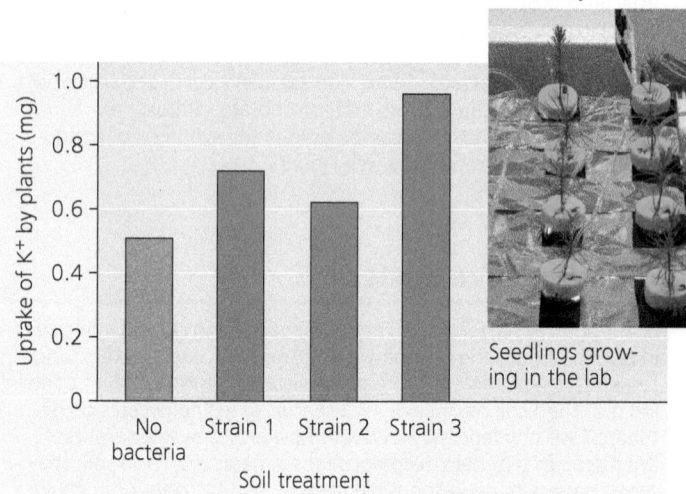

Pascale Frey-Klett

Seedlings growing in the lab

▲ Figure 27.18 **Impact of bacteria on soil nutrient availability.** Pine seedlings grown in sterile soils to which one of three strains of the bacterium *Burkholderia glathei* had been added absorbed more potassium (K+) than did seedlings grown in soil without any bacteria. Other results (not shown) demonstrated that strain 3 increased the amount of K+ released from mineral crystals to the soil.

Source: Based on data from "Root-Associated Bacteria Contribute to Mineral Weathering and to Mineral Nutrition in Trees: A Budgeting Analysis" by Christophe Calvaruso et al., *Applied and Environmental Microbiology*, February 2006, Volume 72(2). © Jane B Reece.

WHAT IF? *Estimate the average uptake of K+ for seedlings in soils with bacteria. What would you expect this average to be if bacteria had no effect on nutrient availability?*

and its host participate in **mutualism**, an ecological interaction between two species in which both benefit. Other interactions take the form of **commensalism**, an ecological relationship in which one species benefits while the other is not harmed or helped in any significant way. For example, more than 150 bacterial species live on the surface of your body, covering portions of your skin with up to 10 million cells per square centimetre. Some of these species are commensalists: You provide them with food, such as the oils that exude from your pores, and a place to live, while they do not harm or benefit you. Finally, some prokaryotes engage in **parasitism**, an ecological relationship in which a **parasite** eats the cell contents, tissues, or body fluids of its host; as a group, parasites harm but usually do not kill their host, at least not immediately (unlike a predator). Parasites that cause disease are known as **pathogens**, many of which are prokaryotic. (We'll discuss mutualism, commensalism, and parasitism in greater detail in Chapter 54.)

The very existence of an ecosystem can depend on prokaryotes. For example, consider the diverse ecological communities found at hydrothermal vents. These communities are densely populated by many different kinds of animals, including worms, clams, snails, and crabs (Figure 27.19). But since sunlight does not penetrate to the deep ocean floor, the community does not include photosynthetic organisms. Instead, the energy that supports the community is derived from the metabolic activities of chemoautotrophic bacteria (both free-living and symbiotic). These bacteria harvest chemical energy from compounds such as hydrogen sulphide (H_2S) that are released from the vent. An active hydrothermal vent may support hundreds of eukaryotic species, but when the vent stops releasing chemicals, the chemoautotrophic bacteria cannot survive. As a result, the

▲ Figure 27.19 **A "black smoker" hydrothermal vent with tube worms.** Tube worms are dependent upon endosymbiotic, chemotrophic bacteria for nutrition. The black "smoke" is the precipitation of metal sulphides as the superheated hydrothermal fluids hit the cold sea water. This vent is from the Endeavour segment of the Juan de Fuca Ridge, about 300 km off the British Columbian coast.

entire vent community collapses. Ecosystems such as these are actively monitored by Ocean Networks Canada using ocean observatories, including hydrothermal vents that are 2200 metres deep at the Juan de Fuca Ridge off the coast of British Columbia.

CONCEPT CHECK 27.5

1. Explain how prokaryotes, though small, can be considered giants in their collective impact on Earth and its life.

2. **MAKE CONNECTIONS** Read the section on nitrogen-fixing bacteria on page 612. Plants cannot use N_2 from the atmosphere directly, but many legumes have developed symbioses with bacteria that can fix N_2 and supply the plant with NH_3. In Canada, alfalfa is an important forage crop (used for hay to feed cattle) that has root nodules with symbiotic bacteria for N_2 fixation. What is the significance of these N_2-fixing symbioses for farmers and crop rotations?

For suggested answers, see Appendix A.

CONCEPT 27.6

Prokaryotes have both beneficial and harmful impacts on humans

Though the best-known prokaryotes tend to be the bacteria that cause illness in humans, these pathogens represent only a small fraction of prokaryotic species. Many other prokaryotes have positive interactions with humans, and some play essential roles in agriculture and industry.

Mutualistic Bacteria

As is true for many other eukaryotes, human well-being can depend on mutualistic prokaryotes that collectively comprise the human **microbiome** (Figure 27.20). For example, our intestines are home to an estimated 500–1000 species of bacteria. Different species live in different portions of the intestines, and they vary in their ability to process different foods. Many of these species are mutualists, digesting food that our own intestines cannot break down. In 2003, scientists published the first complete genome of one of these gut mutualists, *Bacteroides thetaiotaomicron*. The genome includes a large array of genes involved in synthesizing carbohydrates, vitamins, and other nutrients needed by humans. Signals from the bacterium activate human genes that build the network of intestinal blood vessels necessary to absorb nutrient molecules. Other signals induce human cells to produce antimicrobial compounds to which *B. thetaiotaomicron* is not susceptible. This action may reduce the population sizes of other, competing species, thus potentially benefitting both *B. thetaiotaomicron* and its human host. Disruption of the gut microbiome, which can occur through the use of antibiotics, can allow

Impact

The Human Microbiome and Health

It's been estimated that the number of bacteria living on or within humans is larger than the number of human cells by a factor of 10—that's about 100 trillion bacteria! These bacterial communities live symbiotically in many locations including on the skin, in mouths, the stomach, intestines, and vagina. This microbial community on and within us is collectively called the microbiome. These bacteria are not simply unwanted guests but are often mutualistic and have a functional role in human physiology and health.

Colourized SEM of bacteria on the colon wall.

Why It Matters As an example, scientists have been making links between the gut microbiome and obesity. The bacteria in our guts are essential for assisting with the digestion of foods, but in obese subjects, the gut bacterial community is changed in several ways. The population of bacteria is shifted taxonomically, is less diverse, and has different metabolic capabilities as inferred by the collection of genes in the different species. The immediate relationship to obesity is not certain, but the different microbiome composition in obese subjects may affect the efficiency of energy harvesting from the available food or influence how this energy is used by the host.

Further Reading P. J. Turnbaugh et al., A core gut microbiome in obese and lean twins, *Nature* 457:480–484 (2009).

WHAT IF? *What would happen to the human microbiome after a standard 10-day treatment with antibiotics?*

opportunistic bacteria like the diarrhea-causing *Clostridium difficile* to take hold. *C. difficile* has become a concern in many hospitals across Canada and the industrialized world. There is now an international effort, including Canadian researchers, to identify the entire human microbiome, how it changes, and to discover its role in human health. The ability to undertake such an initiative is driven by technology that allows scientists to sequence the genomes of populations of organisms, and hence identify them, without having to culture them individually, an approach referred to as **metagenomics** (see Concept 21.1, p. 465).

Pathogenic Bacteria

All the pathogenic prokaryotes known to date are bacteria, and they deserve their negative reputation. Bacteria cause about half of all human diseases. Roughly 2 million people die each year of the lung disease tuberculosis, caused by *Mycobacterium tuberculosis*. And another 2 million people die each year from diarrheal diseases caused by various bacteria.

Some bacterial diseases are transmitted by other species, such as fleas or ticks. Lyme disease is a serious emerging health issue in Canada (**Figure 27.21**) that is caused by a bacterium carried by ticks (*Ixodes scapularis*) that live on deer and field mice. Lyme disease can result in debilitating arthritis, heart disease, nervous disorders, and death if untreated. One concern with the increasing temperatures associated with climate change is the expansion of the deer tick into increasingly northern areas, and with it an increased occurrence of Lyme disease in Canada.

Pathogenic prokaryotes usually cause illness by producing poisons, which are classified as exotoxins or endotoxins. **Exotoxins** are proteins secreted by certain bacteria and other organisms. Cholera, a dangerous diarrheal disease, is caused by an exotoxin secreted by the proteobacterium *Vibrio cholerae*. The exotoxin stimulates intestinal cells to release

▲ Figure 27.21 **Lyme disease.** Ticks in the genus *Ixodes* spread the disease by transmitting the spirochete *Borrelia burgdorferi* (colourized SEM). A rash may develop at the site of the tick's bite; the rash may be large and ring-shaped (as shown) or much less distinctive.

chloride ions into the gut, and water follows by osmosis. In another example, the potentially fatal disease botulism is caused by botulinum toxin, an exotoxin secreted by the gram-positive bacterium *Clostridium botulinum* as it ferments various foods, including improperly canned meat, seafood, and vegetables. Like other exotoxins, the botulinum toxin can produce disease even if the bacteria that manufacture it are not present. In one such case, eight people contracted botulism after eating salted fish that did not contain any *C. botulinum* bacteria, but did contain the botulinum toxin. Even though the bacterium was no longer present, at some point in the fish preparation process, the bacterium had been able to grow and secrete the toxin.

Endotoxins are lipopolysaccharide components of the outer membrane of gram-negative bacteria. In contrast to exotoxins, endotoxins are released only when the bacteria die and their cell walls break down. Endotoxin-producing bacteria include species in the genus *Salmonella*, such as *Salmonella typhi*, which causes typhoid fever. You might have heard of food poisoning caused by other *Salmonella* species that are frequently found in poultry.

Since the 19th century, improved sanitation systems in the industrialized world have greatly reduced the threat of pathogenic bacteria. Antibiotics have saved a great many lives and reduced the incidence of disease. However, resistance to antibiotics is currently evolving in many bacterial strains. As you read earlier, the rapid reproduction of bacteria enables cells carrying resistance genes to quickly give rise to large populations as a result of natural selection, and these genes can also spread to other species by horizontal gene transfer.

Horizontal gene transfer can also spread genes associated with virulence, turning normally harmless bacteria into potent pathogens. *E. coli*, for instance, is ordinarily a harmless symbiont in the human intestines, but pathogenic strains that cause bloody diarrhea have emerged. One of the most dangerous strains, called O157:H7, is a global threat that is often transmitted through contaminated beef or produce. In Canada, there are roughly 1300 cases per year. In 2000, however, groundwater contamination of the municipal water supply in Walkerton, Ontario, introduced *E. coli* O157:H7, likely from surrounding fields. Ultimately, over 2000 residents became ill and 7 died, making this Canada's most severe outbreak of *E. coli*. In 2001, scientists sequenced the genome of O157:H7 and compared it with the genome of a harmless strain of *E. coli* called K-12. They discovered that 1387 out of the 5416 genes in O157:H7 have no counterpart in K–12. Many of these 1387 genes are found in chromosomal regions that include phage DNA. This result suggests that at least some of the 1387 genes were incorporated into the genome of O157:H7 through phage-mediated horizontal gene transfer (transduction). Some of the genes found only in O157:H7

are associated with virulence, including genes that code for adhesive fimbriae that enable O157:H7 to attach itself to the intestinal wall and extract nutrients.

Pathogenic bacteria also pose a potential threat as weapons of bioterrorism. For example, endospores of *Bacillus anthracis* sent through the mail in 2001 caused 18 people to develop inhalation anthrax, which was fatal in 5 of the cases. Such scenarios have stimulated more research on pathogenic prokaryotic species in the hope of developing new vaccines and antibiotics.

Prokaryotes in Research and Technology

On a positive note, we reap many benefits from the metabolic capabilities of both bacteria and archaea. For example, humans have long used bacteria to convert milk to cheese and yogurt. In recent years, our greater understanding of prokaryotes has led to an explosion of new applications in biotechnology; two examples are the use of *E. coli* in gene cloning and the use of *Agrobacterium tumefaciens* in producing transgenic plants. Naturally occurring soil bacteria may have potential for combatting diseases that affect crop plants; in the Scientific Skills Exercise you can interpret data from an experiment studying the effect of these bacteria.

Bacteria may soon figure prominently in a major industry: plastics. Globally each year about 159 billion kilograms of plastic are produced from petroleum and used to make toys, storage containers, soft drink bottles, and many other items. These products degrade slowly, creating environmental problems. Bacteria can now be used to make natural plastics (**Figure 27.22**). For example, some bacteria synthesize a type of polymer known as PHA (polyhydroxyalkanoate), which they use to store chemical energy. The PHA they produce can be extracted, formed into pellets, and used to make durable, biodegradable plastics.

Another way to harness prokaryotes is in **bioremediation**, the use of organisms to remove pollutants from soil, air, or water. For example, anaerobic bacteria and archaea decompose the organic matter in sewage, converting it to material that can be used as landfill or fertilizer after chemical sterilization. Other bioremediation applications include cleaning up oil spills (**Figure 27.23**) and precipitating radioactive material (such as uranium) out of groundwater. You'll learn more about bioremediation in Chapter 55.

Through genetic engineering, humans can now modify bacteria to produce

▲ Figure 27.22 **Bacteria synthesizing and storing PHA, a component of biodegradeable plastics.**

SCIENTIFIC SKILLS EXERCISE

Making a Bar Graph and Interpreting Data

Do Soil Microorganisms Protect Against Crop Disease? The soil layer surrounding plant roots, called the *rhizosphere*, is a complex community in which archaea, bacteria, fungi, and plants interact with one another. When crop plants are attacked by fungal or bacterial pathogens, in some cases soil from the rhizosphere protects plants from future attacks. Such protective soil is called disease-suppressive soil. Plants grown in disease-suppressive soils appear to be less vulnerable to pathogen attack. In this exercise, you'll interpret data from an experiment studying whether microorganisms were responsible for the protective effects of disease-suppressive soils.

igor.stevanovic/Shutterstock

How the Experiment Was Done The researchers obtained disease-suppressive soil from 25 random sites in an agricultural field in the Netherlands in which sugar beet crops had previously been attacked by *Rhizoctonia solani*, a fungal pathogen that also afflicts potatoes and rice. The researchers collected other soil samples from the grassy margins of the field where sugar beets had not been grown. The researchers predicted that these soil samples from the margins would not offer protection against pathogens.

The researchers then planted and raised sugar beets in greenhouses, using five different soil treatments. Each soil treatment was applied to four pots, and each pot contained eight plants. The pots were inoculated with *R. solani*. After 20 days, the percentage of infected sugar beet seedlings was determined for each pot and then averaged for each soil treatment.

Data from the Experiment

Soil Treatment	Average Percentage of Seedlings Afflicted with Fungal Disease
Disease-suppressive soil	3.0
Soil from margin of field	62
Soil from margin of field + 10% disease-suppressive soil	39
Disease-suppressive soil heated to 50°C for 1 hour	31
Disease-suppressive soil heated to 80°C for 1 hour	70

Interpret the Data

1. What hypothesis were the researchers testing in this study? What is the independent variable in this study? What is the dependent variable?

2. What is the total number of pots used in this experiment, and how many plants received each soil treatment? Explain why multiple pots and plants were used for each treatment.

3. Use the data in the table to create a bar graph. Then, in words, describe and compare the results for the five soil treatments.

4. The researchers stated, "Collectively, these results indicated that disease suppressiveness [of soil] toward *Rhizoctonia solani* was microbiological in nature." Is this statement supported by the results shown in the graph? Explain.

Data from R. Mendes et al., Deciphering the rhizosphere for disease-suppressive bacteria, *Science* 332:1097–1100 (2011). © Jane B Reece.

---

vitamins, antibiotics, hormones, and other products (see Chapter 20). Researchers are seeking to reduce fossil fuel use by engineering bacteria that can produce ethanol from various forms of biomass, including agricultural waste, switchgrass, municipal waste (such as paper products that are not recycled), and corn **(Figure 27.24)**.

The usefulness of prokaryotes largely derives from their diverse forms of nutrition and metabolism. All this metabolic versatility evolved prior to the appearance of the structural novelties that heralded the evolution of eukaryotic organisms, to which we devote the remainder of this unit.

ExxonMobil Corporation

▲ **Figure 27.23 Bioremediation of an oil spill.** Spraying fertilizer stimulates the growth of native bacteria that metabolize oil, increasing the breakdown process up to fivefold.

Kathleen Spuhler

▲ **Figure 27.24 Fuel production.** Researchers are developing bacteria that produce ethanol (E-85) fuel from renewable plant products.

CONCEPT CHECK 27.6

1. Identify at least two ways that prokaryotes have affected you positively today.

2. A pathogenic bacterium's toxin causes symptoms that increase the bacterium's chance of spreading from host to host. Does this information indicate whether the poison is an exotoxin or endotoxin? Explain.

3. **WHAT IF?** How might a sudden and dramatic change in your diet affect the diversity of prokaryotic species that live in your digestive tract?

For suggested answers, see Appendix A.

27 Chapter Review

Go to **MasteringBiology®** for Assignments, the eText, and the Study Area with Animations, Activities, Vocab Self-Quiz, and Practice Tests.

SUMMARY OF KEY CONCEPTS

CONCEPT 27.1

Structural and functional adaptations contribute to prokaryotic success (pp. 604–608)

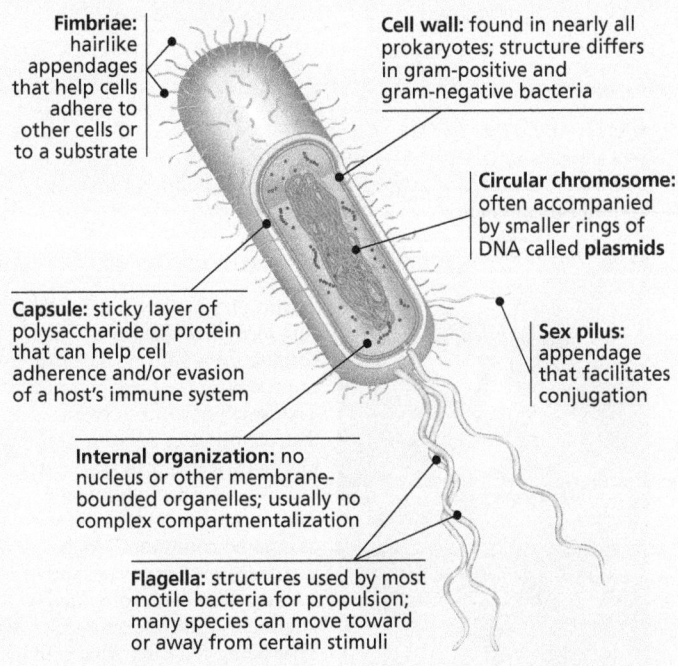

Fimbriae: hairlike appendages that help cells adhere to other cells or to a substrate

Cell wall: found in nearly all prokaryotes; structure differs in gram-positive and gram-negative bacteria

Circular chromosome: often accompanied by smaller rings of DNA called **plasmids**

Capsule: sticky layer of polysaccharide or protein that can help cell adherence and/or evasion of a host's immune system

Sex pilus: appendage that facilitates conjugation

Internal organization: no nucleus or other membrane-bounded organelles; usually no complex compartmentalization

Flagella: structures used by most motile bacteria for propulsion; many species can move toward or away from certain stimuli

- Prokaryotes can reproduce quickly by binary fission. Some form endospores, which can remain viable in harsh conditions for centuries. Prokaryotic populations can evolve in short periods of time in response to changing environmental conditions.

? *Describe features of prokaryotes that enable them to thrive in many different environments.*

CONCEPT 27.2

Rapid reproduction, mutation, and genetic recombination promote genetic diversity in prokaryotes (pp. 608–612)

- Because prokaryotes can often proliferate rapidly, mutations can quickly increase a population's genetic variation, making adaptive evolution possible.
- Genetic diversity in prokaryotes also can arise by recombination of the DNA from two different cells (via transformation, transduction, or conjugation). By transferring advantageous alleles, such as ones for antibiotic resistance, genetic recombination can promote adaptive evolution in prokaryotic populations.

? *Mutations are rare and prokaryotes reproduce asexually; yet their populations can have high genetic diversity. Explain how this can occur.*

CONCEPT 27.3

Diverse nutritional and metabolic adaptations have evolved in prokaryotes (pp. 612–613)

- Nutritional diversity is much greater in prokaryotes than in eukaryotes. As a group, prokaryotes perform all four modes of nutrition: **photoautotrophy**, **chemoautotrophy**, **photoheterotrophy**, and **chemoheterotrophy**.
- Among prokaryotes, **obligate aerobes** require O_2, **obligate anaerobes** are poisoned by O_2, and **facultative anaerobes** can survive with or without O_2.
- Unlike eukaryotes, prokaryotes can metabolize nitrogen in many different forms. Some can convert atmospheric nitrogen to ammonia, a process called **nitrogen fixation**.
- Prokaryotic cells and even species may cooperate metabolically. In *Anabaena*, photosynthetic cells and nitrogen-fixing cells exchange metabolic products. Metabolic cooperation also occurs in surface-coating **biofilms** that include different species.

? *Describe the range of prokaryotic metabolic adaptations.*

CONCEPT 27.4

Prokaryotes have radiated into a diverse set of lineages (pp. 613–618)

- Molecular systematics is leading to a phylogenetic classification of prokaryotes, allowing systematists to identify major new clades.
- Some archaea, such as extreme thermophiles and extreme halophiles, live in extreme environments. Other archaea live in moderate environments such as soils and lakes.
- Diverse nutritional types are scattered among the major groups of bacteria. The two largest groups are the proteobacteria and the gram-positive bacteria.

? *What impact have molecular data had on constructing prokaryotic phylogeny?*

CONCEPT 27.5

Prokaryotes play crucial roles in the biosphere (pp. 618–619)

- Decomposition by heterotrophic prokaryotes and the synthetic activities of autotrophic and nitrogen-fixing prokaryotes contribute to the recycling of elements in ecosystems.
- Many prokaryotes have a symbiotic relationship with a host; the relationships between prokaryotes and their hosts range from mutualism to commensalism to parasitism.

? *In what ways are prokaryotes key to the survival of many species?*

CONCEPT 27.6

Prokaryotes have both beneficial and harmful impacts on humans (pp. 619–622)

- Humans depend on mutualistic prokaryotes, including hundreds of species that live in our intestines and help digest food.
- Pathogenic bacteria typically cause disease by releasing **exotoxins** or **endotoxins** and are potential weapons of bioterrorism. Horizontal gene transfer can spread genes associated with virulence to harmless species or strains.
- Experiments with bacteria such as *E. coli* have led to important advances in DNA technology. Prokaryotes can be used in bioremediation, production of biodegradable plastics, and the synthesis of vitamins, antibiotics, and other products.

? *Describe beneficial and harmful impacts of prokaryotes on humans.*

LEVEL 1: KNOWLEDGE/COMPREHENSION

1. Genetic variation in bacterial populations cannot result from
   a. transduction.
   c. mutation.
   b. conjugation.
   d. meiosis.

2. Photoautotrophs use
   a. light as an energy source and CO_2 as a carbon source.
   b. light as an energy source and methane as a carbon source.
   c. N_2 as an energy source and CO_2 as a carbon source.
   d. CO_2 as both an energy source and a carbon source.

3. Which of the following statements is *not* true?
   a. Archaea and bacteria have different membrane lipids.
   b. The cell walls of archaea lack peptidoglycan.
   c. Only bacteria have histones associated with DNA.
   d. Only some archaea use CO_2 to oxidize H_2, releasing methane.

4. Which of the following involves metabolic cooperation among prokaryotic cells?
   a. binary fission
   c. biofilms
   b. endospore formation
   d. photoautotrophy

5. Bacteria perform the following ecological roles. Which role typically does *not* involve symbiosis?
   a. skin commensalist
   c. gut mutualist
   b. decomposer
   d. pathogen

6. Plantlike photosynthesis that releases O_2 occurs in
   a. cyanobacteria.
   c. archaea.
   b. gram-positive bacteria.
   d. chemoautotrophic bacteria.

LEVEL 2: APPLICATION/ANALYSIS

7. **EVOLUTION CONNECTION**
   In patients infected with nonresistant strains of the tuberculosis bacterium, antibiotics can relieve symptoms in a few weeks. However, it takes much longer to halt the infection, and patients may discontinue treatment while bacteria are still present. How might this result in the evolution of drug-resistant pathogens?

LEVEL 3: SYNTHESIS/EVALUATION

8. **SCIENTIFIC INQUIRY**
   INTERPRET THE DATA The nitrogen-fixing bacterium *Rhizobium* infects the roots of some plant species, forming a mutualism in which the bacterium provides nitrogen, and the plant provides carbohydrates. Scientists measured the 12-week growth of one such plant species (*Acacia irrorata*) when infected by six different *Rhizobium* strains. (a) Graph the data. (b) Interpret your graph.

Rhizobium strain	1	2	3	4	5	6
Plant mass (g)	0.91	0.06	1.56	1.72	0.14	1.03

Source: Based on J. J. Burdon et al., Variation in the effectiveness of symbiotic associations between native rhizobia and temperate Australian *Acacia*: Within species interactions, *Journal of Applied Ecology* 36:398–408 (1999). © Jane B Reece.

Note: Without *Rhizobium*, after 12 weeks, *Acacia* plants have a mass of about 0.1 g.

9. **WRITE ABOUT A THEME: ENERGY**
   In a short essay (about 100–150 words), discuss how prokaryotes and other members of hydrothermal vent communities transfer and transform energy.

10. **SYNTHESIZE YOUR KNOWLEDGE**

Dion Durnford

If you play hockey, you'll probably recognize that stale odour coming from your hockey bag or present in the dressing room. That smell starts from sweat that accumulates on your gear. Human sweat is primarily water but also contains sodium chloride, ammonia, and a variety of organic compounds such as lactate, urea, pyruvate, and amino acids—none of which smells like your hockey bag. That being the case, what is the source of the smell?

For selected answers, see Appendix A.

28

Protists

▲ **Figure 28.1** This protist has a second, relic nuclear genome related to a green alga—a completely different organism. How could such a cell structure have appeared?

KEY CONCEPTS

28.1 Protists are a diverse group of eukaryotes that span all four supergroups

28.2 Excavates include protists with modified mitochondria and protists with unique flagella

28.3 The SAR clade is a highly diverse group of protists defined by DNA similarities

28.4 Red algae and green algae are the closest relatives of land plants

28.5 Unikonts include protists that are closely related to fungi and animals

28.6 Protists play key roles in ecological communities

The Hidden Diversity

Dutch microscopist Antoni van Leeuwenhoek first observed a variety of microbes, including protists, using a hand-held microscope he invented. His microscope was little more than a polished drop of glass sandwiched between metal plates, yet he achieved extraordinary magnification. This discovery of an entirely new layer of the biosphere previously hidden to the naked eye has intrigued scientists for more than 300 years. Recalling his observations, van Leeuwenhoek wrote, "No more pleasant sight has met my eye than this, of so many thousands of living creatures in one small drop of water." Little did he know that this microscopic biosphere was composed of diverse unicellular organisms found in all eukaryotic supergroups.

The term *protist* was first coined by Ernst Haeckel in 1866 when he classified life into three kingdoms: Plantae, Animalia, and Protista. What has been particularly intriguing is how this diversity of the "Protista" evolved over the last billion years. **Figure 28.1** shows an image of a chlorarachniophyte, a photosynthetic protist that often has an amoeboid stage with extensions of the cytoplasm called filopodia (shown). Chlorarachniophytes are mixotrophic, meaning they are photosynthetic yet can still ingest bacteria and smaller protists for nutrition. Feeding

◄ **Heterotrophic protist (*Frontonia leucas*) feeding on photosynthetic protists**

625

appears to be a key function of the filopodia. Chlorarachniophytes are fascinating because of their cellular complexity and are a great example of how eukaryotic cells evolve through endosymbiosis (union between different organisms living together, discussed in detail in Concept 28.1). The chlorarachniophytes are a union between a non-photosynthetic eukaryote and a green alga. The best evidence for this lies in the presence of a second small, nuclear genome within the chlorarachniophyte chloroplast that is the remains of a nucleus from an early green algal symbiont. These vestigial nuclei (or *nucleomorphs*) have excited Dalhousie University researcher John Archibald, whose research program is focused on understanding the structure, evolution, and function of these tiny genomes and how endosymbiosis shaped the evolution of eukaryotic cells.

Until recently, biologists thought that 300 years of observation had uncovered a representative sample of protist diversity. But in the last decade, metagenomic studies have turned up a treasure trove of previously unknown protists within the world of microscopic life. Many of these newly discovered organisms are just 0.5–2 μm in diameter—as small as many prokaryotes. The functional, biochemical, and structural diversity of the protists continues to amaze scientists, and research on these organisms is allowing us to understand how eukaryotic cells first evolved.

In this chapter, you will become acquainted with some of the most significant groups of protists. You will learn about their structural and biochemical adaptations as well as their enormous impact on ecosystems, agriculture, industry, and human health.

<hr>

CONCEPT 28.1

Protists are a diverse group of eukaryotes that span all four supergroups

Protists, along with plants, animals, and fungi, are classified as eukaryotes; they are in domain Eukarya, one of the three domains of life. Unlike the cells of prokaryotes, eukaryotic cells have a nucleus and other membrane-enclosed organelles, such as mitochondria and the Golgi apparatus. Such organelles provide specific locations where particular cellular functions are accomplished, making the structure and organization of eukaryotic cells more complex than those of prokaryotic cells.

Eukaryotic cells also have a well-developed cytoskeleton that extends throughout the cell (see Figure 6.20). The cytoskeleton provides the structural support that enables eukaryotic cells to have asymmetric (irregular) forms, as

well as to change in shape as they feed, move, or grow. In contrast, prokaryotic cells lack a well-developed cytoskeleton, thus limiting the extent to which they can maintain asymmetric forms or change shape over time.

We'll survey the diversity of eukaryotes throughout the rest of this unit, beginning in this chapter with the protists. As you explore this material, bear in mind that

- the organisms in most eukaryotic lineages are protists, and
- most protists are unicellular.

Thus, life differs greatly from how most of us commonly think of it. The large, multicellular organisms that we know best (plants, animals, and fungi) are the tips of just a few branches on the great tree of life (see Figure 26.20).

Structural and Functional Diversity in Protists

Most protists are unicellular, although there are some colonial and multicellular species. Single-celled protists are justifiably considered the simplest eukaryotes, but at the cellular level many protists are very complex—the most elaborate of all cells. In multicellular organisms, essential biological functions are carried out by organs. Unicellular protists carry out the same essential functions, but they do so using subcellular organelles, not multicellular organs. The organelles that protists use are mostly those discussed in Chapter 6, including the nucleus, endoplasmic reticulum, Golgi apparatus, and lysosomes. Certain freshwater protists also rely on organelles not found in most other eukaryotic cells, such as contractile vacuoles that pump excess water from the protistan cell (see Figure 7.13).

Protists have a wide variety of nutritional lifestyles. Some protists are photoautotrophs, which use energy from light to acquire carbon from carbon dioxide, and contain chloroplasts. Some are heterotrophs, absorbing organic molecules or ingesting larger food particles. Still other protists, called **mixotrophs**, combine photosynthesis *and* heterotrophic nutrition. Photoautotrophy, heterotrophy, and mixotrophy have all arisen independently in many protist lineages.

Reproduction and life cycles also are highly varied among protists. Some protists are only known to reproduce asexually; others can also reproduce sexually or at least employ the sexual processes of meiosis and fertilization. All three basic types of sexual life cycles (see Figure 13.6) are represented among protists, along with some variations that do not quite fit any of these types. We will examine the life cycles of several protist groups later in this chapter.

Four Supergroups of Eukaryotes

Protists, along with plants, animals, and fungi, are classified as eukaryotes; they are in domain Eukarya, one of the three domains of life. All protists were once classified in a single kingdom, Protista, but advances in eukaryotic systematics have caused the kingdom to crumble. It has become clear that the kingdom Protista is in fact polyphyletic (see Figure 26.10); some protists are more closely related to plants, fungi, or animals than they are to other protists. As a result, the kingdom Protista has been abandoned, and various lineages of protists are now recognized as kingdoms in their own right. Most biologists still use the term *protist*, but only as a convenient way to refer to eukaryotes that are not plants, animals, or fungi.

Not only has kingdom Protista been abandoned, but a variety of other hypotheses have been discarded as well. For example, in the early 1990s, many biologists thought that the oldest lineage of living eukaryotes consisted of the *amitochondriate protists*, organisms without conventional mitochondria and with fewer membrane-bounded organelles than other protist groups. But recent structural and DNA data have undermined this hypothesis. Many of the so-called amitochondriate protists have been shown to have mitochondria—though reduced ones—and some of these organisms are now classified in entirely different groups. For example, microsporidians, once considered amitochondriate protists, are now classified as fungi.

The ongoing changes in our understanding of the phylogeny of protists pose challenges to students and instructors alike. Hypotheses about these relationships are a focus of scientific activity, changing rapidly as new data cause previous ideas to be modified or discarded. We'll focus here on one current hypothesis: the four supergroups of eukaryotes shown in Figure 28.2. Because the root of the eukaryotic tree is not known, all five supergroups are shown as diverging simultaneously from a common ancestor. We know that is not correct, but we do not know which organisms were the first to diverge from the others. In addition, while some of the groups in Figure 28.2 are well supported by morphological and DNA data, others are more controversial. As you read this chapter, it may be helpful to focus less on the specific names of groups of organisms and more on why the organisms are important and how ongoing research is elucidating their evolutionary relationships.

Endosymbiosis and the Spread of Photosynthesis During Protist Evolution

Some ideas are worth spreading, and when it comes to acquiring photosynthesis during eukaryotic evolution, why reinvent the wheel? Photosynthesis is one of those processes that have been passed around among organisms during diversification of eukaryotes. Oxygenic photosynthesis first appeared in cyanobacteria and, in a pivotal event,

this function was transferred to the first eukaryotic cell as described by the endosymbiont theory (Figure 25.10). What started as an endosymbiosis between cyanobacteria and a eukaryote ended with the formation of an organelle and the integration of photosynthetic metabolism into a previously nonphotosynthetic organism. The formation of a chloroplast (or more generally, **plastid**) from an endosymbiotic cyanobacterium within a eukaryotic host is called **primary endosymbiosis**. Evidence supporting the origin of the plastid from cyanobacteria is overwhelming and comes from comparing plastid genes and other biochemical features with those of free-living cyanobacteria. This newly created photosynthetic eukaryote is believed to have diverged over time into the **Archaeplastida**, a group that includes land plants plus green and red algae (see Concept 28.4). This scenario suggests that the primary endosymbiosis occurred only once. To test this hypothesis, you have to demonstrate that the members of this group share a common ancestor, as implied in Figure 28.3 on page 630. Scientists have examined genes from the nuclei of red and green algae, and much of the evidence suggests that these genes are more similar to each other than they are to other groups of eukaryotes. This supports the hypothesis that they shared a common ancestor and that there was a single primary endosymbiotic event that gave rise to the plastid (Figure 28.2). Of course, these are very early events in the history of eukaryotic cell evolution. Getting conclusive molecular evidence can be a challenge, especially since the primary endosymbiotic event is estimated to have occurred between 1 and 1.5 billion years ago.

Photosynthesis continued to be passed to diverse groups and across kingdoms. Presently there are photosynthetic members in three out of the four eukaryotic supergroups (Figure 28.2). There is considerable evidence to suggest these plastid acquisition events occurred on several different occasions via an endosymbiosis between red or green algae with a nonphotosynthetic, eukaryotic host—a process called **secondary endosymbiosis** (Figure 28.3). These early heterotrophic eukaryotes must have had the ability to phagocytose, or swallow, whole algal cells, an ability possessed by the ciliate, *Frontonia leucas,* shown in the photo on the first page of this chapter. Maintaining these cells as endosymbionts within a vacuole in the host's cytoplasm would have been a first step in organelle evolution (see Figure 6.16). A classic piece of evidence suggesting plastids were derived through secondary endosymbioses is the presence of additional membranes around the organelle. Typically there are a total of three or four surrounding plastid membranes depending on the group. Scientists believe these additional membranes were derived from the endosymbiont's plasma membrane and/or the host's vacuolar membrane.

Exploring Protistan Diversity

The tree below represents a phylogenetic hypothesis for the relationships among all the eukaryotes on Earth today. The eukaryotic groups at the branch tips are related in larger "supergroups," labelled vertically at the far right of the tree. The kingdoms Plantae (land plants), Fungi, and Animalia (animals) have survived from the five-kingdom system of classification. Groups that were formerly classified in the kingdom Protista are listed in yellow boxes. Dotted lines indicate evolutionary relationships that are uncertain and proposed clades that are under active debate. For clarity, this tree only includes representative clades from each supergroup. The relationship of other eukaryotic groups, such as the haptophytes and cryptomonads, to the four supergroups is uncertain and they were left off the tree. In addition, the recent discoveries of many new groups of eukaryotes indicate that eukaryotic diversity is much greater than shown here.

Excavata

Some members of this supergroup have an "excavated" groove on one side of the cell body. Two major clades (the parabasalids and diplomonads) have modified mitochondria; others (the euglenozoans) have flagella that differ in structure from those of other organisms. Excavates include parasites such as *Giardia*, as well as many predatory and photosynthetic species.

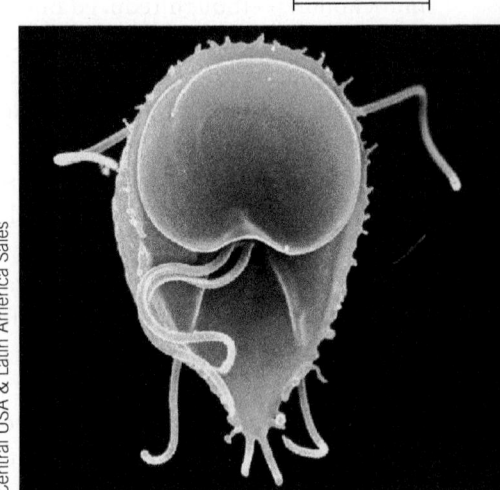

5 μm

Central USA & Latin America Sales

***Giardia intestinalis*, a diplomonad parasite.** This diplomonad (colourized SEM), which lacks the characteristic surface groove of the Excavata, can infect people when they drink water contaminated with feces containing *Giardia* cysts. Drinking such water—even from a seemingly pristine stream—can cause severe diarrhea. Boiling the water kills the parasite.

Excavata
- Diplomonads
- Parabasalids
- Euglenozoans

SAR clade

Stramenopiles
- Diatoms
- Golden algae
- Brown algae

Alveolates
- Dinoflagellates
- Apicomplexans
- Ciliates

Rhizarians
- Forams
- Cercozoans
- Radiolarians

Archaeplastida
- Red algae
- Chlorophytes — Green algae
- Charophytes — Green algae
- Land plants

Unikonta

Amoebozoans
- Slime moulds
- Tubulinids
- Entamoebas

Opisthokonts
- Nucleariids
- Fungi
- Choanoflagellates
- Animals

■ SAR Clade

This supergroup contains (and is named after) three large and very diverse clades: Stramenopila, Alveolata, and Rhizaria. Stramenopiles include some of the most important photosynthetic organisms on Earth, such as the diatoms shown here. Alveolates also include many photosynthetic species as well as important pathogens, such as *Plasmodium*, which causes malaria. Many of the key groups of photosynthetic stramenopiles and alveolates are thought to have arisen by secondary endosymbiosis.

M. I. Walker/Photoshot
50 μm

Diatom diversity. These beautiful single-celled protists are important photosynthetic organisms in aquatic communities (LM).

The rhizarian subgroup of the SAR clade contains many species of amoebas, most of which have pseudopodia that are threadlike in shape. Pseudopodia are extensions that can bulge from any portion of the cell; they are used in movement and in the capture of prey. The chlorarachniophytes, discussed at the start of this chapter, are also in the Rhizaria.

National Oceanic and Atmospheric Administration

100 μm

University of California Davis

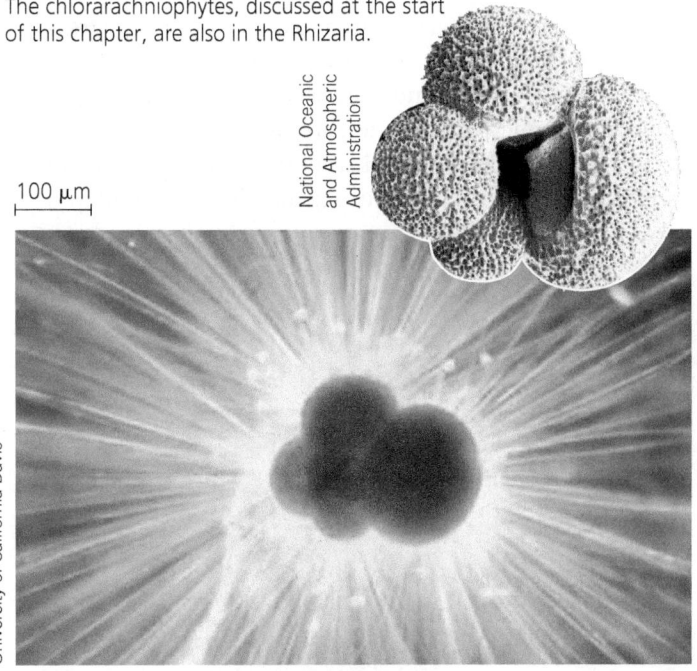

Globigerina, a rhizarian in the SAR clade. This species is a foram, a group whose members have threadlike pseudopodia extending through pores in the shell, or *test* (LM). The inset SEM shows a foram test, which is hardened by calcium carbonate.

■ Archaeplastida

This group of eukaryotes includes red algae and green algae, along with land plants (kingdom Plantae). Red algae and green algae include unicellular species, colonial species (such as the green alga *Volvox*), and multicellular species. Many of the large algae known informally as "seaweeds" are multicellular red or green algae. Protists in Archaeplastida include key photosynthetic species that form the base of the food web in some aquatic communities.

20 μm

David J. Patterson
50 μm

blickwinkel/Alamy Stock Photo

Volvox, a colonial freshwater green alga. The colony is a hollow ball whose wall is composed of hundreds of biflagellated cells (see inset LM) embedded in a gelatinous matrix. The cells are usually connected by cytoplasmic strands; if isolated, these cells cannot reproduce. The large colonies seen here will eventually release the small "daughter" colonies within them (LM).

■ Unikonta

This group of eukaryotes includes amoebas that have lobe- or tube-shaped pseudopodia, as well as animals, fungi, and non-amoeba protists that are closely related to animals or fungi. According to one current hypothesis, the unikonts may have been the first group of eukaryotes to diverge from other eukaryotes; however, this hypothesis has yet to be widely accepted.

100 μm

Michael Abbey/Science Source

A unikont amoeba. This amoeba (*Amoeba proteus*) is using its pseudopodia to move.

▼ **Figure 28.3 Diversity of plastids produced by endosymbiosis.** Studies of plastid-bearing eukaryotes suggest that plastids evolved from a gram-negative cyanobacterium that was engulfed by an ancestral heterotrophic eukaryote (primary endosymbiosis). That ancestor then diversified into red algae and green algae, some of which were subsequently engulfed by other eukaryotes (secondary endosymbiosis).

MAKE CONNECTIONS *How many distinct genomes does a chlorarachniophyte cell contain? Explain. (See Figures 6.17 and 6.18.)*

Cyanobacterium

Heterotrophic eukaryote

Primary endosymbiosis

Membranes are represented as dark lines in the cell.

1 2 3

One of these membranes was lost in red and green algal descendants.

Red alga

Green alga

Secondary endosymbiosis

Secondary endosymbiosis

Secondary endosymbiosis

Plastid

Dinoflagellates

Apicomplexans

Stramenopiles

Plastid

Euglenids

Nucleomorph

Chlorarachniophytes

The best evidence for the occurrence of secondary endosymbiosis exists with two groups of organisms that possess vestigial nuclei, or **nucleomorphs** (Figure 28.4): the chlorarachniophytes (Rhizaria) and cryptomonads (a group whose relationship to the four eukaryotic supergroups is uncertain). This rather amazing organelle is sandwiched between the two sets of surrounding plastid membranes, in a location analogous to the endosymbiont's former cytoplasm (see Figure 28.4). Work on cryptomonads led by Susan Douglas of the National Research Council in Halifax and Michael Gray from Dalhousie University examined the evolution of the cryptomonad nucleomorph by comparing genetic sequences. In the Scientific Skills Exercise, you will interpret the data they used to make their conclusions on the nucleomorph origin. This study was the first to provide molecular evidence that the cryptomonad nucleomorph is derived from the nucleus of a photosynthetic eukaryote, specifically a red alga, and that this was acquired through an endosymbiosis.

Nucleomorphs have a double membrane with nuclear pores (Figure 28.4), similar to a typical nuclear envelope.

While nucleomorph genes are organized on linear chromosomes, the genes are very densely packed with little repetitive DNA or spacer regions between the different genes, unlike the typical eukaryotic chromosome. It is astonishing that these two groups of eukaryotes (chlorarachniophytes and cryptomonads) have four separate genomes within one

Outer plastid membranes

Nuclear pore-like gap

Nucleomorph

Inner plastid membranes

Thylakoid membranes

Ken Ishida

▲ **Figure 28.4 Nucleomorph within a plastid of a chlorarachniophyte.**

Interpreting Comparisons of Genetic Sequences

What Is the Origin of the Cryptomonad Nucleomorph? Cryptomonads, like *Rhodomonas salina* shown in the photograph, are marine protists and are one of two groups that contain nucleomorphs—the vestigial nucleus left over from a secondary endosymbiosis. In studying which living eukaryotes might be most closely related to the cryptomonad nucleomorph, thereby identifying the group of organisms from which the nucleomorph likely evolved, Canadian researchers compared ribosomal RNA (rRNA) sequences. Because most cells contain thousands of ribosomes, rRNA is the most abundant form of RNA in living cells and is suitable for comparing even distantly related species. In this exercise, you'll interpret some of the research data to draw conclusions about the evolution of nucleomorphs.

5 μm

Courtesy of Bigelow Laboratory for Ocean Sciences

How the Research Was Done Researchers used the polymerase chain reaction and rRNA-specific primers to amplify the gene that codes for the small-subunit (18s) rRNA molecule from cryptomonads. The rRNA genes were then sequenced and compared to rRNAs from other organisms to determine evolutionary relationships.

Data from the Research The PCR reaction yielded two different rRNA sequences: one from the nucleus and one from the nucleomorph. The 1001 nucleotides were then compared to rRNAs from different organisms and the percent differences between them calculated and tabulated in a *distance matrix*. A distance matrix is a table showing the calculated divergence (number of nucleotide differences) between every pair of sequences. A tree-building program is then used to construct a tree to represent the evolutionary relationships.

Interpret the Data

1. First, make sure you understand how to read the tree. This is a phylogram (see Figure 26.15), so the branch lengths (horizontal) are proportional to the divergence between the sequences. In this type of tree, there is a scale bar indicating the number of nucleotide differences with a given length. To get an estimate of the divergence

between two species on the tree, you have to add the differences of all horizontal branches connecting them.

2. Why didn't the two cryptomonad rRNA sequences group together in the tree?
3. Which eukaryotic group has an rRNA gene that is most similar to that of the cryptomonad nucleomorph? What is the significance of this similarity?
4. If you sequenced the chloroplast genome, to what group of organisms would you predict it would be similar?

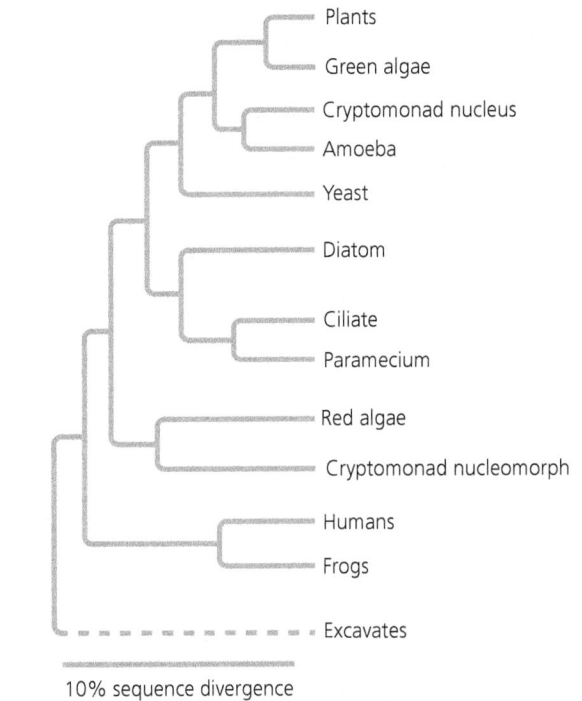

10% sequence divergence

Data from S. E. Douglas et al., Cryptomonad algae are evolutionary chimeras of two phylogenetically distinct unicellular eukaryotes, *Nature* 350:148–151 (1991).

---

eukaryotic cell: a nuclear, nucleomorph, plastid, and mitochondrial genome. This example itself illustrates the importance of endosymbiosis for eukaryote evolution— three of the four genomes were derived from endosymbionts.

How Do You Create an Organelle Through Endosymbiosis?

EVOLUTION **Endosymbiosis has shaped the evolution of eukaryotic cells.** The rationale for the formation of endosymbiotic relationships is debatable and varied, but for photosynthetic endosymbionts, it is likely that the host was able to "steal" a proportion of the sugars being made by the algae through photosynthesis or was acquiring some other essential metabolite. Over time, the relationship

became more interdependent until the alga was eventually reduced to an organelle. But how does this happen and what must occur? The process of reducing an endosymbiont to an organelle is complex. Think about photosynthesis (see Chapter 10) and all the genes/proteins required for making sugar from CO_2 and light—there are hundreds! Most of these genes, except for a few remaining on the plastid genome, were moved into the nucleus of the host; many others that were not essential were lost entirely. The mechanism of gene transfer from the endosymbiont to the nucleus of the host is unknown, but we know it happens. But getting to the nucleus is only half the battle. Algal genes that make it to the host nucleus must then be expressed properly (need proper promoters), they have to be translated (if they encode a protein), and the protein must find its way back into the plastid (which requires specific targeting sequences in the protein). So there are lots of presumed steps to complete a process that took millions of years, but nevertheless occurred independently on several occasions.

CONCEPT CHECK 28.1

1. Cite at least four examples of structural and functional diversity among protists.

2. Summarize the role of endosymbiosis in eukaryotic evolution.

3. **WHAT IF?** After studying Figure 28.2, draw a simplified version of the phylogenetic tree that shows only the four supergroups of eukaryotes. Now sketch how the tree would look if the unikonts were the first group of eukaryotes to diverge from other eukaryotes.

For suggested answers, see Appendix A.

CONCEPT 28.2

Excavates include protists with modified mitochondria and protists with unique flagella

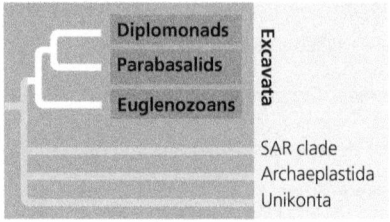

Now that we have examined some of the broad patterns in eukaryotic evolution, we will look more closely at the five main groups of protists shown in Figure 28.2.

We begin this tour with **Excavata** (the excavates), a clade recently proposed based on morphological studies of the cytoskeleton. Some members of this diverse group also have an "excavated" feeding groove on one side of the cell body.

The excavates include the diplomonads, the parabasalids, and the euglenozoans. Molecular data indicate that each of these three groups is monophyletic, and recent genomic studies support the monophyly of the excavate supergroup.

Diplomonads and Parabasalids

The protists in these two groups lack plastids and have modified mitochondria (until recently, they were thought to lack mitochondria altogether). Most diplomonads and parabasalids are found in anaerobic environments.

Diplomonads have modified mitochondria called *mitosomes*. These organelles lack functional electron transport chains and hence cannot use oxygen to help extract energy from carbohydrates and other organic molecules. Instead, diplomonads get the energy they need from anaerobic

biochemical pathways. Many diplomonads are parasites, including the infamous *Giardia intestinalis* (see Figure 28.2), which inhabits the intestines of mammals.

Structurally, diplomonads have two equal-sized nuclei and multiple flagella. Recall that eukaryotic flagella are extensions of the cytoplasm, consisting of bundles of microtubules covered by the cell's plasma membrane (see Figure 6.24). They are quite different from prokaryotic flagella, which are filaments composed of the globular protein flagellin attached to the cell surface (see Figure 27.7).

Parabasalids also have reduced mitochondria; called *hydrogenosomes*, these organelles generate some energy anaerobically, releasing hydrogen gas as a by-product. The best-known parabasalid is *Trichomonas vaginalis*, a sexually transmitted parasite that infects some 5 million people each year. *T. vaginalis* travels along the mucus-coated lining of the human reproductive and urinary tracts by moving its flagella and by undulating part of its plasma membrane (Figure 28.5). In females, if the vagina's normal acidity is disturbed, *T. vaginalis* can outcompete beneficial microorganisms there and infect the vagina. (*Trichomonas* infections also can occur in the urethra of males, though often without symptoms.) *T. vaginalis* has a gene that allows it to feed on the vaginal lining, promoting infection. Studies suggest that the protist acquired this gene by horizontal gene transfer from bacterial parasites in the vagina.

Euglenozoans

Protists called **euglenozoans** belong to a diverse clade that includes predatory heterotrophs, photosynthetic autotrophs, mixotrophs, and parasites. The main morphological feature that distinguishes protists in this clade is the presence of a rod with either a spiral or a crystalline structure inside each of their flagella (Figure 28.6). The two best-studied groups of euglenozoans are the kinetoplastids and the euglenids.

Kinetoplastids

Protists called **kinetoplastids** have a single, large mitochondrion that contains an unusual organized mass of DNA composed of thousands of interlocking circles called a *kinetoplast*. These protists include species that feed on

David M. Phillips/The Population Council/Science Source

▲ Figure 28.5 The parabasalid *Trichomonas vaginalis* (colourized SEM).

Flagella

0.2 μm

8 μm

Crystalline rod
(cross section)

Ring of microtubules
(cross section)

David J. Patterson

▲ **Figure 28.6 Euglenozoan flagellum.** Most euglenozoans have a crystalline rod inside one of their flagella (the TEM is a flagellum shown in cross section). The rod lies alongside the 9 + 2 ring of microtubules found in all eukaryotic flagella (compare with Figure 6.24).

9 μm

Oliver Meckes/Science Source

▲ **Figure 28.7 *Trypanosoma*, a kinetoplastid that causes sleeping sickness.** The purple, ribbon-shaped cells among these red blood cells are the trypanosomes (colourized SEM).

prokaryotes in freshwater, marine, and moist terrestrial ecosystems, as well as species that parasitize animals, plants, and other protists. For example, kinetoplastids in the genus *Trypanosoma* infect humans and cause sleeping sickness, a neurological disease that is invariably fatal if not treated (**Figure 28.7**). The infection occurs via the bite of a vector (carrier) organism, the African tsetse fly. Trypanosomes also cause Chagas' disease, which is transmitted by bloodsucking insects and can lead to congestive heart failure.

Trypanosomes evade immune responses with an effective "bait-and-switch" defence. The surface of a trypanosome is coated with millions of copies of a single protein. However, before the host's immune system can recognize the protein and mount an attack, new generations of the parasite switch to another surface protein with a different molecular structure. Frequent changes in the surface protein prevent the host from developing immunity (See the Scientific Skills Exercise in Chapter 43 to explore this topic further). About a third of *Trypanosoma*'s genome is dedicated to producing these surface proteins.

Euglenids

A **euglenid** has a pocket at one end of the cell from which one or two flagella emerge (**Figure 28.8**). Some euglenids are mixotrophs: They perform photosynthesis when sun is available, but when it is not, they can

become heterotrophic, absorbing organic nutrients from their environment. Many other euglenids engulf prey by phagocytosis.

CONCEPT CHECK 28.2

1. Why do some biologists describe the mitochondria of diplomonads and parabasalids as "highly reduced"?

2. **WHAT IF?** DNA sequence data for a diplomonad, a euglenid, a plant, and an unidentified protist suggest that the unidentified species is most closely related to the diplomonad. Further studies reveal that the unknown species has fully functional mitochondria. Based on these data, at what point on the phylogenetic tree in Figure 28.2 did the mystery protist's lineage probably diverge from other eukaryote lineages? Explain.

For suggested answers, see Appendix A.

▼ **Figure 28.8 *Euglena*, a euglenid commonly found in pond water.**

Long flagellum

Eyespot: pigmented organelle that functions as a light shield, allowing light from only a certain direction to strike the light detector

Short flagellum

Contractile vacuole

Nucleus

Chloroplast

Plasma membrane

Euglena (LM)

5 μm

David J. Patterson

Light detector: swelling near the base of the long flagellum; detects light that is not blocked by the eyespot. As a result, *Euglena* moves toward light of appropriate intensity, an important adaptation that enhances photosynthesis.

Pellicle: protein bands beneath the plasma membrane that provide strength and flexibility (*Euglena* lacks a cell wall.)

The SAR clade is a highly diverse group of protists defined by DNA similarities

▲ **Figure 28.9 Stramenopile flagella.** Most stramenopiles, such as *Synura petersenii*, have two flagella: one covered with fine, stiff hairs and a shorter one that is smooth.

Our second supergroup, the so-called **SAR clade**, was proposed recently based on whole-genome DNA sequence analyses. These studies have found that three major clades of protists—the stramenopiles, alveolates, and rhizarians—form a monophyletic supergroup. This supergroup contains a large, extremely diverse collection of protists. To date, this supergroup has not received a formal name but is instead known by the first letters of its major clades: the SAR clade.

Some morphological and DNA sequence data suggest that two of these groups, the stramenopiles and alveolates, originated more than a billion years ago, when a common ancestor of these two clades engulfed a single-celled, photosynthetic red alga and gave rise to a plastid through secondary endosymbiosis (Figure 28.3). Some species in these clades, however, lack plastids, implying that they were lost during evolution.

As its lack of a formal name suggests, the SAR clade is one of the most controversial of the four supergroups we describe in this chapter. Even so, for many scientists, this supergroup represents the best current hypothesis for the phylogeny of the three large protist clades to which we now turn.

Stramenopiles

One major subgroup of the SAR clade, the **stramenopiles**, includes some of the most important photosynthetic organisms on the planet. Their name (from the Latin *stramen*, straw, and *pilos*, hair) refers to their characteristic flagellum, which has numerous fine, hairlike projections. In most stramenopiles, this "hairy" flagellum is paired with a shorter "smooth" (nonhairy) flagellum (Figure 28.9). In multicellular stramenopiles, it is usually the reproductive structures (zoospores, sperm) that have the flagellar apparatus characteristic of the group. Here we'll focus on four groups of stramenopiles: diatoms, golden algae, and brown algae.

Diatoms

Diatoms are unicellular algae that have a unique glass-like wall made of hydrated silica (silicon dioxide) embedded in an organic matrix. The wall consists of two parts that overlap like a shoe box and its lid (Figure 28.10). These walls provide effective protection from the crushing jaws of predators: Live diatoms can withstand pressures as great as 1.4 million kg/m^2, equal to the pressure under each leg of a table supporting an elephant! Some diatoms can produce toxins, like domoic acid, that accumulate in shellfish and cause amnesic shellfish poisoning in humans, resulting in short-term memory loss and sometimes death. In 1987, shellfish from Prince Edward Island caused the deaths of three people and left over 100 with symptoms in what was the first documented outbreak of domoic acid poisoning. Shellfish from the island are now routinely monitored for domoic acid to ensure they are safe.

With an estimated 100 000 living species, diatoms are a highly diverse group of protists (see Figure 28.2). They are a major component of phytoplankton both in the ocean and in lakes. The abundance of diatoms in the past is also evident in the fossil record, where massive accumulations of fossilized diatom walls are major constituents of sediments known as *diatomaceous earth*. These sediments are mined for their quality as a filtering medium and for many other uses.

Diatoms are so widespread and abundant, their photosynthetic activity would affect global carbon dioxide levels, and this is indeed the case. Diatoms have this effect in part because of the chain of

▲ **Figure 28.10 The diatom *Triceratium morlandii* (colourized SEM).**

events that follows their rapid population growth (a bloom) when ample nutrients are available. Typically, diatoms are eaten by a variety of protists and invertebrates, but during a bloom, many escape this fate. When these uneaten diatoms die, their bodies sink to the ocean floor. It takes decades to centuries for diatoms that sink to the ocean floor to be broken down by bacteria and other decomposers. As a result, the carbon in their bodies remains there for some time, rather than being released immediately as carbon dioxide as the decomposers respire. The overall effect of these events is that carbon dioxide absorbed by diatoms during photosynthesis is transported, or "pumped," to the ocean floor.

With the goal of reducing climate change by lowering atmospheric carbon dioxide levels, some scientists advocate promoting diatom blooms by fertilizing the ocean with essential nutrients such as iron. In a 2012 study, researchers found that iron fertilization of the ocean doubled diatom biomass within a couple weeks and about half of the organic carbon from this bloom (representing captured carbon dioxide) sank below 1000 metres, and likely to the ocean floor. Whether governments should use these geoengineering approaches to combat climate change is controversial and further experiments are required to test whether iron fertilization has undesirable side effects (such as oxygen depletion or the production of nitrous oxide, a more potent greenhouse gas than carbon dioxide). In a surprise development, the Haida Salmon Restoration Corporation independently commissioned a project that added 100 tons of iron sulphate to the ocean off the western coast of Canada in an effort to stimulate the base of the food web (phytoplankton) and ultimately increase salmon productivity. Since the project did not have Environment Canada approval and because of an international moratorium on iron fertilization, the case is currently before the courts.

Golden Algae

The characteristic colour of **golden algae** results from their yellow and brown carotenoids. The cells of golden algae are typically biflagellated, with both flagella attached near one end of the cell.

Many golden algae are components of freshwater and marine plankton. While all golden algae are photosynthetic, some species are mixotrophic. These mixotrophs can absorb dissolved organic compounds or ingest food particles, including living cells, by phagocytosis. Most species are unicellular, but some, such as those in the freshwater genus *Dinobryon*, are colonial (Figure 28.11). If environmental conditions deteriorate, many species form protective cysts that can survive for decades.

Brown Algae

The largest and most complex algae are **brown algae**. All are multicellular, and most are marine. Brown algae

Flagellum
Outer container
Living cell

25 μm

Stephen Durr

▲ Figure 28.11 *Dinobryon*, a colonial golden alga found in fresh water (LM).

are especially common along temperate coasts, where the water is cool. They owe their characteristic brown or olive colour to the carotenoids in their plastids.

Many of the species commonly called "seaweeds" are brown algae. Some brown algal seaweeds have specialized tissues and organs that resemble those in plants, such as a root-like **holdfast**, which anchors the alga, and a stemlike **stipe**, which supports the leaflike **blades** (Figure 28.12). However, morphological and DNA evidence show that these similarities evolved independently in the algal and plant lineages and are thus analogous, not homologous. In addition, while plants have adaptations (such as rigid stems) that provide support

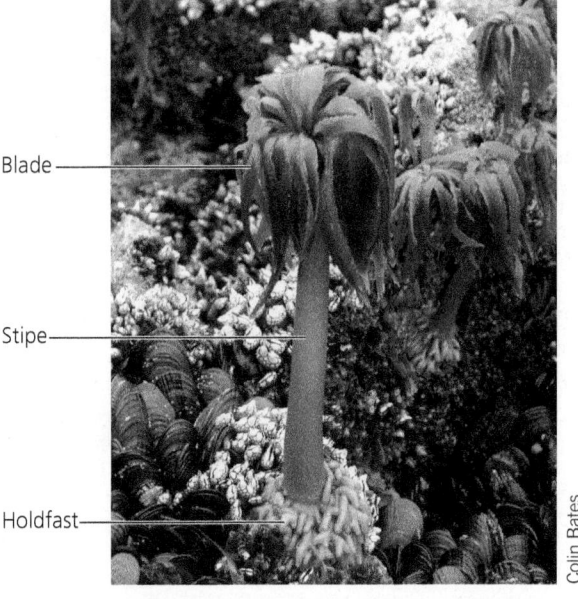

Blade
Stipe
Holdfast

Colin Bates

▲ Figure 28.12 **Seaweeds: Adapted to life at the ocean's margins.** The sea palm (*Postelsia*) lives on rocks along the coast of the northwestern United States and western Canada. The thallus of this brown alga is well adapted to maintaining a firm foothold despite the crashing surf.

against gravity, brown algae have adaptations that enable their main photosynthetic surfaces (the leaflike blades) to be near the water surface. Some brown algae accomplish this task with gas-filled, bubble-shaped floats. Giant brown algae known as kelps that live in deep waters use a different means: Their blades are attached to stipes that can rise as much as 60 metres from the seafloor, more than half the length of a football field.

Brown algae are important commodities for humans. Some species are eaten, such as *Laminaria* (Japanese "kombu"), which is used in soups. In addition, the gel-forming substance in the cell walls of brown algae, called algin, is used to thicken many processed foods, including pudding and salad dressing.

Alternation of Generations

A variety of life cycles have evolved among the multicellular algae. The most complex life cycles include an **alternation of generations**, the alternation of multicellular haploid and diploid forms. Although haploid and diploid conditions alternate in *all* sexual life cycles—human gametes, for example, are haploid—the term *alternation of generations* applies only to life cycles in which both haploid and diploid stages are multicellular. As you will read in Chapter 29, alternation of generations also evolved in plants.

The complex life cycle of the brown alga *Laminaria* provides an example of alternation of generations (Figure 28.13). The diploid individual is called the *sporophyte* because it

1 The sporophytes are usually found in water just below the line of the lowest tides, attached to rocks by branching holdfasts.

2 Cells on the surface of the blade develop into sporangia.

3 Sporangia produce zoospores by meiosis.

4 The zoospores are all structurally alike, but about half of them develop into male gametophytes and half into female gametophytes. The gametophytes are short, branched filaments that grow on subtidal rocks.

5 Male gametophytes release sperm, and female gametophytes produce eggs, which remain attached to the female gametophyte. Eggs secrete a chemical signal that attracts sperm of the same species, thereby increasing the probability of fertilization in the ocean.

6 Sperm fertilize the eggs.

7 The zygotes grow into new sporophytes while attached to the remains of the female gametophyte.

Sporangia

MEIOSIS

Zoospore

Sporophyte (2n)

Female

Gametophytes (n)

Male

Developing sporophyte

Zygote (2n)

Mature female gametophyte (n)

FERTILIZATION

Egg

Sperm

Key

Haploid (n)

Diploid (2n)

10 cm

J.R. Waaland/Biological Photo Service

▲ Figure 28.13 **The life cycle of the brown alga *Laminaria*: An example of alternation of generations.**

? *Are the sperm shown in* **5** *genetically identical to one another? Explain.*

produces spores. The spores are haploid and move by means of flagella; they are called zoospores. The zoospores develop into haploid, multicellular male and female *gametophytes*, which produce gametes. The union of two gametes (fertilization, or syngamy) results in a diploid zygote, which matures and gives rise to a new multicellular sporophyte.

In *Laminaria*, the two generations are **heteromorphic**, meaning that the sporophytes and gametophytes are structurally different. Other algal life cycles have an alternation of **isomorphic** generations, in which the sporophytes and gametophytes look similar to each other, although they differ in chromosome number.

Alveolates

Members of the next subgroup of the SAR clade, the **alveolates**, have membrane-bounded sacs (alveoli) just under the plasma membrane **(Figure 28.14)**. The function of the alveoli is unknown; researchers hypothesize that they may help stabilize the cell surface or regulate the cell's water and ion content.

Alveolates are abundant in many habitats and include a wide range of photosynthetic and heterotrophic protists. We'll discuss three alveolate clades here: a group of flagellates (the dinoflagellates), a group of parasites (the apicomplexans), and a group of protists that move using cilia (the ciliates).

Dinoflagellates

The cells of many **dinoflagellates** are reinforced by cellulose plates. Two flagella located in grooves in this "armour" make dinoflagellates (from the Greek *dinos*, whirling) spin as they move through the water **(Figure 28.15a)**. Although the ancestors of dinoflagellates are thought to have acquired

Virginia Institute of Marine Science

Flagella

(a) Dinoflagellate flagella. Beating of the spiral flagellum, which lies in a groove that encircles the cell, makes this specimen of *Pfiesteria shumwayae* spin (colourized SEM).

3 μm

(b) Red tide in the Gulf of Carpentaria in northern Australia. The red colour is due to high concentrations of a carotenoid-containing dinoflagellate.

Bill Bachman/Science Source

▲ Figure 28.15 **Dinoflagellates.**

photosynthesis by secondary endosymbiosis (see Figure 28.3), roughly half of all dinoflagellates are now purely heterotrophic and many are mixotrophic.

Periods of explosive population growth, or *blooms*, in dinoflagellates sometimes cause a phenomenon called "red tide" **(Figure 28.15b)**. The blooms make coastal waters appear brownish red or pink because of the presence of pigments called carotenoids, located in the dinoflagellate plastid. Toxins produced by certain dinoflagellates (such as *Karenia brevis*, which inhabits the Gulf of Mexico) have caused massive kills of invertebrates and fishes. Humans who eat molluscs that have accumulated the toxins are affected as well, sometimes fatally.

Apicomplexans

Nearly all **apicomplexans** are parasites of animals, and some cause serious human diseases. The parasites spread through their host as tiny infectious cells called *sporozoites*. Apicomplexans are so named because one end (the *apex*) of the sporozoite cell contains a *complex* of organelles

Flagellum   Alveoli

Alveolate

Guy Brugerolle

0.2 μm

▲ Figure 28.14 **Alveoli.** These sacs under the plasma membrane are a characteristic that distinguishes alveolates from other eukaryotes (TEM).

specialized for penetrating host cells and tissues. Although apicomplexans are not photosynthetic, recent data show that they retain a modified plastid (apicoplast), most likely of red algal origin.

Most apicomplexans have intricate life cycles with both sexual and asexual stages. Those life cycles often require two or more host species for completion. For example, *Plasmodium*, the parasite that causes malaria, lives in both mosquitoes and humans (Figure 28.16).

Historically, malaria has rivalled tuberculosis as the leading cause of human death by infectious disease. The incidence of malaria was greatly diminished in the 1960s by insecticides that reduced carrier populations of *Anopheles* mosquitoes and by drugs that killed *Plasmodium* in humans. But the emergence of resistant varieties of both *Anopheles* and *Plasmodium* has led

to a resurgence of malaria. About 250 million people in the tropics are currently infected, and 900 000 die each year.

In regions where malaria is common, the lethal effects of this disease have resulted in the evolution of high frequencies of the sickle-cell allele; for an explanation of this connection, see Figure 23.16, as well as the Make Connections figure at the beginning of Unit Four.

The search for malarial vaccines has been hampered by the fact that *Plasmodium* lives mainly inside cells, hidden from the host's immune system. And, like trypanosomes, *Plasmodium* continually changes its surface proteins. The urgent need for treatments has led researchers to track the expression of most of the parasite's genes at numerous points in its life cycle. This research could help identify vaccine targets. Drugs that target the apicoplast are also in development. This approach

▼ Figure 28.16 **The two-host life cycle of *Plasmodium*, the apicomplexan that causes malaria.**

? *Are morphological differences between sporozoites, merozoites, and gametocytes caused by different genomes or by differences in gene expression? Explain.*

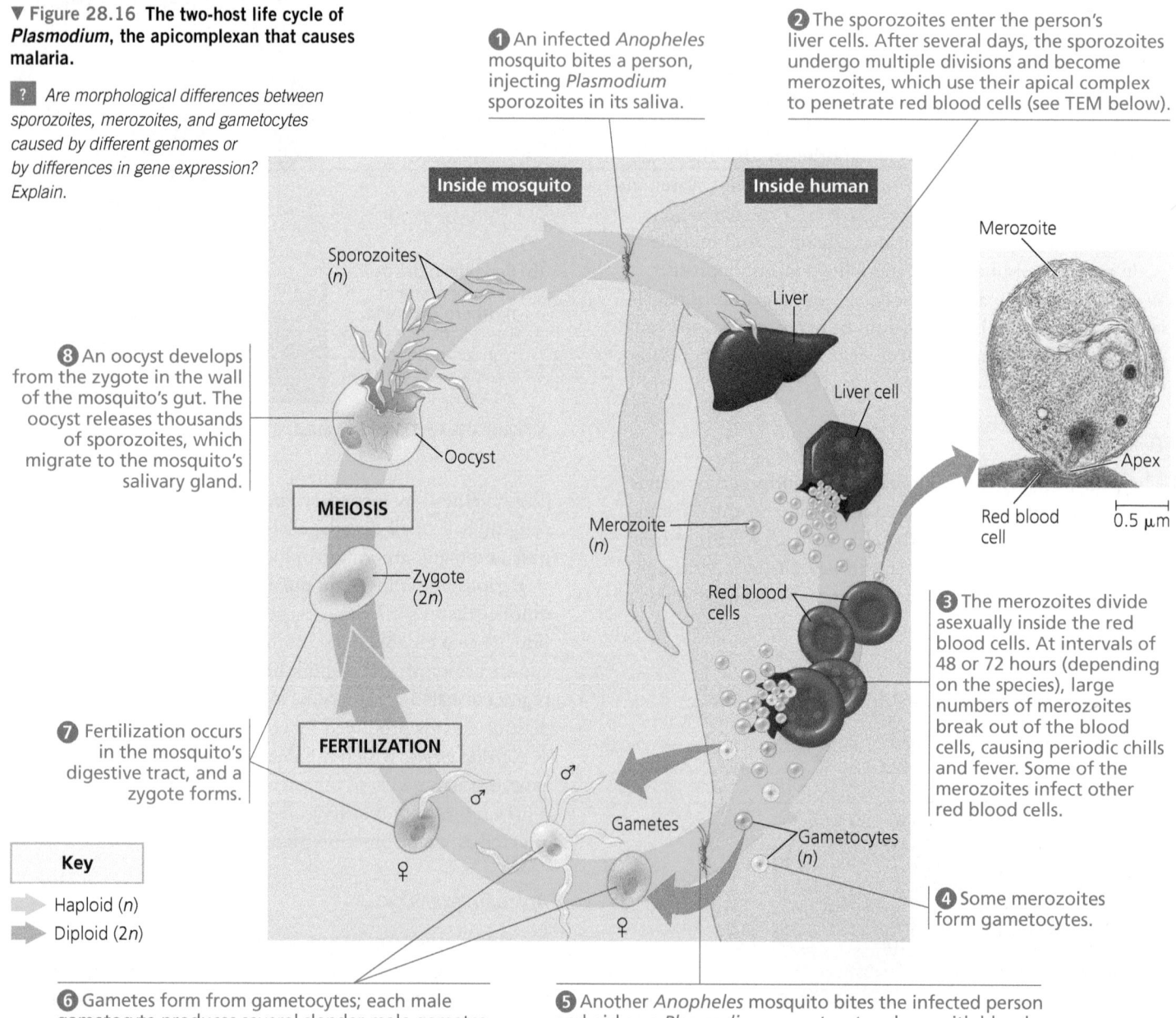

1 An infected *Anopheles* mosquito bites a person, injecting *Plasmodium* sporozoites in its saliva.

2 The sporozoites enter the person's liver cells. After several days, the sporozoites undergo multiple divisions and become merozoites, which use their apical complex to penetrate red blood cells (see TEM below).

Inside mosquito

Inside human

Sporozoites (*n*)

8 An oocyst develops from the zygote in the wall of the mosquito's gut. The oocyst releases thousands of sporozoites, which migrate to the mosquito's salivary gland.

Oocyst

Liver

Liver cell

Merozoite

Apex

Red blood cell

0.5 μm

Masamichi Aikawa

MEIOSIS

Zygote (2*n*)

Merozoite (*n*)

Red blood cells

3 The merozoites divide asexually inside the red blood cells. At intervals of 48 or 72 hours (depending on the species), large numbers of merozoites break out of the blood cells, causing periodic chills and fever. Some of the merozoites infect other red blood cells.

7 Fertilization occurs in the mosquito's digestive tract, and a zygote forms.

FERTILIZATION

♂

Gametes

Gametocytes (*n*)

♀

4 Some merozoites form gametocytes.

Key

Haploid (*n*)
Diploid (2*n*)

6 Gametes form from gametocytes; each male gametocyte produces several slender male gametes.

5 Another *Anopheles* mosquito bites the infected person and picks up *Plasmodium* gametocytes along with blood.

Source: Adaptation of illustration by Kenneth X. Probst, from *Microbiology* by R.W. Bauman. Copyright ©2004 by Kenneth X. Probst. Reprinted with permission of the illustrator.

may be effective because the apicoplast, derived by secondary endosymbiosis from a prokaryote, has metabolic pathways different from those in humans (Figure 28.17).

Ciliates

Ciliates are a large and varied group of protists named for their use of cilia to move and feed (Figure 28.18a). Most ciliates are predators, typically of bacteria or small protists. Their cilia may completely cover the cell surface or may be clustered in a few rows or tufts. In certain species, rows of tightly packed cilia function collectively in locomotion. Other ciliates scurry about on leg-like structures constructed from many cilia bonded together.

A distinctive feature of ciliates is the presence of two types of nuclei: tiny micronuclei and large macronuclei. A cell has one or more nuclei of each type. The micronuclei are reserved for the exchange of genetic information during sexual reproduction that occurs during **conjugation**, a process in which two individuals exchange haploid micronuclei but do not fuse (Figure 28.18b). The macronucleus is the transcriptionally active one and required for producing RNAs and proteins that support everyday functions of the cell. The macronucleus is derived from the micronucleus, but is quite different in content and structure. As the macronucleus differentiates, many chromosomes are amplified so there are many extra copies (dozens to thousands!) and the chromosomes can become fragmented, with the elimination of specific genomic regions. Ciliates generally reproduce asexually by binary fission, during which the existing macronucleus disintegrates and a new one is formed from the cell's micronuclei.

▼ Figure 28.17 | **Impact**

Will the Study of Protist Diversity Lead to a Treatment for Malaria?

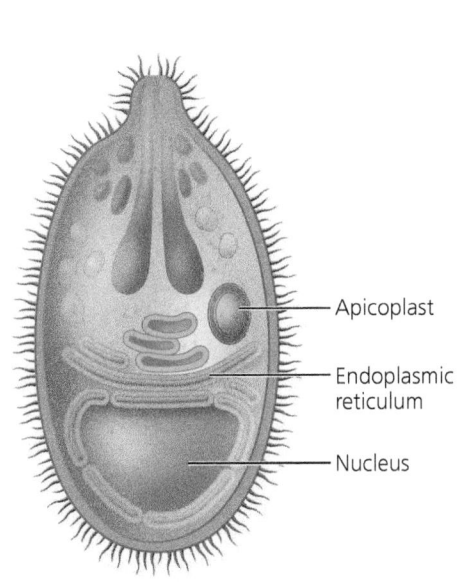

(a) *Diagram of an Apicomplexan with the apicoplast shown in green.*

Apicoplast
Endoplasmic reticulum
Nucleus

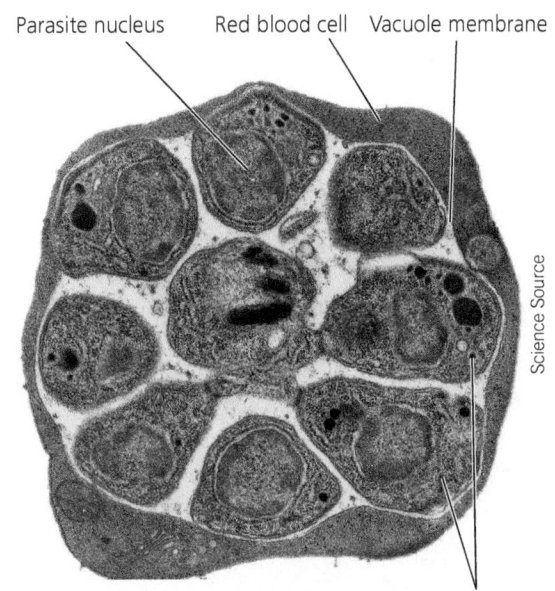

Parasite nucleus · Red blood cell · Vacuole membrane

Science Source

Malaria parasites (*Plasmodium* sp.)

(b) *Transmission electron micrograph of a red blood cell infected with* Plasmodium. *The parasites are within a vacuole where they feed upon the cell cytoplasm and replicate before breaking the cell.*

Malaria in humans is caused by four main species of the parasite *Plasmodium,* of which *Plasmodium falciparum* is the most common and dangerous. Investigations into the genomes of these and related parasites led to the discovery of an organelle called the apicoplast (above). The apicoplast contains a circular genome that shares many sequence similarities with the chloroplast genomes of plants and algae, providing strong evidence these organelles were once, but are no longer, photosynthetic. Dr. Keeling, a professor at the University of British Columbia whose interview starts off Unit Five, studies the endosymbiotic origin and function of the apicoplast. The surprise discovery that this notorious group of human parasites has an organelle with a photosynthetic ancestry was met with excitement at the possibility of finding effective drug treatments for malaria by targeting enzymes involved with apicoplast metabolism.

Why It Matters Malaria is a global health problem, with nearly 1 million deaths attributed to the disease every year. In many parts of the world, malaria is resistant to the cheaper, conventional antimalarial medications, and treatment of the severe form of malaria now relies on a combination of drugs to prevent the emergence of resistance. Considering the number of people (approximately half the world's population) is at risk of contracting malaria and the scale of antimalarial drug resistance, the development of new treatment options is an urgent matter. The discovery of a unique organelle within *Plasmodium* with metabolic pathways potentially distinct from those in humans provides an obvious target for the development of antimalarial drugs with fewer side effects. To accomplish this, additional research is required to determine the biochemical function of the apicoplast at different stages of the parasite's life cycle and to develop drugs that inhibit apicoplast metabolic pathways.

Further Reading G. I. McFadden, The apicoplast, *Protoplasma.* doi: 10.1007/s00709-010-0250-5 (2010).

MAKE CONNECTIONS *Read Concept 6.5. What additional functions do chloroplasts have that would give you a hint as to possible metabolic functions of the apicoplast?*

Rhizarians

Our next subgroup of the SAR clade is the **rhizaria**. Many species in this group are **amoebas**, protists that move and feed by means of **pseudopodia**, extensions that may bulge from almost anywhere on the cell surface. As it moves, an amoeba extends a pseudopodium and anchors the tip; more cytoplasm then streams into the

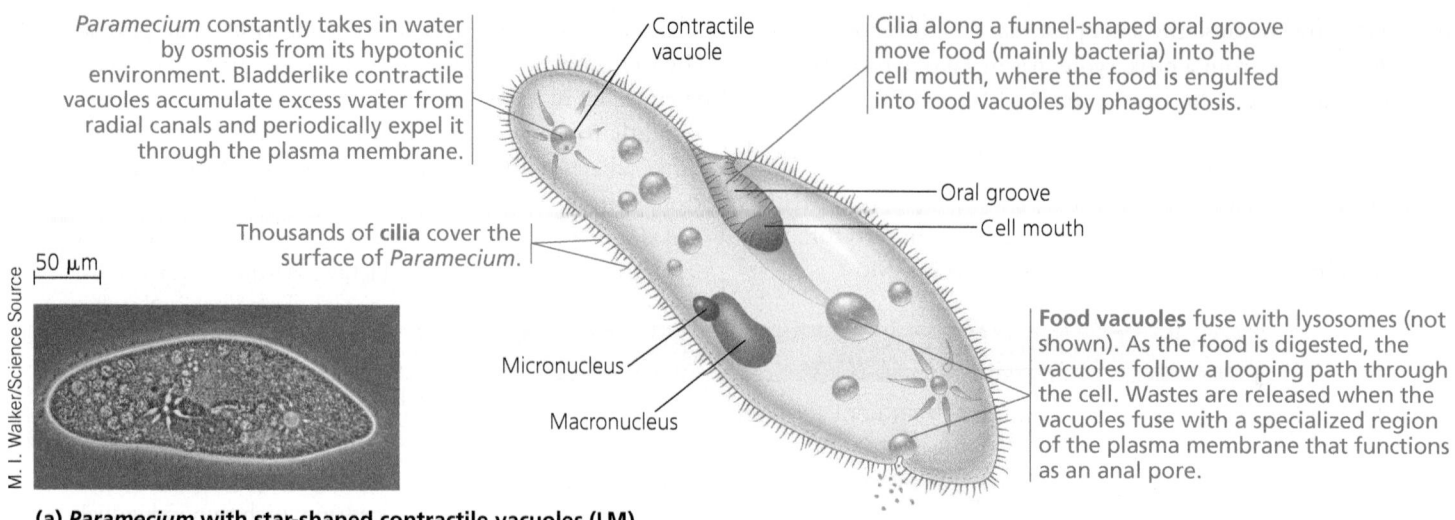

Paramecium constantly takes in water by osmosis from its hypotonic environment. Bladderlike contractile vacuoles accumulate excess water from radial canals and periodically expel it through the plasma membrane.

Contractile vacuole

Cilia along a funnel-shaped oral groove move food (mainly bacteria) into the cell mouth, where the food is engulfed into food vacuoles by phagocytosis.

Thousands of **cilia** cover the surface of *Paramecium*.

50 μm

M. I. Walker/Science Source

Oral groove
Cell mouth

Micronucleus

Macronucleus

Food vacuoles fuse with lysosomes (not shown). As the food is digested, the vacuoles follow a looping path through the cell. Wastes are released when the vacuoles fuse with a specialized region of the plasma membrane that functions as an anal pore.

(a) *Paramecium* **with star-shaped contractile vacuoles (LM).**

❶ Two cells of compatible mating strains align side by side and partially fuse.

❷ Meiosis of micronuclei produces four haploid micronuclei in each cell.

❸ Three micronuclei in each cell disintegrate. The remaining micronucleus in each cell divides by mitosis.

MEIOSIS

❹ The cells swap one micronucleus.

Diploid micronucleus

Haploid micronucleus

Compatible mates

The original macronucleus disintegrates.

Diploid micronucleus

Diploid micronucleus

MICRONUCLEAR FUSION

❺ The cells separate.

❾ Two rounds of binary fission yield four daughter cells.

❽ Four micronuclei become macronuclei.

❼ Three rounds of mitosis produce eight micronuclei.

❻ The two micronuclei fuse.

Key

Conjugation

Asexual reproduction

(b) Conjugation and reproduction.

▲ Figure 28.18 **Structure and function in the ciliate** *Paramecium caudatum.*

pseudopodium. Amoebas do not constitute a monophyletic group; instead, they are dispersed across many distantly related eukaryotic taxa. Most amoebas that are rhizarians differ morphologically from other amoebas by having threadlike pseudopodia. Rhizarians also include flagellated (non-amoeboid) protists that feed using threadlike pseudopodia.

We'll examine three groups of rhizarians here: radiolarians, forams, and cercozoans.

Radiolarians

The protists called **radiolarians** have delicate, intricately symmetrical internal skeletons that are generally made of silica. The pseudopodia of these mostly marine protists radiate from the central body (**Figure 28.19**) and are reinforced by bundles of microtubules. The microtubules are covered by a thin layer of cytoplasm, which engulfs

▲ **Figure 28.19 A radiolarian.** Numerous threadlike pseudopodia radiate from the central body of this radiolarian (LM).

▲ **Figure 28.20 Fossil forams.** By measuring the magnesium content in fossilized forams like these, researchers seek to learn how ocean temperatures have changed over time. Forams take up more magnesium when they are in warmer water than in colder water.

smaller microorganisms that become attached to the pseudopodia. Cytoplasmic streaming then carries the captured prey into the main part of the cell. After radiolarians die, their skeletons settle to the seafloor, where they have accumulated as an ooze that is hundreds of metres thick in some locations.

Forams

The protists called **foraminiferans** (from the Latin *foramen*, little hole, and *ferre*, to bear), or **forams**, are named for their porous shells, called **tests** (see Figure 28.2). Foram tests consist of a single piece of organic material hardened with calcium carbonate. The pseudopodia that extend through the pores function in swimming, test formation, and feeding. Many forams also derive nourishment from the photosynthesis of symbiotic algae that live within the tests.

Forams are found in both the ocean and fresh water. Most species live in sand or attach themselves to rocks or algae, but some are abundant in plankton. The largest forams, though single-celled, have tests measuring several centimetres in diameter.

Ninety percent of all identified species of forams are known from fossils. Along with the calcium-containing remains of other protists, the fossilized tests of forams are part of marine sediments, including sedimentary rocks that are now land formations. Foram fossils are excellent markers for correlating the ages of sedimentary rocks in different parts of the world. Researchers are also studying these fossils to obtain information about climate change and its effects on the oceans and their life (**Figure 28.20**).

Cercozoans

First identified in molecular phylogenies, the **cercozoans** form a large group that contains most of the amoeboid and flagellated

protists that feed with threadlike pseudopodia. Cercozoan protists are common in marine, freshwater, and soil ecosystems.

Most cercozoans are heterotrophs. Many are parasites of plants, animals, or other protists; many others are predators. The predators include the most important consumers of bacteria in aquatic and soil ecosystems, along with species that eat other protists, fungi, and even small animals. One small group of cercozoans, the chlorarachniophytes (mentioned earlier in the discussion of secondary endosymbiosis), are mixotrophic: These organisms ingest smaller protists and bacteria as well as perform photosynthesis. At least one other cercozoan, *Paulinella chromatophora*, is an autotroph, deriving its energy from light and its carbon from carbon dioxide. As described in **Figure 28.21**, *Paulinella*

▲ **Figure 28.21 A second case of primary endosymbiosis?** The cercozoan *Paulinella* conducts photosynthesis in a unique structure called a chromatophore (LM). Chromatophores are surrounded by a membrane with a peptidoglycan layer, suggesting that they are derived from a bacterium. DNA evidence indicates that chromatophores are derived from a different cyanobacterium than that from which other plastids are derived.

appears to represent an intriguing additional evolutionary example of a eukaryotic lineage that obtained its photosynthetic apparatus directly from a cyanobacterium.

CONCEPT CHECK 28.3

1. Explain why forams have such a well-preserved fossil record.

2. **WHAT IF?** Would you expect the plastid DNA of photosynthetic dinoflagellates, diatoms, and golden algae to be more similar to the nuclear DNA of plants (domain Eukarya) or to the chromosomal DNA of cyanobacteria (domain Bacteria)? Explain.

3. **MAKE CONNECTIONS** Which of the three life cycles in Figure 13.6 exhibits alternation of generations? How does it differ from the other two?

4. **MAKE CONNECTIONS** Review Figures 9.2 and 10.6, and then summarize how CO_2 and O_2 are both used and produced by chlorarachniophytes and other aerobic algae.

For suggested answers, see Appendix A.

CONCEPT 28.4

Red algae and green algae are the closest relatives of land plants

As described earlier, morphological and molecular evidence indicates that plastids arose when a heterotrophic protist acquired a cyanobacterial endosymbiont. Later, photosynthetic descendants of this ancient protist evolved into red algae and green algae (see Figure 28.3), and the lineage that produced green algae then gave rise to land plants.

Together, red algae, green algae, and land plants make up the fourth eukaryotic supergroup, which is called **Archaeplastida**. Archaeplastida is a monophyletic group that descended from the ancient protist that engulfed a cyanobacterium. We will examine land plants in Chapters 29 and 30; here we will look at the diversity of their closest algal relatives, red algae and green algae.

Red Algae

Many of the 6000 known species of **red algae** (rhodophytes, from the Greek *rhodos*, red) are reddish, owing to a photosynthetic accessory pigment called phycoerythrin,

which masks the green of chlorophyll (Figure 28.22). However, species adapted to more shallow water have less phycoerythrin. As a result, red algal species may be greenish red in very shallow water, bright red at moderate depths, and almost black in deep water. Some species lack pigmentation altogether and function heterotrophically as parasites on other red algae.

▶ *Bonnemaisonia hamifera.* This red alga has a filamentous form.

20 cm

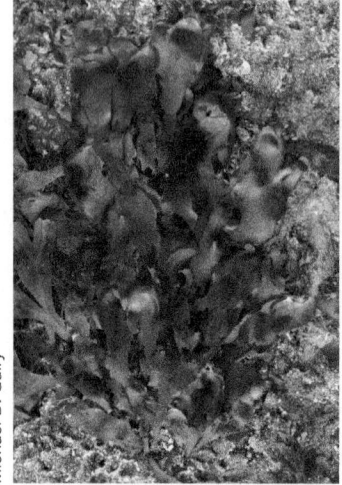

8 mm

◀ **Dulse (*Palmaria palmata*).** This edible species has a "leafy" form.

▼ **Nori.** The red alga *Porphyra* is the source of a traditional Japanese food.

The seaweed is grown on nets in shallow coastal waters.

Paper-thin, glossy sheets of nori make a mineral-rich wrap for rice, seafood, and vegetables in sushi.

▲ **Figure 28.22 Red algae.**

Red algae are the most abundant large algae in the warm coastal waters of tropical oceans. Their accessory pigments, including phycoerythrin, allow them to absorb blue and green light, which penetrate relatively far into the water. A species of red alga has been discovered near the Bahamas at a depth of more than 260 m. There are also a small number of freshwater and terrestrial species.

Most red algae are multicellular. Although none are as big as the giant brown kelps, the largest multicellular red algae are included in the informal designation "seaweeds." You may have eaten one of these multicellular red algae, *Porphyra* (Japanese "nori"), as crispy sheets or as a wrap for sushi (see Figure 28.22). Red algae have especially diverse life cycles, and alternation of generations is common. But unlike other algae, they have no flagellated stages in their life cycle and depend on water currents to bring gametes together for fertilization.

Green Algae

The grass-green chloroplasts of **green algae** have a structure and pigment composition much like the chloroplasts of land plants. Molecular systematics and cellular morphology leave little doubt that green algae and land plants are closely related. In fact, some systematists now advocate including green algae in an expanded "plant" kingdom, Viridiplantae (from the Latin *viridis*, green). Phylogenetically, this change makes sense, since otherwise the green algae are a paraphyletic group.

Green algae are divided into several groups, but the main ones are the charophytes and the chlorophytes. The charophytes are the algae most closely related to land plants, and so we will discuss them along with plants in Chapter 29.

The second group, the chlorophytes (from the Greek *chloros*, green), include more than 7000 species. Most live in fresh water, but there are also many marine and some terrestrial species. The simplest chlorophytes are unicellular organisms such as *Chlamydomonas*, which resemble gametes or zoospores of more complex chlorophytes. Various species of unicellular chlorophytes live in aquatic habitats as phytoplankton or inhabit damp soil. Some live symbiotically within other eukaryotes, contributing part of their photosynthetic output to the food supply of their hosts. Some chlorophytes have even adapted to one of the last habitats you might expect to find them: snow. These chlorophytes carry out photosynthesis despite subfreezing temperatures and intense visible and ultraviolet radiation. They are protected by the snow itself, which acts as a shield, and by radiation-blocking compounds in their cytoplasm. These pigments are red in colour, and the presence of these algae in the mountains of British Columbia

(a) *Ulva*, or sea lettuce. This edible chlorophyte has a multicellular thallus differentiated into leaflike blades. Its rootlike holdfast anchors the alga.

David L. Ballantine

(b) *Caulerpa*, an intertidal chlorophyte. The branched filaments lack cross-walls and thus are multinucleate. In effect, the thallus is one huge "supercell."

Laurie Campbell/Photoshot License Limited

▲ Figure 28.23 **Multicellular chlorophytes.**

or Alberta are made obvious by the long, red streaks in the snow.

Larger size and greater complexity evolved in chlorophytes by three different mechanisms:

1. The formation of colonies of individual cells, as seen in *Volvox* (see Figure 28.2) and in filamentous forms that contribute to the stringy masses known as pond scum
2. The formation of true multicellular bodies by cell division and differentiation, as in *Ulva* (Figure 28.23a)
3. The repeated division of nuclei with no cytoplasmic division, as in *Caulerpa* (Figure 28.23b)

Most chlorophytes have complex life cycles, with both sexual and asexual reproductive stages. Nearly all species of chlorophytes reproduce sexually by means of biflagellated gametes that have cup-shaped chloroplasts (Figure 28.24). Alternation of generations has evolved in some chlorophytes, including *Ulva*.

CONCEPT CHECK 28.4

1. Contrast red algae and brown algae.
2. Why is it accurate to say that *Ulva* is truly multicellular but *Caulerpa* is not?
3. **WHAT IF?** Suggest a possible reason why species in the green algal lineage may have been more likely to colonize land than species in the red algal lineage.

For suggested answers, see Appendix A.

Flagella

Cell wall

Nucleus

Cross section of cup-shaped chloroplast

1 μm

William L. Dentler

(TEM)

1 In *Chlamydomonas*, mature cells are haploid and contain a single cup-shaped chloroplast.

2 In response to a nutrient shortage, drying of the environment, or other stress, cells develop into gametes.

3 Gametes of different mating types (designated + and −) fuse (fertilization), forming a diploid zygote.

Gamete (*n*)

7 These daughter cells develop flagella and cell walls and then emerge as swimming zoospores from the parent cell. The zoospores develop into mature haploid cells.

Zoospore

Mature cell (*n*)

ASEXUAL REPRODUCTION

SEXUAL REPRODUCTION

FERTILIZATION

Zygote (2*n*)

Key

➤ Haploid (*n*)
➤ Diploid (2*n*)

6 When a mature cell reproduces asexually, it resorbs its flagella and then undergoes two rounds of mitosis, forming four cells (more in some species).

MEIOSIS

4 The zygote secretes a durable coat that protects the cell from harsh conditions.

▲ **Figure 28.24 The life cycle of *Chlamydomonas*, a unicellular chlorophyte.**

DRAW IT *Circle the stage(s) in the diagram in which clones are formed, producing additional new daughter cells that are genetically identical to the parent cell(s).*

5 After a dormant period, meiosis produces four haploid individuals (two of each mating type) that emerge and mature.

CONCEPT 28.5

Unikonts include protists that are closely related to fungi and animals

Unikonta is an extremely diverse supergroup of eukaryotes that includes animals, fungi, and some protists. There are two major clades of unikonts, the amoebozoans and the opisthokonts (animals, fungi, and closely related protist groups). Each of these two major clades is strongly

supported by molecular systematics. The close relationship between amoebozoans and opisthokonts is more controversial. Support for this close relationship is provided by comparisons of myosin proteins and by some (but not all) studies based on multiple genes or whole genomes.

Another controversy involving the unikonts concerns the root of the eukaryotic tree. Recall that the root of a phylogenetic tree anchors the tree in time: Branch points close to the root are the oldest. At present, the root of the eukaryotic tree is uncertain; thus, we do not know which group of eukaryotes was the first to diverge from other eukaryotes. Some hypotheses, such as the amitochondriate hypothesis described earlier, have been abandoned, but researchers have yet to agree on an alternative. If the root of the eukaryotic tree were known, scientists could infer characteristics of the common ancestor of all eukaryotes.

In trying to determine the root of the eukaryotic tree, researchers have based their phylogenies on different sets of genes, some of which have produced conflicting results.

What is the root of the eukaryotic tree?

Experiment Responding to the difficulty in determining the root of the eukaryotic phylogenetic tree, Alexandra Stechmann and Thomas Cavalier-Smith, of Oxford University, proposed a new approach. They studied two genes, one for the enzyme dihydrofolate reductase (DHFR), the other for the enzyme thymidylate synthase (TS). Their approach took advantage of a rare evolutionary event: In some organisms, the DHFR and TS genes have fused, leading to the production of a single protein with both enzyme activities. Stechmann and Cavalier-Smith amplified (using PCR; see Figure 20.8) and sequenced DHFR and TS genes in nine species (one choanoflagellate; two amoebozoans; one euglenozoan; one stramenopile; one alveolate; and three rhizarians). They combined their data with previously published data for species of bacteria, animals, plants, and fungi.

Results The bacteria studied all have separate DHFR and TS genes, suggesting that this is the ancestral condition (red dot on the tree below). Other taxa with separate genes are denoted by red type. Fused genes are a derived character, found in certain members (blue type) of the supergroups Excavata, SAR clade, Rhizaria, and Archaeplastida:

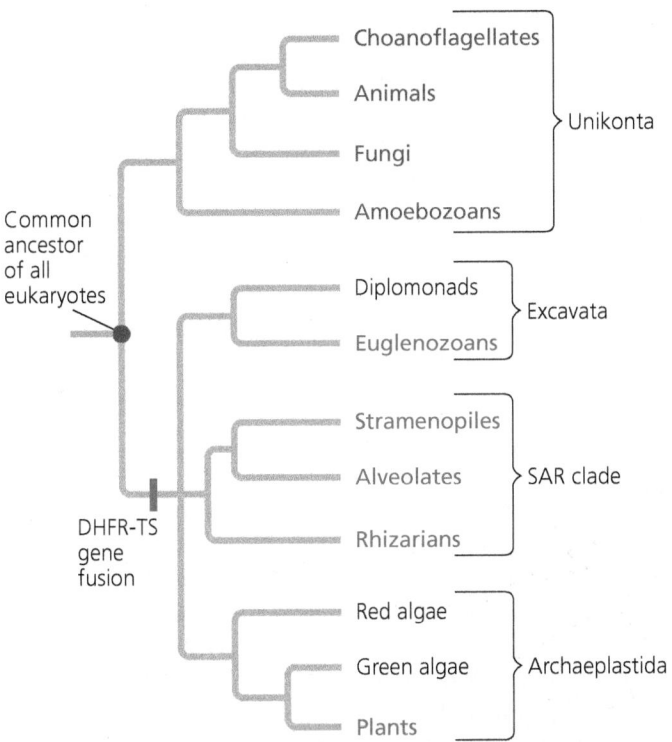

Conclusion These results support the hypothesis that the root of the tree is located between the unikonts and all other eukaryotes, suggesting that the unikonts were the first group of eukaryotes to diverge. Because support for this hypothesis is based on only one trait—the fusion of the DHFR and TS genes—more data are needed to evaluate its validity.

Source: Based on A. Stechmann and T. Cavalier-Smith, Rooting the eukaryote tree by using a derived gene fusion, *Science* 297:89–91 (2002). © Jane B Reece.

WHAT IF? *Stechmann and Cavalier-Smith wrote that their conclusions are "valid only if the genes fused just once and were never secondarily split." Why is this assumption critical to their approach?*

Researchers have also tried a different approach, based on tracing the occurrence of a rare evolutionary event (Figure 28.25). Results from this "rare event" approach suggest that unikonts were the first eukaryotes to diverge from other eukaryotes. This hypothesis proposes that animals and fungi belong to an early-diverging group of eukaryotes, while protists that lack typical mitochondria (such as the diplomonads and parabasalids) diverged much later in the history of life. This idea remains controversial and will require more supporting evidence to be widely accepted.

Amoebozoans

As already mentioned, **amoebozoans** form a clade that is well supported by molecular data. This clade includes many species of amoebas that have lobe- or tube-shaped, rather than threadlike, pseudopodia. Amoebozoans include slime moulds, gymnamoebas, and entamoebas.

Slime Moulds

Slime moulds, or **mycetozoans** (from the Latin, meaning "fungus animals"), were once thought to be fungi because, like fungi, they produce fruiting bodies that aid in spore dispersal. However, the resemblance between slime moulds and fungi appears to be another example of evolutionary convergence. Molecular systematics places slime moulds in Amoebozoa and suggests that they descended from unicellular ancestors. Slime moulds have diverged into two main branches, plasmodial slime moulds and cellular slime moulds, distinguished in part by their unique life cycles.

Plasmodial Slime Moulds Many **plasmodial slime moulds** are brightly coloured, often yellow or orange (Figure 28.26). At one stage in their life cycle, they form a mass called a **plasmodium**, which may grow to a diameter of many centimetres. (Don't confuse a slime mould's plasmodium with the genus *Plasmodium*, which includes the parasitic apicomplexan that causes malaria.) Despite its size, the plasmodium is not multicellular; it is a single mass of cytoplasm that is undivided by plasma membranes and that contains many nuclei. This "supercell" is the product of mitotic nuclear divisions that are not followed by cytokinesis. The plasmodium extends pseudopodia through moist soil, leaf mulch, or rotting logs, engulfing food particles by phagocytosis as it grows. If the habitat begins to dry up or there is no food left, the plasmodium stops growing and differentiates into fruiting bodies, which function in sexual reproduction.

Cellular Slime Moulds The life cycle of the protists called **cellular slime moulds** can prompt us to question what it means to be an individual organism. The feeding stage of these organisms consists of solitary cells that function

7 Repeated mitotic divisions of the zygote's nucleus, without cytoplasmic division, form the plasmodium.

1 The feeding stage is a multinucleate plasmodium.

6 The cells fuse, forming diploid zygotes.

FERTILIZATION

Zygote (2n)

Feeding plasmodium

Mature plasmodium (preparing to fruit)

Dr. George L. Barron

4 cm

Flagellated cells (n)

Amoeboid cells (n)

Young sporangium

Germinating spore

Mature sporangium

5 The motile haploid cells are either amoeboid or flagellated; the two forms readily convert from one to the other.

Spores (n)

MEIOSIS

Stalk

2 The plasmodium erects stalked fruiting bodies (sporangia) when conditions become harsh.

4 The resistant spores germinate in favourable conditions, releasing motile cells.

3 In the sporangia, meiosis produces haploid spores, which disperse through the air.

Key

→ Haploid (n)

→ Diploid (2n)

▲ **Figure 28.26 The life cycle of a plasmodial slime mould.** The photograph shows a mature plasmodium, the feeding stage in the life cycle of a plasmodial slime mould. When food becomes scarce, the plasmodium forms stalked fruiting bodies that produce haploid spores that function in sexual reproduction.

individually, but when food is depleted, the cells form an aggregate that functions as a unit (**Figure 28.27**). Unlike the feeding stage (plasmodium) of a plasmodial slime mould, these aggregated cells remain separated by their individual plasma membranes. Ultimately, the aggregated cells form an asexual fruiting body.

Dictyostelium discoideum, a cellular slime mould commonly found on forest floors, has become a model organism for studying the evolution of multicellularity. One line of research has focused on the slime mould's fruiting body stage. During this stage, the cells that form the stalk die as they dry out, while the spore cells at the top survive and have the potential to reproduce. Scientists have found that mutations in a single gene can turn individual *Dictyostelium* cells into "cheaters" that never become part of the stalk. Because these mutants gain a strong reproductive advantage over noncheaters, why don't all *Dictyostelium* cells cheat?

Recent discoveries suggest an answer to this question. Cheating mutants lack a protein on their cell surface, and noncheating cells can recognize this difference. Noncheaters preferentially aggregate with other noncheaters, thus depriving cheaters of the opportunity to exploit them. Such a recognition system may have been important in the evolution of multicellular eukaryotes such as animals and plants.

Tubulinids

Tubulinids constitute a large and varied group of amoebozoans. These unicellular protists are ubiquitous in soil as well as freshwater and marine environments. Most are heterotrophs that actively seek and consume bacteria and other protists; one such tubulinid species, *Amoeba proteus*, is shown in Figure 28.2. Some tubulinids also feed on detritus (nonliving organic matter).

Entamoebas

Whereas most amoebozoans are free-living, those that belong to the genus *Entamoeba* are parasites. They infect all classes of vertebrate animals as well as some invertebrates. Humans are host to at least six species of *Entamoeba*, but only one, *E. histolytica*, is known to be pathogenic. *E. histolytica* causes amoebic dysentery and is spread via contaminated drinking water, food, or eating utensils. Responsible for up to 100 000 deaths worldwide every year, the disease is the third leading cause of death due to eukaryotic parasites, after malaria (see Figure 28.16) and schistosomiasis (see Figure 33.11).

Opisthokonts

Opisthokonts are an extremely diverse group of eukaryotes that includes animals, fungi, and several groups of protists. We will discuss the evolutionary history of fungi and animals in Chapters 31–34. Of the opisthokont protists, we will discuss the nucleariids in Chapter 31 because they are more closely related to fungi than they are to other protists. Similarly, we will discuss

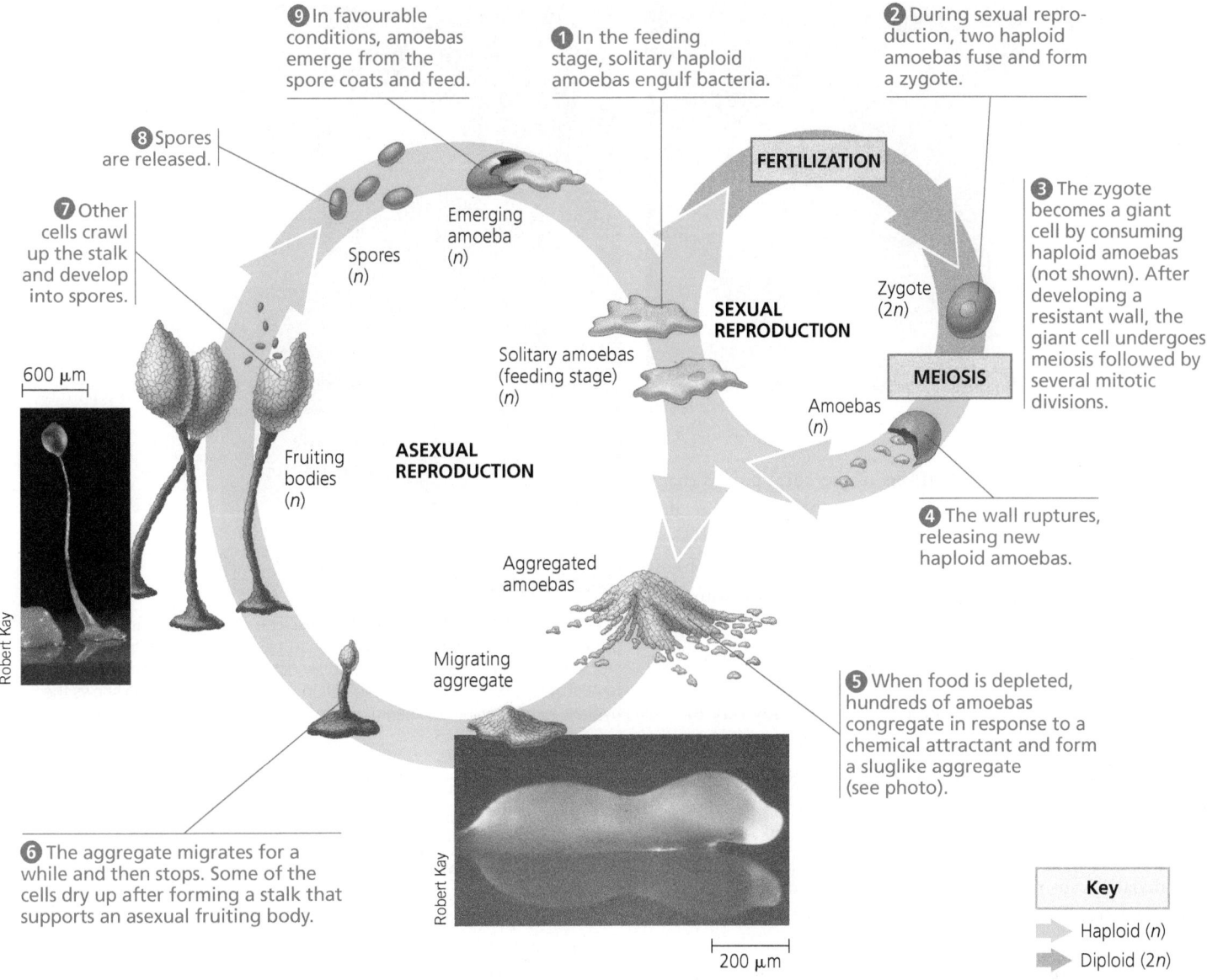

① In the feeding stage, solitary haploid amoebas engulf bacteria.

② During sexual reproduction, two haploid amoebas fuse and form a zygote.

FERTILIZATION

③ The zygote becomes a giant cell by consuming haploid amoebas (not shown). After developing a resistant wall, the giant cell undergoes meiosis followed by several mitotic divisions.

Zygote (*n*)

SEXUAL REPRODUCTION

MEIOSIS

Amoebas (*n*)

④ The wall ruptures, releasing new haploid amoebas.

⑨ In favourable conditions, amoebas emerge from the spore coats and feed.

⑧ Spores are released.

⑦ Other cells crawl up the stalk and develop into spores.

Emerging amoeba (*n*)

Spores (*n*)

Solitary amoebas (feeding stage) (*n*)

ASEXUAL REPRODUCTION

Fruiting bodies (*n*)

600 μm

Robert Kay

Aggregated amoebas

Migrating aggregate

⑤ When food is depleted, hundreds of amoebas congregate in response to a chemical attractant and form a sluglike aggregate (see photo).

⑥ The aggregate migrates for a while and then stops. Some of the cells dry up after forming a stalk that supports an asexual fruiting body.

Robert Kay

200 μm

Key

Haploid (*n*)
Diploid (2*n*)

▲ Figure 28.27 **The life cycle of *Dictyostelium*, a cellular slime mould.**

choanoflagellates in Chapter 32, since they are more closely related to animals than they are to other protists. The nucleariids and choanoflagellates illustrate why scientists have abandoned the former kingdom Protista: A monophyletic group that included these single-celled eukaryotes would also have to include the multicellular animals and fungi that are closely related to them.

CONCEPT CHECK 28.5

1. Contrast the pseudopodia of amoebozoans and forams.
2. In what sense is "fungus animal" a fitting description of a slime mould? In what sense is it not fitting?
3. **WHAT IF?** If further evidence indicates that the root of the eukaryotic tree is as shown in Figure 28.25, would this evidence support, contradict, or have no bearing on the hypothesis that Excavata is monophyletic?

For suggested answers, see Appendix A.

CONCEPT 28.6

Protists play key roles in ecological communities

Most protists are aquatic, and they are found almost anywhere there is water, including moist terrestrial habitats such as damp soil and leaf litter. In oceans, ponds, and lakes, many protists are bottom-dwellers that attach to rocks and other substrates or creep through the sand and silt. Other protists are important constituents of plankton. We'll focus here on two key roles that protists play in the varied habitats in which they live: that of symbiont and that of producer.

Symbiotic Protists

Many protists form symbiotic associations with other species. For example, photosynthetic dinoflagellates are

► Figure 28.28 **A symbiotic protist.** This organism is a hypermastigote, a member of a group of parabasalids that live in the gut of termites and certain cockroaches and enable the hosts to digest wood (SEM).

10 μm

Patrick Keeling

Andrew Syred/Science Source

Sporangia

Hyphae

Leaf mesophyll cell

▲ Figure 28.29 **Phytopthtora infestans.** The reproductive structures of the potato blight-causing stramenopile can be seen emerging from the leaf's stomates. The sporangia (tips) eventually detach and are carried by wind to nearby plants to start another infection cycle. This image also shows the hyphae extending into the centre of the leaf (colourized SEM).

food-providing symbiotic partners of the coral polyps that build coral reefs. Coral reefs are highly diverse ecological communities. That diversity ultimately depends on corals—and on the mutualistic protist symbionts that nourish them. Corals support reef diversity by providing food to some species and habitat to many others.

Another example is the wood-digesting protists that inhabit the gut of many termite species (**Figure 28.28**). Unaided, termites cannot digest wood, and they rely on protistan or prokaryotic symbionts to do so. Termites cause over $3.5 billion in damage annually to wooden homes in North America.

Symbiotic protists also include parasites that have compromised the economies of entire countries. Consider the malaria-causing protist *Plasmodium*: Income levels in countries hard hit by malaria are 33% lower than in similar countries free of the disease. Protists can have devastating effects on other species too. Massive fish kills have been attributed to *Pfiesteria shumwayae* (see Figure 28.15), a dinoflagellate parasite that attaches to its victims and eats their skin. *Anophryoides haemophila* is a ciliate that causes "bumper car" disease in lobster, so named because of the ciliate's movement in lobster blood. Outbreaks are thought to be associated with confinement in holding tanks and are a concern for the lobster industry in Atlantic Canada.

One of the most significant plant pathogens is *Phytophthora infestans* (**Figure 28.29**), a member of the SAR clade called an oomycete. This protist causes potato late blight, which turns the stalks and stems of potato (and tomato) plants into black slime. Late blight contributed to the devastating Irish famine of the 19th century, in which a million people died and at least that many were forced to leave Ireland. The disease continues to be a major problem in Canada, especially in Prince Edward Island and New Brunswick where potatoes are an important crop. Globally,

it is estimated that $1 billion is being spent on fungicides to control the parasite.

Photosynthetic Protists

Many protists are important **producers**, organisms that use energy from light (or inorganic chemicals) to convert carbon dioxide to organic compounds. Producers form the base of ecological food webs. In aquatic communities, the main producers are photosynthetic protists and prokaryotes. All other organisms in the community depend on them for food, either directly (by eating them) or indirectly (by eating an organism that ate a producer; **Figure 28.30**). Scientists estimate that roughly 30% of the world's photosynthesis is performed by diatoms, dinoflagellates, multicellular algae, and other aquatic protists. Photosynthetic prokaryotes contribute another 20%, and land plants are responsible for the remaining 50%.

Because producers form the foundation of food webs, factors that affect producers can dramatically affect their entire community. In aquatic environments, photosynthetic protists are often held in check by low concentrations of nitrogen, phosphorus, or iron. Various human actions can increase the concentrations of these elements in aquatic communities. For example, when fertilizer is applied to a field, some of the fertilizer may be washed by rainfall into

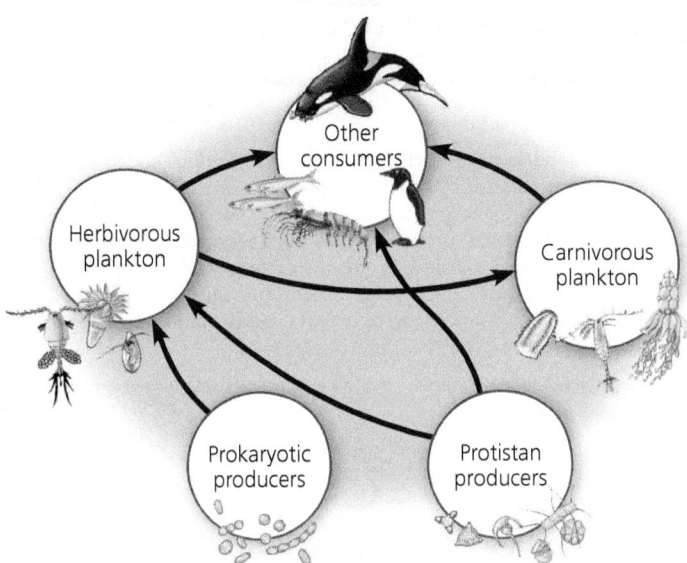

▲ **Figure 28.30 Protists: key producers in aquatic communities.** Arrows in this simplified food web lead from food sources to the organisms that eat them.

a river that drains into a lake or ocean. When people add nutrients to aquatic communities in this or other ways, the abundance of photosynthetic protists can increase spectacularly. In Canada, the Experimental Lakes Area in northwestern Ontario is world renowned for the manipulation of whole-lake ecosystems to investigate the effect of nutrient runoff on algal growth and a variety of other ecosystem responses, as you will learn in Chapter 55.

A pressing question is how global warming will affect protists and other producers. Satellite data indicate that the growth and biomass of photosynthetic protists and prokaryotes have declined in many regions as sea surface temperatures have increased (Figure 28.31). If sustained, these changes would likely have far-reaching effects on marine ecosystems, fishery yields, and the global carbon cycle (see Chapter 55). Global warming can also affect producers on land, but there the base of food webs is occupied not by protists but by land plants, which we will discuss in Chapters 29 and 30.

CONCEPT CHECK 28.6

1. Justify the claim that photosynthetic protists are among the biopshere's most important oranisms.

2. Describe three symbioses that include protists.

3. **WHAT IF?** High water temperatures and pollution can cause corals to expel their dinoflagellate symbionts. Predict how such "coral bleaching" would affect corals and other species in the community.

---

4. **MAKE CONNECTIONS** The bacterium *Wolbachia* is a symbiont that lives in mosquito cells and spreads rapidly through mosquito populations. *Wolbachia* can make mosquitoes resistant to infection by *Plasmodium*; researchers are seeking a strain that confers resistance and does not harm mosquitoes. Compare evolutionary changes that could occur if malaria control is attempted using such a *Wolbachia* strain versus using insecticides to kill mosquitoes. (Review Figures 28.16 and Concept 23.4.)

For suggested answers, see Appendix A.

▼ **Figure 28.31** | **Impact**

Marine Protists in a Warmer World

Photosynthetic protists are important components of marine food webs, each day converting millions of tonnes of carbon in CO_2 to organic molecules on which other organisms depend. How has global warming affected these key marine producers? Satellite data indicate that the growth and biomass of marine producers are negatively correlated to sea surface temperature (SST) across much of the tropical and midlatitude oceans (between the heavy black lines on the map below). In regions where SSTs have risen and growth has declined, the available nutrient supply may have been reduced by the formation of a light, warm layer of water that acts as a barrier preventing the rise, or upwelling, of cold, nutrient-rich waters from below.

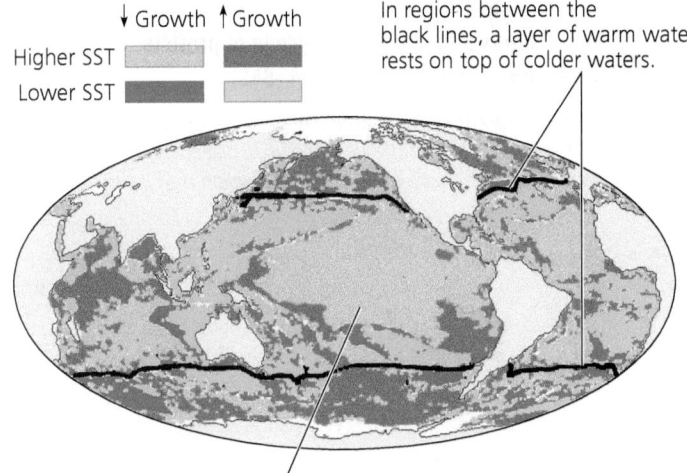

In the yellow regions, high SSTs increase the temperature differences between warm and cold waters, which reduces upwelling. Marine producers rely on upwelled nutrients, so their growth decreases when upwelling decreases.

Why It Matters Major changes to marine ecosystems are expected if the growth and biomass of producers decrease as SSTs increase due to global warming. A decrease in diatom biomass, for example, would likely reduce both the amount of carbon pumped to the ocean floor and the catch of economically important fish such as salmon and anchovies that feed on phytoplankton.

Further Reading M. J. Behrenfeld et al., Climate-driven trends in contemporary ocean productivity, *Nature* 444:752–755 (2006).

WHAT IF? *If diatom populations continue to drop as the oceans warm, how might climate be affected in the future?*

28 Chapter Review

Go to **MasteringBiology**® for Assignments, the eText, and the Study Area with Animations, Activities, Vocab Self-Quiz, and Practice Tests.

SUMMARY OF KEY CONCEPTS

CONCEPT **28.1**

Protists are a diverse group of eukaryotes that span all four supergroups (pp. 626–632)

- Protists are more diverse than all other eukaryotes and are no longer classified in a single kingdom. Most are unicellular. Protists include photoautotrophs, heterotrophs, and **mixotrophs**. Protists are characterized by a wide diversity of life cycles.

- Mitochondria and **plastids** are thought to be descendants of bacteria that were engulfed by other cells and became endosymbionts. The plastid-bearing lineage eventually evolved into red algae and green algae. Other protist groups evolved from **secondary endosymbiosis** events in which red algae or green algae were themselves engulfed.

- In one hypothesis, eukaryotes are grouped into five supergroups, each a monophyletic clade: **Excavata**, **SAR clade**, **Archaeplastida**, and **Unikonta**.

? *What evidence supports the idea that many plastids evolved from endo-symbiotic algae?*

Key Concept/Eukaryote Supergroup	Major Groups	Key Morphological Characteristics	Specific Examples	
CONCEPT **28.2** **Excavates include protists with modified mitochondria and protists with unique flagella (pp. 632–633)** ? *What evidence indicates that the excavates form a clade?*	**Diplomonads and parabasalids**	Modified mitochondria	*Giardia, Trichomonas*	
	Euglenozoans Kinetoplastids Euglenids	Spiral or crystalline rod inside flagella	*Trypanosoma, Euglena*	
CONCEPT **28.3** **The SAR clade is a highly diverse group of protists defined by DNA similarities (pp. 634–642)** ? *Although they are not photosynthetic, apicomplexan parasites such as* Plasmodium *have modified plastids. Describe a current hypothesis that explains this observation.*	**Stramenopiles** Diatoms Golden algae Brown algae Alternation of Generations	Hairy and smooth flagella	*Phytophthora, Laminaria*	
	Alveolates Dinoflagellates Apicomplexans Ciliates	Membrane-bounded sacs (alveoli) beneath plasma membrane	*Pfiesteria, Plasmodium, Paramecium*	
	Rhizarians Radiolarians Forams Cercozoans	Amoebas with thread-like pseudopodia	*Globigerina*	
CONCEPT **28.4** **Red algae and green algae are the closest relatives of land plants (pp. 642–644)** ? *On what basis do some systematists place land plants in the same supergroup (Archaeplastida) as red and green algae?*	**Red algae**	Phycoerythrin (accessory pigment)	*Porphyra*	
	Green algae	Plant-type chloroplasts	*Chlamydomonas, Ulva*	
	Land plants	(See Chapters 29 and 30.)	Mosses, ferns, conifers, flowering plants	
CONCEPT **28.5** **Unikonts include protists that are closely related to fungi and animals (pp. 644–647)** ? *Describe a key feature for each of the main protist subgroups of Unikonta.*	**Amoebozoans** Slime moulds Tubulinids Entamoebas	Amoebas with lobe-shaped pseudopodia	Amoeba, Entamoeba, Dictyostelium	
	Opisthokonts	(Highly variable; see Chapters 31–34.)	Nucleariids, choanoflagellates, animals, fungi	

Protists play key roles in ecological communities (pp. 647–649)

- Protists form a wide range of mutualistic and parasitic relationships that affect their symbiotic partners and many other members of the community.
- Photosynthetic protists are among the most important producers in aquatic communities. Because they are at the base of the food web, factors that affect photosynthetic protists affect many other species in the community.

? *Describe several protists that are ecologically important.*

TEST YOUR UNDERSTANDING

LEVEL 1: KNOWLEDGE/COMPREHENSION

1. Plastids that are surrounded by more than two membranes are evidence of
   a. evolution from mitochondria.
   b. fusion of plastids.
   c. origin of the plastids from archaea.
   d. secondary endosymbiosis.

2. Biologists suspect that endosymbiosis gave rise to mitochondria before plastids partly because
   a. the products of photosynthesis could not be metabolized without mitochondrial enzymes.
   b. all eukaryotes have mitochondria (or their remnants), whereas many eukaryotes do not have plastids.
   c. mitochondrial DNA is less similar to prokaryotic DNA than is plastid DNA.
   d. without mitochondrial CO_2 production, photosynthesis could not occur.

3. Which group is *incorrectly* paired with its description?
   a. diatoms—important producers in aquatic communities
   b. red algae—acquired plastids by secondary endosymbiosis
   c. apicomplexans—parasites with intricate life cycles
   d. diplomonads—protists with modified mitochondria

4. Which protists are in the same eukaryotic supergroup as land plants?
   a. dinoflagellates
   b. red algae
   c. brown algae
   d. euglenids

5. In life cycles with an alternation of generations, multicellular haploid forms alternate with
   a. unicellular haploid forms.
   b. unicellular diploid forms.
   c. multicellular haploid forms.
   d. multicellular diploid forms.

LEVEL 2: APPLICATION/ANALYSIS

6. Based on the phylogenetic tree in Figure 28.2, which of the following statements is correct?
   a. The most recent common ancestor of Excavata is older than that of the SAR clade.
   b. The most recent common ancestor of the SAR clade is older than that of Unikonta.

   c. The most basal (first to diverge) eukaryotic supergroup cannot be determined.
   d. Excavata is the most basal eukaryotic supergroup.

7. **EVOLUTION CONNECTION**
   DRAW IT Medical researchers seek to develop drugs that can kill or restrict the growth of human pathogens yet have few harmful effects on patients. These drugs often work by disrupting the metabolism of the pathogen or by targeting its structural features.

   Draw and label a phylogenetic tree that includes an ancestral prokaryote and the following groups of organisms: Excavata, SAR clade, Archaeplastida, Unikonta, and, within Unikonta, amoebozoans, animals, choanoflagellates, fungi, and nucleariids. Based on this tree, hypothesize whether it would be most difficult to develop drugs to combat human pathogens that are prokaryotes, protists, animals, or fungi. (You do not need to consider the evolution of drug resistance by the pathogen.)

LEVEL 3: SYNTHESIS/EVALUATION

8. **SCIENTIFIC INQUIRY**
   Read the passages on global climate change (pp. 1230-1231 and pp. 1339-1340). Would you expect the proportion of the global population at risk of/for malaria to be affected by climate change?

9. **WRITE ABOUT A THEME: ENVIRONMENTAL INTERACTIONS**
   Organisms interact with each other and the physical environment. In a short essay (100–150 words), explain how the response of diatom populations to a drop in nutrient availability can affect both other organisms and aspects of the physical environment (such as carbon dioxide concentrations).

10. **SYNTHESIZE YOUR KNOWLEDGE**

Dion Durnford

This photograph shows a "Dog Vomit fungus" growing on the campus of the University of New Brunswick. It is actually a plasmodial slime mould and is commonly found in urban areas growing on bark mulch when conditions are moist and humid. What stage of the plasmodial slime mould life cycle are you looking at and what are its features? Though often incorrectly called a fungus, what distinguishes this organism from true fungi?

For selected answers, see Appendix A.

29

Plant Diversity I: How Plants Colonized Land

KEY CONCEPTS

29.1   Land plants evolved from green algae

29.2   Mosses and other nonvascular plants have life cycles dominated by gametophytes

29.3   Ferns and other seedless vascular plants were the first plants to grow tall

Walter Myers/Science Source

▲ **Figure 29.1 What does this fossil from Quebec tell us about the colonization of land?**

The Greening of Earth

For more than 3 billion years of Earth's history, the land surface was largely lifeless, quite different from the lush forests and grasslands that now dominate the planet. Thin coatings of cyanobacteria likely existed on land about 1.2 billion years ago, but it was only within the last 500 million years that small plants, fungi, and animals joined them ashore. Finally, by about 385 million years ago, some plants appeared that could grow much taller, leading to the formation of the first forests, changing not only the landscape but also the climate.

Fossils of the earliest known trees can be found at Miguasha, Quebec. Miguasha National Park fossil beds formed approximately 380 million years ago and several important fossils have been discovered at the site, leading to it being declared a UNESCO World Heritage Site in 1999. Some of these fossils are from two species of *Archaeopteris*, one of which is shown in **Figure 29.1**. These early trees dominated the forest surrounding the Miguasha estuary and had extensive root systems and woody trunks, both adaptations that provided the stability and strength to grow tall (upwards of 30 m) and compete for sunlight. They also had fern-like leaves with a greater surface area that would have been more efficient at capturing sunlight than the narrow leaves of earlier land plants.

Walter Myers/Science Source

◄ **Artist's concept of *Archaeopteris***

Archaeopteris is classified as a progymnosperm, meaning that it is ancestral to true gymnosperms. Unlike gymnosperms, *Archaeopteris* reproduced by spores rather than seeds; reproduction by seeds is a key characteristic of gymnosperms and angiosperms (seed plants). The female spore of *Archaeopteris*, however, was larger than the male spore (heterospory), suggesting it contained a food source, making this an important first step toward modern seeds (discussed in Chapter 30).

Archaeopteris was a dominant tree species across the globe, but became extinct during the Carboniferous period. Plants have since diversified widely; today, there are more than 290 000 known plant species. Plants inhabit all but the harshest environments, such as some mountaintop and desert areas and the polar ice sheets. A few plant species, such as sea grasses, returned to aquatic habitats during their evolution. In this chapter, we'll refer to all plants as *land* plants, even those that are now aquatic, to distinguish them from algae, which are photosynthetic protists.

Land plants enabled other life-forms to survive on land. Plants supply oxygen and ultimately most of the food eaten by terrestrial animals. Also, [...] other organisms by stabiliz[...] the first 100 million years [...] emergence of seedless plan[...]

◀ *Chara* species, a pond organism

▼ *Coleochaete orbicularis*, a disk-shaped charophyte that also lives in ponds (LM)

5 mm

40 µm

Dr. Linda E. Graham

▲ Figure 29.2 **Examples of charophytes, the closest algal relatives of land plants.**

CONCEPT 29.1

Land plants evolve[...]

Researchers have identifie[...] as the closest relatives of l[...] for this relationship, and v[...] algal ancestors of land plan[...]

Morphological and Mol[...]

Many important traits of [...] of protists, including mul[...] pigments, and cell walls c[...] these traits were acquired [...] plete story with respect to [...] phytes, however, are the [...] three distinctive traits wit[...] that they are their closest [...]

- **Rings of cellulose-s[...]** cells of both land plan[...] distinctive circular rings or proteins in the plasma membrane (see SEM on right). These protein rings synthesize the cellulose microfibrils of the cell wall. In contrast, noncharophyte algae have linear sets of proteins that synthesize cellulose.

Brown Jr, M

30 nm

- **Structure of flagellated sperm.** In species of land plants that have flagellated sperm, the structure of the sperm closely resembles that of charophyte sperm.

- [...]**tion of a phragmoplast.** Particular details of cell [...] occur only in land plants and certain charophytes, [...]ng the genera *Chara* and *Coleochaete*. For example, [...] plants and certain charophytes, a group of micro[...] known as the **phragmoplast** forms between the [...]r nuclei of a dividing cell. A cell plate then devel[...] the middle of the phragmoplast, across the midline [...] dividing cell (see Figure 12.10b). The cell plate, [...], gives rise to a new cross wall that separates the [...]r cells.

[...]es of whole genomes plus different nuclear and [...]st genes from a wide range of plants and algae [...] hat charophytes **(Figure 29.2)** are the closest living [...] of land plants **(Figure 29.3)**. Note that this does [...] that plants are descended from these living algae; [...], present-day charophytes may tell us something [...]at the algal ancestors of plants were like.

[...]ions Enabling the Move to Land

[...]ecies of charophyte algae inhabit shallow waters [...] he edges of ponds and lakes, where they are sub[...]ccasional drying. In such environments, natural [...] favours individual algae that can survive periods [...]ey are not submerged in water. In charophytes, [...] layer of a durable polymer called **sporopollenin** [...]revents exposed zygotes from drying out. A similar [...] hemical adaptation is found in the tough sporopollenin walls that encase the spores of plants.

The accumulation of such traits by at least one population of charophyte ancestors probably enabled their descendants—the first land plants—to

▲ Figure 29.3 Three possible "plant" kingdoms.

> **?** *A branch with three parallel lines leading to a group indicates that the group is paraphyletic. Explain why charophyte algae are represented as a paraphyletic group.*

live permanently above the waterline. These evolutionary novelties opened a new frontier: a terrestrial habitat that offered enormous benefits. The bright sunlight was unfiltered by water and plankton; the atmosphere offered more plentiful carbon dioxide than did water; the soil by the water's edge was rich in some mineral nutrients; and initially there were relatively few herbivores and pathogens. But these benefits were accompanied by challenges: a relative scarcity of water and a lack of structural support against gravity. (To appreciate why such support is important, picture how the soft body of a jellyfish sags when taken out of water.) Land plants diversified as adaptations evolved that enabled plants to thrive despite these challenges.

Today, what adaptations are unique to plants? The answer to this question depends on where you draw the boundary dividing land plants from algae (Figure 29.3). Many biologists equate the kingdom Plantae with embryophytes (plants with embryos). Others propose that the boundaries of the plant kingdom should be expanded to include some or all of the green algae (kingdoms Streptophyta and Viridiplantae). Since the debate is ongoing, this text retains the embryophyte definition of the plant kingdom and uses Plantae as the formal name for the taxon. In this context, let's now identify the derived traits that separate land plants from their closest algal relatives.

Derived Traits of Plants

Many of the adaptations that appear to have emerged after land plants diverged from their algal relatives facilitated

survival and reproduction on dry land. **Figure 29.4**, on the next two pages, depicts four key traits that appear in land plants but not in the charophyte algae.

In addition to the four traits shown in Figure 29.4, other derived traits that relate to terrestrial life have evolved in many plant species. For example, the epidermis in many species has a covering, the **cuticle**, which consists of wax and other polymers. Permanently exposed to the air, land plants run a far greater risk of desiccation (drying out) than their algal ancestors. The cuticle acts as waterproofing, helping prevent excessive water loss from the above-ground plant organs, while also providing some protection from microbial attack.

Early land plants lacked true roots and leaves. Without roots, how did these plants absorb nutrients from the soil? Fossils dating from 420 million years ago reveal an adaptation that may have aided early plants in nutrient uptake: They formed symbiotic associations with fungi, similar in structure to beneficial associations observed today between plants and fungi. We'll describe these associations, called *mycorrhizae*, and their benefits to both plants and fungi in more detail in Chapter 31. For now, the main point is that mycorrhizal fungi form extensive networks of filaments through the soil, enabling them to absorb nutrients more effectively than a plant can on its own. The fungi transfer nutrients to their symbiotic plant partner, a benefit that may have helped plants without roots to colonize land.

The Origin and Diversification of Plants

When did plants start making the transition to land? To answer this question, you have to examine the fossil record, but the fossil record is fragmentary, and the best evidence to date comes from the discovery of fossilized spores dating to 470 million years ago. However, the earliest fossils (megafossils) that are clearly from a land plant are about 45 million years younger than the earliest spore microfossils; the conclusion that these microscopic spores are from land plants is tenuous and one could argue that they could be of algal or fungal origin.

Clues to their origin come in the arrangement of spores into groups of four (tetrads) that are common to early land plants (**Figure 29.5a**). The structure of the spore walls and their deduced chemical composition both indicate sporopollenin is present—a key characteristic derived from land plants. Significantly, fossilized sporophyte tissue from 450-million-year-old rocks was found that had structural resemblance to liverworts, a land plant, providing evidence that the common spore microfossils from this time were indeed derived from land plants. Fossils of larger plant structures, such as the *Cooksonia* sporangium shown here

0.3 mm

▲ Cooksonia sporangium fossil

Exploring Derived Traits of Land Plants

Charophyte algae lack the key traits of land plants described in this figure: alternation of generations; multicellular, dependent embryos; walled spores produced in sporangia; multicellular gametangia; and apical meristems. This suggests that these traits were absent in the ancestor common to land plants and charophytes but instead evolved as derived traits of land plants. Not every land plant exhibits all of these traits; certain lineages of plants have lost some traits over time.

Alternation of Generations

The life cycles of all land plants alternate between two generations of distinct multicellular organisms: gametophytes and sporophytes. As shown in the diagram below (using a fern as an example), each generation gives rise to the other, a process that is called **alternation of generations**. This type of reproductive cycle evolved in various groups of algae but does not occur in the charophytes, the algae most closely related to land plants. Take care not to confuse the alternation of generations in plants with the haploid and diploid stages in the life cycles of other sexually reproducing organisms (see Figure 13.6). Alternation of generations is distinguished by the fact that the life cycle includes both multicellular haploid organisms and multicellular diploid organisms.

Alternation of generations: five generalized steps

The multicellular haploid **gametophyte** ("gamete-producing plant") is named for its production by mitosis of haploid gametes—eggs and sperm—that fuse during fertilization, forming diploid zygotes. Mitotic division of the zygote produces a multicellular diploid **sporophyte** ("spore-producing plant"). Meiosis in a mature sporophyte produces haploid **spores**, reproductive cells that can develop into a new haploid organism without fusing with another cell. Mitotic division of the spore cell produces a new multicellular gametophyte, and the cycle begins again.

❶ The gametophyte produces haploid gametes by mitosis.

Gametophyte (*n*)

Gamete from another plant

Mitosis

Mitosis

Spore

Gamete

❷ Two gametes unite (fertilization) and form a diploid zygote.

❺ The spores develop into multicellular haploid gametophytes.

MEIOSIS

FERTILIZATION

Zygote

❹ The sporophyte produces unicellar haploid spores by meiosis.

2*n*

❸ The zygote develops into a multicellular diploid sporophyte.

Sporophyte (2*n*)

Mitosis

Key

Haploid (*n*)

Diploid (2*n*)

Multicellular, Dependent Embryos

As part of a life cycle with alternation of generations, multicellular plant embryos develop from zygotes that are retained within the tissues of the female parent (a gametophyte). The parental tissues protect the developing embryo from harsh environmental conditions and provide nutrients such as sugars and amino acids. The embryo has specialized *placental transfer cells* that enhance the transfer of nutrients to the embryo through elaborate ingrowths of the wall surface (plasma membrane and cell wall). The multicellular, dependent embryo of land plants is such a significant derived trait that land plants are also known as **embryophytes**.

Embryo (LM) and placental transfer cell (TEM) of *Marchantia* (a liverwort)

Renzaglia, Karen S.

Embryo

Maternal tissue

Wall ingrowths

Placental transfer cell (blue outline)

10 μm

2 μm

Dr. Linda E. Graham

MAKE CONNECTIONS *Review sexual life cycles in Figure 13.6. Identify which type of sexual life cycle has alternation of generations, and summarize how it differs from other life cycles.*

Continued on next page

Exploring Derived Traits of Land Plants

Walled Spores Produced in Sporangia

Plant spores are haploid reproductive cells that can grow into multicellular haploid gametophytes by mitosis. The polymer sporopollenin makes the walls of plant spores tough and resistant to harsh environments. This chemical adaptation enables spores to be dispersed through dry air without harm.

The sporophyte has multicellular organs called **sporangia** (singular, *sporangium*) that produce the spores. Within a sporangium, diploid cells called **sporocytes**, or spore mother cells, undergo meiosis and generate the haploid spores. The outer tissues of the sporangium protect the developing spores until they are released into the air. Multicellular sporangia that produce spores with sporopollenin-enriched walls are key terrestrial adaptations of land plants. Although charophytes also produce spores, these algae lack multicellular sporangia, and their flagellated, water-dispersed spores lack sporopollenin.

Alan S. Heilman

Michael Clayton

Spores
Sporangium

Longitudinal section of *Sphagnum* sporangium (LM)

Sporophyte

Gametophyte

Sporophytes and sporangia of *Sphagnum* (a moss)

Multicellular Gametangia

Another feature distinguishing early land plants from their algal ancestors was the production of gametes within multicellular organs called **gametangia**. The female gametangia are called **archegonia** (singular, archegonium). Each archegonium is a pear-shaped organ that produces a single nonmotile egg retained within the bulbous part of the organ (the top for the species shown here). The male gametangia, called **antheridia** (singular, antheridium), produce sperm and release them into the environment. In many groups of present-day plants, the sperm have flagella and swim to the eggs through water droplets or a film of water. Each egg is fertilized within an archegonium, where the zygote develops into an embryo. As you will see in Chapter 30, the gametophytes of seed plants are so reduced in size that the archegonia and antheridia have been lost in many lineages.

Courtesy of David John Jones

Female gametophyte

Archegonia, each with an egg (yellow)

Antheridia (brown), containing sperm

Male gametophyte

Archegonia and antheridia of *Marchantia* (a liverwort)

Apical Meristems

In terrestrial habitats, a photosynthetic organism finds essential resources in two very different places. Light and CO_2 are mainly available above ground; water and mineral nutrients are found mainly in the soil. Though plants cannot move from place to place, their roots and shoots can elongate, increasing exposure to environmental resources. This growth in length is sustained throughout the plant's life by the activity of **apical meristems**, localized regions of cell division at the tips of roots and shoots. Cells produced by apical meristems differentiate into the outer epidermis, which protects the body, and various types of internal tissues. Shoot apical meristems also generate leaves in most plants. Thus, the complex bodies of plants have specialized below- and aboveground organs.

Apical meristems of plant roots and shoots. The LMs are longitudinal sections at the tips of a root and shoot.

Centers for Disease Control & Prevention

Apical meristem of shoot

Developing leaves

Ed Reschke/Getty Images

Apical meristem of root

Root

100 μm

Shoot

100 μm

(a) **Fossilized spores.** The chemical composition and wall structure of these 450-million-year-old spores match those found in land plants.

Charles H. Wellman

(b) **Fossilized sporophyte tissue.** The spores were embedded in tissue that appears to be from plants.

▲ Figure 29.5 **Ancient plant spores and tissue** (colourized SEMs).

Table 29.1 Ten Phyla of Extant Plants		
	Common Name	Number of Known Species
Nonvascular Plants (Bryophytes)		
Phylum Hepatophyta	Liverworts	9000
Phylum Bryophyta	Mosses	15 000
Phylum Anthocerophyta	Hornworts	100
Vascular Plants		
Seedless Vascular Plants		
Phylum Lycophyta	Lycophytes	1200
Phylum Monilophyta	Monilophytes	12 000
Seed Plants		
Gymnosperms		
Phylum Ginkgophyta	Ginkgo	1
Phylum Cycadophyta	Cycads	130
Phylum Gnetophyta	Gnetophytes	75
Phylum Coniferophyta	Conifers	600
Angiosperms		
Phylum Anthophyta	Flowering plants	250 000

(Figure 29.5b), date to 425 million years ago—45 million years after the appearance of plant spores in the fossil record.

Whatever the precise age of the first land plants, those ancestral species gave rise to the vast diversity of living plants. Table 29.1 summarizes the 10 extant phyla in the taxonomic scheme used in this text. (Extant lineages are those that have surviving members, not only extinct ones.)

As you read the rest of this section, look at Table 29.1 together with **Figure 29.6**, which reflects a view of plant phylogeny based on plant morphology, biochemistry, and molecular genetics.

One way to distinguish groups of plants is whether or not they have an extensive system of **vascular tissue**, cells joined

▲ Figure 29.6 **Highlights of plant evolution.** The phylogeny shown here illustrates a leading hypothesis about the relationships between plant groups.

into tubes that transport water and nutrients throughout the plant body. Most present-day plants have a complex vascular tissue system and are therefore called **vascular plants**. Plants that do not have an extensive transport system—liverworts, mosses, and hornworts—are described as "nonvascular" plants, even though some mosses do have simple vascular tissue. Nonvascular plants are often informally called **bryophytes** (from the Greek *bryon*, moss, and *phyton*, plant).

Although the term *bryophyte* is commonly used to refer to all nonvascular plants, molecular studies and morphological analyses of sperm structure have concluded that bryophytes do not form a monophyletic group (a clade; see Figure 26.10). Debate continues, however, over the relationships of liverworts, mosses, and hornworts to each other and to vascular plants. Regardless of the outcome of this debate, bryophytes share some derived traits with vascular plants, such as multicellular embryos and apical meristems, while lacking many innovations of vascular plants, such as roots and true leaves.

Vascular plants, which form a clade that comprises about 93% of all extant plant species, can be categorized further into smaller clades. Two of these clades are the **lycophytes** (club mosses and their relatives) and the **monilophytes** (ferns and their relatives). The plants in each of these clades lack seeds, which is why collectively the two clades are often informally called **seedless vascular plants**. However, notice in Figure 29.6 that seedless vascular plants do not form a clade. Groups such as the seedless vascular plants are sometimes referred to as a **grade**, a collection of organisms that share a key biological feature. Grades can be informative by grouping organisms according to features, such as lack of seeds. But members of a grade, unlike members of a clade, do not necessarily share the same ancestry. For example, even though monilophytes and lycophytes are all seedless plants, monilophytes share a more recent common ancestor with seed plants. As a result, we would expect monilophytes and seed plants to share key traits not found in lycophytes—and they do, as you'll read in Concept 29.3.

A third clade of vascular plants consists of seed plants, which represent the vast majority of living plant species. A **seed** is an embryo packaged with a supply of nutrients inside a protective coat. Seed plants can be divided into two groups, gymnosperms and angiosperms, based on the absence or presence of enclosed chambers in which seeds mature. **Gymnosperms** (from the Greek *gymnos*, naked, and *sperm*, seed) are grouped together as "naked seed" plants because their seeds are not enclosed in chambers. Living gymnosperm species, the most familiar of which are the conifers, probably form a clade. **Angiosperms** (from the Greek *angion*, container) are a huge clade consisting of all flowering plants. Angiosperm seeds develop inside chambers called ovaries, which originate within flowers and mature into fruits. Nearly 90% of living plant species are angiosperms.

Note that the phylogeny depicted in Figure 29.6 focuses only on the relationships between extant plant lineages. Paleobotanists have also discovered fossils belonging to extinct plant lineages. As you'll read later in the chapter, many of these fossils reveal intermediate steps in the emergence of the distinctive plant groups found on Earth today.

CONCEPT CHECK 29.1

1. Why do researchers identify charophytes rather than another group as the closest relatives of land plants?
2. Identify four derived traits that distinguish plants from charophytes *and* facilitate life on land. Explain.
3. **WHAT IF?** What would the human life cycle be like if we had alternation of generations? Assume that the multicellular diploid stage is similar in form to an adult human.
4. **MAKE CONNECTIONS** The transition to land required a variety of evolutionary adaptations in plants, but animals also faced similar problems. Compare the strategies plants evolved with various animal adaptations that helped overcome problems with water loss, gas exchange, and gravity.

For suggested answers, see Appendix A.

CONCEPT 29.2

Mosses and other nonvascular plants have life cycles dominated by gametophytes

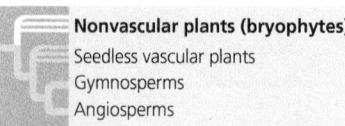
Nonvascular plants (bryophytes)
Seedless vascular plants
Gymnosperms
Angiosperms

The nonvascular plants (bryophytes) are represented today by three phyla of small herbaceous (nonwoody) plants: **liverworts** (phylum Hepatophyta), **mosses** (phylum Bryophyta), and **hornworts** (phylum Anthocerophyta). Liverworts and hornworts are named for their shapes, plus the suffix *wort* (from the Anglo-Saxon for "herb"). Mosses are familiar to many people, although some plants commonly called "mosses" are not really mosses at all. These include Irish moss (a red seaweed), reindeer moss (a lichen), club mosses (lycopods), and Spanish mosses (lichens in some regions and flowering plants in others).

Researchers think that liverworts, mosses, and hornworts were the earliest lineages to have diverged from the common ancestor of land plants (see Figure 29.6). Fossil evidence provides some support for this idea: The earliest spores of land plants (dating from 470 to 450 million years ago) have structural features found only in the spores of liverworts, and by 430 million years ago spores similar to those of mosses and hornworts also occur in the fossil record. The earliest fossils of vascular plants date to about 425 million years ago.

Over the long course of their evolution, liverworts, mosses, and hornworts have acquired many unique adaptations. Next, we'll examine some of those features.

Bryophyte Gametophytes

Unlike vascular plants, in all three bryophyte phyla the haploid gametophytes are the dominant stage of the life cycle: That is, they are usually larger and longer-living than the sporophytes, as shown in the moss life cycle in Figure 29.7. Sporophytes are typically present only part of the time.

When bryophyte spores are dispersed to a favourable habitat, such as moist soil or tree bark, they may germinate and grow into gametophytes. Germinating moss spores, for example, characteristically produce a mass of green,

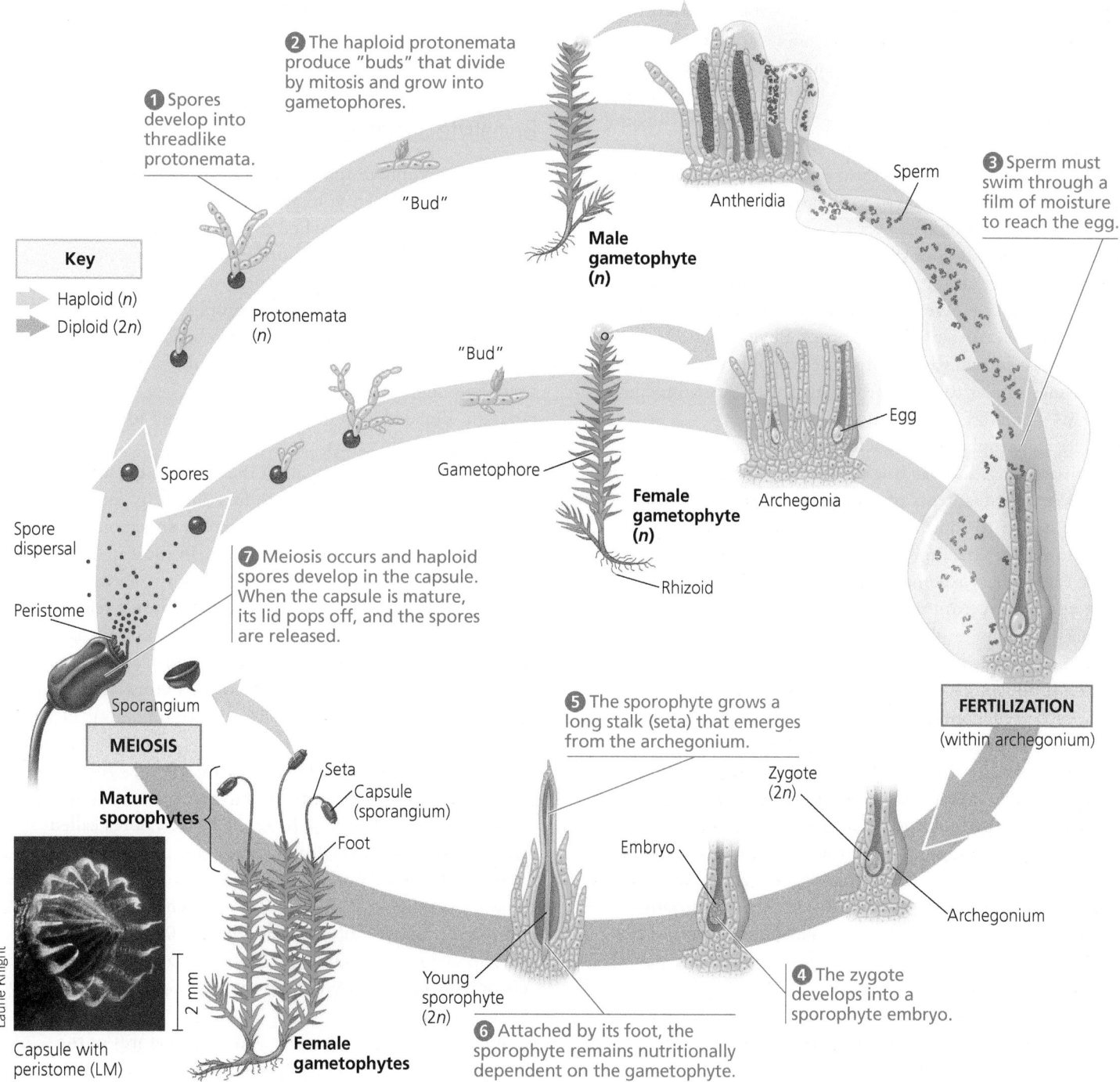

Key

➤ Haploid (*n*)
➤ Diploid (2*n*)

1 Spores develop into threadlike protonemata.

2 The haploid protonemata produce "buds" that divide by mitosis and grow into gametophores.

"Bud"

Protonemata (*n*)

Spores

Spore dispersal

Peristome

7 Meiosis occurs and haploid spores develop in the capsule. When the capsule is mature, its lid pops off, and the spores are released.

Sporangium

MEIOSIS

Mature sporophytes

Seta
Capsule (sporangium)
Foot

Capsule with peristome (LM)

2 mm

Laurie Knight

Female gametophytes

Young sporophyte (2*n*)

6 Attached by its foot, the sporophyte remains nutritionally dependent on the gametophyte.

5 The sporophyte grows a long stalk (seta) that emerges from the archegonium.

Embryo

4 The zygote develops into a sporophyte embryo.

Archegonium

Zygote (2*n*)

FERTILIZATION
(within archegonium)

"Bud"

Gametophore

Female gametophyte (*n*)

Rhizoid

Archegonia

Egg

Male gametophyte (*n*)

Antheridia

Sperm

3 Sperm must swim through a film of moisture to reach the egg.

Figure 29.7 The life cycle of a moss.

? *In this diagram, does the sperm cell that fertilizes the egg cell differ genetically from the egg? Explain.*

branched, one-cell-thick filaments known as a **protonema** (plural, *protonemata*; from the Greek *proto*, first, and *nema*, threads). A protonema has a large surface area that enhances absorption of water and minerals. In favourable conditions, a protonema produces one or more "buds." (Note that when referring to nonvascular plants, we typically use quotation marks for structures similar to the buds, stems, and leaves of vascular plants because the definitions of these terms are based on vascular plant organs.) Each of these bud-like growths has an apical meristem that generates a gamete-producing structure known as a **gametophore** ("gamete bearer"). Together, a protonema and one or more gametophores make up the body of a moss gametophyte.

Bryophyte gametophytes generally form ground-hugging carpets, partly because their body parts are too thin to support a tall plant. A second constraint on the height of many bryophytes is the absence of vascular tissue, which would enable long-distance transport of water and nutrients. (The thin structure of bryophyte organs makes it possible to distribute materials for short distances without specialized vascular tissue.) However, some mosses have conducting tissues in the centre of their "stems." Phylogenetic analyses suggest that in these and some other bryophytes, conducting tissues similar to those of vascular plants arose independently by convergent evolution.

The gametophytes are anchored by delicate **rhizoids**, which are long, tubular single cells (in liverworts and hornworts) or filaments of cells (in mosses). While structurally similar to root hairs (not roots!), rhizoids primary function is for attachment to the substrate. They do not have the primary role in water and mineral absorption that you expect from the more complex roots of vascular plants.

Gametophytes can form multiple gametangia, each of which produces gametes and is covered by protective tissue. Each archegonium produces one egg, whereas each antheridium produces many sperm. Some bryophyte gametophytes are bisexual, but in mosses the archegonia and antheridia are typically carried on separate female and male gametophytes. Flagellated sperm swim through a film of water toward eggs, entering the archegonia in response to chemical attractants. Eggs are not released but instead remain within the bases of archegonia. After fertilization, embryos are retained within the archegonia. Layers of placental transfer cells help transport nutrients to the embryos as they develop into sporophytes.

Bryophyte sperm typically require a film of water to reach the eggs. Given this requirement, it is not surprising that many bryophyte species are found in moist habitats. The fact that sperm swim through water to reach the egg also means that in species with separate male and female gametophytes (most mosses), sexual reproduction is likely to be more successful when individuals are located close to one another. However, small arthropods may also be involved in transferring sperm between the male and female plants over relatively larger distances and across a swimming barrier (**Figure 29.8**). Many bryophyte species can increase the number of individuals in a local area through various methods of asexual reproduction. For example, some mosses reproduce asexually by forming *brood bodies*, small plantlets (as shown to the right) that detach from the parent plant and grow into new, genetically identical copies of their parent.

Bryophyte Sporophytes

Although bryophyte sporophytes are usually green and photosynthetic when young, they cannot live independently. They remain attached to their parental gametophytes, from which they absorb sugars, amino acids, minerals, and water.

Bryophytes have the smallest sporophytes of all extant plant groups, consistent with the hypothesis that larger sporophytes evolved only later, in the vascular plants. A typical bryophyte sporophyte consists of a foot, a seta, and a sporangium. Embedded in the archegonium, the **foot** absorbs nutrients from the gametophyte. The **seta** (plural, *setae*), or stalk, conducts these materials to the sporangium, also called a **capsule**, which uses them to produce spores by meiosis.

A single moss capsule can produce an enormous number of spores—upwards of 50 million. In most mosses, the seta elongates, enhancing spore dispersal by elevating the capsule. Typically, the upper part of the capsule features a ring of interlocking, tooth-like structures known as the **peristome** (see Figure 29.7). These "teeth" open under dry conditions and close again when it is moist. This allows spores to be discharged gradually, via periodic gusts of wind that can carry them long distances.

Moss and hornwort sporophytes are often larger and more complex than those of liverworts. Both moss and hornwort sporophytes also have specialized pores called **stomata** (singular, *stoma*), which are also found in all vascular plants. These pores support photosynthesis by allowing the exchange of CO_2 and O_2 between the outside air and the sporophyte interior (see Figure 10.4). Stomata are also the main avenues by which water evaporates from the sporophyte. In hot, dry conditions, the stomata close, minimizing water loss.

Within the bryophytes, the structural features of the sporophytes are diverse. Moss and hornwort sporophytes are often larger and more complex than those of liverworts. Moss and hornwort sporophytes also have stomata, as do all vascular plants, but these are absent in the liverworts,

Do animals facilitate fertilization in mosses?

Experiment Step 3 of Figure 29.7 indicates that sperm from antheridia swim through a film of moisture to reach an egg present in archegonia. This is considered a major challenge during the colonization of land. It is generally thought that sperm are poorly adapted to land, unlike pollen of the seed plants, which are drought resistant. A dependence upon the sperm swimming would appear to limit reproduction to wet conditions and close distances. A group at Lund University, in Sweden, tested whether microarthropods (springtails and mites) are able to facilitate fertilization at different distances in the presence of a moisture barrier. The experiment involved separating male and female gametophytes by different distances (0, 2, and 4 cm) on a surface that acted as a physical barrier to swimming in the presence or absence of the microarthropods.

Results While fertilization (as evident by the number of sporophytes produced) was efficient with or without the microarthropods when male and female plants were grown together (0 cm), both species of microarthropods were able to increase the number of fertilization events when the male and female gametophyte were separated (2 or 4 cm).

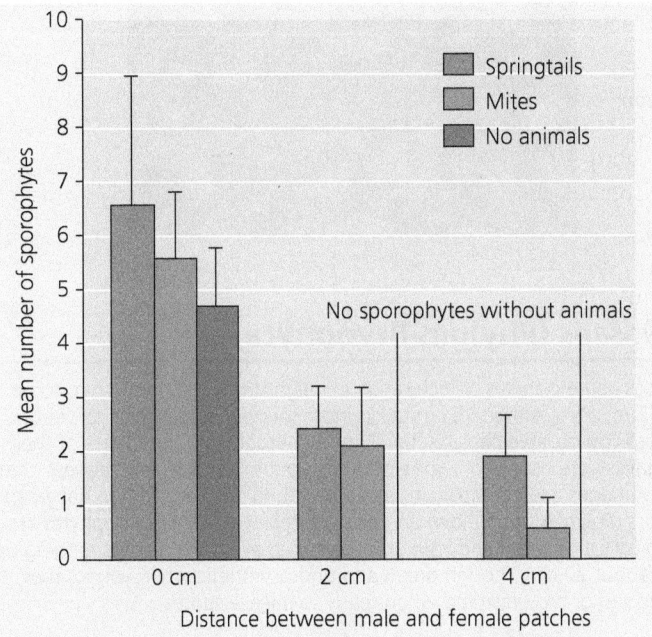

Source: N. Cronberg, R. Natcheva, and K. Hedlund, Microarthropods mediate sperm transfer in moss, *Science* 313: 1255, AAAS (2006). Reprinted with permission.

Conclusion Microarthropod interaction has a positive outcome for bryophytes, increasing the distance and conditions under which fertilization can occur. This also suggests that animal-mediated fertilization, well known in the angiosperms (bee pollination, for instance), developed early in the transition to land.

Source: Based on N. Cronberg, R. Natcheva, and K. Hedlund, Microarthropods mediate sperm transfer in moss, *Science* 313:1255 (2006). © Jane B Reece.

WHAT IF? *The researchers did a second experiment and found that the microarthropods preferred to visit fertile rather than sterile gametophytes. Examine Figure 38.5 and propose a hypothesis to explain the preference.*

supporting the placement of the liverworts as the earliest-diverging members of the land plants (Figure 29.6).

Figure 29.9 shows some examples of gametophytes and sporophytes in the bryophyte phyla.

The Ecological and Economic Importance of Mosses

Wind dispersal of lightweight spores has distributed mosses throughout the world. These plants are particularly common and diverse in moist forests and wetlands. Some mosses colonize bare, sandy soil, where researchers have found they help retain nitrogen in the soil. In northern coniferous forests, species such as the feather moss *Pleurozium* harbour nitrogen-fixing cyanobacteria that increase the availability of nitrogen in the ecosystem. Other mosses inhabit such extreme environments as mountaintops, tundra, and deserts. Many mosses are able to live in very cold or dry habitats because they can survive the loss of most of their body water, then rehydrate when moisture is available. Few vascular plants can survive the same degree of desiccation.

One wetland moss genus, *Sphagnum*, or "peat moss," is often a major component of deposits of partially decayed organic material known as **peat** (Figure 29.10a). Boggy regions with thick layers of peat are called peatlands. *Sphagnum* does not decay readily, in part because of phenolic compounds embedded in its cell walls. The low temperature, pH, and oxygen level of peatlands also inhibit decay of moss and other organisms in these boggy wetlands. The slow decay in these bog environments is evident from the many corpses that have been preserved for thousands of years. The best preserved of these "bog bodies" is Tollund man, who was found in Denmark in 1950. He lived during the Iron Age, over 2400 years ago (Figure 29.10b)!

Peat has long been a fuel source in Europe and Asia, and it is still harvested for fuel today, notably in Finland and Ireland. Peat moss is also useful as a soil conditioner and for packing plant roots during shipment because it has large dead cells that can absorb roughly 20 times the moss's weight in water. Canada is one of the largest producers of horticultural peat, but this is less than 5% of global production.

Peatlands cover 3% of Earth's land surface and contain roughly 30% of the world's soil carbon: Globally, an estimated 450 billion tonnes of organic carbon is stored as peat. These carbon reservoirs have helped to stabilize atmospheric CO_2 concentrations (see Chapter 55). Current overharvesting of *Sphagnum* may reduce peat's beneficial ecological effects and contribute to global warming by releasing stored CO_2. In addition, if global temperatures continue to rise, the water levels of some peatlands are expected to drop. Such a change would expose peat to air and cause it to decompose, thereby releasing additional stored CO_2 and contributing further to global warming. The historical and expected future effects of *Sphagnum* on the global climate underscore the importance of preserving and managing peatlands.

Mosses may have a long history of affecting climate change. In the Scientific Skills Exercise, you will explore the question of whether mosses did so by contributing to the weathering of rocks during the Ordovician period.

Exploring Bryophyte Diversity

Liverworts (Phylum Hepatophyta)

This phylum's common and scientific names (from the Latin *hepaticus*, liver) refer to the liver-shaped gametophytes of its members, such as *Marchantia*, shown below. In medieval times, their shape was thought to be a sign that the plants could help treat liver diseases, a belief referred to as the "Doctrine of Signatures." Some liverworts, including *Marchantia*, are described as "thalloid" because of the flattened shape of their gametophytes. (Recall from Chapter 28 that the body of a multicellular alga is called a thallus.) *Marchantia* gametangia are elevated on gametophores that look like miniature trees. You would need a magnifying glass to see the sporophytes, which have a short seta (stalk) with an oval or round capsule. Other liverworts, such as *Plagiochila*, below, are called "leafy" because their stemlike gameto-phytes have many leaflike appendages. There are many more species of leafy liverworts than thalloid liverworts.

Thallus

Gametophore of female gametophyte

Sporophyte

Alvin E. Staffan/Science Source

Marchantia polymorpha, a "thalloid" liverwort

Marchantia sporophyte (LM)

Foot
Seta
Capsule (sporangium)

500 μm

Dr. Linda E. Graham

Plagiochila deltoidea, a "leafy" liverwort

Hidden Forest

Hornworts (Phylum Anthocerophyta)

This phylum's common and scientific names (from the Greek *keras*, horn) refer to the long, tapered shape of the sporophyte. A typical sporophyte can grow to about 5 cm high. Unlike a liverwort or moss sporophyte, a hornwort sporophyte lacks a seta and consists only of a sporangium. The sporangium releases mature spores by splitting open, starting at the tip of the horn. The gametophytes, which are usually 1–2 cm in diameter, grow mostly horizontally and often have multiple sporophytes attached. Hornworts are frequently among the first species to colonize open areas with moist soils; a symbiotic relationship with nitrogen-fixing cyanobacteria contributes to their ability to do this (nitrogen is often in short supply in such areas).

Mosses (Phylum Bryophyta)

Moss gametophytes, which range in height from less than 1 mm to up to 2 m, are less than 15 cm tall in most species. The familiar carpet of moss you observe consists mainly of gametophytes. The blades of their "leaves" are usually only one cell thick, but more complex "leaves" that have ridges coated with cuticle can be found on the common hairy-cap moss (*Polytrichum*, below) and its close relatives. Moss sporophytes are typically elongated and visible to the naked eye, with heights ranging up to about 20 cm. Though green and photosynthetic when young, they turn tan or brownish red when ready to release spores.

An *Anthoceros* hornwort species

Sporophyte

Gametophyte

Hidden Forest

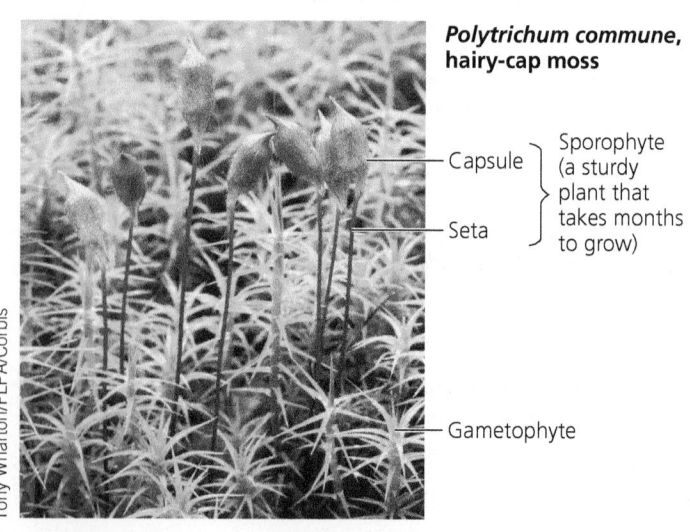

Polytrichum commune, hairy-cap moss

Capsule
Seta

Sporophyte (a sturdy plant that takes months to grow)

Gametophyte

Tony Wharton/FLPA/Corbis

(a) Peat being harvested from a peatland

▲ Figure 29.10 *Sphagnum*, or peat moss: a bryophyte with economic, ecological, and archaeological significance.

(b) "Tollund Man," a bog mummy dating from 405–100 BCE. The acidic, oxygen-poor conditions produced by *Sphagnum* can preserve human or other animal bodies for thousands of years.

SCIENTIFIC SKILLS EXERCISE

Making Bar Graphs and Interpreting Data

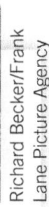

Could Nonvascular Plants Have Caused Weathering of Rocks and Contributed to Climate Change During the Ordovician Period? The oldest traces of terrestrial plants are fossilized spores formed 470 million years ago. Between that time and the end of the Ordovician period 444 million years ago, the atmospheric CO_2 level dropped by half and the climate cooled dramatically.

One possible cause of the drop in CO_2 during the Ordovician period is the breakdown, or weathering, of rock. As rock weathers, calcium silicate (Ca_2SiCO_3) is released and combines with CO_2 from the air, producing calcium carbonate ($CaCO_3$). In later periods of time, the roots of vascular plants increased rock weathering and mineral release by producing acids that break down rock and soil. Although nonvascular plants lack roots, they require the same mineral nutrients as vascular plants. Could nonvascular plants also increase chemical weathering of rock? If so, they could have contributed to the decline in atmospheric CO_2 during the Ordovician period. In this exercise, you will interpret data from a study of the effects of moss on releasing minerals from two types of rock.

How the Experiment Was Done The researchers set up experimental and control microcosms, or small artificial ecosystems, to measure mineral release from rocks. First, they placed rock fragments of volcanic origin, either granite or andesite, into small glass containers. Then they mixed water and macerated (chopped and crushed) moss of the species *Physcomitrella patens*. They added this mixture to the experimental microcosms (72 granite and 41 andesite). For the control microcosms (77 granite and 37 andesite), they filtered out the moss and just added the water. After 130 days, they measured the amounts of various minerals found in the water in the control microcosms and in the water and moss in the experimental microcosms.

Data from the Experiment The moss grew (increased its biomass) in the experimental microcosms. The table shows the mean amounts in micromoles (μmol) of several minerals measured in the water and the moss in the microcosms.

Interpret the Data

1. Why did the researchers add filtrate from which macerated moss had been removed to the control microcosms?

2. Make two bar graphs (for granite and andesite) comparing the mean amounts of each element weathered from rocks in the control and experimental microcosms. (Hint: For an experimental microcosm, what sum represents the total amount weathered from rocks?)

3. Overall, what is the effect of moss on chemical weathering of rock? Are the results similar or different for granite and andesite?

4. Based on their experimental results, the researchers added weathering of rock by nonvascular plants to simulation models of the Ordovician climate. The new models predicted decreased CO_2 levels and global cooling sufficient to produce the glaciations in the late Ordovician period. What assumptions did the researchers make in using results from their experiments in climate simulation models?

5. "Life has profoundly changed the Earth." Explain whether or not these experimental results support this statement.

Data from T. M. Lenton et al., First plants cooled the Ordovician, *Nature Geoscience* 5:86–89 (2012).

	Ca^{2+} (μmol)		Mg^{2+} (μmol)		K^+ (μmol)	
	Granite	Andesite	Granite	Andesite	Granite	Andesite
Mean weathered amount released in water in the control microcosms	1.68	1.54	0.42	0.13	0.68	0.60
Mean weathered amount released in water in the experimental microcosms	1.27	1.84	0.34	0.13	0.65	0.64
Mean weathered amount taken up by moss in the experimental microcosms	1.09	3.62	0.31	0.56	1.07	0.28

1. How do bryophytes differ from other plants?

2. Give three examples of how structure fits function in bryophytes.

3. **MAKE CONNECTIONS** Review the discussion of feedback regulation in Concept 1.1. Could effects of global warming on peatlands alter CO_2 concentrations in ways that result in negative or positive feedback? Explain.

For suggested answers, see Appendix A.

◀ Figure 29.11 **Sporophytes of *Aglaophyton major*, an ancient relative of present-day vascular plants.** This reconstruction from 405-million-year-old fossils exhibits dichotomous (Y-shaped) branching with sporangia at the ends of the branches. Sporophyte branching characterizes living vascular plants but is lacking in living nonvascular plants (bryophytes). *Aglaophyton* had rhizoids that anchored it to the ground. The inset shows a fossilized stoma of *A. major* (colourized LM).

CONCEPT 29.3

Ferns and other seedless vascular plants were the first plants to grow tall

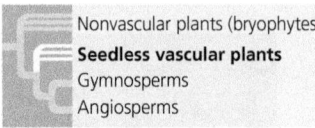

Nonvascular plants (bryophytes)
Seedless vascular plants
Gymnosperms
Angiosperms

During the first 100 million years of plant evolution, bryophytes or bryophyte-like plants were the prevalent vegetation. But it is vascular plants that dominate most landscapes today. Fossils and living seedless vascular plants can provide insights into plant evolution during the Devonian and Carboniferous periods, when vascular plants began to diversify but most groups of seed plants had not yet evolved. Fossils show that lycophytes, ferns, and other seedless vascular plants had well-developed vascular systems by the Devonian period. As we'll see, this evolutionary innovation set the stage for vascular plants to grow taller than their bryophyte counterparts. As in nonvascular plants, however, the sperm of ferns and all other seedless vascular plants are flagellated and swim through a film of water to reach eggs. In part because of these swimming sperm, seedless vascular plants today are most common in damp environments.

Origins and Traits of Vascular Plants

Fossils of the forerunners of present-day vascular plants date back about 425 million years. Unlike the nonvascular plants, these species had branched sporophytes that were not dependent on gametophytes for nutrition (Figure 29.11). Although these ancestors of vascular plants were less than 20 cm tall, their branching allowed more complex bodies with multiple sporangia to evolve. As plant bodies became increasingly complex, competition for space and sunlight probably increased. As we'll see, that competition may have stimulated still more evolution in vascular plants.

The ancestors of vascular plants already had some derived traits of today's vascular plants, but they lacked roots and some other adaptations that evolved later. This section describes the main traits that characterize living vascular plants: life cycles with dominant sporophytes, transport in vascular tissues called xylem and phloem, and well-developed roots and leaves, including spore-bearing leaves called sporophylls.

Life Cycles with Dominant Sporophytes

Fossils suggest that the ancestors of vascular plants had gametophytes and sporophytes that were about equal in size. Among living vascular plants, however, the sporophyte (diploid) generation is the larger and more complex plant in the alternation of generations (Figure 29.12). In ferns, for example, the familiar leafy plants are the sporophytes. You would have to get down on your hands and knees and search the ground carefully to find fern gametophytes, which are tiny structures that often grow on or just below the soil surface. Until you have a chance to do that, you can study the sporophyte-dominant life cycle of seedless vascular plants in Figure 29.12, which uses a fern as an example. Then, for review, compare this life cycle with Figure 29.7, which represents a gametophyte-dominated life cycle typical of mosses and other nonvascular plants. In Chapter 30, you will see that gametophytes became even more reduced during the evolution of seed plants.

Transport in Xylem and Phloem

Vascular plants have two types of vascular tissue: xylem and phloem. **Xylem** conducts most of the water and minerals. The xylem of most vascular plants includes **tracheids**, tube-shaped cells that carry water and minerals up from roots (see Figure 35.10). (Tracheids have been lost in some highly specialized species, such as *Wolffia*, a tiny aquatic angiosperm.) Because nonvascular plants lack tracheids, vascular plants are sometimes referred to as tracheophytes.

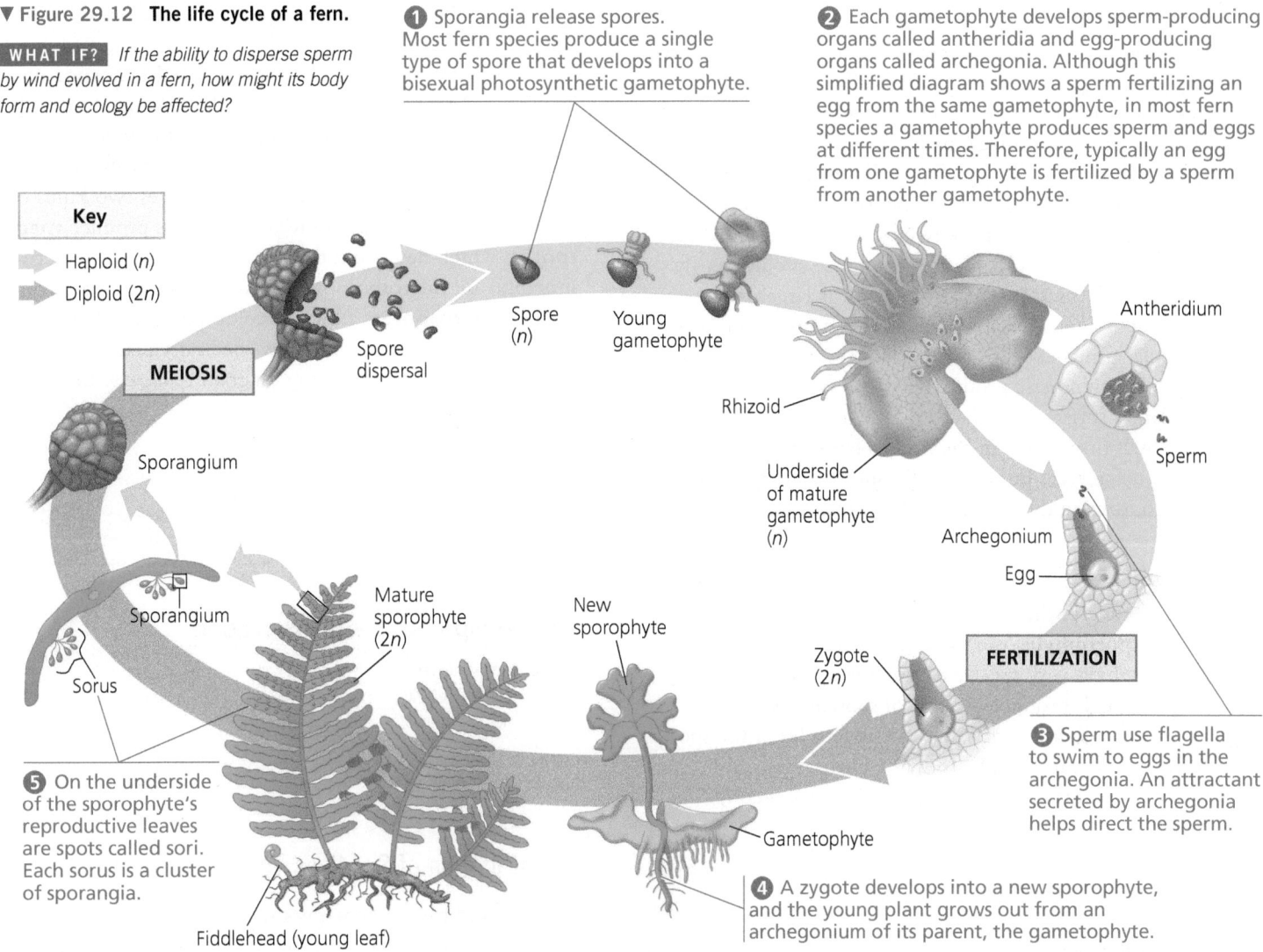

▼ **Figure 29.12 The life cycle of a fern.**

WHAT IF? *If the ability to disperse sperm by wind evolved in a fern, how might its body form and ecology be affected?*

1 Sporangia release spores. Most fern species produce a single type of spore that develops into a bisexual photosynthetic gametophyte.

2 Each gametophyte develops sperm-producing organs called antheridia and egg-producing organs called archegonia. Although this simplified diagram shows a sperm fertilizing an egg from the same gametophyte, in most fern species a gametophyte produces sperm and eggs at different times. Therefore, typically an egg from one gametophyte is fertilized by a sperm from another gametophyte.

Key
➡ Haploid (*n*)
➡ Diploid (*2n*)

MEIOSIS

Spore dispersal

Sporangium

Spore (*n*)

Young gametophyte

Rhizoid

Antheridium

Sperm

Underside of mature gametophyte (*n*)

Archegonium

Egg

Sporangium

Mature sporophyte (*2n*)

New sporophyte

Zygote (*2n*)

FERTILIZATION

Sorus

5 On the underside of the sporophyte's reproductive leaves are spots called sori. Each sorus is a cluster of sporangia.

Fiddlehead (young leaf)

Gametophyte

3 Sperm use flagella to swim to eggs in the archegonia. An attractant secreted by archegonia helps direct the sperm.

4 A zygote develops into a new sporophyte, and the young plant grows out from an archegonium of its parent, the gametophyte.

The water-conducting cells in vascular plants are *lignified*; that is, their cell walls are strengthened by the polymer **lignin**. The tissue called **phloem** has cells arranged into tubes that distribute sugars, amino acids, and other organic products (see Figure 35.10).

Lignified vascular tissue permitted vascular plants to grow tall. Their stems became strong enough to provide support against gravity, and they could transport water and mineral nutrients high above the ground. Tall plants could also outcompete short plants for access to the sunlight needed for photosynthesis. In addition, the spores of tall plants could disperse farther than those of short plants, enabling tall species to colonize new environments rapidly. Overall, the ability to grow tall was a major evolutionary innovation that gave vascular plants a competitive edge over nonvascular plants, which rarely grow above 20 cm in height. Competition among vascular plants also increased, and taller growth forms were favoured by natural selection—such as the trees that formed the first forests about 385 million years ago.

Evolution of Roots

Lignified vascular tissue also provides benefits below ground. Instead of the rhizoids seen in bryophytes, roots evolved in the sporophytes of almost all vascular plants. **Roots** are organs that absorb water and nutrients from the soil. Roots also anchor vascular plants, hence allowing the shoot system to grow taller.

Root tissues of living plants closely resemble stem tissues of early vascular plants preserved in fossils. This suggests that roots may have evolved from the lowest belowground portions of stems in ancient vascular plants. It is unclear whether roots evolved only once in the common ancestor of all vascular plants or independently in different lineages. Although the roots of living members of these lineages of vascular plants share many similarities, fossil evidence hints at convergent evolution. The oldest lycophyte fossils, for example, already displayed simple roots 400 million years ago, when the ancestors of ferns and seed plants still had none. Studying genes that control root development in different vascular plant species may help resolve this question.

Evolution of Leaves

Leaves increase the surface area of the plant body and serve as the primary photosynthetic organ of vascular plants. In terms of size and complexity, leaves can be classified as either microphylls or megaphylls (Figure 29.13). **Microphylls** are leaves that are small, usually spine-shaped, and supported by a single strand of vascular tissue. They are a simple structure present in only lycophytes, which are the oldest lineage of vascular plants. The more evolutionarily advanced leaf structure, the **megaphyll**, is larger leaves with a highly branched vascular system and is present in all vascular plants except lycophytes. Megaphylls support greater photosynthetic productivity than microphylls due to the larger surface area served by the network of veins. Microphylls first appear in the fossil record 410 million years ago, but megaphylls do not emerge until about 370 million years ago, toward the end of the Devonian period.

Sporophylls and Spore Variations

One milestone in the evolution of plants was the emergence of **sporophylls**, modified leaves that bear sporangia. Sporophylls vary greatly in structure. For example, fern sporophylls produce clusters of sporangia known as **sori** (singular, *sorus*), usually on the undersides of the sporophylls (see Figure 29.12). In many lycophytes and in most gymnosperms, groups of sporophylls form cone-like structures called **strobili** (singular, *strobilus*; from the Greek *strobilos*, cone).

Most seedless vascular plant species are **homosporous**: They have one type of sporangium that produces one type of spore, which typically develops into a bisexual gametophyte, as in most ferns. In contrast, a **heterosporous** species has two types of sporangia and produces two kinds of spores: Megasporangia on megasporophylls produce **megaspores**, which develop into female gametophytes; microsporangia on microsporophylls produce the comparatively smaller **microspores**, which develop into male gametophytes. All seed plants and a few seedless vascular plants are heterosporous. The following diagram compares the two conditions:

Homosporous spore production

Sporangium on sporophyll → Single type of spore → Typically a bisexual gametophyte → Eggs / Sperm

Heterosporous spore production

Megasporangium on megasporophyll → Megaspore → Female gametophyte → Eggs

Microsporangium on microsporophyll → Microspore → Male gametophyte → Sperm

Classification of Seedless Vascular Plants

As we noted earlier, biologists recognize two clades of living seedless vascular plants: the lycophytes (phylum Lycophyta) and the monilophytes (phylum Monilophyta). The lycophytes include the club mosses, the spike mosses, and the quillworts. The monilophytes include the ferns, the horsetails, and the whisk ferns and their relatives. Although the ferns, horsetails, and whisk ferns may look quite different, recent anatomical molecular comparisons provide convincing evidence that all three groups make up a clade. Accordingly, many systematists now classify them together as the phylum Monilophyta as we do in this chapter.

Characteristics of the two main groups of seedless vascular plants are described in Figure 29.14.

Phylum Lycophyta: Club Mosses, Spike Mosses, and Quillworts

Present-day species of lycophytes, the most ancient group of vascular plants, are relics of a far more impressive past (Figure 29.15 on page 668). By the Carboniferous period (359–299 million years ago), the lycophyte evolutionary lineage included small herbaceous plants and giant trees with diameters of more than 2 m and heights of more than 40 m. The giant lycophyte trees thrived for millions

---

▼ Figure 29.13 **Microphyll and megaphyll leaves.**

Microphyll leaves

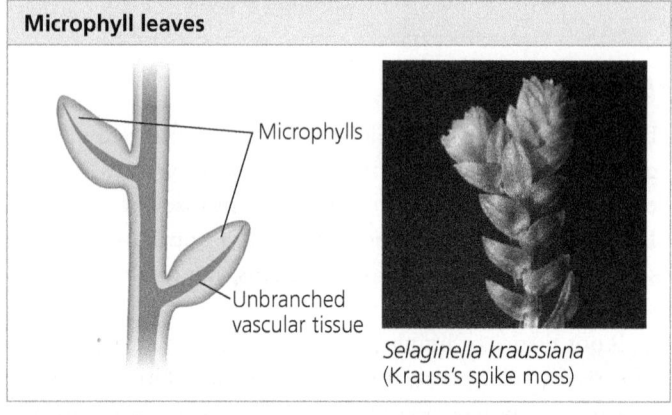

Microphylls

Unbranched vascular tissue

Selaginella kraussiana (Krauss's spike moss)

Megaphyll leaves

Megaphylls

Branched vascular tissue

Hymenophyllum tunbrigense (Tunbridge filmy fern)

David Fenwick

▼ Figure 29.14

Exploring Seedless Vascular Plant Diversity

Lycophytes (Phylum Lycophyta)

Many lycophytes grow on tropical trees as *epiphytes*, plants that use other plants as a substrate but are not parasites. Other species grow on temperate forest floors. In some species, the tiny gametophytes live above ground and are photosynthetic. Others live below ground, nurtured by symbiotic fungi.

Sporophytes have upright stems with many small leaves, as well as ground-hugging stems that produce dichotomously branching roots. Spike mosses are usually relatively small and often grow horizontally. In many club mosses and spike mosses, sporophylls are clustered into club-shaped cones (strobili). Quillworts, named for their leaf shape, form a single genus whose members live in marshy areas or as submerged aquatic plants. Club mosses are all homosporous, whereas spike mosses and quillworts are all heterosporous. The spores of club mosses are released in clouds and are so rich in oil that magicians and photographers once ignited them to create smoke or flashes of light.

2.5 cm

Selaginella moellendorffii, a spike moss

Purdue University

Isoetes gunnii, a quillwort

Murray Fagg/
Australian National
Botanic Gardens

1 cm

Strobili (clusters of sporophylls)

Rasbach, Helga & Kurt

Diphasiastrum tristachyum, a club moss

Monilophytes (Phylum Monilophyta)

Bildagentur Zoonar GmbH/Shutterstock

Athyrium filix-femina, lady fern

25 cm

Ferns

Unlike the lycophytes, ferns have megaphylls (see Figure 29.13). The sporophytes typically have horizontal stems that give rise to large leaves called fronds, often divided into leaflets. A frond grows as its coiled tip, the fiddlehead, unfurls.

Almost all species are homosporous. The gametophyte in some species shrivels and dies after the young sporophyte detaches itself. In most species, sporophytes have stalked sporangia with springlike devices that catapult spores several metres. Airborne spores can be carried far from their origin. Some species produce more than a trillion spores in a plant's lifetime.

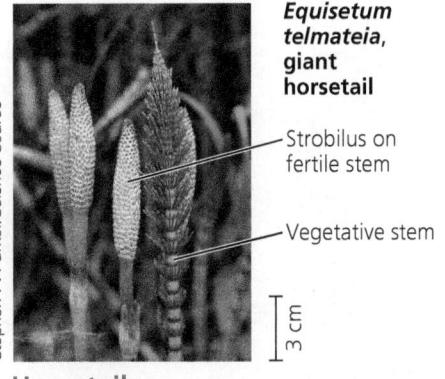

Stephen P. Parker/Science Source

Equisetum telmateia, giant horsetail

Strobilus on fertile stem

Vegetative stem

3 cm

Horsetails

The group's name refers to the brushy appearance of the stems, which have a gritty texture that made them historically useful as "scouring rushes" for pots and pans. Some species have separate fertile (cone-bearing) and vegetative stems. Horsetails are homosporous, with cones releasing spores that typically give rise to bisexual gametophytes.

Horsetails are also called arthrophytes ("jointed plants") because their stems have joints. Rings of small leaves or branches emerge from each joint, but the stem is the main photosynthetic organ. Large air canals carry oxygen to the roots, which often grow in waterlogged soil.

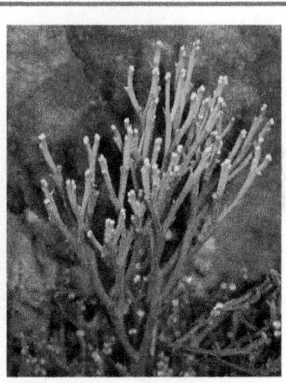

Francisco Javier Yeste Garcia

Psilotum nudum, a whisk fern

4 cm

Whisk Ferns and Relatives

Like primitive vascular plant fossils, the sporophytes of whisk ferns (genus *Psilotum*) have dichotomously branching stems but no roots. Stems have scalelike outgrowths that lack vascular tissue and may have resulted from the evolutionary reduction of leaves. Each yellow knob on a stem consists of three fused sporangia. Species of the genus *Tmesipteris*, closely related to whisk ferns and found only in the South Pacific, also lack roots but have small, leaflike outgrowths in their stems, giving them a vine-like appearance. Both genera are homosporous, with spores giving rise to bisexual gametophytes that grow underground and are only about a centimetre long.

Impact

The First Forests Were Composed of Seedless Vascular Plants That Eventually Became Coal

Seedless vascular plants dominated the Carboniferous period (359–299 million years ago) and it would have been an impressive sight. Scattered throughout the warm, swampy ecosystem, lycophyte trees stood up to 40 metres tall along with large horsetails and tree ferns. In the understory would have been some seed plants, which eventually replaced these spore-producers as the dominant land plant. The abundant organic material produced during the Carboniferous period didn't always decay in the swampy environment and eventually turned into thick layers of peat that was later covered by the sea.

Over millions of years, marine sediments piled on top and the heat and pressure converted the peat to coal.

Nowhere is the story of the Carboniferous period better told than in the fossils and geology of the Joggins Fossil Cliffs **(a)**. Located at Joggins, Nova Scotia, this UNESCO heritage site houses the fossilized remnants of the giant lycopods, as evidenced by the fossilized lycopod root (complete with emerging rootlets) embedded within its cliffs **(b)**. The Carboniferous period has the most extensive coal deposits ever formed, and this is clearly evident from the presence of many coal seams throughout the Joggins area **(c)**.

(a)

Dion Durnford

(b)

Root
Rootlet

Dion Durnford

(c)

Dion Durnford

Why It Matters Coal was crucial to the Industrial Revolution, and humans still burn 7 billion tonnes of coal a year, primarily for the generation of electricity. Despite its size, Canada holds only 1% of the proven global reserves for coal and produces around 65 million tonnes a year. Much of the coal we mine was produced from plant material that grew during the Carboniferous period. The massive amount of biomass produced during the Carboniferous period required a lot of photosynthesis, leading to significant reductions in atmospheric CO_2 levels that contributed to global cooling. Ironically, modern combustion

of coal liberates CO_2 sequestered for millions of years that now contributes to global warming.

Further Reading H. J. Falcon-Lang et al., The Pennsylvanian tropical biome reconstructed from the Joggins Formation of Nova Scotia, Canada, *Journal of the Geological Society* 163:561–576 (2006).

MAKE CONNECTIONS *Examine Table 25.1 and Figures 25.16 and 34.21. What did the continents look like during the Carboniferous period and what animals were dominant at the time in the Joggins area?*

of years in moist swamps, but they became extinct when Earth's climate became drier at the end of the Carboniferous period. The small lycophytes survived, represented today by about 1200 species.

Phylum Monilophyta Ferns, Horsetails, and Whisk Ferns and Relatives

Ferns radiated extensively from their Devonian origins and grew alongside lycophyte trees and horsetails in the great Carboniferous swamp forests. Today, ferns are by far the most widespread seedless vascular plants, numbering more than 12 000 species. Though most diverse in the tropics, many ferns thrive in temperate forests, and some species are even adapted to arid habitats.

As mentioned earlier, ferns and other monilophytes are more closely related to seed plants than to lycophytes. As a result, monilophytes and seed plants share traits that are not found in lycophytes: megaphyll leaves and roots that can branch at various points along the length of an existing root. In lycophytes, by contrast, roots branch only at the growing tip of the root, forming a Y-shaped structure.

The monilophytes called horsetails were very diverse during the Carboniferous period, some growing as tall as 15 m. Today, only 15 species survive as a single, widely distributed genus, *Equisetum*, found in marshy places and along streams.

Psilotum (whisk ferns) and a closely related genus, *Tmesipteris*, form a clade consisting mainly of tropical epiphytes. Plants in these two genera, the only vascular plants lacking true roots, are called "living fossils" because of their resemblance to fossils of ancient relatives of living vascular plants (see Figures 29.11 and 29.14). However, much evidence, including analyses of DNA sequences and sperm structure, indicates that the genera *Psilotum* and *Tmesipteris* are closely related to ferns. This hypothesis suggests that their ancestor's true roots were lost during evolution. Today, plants in these two genera absorb water and nutrients through numerous absorptive rhizoids.

The Significance of Seedless Vascular Plants

The ancestors of living lycophytes, horsetails, and ferns, along with their extinct seedless vascular relatives, grew to great heights during the Devonian and early Carboniferous periods, forming the first forests (Figure 29.15). How did their dramatic growth affect Earth and its other life? With the evolution of vascular tissue, roots, and leaves, these plants accelerated their rate of photosynthesis, dramatically increasing the removal of CO_2 from the atmosphere. Scientists estimate that CO_2 levels dropped by as much as a factor of five during the Carboniferous period, causing global cooling that resulted in widespread glacier formation. Ancient CO_2 levels can be estimated in several ways. These include counting the number of stomata in fossil leaves (data from living species show that this number increases as CO_2 levels drop) and measuring carbon isotope levels in fossils of plankton. Different methods yield similar results, suggesting that reconstructions of past CO_2 levels are accurate.

Growing along with the seedless plants in Carboniferous swamps were primitive seed plants. Though seed plants were not dominant at that time, they rose to prominence after the swamps began to dry up at the end of the Carboniferous period. The next chapter traces the origin and diversification of seed plants, continuing our story of adaptation to life on land.

CONCEPT CHECK 29.3

1. List the key derived traits found in monilophytes and seed plants, but not in lycophytes.

2. How do the main similarities and differences between seedless vascular plants and nonvascular plants influence function in these plants?

3. **WHAT IF?** If (contrary to the evidence) lycophytes and monilophytes formed a clade, what could you conclude about how members of this clade gained (or lost) traits shared by monilophytes and seed plants?

4. **MAKE CONNECTIONS** In Figure 29.12, if fertilization occurred between gametes from one gametophyte, how would this affect the production of genetic variation from sexual reproduction? See pages 277–278 of Concept 13.4.

For suggested answers, see Appendix A.

29 Chapter Review

Go to **MasteringBiology**® for Assignments, the eText, and the Study Area with Animations, Activities, Vocab Self-Quiz, and Practice Tests.

SUMMARY OF KEY CONCEPTS

CONCEPT 29.1

Land plants evolved from green algae (pp. 653–658)

- Morphological and biochemical traits, as well as similarities in nuclear and chloroplast genes, suggest that charophytes are the closest living relatives of land plants.

- A protective layer of **sporopollenin** and other traits allow charophytes to tolerate occasional drying along the edges of ponds and lakes. Such traits may have enabled the algal ancestors of plants to survive in terrestrial conditions, opening the way to the colonization of dry land.

- Derived traits that distinguish the clade of land plants from charophytes, their closest algal relatives, include the four shown here:

① Alternation of generations

Gametophyte

Mitosis Mitosis

n *n*

n — Spore Gamete

MEIOSIS **FERTILIZATION**

2n — Zygote

Mitosis

Sporophyte

Haploid

Diploid

Apical meristem Developing
of shoot leaves

② Apical meristems

Archegonium
with egg

Antheridium
with sperm

Sporangium Spores

③ Multicellular gametangia **④ Walled spores in sporangia**

- Fossil evidence indicates that plants were on land at least 475 million years ago. Subsequently, plants diverged into several major groups, including nonvascular plants (bryophytes); **seedless vascular plants**, such as lycophytes and ferns; and the two groups of seed plants: **gymnosperms** and **angiosperms**.

? *Draw a phylogenetic tree illustrating our current understanding of land plant phylogeny; label the common ancestor of land plants and the origins of multicellular gametangia, vascular tissue, and seeds.*

CONCEPT 29.2

Mosses and other nonvascular plants have life cycles dominated by gametophytes (pp. 658–664)

- Three clades of nonvascular plants are collectively referred to as **bryophytes**: liverworts, mosses, and hornworts. These are the earliest-diverging plant lineages.
- In bryophytes, the dominant and typically most visible generation consists of haploid **gametophytes**, such as those that make up a carpet of moss. **Rhizoids** anchor gametophytes to the substrate on which they grow. The flagellated sperm produced by **antheridia** typically require a film of water to travel to the eggs in the **archegonia**.
- The diploid stage of the bryophyte life cycle—the **sporophyte**—grows out of the archegonium and is attached to the gametophyte and dependent on it for nourishment. Smaller and simpler than vascular plant sporophytes, byrophyte sporophytes typically consist of a **foot**, **seta** (stalk), and **sporangium**.
- *Sphagnum*, or peat moss, is common in large regions known as peatlands and has many practical uses, including as a fuel.

? *Summarize the ecological importance of mosses.*

CONCEPT 29.3

Ferns and other seedless vascular plants were the first plants to grow tall (pp. 664–669)

- Fossils of the forerunners of today's vascular plants date back about 425 million years and show that these small plants had independent,

branching sporophytes. However, these ancestral species lacked other derived traits of living vascular plants, such as a life cycle with dominant sporophytes, lignified vascular tissue, well-developed roots and leaves, and sporophylls.
- Seedless vascular plants include the **lycophytes** (phylum Lycophyta: club mosses, spike mosses, and quillworts) and the **monilophytes** (phylum Monilophyta: ferns, horsetails, and whisk ferns and relatives). Ancient lycophytes included both small herbaceous plants and large trees. Present-day lycophytes are small herbaceous plants.
- Seedless vascular plants dominated the earliest forests. Their growth may have helped produce the major global cooling that characterized the end of the Carboniferous period. The decaying remnants of the first forests eventually became coal.

? *What trait(s) allowed vascular plants to grow tall, and why might increased height have been advantageous?*

TEST YOUR UNDERSTANDING

LEVEL 1: KNOWLEDGE/COMPREHENSION

1. Three of the following are evidence that charophytes are the closest algal relatives of plants. Select the exception.
   a. similar sperm structure
   b. the presence of chloroplasts
   c. similarities in cell wall formation during cell division
   d. genetic similarities in chloroplasts

2. Which of the following characteristics of plants is absent in their closest relatives, the charophyte algae?
   a. chlorophyll *b*
   b. cellulose in cell walls
   c. sexual reproduction
   d. alternation of multicellular generations

3. What key feature distinguishes a fern from a moss?
   a. production of spores
   b. alternation of generations
   c. seed production
   d. vascular system

4. Microphylls are found in which plant group?
   a. liverworts c. ferns
   b. lycophytes d. hornworts

5. Which of the following is a land plant that has flagellated sperm and a sporophyte-dominated life cycle?
   a. fern c. liverwort
   b. moss d. hornwort

LEVEL 2: APPLICATION/ANALYSIS

6. Suppose an efficient conducting system evolved in a moss that could transport water and other materials as high as a tall tree. Which of the following statements about "trees" of such a species would *not* be true?
   a. Spore dispersal distances would probably increase.
   b. Females could produce only one archegonium.
   c. Unless its body parts were strengthened, such a "tree" would probably flop over.
   d. Individuals would probably compete more effectively for access to light.

7. Identify each of the following structures as haploid or diploid.
   a. sporophyte d. zygote
   b. spore e. sperm
   c. gametophyte

8. **EVOLUTION CONNECTION**
   DRAW IT Draw a phylogenetic tree that represents our current understanding of evolutionary relationships between a moss,

a gymnosperm, a lycophyte, and a fern. Use a charophyte alga as the outgroup. (See Chapter 26 to review phylogenetic trees.) Label each branch point of the phylogeny with at least one derived character unique to the clade descended from the common ancestor represented by the branch point.

LEVEL 3: SYNTHESIS/EVALUATION

9. SCIENTIFIC INQUIRY

INTERPRET THE DATA The feather moss *Pleurozium schreberi* harbours species of symbiotic nitrogen-fixing bacteria. Scientists studying this moss in northern forests found that the percentage of the ground surface "covered" by the moss increased from about 5% in forests that had burned 35 to 41 years ago to about 70% in forests that had burned 170 or more years ago. From mosses growing in these forests, they also obtained the following data on nitrogen fixation:

Age (years after fire)	N Fixation Rate (kg N per ha per yr)
35	0.001
41	0.005
78	0.08
101	0.3
124	0.9
170	2.0
220	1.3
244	2.1
270	1.6
300	3.0
355	2.3

Source: Data from O. Zackrisson et al., Nitrogen fixation increases with successional age in boreal forests, *Ecology* 85:3327–3334 (2006). © Jane B Reece.

a. Use the data to draw a line graph, with age on the *x*-axis and the nitrogen fixation rate on the *y*-axis.

b. Along with the nitrogen added by nitrogen fixation, about 1 kg of nitrogen per hectare per year is deposited into northern forests from the atmosphere as rain and small particles. Evaluate the extent to which *Pleurozium* affects nitrogen availability in northern forests of different ages.

10. WRITE ABOUT A THEME: INTERACTIONS

Giant lycophyte trees had microphylls, whereas ferns and seed plants have megaphylls. Write a short essay (100–150 words) describing how a forest of lycophyte trees may have differed from a forest of large ferns or seed plants. In your answer, consider how the type of forest in which they grew may have affected interactions among small plants growing beneath the tall ones.

11. SYNTHESIZE YOUR KNOWLEDGE

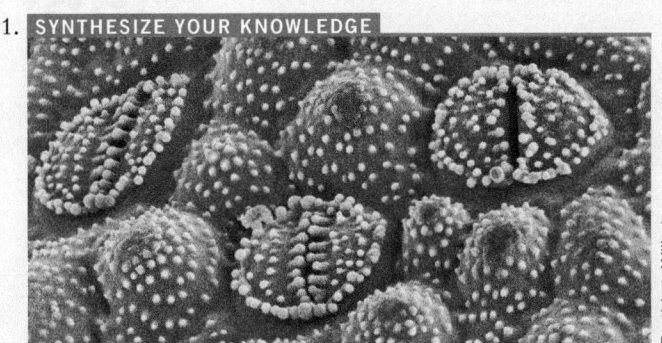

Barthlott, Wilhelm

These stomata are from the leaf of a common horsetail. Describe how stomata and other adaptations facilitated life on land and ultimately led to the formation of the first forests.

For selected answers, see Appendix A.

30

Plant Diversity II: The Evolution of Seed Plants

KEY CONCEPTS

30.1 Seeds and pollen grains are key adaptations for life on land

30.2 Gymnosperms bear "naked" seeds, typically on cones

30.3 The reproductive adaptations of angiosperms include flowers and fruits

30.4 Human welfare depends greatly on seed plants

Lynwood M. Chace/Science Source

▲ Figure 30.1 **What adaptations facilitated the colonization of land?**

Transforming the World

Dandelions are thought to be native to Europe and Asia, but have dispersed throughout the world mainly from intentional introductions by humans for their believed medicinal value. Though now maligned by many in Canada, this distinctive yellow flower pops up early in spring in exposed areas like your lawn. The success of the dandelion in colonizing new habitats, however, is partly due to its wonderful dispersal mechanism.

If you were like many children, you probably found it hard to resist picking a dandelion seed head (Figure 30.1) and blowing the fruits free into the air. The released plumes can drift on turbulent wind currents, some moving many metres away from the parent plant. This is possible because dandelion seeds have an adaptation called a pappus, which is composed of fine hairs that act like a parachute (lower left image). Its function is to reduce the falling velocity of the seed to aid dispersal on wind currents. A mechanism for dispersal is important for plants to locate new resources, reduce the probability of inbreeding (for sexually reproducing species) and limit competition among individuals with similar genotypes. The ease with which the dandelion spreads from one disturbed habitat to another mirrors the success of all seed plants during the colonization of land. However, it's what these hairy plumes carry that is the most important feature—a **seed**.

Jun Ji/123RF

◀ **Dandelion seed**

The seed is a remarkable evolutionary innovation that explains the dominance of seed plants on the terrestrial environment. The seed enhances survival of plants during reproduction by enclosing the embryo and a food source in a shell that can withstand periods of drought, low temperatures, and other environmental assaults. When the conditions are appropriate, the seed germinates, using the enclosed food supply to support its growth as it develops the capacity for photosynthesis.

In this chapter, we will first examine the general characteristics of seed plants. Then we will look at their evolutionary history and the key adaptations that allowed them to dominate the terrestrial ecosystem.

CONCEPT 30.1

Seeds and pollen grains are key adaptations for life on land

We begin with an overview of terrestrial adaptations that seed plants added to those already present in nonvascular plants (bryophytes) and seedless vascular plants (see Chapter 29). In addition to seeds, the following are common to all seed plants: reduced gametophytes, heterospory, ovules, and pollen. As you'll read, these adaptations provided new ways for seed plants to cope with terrestrial conditions such as drought and exposure to the ultraviolet (UV) radiation in sunlight. Novel adaptations also freed seed plants from requiring water for fertilization, enabling reproduction to occur under a broader range of conditions than in seedless plants.

Advantages of Reduced Gametophytes

Mosses and other bryophytes have life cycles dominated by gametophytes, whereas ferns and other seedless vascular plants have sporophyte-dominated life cycles. The evolutionary trend of gametophyte reduction continued further in the vascular plant lineage that led to seed plants. While the gametophytes of seedless vascular plants are visible to the naked eye, the gametophytes of seed plants are mostly microscopic.

This miniaturization allowed for an important evolutionary innovation in seed plants: Their tiny gametophytes can develop from spores retained within the sporangia of the parental sporophyte. This arrangement protects the gametophytes from environmental stresses. The moist reproductive tissues of the sporophyte shield the gametophytes from UV radiation and protect them from drying out. This relationship also enables the dependent gametophytes to obtain nutrients from the sporophyte. In contrast, the free-living gametophytes of seedless plants must fend for themselves. **Figure 30.2** contrasts the gametophyte-sporophyte relationships in nonvascular plants, seedless vascular plants, and seed plants.

Heterospory: The Rule Among Seed Plants

You read in Chapter 29 that most seedless plants are *homosporous*—they produce one kind of spore, which usually gives rise to a bisexual gametophyte. Ferns and other close relatives of seed plants are homosporous, suggesting that seed plants had homosporous ancestors. At some point, seed plants or their ancestors became *heterosporous*, producing two kinds of spores: Megasporangia produce *megaspores* that give rise to female gametophytes, and microsporangia produce *microspores* that give rise to male gametophytes. Each megasporangium has a single functional megaspore, whereas each microsporangium contains vast numbers of microspores.

As we noted previously, the miniaturization of seed plant gametophytes likely contributed to the great success of this clade. Next we will look at the development of the female gametophyte within an ovule and the development of the male gametophyte in a pollen grain. Then we will follow the transformation of a fertilized ovule into a seed.

Ovules and Production of Eggs

Although a few species of seedless plants are heterosporous, seed plants are unique in retaining the megasporangium within the parent sporophyte. A layer of sporophyte tissue called **integument** envelops and protects the megasporangium. Gymnosperm megasporangia are surrounded by one integument, whereas those in angiosperms usually have two integuments. The whole structure—megasporangium, megaspore, and their integument(s)—is called an **ovule** (Figure 30.3a). Inside each ovule (from the Latin *ovulum*, little egg) a female gametophyte develops from a megaspore and produces one or more eggs.

Pollen and Production of Sperm

A microspore develops into a **pollen grain** that consists of a male gametophyte enclosed within the pollen wall. The outer layer of the pollen cell wall, however, is composed of molecules secreted by sporophyte cells, so the male gametophyte is considered to be in the pollen grain, not equivalent to the pollen grain. The tough pollen wall, which contains the polymer sporopollenin, protects a pollen grain as it is transported from the parent plant by wind, for example, or by hitchhiking on the body of an animal. The pollen outer wall often has elaborate spikes or ridges, as shown on the right, that are adapted for their mode of travel. Because of the tough

▲ Colourized scanning electron micrograph of pollen grains.

PLANT GROUP		
	Mosses and other nonvascular plants	Ferns and other seedless vascular plants	Seed plants (gymnosperms and angiosperms)
Gametophyte	Dominant	Reduced, independent (photosynthetic and free-living)	Reduced (usually microscopic), dependent on surrounding sporophyte tissue for nutrition
Sporophyte	Reduced, dependent on gametophyte for nutrition	Dominant	Dominant
Example	Sporophyte (2n) / Gametophyte (n)	Sporophyte (2n) / Gametophyte (n)	**Gymnosperm** Microscopic female gametophytes (n) inside ovulate cone / Microscopic male gametophytes (n) inside pollen cone / Sporophyte (2n) — **Angiosperm** Microscopic female gametophytes (n) inside these parts of flowers / Microscopic male gametophytes (n) inside these parts of flowers / Sporophyte (2n)

▲ **Figure 30.2 Gametophyte-sporophyte relationships in different plant groups.**

MAKE CONNECTIONS *In seed plants, how does retaining the gametophyte within the sporophyte likely affect embryo fitness? (See Concepts 17.5, 23.1, and 23.4 to review mutagens, mutations, and fitness.)*

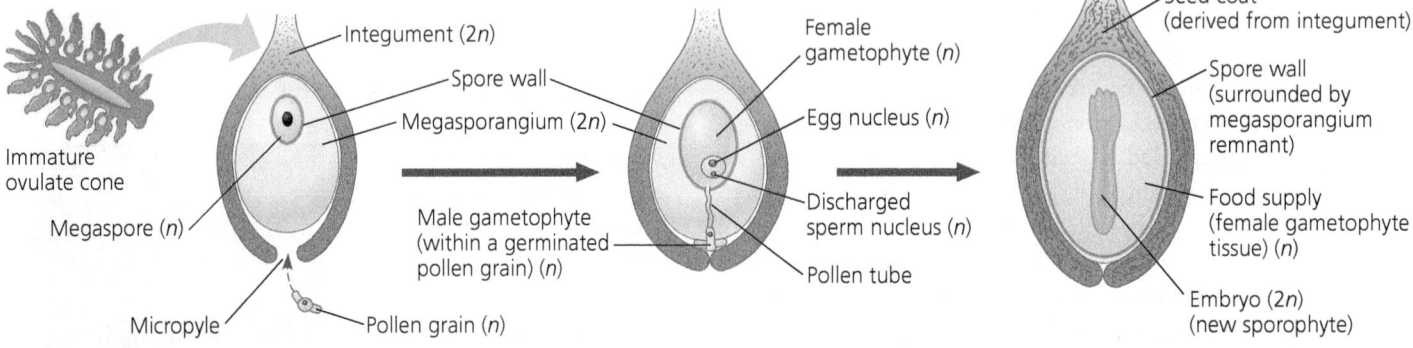

(a) Unfertilized ovule. In this longitudinal section through the ovule of a pine (a gymnosperm), a fleshy megasporangium is surrounded by a protective layer of tissue called an integument. The micropyle, the only opening through the integument, allows entry of a pollen grain.

(b) Fertilized ovule. A megaspore develops into a female gametophyte, which produces an egg. The pollen grain, which had entered through the micropyle, contains a male gametophyte. The male gametophyte develops a pollen tube that discharges sperm, thereby fertilizing the egg.

(c) Gymnosperm seed. Fertilization initiates the transformation of the ovule into a seed, which consists of a sporophyte embryo, a food supply, and a protective seed coat derived from the integument. The megasporangium dries out and collapses.

▲ **Figure 30.3 From ovule to seed in a gymnosperm.**

? *A gymnosperm seed contains cells from how many different plant generations? Identify the cells and whether each is haploid or diploid.*

sporopollenin, these ornamentations fossilize and are unique enough to identify specific genera or species of plants. The transfer of pollen to the part of a seed plant that contains the ovules is called **pollination**. If a pollen grain germinates (begins growing), it gives rise to a pollen tube that discharges sperm into the female gametophyte within the ovule, as shown in Figure 30.3b.

Recall that in nonvascular plants and seedless vascular plants such as ferns, free-living gametophytes release flagellated sperm that swim through a film of water to reach eggs. The distance for this sperm transport rarely exceeds a few centimetres. By contrast, in seed plants a sperm-producing male gametophyte inside a pollen grain can be carried long distances by wind or by animals, eliminating the dependence on water for sperm transport. The sperm of seed plants also do not require motility because sperm are carried directly to the eggs by pollen tubes. Living gymnosperms provide evidence of the evolutionary transition to nonmotile sperm. The sperm of some gymnosperm species (such as ginkgos and cycads, shown in Figure 30.7) retain the ancient flagellated condition, but flagella have been lost in the sperm of most gymnosperms and all angiosperms.

The Evolutionary Advantage of Seeds

If a sperm fertilizes an egg of a seed plant, the zygote grows into a sporophyte embryo. As shown in Figure 30.3c, the whole ovule develops into a seed: the embryo, along with a food supply, packaged within a protective coat derived from the integument(s).

Until the advent of seeds, the spore was the only protective stage in any plant life cycle. Moss spores, for example, may survive even if the local environment becomes too cold, too hot, or too dry for the mosses themselves to live. Their tiny size enables the spores to be dispersed in a dormant state to a new area, where they can germinate and give rise to new moss gametophytes if and when conditions are favourable enough for them to break dormancy. Spores were the main way that mosses, ferns, and other seedless plants spread over Earth for the first 100 million years of plant life on land.

Although mosses and other seedless plants continue to be very successful today, seeds represent a major evolutionary innovation that contributed to the opening of new ways of life for seed plants. What advantages do seeds provide over spores? Spores are usually single-celled, whereas seeds are multicellular, consisting of an embryo protected by a layer of tissue, the seed coat. A seed can remain dormant for days, months, or even years after being released from the parent plant, whereas most spores have shorter lifetimes. Also, unlike spores, seeds have a supply of stored food. Under favourable conditions, the seed can emerge from dormancy and germinate, with its stored food providing critical support for growth as the sporophyte embryo emerges as a seedling. As we explore in the Scientific Skills Exercise, some seeds have germinated after more than 1000 years.

SCIENTIFIC SKILLS EXERCISE

Using Natural Logarithms to Interpret Data

Eisner, Guy

How Long Can Seeds Remain Viable in Dormancy? Environmental conditions can vary greatly over time, and they may not be favourable for germination when seeds are produced. One way that plants cope with such variation is through seed dormancy. Under favourable conditions, seeds of some species can germinate after many years of dormancy.

One unusual opportunity to test how long seeds can remain viable occurred when seeds from date palm trees (*Phoenix dactylifera*) were discovered under the rubble of a 2000-year-old fortress near the Dead Sea.

As you saw in the Chapter 2 Scientific Skills Exercise and Concept 25.2, scientists use radiometric dating to estimate the ages of fossils and other old objects. In this exercise, you will estimate the ages of three of these ancient seeds by using natural logarithms.

How the Experiment Was Done Scientists measured the fraction of carbon-14 that remained in three ancient date palm seeds: two that were not planted and one that was planted and germinated. For the germinated seed, the scientists used a seed-coat fragment found clinging to a root of the seedling. (The seedling grew into the plant in the photo.)

Data from the Experiment This table shows the fraction of carbon-14 remaining from the three ancient date palm seeds.

	Fraction of Carbon-14 Remaining
Seed 1 (not planted)	0.7656
Seed 2 (not planted)	0.7752
Seed 3 (germinated)	0.7977

Interpret the Data A logarithm is the power to which a base is raised to produce a given number x. For example, if the base is 10 and $x = 100$, the logarithm of 100 equals 2 (because $10^2 = 100$). A natural logarithm (ln) is the logarithm of a number x to the base e, where e is about 2.718. Natural logarithms are useful in calculating rates of some natural processes, such as radioactive decay.

1. The equation $F = e^{-kt}$ describes the fraction F of an original isotope remaining after a period of t years; the exponent is negative because it refers to a *decrease* over time. The constant k provides a measure of how rapidly the original isotope decays. For the decay of carbon-14 to nitrogen-14, $k = 0.00012097$. To find t, rearrange the equation by following these steps: (a) Take the natural logarithm of both sides of the equation: $\ln(F) = \ln(e^{-kt})$. Rewrite the right side of this equation by applying the following rule: $\ln(e^x) = x \ln(e)$. (b) Since $\ln(e) = 1$, simplify the equation. (c) Now solve for t and write the equation in the form "$t = $ _____."

2. Using the equation you developed, the data from the table, and a calculator, estimate the ages of Seed 1, Seed 2, and Seed 3.

3. Why do you think there was more carbon-14 in the germinated seed?

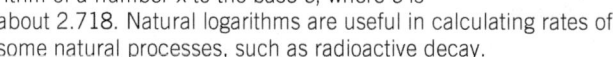

Data from S. Sallon et al., Germination, genetics, and growth of an ancient date seed, *Science* 320:1464 (2008). © Jane B Reece.

Evolution of the Seed

The origins of characteristics that are shared by all seed plants date back to the late Devonian period (about 380 million years ago). For example, *Archaeopteris*, as discussed at the start of Chapter 29, was significant because of the presence of secondary growth that allowed the production of a woody stem, an innovation that allowed the plant to grow very tall, producing the first trees. Like seed plants, *Archaeopteris* was heterosporous, but it reproduced via spores, not seeds. Such transitional species of seedless vascular plants are sometimes called **progymnosperms**. The first seed plants to appear in the fossil record date from around 360 million years ago; 55 million years before the first gymnosperm fossils and more than 200 million years before the first angiosperm fossils. They are called a "seed fern" because their leaves were fern-like but they had woody stems and produced seed-like structures. The seeds were composed of a partially covered ovule surrounded by finger-like projections called cupules, structures resembling cupped hands that protect the ovule (Figure 30.4). These early seed ferns became extinct, as did several later lineages, so don't confuse them with extant "tree ferns" that are true ferns (no seeds) found in humid, tropical locations. It remains uncertain which of these extinct seed fern lineages ultimately gave rise to the gymnosperms.

5 mm

▲ Figure 30.4 **A primitive seed fern.** Diagram of a cupulate seed showing the ovule and the surrounding cupula (left) along with a fossilized cupulate seeds from *Archaeosperma arnoldii*, from which the diagram was reconstructed.

Source: Based on Pettitt and Beck (1968) Archaeosperma Arnoldii— A cupulate seed from the upper Devonian of North America. *Contributions from the Museum of Paleontology, The University of Michigan*, 22 (10) pp.139–154. © Jane B Reece.

CONCEPT CHECK 30.1

1. Contrast sperm delivery in seedless plants with sperm delivery in seed plants.
2. What features not present in seedless plants have contributed to the enormous success of seed plants on land?
3. **WHAT IF?** If a seed could not enter dormancy, how might that affect the embryo's transport or survival?

For suggested answers, see Appendix A.

CONCEPT 30.2

Gymnosperms bear "naked" seeds, typically on cones

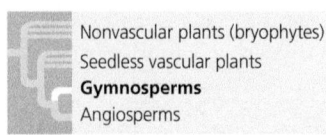
Nonvascular plants (bryophytes)
Seedless vascular plants
Gymnosperms
Angiosperms

Extant seed plants form two sister clades: gymnosperms and angiosperms. Recall from Chapter 29 that gymnosperms have "naked" seeds exposed on modified leaves (sporophylls) that usually form cones (strobili). (Angiosperm seeds are enclosed in chambers that mature into fruits.) Most gymnosperms are cone-bearing plants called **conifers**, such as pines, firs, and redwoods.

The Life Cycle of a Pine

As you read earlier, seed plant evolution has included three key reproductive adaptations: the increasing dominance of the sporophyte; the advent of the seed as a resistant, dispersible stage in the life cycle; and the appearance of pollen as an airborne agent that brings gametes together. Figure 30.5 shows how these adaptations come into play during the life cycle of a pine, a familiar conifer.

The pine tree is the sporophyte; its sporangia are located on scalelike structures packed densely in cones. Like all seed plants, conifers are heterosporous. In conifers, the two types of spores are produced by separate cones: small pollen cones and large ovulate cones. In most pine species, each tree has both types of cones. In pollen cones, like the lodgepole pine pollen cones shown on the cover, microsporocytes (microspore mother cells) undergo meiosis, producing haploid microspores. Each microspore develops into a pollen grain containing a male gametophyte. In pines and other conifers, the yellow pollen is released in large amounts and carried by the wind, dusting everything in its path. Meanwhile, in ovulate cones, megasporocytes (megaspore mother cells) undergo meiosis and produce haploid

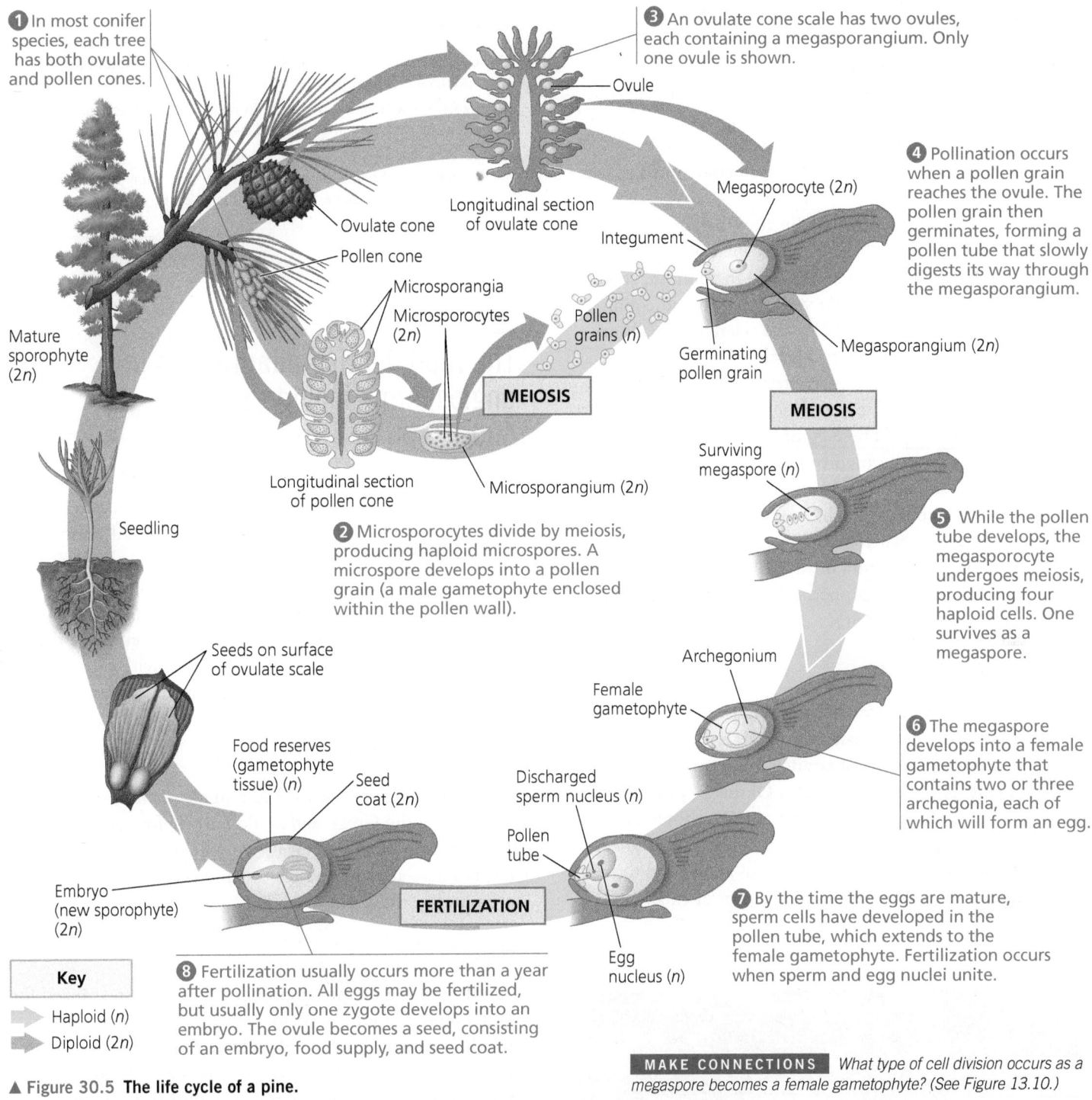

1 In most conifer species, each tree has both ovulate and pollen cones.

3 An ovulate cone scale has two ovules, each containing a megasporangium. Only one ovule is shown.

Ovule

Longitudinal section of ovulate cone

Ovulate cone

Pollen cone

Microsporangia

Microsporocytes (2n)

Pollen grains (n)

MEIOSIS

Megasporocyte (2n)

Integument

Germinating pollen grain

Megasporangium (2n)

4 Pollination occurs when a pollen grain reaches the ovule. The pollen grain then germinates, forming a pollen tube that slowly digests its way through the megasporangium.

Mature sporophyte (2n)

Longitudinal section of pollen cone

Microsporangium (2n)

2 Microsporocytes divide by meiosis, producing haploid microspores. A microspore develops into a pollen grain (a male gametophyte enclosed within the pollen wall).

MEIOSIS

Surviving megaspore (n)

5 While the pollen tube develops, the megasporocyte undergoes meiosis, producing four haploid cells. One survives as a megaspore.

Seedling

Archegonium

Female gametophyte

6 The megaspore develops into a female gametophyte that contains two or three archegonia, each of which will form an egg.

Seeds on surface of ovulate scale

Food reserves (gametophyte tissue) (n)

Seed coat (2n)

Discharged sperm nucleus (n)

Pollen tube

Embryo (new sporophyte) (2n)

FERTILIZATION

Egg nucleus (n)

7 By the time the eggs are mature, sperm cells have developed in the pollen tube, which extends to the female gametophyte. Fertilization occurs when sperm and egg nuclei unite.

Key

➡ Haploid (n)

➡ Diploid (2n)

8 Fertilization usually occurs more than a year after pollination. All eggs may be fertilized, but usually only one zygote develops into an embryo. The ovule becomes a seed, consisting of an embryo, food supply, and seed coat.

▲ Figure 30.5 **The life cycle of a pine.**

MAKE CONNECTIONS *What type of cell division occurs as a megaspore becomes a female gametophyte? (See Figure 13.10.)*

megaspores inside the ovule. Surviving megaspores develop into multicellular female gametophytes, which are retained within the sporangia.

From the time young pollen and ovulate cones appear on the tree, it takes nearly three years for the male and female gametophytes to be produced and brought together and for mature seeds to form from the fertilized ovules. The scales of each ovulate cone then separate, and the seeds

are dispersed by the wind. A seed that lands in a suitable environment then germinates, its embryo emerging as a pine seedling.

Evolution of Gymnosperms

The earliest fossils of extant gymnosperms are about 305 million years old. These early gymnosperms lived in moist Carboniferous ecosystems still dominated by lyco-phytes, horsetails, ferns, and other seedless vascular plants. As the Carboniferous period gave way to the Permian period (299 to 251 million years ago), the climate became much drier. As a result, the lycophytes, horsetails, and ferns that dominated Carboniferous swamps were largely replaced by gymnosperms, which were better suited to the drier climate.

Gymnosperms thrived as the climate dried, in part because they have the key terrestrial adaptations found in all seed plants, such as seeds and pollen. In addition, some gymnosperms were particularly well suited to arid condi-tions because of the thick cuticles and relatively small sur-face areas of their needle-shaped leaves.

Gymnosperms dominated terrestrial ecosystems through-out much of the Mesozoic era, which lasted from 251 to 65.5 million years ago. These gymnosperms served as the food supply for giant herbivorous dinosaurs, and they also interacted with animals in other ways. Recent fossil dis-coveries, for example, show that insects pollinated some gymnosperms more than 100 million years ago—the earliest evidence of insect pollination in any plant group (**Figure 30.6**). Late in the Mesozoic, angiosperms began to replace gym-nosperms in some ecosystems.

Gymnosperm Diversity

Although angiosperms now dominate most terrestrial eco-systems, gymnosperms remain an important part of Earth's flora. For example, forests of conifers cover vast regions in northern latitudes (see Figure 52.8). Of the 10 plant phyla (see Table 29.1), four are gymnosperms: Cycadophyta, Ginkgophyta, Gnetophyta, and Coniferophyta. It is uncer-tain how the four phyla of gymnosperms are related to each other. **Figure 30.7** surveys the diversity of extant gymnosperms.

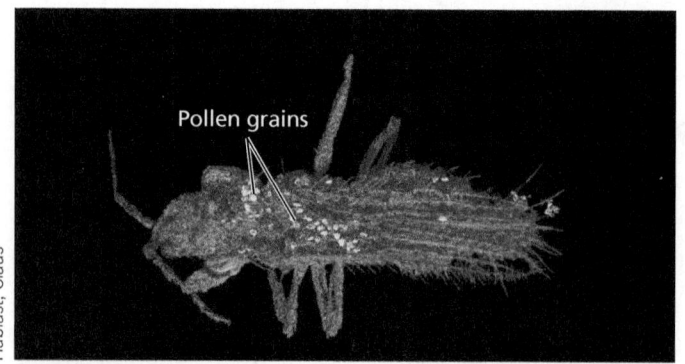

▲ **Figure 30.6 An ancient pollinator.** This 110-million-year-old fossil shows pollen on an insect, the thrip *Gymnopollisthrips minor.* Structural features of the pollen suggest that it was produced by gym-nosperms (most likely by species related to extant ginkgos or cycads). Although most gymnosperms today are wind-pollinated, many cycads are insect-pollinated.

CONCEPT CHECK 30.2

1. Use examples from Figure 30.7 to describe how various gymno-sperms are similar yet distinctive.
2. Explain how the pine life cycle in Figure 30.5 reflects the five adaptations common to all seed plants.
3. MAKE CONNECTIONS Does the hypothesis that gym-nosperms and angiosperms are sister clades imply that they originated at the same time? See Figure 26.6.

For suggested answers, see Appendix A.

CONCEPT 30.3

The reproductive adaptations of angiosperms include flowers and fruits

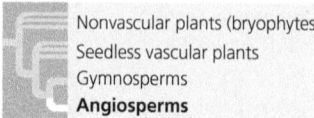

Nonvascular plants (bryophytes)
Seedless vascular plants
Gymnosperms
Angiosperms

Commonly known as flowering plants, angio-sperms are seed plants that produce the reproductive structures called flowers and fruits. The name *angiosperm* (from the Greek *angion*, container) refers to seeds contained in fruits, the mature ovaries. Today, angiosperms are the most diverse and widespread of all plants, with more than 250 000 species (about 90% of all plant species).

Characteristics of Angiosperms

All angiosperms are classified in a single phylum, Antho-phyta (from the Greek *anthos*, flower). Before considering the evolution of angiosperms, we will examine their key adaptations—flowers and fruits—and the roles of these structures in the angiosperm life cycle.

Flowers

The **flower** is a unique angiosperm structure specialized for sexual reproduction. In many angiosperm species, insects or other animals transfer pollen from one flower to the sex organs on another flower, which makes pollination more directed than the wind-dependent pollination of most gymnosperms. However, some angiosperms *are* wind-pollinated, particularly those species that occur in dense populations, such as grasses and tree species in temperate forests. Wind-pollinated plants are responsible for seasonal allergies when our immune systems react to the proteins present on the outer surface of the pollen grains (see Con-cept 43.4). In Canada, the dominant allergies are to tree pollen in the spring (birch, oak), grass pollen in early sum-mer, and ragweed pollen in late summer.

A flower is a specialized shoot that can have up to four rings of modified leaves (sporophylls) called floral

Exploring Gymnosperm Diversity

Phylum Cycadophyta

The 300 species of living cycads have large cones and palmlike leaves (true palm species are angiosperms). Unlike most seed plants, cycads have flagellated sperm, indicating their descent from seedless vascular plants that had motile sperm. Cycads thrived during the Mesozoic era, known as the age of cycads as well as the age of dinosaurs. Today, however, cycads are the most endangered of all plant groups: 75% of their species are threatened by habitat destruction and other human actions.

Phylum Ginkgophyta

Johannes Greyling/Getty Images

Cycas revoluta

Kurt Stueber

Travis Amos/Pearson Education

Ginkgo biloba is the only surviving species of this phylum; like cycads, ginkgos have flagellated sperm. Also known as the maiden-hair tree, Ginkgo biloba has deciduous fanlike leaves that turn gold in autumn. It is a popular ornamental tree in cities because it tolerates air pollution well. Landscapers often plant only pollen-producing trees because the fleshy seeds smell rancid as they decay.

Phylum Gnetophyta

Phylum Gnetophyta includes plants in three genera: Gnetum, Ephedra, and Welwitschia. Some species are tropical, whereas others live in deserts. Although very different in appearance, the genera are grouped together based on molecular data.

Jeroen Peys/E+/Getty Images

► **Welwitschia.** This genus consists of one species, *Welwitschia mirabilis*, a plant that can live for thousands of years and is found only in the deserts of southwestern Africa. Its straplike leaves are among the largest leaves known.

Ovulate cones

Thomas Schoepke

► **Ephedra.** This genus includes about 40 species that inhabit arid regions worldwide. These desert shrubs, commonly called "Mormon tea," produce the compound ephedrine, which is used medicinally as a decongestant.

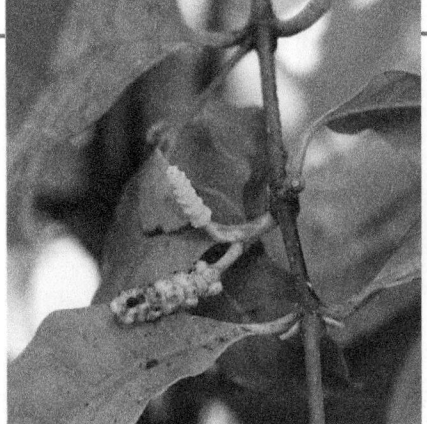

Michael Clayton

◄ **Gnetum.** This genus includes about 35 species of tropical trees, shrubs, and vines, mainly native to Africa and Asia. Their leaves look similar to those of flowering plants, and their seeds look somewhat like fruits.

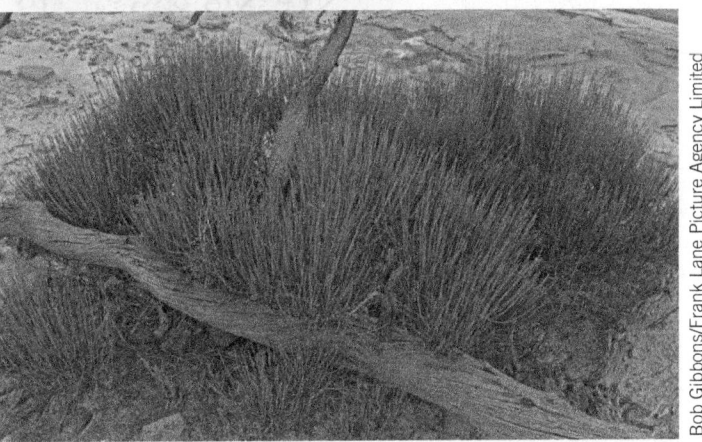

Bob Gibbons/Frank Lane Picture Agency Limited

Continued on next page

Exploring Gymnosperm Diversity

Phylum Coniferophyta

Phylum Coniferophyta, the largest gymnosperm phyla, consists of about 600 species of conifers (from the Latin *conus*, cone, and *ferre*, to carry), including many large trees. Most species have woody cones, but a few have fleshy cones. Some, such as pines, have needle-like leaves. Others, such as redwoods, have scale-like leaves. Some species dominate vast northern forests, whereas others are native to the Southern Hemisphere.

Most conifers are evergreens, they retain their leaves throughout the year. Even during winter, a limited amount of photosynthesis occurs on sunny days. When spring comes, conifers already have fully developed leaves that can take advantage of the sunnier, warmer days. Some conifers, such as the dawn redwood, tamarack, and larch, are deciduous trees that lose leaves each autumn.

▶ **Douglas fir.** This evergreen tree (*Pseudotduga menziesii*) provides more timber than any other North American tree species. Some uses include house framing, plywood, pulpwood for paper, railroad ties, and boxes and crates.

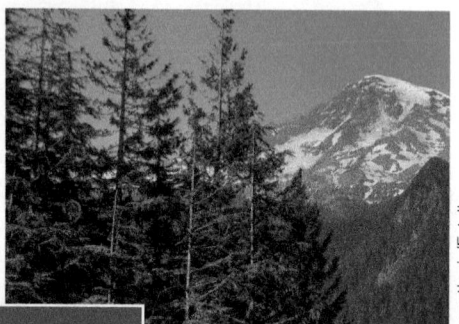

vincentlouis/Fotolia

Adam Jones/Getty Images

◀ **European larch.** The needle-like leaves of this deciduous conifer (*Larix decidua*) turn yellow before they are shed in autumn. Native to the mountains of central Europe, including Switzerland's Matterhorn, depicted here, this species is extremely cold-tolerant, able to survive winter temperatures that plunge to −50°C.

▶ **Common juniper.** The "berries" of the common juniper (*Juniperus communis*) are actually ovule-producing cones consisting of fleshy sporophylls.

Svetlana Tikhonova/Shutterstock

Royal Botanic Gardens Sydney

◀ **Wollemi pine.** Survivors of a conifer group once known only from fossils, living Wollemi pines (*Wollemia nobilis*) were discovered in 1994 in a national park only 150 km from Sydney, Australia. The species consists of just 40 known individuals in two small groves. The inset photo compares the leaves of this "living fossil" with actual fossils.

▶ **Sequoia.** This giant sequoia (*Sequoiadendron giganteum*) in California's Sequoia National Park weighs about 2500 metric tons, equivalent to about 24 blue whales (the largest animals) or 40 000 people. The giant sequoia is one of the largest living organisms and also among the most ancient, with some individuals estimated to be between 1800 and 2700 years old. Their cousins, the coast redwoods (*Sequoia sempervirens*), grow to heights of more than 110 m (taller than the Statue of Liberty) and are found only in a narrow coastal strip of northern California and southern Oregon.

Tips Images/Alamy

AP Images

▶ **Bristlecone pine.** This species (*Pinus longaeva*), which is found in the White Mountains of California, includes some of the oldest living organisms, reaching ages of more than 4600 years. One tree (not shown here) is called Methuselah because it may be the world's oldest living tree. To protect the tree, scientists keep its location a secret.

Russ Bishop/Alamy

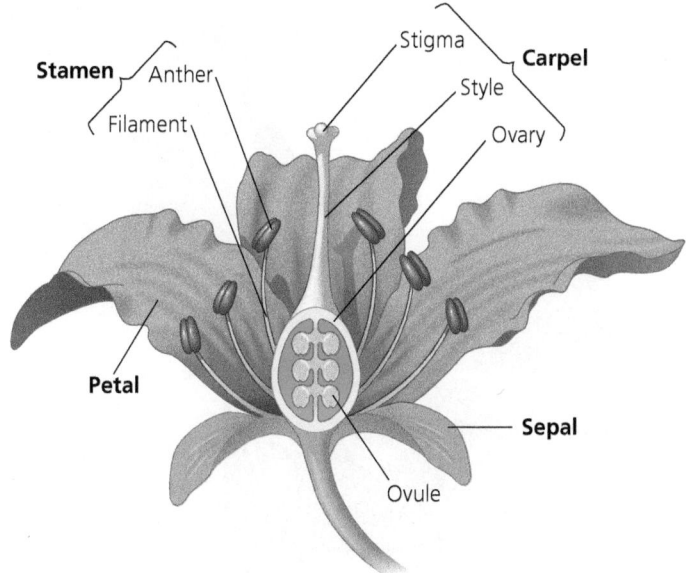

▲ Figure 30.8 **The structure of an idealized flower.**

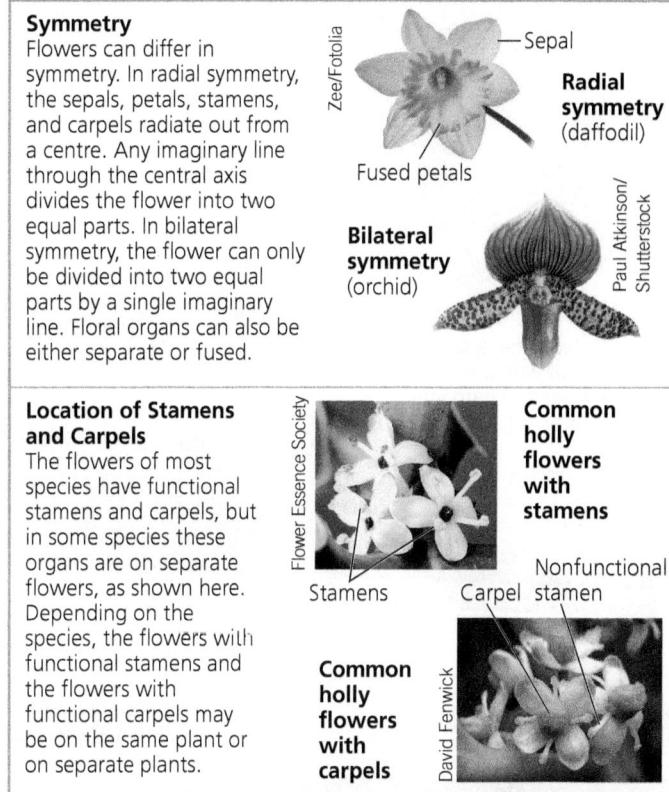

▲ Figure 30.9 **Some variations in flower structure.**

organs: sepals, petals, stamens, and carpels (Figure 30.8). Starting at the base of the flower are the **sepals**, which are usually green and enclose the flower before it opens (think of a rosebud). Interior to the sepals are the **petals**, which are brightly coloured in most flowers and aid in attracting pollinators. Flowers that are wind-pollinated, however, generally lack brightly coloured parts, like the flowers of grasses that are inconspicuous. In all angiosperms, the sepals and petals are sterile floral organs, meaning that they do not produce sperm or eggs. Within the petals are two whorls of fertile floral organs that produce spores, the stamens and carpels. **Stamens** produce microspores that develop into pollen grains containing male gametophytes. A stamen consists of a stalk called the **filament** and a terminal sac, the **anther**, where pollen is produced. **Carpels** make megaspores and their products, female gametophytes. Some flowers have a single carpel, whereas others have multiple carpels, which are either separate or fused together. At the tip of the carpel is a sticky **stigma** that receives pollen. A **style** leads from the stigma to the **ovary** at the base of the carpel; the ovary contains one or more ovules. If fertilized, an ovule develops into a seed. Flowers that have all four organs are called complete flowers. Those that lack one or more of these organs are known as incomplete flowers. For example, some lack functional stamens, and others lack functional carpels. Flowers also vary in structure (Figure 30.9), as well as size, colour, and odour. Much of this diversity results from adaptation to specific pollinators (see Figures 38.4 and 38.5).

Fruits

As seeds develop from ovules after fertilization, the ovary wall thickens and the ovary matures into a **fruit**. A pea

pod is an example of a fruit, with seeds (mature ovules, the peas) encased in the ripened ovary (the pod).

Fruits protect seeds and aid in their dispersal. Mature fruits can be either fleshy or dry (Figure 30.10). Tomatoes, plums, and grapes are examples of fleshy fruits, in which the wall (pericarp) of the ovary becomes soft during ripening. Dry fruits include beans, nuts, and grains. Some dry fruits split open at maturity to release seeds, whereas others remain closed. The fruits of grasses, harvested while on the plant, are major staple foods for humans. The cereal grains of maize, rice, wheat, and other grasses, though easily mistaken for seeds, are each actually a fruit with a dry outer covering (the former wall of the ovary) that adheres to the seed coat of the seed within.

As shown in Figure 30.11, various adaptations of fruits and seeds help to disperse seeds (see also Figure 38.12). The seeds of some flowering plants, such as dandelions and maples, are contained within fruits that function like parachutes or propellers, adaptations that enhance dispersal by wind. Some fruits, such as coconuts, are adapted to dispersal by water (see Figure 38.12). And many angiosperms rely on animals to carry seeds. Some of these plants have fruits modified as burrs that cling to animal fur (or the clothes of humans). Other angiosperms produce edible fruits, which are usually nutritious, sweet tasting, and vividly coloured, advertising their ripeness. When an animal eats the fruit,

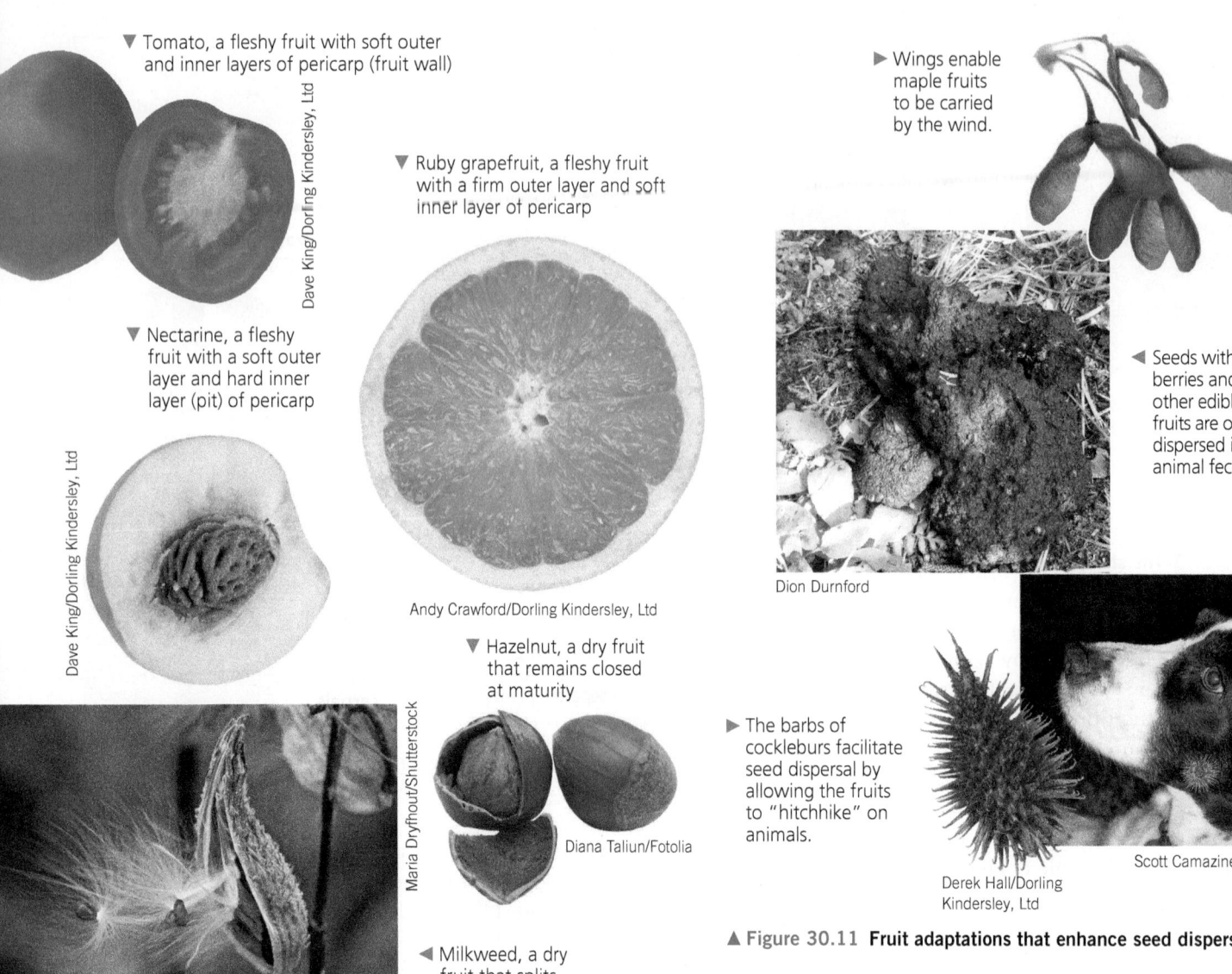

▼ Tomato, a fleshy fruit with soft outer and inner layers of pericarp (fruit wall)

Dave King/Dorling Kindersley, Ltd

▶ Ruby grapefruit, a fleshy fruit with a firm outer layer and soft inner layer of pericarp

▼ Nectarine, a fleshy fruit with a soft outer layer and hard inner layer (pit) of pericarp

Dave King/Dorling Kindersley, Ltd

Andy Crawford/Dorling Kindersley, Ltd

▼ Hazelnut, a dry fruit that remains closed at maturity

Maria Dryfhout/Shutterstock

Diana Taliun/Fotolia

◀ Milkweed, a dry fruit that splits open at maturity

▲ Figure 30.10 Some variations in fruit structure.

▶ Wings enable maple fruits to be carried by the wind.

PIXTAL/AGE Fotostock

◀ Seeds within berries and other edible fruits are often dispersed in animal feces.

Dion Durnford

▶ The barbs of cockleburs facilitate seed dispersal by allowing the fruits to "hitchhike" on animals.

Derek Hall/Dorling Kindersley, Ltd

Scott Camazine/Science Source

▲ Figure 30.11 Fruit adaptations that enhance seed dispersal.

it digests the fruit's fleshy part, but the tough seeds usually pass unharmed through the animal's digestive tract. Animals may deposit the seeds, along with a supply of natural fertilizer, many kilometres from where the fruit was eaten.

The Angiosperm Life Cycle

You can follow a typical angiosperm life cycle in **Figure 30.12**. The flower of the sporophyte produces microspores that form male gametophytes and megaspores that form female gametophytes. The male gametophytes are in the pollen grains, which develop within microsporangia in the anthers. Each male gametophyte has two haploid cells: a *generative cell* that divides, forming two sperm, and a *tube cell* that produces a pollen tube. Each ovule, which develops in the ovary, contains a female gametophyte, also known as an

embryo sac. The embryo sac consists of only a few cells, one of which is the egg. (We will discuss gametophyte development in more detail in Chapter 38.)

After its release from the anther, the pollen is carried to the sticky stigma at the tip of a carpel. Although some flowers self-pollinate, most have mechanisms that ensure **cross-pollination**, which in angiosperms is the transfer of pollen from an anther of a flower on one plant to the stigma of a flower on another plant of the same species. Cross-pollination enhances genetic variability and can be promoted by a variety of mechanisms. For example, stamens and carpels of a single flower may mature at different times, or the reproductive organs may be arranged to make self-pollination unlikely.

The pollen grain absorbs water and germinates after it adheres to the stigma of a carpel. The tube cell produces a pollen tube that grows down within the style of the carpel. After reaching the ovary, the pollen tube penetrates through the **micropyle**, a pore in the integuments of the ovule, and discharges two sperm cells into the female

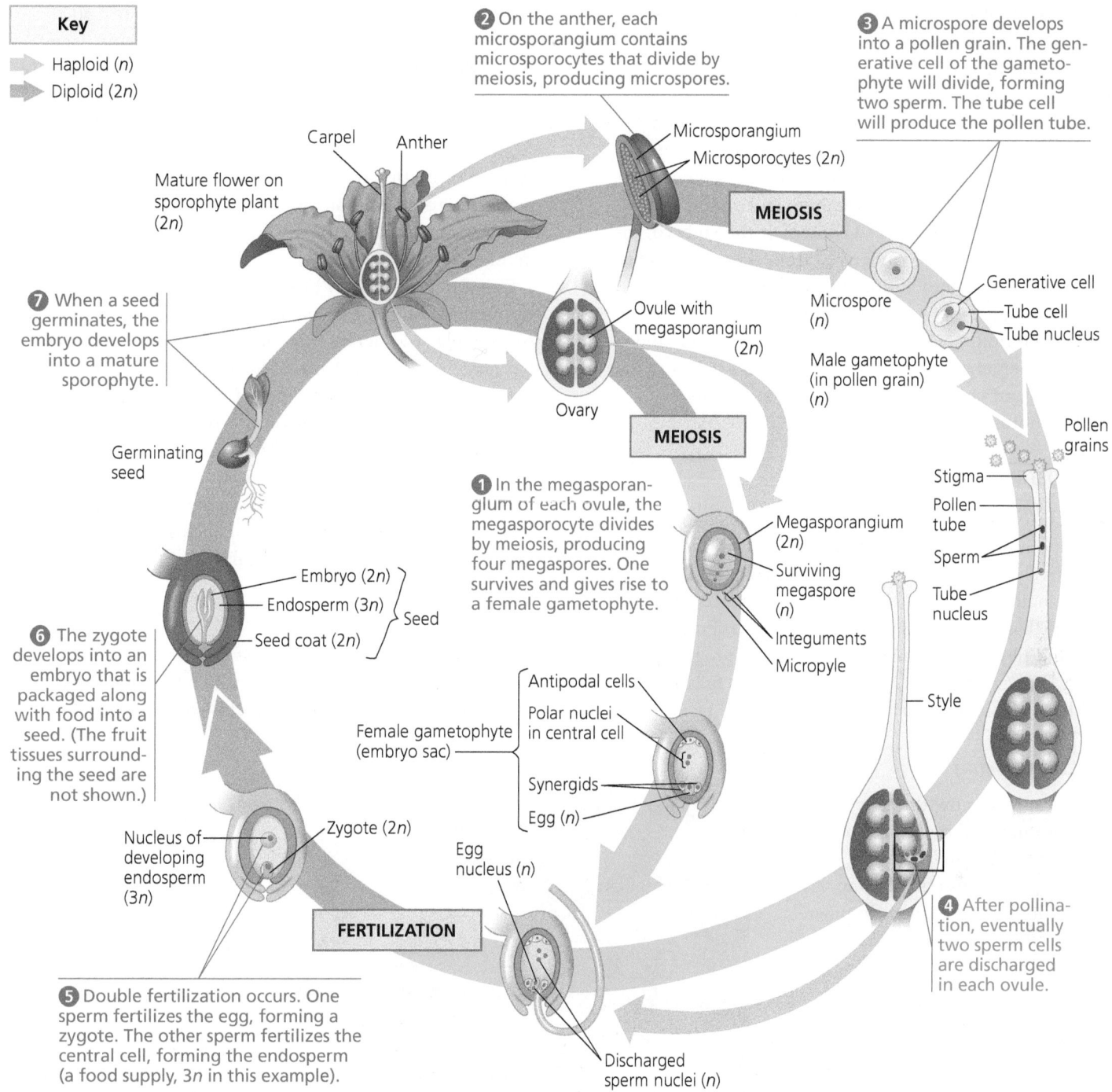

2 On the anther, each microsporangium contains microsporocytes that divide by meiosis, producing microspores.

3 A microspore develops into a pollen grain. The generative cell of the gametophyte will divide, forming two sperm. The tube cell will produce the pollen tube.

Carpel
Anther

Mature flower on sporophyte plant (2*n*)

Microsporangium
Microsporocytes (2*n*)

MEIOSIS

Ovule with megasporangium (2*n*)

Microspore (*n*)

Generative cell
Tube cell
Tube nucleus

7 When a seed germinates, the embryo develops into a mature sporophyte.

Ovary

Male gametophyte (in pollen grain) (*n*)

MEIOSIS

Pollen grains

1 In the megasporangium of each ovule, the megasporocyte divides by meiosis, producing four megaspores. One survives and gives rise to a female gametophyte.

Megasporangium (2*n*)

Surviving megaspore (*n*)

Integuments

Micropyle

Stigma
Pollen tube
Sperm
Tube nucleus

Germinating seed

Embryo (2*n*)
Endosperm (3*n*) } Seed
Seed coat (2*n*)

6 The zygote develops into an embryo that is packaged along with food into a seed. (The fruit tissues surrounding the seed are not shown.)

Antipodal cells
Polar nuclei in central cell

Style

Female gametophyte (embryo sac)

Synergids
Egg (*n*)

Nucleus of developing endosperm (3*n*)

Zygote (2*n*)

Egg nucleus (*n*)

4 After pollination, eventually two sperm cells are discharged in each ovule.

FERTILIZATION

5 Double fertilization occurs. One sperm fertilizes the egg, forming a zygote. The other sperm fertilizes the central cell, forming the endosperm (a food supply, 3*n* in this example).

Discharged sperm nuclei (*n*)

▲ Figure 30.12 **The life cycle of an angiosperm.**

gametophyte (embryo sac). One sperm fertilizes the egg, forming a diploid zygote. The other sperm fuses with the two nuclei in the large central cell of the female gametophyte, producing a triploid cell. This type of **double fertilization**, in which one fertilization event produces a zygote and the other produces a triploid cell, is unique to angiosperms.

After double fertilization, the ovule matures into a seed. The zygote develops into a sporophyte embryo with a rudimentary root and one or two seed leaves called **cotyledons**. The triploid central cell of the female gametophyte develops into **endosperm**, tissue rich in starch and other food reserves that nourish the developing embryo.

What is the function of double fertilization in angiosperms? One hypothesis is that double fertilization synchronizes the development of food storage in the seed with the development of the embryo. If a particular flower is not pollinated or sperm cells are not discharged into the embryo sac, fertilization does not occur, and neither endosperm nor embryo forms. So perhaps double fertilization is an adaptation that prevents flowering plants from squandering nutrients on infertile ovules.

Another type of double fertilization occurs in some gymnosperm species belonging to the phylum Gnetophyta. However, double fertilization in these species gives rise to two embryos rather than to an embryo and endosperm.

As you read earlier, the seed consists of the embryo, the endosperm, and a seed coat derived from the integuments. An ovary develops into a fruit as its ovules become seeds. After being dispersed, a seed may germinate if environmental conditions are favourable. The coat ruptures and the embryo emerges as a seedling, using food stored in the endosperm and cotyledons until it can produce its own food by photosynthesis.

Angiosperm Evolution

Charles Darwin once referred to the origin of angiosperms as an "abominable mystery." He was particularly troubled by the relatively sudden and geographically widespread appearance of angiosperms in the fossil record (about 100 million years ago, based on fossils known to Darwin). Fossil evidence and phylogenetic analyses have led to progress in solving Darwin's mystery, but we still do not fully understand how angiosperms arose from earlier seed plants.

Fossil Angiosperms

Angiosperms are now thought to have originated in the early Cretaceous period, about 140 million years ago. By the mid-Cretaceous (100 million years ago), angiosperms began to dominate some terrestrial ecosystems. Landscapes changed dramatically as conifers and other gymnosperms gave way to flowering plants in many parts of the world. The Cretaceous period ended about 65 million years ago with mass extinctions of dinosaurs and many other animal groups and further increases in the diversity and importance of angiosperms.

What evidence suggests that angiosperms arose 140 million years ago? First, although pollen grains are common in rocks from the Jurassic period (200 to 145 million years ago), none of these pollen fossils have features characteristic of angiosperms, suggesting that angiosperms may have originated after the Jurassic. Indeed, the earliest

fossils with distinctive angiosperm features are of 130-million-year-old pollen grains discovered in China, Israel, and England. Early fossils of larger flowering plant structures include those of *Archaefructus* (Figure 30.13) and *Leefructus*, both of which were discovered in China in rocks that are about 125 million years old. Overall, early angiosperm fossils indicate that the group arose and began to diversify over a 20- to 30-million year period—a less sudden event than was suggested by the fossils known during Darwin's lifetime.

Can we infer traits of the angiosperm common ancestor from traits found in early fossil angiosperms? *Archaefructus*, for example, was herbaceous and had bulbous structures that may have served as floats, suggesting it was aquatic. But investigating whether the angiosperm common ancestor was herbaceous and aquatic also requires examining fossils of other seed plants thought to have been closely related to angiosperms. All of those plants were woody, indicating that the common ancestor was probably woody and probably not aquatic. As we'll see, this conclusion has been supported by recent phylogenetic analyses.

Angiosperm Phylogeny

To shed light on the body plan of early angiosperms, scientists have long sought to identify which seed plants, including fossil species, are most closely related to

(a) *Archaefructus sinensis*, **a 125-million-year-old fossil.** This species may represent the sister group to all other angiosperms, or it may belong to the water lily group. Researchers are testing these two hypotheses with phylogenetic analyses.

David L. Dilcher

5 cm

Carpel

Stamen

(b) Artist's reconstruction of *Archaefructus sinensis*

▲ Figure 30.13 **An early flowering plant.**

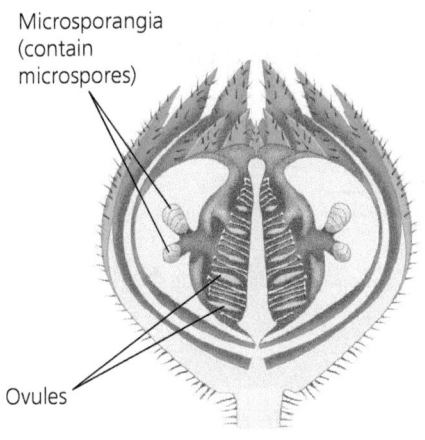

Microsporangia
(contain
microspores)

Ovules

(a) A possible ancestor of the angiosperms?
This reconstruction shows a cross section through the flowerlike structures found in the Bennettitales, an extinct group of seed plants hypothesized to be more closely related to extant angiosperms than to extant gymnosperms.

Source: Adapted from the source: "A Revision of Williamsoniella" by T. M. Harris, from *Proceedings of the Royal Society B: Biological Sciences*, October 1944, Volume 231(583):313–328. © Jane B Reece.

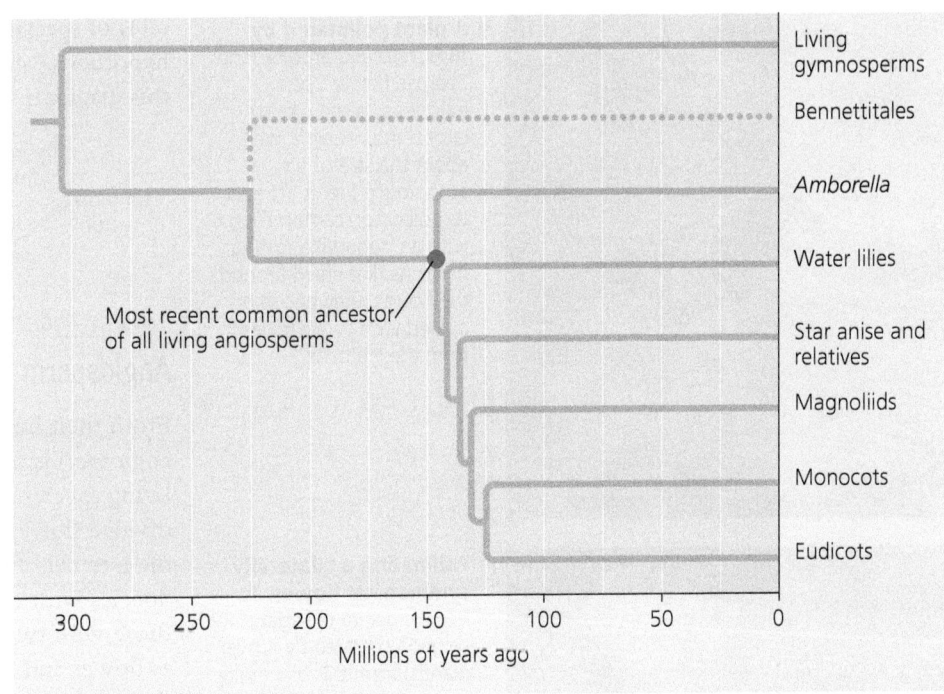

Most recent common ancestor of all living angiosperms

Living gymnosperms
Bennettitales
Amborella
Water lilies
Star anise and relatives
Magnoliids
Monocots
Eudicots

300   250   200   150   100   50   0
Millions of years ago

(b) Angiosperm phylogeny. This tree represents one current hypothesis of angiosperm evolutionary relationships, based on morphological and molecular evidence. Angiosperms originated at least 140 million years ago. The dotted line indicates the uncertain position of the Bennettitales, a possible sister group to the extant angiosperms.

Source: Adaptation of Figure 2.3 from *Phylogeny and Evolution of Angiosperm*, 2nd Edition, by Douglas E. Soltis et al. Copyright © 2005 by Sinauer Associates, Inc. Reprinted with permission.

▲ **Figure 30.14 Angiosperm evolutionary history.**

? *Would the branching order of the phylogeny in (b) necessarily have to be redrawn if a 150-million-year-old fossil monocot were discovered? Explain.*

angiosperms. Molecular and morphological evidence suggests that living gymnosperms are a monophyletic group whose earliest lineages diverged from the ancestors of angiosperms about 305 million years ago. Note that this does not necessarily imply that angiosperms originated 305 million years ago, but that the most recent common ancestor of gymnosperms and angiosperms lived at that time. Angiosperms may in fact be most closely related to extinct seed plants such as the Bennettitales, a group with flowerlike structures that may have been pollinated by insects (**Figure 30.14a**).

Making sense of the origin of angiosperms also depends on working out the order in which angiosperm clades diverged from one another. Here, dramatic progress has been made in recent years. Molecular and morphological evidence suggests that water lilies and a small South Pacific shrub called *Amborella trichopoda* are living representatives of two of the most ancient angiosperm lineages (**Figure 30.14b**). *Amborella* is woody, supporting the conclusion mentioned earlier that the angiosperm common ancestor was probably woody. Like the Bennettitales, *Amborella* and other basal angiosperms lacked vessel elements, efficient water-conducting cells that are found in angiosperms from later-diverging lineages. Overall, based on the features of ancestral species and basal angiosperms such as *Amborella*, some researchers have hypothesized that early angiosperms were shrubs that had small flowers and relatively simple water-conducting cells.

Evolutionary Links Between Angiosperms and Animals

Plants and animals have interacted for hundreds of millions of years, and those interactions have led to evolutionary change. For example, herbivores can reduce a plant's reproductive success by eating its roots, leaves, or seeds. As a result, if a novel and effective defence against herbivores originates in a group of plants, those plants may be favoured by natural selection—as will any herbivores that can overcome this new defence. Plant-pollinator and other mutually beneficial interactions can have reciprocal evolutionary effects, as seen in **Figure 30.15**.

Plant-pollinator interactions also may have affected the rates at which new species form. Consider the impact of a flower's symmetry (see Figure 30.9). On a flower with bilateral symmetry, an insect pollinator can obtain nectar only when approaching from a certain direction (Figure 30.15, lower panel). This constraint makes it more likely that pollen is placed on a part of the insect's body that will come

◀ **A plant pollinated by flies.** *Rafflesia arnoldii*, the "corpse flower" of Indonesia, is the world's largest individual flower, about the size of an automobile tire. It attracts its pollinator, carrion flies, with an odour like rotting flesh. As flies crawl around the flower, they become dusted with sticky pollen from the stamens.

kkaplin/Shutterstock

◀ **Pollinating a bilaterally symmetrical flower.** To harvest nectar (a sugary solution secreted by flower glands) from this bilaterally symmetrical Scottish broom flower, a honeybee must land as shown. This releases a tripping mechanism that arches the flower's stamens over the bee and dusts it with pollen. Later, some of this pollen will rub off onto the stigma of the next flower of this species that the bee visits.

D. Wilder

▲ Figure 30.15 **Animals participating in plant reproduction.**

into contact with the stigma of a flower of the same species. Such specificity of pollen transfer reduces gene flow between diverging populations and could lead to increased

rates of speciation in plants with bilateral symmetry. This hypothesis can be tested using the approach illustrated in this diagram:

Angiosperm Diversity

From their humble beginnings in the Mesozoic period, angiosperms have diversified into more than 250 000 living species. Until the late 1990s, most systematists divided flowering plants into two groups, based partly on the number of cotyledons, or seed leaves, in the embryo. Species with one cotyledon were called **monocots**, and those with two were called **dicots**. Other features, such as flower and leaf structure, were also used to define the two groups. Recent DNA studies, however, indicate that the species traditionally called dicots are paraphyletic. The vast majority of species once categorized as dicots form a large clade, now known as **eudicots** ("true" dicots). **Figure 30.16** compares the main characteristics of monocots and eudicots. The rest of the former dicots are now grouped into four small lineages. Three of these are informally called basal angiosperms because they appear to include the flowering plants belonging to the oldest lineages (see Figure 30.14b). A fourth lineage, the **magnoliids**, evolved later. **Figure 30.17** provides an overview of angiosperm diversity.

A key step is to identify cases in which a clade with bilaterally symmetrical flowers shares an immediate common ancestor with a clade whose members have radially

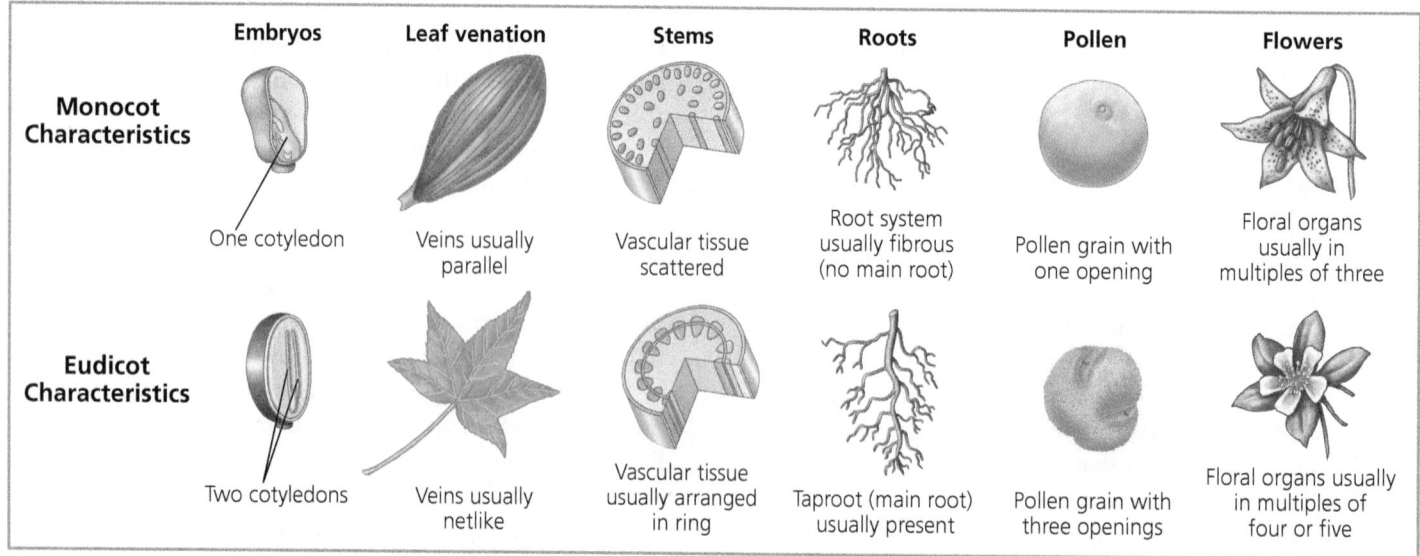

▲ Figure 30.16 **Characteristics of monocots and eudicots.**

Exploring Angiosperm Diversity

Basal Angiosperms

Surviving basal angiosperms are currently thought to consist of three lineages comprising only about 100 species. The oldest lineage seems to be represented by a single species, *Amborella trichopoda* (far right). The other surviving lineages diverged later: a clade that includes water lilies and a clade consisting of the star anise and its relatives.

Amborella trichopoda. ▶ This small shrub, found only on the South Pacific island of New Caledonia, may be the sole survivor of a branch at the base of the angiosperm tree.

McNeal, Joel

◀ **Water lily (*Nymphaea "Rene Gerard"*).** Species of water lilies are found in aquatic habitats throughout the world. Water lilies are living members of a clade that may be predated only by the *Amborella* lineage.

Howard Rice/Dorling Kindersley, Ltd

Floridata.com

◀ **Star anise (*Illicium*).** This genus belongs to a third surviving lineage of basal angiosperms.

Magnoliids

Magnoliids consist of about 8000 species, most notably magnolias, laurels, and black pepper plants. They include both woody and herbaceous species. Although they share some traits with basal angiosperms, such as a typically spiral rather than whorled arrangement of floral organs, magnoliids are more closely related to eudicots and monocots.

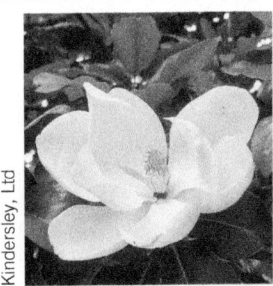

Andrew Butler/Dorling Kindersley, Ltd

◀ **Southern magnolia (*Magnolia grandiflora*).** This member of the magnolia family is a large tree. The variety of southern magnolia shown here, called "Goliath," has flowers that measure up to about a foot across.

Monocots

About one-quarter of angiosperm species are monocots—about 70 000 species. Some of the largest groups are the orchids, grasses, and palms. Grasses include some of the most important crops, such as maize, rice, and wheat.

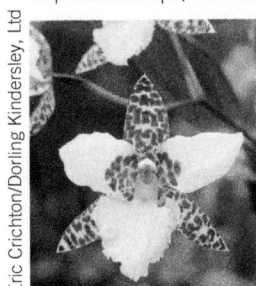

Eric Crichton/Dorling Kindersley, Ltd

◀ **Orchid (*Lemboglossum rossii*)**

Pygmy date palm (*Phoenix roebelenii*) ▶

John Dransfield

Terry W. Eggers/Corbis

▲ **Barley (*Hordeum vulgare*), a grass**

Eudicots

More than two-thirds of angiosperm species are eudicots—roughly 170 000 species. The largest group is the legume family, which includes such crops as peas and beans. Also important economically is the rose family, which includes many plants with ornamental flowers as well as some species with edible fruits, such as strawberry plants and apple and pear trees. Most of the familiar flowering trees are eudicots, such as oak, walnut, maple, willow, and birch.

◀ **Pyrenean oak (*Quercus pyrenaica*)**

Matthew Ward/Dorling Kindersley, Ltd

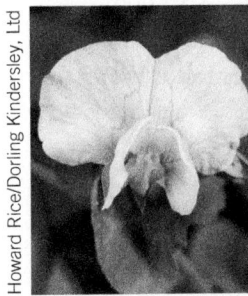

Howard Rice/Dorling Kindersley, Ltd

◀ **Snow pea (*Pisum sativum*), a legume**

Dog rose (*Rosa canina*), a wild rose ▶

Glam/Shutterstock

▼ Figure 30.18 | Impact

Modern Agriculture and Honeybee Colony Losses

Domestic honeybee-colony losses (including those caused by Colony Collapse Disorder, which is characterized by a sudden loss of adult worker bees), are a global concern. In Canada, over-wintering losses usually range between 10–20%, but between 2007 and 2009, these losses increased to 35%. The United States has been particularly hard hit, with losses up to 50% in some regions. What is responsible for the decline? A single cause has not been identified, but a combination of factors may be involved. Pathogens, for instance, are associated with colony loss. The main ones include mites and microsporidians. A variety of other fungal, bacterial, and viral pathogens have also been implicated in colony collapse. Managerial practices likely play a role in the declines by putting stress on colonies and making them more susceptible to pathogens. This may include the use of pesticides within (miticides) and near the hives (agrochemicals). Nutritional deficiencies due to bees foraging on single plant species (monocultures) may also reduce colony vigour.

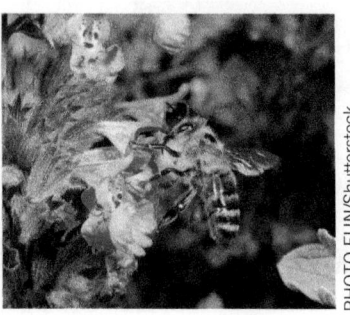

Michael Maloney/San Francisco Chronicle/Corbis

PHOTO FUN/Shutterstock

Why It Matters Canadian agriculture is dependent upon animal pollinators for the fertilization of a variety of crops, including alfalfa, apples, and blueberries, that collectively have a value of at least $1 billion. Globally, 70% of 124 crops used for human consumption depend upon pollinators for production with a value surpassing $200 billion. Many of these crops depend upon domesticated honeybee populations (rather than native, wild pollinators), like the hives shown in the apple orchard in the upper left image. Bees, like the Western honeybee (*Apis mellifera*, right image), mediate pollen transfer required for successful fertilization and fruit production, and thus are an important factor in increasing yield.

Further Reading F. L. Ratnieks and N. L. Carreck, Clarity on honey bee collapse? *Science* 327:152–153 (2010).

MAKE CONNECTIONS *Flowers and their animal pollinators are considered to have coevolved. Examine Figure 38.6 and think about implications for the pair should one suffer population declines.*

symmetrical flowers. One recent study identified 19 such pairs of closely related "bilateral" and "radial" clades. On average, the clade with bilaterally symmetrical flowers had nearly 2400 more species than did its closely related clade with radially symmetrical flowers. This result suggests that flower shape can affect the rate at which new species form, with speciation occurring more rapidly in clades with bilateral symmetry. Overall, the effects of plant-pollinator interactions are thought to have contributed to the increasing

dominance of flowering plants in the Cretaceous period, helping to make angiosperms of central importance in ecological communities.

Pollinator–plant interactions are a significant component of modern agriculture, accounting for 35% of global food production and worth billions of dollars in trade. Domesticated honeybees are one of the most important insect pollinators for global food production, without which yields can decline by up to 90% depending on the crop in question (Figure 30.18). The role of insects in mediating fertilization in angiosperms makes an interesting codependence between insects, plants, and humans, whose welfare is dependent on seed plants.

CONCEPT CHECK 30.3

1. It has been said that an oak is an acorn's way of making more acorns. Write an explanation that includes these terms: sporophyte, gametophyte, ovule, seed, ovary, and fruit.

2. Compare and contrast a pine cone and a flower in terms of structure and function.

3. **MAKE CONNECTIONS** Assume you are an arborist deciding what trees to plant in a new subdivision to both beautify the area and to add privacy. What aspects of plant reproduction would be useful to consider when deciding which plants to select?

For suggested answers, see Appendix A.

CONCEPT 30.4

Human welfare depends greatly on seed plants

In forests and on farms, seed plants are key sources of food, fuel, wood products, and medicine. Our reliance on them makes the preservation of plant diversity critical.

Products from Seed Plants

Most of our food comes from angiosperms. Just six crops—maize, rice, wheat, potatoes, cassava, and sweet potatoes—yield 80% of all the calories consumed by humans. We also depend on angiosperms to feed livestock: It takes 5–7 kg of grain to produce 1 kg of grain-fed beef.

Today's crops are the products of artificial selection—the result of plant domestication that began about 12 000 years ago. To appreciate the scale of this transformation, note how the number and size of seeds in domesticated plants are greater than those of their wild relatives, as in the case of maize and the grass teosinte (see Figure 38.16). Scientists can glean information about domestication by comparing the genes of crops with those of wild relatives. With maize, dramatic changes such as increased cob size and loss of the hard coating around teosinte kernels may have been initiated by as few as five mutations.

Flowering plants also provide other edible products. Two popular beverages come from tea leaves and coffee beans, and you can thank the tropical cacao tree for cocoa and chocolate. Spices are derived from various plant parts, such as flowers (cloves, saffron), fruits and seeds (vanilla, black pepper, mustard), leaves (basil, mint, sage), and even bark (cinnamon).

Many seed plants are sources of wood, which is absent in all living seedless plants. Wood consists of tough-walled xylem cells (see Figure 35.22). It is the primary source of fuel for much of the world, and wood pulp, typically derived from conifers such as fir and pine, is used to make paper. Wood also remains the most widely used construction material.

For centuries, humans have also depended on seed plants for medicines. Many cultures use herbal remedies, and scientists have extracted and identified the relevant secondary compounds from many of these plants, and later synthesized them. Willow leaves and bark, for instance, have long been used in pain-relieving remedies, including prescriptions by the Greek physician Hippocrates. In the 1800s, scientists traced the willow's medicinal property to the chemical salicin. A synthesized derivative, acetylsalicylic acid, is what we call aspirin. Plants also remain a direct source of medicinal compounds. Other ingredients were discovered in seed plants and then synthesized artificially. Table 30.1 lists some medicinal uses of secondary compounds found in seed plants.

Threats to Plant Diversity

Although plants may be a renewable resource, plant diversity is not. The exploding human population and its demand for space and resources are extinguishing plant species at a high rate. The problem is especially severe in the tropics, where more than two-thirds of the human population live and where population growth is fastest.

▲ Figure 30.19 **Clear-cutting of tropical forests.** Over the past several hundred years, nearly half of Earth's tropical forests have been cut down and converted to farmland and other uses. A satellite image from 1975 (left) shows a dense forest in Brazil. By 2012, much of this forest had been cut down. Deforested and urban areas are shown as light purple.

About 55 000 km^2 of tropical rain forest are cleared each year (Figure 30.19), a rate that would completely eliminate the remaining 11 million km^2 of tropical forests in 200 years. The loss of forests reduces the absorption of atmospheric carbon dioxide (CO_2) that occurs during photosynthesis, contributing to the increase in greenhouse gases that are causing higher average global temperatures. As forests disappear, so do large numbers of plant species. Of course, once a species becomes extinct, it can never return.

The loss of plant species is often accompanied by the loss of insects and other rain forest animals. Scientists estimate that within the next few centuries, 50% or more of Earth's species will become extinct. Such losses would constitute a global mass extinction, rivalling the Permian and Cretaceous mass extinctions and forever changing the evolutionary history of land plants (and many other organisms).

Many people have ethical concerns about contributing to the extinction of living forms. In addition, there are practical reasons to be concerned about the loss of plant diversity. So far, we have explored the potential uses of only a tiny fraction of the more than 290 000 known plant species. For example, almost all our food is based on the cultivation of only about two dozen species of seed plants. And fewer than 5000 plant species have been studied as potential sources of medicines. The tropical rain forest may be a medicine chest of healing plants that could be extinct before we even know they exist. If we begin to view rain forests and other ecosystems as living treasures that can regenerate only slowly, we may learn to harvest their products at sustainable rates.

Table 30.1	Examples of Plant-Derived Medicines	
Compound	**Source**	**Use**
Atropine	Belladonna plant	Eye pupil dilator
Morphine	Poppy	Pain reliever
Digitalin	Foxglove	Heart medication
Menthol	Eucalyptus tree	Throat soother
Quinine	Cinchona tree	Malaria preventive
Taxol	Pacific yew	Ovarian cancer drug
Tubocurarine	Curare tree	Muscle relaxant
Vinblastine	Periwinkle	Leukemia drug

CONCEPT CHECK 30.4

1. Explain why plant diversity can be considered a nonrenewable resource.

2. **WHAT IF?** How could phylogenies be used to help researchers search more efficiently for novel medicines derived from seed plants?

For suggested answers, see Appendix A.

30 Chapter Review

Go to **MasteringBiology**® for Assignments, the eText, and the Study Area with Animations, Activities, Vocab Self-Quiz, and Practice Tests.

SUMMARY OF KEY CONCEPTS

CONCEPT 30.1

Seeds and pollen grains are key adaptations for life on land (pp. 673–676)

Five Derived Traits of Seed Plants		
Reduced gametophytes	Microscopic male and female gametophytes (*n*) are nourished and protected by the sporophyte (2*n*)	Male gametophyte — Female gametophyte
Heterospory	Microspore (gives rise to a male gametophyte)	
	Megaspore (gives rise to a female gametophyte)	
Ovules	Ovule (gymnosperm) { Integument (2*n*) — Megaspore (*n*) — Megasporangium (2*n*)	
Pollen	Pollen grains make water unnecessary for fertilization as they are easily transported by wind or animals.	
Seeds	Seeds: survive better than unprotected spores, can be transported long distances	Seed coat — Food supply — Embryo

? *Describe how the parts of an ovule (integument, megaspore, megasporangium) correspond to the parts of a seed.*

CONCEPT 30.2

Gymnosperms bear "naked" seeds, typically on cones (pp. 676–678)

- Dominance of the sporophyte generation, the development of seeds from fertilized ovules, and the role of pollen in transferring sperm to ovules are key features of a typical gymnosperm life cycle.
- Gymnosperms appear early in the plant fossil record and dominated many Mesozoic terrestrial ecosystems. Living seed plants can be divided into two monophyletic groups: gymnosperms and angiosperms. Extant gymnosperms include cycads, *Ginkgo biloba*, gnetophytes, and conifers.

? *Although there are fewer than 1000 species of gymnosperms, the group is still very successful in terms of its evolutionary longevity, adaptations, and geographic distribution. Explain.*

CONCEPT 30.3

The reproductive adaptations of angiosperms include flowers and fruits (pp. 678–688)

- Flowers generally consist of four whorls of modified leaves: **sepals**, **petals**, **stamens** (which produce pollen), and **carpels** (which produce ovules). **Ovaries** ripen into **fruits**, which often carry seeds by wind, water, or animals to new locations.
- Flowering plants originated about 140 million years ago, and by the mid-Cretaceous (100 mya) had begun to dominate some terrestrial ecosystems. Fossils, phylogenetic analyses, and developmental studies offer insights into the origin of flowers.
- Several groups of basal angiosperms have been identified. Other major clades of angiosperms include **magnoliids**, **monocots**, and **eudicots**.
- Pollination and other interactions between angiosperms and animals may have contributed to the success of flowering plants during the last 100 million years.

? *Explain why Darwin called the origin of angiosperms an "abominable mystery," and describe what has been learned from fossil evidence and phylogenetic analyses.*

CONCEPT 30.4

Human welfare depends greatly on seed plants (pp. 688–689)

- Humans depend on seed plants for products such as food, wood, and many medicines.
- Destruction of habitat threatens the extinction of many plant species and the animal species they support.

? *In what ways are humans, plants, and insects co-dependent?*

TEST YOUR UNDERSTANDING

LEVEL 1: KNOWLEDGE/COMPREHENSION

1. Where in an angiosperm would you find a megasporangium?
   a. in the style of a flower
   b. enclosed in the stigma of a flower
   c. within an ovule contained within an ovary of a flower
   d. packed into pollen sacs within the anthers found on a stamen

2. A fruit is most commonly
   a. a mature ovary.
   b. a thickened style.
   c. an enlarged ovule.
   d. a mature female gametophyte.

3. With respect to angiosperms, which of the following is *incorrectly* paired with its chromosome count?
   a. egg—*n*
   b. megaspore—2*n*
   c. microspore—*n*
   d. zygote—2*n*

4. Seeds were a major evolutionary innovation that, in part, accounts for the success of gymnosperms and angiosperms. Which best describes the evolutionary adaptation?
   a. allows reproduction under diverse conditions
   b. easily transported by wind, unlike spores
   c. allows sexual reproduction
   d. allows for alternation of generations

5. Gymnosperms and angiosperms have the following in common *except*
   a. seeds.   c. ovaries.
   b. pollen.   d. ovules.

LEVEL 2: APPLICATION/ANALYSIS

6. **DRAW IT** Use the letters a–d to label where on the phylogenetic tree each of the following derived characters appear.
   a. flowers
   b. embryos
   c. seeds
   d. vascular tissue

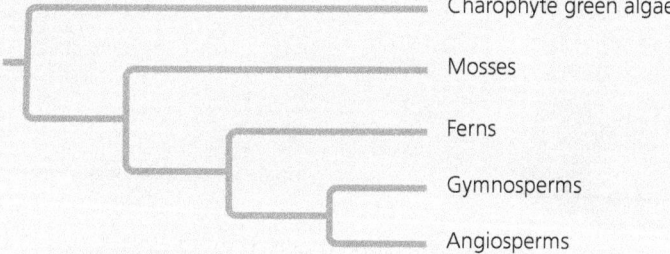

Charophyte green algae

Mosses

Ferns

Gymnosperms

Angiosperms

7. EVOLUTION CONNECTION

The history of life has been punctuated by several mass extinctions. For example, the impact of a meteorite may have wiped out most of the dinosaurs and many forms of marine life at the end of the Cretaceous period (see Chapter 25). Fossils indicate that plants were less severely affected by this and other mass extinctions. What adaptations may have enabled plants to withstand these disasters better than animals?

LEVEL 3: SYNTHESIS/EVALUATION

8. SCIENTIFIC INQUIRY

DRAW IT As will be described in detail in Chapter 38, the female gametophyte of angiosperms typically has seven cells, one of which, the central cell, contains two haploid nuclei. After double fertilization, the central cell develops into endosperm, which is triploid. Because magnoliids, monocots, and eudicots typically have female gametophytes with seven cells and triploid endosperm, scientists assumed that this was the ancestral state for angiosperms. Consider, however, the following recent discoveries:

- Our understanding of angiosperm phylogeny has changed to that shown in Figure 30.14b.
- *Amborella trichopoda* has eight-celled female gametophytes and triploid endosperm.
- Water lilies and star anise have four-celled female gametophytes and diploid endosperm.

a. Draw a phylogeny of the angiosperms (see Figure 30.14b), incorporating the data given above about the number of cells in female gametophytes and the ploidy of the endosperm. Assume that all of the star anise relatives have four-celled female gametophytes and diploid endosperm.

b. What does your labelled phylogeny suggest about the evolution of the female gametophyte and endosperm in angiosperms?

9. WRITE ABOUT A THEME: THE CELLULAR BASIS OF LIFE

Cells are the basic units of structure and function in all organisms. A key feature in the life cycle of plants is the alternation of multicellular haploid and diploid generations. Imagine a lineage of flowering plants in which mitotic cell division did not occur between the events of meiosis and fertilization (see Figure 30.12). In a short essay (100–150 words), describe how this change in the timing of cell division would affect the structure and life cycle of plants in this lineage.

10. SYNTHESIZE YOUR KNOWLEDGE

tomoki1970/123RF

Tree ferns are impressive tropical and sub-tropical plants found in damp, humid ecosystems that were dominant during the Carboniferous period (see Chapter 29). Describe how these ferns differ from the now dominant gymnosperms and angiosperms and what accounts for the success of the latter.

For selected answers, see Appendix A.

31

Fungi

KEY CONCEPTS

31.1 Fungi are heterotrophs that feed by absorption

31.2 Fungi produce spores through sexual or asexual life cycles

31.3 The ancestor of fungi was an aquatic, single-celled, flagellated protist

31.4 Fungi have radiated into a diverse set of lineages

31.5 Fungi play key roles in nutrient cycling, ecological interactions, and human welfare

▲ Figure 31.1 **What is the commercial importance of this unicellular fungus?**

Brewer's Yeast and Climate Change

If you drive a motor vehicle, you've probably noticed the "May contain up to 10% ethanol" stickers on the gas pump when you fill up. This so-called E10 gasoline contains a mixture of gas and ethanol as there is a requirement to have at least 5% ethanol added to gasoline sold in Canada. Roughly 200 million litres of gasoline per day is pumped into fuel tanks, requiring over 10 million litres of ethanol per day. That's a lot of ethanol!

Ethanol is produced from plant biomass and as a result is considered a biofuel. Its use effectively reduces emissions of CO_2 compared to burning straight gasoline because the CO_2 released during combustion was captured by the plant recently rather than 300 million years ago, thus reducing the emission of net CO_2. In Canada, wheat and corn are the primary feedstocks for ethanol production. Amazingly, all this ethanol production is done through fermentation (see Concept 9.5) of plant starch by a single-celled fungus, or yeast. Once the starch is partially degraded to sugars, the yeast ferments the sugar to ethanol and CO_2. In fact, this is the same yeast whose fermentation produces the alcohol in our beer and wine and produces the CO_2 that causes our bread to rise. It is extraordinary that this one yeast, *Saccharomyces cerevisiae* (Figure 31.1), has been such an important part of the human experience.

◀ **King of the forest—*Armillaria ostoyae***

While about 100 000 species have been described, it is estimated that there are as many as 1.5 million species of **fungi**. Some fungi are exclusively single celled, like *Saccharomyces*, though most have complex multicellular bodies, which includes the structures we know as mushrooms. Fungi can be amongst the largest organisms on the planet, and with honey mushrooms (genus *Armillaria*) the above-ground mushroom structure is only a tiny fraction of the total individual biomass. Underground, the network of filaments (hyphae) can spread over 965 hectares of the forest with an estimated biomass of 10 000 kg!

The inconspicuous honey mushrooms on the forest floor are a fitting symbol of the neglected grandeur of the kingdom Fungi. Most of us are barely aware of these eukaryotes beyond the mushrooms we eat or the yeast we use in cooking. Yet fungi are a huge and important component of the biosphere. These diverse organisms are found in just about every imaginable terrestrial and aquatic habitat; airborne spores have been found 160 km above ground and even growing in the highly radioactive nuclear reactor of the Chernobyl power plant.

Fungi are not only diverse and widespread, they are also essential for the well-being of most ecosystems. They break down organic material and recycle nutrients, allowing other organisms to assimilate essential chemical elements. Humans make use of fungi as a food source, for applications in agriculture and forestry, and in the manufacturing of products ranging from alcohol to antibiotics. Certain fungi can also cause diseases in animals and plants, and as such are important effectors of our food production systems and our general well-being.

In this chapter, we will investigate the structure and evolutionary history of fungi, survey the major groups of fungi, and discuss their ecological and commercial significance.

CONCEPT 31.1

Fungi are heterotrophs that feed by absorption

Despite their vast diversity, all fungi share some key traits, most importantly the way they derive nutrition. In addition, many fungi grow by forming multicellular filaments, a body structure that plays an important role in how they obtain food.

Nutrition and Ecology

Like animals, fungi are heterotrophs: They cannot make their own food as plants and algae can. But unlike animals, fungi do not ingest (eat) their food. Instead, a fungus absorbs nutrients from the environment outside of its body. Many fungi accomplish this task by secreting powerful hydrolytic enzymes into their surroundings. These enzymes break down complex molecules to smaller organic compounds that the fungi can absorb into their bodies and use. Other fungi use enzymes to penetrate the walls of cells, enabling the fungi to absorb nutrients from the cells. Collectively, the different enzymes found in various fungal species can digest compounds from a wide range of sources, living or dead, including the most abundant biomolecules on the planet—cellulose and lignin.

This diversity of food sources corresponds to the varied roles of fungi in ecological communities, with different species living as decomposers, parasites, or mutualists. Decomposer fungi break down and absorb nutrients from nonliving organic material, such as fallen logs, animal corpses, and the wastes of living organisms, and are an essential component of global carbon cycling. Parasitic fungi absorb nutrients from the cells of living hosts. Some parasitic fungi are pathogenic, including many species that cause diseases in plants. Mutualistic fungi also absorb nutrients from a host organism, but they reciprocate with actions that benefit the host. For example, mutualistic fungi that live inside certain termite species use their enzymes to break down wood, as do mutualistic protists in other termite species (see Figure 28.28).

The success of fungi in the environment is due to the diverse metabolic enzymes they produce that allow them to use a broad range of food sources. Their body structure is also well adapted for efficient uptake of the nutrients the enzymes release.

Body Structure

The most common fungal body structures are multicellular filaments and single cells (**yeasts**). Many species can grow as both filaments and yeasts, but even more grow only as filaments; relatively few species grow only as yeasts. Yeasts often inhabit moist environments, including plant sap and animal tissues, where there is a ready supply of soluble nutrients, such as sugars and amino acids. We'll discuss yeasts again later in the chapter.

The morphology of multicellular fungi enhances their ability to grow into and absorb nutrients from their surroundings (**Figure 31.2**). The bodies of these fungi typically form a network of tiny filaments called **hyphae** (singular, *hypha*). Hyphae consist of tubular cell walls surrounding the plasma membrane and cytoplasm of the cells. Unlike plant cell walls, which contain cellulose, fungal cell walls are strengthened by **chitin**. This strong

Reproductive structure. Tiny haploid cells called spores are produced inside the mushroom.

Hyphae. The mushroom and its subterranean mycelium are a continuous network of hyphae.

Spore-producing structures

George Barron

60 μm

Nata-Lia/Shutterstock

Fred Rhoades

Mycelium (a mass of hyphae)

▲ **Figure 31.2 Structure of a multicellular fungus.** The top photograph shows the sexual structures, in this case called mushrooms, of the penny bun fungus (*Boletus edulis*). The bottom photograph shows a mycelium growing on fallen conifer needles. The inset SEM shows hyphae.

? *Although the mushrooms in the top photograph appear to be different individuals, could their DNA be identical? Explain.*

Fungal hyphae form an interwoven mass called a **mycelium** (plural, *mycelia*) that infiltrates the material on which the fungus feeds. A mycelium's structure maximizes its surface-to-volume ratio, making absorption of nutrients very efficient. Just 1 cm^3 of rich soil may contain as much as 1 km of hyphae with a total surface area of 300 cm^2 in contact with the soil. A fungal mycelium grows rapidly, as proteins and other materials synthesized by the fungus are channelled through cytoplasmic streaming to the tips of the extending hyphae. The fungus concentrates its energy and resources on adding hyphal length and thus overall absorptive surface area, rather than on increasing hyphal girth. As we learned with the honey mushroom, these hyphae biomass can grow to cover an enormous area. Fungi are not motile in the typical sense—they cannot run, swim, or fly in search of food or mates. However, as they grow, fungi can move into new territory, swiftly extending the tips of their hyphae.

but flexible nitrogen-containing polysaccharide is also found in the external skeletons of insects and other arthropods.

In most fungi, the hyphae are divided into cells by cross-walls, or **septa** (singular, *septum*) (Figure 31.3a). Septa generally have pores large enough to allow ribosomes, mitochondria, and even nuclei to flow from cell to cell. Some fungi lack septa (Figure 31.3b). Known as **coenocytic fungi**, these organisms consist of a continuous cytoplasmic mass having hundreds or thousands of nuclei. The coenocytic condition results from the repeated division of nuclei without cytokinesis.

Cell wall

Pore

Septum

Nuclei

(a) Septate hypha

Cell wall

Nuclei

(b) Coenocytic hypha

▲ **Figure 31.3 Two forms of hyphae.**

Specialized Hyphae in Mycorrhizal Fungi

Some fungi have specialized hyphae that allow them to feed on living animals (Figure 31.4a). Other fungal species have specialized hyphae called **haustoria**, which the fungi use to extract nutrients from, or exchange nutrients with, their plant hosts (Figure 31.4b). Mutually beneficial relationships between such fungi and plant roots are called **mycorrhizae** (the term means "fungus roots").

Mycorrhizal fungi (fungi that form mycorrhizae) can improve delivery of phosphate ions and other minerals to plants because the vast mycelial networks of the fungi are more efficient than the plants' roots at acquiring these minerals from the soil. In exchange, the plants supply the fungi with organic nutrients such as carbohydrates. There are two main types of mycorrhizal fungi. **Ectomycorrhizal fungi** (from the Greek *ektos*, out) form sheaths of hyphae over the surface of a root and typically grow into the extracellular spaces of the root cortex (see Figure 37.13a). **Arbuscular mycorrhizal fungi** (from the Latin *arbor*, tree) extend branching hyphae through the root cell wall and into tubes formed by invagination (pushing inward) of the root cell plasma membrane (Figures 31.4b, 31.14, and 37.13b).

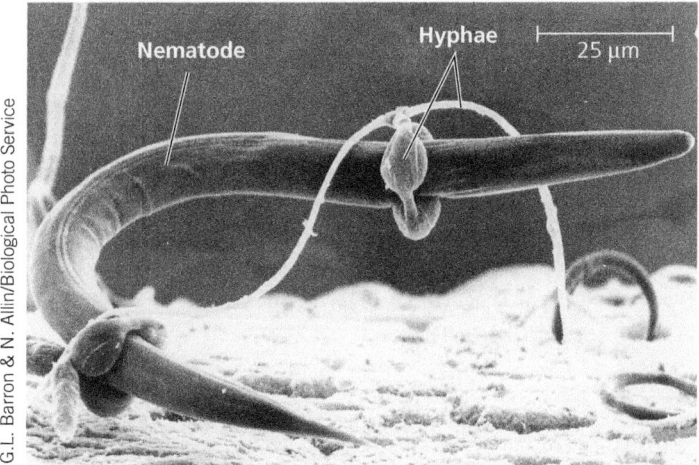

(a) Hyphae adapted for trapping and killing prey. In *Arthrobotrys*, a soil fungus, portions of the hyphae are modified as hoops that can constrict around a nematode (roundworm) in less than a second. The fungus then penetrates its prey with hyphae and digests the prey's inner tissues (SEM).

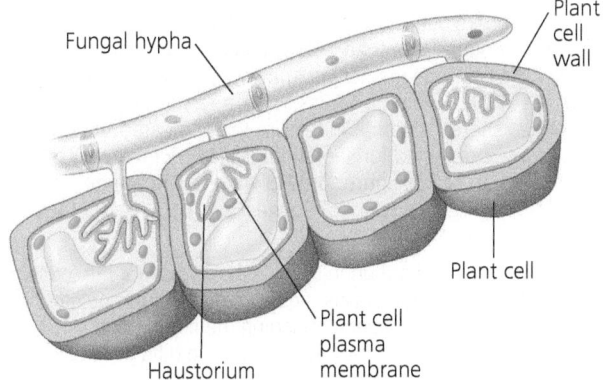

(b) Haustoria. Some mutualistic and parasitic fungi grow specialized hyphae called haustoria that can extract nutrients from living plant cells. Haustoria remain separated from a plant cell's cytoplasm by the plasma membrane of the plant cell (orange).

▲ **Figure 31.4 Specialized hyphae.**

In the Scientific Skills Exercise, you'll compare genomic data from fungi that form mycorrhizae and fungi that do not.

Mycorrhizae are enormously important in natural ecosystems and agriculture. Almost all vascular plants have mycorrhizae and rely on their fungal partners for essential nutrients. In fact, one fungal species can form mycorrhizae with different plant species, forming an interconnected mycorrhizal network in the soil. Interestingly, Dr. Suzanne Simard, at the University of British Columbia, was the lead researcher who discovered nutrients are transferred between different trees via the mycorrhizal network, and the magnitude of the nutrient transfer depended on the light conditions. In this work, shading trees of one species increased the transfer of nutrients from another via the fungal hyphae network; thus, these underground networks may have very important roles in the forest ecosystem.

Many studies have demonstrated the significance of mycorrhizae by comparing the growth of plants with and without them. Foresters commonly inoculate pine seedlings with mycorrhizal fungi to promote growth. In the absence of human intervention, mycorrhizal fungi colonize soils by dispersing haploid cells called **spores** that form new mycelia after germinating. Spore dispersal is a key component of how fungi reproduce and spread to new areas, as we discuss next.

CONCEPT CHECK 31.1

1. Compare and contrast the nutritional mode of a fungus with your own nutritional mode.

2. **WHAT IF?** Suppose a certain fungus is a mutualist that lives within an insect host, yet its ancestors were parasites that grew in and on the insect's body. What derived traits might you find in this mutualistic fungus?

3. **MAKE CONNECTIONS** Review Figure 10.4 and Figure 10.6. If a plant has mycorrhizae, where might carbon that enters the plant's stomata as CO_2 eventually be deposited: in the plant, in the mycorrhizal fungus, or in both? Explain.

For suggested answers, see Appendix A.

CONCEPT **31.2**

Fungi produce spores through sexual or asexual life cycles

Most fungi propagate themselves by producing vast numbers of spores, either sexually or asexually. For example, puffballs, the reproductive structures of certain fungal species, may release trillions of spores in cloud-like bursts (see Figure 31.17). Spores can be carried long distances by wind or water. If they land in a moist place where there is food, they germinate, producing new mycelia. To appreciate how effective spores are at dispersing, leave a slice of melon exposed to the air. Even without a visible source of spores nearby, within a week or so you will likely observe fuzzy mycelia growing from the microscopic spores that have fallen onto the melon.

Figure 31.5 on page 697 generalizes the many different life cycles that can produce fungal spores. In this section, we will survey general aspects of the sexual and asexual life cycles of fungi. Later, we'll examine more closely the life cycles of specific fungi.

Sexual Reproduction

The nuclei of fungal hyphae and the spores of most fungal species are haploid, although many fungi have transient diploid stages that form during sexual life cycles. In fungi, sexual reproduction often begins when hyphae from two mycelia release sexual signalling molecules called

Interpreting Genomic Data and Generating Hypotheses

What Can Genomic Analysis of a Mycorrhizal Fungus Reveal About Mycorrhizal Interactions? The first genome of a mycorrhizal fungus to be sequenced was that of the basidiomycete *Laccaria bicolor* (see photo). In nature, *L. bicolor* is a common ectomycorrhizal fungus of trees such as poplar and fir, as well as a free-living soil organism. In forest nurseries, it is used in large-scale inoculation programs to enhance seedling growth. The fungus can easily be grown alone

DOE Photo

in culture and can establish mycorrhizae with tree roots in the laboratory. Researchers hope that studying the genome of *Laccaria* will yield clues to the processes by which it interacts with its mycorrhizal partners—and by extension, to mycorrhizal interactions involving other fungi.

How the Study Was Done Using the whole-genome shotgun method (see Figure 21.2) and bioinformatics, researchers sequenced the genome of *L. bicolor* and compared it with the genomes of some nonmycorrhizal basidiomycete fungi. By analyzing gene expression using microarrays, the researchers were able to compare gene expression levels for different protein-coding genes and for the same genes in a mycorrhizal mycelium and a free-living mycelium. They could thus identify the genes for fungal proteins that are made specifically in mycorrhizae.

Data from the Study

Table 1. Numbers of Genes in *L. bicolor* and Four Nonmycorrhizal Fungal Species

	L. bicolor	1	2	3	4
Protein-coding genes	20 614	13 544	10 048	7302	6522
Genes for membrane transporters	505	412	471	457	386
Genes for small secreted proteins (SSPs)	2191	838	163	313	58

Table 2. *L. bicolor* Genes Most Highly Upregulated in Ectomycorrhizal Mycelium (ECM) of Douglas Fir or Poplar vs. Free-Living Mycelium (FLM)

Protein ID	Protein Feature or Function	Douglas Fir ECM/FLM Ratio	Poplar ECM/FLM Ratio
298599	Small secreted protein	22 877	12 913
293826	Enzyme inhibitor	14 750	17 069
333839	Small secreted protein	7844	1931
316764	Enzyme	2760	1478

Interpret the Data

1. (a) From the data in Table 1, which fungal species has the most genes encoding membrane transporters (membrane transport proteins; see Chapter 7)? (b) Why might these genes be of particular importance to *L. bicolor*?

2. The researchers used the phrase "small secreted proteins" (SSPs) to refer to proteins less than 100 amino acids in length that the fungi secrete; their function is not yet known. (a) What is most striking about the Table 1 data on SSPs? (b) The researchers found that the SSP genes shared a common feature that indicated the encoded proteins were destined for secretion. Based on Figure 17.21 and the text discussion of this figure, predict what this common characteristic of the SSP genes was. (c) Suggest a hypothesis for the roles of SSPs in mycorrhizae.

3. Table 2 shows data from gene expression studies for the four *L. bicolor* genes whose transcription was most increased ("upregulated") in mycorrhizae. (a) For the gene encoding the first protein listed, what does the number 22 877 indicate? (b) Do the data in Table 2 support your hypothesis in 2(c)? Explain.

4. (a) In Table 2, how do the data for poplar mycorrhizae compare with those for Douglas fir mycorrhizae? (b) Suggest a general hypothesis for this difference.

Data from F. Martin et al., The genome of *Laccaria bicolor* provides insights into mycorrhizal symbiosis, *Nature* 452:88–93 (2008). © Jane B. Reece.

pheromones. If the mycelia are of different mating types, the pheromones from each partner bind to receptors on the other, and the hyphae extend toward the source of the pheromones. When the hyphae meet, they fuse. In species with such a "compatibility test," this process contributes to genetic variation by preventing hyphae from fusing with other hyphae from the same mycelium or another genetically identical mycelium.

The union of the cytoplasms of two parent mycelia is known as **plasmogamy**. In most fungi, the haploid nuclei contributed by each parent do not fuse right away. Instead, parts of the fused mycelium contain coexisting, genetically different nuclei. Such a mycelium is said to be a **heterokaryon** (meaning "different nuclei"). In some species, the different nuclei may even exchange chromosomes and genes in a process similar to crossing over (see Chapter 13). In other species, the haploid nuclei pair off two to a cell, one from each parent. Such a mycelium is **dikaryotic** (meaning "two nuclei"). As a dikaryotic mycelium grows, the two nuclei in each cell divide in tandem without fusing. Because these cells retain two separate haploid nuclei, they differ from diploid cells, which have pairs of homologous chromosomes within a single nucleus.

Hours, days, or (in some fungi) even centuries may pass between plasmogamy and the next stage in the sexual cycle, **karyogamy**. During karyogamy, the haploid nuclei

Key

→ Haploid (n)

→ Heterokaryotic (unfused nuclei from different parents)

→ Diploid (2n)

PLASMOGAMY (fusion of cytoplasm)

Heterokaryotic stage

Spore-producing structures

Spores

ASEXUAL REPRODUCTION

Mycelium

SEXUAL REPRODUCTION

KARYOGAMY (fusion of nuclei)

Zygote

GERMINATION

GERMINATION

MEIOSIS

Spores

▲ **Figure 31.5 Generalized life cycle of fungi.** Many—but not all—fungi reproduce both sexually and asexually. Some reproduce only sexually, others only asexually.

? *Compare the genetic variation found in spores produced in the sexual and asexual portions of the life cycle and explain why these differences occur.*

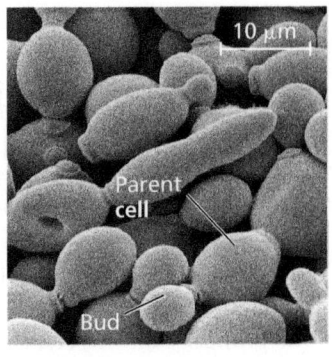

▲ **Figure 31.7 The yeast *Saccharomyces cerevisiae* in several stages of budding (*SEM*).**

Parent cell

Bud

10 μm

Stephen J. Kron

Asexual Reproduction

Many fungi can reproduce both sexually and asexually. Some 20 000 fungal species are only known to reproduce asexually. As with sexual reproduction, the processes of asexual reproduction vary widely among fungi.

Many fungi reproduce asexually by growing as filamentous fungi that produce (haploid) spores by mitosis; such species are known informally as **moulds** if they form visible mycelia. Depending on your housekeeping habits, you may have observed moulds in your kitchen, forming furry carpets on fruit, bread, and other foods (Figure 31.6). Moulds typically grow rapidly and produce many spores asexually, enabling the fungi to colonize new sources of food. Many species that produce such spores can also reproduce sexually if they happen to contact a member of their species of a different mating type.

Other fungi reproduce asexually by growing as single-celled yeasts. Instead of producing spores, asexual reproduction in yeasts occurs by ordinary cell division or by the pinching of small "bud cells" off a parent cell (Figure 31.7). As already mentioned, some fungi that grow as yeasts can also grow as filamentous mycelia, depending on the availability of nutrients.

contributed by the two parents fuse, producing diploid cells. Zygotes and other transient structures form during karyogamy, the only diploid stage in most fungi. Meiosis then restores the haploid condition, leading to the formation of spores that enable the fungus to disperse.

The sexual processes of karyogamy and meiosis generate extensive genetic variation, a prerequisite for natural selection. (See Chapters 13 and 23 to review how sex can increase genetic diversity in a population.) The heterokaryotic condition also offers some of the advantages of diploidy in that one haploid genome may compensate for harmful mutations in the other.

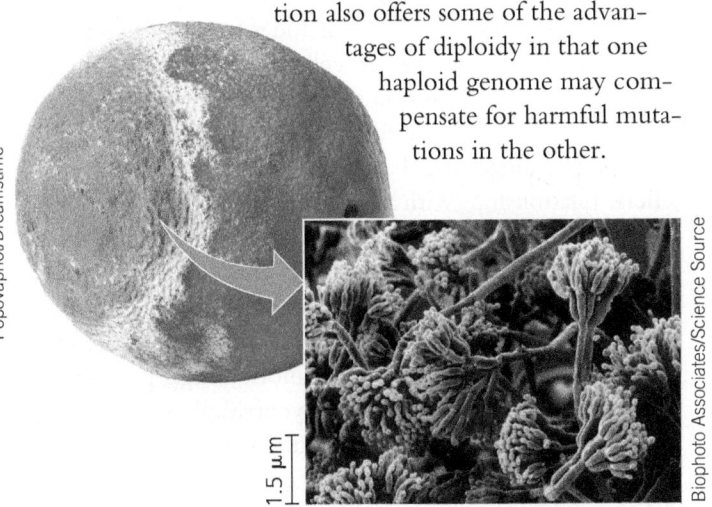

Popovaphot/Dreamstime

Biophoto Associates/Science Source

1.5 μm

▲ **Figure 31.6 *Penicillium*, a mould commonly encountered as a decomposer of food.** The bead-like clusters in the colourized SEM are conidia, structures involved in asexual reproduction.

CONCEPT CHECK 31.2

1. **MAKE CONNECTIONS** Compare Figure 31.5 with Figure 13.5. In terms of haploidy versus diploidy, how do the life cycles of fungi and humans differ?

2. **WHAT IF?** Suppose that you sample the DNA of two mushrooms on opposite sides of your yard and find that they are identical. Propose two hypotheses that could reasonably account for this result.

For suggested answers, see Appendix A.

CONCEPT 31.3

The ancestor of fungi was an aquatic, single-celled, flagellated protist

Fungi were often discussed in botany courses or included in the plant section of textbooks, but paleontology and molecular systematics indicate that fungi are more closely related to animals than either is to plants or other eukaryotic groups. Collectively, animals and fungi are in the same clade called **opisthokonts**, a name that refers to the posterior (opistho-) location of the flagellum in these organisms (Figure 31.8). While most fungi lack flagella, the earliest diverging ancestors had them, suggesting they were lost during evolution. Opisthokonts can be broadly separated into fungi and animals. However, DNA sequence evidence suggests these two groups arose from different unicellular ancestors. While animals are closely related to the choanoflagellates (see Figure 32.3), fungi are more closely related to a different group of protists, specifically the **nucleariids**, which are amoeba that feed on algae and bacteria. This indicates that multicellularity evolved independently in animals and fungi from different single-celled ancestors.

To estimate when the separation of fungi and animals occurred you have to rely on the fossil record or molecular clock calculations based on sequence data (see Chapter 26). Molecular clock approaches estimate the division occurred 1.5–1 billion years ago, however, the earliest undisputed fossils of fungi are only 460 million years old (Figure 31.9). This discrepancy may be related to the challenges associated with locating and identifying microscopic fossils. While there are fossils of unicellular marine eukaryotes that existed about 1.5 billion years ago, identifying them definitively as fungi over other unicellular eukaryotes is difficult.

Early-Diverging Fungal Groups

Understanding the biology of extant groups of early-diverging organisms can provide clues as to when specific

▲ Figure 31.8 **Fungi and their close relatives.** Molecular evidence indicates that the nucleariids, a group of single-celled protists, are the closest living relatives of fungi. The three parallel lines leading to the chytrids indicate that this group may be paraphyletic.

traits appeared in a group. Recent genomic studies have identified one of the earliest diverging fungi as a chytrid in the genus *Rozella*. Studies have also indicated that *Rozella* is part of a previously unknown clade of unicellular fungi called the "cryptomycota" (meaning hidden fungi), both of which have flagellated spores. Current evidence indicates that *Rozella* and other members of the cryptomycota are unique among fungi in that they do not synthesize a chitin-rich cell wall during any of their life cycle stages. This suggests that a cell wall strengthened by chitin—a key structural feature of the fungi—may have arisen after the cryptomycota diverged from other fungi.

Dirk Redecker

▲ Figure 31.9 **Fossil fungal hyphae and spores from the Ordovician period (about 460 million years ago) (LM).**

The Move to Land

Plants colonized land about 470 million years ago (see Chapter 29), and fungi may well have colonized land before plants did so. Indeed, some researchers have described life on land before the arrival of plants as a "green slime" that consisted of cyanobacteria, algae, and a variety of small, heterotrophic species, including fungi. With their capacity for extracellular digestion, fungi would have been well suited for feeding on other early terrestrial organisms (or their remains).

Once on land, some fungi formed symbiotic associations with early land plants. For example, 405-million-year-old fossils of the early land plant *Aglaophyton* contain evidence of mycorrhizal relationships between plants and fungi (see Figure 25.12). This evidence includes fossils of hyphae that have penetrated within plant cells and formed structures that resemble the haustoria of arbuscular mycorrhizae. Similar structures have been found in a variety of other early land plants, suggesting that plants probably existed in beneficial relationships with fungi from the earliest periods of colonization of land. The earliest land plants lacked roots, limiting their ability to extract nutrients from the soil. As occurs in mycorrhizal associations today, it is likely that soil nutrients were transferred to early land plants via the extensive mycelia formed by their symbiotic fungal partners.

Support for the antiquity of mycorrhizal associations has also come from recent molecular studies. For a mycorrhizal fungus and its plant partner to establish a symbiotic relationship, certain genes must be expressed by the fungus and other genes must be expressed by the plant. Researchers focused on three plant genes (called "*sym*" genes) whose expression is required for the formation of mycorrhizae in flowering plants. They found that these genes were present in all major plant lineages, including basal lineages such as liverworts (see Figure 29.6). Furthermore, after they transferred a liverwort *sym* gene to a flowering plant mutant that could not form mycorrhizae, the mutant recovered its ability to form mycorrhizae. These results suggest that mycorrhizal *sym* genes were present in the common ancestor of land plants—and that the function of these genes has been conserved for hundreds of millions of years as plants continued to adapt to life on land.

The early presence of fungi on land may have been more spectacular than imagined. Fossils discovered in the Gaspé Bay region of Quebec from the Devonian period (419–359 million years ago) suggest that one of the largest organisms on land during this time, standing up to 6 m in height, may have been a fungus. Called *Prototaxites*, these fossils have anatomy and carbon isotope ratios (indicating heterotrophic nutrition) that are consistent with fungi, though this is hotly debated! While these large trunk-like structures may be a large fungal sporophyte, others have interpreted them as algae, lichens, or even fossils of rolled liverwort mats. Scientists continue to search for evidence to support or refute the different hypotheses regarding the identity of these curious and unexpected organisms.

CONCEPT CHECK 31.3

1. Why are fungi classified as opisthokonts despite the fact that most fungi lack flagella?
2. Explain the evolutionary significance of the presence of mycorrhizae in the earliest vascular plants.
3. **WHAT IF?** If fungi had colonized land before plants, where might the fungi have lived? How would their food sources have differed from what they feed on today?

For suggested answers, see Appendix A.

CONCEPT 31.4

Fungi have radiated into a diverse set of lineages

In the past decade, molecular analyses have helped clarify the evolutionary relationships between fungal groups, although there are still areas of uncertainty. Figure 31.10, on the next page, presents a simplified version of one current hypothesis. In this section, we will survey each of the major fungal groups identified in this phylogenetic tree.

The groups shown in Figure 31.10 account for roughly 100 000 known species of fungi, but based on molecular evidence, the actual number may be over 10 times larger. Since many fungi are difficult to isolate and grow in culture, the diversity has been underestimated. Metagenomic studies that randomly sequence environmental

DNA samples are now revealing this hidden diversity. For instance, the cryptomycota (see Concept 31.3) and other entirely new groups of unicellular fungi were discovered in these metagenomic screens. The genetic variation found in some of these groups is as large as that found across all of the groups shown in Figure 31.10.

Chytrids

The fungi classified in the phylum Chytridiomycota, called **chytrids**, are ubiquitous in lakes and soil. Some of the approximately 1000 chytrid species are decomposers, while others are parasites of protists, other fungi, plants, or animals; one such chytrid parasite (*Batrachochytrium dendrobatidis*) has likely contributed to the global decline of amphibian populations. Still other chytrids are important mutualists. For example, anaerobic chytrids that live in the digestive tracts of sheep and cattle help to break down plant matter, thereby contributing significantly to the animal's growth.

As discussed earlier, molecular evidence indicates that some chytrid lineages diverged early in fungal evolution. The fact that chytrids are unique among fungi in having flagellated spores, called **zoospores** (Figure 31.11), agrees with this hypothesis. Like other fungi, chytrids (other than those in the recently discovered cryptomycota clade) have cell walls made of chitin, and they also share certain key enzymes and metabolic pathways with other fungal groups. Some chytrids form colonies with hyphae, while others exist as single spherical cells.

Zygomycetes

There are approximately 1000 known species of **zygomycetes**, fungi in the phylum Zygomycota. This diverse phylum includes species of fast-growing moulds responsible for causing foods such as bread, peaches, strawberries, and sweet potatoes to rot during storage. Other zygomycetes live as parasites or as commensal (neutral) symbionts of animals.

The life cycle of *Rhizopus stolonifer* (black bread mould) is fairly typical of zygomycete species (Figure 31.12). Its hyphae spread out over the food surface, penetrate it, and absorb nutrients. The hyphae are coenocytic, with septa found only where reproductive cells are formed. In the asexual phase, bulbous black sporangia develop at the tips of upright hyphae. Within each sporangium, hundreds of haploid spores develop and are dispersed through the air. Spores that happen to land on moist food germinate, growing into new mycelia.

If environmental conditions deteriorate—for instance, if the mould consumes all its food—*Rhizopus* may reproduce

Exploring Fungal Diversity

Many mycologists currently recognize five major groups of fungi, although recent genomic evidence indicates that the chytrids and zygomycetes are probably paraphyletic (as indicated by the parallel lines).

Chytrids (1000 species)

In chytrids such as *Chytridium*, the globular fruiting body forms multicellular, branched hyphae (LM); other species are single-celled. Chytrids have flagellated spores and are thought to include some of the earliest fungal groups to diverge from other fungi.

Hyphae

25 μm

John Taylor

Zygomycetes (1000 species)

The hyphae of some zygomycetes, including this mould in the genus *Mucor* (LM), grow rapidly into foods such as fruits and bread. As such, the fungi may act as decomposers (if the food is not alive) or parasites; other species live as neutral (commensal) symbionts.

Ray Watson

Glomeromycetes (160 species)

The glomeromycetes (arbuscular mycorrhizal fungi) are of great ecological importance. Many plants form mycorrhizal associations with these fungi. This LM shows glomeromycete hyphae (stained dark blue) within a plant root.

Fungal hypha

25 μm

Ecological Society of America

Ascomycetes (65 000 species)

Also called sac fungi, members of this diverse group are common to many marine, freshwater, and terrestrial habitats. The cup-shaped ascocarp (fruiting body) of the ascomycete shown here (*Aleuria aurantia*) gives this species its common name: orange peel fungus.

Lenz/blickwinkel/Alamy

Science Source

Basidiomycetes (30 000 species)

Widely important as decomposers and ectomycorrhizal fungi, basidiomycetes, or club fungi, are unusual in having a long-lived, dikaryotic mycelium. The fruiting bodies—commonly called mushrooms—of this fly agaric (*Amanita muscaria*) are a familiar sight in coniferous forests of the Northern Hemisphere.

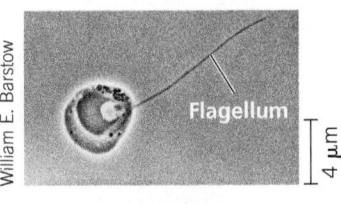

William E. Barstow

Figure 31.11 Flagellated chytrid zoospore (TEM).

Flagellum

4 μm

sexually. The parents in a sexual union are mycelia of different mating types, which possess different chemical markers but may appear identical. Plasmogamy produces a sturdy structure called a **zygosporangium**, in which karyogamy and then meiosis occur. Note that while a zygosporangium represents the zygote (2n) stage in the life cycle, it is not a zygote in the usual sense (that is, a cell with one diploid nucleus). Rather, a zygosporangium is a multinucleate structure, first heterokaryotic with many haploid nuclei from the two parents, then with many diploid nuclei after karyogamy.

Zygosporangia are resistant to freezing and drying and are metabolically inactive. When conditions improve, the nuclei of the zygosporangium undergo meiosis, the zygosporangium germinates into a sporangium, and the sporangium releases genetically diverse haploid spores that may colonize a new substrate. Some zygomycetes, such as *Pilobolus*, can actually "aim" and then shoot their sporangia toward bright light (Figure 31.13).

Glomeromycetes

Chytrids
Zygomycetes
Glomeromycetes
Ascomycetes
Basidiomycetes

The **glomeromycetes**, fungi assigned to the phylum Glomeromycota, were formerly thought to be zygomycetes. But recent molecular studies, including a

---

Key

→ Haploid (*n*)

→ Heterokaryotic (*n* + *n*)

→ Diploid (2*n*)

❶ Mycelia have various mating types (here designated (–), with red nuclei, and (+), with blue nuclei).

❷ Neighbouring mycelia of different mating types form hyphal extensions (gametangia), each of which encloses several haploid nuclei.

❸ A zygosporangium forms, containing multiple haploid nuclei from the two parents.

PLASMOGAMY

Gametangia with haploid nuclei

Mating type (–)

Mating type (+)

Young zygosporangium (heterokaryotic)

100 μm

Ed Reschke/Getty Images

Rhizopus growing on bread

Culture Collection of Fungi (CCF)

Mukhina Viktoriia/Shutterstock

❽ The spores germinate and grow into new mycelia.

SEXUAL REPRODUCTION

Dispersal and germination

Zygosporangium

❹ The zygosporangium develops a rough, thick-walled coating that can resist harsh conditions for months.

KARYOGAMY

Diploid nuclei

❾ Mycelia can also reproduce asexually by forming sporangia that produce genetically identical haploid spores.

❼ The sporangium disperses genetically diverse haploid spores.

Sporangia

ASEXUAL REPRODUCTION

Sporangium

MEIOSIS

Dr. George L. Barron

50 μm

Dispersal and germination

Mycelium

❺ When conditions are favourable, karyogamy occurs, then meiosis.

❻ The zygosporangium germinates into a sporangium on a short stalk.

▲ Figure 31.12 **The life cycle of the zygomycete** *Rhizopus stolonifer* (black bread mould).

◀ **Figure 31.13** *Pilobolus* **aiming its sporangia.** This zygomycete decomposes animal dung. Its spore-bearing hyphae bend toward light, where there are likely to be openings in the vegetation through which spores may reach fresh grass. Due to a buildup of hydrostatic pressure in the stalk, the fungus can launch its sporangia in a jet of water that can travel up to 2.5 m. Grazing animals ingest the fungi with the grass and then scatter the spores in feces, thereby enabling the next generation of fungi to grow.

G.L. Barron/Biological Photo Service

phylogenetic analysis of DNA sequence data from hundreds of fungal species, indicate that glomeromycetes form a separate clade (monophyletic group). Although only 160 species have been identified to date, the glomeromycetes are an ecologically significant group in that nearly all of them form arbuscular mycorrhizae (**Figure 31.14**). The tips of the hyphae that push into plant root cells branch into tiny tree-like arbuscules. About 80% of all plant species have such mutualistic partnerships with glomeromycetes.

Ascomycetes

Chytrids
Zygomycetes
Glomeromycetes
Ascomycetes
Basidiomycetes

Mycologists have described 65 000 species of **ascomycetes**, fungi in the phylum Ascomycota, from a wide variety of marine, freshwater, and terrestrial habitats. The defining feature of ascomycetes is the production of spores in saclike **asci** (singular, *ascus*) during sexual reproduction; thus, they

M. F. Brown/Biological Photo Service

▲ **Figure 31.14** **Arbuscular mycorrhizae.** Most glomeromycetes form arbuscular mycorrhizae with plant roots, supplying minerals and other nutrients to the roots. This SEM depicts the branched hyphae—an arbuscule—of *Glomus mosseae* bulging into a root cell by pushing in the membrane (the root has been treated to remove the cytoplasm).

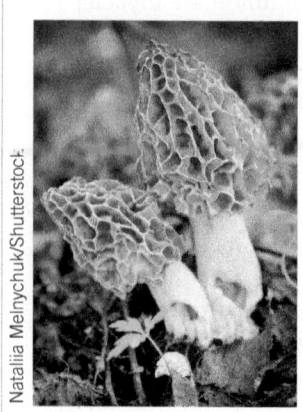

▶ *Tuber melanosporum* is a truffle species that forms ectomycorrhizae with trees. The ascocarp grows underground and emits a strong odour. These ascocarps have been dug up and the bottom one sliced open.

Jacana/Scien Source

◀ The edible ascocarp of *Morchella esculenta*, the tasty morel, is often found under trees in orchards.

Natalia Melnychuk/Shutterstock

▲ **Figure 31.15** **Ascomycetes (sac fungi).**

[?] *Ascomycetes vary greatly in morphology (see also Figure 31.10). How could you confirm that a fungus is an ascomycete?*

are commonly called *sac fungi*. Unlike zygomycetes, during their sexual stage most ascomycetes develop fruiting bodies, called **ascocarps**, which range in size from microscopic to macroscopic (**Figure 31.15**). The ascocarps contain the spore-forming asci.

Ascomycetes vary in size and complexity from unicellular yeasts to elaborate cup fungi and morels (see Figure 31.15). They include some of the most devastating plant pathogens, which we will discuss later. However, many ascomycetes are important decomposers, particularly of plant material. More than 25% of all ascomycete species live with green algae or cyanobacteria in beneficial symbiotic associations called lichens. Some ascomycetes form mycorrhizae with plants. Many others live between mesophyll cells in leaves; some of these species release toxic compounds that help protect the plant from insects.

Although the life cycles of various ascomycete groups differ in the details of their reproductive structures and processes, we'll illustrate some common elements using the bread mould *Neurospora crassa* (**Figure 31.16**). Ascomycetes reproduce asexually by producing enormous numbers of asexual spores called **conidia** (singular, *conidium*). Conidia are not formed inside sporangia, as are the asexual spores of most zygomycetes. Rather, they are produced externally at the tips of specialized hyphae called conidiophores, often in clusters or long chains, from which they may be dispersed by the wind.

Conidia may also be involved in sexual reproduction, fusing with hyphae from a mycelium of a different mating type, as occurs in *Neurospora*. Fusion of two different mating types is followed by plasmogamy, resulting in the formation of dikaryotic cells, each with two haploid nuclei representing the two parents. The cells at the tips of these

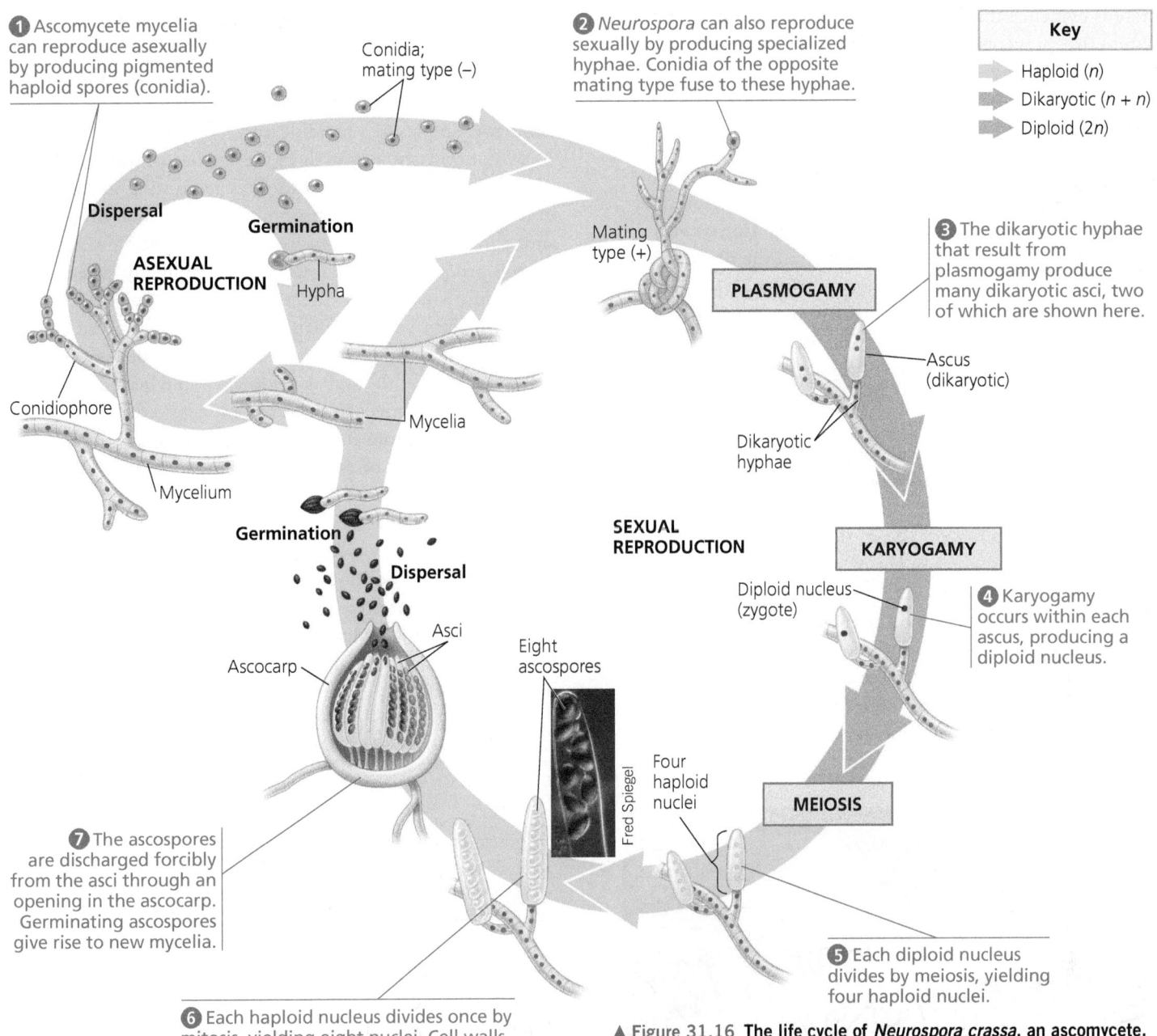

1 Ascomycete mycelia can reproduce asexually by producing pigmented haploid spores (conidia).

Conidia; mating type (–)

Dispersal

Germination

ASEXUAL REPRODUCTION

Hypha

Conidiophore

Mycelia

Mycelium

Germination

Dispersal

Ascocarp

Asci

Eight ascospores

Fred Spiegel

2 *Neurospora* can also reproduce sexually by producing specialized hyphae. Conidia of the opposite mating type fuse to these hyphae.

Key

→ Haploid (*n*)

→ Dikaryotic (*n* + *n*)

→ Diploid (2*n*)

Mating type (+)

PLASMOGAMY

3 The dikaryotic hyphae that result from plasmogamy produce many dikaryotic asci, two of which are shown here.

Ascus (dikaryotic)

Dikaryotic hyphae

SEXUAL REPRODUCTION

KARYOGAMY

Diploid nucleus (zygote)

4 Karyogamy occurs within each ascus, producing a diploid nucleus.

Four haploid nuclei

MEIOSIS

7 The ascospores are discharged forcibly from the asci through an opening in the ascocarp. Germinating ascospores give rise to new mycelia.

5 Each diploid nucleus divides by meiosis, yielding four haploid nuclei.

6 Each haploid nucleus divides once by mitosis, yielding eight nuclei. Cell walls and plasma membranes develop around the nuclei, forming ascospores (LM).

▲ **Figure 31.16 The life cycle of *Neurospora crassa*, an ascomycete.** *Neurospora* is a bread mould and research organism that also grows in the wild on burned vegetation.

dikaryotic hyphae develop into many asci. Within each ascus, karyogamy combines the two parental genomes, and then meiosis forms four genetically different nuclei. This is usually followed by a mitotic division, forming eight ascospores. The ascospores develop in and are eventually discharged from the ascocarp.

Compared to the life cycle of zygomycetes, the extended dikaryotic stage of ascomycetes (and also basidiomycetes) provides increased opportunity for genetic recombination. In *Neurospora*, for example, many dikaryotic cells can develop into asci. The haploid nuclei in these asci fuse, and their genomes recombine during meiosis, resulting in a

multitude of genetically different offspring from one mating event (see steps 3–5 in Figure 31.16).

As we discussed in Chapter 17, biologists in the 1930s used *Neurospora* in research that led to the one gene–one enzyme hypothesis. Today, this ascomycete continues to serve as a model research organism. In 2003, its entire genome was published. With about 10 000 genes, this tiny fungus has about one-quarter fewer genes than the fruit fly *Drosophila* and about half as many as a human. The *Neurospora* genome is relatively compact, having few of the stretches of noncoding DNA that occupy so much space in the genomes of humans and many other eukaryotes. In fact, there is evidence that *Neurospora* has a genomic defence system that prevents noncoding DNA such as transposons from accumulating.

Basidiomycetes

Chytrids
Zygomycetes
Glomeromycetes
Ascomycetes
Basidiomycetes

An estimated 30 000 species, including mushrooms, puffballs, and shelf fungi, are called **basidiomycetes** and are classified in the phylum Basidiomycota (**Figure 31.17**). This phylum also includes mutualists that form mycorrhizae and two groups of destructive plant parasites: rusts and smuts. The name of the phylum derives from the **basidium** (Latin for "little pedestal"), a cell in which karyogamy occurs, followed immediately by meiosis. The club-like shape of the basidium also gives rise to the common name *club fungus*.

Basidiomycetes are important decomposers of wood and other plant material. Of all the fungi, certain basidiomycetes are the best at decomposing the complex polymer lignin, an abundant component of wood. Many shelf fungi break down the wood of weak or damaged trees and continue to decompose the wood after the tree dies.

The life cycle of a basidiomycete usually includes a long-lived dikaryotic mycelium (**Figure 31.18**). As in ascomycetes, this extended dikaryotic stage provides opportunities for many genetic recombination events, in effect multiplying

the result of a single mating. Periodically, in response to environmental stimuli, the mycelium reproduces sexually by producing elaborate fruiting bodies called **basidiocarps**. The common white mushrooms in the supermarket are familiar examples of a basidiocarp.

By concentrating growth in the hyphae of mushrooms, a basidiomycete mycelium can erect its fruiting structures in just a few hours; a mushroom pops up as it absorbs water and as cytoplasm streams in from the dikaryotic mycelium. By this process, a ring of mushrooms, popularly called a "fairy ring," may appear literally overnight (**Figure 31.19**). The mycelium below the fairy ring expands outward concentrically at a rate of about 30 cm per year, decomposing organic matter in the soil as it grows. Some giant fairy rings are produced by mycelia that are centuries old.

After a mushroom forms, its cap supports and protects a large surface area of dikaryotic basidia on gills. During karyogamy, the two nuclei in each basidium fuse, producing a diploid nucleus (see Figure 31.18). This nucleus then undergoes meiosis, yielding four haploid nuclei, each of which ultimately develops into a basidiospore. Large numbers of basidiospores are produced: The gills of a common white mushroom have a surface area of about 200 cm^2 and may release a billion basidiospores, which drop from the bottom of the cap and are blown away.

CONCEPT CHECK 31.4

1. What feature of chytrids supports the hypothesis that they represent an early-diverging fungal lineage?

2. Give examples of how form fits function in zygomycetes, glomeromycetes, ascomycetes, and basidiomycetes.

3. **WHAT IF?** Suppose that the mutation of an ascomycete changed its life cycle so that plasmogamy, karyogamy, and meiosis occurred in quick succession. How might this affect the ascospores and ascocarp?

For suggested answers, see Appendix A.

CONCEPT 31.5

Fungi play key roles in nutrient cycling, ecological interactions, and human welfare

In our survey of fungal classification, we've touched on some of the ways fungi influence other organisms. We will now look more closely at these impacts, focusing on how fungi act as **decomposers**, or **saprotrophs**, by acquiring nutrition from nonliving organic material; **mutualists**, where the fungus and another organism benefit from a symbiosis; and **pathogens**, when fungal growth harms an organism it is feeding on.

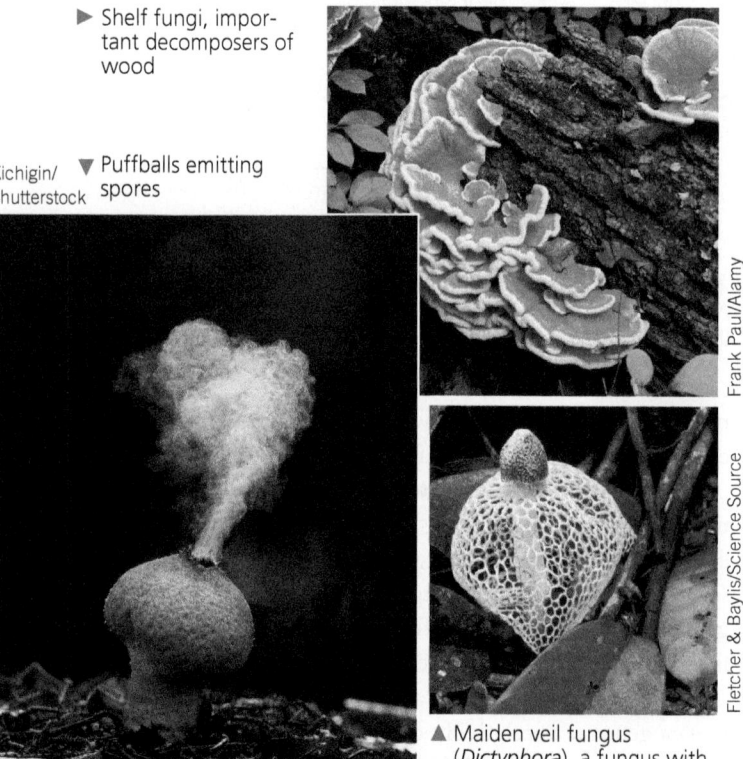

▶ Shelf fungi, important decomposers of wood

Kichigin/ Shutterstock

▼ Puffballs emitting spores

Frank Paul/Alamy

Fletcher & Baylis/Science Source

▲ Maiden veil fungus (*Dictyphora*), a fungus with an odour like rotting meat

▲ Figure 31.17 **Basidiomycetes (club fungi).**

▼ **Figure 31.18 The life cycle of a mushroom-forming basidiomycete.**

❶ Two haploid mycelia of different mating types undergo plasmogamy.

PLASMOGAMY

❷ A dikaryotic mycelium forms, growing faster than, and ultimately crowding out, the haploid parental mycelia.

Dikaryotic mycelium

❸ Environmental cues such as rain or change in temperature induce the dikaryotic mycelium to form compact masses that develop into basidiocarps (mushrooms, in this case).

Mating type (–)

Mating type (+)

❽ In a suitable environment, the basidiospores germinate and grow into short-lived haploid mycelia.

Haploid mycelia

SEXUAL REPRODUCTION

Gills lined with basidia

Basidiocarp (n + n)

❼ When mature, the basidiospores are ejected and then dispersed by the wind.

Dispersal and germination

Basidiospores (n)

Basidia (n + n)

Basidium with four basidiospores

Basidium containing four haploid nuclei

❹ The basidiocarp gills are lined with terminal dikaryotic cells called basidia.

KARYOGAMY

Basidium

Biophoto Associates/Science Source

MEIOSIS

❻ Each diploid nucleus yields four haploid nuclei, each of which develops into a basidiospore (SEM).

Diploid nuclei

❺ Karyogamy in each basidium produces a diploid nucleus, which then undergoes meiosis.

1 μm   Basidiospore

Key

Haploid (n)

Dikaryotic (n + n)

Diploid (2n)

University of Tennessee Entomology and Plant Pathology

▲ **Figure 31.19 A fairy ring.** According to legend, these mushrooms spring up where fairies have danced in a ring on a moonlit night. The text provides a biological explanation of how fairy rings form.

Fungi as Decomposers (Saprotrophs)

Fungi are well adapted as decomposers of organic material, including the cellulose and lignin of plant cell walls. In fact, almost any carbon-containing substrate—even jet fuel and house paint—can be consumed by at least some fungi. As you might expect, researchers are developing ways to use a variety of fungal species in bioremediation projects. In addition, fungi and bacteria are primarily responsible for keeping ecosystems stocked with the inorganic nutrients essential for plant growth. Without these decomposers, carbon, nitrogen, and other elements would remain tied up in organic matter. Plants and the animals that eat them could not exist because elements taken from the soil would not be returned (see Chapter 55). Without decomposers, life as we know it would cease.

Fungi as Mutualists

Fungi may form mutualistic relationships with plants, algae, cyanobacteria, and animals. Mutualistic fungi absorb nutrients from a host organism, but they reciprocate with actions that benefit the host—as we already saw for the key mycorrhizal associations that fungi form with most vascular plants.

Fungus-Plant Mutualisms

All plants in their natural ecosystem seem to harbour fungal **endophytes** (but keep in mind that bacteria can be endophytes as well). These symbiotic fungi live entirely within the tissue (leaves, stems, flowers, and so on), often living in the space between the cells, without causing noticeable harm. Fungal endophytes differ from mycorrhizal fungi because their association is not limited to the roots, and they exist entirely within the plant tissue, emerging only during reproduction, usually when the plant is dead or dying. Most endophytes identified to date are ascomycetes and are distinct from mycorrhizal fungi. While mycorrhizal fungi have a defined function in nutrient transfer in the soil, the interaction between endophytes and the plant host is diverse. Endophytes have been shown to benefit certain grasses and other nonwoody plants by making toxins that deter herbivores or by increasing host plant tolerance of heat, drought, or heavy metals. Seeking to discover how endophytes affect a woody plant, researchers tested whether leaf endophytes benefit seedlings of the cacao tree, *Theobroma cacao* (Figure 31.20). Their findings show that the endophytes of woody flowering plants can play an important role in defending against pathogens.

Fungus-Animal Mutualisms

As mentioned earlier, some fungi share their digestive services with animals, helping break down plant material in the guts of cattle and other grazing mammals. Many species of ants take advantage of the digestive power of fungi by raising them in "farms." Leaf-cutter ants, for example, scour tropical forests in search of leaves, which they cannot digest on their own but carry back to their nests and feed to the fungi (Figure 31.21). As the fungi grow, their hyphae develop specialized swollen tips that are rich in proteins and carbohydrates. The ants feed primarily on these nutrient-rich tips. The fungi break down plant leaves into substances the insects can digest, and they also detoxify plant defensive compounds that would otherwise kill or harm the ants. In some tropical forests, the

---

▼ Figure 31.20 **Inquiry**

Do endophytes benefit a woody plant?

Experiment Fungal endophytes are symbiotic fungi found within the bodies of all plants examined to date. A. Elizabeth Arnold, at the University of Arizona, Tucson, and colleagues tested whether endophytes benefit the cacao tree (*Theobroma cacao*). This tree, whose name means "food of the gods" in Greek, is the source of the beans used to make chocolate, and it is cultivated throughout the tropics. Endophytes were added to the leaves of some cacao seedlings, but not others. (In cacao, endophytes colonize leaves after the seedling germinates.) The seedlings were then inoculated with a virulent pathogen, the protist *Phytophthora*.

Results Fewer leaves were killed by the pathogen in seedlings with endophytes than in seedlings without endophytes. Among leaves that survived, pathogens damaged less of the leaf surface area in seedlings with endophytes than in seedlings without endophytes.

■ Endophyte not present; pathogen present (E–P+)
■ Both endophyte and pathogen present (E+P+)

Conclusion The presence of endophytes appears to benefit cacao trees by reducing the leaf mortality and damage caused by *Phytophthora*.

Source: Adaptation of figures 4 and 5 from "Fungal Endophytes Limit Pathogen Damage in a Tropical Tree" by A. Elizabeth Arnold et al., *PNAS*, December 2003, Volume 100(26). Copyright © 2003 by National Academy of Sciences. Reprinted with permission.

WHAT IF? *Arnold and colleagues also performed control treatments. Suggest two controls they might have used, and explain how each would be helpful in interpreting the results described here.*

▲ Figure 31.21 **Fungus-gardening insects.** These leaf-cutting ants depend on fungi to convert plant material to a form the insects can digest. The fungi, in turn, depend on the nutrients from the leaves the ants feed them.

fungi have helped these insects become the major consumers of leaves.

The evolution of such farmer ants and that of their fungal "crops" have been tightly linked for over 50 million years. The fungi have become so dependent on their caretakers that in many cases they can no longer survive without the ants, and vice versa.

Fungus-Algal Mutualisms: Lichens

A **lichen** is a symbiotic association between a photosynthetic microorganism and a fungus in which millions of photosynthetic cells are held in a mass of fungal hyphae. Lichens grow on the surfaces of rocks, rotting logs, trees, and roofs in various forms **(Figure 31.22)**. The photosynthetic partners are unicellular or filamentous green algae or cyanobacteria. The fungal component is most often an ascomycete, but one glomeromycete and 75 basidiomycete lichens are known. In 2016, there was a surprising discovery that some common lichens have a third, symbiotic partner—a yeast! The fungal components usually give a lichen its overall shape and structure, and tissues formed by hyphae account for most of the lichen's mass. The algae or cyanobacteria generally occupy an inner layer below the lichen surface **(Figure 31.23)**.

The merger of fungus and alga or cyanobacterium is so complete that lichens are given scientific names as though they were single organisms; to date, 17 000 lichen species have been described. As might be expected of such "dual organisms," asexual reproduction as a symbiotic unit is common. This can occur either by fragmentation of the parental lichen or by the formation of **soredia**, small clusters of hyphae with embedded algae (see Figure 31.23). The fungi of many lichens also reproduce sexually. Despite the tight interaction, these partners can be coaxed about to live independently in the laboratory.

In most lichens, each partner provides something the other could not obtain on its own. The algae provide carbon compounds; the cyanobacteria also fix nitrogen (see Chapter 27) and provide organic nitrogen compounds. The fungi provide their photosynthetic partners with a suitable environment for growth. The physical arrangement of hyphae allows for gas exchange, protects

▼ Crustose (encrusting) lichens

▼ A foliose (leaflike) lichen
Geoff Simpson/Nature Picture Library

Ralph Lee Hopkins/National Geographic/Getty Images

▶ A fruticose (shrublike) lichen

Wild-Wonders of Europe/Nature Picture Library

▲ Figure 31.22 **Variation in lichen growth forms.**

the photosynthetic partner, and retains water and minerals, most of which are absorbed either from airborne dust or from rain. The fungi also secrete acids, which aid in the uptake of minerals.

Lichens are important pioneers on cleared rock and soil surfaces, such as volcanic flows and burned forests. They break down the surface by physically penetrating and chemically attacking it, and they trap windblown soil. Nitrogen-fixing lichens also add organic nitrogen to some ecosystems. These processes make it possible for a succession of plants to grow (see Chapter 54). Lichens may also have aided the colonization of land by plants. Fossils of lichens or lichen-like organisms date to 550–600 million years ago, long before plants grew on land. Early lichens may have modified rocks and soil much as they do today, helping pave the way for plants.

Ascocarp of fungus

Fungal hyphae

Algal layer

Soredia

50 μm

Fungal hyphae

Algal cell

Eye of Science/Science Source

▲ Figure 31.23 **Anatomy of an ascomycete lichen (colourised SEM).**

Fungi as Pathogens

About 30% of the 100 000 known species of fungi make a living as parasites or pathogens, mostly of plants. For example, the ascomycete fungus *Grosmannia clavigera* (blue stain fungus), along with the mountain pine beetle, have been responsible for the loss of over 17.5 million hectares (5 times the size of Vancouver Island) of lodgepole pine in British Columbia alone (Figure 31.24). The blue stain fungus, so called because of the characteristic colour left in the wood (Figure 31.24b), is found on specialized head structures of the beetle. The fungus is transferred between trees by this burrowing insect and, once the beetle bores into the tree, the fungus is transferred to the nutrient-rich portion of the tree where it grows. It is thought that the fungus may compromise the tree's defences against the beetle and cut off nutrient and water transport, leading to tree mortality. Another ascomycete, *Ophiostoma ulmi*, is the cause of Dutch elm disease that has devastated populations of the elm tree in Europe and North America. Transmitted by the elm bark beetle, infection by this fungus ultimately leads to a blockage of water and nutrient transport, and death of the tree. At the University of Guelph, Praveen Saxena has taken the approach of cloning American elms that have survived the fungal outbreak, with the goal of propagating resistant trees for future generations. Interestingly, one such tree is located on the Guelph campus. While the disease has changed the landscape of many cities, in Fredericton, New Brunswick, magnificent elm trees still line some city streets due to an active disease-monitoring program.

Fungal pathogens have a significant effect on world food production, and between 10% and 50% of the world's fruit harvest is lost annually due to fungi, with grain crops also suffering major losses each year. Some fungi that attack food crops produce compounds that are toxic to humans. Certain species of the ascomycete *Aspergillus* contaminate grain and peanuts by secreting compounds called aflatoxins. Another example is the ascomycete *Claviceps purpurea*, which grows on rye plants, forming purple structures called ergots. If infected rye is milled into flour, toxins from the ergots can cause ergotism, characterized by gangrene, nervous spasms, burning sensations, hallucinations, and temporary insanity. An epidemic of ergotism around 944 CE killed more than 40 000 people in France. One compound that has been isolated from ergots is lysergic acid, the raw material from which the hallucinogen LSD is made.

Although animals are less susceptible to parasitic fungi than are plants, about 500 fungi are known to parasitize animals. One such parasite, the ascomycete *Pseudogymnoascus destructans* (formerly *Geomyces destructans*), is the cause of bat white-nose syndrome that has been reducing the populations of cave-hibernating bats across eastern North America (Figure 31.25). The infection is obvious by white, fuzzy fungal growth on the nose, ears, and wing membranes. When infected, bats have more frequent arousal time during hibernation, leading to depleted fat reserves and ultimately death. The fungus is psychrophilic, meaning it grows optimally at low temperatures, coinciding with the temperatures in caves and mine shafts where bats hibernate. Recent evidence suggests that the fungus was introduced from Europe, where it is endemic (commonly found) but does not cause the mortality observed in North American bat populations.

The general term for an infection caused by a fungal parasite is **mycosis**. In humans, skin mycoses include the disease ringworm, so named because it appears as circular red areas on the skin. The ascomycetes that cause ringworm can infect almost any skin surface. Most commonly, they grow on the feet, causing the intense itching and blisters known as athlete's foot. Though highly contagious, athlete's foot and other ringworm infections can be treated with fungicidal lotions and powders.

Systemic mycoses, by contrast, spread through the body and usually cause very serious illnesses. They are typically caused by inhaled spores. For example, coccidioidomycosis is a systemic mycosis that produces tuberculosis-like symptoms in the lungs. While most recover without treatment, each year, hundreds of cases in North America require treatment with antifungal drugs, without which the disease would be fatal.

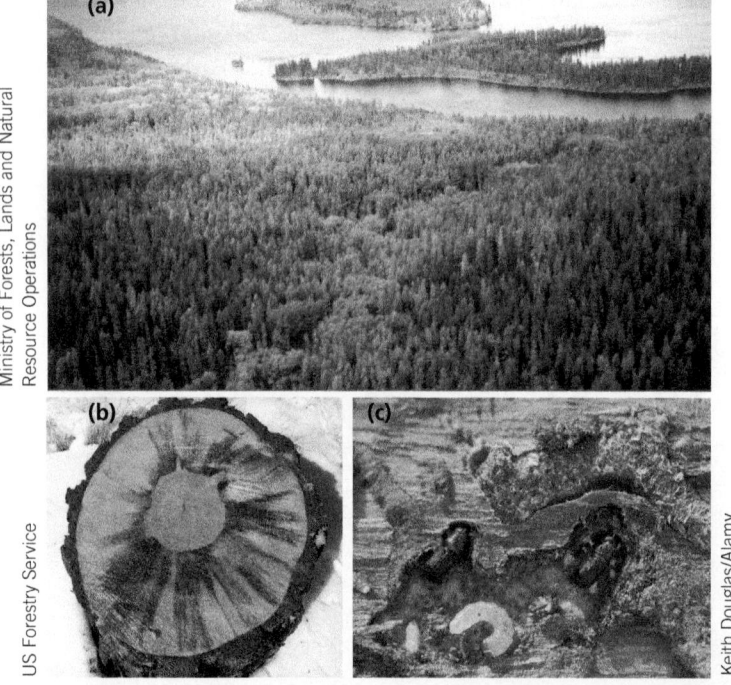

Ministry of Forests, Lands and Natural Resource Operations

US Forestry Service

Keith Douglas/Alamy

▲ **Figure 31.24 Extensive damage to the lodgepole pine forests of British Columbia.** This damage is caused by the fungus *Grosmannia clavigera*, which leaves a blue stain in the wood (b), and is transmitted by the mountain pine beetle (c).

Impact

Demise of North American, Cave-Hibernating Bats

No one had ever heard about bat white-nose syndrome (WNS), a disease caused by the ascomycete fungus *Pseudogymnoascus destructans*, until 2006 when the first infections were detected in bats hibernating in Howes Cave, in upstate New York. Since then, it has spread throughout the Eastern United States and Canada (Ontario, Quebec, New Brunswick, Nova Scotia, and Prince Edward Island), as shown in the WNS occurrence map below. The disease has been devastating to bat populations. Bat mortality has so far been estimated at over 6 million individuals. In New Brunswick, losses of cave-hibernating bat species are estimated to be 99%, and in 2013 only 22 brown bats were counted from a population that once surpassed 7000. Similar mortality has been observed at other bat hibernation sites in central and eastern Canada.

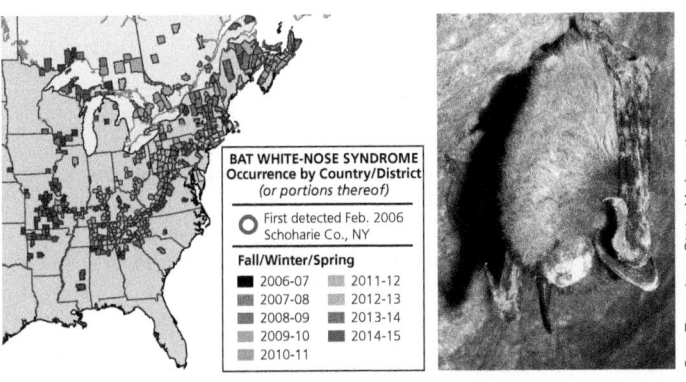

Source: Adaption of figure 1 from "Reversing Introduced Species Effects: Experimental Removal of Introduced Fish Leads to Rapid Recovery of a Declining Frog" by Vance T. Vredenburg, from PNAS, May 2004, Volume 101(20). Copyright © 2004 by National Academy of Sciences. Reprinted with permission.

Map: Spread of WNS throughout eastern North America since 2006.
Right: Little brown bat (*Myotis lucifugus*) with WNS

Why It Matters Three species of cave-hibernating bats in Canada—little brown bat, northern long-eared bat, and tri-coloured bat—are now on the federal endangered species list as a result of WNS. The loss of biodiversity is always a concern, but bats play important roles in forest ecosystems as insect predators. They help control insect populations, including agricultural pests. This case also illustrates the effect an introduced parasitic species can have on populations with no natural immunity to the infection.

Further Reading J. M. Lorch et al., Experimental infection of bats with *Geomyces destructans* causes white-nose syndrome. *Nature* 480: 376–379 (2011).

Some mycoses are opportunistic, occurring only when a change in the body's microorganisms, chemical environment, or immune system allows fungi to grow unchecked. *Candida albicans*, for example, is one of the normal inhabitants of moist epithelia, such as the vaginal lining. Under certain circumstances, *Candida* can grow too rapidly and become pathogenic, leading to so-called "yeast infections." Many other opportunistic mycoses in humans have become more common in recent decades, due in part to AIDS, which compromises the immune system.

Cryptococcus gattii is an emerging fungal disease in the Pacific North West, first reported on Vancouver Island. While typically a tropical disease, there are now around 15-20 cases a year in British Columbia; a small number of them are fatal. *Cryptococcus* exists on plant leaves and in the soil, and it is thought that patients contract the disease primarily through inhalation, where it initiates a lung infection. Why or how the disease has appeared in British Columbia is not known, but a change in climate has been one proposed factor.

Practical Uses of Fungi

The dangers posed by fungi should not overshadow their immense benefits. We depend on their ecological services as decomposers and recyclers of organic matter. And without mycorrhizae, farming would be far less productive.

Mushrooms are not the only fungi of interest for human consumption. Fungi are used to ripen Roquefort and other blue cheeses. A species of *Aspergillus* produces citric acid used in colas. Morels and truffles, the edible fruiting bodies of various ascomycetes, are highly prized for their complex flavours (see Figure 31.15). These fungi can sell for hundreds to thousands of dollars a kilogram. Truffles release strong odours that attract mammals and insects, which in nature feed on them and disperse their spores. In some cases, the odours mimic the pheromones (sex attractants) of certain mammals. For example, the odours of several European truffles mimic the pheromones released by male pigs, which explains why *female* pigs are used to help find these delicacies.

Humans have used yeasts to produce alcoholic beverages and bread for thousands of years. Under anaerobic conditions, yeasts ferment sugars to alcohol and CO_2, which causes dough to rise. Only relatively recently have the yeasts involved been separated into pure cultures for more controlled use. The yeast *Saccharomyces cerevisiae* is the most important of all cultured fungi (see Figure 31.1). It is available as many strains of baker's yeast and brewer's yeast.

Many fungi have great medical value as well. For example, a compound extracted from ergots is used to reduce high blood pressure and to stop maternal bleeding after childbirth. Some fungi produce antibiotics that are effective in treating bacterial infections. In fact, the first antibiotic discovered was penicillin, made by the ascomycete mould *Penicillium* (**Figure 31.26**). Other examples of pharmaceuticals derived from fungi include cholesterol-lowering drugs and cyclosporine, a drug used to suppress the immune system after organ transplants.

Fungi also figure prominently in research. For example, the yeast *Saccharomyces cerevisiae* is used to study the molecular genetics of eukaryotes because its cells are easy to culture and manipulate. Scientists are gaining insight into

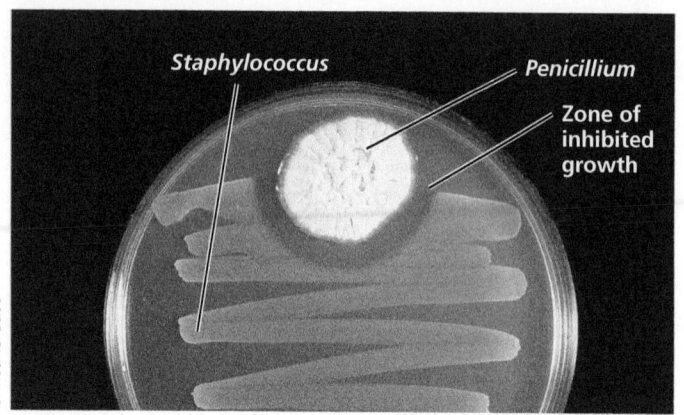

Staphylococcus

Penicillium

Zone of inhibited growth

Christine Case

▲ Figure 31.26 **Fungal production of an antibiotic.** The mould *Penicillium* produces an antibiotic (penicillin) that inhibits the growth of *Staphylococcus* bacteria, resulting in the clear area between the mould and the bacteria.

the genes involved in Parkinson's disease and other human diseases by examining the functions of homologous genes in *S. cerevisiae*.

Genetically modified fungi also hold much promise. For example, scientists have succeeded in engineering a strain of *S. cerevisiae* that produces human glycoproteins, including insulin-like growth factor. Such fungus-produced glycoproteins have the potential to treat people with medical

conditions that prevent them from producing these compounds. Meanwhile, other researchers are sequencing the genome of *Gliocladium roseum*, an ascomycete that can grow on wood or agricultural waste and that naturally produces hydrocarbons similar to those in diesel fuel. They hope to decipher the metabolic pathways by which *G. roseum* synthesizes hydrocarbons, with the goal of harnessing those pathways to produce biofuels without reducing land area for growing food crops (as occurs when ethanol is produced from corn).

Having now completed our survey of the kingdom Fungi, we will turn in the remaining chapters of this unit to the closely related kingdom Animalia, to which we humans belong.

CONCEPT CHECK 31.5

1. What are some of the benefits that lichen algae can derive from their relationship with fungi?
2. What characteristics of pathogenic fungi result in their being efficiently transmitted?
3. **WHAT IF?** How might life on Earth differ from what we know today if no mutualistic relationships between fungi and other organisms had ever evolved?

For suggested answers, see Appendix A.

---

31 Chapter Review

Go to **MasteringBiology**® for Assignments, the eText, and the Study Area with Animations, Activities, Vocab Self-Quiz, and Practice Tests.

SUMMARY OF KEY CONCEPTS

CONCEPT 31.1

Fungi are heterotrophs that feed by absorption (pp. 693–695)

- All **fungi** (including decomposers and symbionts) are heterotrophs that acquire nutrients by absorption. Many fungi secrete enzymes that break down complex molecules to smaller molecules that can be absorbed.
- Most fungi grow as thin, multicellular filaments called **hyphae**; relatively few species grow only as single-celled **yeasts**. In their multicellular form, fungi consist of **mycelia**, networks of branched hyphae adapted for absorption. Mycorrhizal fungi have specialized hyphae that enable them to form a mutually beneficial relationship with plants.

? *How does the morphology of multicellular fungi affect the efficiency of nutrient absorption?*

CONCEPT 31.2

Fungi produce spores through sexual or asexual life cycles (pp. 695–697)

- The sexual cycle involves cytoplasmic fusion (**plasmogamy**) and nuclear fusion (**karyogamy**), with an intervening heterokaryotic

stage in which cells have haploid nuclei from two parents. The diploid cells resulting from karyogamy are short-lived and undergo meiosis, producing haploid **spores**.
- Many fungi can reproduce asexually as filamentous fungi or yeasts.

DRAW IT *Draw a generalized fungal life cycle, labelling asexual and sexual reproduction, meiosis, plasmogamy, karyogamy, and the points in the cycle when spores and the zygote are produced.*

CONCEPT 31.3

The ancestor of fungi was an aquatic, single-celled, flagellated protist (pp. 698–699)

- Molecular evidence indicates that fungi and animals are more closely related to each other than either is to plants or other eukaryotic groups.
- Molecular evidence also supports the hypothesis that fungi and animals diverged from a common ancestor that was unicellular and had a flagellum.
- Fungi were among the earliest colonizers of land, including species that were symbionts with early land plants.

? *Did multicellularity originate independently in fungi and animals? Explain.*

CONCEPT 31.4

Fungi have radiated into a diverse set of lineages (pp. 699–704)

Fungal Phylum	Distinguishing Features of Morphology and Life Cycles	
Chytridiomycota (chytrids)	Flagellated spores	
Zygomycota (zygote fungi)	Resistant zygosporangium as sexual stage	
Glomeromycota (arbuscular mycorrhizal fungi)	Arbuscular mycorrhizae formed with plants	
Ascomycota (ascomycetes, or sac fungi)	Sexual spores (ascospores) borne internally in sacs called asci; vast numbers of asexual spores (conidia) produced	
Basidiomycota (basidiomycetes, or club fungi)	Elaborate fruiting body (basidiocarp) containing many basidia that produce sexual spores (basidiospores)	

DRAW IT *Draw a phylogenetic tree showing relationships among the five major groups of fungi.*

CONCEPT 31.5

Fungi play key roles in nutrient cycling, ecological interactions, and human welfare (pp. 704–710)

- Fungi perform essential recycling of chemical elements between the living and nonliving world.
- Some **endophytes** help protect plants from herbivores and pathogens, while other fungi help certain animals digest plant tissue. **Lichens** are highly integrated symbiotic associations of fungi and algae or cyanobacteria.
- About 30% of all known fungal species are parasites, mostly of plants. Some fungi also cause disease in animals.
- Humans eat many fungi and use others to make cheeses, alcoholic beverages, and bread. Antibiotics produced by fungi treat bacterial infections. Genetic research on fungi is leading to applications in biotechnology.

? *Summarize how fungi are important as decomposers, mutualists, and pathogens.*

TEST YOUR UNDERSTANDING

LEVEL 1: KNOWLEDGE/COMPREHENSION

1. *All* fungi share which of the following characteristics?
   - a. symbiotic
   - b. heterotrophic
   - c. flagellated
   - d. decomposers

2. Which of the following cells or structures are associated with *asexual* reproduction in fungi?
   - a. ascospores
   - b. basidiospores
   - c. zygosporangia
   - d. conidiophores

3. Among the organisms listed here, which are thought to be the closest relatives of fungi?
   - a. animals
   - b. vascular plants
   - c. mosses
   - d. slime moulds

LEVEL 2: APPLICATION/ANALYSIS

4. The most important adaptive advantage associated with the filamentous nature of fungal mycelia is
   - a. the ability to form haustoria and parasitize other organisms.
   - b. the potential to inhabit almost all terrestrial habitats.
   - c. the increased chance of contact between mating types.
   - d. an extensive surface area well suited for invasive growth and absorptive nutrition.

5. **SCIENTIFIC INQUIRY**

   INTERPRET THE DATA The grass *Dichanthelium languinosum* lives in hot soils and houses fungi of the genus *Curvularia* as endophytes. Regina Redman, of Montana State University, and colleagues performed field experiments to test the impact of *Curvularia* on the heat tolerance of this grass. They grew plants without (E–) and with (E+) *Curvularia* endophytes in soils of different temperatures and measured plant mass and the number of new shoots the plants produced. Draw a bar graph of the results for plant mass versus temperature and interpret it.

Soil Temp.	*Curvularia* Presence	Plant Mass (g)	Number of New Shoots
30°C	E–	16.2	32
	E+	22.8	60
35°C	E–	21.7	43
	E+	28.4	60
40°C	E–	8.8	10
	E+	22.2	37
45°C	E–	0	0
	E+	15.1	24

Source: Based on R. S. Redman et al., Thermotolerance generated by plant/fungal symbiosis, *Science* 298:1581 (2002). © Jane B Reece.

LEVEL 3: SYNTHESIS/EVALUATION

6. **EVOLUTION CONNECTION**

   The fungus-alga symbiosis that makes up a lichen is thought to have evolved multiple times independently in different fungal groups. However, lichens fall into three well-defined growth forms (see Figure 31.22). What research could you perform to test the following hypotheses?

   Hypothesis 1: Crustose, foliose, and fruticose lichens each represent a monophyletic group.

   Hypothesis 2: Each lichen growth form represents convergent evolution by taxonomically diverse fungi.

7. **WRITE ABOUT A THEME: ORGANIZATION**

   As you read in this chapter, fungi have long formed symbiotic associations with plants and with algae. In a short essay (100–150 words), describe how these two types of associations may lead to emergent properties in biological communities.

8. **SYNTHESIZE YOUR KNOWLEDGE**

The compression fossil of the giant *Prototaxites* from the Devonian period is hypothesized to be a fungus, though this is controversial. Ecologically speaking, why may *Prototaxites* have grown so large?

Boyce et al (2007) Devonian landscape heterogeneity recorded by a giant fungus. *Geology*, 35(5), 399. © 2007 The Geological Society of America

For selected answers, see Appendix A.

32

An Overview of Animal Diversity

Figure 32.1 caption attribution:

top left, Bernard Safran Estate; top centre, andreanita/Fotolia; top right, blickwinkel/Alamy; bottom left, Paul Whitten/Science Source; bottom centre, Andrew J. Martinez/Science Source; bottom right, Andrew J. Martinez/Science Source

▲ **Figure 32.1 What do all these animals found in Newfoundland have in common?**

KEY CONCEPTS

32.1 Animals are multicellular, heterotrophic eukaryotes with tissues that develop from embryonic layers

32.2 The history of animals spans more than half a billion years

32.3 Animals can be characterized by "body plans"

32.4 Views of animal phylogeny continue to be shaped by new molecular and morphological data

Welcome to Your Kingdom

Reading the last few chapters, you may have felt like a tourist among some unfamiliar organisms, such as slime moulds, whisk ferns, and sac fungi. You probably are more at home with the topic introduced in this chapter—the animal kingdom, which of course includes yourself. While humans are part of the animal kingdom, we are but a small portion of the evolutionary diversity in this group. **Figure 32.1**, for instance, shows a selection of animals found in Newfoundland. Foremost is Joey Smallwood, shown in a painting by Bernard Safran, the politician who led Newfoundland into Confederation in 1949 and the first premier of the new province. Some of the other animals, like the puffin (provincial bird of Newfoundland and Labrador) and the iconic codfish, are quite different, but still have a number of features that are obviously similar to humans. But look at the green darner dragonfly, the green sea urchin, and the northern red sea anemone in the bottom panels. What similarities do they share with the animals shown on the top panel? To date, biologists have identified 1.3 million extant (living) species of animals. Estimates of the actual number of animal species run far higher. This vast diversity encompasses a spectacular range of morphological variation, from corals to cockroaches to crocodiles and to you.

◄ **Woodland caribou (*Rangifer tarandus*)**

In this chapter, we embark on a tour of the animal kingdom that will continue in the next two chapters. We will consider the characteristics that all animals share, as well as those that distinguish various taxonomic groups. This information is central to understanding animal phylogeny, a topic that is a lively arena of biological research and debate, as you will read.

CONCEPT 32.1

Animals are multicellular, heterotrophic eukaryotes with tissues that develop from embryonic layers

Listing features shared by all animals is challenging, as there are exceptions to nearly every criterion we might select. When taken together, however, several characteristics of animals sufficiently describe the group for our discussion.

Nutritional Mode

Animals differ from both plants and fungi in their mode of nutrition. Plants are autotrophic eukaryotes capable of generating organic molecules through photosynthesis. Fungi are heterotrophs that grow on or near their food and that feed by absorption (often after they have released enzymes that digest the food outside their bodies). Unlike plants, animals cannot construct all of their own organic molecules and so, in most cases, they ingest them—either by eating other living organisms or by eating nonliving organic material. But unlike fungi, most animals do not feed by absorption; instead, animals ingest their food and then use enzymes to digest it within their bodies.

Cell Structure and Specialization

Animals are eukaryotes, and like plants and most fungi, animals are multicellular. In contrast to plants and fungi, however, animals lack the structural support of cell walls. Instead, a variety of proteins external to the cell membrane provide structural support to animal cells and connect them to one another (see Figure 6.28). The most abundant of these proteins is collagen, which is not found in plants or fungi.

The cells of most animals are organized into tissues, groups of similar cells that act as a functional unit. For example, muscle tissue and nervous tissue are responsible for moving the body and conducting nerve impulses, respectively. The ability to move and conduct nerve impulses underlies many of the adaptations that differentiate animals from plants and fungi. For this reason, muscle and nerve cells are central to the animal lifestyle.

Reproduction and Development

Most animals reproduce sexually, and the diploid stage usually dominates the life cycle. In the haploid stage, sperm and egg cells are produced directly by meiotic division, unlike what occurs in plants and fungi (see Figure 13.6). In most animal species, a small, flagellated sperm fertilizes a larger, nonmotile egg, forming a diploid zygote. The zygote then undergoes **cleavage**, a succession of mitotic cell divisions without cell growth between the divisions. During the development of most animals, cleavage leads to the formation of a multicellular stage called a **blastula**, which in many animals takes the form of a hollow ball (Figure 32.2).

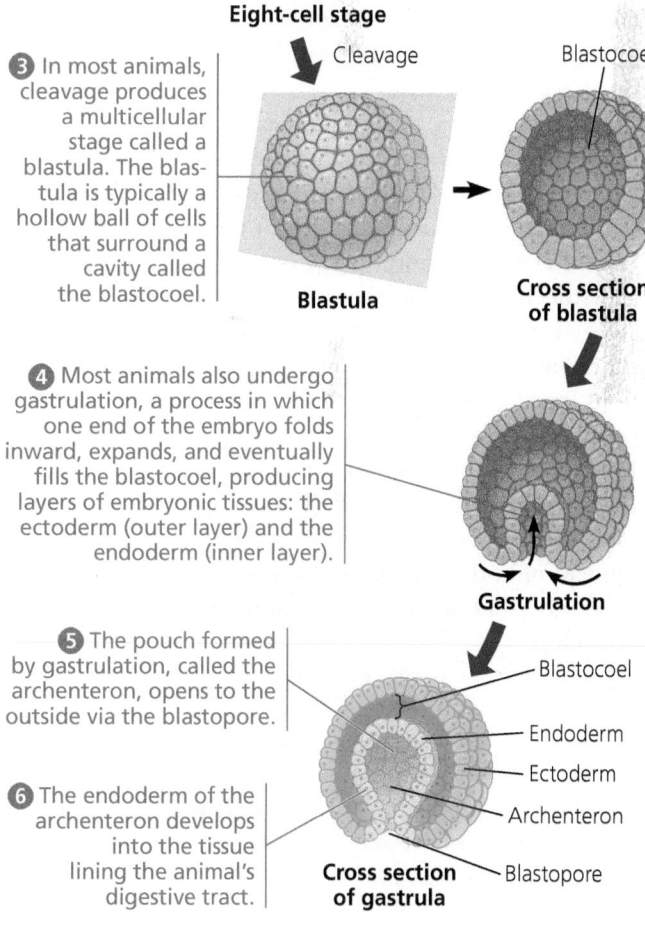

❶ The zygote of an animal undergoes a series of mitotic cell divisions called cleavage.

Zygote

Cleavage

❷ An eight-cell embryo is formed by three rounds of cell division.

Eight-cell stage

Cleavage

❸ In most animals, cleavage produces a multicellular stage called a blastula. The blastula is typically a hollow ball of cells that surround a cavity called the blastocoel.

Blastula

Blastocoel

Cross section of blastula

❹ Most animals also undergo gastrulation, a process in which one end of the embryo folds inward, expands, and eventually fills the blastocoel, producing layers of embryonic tissues: the ectoderm (outer layer) and the endoderm (inner layer).

Gastrulation

❺ The pouch formed by gastrulation, called the archenteron, opens to the outside via the blastopore.

❻ The endoderm of the archenteron develops into the tissue lining the animal's digestive tract.

Blastocoel
Endoderm
Ectoderm
Archenteron
Blastopore

Cross section of gastrula

▲ Figure 32.2 **Early embryonic development in animals.**

Following the blastula stage is the process of **gastrulation**, during which the layers of embryonic **tissues** that will develop into adult body parts are produced. The resulting developmental stage is called a **gastrula**.

Although some animals, including humans, develop directly into adults, the life cycles of most animals include at least one larval stage. A **larva** is a sexually immature form of an animal that is morphologically distinct from the adult, usually eats different food, and may even have a different habitat than the adult, as in the case of the aquatic larva of a mosquito or dragonfly. Animal larvae eventually undergo **metamorphosis**, a developmental transformation that turns the animal into a juvenile that resembles an adult but is not yet sexually mature.

Although adult animals vary widely in morphology, the genes that control animal development are similar across a broad range of taxa. All animals have developmental genes encoding transcription factors that regulate the expression of other genes, and many of these regulatory genes contain sets of DNA sequences called *homeoboxes* (see Chapter 21). Most animals share a unique homeobox-containing family of genes, known as *Hox* genes. *Hox* genes play important roles in the development of animal embryos, controlling the expression of dozens or even hundreds of other genes that influence animal morphology (see Chapter 25).

Sponges, which are among the simplest extant animals, lack *Hox* genes. However, they have other homeobox genes that influence their shape, such as those that regulate the formation of water channels in the body wall, a key feature of sponge morphology (see Figure 33.4). In the ancestors of more complex animals, the *Hox* gene family arose via the duplication of earlier homeobox genes. Over time, the *Hox* gene family underwent a series of duplications, yielding a versatile "toolkit" for regulating development. In vertebrates, insects, and most other animals, *Hox* genes regulate the formation of the anterior-posterior (front-to-back) axis, as well as other aspects of development. Similar sets of conserved genes govern the development of both flies and humans, despite their obvious differences and hundreds of millions of years of divergent evolution.

CONCEPT CHECK 32.1

1. Summarize the main stages of animal development. What family of control genes plays a major role?

2. **WHAT IF?** What animal characteristics would be needed by an imaginary plant that could chase, capture, and digest its prey—yet could also extract nutrients from soil and conduct photosynthesis?

For suggested answers, see Appendix A.

The history of animals spans more than half a billion years

A variety of studies suggest that the vast morphological diversity in the animal kingdom originated during the last billion years. However, dating the origin of animals is difficult, especially since the early animals lacked the hard, durable structures that normally fossilize well. Some researchers have used the presence of biomarkers in sediments to suggest the presence of specific animal groups. For example, in 710-million-year-old sediments, researchers have detected the chemical remains of certain steroids that today are primarily produced by a particular group of sponges. Hence, these fossil steroids suggest that animals had arisen by at least 710 million years ago.

DNA analyses generally agree with this fossil biochemical evidence; for example, one recent molecular clock study estimated that sponges originated about 700 million years ago. These findings are also consistent with molecular analyses suggesting that the common ancestor of all extant animal species lived about 770 million years ago. What was this common ancestor like, and how did animals arise from their single-celled ancestors?

To learn what this common ancestor may have been like, scientists have sought to identify protist groups that are closely related to animals. As shown in **Figure 32.3**, a combination of morphological and molecular evidence indicates that choanoflagellates are among the closest living relatives of animals. Based on such evidence, researchers hypothesize that the common ancestor of living animals may have been a suspension feeder similar to present-day choanoflagellates. We will next survey the fossil evidence for how animals evolved from their distant common ancestor over four geologic eras (see Table 25.1 to review the geologic time scale).

Neoproterozoic Era (1 Billion–542 Million Years Ago)

Animals first evolved in the Neoproterozoic era, and while steroid biomarkers provide the earliest evidence in this era, the first generally accepted macroscopic fossils of animals date from 565 to 550 million years ago. These fossils are members of an early group of soft-bodied multicellular eukaryotes, known collectively as the **Ediacaran biota**. The name comes from the Ediacara Hills of Australia, where fossils of these animals were first discovered (**Figure 32.4**).

Mistaken Point, on the Avalon Peninsula of Newfoundland, contains some of the oldest Ediacaran fossils that date to approximately 565 million years ago. Fossils common at Mistaken Point include some of the more enigmatic

---

▼ **Figure 32.3 Three lines of evidence that choanoflagellates are closely related to animals.**

? *Are the data described in ❸ consistent with predictions that could be made from the evidence in ❶ and ❷? Explain.*

Choanoflagellates

OTHER EUKARYOTES

Animals

Sponges

Other animals

Individual choanoflagellate

❶ Morphologically, choanoflagellate cells and the collar cells (or *choanocytes*) of sponges are almost indistinguishable.

Collar cell (choanocyte)

❸ DNA sequence data indicate that choanoflagellates and animals are sister groups. In addition, genes for signalling and adhesion proteins previously known only from animals have been discovered in choanoflagellates.

❷ Similar collar cells have been identified in other animals, including cnidarians, flatworms, and echinoderms—but they have never been observed in non-choanoflagellate protists or in plants or fungi.

of this era, such as a group of sessile organisms called the rangeomorphs that are characterized by fractal (self-similar) branching patterns (Figure 32.5). This unique pattern makes them difficult to classify, as they do not seem to be closely related to any living animal or algal groups. Rangeomorphs are, however, found in deep-water sediments where light would be limiting, thus indicating they were likely heterotrophic. Rangeomorphs disappeared from the fossil record in the Paleozoic era.

Other Ediacaran fossils do resemble extant sponges and cnidarians (sea anemones and their relatives) or molluscs (snails and their relatives) in morphology. In addition to

these macroscopic fossils, Neoproterozoic rocks have also yielded what may be microscopic fossils of early animal embryos. Although these microfossils appear to exhibit the basic structural organization of present-day animal embryos, debate continues about whether these fossils are indeed of animals.

The fossil record from the Ediacaran period (635–542 million years ago) also provides early evidence

(a) *Mawsonites spriggi*

(b) *Spriggina floundersi*

South Australian Museum

▲ **Figure 32.4 Ediacaran fossils.** Fossils dating to 565–550 million years ago include animals **(a)** with simple, radial forms and **(b)** with many body segments.

Courtesy of Phoebe A. Cohen

▲ **Figure 32.5 Rangeomorph (*Fractofusus*) fossils.** These fossils are commonly found on the exposed rock of Mistaken Point, Newfoundland.

of predation. Some animals of the time have a body protected by a shell that show signs of attack: round "bore holes" that resemble those formed today by predators that drill through the shells of their prey to gain access to the soft-bodied organisms lying within. Other small Ediacaran animals had shells or other defensive structures that may have been selected for because of predation. Overall, the fossil evidence indicates that the Ediacaran was a time of increasing animal diversity— a trend that continued in the Paleozoic era.

Paleozoic Era (542–251 Million Years Ago)

Another wave of animal diversification occurred 535–525 million years ago, during the Cambrian period of the Paleozoic era—a phenomenon referred to as the **Cambrian explosion** (see Chapter 25). In strata formed before the Cambrian explosion, only a few animal phyla have been observed. But in strata that are 535–525 million years old, paleontologists have found the oldest fossils of about half of all extant animal phyla, including the first arthropods, chordates, and echinoderms. The Burgess Shale, in British Columbia, is dated at around 505 million years old and has an incredible record of animal fossils from after the Cambrian explosion. Many of these distinctive fossils, which include the first animals with hard, mineralized skeletons, look very different from most living animals (Figure 32.6). Some fossils, like *Hallucigenia*, are perplexing, and it is difficult to distinguish what may be spines from legs or which end is the head. New electron microscopy approaches, however, are starting to reveal these details and are providing clues to the taxonomic position of these bizarre organisms. In the case of *Hallucigenia*, this work was able to distinguish spines, claws and a head with a simple pair of eyes and even teeth! These features provided evidence that *Hallucigenia* is distantly related to extant velvet worms (Ecdysoza). Jean-Bernard Caron, Curator of Invertebrate Paleontology at the Royal Ontario Museum, was involved in discovering *Hallucigenia*'s features and has a long-held interest in the Burgess Shale. You can even explore the amazing fossils of the Burgess Shale yourself at the Burgess Shale virtual museum (burgess-shale.rom.on.ca). One of the most famous fossils from this area is also one of the largest predators of its time, *Anomalocaris canadensis* (Figure 32.7). For

Chip Clark

The Natural History Museum, London

Hallucigenia fossil (530 mya)

1 cm

▲ **Figure 32.6 A Cambrian seascape.** This artist's reconstruction depicts a diverse array of organisms found in fossils from the Burgess Shale site in British Columbia, Canada. The animals include *Pikaia* (eel-like chordate at top left), *Marella* (arthropod swimming at left), an *anomalocaridid* (large animal with anterior grasping limbs and a circular mouth), and *Hallucigenia* (animals on the seafloor with toothpick-like spikes).

the most part, paleontologists have established that these Cambrian fossils are members of extant animal phyla, or at least are close relatives. In particular, most of the fossils from the Cambrian explosion are of **bilaterians**, an enormous clade whose members (unlike sponges and cnidarians) have a two-sided or bilaterally symmetric form (see Figure 32.8) and a complete digestive tract, an efficient digestive system that has a mouth at one end and an anus at the other. As we'll discuss later in the chapter, bilaterians include molluscs, arthropods, chordates, and most other living animal phyla.

As the diversity of animal phyla increased during the Cambrian period, the diversity of Ediacaran life-forms declined. What caused these trends? There are several current hypotheses. Some evidence suggests that during the Cambrian period, predators acquired novel adaptations, such as forms of locomotion that helped them catch prey, while prey species acquired new defences, such as protective shells. As new predator-prey relationships emerged, natural selection may have led to the decline of some groups and the rise of others. Another hypothesis focuses on an increase in atmospheric oxygen that preceded the Cambrian explosion. More plentiful oxygen would have enabled animals with higher metabolic rates and larger body sizes to thrive, while potentially harming other species. A third hypothesis proposes that the origin of *Hox* genes and the addition of new microRNAs (small RNAs involved in gene regulation) facilitated the evolution of

▼ Figure 32.7 **Impact**

The Burgess Shale and *Anomalocaris canadensis*

Located in Yoho National Park in the mountains of British Columbia, the Burgess Shale is a UNESCO World Heritage Site because of the significance of its Cambrian period fossil beds. Richard McConnell of the Canadian Geological Survey was one of the first to make collections of fossils from this area around 1885. Amongst the many discoveries were fossils from the arthropod *Anomalocaris* (meaning "unlike other shrimps"). It was Charles Walcott in 1907, however, working for the American Geological Survey, who made some of the most famous discoveries in an area he named the Burgess Shale, shown in the panel on the left. Interestingly, it took the efforts of dozens of paleontologists analyzing many different fossils, like the one in the top-right panel, to come up with a reconstruction of *Anomalocaris canadensis* (bottom right panel). *Anomalocaris* had compound eyes like other arthropods, lateral fins and a fantail that likely made it an agile swimmer, plus a bottom-facing, circular mouth with sharp plates. The largest of the Anomalocarids may have grown to 1 metre in length. Most have predicted that this species was the main predator of the Cambrian seas, though exactly what these animals ate is a matter of debate.

Why It Matters The Burgess Shale is one of the most significant fossil sites in the world because, in this area that was once a shallow sea teaming with life, many animal specimens from the middle of the Cambrian period are preserved. The fossils are from every major animal phylum and include many soft-bodied animals. While soft-bodied animals do not fossilize as frequently as the calcified bones of the vertebrates, here there are many such specimens, allowing for the reconstruction of the anatomy of individual species and the composition of the early animal community. The Burgess shale continues to provide evidence for many early diverging, now extinct, groups of animals like *Anomalocaris*. This helps us understand the origin of the main animal phyla you'll discuss in the next two chapters.

Further Reading D. Collins, The "evolution" of *Anomalocaris* and its classification in the arthropod class Dinocarida (nov.) and order Radiodonta (nov.), *Journal of Paleontology* 70:280–293 (1996).

MAKE CONNECTIONS *Figure 32.6 shows a variety of animals that existed in the Cambrian seas, but there is no depiction of algal/plant life. Review Figures 29.6 and 28.2 and predict what types of photosynthetic organisms may have existed during this period.*

new body forms. In the Scientific Skills Exercise, you can investigate whether there is a correlation between micro-RNAs (miRNAs; see Figure 18.14) and body complexity in various animal phyla. These hypotheses are not mutually exclusive, however; predator-prey relationships, atmospheric changes, and changes in the regulation of development may each have played a role.

The Cambrian period was followed by the Ordovician, Silurian, and Devonian periods, when animal diversity continued to increase, although punctuated by episodes of mass extinction (see Figure 25.17). Vertebrates (fishes) emerged as the top predators of the marine food web. By 460 million years ago, groups that diversified during the Cambrian period were making an impact on land. Arthropods began to adapt to terrestrial habitats, as indicated by the appearance of millipedes and centipedes. Another clue is seen in fossilized fern galls—enlarged cavities that fern plants form in response to stimulation by resident insects, which then use the galls for protection. Fossils indicate that fern galls date back at least 302 million years, suggesting that insects and plants were influencing each other's evolution by that time.

Vertebrates made the transition to land around 365 million years ago and diversified into numerous terrestrial groups. Two of these survive today: the amphibians (such as frogs and salamanders) and the amniotes (reptiles, including birds, and mammals). We will explore these groups, known collectively as the tetrapods, in more detail in Chapter 34.

Mesozoic Era (251–65.5 Million Years Ago)

The animal phyla that had evolved during the Paleozoic era now began to spread into new habitats. In the oceans, the first coral reefs formed, providing other marine animals with new habitats. Some reptiles returned to the water, leaving plesiosaurs (see Figure 25.5) and other large aquatic predators as their descendants. On land, descent with modification in some tetrapods led to the origin of wings and other flight equipment in pterosaurs and birds. Large and small dinosaurs emerged, both as predators and herbivores. At the same time, the first mammals—tiny nocturnal insect-eaters—appeared on the scene. In addition, as you read in Chapter 30, flowering plants (angiosperms) and insects both underwent dramatic diversifications during the late Mesozoicera.

Cenozoic Era (65.5 Million Years Ago to the Present)

Mass extinctions of both terrestrial and marine animals ushered in a new era, the Cenozoic. Among the groups of species that disappeared were the large, nonflying

Calculating and Interpreting Correlation Coefficients

Is Animal Complexity Correlated with miRNA Diversity? Animal phyla vary greatly in morphology, from simple sponges that lack tissues and symmetry to complex vertebrates. Members of different animal phyla have similar developmental genes, but the number of miRNAs varies considerably. In this exercise, you will explore whether miRNA diversity is correlated to morphological complexity.

How the Study Was Done In the analysis, miRNA diversity is represented by the average number of miRNAs in a phylum (x), while morphological complexity is represented by the average number of cell types (y). The researchers examined the relationship between these two variables by calculating the correlation coef-

Data from the Study

Animal Phylum	i	No. of miRNAs (x_i)	($x_i - \bar{x}$)	($x_i - \bar{x}$)²	No. of Cell Types (y_i)	($y_i - \bar{y}$)	($y_i - \bar{y}$)²	($x_i - \bar{x}$)($y_i - \bar{y}$)
Porifera	1	5.8			25			
Platyhelminthes	2	35			30			
Cnidaria	3	2.5			34			
Nematoda	4	26			38			
Echinodermata	5	38.6			45			
Cephalochordata	6	33			68			
Arthropoda	7	59.1			73			
Urochordata	8	25			77			
Mollusca	9	50.8			83			
Annelida	10	58			94			
Vertebrata	11	147.5			172.5			
		$\bar{x} =$ $s_x =$		$\Sigma =$	$\bar{y} =$ $s_y =$		$\Sigma =$	$\Sigma =$

ficient (r). The correlation coefficient indicates the extent and direction of a linear relationship between two variables (x and y) and ranges in value between -1 and 1. When $r < 0$, y and x are negatively correlated, meaning that values of y become smaller as values of x become larger. When $r > 0$, y and x are positively correlated (y becomes larger as x becomes larger). When $r = 0$, the variables are not correlated.

The formula for the correlation coefficient r is

$$r = \frac{\frac{1}{n-1}\sum(x_i - \bar{x})(y_i - \bar{y})}{s_x s_y}$$

In this formula, n is the number of observations, x_i is the value of the ith observation of variable x, and y_i is the value of the ith observation of variable y. $\bar{x}$ and $\bar{y}$ are the means of variables x and y, and s_x and s_y are the standard deviations of variables x and y. The Σ symbol indicates that the n values of the product $(x_i - \bar{x})(y_i - \bar{y})$ are to be added together.

Interpret the Data

1. First, practise reading the data table. For the eighth observation ($i = 8$), what are x_i and y_i? For which phylum are these data?

2. Next, we'll calculate the mean and standard deviation for each variable. (a) The mean ($\bar{x}$) is the sum of the data values divided by n, the number of observations: $\bar{x} = \dfrac{\sum x_i}{n}$. Calculate the mean number of

miRNAs ($\bar{x}$) and the mean number of cell types ($\bar{y}$) and enter them in the data table (for $\bar{y}$, replace each x in the formula with a y). (b) Next, calculate ($x_i - \bar{x}$) and ($y_i - \bar{y}$) for each observation, recording your results in the appropriate column. Square each of those results to complete the ($x_i - \bar{x}$)² and ($y_i - \bar{y}$)² columns; sum the results for those columns. (c) The standard deviation, s_x, which describes the variation found in the data, is calculated using the following formula:

$$s_x = \sqrt{\frac{1}{n-1}\sum(x_i - \bar{x})^2}$$

(d) Calculate s_x and s_y by substituting the results in (b) into the formula for the standard deviation.

3. Next, calculate the correlation coefficient r for the variables x and y. (a) First, use the results in 2(b) to complete the ($x_i - \bar{x}$)($y_i - \bar{y}$) column; sum the results in that column. (b) Now use the values for s_x and s_y from 2(c) along with the results from 3(a) in the formula for r.

4. Do these data indicate that miRNA diversity and animal complexity are negatively correlated, positively correlated, or uncorrelated? Explain.

5. What does your analysis suggest about the role of miRNA diversity in the evolution of animal complexity?

Data from Bradley Deline, University of West Georgia, and Kevin Peterson, Dartmouth College, 2013. © Jane B. Reece.

---

dinosaurs and the marine reptiles. The fossil record of the early Cenozoic documents the rise of large mammalian herbivores and predators as mammals began to exploit the vacated ecological niches. The global climate gradually cooled throughout the Cenozoic, triggering significant shifts in many animal lineages. Among primates, for example, some species in Africa adapted to the open woodlands and savannas that replaced many of the former dense forests. The ancestors of our own species were among those grassland apes.

CONCEPT CHECK 32.2

1. Put the following milestones in animal evolution in chronological order from oldest to most recent: (a) origin of mammals, (b) earliest evidence of terrestrial arthropods, (c) Ediacaran fauna, (d) extinction of large, nonflying dinosaurs.

2. **WHAT IF?** Suppose the most recent common ancestor of fungi and animals lived 1 billion years ago. If the first fungi lived 990 million years ago, would animals also have been alive at that time? Explain.

For suggested answers, see Appendix A.

CONCEPT 32.3

Animals can be characterized by "body plans"

Animal species vary tremendously in morphology, but their great diversity in form can be described by a relatively small number of major "body plans." A **body plan** is a particular set of morphological and developmental traits integrated into a functional whole—the living animal. The term *plan* here does not imply that animal forms are the result of conscious planning or invention. But body plans do provide a succinct way to compare and contrast key animal features. They also are of interest in the study of *evo-devo*, the interface between evolution and development (see Chapters 21 and 25).

Like all features of organisms, animal body plans have evolved over time. Some of the evolutionary changes appear to have occurred early in the history of animal life. For example, recent research suggests that a key step in the molecular control of gastrulation has remained unchanged for more than 500 million years. This early evolutionary innovation was of fundamental importance: Gastrulation helps to explain why most animals are not a hollow ball of cells. As we'll discuss, however, other aspects of animal body plans have changed multiple times over the course of evolution. Thus, as we explore the major features of animal body plans, bear in mind that similar body forms may have evolved independently in different lineages. In addition, body features can be lost over the course of evolution, causing some closely related species to look very different from one another.

Symmetry

A basic feature of animal bodies is their type of symmetry—or absence of symmetry. (Many sponges, for example, lack symmetry altogether.) Some animals exhibit **radial symmetry**, the type of symmetry found in a flowerpot (Figure 32.8a). Sea anemones, for example, have a top side (where the mouth is located) and a bottom side. But they have no front and back ends and no left and right sides.

The two-sided symmetry seen in a shovel is an example of **bilateral symmetry** (Figure 32.8b). A bilateral animal has two axes of orientation: front to back and top to bottom. Such animals have a **dorsal** (top) side and a **ventral** (bottom) side, a left side and a right side, and an **anterior** (front) end and a **posterior** (back) end. Many animals with a bilaterally symmetrical body plan (such as arthropods and mammals) have sensory equipment concentrated at their anterior end, including a central nervous system ("brain") in the head—an evolutionary trend called **cephalization** (from the Greek *kephale*, head).

(a) Radial symmetry.
A radial animal, such as a sea anemone (phylum Cnidaria), does not have a left side and a right side. Any imaginary slice through the central axis divides the animal into mirror images.

(b) Bilateral symmetry.
A bilateral animal, such as a lobster (phylum Arthropoda), has a left side and a right side. Only one imaginary cut divides the animal into mirror-image halves.

▲ Figure 32.8 **Body symmetry.** The flowerpot and shovel are included to help you remember the radial-bilateral distinction.

The symmetry of an animal generally fits its lifestyle. Many radial animals are sessile (living attached to a substrate) or planktonic (drifting or weakly swimming, such as jellies, commonly called jellyfish). Their symmetry equips them to meet the environment equally well from all sides. In contrast, bilateral animals typically move actively from place to place. Most bilateral animals have a central nervous system that enables them to coordinate the complex movements involved in crawling, burrowing, flying, or swimming. Fossil evidence indicates that these two fundamentally different kinds of symmetry have been present for at least 550 million years.

Tissues

Animal body plans also vary with regard to tissue organization. In animals, true tissues are collections of specialized cells isolated from other tissues by membranous layers. Sponges and a few other groups lack true tissues. In all other animals, the embryo becomes layered through the process of gastrulation. As development progresses, these layers, called *germ layers*, form the various tissues and organs of the body. **Ectoderm**, the germ layer covering the surface of the embryo, gives rise to the outer covering of the animal and, in some phyla, to the central nervous system. **Endoderm**, the innermost germ layer, lines the pouch that forms during gastrulation (the archenteron) and gives rise to the lining of the digestive tract (or cavity) and organs such as the liver and lungs of vertebrates.

Cnidarians and a few other animal groups that have only these two germ layers are said to be **diploblastic**. All bilaterally symmetrical animals have a third germ layer, called the **mesoderm**, which fills much of the space between the ectoderm and endoderm. Thus, animals with bilateral symmetry are also said to be **triploblastic** (having three germ layers). In triploblasts, the mesoderm forms the muscles and most other organs between the digestive tract and the outer covering of the animal. Triploblasts include a broad range of animals, from flatworms to arthropods to vertebrates. (Although some diploblasts actually do have a third germ layer, it is not nearly as well developed as the mesoderm of animals considered to be triploblastic.)

Body Cavities

Most triploblastic animals have a **body cavity**, a fluid- or air-filled space located between the digestive tract and the outer body wall. This body cavity is also called a **coelom** (from the Greek *koilos*, hollow). A so-called "true" coelom forms from tissue derived from mesoderm. The inner and outer layers of tissue that surround the cavity connect and form structures that suspend the internal organs. Animals with a true coelom are known as **coelomates** (Figure 32.9a).

Some triploblastic animals have a body cavity that is formed from mesoderm and endoderm (Figure 32.9b). Such a cavity is called a "pseudocoelom" (from the Greek *pseudo*, false), and the animals that have one are called **pseudocoelomates**. Despite its name, however, a pseudocoelom is not false; it is a fully functional body cavity. Finally, some triploblastic animals lack a body cavity altogether (Figure 32.9c). They are known collectively as **acoelomates** (from the Greek *a-*, without).

A body cavity has many functions. Its fluid cushions the suspended organs, helping to prevent internal injury. In soft-bodied coelomates, such as earthworms, the coelom contains noncompressible fluid that acts like a skeleton against which muscles can work. The cavity also enables the internal organs to grow and move independently of the outer body wall. If it were not for your coelom, for example, every beat of your heart or ripple of your intestine would warp your body's surface.

Terms such as *coelomates* and *pseudocoelomates* categorize organisms based on shared biological features (body plan). However, phylogenetic studies show that true coeloms and pseudocoeloms have been independently gained or lost multiple times in the course of evolution; thus, they did not inherit these traits from a common ancestor and would not form an evolutionary clade (a group that includes an ancestral species and all of its descendants). Groups that share biological traits not derived from the same ancestor form what is called an evolutionary **grade**. Thus, while describing an organism as a coelomate or pseudocoelomate can be helpful in describing its features,

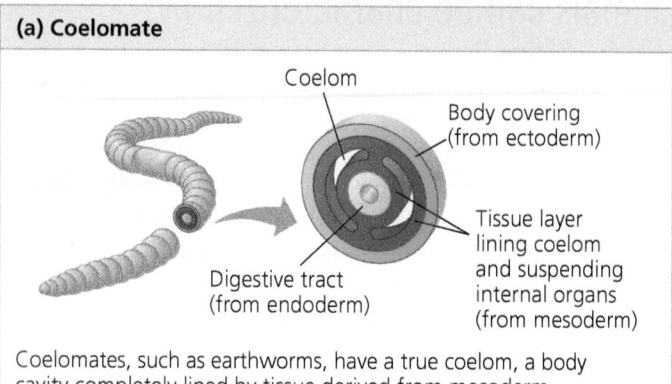

▼ Figure 32.9 **Body cavities of triploblastic animals.** The organ systems develop from the three embryonic germ layers.

(a) Coelomate

Coelom

Body covering (from ectoderm)

Digestive tract (from endoderm)

Tissue layer lining coelom and suspending internal organs (from mesoderm)

Coelomates, such as earthworms, have a true coelom, a body cavity completely lined by tissue derived from mesoderm.

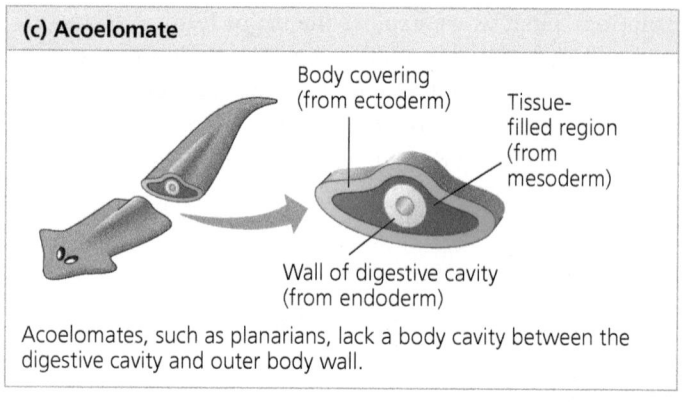

(b) Pseudocoelomate

Body covering (from ectoderm)

Pseudocoelom

Muscle layer (from mesoderm)

Digestive tract (from endoderm)

Pseudocoelomates, such as roundworms, have a body cavity lined by tissue derived from mesoderm and by tissue derived from endoderm.

(c) Acoelomate

Body covering (from ectoderm)

Tissue-filled region (from mesoderm)

Wall of digestive cavity (from endoderm)

Acoelomates, such as planarians, lack a body cavity between the digestive cavity and outer body wall.

Key

Ectoderm   Mesoderm   Endoderm

these terms don't necessarily reflect the organisms' evolutionary history.

Protostome and Deuterostome Development

Based on certain aspects of early development, many animals can be described as having one of two developmental modes: **protostome development** or **deuterostome development**. These modes can generally be distinguished by differences in cleavage, coelom formation, and fate of the blastopore.

Cleavage

Many animals with protostome development undergo **spiral cleavage**, in which the planes of cell division are diagonal to the vertical axis of the embryo; as seen in the eight-cell stage of the embryo, smaller cells are centred over the grooves between larger, underlying cells (**Figure 32.10a**, left). Furthermore, the so-called **determinate cleavage** of some animals with protostome development rigidly casts ("determines") the developmental fate of each embryonic cell very early. A cell isolated from a snail at the four-cell stage, for example, cannot develop into a whole animal. Instead, after repeated divisions, such a cell will form an inviable embryo that lacks many parts.

In contrast to the spiral cleavage pattern, deuterostome development is predominantly characterized by **radial cleavage**. The cleavage planes are either parallel or perpendicular to the vertical axis of the embryo; as seen at the eight-cell stage, the tiers of cells are aligned, one directly above the other (see Figure 32.10a, right). Most animals with deuterostome development also have **indeterminate cleavage**, meaning that each cell produced by early cleavage divisions retains the capacity to develop into a complete embryo. For example, if the cells of a sea urchin embryo are separated at the four-cell stage, each can form a complete larva. Similarly, it is the indeterminate cleavage of the human zygote that makes identical twins possible.

Coelom Formation

During gastrulation, an embryo's developing digestive tube initially forms as a blind pouch (a cavity closed at one end), the **archenteron**, which becomes the gut (**Figure 32.10b**). As the archenteron forms in protostome development, the solid masses of mesoderm cells split to form the fluid-filled cavity, the coelom. In contrast, in deuterostome development, the mesoderm buds from the wall of the archenteron, and its cavity becomes the coelom.

Fate of the Blastopore

Protostome and deuterostome development often differ in the fate of the **blastopore**, the indentation that during gastrulation leads to the formation of the archenteron (**Figure 32.10c**). After the archenteron develops, in most animals a second opening forms at the opposite end of the gastrula. In many species, the blastopore and this second opening become the two openings of the digestive tube: the mouth and the anus. In protostome development, the mouth generally develops from the first opening, the blastopore, and it is for this characteristic that the term *protostome* derives (from the Greek *protos*, first, and *stoma*, mouth). In deuterostome development (from the Greek *deuteros*, second), the mouth is derived from the secondary opening, and the blastopore usually forms the anus.

	Protostome development (examples: molluscs, annelids)	Deuterostome development (examples: echinoderms, chordates)
(a) Cleavage. In general, protostome development begins with spiral, determinate cleavage. Deuterostome development is characterized by radial, indeterminate cleavage.	Eight-cell stage Spiral and determinate	Eight-cell stage Radial and indeterminate
(b) Coelom formation. Coelom formation begins in the gastrula stage. In protostome development, the coelom forms from splits in the mesoderm. In deuterostome development, the coelom forms from mesodermal outpocketings of the archenteron.	Archenteron — Coelom Mesoderm / Blastopore Solid masses of mesoderm split and form coelom.	Coelom — Archenteron Blastopore / Mesoderm Folds of archenteron form coelom.
(c) Fate of the blastopore. In protostome development, the mouth forms from the blastopore. In deuterostome development, the mouth forms from a secondary opening.	Anus — Digestive tube — Mouth Mouth develops from blastopore.	Mouth — Digestive tube — Anus Anus develops from blastopore.

◄ Figure 32.10 **A comparison of protostome and deuterostome development.** These are useful general distinctions, though there are many variations and exceptions to these patterns.

MAKE CONNECTIONS *Review Figure 20.21. As an early embryo, which would more likely have stem cells capable of giving rise to cells of any type: an animal with protostome development or with deuterostome development? Explain.*

Key
- Ectoderm
- Mesoderm
- Endoderm

1. Distinguish the terms *grade* and *clade*.
2. Compare three aspects of the early development of a snail (a mollusc) and a human (a chordate).
3. **WHAT IF?** Evaluate this claim: Ignoring the details of their specific anatomy, worms, humans, and most other triploblasts have a shape analogous to that of a doughnut.

For suggested answers, see Appendix A.

CONCEPT **32.4**

Views of animal phylogeny continue to be shaped by new molecular and morphological data

As animals with diverse body plans radiated during the early Cambrian period, some lineages arose, thrived for a period of time, and then became extinct, leaving no descendants. However, by 500 million years ago, most animal phyla with members alive today were established. Next, we'll examine relationships among these taxa along with some remaining questions that are currently being addressed using genomic data.

The Diversification of Animals

Zoologists currently recognize about three dozen phyla of extant animals, 15 of which are shown in **Figure 32.11**. Researchers infer evolutionary relationships among these phyla by analyzing whole genomes, as well as morphological traits, ribosomal RNA (rRNA) genes, *Hox* genes, protein-coding nuclear genes, and mitochondrial genes. Notice how the following points are reflected in Figure 32.11.

1. **All animals share a common ancestor.** Current evidence indicates that animals are monophyletic, forming a clade called Metazoa. All extant and extinct animal lineages have descended from a common ancestor.

2. **Sponges are basal animals.** Among the extant taxa, sponges (phylum Porifera) branch from the base of the animal tree.

Recent morphological and molecular analyses indicate that sponges are monophyletic, as shown here.

3. **Eumetazoa is a clade of animals with true tissues.** All animals except for sponges and a few others belong to a clade of **eumetazoans** ("true animals"). True tissues evolved in the common ancestor of living eumetazoans. Basal eumetazoans, which include the phyla Ctenophora (comb jellies) and Cnidaria, are diploblastic and generally have radial symmetry.

4. **Most animal phyla belong to the clade Bilateria.** Bilateral symmetry and the presence of three germ layers are shared derived characters that help define the clade Bilateria. This clade contains the majority of animal phyla, and its members are known as bilaterians. The Cambrian explosion was primarily a rapid diversification of bilaterians.

5. **There are three major clades of bilaterian animals.** Bilaterians have diversified into three main lineages, Deuterostomia, Lophotrochozoa, and Ecdysozoa. With one

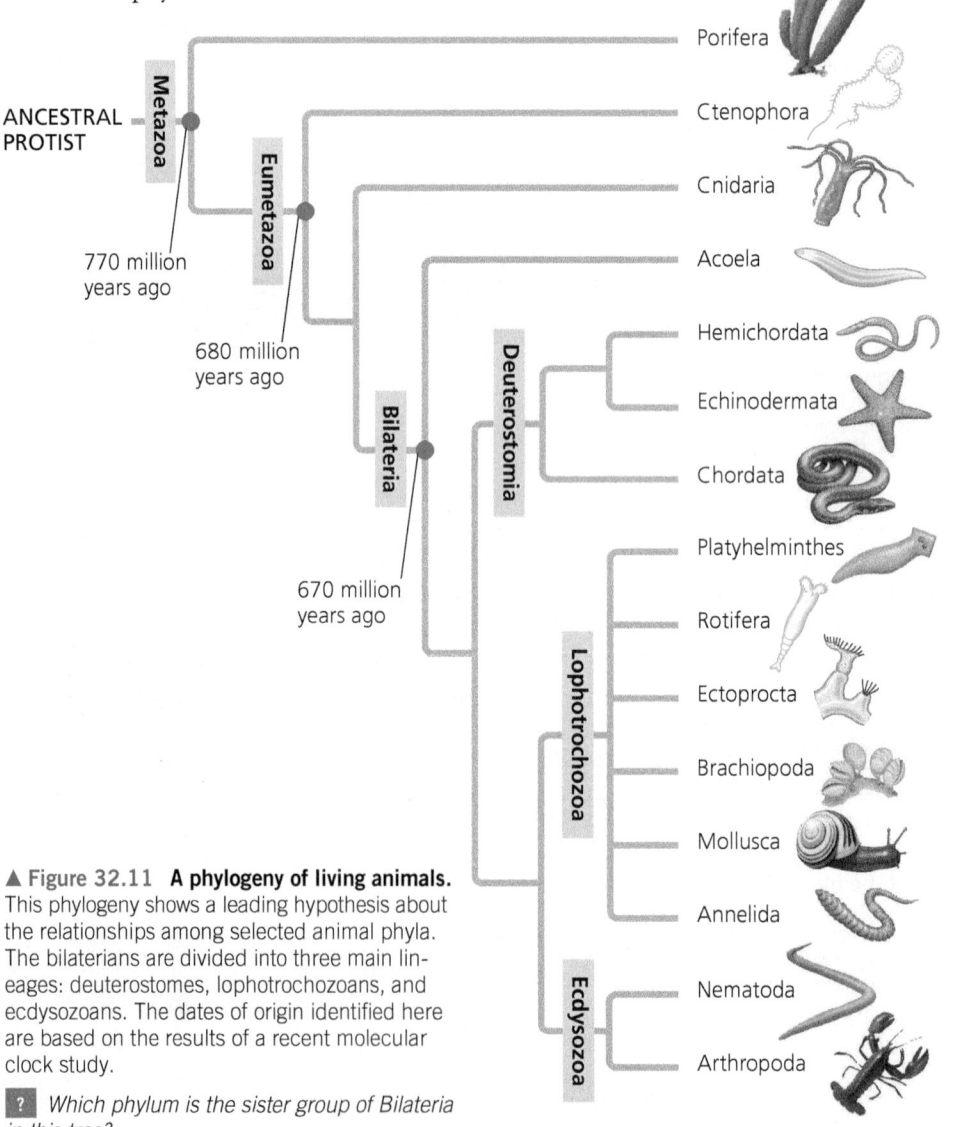

▲ Figure 32.11 **A phylogeny of living animals.** This phylogeny shows a leading hypothesis about the relationships among selected animal phyla. The bilaterians are divided into three main lineages: deuterostomes, lophotrochozoans, and ecdysozoans. The dates of origin identified here are based on the results of a recent molecular clock study.

? *Which phylum is the sister group of Bilateria in this tree?*

exception, the phyla in these clades consist entirely of **invertebrates**, animals that lack a backbone; Chordata is the only phylum that includes **vertebrates**, animals with a backbone.

As seen in Figure 32.11, hemichordates (acorn worms), echinoderms (sea stars and relatives), and chordates are members of the bilaterian clade **Deuterostomia**; thus, the term *deuterostome* refers not only to a mode of animal development, but also to the members of this clade. (The dual meaning of this term can be confusing since some organisms with a deuterostome developmental pattern are *not* members of clade Deuterostomia.) Hemichordates share some characteristics with chordates, such as gill slits and a dorsal nerve cord; echinoderms lack these characteristics. These shared traits may have been present in the common ancestor of the deuterostome clade (and lost in the echinoderm lineage). As mentioned earlier, phylum Chordata, the only phylum with vertebrate members, also includes invertebrates like tunicates that possess a dorsal notochord.

Bilaterians also diversified in two major clades that are composed entirely of invertebrates: the *ecdysozoans* and the *lophotrochozoans*. The clade name **Ecdysozoa** refers to a characteristic shared by nematodes, arthropods, and some of the other ecdysozoan phyla that are not included in our survey. These animals secrete external skeletons (exoskeletons); the stiff covering of a cricket and the flexible cuticle of a nematode are examples. As the animal grows, it molts, squirming out of its old exoskeleton and secreting a larger one (**Figure 32.12**). The process of shedding the old exoskeleton is called *ecdysis*. Though named for this characteristic, the clade was proposed mainly on the basis of molecular data that support the common ancestry of its members. Furthermore, some taxa excluded from this clade by their molecular data, such as certain species of leeches, do in fact molt.

The name **Lophotrochozoa** refers to two different features observed in some animals belonging to this clade. Some lophotrochozoans, such as ectoprocts, develop a unique structure called a **lophophore** (from the Greek *lophos*, crest, and *pherein*, to carry), a crown of ciliated tentacles that function in feeding (**Figure 32.13a**). Individuals in other phyla, including molluscs and annelids, go through a distinctive developmental stage called the **trochophore larva** (**Figure 32.13b**)—hence the name lophotrochozoan.

Future Directions in Animal Systematics

While many scientists think that current evidence supports the evolutionary relationships shown in Figure 32.11, aspects of this phylogeny continue to be debated. Although it can be frustrating that the phylogenies in textbooks cannot be memorized as set-in-stone truths, it's important to remember that the trees represent hypotheses based on collected data and that science is an ongoing, dynamic process of inquiry. We'll conclude with three questions that are the focus of ongoing research:

1. **Are sponges monophyletic?** Traditionally, sponges were placed in a single phylum, Porifera. This view began

to change in the 1990s, when molecular studies indicated that sponges were paraphyletic; as a result, sponges were placed into several different phyla that branched near the base of the animal tree. Since 2009, however, several morphological and molecular studies have concluded that sponges are a monophyletic group after all, as traditionally thought and as shown in Figure 32.11. Researchers are currently sequencing the entire genomes of various sponges to investigate whether sponges are indeed monophyletic.

▲ **Figure 32.12 Ecdysis.** This moulting cicada is in the process of emerging from its old exoskeleton. The animal will now secrete a new, larger exoskeleton.

2. **Are ctenophores basal metazoans?** Many researchers have concluded that sponges are basal metazoans (see Figure 32.11). However, several recent studies have placed the comb jellies (phylum Ctenophora) at the base of the animal tree. Data that are consistent with placing sponges at the base of the animal tree include fossil steroid evidence, molecular clock analyses, the morphological similarity of sponge collar cells to the cells of choanoflagellates (see Figure 32.3), and the fact that sponges are one of the few animal groups that lack true tissues (as might be expected for basal animals). Ctenophores, on the other hand, have true tissues and their cells do not resemble the cells of choanoflagellates. At present, the idea that ctenophores are basal metazoans remains an intriguing but controversial hypothesis.

3. **Are acoelomate flatworms basal bilaterians?** A series of recent molecular papers have indicated that acoelomate

(a) **Lophophore feeding structures of an ectoproct**

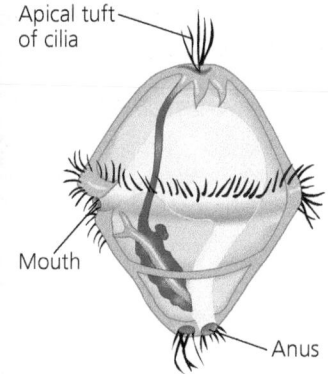

(b) **Structure of a trochophore larva**

▲ **Figure 32.13 Morphological characteristics of lophotrochozoans.**

flatworms (phylum Acoela) are basal bilaterians, as shown in Figure 32.11. A different conclusion was supported by a 2011 analysis, which placed acoelomates within Deuterostomia. Researchers are currently sequencing the genomes of several acoelomates and species from closely related groups to provide a more definitive test of the hypothesis that acoelomate flatworms are basal bilaterians. If further evidence supports this hypothesis, this would suggest that the bilaterians may have descended from a common ancestor that resembled living acoelomate flatworms—that is, from an ancestor that had a simple nervous system, a saclike gut with a single opening (the "mouth"), and no excretory system.

CONCEPT CHECK 32.4

1. Describe the evidence that cnidarians share a more recent common ancestor with other animals than with sponges.
2. **WHAT IF?** Suppose ctenophores are basal metazoans and sponges are the sister group of all remaining animals. Under this hypothesis, redraw Figure 32.11 and discuss whether animals with true tissues would form a clade.
3. **MAKE CONNECTIONS** Based on the phylogeny in Figure 32.11 and the information in Figure 25.11, evaluate this statement: "The Cambrian explosion actually consists of three explosions, not one."

For suggested answers, see Appendix A.

32 Chapter Review

Go to **MasteringBiology®** for Assignments, the eText, and the Study Area with Animations, Activities, Vocab Self-Quiz, and Practice Tests.

SUMMARY OF KEY CONCEPTS

CONCEPT 32.1

Animals are multicellular, heterotrophic eukaryotes with tissues that develop from embryonic layers (pp. 713–714)

- Animals are heterotrophs that ingest their food.
- Animals are multicellular eukaryotes. Their cells are supported and connected to one another by collagen and other structural proteins located outside the cell membrane. Nervous tissue and muscle tissue are key animal features.
- In most animals, **gastrulation** follows the formation of the **blastula** and leads to the formation of embryonic tissue layers. All animals except sponges have *Hox* genes that regulate the development of body form. Although *Hox* genes have been highly conserved over the course of evolution, they can produce a wide diversity of animal morphology.

? *Describe key ways that animals differ from plants and fungi.*

CONCEPT 32.2

The history of animals spans more than half a billion years (pp. 714–718)

? *What caused the Cambrian explosion? Describe current hypotheses.*

CONCEPT 32.3

Animals can be characterized by "body plans" (pp. 719–722)

- Animals may lack symmetry or may have **radial** or **bilateral symmetry**. Bilaterally symmetrical animals have **dorsal** and **ventral** sides, as well as **anterior** and **posterior** ends.
- Embryos of eumetazoans (animals with true tissues) may be **diploblastic** (two germ layers) or **triploblastic** (three germ layers). In triploblastic animals a body cavity may have a **pseudocoelom** (derived from both mesoderm and endoderm) or a true **coelom** (derived only from mesoderm).
- **Protostome** and **deuterostome development** often differ in patterns of **cleavage**, coelom formation, and blastopore fate.

? *Describe how body plans provide useful information yet should be interpreted cautiously when scientists are trying to understand evolutionary relationships.*

CONCEPT 32.4

Views of animal phylogeny continue to be shaped by new molecular and morphological data (pp. 722–724)

This phylogenetic tree shows key steps in animal evolution:

Common ancestor of all animals

Porifera (basal animals)

Ctenophora

Cnidaria

True tissues

Acoela (basal bilaterians)

Deuterostomia

Bilateral symmetry

Lophotrochozoa

Three germ layers

Ecdysozoa

Metazoa

Eumetazoa

Bilateria (most animals)

? *Consider clades Bilateria, Lophotrochozoa, Metazoa, Chordata, Ecdysozoa, Eumetazoa, and Deuterostomia. List the clades to which humans belong in order from the most to the least inclusive clade.*

LEVEL 1: KNOWLEDGE/COMPREHENSION

1. Among the characteristics unique to animals is
   a. gastrulation.
   b. multicellularity.
   c. sexual reproduction.
   d. flagellated sperm.

2. The distinction between sponges and other animal phyla is based mainly on the absence versus the presence of
   a. a body cavity.
   b. a complete digestive tract.
   c. true tissues.
   d. mesoderm.

3. Which one of the following terms does not apply to you?
   a. bilaterian
   b. triploblastic
   c. deuterosome
   d. acoelomate

4. Which of the following was probably the *least* important factor in bringing about the Cambrian explosion?
   a. the emergence of predator-prey relationships
   b. an increase in the concentration of atmospheric oxygen
   c. the movement of animals onto land
   d. the origin of *Hox* genes

LEVEL 2: APPLICATION/ANALYSIS

5. Based on the tree in Figure 32.11, which statement is false?
   a. The animal kingdom is monophyletic.
   b. Acoela are more closely related to echinoderms than to annelids.
   c. Sponges are basal animals.
   d. Bilaterians form a clade.

LEVEL 3: SYNTHESIS/EVALUATION

6. **EVOLUTION CONNECTION**
   A professor begins a lecture on animal phylogeny by saying, "We are all worms." In this context, what did she mean?

7. **SCIENTIFIC INQUIRY**
   INTERPRET THE DATA Redraw the bilaterian portion of Figure 32.11 for the nine phyla in the table in the next column. Consider these blastopore fates: protostomy (mouth develops from the blastopore), deuterostomy (anus develops from the blastopore), or neither (the blastopore closes and the mouth develops elsewhere). Depending on the blastopore fate of its members, label each branch that leads to a phylum with P, D, N, or a combination of these letters. What is the ancestral blastopore fate? How many times has blastopore fate changed over the course of evolution? Explain.

Blastopore Fate	Phyla
Protostomy (P)	Platyhelminthes, Rotifera, Nematoda; most Mollusca, most Annelida; few Arthropoda
Deuterostomy (D)	Echinodermata, Chordata; most Arthropoda; few Mollusca, few Annelida
Neither (N)	Acoela

Source: A. Hejnol and M. Martindale, The mouth, the anus, and the blastopore—open questions about questionable openings. In *Animal Evolution: Genomes, Fossils and Trees,* eds. D. T. J. Littlewood and M. J. Telford, Oxford University Press, pp. 33–40 (2009). © Jane B. Reece.

8. **WRITE ABOUT A THEME: INTERACTIONS**
   Animal life changed greatly during the Cambrian explosion, with some groups expanding in diversity and others declining. Write a short essay (100–150 words) interpreting these events as feedback regulation at the level of the biological community.

9. **SYNTHESIZE YOUR KNOWLEDGE**

WaterFrame/Alamy Stock Photo

This organism is an animal. What can you infer about its body structure and lifestyle (that might not be obvious from its appearance)? This animal has a deuterostome developmental pattern and a lophophore. To which major clades does this animal belong? Explain your selection, and describe when these clades originated and how they are related to one another.

For selected answers, see Appendix A.

33

An Introduction to Invertebrates

KEY CONCEPTS

33.1 Sponges are basal animals that lack true tissues

33.2 Cnidarians are an ancient phylum of eumetazoans

33.3 Lophotrochozoans, a clade identified by molecular data, have the widest range of animal body forms

33.4 Ecdysozoans are the most species-rich animal group

33.5 Echinoderms and chordates are deuterostomes

Dion Durnford

▲ Figure 33.1 **Can you locate the fossilized snail in a stone from the Parliament Buildings in Ottawa?**

Life Without a Backbone

Embedded within the stone walls of the Parliament Buildings in Ottawa, the very seat of power in the country, are hundreds of fossil animals without backbones (Figure 33.1). While perhaps not the most flattering image for our honourable members, these are a remarkable reminder of the past dominance of the **invertebrates**. Parts of the Parliament Buildings, in particular The House of Commons, were made with Tyndall stone, a limestone with a distinctive mottled appearance made from the dolomitization (where magnesium replaces calcium in calcium carbonate) of the burrows from marine animals. Tyndall stone is mined from a quarry just outside Winnipeg, Manitoba, that was part of an area once covered by a shallow, warm sea around 450 million years ago. Within this stone are representatives of many of the major groups you'll discuss in this chapter. If you visit the Parliament Buildings, take some time to examine the diversity within the walls, in addition to the beautiful architecture.

In this chapter, we'll take a tour of the invertebrate world, using the phylogenetic tree in **Figure 33.2** as a guide. **Figure 33.3** surveys

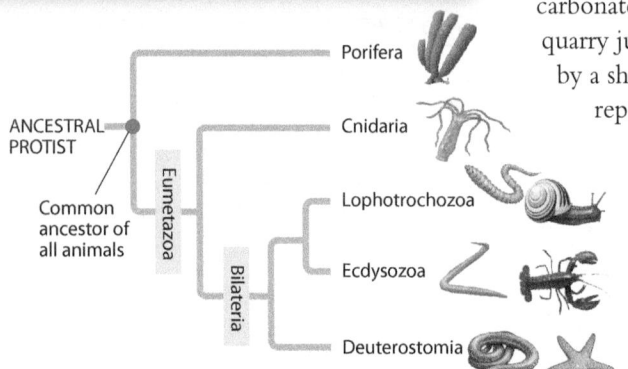

ANCESTRAL PROTIST

Common ancestor of all animals

Eumetazoa

Bilateria

Porifera

Cnidaria

Lophotrochozoa

Ecdysozoa

Deuterostomia

◀ Figure 33.2 **Review of animal phylogeny.** Except for sponges (basal animals in phylum Porifera) and a few other groups, all animals have tissues and are in the clade Eumetazoa. Most animals are in the diverse clade Bilateria (for a more complete view of animal relationships, see Figure 32.11).

Exploring Invertebrate Diversity

Kingdom Animalia encompasses about 1.3 million known species, but estimates of total species approach 8 million. Of the 23 phyla surveyed here, 12 are discussed more fully in this chapter, Chapter 32, or Chapter 34; cross-references are given at the end of their descriptions.

Porifera (5500 species)

Animals in this phylum are informally called sponges. Sponges are sessile animals that lack true tissues. They live as suspension feeders, trapping particles that pass through the internal channels of their body (see Concept 33.1).

Andrew J. Martinez/Science Source

A sponge

Cnidaria (10 000 species)

Cnidarians include corals, jellies, and hydras. These animals have a diploblastic, radially symmetrical body plan that includes a gastrovascular cavity with a single opening that serves as both mouth and anus (see Concept 33.2).

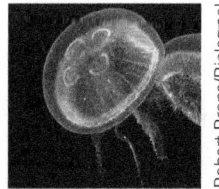

Robert Brons/Biological Photo Service

A jelly

Acoela (400 species)

Acoel flatworms have a simple nervous system and a saclike gut, and thus were once placed in phylum Platyhelminthes. Molecular analyses, however, indicate that Acoela is a separate lineage that diverged before the three main bilaterian clades (see Concept 32.4)

Teresa Zuberbühler

1.5 mm

Acoel flatworms (LM)

Placozoa (1 species)

This phylum contains one known species—*Trichoplax adhaerens*—with a simple morphology, having only a few thousand cells and four distinct cell types. It resembles a flattened, hairy ball with no internal structures other than a few scattered cells. Placozoans are thought to be basal animals, but it is not yet known how they are related to other early diverging animal groups such as Porifera and Cnidaria. *Trichoplax* can reproduce asexually by dividing into two individuals or by budding off many multicellular individuals.

0.5 mm

Stephen Dellaporta

A placozoan (LM)

Ctenophora (100 species)

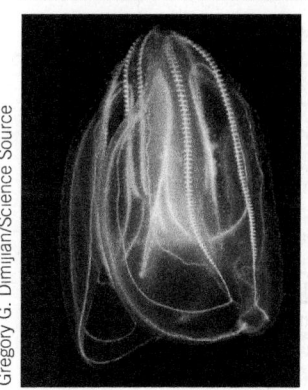

Ctenophores (comb jellies, like the one you saw in Figure 8.1) are diploblastic and radially symmetrical like cnidarians, suggesting that both phyla diverged from other animals very early (see Figure 32.11). Comb jellies make up much of the ocean's plankton. They have many distinctive traits, including eight "combs" of cilia that propel the animals through the water. When a small animal contacts the tentacles of some comb jellies, specialized cells burst open, covering the prey with sticky threads.

Gregory G. Dimijian/Science Source

A ctenophore, or comb jelly

Lophotrochozoa

Platyhelminthes (20 000 species)

Robinson Ed/Perspectives/Getty Images

Flatworms (including tapeworms, planarians, and flukes) have bilateral symmetry and a central nervous system that processes information from sensory structures. They have no body cavity or organs for circulation (see Concept 33.3).

A marine flatworm

Rotifera (1800 species)

Despite their microscopic size, rotifers have specialized organ systems, including an *alimentary canal* (a digestive tract with both a mouth and an anus). They feed on microorganisms suspended in water (see Concept 33.3).

100 µm

M. I. Walker/Science Source

A rotifer (LM)

Ectoprocta (4500 species)

Ectoprocts (also known as bryozoans) live as sessile colonies and are covered by a tough exoskeleton (see Concept 33.3).

Lacy crust (*Membranipora membranacea*) is a bryozoan that commonly forms whitish-grey crusts on the fronds of seaweeds on both anadian coasts.

Hecker/Sauer/AGE Fotostock

An ectoproct

Brachiopoda (335 species)

Brachiopods, or lamp shells, may be easily mistaken for clams or other molluscs. However, most brachiopods have a unique stalk that anchors them to their substrate, as well as a crown of cilia called a lophophore (see Concept 33.3).

Kåre Telnes/Image Quest Marine

A brachiopod

Continued on next page

Exploring Invertebrate Diversity

Lophotrochozoa (continued)

Acanthocephala (1100 species)

Acanthocephalans are called spiny-headed worms because of the curved hooks on the proboscis at the anterior end of their body. All species are parasites. Some acanthocephalans manipulate the behaviour of their intermediate hosts (generally arthropods) in ways that increase their chances of reaching their final hosts (generally vertebrates). For example, acanthocephalans that infect New Zealand mud crabs force their hosts to move to more visible areas on the beach, where the crabs are more likely to be eaten by birds, the worms' final hosts. Some phylogenetic analyses place the acanthocephalans within Rotifera.

Proboscis

An acanthocephalan

Neil Campbell/University of Aberdeen

Cycliophora (1 species)

A cycliophoran (colourized SEM)

100 μm

Peter Funch

The only known cycliophoran species, *Symbion pandora*, was discovered in 1995 on the mouthparts of a lobster. This tiny, vase-shaped creature has a unique body plan and a particularly bizarre life cycle. Males impregnate females that are still developing in their mothers' bodies. The fertilized females then escape, settle elsewhere on the lobster, and release their offspring. The offspring apparently leave that lobster and search for another one to which they attach.

Nemertea (900 species)

A ribbon worm

Erling Svensen/UWPhoto ANS

Also called proboscis worms or ribbon worms, nemerteans swim through water or burrow in sand, extending a unique proboscis to capture prey. Like flatworms, they lack a true coelom. However, unlike flatworms, nemerteans have an alimentary canal and a closed circulatory system in which the blood is contained in vessels and hence is distinct from fluid in the body cavity.

Annelida (16 500 species)

Annelids, or segmented worms, are distinguished from other worms by their body segmentation. Earthworms are the most familiar annelids, but the phylum consists primarily of marine and freshwater species (see Concept 33.3).

A marine annelid

Pleijel, Fredrik

Mollusca (93 000 species)

Molluscs (including snails, clams, squids, and octopuses) have a soft body that in many species is protected by a hard shell (see Concept 33.3).

An octopus

Photonimo/Shutterstock

Ecdysozoa

Loricifera (10 species)

Loriciferans (from the Latin *lorica*, corset, and *ferre*, to bear) are tiny animals that inhabit the deep-sea bottom. A loriciferan can telescope its head, neck, and thorax in and out of the lorica, a pocket formed by six plates surrounding the abdomen. Though the natural history of loriciferans is mostly a mystery, at least some species likely eat bacteria.

50 μm

A loriciferan (LM)

Reinhart Mobjerg Kristensen

Priapula (16 species)

A priapulan

Erling Svensen/ UWPhoto ANS

Priapulans are worms with a large, rounded proboscis at the anterior end. (They are named after Priapos, the Greek god of fertility, who was symbolized by a giant penis.) Ranging from 0.5 mm to 20 cm in length, most species burrow through seafloor sediments. Fossil evidence from the Burgess Shale suggests that priapulans were among the major predators during the Cambrian period (see diagram in Figure 32.7, lower right).

Onychophora (110 species)

Thomas Stromberg

An onychophoran

Onychophorans, also called velvet worms, originated during the Cambrian explosion (see Chapter 32). Originally, they thrived in the ocean, but at some point they succeeded in colonizing land. Today they live only in humid forests. Onychophorans have fleshy antennae and several dozen pairs of saclike legs.

Nematoda (25 000 species)

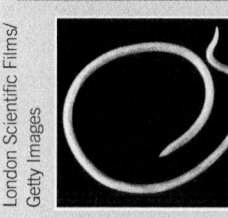

London Scientific Films/ Getty Images

A roundworm (colourized SEM)

Also called roundworms, nematodes are enormously abundant and diverse in the soil and in aquatic habitats; many species parasitize plants and animals. Their most distinctive feature is a tough cuticle that coats the body (see Concept 33.4).

Tardigrada (800 species)

Tardigrades (from the Latin *tardus*, slow, and *gradus*, step) are sometimes called water bears for their rounded shape, stubby appendages, and lumbering, bearlike gait. Most tardigrades are less than 0.5 mm in length. While commonly associated with moss where as many as 2 million tardigrades can be found per square metre, they can live almost anywhere, including the oceans, on animals, in hot springs, or under ice. Their incredible ability to transform

100 μm

Andrew Syred/Science Source

Tardigrades (colourized SEM)

into a dehydrated, dormant state (called a "tun") means they can survive extreme temperatures, pressures, and even the vacuum of space!

Arthropoda (1 000 000 species)

The vast majority of known animal species, including insects, crustaceans, and arachnids, are arthropods. All arthropods have a segmented exoskeleton and jointed appendages (see Concept 33.4).

Tim Flach/The Image Bank/Getty Images

Deuterostomia

Hemichordata (85 species)

Leslie Newman/Andrew Flowers/ Science Source

An acorn worm

Like echinoderms and chordates, hemichordates are members of the deuterostome clade (see Chapter 32). Hemichordates share some traits with chordates, such as gill slits and a dorsal nerve cord. The largest group of hemichordates is the enteropneusts, or acorn worms. Acorn worms are marine and generally live buried in mud or under rocks; they may grow to more than 2 m in length.

Chordata (52 000 species)

More than 90% of all known chordate species have backbones (and thus are vertebrates). However, the phylum Chordata also includes three groups of invertebrates: lancelets, tunicates, and hagfishes. See Chapter 34 for a full discussion of this phylum.

Robert Brons/Biological Photo Service

A tunicate

Echinodermata (7000 species)

Robert Harding World Imagery/Alamy

Echinoderms, such as sand dollars, sea stars, and sea urchins, are marine animals in the deuterostome clade that are bilaterally symmetrical as larvae but not as adults. They move and feed by using a network of internal canals to pump water to different parts of their body (see Concept 33.5).

A sea urchin

23 invertebrate phyla. Serving as representatives of invertebrate diversity, many of those phyla are explored in more detail in the rest of this chapter.

Invertebrates account for 95% of known animal species. They occupy almost every habitat on Earth, from the scalding water released by deep-sea hydrothermal vents to the rocky, frozen ground of Antarctica. Adaptation to these varied environments has produced an immense diversity of forms, ranging from a species consisting of a flat bilayer of cells to other species with features such as silk-spinning glands, pivoting spines, and tentacles covered with suction cups. Invertebrate species also show enormous variation in size, from microscopic organisms to organisms that can grow to 18 m long (1.5 times the length of a school bus).

CONCEPT 33.1

Sponges are basal animals that lack true tissues

Porifera
Cnidaria
Lophotrochozoa
Ecdysozoa
Deuterostomia

Animals in the phylum Porifera are known informally as sponges. (Recent molecular studies indicate that sponges are monophyletic, and that is the phylogeny we follow here; this remains under debate, however, as some studies suggest that sponges are paraphyletic.) Among the simplest of animals, sponges are sedentary and were mistaken for plants by the ancient Greeks. They range in size from a few millimetres to a few metres, and most species are marine, though a few live in fresh water. Sponges are **suspension feeders**: They capture food particles suspended in the water that passes through their body, which in some species resembles a sac perforated with pores. Water is drawn through the pores into a central cavity, the **spongocoel**, and then flows out of the sponge through a larger opening called the **osculum** (Figure 33.4). More complex sponges have folded body walls, and many contain branched water canals and several oscula.

Sponges represent a lineage that originates near the root of the phylogenetic tree of animals; thus, they are said to be *basal animals*. Unlike nearly all other animals, sponges lack true tissues, groups of similar cells that act as a functional unit and are isolated from other tissues by membranous layers. However, the sponge body does contain several different cell types. For example, lining the interior of the spongocoel are flagellated **choanocytes**, or collar cells (named for the finger-like projections that form a "collar" around the flagellum). These cells engulf

Andrew J. Martinez/Science Source

Sponge from the Bay of Fundy (*Polymastia mammillaris*)

❺ **Choanocytes.** The spongocoel is lined with flagellated cells called choanocytes. By beating flagella, the choanocytes create a current that draws water in through the pores and out through the osculum.

▼ **Figure 33.4 Anatomy of a sponge.**

Food particles in mucus

Collar

Choanocyte

Osculum

Flagellum

Phagocytosis of food particles

Amoebocyte

❹ **Spongocoel.** Water passing through pores enters a cavity called the spongocoel.

❸ **Pores.** Water enters the sponge through pores formed by doughnut-shaped cells that span the body wall.

❷ **Epidermis.** The outer layer consists of tightly packed epidermal cells.

Water flow

Spicules

❶ **Mesohyl.** The wall of this sponge consists of two layers of cells separated by a gelatinous matrix, the mesohyl ("middle matter").

❻ The movement of a choanocyte's flagellum also draws water through its collar of finger-like projections. Food particles are trapped in the mucus that coats the projections, engulfed by phagocytosis, and either digested or transferred to amoebocytes.

❼ **Amoebocytes.** These cells can transport nutrients to other cells of the sponge body, produce materials for skeletal fibres (spicules), or become any type of sponge cell as needed.

bacteria and other food particles by phagocytosis. The similarity between choanocytes and the cells of choanoflagellates supports molecular evidence suggesting that animals evolved from a choanoflagellate-like ancestor (see Figure 32.3).

The body of a sponge consists of two layers of cells separated by a gelatinous region called the **mesohyl**. Because both cell layers are in contact with water, processes such as gas exchange and waste removal can occur by diffusion across the membranes of these cells. Other tasks are performed by cells called **amoebocytes**, named for their use of pseudopodia. These cells move through the mesohyl and have many functions. For example, they take up food from the surrounding water and from choanocytes, digest it, and carry nutrients to other cells. Amoebocytes also manufacture tough skeletal fibres within the mesohyl. In some sponges, these fibres are sharp spicules made from calcium carbonate or silica. Other sponges produce more flexible fibres composed of a protein called spongin; you may have seen these pliant skeletons being sold as brown bath sponges. Finally, and perhaps most importantly, amoebocytes are totipotent, meaning they can differentiate into other types of sponge cells. This gives the sponge body remarkable flexibility, enabling it to adjust its shape in response to changes in its physical environment (such as the direction of water currents).

Most sponges are **hermaphrodites**, meaning that each individual functions as both male and female in sexual reproduction by producing sperm *and* eggs. Almost all sponges exhibit sequential hermaphroditism: They function first as one sex and then as the other. Cross-fertilization results from some of the sperm being drawn into neighbouring individuals. Fertilization occurs in the mesohyl, where the zygotes develop into flagellated, swimming larvae that disperse from the parent sponge. After settling on a suitable substrate, a larva develops into a sessile adult.

Sponges produce a variety of antibiotics and other defensive compounds. For example, a compound called cribrostatin isolated from marine sponges can kill penicillin-resistant strains of the bacterium *Streptococcus*. Other sponge-derived compounds are being tested as possible anticancer agents.

CONCEPT CHECK 33.1

1. Describe how sponges feed.
2. **WHAT IF?** Some molecular evidence suggests that the sister group of animals is not the choanoflagellates, but rather a group of parasitic protists, Mesomycetozoa. Given that these parasites lack collar cells, can this hypothesis be correct? Explain.

For suggested answers, see Appendix A.

Cnidarians are an ancient phylum of eumetazoans

Porifera
Cnidaria
Lophotrochozoa
Ecdysozoa
Deuterostomia

Eumetazoa

All animals except sponges and a few other groups belong to the clade Eumetazoa, animals with true tissues (see Chapter 32). One of the oldest lineages in this clade is the phylum Cnidaria, which originated about 680 million years ago as estimated by DNA analyses. Cnidarians have diversified into a wide range of sessile and motile forms, including hydras, corals, and jellies (commonly called "jellyfish"). Yet most cnidarians still exhibit the relatively simple, diploblastic, radial body plan that existed in early members of the group some 560 million years ago.

The basic body plan of a cnidarian is a sac with a central digestive compartment, the **gastrovascular cavity**. A single opening to this cavity functions as both mouth and anus. There are two variations on this body plan: the sessile polyp and the motile medusa (Figure 33.5). **Polyps** are cylindrical forms that adhere to the substrate by the aboral end of their body (the end opposite the mouth) and extend their tentacles, waiting for prey. Examples of the polyp form include hydras and sea anemones. A **medusa** (plural, *medusae*) resembles a flattened, mouth-down version of the polyp. It moves freely in the water by a combination of passive drifting and contractions of its bell-shaped body. Medusae include free-swimming jellies. The tentacles of a jelly dangle from the oral surface, which points downward. Some cnidarians exist only as polyps or only as medusae; others have both a polyp stage and a medusa stage in their life cycle.

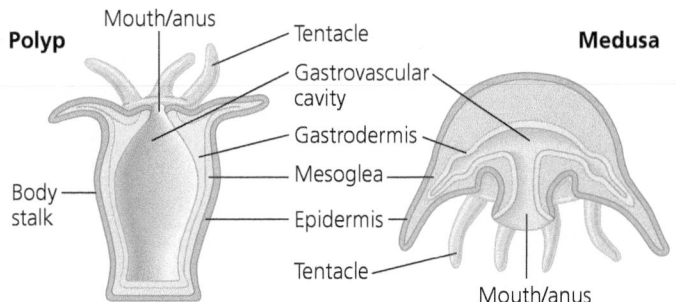

Polyp
Mouth/anus
Tentacle
Gastrovascular cavity
Gastrodermis
Mesoglea
Epidermis
Tentacle
Body stalk
Medusa
Mouth/anus

▲ Figure 33.5 **Polyp and medusa forms of cnidarians.** The body wall of a cnidarian has two layers of cells: an outer layer of epidermis (darker blue; derived from ectoderm) and an inner layer of gastrodermis (yellow; derived from endoderm). Digestion begins in the gastrovascular cavity and is completed inside food vacuoles in the gastrodermal cells. Sandwiched between the epidermis and gastrodermis is a gelatinous layer, the mesoglea.

Cnidarians are carnivores that often use tentacles arranged in a ring around their mouth to capture prey and push the food into their gastrovascular cavity, where digestion begins. Enzymes are secreted into the cavity, thus breaking down the prey into a nutrient-rich broth. Cells lining the cavity then absorb these nutrients and complete the digestive process; any undigested remains are expelled through the mouth/anus. The tentacles are armed with batteries of **cnidocytes**, cells unique to cnidarians that function in defence and prey capture (**Figure 33.6**). Cnidocytes contain *cnidae* (from the Greek *cnide*, nettle), capsule-like organelles that are capable of exploding outward and that give phylum Cnidaria its name. Specialized cnidae called **nematocysts** contain a stinging thread that can penetrate the body wall of the cnidarian's prey. Other kinds of cnidae have long threads that stick to or entangle small prey that bump into the cnidarian's tentacles. Amazingly, some animals that feed on the tentacles of cnidarians (such as certain sea slugs), can pass the nematocyst cells through their digestive system without firing and store them in pouches to be used as their own defence mechanism!

Contractile tissues and nerves occur in their simplest forms in cnidarians. Cells of the epidermis (outer layer) and gastrodermis (inner layer) have bundles of microfilaments arranged into contractile fibres. The gastrovascular cavity acts as a hydrostatic skeleton (see Concept 50.6) against which the contractile cells can work. When a cnidarian closes its mouth, the volume of the cavity is fixed, and contraction of selected cells causes the animal to change shape. Movements are coordinated by a nerve net. Cnidarians have no brain, and the noncentralized nerve net is associated with sensory structures that are distributed around the body. Thus, the animal can detect and respond to stimuli from all directions.

Fossil and molecular evidence suggests that early in its evolutionary history, the phylum Cnidaria diverged into two major clades, Medusozoa and Anthozoa (**Figure 33.7**).

Medusozoans

All cnidarians that produce a medusa are members of clade Medusozoa, a group that includes the *scyphozoans* (jellies)

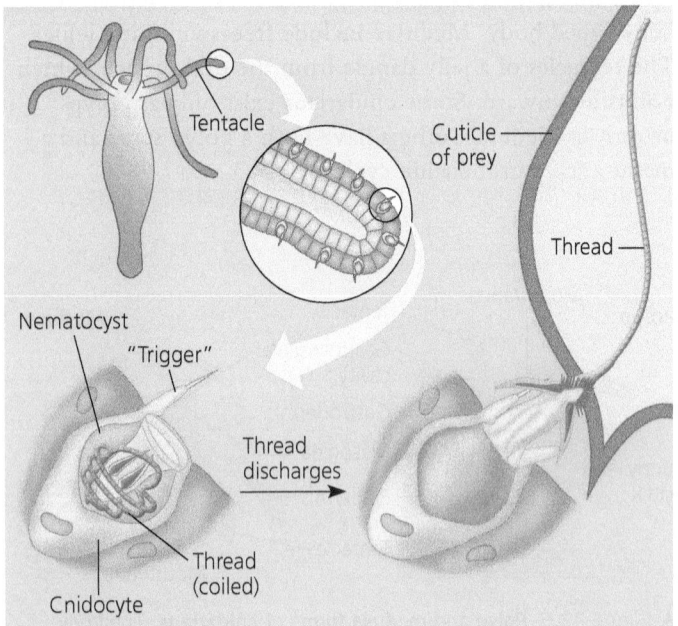

▲ Figure 33.6 **A cnidocyte of a hydra.** This type of cnidocyte contains a stinging capsule, the nematocyst, which contains a coiled thread. When a "trigger" is stimulated by touch or by certain chemicals, the thread shoots out, puncturing and injecting toxins into prey.

▼ Figure 33.7 **Cnidarians.**

(a) Medusozoans

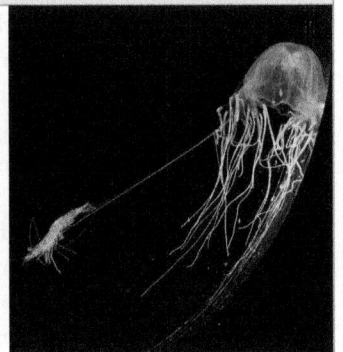

Many jellies are bioluminescent. Food captured by nematocyst-bearing tentacles is transferred to specialized oral arms (that lack nematocysts) for transport to the mouth.

This sea wasp produces a venom that can subdue fish and other large prey (as seen here). The sea wasp venom is more potent than cobra venom.

(b) Anthozoans

Sea anemones and other anthozoans exist only as polyps. Many anthozoans form symbiotic relationships with photosynthetic algae.

These star corals live as colonies of polyps. Their soft bodies are enclosed at the base by a hard exoskeleton.

and *cubozoans* (box jellies) shown in Figure 33.7a, along with the *hydrozoans*. Most hydrozoans alternate between the polyp and medusa forms, as seen in the life cycle of *Obelia* (Figure 33.8). The polyp stage, a colony of interconnected polyps in the case of *Obelia*, is more conspicuous than the medusa. Hydras, among the few cnidarians found in fresh water, are also unusual hydrozoans in that they exist only in polyp form.

Unlike hydrozoans, most scyphozoans and cubozoans spend the majority of their life cycles in the medusa stage. Coastal scyphozoans, for example, often have a brief polyp stage during their life cycle, whereas those that live in the open ocean generally lack the polyp stage altogether. As their name (which means "cube animals") suggests,

cubozoans have a box-shaped medusa stage. Most cubozoans live in tropical oceans and are equipped with highly toxic cnidocytes. The sea wasp (*Chironex fleckeri*), a cubozoan that lives off the coast of northern Australia, is one of the deadliest organisms known: Its sting causes intense pain and can lead to respiratory failure, cardiac arrest, and death within minutes.

Anthozoans

Sea anemones and corals belong to the clade Anthozoa (see Figure 33.7b). These cnidarians occur only as polyps. Corals live as solitary or colonial forms, often forming symbioses with algae. Many species secrete a hard **exoskeleton**

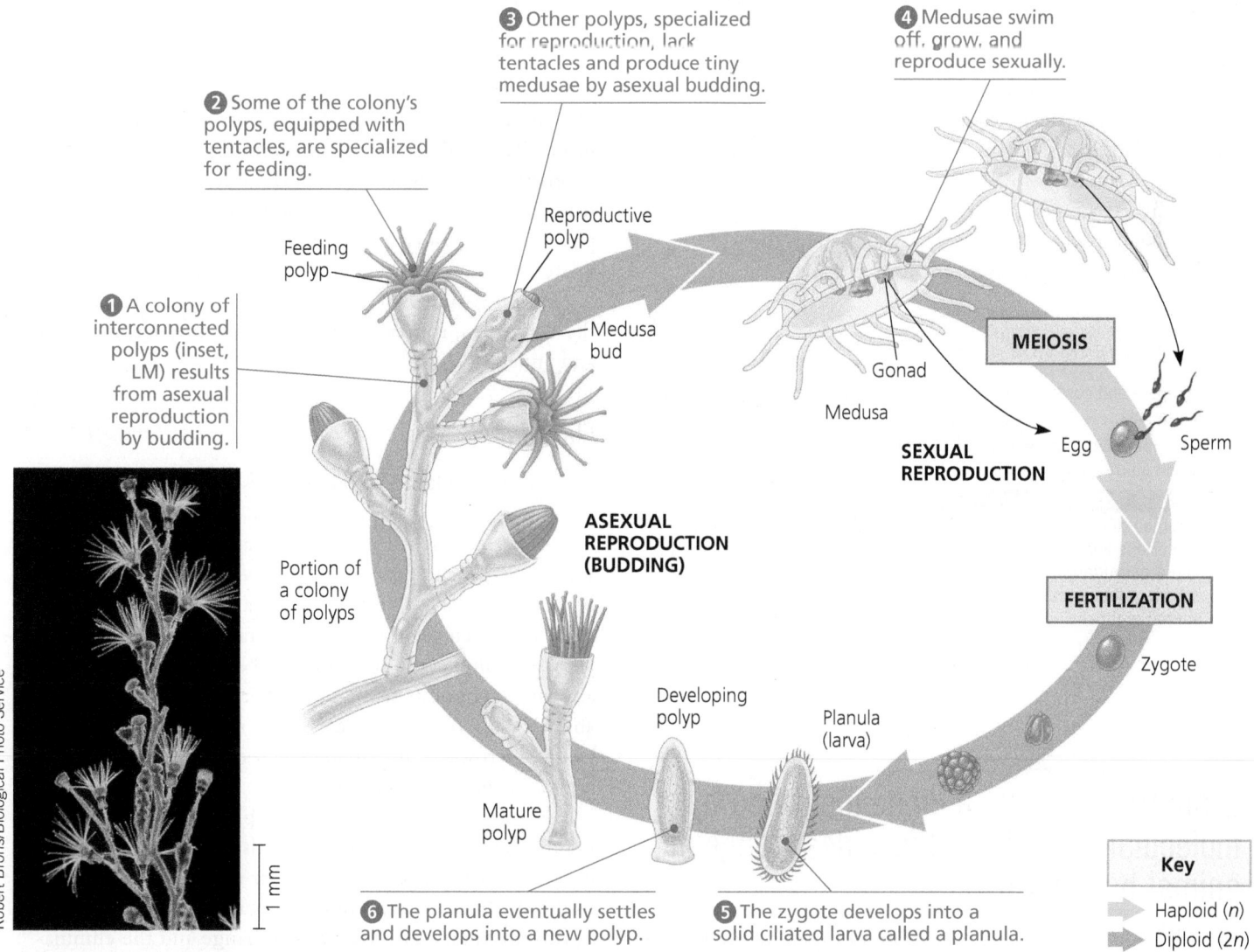

2 Some of the colony's polyps, equipped with tentacles, are specialized for feeding.

3 Other polyps, specialized for reproduction, lack tentacles and produce tiny medusae by asexual budding.

4 Medusae swim off, grow, and reproduce sexually.

1 A colony of interconnected polyps (inset, LM) results from asexual reproduction by budding.

Feeding polyp

Reproductive polyp

Medusa bud

Portion of a colony of polyps

ASEXUAL REPRODUCTION (BUDDING)

Developing polyp

Mature polyp

6 The planula eventually settles and develops into a new polyp.

5 The zygote develops into a solid ciliated larva called a planula.

Planula (larva)

MEIOSIS

Gonad

Medusa

SEXUAL REPRODUCTION

Egg

Sperm

FERTILIZATION

Zygote

Key

Haploid (*n*)

Diploid (*2n*)

Robert Brons/Biological Photo Service

1 mm

▲ **Figure 33.8 The life cycle of the hydrozoan *Obelia*.** The polyp is asexual, and the medusa is sexual, releasing eggs and sperm. These two stages alternate, one producing the other. Do not confuse this with the alternation of generations that occurs in plants and some algae:

In *Obelia*, both the polyp and the medusa are diploid organisms. Typical of animals, only the single-celled gametes are haploid. By contrast, plants have a multicellular haploid generation and a multicellular diploid generation.

WHAT IF? *Suppose that Obelia medusae and gametes were haploid, but all other stages were diploid. What aspects of its actual life cycle would have to change for this to occur?*

(external skeleton) of calcium carbonate. Each polyp generation builds on the skeletal remains of earlier generations, constructing "rocks" with shapes characteristic of their species. These skeletons are what we usually think of as coral. While most associate corals with shallow-water tropical reefs, there are also cold-water corals that are prevalent in the Atlantic, including on the Scotian Shelf off the coast of Nova Scotia. These cold-water corals can be found in very deep waters and lack algal symbionts (because there is no light). The low temperature means that these corals grow very slowly and individuals can be hundreds of years old.

Coral reefs are to tropical seas what rain forests are to tropical land areas: They provide habitat for many other species. Unfortunately, these reefs are being destroyed at an alarming rate. Pollution, overharvesting, and ocean acidification (see Figure 3.13) are major threats; global warming may also be contributing to their demise by raising seawater temperatures above the range in which corals thrive. The deep-water corals are also feeling the impact of fishing, especially by trawlers that drag a net along the ocean bottom. Because of their slow growth rate, recovery can take a very long time. In Atlantic Canada, we now have coral conservation areas to protect these delicate ecosystems.

CONCEPT CHECK 33.2

1. Compare and contrast the polyp and medusa forms of cnidarians.

2. Describe the structure and function of the stinging cells for which cnidarians are named.

3. **MAKE CONNECTIONS** Many new animal body plans emerged during and after the Cambrian explosion. In contrast, cnidarians today retain the same diploblastic, radial body plan found in cnidarians 560 million years ago. Are cnidarians therefore less successful or less "highly evolved" than other animal groups? Explain. (See also Concepts 25.3 and 25.6)

For suggested answers, see Appendix A.

CONCEPT 33.3

Lophotrochozoans, a clade identified by molecular data, have the widest range of animal body forms

The vast majority of animal species belong to the clade Bilateria, whose members exhibit bilateral symmetry and triploblastic development (see Chapter 32). Most bilaterians also have a digestive tract with two openings (a mouth and an

anus) and a coelom. Recent DNA analyses suggest that the common ancestor of living bilaterians lived about 670 million years ago. Many of the major groups of bilaterians first appeared in the fossil record during the Cambrian explosion (535 to 525 million years ago).

As you read in Chapter 32, molecular evidence suggests that there are three major clades of bilaterally symmetrical animals: Lophotrochozoa, Ecdysozoa, and Deuterostomia. This section will focus on the first of these clades, the lophotrochozoans. Concepts 33.4 and 33.5 will explore the other two clades.

Although the clade Lophotrochozoa was identified by molecular data, its name comes from features found in some of its members. Some lophotrochozoans develop a structure called a *lophophore*, a crown of ciliated tentacles that functions in feeding, while others go through a distinctive stage called the *trochophore larva* (see Figure 32.13). Other members of the group have neither of these features. Few other unique morphological features are widely shared within the group—in fact, the lophotrochozoans are the most diverse bilaterian clade in terms of body plan. This diversity in form is reflected in the number of phyla classified in the group: Lophotrochozoa includes about 18 phyla, more than twice the number in any other clade of bilaterians.

We'll now introduce six diverse lophotrochozoan phyla: the flatworms, rotifers, ectoprocts, brachiopods, molluscs, and annelids.

Flatworms

Flatworms (phylum Platyhelminthes) live in marine, freshwater, and damp terrestrial habitats. In addition to free-living species, flatworms include many parasitic species, such as flukes and tapeworms. Flatworms are so named because they have thin bodies that are flattened dorsoventrally (between the dorsal and ventral surfaces); the word *platyhelminth* means "flat worm." (Note that *worm* is not a formal taxonomic name but rather refers to a grade of animals with long, thin bodies.) The smallest flatworms are nearly microscopic free-living species, while some tapeworms are more than 20 m long.

Although flatworms undergo triploblastic development, they are acoelomates (animals that lack a body cavity). Their flat shape places all their cells close to water in the surrounding environment or in their gut. Because of this proximity to water, gas exchange and the elimination of nitrogenous waste (ammonia) can occur by diffusion across the body surface. A flat shape is one way to maximize surface area for efficient exchange processes and have arisen (by convergent evolution) in different groups of animals and other organisms. Flatworms have no organs specialized for gas exchange, and their relatively simple excretory apparatus functions mainly to maintain osmotic balance with their surroundings. This apparatus consists of **protonephridia**, networks of tubules with ciliated structures called *flame bulbs* that pull fluid through branched ducts opening to the outside (see Figure 44.10). Most flatworms have a gastrovascular cavity with only one opening. Though flatworms lack a circulatory system, the fine branches of the gastrovascular cavity distribute food directly to the animal's cells.

Early in their evolutionary history, flatworms separated into two lineages, Catenulida and Rhabditophora. Catenulida is a small clade of about 100 flatworm species, most of which live in freshwater habitats. Catenulids typically reproduce asexually by budding at their posterior end. The offspring often produce their own buds before detaching from the parent, thereby forming a chain of two to four genetically identical individuals—hence their informal name, "chain worms."

The other ancient flatworm lineage, Rhabditophora, is a diverse clade of about 20 000 freshwater and marine species, one example of which is shown in Figure 33.9. We'll explore this group in more detail, focusing on free-living and parasitic members of this clade.

Free-Living Species

Free-living rhabditophorans are important as predators and scavengers in a wide range of freshwater and marine habitats. The best-known members of this group are freshwater species in the genus *Dugesia*, commonly called **planarians**. Abundant in unpolluted ponds and streams, planarians prey on smaller animals or feed on dead animals. They move by using cilia on their ventral surface, gliding along a film of mucus they secrete. Some other rhabditophorans also use their muscles to swim through water with an undulating motion.

A planarian's head is equipped with a pair of light-sensitive eyespots and lateral flaps that function mainly to detect specific chemicals. The planarian nervous system is more complex and centralized than the nerve nets of cnidarians (Figure 33.10). Experiments have shown that planarians can learn to modify their responses to stimuli.

Some planarians can reproduce asexually through fission. The parent constricts roughly in the middle of its body, separating into a head end and a tail end; each end then regenerates the missing parts. Sexual reproduction also occurs. Planarians are hermaphrodites, and copulating mates typically cross-fertilize each other.

Parasitic Species

More than half of the known species of rhabditophorans live as parasites in or on other animals. Many have suckers that attach to the internal organs or outer surfaces of the host animal. In most species, a tough covering helps protect the parasites within their hosts. Reproductive organs occupy nearly the entire interior of these worms. We'll discuss two ecologically and economically important subgroups of parasitic rhabditophorans, the trematodes and the tapeworms.

Trematodes As a group, trematodes parasitize a wide range of hosts, and most species have complex life cycles with alternating sexual and asexual stages. Many trematodes require an intermediate host in which larvae develop before infecting the final host (usually a vertebrate), where the adult worms live. For example, trematodes that parasitize

▲ Figure 33.9 **A free-living marine flatworm.**

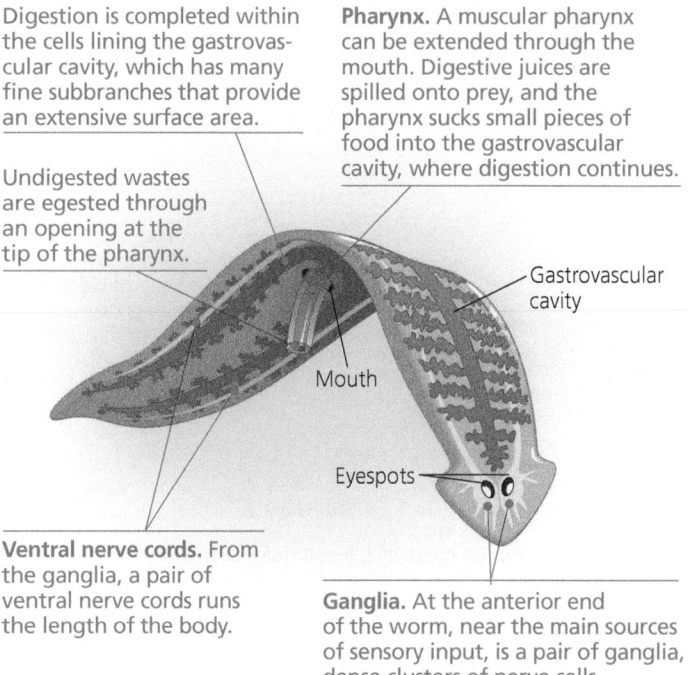

Digestion is completed within the cells lining the gastrovascular cavity, which has many fine subbranches that provide an extensive surface area.

Undigested wastes are egested through an opening at the tip of the pharynx.

Pharynx. A muscular pharynx can be extended through the mouth. Digestive juices are spilled onto prey, and the pharynx sucks small pieces of food into the gastrovascular cavity, where digestion continues.

Gastrovascular cavity

Mouth

Eyespots

Ventral nerve cords. From the ganglia, a pair of ventral nerve cords runs the length of the body.

Ganglia. At the anterior end of the worm, near the main sources of sensory input, is a pair of ganglia, dense clusters of nerve cells.

▲ Figure 33.10 **Anatomy of a planarian.**

humans spend part of their lives in snail hosts (Figure 33.11). Around the world, some 200 million people are infected with trematodes called blood flukes (*Schistosoma*) and suffer from schistosomiasis, a disease whose symptoms include pain, anemia, and diarrhea.

In Canada you are more likely to come across schistosomes with non-human host specificity, like those that cause swimmer's itch. These flatworms are similar, but their normal vertebrate host is a bird. After developing in a snail, these flatworms swim in the water in search of the next host. If a flatworm comes across a human, it can burrow into the skin but will soon die and not cause an infection; however, your immune system will cause an inflammatory reaction that produces the rash and itching associated with the condition.

Living within different hosts puts demands on trematodes that free-living animals don't face. A blood fluke, for instance, must evade the immune systems of both snails and humans. By mimicking the surface proteins of its hosts, the blood fluke creates a partial immunological camouflage for itself. It also releases molecules that manipulate the hosts' immune systems into tolerating the parasite's existence. These defences are so effective that individual blood flukes can survive in humans for more than 40 years.

Tapeworms The tapeworms are a second large and diverse group of parasitic rhabditophorans (Figure 33.12). The adults live mostly inside vertebrates, including humans. In many tapeworms, the anterior end, or scolex, is armed with suckers and often hooks that the worm uses to attach itself to the

Centers for Disease Control and Prevention

1 Mature flukes live in the blood vessels of the human intestine. A female fluke fits into a groove running the length of the larger male's body, as shown in the LM at right.

Male

Female

1 mm

5 These larvae penetrate the skin and blood vessels of humans working in fields irrigated with water contaminated with fluke larvae.

2 Blood flukes reproduce sexually in the human host. The fertilized eggs exit the host in feces.

3 If the human feces reach a pond or other source of water, the eggs develop into ciliated larvae. These larvae infect snails, the intermediate host.

4 Asexual reproduction within a snail results in another type of motile larva, which escapes from the snail host.

Snail host

▲ Figure 33.11 **The life cycle of a blood fluke (*Schistosoma mansoni*), a trematode.**

WHAT IF? *Snails eat algae, whose growth is stimulated by nutrients found in fertilizer. How would the contamination of irrigation water with fertilizer likely affect the occurrence of schistosomiasis? Explain.*

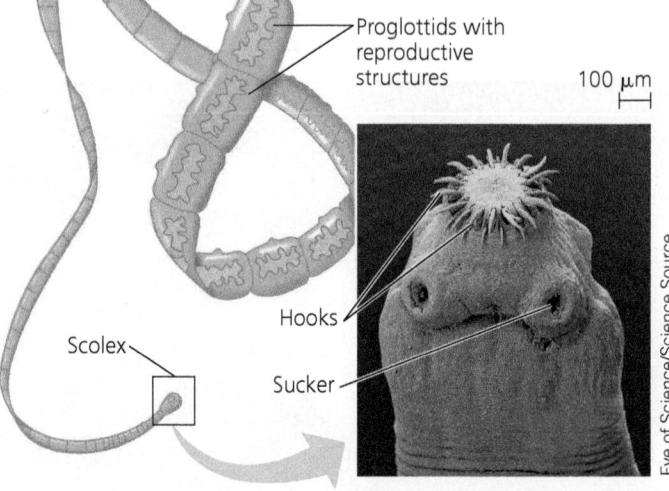

Proglottids with reproductive structures

100 μm

Scolex

Hooks

Sucker

Eye of Science/Science Source

▲ Figure 33.12 **Anatomy of a tapeworm.** The inset shows a close-up of the scolex (colourized SEM).

intestinal lining of its host. Tapeworms lack a mouth and gastrovascular cavity; they simply absorb nutrients released by digestion in the host's intestine. Absorption occurs across the tapeworm's body surface.

Posterior to the scolex is a long ribbon of units called proglottids, which are little more than sacs of sex organs. After sexual reproduction, proglottids loaded with thousands of fertilized eggs are released from the posterior end of a tapeworm and leave the host's body in feces. In one type of life cycle, feces carrying the eggs contaminate the food or water of intermediate hosts, such as pigs or cattle, and the tapeworm eggs develop into larvae that encyst in muscles of these animals. A human acquires the larvae by eating undercooked meat containing the cysts, and the worms develop into mature adults within the human. Large tapeworms can block the intestines and rob enough nutrients from the human host to cause nutritional deficiencies. Doctors have patients take the drug niclosamide by mouth to kill the adult worms. Although tapeworm infections are rare in Canada, they are a concern in parts of Asia, Africa, Eastern Europe, and Latin America.

Rotifers

Rotifers (phylum Rotifera) are tiny animals that inhabit freshwater, marine, and damp soil habitats. Ranging in size from about 50 μm to 2 mm, rotifers are smaller than many protists but nevertheless are multicellular and have specialized organ systems **(Figure 33.13)**. In contrast to cnidarians and flatworms, which have a gastrovascular cavity, rotifers have an **alimentary canal**, a digestive tube with two openings, a mouth and an anus. Internal organs lie within the pseudocoelom, a body cavity that is not completely lined by mesoderm (see Figure 32.9b). Fluid in the pseudocoelom serves as a hydrostatic skeleton. Movement of a

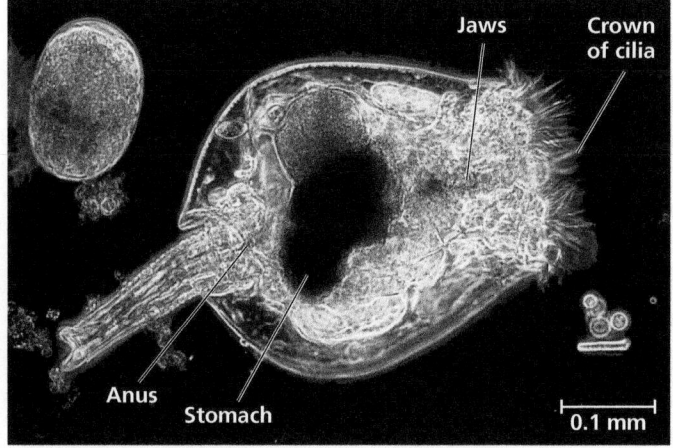

▲ **Figure 33.13 A rotifer.** These pseudocoelomates, smaller than many protists, are generally more anatomically complex than flatworms (LM).

rotifer's body distributes the fluid throughout the body, circulating nutrients.

The word *rotifer* is derived from the Latin meaning "wheel-bearer," a reference to the crown of cilia that draws a vortex of water into the mouth. Posterior to the mouth, a region of the digestive tract called the pharynx bears jaws called trophi that grind up food, mostly microorganisms suspended in the water. Digestion is then completed farther along the alimentary canal. Most other bilaterians also have an alimentary canal, which enables the stepwise digestion of a wide range of food particles.

Rotifers exhibit some unusual forms of reproduction. Some species consist only of females that produce more females from unfertilized eggs, a type of asexual reproduction called **parthenogenesis**. Some other invertebrates (for example, aphids and some bees) and even some vertebrates (for example, some lizards and some fish) can also reproduce in this way. In addition to being able to produce females by parthenogenesis, some rotifers can also reproduce sexually under certain conditions, such as high levels of crowding. When this occurs, a female produces two types of eggs. Eggs of one type develop into females, and eggs of the other type develop into males. In some cases, the males do not feed and survive only long enough to fertilize eggs. The fertilized eggs develop into resistant embryos capable of remaining dormant for years. Once the embryos break dormancy, they develop into a new female generation that reproduces by parthenogenesis until conditions once again favour sexual reproduction.

It is puzzling that many rotifer species survive without males. The vast majority of animals and plants reproduce sexually at least some of the time, and sexual reproduction has certain advantages over asexual reproduction (see Concept 46.1). For example, species that reproduce asexually tend to accumulate harmful mutations in their genomes faster than sexually reproducing species. As a result, asexual species should experience higher rates of extinction and lower rates of speciation.

Seeking to understand this unusual group, researchers have been studying a clade of asexual rotifers named Bdelloidea. Some 360 species of bdelloid rotifers are known, and all of them reproduce by parthenogenesis without any males. Paleontologists have discovered bdelloid rotifers preserved in 35-million-year-old amber, and the morphology of these fossils resembles only the female form, with no evidence of males. By comparing the DNA of bdelloids with that of their closest sexually reproducing rotifer relatives, scientists have concluded that bdelloids have likely been asexual for 100 million years. How these animals manage to flout the general rule against long-lasting asexuality remains a puzzle.

Lophophorates: Ectoprocts and Brachiopods

Bilaterians in the phyla Ectoprocta and Brachiopoda are among those known as lophophorates. These animals have a *lophophore*, a crown of ciliated tentacles around their mouth (see Figure 32.13a). As the cilia draw water toward the mouth, the tentacles trap suspended food particles. Other similarities, such as a U-shaped alimentary canal and the absence of a distinct head, reflect these organisms' sessile existence. In contrast to flatworms, which lack a body cavity, and rotifers, which have a pseudocoelom, lophophorates have a true coelom that is completely lined by mesoderm (see Figure 32.9a).

Ectoprocts (from the Greek *ecto*, outside, and *procta*, anus) are colonial animals that superficially resemble clumps of moss. (In fact, their common name, bryozoans, means "moss animals.") In most species, the colony is encased in a hard exoskeleton (external skeleton) studded with pores through which the lophophores extend (Figure 33.14a). Most ectoproct species live in the sea, where they are among the most widespread and numerous sessile animals. Several species are important reef builders. Ectoprocts also live in lakes and rivers. Colonies of the freshwater ectoproct *Pectinatella magnifica* grow on submerged sticks or rocks and can grow into a gelatinous, ball-shaped mass more than 10 cm across.

Brachiopods, or lamp shells, superficially resemble clams and other hinge-shelled molluscs, but the two halves of the brachiopod shell are dorsal and ventral rather than lateral, as in clams (Figure 33.14b). All brachiopods are marine. Most live attached to the seafloor by a stalk, opening their shell slightly to allow water to flow through the lophophore. The living brachiopods are remnants of a much richer past that included 30 000 species in the

Paleozoic and Mesozoic eras. Some living brachiopods, such as those in the genus *Lingula*, appear nearly identical to fossils of species that lived 400 million years ago.

Molluscs

Snails and slugs, oysters and clams, and octopuses and squids are all molluscs (phylum Mollusca). There are over 100 000 known species, making them the second most diverse phylum of animals (after the arthropods, discussed later). Although the majority of molluscs are marine, roughly 8000 species inhabit fresh water, and 28 000 species of snails and slugs live on land. All molluscs are soft-bodied (from the Latin *molluscus*, soft), and most secrete a hard protective shell made of calcium carbonate. Slugs, squids, and octopuses have a reduced internal shell or have lost their shell completely during their evolution.

Despite their apparent differences, all molluscs have a similar body plan (Figure 33.15). Molluscs are coelomates, and their bodies have three main parts: a muscular **foot**, usually used for movement; a **visceral mass** containing most of the internal organs; and a **mantle**, a fold of tissue that drapes over the visceral mass and secretes a shell (if one is present). In many molluscs, the mantle extends beyond the visceral mass, producing a water-filled chamber, the **mantle cavity**, which houses the gills, anus, and excretory pores. Many molluscs feed by using a straplike organ called a **radula** to scrape up food.

Most molluscs have separate sexes, and their gonads (ovaries or testes) are located in the visceral mass. Many snails, however, are hermaphrodites. The life cycle of many marine molluscs includes a ciliated larval stage, the trochophore (see Figure 32.13b), which is also characteristic of marine annelids (segmented worms) and some other lophotrochozoans.

The basic body plan of molluscs has evolved in various ways in the phylum's seven or eight clades (experts disagree on the number). We'll examine four of those clades here: Polyplacophora (chitons), Gastropoda (snails and slugs), Bivalvia (clams, oysters, and other bivalves), and Cephalopoda (squids, octopuses, cuttlefishes, and chambered nautiluses). We will then focus on threats facing some groups of molluscs.

Chitons

Chitons have an oval-shaped body and a shell composed of eight dorsal plates (Figure 33.16). The chiton's body itself, however, is unsegmented. You can find these marine animals clinging to rocks along the seashore during low tide. If you try to dislodge a chiton by hand, you will be surprised at how well its foot, acting as a suction cup, grips the rock. A chiton can also use its foot to creep

(a) Ectoprocts, such as this creeping bryozoan (*Plumatella repens*), are colonial lophophorates.

(b) Brachiopods, such as this lampshell (*Terebratulina retusa*), have a hinged shell. The two parts of the shell are dorsal and ventral.

▲ Figure 33.14 **Lophophorates.**

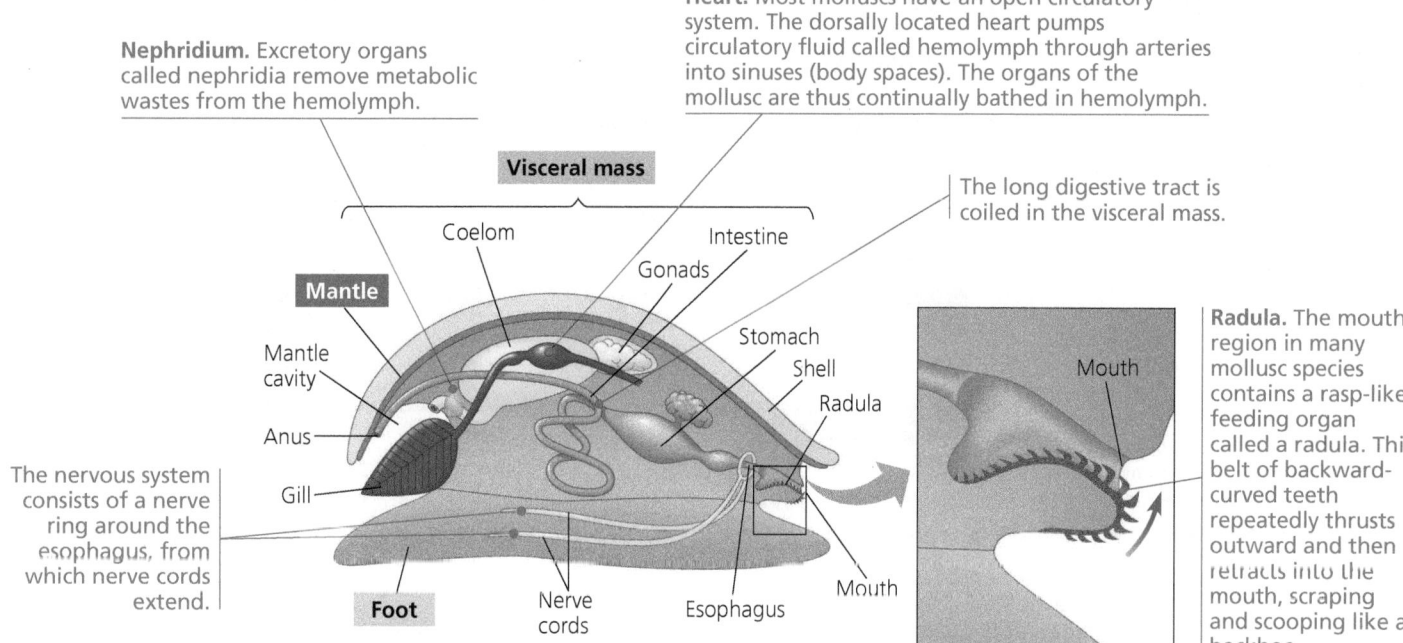

Nephridium. Excretory organs called nephridia remove metabolic wastes from the hemolymph.

Heart. Most molluscs have an open circulatory system. The dorsally located heart pumps circulatory fluid called hemolymph through arteries into sinuses (body spaces). The organs of the mollusc are thus continually bathed in hemolymph.

Visceral mass

Coelom

Intestine

Gonads

The long digestive tract is coiled in the visceral mass.

Mantle

Stomach

Mantle cavity

Shell

Radula

Anus

Radula. The mouth region in many mollusc species contains a rasp-like feeding organ called a radula. This belt of backward-curved teeth repeatedly thrusts outward and then retracts into the mouth, scraping and scooping like a backhoe.

Mouth

The nervous system consists of a nerve ring around the esophagus, from which nerve cords extend.

Gill

Foot

Nerve cords

Esophagus

Mouth

▲ Figure 33.15 **The basic body plan of a mollusc.**

slowly over the rock surface. Chitons use their radula to scrape algae off the rock surface.

Gastropods

About three-quarters of all living species of molluscs are gastropods (Figure 33.17). Most gastropods are marine, but there are also freshwater species. Still other gastropods have adapted to life on land, where snails and slugs thrive in habitats ranging from deserts to rain forests. Terrestrial snails lack the gills typical of most aquatic gastropods. Instead, the lining of their mantle cavity functions as a lung, exchanging respiratory gases with the air.

Most gastropods have a single, spiralled shell that is often conical but is somewhat flattened in abalones and limpets. Many gastropods have a distinct head with eyes at the tips

of tentacles. Gastropods rely heavily on olfactory cues and the tentacles also contain receptors for sensing different chemicals in the environment. Gastropods move literally at a snail's pace by a rippling motion of their foot or by means of cilia, often leaving a trail of slime in their wake. The gastropod's shell is secreted by glands at the edge of the mantle. The shell has several functions, including protecting the animal's soft body from injury and dehydration. One of its most important roles is as a defence against predators, as is demonstrated by comparing populations with different histories of predation (see the Scientific Skills Exercise). As they move slowly about, most gastropods use their radula to graze on algae or plants. Several groups, however, are predators, and their radula has become modified for boring holes in the shells of other molluscs or for tearing apart prey. In the cone snails, the teeth of the radula act as poison darts that are used to subdue prey.

▲ Figure 33.16 **A chiton.** Note the eight-plate shell characteristic of molluscs in the clade Polyplacophora.

Dray van Beeck/Image Quest Marine

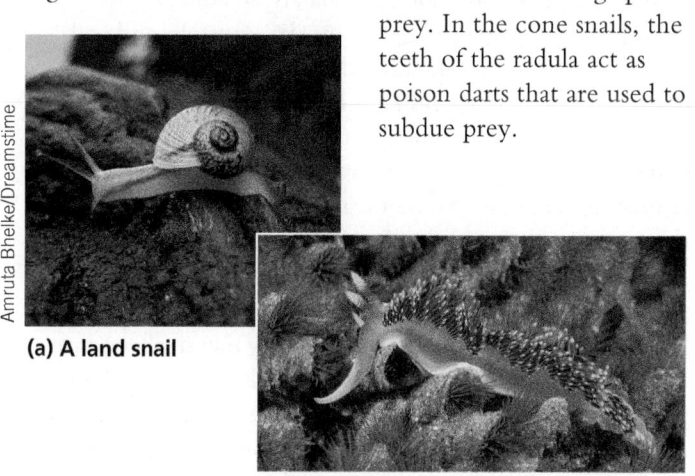

Amruta Bhelke/Dreamstime

(a) A land snail

Corbis

▲ Figure 33.17 **Gastropods.**

(b) A sea slug. Nudibranchs, or sea slugs, lost their shell during their evolution.

Understanding Experimental Design and Interpreting Data

Is There Evidence of Selection for Defensive Adaptations in Mollusc Populations Exposed to Predators? The fossil record shows that, historically, increased risk to prey species from predators is often accompanied by increased incidence and expression of prey defences. Researchers tested whether populations of the predatory European green crab (*Carcinus maenas*) have exerted similar selective pressures on its gastropod prey, the flat periwinkle (*Littorina obtusata*). Periwinkles from southern sites in the Gulf of Maine have experienced predation by European green crabs for over 100 generations, at about one generation per year. Periwinkles from northern sites in the Gulf have been interacting with the invasive green crabs for relatively few generations, as the invasive crabs spread to the northern Gulf comparatively recently.

Christophe Courteau/naturepl.com
▲ **A periwinkle**

Previous research shows that (1) flat periwinkle shells recently collected from the Gulf are thicker than those collected in the late 1800s, and (2) periwinkle populations from southern sites in the Gulf have thicker shells than periwinkle populations from northern sites. In this exercise, you'll interpret the design and results of the researchers' experiment studying the rates of predation by European green crabs on periwinkles from northern and southern populations.

How the Experiment Was Done The researchers collected periwinkles and crabs from sites in the northern and southern Gulf of Maine, separated by 450 km of coastline. A single crab was placed in a cage with eight periwinkles of different sizes. After three days, researchers assessed the fate of the eight periwinkles. Four different treatments were set up, with crabs from northern or southern populations offered periwinkles from northern and southern populations. All crabs were of similar size and included equal numbers of males and females. Each experimental treatment was tested 12 to 14 times.

In a second part of the experiment, the bodies of periwinkles from northern and southern populations were removed from their shells and presented to crabs from northern and southern populations.

Data from the Experiment

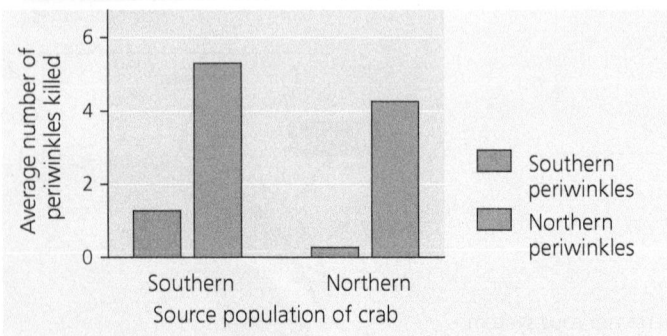

Source: Adaptation of figure 1 from "Interaction between an Invasive Decapod and a Native Gastropod: Predator Foraging Tactics and Prey Architectural Defenses" by Remy Rochette et al., from *Marine Ecology Progress Series*, January 2007, Volume 330. Copyright © 2007 by Inter-Research Science Center. Reprinted with permission.

When the researchers presented the crabs with unshelled periwinkles, all the unshelled periwinkles were consumed in less than an hour.

Interpret the Data

1. What hypotheses were the researchers testing in this study? What are the independent variables in this study? What are the dependent variables in this study?

2. Why did the research team set up four different treatments?

3. Why did researchers present unshelled periwinkles to the crabs? Explain what the results of this part of the experiment indicate.

4. Summarize the results of the experiment in words. Do these results support the hypothesis you identified in question 1? Explain.

5. Suggest how natural selection may have affected populations of flat periwinkles in the southern Gulf of Maine over the last 100 years.

Data from R. Rochette et al., Interaction between an invasive decapod and a native gastropod: Predator foraging tactics and prey architectural defenses, *Marine Ecology Progress Series* 330:179–188 (2007). © Jane B. Reece.

Bivalves

The molluscs of the clade Bivalvia are all aquatic and include many species of clams, oysters, mussels, and scallops. Bivalves have a shell divided into two halves (**Figure 33.18**). The halves are hinged, and powerful adductor muscles draw them tightly together to protect the animal's soft body. Bivalves have no distinct head, and the radula has been lost. Some bivalves have eyes and sensory tentacles along the outer edge of their mantle.

The mantle cavity of a bivalve contains gills that are used for gas exchange as well as feeding in most species (**Figure 33.19**). Most bivalves are suspension feeders. They trap small food particles in mucus that coats their gills, and cilia then convey those particles to the mouth. Water enters the mantle cavity through an incurrent siphon, passes over the gills, and then exits the mantle cavity through an excurrent siphon.

Harold W. Pratt/Biological Photo Service

▲ **Figure 33.18 A bivalve.** This scallop has many eyes (dark blue spots) lining each half of its hinged shell.

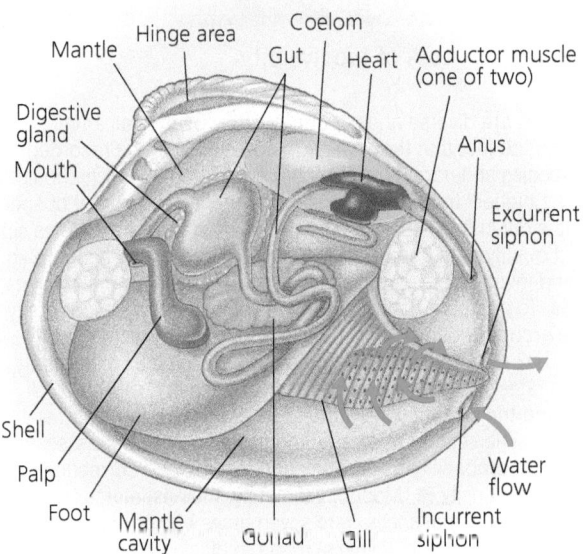

Mantle — Hinge area — Coelom — Gut — Heart — Adductor muscle (one of two)

Digestive gland

Mouth

Anus

Excurrent siphon

Shell

Palp

Foot

Mantle cavity — Gonad — Gill — Incurrent siphon

Water flow

▲ Figure 33.19 **Anatomy of a clam.** Food particles suspended in water that enters through the incurrent siphon are collected by the gills and passed via cilia and the palps to the mouth.

Most bivalves lead sedentary lives, a characteristic suited to suspension feeding. Mussels secrete strong threads that tether them to rocks, docks, boats, and the shells of other animals. However, clams can pull themselves into the sand or mud, using their muscular foot for an anchor, and scallops can skitter along the seafloor by flapping their shells, rather like the mechanical false teeth sold in novelty shops.

Cephalopods

Cephalopods are active marine predators (**Figure 33.20**). They use their tentacles to grasp prey, which they then bite with beak-like jaws and immobilize with a toxin present in their saliva. The foot of a cephalopod has become modified into a muscular excurrent siphon and part of the tentacles. Squids dart about by drawing water into their mantle cavity and then firing a jet of water through the excurrent siphon; they steer by pointing the siphon in different directions. Octopuses use a similar mechanism to escape predators.

The mantle covers the visceral mass of cephalopods, but the shell is generally reduced and internal (in most species) or missing altogether (in some cuttlefishes and some octopuses). One small group of cephalopods with external shells, the chambered nautiluses, survives today.

Cephalopods are the only molluscs with a *closed circulatory system*, in which the blood remains separate from fluid in the body cavity. They also have well-developed

▶ Squids are speedy carnivores with beak-like jaws and well-developed eyes.

◀ Octopuses are considered among the most intelligent invertebrates.

▶ Chambered nautiluses are the only living cephalopods with an external shell.

▲ Figure 33.20 **Cephalopods.**

sense organs and a complex brain. The ability to learn and behave in a complex manner is probably more critical to fast-moving predators than to sedentary animals such as clams.

The ancestors of octopuses and squids were probably shelled molluscs that took up a predatory lifestyle; the shell was lost in later evolution. Shelled cephalopods called **ammonites**, some of them as large as truck tires, were the dominant invertebrate predators of the seas for hundreds of millions of years until their disappearance during the mass extinction at the end of the Cretaceous period, 65.5 million years ago (see Table 25.1).

Most species of squid are less than 75 cm long, but some are considerably larger. The giant squid (*Architeuthis dux*), for example, has an estimated maximum length of 13 m for females and 10 m for males. The colossal squid (*Mesonychoteuthis hamiltoni*) is even larger, with an estimated maximum length of 14 m. Unlike *A. dux*, which has large suckers and small teeth on its tentacles, *M. hamiltoni* has two rows of sharp hooks at the ends of its tentacles that can inflict deadly lacerations.

It is likely that *A. dux* and *M. hamiltoni* spend most of their time in the deep ocean, where they may feed on large fishes. Remains of both giant squid species have been found in the stomachs of sperm whales, which are probably their only natural predator. In 2005, scientists reported the first observations of *A. dux* in the wild, photographed while attacking baited hooks at a depth of 900 m. *M. hamiltoni* has yet to be observed in nature. Overall, these marine giants remain among the great mysteries of invertebrate life.

Protecting Freshwater and Terrestrial Molluscs

Species extinction rates have increased dramatically in the last 400 years, raising concern that a sixth human-caused mass extinction may be under way (see Concept 25.4). Of the documented animal extinctions, almost 40% are molluscs. In Canada, there are 22 mollusc species that are threatened or endangered according to the Committee on the Status of Endangered Wildlife in Canada (COSEWIC), including the Banff Springs snail (*Physella johnsoni*) **(Figure 32.21)**, which was the first species COSEWIC placed on the endangered species list in 1997. This tiny snail (<1 cm) is a specialist and is found in five thermal springs on Sulphur Mountain located in Banff National Park. It has adapted to the warm water (around 33°C), low oxygen, and high hydrogen sulphide content of these thermal springs. In fact, this snail is found nowhere else on earth! The Banff Springs snail is endangered for several reasons, including habitat loss due to thermal water reductions and redirections (both natural and managed) plus human activities, including trampling of the snail around the pools. Recovery plans are in effect that include habitat protection and reduced visitor access to the natural thermal springs.

The threat to invertebrate biodiversity is certainly not limited to molluscs, but collecting the data to determine the conservation status of a population requires a lot of effort and expertise. As you probably would predict, invertebrates are not as closely monitored by biologists as are vertebrates, so the true loss of invertebrate biodiversity is likely much higher than currently recorded **(Figure 33.22)**.

▲ Figure 33.21 *Physella johnsoni*—the **Banff Springs snail**

Annelids

Annelida means "little rings," referring to the annelid body's resemblance to a series of fused rings. Annelids are segmented worms that live in the sea, in most freshwater habitats, and in damp soil. Annelids are coelomates, and they range in length from less than 1 mm to more than 3 m, the length of a giant Australian earthworm.

▼ Figure 33.22 | **Impact**

Invertebrates: Loss of biodiversity

Invertebrates are diverse and account for over 95% of all animal species, so the fact that they make up about 50% of the recorded extinct species shouldn't be a surprise, in fact, the question should be why isn't it higher? In short, there is a bias in the assessment of species at risk. It is difficult to assess the conservation status of a species since you need quality data on population trends, habitat, and geographic range, and invertebrates are not as well studied as mammals, fishes, and birds. To get more realistic estimates of invertebrate biodiversity loss, one group randomly selected 200 species of terrestrial snails (from 17 102 global records) and used two approaches to assess extinction rates. The first relied on reports of experts, museum records, and the scientific literature to assess the conservation status ■ (Experts). The second used a mathematical model that assessed the extinction probability using collection records and correcting for sampling intensity ■ (Model). Ultimately, their estimates for extinction for terrestrial snails were seven times higher (and showing 10% extinction of terrestrial snails) than the official records from the International Union for the Conservation of Nature ■ (IUCN).

Why It Matters The extinctions of molluscs and other invertebrates represent an irreversible loss of biological diversity and these losses threaten other organisms. Terrestrial snails, for example, play a role in nutrient recycling while other invertebrates are integral to most global ecosystems, whether as consumers or decomposers.

Further Reading C. Régnier et al., Mass extinction in poorly known taxa, *Proceedings National Academy of Science* 112:7761–7766 (2015).

MAKE CONNECTIONS *Ten percent of freshwater mussel species in North America have become extinct in the last 300 years. These bivalves feed on photosynthetic protists and bacteria. As such, what effect could the extinction of freshwater mussels have on their aquatic communities (see Concept 28.6)?*

Traditionally, the phylum Annelida was divided into three main groups, Polychaeta (the polychaetes), Oligochaeta (the oligochaetes), and Hirudinea (the leeches). The names of the first two of these groups reflected the relative number of chaetae, bristles made of chitin, on their bodies: polychaetes (from the Greek *poly*, many, and *chaitē*, long hair) have many more chaetae per segment than do oligochaetes.

However, a 2011 phylogenomic study and other recent molecular analyses have indicated that the oligochaetes are a subgroup of the polychaetes, making the polychaetes (as defined morphologically) a paraphyletic group. Likewise, the leeches have been shown to be a subgroup of the oligochaetes. As a result, these traditional names are no longer used to describe the evolutionary history of the annelids. Instead, current evidence indicates that the annelids can be divided into two major clades, Errantia and Sedentaria—a grouping that reflects broad differences in lifestyle.

Errantians

Clade Errantia (from the Old French *errant*, travelling) is a large and diverse group, most of whose members are marine. As their name suggests, many errantians are mobile; some swim among the plankton (small, drifting organisms), while many others crawl on or burrow in the seafloor. Many are predators, while others are grazers that feed on large, multicellular algae. The group also includes some relatively immobile species, such as the tube-dwelling *Platynereis*, a marine species that recently has become a model organism for studying neurobiology and development.

In many errantians, each body segment has a pair of prominent paddle-like or ridge-like structures called parapodia ("beside feet") that function in locomotion (Figure 33.23). Each parapodium has numerous chaetae. (Possession of parapodia with numerous chaetae is not unique to Errantia, however, as some members of the other major clade of annelids, Sedentaria, also have these features.) In many species, the parapodia are richly supplied with blood vessels and also function as gills. Errantians also tend to have well-developed jaws and sensory organs, as might be expected of predators or grazers that move about in search of food.

Sedentarians

Species in the other major clade of annelids, Sedentaria (from the Latin *sedere*, sit), tend to be less mobile than those

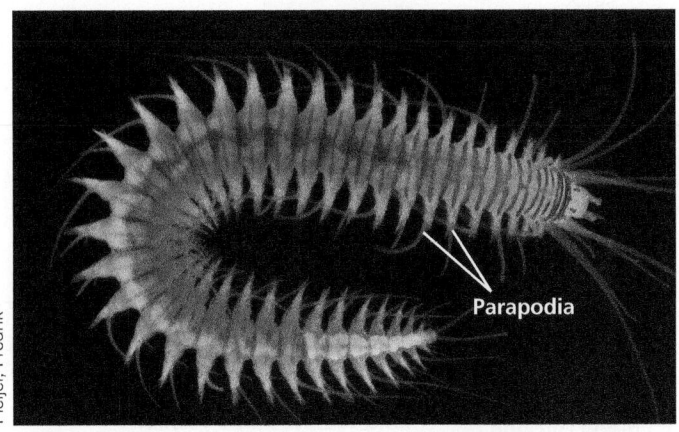

▲ Figure 33.23 **An errantian, the predator *Nereimyra punctata*.** This marine annelid ambushes prey from burrows it has constructed on the seafloor. *N. punctata* hunts by touch, detecting its prey with long sensory organs called cirri that extend from the burrow.

▲ Figure 33.24 **The Christmas tree worm, *Spirobranchus giganteus*.** The two tree-shaped whorls of this sedentarian are tentacles, which the worm uses for gas exchange and for removing small food particles from the surrounding water. The tentacles emerge from a tube of calcium carbonate secreted by the worm that protects and supports its soft body.

in Errantia. Some species burrow slowly through marine sediments or soil, while others live within tubes that protect and support their soft bodies. Tube-dwelling sedentarians often have elaborate gills or tentacles used for filter feeding (Figure 33.24).

Although the Christmas tree worm shown in Figure 33.24 once was classified as a "polychaete," current evidence indicates it is a sedentarian. The clade Sedentaria also contains former "oligochaetes," including the two groups we turn to next, the leeches and the earthworms.

Leeches Most leeches inhabit fresh water, but there are also marine species and terrestrial leeches, which live in moist vegetation. Leeches range in length from 1 to 30 cm. Many are predators that feed on other invertebrates, but some are parasites that suck blood by attaching temporarily to other animals, including humans (Figure 33.25). Some parasitic species use bladelike jaws to slit the skin of their host. The host is usually oblivious to this attack because the leech secretes an anaesthetic. After making the incision, the leech secretes a chemical, hirudin, which keeps the blood of the host from

▲ Figure 33.25 **A leech.** A nurse applied this medicinal leech (*Hirudo medicinalis*) to a patient's sore thumb to drain blood from a hematoma (an abnormal accumulation of blood around an internal injury).

coagulating near the incision. The parasite then sucks as much blood as it can hold, often more than 10 times its own weight. After this gorging, a leech can last for months without another meal.

Until the 20th century, leeches were frequently used for bloodletting. Today they are used to drain blood that accumulates in tissues following certain injuries or surgeries. In addition, forms of hirudin produced with recombinant DNA techniques can be used to dissolve unwanted blood clots that form during surgery or as a result of heart disease.

Earthworms Earthworms eat their way through the soil, extracting nutrients as the soil passes through the alimentary canal. Undigested material, mixed with mucus secreted into the canal, is eliminated as fecal castings through the anus. Farmers value earthworms because the animals till and aerate the earth, and their castings improve the texture of the soil. (Charles Darwin estimated that one acre of farmland contains about 50 000 earthworms, producing 18 tonnes of castings per year.)

A guided tour of the anatomy of an earthworm, which is representative of annelids, is shown in **Figure 33.26**.

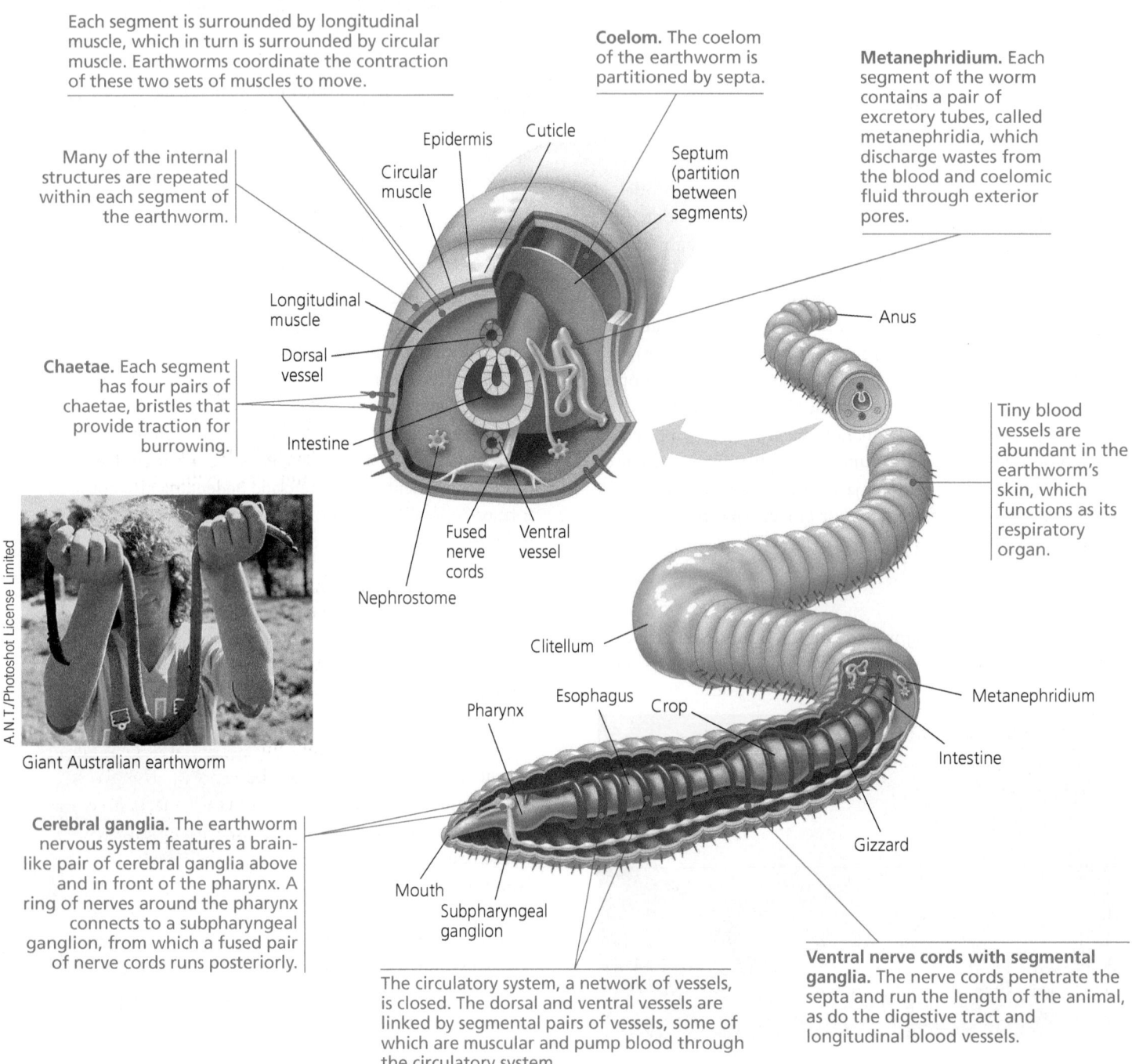

Each segment is surrounded by longitudinal muscle, which in turn is surrounded by circular muscle. Earthworms coordinate the contraction of these two sets of muscles to move.

Many of the internal structures are repeated within each segment of the earthworm.

Chaetae. Each segment has four pairs of chaetae, bristles that provide traction for burrowing.

Coelom. The coelom of the earthworm is partitioned by septa.

Metanephridium. Each segment of the worm contains a pair of excretory tubes, called metanephridia, which discharge wastes from the blood and coelomic fluid through exterior pores.

Epidermis
Cuticle
Circular muscle
Septum (partition between segments)
Longitudinal muscle
Dorsal vessel
Intestine
Fused nerve cords
Ventral vessel
Nephrostome

Anus

Tiny blood vessels are abundant in the earthworm's skin, which functions as its respiratory organ.

Clitellum

Pharynx
Esophagus
Crop
Mouth
Subpharyngeal ganglion

Metanephridium
Intestine
Gizzard

A.N.T./Photoshot License Limited

Giant Australian earthworm

Cerebral ganglia. The earthworm nervous system features a brain-like pair of cerebral ganglia above and in front of the pharynx. A ring of nerves around the pharynx connects to a subpharyngeal ganglion, from which a fused pair of nerve cords runs posteriorly.

The circulatory system, a network of vessels, is closed. The dorsal and ventral vessels are linked by segmental pairs of vessels, some of which are muscular and pump blood through the circulatory system.

Ventral nerve cords with segmental ganglia. The nerve cords penetrate the septa and run the length of the animal, as do the digestive tract and longitudinal blood vessels.

▲ Figure 33.26 **Anatomy of an earthworm, a sedentarian.**

Earthworms are hermaphrodites, but they do cross-fertilize. Two earthworms mate by aligning themselves in opposite directions in such a way that they exchange sperm, and then they separate. Some earthworms can also reproduce asexually by fragmentation followed by regeneration.

As a group, Lophotrochozoa encompasses a remarkable range of body plans, as illustrated by members of such phyla as Rotifera, Ectoprocta, Mollusca, and Annelida. Next we'll explore the diversity of Ecdysozoa, a dominant presence on Earth in terms of sheer number of species.

CONCEPT CHECK 33.3

1. Explain how tapeworms can survive without a coelom, a mouth, a digestive system, or an excretory system.
2. Annelid anatomy can be described as "a tube within a tube." Explain.
3. **MAKE CONNECTIONS** Explain how the molluscan foot in gastropods and the excurrent siphon in cephalopods represent an example of descent with modification (see Concept 22.2).

For suggested answers, see Appendix A.

CONCEPT 33.4

Ecdysozoans are the most species-rich animal group

Porifera
Cnidaria
Lophotrochozoa
Ecdysozoa
Deuterostomia

Although defined primarily by molecular evidence, the clade Ecdysozoa includes animals that shed a tough external coat (**cuticle**) as they grow; in fact, the group derives its name from this process, which is called *ecdysis*, or **moulting**. Ecdysozoa consists of about eight animal phyla and contains more known species than all other animal, protist, fungus, and plant groups combined. Here we'll focus on the two largest ecdysozoan phyla, the nematodes and arthropods, which are among the most successful and abundant of all animal groups.

Nematodes

Among the most ubiquitous of animals, nematodes (phylum Nematoda), or roundworms, are found in most aquatic habitats, in the soil, in the moist tissues of plants, and in the body fluids and tissues of animals. In contrast to annelids, nematodes do not have segmented bodies. The cylindrical bodies of nematodes range from less than 1 mm to more than 1 m long, often tapering to a fine tip at the posterior end and to a blunter tip at the anterior end (Figure 33.27).

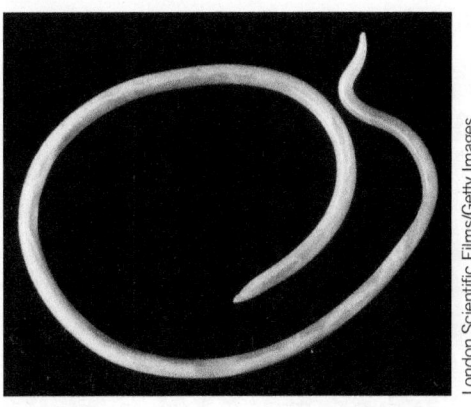

◀ Figure 33.27 A free-living nematode (colourized SEM).

London Scientific Films/Getty Images

A nematode's body is covered by a tough cuticle (a type of exoskeleton); as the worm grows, it periodically sheds its old cuticle and secretes a new, larger one. Nematodes have an alimentary canal, though they lack a circulatory system. Nutrients are transported throughout the body via fluid in the pseudocoelom. The body wall muscles are all longitudinal, and their contraction produces a thrashing motion.

Multitudes of nematodes live in moist soil and in decomposing organic matter on the bottoms of lakes and oceans. While 25 000 species are known, perhaps 20 times that number actually exist. It has been said that if nothing of Earth or its organisms remained but nematodes, they would still preserve the outline of the planet and many of its features. These free-living worms play an important role in decomposition and nutrient cycling, but little is known about most species. One species of soil nematode, *Caenorhabditis elegans*, however, is very well studied and has become a model research organism in biology (see Chapter 47). Ongoing studies of *C. elegans* are revealing some of the mechanisms involved in aging in humans, among many other topics.

Phylum Nematoda includes many species that parasitize plants, and some are major agricultural pests that attack the roots of crops. Other nematodes parasitize animals. Some of these species benefit humans by attacking insects such as cutworms that feed on the roots of crop plants. On the other hand, humans are hosts to at least 50 nematode species, including various pinworms and hookworms. One notorious nematode is *Trichinella spiralis*, the worm that causes trichinosis (Figure 33.28). Humans acquire this nematode by eating raw or undercooked pork or other meat (including wild game such as bear or walrus) that has juvenile worms encysted in the muscle tissue. Within the human intestines, the juveniles develop into sexually mature adults. Females burrow into the intestinal muscles and produce more juveniles, which bore through the body or travel in lymphatic vessels to other organs, including skeletal muscles, where they encyst.

Encysted juveniles   Muscle tissue   50 μm

▲ Figure 33.28 Juveniles of the parasitic nematode *Trichinella spiralis* encysted in human muscle tissue (LM).

Parasitic nematodes have an extraordinary molecular toolkit that enables them to redirect some of the cellular functions of their hosts and thus evade their immune systems. Some species inject their plant hosts with molecules that induce the development of root cells, which then supply nutrients to the parasites. When *Trichinella* parasitizes animals, it regulates the expression of specific muscle cell genes that code for proteins that make the cell elastic enough to house the nematode. Additionally, the infected muscle cell releases signals that promote the growth of new blood vessels, which then supply the nematode with nutrients.

Arthropods

Zoologists estimate that there are about a billion billion (10^{18}) arthropods living on Earth. More than 1 million arthropod species have been described, most of which are insects. In fact, two out of every three known species are arthropods, and members of the phylum Arthropoda can be found in nearly all habitats of the biosphere. By the criteria of species diversity, distribution, and sheer numbers, arthropods must be regarded as the most successful of all animal phyla.

Arthropod Origins

Biologists hypothesize that the diversity and success of **arthropods** are related to their body plan—their segmented body, hard exoskeleton, and jointed appendages (*arthropod* means "jointed feet"). The earliest fossils with this body plan are from the Cambrian explosion (535–525 million years ago), indicating that the arthropods are at least that old.

Along with arthropods, the fossil record of the Cambrian explosion contains many species of *lobopods*, an extinct

group from which arthropods may have evolved. Lobopods such as *Hallucigenia* (see Figure 32.6) had segmented bodies, but most of their body segments were identical to one another. Early arthropods, such as the trilobites, also showed little variation from segment to segment (Figure 33.29). Fossils from these extinct groups are represented at the Burgess Shale site in British Columbia (Figure 32.6). As arthropods continued to evolve, the segments tended to fuse and become fewer, and the appendages became specialized for a variety of functions. These evolutionary changes resulted not only in great diversification but also in an efficient body plan that permits the division of labour among different body regions.

What genetic changes led to the increasing complexity of the arthropod body plan? Arthropods today have two unusual *Hox* genes, both of which influence segmentation. To test whether these genes could have driven the evolution of increased body segment diversity in arthropods, researchers studied *Hox* genes in onychophorans (see Figure 33.3), close relatives of arthropods (Figure 33.30). Their results indicate that the diversity of arthropod body plans did *not* arise from the acquisition of new *Hox* genes. Instead, the evolution of body segment diversity in arthropods was probably driven by changes in the sequence or regulation of existing *Hox* genes. (See Concept 25.5 for a discussion of how changes in form can result from changes in the sequence or regulation of existing *Hox* genes.

General Characteristics of Arthropods

Over the course of evolution, the appendages of some arthropods have become modified, specializing in functions such as walking, feeding, sensory reception, reproduction, and defence. Like the appendages from which they were derived, these modified structures are jointed and come in pairs. Figure 33.31 illustrates the diverse appendages and other arthropod characteristics of a lobster.

The body of an arthropod is completely covered by the cuticle, an exoskeleton constructed from layers of protein

◀ Figure 33.29 A trilobite fossil. Trilobites were common denizens of the shallow seas throughout the Paleozoic era but disappeared with the great Permian extinctions about 250 million years ago. Paleontologists have described about 4000 trilobite species.

▼ Figure 33.30 Inquiry

Did the arthropod body plan result from new *Hox* genes?

Experiment One hypothesis suggests that the arthropod body plan resulted from the origin (by a gene duplication followed by mutation) of two unusual *Hox* genes found in arthropods: *Ultrabithorax* (*Ubx*) and *abdominal-A* (*abd-A*). Hox genes are known to encode transcription factors involved in development in animals. To test this hypothesis, Sean Carroll, of the University of Wisconsin, Madison, and colleagues turned to the onychophorans, a group of invertebrates closely related to arthropods. Unlike many living arthropods, onychophorans have a body plan in which most body segments are identical to one another. Thus, Carroll and colleagues reasoned that if the origin of the *Ubx* and *abd-A Hox* genes drove the evolution of body segment diversity in arthropods, these genes probably arose on the arthropod branch of the evolutionary tree:

According to this hypothesis, *Ubx* and *abd-A* would not have been present in the common ancestor of arthropods and onychophorans; hence, onychophorans should not have these genes. To find out whether this was the case, Carroll and colleagues examined the *Hox* genes of the onychophoran *Acanthokara kaputensis*.

Results The onychophoran *A. kaputensis* has all arthropod *Hox* genes, including *Ubx* and *abd-A*.

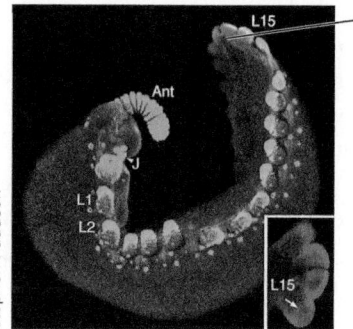

Red indicates the body regions of this onychophoran embryo in which *Ubx* or *abd-A* genes were expressed. (The inset shows this area enlarged.)

Ant = antenna
J = jaws
L1–L15 = body segments

Conclusion The evolution of increased body segment diversity in arthropods was not related to the origin of new *Hox* genes; thus, their hypothesis was not supported.

Source: Based on J. K. Grenier, S. Carroll, et al., Evolution of the entire arthropod Hox gene set predated the origin and radiation of the onychophoran/arthropod clade, Current Biology 7:547–553 (1997). © Jane B. Reece.

WHAT IF? *Suppose* A. kaputensis *did not have the* Ubx *and* abd-A Hox *genes, how would their conclusion have been affected? Explain.*

---

and the polysaccharide chitin. The cuticle can be thick and hard over some parts of the body and paper-thin and flexible over others, such as the joints. The rigid exoskeleton protects the animal and provides points of attachment for

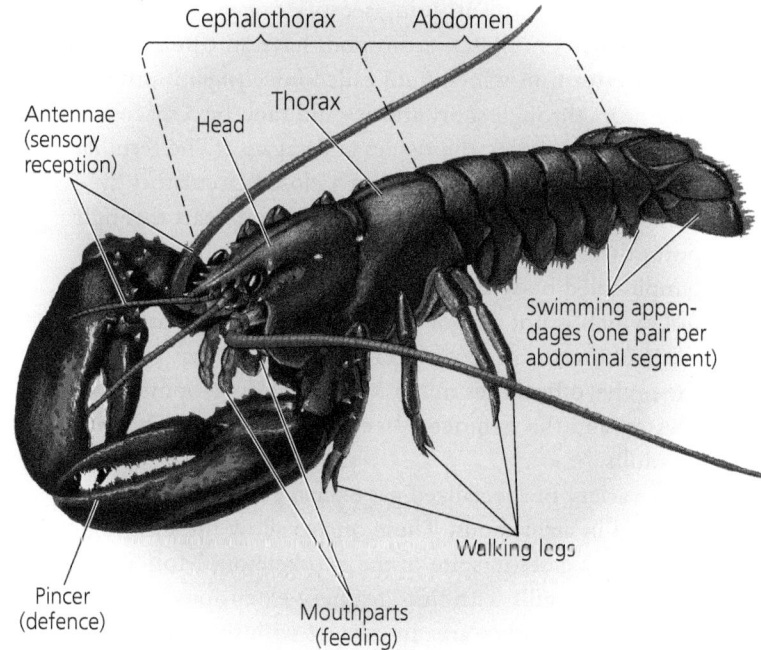

▲ **Figure 33.31 External anatomy of an arthropod.** Many of the distinctive features of arthropods are apparent in this dorsal view of a lobster, along with some uniquely crustacean characteristics. The body is segmented, but this characteristic is obvious only in the abdomen. The appendages (including antennae, pincers, mouthparts, walking legs, and swimming appendages) are jointed. The head bears a pair of compound (multilens) eyes, each situated on a movable stalk. The whole body, including appendages, is covered by an exoskeleton.

the muscles that move the appendages. But it also prevents the arthropod from growing, unless it occasionally sheds its exoskeleton and produces a larger one. This moulting process is energetically expensive. A moulting or recently moulted arthropod is also vulnerable to predation and other dangers until its new, soft exoskeleton hardens.

When the arthropod exoskeleton first evolved in the sea, its main functions were probably protection and anchorage for muscles, but it later enabled certain arthropods to live on land. The exoskeleton's relative impermeability to water helped prevent desiccation, and its strength solved the problem of support when arthropods left the buoyancy of water. Fossil evidence suggests that arthropods were among the first animals to colonize land, roughly 450 million years ago. These fossils include fragments of arthropod remains, as well as possible millipede burrows. Arthropod fossils from several continents indicate that by 410 million years ago, millipedes, centipedes, spiders, and a variety of wingless insects all had colonized land.

Arthropods have well-developed sensory organs, including eyes, olfactory (smell) receptors, and antennae that function in both touch and smell. Most sensory organs are concentrated at the anterior end of the animal, although there are interesting exceptions. Female butterflies, for example, "taste" plants using sensory organs on their feet.

Like many molluscs, arthropods have an **open circulatory system**, in which fluid called *hemolymph* is propelled by a heart through short arteries and then into spaces called sinuses surrounding the tissues and organs. (The term *blood* is generally reserved for fluid in a closed circulatory system.) Hemolymph reenters the arthropod heart through pores that are usually equipped with valves. The hemolymph-filled body sinuses are collectively called the *hemocoel*, which is not part of the coelom. Although arthropods are coelomates, in most species the coelom that forms in the embryo becomes much reduced as development progresses, and the hemocoel becomes the main body cavity in adults.

A variety of specialized gas exchange organs have evolved in arthropods. These organs allow the diffusion of respiratory gases in spite of the exoskeleton. Most aquatic species have gills with thin, feathery extensions that place an extensive surface area in contact with the surrounding water. Terrestrial arthropods generally have internal surfaces specialized for gas exchange. Most insects, for instance, have tracheal systems, branched air ducts leading into the interior from pores in the cuticle.

Morphological and molecular evidence suggests that living arthropods consist of three major lineages that diverged early in the evolution of the phylum: **chelicerates** (sea spiders, horseshoe crabs, scorpions, ticks, mites, and spiders); **myriapods** (centipedes and millipedes); **hexapods** (insects and their wingless, six-legged relatives); and **pancrustaceans** (a recently defined group that includes insects as well as lobsters, shrimp, barnacles, and other crustaceans).

Chelicerates

Chelicerates (clade Chelicerata) are named for clawlike feeding appendages called **chelicerae**, which serve as pincers or fangs. Chelicerates have an anterior cephalothorax and a posterior abdomen. They lack antennae, and most have simple eyes (eyes with a single lens).

The earliest chelicerates were **eurypterids**, or water scorpions. These marine and freshwater predators grew up to 3 m long; it is thought that some species could have walked on land, much as land crabs do today. Most of the marine chelicerates, including all of the eurypterids, are extinct. Among the marine chelicerates that survive today are the sea spiders (pycnogonids) and horseshoe crabs (Figure 33.32). The horseshoe crabs are often considered "living fossils" because their gross morphology has remained the same for millions of years. The oldest horseshoe crab fossil was found in Manitoba and was dated to around 454 million years ago. Interestingly, the hemolymph of the horseshoe crab clots readily in the presence of bacterial

▲ Figure 33.32 **Horseshoe crabs (*Limulus polyphemus*).** Common on the Atlantic and Gulf coasts of the United States, these "living fossils" have changed little in hundreds of millions of years. They are surviving members of a rich diversity of chelicerates that once filled the seas.

Mark Newman/Frank Lane Picture Agency Limited

endotoxins and is used to screen pharmaceutical products for the presence of endotoxins and in the diagnosis of disease. While the horseshoe crab has survived for millions of years, their numbers are reportedly declining due to a number of factors, including habitat loss and harvesting.

The bulk of modern chelicerates are **arachnids**, a group that includes scorpions, spiders, ticks, and mites (Figure 33.33). Ticks and many mites are among a large group of parasitic arthropods. Nearly all ticks are blood-sucking parasites that live on the body surfaces of reptiles or mammals. Parasitic mites live on or in a wide variety of vertebrates, invertebrates, and plants.

Arachnids have six pairs of appendages: the chelicerae; a pair of appendages called *pedipalps* that function in sensing, feeding, or reproduction; and four pairs of walking legs (Figure 33.34). Spiders use their fang-like chelicerae, which are equipped with venom glands, to attack prey. As the chelicerae pierce the prey, the spider secretes digestive juices onto the prey's torn tissues. These secretions contain a variety of enzymes that soften the tissue, and the spider sucks up the liquid meal.

In most spiders, gas exchange is carried out by **book lungs**, stacked platelike structures contained in an internal chamber (see Figure 33.34). The extensive surface area of these respiratory organs is a structural adaptation that enhances the exchange of O_2 and CO_2 between the hemolymph and air.

A unique adaptation of many spiders is the ability to catch insects by constructing webs of silk, a liquid protein produced by specialized abdominal glands. The silk is spun by organs called spinnerets into fibres that then solidify. Each spider engineers a web characteristic of its species and builds it perfectly on the first try, indicating that this complex behaviour is inherited. Various spiders also use

▲ Scorpions have pedipalps that are pincers specialized for defence and the capture of food. The tip of the tail bears a stinger that delivers a venom.

Tim Flach/The Image Bank/Getty Images

50 µm

Andrew Syred/Science Source

▲ Dust mites are ubiquitous scavengers in human dwellings but are harmless except to those people who are allergic to them (colourized SEM).

Spydr/Getty Images

◄ Web-building spiders are generally most active during the daytime.

▲ **Figure 33.33 Arachnids.**

silk in other ways: as droplines for rapid escape, as a cover for eggs, and even as "gift wrap" for food that males offer females during courtship. Many small spiders also extrude silk into the air and let themselves be transported by wind, a behaviour known as "ballooning."

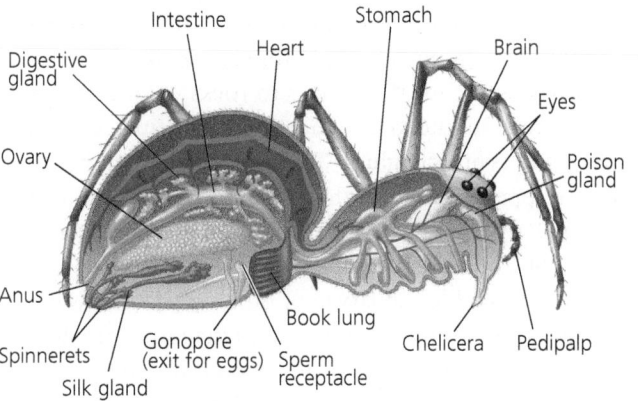

Intestine | Stomach | Brain

Digestive gland | Heart | Eyes

Ovary | Poison gland

Anus | Book lung

Spinnerets | Gonopore (exit for eggs) | Chelicera | Pedipalp

Silk gland | Sperm receptacle

▲ **Figure 33.34 Anatomy of a spider.**

Myriapods

Millipedes and centipedes belong to the subphylum Myriapoda (Figure 33.35). All living myriapods are terrestrial. The myriapod head has a pair of antennae and three pairs of appendages modified as mouthparts, including the jaw-like **mandibles**.

Millipedes have a large number of legs, though fewer than the thousand their name implies. Each trunk segment is formed from two fused segments and bears two pairs of legs (see Figure 33.35a). Millipedes eat decaying leaves and other plant matter. They may have been among the earliest animals on land, living on mosses and early vascular plants.

The now extinct genus *Arthropleura* likely represented the largest terrestrial invertebrates on Earth, estimated to have grown up to 2 m in length. There are fossil trackways from the giant *Arthropleura* at the Joggins Fossil Cliffs in Nova Scotia dating from the Carboniferous period.

Unlike millipedes, centipedes are carnivores. Each segment of a centipede's trunk region has one pair of legs (see Figure 33.35b). Centipedes have venomous claws on their foremost trunk segment that paralyze prey and aid in defence.

Pancrustaceans

A series of recent papers, including a 2010 phylogenomic study, present evidence that terrestrial insects are more closely related to lobsters and other crustaceans than they are to the terrestrial group we just discussed, the myriapods (millipedes and centipedes). These studies also suggest that the diverse group of organisms referred to as crustaceans are paraphyletic: Some lineages of crustaceans are more closely related to insects than they are to other crustaceans

PREMAPHOTOS/Nature Picture Library

(a) Millipede

(b) Centipede

Tom McHugh/Science Source

▲ **Figure 33.35 Myriapods.**

(Figure 33.36). However, together the insects and crustaceans form a clade, which systematists have named Pancrustacea (from the Greek *pan*, all). We turn next to a description of the members of Pancrustacea, focusing first on crustaceans and then on the insects.

Crustaceans

Crustaceans (crabs, lobsters, shrimps, barnacles, and many others) thrive in a broad range of marine, freshwater, and terrestrial environments. Many crustaceans have highly specialized appendages. Lobsters and crayfishes, for instance, have a toolkit of 19 pairs of appendages (see Figure 33.31). The anterior-most appendages are antennae; crustaceans are the only arthropods with two pairs. Three or more pairs of appendages are modified as mouthparts, including the hard mandibles. Walking legs are present on the thorax, and, unlike insects, crustaceans also have appendages on their abdomen.

Small crustaceans exchange gases across thin areas of the cuticle; larger species have gills. Nitrogenous wastes also diffuse through thin areas of the cuticle, but a pair of glands regulates the salt balance of the hemolymph.

Sexes are separate in most crustaceans. In the case of lobsters and crayfishes, the male uses a specialized pair of abdominal appendages to transfer sperm to the reproductive pore of the female during copulation. Most aquatic crustaceans go through one or more swimming larval stages.

One of the largest groups of crustaceans (numbering over 11 000 species) is the **isopods**, which include terrestrial, freshwater, and marine species. Some isopod species are abundant in habitats at the bottom of the deep ocean. Among the terrestrial isopods are the pill

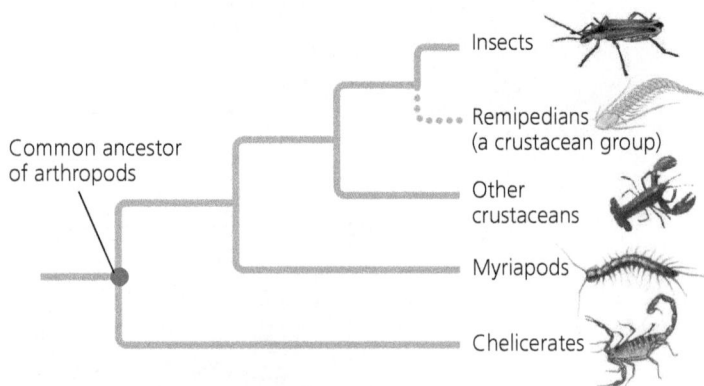

Common ancestor of arthropods

Insects

Remipedians (a crustacean group)

Other crustaceans

Myriapods

Chelicerates

▲ **Figure 33.36 The phylogenetic position of the insects.** Recent results have shown that the insects are nested within lineages of aquatic crustaceans. The remipedians are one of several groups of aquatic crustaceans that may be the sister group to the insects.

? *Circle the portions of this tree that comprise the clade Pancrustacea.*

Maximilian Weinzierl/Alamy

▲ **Figure 33.37 A ghost crab, an example of a decapod.** Ghost crabs live on sandy ocean beaches worldwide. Primarily nocturnal, they take shelter in burrows during the day.

bugs, or wood lice, common on the undersides of moist logs and leaves.

Lobsters, crayfishes, crabs, and shrimps are all relatively large crustaceans called **decapods** (Figure 33.37). The cuticle of decapods is hardened by calcium carbonate; the portion that covers the dorsal side of the cephalothorax forms a shield called the carapace. Most decapod species are marine. Crayfishes, however, live in fresh water, and some tropical crabs live on land.

Many small crustaceans are important members of marine and freshwater plankton communities. Planktonic crustaceans include many species of **copepods**, which are among the most numerous of all animals. Some copepods are grazers that feed upon algae, while others are predators that eat small animals (including smaller copepods!). Copepods are rivalled in abundance by the shrimplike krill, which grow to about 5 cm long (Figure 33.38). A major food source for baleen whales (including blue whales, humpbacks, and right whales), krill are now being harvested in great numbers by humans for food and agricultural fertilizer. The larvae of many larger-bodied crustaceans are also planktonic.

With the exception of a few parasitic species, barnacles are a group of sessile crustaceans whose cuticle is hardened into a shell containing calcium carbonate (Figure 33.39). Most barnacles anchor themselves to rocks, boat hulls, pilings, and other submerged surfaces. Their natural adhesive is as strong as synthetic glues. These barnacles feed by extending appendages from their shell to strain food from the water. Barnacles were not recognized as crustaceans until the 1800s, when naturalists discovered that barnacle larvae resemble the larvae of other crustaceans. The remarkable mix of unique traits and crustacean homologies found in barnacles was a major inspiration to Charles Darwin as he developed his theory of evolution.

We turn now to a group nested within the paraphyletic crustaceans—the insects.

▲ **Figure 33.38 Krill.** These planktonic crustaceans are consumed in vast quantities by some whales.

▲ **Figure 33.39 Barnacles.** The jointed appendages projecting from the barnacles' shells capture organisms and organic particles suspended in the water.

Insects

Insects and their six-legged terrestrial relatives form an enormous clade, Hexapoda; we'll focus here on the insects, since as a group they have more species than any other eukaryotic group. Insects live in almost every terrestrial habitat and in fresh water, and flying insects fill the air.

Insects are rare, though not absent, in marine habitats, where crustaceans are the dominant arthropods. The internal anatomy of an insect includes several complex organ systems, which are highlighted in **Figure 33.40**.

The oldest insect fossils date to about 415 million years ago. Later, an explosion in insect diversity took place when insect flight evolved during the Carboniferous and Permian periods (359–251 million years ago). An animal that can fly can escape predators, find food and mates, and disperse to new habitats more effectively than an animal that must crawl about on the ground. Many insects have one or two pairs of wings that emerge from the dorsal side of the thorax. Because the wings are extensions of the cuticle, insects can fly without sacrificing any walking legs (**Figure 33.41**). By contrast, the flying vertebrates—birds and bats—have one of their two pairs of walking legs modified into wings, making some of these species clumsy on the ground.

Insects also radiated in response to the origin of new plant species, which provided new sources of food. By the speciation mechanisms described in Chapter 24, an insect population feeding on a new plant species can diverge from other populations, eventually forming a new species of insect. A fossil record of diverse insect mouthparts, for example, suggests that specialized modes of feeding on gymnosperms and other Carboniferous plants contributed to early adaptive radiations of insects. Later, a major

Cerebral ganglion. The two nerve cords meet in the head, where the ganglia of several anterior segments are fused into a cerebral ganglion (brain, coloured white below). The antennae, eyes, and other sense organs are concentrated on the head.

Heart. The insect heart drives hemolymph through an open circulatory system.

Malpighian tubules. Metabolic wastes are removed from the hemolymph by excretory organs called Malpighian tubules, which are outpocketings of the digestive tract.

Tracheal tubes. Gas exchange in insects is accomplished by a tracheal system of branched, chitin-lined tubes that infiltrate the body and carry oxygen directly to cells. The tracheal system opens to the outside of the body through spiracles, pores that can control air flow and water loss by opening or closing.

Nerve cords. The insect nervous system consists of a pair of ventral nerve cords with several segmental ganglia.

Insect mouthparts are formed from several pairs of modified appendages. The mouthparts include mandibles, which grasshoppers use for chewing. In other insects, mouthparts are specialized for lapping, piercing, or sucking.

▲ **Figure 33.40 Anatomy of a grasshopper, an insect.** The insect body has three regions: head, thorax, and abdomen. The segmentation of the thorax and abdomen is obvious, but the segments that form the head are fused.

▲ **Figure 33.41 Ladybird beetle in flight.**

increase in insect diversity appears to have been stimulated by the evolutionary expansion of flowering plants during the mid-Cretaceous period (about 90 million years ago). Although insect and plant diversity decreased during the Cretaceous mass extinction, both groups have rebounded over the past 65 million years. Increases in the diversity of particular insect groups have often been associated with radiations of the flowering plants on which they fed.

Many insects undergo metamorphosis during their development. In the **incomplete metamorphosis** of grasshoppers and some other insect groups, the young (called nymphs) resemble adults but are smaller, have different body proportions, and lack wings. The nymph undergoes a series of moults, each time looking more like an adult. With the final moult, the insect reaches full size, acquires functional wings, and becomes sexually mature. Insects with **complete metamorphosis** have larval stages specialized for eating and growing that are known by such names as caterpillar,

maggot, or grub. The larval stage looks entirely different from the adult stage, which is specialized for dispersal and reproduction. Metamorphosis from the larval stage to the adult occurs during a pupal stage (Figure 33.42).

Reproduction in insects is usually sexual, with separate male and female individuals. Adults come together and recognize each other as members of the same species by advertising with bright colours (as in butterflies), sounds (as in crickets), or odours (as in moths). Fertilization is generally internal. In most species, sperm are deposited directly into the female's vagina at the time of copulation, though in some species the male deposits a sperm packet outside the female, and the female picks it up. An internal structure in the female called the spermatheca stores the sperm, usually enough to fertilize more than one batch of eggs. Many insects mate only once in a lifetime. After mating, a female often lays her eggs on an appropriate food source where the next generation can begin eating as soon as it hatches.

Insects are classified in more than 30 orders, 8 of which are introduced in Figure 33.43.

Animals as numerous, diverse, and widespread as insects are bound to affect the lives of most other terrestrial organisms, including humans. Insects consume enormous quantities of plant matter; play key roles as predators, parasites, and decomposers; and are an essential source of food for larger animals such as lizards, rodents, and birds. Humans depend on bees, flies, and many other insects to pollinate

(a) Larva (caterpillar)

(b) Pupa

(c) Later-stage pupa

(d) Emerging adult

(e) Adult

▲ **Figure 33.42 Complete metamorphosis of a butterfly. (a)** The larva (caterpillar) spends its time eating and growing, moulting as it grows. **(b)** After several moults, the larva develops into a pupa. **(c)** Within the pupa, the larval tissues are broken down, and the adult is built by the division and differentiation of cells that were quiescent in the larva. **(d)** Eventually, the adult begins to emerge from the pupal cuticle. **(e)** Hemolymph is pumped into veins of the wings and then withdrawn, leaving the hardened veins as struts supporting the wings. The insect will fly off and reproduce, deriving much of its nourishment from the food reserves stored by the feeding larva.

▼ Figure 33.43

Exploring Insect Diversity

Although there are more than 30 orders of insects, we'll focus on just 8 here. Two early-diverging groups of wingless insects are the bristletails (Archaeognatha) and silverfish (Thysanura). Evolutionary relationships among the other groups discussed here are under debate and so are not depicted on the tree.

Kevin Murphy

Archaeognatha (bristletails; 350 species)

These wingless insects are found under bark and in other moist, dark habitats such as leaf litter, compost piles, and rock crevices. They feed on algae, plant debris, and lichens.

Thysanura (silverfish; 450 species)

These small, wingless insects have a flattened body and reduced eyes. They live in leaf litter or under bark. They can also infest buildings, where they can become pests.

Perry Babin

Winged insects (many orders; six are shown below)

Complete Metamorphosis

PREMAPHOTOS/Nature Picture Library

Coleoptera (beetles; 350 000 species)

Beetles, such as this male snout weevil (*Rhiastus lasternus*), constitute the most species-rich order of insects. They have two pairs of wings, one of which is thick and stiff, the other membranous. They have an armoured exoskeleton and mouthparts adapted for biting and chewing.

Diptera (151 000 species)

Dipterans have one pair of wings; the second pair has become modified into balancing organs called halteres. Their mouthparts are adapted for sucking, piercing, or lapping. Flies and mosquitoes are among the best-known dipterans, which live as scavengers, predators, and parasites. Like many other insects, flies such as this red tachinid (*Adejeania vexatrix*) have well-developed compound eyes that provide a wide-angle view and excel at detecting fast movements.

Bruce Marlin

Hymenoptera (125 000 species)

John Cancalosi/Nature Picture Library

Most hymenopterans, which include ants, bees, and wasps, are highly social insects. They have two pairs of membranous wings, a mobile head, and chewing or sucking mouthparts. The females of many species have a posterior stinging organ. Many species, such as this European paper wasp (*Polistes dominulus*), build elaborate nests.

Lepidoptera (120 000 species)

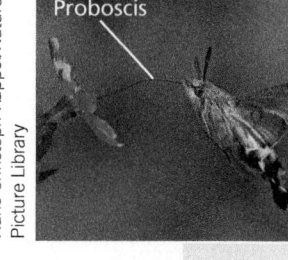

Hans Christoph Kappel/Nature Picture Library

Proboscis

Butterflies and moths have two pairs of wings covered with tiny scales. To feed, they uncoil a long proboscis, visible in this photograph of a hummingbird hawkmoth (*Macroglossum stellatarum*). This moth's name refers to its ability to hover in the air while feeding from a flower. Most lepidopterans feed on nectar, but some species feed on other substances, including animal blood or tears.

Incomplete Metamorphosis

Hemiptera (85 000 species)

Hemipterans include so-called "true bugs," such as stink bugs, bed bugs, and assassin bugs. (Insects in other orders are sometimes erroneously called bugs.) Hemipterans have two pairs of wings, one pair partly leathery, the other pair membranous. They have piercing or sucking mouthparts and undergo incomplete metamorphosis, as shown in this image of an adult stink bug guarding its offspring (nymphs).

Dante Fenolio/Science Source

Orthoptera (13 000 species)

Nigel Cattlin/Science Source

Grasshoppers, crickets, and their relatives are mostly herbivorous. They have large hind legs adapted for jumping, two pairs of wings (one leathery, one membranous), and biting or chewing mouthparts. This desert locust (*Schistocerca gregaria*) has an infamous place in human history as the cause of famines. Under ideal conditions, locusts can change behaviour, going from a solitary existence to a "gregarious" phase where they form swarms that can devastate crops.

crops and orchards. In addition, people in many parts of the world eat insects as an important source of protein. On the other hand, insects are carriers for many diseases, including African sleeping sickness (spread by tsetse flies that carry the protist *Trypanosoma*; see Figure 28.7) and malaria (spread by mosquitoes that carry the protist *Plasmodium*; see Figure 28.16).

Insects also compete with humans for food. In parts of Africa, for instance, insects claim about 75% of the crops. In Canada and the United States, billions of dollars are spent each year on pesticides. Try as they may, not even humans have challenged the preeminence of insects and their arthropod kin. As Cornell University entomologist Thomas Eisner put it: "Bugs are not going to inherit the Earth. They own it now. So we might as well make peace with the landlord."

CONCEPT CHECK 33.4

1. How do nematode and annelid body plans differ?
2. Describe two adaptations that have enabled insects to thrive on land.
3. **MAKE CONNECTIONS** Historically, annelids and arthropods were viewed as closely related because both have body segmentation. Yet DNA sequence data indicate that annelids belong to one clade (Lophotrochozoa) and arthropods to another (Ecdysozoa). Could traditional and molecular hypotheses be tested by studying the expression of *Hox* genes that control body segmentation (see Concept 21.6)? Explain.

For suggested answers, see Appendix A.

Echinoderms and chordates are deuterostomes

Porifera
Cnidaria
Lophotrochozoa
Ecdysozoa
Deuterostomia

Sea stars, sea urchins, and other echinoderms (phylum Echinodermata) may seem to have little in common with vertebrates (animals that have a backbone) and other members of phylum Chordata. Nevertheless, DNA evidence indicates that echinoderms and chordates are closely related, with both phyla belonging to the Deuterostomia clade of bilaterian animals. Echinoderms and chordates also share features characteristic of a deuterostome mode of development, such as radial cleavage and formation of the anus from the blastopore (see Figure 32.10). As discussed in Chapter 32, however, some animal phyla with members that have deuterostome developmental features, including ectoprocts and

brachiopods, are not in the deuterostome clade. Hence, despite its name, the clade Deuterostomia is defined primarily by DNA similarities, not developmental similarities.

Echinoderms

Sea stars (commonly called starfish) and most other **echinoderms** (from the Greek *echin*, spiny, and *derma*, skin) are slow-moving or sessile marine animals. A thin epidermis covers an endoskeleton of hard calcareous plates. Most echinoderms are prickly from skeletal bumps and spines. Unique to echinoderms is the **water vascular system**, a network of hydraulic canals branching into extensions called **tube feet** that function in locomotion and feeding (Figure 33.44). Sexual reproduction of echinoderms usually involves separate male and female individuals that release their gametes into the water.

The internal and external parts of most adult echinoderms radiate from the centre, often as five spokes. However, echinoderm larvae have bilateral symmetry. Furthermore, the symmetry of adult echinoderms is not truly radial. For example, the opening (madreporite) of a sea star's water vascular system is not central but shifted to one side.

Living echinoderms are divided into five clades.

Asteroidea: Sea Stars and Sea Daisies

Sea stars have arms radiating from a central disk; the undersurfaces of the arms bear tube feet. By a combination of muscular and chemical actions, the tube feet can attach to or detach from a substrate. The sea star adheres firmly to rocks or creeps along slowly as its tube feet extend, grip, release, extend, and grip again. Although the base of the tube foot has a flattened disk that resembles a suction cup, the gripping action results from adhesive chemicals, not suction (see Figure 33.44).

Sea stars also use their tube feet to grasp prey, such as clams and oysters. The arms of the sea star embrace the closed bivalve, clinging tightly with their tube feet. The sea star then turns part of its stomach inside out, everting it through its mouth and into the narrow opening between the halves of the bivalve's shell. Next, the digestive system of the sea star secretes juices that begin digesting the mollusc within its own shell. The stomach is then brought back inside the sea star's body, where digestion of the mollusc's (now liquefied) body is completed. The ability to begin the digestive process outside of its body allows a sea star to consume bivalves and other prey species that are much larger than its mouth.

Sea stars and some other echinoderms have considerable powers of regeneration. Sea stars can regrow lost arms, and members of one genus can even regrow an entire body from a single arm if part of the central disk remains attached.

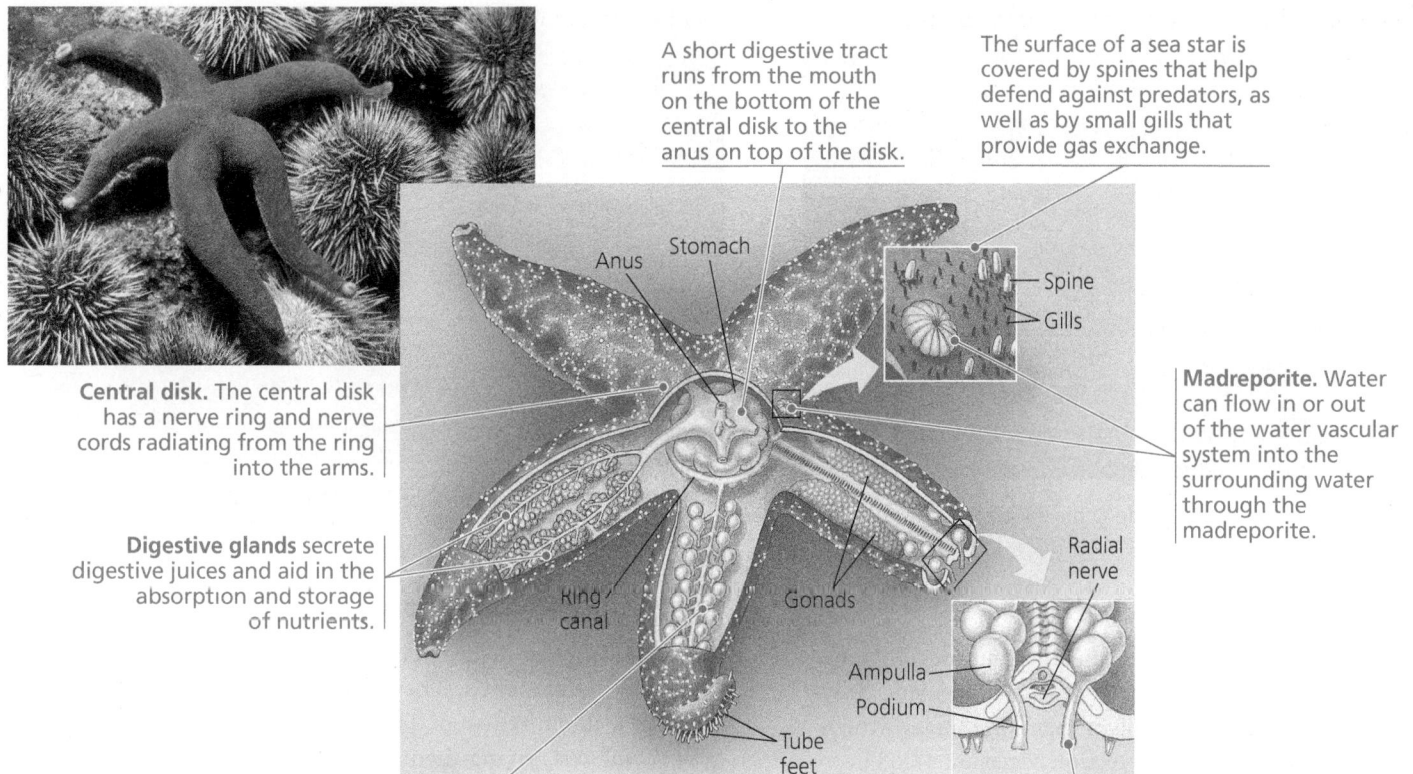

A short digestive tract runs from the mouth on the bottom of the central disk to the anus on top of the disk.

The surface of a sea star is covered by spines that help defend against predators, as well as by small gills that provide gas exchange.

Central disk. The central disk has a nerve ring and nerve cords radiating from the ring into the arms.

Digestive glands secrete digestive juices and aid in the absorption and storage of nutrients.

Madreporite. Water can flow in or out of the water vascular system into the surrounding water through the madreporite.

Anus

Stomach

Spine

Gills

Radial nerve

Ring canal

Gonads

Ampulla

Podium

Tube feet

Radial canal. The water vascular system consists of a ring canal in the central disk and five radial canals, each running in a groove down the entire length of an arm. Branching from each radial canal are hundreds of hollow, muscular tube feet filled with fluid.

Each tube foot consists of a bulb-like ampulla and a podium (foot portion). When the ampulla squeezes, water is forced into the podium, which expands and contacts the substrate. Adhesive chemicals are then secreted from the base of the podium, attaching it to the substrate. To detach the tube foot, de-adhesive chemicals are secreted and muscles in the podium contract, forcing water back into the ampulla and shortening the podium. As it moves, a sea star leaves an observable "footprint" of adhesive material on the substrate.

▲ Figure 33.44 **Anatomy of a sea star, an echinoderm.**

The clade Asteroidea, to which sea stars belong, also includes a small group of armless species, the *sea daisies*. Discovered in 1986, only three species of sea daisies are known, all of which live on submerged wood. A sea daisy's body is typically disk-shaped; it has a five-sided organization and measures less than a centimetre in diameter (Figure 33.45). The edge of the body is ringed with small spines. Sea daisies absorb nutrients through a membrane that surrounds their body.

Ophiuroidea: Brittle Stars

Brittle stars have a distinct central disk and long, flexible arms (Figure 33.46). They move primarily by lashing their arms in serpentine movements. The

base of a brittle star tube foot lacks the flattened disk found in sea stars but does secrete adhesive chemicals. Hence, like sea stars and other echinoderms, brittle stars can use their tube feet to grip substrates. Some species are suspension feeders; others are predators or scavengers.

Daniel Janies

◄ Figure 33.45 **A sea daisy (clade Asteroidea).**

Jeff Rotman/Science Source

▲ Figure 33.46 **A brittle star (clade Ophiuroidea).**

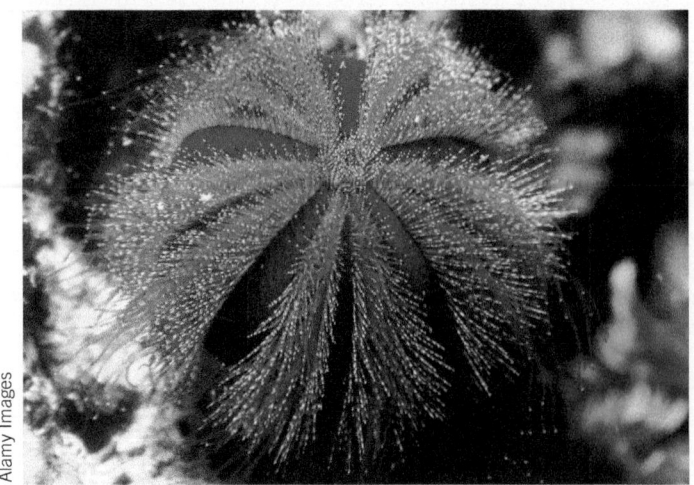

Alamy Images

▲ Figure 33.47 **A sea urchin (clade Echinoidea).**

Echinoidea: Sea Urchins and Sand Dollars

Sea urchins and sand dollars have no arms, but they do have five rows of tube feet that function in slow movement. Sea urchins also have muscles that pivot their long spines, which aid in locomotion as well as protection (**Figure 33.47**). The mouth of a sea urchin is ringed by highly complex, jaw-like structures that are well adapted to eating seaweed. Sea urchins are roughly spherical, whereas sand dollars are flat disks.

Crinoidea: Sea Lilies and Feather Stars

Sea lilies live attached to the substrate by a stalk; feather stars crawl about by using their long, flexible arms. Both use their arms in suspension feeding. The arms encircle the mouth, which is directed upward, away from the substrate (**Figure 33.48**). Crinoidea is an ancient group whose morphology has changed little over the course of evolution; fossilized sea lilies some 500 million years old are extremely similar to present-day members of the clade.

Jurgen Freund/Nature Picture Library

▲ Figure 33.48 **A feather star (clade Crinoidea).**

Andrew J. Martinez/Science Source

▲ Figure 33.49 **A sea cucumber (clade Holothuroidea).**

Holothuroidea: Sea Cucumbers

On casual inspection, sea cucumbers do not look much like other echinoderms. They lack spines, and their endoskeleton is much reduced. They are also elongated in their oral-aboral axis, giving them the shape for which they are named and further disguising their relationship to sea stars and sea urchins (**Figure 33.49**). Closer examination, however, reveals that sea cucumbers have five rows of tube feet. Some of the tube feet around the mouth are developed as feeding tentacles, as seen in this "orange-footed" sea cucumber that is common on the North Atlantic coast.

Chordates

Phylum Chordata consists of two subphyla of invertebrates, as well as the hagfishes and the vertebrates. Chordates are bilaterally symmetrical coelomates with segmented bodies. The close relationship between echinoderms and chordates does not mean that one phylum evolved from the other. In fact, echinoderms and chordates have evolved independently of one another for over 500 million years. We will trace the phylogeny of chordates in Chapter 34, focusing on the history of vertebrates.

CONCEPT CHECK 33.5

1. How do sea star tube feet attach to substrates?

2. **WHAT IF?** The insect *Drosophila melanogaster* and the nematode *Caenorhabditis elegans* are prominent model organisms. Are these species the most appropriate invertebrates for making inferences about humans and other vertebrates? Explain.

3. **MAKE CONNECTIONS** Describe how the features and diversity of echinoderms illustrate the unity of life, the diversity of life, and the match between organisms and their environments (see Concept 22.2).

For suggested answers, see Appendix A.

33 Chapter Review

SUMMARY OF KEY CONCEPTS

This table reviews the animal groups surveyed in this chapter.

Key Concept				Phylum	Description
CONCEPT 33.1 **Sponges are basal animals that lack true tissues (pp. 730–731)** [?] *Lacking tissues and organs, how do sponges accomplish tasks such as gas exchange, nutrient transport, and waste disposal?*				Porifera (sponges)	Lack true tissues; have choanocytes (collar cells—flagellated cells that ingest bacteria and tiny food particles)
CONCEPT 33.2 **Cnidarians are an ancient phylum of eumetazoans (pp. 731–734)** [?] *Describe the cnidarian body plan and its two major variations.*				Cnidaria (hydras, jellies, sea anemones, corals)	Unique stinging structures (nematocysts) housed in specialized cells (cnidocytes); diploblastic; radially symmetrical; gastrovascular cavity (digestive compartment with a single opening)
CONCEPT 33.3 **Lophotrochozoans, a clade identified by molecular data, have the widest range of animal body forms (pp. 734–745)** [?] *Is the lophotrochozoan clade united by unique morphological features shared by all of its members? Explain.*				Platyhelminthes (flatworms)	Dorsoventrally flattened acoelomates; gastrovascular cavity or no digestive tract
				Rotifera (rotifers)	Pseudocoelomates with alimentary canal (digestive tube with mouth and anus); jaws (trophi); head with ciliated crown
				Lophophorates: Ectoprocta, Brachiopoda	Coelomates with lophophores (feeding structures bearing ciliated tentacles)
				Mollusca (clams, snails, squids)	Coelomates with three main body parts (muscular foot, visceral mass, mantle); coelom reduced; most have hard shell made of calcium carbonate
				Annelida (segmented worms)	Coelomates with segmented body wall and internal organs (except digestive tract, which is unsegmented)
CONCEPT 33.4 **Ecdysozoans are the most species-rich animal group (pp. 745–754)** [?] *Describe some ecological roles of nematodes and arthropods.*				Nematoda (roundworms)	Cylindrical pseudocoelomates with tapered ends; no circulatory system; undergo ecdysis
				Arthropoda (spiders, centipedes, crustaceans, and insects)	Coelomates with segmented body, jointed appendages, and exoskeleton made of protein and chitin
CONCEPT 33.5 **Echinoderms and chordates are deuterostomes (pp. 754–756)** [?] *You've read that echinoderms and chordates are closely related and have evolved independently for over 500 million years. Explain how both of these statements can be correct.*				Echinodermata (sea stars, sea urchins)	Coelomates with bilaterally symmetrical larvae and five-part body organization as adults; unique water vascular system; endoskeleton
				Chordata (lancelets, tunicates, vertebrates)	Coelomates with notochord; dorsal, hollow nerve cord; pharyngeal slits; post-anal tail (see Chapter 34)

Bracket labels: Metazoa; Eumetazoa; Bilateria; Lophotrochozoa; Ecdysozoa; Deuterostomia

LEVEL 1: KNOWLEDGE/COMPREHENSION

1. A land snail, a clam, and an octopus all share
   a. a mantle.
   b. a radula.
   c. gills.
   d. distinct cephalization.

2. Which phylum is characterized by animals that have a segmented body?
   a. Cnidaria
   b. Platyhelminthes
   c. Arthropoda
   d. Mollusca

3. The water vascular system of echinoderms
   a. functions as a circulatory system that distributes nutrients to body cells.
   b. functions in locomotion and feeding.
   c. is bilateral in organization, even though the adult animal is not bilaterally symmetrical.
   d. moves water through the animal's body during suspension feeding.

4. Which of the following combinations of phylum and description is *incorrect*?
   a. Echinodermata—bilateral symmetry as a larva, coelom present
   b. Nematoda—roundworms, pseudocoelomate
   c. Platyhelminthes—flatworms, gastrovascular cavity, acoelomate
   d. Porifera—gastrovascular cavity, coelomate

LEVEL 2: APPLICATION/ANALYSIS

5. In Figure 33.2, which two main clades branch from the most recent common ancestor of the eumetazoans?
   a. Porifera and Cnidaria
   b. Lophotrochozoa and Ecdysozoa
   c. Cnidaria and Bilateria
   d. Deuterostomia and Bilateria

6. **MAKE CONNECTIONS** In Figure 33.8, assume that the two medusae shown at step 4 were produced by one polyp colony. Review Concept 12.1 and Concept 13.4, and then use your understanding of mitosis and meiosis to evaluate whether the following sentence is true or false. If false, select the answer that provides the correct reason. *Although the two medusae are genetically identical, a sperm produced by one will differ genetically from an egg produced by the other.*
   a. F (the medusae are genetically identical, but so are the gametes)
   b. F (neither the medusae or the gametes are genetically identical)
   c. F (the medusae are not identical but the gametes are)
   d. T

LEVEL 3: SYNTHESIS/EVALUATION

7. **EVOLUTION CONNECTION**
   INTERPRET THE DATA Draw a phylogenetic tree of Bilateria that includes the 10 phyla of bilaterians discussed in detail in this chapter. Label each branch that leads to a phylum with a C, P, or A, depending on whether members of the phylum are coelomates (C), pseudocoelomates (P), or acoelomates (A). Use your labelled tree to answer the following questions:
   (a) For each of the three major clades of bilaterians, what (if anything) can be inferred about whether the common ancestor of the clade had a true coelom?

(b) To what extent has the presence of a true coelom in animals changed over the course of evolution?

8. **SCIENTIFIC INQUIRY**
   Bats emit ultrasonic sounds and then use the returning echoes of those sounds to locate and capture flying insects, such as moths, in the dark. In response to bat attacks, some tiger moths make ultrasonic clicks of their own. Researchers hypothesize that tiger moth clicks likely either (1) jam the bat's sonar or (2) warn the bat about the moth's toxic chemical defences. The graph below shows two patterns observed in studies of moth capture rates over time for two different species of tiger moths.

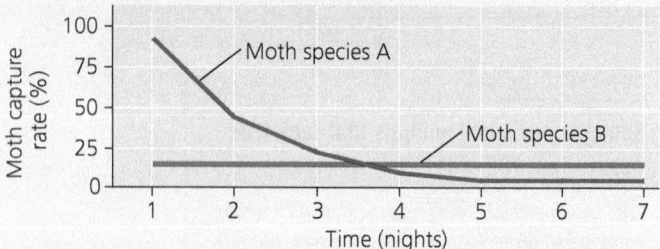

Bats in these experiments were "naive," meaning that prior to the study the bats had not previously hunted tiger moths. Do the results support hypothesis (1), hypothesis (2), or both? Why did the researchers use naive bats? Explain.

9. **WRITE ABOUT A THEME: STRUCTURE AND FUNCTION**
   Write a short essay (100–150 words) that explains how the structure of the digestive tract in different invertebrate groups affects the size of the organisms that they can eat.

10. **SYNTHESIZE YOUR KNOWLEDGE**

Lucy Arnold

Collectively, do these beetles and all other invertebrate species combined form a monophyletic group? Explain your answer and provide an overview of the evolutionary history of invertebrate life.

For selected answers, see Appendix A.

34

The Origin and Evolution of Vertebrates

KEY CONCEPTS

34.1 Chordates have a notochord and a dorsal, hollow nerve cord

34.2 Vertebrates are chordates that have a backbone

34.3 Gnathostomes are vertebrates that have jaws

34.4 Tetrapods are gnathostomes that have limbs

34.5 Amniotes are tetrapods that have a terrestrially adapted egg

34.6 Mammals are amniotes that have hair and produce milk

34.7 Humans are mammals that have a large brain and bipedal locomotion

Arco Images GmbH/Alamy Stock Photo

▲ Figure 34.1 **What are the closest living relatives to cetaceans?**

Half a Billion Years of Backbones

For more than 150 million years, **vertebrates** were restricted to the oceans and our discussion of vertebrate evolution in this chapter will ultimately lead us from sea to land. Around 365 million years ago, a lineage of aquatic vertebrates evolved limbs and other characteristics as adaptations to the terrestrial environment. However, three major groups of mammals have since made the transition in the other direction—from land to sea. Killer whales, like those found along the west coast of British Columbia, represent one such group (Figure 34.1). Cetaceans (whales and dolphins) appeared about 50 million years ago and their closest living relatives are the hippopotamuses and other terrestrial, even-toed ungulates (animals with hooves). In 2007, paleontologists found fossils in India belonging to an extinct group of animals, called raoellids, that turned out to be close relatives to cetaceans. This raccoon-sized animal was likely an aquatic wader (walked on the bottom), but probably not an adept swimmer, based on bone structure. Over 50 million years, cetaceans adapted to the marine environment acquiring many of the morphological characteristics that were lost by their ancestors during the transition to land.

The other two major transitions of mammals from land to sea include the sirenians (manatees, see the picture to the left) and pinnipeds (seals, walruses).

◀ **The Florida manatee (*Trichechus manatus*)**

Douglas Faulkner/Science Source

759

Sirenians diverged about the same time as cetaceans (50 million years ago) but are within a group called the Afrotheria, which includes elephants. Pinnipeds are aquatic carnivores that emerged more recently (about 20 million years ago) and whose closest living relatives are bears. The transitions of these mammals to the sea are incredible examples of phenotypic convergence, where different groups independently evolve similar morphological features for adaptation to similar environments. These are just some of the wonderful examples of vertebrate diversity we will cover in this chapter.

There are approximately 52 000 species of vertebrates, a relatively small number compared to, say, the 1 million insect species on Earth. But what vertebrates lack in species diversity they make up for in *disparity*, varying enormously in characteristics such as body mass. Vertebrates include the heaviest animals ever to walk on land, plant-eating dinosaurs as massive as 40 000 kg (more than two fully loaded city buses). They also include the biggest animal ever to exist on Earth, the blue whale, which can exceed a mass of 100 000 kg. On the other end of the spectrum, a

fish discovered in 2004 is just 8.4 mm long and has a mass roughly 100 billion times smaller than that of a blue whale.

In this chapter, you will learn about current hypotheses regarding the origins of vertebrates from invertebrate ancestors. We will track the evolution of the vertebrate body plan, from a notochord to a head to a mineralized skeleton. We'll also explore the major groups of vertebrates (both living and extinct), as well as the evolutionary history of our own species.

CONCEPT 34.1

Chordates have a notochord and a dorsal, hollow nerve cord

Vertebrates are members of the phylum Chordata, the chordates. **Chordates** are bilaterian (bilaterally symmetrical) animals, and within Bilateria, they belong to the clade of animals known as Deuterostomia (see Chapter 32). The best-known deuterostomes, aside from vertebrates, are the echinoderms, the group that includes sea stars and sea urchins. However, as shown in **Figure 34.2**, the

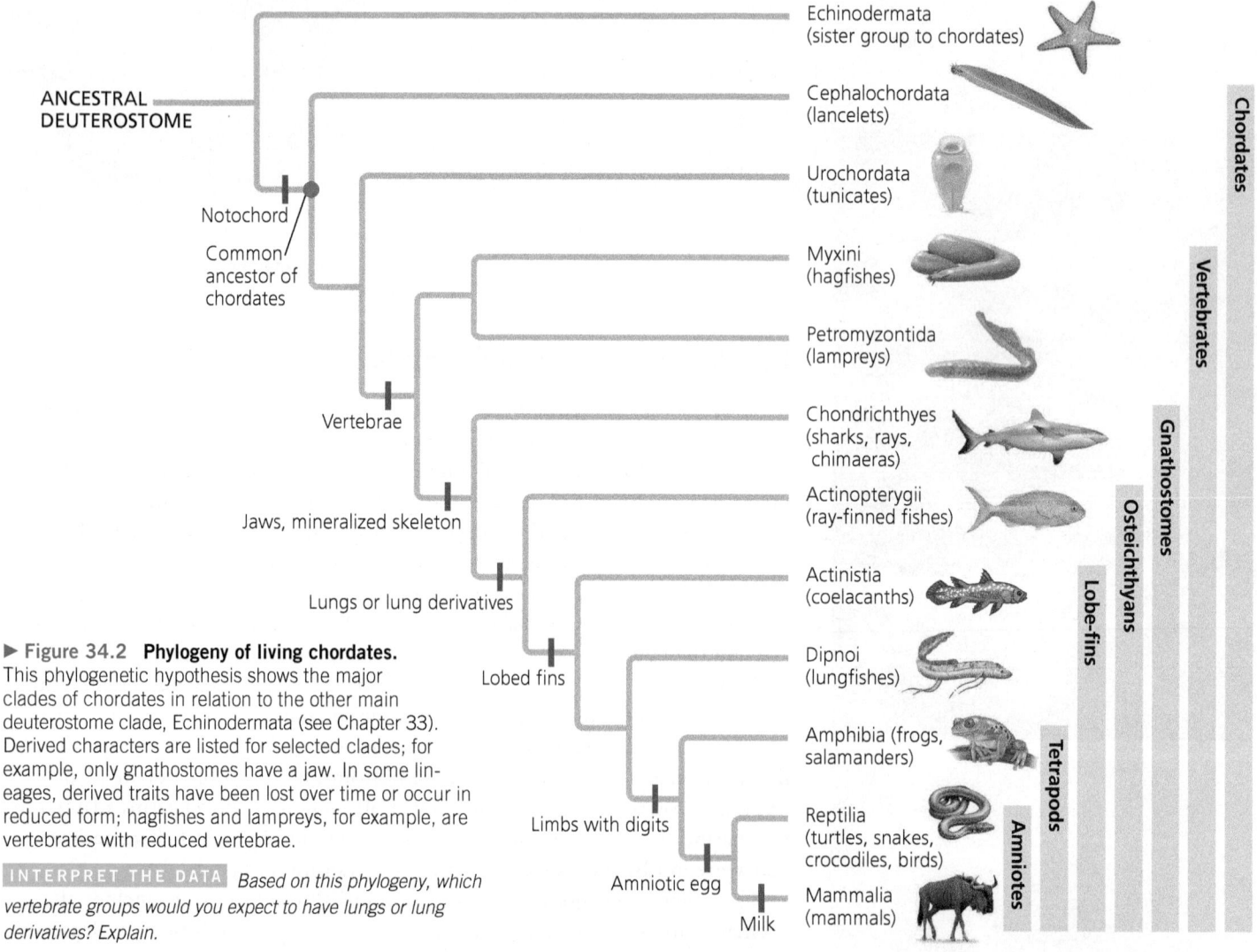

▶ Figure 34.2 **Phylogeny of living chordates.** This phylogenetic hypothesis shows the major clades of chordates in relation to the other main deuterostome clade, Echinodermata (see Chapter 33). Derived characters are listed for selected clades; for example, only gnathostomes have a jaw. In some lineages, derived traits have been lost over time or occur in reduced form; hagfishes and lampreys, for example, are vertebrates with reduced vertebrae.

INTERPRET THE DATA *Based on this phylogeny, which vertebrate groups would you expect to have lungs or lung derivatives? Explain.*

cephalochordates and the urochordates are two groups of invertebrate deuterostomes that are more closely related to vertebrates than to other invertebrates. Thus, these two invertebrate groups are classified within the chordates along with the vertebrates.

Derived Characters of Chordates

All chordates share a set of derived characters, though many species possess some of these traits only during embryonic development. Figure 34.3 illustrates four key characters of chordates: a notochord; a dorsal, hollow nerve cord; pharyngeal slits or clefts; and a muscular, post-anal tail.

Notochord

Chordates are named for a skeletal structure, the notochord, present in all chordate embryos as well as in some adult chordates. The **notochord** is a longitudinal, flexible rod located between the digestive tube and the nerve cord. It is composed of large, fluid-filled cells encased in fairly stiff, fibrous tissue. The notochord provides skeletal support throughout most of the length of a chordate, and in larvae or adults that retain it, it also provides a firm but flexible structure against which muscles can work during swimming. In most vertebrates, a more complex, jointed skeleton develops around the ancestral notochord, and the adult retains only remnants of the embryonic notochord. In humans, the notochord is reduced and forms part of the gelatinous disks sandwiched between the vertebrae.

Dorsal, Hollow Nerve Cord

The nerve cord of a chordate embryo develops from a plate of ectoderm that rolls into a tube located dorsal to the notochord. The resulting dorsal, hollow nerve cord is unique to chordates. Other animal phyla have solid nerve cords, and in most cases they are ventrally located. The nerve cord of a chordate embryo develops into the central nervous system: the brain and spinal cord.

Pharyngeal Slits or Clefts

The digestive tube of chordates extends from the mouth to the anus. The region just posterior to the mouth is the pharynx. In all chordate embryos, a series of arches separated by grooves forms along the sides of the pharynx. In most chordates, these grooves (known as **pharyngeal clefts**) develop into slits that open to the outside of the body. These **pharyngeal slits** allow water entering the mouth to exit the body without passing through the entire digestive tract. Pharyngeal slits function as suspension-feeding devices in many invertebrate chordates. In vertebrates (with the exception of vertebrates with limbs, the tetrapods), these slits and the structures that support them have been modified for gas exchange and are known as gill slits. In tetrapods, the pharyngeal clefts do not develop into slits. Instead, they play an important role in the development of parts of the ear and other structures in the head and neck.

Muscular, Post-Anal Tail

Chordates have a tail that extends posterior to the anus, although in many species it is greatly reduced during embryonic development. In contrast, most nonchordates have a digestive tract that extends nearly the whole length of the body. The chordate tail contains skeletal elements and muscles, and it helps propel many aquatic species in the water.

Lancelets

The most basal (earliest-diverging) group of living chordates are animals called **lancelets** (Cephalochordata), which get their name from their bladelike shape (Figure 34.4). As larvae, lancelets develop a notochord, a dorsal, hollow nerve cord, numerous pharyngeal slits, and a post-anal tail. The larvae feed on plankton in the water column, alternating between upward swimming and passive sinking. As the larvae sink, they trap plankton and other suspended particles in their pharynx.

Adult lancelets can reach 6 cm in length. They retain key chordate traits, closely resembling the idealized chordate shown in Figure 34.3. Following metamorphosis, an adult lancelet swims down to the sea floor and wriggles

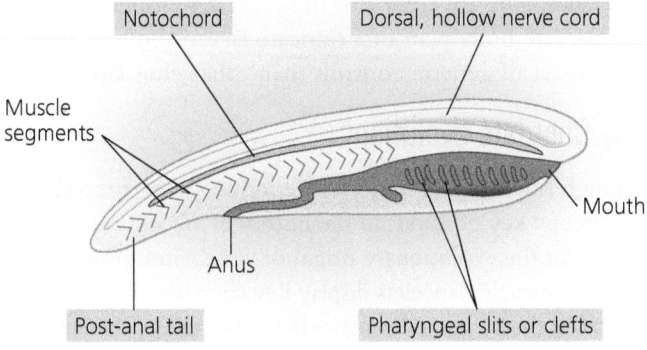

▲ Figure 34.3 **Chordate characteristics.** All chordates possess the four highlighted structural trademarks at some point during their development.

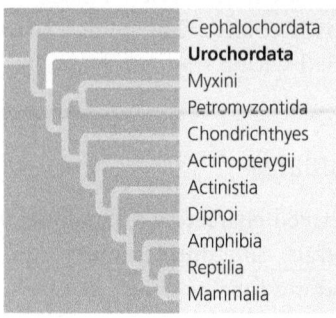

▲ **Figure 34.4 The lancelet *Branchiostoma*, a cephalochordate.** This small invertebrate displays all four main chordate characters. Water enters the mouth and passes through the pharyngeal slits into the atrium, a chamber that vents to the outside via the atriopore; large particles are blocked from entering the mouth by tentacle-like cirri. The serially arranged segmental muscles produce the lancelet's wavelike swimming movements.

backward into the sand, leaving only its anterior end exposed. Cilia draw sea water into the lancelet's mouth. A net of mucus secreted across the pharyngeal slits removes tiny food particles as the water passes through the slits, and the trapped food enters the intestine. The pharynx and pharyngeal slits play a minor role in gas exchange, which occurs mainly across the external body surface.

A lancelet frequently leaves its burrow to swim to a new location. Though feeble swimmers, these invertebrate chordates display, in a simple form, the swimming mechanism of fishes. Coordinated contraction of muscles arranged like rows of chevrons (<<<<) along the sides of the notochord flexes the notochord, producing side-to-side undulations that thrust the body forward. This serial arrangement of muscles is evidence of the lancelet's segmentation. The muscle segments develop from blocks of mesoderm called *somites*, which are found along each side of the notochord in all chordate embryos.

Globally, lancelets are rare, but in a few regions (including Tampa Bay, along the Florida coast), they occasionally reach densities in excess of 5000 individuals per square metre.

Tunicates

Contrary to what was formerly thought, molecular studies suggest that the **tunicates** (Urochordata) are more closely related to other chordates than are lancelets. The chordate characters of tunicates are most apparent during their larval stage, which may be as brief as a few minutes (**Figure 34.5a**). In many species, the larva uses its tail muscles and notochord to swim through water in search of a suitable substrate on which it can settle, guided by cues it receives from light- and gravity-sensitive cells.

Once a tunicate has settled on a substrate, it undergoes a radical metamorphosis in which many of its chordate characters disappear. Its tail and notochord are resorbed; its nervous system degenerates; and its remaining organs rotate 90°. As an adult, a tunicate draws in water through an incurrent siphon; the water then passes through the pharyngeal slits into a chamber called the atrium and exits through an excurrent siphon (**Figure 34.5b** and **c**). Food particles are filtered from the water by a mucous net and transported by cilia to the esophagus. The anus empties into the excurrent siphon. Some tunicate species shoot a jet of water through their excurrent siphon when attacked, earning them the informal name of "sea squirts." Tunicates are widely distributed and can be a nuisance to the aquaculture industry. On Prince Edward Island, some invasive tunicates can limit mussel yields and foul equipment, making harvesting and processing the mussels difficult and expensive.

The loss of chordate characters in the adult stage of tunicates appears to have occurred after the tunicate lineage branched off from other chordates. Even the tunicate larva appears to be highly derived. For example, tunicates have 9 *Hox* genes, whereas all other chordates studied to date—including the early-diverging lancelets—share a set of 13 *Hox* genes. The apparent loss of 4 *Hox* genes indicates that the chordate body plan of a tunicate larva is built using a different set of genetic controls than other chordates.

Early Chordate Evolution

Although lancelets and tunicates are relatively obscure animals, they occupy key positions in the history of life and can provide clues about the evolutionary origin of vertebrates. As you have read, for example, lancelets display key chordate characters as adults, and their lineage branches from the base of the chordate phylogenetic tree. These findings suggest that the ancestral chordate may have looked something like a lancelet—that is, it had an anterior end with a mouth; a notochord; a dorsal, hollow nerve cord; pharyngeal slits; and a post-anal tail.

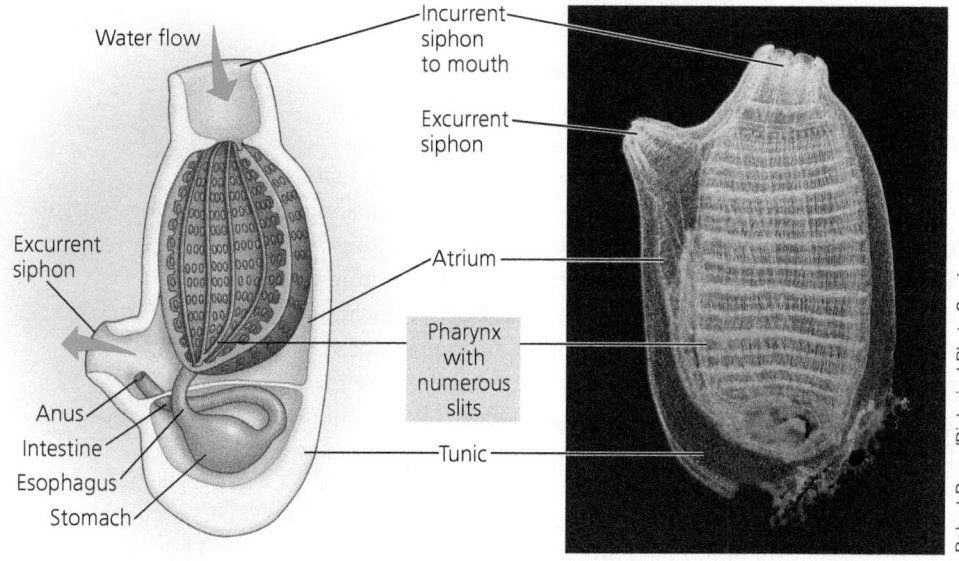

(a) A tunicate larva is a free-swimming but nonfeeding "tadpole" in which all four main characters of chordates are evident.

(b) In the adult, prominent pharyngeal slits function in suspension feeding, but other chordate characters are not obvious.

(c) An adult tunicate, or sea squirt, is a sessile animal (photo is approximately life-sized).

Robert Brons/Biological Photo Service

▲ Figure 34.5 **A tunicate, a urochordate.**

Research on lancelets has also revealed important clues about the evolution of the chordate brain. Rather than a full-fledged brain, lancelets have only a slightly swollen tip on the anterior end of their dorsal nerve cord (Figure 34.6). But the same *Hox* genes that organize major regions of the forebrain, midbrain, and hindbrain of vertebrates express themselves in a corresponding pattern in this small cluster of cells in the lancelet's nerve cord. This suggests that the vertebrate brain is an elaboration of an ancestral structure similar to the lancelet's simple nerve cord tip.

As for tunicates, their genome has been completely sequenced and can be used to identify genes likely to have

been present in early chordates. Researchers taking this approach have suggested that ancestral chordates had genes associated with vertebrate organs such as the heart and thyroid gland. These genes are found in tunicates and vertebrates but are absent from nonchordate invertebrates. In contrast, tunicates lack many genes that in vertebrates are associated with the long-range transmission of nerve impulses. This result suggests that such genes arose in an early vertebrate and are unique to the vertebrate evolutionary lineage.

▲ Figure 34.6 **Expression of developmental genes in lancelets and vertebrates.** *Hox* genes (including *BF1*, *Otx*, and *Hox3*) control the development of major regions of the vertebrate brain. These genes are expressed in the same anterior-to-posterior order in lancelets and vertebrates. Each coloured bar is positioned above the portion of the brain whose development that gene controls.

MAKE CONNECTIONS *What do these results and those in Figure 21.20 indicate about* Hox *genes and their evolution?*

CONCEPT 34.2

Vertebrates are chordates that have a backbone

During the Cambrian period, half a billion years ago, a lineage of chordates gave rise to vertebrates. With a skeletal system and a more complex nervous system than that of their ancestors, vertebrates became more efficient at two essential tasks: capturing food and avoiding being eaten.

Derived Characters of Vertebrates

Living vertebrates share a set of derived characters that distinguish them from other chordates. As a result of gene duplication, vertebrates possess two or more sets of *Hox* genes (lancelets and tunicates have only one). Other important families of genes that produce transcription factors and signalling molecules are also duplicated in vertebrates. The resulting additional genetic complexity may be associated with innovations in the vertebrate nervous system and skeleton, including the development of a skull and a backbone composed of vertebrae. In some vertebrates, the vertebrae are little more than small prongs of cartilage arrayed dorsally along the notochord. In the majority of vertebrates, however, the vertebrae enclose the spinal cord and have taken over the mechanical roles of the notochord. Over time, dorsal, ventral, and anal fins stiffened by bony structures called fin rays also evolved in aquatic vertebrates. Fin rays provide thrust and steering control when aquatic vertebrates swim after prey or away from predators. Faster swimming was supported by other adaptations, including a more efficient gas exchange system in the gills.

Hagfishes and Lampreys

The **hagfishes** (Myxini) and the **lampreys** (Petromyzontida) are the only lineages of living vertebrates whose members lack jaws. Unlike most vertebrates, lampreys and hagfishes also do not have a backbone. Nevertheless, lampreys were traditionally classified as vertebrates because they have rudimentary vertebrae (composed of cartilage, not bone). The hagfishes, in contrast, were thought to lack vertebrae altogether; hence, they were classified as invertebrate chordates closely related to vertebrates.

In the past few years, however, this interpretation has changed. Recent research has shown that hagfishes, like lampreys, have rudimentary vertebrae. In addition, a series of molecular phylogenetic studies have supported the hypothesis that hagfishes are vertebrates.

Molecular analyses also have indicated that hagfishes and lampreys are sister groups, as shown in the phylogenetic tree at the beginning of this section. Together, the hagfishes and lampreys form a clade of living jawless vertebrates, the **cyclostomes**. (Vertebrates with jaws make up a much larger clade, the gnathostomes, which we will discuss in Concept 34.3.)

Hagfishes

The hagfishes are jawless vertebrates that have highly reduced vertebrae and a skull that is made of cartilage.

▲ Figure 34.7 **A hagfish.**

They swim in a snakelike fashion by using their segmental muscles to exert force against their notochord, which they retain in adulthood as a strong, flexible rod of cartilage. Hagfishes have a small brain, eyes, ears, and a nasal opening that connects with the pharynx. Their mouths contain tooth-like formations made of the protein keratin.

All of the 30 living species of hagfishes are marine. Measuring up to 60 cm in length, most are bottom-dwelling scavengers that feed on worms and sick or dead fish (Figure 34.7). Rows of slime glands on a hagfish's flanks secrete a substance that absorbs water, forming a slime that may repulse other scavengers when a hagfish is feeding. When attacked by a predator, a hagfish can produce several litres of slime in less than a minute. The slime coats the gills of the attacking fish, sending it into retreat or even suffocating it. Several teams of biologists and engineers are investigating the properties of hagfish slime in hopes of producing an artificial slime that could act as a space-filling gel. Such a gel might be used, for instance, to curtail bleeding during surgery.

Lampreys

The second group of living jawless vertebrates, the lampreys, consists of about 35 species inhabiting various marine and freshwater environments (Figure 34.8). Most are parasites that feed by clamping their round, jawless mouth onto the flank of a live fish, their "host." They then use their rasping tongue to penetrate the skin of the fish and ingest the fish's blood and other tissues.

As larvae, lampreys live in freshwater streams. The larva is a suspension feeder that resembles a lancelet and spends much of its time partially buried in sediment. Some species of lampreys feed only as larvae; following several years in streams, they mature sexually, reproduce, and die within a few days. Most lampreys, however, migrate to the sea or lakes as they mature into adults.

Sea lampreys (*Petromyzon marinus*) have invaded the Great Lakes, likely from the St. Lawrence River, over the last

▲ **Figure 34.8 A sea lamprey.** Most lampreys use their mouth (inset) and tongue to bore a hole in the side of a fish. The lamprey then ingests the blood and other tissues of its host.

170 years following the construction of canals for shipping. This invasion of lampreys has devastated a number of fisheries in the region. Lampreys can reduce predatory fish populations (like trout) and thus upset the ecosystem dynamics and allow other, more invasive, fish species to thrive.

The skeleton of lampreys is made of cartilage. Unlike the cartilage found in most vertebrates, lamprey cartilage contains no collagen. Instead, it is a stiff matrix of other proteins. The notochord of lampreys persists as the main axial skeleton in the adult, as it does in hagfishes. However, lampreys also have a flexible sheath around their rodlike notochord. Along the length of this sheath, pairs of cartilaginous projections related to vertebrae extend dorsally, partially enclosing the nerve cord.

Early Vertebrate Evolution

In the late 1990s, paleontologists working in China discovered a vast collection of fossils of early chordates that appear to straddle the transition to vertebrates. The fossils were formed during the Cambrian explosion 530 million years ago, when many animal groups were undergoing rapid diversification (see Concept 32.2).

The most primitive of the fossils are the 3-cm-long *Haikouella* (Figure 34.9). In many ways, *Haikouella* resembled a lancelet. Its mouth structure indicates that, like lancelets, it probably was a suspension feeder. However, *Haikouella* also had some of the characters of vertebrates. For example, it had a well-formed brain, small eyes, and muscle segments along the body, as do the vertebrate fishes. Unlike the vertebrates, however, *Haikouella* did not have a skull or ear organs, suggesting that these characters emerged with further innovations to the chordate nervous system. (The earliest "ears" were organs for maintaining balance, a function still performed by the ears of humans and other living vertebrates.)

Early signs of a skull can be seen in *Myllokunmingia* (Figure 34.10). About the same size as *Haikouella*, *Myllokunmingia* had ear capsules and eye capsules, parts of the

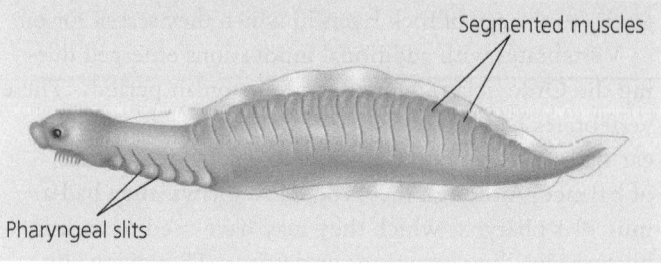

▲ **Figure 34.9 Fossil of an early chordate.** Discovered in 1999 in southern China, *Haikouella* had eyes and a brain but lacked a skull, a derived trait of craniates. The colours in the illustration are fanciful.

Source: Adaptation of figure 1a from "Fossil Sister Group of Craniates: Predicted and Found" by Jon Mallatt and Jun-yuan Chen, from *Journal of Morphology*, May 15, 2003, Volume 258(1). Copyright © 2003 by Wiley Periodicals Inc. Reprinted with permission of Wiley Inc.

skull that surround these organs. Based on these and other characters, *Myllokunmingia* is considered the first chordate to have a head. The origin of a head—consisting of a brain at the anterior end of the dorsal nerve cord, eyes and other sensory organs, and a skull—enabled chordates to coordinate more complex movement and feeding behaviours. Although it had a head, *Myllokunmingia* lacked vertebrae and hence is not classified as a vertebrate.

▲ **Figure 34.10 Fossil of chordate from the Cambrian.** Found in southern China, *Myllokunmingia fengjiao* is only around 3 cm long and one of the earliest (530 million years ago) chordate fossils found that has a head.

The earliest fossils of vertebrates date to 500 million years ago and include those of **conodonts**, a group of slender, soft-bodied vertebrates that lacked jaws and whose internal skeleton was composed of cartilage. Conodonts had large eyes, which they may have used in locating prey that were then impaled on a set of barbed hooks at the anterior end of their mouth. These hooks were made of dental tissues that were *mineralized*—hardened by the incorporation of minerals such as calcium (Figure 34.11). The food was then passed back to the pharynx, where a different set of dental elements sliced and crushed the food.

Conodonts were extremely abundant for over 300 million years. Their fossilized dental elements are so plentiful that they have been used for decades by petroleum geologists as guides to the age of rock layers in which they search for oil.

Vertebrates with additional innovations emerged during the Ordovician, Silurian, and Devonian periods. These vertebrates had paired fins and, as in lampreys, an inner ear with two semicircular canals that provided a sense of balance. Although they, too, lacked jaws, they had a muscular pharynx, which they may have used to suck in bottom-dwelling organisms or detritus. They were also armoured with mineralized bone, which covered varying amounts of their body (Figure 34.12). The armour, which in some species included spines, may have offered protection from predators. There were many species of these jawless, armoured swimming vertebrates, but they all became extinct by the end of the Devonian.

Origins of Bone and Teeth

The human skeleton is heavily mineralized bone, whereas cartilage plays a fairly minor role. But a bony skeleton was a relatively late development in the history of vertebrates. As we've seen, the vertebrate

Dental elements
(within
head)

▲ **Figure 34.11 A conodont.** Conodonts were early vertebrates that lived from the late Cambrian until the late Triassic. Unlike lampreys, conodonts had mineralized mouthparts, which they used for either predation or scavenging.

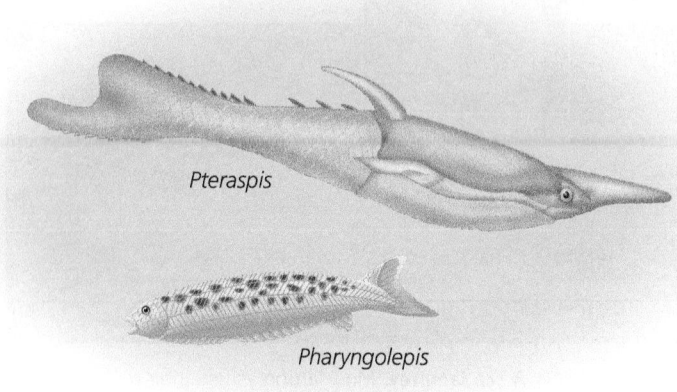

Pteraspis

Pharyngolepis

▲ **Figure 34.12 Jawless armoured vertebrates.** *Pteraspis* and *Pharyngolepis* were two of many genera of jawless vertebrates that emerged during the Ordovician, Silurian, and Devonian periods.

Source: Based on *Vertebrates: Comparative Anatomy, Function, Evolution*, 2002, The McGraw-Hill Companies, Inc. © Jane B Reece.

skeleton evolved initially as a structure made of unmineralized cartilage.

What initiated the process of mineralization in vertebrates? One hypothesis is that mineralization was associated with a transition in feeding mechanisms. Early chordates probably were suspension feeders, like lancelets, but over time they became larger and were able to ingest larger particles, including some small animals. The earliest known mineralized structures in vertebrates—conodont dental elements—were an adaptation that may have allowed these animals to become scavengers and predators. In addition, when the bony armour of later jawless vertebrates was examined under the microscope, scientists found that it was composed of small tooth-like structures. These findings suggest that mineralization of the vertebrate body may have begun in the mouth and later was incorporated into protective armour. Only in more derived vertebrates did the endoskeleton begin to mineralize, starting with the skull. As you'll read in the next section, more recent lineages of vertebrates underwent even further mineralization.

CONCEPT CHECK 34.2

1. How are differences in the anatomy of lampreys and conodonts reflected in each animal's feeding method?

2. **WHAT IF?** In several different animal lineages, organisms with a head first appeared around 530 million years ago. Does this finding constitute proof that having a head is favoured by natural selection? Explain.

3. **WHAT IF?** Suggest key roles that mineralized bone might have played in early vertebrates.

For suggested answers, see Appendix A.

Gnathostomes are vertebrates that have jaws

Hagfish and lampreys are survivors from the early Paleozoic era, when jawless vertebrates were common. Since then, jawless vertebrates have been far outnumbered by jawed vertebrates, known as **gnathostomes**. Living gnathostomes are a diverse group that includes sharks and their relatives, ray-finned fishes, lobe-finned fishes, amphibians, reptiles (including birds), and mammals.

Derived Characters of Gnathostomes

Gnathostomes ("jaw mouth") are named for their jaws, hinged structures that, especially with the help of teeth, enable gnathostomes to grip food items firmly and slice them. According to one hypothesis, gnathostome jaws evolved by modification of the skeletal rods that had previously supported the anterior pharyngeal (gill) slits. Figure 34.13 shows a stage in this evolutionary process in which several of these skeletal rods have been modified into precursors of jaws (green) and their structural supports (red). The remaining gill slits, no longer required for suspension feeding, remained as the major sites of respiratory gas exchange with the external environment.

Gnathostomes share other derived characters besides jaws. The common ancestors of all gnathostomes underwent an additional duplication of *Hox* genes, such that the single set present in early chordates became four. In fact, the entire genome appears to have duplicated, and together these genetic changes likely enabled the origin of jaws and other novel features in gnathostomes. The gnathostome forebrain is enlarged compared to that of other vertebrates, mainly in association with enhanced senses of smell and vision. Another characteristic of aquatic gnathostomes is the **lateral line system**, a row of organs along each side of the body that are sensitive to vibrations in the surrounding water. Precursors of these organs were present in the head shields of some jawless vertebrates.

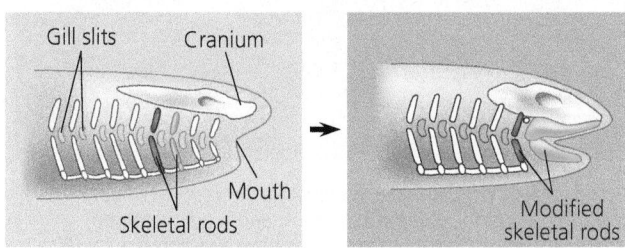

▲ Figure 34.13 **Possible step in the evolution of jawbones.**

Fossil Gnathostomes

Gnathostomes appeared in the fossil record in the late Ordovician period, about 450 million years ago, and steadily became more diverse. Their success probably resulted from a combination of anatomical features: Their paired fins and tail (which were also found in jawless vertebrates) allowed them to swim efficiently after prey, and their jaws enabled them to grab prey or simply bite off chunks of flesh.

Miguasha national park

▲ Figure 34.14 **Fossil of early gnathostome.** Numerous examples of one of the best-known placoderms, *Bothriolepis Canadensis*, have been found in Miguasha National Park in Eastern Quebec. This placoderm has armoured plates covering the head, body and even the pectoral fins and is approximately 40 cm in length. Likely a bottom-dwelling fish, *Bothriolepis* may have used its pectoral fins for manoeuvrability rather than propulsion.

The earliest gnathostomes in the fossil record include extinct lineages of armoured vertebrates known as **placoderms**, which means "plate-skinned" (Figure 34.14). Most placoderms were less than a metre long, though some giants measured more than 10 m. Other groups of jawed vertebrates, collectively called **acanthodians**, emerged at roughly the same time and radiated during the Silurian and Devonian periods (444–359 million years ago). Placoderms had disappeared by 359 million years ago, and acanthodians became extinct about 70 million years later.

Overall, a series of recent fossil discoveries have revealed that 450–420 million years ago was a period of tumultuous evolutionary change. Gnathostomes that lived during this period had highly variable forms, and by 420 million years ago, they had diverged into the three lineages of jawed vertebrates that survive today: chondrichthyans, ray-finned fishes, and lobe-fins.

Chondrichthyans (Sharks, Rays, and Their Relatives)

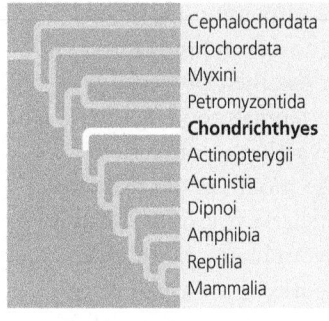

Cephalochordata
Urochordata
Myxini
Petromyzontida
Chondrichthyes
Actinopterygii
Actinistia
Dipnoi
Amphibia
Reptilia
Mammalia

Sharks, rays, and their relatives include some of the biggest and most successful vertebrate predators in the oceans. They belong to the clade Chondrichthyes, which means "cartilage fish." As their name indicates, the **chondrichthyans** have a skeleton composed predominantly of cartilage. Cartilage is composed of extracellular matrix proteins, like collagen, that form a tough, interconnected network containing cartilage-producing cells, the **chondrocytes**. However, cartilage of the chodrichthyans can be mineralized with calcium for added support.

When the name Chondrichthyes was first coined in the 1800s, scientists thought that chondrichthyans represented an early stage in the evolution of the vertebrate skeleton and that mineralization had evolved only in more derived lineages (such as "bony fish"). However, as conodonts and armoured jawless vertebrates demonstrate, the mineralization of the vertebrate skeleton had already begun before the chondrichthyan lineage branched off from other vertebrates. Moreover, bone-like tissues have been found in early chondrichthyans, such as the fin skeleton of a shark that lived in the Carboniferous period. Traces of bone can also be found in living chondrichthyans—in their scales, at the base of their teeth, and, in some sharks, in a thin layer on the surface of their vertebrae. Such findings strongly suggest that the restricted distribution of bone in the chondrichthyan body is a derived condition, emerging after chondrichthyans diverged from other gnathostomes.

There are about 1000 species of living chondrichthyans. The largest and most diverse group consists of the sharks, rays, and skates (Figure 34.15a and b). A second group is composed of a few dozen species of ratfishes, or chimaeras (Figure 34.15c).

Most sharks have a streamlined body and are swift swimmers, but they do not manoeuvre very well. Powerful movements of the trunk and the tail fin propel them forward. The dorsal fins function mainly as stabilizers, and the paired pectoral (fore) and pelvic (hind) fins are important for manoeuvring. Although a shark gains buoyancy by storing a large amount of oil in its huge liver, the animal is still more dense than water, and if it stops swimming it sinks. Continual swimming also ensures that water flows into the shark's mouth and out through the gills, where gas exchange occurs. However, some sharks and many skates and rays spend a good deal of time resting on the seafloor. When resting, they use muscles of their jaws and pharynx to pump water over the gills.

The largest sharks and rays are suspension feeders that consume plankton. Most sharks, however, are carnivores that swallow their prey whole or use their powerful jaws and sharp teeth to tear flesh from animals too large to swallow in one piece. Sharks have several rows of teeth that gradually move to the front of the mouth as old teeth are lost. The digestive tract of many sharks is proportionately shorter than that of many other vertebrates. Within the shark intestine is a *spiral valve*, a corkscrew-shaped ridge that increases surface area and prolongs the passage of food through the digestive tract.

Acute senses are adaptations that go along with the active, carnivorous lifestyle of sharks. Sharks have sharp

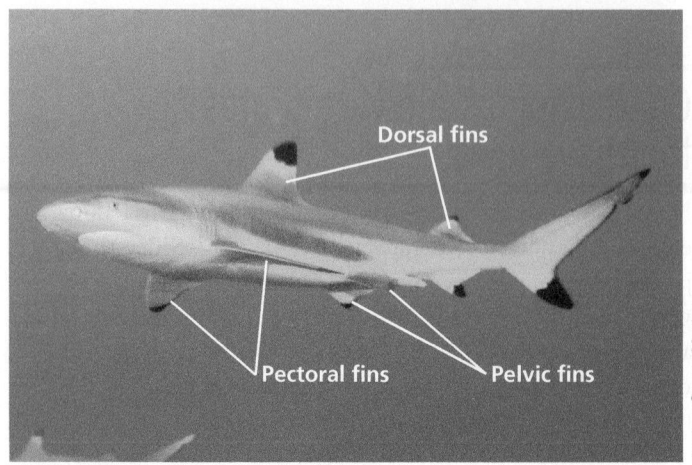

(a) **Blacktip reef shark (*Carcharhinus melanopterus*).** Sharks are fast swimmers with acute senses. Like all gnathostomes, they have paired pectoral and pelvic fins.

(b) **Southern stingray (*Dasyatis americana*).** Most rays are bottom-dwellers that feed on molluscs and crustaceans. Some rays cruise in open water and scoop food into their gaping mouths.

(c) **Spotted ratfish (*Hydrolagus colliei*).** Ratfishes, or chimaeras, typically live at depths greater than 80 m and feed on shrimp, molluscs, and sea urchins. Some species have a venomous spine at the front of their first dorsal fin.

▲ Figure 34.15   **Chondrichthyans.**

vision but cannot distinguish colours. The nostrils of sharks, like those of most aquatic vertebrates, open into dead-end cups. They function only for olfaction (smelling), not for breathing. Like some other vertebrates, sharks have a pair of regions in the skin of their head that can detect electric fields generated by the muscle contractions of nearby animals. Like all (nonmammalian) aquatic vertebrates, sharks have no eardrums, structures that terrestrial vertebrates use to transmit sound waves in air to the auditory organs. Sound reaches a shark through water, and the animal's entire body transmits the sound to the hearing organs of the inner ear.

Shark eggs are fertilized internally. The male has a pair of claspers on its pelvic fins that transfer sperm into the female's reproductive tract. Some species of sharks are **oviparous**; they lay eggs that hatch outside the mother's body. These sharks release their eggs after encasing them in protective coats. Other species are **ovoviviparous**; they retain the fertilized eggs in the oviduct. Nourished by the egg yolk, the embryos develop into young that are born after hatching within the uterus. A few species are **viviparous**; the young develop within the uterus and obtain nourishment prior to birth by receiving nutrients from the mother's blood through a yolk sac placenta, by absorbing a nutritious fluid produced by the uterus, or by eating other eggs. The reproductive tract of the shark empties along with the excretory system and digestive tract into the **cloaca**, a common chamber that has a single opening to the outside.

Although rays are closely related to sharks, they have adopted a very different lifestyle. Most rays are bottom-dwellers that feed by using their jaws to crush molluscs and crustaceans. They have a flattened shape and use their greatly enlarged pectoral fins like water wings to propel themselves through the water. The tail of many rays is whiplike and, in some species, bears venomous barbs that function in defence.

Chondrichthyans have thrived for over 400 million years. Today, however, they are severely threatened with overfishing. A 2012 report, for example, indicated that shark populations in the Pacific have plummeted by up to 95%, and shark populations that live closest to people have declined the most.

Ray-Finned Fishes and Lobe-Fins

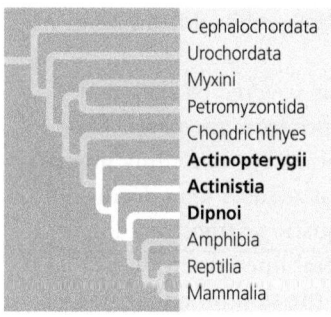

The vast majority of vertebrates belong to the clade of gnathostomes called Osteichthyes. Unlike chondrichthyans, nearly all living **osteichthyans** have an ossified (bony) endoskeleton with a hard matrix of calcium phosphate. Like many other taxonomic names, the name Osteichthyes ("bony fish") was coined long before the advent of phylogenetic systematics. When it was originally defined, the group excluded tetrapods, but we now know that such a taxon would be paraphyletic (see Figure 34.2). Therefore, systematists today include tetrapods along with bony fishes in the clade Osteichthyes. Clearly, the name of the group does not accurately describe all of its members.

This section discusses the aquatic osteichthyans known informally as fishes. Most fishes breathe by drawing water over four or five pairs of gills located in chambers covered by a protective bony flap called the **operculum** (Figure 34.16). Water is drawn into the mouth, through the pharynx, and out between the gills by movement of the operculum and contraction of muscles surrounding the gill chambers.

Most fishes can control their buoyancy with an air sac known as a **swim bladder**. If a fish swims to greater

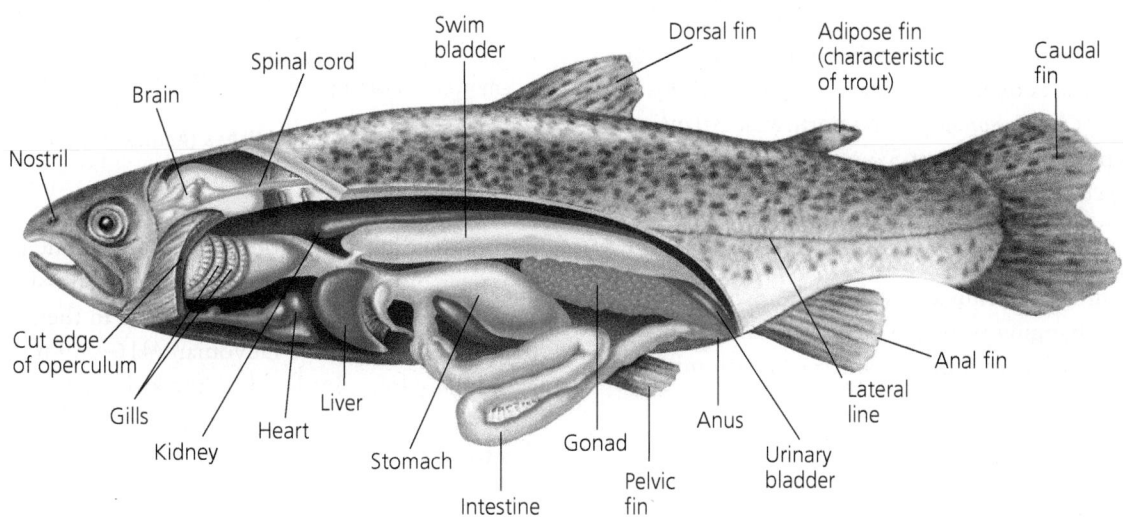

▲ Figure 34.16 **Anatomy of a trout, a ray-finned fish.**

depths or toward the surface, where water pressure differs, the fish shuttles gas between its blood and swim bladder, keeping the volume of gas in the bladder constant. Charles Darwin proposed that the lungs of tetrapods evolved from swim bladders, but strange as it may sound, the opposite seems to be true. Osteichthyans in many early-branching lineages have lungs, which they use to breathe air as a supplement to gas exchange in their gills. The weight of evidence indicates that lungs arose in early osteichthyans; later, swim bladders evolved from lungs in some lineages.

In nearly all fishes, the skin is covered by flattened, bony scales that differ in structure from the tooth-like scales of sharks. Glands in the skin secrete a slimy mucus over the skin, an adaptation that reduces drag during swimming. Like the ancient aquatic gnathostomes mentioned earlier, fishes have a lateral line system, which is evident as a row of tiny pits in the skin on either side of the body.

The details of fish reproduction vary extensively. Most species are oviparous, reproducing by external fertilization after the female sheds large numbers of small eggs. However, internal fertilization and birthing characterize other species.

Ray-Finned Fishes

Nearly all the aquatic osteichthyans familiar to us are among the over 27 000 species of **ray-finned fishes** (Actinopterygii) (Figure 34.17). Named for the bony rays that support their fins, the ray-finned fish originated during the Silurian period (444–416 million years ago). The group has diversified greatly since that time, as suggested by modifications in body form and fin structure that affect manoeuvring, defence, and other functions (see Figure 34.17).

Ray-finned fishes serve as a major source of protein for humans, who have harvested them for thousands of years. However, industrial-scale fishing operations appear to have driven some of the world's biggest fisheries to collapse. For example, after decades of abundant harvests, in the 1990s the catch of cod (*Gadus morhua*) in the northwest Atlantic (Figure 34.17) plummeted to just 5% of its historic maximum, bringing codfishing there to a near halt. Despite ongoing restrictions on the fishery, cod populations have yet to recover to sustainable levels. Ray-finned fishes also face other pressures from humans, such as the diversion of rivers by dams. Changing water flow patterns can hamper the fishes' ability to obtain food and interferes with migratory pathways and spawning grounds.

Lobe-Fins

Like the ray-finned fishes, the other major lineage of osteichthyans, the **lobe-fins** (Sarcopterygii), also originated

▲ Atlantic cod (*Gadus morhua*) was commercially important worldwide and a symbol of the Atlantic Canada fishery. The commercial fishery was shut down in the 1990s due to overfishing, ending a way of life for many in small communities.

▶ Native to coral reefs of the Pacific Ocean, the brightly coloured red lionfish (*Pterois volitans*) can inject venom through its spines, causing a severe and painful reaction in humans.

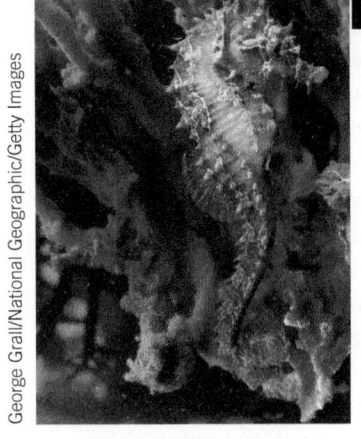

▲ The seahorse has a highly modified body form, as exemplified by *Hippocampus ramulosus,* shown above. Sea horses are unusual among animals in that the male carries the young during their embryonic development.

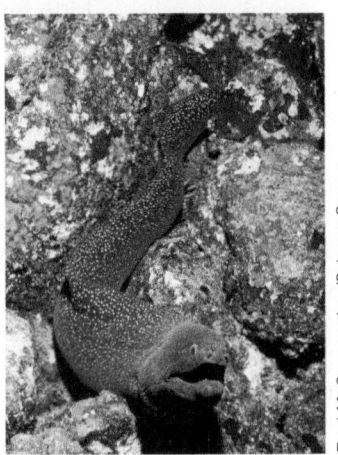

▲ The fine-spotted moray eel (*Gymnothorax dovii*) is a predator that ambushes prey from crevices in its coral reef habitat.

▲ Figure 34.17 **Ray-finned fishes (Actinopterygii).**

during the Silurian period (Figure 34.18). The key derived character of lobe-fins is the presence of rod-shaped bones surrounded by a thick layer of muscle in their pectoral and pelvic fins. During the Devonian (416–359 million years ago), many lobe-fins lived in brackish waters, such as in coastal wetlands. There they may have used their lobed fins to swim and "walk" underwater across the substrate (as do some living lobe-fins). Some Devonian lobe-fins were gigantic predators. It is not uncommon to find spike-shaped fossils of Devonian lobe-fin teeth as big as your thumb.

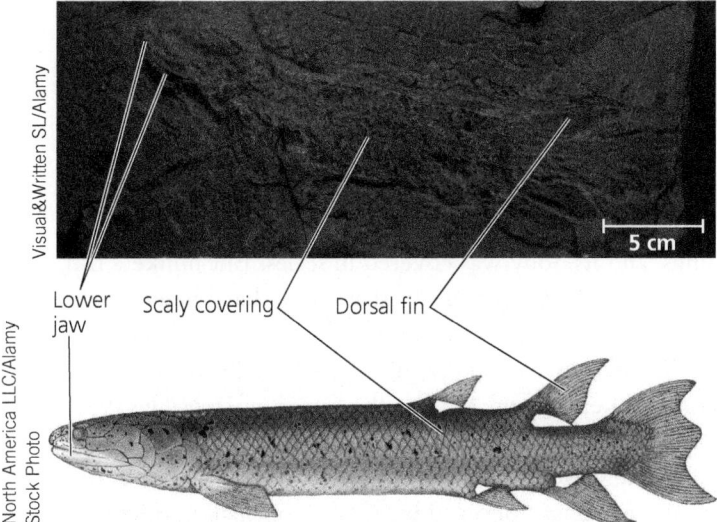

▲ **Figure 34.18 Reconstruction of an ancient lobe-fin.** The rich fossil beds of Miguasha National Park, which include the fossil in the upper panel, were the basis for this artist's reconstruction of the lobe-fin fish *Eusthenopteron foordi* (bottom panel).

Miguasha National Park, located on the southern end of the Gaspé Peninsula in eastern Quebec, is home to numerous fossils from the Devonian period in what is commonly called the "Age of Fishes." Lobe-finned fish, such as those from the genus *Eusthenopteron*, are commonly found at the park (Figure 34.18). The fossil beds at the park were first discovered by a Nova Scotian geologist, Abraham Gesner (the inventor of kerosene), in 1842.

By the end of the Devonian period, lobe-fin diversity was dwindling, and today only three lineages survive. One lineage, the coelacanths (Actinistia), was thought to have become extinct 75 million years ago. However, in 1938, fishermen caught a living coelacanth off the east coast of South Africa (Figure 34.19). Until the 1990s, all subsequent discoveries were near the Comoros Islands in the western Indian Ocean. Since 1999, coelacanths have also been found at various places along the eastern coast of Africa and in the eastern Indian Ocean, near Indonesia. The Indonesian population may represent a second species.

▲ **Figure 34.19 A coelacanth (*Latimeria*).** These lobe-fins were found living off the coasts of southern Africa and Indonesia.

The second lineage of living lobe-fins, the lungfishes (Dipnoi), is represented today by six species in three genera, all of which are found in the Southern Hemisphere. Lungfishes arose in the ocean but today are found only in fresh water, generally in stagnant ponds and swamps. They surface to gulp air into lungs connected to their pharynx. Lungfishes also have gills, which are the main organs for gas exchange in Australian lungfishes. When ponds shrink during the dry season, some lungfishes can burrow into the mud and aestivate (wait in a state of torpor; see Chapter 40).

The third lineage of lobe-fins that survives today is far more diverse than the coelacanths or the lungfishes. During the mid-Devonian, these organisms adapted to life on land and gave rise to vertebrates with limbs and feet, called tetrapods—a lineage that includes humans.

CONCEPT CHECK 34.3

1. What derived characters do sharks and codfish share? What are some characteristics that distinguish codfish from sharks?

2. Describe key adaptations of aquatic gnathostomes.

3. **DRAW IT** Redraw Figure 34.2 to show four lineages: cyclostomes, lancelets, gnathostomes, and tunicates. Label the vertebrate common ancestor and circle the lineage that includes humans.

4. **WHAT IF?** Imagine that we could replay the history of life. Is it possible that a group of vertebrates that colonized land could have arisen from aquatic gnathostomes other than the lobe-fins? Explain.

For suggested answers, see Appendix A.

CONCEPT 34.4

Tetrapods are gnathostomes that have limbs

One of the most significant events in vertebrate history took place about 365 million years ago, when the fins of some lobe-fins evolved into the limbs and feet of tetrapods. Until then, all vertebrates had shared the same basic fishlike anatomy. After tetrapods moved onto land, they took on many new forms, from leaping frogs to flying eagles to bipedal humans.

Derived Characters of Tetrapods

The most significant character of **tetrapods** gives the group its name, which means "four feet" in Greek. In place of pectoral and pelvic fins, tetrapods have limbs with digits. Limbs support a tetrapod's weight on land, while feet with digits efficiently transmit muscle-generated forces to the ground when it walks.

Life on land brought numerous other changes to the tetrapod body plan. In tetrapods, the head is separated from the body by a neck that originally had one vertebra on which the skull could move up and down. Later, with the origin of a second vertebra in the neck, the head could also swing from side to side. The bones of the pelvic girdle, to which the hind legs are attached, are fused to the backbone, permitting forces generated by the hind legs against the ground to be transferred to the rest of the body. Except for some fully aquatic species (such as the axolotl discussed below), the adults of living tetrapods do not have gills; during embryonic development, the pharyngeal clefts instead give rise to parts of the ears, certain glands, and other structures.

As you will see, some of these characters were dramatically altered or lost in various lineages of tetrapods. In birds, for example, the pectoral limbs became wings, and in whales, the entire body converged toward a fishlike shape.

The Origin of Tetrapods

As you have read, the Devonian coastal wetlands were home to a wide range of lobe-fins. Those that entered particularly shallow, oxygen-poor water could use their lungs to breathe air. Some species probably used their stout fins to help them move across logs or the muddy bottom. Thus, the tetrapod body plan did not evolve "out of nowhere" but was simply a modification of a preexisting body plan.

The discovery in 2006 of a fossil called *Tiktaalik* in northern Canada has provided new details on how this process occurred. Like a fish, this species had fins, gills, and lungs, and its body was covered in scales. But unlike a fish, *Tiktaalik* had a full set of ribs that would have helped it breathe air and support its body (**Figure 34.20**). Also unlike a fish, *Tiktaalik* had a neck and shoulders, allowing it to move its head about. Finally, the bones of *Tiktaalik*'s front fin have the same basic pattern found in all limbed animals: one bone (the humerus), followed by two bones (the radius and ulna), followed by a group of small bones that

---

▼ Figure 34.20

Impact

Discovery of a "Fishapod": *Tiktaalik*

Paleontologists were on the hunt for fossils that could shed light on the evolutionary origin of tetrapods. Based on the ages of previously discovered fossils, researchers were looking for a dig site with rocks about 385–365 million years old. Ellesmere Island, in Nunavut, Canada, was one of the few such sites likely to contain fossils, because the site was once a river. The search at this site was rewarded by the discovery of fossils of a 375-million-year-old lobe-fin, named *Tiktaalik*. As shown in the chart and photographs below, *Tiktaalik* exhibits both fish and tetrapod characters. (Figure 34.21, on the facing page, includes an artist's conception of what *Tiktaalik* might have looked like.)

Why It Matters As the most tetrapod-like fish known, *Tiktaalik* documents key steps in the vertebrate transition from water to land.

Since *Tiktaalik* predates the oldest known tetrapod by 10 million years, its features suggest that key "tetrapod" traits, such as a wrist, ribs, and a neck, were in fact ancestral to the tetrapod lineage. The discovery also shows the predictive capacity of paleontology in identifying likely locations of fossils of interest.

Further Reading E. B. Daeschler, N. H. Shubin, and F. A. Jenkins, A Devonian tetrapod-like fish and the evolution of the tetrapod body plan, *Nature* 440:757–763 (2006).

MAKE CONNECTIONS *Describe how* Tiktaalik's *features illustrate Darwin's concept of descent with modification (see Concept 22.2).*

Fish Characters	Tetrapod Characters
Scales	Neck
Fins	Ribs
Gills and lungs	Fin skeleton
	Flat skull
	Eyes on top of skull

Ted Daeschler/Academy of Natural Sciences

comprise the wrist. Although it is unlikely that *Tiktaalik* could walk on land, its front fin skeleton suggests that it could prop itself up in water on its fins.

Tiktaalik and other extraordinary fossil discoveries have allowed paleontologists to reconstruct how fins became progressively more limb-like over time, culminating in the appearance of the first tetrapods 365 million years ago **(Figure 34.21)**. Over the next 60 million years, a great diversity of tetrapods arose. Judging from the morphology and locations of their fossils, most of these early tetrapods probably remained tied to water, a characteristic they share with some members of a group of living tetrapods called amphibians.

Amphibians

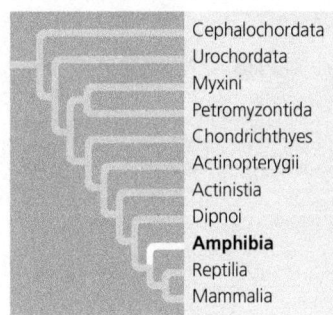

Cephalochordata
Urochordata
Myxini
Petromyzontida
Chondrichthyes
Actinopterygii
Actinistia
Dipnoi
Amphibia
Reptilia
Mammalia

The **amphibians** (class Amphibia) are represented today by about 6150 species of salamanders (order Urodela, "tailed ones"), frogs (order Anura, "tailless ones"), and caecilians (order Apoda, "legless ones").

Salamanders

There are about 550 known species of urodeles, or salamanders. Some are entirely aquatic, but others live on land as adults or throughout life. Most salamanders that live on land walk with a side-to-side bending of the body, a trait also found in early terrestrial tetrapods **(Figure 34.22a)**. Paedomorphosis, the retention of juvenile characteristics after maturation, is common among aquatic salamanders; the axolotl, for instance, retains larval features even when it is sexually mature (see Figure 25.25).

Frogs

Numbering about 5420 species, anurans, or frogs, are better suited than salamanders for moving on land **(Figure 34.22b)**. Adult frogs use their powerful hind legs to hop along the terrain. Although often distinctive in appearance, the animals known as "toads" are simply frogs that have leathery skin or other adaptations for life on land. A frog nabs insects and other prey by flicking out its long, sticky tongue, which is attached to the front of the mouth. Frogs display a great variety of adaptations that help them avoid being eaten by larger predators. Their skin glands secrete distasteful or even poisonous mucus. Many poisonous species have bright colouration, which predators apparently associate with danger. Other

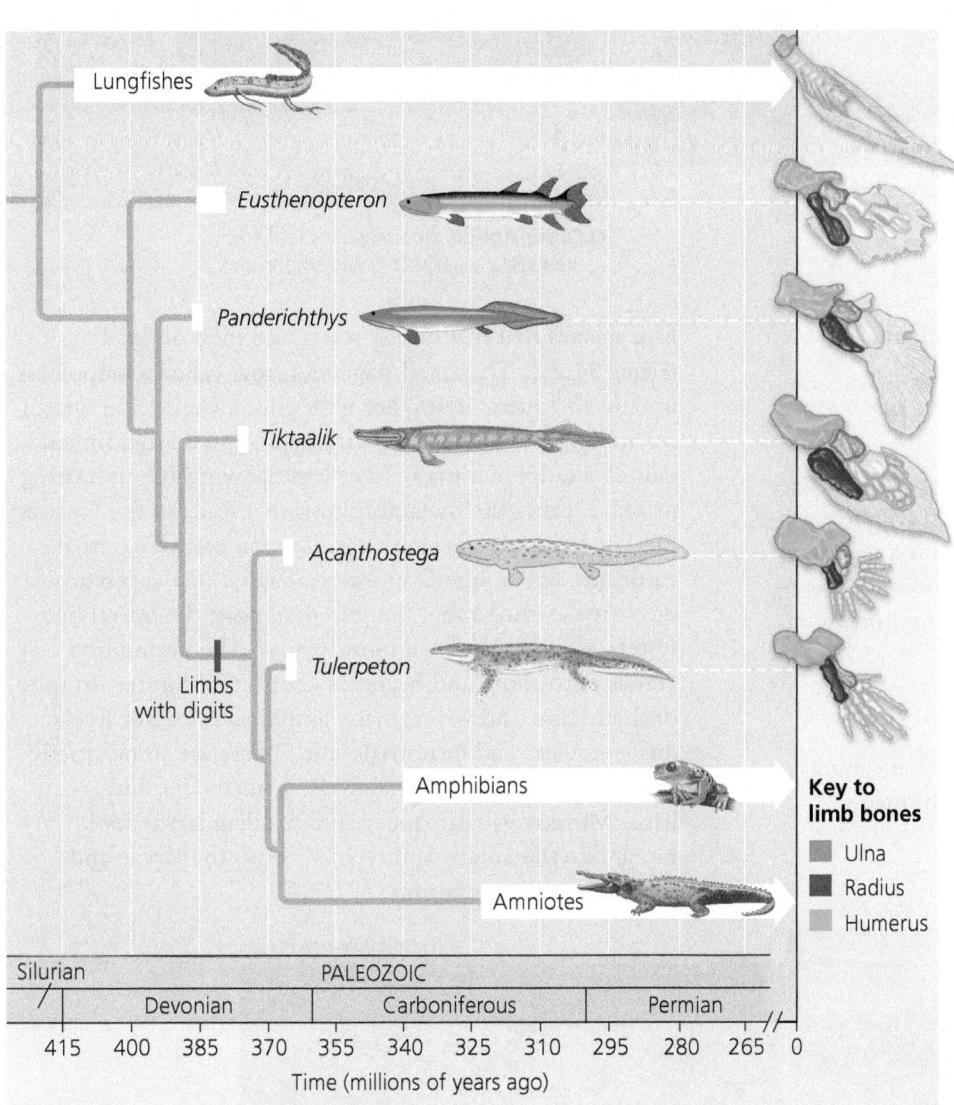

Lungfishes
Eusthenopteron
Panderichthys
Tiktaalik
Acanthostega
Tulerpeton
Limbs with digits
Amphibians
Amniotes

Key to limb bones
Ulna
Radius
Humerus

Silurian | PALEOZOIC
Devonian | Carboniferous | Permian
415 400 385 370 355 340 325 310 295 280 265 0
Time (millions of years ago)

▲ **Figure 34.21 Steps in the origin of limbs with digits.** The white bars on the branches of this diagram place known fossils in time; arrowheads indicate lineages that extend to today. The drawings of extinct organisms are based on fossilized skeletons, but the colours are fanciful.

Sources: Adaptation of figure 4 from "The Pectoral Fin of Tiktaalik roseae and the Origin of the Tetrapod Limb" by Neil H. Shubin et al., from *Nature*, April 6, 2006, Volume 440(7085). Copyright © 2006 by Macmillan Publishers Ltd. Reprinted with permission; Adaptation of Figure 27 from "The Devonian Tetrapod Acanthostega gunnari Jarvik: Postcranial Anatomy, Basal Tetrapod Relationships and Patterns of Skeletal Evolution" by Michael I. Coates, from *Transactions of the Royal Society of Edinburgh: Earth Sciences*, Volume 87: 398. Copyright © 1996 by Royal Society of Edinburgh. Reprinted with permission.

WHAT IF? *If the most recent common ancestor of Tulerpeton and living tetrapods originated 380 million years ago, what range of dates would include the origin of amphibians?*

Alberto Fernández/AGE Fotostock

(a) Order Urodela. Urodeles (salamanders) retain their tail as adults.

Dr. Paul A. Zahl/Science Source

(b) Order Anura. Anurans, such as this variable harlequin toad, lack a tail as adults.

blickwinkel/Alamy Stock Photo

(c) Order Apoda. Apodans, or caecilians, are legless, mainly burrowing amphibians.

▲ **Figure 34.22 Amphibians.**

frogs have colour patterns that camouflage them (see Figure 54.5).

Caecilians

The roughly 170 species of apodans, or caecilians, are legless and nearly blind, and superficially they resemble earthworms (**Figure 34.22c**). Their absence of legs is a secondary adaptation, as they evolved from a legged ancestor. Caecilians inhabit tropical areas, where most species burrow in moist forest soil.

Lifestyle and Ecology of Amphibians

The term *amphibian* (derived from *amphibious*, meaning "both ways of life") refers to the life stages of many

frog species that live first in water and then on land (**Figure 34.23**). The larval stage of a frog, called a tadpole, is usually an aquatic herbivore with gills, a lateral line system resembling that of aquatic vertebrates, and a long, finned tail. The tadpole initially lacks legs; it swims by undulating its tail. During the metamorphosis that leads to the "second life," the tadpole develops legs, lungs, a pair of external eardrums, and a digestive system adapted to a carnivorous diet. At the same time, the gills disappear; the lateral line system also disappears in most species. The young frog crawls onto shore and becomes a terrestrial hunter. In spite of their name, however, many amphibians do not live a dual—aquatic and terrestrial—life. There are some strictly aquatic or strictly terrestrial frogs, salamanders, and caecilians. Moreover, salamander and caecilian larvae look much like the adults, and typically both the larvae and the adults are carnivorous.

Terry Whittaker/Alamy Stock Photo

Dave Pressland/Frank Lane Picture Agency

John Cancalosi/Getty Images

(a) The tadpole is an aquatic herbivore with a fishlike tail and internal gills.

(b) During metamorphosis, the gills and tail are resorbed, and walking legs develop. The adult frog will live on land.

(c) The adults return to water to mate. The male grasps the female, stimulating her to release eggs. The eggs are laid and fertilized in water. They have a jelly coat but lack a shell and would desiccate in air.

▲ **Figure 34.23 The "dual life" of a frog (*Rana temporaria*).**

Most amphibians are found in damp habitats such as swamps and rain forests. Even those adapted to drier habitats spend much of their time in burrows or under moist leaves, where humidity is high. Amphibians generally rely heavily on their moist skin for gas exchange with the environment. Some terrestrial species lack lungs and breathe exclusively through their skin and oral cavity.

Fertilization is external in most amphibians; the male grasps the female and spills his sperm over the eggs as the female sheds them (see Figure 34.23c). Amphibians typically lay their eggs in water or in moist environments on land; the eggs lack a shell and dehydrate quickly in dry air. Some amphibian species lay vast numbers of eggs in temporary pools, and egg mortality is high. In contrast, other species lay relatively few eggs and display various types of parental care. Depending on the species, either males or females may house eggs on their back (Figure 34.24), in their mouth, or even in their stomach. Certain tropical tree frogs stir their egg masses into moist, foamy nests that resist drying. There are also some ovoviviparous and viviparous species that retain the eggs in the female reproductive tract, where embryos can develop without drying out.

Many amphibians exhibit complex and diverse social behaviours, especially during their breeding seasons. Frogs are usually quiet, but the males of many species vocalize to defend their breeding territory or to attract females. In some species, migrations to specific breeding sites may involve vocal communication, celestial navigation, or chemical signalling.

Over the past 30 years, zoologists have documented a rapid and alarming decline in amphibian populations in locations throughout the world. There appear to be several causes, including the spread of a disease-causing chytrid fungus, habitat loss, climate change, and pollution. These and other factors have not only reduced populations, but led to extinctions. A recent study indicates that at least nine amphibian species have become extinct since 1980; more than 100 other species have not been seen since that time and are considered possibly extinct.

CONCEPT CHECK 34.4

1. Describe the origin of tetrapods and identify some of their key derived traits.

2. Some amphibians never leave the water, whereas others can survive in relatively dry terrestrial environments. Contrast the adaptations that facilitate these two lifestyles.

3. **WHAT IF?** Scientists think that amphibian populations may provide an early warning system of environmental problems. What features of amphibians might make them particularly sensitive to environmental problems?

For suggested answers, see Appendix A.

CONCEPT 34.5

Amniotes are tetrapods that have a terrestrially adapted egg

The **amniotes** are a group of tetrapods whose extant members are the reptiles (including birds) and mammals (Figure 34.25). During their evolution, amniotes acquired a number of new adaptations to life on land.

Derived Characters of Amniotes

Amniotes are named for the major derived character of the clade, the **amniotic egg**, which contains four specialized membranes: the amnion, the chorion, the yolk sac, and the allantois (Figure 34.26). Called *extraembryonic membranes* because they are not part of the body of the embryo itself, these membranes develop from tissue layers that grow out from the embryo. The amniotic egg is named for the amnion, which encloses a compartment of fluid that bathes the embryo and acts as a hydraulic shock absorber. The other membranes in the egg function in gas exchange, the transfer of stored nutrients to the embryo, and waste storage. The amniotic egg was a key evolutionary innovation for terrestrial life: It allowed the embryo to develop on land in its own private "pond," hence reducing the dependence of tetrapods on an aqueous environment for reproduction.

In contrast to the shell-less eggs of amphibians, the amniotic eggs of most reptiles and some mammals have a shell. The shells of bird eggs are calcareous (made of calcium carbonate) and inflexible, while the eggshells of

▲ Figure 34.24 **A mobile nursery.** A female pygmy marsupial frog, *Flectonotus pygmaeus*, incubates her eggs in a pouch of skin on her back, helping to protect the eggs from predators. When the eggs hatch, the female deposits the tadpoles in water where they begin life on their own.

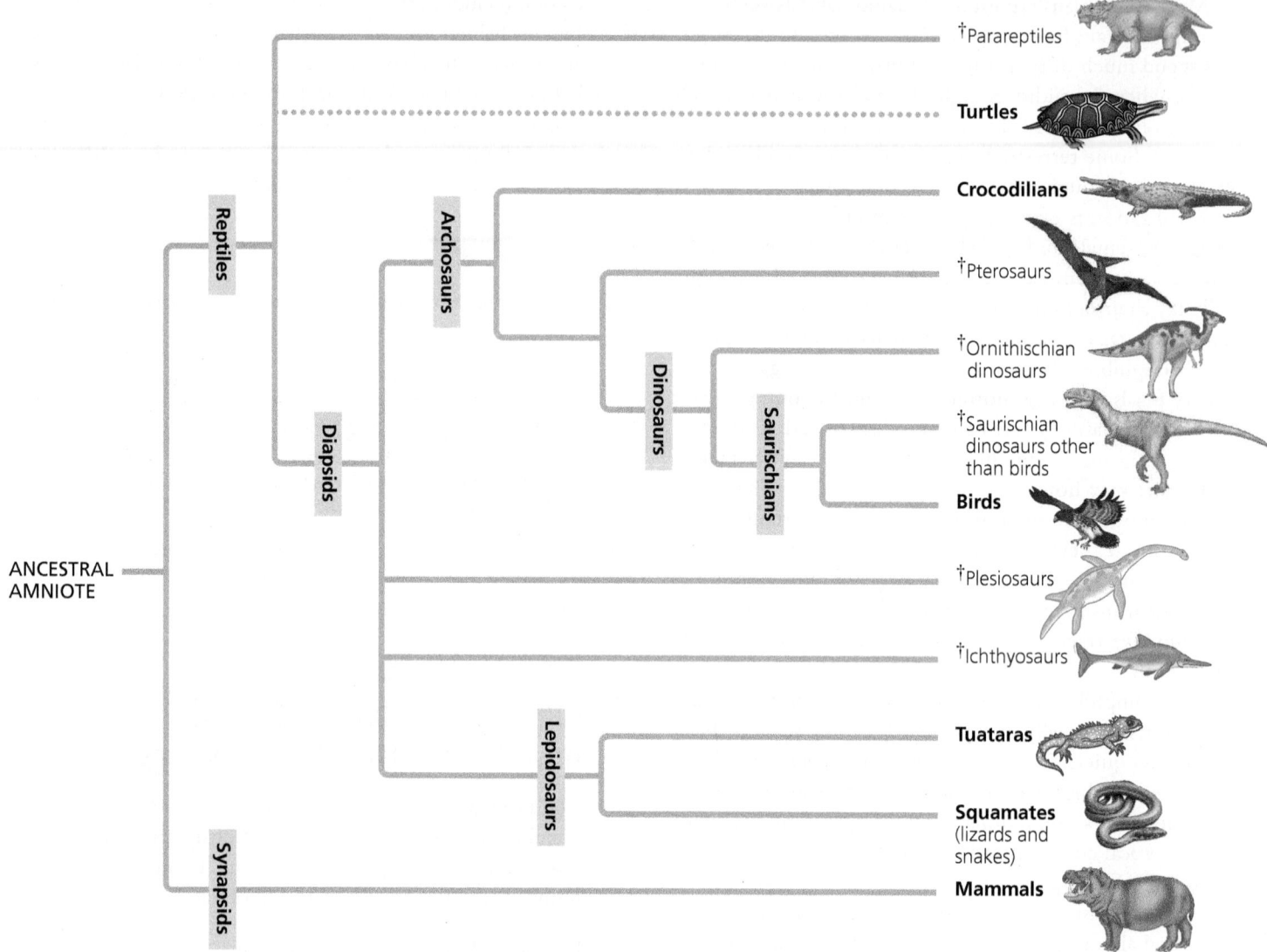

▲ **Figure 34.25 A phylogeny of amniotes.** Extant groups are named at the tips of the branches in boldface type. The dagger symbols (†) indicate extinct groups. The dotted line indicates the uncertain relationship of turtles to other reptiles.

? *Based on this phylogeny, are pterosaurs dinosaurs? Are birds? Explain.*

many other reptiles are leathery and flexible. Either kind of shell significantly slows dehydration of the egg in air, an adaptation that helped amniotes to occupy a wider range of terrestrial habitats than amphibians, their closest living relatives. (Seeds played a similar role in the evolution of land plants, as we discussed in Chapter 30.) Most mammals have dispensed with the eggshell over the course of their evolution, and the embryo avoids desiccation by developing within the amnion inside the mother's body.

Amniotes have acquired other key adaptations to life on land. For example, amniotes use their rib cage to ventilate their lungs. This method is more efficient than throat-based ventilation, which amphibians use as a supplement to breathing through their skin. The increased efficiency of rib cage ventilation may have allowed amniotes to abandon

breathing through their skin and develop less permeable skin, thereby conserving water.

Early Amniotes

The most recent common ancestor of living amphibians and amniotes likely lived about 350 million years ago. No fossils of amniotic eggs have been found from that time, which is not surprising given how delicate they are. Thus, it is not yet possible to say when the amniotic egg evolved, although it must have existed in the last common ancestor of living amniotes, which all have amniotic eggs.

Based on where their fossils have been found, the earliest amniotes lived in warm, moist environments, as did the first tetrapods. Over time, however, early amniotes

Extraembryonic membranes

Allantois. The allantois is a disposal sac for certain metabolic wastes produced by the embryo.

Chorion. The chorion and the membrane of the allantois exchange gases between the embryo and the air.

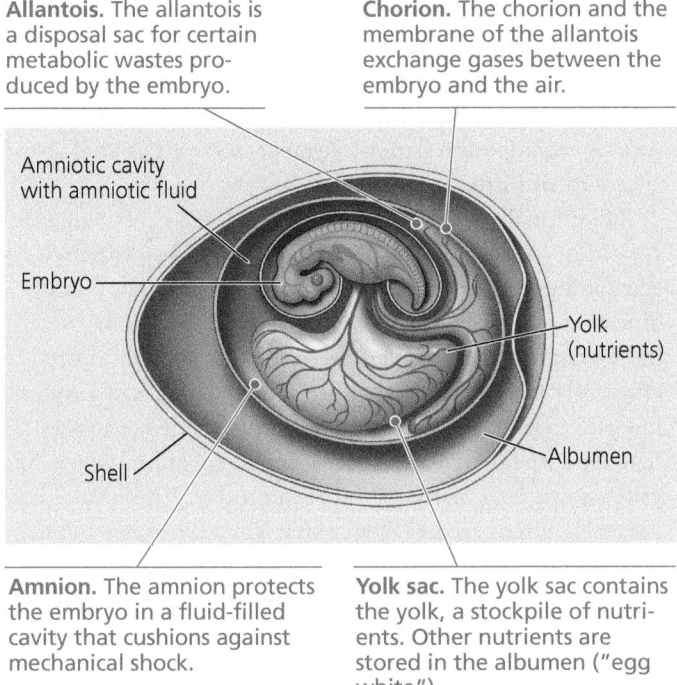

Amniotic cavity with amniotic fluid

Embryo

Shell

Yolk (nutrients)

Albumen

Amnion. The amnion protects the embryo in a fluid-filled cavity that cushions against mechanical shock.

Yolk sac. The yolk sac contains the yolk, a stockpile of nutrients. Other nutrients are stored in the albumen ("egg white").

Extraembryonic membranes

▲ **Figure 34.26 The amniotic egg.** The embryos of reptiles and mammals form four extraembryonic membranes: the amnion, chorion, yolk sac, and allantois. This diagram shows these membranes in the shelled egg of a reptile.

expanded into a wide range of new environments, including dry and high-latitude regions. The earliest amniotes were small and had sharp teeth, a sign that they were predators. The fossilized remains of the earliest known amniote, *Hylonomus lyelli* (Figure 34.27), was discovered by Nova Scotia-born geologist Sir William Dawson along with Sir Charles Lyell in 1852 while studying rocks from the late Carboniferous period at Joggins, Nova Scotia (see Figure 29.15). Later groups also included herbivores, as evidenced by their grinding teeth and other features.

Canada Post

▲ **Figure 34.27 Canadian stamp of an artist's reconstruction of** *Hylonomus lyelli.* About 25 cm long, this early amniote lived 310 million years ago and probably ate insects and other small invertebrates. It was one of the more significant discoveries from the Joggins Fossil Cliffs, situated at the Bay of Fundy in Nova Scotia.

Reptiles

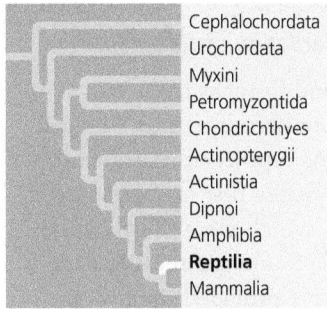

Cephalochordata
Urochordata
Myxini
Petromyzontida
Chondrichthyes
Actinopterygii
Actinistia
Dipnoi
Amphibia
Reptilia
Mammalia

The **reptile** clade includes tuataras, lizards, snakes, turtles, crocodilians, and birds, along with a number of extinct groups, such as plesiosaurs and ichthyosaurs (see Figure 34.25).

Fossil evidence indicates that the earliest reptiles lived about 310 million years ago and resembled lizards. Reptiles have diverged greatly since that time, but as a group they share several derived characters that distinguish them from other tetrapods. For example, unlike amphibians, reptiles have scales that contain the protein keratin (as does a human nail). Scales help protect the animal's skin from desiccation and abrasion. In addition, most reptiles lay their shelled eggs on land (Figure 34.28). Fertilization must occur internally, before the eggshell is secreted.

Reptiles such as lizards and snakes are sometimes described as "cold-blooded" because they do not use their metabolism extensively to control their body temperature. However, they do regulate their body temperature by using behavioural adaptations. For example, many lizards bask in the sun when the air is cool and seek shade when the air is too warm. A more accurate description of these reptiles is to say that they are **ectothermic**, which means that they absorb external heat as their main source of body heat. (This topic is discussed in more detail in Chapter 40.) By warming themselves directly with solar energy rather than through the metabolic breakdown of food, an ectothermic reptile can survive on less than 10% of the food energy required by a mammal of the same size. But the reptile clade is not entirely

age fotostock/Alamy Stock Photo

▲ **Figure 34.28 Hatching reptiles.** This snapping turtle (*Chelydra serpentina*) is breaking out of its flexible shell, a common type of shell among living reptiles other than birds.

ectothermic; birds are **endothermic**, capable of maintaining body temperature through metabolic activity.

The Origin and Evolutionary Radiation of Reptiles

The oldest reptilian fossils, found in rocks from Nova Scotia, date from the late Carboniferous period, 310 million years ago (Figure 34.27). As reptiles diverged from their lizard-like ancestors, one of the first major groups to emerge were the **parareptiles**, which were mostly large, stocky, quadrupedal herbivores. Some parareptiles had plates on their skin that may have provided them with defence against predators. Parareptiles died out by about 200 million years ago, at the end of the Triassic period.

As parareptiles were dwindling, another ancient clade of reptiles, the **diapsids**, was diversifying. One of the most obvious derived characters of diapsids is a pair of holes on each side of the skull, behind the eye socket (on the left); muscles pass through these holes and attach to the jaw, controlling jaw movement. The diapsids are composed of two main lineages. One lineage gave rise to the **lepidosaurs**, which include tuataras, lizards, and snakes. This lineage also produced some marine reptiles, including the giant mosasaurs. Some of these marine species rivalled today's whales in length; all of them are extinct. The other main diapsid lineage, the **archosaurs**, produced the crocodilians, pterosaurs, and dinosaurs. In this section we'll focus on extinct lineages of lepidosaurs and archosaurs, returning to living reptiles afterward.

Pterosaurs, which originated in the late Triassic, were the first tetrapods to exhibit flapping flight. The pterosaur wing was completely different from the wings of birds and bats. It consisted of a collagen-strengthened membrane that stretched between the trunk or hind leg and a very long digit on the foreleg. Well-preserved fossils show evidence of muscles, blood vessels, and nerves in the wing membranes, suggesting that pterosaurs could dynamically adjust their membranes to assist their flight. The smallest pterosaurs were no bigger than a sparrow, and the largest had a wingspan of nearly 11 m. They appear to have converged on many of the ecological roles later played by birds; some were insect-eaters, others grabbed fish out of the ocean, and still others filtered small animals through thousands of fine needlelike teeth. But by 65.5 million years ago, pterosaurs had become extinct.

On land, the **dinosaurs** diversified into a vast range of shapes and sizes, from bipeds the size of a pigeon to 45-m-long quadrupeds with necks long enough to let them browse the tops of trees. One lineage of dinosaurs, the ornithischians, were herbivores; they included many species with elaborate defences against predators, such as tail clubs and horned crests. The other main lineage of dinosaurs, the saurischians, included the long-necked giants and a group called the **theropods**, which were bipedal carnivores. Theropods included the famous *Tyrannosaurus rex* as well as the ancestors of birds.

Traditionally, dinosaurs were considered slow, sluggish creatures. Since the early 1970s, however, fossil discoveries and research have led to the conclusion that many dinosaurs were agile and fast moving. Dinosaurs had a limb structure that enabled them to walk and run more efficiently than could earlier tetrapods, which had a sprawling gait. Fossilized footprints and other evidence suggest that some species were social—they lived and travelled in groups, much as many mammals do today. Paleontologists have also discovered evidence that some dinosaurs built nests and brooded their eggs, as birds do today.

All dinosaurs except birds became extinct by the end of the Cretaceous period (65.5 million years ago). Their extinction may have been caused at least in part by the asteroid or comet impact you read about in Chapter 25. Some analyses of the fossil record are consistent with this idea in that they show a sudden decline in dinosaur diversity at the end of the Cretaceous. However, other analyses indicate that the number of dinosaur species had begun to decline several million years before the Cretaceous ended. Further fossil discoveries and new analyses will be needed to resolve this debate.

Next, we'll discuss extant lineages of reptiles, including turtles, lepidosaurs, and two groups of archosaurs—crocodilians and birds.

Turtles

Turtles are one of the most distinctive groups of reptiles alive today. To date, their phylogenetic position remains uncertain (see Figure 34.25). Turtles may be a sister group to parareptiles or they may be within the diapsid clade, depending on the data used to assess their phylogeny.

All turtles have a boxlike shell made of upper and lower shields that are fused to the vertebrae, clavicles (collarbones), and ribs (**Figure 34.29a**). Most of the 307 known species of turtles have a hard shell, providing excellent defence against predators. A 2008 study reported the

▼ Figure 34.29 **Extant reptiles (other than birds).**

(a) Eastern box turtle (*Terrapene carolina carolina*)

discovery of the oldest known fossil of the turtle lineage, dating to 220 million years ago. This fossil has a complete lower shell but an incomplete upper shell, suggesting that turtles may have acquired full shells in stages. The marine sediments in which this fossil was found also suggest that turtles may have originated in shallow coastal waters. However, as other scientists have argued, it is also possible that turtles originated on land and that the incomplete upper shell of this fossil may have been a specialized adaptation for an aquatic lifestyle. Scientists continue to hunt for fossils that could shed light on the origin of the turtle shell.

The earliest turtles could not retract their head into their shell, but mechanisms for doing so evolved independently in two separate branches of turtles. The side-necked turtles fold their neck horizontally, while the vertical-necked turtles fold their neck vertically.

Some turtles have adapted to deserts, and others live almost entirely in ponds and rivers. Still others have returned to the sea. Sea turtles have a reduced shell and enlarged fore-limbs that function as flippers. They include the largest living turtles, the deep-diving leatherbacks, which can exceed a mass of 1500 kg and feed on jellies. Leatherbacks and other sea turtles are endangered by being caught in fishing nets, as well as by residential and commercial development of the beaches where the turtles lay their eggs.

Lepidosaurs

One surviving lineage of lepidosaurs is represented by two species of lizard-like reptiles called tuataras (Figure 34.29b).

Fossil evidence indicates that tuatara ancestors lived at least 220 million years ago. These organisms thrived on many continents well into the Cretaceous period, reaching up to a metre in length. Today, however, tuataras are found only on 30 islands off the coast of New Zealand. When humans arrived in New Zealand 750 years ago, the rats that accompanied them devoured tuatara eggs, eventually eliminating the reptiles on the main islands. The tuataras that remain on the outlying islands are about 50 cm long and feed on insects, small lizards, and bird eggs and chicks. They can live to be over 100 years old. Their future survival depends on whether their remaining habitats are kept rat-free.

The other major living lineage of lepidosaurs consists of the lizards and snakes, or squamates, which number about 7900 species. Lizards are the most numerous and diverse reptiles (apart from birds) alive today (Figure 34.29c). Many lizards are small; the Jaragua lizard, discovered in the Dominican Republic in 2001, is only 16 mm long—small enough to fit comfortably on a dime. In contrast, the Komodo dragon of Indonesia is a lizard that can reach a length of 3 m. It hunts deer and other large prey, delivering venom with its bite.

Snakes descended from lizards with legs (Figure 34.29d). Today, some species of snakes retain vestigial pelvic and limb bones, providing evidence of their ancestry. Despite their lack of legs, snakes are quite proficient at moving on land, most often by producing waves of lateral bending that pass from head to tail. Force exerted by the bends against solid objects pushes

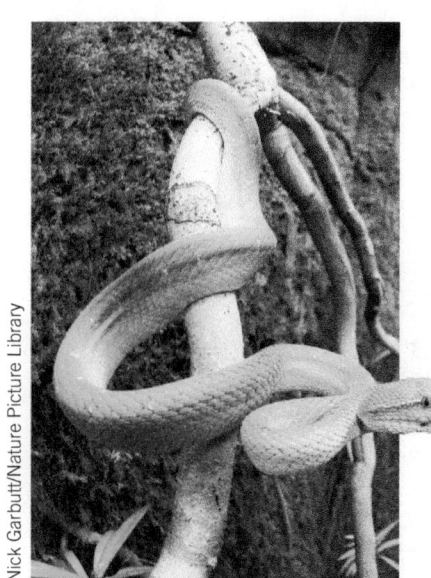

(d) Wagler's pit viper (*Tropidolaemus wagleri*)

(b) Tuatara (*Sphenodon punctatus*)

(c) Australian thorny devil lizard (*Moloch horridus*)

(e) American alligator (*Alligator mississippiensis*)

the snake forward. Snakes can also move by gripping the ground with their belly scales at several points along the body while the scales at intervening points are lifted slightly off the ground and pulled forward.

Snakes are carnivorous, and a number of adaptations aid them in hunting and eating prey. They have acute chemical sensors, and though they lack eardrums, they are sensitive to ground vibrations, which helps them detect the movements of prey. Heat-detecting organs between the eyes and nostrils of pit vipers, including rattlesnakes, are sensitive to minute temperature changes, enabling these night hunters to locate warm animals. Venomous snakes inject their toxin through a pair of sharp teeth that may be hollow or grooved. The flicking tongue is not venomous but helps fan odours toward olfactory (smell) organs on the roof of the mouth. Loosely articulated jawbones and elastic skin enable most snakes to swallow prey larger than the diameter of the snake's head (see Figure 23.13).

Crocodilians

Alligators and crocodiles (collectively called crocodilians) belong to a lineage that reaches back to the late Triassic (Figure 34.29e). The earliest members of this lineage were small terrestrial quadrupeds with long, slender legs. Later species became larger and adapted to aquatic habitats,

breathing air through their upturned nostrils. Some Mesozoic crocodilians grew as long as 12 m and may have attacked dinosaurs and other prey at the water's edge. The 23 known species of living crocodilians are confined to warm regions of the globe.

Birds

There are about 10 000 species of birds in the world. Like crocodilians, birds are archosaurs, but almost every feature of their anatomy has been modified in their adaptation to flight.

Derived Characters of Birds Many of the characters of birds are adaptations that facilitate flight, including weight-saving modifications that make flying more efficient. For example, birds lack a urinary bladder, and the females of most species have only one ovary. The gonads of both females and males are usually small, except during the breeding season, when they increase in size. Living birds are also toothless, an adaptation that trims the weight of the head.

A bird's most obvious adaptations for flight are its wings and feathers (Figure 34.30). Feathers are made of the protein β-keratin, which is also found in the scales of other reptiles. The shape and arrangement of the feathers form the wings into airfoils, and they illustrate some of the same principles of aerodynamics as the wings of an airplane. Power for flapping the wings comes from contractions of large pectoral (breast) muscles anchored to a keel on the sternum

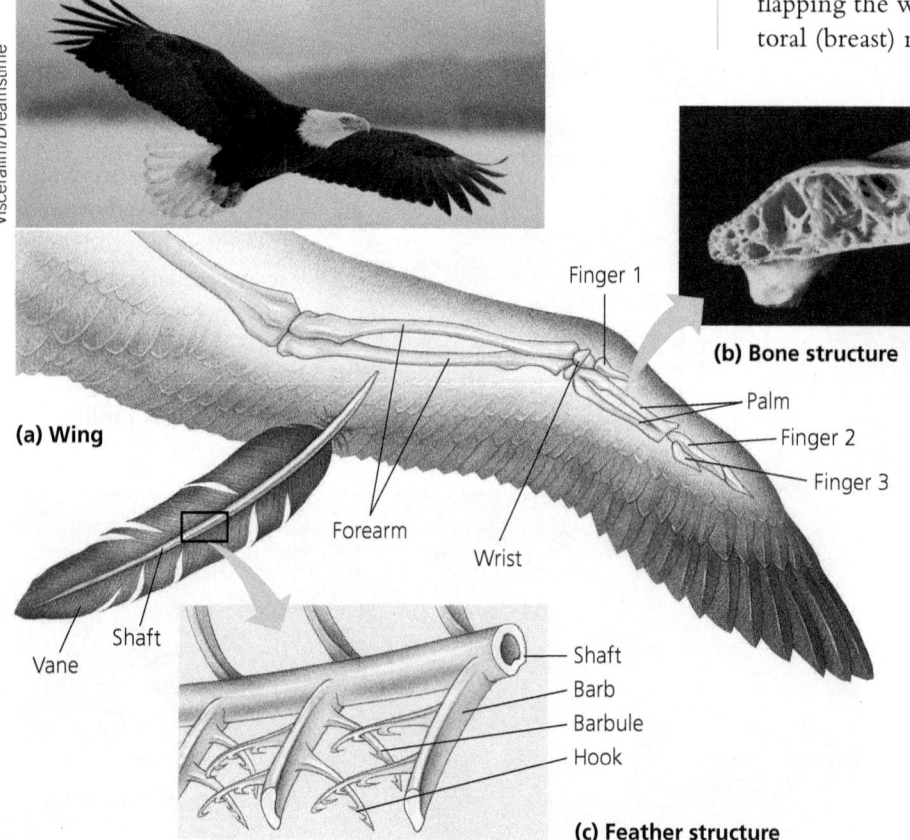

(a) Wing

(b) Bone structure

(c) Feather structure

Finger 1 — Palm — Finger 2 — Finger 3 — Forearm — Wrist — Shaft — Vane — Shaft — Barb — Barbule — Hook

◀ Figure 34.30 **Form fits function: the avian wing and feather. (a)** A wing is a remodelled version of the tetrapod forelimb. **(b)** The bones of many birds have a honeycombed internal structure and are filled with air. **(c)** A feather consists of a central air-filled shaft, from which radiate the vanes. The vanes are made up of barbs, which bear small branches called barbules. Birds have contour feathers and downy feathers. Contour feathers are stiff and contribute to the aerodynamic shapes of the wings and body. Their barbules have hooks that cling to barbules on neighbouring barbs. When a bird preens, it runs the length of each contour feather through its bill, engaging the hooks and uniting the barbs into a precise shape. Downy feathers lack hooks, and the free-form arrangement of their barbs produces a fluffiness that provides insulation by trapping air.

(breastbone). Some birds, such as eagles and hawks, have wings adapted for soaring on air currents and flap their wings only occasionally; other birds, including hummingbirds, must flap continuously to stay aloft (see Figure 34.34). Among the fastest birds are the appropriately named swifts, which can fly up to 170 km/hr.

Flight provides numerous benefits. It enhances hunting and scavenging; many birds consume flying insects, an abundant, highly nutritious food resource. Flight also provides ready escape from earthbound predators and enables some birds to migrate great distances to exploit different food resources and seasonal breeding areas.

Flying requires a great expenditure of energy from an active metabolism. Birds are endothermic; they use their own metabolic heat to maintain a high, constant body temperature. Feathers and in some species a layer of fat provide insulation that enables birds to retain body heat. The lungs have tiny tubes leading to and from elastic air sacs that improve airflow and oxygen uptake. This efficient respiratory system and a circulatory system with a four-chambered heart keep tissues well supplied with oxygen and nutrients, supporting a high rate of metabolism.

Flight also requires both acute vision and fine muscle control. Birds have colour vision and excellent eyesight. The visual and motor areas of the brain are well developed, and the brain is proportionately larger than those of amphibians and nonbird reptiles.

Birds generally display very complex behaviours, particularly during the breeding season, when they engage in elaborate courtship rituals. Because eggs have shells by the time they are laid, fertilization must be internal. Copulation usually involves contact between the mates' vents, the openings to their cloacas. After eggs are laid, the avian embryo must be kept warm through brooding by the mother, the father, or both, depending on the species.

The Origin of Birds Cladistic analyses of birds and reptilian fossils indicate that birds belong to the group of bipedal saurischian dinosaurs called theropods. Since the late 1990s, paleontologists have unearthed a spectacular trove of feathered theropod fossils that are shedding light on the origin of birds (see Figure 26.2). Several species of dinosaurs closely related to birds had feathers with vanes, and a wider range of species had filamentous feathers. Such findings imply that feathers evolved long before powered flight. Among the possible functions of these early feathers were insulation, camouflage, and courtship display.

By 160 million years ago, feathered theropods had evolved into birds. Many researchers consider *Archaeopteryx*, which was discovered in a German limestone quarry in 1861, to be the earliest known animal that shared a common ancestor with birds (Figure 34.31). It had feathered

Toothed beak — Wing claw

Airfoil wing with contour feathers

Long tail with many vertebrae

▲ Figure 34.31 **Artist's reconstruction of *Archaeopteryx*, the earliest known bird-like animal.** Fossil evidence indicates that *Archaeopteryx* was capable of powered flight but retained many characters of nonbird dinosaurs.

wings but retained ancestral characters such as teeth, clawed digits in its wings, and a long, bony tail. *Archaeopteryx* flew well at high speeds, but unlike a present-day bird, it could not take off from a standing position. Fossils of later birds from the Cretaceous show a gradual loss of certain ancestral dinosaur features, such as teeth and clawed forelimbs, as well as the acquisition of innovations found in extant birds, including a short tail covered by a fan of feathers.

Living Birds Clear evidence of Neornithes, the clade that includes the 28 orders of living birds, can be found before the Cretaceous-Paleogene boundary 65.5 million years ago. Several groups of living and extinct birds include one or more flightless species. The **ratites** (order Struthioniformes), which consist of the ostrich, rhea, kiwi, cassowary, and emu, are all flightless (**Figure 34.32**). In ratites,

Boris Karpinski/Alamy

▲ Figure 34.32 **An emu (*Dromaius novaehollandiae*), a flightless bird native to Australia.**

▲ Figure 34.33 **A king penguin (*Aptenodytes patagonicus*) "flying" underwater.** With their streamlined shape and powerful pectoral muscles, penguins are fast and agile swimmers.

the sternal keel is absent, and the pectoral muscles are small relative to those of birds that can fly.

Penguins make up the flightless order Sphenisciformes, but, like flying birds, they have powerful pectoral muscles. They use these muscles to "fly" in the water: As they swim, they flap their flipper-like wings in a manner that resembles the flight stroke of a more typical bird (**Figure 34.33**). Certain species of rails, ducks, and pigeons are also flightless.

Although the demands of flight have rendered the general body forms of many flying birds similar to one another, experienced bird-watchers can distinguish species by their profile, colours, flying style, behaviour, and beak shape. The skeleton of a hummingbird wing is unique, making them the only birds that can hover and fly backwards (**Figure 34.34**). Adult birds lack teeth, but during the course of avian evolution their beaks have taken on a variety of shapes suited to different diets. Some birds, such

▲ Figure 34.34 **Hummingbird feeding while hovering.** A hummingbird can rotate its wings in all directions, enabling it to hover and fly backwards.

▲ Figure 34.35 **Specialized beaks.** This greater flamingo (*Phoenicopterus ruber*) dips its beak into the water and strains out the food.

▲ Figure 34.36 **Feet adapted to perching.** This great tit (*Parus major*) is a member of the Passeriformes, the perching birds. The toes of these birds can lock around a branch or wire, enabling the bird to rest for long periods.

as parrots, have crushing beaks with which they can crack open hard nuts and seeds. Other birds, such as flamingoes, are filter feeders. Their beaks have remarkable "strainers" that enable them to capture food particles from the water (**Figure 34.35**). Foot structure, too, shows considerable variation. Various birds use their feet for perching on branches (**Figure 34.36**), grasping food, defence, swimming or walking, and even courtship (see Figure 24.3e).

CONCEPT CHECK 34.5

1. Describe three key amniote adaptations for life on land.
2. Are snakes tetrapods? Explain.
3. Identify four avian adaptations for flight.
4. **WHAT IF?** Suppose turtles are more closely related to lepidosaurs than to other reptiles. Redraw Figure 34.25 to show this relationship, and mark the node that represents the most recent common ancestor shared by all living reptiles. Defining the reptile clade as consisting of all descendants of that ancestor, list the reptiles.

For suggested answers, see Appendix A.

Mammals are amniotes that have hair and produce milk

The reptiles we have been discussing represent one of the two living lineages of amniotes. The other amniote lineage is our own, the **mammals** (class Mammalia). Today, there are more than 5300 known species of mammals on Earth.

Derived Characters of Mammals

The distinctive character from which mammals derive their name is their mammary glands, which produce milk for offspring. All mammalian mothers nourish their young with milk, a balanced diet rich in fats, sugars, proteins, minerals, and vitamins. Hair, another

Synapsid

Key
- Articular
- Quadrate
- Dentary
- Squamosal

(a) In *Biarmosuchus*, the meeting of the articular and quadrate bones formed the jaw joint.

Present-day reptile   **Present-day mammal**

(b) During the evolutionary remodelling of the mammalian skull, a new jaw joint formed between the dentary and squamosal bones (see Figure 25.7). No longer used in the jaw, the quadrate and articular bones became incorporated into the middle ear as two of the three bones that transmit sound from the eardrum to the inner ear.

▲ **Figure 34.37 The evolution of the mammalian ear bones.** *Biarmosuchus* was a synapsid, a lineage that eventually gave rise to the mammals. Bones that transmit sound in the ear of mammals arose from the modification of bones in the jaw of nonmammalian synapsids.

Source: Based on many sources including figure 4.10 from Evolution, by Douglas J. Futuyma. Sinauer Associates, 2005; and Vertebrate Paleontology and Evolution by Robert L. Carroll. W.H. Freeman & Co., 1988. © Jane B Reece.

MAKE CONNECTIONS *Review the definition of* exaptation *in Concept 25.6. Summarize the process by which exaptation occurs and explain how the incorporation of the articular and quadrate bones into the mammalian inner ear is an example.*

mammalian characteristic, and a fat layer under the skin help the body retain heat. Like birds, mammals are endothermic, and most have a high metabolic rate. Efficient respiratory and circulatory systems (including a four-chambered heart) support a mammal's metabolism. A sheet of muscle called the diaphragm helps ventilate the lungs.

Like birds, mammals generally have a larger brain than other vertebrates of equivalent size, and many species are capable learners. And as in birds, the relatively long duration of parental care extends the time for offspring to learn important survival skills by observing their parents.

Differentiated teeth are another important mammalian trait. Whereas the teeth of reptiles are generally uniform in size and shape, the jaws of mammals bear a variety of teeth with sizes and shapes adapted for chewing many kinds of foods. Humans, like most mammals, have teeth modified for shearing (incisors and canine teeth) and for crushing and grinding (premolars and molars).

Early Evolution of Mammals

Mammals belong to a group of amniotes known as **synapsids**. Early nonmammalian synapsids lacked hair, had a sprawling gait, and laid eggs. A distinctive characteristic of synapsids is the single temporal fenestra, a hole behind the eye socket on each side of the skull (see the picture to the left). Humans retain this feature; your jaw muscles pass through the temporal fenestra and anchor on your temple. Fossil evidence shows that the jaw was remodelled as mammalian features arose gradually in successive lineages of earlier synapsids (see Figure 25.7); in all, these changes took more than 100 million years. In addition, two of the bones that formerly made up the jaw joint were incorporated into the mammalian middle ear **(Figure 34.37)**. This evolutionary change is reflected in changes that occur during development. For example, as a mammalian embryo grows, the posterior region of its jaw—which in a reptile forms the articular bone—can be observed to detach from the jaw and migrate to the ear, where it forms the malleus.

Synapsids evolved into large herbivores and carnivores during the Permian period, and for a time they were the dominant tetrapods. However, the Permian-Triassic extinctions took a heavy toll on them, and their diversity fell during the Triassic (251–200 million years ago). Increasingly mammal-like synapsids emerged by the end of the Triassic. While not true mammals, these synapsids had acquired a number of the derived characters that distinguish mammals from other amniotes. They were small and probably hairy, and they likely fed on insects at night. Their bones show that they grew faster than other synapsids, suggesting that they probably had a relatively high metabolic rate; however, they still laid eggs.

During the Jurassic period (200–145 million years ago), the first true mammals arose and diversified into many short-lived lineages. A diverse set of mammal species coexisted with dinosaurs in Jurassic and Cretaceous periods, but these species were not abundant or dominant members of their community, and most measured less than 1 m. One possible explanation for their small size is that dinosaurs already occupied ecological niches of large-bodied animals.

By the early Cretaceous period, the three major lineages of mammals had emerged: those leading to monotremes (egg-laying mammals), marsupials (mammals with a pouch), and eutherians (placental mammals). After the extinction of large dinosaurs, pterosaurs, and marine reptiles during the late Cretaceous period, mammals underwent an adaptive radiation, giving rise to large predators and herbivores as well as flying and aquatic species.

Monotremes

Monotremes are found only in Australia and New Guinea and are represented by one species of platypus and four species of echidnas (spiny anteaters). Monotremes lay eggs, a character that is ancestral for amniotes and retained in most reptiles (Figure 34.38). Like all mammals, monotremes have hair and produce milk, but they lack nipples. Milk is secreted by glands on the belly of the mother. After hatching, the baby sucks the milk from the mother's fur.

Marsupials

Opossums, kangaroos, and koalas are examples of **marsupials**. Both marsupials and eutherians share derived characters

Keifer/Shutterstock

Mervyn Griffiths/Commonwealth of Scientific and Industrial Research Organization

▲ Figure 34.38 **Short-beaked echidna (*Tachyglossus aculeatus*), an Australian monotreme.** Monotremes have hair and produce milk, but they lack nipples. Monotremes are the only mammals that lay eggs (inset).

not found among monotremes. They have higher metabolic rates and nipples that provide milk, and they give birth to live young. The embryo develops inside the uterus of the female's reproductive tract. The lining of the uterus and the extraembryonic membranes that arise from the embryo form a **placenta**, a structure in which nutrients diffuse into the embryo from the mother's blood.

A marsupial is born very early in its development and completes its embryonic development while nursing. In most species, the nursing young are held within a maternal pouch called a *marsupium* (Figure 34.39a). A red kangaroo, for instance, is about the size of a honeybee at its birth, just 33 days after fertilization. Its back legs are merely buds, but its front legs are strong enough for it to crawl from the exit of its mother's reproductive tract to a pouch that opens to the front of her body, a journey that lasts a few minutes. In other species, the marsupium opens to the rear of the

John Cancalosi/Alamy

(a) A young brushtail possum. The offspring of marsupials are born very early in their development. They finish their growth while nursing from a nipple (in their mother's pouch in most species).

Getty Images

(b) Long-nosed bandicoot. Most bandicoots are diggers and burrowers that eat mainly insects but also some small vertebrates and plant material. Their rear-opening pouch helps protect the young from dirt as the mother digs. Other marsupials, such as kangaroos, have a pouch that opens to the front.

▲ Figure 34.39 **Australian marsupials.**

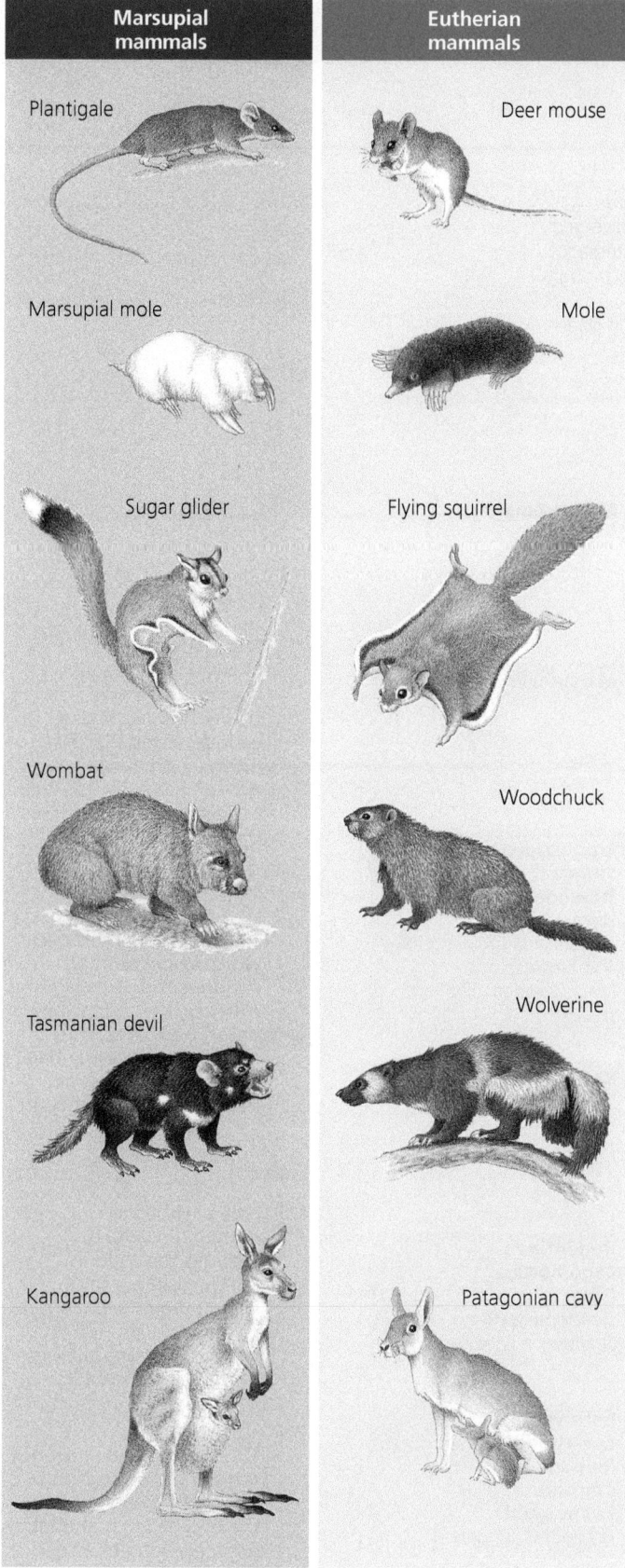

Marsupial mammals	Eutherian mammals
Plantigale	Deer mouse
Marsupial mole	Mole
Sugar glider	Flying squirrel
Wombat	Woodchuck
Tasmanian devil	Wolverine
Kangaroo	Patagonian cavy

▲ Figure 34.40 **Convergent evolution of marsupials and eutherians (placental mammals).** (Note that the drawings are not to scale.)

mother's body; in bandicoots, this protects the young as their mother burrows in the dirt (Figure 34.39b).

Marsupials existed worldwide during the Mesozoic era, but today they are found only in the Australian region and in North and South America. The biogeography of marsupials is an example of the interplay between biological and geologic evolution (see Concept 25.4). After the breakup of the supercontinent Pangaea, South America and Australia became island continents, and their marsupials diversified in isolation from the eutherians that began an adaptive radiation on the northern continents. Australia has not been in contact with another continent since early in the Cenozoic era, about 65 million years ago. In Australia, convergent evolution has resulted in a diversity of marsupials that resemble eutherians in similar ecological roles in other parts of the world (Figure 34.40). In contrast, although South America had a diverse marsupial fauna throughout the Paleogene, it has experienced several migrations of eutherians. One of the most important migrations occurred about 3 million years ago, when North and South America joined at the Panamanian isthmus and extensive two-way traffic of animals took place over the land bridge. Today, only three families of marsupials live outside the Australian region, and the only marsupials found in the wild in North America are a few species of opossum.

Eutherians (Placental Mammals)

Eutherians are commonly called placental mammals because their placentas are more complex than those of marsupials. Eutherians have a longer pregnancy than marsupials. Young eutherians complete their embryonic development within the uterus, joined to their mother by the placenta. The eutherian placenta provides an intimate and long-lasting association between the mother and her developing young.

The major groups of living eutherians are thought to have diverged from one another in a burst of evolutionary change. The timing of this burst is uncertain: It is dated to 100 million years ago by molecular data and 60 million years ago by fossils. Figure 34.41, on the next two pages, explores the major eutherian orders and their possible phylogenetic relationships with each other as well as with the monotremes and marsupials.

Primates

The mammalian order Primates includes the lemurs, tarsiers, monkeys, and apes. Humans are members of the ape group.

Derived Characters of Primates Most primates have hands and feet adapted for grasping, and their digits have flat nails instead of the narrow claws of other mammals. There are other characteristic features of the hands and feet, too, such as skin ridges on the fingers (which account for human fingerprints). Relative to other mammals, primates have a large brain and short jaws, giving them a flat face. Their forward-looking eyes are close together on the front of the face.

Phylogenetic Relationships of Mammals

Evidence from numerous fossils and molecular analyses indicates that monotremes diverged from other mammals about 180 million years ago and that marsupials diverged from eutherians (placental mammals) about 140 million years ago. Molecular systematics has helped to clarify the evolutionary relationships between the eutherian orders, though there is still no broad consensus on a phylogenetic tree. One current hypothesis, represented by the tree shown below, clusters the eutherian orders into four main clades.

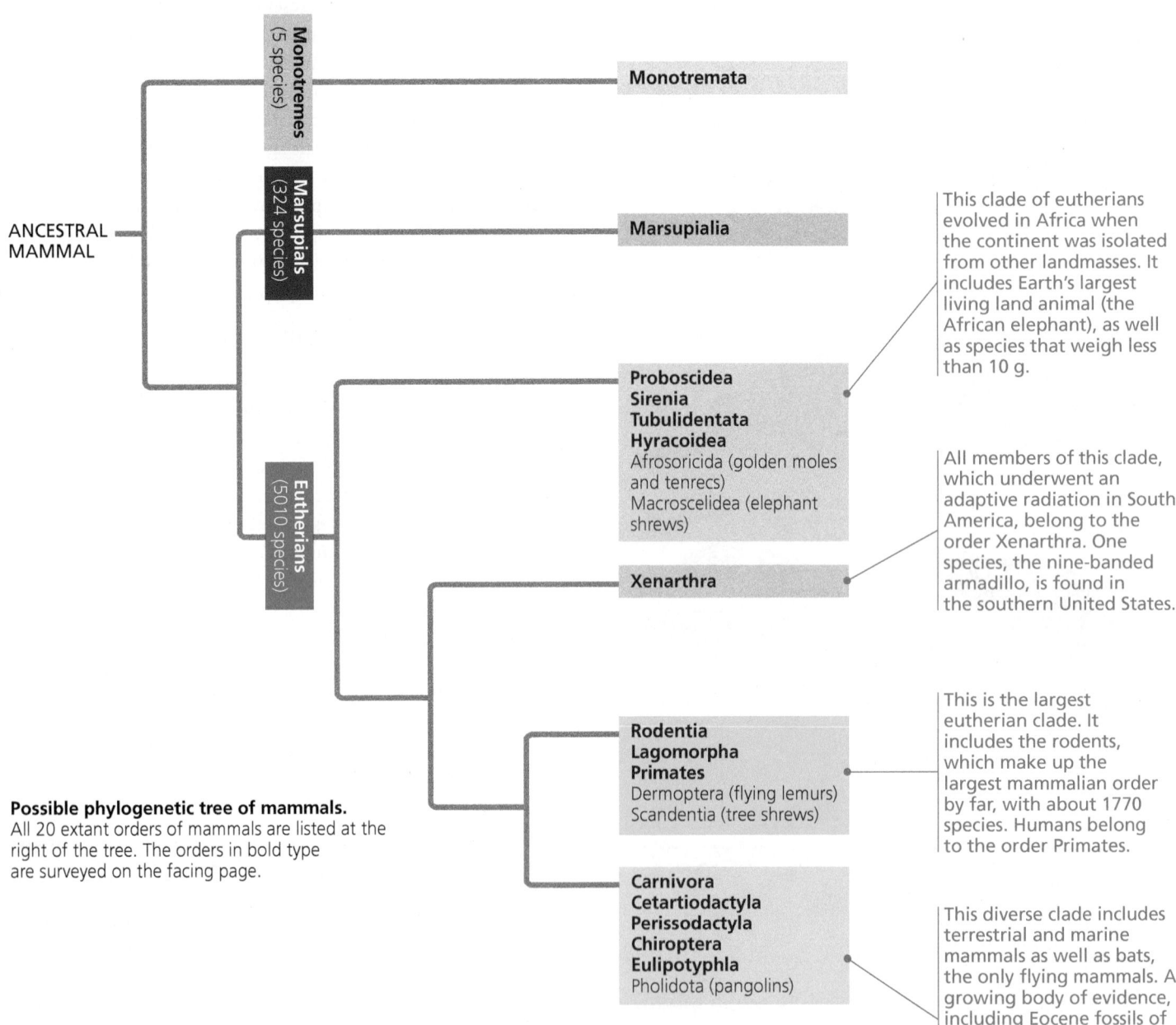

Possible phylogenetic tree of mammals.
All 20 extant orders of mammals are listed at the right of the tree. The orders in bold type are surveyed on the facing page.

This clade of eutherians evolved in Africa when the continent was isolated from other landmasses. It includes Earth's largest living land animal (the African elephant), as well as species that weigh less than 10 g.

All members of this clade, which underwent an adaptive radiation in South America, belong to the order Xenarthra. One species, the nine-banded armadillo, is found in the southern United States.

This is the largest eutherian clade. It includes the rodents, which make up the largest mammalian order by far, with about 1770 species. Humans belong to the order Primates.

This diverse clade includes terrestrial and marine mammals as well as bats, the only flying mammals. A growing body of evidence, including Eocene fossils of whales with feet, supports putting whales in the same order (Cetartiodactyla) as pigs, cows, and hippos (see Figures 22.19 and 22.20).

Orders and Examples	Main Characteristics	Orders and Examples	Main Characteristics
Monotremata Platypuses, echidnas Echidna	Lay eggs; no nipples; young suck milk from fur of mother	**Marsupialia** Kangaroos, opossums, koalas Koala	Complete embryonic development in pouch on mother's body
Proboscidea Elephants African elephant	Long, muscular trunk; thick, loose skin; upper incisors elongated as tusks; herbivorous	**Tubulidentata** Aardvarks Aardvark	Teeth consisting of many thin tubes cemented together; eats ants and termites
Sirenia Manatees, dugongs Manatee	Aquatic; finlike fore-limbs and no hind limbs; herbivorous	**Hyracoidea** Hyraxes Rock hyrax	Short legs; stumpy tail; herbivorous; complex, multi-chambered stomach
Xenarthra Sloths, anteaters, armadillos Tamandua	Reduced teeth or no teeth; herbivorous (sloths) or carnivorous (anteaters, armadillos)	**Rodentia** Squirrels, beavers, rats, porcupines, mice Red squirrel	Chisel-like, continuously growing incisors worn down by gnawing; herbivorous
Lagomorpha Rabbits, hares, pikas Jackrabbit	Chisel-like incisors; hind legs longer than forelegs and adapted for running and jump-ing; herbivorous	**Primates** Lemurs, monkeys, chimpanzees, gorillas, humans Golden lion tamarin	Opposable thumbs; forward-facing eyes; well-developed cerebral cortex; omnivorous
Carnivora Dogs, wolves, bears, cats, weasels, otters, seals, walruses Coyote	Sharp, pointed canine teeth and molars for shearing; carnivorous	**Perissodactyla** Horses, zebras, tapirs, rhinoceroses Indian rhinoceros	Hooves with an odd number of toes on each foot; herbivorous
Cetartiodactyla Artiodactyls Sheep, pigs, cattle, deer, giraffes Bighorn sheep	Hooves with an even number of toes on each foot; herbivorous	**Chiroptera** Bats Frog-eating bat	Adapted for flight; broad skinfold that extends from elongated fingers to body and legs; carnivorous or herbivorous
Cetaceans Whales, dolphins, porpoises Pacific white-sided porpoise	Aquatic; streamlined body; paddle-like forelimbs and no hind limbs; thick layer of insulating blubber; carnivorous	**Eulipotyphla** "Core insectivores": some moles, some shrews Star-nosed mole	Eat mainly insects and other small invertebrates

Primates also exhibit relatively well-developed parental care and complex social behaviour.

The earliest known primates were tree-dwellers, and many of the characteristics of primates are adaptations to the demands of living in the trees. Grasping hands and feet allow primates to hang onto tree branches. All living primates, except humans, have a big toe that is widely separated from the other toes, enabling them to grasp branches with their feet. All primates also have a thumb that is relatively movable and separate from the fingers, but monkeys and apes have a fully **opposable thumb**; that is, they can touch the ventral surface (fingerprint side) of the tip of all four fingers with the ventral surface of the thumb of the same hand. In monkeys and apes other than humans, the opposable thumb functions in a grasping "power grip." In humans, a distinctive bone structure at the base of the thumb allows it to be used for more precise manipulation. The unique dexterity of humans represents descent with modification from our tree-dwelling ancestors. Arboreal manoeuvring also requires excellent eye-hand coordination. The overlapping visual fields of the two forward-facing eyes enhance depth perception, an obvious advantage when brachiating (travelling by swinging from branch to branch in trees).

Living Primates There are three main groups of living primates: (1) the lemurs of Madagascar (**Figure 34.42**) and the lorises and bush babies of tropical Africa and southern Asia; (2) the tarsiers, which live in Southeast Asia; and (3) the **anthropoids**, which include monkeys and apes and are found worldwide. The first group—lemurs, lorises, and bush babies—probably resemble early arboreal primates. The oldest known tarsier fossils date to 55 million years ago, while the oldest anthropoid fossils date to 45 million years ago; along with DNA evidence, these fossils indicate that tarsiers are more closely related to anthropoids than to the lemur group (**Figure 34.43**).

You can see in Figure 34.43 that monkeys do not form a clade but rather consist of two groups, the New and Old World monkeys. Both of these groups are thought to have originated in Africa or Asia. The fossil record indicates that New World monkeys first colonized South America roughly 25 million years ago. By that

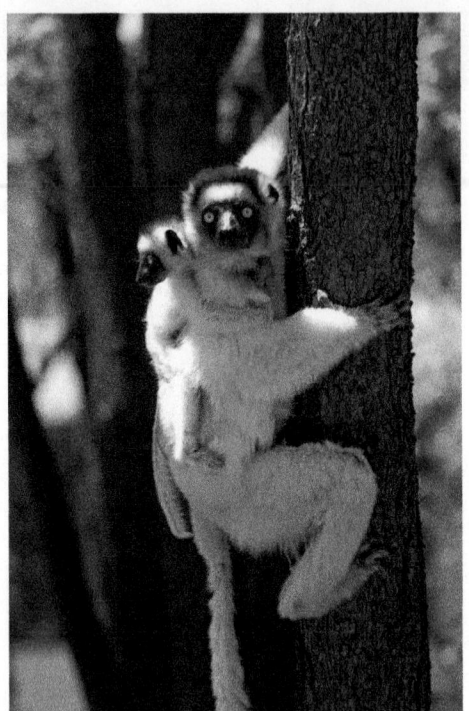

▶ Figure 34.42 **Coquerel's sifakas (*Propithecus verreauxi coquereli*), a type of lemur.**

J & C Sohns/AGE Fotostock

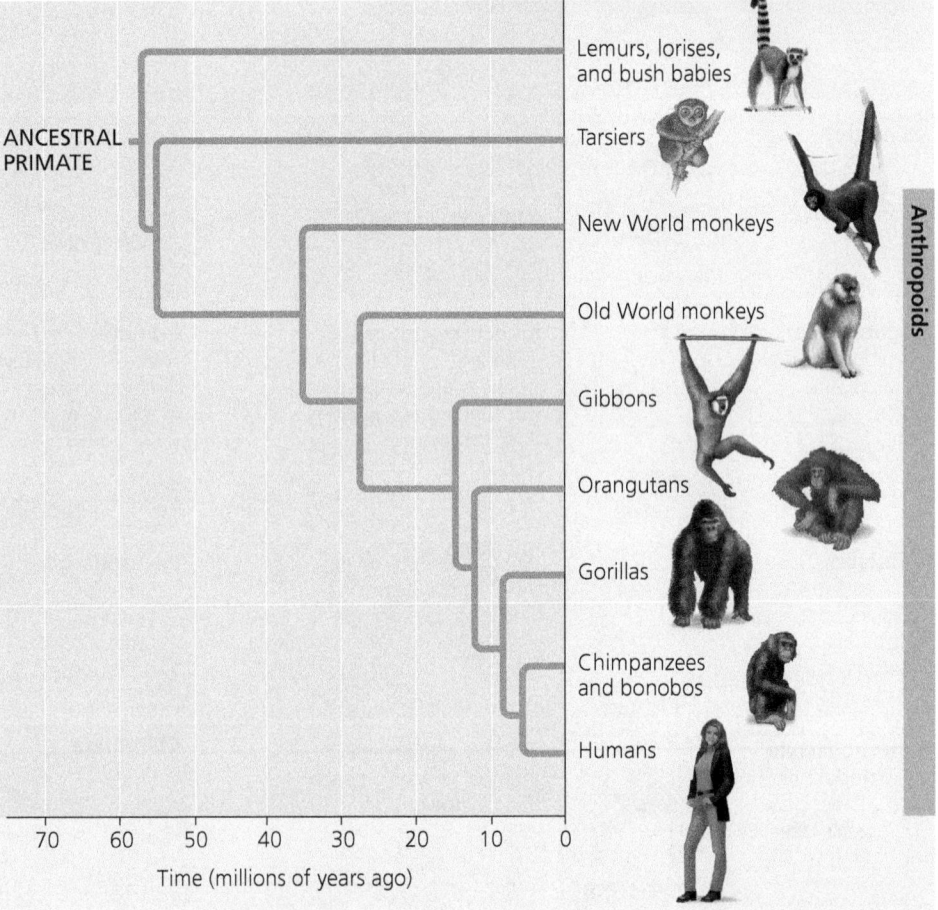

▲ Figure 34.43 **A phylogenetic tree of primates.** The fossil record indicates that anthropoids began diverging from other primates about 55 million years ago. New World monkeys, Old World monkeys, and apes (the clade that includes gibbons, orangutans, gorillas, chimpanzees, and humans) have been evolving as separate lineages for over 25 million years. The lineages leading to humans branched off from other apes sometime between 6 and 7 million years ago.

? *Is the phylogeny shown here consistent with the idea that humans evolved from chimpanzees? Explain.*

time, South America and Africa had drifted apart, and monkeys may have reached South America from Africa by rafting on logs or other debris. What is certain is that New World monkeys and Old World monkeys underwent separate adaptive radiations during their many millions of years of separation (Figure 34.44). All species of New World monkeys are arboreal, whereas Old World monkeys include ground-dwelling as well as arboreal species. Most monkeys in both groups are diurnal (active during the day) and usually live in bands held together by social behaviour.

The other group of anthropoids consists of primates informally called apes (Figure 34.45). The ape group includes the genera *Hylobates* (gibbons), *Pongo* (orangutans), *Gorilla* (gorillas), *Pan* (chimpanzees and bonobos), and *Homo* (humans). The apes diverged from Old World monkeys about 20–25 million years ago. Today, nonhuman apes are found exclusively in tropical regions of the Old World. With the exception of gibbons, living apes are larger than either New or Old World monkeys. All living apes have relatively long arms, short legs, and no tail. Although all nonhuman apes spend time in trees, only gibbons and orangutans are primarily arboreal. Social organization varies

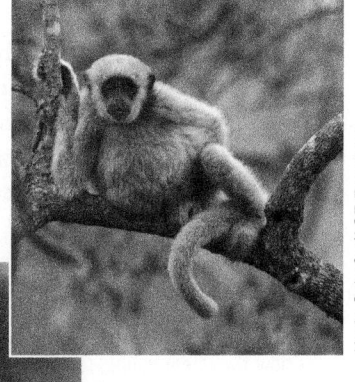

(a) New World monkeys, such as spider monkeys (shown here), squirrel monkeys, and capuchins, have a prehensile (capable of grasping) tail and nostrils that open to the sides.

(b) Old World monkeys lack a prehensile tail, and their nostrils open downward. This group includes macaques (shown here), mandrils, baboons, and rhesus monkeys.

▲ Figure 34.44 **New World monkeys and Old World monkeys.**

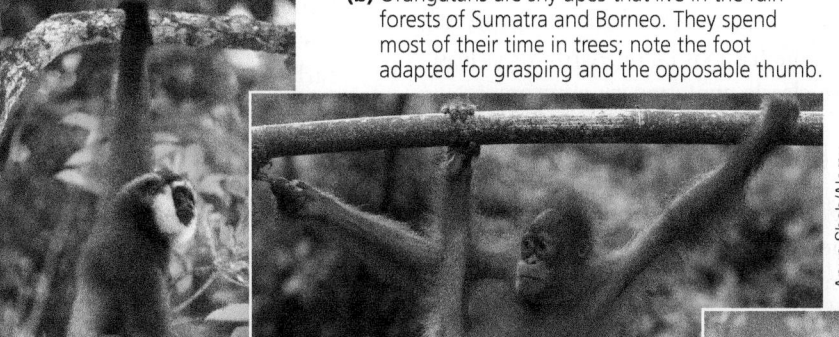

(a) Gibbons, such as this Muller's gibbon, are found only in south-eastern Asia. Their very long arms and fingers are adaptations for brachiating (swinging by the arms from branch to branch).

(b) Orangutans are shy apes that live in the rain forests of Sumatra and Borneo. They spend most of their time in trees; note the foot adapted for grasping and the opposable thumb.

(c) Gorillas are the largest apes; some males are almost 2 m tall and weigh about 200 kg. Found only in Africa, these herbivores usually live in groups of up to about 20 individuals.

(d) Chimpanzees live in tropical Africa. They feed and sleep in trees but also spend a great deal of time on the ground. Chimpanzees are intelligent, communicative, and social.

Martin Harvey/Peter Arnold/Getty Images

(e) Bonobos are in the same genus (*Pan*) as chimpanzees but are smaller. They survive today only in the African nation of Congo.

▲ Figure 34.45 **Nonhuman apes.**

among the apes; gorillas and chimpanzees are highly social. Finally, compared to other primates, apes have a larger brain in proportion to their body size, and their behaviour is more flexible. These two characteristics are especially prominent in the next group we'll consider, the hominins.

CONCEPT CHECK 34.6

1. Contrast monotremes, marsupials, and eutherians in terms of how they bear young.

2. Identify at least five derived traits of primates.

3. **MAKE CONNECTIONS** Develop a hypothesis to explain why the diversity of mammals increased in the Cenozoicera. Your explanation should consider mammalian adaptations as well as factors such as mass extinctions and continental drift (review these factors in Concept 25.4).

For suggested answers, see Appendix A.

CONCEPT 34.7

Humans are mammals that have a large brain and bipedal locomotion

In our tour of Earth's biodiversity, we come at last to our own species, *Homo sapiens*, which is about 200 000 years old. When you consider that life has existed on Earth for at least 3.5 billion years, we are clearly evolutionary newcomers.

Derived Characters of Humans

Many characters distinguish humans from other apes. Most obviously, humans stand upright and are bipedal (walk on two legs). Humans have a much larger brain and are capable of language, symbolic thought, artistic expression, and the manufacture and use of complex tools. Humans also have reduced jawbones and jaw muscles, along with a shorter digestive tract.

At the molecular level, the list of derived characters of humans is growing as scientists compare the genomes of humans and chimpanzees. Although the two genomes are 99% identical, a difference of 1% can translate into a large number of changes in a genome that contains 3 billion base pairs. Furthermore, changes in a small number of genes can have large effects. This point was highlighted by recent results showing that humans and chimpanzees differ in the expression of 19 regulatory genes. These genes turn other genes on and off and hence may account for many differences between humans and chimpanzees.

Bear in mind that such genomic differences—and whatever derived phenotypic traits they code for—separate humans from other *living* apes. But many of these new characters first emerged in our ancestors, long before our own species appeared. We will consider some of these ancestors to see how these characters originated.

The Earliest Hominins

The study of human origins is known as **paleoanthropology**. Paleoanthropologists have unearthed fossils of approximately 20 extinct species that are more closely related to humans than to chimpanzees. These species are known as **hominins** (Figure 34.46). (Although a majority of anthropologists now use the term *hominin*, its older synonym, *hominid*, continues to be used by some.) Since 1994, fossils of four hominin species dating to more than 4 million years ago have been discovered. The oldest of these hominins, *Sahelanthropus tchadensis*, lived about 6.5 million years ago.

Sahelanthropus and other early hominins shared some of the derived characters of humans. For example, they had reduced canine teeth, and some fossils suggest that they had relatively flat faces. They also show signs of having been more upright and bipedal than other apes. One clue to their upright stance can be found in the foramen magnum, the hole at the base of the skull through which the spinal cord exits. In chimpanzees, the foramen magnum is relatively far back on the skull, while in early hominins (and in humans), it is located underneath the skull. This position allows us to hold our head directly over our body, as apparently early hominins did as well. The pelvis, leg bones, and feet of the 4.4-million-year-old *Ardipithecus ramidus* also suggest that early hominins were increasingly bipedal (Figure 34.47). (We will return to the subject of bipedalism later.)

Note that the characters that distinguish humans from other living apes did not all evolve in tight unison. While early hominins were showing signs of bipedalism, their brains remained small—about 300–450 cm^3 in volume, compared with an average of 1300 cm^3 for *Homo sapiens*. The earliest hominins were also small overall. *A. ramidus*, for example, is estimated to have been about 1.2 m tall, with relatively large teeth and a jaw that projected beyond the upper part of the face. Humans, in contrast, average about 1.7 m in height and have a relatively flat face; compare your own face with that of the chimpanzees in Figure 34.45d.

It's important to avoid two common misconceptions when considering early hominins. One is to think of them either as chimpanzees or as having evolved from chimpanzees. Chimpanzees represent the tip of a separate branch of evolution, and they acquired derived characters of their own after they diverged from their common ancestor with humans.

Another misconception is to think of human evolution as a ladder leading directly from an ancestral ape to *Homo sapiens*. This error is often illustrated as a parade of fossil species that become progressively more like ourselves as they march across the page. If human evolution is a parade, it is a very disorderly one, with many groups breaking away to wander other evolutionary paths. At times, several hominin species coexisted. These species often differed in skull shape, body size, and diet

Paranthropus
robustus

*Homo
ergaster*

*Homo
neanderthalensis*

*Homo
sapiens*

*Paranthropus
boisei*

*Australopithecus
africanus*

*Kenyanthropus
platyops*

*Australopithecus
anamensis*

*Australopithecus
garhi*

Homo erectus

*Homo
habilis*

*Homo
rudolfensis*

*Australopithecus
afarensis*

Ardipithecus ramidus

Orrorin tugenensis

*Sahelanthropus
tchadensis*

Millions of years ago — 0, 0.5, 1.0, 1.5, 2.0, 2.5, 3.0, 3.5, 4.0, 4.5, 5.0, 5.5, 6.0, 6.5, 7.0

▲ **Figure 34.46 A timeline for some selected hominin species.** Most of these fossils come from sites in eastern and southern Africa. Note that, at most times in hominin history, two or more hominin species were contemporaries. Some of the species are controversial, reflecting phylogenetic debates about the interpretation of skeletal details and biogeography.

Source: Based on many photos of fossils. Some sources are O. tugenensis photo in "Early Hominid Sows Division" by Michael Balter, from *ScienceNow*, Feb. 22, 2001; A. garhi and H. neanderthalensis based on *The Human Evolution Coloring Book* by Adreienne L. Zihlman and Carla J. Simmons. HarperCollins, 2001; K. platyops based on photo in "New Hominin Genus from Eastern Africa Shows Diverse Middle Pliocene Lineages" by Meave Leakey et al., from *Nature*, March 2001, Volume 410(6827); P. boisei based on a photo by David Bill; H. ergaster based on a photo at www.museum-sinhand.com; S. tchadensis based on figure 1b from "A New Hominid from the Upper Miocene of Chad, Central Africa" by Michel Brunet et al.

David L. Brill/David L. Brill Photography

(as inferred from their teeth). Ultimately, all but one lineage—the one that gave rise to *Homo sapiens*—ended in extinction. But when the characteristics of all hominins that lived over the past 6.5 million years are considered, *H. sapiens* appears not as the end result of a straight evolutionary path, but rather as the only surviving member of a highly branched evolutionary tree.

Australopiths

The fossil record indicates that hominin diversity increased dramatically between 4 and

◀ **Figure 34.47 The skeleton of "Ardi," a 4.4-million-year-old hominin,** *Ardipithecus ramidus*, **found in Ethiopia.**

2 million years ago. Many of the hominins from this period are collectively called australopiths. Their phylogeny remains unresolved on many points, but as a group, they are almost certainly paraphyletic. The earliest member of the group, *Australopithecus anamensis*, lived 4.2–3.9 million years ago, close in time to older hominins such as *Ardipithecus ramidus*.

Australopiths got their name from the 1924 discovery in South Africa of *Australopithecus africanus* ("southern ape of Africa"), which lived between 3 and 2.4 million years ago. With the discovery of more fossils, it became clear that *A. africanus* walked fully erect (was bipedal) and had human-like hands and teeth. However, its brain was only about one-third the size of the brain of a present-day human.

In 1974, in the Afar region of Ethiopia, paleoanthropologists discovered a 3.2-million-year-old *Australopithecus* skeleton that was 40% complete. "Lucy," as the fossil was named, was short—only about 1 m tall. Lucy and similar fossils have been given the species name *Australopithecus afarensis* (for the Afar region). Fossils discovered in the early 1990s show that *A. afarensis* existed as a species for at least 1 million years.

More recently, paleontologists discovered another australopith in the Afar region of Ethiopia, named

Australopithecus deyrimeda, that is the same age as many *A. afarensis* fossils. This means that different hominin species existed in the same time and geographic area. However, *A. deyrimeda* has smaller teeth, suggesting the diet was different and may represent adaptations to different ecological niches.

At the risk of oversimplifying, we could say that *A. afarensis* had fewer of the derived characters of humans above the neck than below. Lucy's brain was the size of a softball, a size similar to that expected for a chimpanzee of Lucy's body size. *A. afarensis* skulls also have a long lower jaw. Skeletons of *A. afarensis* suggest that these hominins were capable of arboreal locomotion, with arms that were relatively long in proportion to body size (compared to the proportions in humans). However, fragments of pelvic and skull bones indicate that *A. afarensis* walked on two legs. Fossilized footprints in Laetoli, Tanzania, corroborate the skeletal evidence that hominins living at the time of *A. afarensis* were bipedal (**Figure 34.48**).

Another lineage of australopiths consisted of the "robust" australopiths. These hominins, which included species such as *Paranthropus boisei*, had sturdy skulls with powerful jaws and large teeth, adapted for grinding and chewing hard, tough foods. They contrast with the "gracile" (slender) australopiths, including *A. afarensis* and *A. africanus*, which had lighter feeding equipment adapted for softer foods. Combining evidence from the earliest hominins with the much richer fossil record of later australopiths makes it possible to formulate hypotheses about significant trends in hominin evolution. In the Scientific Skills Exercise, you'll examine one such trend: how hominin brain volume has changed over time. Let's consider two of these trends: the emergence of bipedalism and tool use.

Bipedalism

Our anthropoid ancestors of 35–30 million years ago were still tree-dwellers. But by about 10 million years ago, the Himalayan mountain range had formed, thrust up in the aftermath of the Indian plate's collision with the Eurasian plate (see Figure 25.15). The climate became drier, and the forests of what are now Africa and Asia contracted. The result was an increased area of savanna (grassland) habitat, with fewer trees. For decades, paleoanthropologists have seen a strong connection between the rise of savannas and the rise of bipedal hominins. According to one hypothesis, tree-dwelling hominins could no longer move through the canopy, so natural selection favoured adaptations that made moving over open ground more efficient. Underlying this idea is the fact that while nonhuman apes are superbly adapted for climbing trees, they are less well suited for ground travel. For example, as a chimpanzee walks, it uses four times the amount of energy used by a human.

Although elements of this hypothesis survive, the picture now appears somewhat more complex. Although all

▶ Figure 34.48 **Evidence that hominins walked upright 3.5 million years ago.**

(a) The Laetoli footprints, more than 3.5 million years old, confirm that upright posture evolved quite early in hominin history.

(b) An artist's reconstruction of *A. afarensis*, a hominin alive at the time of the Laetoli footprints.

John Reader/Science Source

John Gurche Studios

recently discovered fossils of early hominins show indications of bipedalism, none of these hominins lived in savannas. Instead, they lived in mixed habitats ranging from forests to open woodlands. Furthermore, whatever the selective pressure that led to bipedalism, hominins did not become more bipedal in a simple, linear fashion. *Ardipithecus* had skeletal elements indicating that it could switch to upright walking but also was well suited for climbing trees. Australopiths seem to have had various locomotor styles, and some species spent more time on the ground than others. Only about 1.9 million years ago did hominins begin to walk long distances on two legs. These hominins lived in more arid environments, where bipedal walking requires less energy than walking on all fours.

Tool Use

As you read earlier, the manufacture and use of complex tools is a derived behavioural character of humans. Determining the origin of tool use in hominin evolution is one of paleoanthropology's great challenges. Other apes are capable of surprisingly sophisticated tool use. Orangutans, for example, can fashion sticks into probes for retrieving insects from their nests.

Determining the Equation of a Regression Line

How Has Brain Volume Changed over Time in the Hominin Lineage? The hominin taxon includes *Homo sapiens* and about 20 extinct species that are thought to represent early relatives of humans. Researchers have found that the brain volume of the earliest hominins ranged between 300 and 450 cm³, similar to the brain volume of chimpanzees. The brain volumes of modern humans range between 1200 and 1800 cm³. In this exercise, you'll examine how mean brain volume changed over time and across various hominin species.

Shutterstock

How the Study Was Done In this table, *x* is the mean age of each hominin species, and *y* is the mean brain volume (cm³). Ages with negative values represent millions of years before the present (which has an age of 0.0).

Hominin Species	Mean age (millions of years; x)	$x_i - \bar{x}$	Mean Brain Volume (cm³; y)	$y_i - \bar{y}$	$(x_i - \bar{x})$ × $(y_i - \bar{y})$
Ardipithecus ramidus	−4.4		325		
Australopithecus afarensis	−3.4		375		
Homo habilis	−1.9		550		
Homo ergaster	−1.6		850		
Homo erectus	−1.2		1000		
Homo heidelbergensis	−0.5		1200		
Homo neanderthalensis	−0.1		1400		
Homo sapiens	0.0		1350		

Interpret the Data

How did the brain volume of hominin species change over time? In particular, is there a linear (straight-line) relationship between brain volume and time?

To find out, we'll perform a linear regression, a technique for determining the equation for the straight line that provides a "best fit" to a set of data. Recall that the equation for a straight line between two variables, *x* and *y*, is

$$y = mx + b$$

In this equation, *m* represents the slope of the line, while *b* represents the *y*-intercept (the point at which the straight line crosses the *y*-axis). When *m* < 0, the line has a negative slope, indicating that the values of *y* become *smaller* as values of *x* become *larger*. When *m* > 0, the line has a positive slope, meaning that the values of *y* become larger as values of *x* become larger. When *m* = 0, *y* has a constant value (*b*).

The correlation coefficient, *r*, can be used to calculate the values of *m* and *b* in a linear regression:

$$m = r\frac{s_y}{s_x} \quad \text{and} \quad b = \bar{y} - m\bar{x}$$

In these equations, s_x and s_y are the standard deviations of variables *x* and *y*, respectively, while $\bar{x}$ and $\bar{y}$ are the means of those two variables. (See the Scientific Skills Exercise for Chapter 32 for more information about the correlation coefficient, mean, and standard deviation.)

1. Calculate the means ($\bar{x}$ and $\bar{y}$) from data in the table. Next, fill in the ($x_i - \bar{x}$) and ($y_i - \bar{y}$) columns in the data table, and use those results to calculate the standard deviations s_x and s_y.

2. As described in the Scientific Skills Exercise for Chapter 32, the formula for a correlation coefficient is

$$r = \frac{\frac{1}{n-1}\sum(x_i - \bar{x})(y_i - \bar{y})}{s_x s_y}$$

Fill in the column in the data table for the product ($x_i - \bar{x}$) × ($y_i - \bar{y}$). Use these values and the standard deviations calculated in Question 1 to calculate the correlation coefficient *r* between the brain volume of hominin species (*y*) and the ages of those species (*x*).

3. Based on the value of *r* that you calculated in Question 2, describe in words the correlation between mean brain volume of hominin species and the mean age of the species.

4. (a) Use your calculated value of *r* to calculate the slope (*m*) and the *y*-intercept (*b*) of a regression line for this data set. (b) Graph the regression line for the mean brain volume of hominin species versus the mean age of the species. Be careful to select and label your axes correctly. (c) Plot the data from the table on the same graph that shows the regression line. Does the regression line appear to provide a reasonable fit to the data?

5. The equation for a regression line can be used to calculate the value of *y* expected for any particular value of *x*. For example, suppose that a linear regression indicated that *m* = 2 and *b* = 4. In this case, when *x* = 5, we expect that *y* = 2*x* + 4 = (2 × 5) + 4 = 14. Based on the values of *m* and *b* that you determined in Question 4, use this approach to determine the expected mean brain volume for a hominin that lived 4 million years ago (that is, *x* = −4).

6. The slope of a line can be defined as $m = \frac{y_2 - y_1}{x_2 - x_1}$, where ($x_1$, y_1) and (x_2, y_2) are the coordinates of two points on the line. As such, the slope represents the ratio of the rise of a line (how much the line rises vertically) to the run of the line (how much the line changes horizontally). Use the definition of the slope to estimate how long it took for mean brain volume to increase by 100 cm³ over the course of hominin evolution.

Data from Dean Falk, Florida State University, 2013.

Chimpanzees are even more adept, using rocks to smash open food and putting leaves on their feet to walk over thorns. It's likely that early hominins were capable of this sort of simple tool use, but finding fossils of modified sticks or leaves that were used as shoes is practically impossible.

The oldest generally accepted evidence of tool use by hominins is 2.5-million-year-old cut marks on animal bones found in Ethiopia. These marks suggest that hominins cut flesh from the bones of animals using stone tools. Interestingly, the hominins whose fossils were found near the site where the bones were discovered had a relatively small brain. If these hominins, which have been named *Australopithecus garhi*, were in fact the creators of the stone tools used on the bones, that would suggest that stone tool use originated before the evolution of large brains in hominins.

Early *Homo*

The earliest fossils that paleoanthropologists place in our genus, *Homo*, include those of the species *Homo habilis*. These fossils, ranging in age from about 2.4 to 1.6 million years, show clear signs of certain derived hominin characters above the neck. Compared to the australopiths, *H. habilis* had a shorter jaw and a larger brain volume, about 600–750 cm³. Sharp stone tools have also been found with some fossils of *H. habilis* (the name means "handy man").

Fossils from 1.9 to 1.5 million years ago mark a new stage in hominin evolution. A number of paleoanthropologists recognize these fossils as those of a distinct species, *Homo ergaster*. *Homo ergaster* had a substantially larger brain than *H. habilis* (over 900 cm³), as well as long, slender legs with hip joints well adapted for long-distance walking (**Figure 34.49**). The fingers were relatively short and straight, suggesting that *H. ergaster* did not climb trees like earlier hominins. *Homo ergaster* fossils have been discovered in far more arid environments than earlier hominins and have been associated with more sophisticated stone tools. Its smaller teeth also suggest that *H. ergaster* either ate different foods than australopiths (more meat and less plant material) or prepared some of its food before chewing, perhaps by cooking or mashing the food.

Consistent with the possible use of cooking, a 2012 study described 1-million-year-old fragments of burnt bone that were found in a cave; the researchers concluded that human ancestors were using fire by that time.

Homo ergaster marks an important shift in the relative sizes of the sexes. In primates, a size difference between males and females is a major component of sexual dimorphism (see Chapter 23). On average, male gorillas and orangutans weigh about twice as much as females of their species. In chimpanzees and bonobos, males are only about 1.35 times as heavy as females, on average. In *Australopithecus afarensis*, males were 1.5 times as heavy as females. But in early *Homo*, sexual dimorphism was significantly reduced, and this trend continues through our own species: Human males average about 1.2 times the weight of females.

The reduced sexual dimorphism may offer some clues to the social systems of extinct hominins. In extant primates, extreme sexual dimorphism is associated with intense male-male competition for multiple females. In species that undergo more pair-bonding (including our own), sexual dimorphism

Prof. Alan Walker

▲ **Figure 34.49 Fossil of *Homo ergaster*.** This 1.7-million-year-old fossil from Kenya belongs to a young *Homo ergaster* male. This individual was tall, slender, and fully bipedal, and he had a relatively large brain.

is less dramatic. In *H. ergaster*, therefore, males and females may have engaged in more pair-bonding than earlier hominins did. This shift may have been associated with long-term care of the young by both parents. Human babies depend on their parents for food and protection much longer than do the young of other apes.

Fossils now generally recognized as *H. ergaster* were originally considered early members of another species, *Homo erectus*, and some paleoanthropologists still hold this position. *Homo erectus* originated in Africa and was the first hominin to migrate out of Africa. The oldest fossils of hominins outside Africa, dating back 1.8 million years, were discovered in 2000 in the former Soviet Republic of Georgia. *Homo erectus* eventually migrated as far as the Indonesian archipelago. Fossil evidence indicates that *H. erectus* became extinct sometime after 200 000 years ago; one group may have persisted on Java until roughly 50 000 years ago.

Neanderthals

In 1856, miners discovered some mysterious human fossils in a cave in the Neander Valley in Germany. The 40 000-year-old fossils belonged to a thick-boned hominin with a prominent brow. The hominin was named *Homo neanderthalensis* and is commonly called a Neanderthal. Neanderthals were living in Europe by 350 000 years ago and later spread to the Near East, central Asia, and southern Siberia. They had a brain as large as that of present-day humans, buried their dead, and made hunting tools from stone and wood. But despite their adaptations and culture, Neanderthals apparently became extinct about 28 000 years ago.

What is the evolutionary relationship of Neanderthals to *Homo sapiens*? Genetic data indicate that the lineages leading to *H. sapiens* and to Neanderthals diverged about 400 000 years ago. This indicates that while Neanderthals and humans share a recent common ancestor, humans did not descend directly from Neanderthals (as was once thought).

Another long-standing question is whether mating occurred between the two species. Some researchers have argued that evidence of gene flow can be found in fossils that show a mixture of human and Neanderthal characteristics. Other researchers have disputed this conclusion. Sequencing ancient DNA has revolutionized our understanding of Neanderthal evolution and interactions with modern humans. Amazingly, DNA can sometimes be extracted from bone fragments that are tens-of-thousands years old and sequenced, though this has to be done very carefully to avoid contamination. Neanderthal genome sequences have been completed in 2010 and in 2014, and a comparison of the DNA sequence of the Neanderthal genome with that of modern humans demonstrates that 99.7% of the nucleotides sites in the two genomes are identical, but more significantly, also indicates a limited gene flow did occur between the two species (Figure 34.50). If you are of European or Asian descent, then about 2% of your genome is of Neanderthal origin! Adding to the intrigue, another group sequenced the DNA found in a 40 000-year-old bone found in the Denisova cave in Russia, and discovered it was not Neanderthal, but an as-yet unidentified hominin. The work indicated that there was also gene flow between Neanderthals and these "Denisovans"!

Homo sapiens

Evidence from fossils, archaeology, and DNA studies has led to a compelling hypothesis about how our own species, *Homo sapiens*, emerged and spread around the world.

Fossil evidence indicates that the ancestors of humans originated in Africa. Older species (perhaps *H. ergaster* or *H. erectus*) gave rise to later species, ultimately including *H. sapiens*. Furthermore, the oldest known fossils of our own species have been found at two different sites in Ethiopia and include specimens that are 195 000 and 160 000 years old (Figure 34.51). These early humans had less pronounced browridges than those found in *H. erectus* and Neanderthals, and they were more slender than other recent hominins.

The Ethiopian fossils support inferences about the origin of humans from molecular evidence. DNA analyses indicate that all living humans are more closely related to one another than to Neanderthals. Other studies on human DNA show that Europeans and Asians share a relatively recent common ancestor and that many African lineages branched off more basal positions on the human family tree. These findings strongly suggest that all living humans have ancestors that originated as *H. sapiens* in Africa.

▲ Figure 34.51 **A 160 000-year-old fossil of Homo sapiens.** This skull, discovered in Ethiopia in 2003, differs little from the skulls of living humans.

The oldest fossils of *H. sapiens* outside Africa are from the Middle East and date back about 115 000 years. Studies of the human Y chromosome suggest that humans spread beyond Africa in one or more waves, first into Asia and then to Europe and Australia. The date of the first arrival of humans in the New World is uncertain, although the oldest generally accepted evidence puts that date at about 15 000 years ago.

▼ Figure 34.50 | **Inquiry**

Did gene flow occur between Neanderthals and humans?

Experiment Fossils discovered in Europe have been interpreted by some researchers as showing a mixture of Neanderthal and human features, suggesting that humans may have bred with Neanderthals. To assess this idea, Richard Green, Svante Paabo, and their colleagues extracted DNA from several Neanderthal fossils and used this DNA to construct a draft sequence of the Neanderthal genome. Under the hypothesis that little or no gene flow occurred between Neanderthals and *H. sapiens* after their evolutionary lineages diverged, the Neanderthal genome should be equally similar to all human genomes, regardless of the geographic region from which the human genomes were obtained.

To test this hypothesis, the researchers compared the Neanderthal genome to the genomes of five living humans: one from southern Africa, one from western Africa, and three from regions outside of Africa (France, China, and Papua New Guinea). They used a genetic similarity index, D, equal to the percentage of Neanderthal DNA that matched one human population minus the percentage of Neanderthal DNA that matched a second human population. If little or no gene flow occurred between Neanderthals and humans, D should be close to zero for each such comparison. Values of D that are substantially greater than zero indicate that Neanderthals are more similar genetically to the first of the two comparison populations—providing evidence of gene flow between Neanderthals and members of that population.

Results Neanderthals consistently shared more genetic variants with non-Africans than with Africans. In contrast, the Neanderthal genome was equally close to the genomes of humans from each of the three different regions outside of Africa.

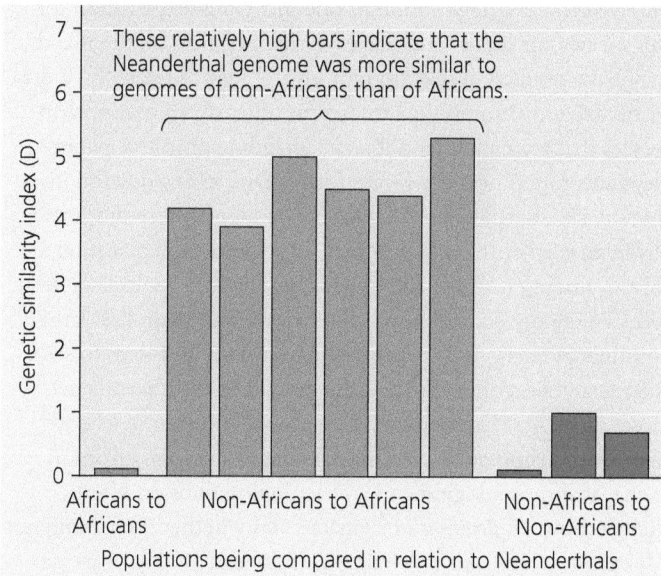

Conclusion Genomic analyses indicate that gene flow occurred between Neanderthals and human populations outside of Africa (where the ranges of the two species overlapped).

Source: Based on R. E. Green et al., A draft sequence of the Neanderthal genome, *Science* 328:710–722 (2010). © Jane B Reece.

WHAT IF? *Neanderthal fossils have been found only in Europe and the Middle East. Explain how Neanderthals could be more similar genetically to non-Africans than to Africans, and yet be equally close to humans from France, China, and Papua New Guinea.*

New findings continually update our understanding of the evolution of *H. sapiens*. For example, in 2004, researchers reported an astonishing find: skeletal remains of adult hominins dating from just 18 000 years ago and representing a previously unknown species, which they named *Homo floresiensis*. Discovered in a limestone cave on the Indonesian island of Flores, the individuals were much shorter and had a much smaller brain volume than *H. sapiens*—more similar, in fact, to an australopith. The researchers who discovered these fossils argue that the skeletons also display many derived traits, including skull thickness and proportions and teeth shape, suggesting that the species is descended from the larger *H. erectus*. Not convinced, some researchers have argued that the fossils represent small *H. sapiens* individuals with deformed, miniature brains, a condition called microcephaly.

However, a 2007 study found that the wrist bones of the Flores fossils are similar in shape to those of nonhuman apes and early hominins, but different from those of Neanderthals and *H. sapiens*. These researchers concluded that the Flores fossils represent a species whose lineage branched off before the origin of the clade that includes Neanderthals and humans. A later study comparing the foot bones of the Flores fossils with those of other hominins also indicated that *H. floresiensis* arose before *H. sapiens*; in fact, these researchers suggested that *H. floresiensis* may have descended from an as-yet-unidentified hominin that lived even earlier than *H. erectus*.

If further evidence continues to support the designation of *H. floresiensis* as a new hominin, one intriguing explanation for this species' apparent "shrinkage" is that isolation on the island may have resulted in selection for greatly reduced size. Such dramatic size reduction is well studied in other dwarf mammalian species that are endemic to islands, including primitive pygmy elephants found near the Flores fossils. One such study found that on islands, the brains of dwarf fossil hippos were proportionally even smaller than their bodies. One possible explanation for this finding is that smaller brains resulted from selection for reduced energy consumption (the mammalian brain uses large amounts of energy). Applying their results to the Flores fossils, the researchers concluded that the brain size of *H. floresiensis* closely matches that predicted for a dwarf hominin of its body size. Compelling questions that may yet be answered from the cache of anthropological and archaeological finds on Flores include how *H. floresiensis* originated and whether it encountered *H. sapiens*, which also was living in Indonesia 18 000 years ago.

The rapid expansion of our species may have been spurred by changes in human cognition as *H. sapiens* evolved in Africa. Evidence of sophisticated thought in *H. sapiens* includes a 2002 discovery in South Africa of 77 000-year-old art—geometric markings made on pieces of ochre (Figure 34.52). And in 2004, archaeologists working in southern and eastern Africa found 75 000-year-old ostrich eggs and snail shells with holes neatly drilled through them. By 17 000 years ago, humans were producing spectacular cave paintings (see Figure 56.32a).

Henshilwood, Chris

▲ Figure 34.52 **Art, a human hallmark.** The engravings on this 77 000-year-old piece of ochre, discovered in South Africa's Blombos Cave, are among the earliest signs of symbolic thought in humans.

While these developments can help us understand the spread of *H. sapiens*, it is not clear whether they played a role in the extinction of other hominins. Neanderthals, for example, also made complex tools and showed a capacity for symbolic thought. As a result, the earlier suggestion that Neanderthals were driven to extinction by competition with *H. sapiens* is now being questioned by some scientists.

Our discussion of humans brings this unit on biological diversity to an end. But this organization isn't meant to imply that life consists of a ladder leading from lowly microorganisms to lofty humanity. Biological diversity is the product of branching phylogeny, not ladderlike "progress," however we choose to measure it. The fact that there are more species of ray-finned fishes alive today than all other vertebrates combined is a clear indication that our finned relatives are not outmoded underachievers that failed to leave the water. The tetrapods—amphibians, reptiles, and mammals—are derived from one lineage of lobe-finned vertebrates. As tetrapods diversified on land, fishes continued their branching evolution in the greatest portion of the biosphere's volume. Similarly, the ubiquity of diverse prokaryotes throughout the biosphere today is a reminder of the enduring ability of these relatively simple organisms to keep up with the times through adaptive evolution. Biology exalts life's diversity, past and present.

CONCEPT CHECK 34.7

1. Identify some characters that distinguish hominins from other apes.
2. Provide an example in which different features of organisms in the hominin evolutionary lineage evolved at different rates.
3. **WHAT IF?** Some genetic studies suggest that the most recent common ancestor of *Homo sapiens* that lived outside of Africa spread from Africa about 50 000 years ago. Compare this date with the dates of fossils given in the text. Can both the genetic results and the dates ascribed to the fossils be correct? Explain.

For suggested answers, see Appendix A.

34 Chapter Review

Go to **MasteringBiology**® for Assignments, the eText, and the Study Area with Animations, Activities, Vocab Self-Quiz, and Practice Tests.

SUMMARY OF KEY CONCEPTS

Key Concept		Clade	Description
CONCEPT 34.1 **Chordates have a notochord and a dorsal, hollow nerve cord (pp. 760–763)** ? *Describe likely features of the chordate common ancestor and explain your reasoning.*	**Chordates:** notochord; dorsal, hollow nerve cord; pharyngeal slits; post-anal tail	Cephalochordata (lancelets)	Basal chordates; marine suspension feeders that exhibit four key derived characters of chordates
		Urochordata (tunicates)	Marine suspension feeders; larvae display the derived traits of chordates
		Myxini (hagfish and relatives)	Jawless marine organisms; have head that includes a skull and brain, eyes, and other sensory organs
CONCEPT 34.2 **Vertebrates are chordates that have a backbone (pp. 763–766)** ? *Identify the shared features of early fossil vertebrates.*	**Vertebrates:** *Hox* genes duplication, backbone of vertebrae	Petromyzontida (lampreys)	Jawless vertebrates; typically feed by attaching to a live fish and ingesting its blood
CONCEPT 34.3 **Gnathostomes are vertebrates that have jaws (pp. 767–771)** ? *How would the appearance of organisms with jaws have altered ecological interactions? Provide supporting evidence.*	**Gnathostomes:** hinged jaws, four sets of *Hox* genes	Chondrichthyes (sharks, rays, skates, ratfishes)	Aquatic gnathostomes; have cartilaginous skeleton, a derived trait formed by the reduction of an ancestral mineralized skeleton
		Actinopterygii (ray-finned fishes)	Aquatic gnathostomes; have bony skeleton and manoeuvrable fins supported by rays
	Osteichthyans: bony skeleton / **Lobe-fins:** muscular fins or limbs	Actinistia (coelacanths)	Ancient lineage of aquatic lobe-fins still surviving in Indian Ocean
		Dipnoi (lungfishes)	Freshwater lobe-fins with both lungs and gills; sister group of tetrapods
CONCEPT 34.4 **Tetrapods are gnathostomes that have limbs (pp. 771–775)** ? *Which features of amphibians restrict most species to living in aquatic or moist terrestrial habitats?*	**Tetrapods:** four limbs, neck, fused pelvic girdle	Amphibia (salamanders, frogs, caecilians)	Have four limbs descended from modified fins; most have moist skin that functions in gas exchange; many live both in water (as larvae) and on land (as adults)
CONCEPT 34.5 **Amniotes are tetrapods that have a terrestrially adapted egg (pp. 775–782)** ? *Explain why birds are considered reptiles.*	**Amniotes:** amniotic egg, rib cage ventilation	Reptilia (tuataras, lizards and snakes, turtles, crocodilians, birds)	One of two groups of living amniotes; have amniotic eggs and rib cage ventilation, key adaptations for life on land
CONCEPT 34.6 **Mammals are amniotes that have hair and produce milk (pp. 783–790)** ? *Describe the origin and early evolution of mammals.*		Mammalia (monotremes, marsupials, eutherians)	Evolved from synapsid ancestors; include egg-laying monotremes (echidnas, platypus); pouched marsupials (such as kangaroos, opossums); and eutherians (placental mammals, such as rodents, primates)

Humans are mammals that have a large brain and bipedal locomotion (pp. 790–796)

- Derived characters of humans include that we are bipedal and have a larger brain and reduced jaw compared with other apes.
- Hominins—humans and species that are more closely related to humans than to chimpanzees—originated in Africa at least 6 million years ago. Early hominins had a small brain but probably walked upright.
- The oldest evidence of tool use is 2.5 million years old.
- *Homo ergaster* was the first fully bipedal, large-brained hominin. *Homo erectus* was the first hominin to leave Africa.
- Neanderthals lived in Europe and the Near East from about 350 000 to 28 000 years ago.
- *Homo sapiens* originated in Africa about 195 000 years ago and began to spread to other continents about 115 000 years ago.

? *Explain why it is misleading to portray human evolution as a "ladder" leading to Homo sapiens.*

TEST YOUR UNDERSTANDING

LEVEL 1: KNOWLEDGE/COMPREHENSION

1. Vertebrates and tunicates share
   a. jaws adapted for feeding.
   b. a high degree of cephalization.
   c. an endoskeleton that includes a skull.
   d. a notochord and a dorsal, hollow nerve cord.

2. Living vertebrates can be divided into two major clades. Select the appropriate pair.
   a. chordates — tetrapods
   b. urochordates — cephalochordates
   c. cyclostomes — gnathostomes
   d. marsupials — eutherians

3. Unlike eutherians, *both* monotremes and marsupials
   a. lack nipples.
   b. have some embryonic development outside the uterus.
   c. lay eggs.
   d. are found in Australia and Africa.

4. Which clade does *not* include humans?
   a. synapsids   c. diapsids
   b. lobe-fins   d. osteichthyans

5. As hominins diverged from other primates, which of the following appeared first?
   a. reduced jawbones   c. the making of stone tools
   b. bipedal locomotion   d. an enlarged brain

6. Which of the following could be considered the most recent common ancestor of living tetrapods?
   a. a sturdy-finned, shallow-water lobe-fin whose appendages had skeletal supports similar to those of terrestrial vertebrates
   b. an armoured, jawed placoderm with two pairs of appendages
   c. an early ray-finned fish that developed bony skeletal supports in its paired fins
   d. a salamander that had legs supported by a bony skeleton but moved with the side-to-side bending typical of fishes

LEVEL 2: APPLICATION/ANALYSIS

7. EVOLUTION CONNECTION
Living members of a vertebrate lineage can be very different from early members of the lineage, and evolutionary reversals (character losses) are common. Give examples that illustrate these observations, and explain their evolutionary causes.

LEVEL 3: SYNTHESIS/EVALUATION

8. SCIENTIFIC INQUIRY
INTERPRET THE DATA As a consequence of size alone, organisms that are large tend to have larger brains than organisms that are small. However, some organisms have brains that are considerably larger than expected for an animal of their size. There are high energetic costs associated with the development and maintenance of brains that are large relative to body size.
   a. The fossil record documents trends in which brains that are large relative to body size evolved in certain lineages, including hominins. In such lineages, what can you infer about the relative magnitude of the costs and benefits of large brains?
   b. Hypothesize how natural selection might favour the evolution of large brains despite their high maintenance costs.
   c. Data for 14 bird species are listed below. Graph the data, placing deviation from expected brain size on the *x*-axis and mortality rate on the *y*-axis. What can you conclude about the relationship between brain size and mortality?

Deviation from Expected Brain Size*	-2.4	-2.1	2.0	-1.8	-1.0	0.0	0.3	0.7	1.2	1.3	2.0	2.3	3.0	3.2
Mortality Rate	0.9	0.7	0.5	0.9	0.4	0.7	0.8	0.4	0.8	0.3	0.6	0.6	0.3	0.6

Source: Based on D. Sol et al., Big-brained birds survive better in nature, *Proceedings of the Royal Society B* 274:763–769 (2007). © Jane B Reece.

*Values <0 indicate brain sizes smaller than expected; values >0 indicate sizes larger than expected.

9. WRITE ABOUT A THEME: ORGANIZATION
Early tetrapods had a sprawling gait (like that of a lizard): As the right front foot moved forward, the body twisted to the left and the left rib cage and lung were compressed; the reverse occurred with the next step. Normal breathing, in which both lungs expand equally with each breath, was hindered during walking and prevented during running. In a short essay (100–150 words), explain how the origin of organisms such as dinosaurs, whose gait allowed them to move without compressing their lungs, could have led to emergent properties in biological communities.

10. SYNTHESIZE YOUR KNOWLEDGE

Tony Heald/Nature Picture Library

This animal is a vertebrate with hair. What can you infer about its phylogeny? Use the information in the chapter to identify as many key derived characters as you can.

For selected answers, see Appendix A.

AN INTERVIEW WITH

Mark Belmonte

Mark Belmonte received his B.Sc. in Biological Sciences and a M.Sc. in Plant Biology at the University of Calgary. He then received a Ph.D. in Plant Science at the University of Manitoba, and also did a post-doctoral fellowship at the University of California Davis in Plant Molecular Biology and Genomics. He is currently an Associate Professor in the Department of Biology at the University of Manitoba.

How did you become interested in science?

I've always been interested in science—always curious about nature and asking why things are happening. I became really excited about science in high school because of a passionate science teacher, and it wasn't until my fourth year of my undergrad that I realized I wanted to become a plant biologist. I am where I am today because of incredible teachers and professors who cared about students and were excited about research!

> " I want students to know how my research is tied to the bigger picture. We're using cutting-edge genomics technologies to protect some of Canada's (and the world's) most valuable crops. "

What type of scientist are you?

I'm a plant biologist. We study everything from the molecular mechanisms guiding biological processes all the way through to how plants respond to the environment and to disease. So we go from molecules to ecosystems.

What are you currently researching?

My lab focuses on fundamental questions in plant biology using discovery-based research. We then try to flip those discoveries into something that is innovative and marketable. So, the lab is divided into two parts: the first part is looking at plant production, and more specifically seed production. We're trying to identify all of the genes required to make oilseeds like canola. To explore this question, we are taking a couple of different approaches using both cutting-edge tools like laser microdissection microscopy and next-generation RNA sequencing. We get to play with lasers and profile individual cells of the seed. We then take that information and try to figure out which genes are essential to the seed.

The second part of the lab is looking at how we can find new ways to protect some of Canada's most important crops. We are trying to harness the genetic potential of plants and trying to understand the mechanisms that drive resistance. You see, some plants are able to overcome disease whereas other plants are not. We want to identify new resistance genes. We're interested in what's happening within individual cells all the way up to the entire plant. We use laser microdissection as well as RNA sequencing to identify genes that are required for resistance. We then translate that back in to the plant—meaning that we discover the genes we think are required for resistance, driving their expression and driving resistance. We use different varieties of canola that show different degrees of resistance against devastating fungal pathogens like *Leptosphaeria maculans* (blackleg) and *Sclerotinia sclerotiorum*. These pathogens cause millions of dollars of damage to crops grown across the country and around the world. We're seeing pathogens evolving quicker than the plant, thus overcoming resistance. So there is an immediate need to identify new resistance genes.

What is the key "take-home" message for students about your research?

I always try to ask my students to think big—think about some of the problems that humanity is currently facing. Once of the biggest problems we are facing is food security and being able to access good nutritious food all while protecting what we have already. In the next 35 years, the human population will pass 9.1 billion people, and we need to find new and innovative ways to produce food to feed the future—getting that food to those who need it most.

I want students to know how my research is tied to the bigger picture. We're using cutting-edge genomics technologies to protect some of Canada's (and the world's) most valuable crops. We're driving innovation through ground-breaking discoveries! Applying research outcomes back to real-world problems is an effective way of driving biological research and sparking interest in the biological sciences.

◀ Canola field

Source: Interview with Mark Belmonte. Used with permission from Mark Belmonte.

AVTG/Getty Images

MAKE CONNECTIONS

Levels of Plant Defences Against Herbivores

Herbivory, animals eating plants, is ubiquitous in nature. Plant defences against herbivores are examples of how biological processes can be observed at multiple levels of biological organization: molecular, cellular, tissue, organ, organism, population, and community (see Figure 1.3).

Molecular-Level Defences

At the molecular level, plants produce chemical compounds that deter attackers. These compounds are typically terpenoids, phenolics, and alkaloids. Some terpenoids mimic insect hormones and cause insects to moult prematurely and die. Some examples of phenolics are tannins, which have an unpleasant taste and hinder the digestion of proteins. Their synthesis is often enhanced following attack. The opium poppy (*Papaver somniferum*) is the source of the narcotic alkaloids morphine, heroin, and codeine. These drugs accumulate in secretory cells called laticifers, which exude a milky-white latex (opium) when the plant is damaged.

Opium poppy fruit

Johan De Meester/Alamy Stock Photo

Cellular-Level Defences

Some plant cells are specialized for deterring herbivores. Trichomes on leaves and stems hinder the access of chewing insects. Laticifers and, more generally, the central vacuoles of plant cells may serve as storage depots for chemicals that deter herbivores. *Idioblasts* are specialized cells found in the leaves and stems of many species, including taro (*Colocasia esculenta*). Some idioblasts contain needle-shaped crystals of calcium oxalate called *raphides*. They penetrate the soft tissues of the tongue and palate, making it easier for an irritant produced by the plant, possibly a protease, to enter animal tissues and cause temporary swelling of the lips, mouth, and throat. The crystals act as a carrier for the irritant, enabling it to seep deeper into the herbivore's tissues. The irritant is destroyed by cooking.

Raphide crystals from taro plant

David T. Webb

Steve GSCHMEISSNER/Science Source

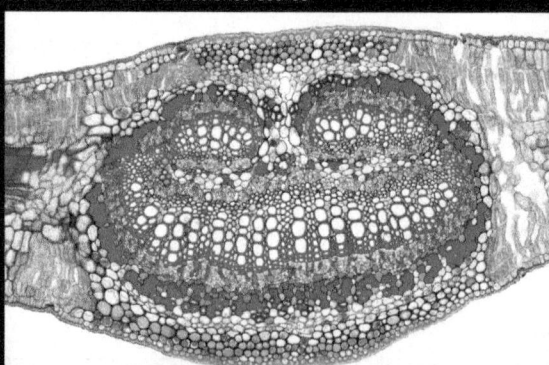

Tissue-Level Defences

Some leaves deter herbivores by being especially tough to chew as a result of extensive growth of thick, hardened sclerenchyma tissue. The bright red cells with thick cell walls seen in this cross section through the major vein of an olive leaf (*Olea europaea*) are tough sclerenchyma fibres.

Organ-Level Defences

The shapes of plant organs may deter herbivores by causing pain or making the plant appear unappealing. Spines (modified leaves) and thorns (modified stems) provide mechanical defences against herbivores. Bristles on the spines of some cacti have fearsome barbs that tear flesh during removal. The leaf of the snowflake plant (*Trevesia palmata*) looks as if it has been partially eaten, perhaps making it less attractive. Some plants mimic the presence of insect eggs on their leaves, dissuading insects from laying eggs there. For example, the leaf glands of some species of *Passiflora* (passion flowers) closely imitate the bright yellow eggs of *Heliconius* butterflies.

Lawrence E. Gilbert

Egg mimicry on leaf of passion flower plant

Giuseppe Mazza

Bristles on cactus spines

Leaf of snowflake plant

Susumu Nishinaga/Science Source

Organismal-Level Defences

Mechanical damage by herbivores can greatly alter a plant's entire physiology, deterring further attack. For example, a species of wild tobacco called *Nicotiana attenuata* changes the timing of its flowering as a result of herbivory. It normally flowers at night, emitting the chemical benzyl acetone, which attracts hawk-moths as pollinators. Unfortunately for the plant, the moths often lay eggs on the leaves as they pollinate, and the larvae are herbivores. When the plants become too larvae- infested, they stop producing the chemical and instead open their flowers at dawn, when the moths are gone. They are then pollinated by hummingbirds. Research has shown that oral secretions from the munching larvae trigger the dramatic shift in the timing of flower opening.

Hummingbird pollinating wild tobacco plant

Danny Kessler

Population-Level Defences

In some species, a coordinated behaviour at the population level helps defend against herbivores. Some plants can communicate their distress from attack by releasing molecules that warn nearby plants of the same species. For example, lima bean (*Phaseolus lunatus*) plants infested with spider mites release a cocktail of chemicals that signal "news" of the attack to noninfested lima bean plants. In response, these neighbours instigate biochemical changes that make them less susceptible to attack. Another type of population-level defence is a phenomenon in some species called masting, in which a population synchronously produces a massive amount of seeds after a long interval. Regardless of environmental conditions, an internal clock signals each plant in the population that it is time to flower. Bamboo populations, for example, grow vegetatively for decades and suddenly flower en masse, set seed, and die. As much as 80 000 kg of bamboo seeds are released per hectare, much more than the local herbivores, mostly rodents, can eat. As a result, some seeds escape the herbivores' attention, germinate, and grow.

/Mode Images/Alamy
ck Photo   Flowering bamboo plants

Community-Level Defences

Some plant species "recruit" predatory animals that help defend the plant against specific herbivores. Parasitoid wasps, for example, inject their eggs into caterpillars feeding on plants. The eggs hatch within the caterpillars, and the larvae eat through their organic containers from the inside out. The larvae then form cocoons on the surface of the host before emerging as adult wasps. The plant has an active role in this drama. A leaf damaged by caterpillars releases compounds that attract parasitoid wasps. The stimulus for this response is a combination of physical damage to the leaf caused by the feeding caterpillar and a specific compound in the caterpillar's saliva.

Custom Life Science Images/Alamy Stock Photo

Parasitoid wasp cocoons on caterpillar host

Adult wasp emerging from a cocoon

Custom Life Science Images/Alamy Stock Photo

AKE CONNECTIONS *As with plant adaptations against herbivores, her biological processes can involve multiple levels of biological ganization* (Figure 1.4). *Discuss examples of specialized photosynthetic aptations involving modifications at the molecular* (Concept 10.4), *sue* (Concept 36.4), *and organismal* (Concept 36.1) *levels.*

35

Plant Structure, Growth, and Development

KEY CONCEPTS

35.1 Plants have a hierarchical organization consisting of organs, tissues, and cells

35.2 Different meristems generate cells for primary and secondary growth

35.3 Primary growth lengthens roots and shoots

35.4 Secondary growth increases the diameter of stems and roots in woody plants

35.5 Growth, morphogenesis, and cell differentiation produce the plant body

Paul Zizka/All Canda Photos

▲ **Figure 35.1 How do these poplar trees, native across North america, respond to different environmental cues?**

A Plant's Growth Is Directed by Environmental Cues

In Chapters 29 and 30 we investigated the evolutionary processes that led to the development of plants as we see them today. Over the course of evolutionary time, factors such as atmospheric carbon dioxide levels, the availability of water, and air temperature have led to altered plant height, leaf size, and leaf patterning. Plants of different heights and leaves of different shapes have evolved because they provide competitive advantages under specific environmental conditions. As our current climate changes, higher temperatures and altered rainfall patterns will have specific and sometimes unexpected effects on the size, shape, and structural organization of plants (Figure 35.1).

In many ways, plants are able to adjust to their environment in ways that animals cannot. Animals generally have a defined body plan, which is genetically determined and fixed within a species. On the other hand, genetically identical plants grown in one location can appear very different from those grown in another place. Because a plant cannot move to a new location when environmental conditions are unfavourable, it needs to be able to perceive changes, and through a set of signals, respond and adjust its growth pattern accordingly.

A good example of what can happen as plants integrate information from different sources, such as temperature and day length, obtained from different

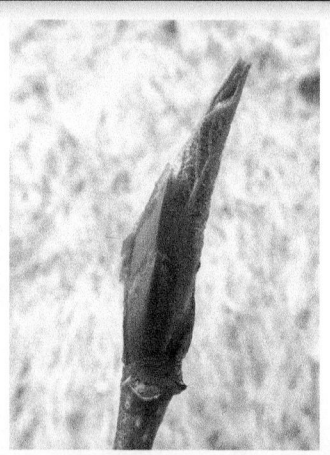

By Donna Kausen. Copyright © 2016
Donna Kausen

◀ **Poplar bud breaking dormancy**

signalling pathways, can be seen in the research of Dr. Rob Guy's lab in the Department of Forest Sciences at the University of British Columbia. While studying balsam poplar trees (*Populus balsamifera*), they found that trees taken from northern Canada and Alaska did not grow as much each year when planted in a garden in Vancouver. When planted in Vancouver, northern trees and those from more southerly locations both broke dormancy at the same time, in February. This reinforced the understanding that rising spring temperatures induce the plants to start growing. However, in late summer, when day length is decreasing, poplar trees enter a dormant state in order to prepare for winter. In northern Canada, poplars normally break dormancy in May, when day length is 20 to 22 hours. They return to dormancy in late August when the day length shortens to less than 18 hours. Interestingly, when planted in Vancouver, northern trees returned to dormancy in April, triggered by "short" day lengths of 12 to 14 hours.

This is an example of the "developmental confusion" that can occur when plants are grown outside of their normal habitat. It also raises significant concerns about the effects of global warming on plant growth. One often assumes that higher temperatures will lead to increased plant growth; however, in the case of the balsam poplar, increased temperature and a longer growing season resulted in severe stunting, even when the plants received the water and nutrients they needed.

In Chapters 35 to 37, we will examine how the structure of plants has evolved to efficiently transport water, absorb sunlight, and obtain nutrients from the soil, all in response to specific cues from its environment.

CONCEPT 35.1

Plants have a hierarchical organization consisting of organs, tissues, and cells

Plants, like most animals, have organs composed of different tissues, which in turn are composed of different cell types. A **tissue** is a group of cells, consisting of one or more cell types, that together perform a specialized function. An **organ** consists of several types of tissues that together carry out particular functions. In looking at the hierarchy of plant organs, tissues, and cells, we begin with organs because they are the most familiar and easily observed plant structures. As you learn about the hierarchy of plant structure, keep in mind how natural selection has produced plant forms that fit plant function at all levels of organization. Note also that vegetative growth—the production of leaves, stems, and roots—is only one stage in a plant's life. Most plants also undergo growth relating to sexual reproduction. In angiosperms, reproductive growth is associated with the production of flowers. Later in this chapter, we'll discuss the transition from vegetative shoot formation to reproductive shoot formation.

The Three Basic Plant Organs: Roots, Stems, and Leaves

The basic morphology of vascular plants reflects their evolutionary history as terrestrial organisms that inhabit and draw resources from two very different environments—below the ground and above the ground. They must absorb water and minerals from below the ground surface and CO_2 and light from above the ground surface. The ability to acquire these resources efficiently is traceable to the evolution of three basic organs—roots, stems, and leaves. These organs form a **root system** and a **shoot system**, the latter consisting of stems and leaves (Figure 35.2). With few exceptions, vascular plants rely completely on both systems for survival. Roots typically are not photosynthetic; they starve unless *photosynthates*, the sugars and other carbohydrates produced during photosynthesis, are imported from the shoot system. Conversely, the shoot system depends on the water and minerals that roots absorb from the soil.

In describing plant organs, we'll draw examples mainly from the two major groups of angiosperms: monocots and eudicots (see Figure 30.17).

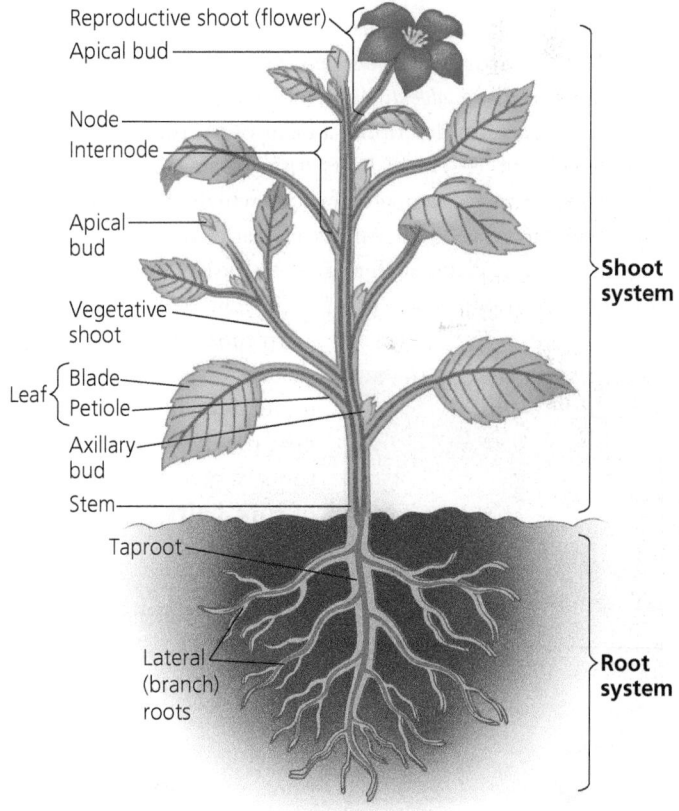

▲ Figure 35.2 **An overview of a flowering plant.** The plant body is divided into a root system and a shoot system, connected by vascular tissue (purple strands in this diagram) that is continuous throughout the plant. The plant shown is an idealized eudicot.

Roots

A **root** is an organ that anchors a vascular plant in the soil, absorbs minerals and water, and often stores carbohydrates and other reserves. The *primary root*, originating in the embryo, is the first root (and the first organ) to emerge from a germinating seed. It soon branches to form **lateral roots** (see Figure 35.2) that greatly enhance the ability of the root system to anchor the plant and to acquire resources such as water and minerals from the soil.

Tall, erect plants with large shoot masses, including most eudicots and gymnosperms, generally have a *taproot system*, consisting of one main vertical root, the **taproot**, which usually develops form the primary root and which helps prevent the plant from toppling. In taproot systems, the role of absorption is restricted largely to lateral roots. A taproot, although energetically expensive to make, allows the plant to be taller, thereby giving it access to more favourable light conditions and, in some cases, providing an advantage for pollen and seed dispersal. Taproots can also be specialized for food storage.

Small plants or those that have a trailing growth habit are particularly susceptible to grazing animals that can potentially uproot the plant and kill it. Such plants are more efficiently anchored by a *fibrous root system*, a thick mat of slender roots spreading out below the soil surface (see Figure 30.16). In plants that have fibrous root systems, including most monocots, the primary root dies early on and does not form a taproot. Instead, many small roots emerge from the stem. Such roots are said to be *adventitious* (from the Latin *adventicus*, extraneous), a term describing a plant organ that grows from an unusual source, such as roots arising from stems or leaves. Each root forms its own lateral roots, which in turn form their own lateral roots. Because this mat of roots holds the topsoil in place, plants such as grasses that have dense fibrous root systems are especially good at preventing soil erosion.

In most plants, the absorption of water and minerals occurs primarily near the tips of elongating roots, where vast numbers of **root hairs**, thin, finger-like extensions of root epidermal cells, emerge and increase the surface area of the root enormously (Figure 35.3). Most terrestrial plant root systems also form mycorrhizal associations, symbiotic interactions with soil fungi that increase a plant's ability to absorb minerals (see Figure 31.14). The roots of many plants are adapted for specialized functions (Figure 35.4).

▲ Figure 35.3 **Root hairs of a radish seedling.** Root hairs grow by the thousands just behind the tip of each root. By increasing the root's surface area, they greatly enhance the absorption of water and minerals from the soil.

Dr. Jeremy Burgess/Science Source

▼ Figure 35.4 **Evolutionary adaptations of roots.**

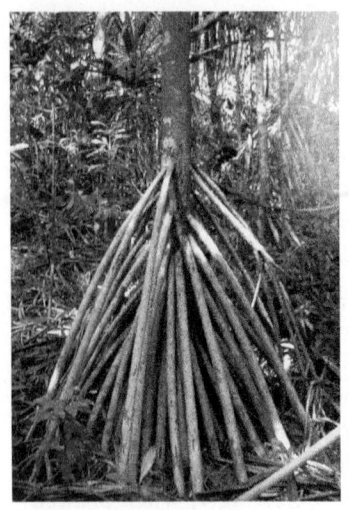

Natalie Bronstein

▲ **Prop roots.** The aerial roots of hala trees are examples of prop roots, so named because they support the tall, top-heavy trees. Hala trees grow along coastal areas in the South Pacific where the sandy soils are shallow and unstable.

Rob Walls/Alamy

▲ **Storage roots.** Many plants, such as the common beet, store food and water in their roots.

Tosporn Preede/Alamy

▲ **Green roots.** Some aerial plant species have essentially no leaves. As a result the roots perform photosynthesis. The green root tissues contain functional chloroplasts that contribute to the plant's food production.

Science Source

▲ **Pneumatophores.** Also known as air roots, pneumatophores are produced by trees such as mangroves that inhabit tidal swamps. By projecting above the water's surface, they enable the root system to obtain oxygen, which is lacking in the thick, waterlogged mud.

YinYang/Getty Images

▶ **"Strangling" aerial roots.** The seeds of this strangler fig germinate in the branches of tall trees of other species and send numerous aerial roots to the ground. These snakelike roots gradually wrap around the host tree and objects such as this Cambodian temple ruin. Eventually, the host tree dies of shading by the fig leaves.

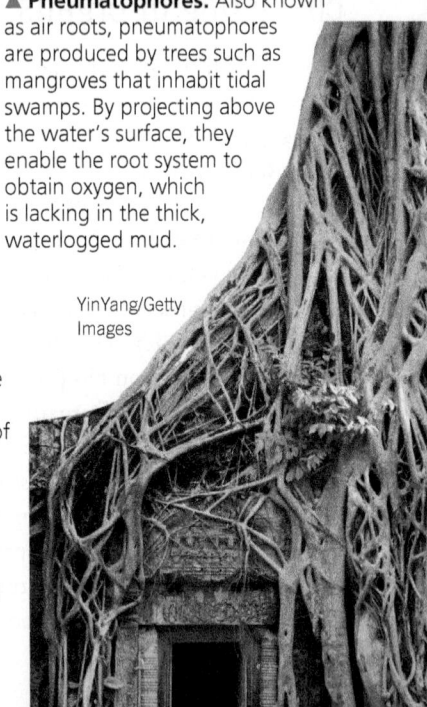

Stems

A **stem** is an organ that raises and separates leaves, exposing them to sunlight. Stems also raise reproductive structures, facilitating dispersal of pollen and fruit. Each stem consists of an alternating system of **nodes**, the points at which leaves are attached, and **internodes**, the stem segments between nodes (see Figure 35.2). In the upper angle (axil) formed by each leaf and the stem is an **axillary bud**, a structure that can form a lateral shoot, commonly called a branch. Young axillary buds typically grow very slowly: Most of the growth of a young shoot is concentrated near the shoot tip, which consists of an **apical bud**, or terminal bud, that is composed of developing leaves and a compact series of nodes and internodes.

Some plants have stems with additional functions, such as food storage and asexual reproduction. These modified stems, which include rhizomes, bulbs, stolons, and tubers, are often mistaken for roots **(Figure 35.5)**.

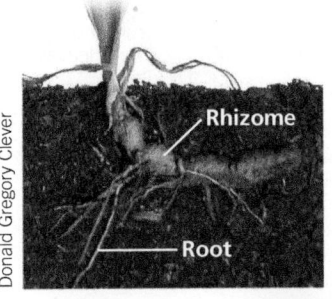

◀ **Rhizomes.** The base of this iris plant is an example of a rhizome, a horizontal shoot that grows just below the surface. Vertical shoots emerge from axillary buds on the rhizome.

Peter Anderson/Dorling Kindersley, Ltd

▶ **Stolons.** Shown here on a strawberry plant, stolons are horizontal shoots that grow along the surface. These "runners" enable a plant to reproduce asexually, as plantlets form at nodes along each runner.

◀ **Tubers.** Tubers, such as these potatoes, are enlarged ends of rhizomes or stolons specialized for storing food. The "eyes" of a potato are clusters of axillary buds that mark the nodes.

▲ Figure 35.5 **Evolutionary adaptations of stems.**

Leaves

In most vascular plants, the **leaf** is the main photosynthetic organ, although green stems and even roots can also perform photosynthesis in some plants. Leaves vary extensively in form but generally consist of a flattened **blade** and a stalk, the **petiole**, which joins the leaf to the stem at a node (see Figure 35.2). Grasses and many other monocots lack petioles; instead, the base of the leaf forms a sheath that envelops the stem.

Monocots and eudicots differ in the arrangement of **veins**, the vascular tissue of leaves. Most monocots have parallel major veins that run the length of the blade. Eudicots generally have a branched network of major veins.

In identifying angiosperms according to structure, taxonomists rely mainly on floral morphology, but they also use variations in leaf morphology, such as leaf shape, the branching pattern of veins, and the spatial arrangement of leaves. **Figure 35.6** illustrates a difference in leaf shape: simple versus compound. Compound leaves may withstand strong wind with less tearing. They may also confine some pathogens (disease-causing organisms and viruses) that invade the leaf to a single leaflet, rather than allowing them to spread to the entire leaf.

The morphological features of leaves are often products of genetic programs that are tweaked by environmental influences. Interpret the data in the Scientific Skills Exercise to explore the roles of genetics and the environment in determining leaf morphology in red maple trees.

Almost all leaves are specialized for photosynthesis. However, some species have leaves with adaptations that

▼ Figure 35.6 **Simple versus compound leaves.**

Simple leaf

A simple leaf has a single, undivided blade. Some simple leaves are deeply lobed, as shown here.

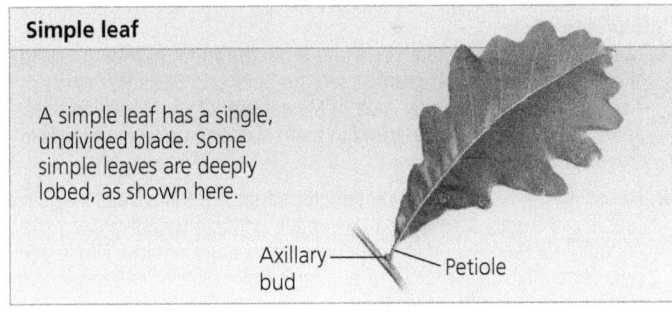

Axillary bud — Petiole

Compound leaf

In a compound leaf, the blade consists of multiple leaflets. A leaflet has no axillary bud at its base. In some plants, each leaflet is further divided into smaller leaflets.

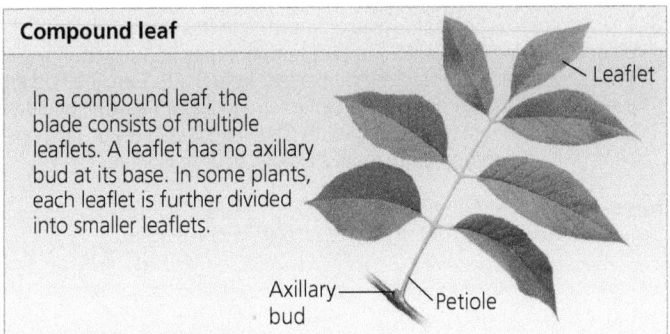

Leaflet

Axillary bud — Petiole

Using Bar Graphs to Interpret Data

Nature versus Nurture: Why Are Leaves from Northern Red Maples "Toothier" Than Leaves from Southern Red Maples? Not all leaves of the red maple (*Acer rubrum*) are the same. The "teeth" along the margins of leaves growing in northern locations differ in size and number compared with their southern counterparts. (The leaf seen here has an intermediate appearance.) Are these morphological differences due to genetic differences between northern and southern *Acer rubrum* populations, or do they arise from environmental differences between northern and southern locations, such as average temperature, that affect gene expression?

Matthew Ward/Dorling Kindersley, Ltd

How the Experiment Was Done Seeds of *Acer rubrum* were collected from four latitudinally distinct sites: Ontario, Pennsylvania, South Carolina, and Florida. The seeds from the four sites were then grown in a northern location (Rhode Island) and a southern location (Florida). After a few years of growth, leaves were harvested from the four sets of plants growing in the two locations. The average area of single teeth and the average number of teeth per leaf area were determined.

Data from the Experiment

Seed Collection Site	Average Area of a Single Tooth (cm²)		Number of Teeth per cm² of Leaf Area	
	Grown in Rhode Island	Grown in Florida	Grown in Rhode Island	Grown in Florida
Ontario (43.32°N)	0.017	0.017	3.9	3.2
Pennsylvania (42.12°N)	0.020	0.014	3.0	3.5
South Carolina (33.45°N)	0.024	0.028	2.3	1.9
Florida (30.65°N)	0.027	0.047	2.1	0.9

Interpret the Data

1. Make a bar graph for tooth size and a bar graph for number of teeth. (For information on bar graphs, see the Scientific Skills Review in Appendix E and the Study Area in MasteringBiology.) From north to south, what is the general trend in tooth size and number of teeth in leaves of *Acer rubrum*?

2. Based on the data, would you conclude that leaf tooth traits in the red maple are largely determined by genetic heritage (genotype), by the capacity for responding to environmental change within a single genotype (phenotypic plasticity), or by both? Make specific reference to the data in answering the question.

3. The "toothiness" of leaf fossils of known age has been used by paleoclimatologists to estimate past temperatures in a region. If a 10 000-year-old fossilized red maple leaf from South Carolina had an average of 4.2 teeth per square centimetre of leaf area, what could you infer about the temperature of South Carolina 10 000 years ago compared with the temperature today? Explain your reasoning.

Data from D. L. Royer et al., Phenotypic plasticity of leaf shape along a temperature gradient in *Acer rubrum*, PLoS ONE 4(10):e7653 (2009). © Jane B Reece.

▶ **Tendrils.** The tendrils by which this pea plant clings to a support are modified leaves. After it has "lassoed" a support, a tendril forms a coil that brings the plant closer to the support. Tendrils are typically modified leaves, but some tendrils are modified stems, as in grapevines.

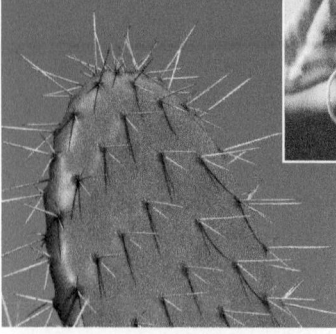

Neil Cooper/Alamy

◀ **Spines.** The spines of cacti, such as this prickly pear, are actually leaves; photosynthesis is carried out by the fleshy green stems.

Martin Ruegner/Photodisc/Getty Images

Jerome Wexler/Science Source

Gusto Production/Science Source

Storage leaves

Stem

▲ **Storage leaves.** Bulbs, such as this cut onion, have short underground stems and modified leaves that store food and water.

▲ **Reproductive leaves.** The leaves of some succulents, such as *Kalanchoë daigremontiana*, produce adventitious plantlets, which fall off the leaf and take root in the soil.

▲ Figure 35.7 **Evolutionary adaptations of leaves.**

enable them to perform additional functions, such as support, protection, storage, or reproduction (**Figure 35.7**).

Dermal, Vascular, and Ground Plant Tissues

Each plant organ—root, stem, or leaf—has dermal, vascular, and ground tissues. Each tissue type forms a **tissue system** that connects all of the plant's organs. Tissue systems are continuous throughout the plant, but their specific characteristics and their spatial relationships to one another vary in different organs (**Figure 35.8**).

The **dermal tissue system** is the plant's outer protective covering. Like our skin, it forms the first line of defence against physical damage and pathogens. In nonwoody and very young parts of woody plants, it is usually a single tissue called the **epidermis**, a layer of tightly packed cells. In leaves and most stems, the **cuticle**, a waxy coating on the epidermal surface, helps prevent water loss. In woody

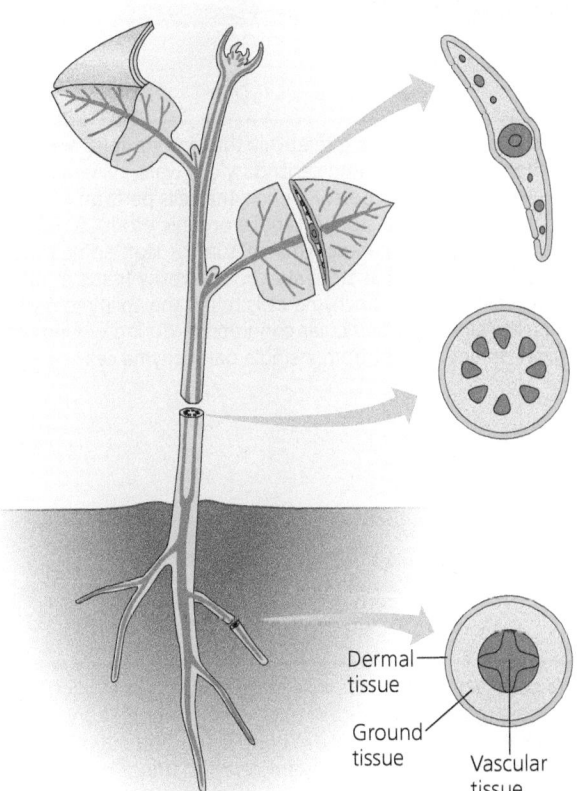

▲ Figure 35.8 **The three tissue systems.** The dermal tissue system (blue) provides a protective cover for the entire body of a plant. The vascular tissue system (purple), which transports materials between the root and shoot systems, is also continuous throughout the plant, but is arranged differently in each organ. The ground tissue system (yellow), which is responsible for most of the plant's metabolic functions, is located between the dermal tissue and the vascular tissue in each organ.

plants, protective tissues called **periderm** replace the epidermis in older regions of stems and roots. In addition to protecting the plant from water loss and disease, the epidermis has specialized characteristics in each organ. In roots, water and minerals absorbed from the soil enter through the epidermis, especially in root hairs. In shoots, specialized epidermal cells called guard cells are involved in gaseous exchange. Trichomes are another class of highly specialized epidermal cells found in shoots. In some desert species, hairlike trichomes reduce water loss and reflect excess light. Some trichomes defend against insects through shapes that hinder movement or glands that secrete sticky fluids or toxic compounds (Figure 35.9).

The **vascular tissue system** carries out long-distance transport of materials between the root and shoot systems and provides mechanical support. The two types of vascular tissues are xylem and phloem. **Xylem** conducts water and dissolved minerals upward from roots into the shoots in much the same way water moves through a drinking straw. **Phloem** transports sugars, the products of photosynthesis, from where they are made (usually the leaves) to where

300 μm

▲ Figure 35.9 **Trichome diversity on the surface of a leaf.** Three types of trichomes are found on the surface of marjoram (*Origanum majorana*). Spear-like trichomes help hinder the movement of crawling insects, while the other two types of trichomes secrete oils and other chemicals involved in defence (colourized SEM).

they are needed—usually roots and sites of growth, such as developing leaves and fruits. The vascular tissue of a root or stem is collectively called the **stele** (the Greek word for "pillar"). The arrangement of the stele varies, depending on the species and organ. In angiosperms, for example, the root stele is a solid central *vascular cylinder* of xylem and phloem, whereas the stele of stems and leaves consists of *vascular bundles*, separate strands containing xylem and phloem (see Figure 35.8). Both xylem and phloem are composed of a variety of cell types, including cells that are highly specialized for transport or support.

Tissues that are neither dermal nor vascular are part of the **ground tissue system**. Ground tissue that is internal to the vascular tissue is known as **pith**, and ground tissue that is external to the vascular tissue is called **cortex**. The ground tissue system is not just filler. It includes various cells specialized for functions such as storage, photosynthesis, and support.

Common Types of Plant Cells

In a plant, as in any multicellular organism, cells undergo cell *differentiation*; that is, they become specialized in structure and function during the course of development. Cell differentiation may involve changes both in the cytoplasm and its organelles and in the cell wall. Figure 35.10, on the next two pages, focuses on the major types of plant cells. Notice the structural adaptations in the different cells that make their specific functions possible. You may also wish to review Figure 6.8, which shows basic plant cell structure.

CONCEPT CHECK 35.1

1. How does the vascular tissue system enable leaves and roots to function together in supporting growth and development of the whole plant?

2. **WHAT IF?** If humans were photoautotrophs, making food by capturing light energy for photosynthesis, how might our anatomy be different?

3. **MAKE CONNECTIONS** Explain how central vacuoles and cellulose cell walls contribute to plant growth (see Chapter 6).

For suggested answers, see Appendix A.

Exploring Examples of Differentiated Plant Cells

Parenchyma Cells

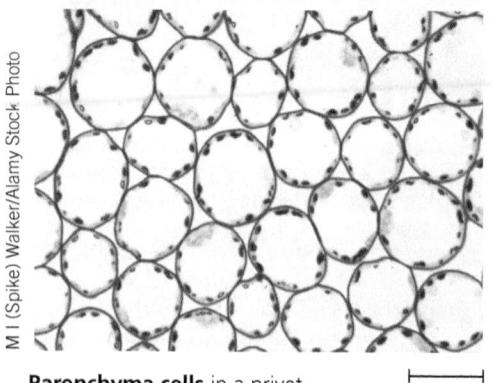

M I (Spike) Walker/Alamy Stock Photo

Mature **parenchyma cells** have primary walls that are relatively thin and flexible, and most lack secondary walls. (See Figure 6.27 to review primary and secondary cell walls.) When mature, parenchyma cells generally have a large central vacuole. Parenchyma cells perform most of the metabolic functions of the plant, synthesizing and storing various organic products. For example, photosynthesis occurs within the chloroplasts of parenchyma cells in the leaf. Some parenchyma cells in stems and roots have colourless plastids that store starch. The fleshy tissue of many fruits is composed mainly of parenchyma cells. Most parenchyma cells retain the ability to divide and differentiate into other types of plant cells under particular conditions—during wound repair, for example. It is even possible to grow an entire plant from a single parenchyma cell.

Parenchyma cells in a privet (*Ligustrum*) leaf (LM) 25 μm

Collenchyma Cells

Clouds Hill Imaging/Last Refuge Limited

Grouped in strands, **collenchyma cells** (seen here in cross section) help support young parts of the plant shoot. Collenchyma cells are generally elongated cells that have thicker primary walls than parenchyma cells, though the walls are unevenly thickened. Young stems and petioles often have strands of collenchyma cells just below their epidermis (for example, the "strings" of a celery stalk, which is a petiole). Collenchyma cells provide flexible support without restraining growth. At maturity, these cells are living and flexible, elongating with the stems and leaves they support.

Collenchyma cells (in *Helianthus* stem) (LM) 5 μm

Sclerenchyma Cells

Graham Kent/Last Refuge Limited

5 μm

Sclereid cells in pear (LM)

25 μm

Cell wall

Graham Kent/Last Refuge Limited

Fibre cells (cross section from ash tree) (LM)

Sclerenchyma cells also function as supporting elements in the plant, but are much more rigid than collenchyma cells. The secondary walls of sclerenchyma cells are thick and contain large amounts of lignin. This relatively indigestible strengthening polymer accounts for more than a quarter of the dry mass of wood. Lignin is present in all vascular plants, but not in bryophytes. Mature sclerenchyma cells cannot elongate, and they occur in regions of the plant that have stopped growing in length. Sclerenchyma cells are so specialized for support that many are dead at functional maturity, but they produce secondary walls before the protoplast (the living part of the cell) dies. The rigid walls remain as a "skeleton" that supports the plant, in some cases for hundreds of years.

Two types of sclerenchyma cells, known as **sclereids** and **fibres**, are specialized entirely for support and strengthening. Sclereids, which are boxier than fibres and irregular in shape, have very thick, lignified secondary walls. Sclereids impart the hardness to nutshells and seed coats and the gritty texture to pear fruits. Fibres, which are usually grouped in strands, are long, slender, and tapered. Some are used commercially, such as hemp fibres for making rope and flax fibres for weaving into linen.

Water-Conducting Cells of the Xylem

The two types of water-conducting cells, **tracheids** and **vessel elements**, are tubular, elongated cells that are dead at functional maturity. Tracheids are in the xylem of nearly all vascular plants. In addition to tracheids, most angiosperms, as well as a few gymnosperms and a few seedless vascular plants, have vessel elements. When the living cellular contents of a tracheid or vessel element disintegrate, the cell's thickened walls remain behind, forming a nonliving conduit through which water can flow. The secondary walls of tracheids and vessel elements are often interrupted by pits, thinner regions where only primary walls are present (see Figure 6.27 to review primary and secondary walls). Water can migrate laterally between neighbouring cells through pits.

Tracheids are long, thin cells with tapered ends. Water moves from cell to cell mainly through the pits, where it does not have to cross thick secondary walls.

Vessel elements are generally wider, shorter, thinner walled, and less tapered than the tracheids. They are aligned end to end, forming long micro-pipes known as **vessels**. The end walls of vessel elements have perforation plates that enable water to flow freely through the vessels.

The secondary walls of tracheids and vessel elements are hardened with lignin. This hardening prevents collapse under the tensions of water transport and also provides support.

Vessel   Tracheids   100 µm

N.C Brown Center for Ultrastructure Studies

Tracheids and vessels
(colourized SEM)

Pits

Perforation plate

Vessel element

Vessel elements, with perforated end walls

Tracheids

Sugar-Conducting Cells of the Phloem

Unlike the water-conducting cells of the xylem, the sugar-conducting cells of the phloem are alive at functional maturity. In seedless vascular plants and gymnosperms, sugars and other organic nutrients are transported through long, narrow cells called sieve cells. In the phloem of angiosperms, these nutrients are transported through sieve tubes, which consist of chains of cells called **sieve-tube elements**, or sieve-tube members.

Though alive, sieve-tube elements lack a nucleus, ribosomes, a distinct vacuole, and cytoskeletal elements. This reduction in cell contents enables nutrients to pass more easily through the cell. The end walls between sieve-tube elements, called **sieve plates**, have pores that facilitate the flow of fluid from cell to cell along the sieve tube. Alongside each sieve-tube element is a nonconducting cell called a **companion cell**, which is connected to the sieve-tube element by numerous channels called plasmodesmata (see Figure 6.27). The nucleus and ribosomes of the companion cell serve not only that cell itself but also the adjacent sieve-tube element. In some plants, the companion cells in leaves also help load sugars into the sieve-tube elements, which then transport the sugars to other parts of the plant.

3 µm

Brian Gunning

Sieve-tube element (left) and companion cell: cross section (TEM)

Sieve-tube elements: longitudinal view (LM)

Sieve plate

Companion cells

Sieve-tube elements

Plasmodesma

Sieve plate

Nucleus of companion cell

Sieve-tube elements: longitudinal view

30 µm

15 µm

Professor Ray F. Evert

Pearson Education

Sieve plate with pores (LM)

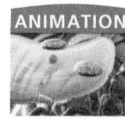

ANIMATION

BioFlix Visit the Study Area in **MasteringBiology** for the BioFlix® 3-D Animation called Tour of a Plant Cell.

CONCEPT 35.2

Different meristems generate cells for primary and secondary growth

How do plant organs develop? A major difference between plants and most animals is that plant growth is not limited to an embryonic or juvenile period. Instead, growth occurs throughout the plant's life, a process known as **indeterminate growth**. Plants can keep growing because they have perpetually dividing, unspecialized tissues called **meristems** that divide when conditions permit, leading to new cells that elongate and become specialized. Except for dormant periods, most plants grow continuously. In contrast, most animals and some plant organs—such as leaves, thorns, and flowers—undergo **determinate growth**; that is, they stop growing after reaching a certain size.

There are two main types of meristems: apical meristems and lateral meristems (**Figure 35.11**). **Apical meristems**, located at the tips of roots and shoots and in axillary buds of shoots, provide additional cells that enable growth in length, a process known as **primary growth**. Primary growth allows roots to extend throughout the soil and shoots to increase their exposure to light. In herbaceous (nonwoody) plants, primary growth produces all, or almost all, of the plant body. Woody plants, however, also grow in diameter in the parts of stems and roots that no longer grow in length. This growth in thickness, known as **secondary growth**, is caused by **lateral meristems** called the vascular cambium and cork cambium. These cylinders of dividing cells extend along the length of roots and stems. The **vascular cambium** adds layers of vascular tissue called secondary xylem (wood) and secondary phloem. The **cork cambium** replaces the epidermis with the thicker, tougher periderm.

The cells within meristems divide relatively frequently, generating additional cells. Some new cells remain in the meristem and produce more cells, while others differentiate and are incorporated into tissues and organs of the growing plant. Cells that remain as sources of new cells have traditionally been called *initials* but are increasingly being called *stem cells* to correspond to animal stem cells that also perpetually divide and remain undifferentiated. The new cells displaced from the meristem, called *derivatives*, divide until the cells they produce become specialized in mature tissues.

The relationship between primary and secondary growth is clearly seen in the winter twig of a deciduous tree. At the shoot tip is the dormant apical bud, enclosed by scales that protect its apical meristem (**Figure 35.12**). In spring, the bud sheds its scales and begins a new spurt of primary growth, producing a series of nodes and internodes. Along each growth segment, nodes are marked by scars that were left when leaves fell. Above each leaf scar is an axillary bud or a branch formed by an axillary bud. Farther down the twig are bud scars from the whorls of scales that enclosed the apical bud during the previous winter. During each growing season, primary growth extends the shoots, and secondary growth thickens the parts that formed in previous years.

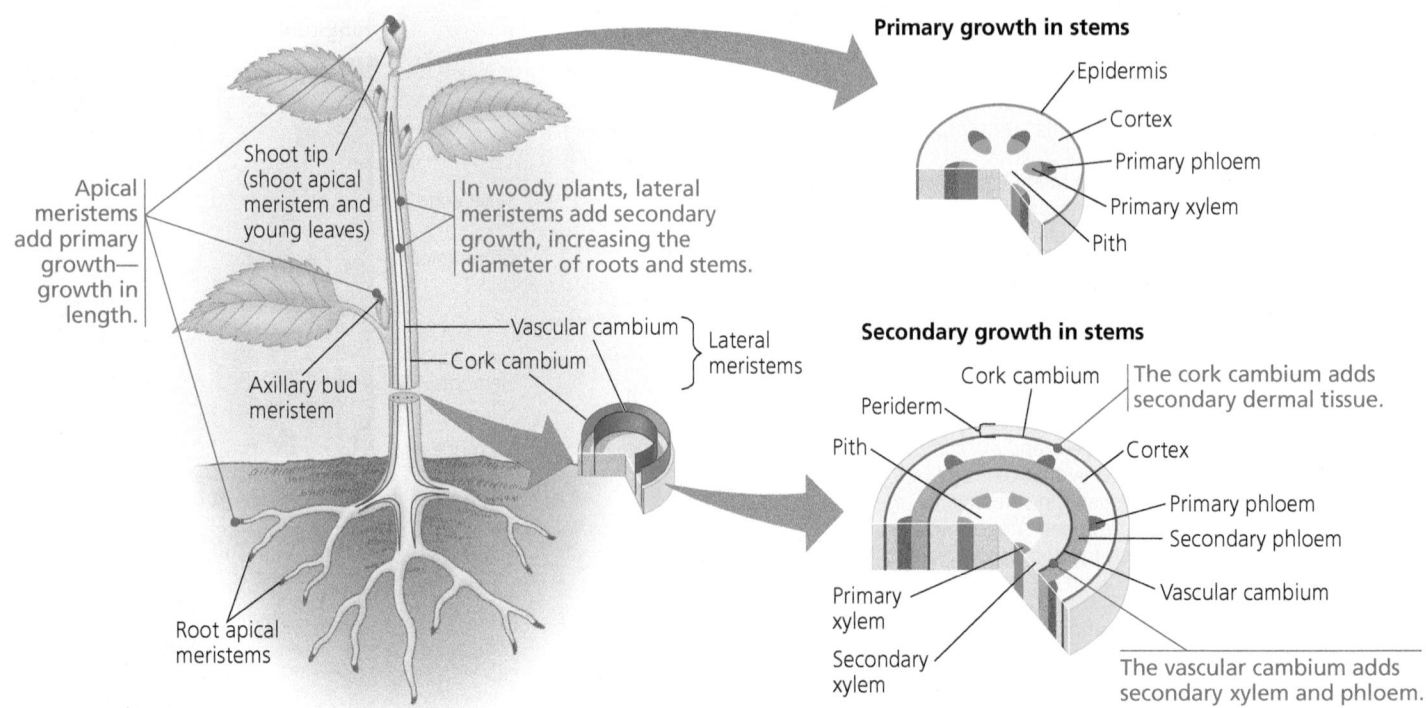

▲ Figure 35.11 **An overview of primary and secondary growth.**

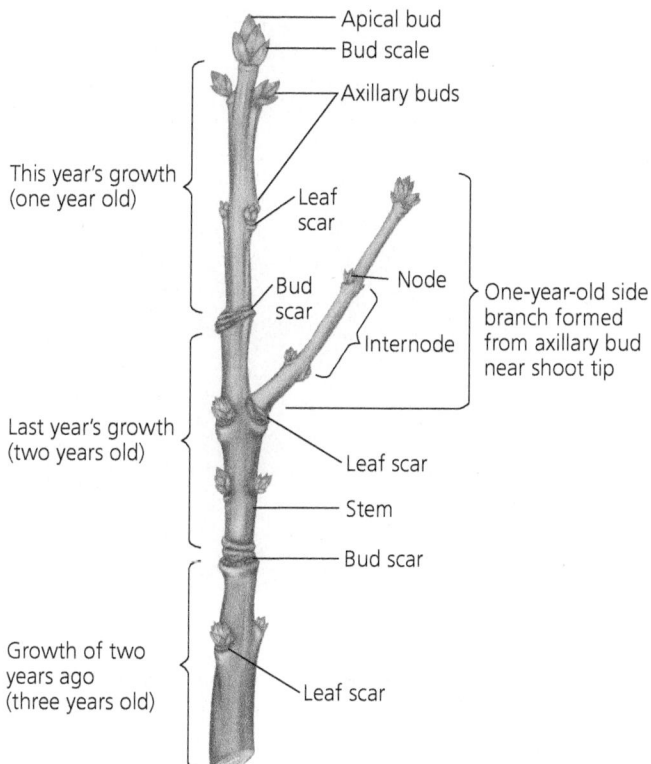

▲ Figure 35.12 **Three years' growth in a winter twig.**

Labels on figure: Apical bud; Bud scale; Axillary buds; This year's growth (one year old); Leaf scar; Bud scar; Node; Internode; One-year-old side branch formed from axillary bud near shoot tip; Last year's growth (two years old); Leaf scar; Stem; Bud scar; Growth of two years ago (three years old); Leaf scar

Although plants grow throughout their lives, they do die, of course. Based on the length of their life cycle, flowering plants can be categorized as annuals, biennials, or perennials. *Annuals* complete their life cycle—from germination to flowering to seed production to death—in a single year or less. Many wildflowers are annuals, as are most staple food crops, including legumes and cereal grains such as wheat and rice. *Biennials*, such as turnips, generally require two growing seasons to complete their life cycle, flowering and fruiting only in their second year. *Perennials* live many years and include trees, shrubs, and some grasses. Some buffalo grass of the North American plains is thought to have been growing for 10 000 years from seeds that sprouted at the close of the last ice age.

CONCEPT CHECK 35.2

1. Would primary and secondary growth ever occur simultaneously in the same plant?

2. Roots and stems grow indeterminately, but leaves do not. How might this benefit the plant?

3. **WHAT IF?** Suppose a gardener uproots some carrots after one season and sees they are too small. Carrots are biennials, so the gardener leaves the remaining plants in the ground, thinking their roots will grow larger during their second year. Is this a good idea? Explain.

For suggested answers, see Appendix A.

Primary growth lengthens roots and shoots

As you have learned, primary growth arises directly from cells produced by apical meristems. In herbaceous plants, the entire plant consists of primary growth, whereas in woody plants, only the nonwoody, more recently formed parts of the plant are primary growth. Although the elongation of both roots and shoots arises from cells derived from apical meristems, the primary growth of roots and primary growth of shoots differ in many ways.

Primary Growth of Roots

The tip of a root is covered by a thimble-like **root cap**, which protects the delicate apical meristem as the root pushes through the abrasive soil. The root cap also secretes a polysaccharide slime that lubricates the soil around the tip of the root. Growth occurs just behind the tip in three overlapping zones of cells at successive stages of primary growth. These are the zones of cell division, elongation, and differentiation (Figure 35.13).

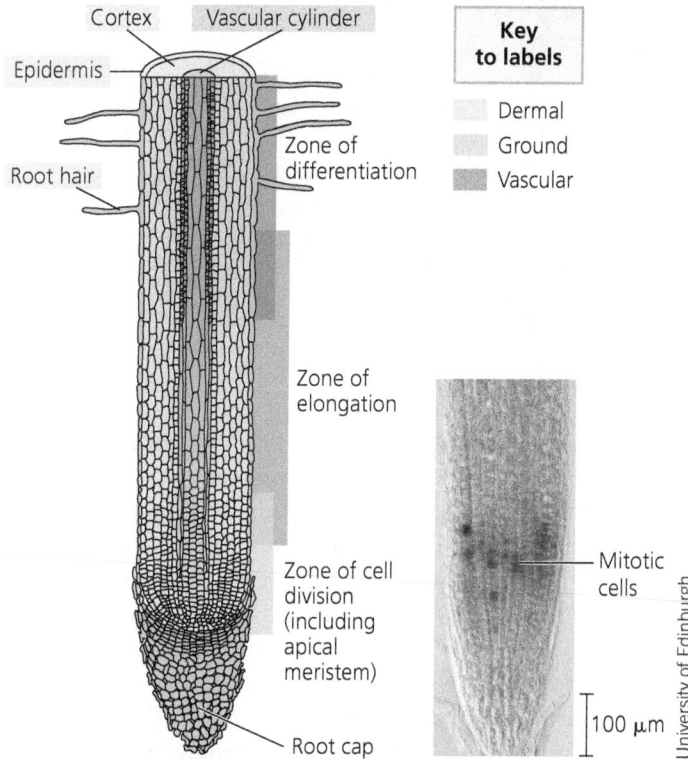

Labels on figure: Cortex; Vascular cylinder; Epidermis; Root hair; Key to labels — Dermal, Ground, Vascular; Zone of differentiation; Zone of elongation; Zone of cell division (including apical meristem); Root cap; Mitotic cells; 100 μm; University of Edinburgh

▲ Figure 35.13 **Primary growth of a root.** The diagram depicts the anatomical features of the tip of a typical eudicot root. The apical meristem produces all the cells of the root and the root cap. Most lengthening of the root occurs in the zone of elongation. In the micrograph, cells undergoing mitosis in the apical meristem are revealed by staining for cyclin, a protein that plays an important role in cell division (LM).

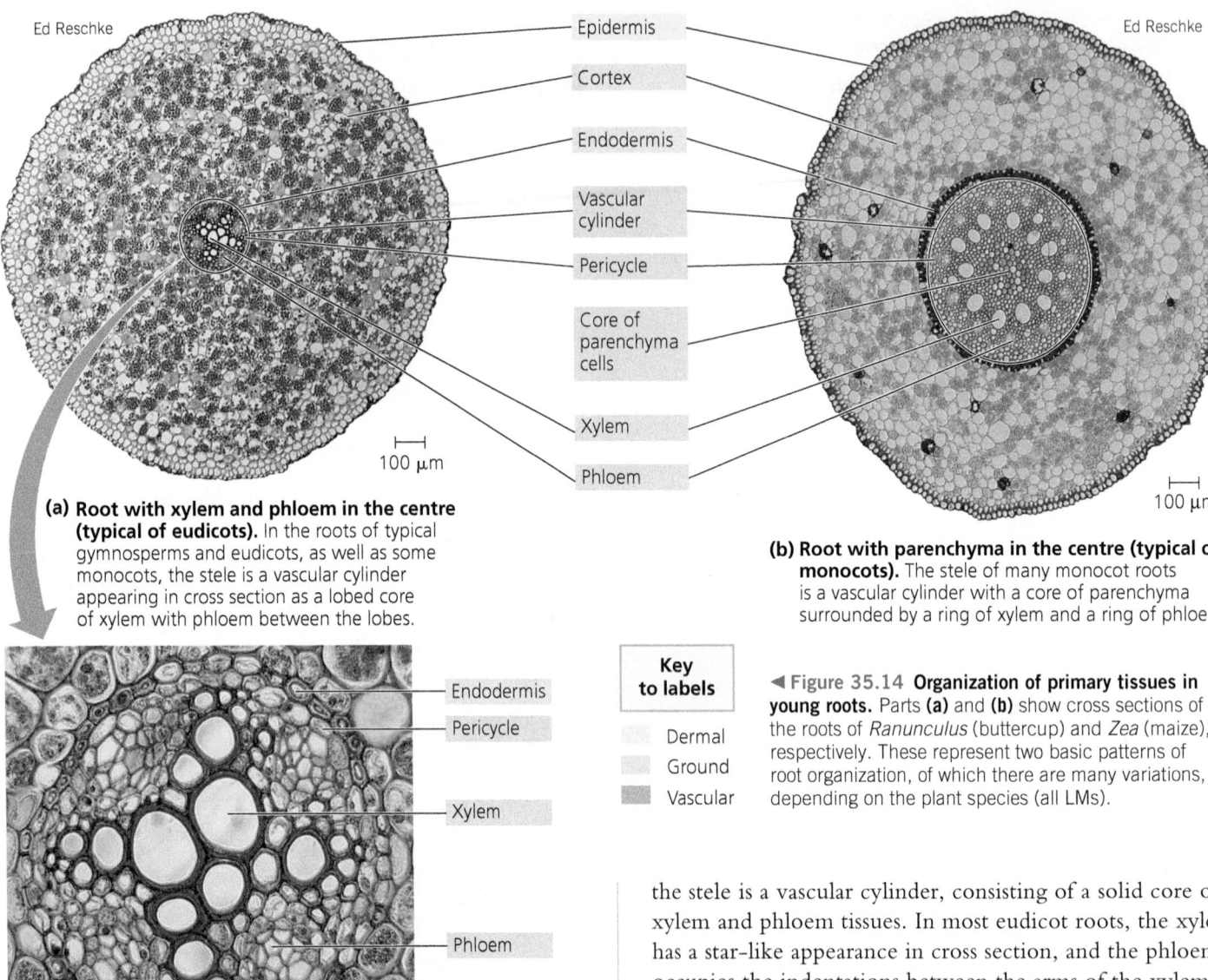

Ed Reschke

Epidermis

Cortex

Endodermis

Vascular cylinder

Pericycle

Core of parenchyma cells

Xylem

Phloem

100 μm

(a) Root with xylem and phloem in the centre (typical of eudicots). In the roots of typical gymnosperms and eudicots, as well as some monocots, the stele is a vascular cylinder appearing in cross section as a lobed core of xylem with phloem between the lobes.

Ed Reschke

100 μm

(b) Root with parenchyma in the centre (typical of monocots). The stele of many monocot roots is a vascular cylinder with a core of parenchyma surrounded by a ring of xylem and a ring of phloem.

Endodermis

Pericycle

Xylem

Phloem

Natalie Bronstein

70 μm

Key to labels

Dermal

Ground

Vascular

◀ **Figure 35.14 Organization of primary tissues in young roots.** Parts **(a)** and **(b)** show cross sections of the roots of *Ranunculus* (buttercup) and *Zea* (maize), respectively. These represent two basic patterns of root organization, of which there are many variations, depending on the plant species (all LMs).

The *zone of cell division* includes the root apical meristem and its derivatives. New root cells are produced in this region, including cells of the root cap. Typically, a few millimetres behind the tip of the root is the *zone of elongation*, where most of the growth occurs as root cells elongate—sometimes to more than 10 times their original length. Cell elongation in this zone pushes the tip farther into the soil. Meanwhile, the root apical meristem keeps adding cells to the younger end of the zone of elongation. Even before the root cells finish lengthening, many begin specializing in structure and function. In the *zone of differentiation*, or zone of maturation, cells complete their differentiation and become distinct cell types.

The primary growth of a root produces its epidermis, ground tissue, and vascular tissue. In angiosperm roots,

the stele is a vascular cylinder, consisting of a solid core of xylem and phloem tissues. In most eudicot roots, the xylem has a star-like appearance in cross section, and the phloem occupies the indentations between the arms of the xylem "star" **(Figure 35.14a)**. In many monocot roots, the vascular tissue consists of a central core of unspecialized parenchyma cells surrounded by a ring of alternating xylem and phloem tissues **(Figure 35.14b)**.

The ground tissue of roots, consisting mostly of parenchyma cells, fills the cortex, the region between the vascular cylinder and epidermis. In addition to storing carbohydrates, cortical cells transport water and salts from the root hairs to the centre of the root. The cortex, because of its large intercellular spaces, also allows for the extracellular diffusion of water, minerals, and oxygen from the root hairs inward. The innermost layer of the cortex is called the **endodermis**, a cylinder one cell thick that forms the boundary with the vascular cylinder. The endodermis is a selective barrier that regulates passage of substances from the soil into the vascular cylinder (see Figure 36.8).

Lateral roots arise from the **pericycle**, the outermost cell layer in the vascular cylinder, which is adjacent to and just inside the endodermis (see Figure 35.14). A lateral root

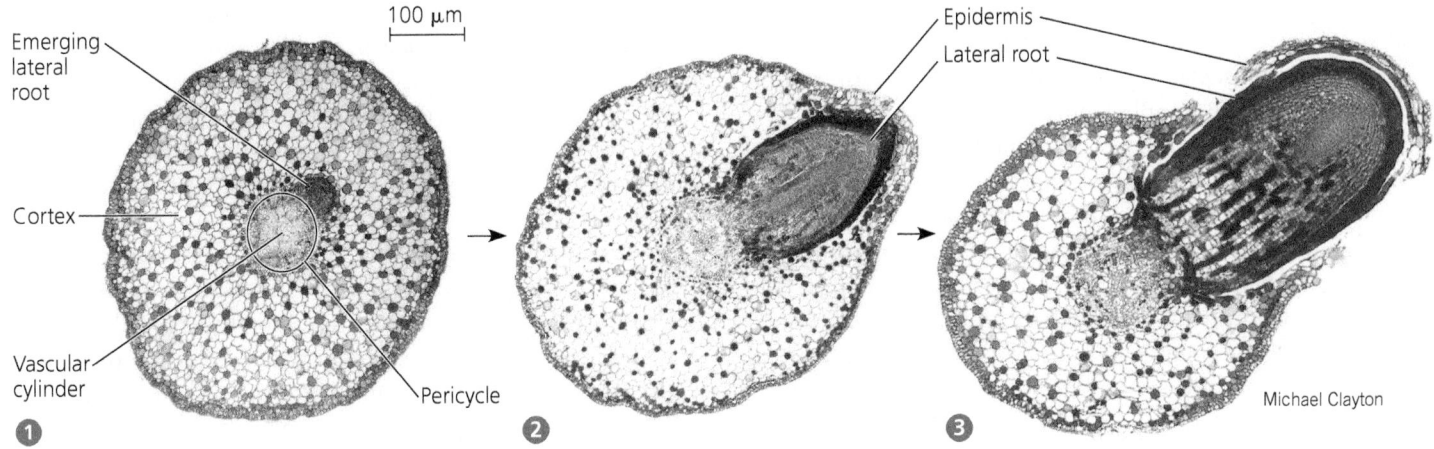

▲ **Figure 35.15 The formation of a lateral root.** A lateral root originates in the pericycle, the outermost layer of the vascular cylinder of a root, and grows out through the cortex and epidermis. In this series of light micrographs, the view of the original root is a cross section, while the view of the lateral root is a longitudinal section.

pushes through the cortex and epidermis until it emerges from the established root (**Figure 35.15**).

Primary Growth of Shoots

A shoot apical meristem is a dome-shaped mass of dividing cells at the shoot tip (**Figure 35.16**). Leaves develop from **leaf primordia** (singular, *primordium*), projections shaped like a cow's horns that emerge along the sides of the apical meristem. Within a bud, young leaves are spaced close together because the internodes are very short. Shoot elongation is due to the lengthening of internode cells below the shoot tip.

Branching, which is also part of primary growth, arises from the activation of axillary buds, each of which has its

▲ **Figure 35.16 The shoot tip.** Leaf primordia arise from the flanks of the dome of the apical meristem. This is a longitudinal section of the shoot tip of *Coleus* (LM).

own shoot apical meristem. Because of chemical communication by plant hormones, the closer an axillary bud is to an active apical bud, the more inhibited it is, a phenomenon called **apical dominance**. (The specific hormonal changes underlying apical dominance are discussed in Chapter 39.) If an animal eats the end of the shoot or if shading results in the light being more intense on the side of the shoot, the chemical communication underlying apical dominance is disrupted. As a result, the axillary buds break dormancy and start to grow. Released from dormancy, an axillary bud eventually gives rise to a lateral shoot, complete with its own apical bud, leaves, and axillary buds. When gardeners prune shrubs and pinch back houseplants, they are reducing the number of apical buds a plant has, thereby allowing branches to elongate and giving the plants a fuller, bushier appearance.

In some monocots, particularly grasses, meristematic activity occurs at the bases of stems and leaves. These areas, called *intercalary meristems*, allow damaged leaves to rapidly regrow, which accounts for the ability of lawns to grow following mowing. The ability of grasses to regrow leaves by intercalary meristems enables the plant to recover more effectively from damage incurred from grazing herbivores.

Tissue Organization of Stems

The epidermis covers stems as part of the continuous dermal tissue system. Vascular tissue runs the length of a stem in vascular bundles. Unlike lateral roots, which arise from vascular tissue deep within a root and disrupt the vascular cylinder, cortex, and epidermis as they emerge (see Figure 35.15), lateral shoots develop from axillary bud meristems on the stem's surface and disrupt no other tissues (see Figure 35.16). The vascular bundles of the stem converge with the root's vascular cylinder in a zone of transition located near the soil surface.

In most eudicot species, the vascular tissue consists of vascular bundles arranged in a ring (Figure 35.17a). The xylem in each vascular bundle is adjacent to the pith, and the phloem in each bundle is adjacent to the cortex. In most monocot stems, the vascular bundles are scattered throughout the ground tissue rather than forming a ring (Figure 35.17b). In the stems of both monocots and eudicots, the ground tissue consists mostly of parenchyma cells. However, collenchyma cells just beneath the epidermis strengthen many stems. Sclerenchyma cells, especially fibre cells, also provide support in those parts of the stems that are no longer elongating.

Tissue Organization of Leaves

Figure 35.18 provides an overview of leaf structure. The epidermis is interrupted by pores called **stomata** (singular, *stoma*), which allow exchange of CO_2 and O_2 between the surrounding air and the photosynthetic cells inside the leaf. In addition to regulating CO_2 uptake for photosynthesis, stomata are major avenues for the evaporative loss of water. The term *stoma* can refer to the stomatal pore or to the entire stomatal complex consisting of a pore flanked by two **guard cells**, which regulate the opening and closing of the pore. We'll discuss stomata in detail in Chapter 36.

The ground tissue of a leaf, a region called the **mesophyll** (from the Greek *mesos*, middle, and *phyll*, leaf), is sandwiched between the upper and lower epidermal layers. Mesophyll consists mainly of parenchyma cells specialized for photosynthesis. The mesophylls of many eudicots have two distinct layers: palisade mesophyll and spongy mesophyll. *Palisade mesophyll* consists of one or more layers of elongated parenchyma cells on the upper part of the leaf. *Spongy mesophyll* is below the palisade mesophyll. These parenchyma cells are more loosely arranged, with a labyrinth of air spaces through which CO_2 and oxygen circulate around the cells and up to the palisade region. The air spaces are particularly large in the vicinity of stomata, where CO_2 is taken up from the outside air and O_2 is released.

The vascular tissue of each leaf is continuous with the vascular tissue of the stem. Veins (vascular bundles of the leaf) subdivide repeatedly and branch throughout the mesophyll. This network brings xylem and phloem into close contact with the photosynthetic tissue, which obtains water and minerals from the xylem and loads its sugars and other organic products into the phloem for transport to other parts of the plant. The vascular structure also functions as a framework that reinforces the shape of the leaf. Each vein is enclosed by a protective *bundle sheath*, consisting of one or more layers of cells, usually parenchyma cells. Bundle sheath cells are particularly prominent in leaves of plant species that undergo C_4 photosynthesis (see Chapter 10).

Phloem   Xylem

Sclerenchyma (fibre cells)

Ground tissue connecting pith to cortex

Ed Reschke

Pith

Epidermis

Vascular bundle

Cortex

1 mm

Key to labels

Dermal

Ground

Vascular

Ground tissue

Ed Reschke

Epidermis

Vascular bundles

1 mm

(a) Cross section of stem with vascular bundles forming a ring (typical of eudicots). Ground tissue toward the inside is called pith, and ground tissue toward the outside is called cortex (LM).

(b) Cross section of stem with scattered vascular bundles (typical of monocots). In such an arrangement, ground tissue is not partitioned into pith and cortex (LM).

▲ Figure 35.17 **Organization of primary tissues in young stems.**

? *Why aren't the terms* pith *and* cortex *used to describe the ground tissue of monocot stems?*

Key to labels

- Dermal
- Ground
- Vascular

Cuticle

Sclerenchyma fibres

Stoma

Bundle sheath cell

Xylem

Phloem

Vein

Guard cells

Cuticle

(a) Cutaway drawing of leaf tissues

Guard cells

Stomatal pore

Epidermal cell

50 μm

Ed Reschke

(b) Surface view of a spiderwort (*Tradescantia*) leaf (LM)

Upper epidermis

Palisade mesophyll

Spongy mesophyll

Lower epidermis

100 μm

Vein   Air spaces   Guard cells

Ed Reschke

(c) Cross section of a lilac (*Syringa*) leaf (LM)

▲ Figure 35.18 **Leaf anatomy.**

CONCEPT CHECK 35.3

1. Contrast primary growth in roots and shoots.

2. **WHAT IF?** If a plant species has vertically oriented leaves, would you expect its mesophyll to be divided into spongy and palisade layers? Explain.

3. **MAKE CONNECTIONS** How are root hairs and microvilli analogous structures? (See Figure 6.8 and the discussion of analogy on p. 586 of Concept 26.2.)

For suggested answers, see Appendix A.

CONCEPT 35.4

Secondary growth increases the diameter of stems and roots in woody plants

Many land plants display secondary growth, the growth in thickness produced by lateral meristems. The advent of secondary growth during plant evolution allowed the production of novel plant forms ranging from massive forest trees to woody vines. All gymnosperm species and many eudicot species undergo secondary growth, but it is unusual in monocots. It occurs in stems and roots of woody plants, but rarely in leaves. Secondary growth consists of the tissues produced by the vascular cambium and cork cambium. The vascular cambium adds secondary xylem (wood) and secondary

phloem, thereby increasing vascular flow and support for the shoots. The cork cambium produces a tough, thick covering of waxy cells that protect the stem from water loss and from invasion by insects, bacteria, and fungi.

In woody plants, primary growth and secondary growth occur simultaneously. As primary growth adds leaves and lengthens stems and roots in the younger regions of a plant, secondary growth thickens stems and roots in older regions where primary growth has stopped. The process is similar in shoots and roots. **Figure 35.19** provides an overview of growth in a woody stem.

The Vascular Cambium and Secondary Vascular Tissue

The vascular cambium, a cylinder of meristematic cells only one cell thick, is wholly responsible for the production of secondary vascular tissue. In a typical woody stem, the vascular cambium is located outside the pith and primary xylem and to the inside of the primary phloem and the cortex.

In a typical woody root, the vascular cambium forms to the exterior of the primary xylem and interior to the primary phloem and pericycle.

In cross section, the vascular cambium appears as a ring of meristematic cells (see Figure 35.19). As these cells divide, they increase the circumference of the vascular cambium and also add secondary xylem to the inside of the cambium and secondary

(a) Primary and secondary growth in a two-year-old woody stem

Epidermis
Cortex
Primary phloem
Vascular cambium
Primary xylem
Pith

Periderm (mainly cork cambia and cork)

Primary phloem
Secondary phloem
Vascular cambium
Secondary xylem
Primary xylem
Pith

①
Pith
Primary xylem
Vascular cambium
Primary phloem
Epidermis
Cortex

②
Growth
③ Vascular ray
Primary xylem
Secondary xylem
Vascular cambium
Secondary phloem
Primary phloem
First cork cambium
④
Cork

⑤ **⑥**
Growth
Secondary xylem (two years of production)
Vascular cambium
Secondary phloem
⑦ Most recent cork cambium
Cork
⑨ Bark
⑧ Layers of periderm

① Primary growth from the activity of the apical meristem is nearing completion. The vascular cambium has just formed.

② Although primary growth continues in the apical bud, only secondary growth occurs in this region. The stem thickens as the vascular cambium forms secondary xylem to the inside and secondary phloem to the outside.

③ Some initials of the vascular cambium give rise to vascular rays (see next page).

④ As the vascular cambium's diameter increases, the secondary phloem and other tissues external to the cambium can't keep pace because their cells no longer divide. As a result, these tissues, including the epidermis, will eventually rupture. A second lateral meristem, the cork cambium, develops from parenchyma cells in the cortex. The cork cambium produces cork cells, which replace the epidermis.

⑤ In year 2 of secondary growth, the vascular cambium produces more secondary xylem and phloem, and the cork cambium produces more cork.

⑥ As the stem's diameter increases, the outermost tissues exterior to the cork cambium rupture and are sloughed off.

⑦ In many cases, the cork cambium re-forms deeper in the cortex. When none of the cortex is left, the cambium develops from phloem parenchyma cells.

⑧ Each cork cambium and the tissues it produces form a layer of periderm.

⑨ Bark consists of all tissues exterior to the vascular cambium.

▲ **Figure 35.19 Primary and secondary growth of a woody stem.** The progress of secondary growth can be tracked by examining the sections through sequentially older parts of the stem.

? *How does the vascular cambium cause some tissues to rupture?*

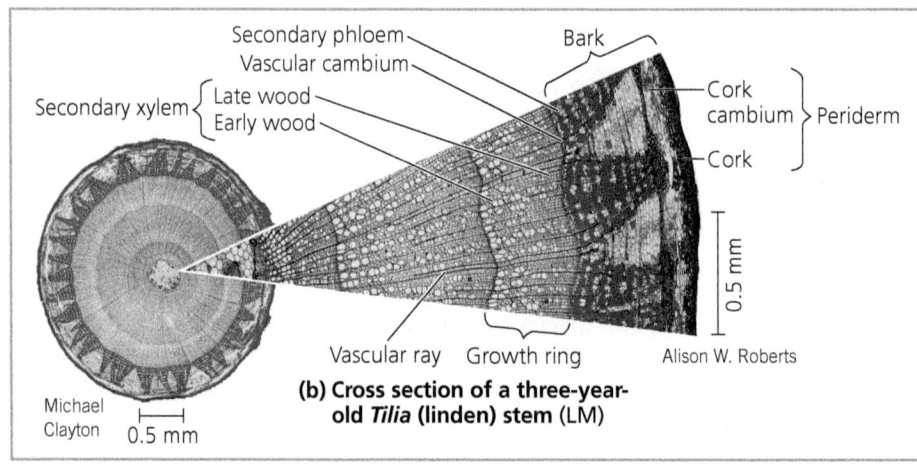

Secondary phloem
Vascular cambium
Bark
Secondary xylem { Late wood / Early wood }
Cork cambium } Periderm
Cork

Vascular ray   Growth ring

Michael Clayton
0.5 mm

Alison W. Roberts
0.5 mm

(b) Cross section of a three-year-old *Tilia* (linden) stem (LM)

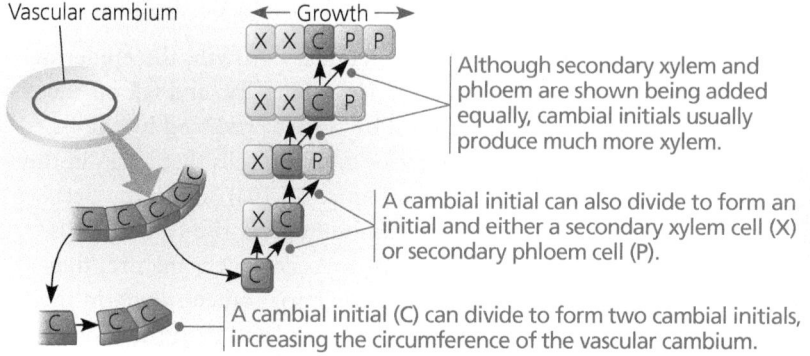

Although secondary xylem and phloem are shown being added equally, cambial initials usually produce much more xylem.

A cambial initial can also divide to form an initial and either a secondary xylem cell (X) or secondary phloem cell (P).

A cambial initial (C) can divide to form two cambial initials, increasing the circumference of the vascular cambium.

Most of the thickening is from secondary xylem.

After one year of growth

After two years of growth

▲ Figure 35.20 **Secondary growth produced by the vascular cambium.**

phloem to the outside (Figure 35.20) Each ring is larger than the previous ring, increasing the diameter of roots and stems.

Some initials are elongated and are oriented with their long axis parallel to the axis of the stem or root. They produce cells such as the tracheids, vessel elements, and fibres of the xylem, as well as the sieve-tube elements, companion cells, axially oriented parenchyma, and fibres of the phloem. The other initials are shorter and are oriented perpendicular to the axis of the stem or root. They produce *vascular rays*—radial files of mostly parenchyma cells that connect the secondary xylem and phloem (see Figure 35.19b). The cells of a vascular ray move water and nutrients between the secondary xylem and phloem, store carbohydrates, and aid in wound repair.

As secondary growth continues, layers of secondary xylem (wood) accumulate, consisting mainly of tracheids, vessel elements, and fibres (see Figure 35.10). In most gymnosperms, tracheids are the only water-conducting cells. Most angiosperms also have vessel elements. The walls of secondary xylem cells are heavily lignified, giving wood its hardness and strength.

In temperate regions, wood that develops early in the spring, known as early (or spring) wood, usually has secondary xylem cells with large diameters and thin cell walls (see Figure 35.19b). This structure maximizes delivery of water to leaves. Wood produced later in the growing season is called late (or summer) wood. It has thick-walled cells that do not transport as much water but provide more support. Because there is a marked contrast between the large cells of the new early wood and the smaller cells of the late wood of the previous growing season, a year's growth appears as a distinct *growth ring* in cross sections of most tree trunks and roots. Therefore, researchers can estimate a tree's age by counting growth rings. *Dendrochronology* is the science of analyzing tree growth ring patterns. Growth rings vary in thickness, depending on seasonal growth. Trees grow well in wet and warm years but may grow hardly at all in cold or dry years. Since a thick ring indicates a warm year and a thin ring indicates a cold or dry one, scientists use ring patterns to study climate change (Figure 35.21).

As a tree or woody shrub ages, the older layers of secondary xylem no longer transport water and minerals (a solution called xylem sap). These layers are called

▼ Figure 35.21 | **Research Method**

Using Dendrochronology to Study Climate

Application Dendrochronology, the science of analyzing tree rings, is useful in studying climate change. Most scientists attribute recent global warming to the burning of fossil fuels and release of CO_2 and other greenhouse gases, whereas a minority think it is a natural variation. Studying climate patterns requires comparing past and present temperatures, but instrumental climate records span only the last two centuries and apply only to some regions. By examining growth rings of Mongolian conifers dating back to the mid-1500s, G. C. Jacoby and Rosanne D'Arrigo, of the Lamont-Doherty Earth Observatory, and colleagues sought to learn whether Mongolia experienced similar warm periods in the past.

Technique Researchers can analyze patterns of rings in living and dead trees. They can even study wood used for building long ago by matching samples with those from naturally situated specimens of overlapping age. Core samples, each about the diameter of a pencil, are taken from the bark to the centre of the trunk. Each sample is dried and sanded to reveal the rings. By comparing, aligning, and averaging many samples from the Mongolian conifers, the researchers compiled a chronology. In this way, the trees served as a chronicle of environmental change.

Results This graph summarizes a composite record of ring-width indices for the Mongolian conifers from 1550 to 1993. The higher indices indicate wider rings and higher temperatures.

INTERPRET THE DATA *What does this graph indicate about the environmental change during the period 1550–1993?*

Source: G. C. Jacoby et al., Mongolian tree rings and 20th-century warming, *Science* 273:771–773 (1996). © Jane B Reece.

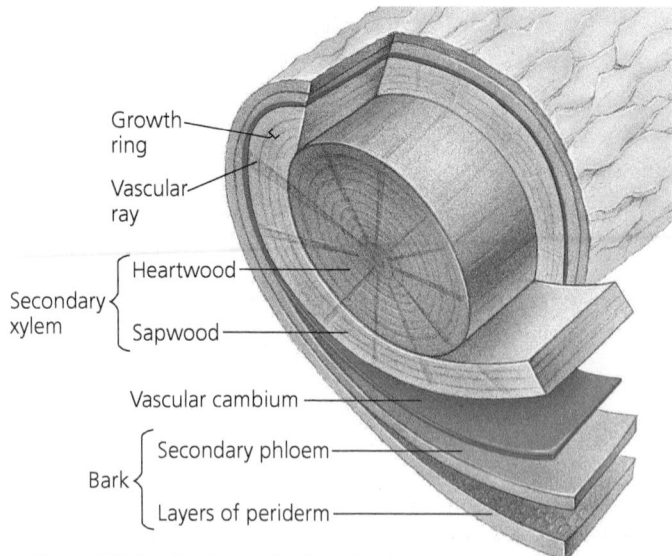

Figure 35.22 **Anatomy of a tree trunk.**

Labels: Growth ring, Vascular ray, Secondary xylem { Heartwood, Sapwood }, Vascular cambium, Bark { Secondary phloem, Layers of periderm }

heartwood because they are closer to the centre of a stem or root (**Figure 35.22**). The newest, outer layers of secondary xylem still transport xylem sap and are therefore known as *sapwood*. That is why a large tree can survive even if the centre of its trunk is hollow (**Figure 35.23**). Because each new layer of secondary xylem has a larger circumference, secondary growth enables the xylem to transport more sap each year, supplying an increasing number of leaves. The heartwood is generally darker than sapwood because of resins and other compounds that permeate the cell cavities and help protect the core of the tree from fungi and wood-boring insects.

Only the youngest secondary phloem, closest to the vascular cambium, functions in sugar transport. As a stem or root increases in circumference, the older secondary phloem is sloughed off, which is one reason secondary phloem does not accumulate as extensively as secondary xylem.

◄ **Figure 35.23 Is this tree living or dead?** The Wawona Sequoia tunnel in Yosemite National Park in California was cut in 1881 as a tourist attraction. This giant sequoia (*Sequoiadendron giganteum*) lived for another 88 years before falling during a severe winter. It was 71.3 m tall and estimated to be 2100 years old. Though conservation policies today would forbid the mutilation of such an important specimen, the Wawona Sequoia did teach a valuable botanical lesson: Trees can survive the excision of large portions of their heartwood.

University of Southern California, Central Library System

The Cork Cambium and the Production of Periderm

During the early stages of secondary growth, the epidermis is pushed outward, causing it to split, dry, and fall off the stem or root. It is replaced by tissues produced by the first cork cambium, a cylinder of dividing cells that arises in the outer cortex of stems (see Figure 35.19a) and in the pericycle in roots. The cork cambium gives rise to cork cells that accumulate to its exterior. As cork cells mature, they deposit a waxy, hydrophobic material called *suberin* in their walls and then die. This waxy cork layer then functions as a barrier that helps protect the stem or root from water loss, physical damage, and pathogens. Each cork cambium and the tissues it produces comprise a layer of periderm.

How can living cells in the interior tissues of woody organs absorb oxygen and respire if they are surrounded by a waxy periderm? Dotting the periderm are small, raised areas called **lenticels**, in which there is more space between cork cells, enabling living cells within a woody stem or root to exchange gases with the outside air. Lenticels often appear as horizontal slits, as shown on the stem in Figure 35.19a.

The thickening of a stem or root often splits the first cork cambium, which loses its meristematic activity and differentiates into cork cells. A new cork cambium forms to the inside, resulting in another layer of periderm. As this process continues, older layers of periderm are sloughed off, as you can see in the cracked, peeling bark of many tree trunks.

There is a popular misconception that bark consists only of the protective outer covering of a woody stem or root. Actually, **bark** includes all tissues external to the vascular cambium. Moving outward, its main components are the secondary phloem (produced by the vascular cambium), the most recent periderm, and all the older layers of periderm (see Figure 35.22).

Evolution of Secondary Growth

EVOLUTION Surprisingly, some insights into the evolution of secondary growth have been achieved by studying the herbaceous plant *Arabidopsis thaliana*. Researchers have found that they can stimulate some secondary growth in *Arabidopsis* stems by adding weights to the plant. These findings suggest that weight carried by the stem activates a developmental program leading to wood formation. Moreover, several developmental genes that regulate shoot apical meristems in *Arabidopsis* have been found to regulate vascular cambium activity in *Populus*. This suggests that the processes of primary and secondary growth are evolutionarily more closely related than previously thought.

Wood Development

Forests cover approximately 400 million hectares of land in Canada, which is an area greater than half of the total land mass of the country. Besides playing an important ecological role as home to many endangered species of plants and animals, the forestry industry in Canada contributes more than $23 billion to the national economy every year and directly or indirectly employs over 400 000 people. Wood harvested is used for construction, furniture, flooring, and the production of paper. Today, we are moving beyond traditional logging practices and seeking to develop sustainable and innovative techniques to provide better forestry products with less environmental impact. Research is a factor in this transition. Nine Canadian universities offer degree programs in forestry. The faculty associated with these programs carry out research in fields as diverse as forest ecology, microbiology, tree physiology, and process engineering.

An area where current research utilizes our basic knowledge of plant secondary growth and stem architecture is in the selection and design of tree species optimized for biofuel production. As our understanding of the genetic and hormonal control of wood formation has improved, it has allowed researchers to explore ways to alter the ratio of xylem to phloem production and the amounts of cellulose and lignin laid down by the cells of the xylem. Selecting for changes in these traits could improve the biofuel potential of specific trees. Armed with this information, perhaps the most difficult challenge facing tree biologists is the slow growth rates and long generation times of tree species.

CONCEPT CHECK 35.4

1. A sign is hammered into a tree 2 m above the tree's base. If the tree is 10 m tall and elongates 1 m each year, how high will the sign be after 10 years?

2. Stomata and lenticels are both involved in exchange of CO_2 and O_2. Why is it that stomata need to be able to close, but lenticels do not?

3. Would you expect a tropical tree to have distinct growth rings? Why or why not?

4. **WHAT IF?** If a complete ring of bark is removed around a tree trunk (a process called girdling), the tree usually dies. Explain why.

For suggested answers, see Appendix A.

CONCEPT 35.5

Growth, morphogenesis, and cell differentiation produce the plant body

The specific series of changes by which cells form tissues, organs, and organisms is called **development**. Development unfolds according to the genetic information that an organism inherits from its parents but is also influenced by the external environment. A single genotype can produce different phenotypes in different environments. For example, the aquatic plant called the fanwort (*Cabomba caroliniana*) forms two very different types of leaves, depending on whether or not the shoot apical meristem is submerged (**Figure 35.24**). This ability to alter form in response to local environmental conditions is called *developmental plasticity*. Dramatic examples of plasticity, as in *Cabomba*, are much more common in plants than in animals and may help compensate for plants' inability to escape adverse conditions by moving.

Plant development can also be affected by changing environmental conditions. For example, the warmer temperatures associated with climate change are known to have significant negative impacts on plant growth and development. As mentioned in the chapter opener, trees moved from colder to warmer growing conditions experienced stunted growth. Similar responses are seen with many other plants, including cereal crops. Decreasing crop yields as temperatures continue to rise will be a major concern for farmers trying to meet a growing demand for food as the human population increases. The development of heat stress-tolerant crops by plant scientists will be essential to the solution for this problem.

Let's briefly review the three overlapping processes in development: growth, morphogenesis, and cell differentiation. **Growth** is an irreversible increase in size. **Morphogenesis** (from the Greek *morphê*, shape, and *genesis*, creation) is the process that gives a tissue, organ, or organism its shape and determines the positions of cell types. Cell **differentiation** is the process by which cells with the same genes become different from one another. We'll examine these three processes in turn, but first we'll discuss how applying techniques of modern molecular biology and genetics to model organisms, particularly *Arabidopsis thaliana*, has revolutionized the study of plant development.

▲ Figure 35.24 **Developmental plasticity in the aquatic plant *Cabomba caroliniana*.** The underwater leaves of *Cabomba* are feathery, an adaptation that protects them from damage by lessening their resistance to moving water. In contrast, the surface leaves are pads that aid in flotation. Both leaf types have genetically identical cells, but their different environments result in the turning on or off of different genes during leaf development.

Model Organisms: Revolutionizing the Study of Plants

As in other branches of biology, molecular biological techniques and a focus on model organisms such as *Arabidopsis thaliana* have catalyzed a research explosion in the last two decades. *Arabidopsis*, a tiny weed in the mustard family, has no inherent agricultural value but is a favoured model organism of plant geneticists and molecular biologists for many reasons. It is so small that thousands of plants can be cultivated in a few square metres of lab space. It also has a short generation time, taking about six weeks for a seed to grow into a mature plant that produces more seeds. This rapid maturation enables biologists to conduct genetic cross experiments in a relatively short time frame. One plant can produce over 5000 seeds, another property that makes *Arabidopsis* useful for genetic analysis.

Beyond these basic traits, the plant's genome makes it particularly well suited for analysis by molecular genetic methods. The *Arabidopsis* genome, which includes about 27 000 protein-encoding genes, is among the smallest known in plants. Furthermore, the plant has only five pairs of chromosomes, making it easier for geneticists to locate specific genes. Because *Arabidopsis* has such a small genome, it was the first plant to have its entire genome sequenced—a six-year, multinational effort.

Another property that makes *Arabidopsis* attractive to molecular biologists is that its cells can easily be transformed with transgenes, genes from different organisms. Biologists usually transform plant cells by infecting them with genetically altered varieties of the bacterium *Agrobacterium tumefaciens* (Figure 35.25). *Arabidopsis* researchers also use a variation of this technique to create a plant with a particular mutation. Studying the effect of a mutation in a gene often yields important information about the gene's normal function. Because *Agrobacterium* inserts its transforming DNA randomly into the genome, the DNA may be inserted in the middle of a gene. Such an insertion usually destroys the function of the disrupted gene, resulting in a "knock-out mutant."

Large-scale projects using this technique are under way to determine the function of every gene in *Arabidopsis*. By identifying each gene's function and tracking every biochemical pathway, researchers aim to determine the blueprints for plant development, a major goal of systems biology. It may one day be possible to create a computer-generated "virtual plant" that enables researchers to visualize which genes are activated in different parts of the plant as the plant develops.

Basic research involving model organisms such as *Arabidopisis* has accelerated the pace of discovery in the plant sciences, including the identification of the complex genetic pathways underlying

Elsevier Science Ltd

▼ Figure 35.25 | **Research Method**

Using the Ti Plasmid to Produce Transgenic Plants

Application Genes conferring useful traits, such as pest resistance, herbicide resistance, delayed ripening, and increased nutritional value, can be transferred from one plant variety or species to another using the Ti plasmid as a vector.

Agrobacterium tumefaciens

1. The Ti plasmid is isolated from the bacterium *Agrobacterium tumefaciens*. The segment of the plasmid that integrates into the genome of host cells is called T DNA.

Ti plasmid

Site where restriction enzyme cuts

T DNA

DNA with the gene of interest

2. The foreign gene of interest is inserted into the middle of the T DNA.

Recombinant Ti plasmid

3. Recombinant plasmids can be introduced into cultured plant cells by electroporation. Or plasmids can be returned to *Agrobacterium*, which is then applied as a liquid suspension to the leaves of susceptible plants, infecting them. Once a plasmid is taken into a plant cell, its T DNA integrates into the cell's chromosomal DNA.

Plant with new trait

Results Transformed cells carrying the transgene of interest can regenerate complete plants that exhibit the new trait conferred by the transgene.

plant structure. As you read more about this, you'll be able to appreciate not just the power of studying model organisms but also the rich history of plant investigation that underpins all modern plant research.

Growth: Cell Division and Cell Expansion

Cell division enhances the potential for growth by increasing the number of cells, but plant growth itself is brought about by cell enlargement. The process of plant cell division is described more fully in Chapter 12 (see Figure 12.10), and Chapter 39 discusses the process of cell elongation (see Figure 39.7). Here we are more concerned with how these processes contribute to plant form.

The Plane and Symmetry of Cell Division

The new cell walls that bisect plant cells during cytokinesis develop from the cell plate (see Figure 12.10). The precise plane of cell division, determined during late interphase, usually corresponds to the shortest path that will halve the volume of the parent cell. The first sign of this spatial orientation is rearrangement of the cytoskeleton. Microtubules in the cytoplasm become concentrated into a ring called the *preprophase band* (Figure 35.26). The band disappears before metaphase but predicts the future plane of cell division.

It had long been thought that the plane of cell division provides the foundation for the forms of plant organs, but studies of an internally disorganized maize mutant called *tangled-1* now indicate that this is not the case. In wild-type maize plants, leaf cells divide either transversely (crosswise) or longitudinally relative to the axis of the parent cell. Transverse divisions are associated with leaf elongation, and longitudinal divisions are associated with leaf broadening. In *tangled-1* leaves, transverse divisions are normal, but most

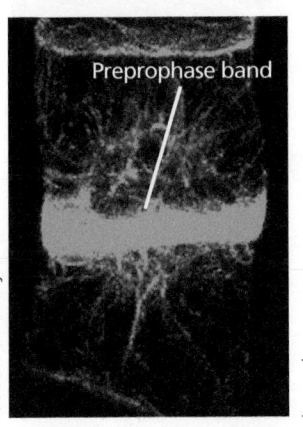

Preprophase band

7 µm

▲ Figure 35.26 **The preprophase band and the plane of cell division.** The location of the preprophase band predicts the plane of cell division. In this light micrograph, the preprophase band has been stained with green fluorescent protein bound to a microtubule-associated protein.

longitudinal divisions are oriented abnormally, leading to cells that are crooked or curved (Figure 35.27). However, these abnormal cell divisions do not affect leaf shape. Mutant leaves grow more slowly than wild-type leaves, but their overall shapes remain normal, indicating that leaf shape does not depend solely on precise spatial control of cell division. In addition, recent evidence suggests that the shape of the shoot apex in *Arabidopsis*

30 µm

Leaf epidermal cells of wild-type maize

Leaf epidermal cells of *tangled-1* maize mutant

▲ Figure 35.27 **Cell division patterns in wild-type versus mutant maize plants.** Compared with the epidermal cells of wild-type maize plants (left), the epidermal cells of the *tangled-1* mutant of maize (right) are highly disordered. Nevertheless, *tangled-1* maize plants produce normal-looking leaves.

depends not on the plane of cell division but on microtubule-dependent mechanical stresses stemming from the "crowding" associated with cell proliferation and growth.

Although the *plane* of cell division does not determine the shape of plant organs, the *symmetry* of cell division—the distribution of cytoplasm between daughter cells—is important in determining cell fate. Not all plant cells divide into two equal halves during mitosis. Although chromosomes are allocated to daughter cells equally during mitosis, the cytoplasm may sometimes divide asymmetrically. *Asymmetrical cell division*, in which one daughter cell receives more cytoplasm than the other during mitosis, usually signals a key event in development. For example, the formation of guard cells typically involves both an asymmetrical cell division and a change in the plane of cell division. An epidermal cell divides asymmetrically, forming a large cell that remains an unspecialized epidermal cell and a small cell that becomes the guard cell "mother cell." Guard cells form when this small mother cell divides in a plane perpendicular to the first cell division (Figure 35.28). Thus, asymmetrical cell division generates cells with different fates—that is, cells that mature into different types.

Asymmetrical cell divisions also play a role in the establishment of **polarity**, the condition of having structural or chemical differences at opposite ends of an organism. Plants typically have an axis, with a root end and a shoot end. Such polarity is most obvious in morphological differences, but it is also apparent in physiological properties, including the movement of the hormone auxin in a single direction and the emergence of adventitious roots and shoots from "cuttings." Adventitious roots form within the root end of a stem cutting, and adventitious shoots arise from the shoot end of a root cutting.

The first division of a plant zygote is normally asymmetrical, initiating polarization of the plant body into shoot and root.

▲ **Figure 35.28 Asymmetrical cell division and stomatal development.** An asymmetrical cell division precedes the development of epidermal guard cells, the cells that border stomata (see Figure 35.18).

This polarity is difficult to reverse experimentally, indicating that the proper establishment of axial polarity is a critical step in a plant's morphogenesis. In the *gnom* (from the German for a dwarf and misshapen creature) mutant of *Arabidopsis*, the establishment of polarity is defective. The first cell division of the zygote is abnormal because it is symmetrical, and the resulting ball-shaped plant has neither roots nor leaves (Figure 35.29).

Orientation of Cell Expansion

Before discussing how cell expansion contributes to plant form, it is useful to consider the difference in cell expansion between plants and animals. Animal cells grow mainly by synthesizing protein-rich cytoplasm, a metabolically expensive process. Growing plant cells also produce additional protein-rich material in their cytoplasm, but water uptake typically accounts for about 90% of expansion. Most of this water is packaged in the large central vacuole. The vacuolar solution or *vacuolar sap* is very dilute and nearly devoid of the energetically expensive macromolecules that are found in great abundance in the rest of the cytoplasm. Large vacuoles are therefore a "cheap" way of filling space, enabling a plant to grow rapidly and economically.

Bamboo shoots, for instance, can elongate more than 2 m per week. Rapid and efficient extensibility of shoots and roots was an important evolutionary adaptation that increased their exposure to light and soil.

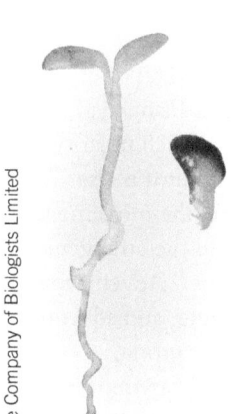

◀ **Figure 35.29 Establishment of axial polarity.** The normal *Arabidopsis* seedling (left) has a shoot end and a root end. In the *gnom* mutant (right), the first division of the zygote was not asymmetrical; as a result, the plant is ball-shaped and lacks leaves and roots. The defect in *gnom* mutants has been traced to an inability to transport the hormone auxin in a polar manner.

Plant cells rarely expand equally in all directions. Their greatest expansion is usually oriented along the plant's main axis. For example, cells near the tip of the root may elongate up to 20 times their original length, with relatively little increase in width. The orientation of cellulose microfibrils in the innermost layers of the cell wall causes this differential growth. The microfibrils do not stretch, so the cell expands mainly perpendicular to the main orientation of the microfibrils, as shown in Figure 35.30. As with the plane of cell division, microtubules play a key role in regulating the plane of cell expansion. It is the orientation of microtubules in the cell's outermost cytoplasm that determines the orientation of cellulose microfibrils, the basic structural units of the cell wall.

Morphogenesis and Pattern Formation

A plant's body is more than a collection of dividing and expanding cells. During morphogenesis, cells acquire different identities in an ordered spatial arrangement. For example, dermal tissue forms on the exterior, and vascular tissue in the interior—never the other way around. The development of specific structures in specific locations is called **pattern formation**.

Two types of hypotheses have been put forward to explain how the fate of plant cells is determined during pattern

▲ **Figure 35.30 The orientation of plant cell expansion.** Growing plant cells expand mainly through water uptake. In a growing cell, enzymes weaken cross-links in the cell wall, allowing it to expand as water diffuses into the vacuole by osmosis; at the same time, more microfibrils are made. The orientation of cell growth is mainly in the plane perpendicular to the orientation of cellulose microfibrils in the wall. The orientation of microtubules in the cell's outermost cytoplasm determines the orientation of the cellulose microfibrils (fluorescent LM). The microfibrils are embedded in a matrix of other (noncellulose) polysaccharides, some of which form the cross-links visible in the TEM.

formation. Hypotheses based on *lineage-based mechanisms* propose that cell fate is determined early in development and that cells pass on this destiny to their progeny. According to this view, the basic pattern of cell differentiation is mapped out according to the directions in which meristematic cells divide and expand. On the other hand, hypotheses based on *position-based mechanisms* propose that the cell's final position in an emerging organ determines what kind of cell it will become. In support of this view, experimental manipulations of cell positions by surgically destroying certain cells with lasers have demonstrated that a plant cell's fate is established late in development and largely depends on signalling from neighbouring cells.

In contrast, cell fate in animals is largely determined by lineage-dependent mechanisms involving transcription factors. The homeotic (*Hox*) genes that encode such transcription factors are critical for the proper number and placement of embryonic structures, such as legs and antennae, in the fruit fly *Drosophila* (see Figure 18.20). Interestingly, maize has a homolog of *Hox* genes called *KNOTTED-1*, but unlike its counterparts in the animal world, *KNOTTED-1* does not affect the proper number or placement of plant organs. As you will see, an unrelated class of transcription factors called *MADS-box* proteins plays that role in plants. *KNOTTED-1* is, however, important in the development of leaf morphology, including the production of compound leaves. If the *KNOTTED-1* gene is expressed in greater quantity than normal in the genome of tomato plants, the normally compound leaves become "super-compound" (Figure 35.31).

Gene Expression and Control of Cell Differentiation

Cells of a developing organism can synthesize different proteins and diverge in structure and function even though they contain the same genetic information. If a mature cell removed from a root or leaf can dedifferentiate in tissue culture and give rise to the diverse cell types of a plant, then it must possess all the genes necessary to make any kind of plant cell. Therefore, cell differentiation depends, to a large degree, on the control of

gene expression—the regulation of transcription and translation, resulting in the production of specific proteins.

Evidence suggests that the activation or inactivation of specific genes involved in cell differentiation depends largely on cell-to-cell communication. For example, two cell types arise in the root epidermis of *Arabidopsis*: root hair cells and hairless epidermal cells. Cell fate is associated with the position of the epidermal cells. The immature epidermal cells that are in contact with two underlying cells of the root cortex differentiate into root hair cells, whereas the immature epidermal cells in contact with only one cortical cell differentiate into mature hairless cells. Differential expression of a homeotic gene called *GLABRA-2* (from the Latin *glaber*, bald) is required for appropriate root hair distribution (Figure 35.32). Researchers have demonstrated this by coupling the *GLABRA-2* gene to a "reporter gene" that causes every cell expressing *GLABRA-2* in the root to turn pale blue following a certain treatment. The *GLABRA-2* gene is normally expressed only in epidermal cells that will not develop root hairs.

Shifts in Development: Phase Changes

Multicellular organisms generally pass through developmental stages. In humans, these are infancy, childhood, adolescence, and adulthood, with puberty as the dividing line between the nonreproductive and reproductive stages. Plants also pass through stages, much like animals, developing from a juvenile stage to an adult vegetative stage to an adult reproductive stage. In animals, the developmental changes take place throughout the entire organism, such as when a larva develops into an adult animal. In contrast, plant developmental stages,

▲ **Figure 35.31 Overexpression of a *Hox*-like gene in leaf formation.** *KNOTTED-1* is a gene involved in leaf and leaflet formation. An increase in its expression in tomato plants results in leaves that are "super-compound" (right) compared with normal leaves (left).

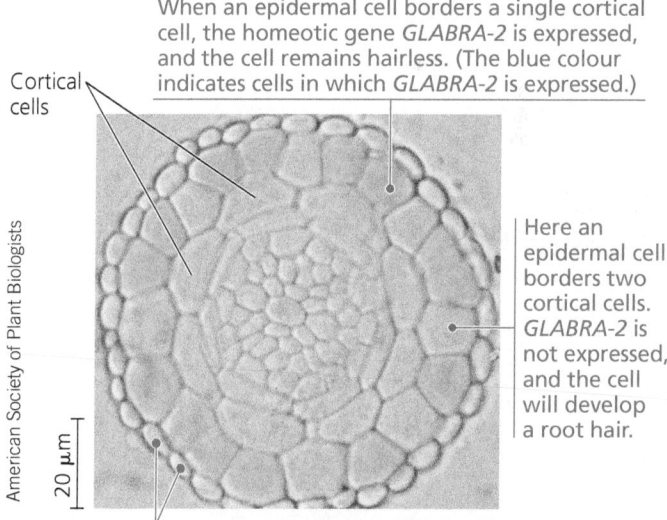

When an epidermal cell borders a single cortical cell, the homeotic gene *GLABRA-2* is expressed, and the cell remains hairless. (The blue colour indicates cells in which *GLABRA-2* is expressed.)

Cortical cells

Here an epidermal cell borders two cortical cells. *GLABRA-2* is not expressed, and the cell will develop a root hair.

20 μm

American Society of Plant Biologists

The root cap cells external to the epidermal layer will be sloughed off before root hairs emerge.

▲ **Figure 35.32 Control of root hair differentiation by a homeotic gene (LM).**

WHAT IF? *What would the roots look like if GLABRA-2 were rendered dysfunctional by a mutation?*

called *phases*, occur within a single region, the shoot apical meristem. The morphological changes that arise from these transitions in shoot apical meristem activity are called **phase changes**. During the transition from a juvenile phase to an adult phase, some species exhibit some striking changes in leaf morphology (**Figure 35.33**). Juvenile nodes and internodes retain their juvenile status even after the shoot continues to elongate and the shoot apical meristem has changed to the adult phase. Therefore, any *new* leaves that develop on branches that emerge from axillary buds at juvenile nodes will also be juvenile, even though the apical meristem of the stem's main axis may have been producing mature nodes for years.

If environmental conditions permit, an adult plant is induced to flower. Biologists have made great progress in explaining the genetic control of floral development—the topic of the next section.

Genetic Control of Flowering

Flower formation involves a phase change from vegetative growth to reproductive growth. This transition is triggered by a combination of environmental cues, such as day length, temperature, and internal signals, such as hormones. (You will learn more about the roles of these signals in flowering in Chapter 39.) Unlike vegetative growth, which is indeterminate, floral growth is usually determinate: The production of a flower by a shoot apical meristem generally stops the primary growth of that shoot. The transition from vegetative growth to flowering is associated with the switching on of floral **meristem identity genes**. The protein products of these genes are transcription factors that regulate the genes required for the conversion of the indeterminate vegetative meristems to determinate floral meristems.

When a shoot apical meristem is induced to flower, the order of each primordium's emergence determines its development into a specific type of floral organ—a sepal, petal, stamen, or carpel (see Figure 30.8 to review basic flower structure). These floral organs form four whorls that can be described roughly as concentric "circles" when viewed from above. Sepals form the first (outermost) whorl; petals form the second; stamens form the third; and carpels form the fourth (innermost) whorl. Plant biologists have identified several **organ identity genes** belonging to the *MADS-box* family that encode transcription factors that regulate the development of this characteristic floral pattern. Positional information determines which organ identity genes are expressed in a particular floral organ primordium. The result is the development of an emerging floral primordium into a specific floral organ. A mutation in a plant organ identity gene can cause abnormal floral development, such as petals growing in place of stamens (**Figure 35.34**). Some homeotic

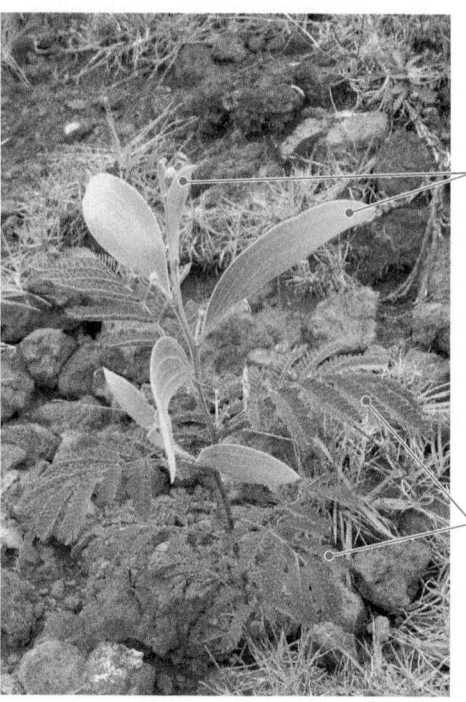

James B. Friday

▲ **Figure 35.33 Phase change in the shoot system of *Acacia koa*.** This native of Hawaii has compound juvenile leaves, consisting of many small leaflets, and simple mature leaves. This dual foliage reflects a phase change in the development of the apical meristem of each shoot. Once a node forms, the developmental phase—juvenile or adult—is fixed; that is, compound leaves do not mature into simple leaves.

Leaves produced by adult phase of apical meristem

Leaves produced by juvenile phase of apical meristem

E. M. Meyerowitz and J. Bowman, *Development* 112:1–231.2 (1991). Division of Biology, California Institute of Technology

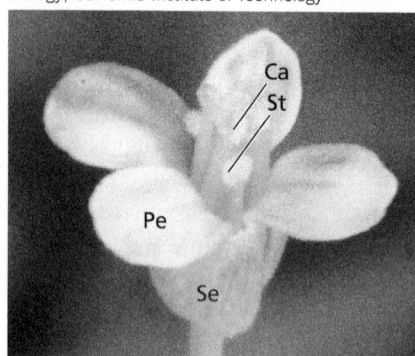

▲ **Normal *Arabidopsis* flower.** *Arabidopsis* normally has four whorls of flower parts: sepals (Se), petals (Pe), stamens (St), and carpels (Ca).

▶ **Abnormal *Arabidopsis* flower.** Researchers have identified several mutations of organ identity genes that cause abnormal flowers to develop. This flower has an extra set of petals in place of stamens and an internal flower where normal plants have carpels.

▲ **Figure 35.34 Organ identity genes and pattern formation in flower development.**

MAKE CONNECTIONS *Review Concept 18.4 and provide another example of a homeotic gene mutation that leads to organs being produced in the wrong place.*

◀ Figure 35.35 **The ABC hypothesis for the functioning of organ identity genes in flower development.**

WHAT IF? *What would a flower look like if the A genes and B genes were inactivated?*

(a) A schematic diagram of the ABC hypothesis. Studies of plant mutations reveal that three classes of organ identity genes are responsible for the spatial pattern of floral parts. These genes, designated *A*, *B*, and *C*, regulate expression of other genes responsible for development of sepals, petals, stamens, and carpels. Sepals develop from the meristematic region where only *A* genes are active. Petals develop where both *A* and *B* genes are expressed. Stamens arise where *B* and *C* genes are active. Carpels arise where only *C* genes are expressed.

(b) Side view of flowers with organ identity mutations. The phenotype of mutants lacking a functional *A*, *B*, or *C* organ identity gene can be explained by combining the model in part (a) with the rule that if *A* or *C* activity is missing, the other activity occurs through all four whorls.

mutants with increased petal numbers produce showier flowers that are prized by gardeners.

By studying mutants with abnormal flowers, researchers have identified and cloned three classes of floral organ identity genes, and their studies are beginning to reveal how these genes function. Figure 35.35a shows a simplified version of the **ABC hypothesis** of flower formation, which proposes that three classes of genes direct the formation of the four types of floral organs. According to the ABC hypothesis, each class of organ identity genes is switched on in two specific whorls of the floral meristem. Normally, *A* genes are switched on in the two outer whorls (sepals and petals); *B* genes are switched on in the two middle whorls (petals and stamens); and *C* genes are switched on in the two inner whorls (stamens and carpels). Sepals arise from those parts of the floral meristems in which only *A* genes are active; petals arise where *A* and *B* genes are active; stamens where *B* and *C* genes are active; and carpels where only *C* genes are active. The ABC hypothesis can account for the phenotypes of mutants lacking *A*, *B*, or *C* gene activity, with one addition: Where gene *A* activity is present, it inhibits *C*, and vice versa. If either *A* or *C* is missing, the other takes its place.

Figure 35.35b shows the floral patterns of mutants lacking each of the three classes of organ identity genes and depicts how the hypothesis accounts for the floral phenotypes. By constructing such hypotheses and designing experiments to test them, researchers are tracing the genetic basis of plant development.

In dissecting the plant to examine its parts, as we have done in this chapter, we must remember that the whole plant functions as an integrated organism. Plant structures largely reflect evolutionary adaptations to the challenges of a photoautotrophic existence on land.

CONCEPT CHECK 35.5

1. How can two cells in a plant have vastly different structures even though they have the same genome?

2. What are three differences between animal development and plant development?

3. **WHAT IF?** In some species, sepals look like petals, and both are collectively called "tepals." Suggest an extension to the ABC hypothesis that could hypothetically account for the origin of tepals.

For suggested answers, see Appendix A.

SUMMARY OF KEY CONCEPTS

CONCEPT 35.1

Plants have a hierarchical organization consisting of organs, tissues, and cells (pp. 803–809)

- Vascular plants have shoots consisting of **stems, leaves**, and, in angiosperms, flowers. **Roots** anchor the plant, absorb and conduct water and minerals, and store food. Leaves are attached to stem **nodes** and are the main **organs** of photosynthesis. **Axillary buds**, in axils of leaves and stems, give rise to branches. Plant organs may be adapted for specialized functions.
- Vascular plants have three **tissue systems**—dermal, vascular, and ground—which are continuous throughout the plant. **Dermal tissue** protects against pathogens, herbivores, and drought and aids in the absorption of water, minerals, and carbon dioxide. **Vascular tissues** (**xylem** and **phloem**) facilitate the long-distance transport of substances. **Ground tissues** function in storage, metabolism, and regeneration.
- **Parenchyma cells** are relatively unspecialized and thin-walled cells that retain the ability to divide; they perform most of the plant's metabolic functions of synthesis and storage. **Collenchyma cells** have unevenly thickened walls; they support young, growing parts of the plant. **Sclerenchyma cells**—fibres and **sclereids**—have thick, lignified walls that help support mature, nongrowing parts of the plant. **Tracheids** and **vessel elements**, the water-conducting cells of xylem, have thick walls and are dead at functional maturity. **Sieve-tube elements** are living but highly modified cells that are largely devoid of internal organelles; they function in the transport of sugars through the phloem of angiosperms.

? *Describe at least three specializations in plant organs and plant cells that are adaptations to life on land.*

CONCEPT 35.2

Different meristems generate cells for primary and secondary growth (pp. 810–811)

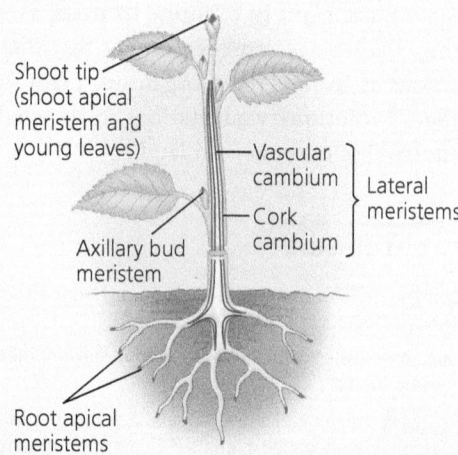

? *Which plant organs originate from the activity of meristems?*

CONCEPT 35.3

Primary growth lengthens roots and shoots (pp. 811–815)

- The root **apical meristem** is located near the tip of the root, where it generates cells for the growing root axis and the **root cap**.
- The apical meristem of a shoot is located in the **apical bud**, where it gives rise to alternating **internodes** and leaf-bearing **nodes**.
- Eudicot stems have vascular bundles in a ring, whereas monocot stems have scattered vascular bundles.
- **Mesophyll** cells are adapted for photosynthesis. **Stomata**, epidermal pores formed by pairs of **guard cells**, allow for gaseous exchange and are major avenues for water loss.

? *How does branching differ in roots versus stems?*

CONCEPT 35.4

Secondary growth increases the diameter of stems and roots in woody plants (pp. 815–819)

- The **vascular cambium** is a meristematic cylinder that produces secondary xylem and secondary phloem during **secondary growth**. Older layers of secondary xylem (heartwood) become inactive, whereas younger layers (sapwood) still conduct water.
- The **cork cambium** gives rise to a thick protective covering called the periderm, which consists of the cork cambium plus the layers of cork cells it produces.

? *What advantages did plants gain from the evolution of secondary growth?*

CONCEPT 35.5

Growth, morphogenesis, and cell differentiation produce the plant body (pp. 819–825)

- Cell division and cell expansion are the primary determinants of **growth**. A preprophase band of microtubules determines where a cell plate will form in a dividing cell. Microtubule orientation also affects the direction of cell elongation by controlling the orientation of cellulose microfibrils in the cell wall.
- **Morphogenesis**, the development of body shape and organization, depends on cells responding to positional information from its neighbours.
- Cell **differentiation**, arising from differential gene activation, enables cells within the plant to assume different functions despite having identical genomes. The way in which a plant cell differentiates is determined largely by the cell's position in the developing plant.
- Internal or environmental cues may cause a plant to switch from one developmental stage to another—for example, from developing juvenile leaves to developing mature leaves. Such morphological changes are called **phase changes**.
- Research on **organ identity genes** in developing flowers provides a model system for studying **pattern formation**. The **ABC hypothesis** identifies how three classes of organ identity genes control formation of sepals, petals, stamens, and carpels.

? *By what mechanism do plant cells tend to elongate along one axis instead of expanding like a balloon in all directions?*

TEST YOUR UNDERSTANDING

LEVEL 1: KNOWLEDGE/COMPREHENSION

1. Most of the growth of a plant body is the result of
   a. cell differentiation.
   c. cell division.
   b. morphogenesis.
   d. cell elongation.

2. The innermost layer of the root cortex is the
   a. core.
   c. endodermis.
   b. pericycle.
   d. pith.

3. Heartwood and sapwood consist of
   a. bark.
   c. secondary xylem.
   b. periderm.
   d. secondary phloem.

4. The phase change of an apical meristem from the juvenile to the mature vegetative phase is often revealed by
   a. a change in the morphology of the leaves produced.
   b. the initiation of secondary growth.
   c. the formation of lateral roots.
   d. the activation of floral meristem identity genes.

LEVEL 2: APPLICATION/ANALYSIS

5. Based on the ABC hypothesis, what would be the structure of a flower from the outermost whorl that had normal expression of genes *A* and *C* and expression of gene *B* in all four whorls?
   a. carpel-petal-petal-carpel
   c. sepal-carpel-carpel-sepal
   b. petal-petal-stamen-stamen
   d. sepal-sepal-carpel-carpel

6. Which of the following arise, directly or indirectly, from meristematic activity?
   a. secondary xylem
   c. dermal tissue
   b. leaves
   d. all of the above

7. Which of the following would not be seen in a cross section through the woody part of a root?
   a. vascular cambium
   c. sieve-tube elements
   b. parenchyma cells
   d. root hairs

8. **DRAW IT** On this cross section from a woody eudicot, label a growth ring, late wood, early wood, and a vessel element. Then draw an arrow in the pith-to-cork direction.

Peter Kitin

LEVEL 3: SYNTHESIS/EVALUATION

9. **EVOLUTION CONNECTION**
   Evolutionary biologists have coined the term *exaptation* to describe a common occurrence in the evolution of life: A limb or organ evolves in a particular context but over time takes on a new function (see Chapter 25). What are some examples of exaptations in plant organs?

10. **SCIENTIFIC INQUIRY**
    Grasslands typically do not flourish when large herbivores are removed. In fact, they are soon replaced by broad-leaved herbaceous eudicots, shrubs, and trees. Based on your knowledge of the structure and growth habits of monocots versus eudicots, suggest a reason why.

11. **SCIENCE, TECHNOLOGY, AND SOCIETY**
    Hunger and malnutrition are urgent problems for many poor countries, and yet plant biologists in wealthy nations have focused most of their research efforts on *Arabidopsis thaliana*. Some people have argued that if plant biologists are truly concerned about fighting world hunger, they should focus their studies on crops such as cassava and plantain because they are staples for many of the world's poor. If you were an *Arabidopsis* researcher, how might you respond to these arguments?

12. **WRITE ABOUT A THEME: ORGANIZATION**
    In a short essay (100–150 words), explain how the evolution of lignin affected vascular plant structure and function.

13. **SYNTHESIZE YOUR KNOWLEDGE**

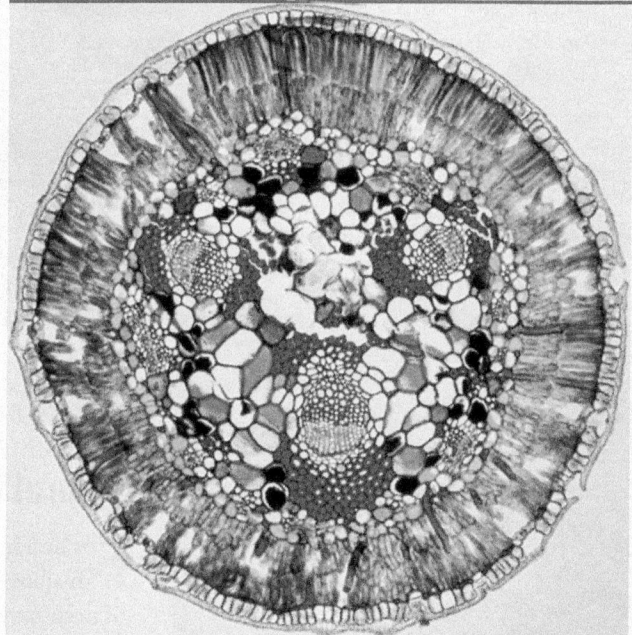

Biophoto Associates/Science Source

This is a light micrograph of a cross section through a plant organ from an angiosperm with an unusual morphology. Is the organ a stem, leaf, or root? Explain your reasoning.

For selected answers, see Appendix A.

36

Resource Acquisition and Transport in Vascular Plants

KEY CONCEPTS

36.1 Adaptations for acquiring resources were key steps in the evolution of vascular plants

36.2 Different mechanisms transport substances over short or long distances

36.3 Transpiration drives the transport of water and minerals from roots to shoots via the xylem

36.4 The rate of transpiration is regulated by stomata

36.5 Sugars are transported from sources to sinks via the phloem

36.6 The symplast is highly dynamic

Larson, Douglas W.

▲ Figure 36.1 **What causes these white cedar trees (*Thuja occidentalis*) on the face of the Niagara Escarpment to grow as natural bonsai?**

Natural Bonsai Trees

For hundreds of years, Japanese gardeners have been practising the art of bonsai. Small trees are pruned, wired into specific shapes, kept in small pots, and deprived of both nutrients and water to keep them in a compact growth form, despite great age. Desired traits in bonsai trees are great age, small size, and artistic form. In the late 1980s, while surveying trees along the Niagara Escarpment in southern Ontario, Dr. Doug Larson from the University of Guelph discovered that the twisted, weathered cedars growing out of the rock face were in many ways natural bonsai trees. Using dendrochronology (Figure 35.21), trees were identified that were over 800 years old, making them the oldest trees in Canada east of the Rocky Mountains. However, unlike the majestic Douglas Firs of the west coast of Canada, these ancient cedar trees are only two to three metres tall and the diameters of their trunks can be measured in centimetres. Based on initial observations, it was hypothesized that the small size of these trees must be due to a lack of water and nutrients, exactly the way bonsai trees are kept small. The bald cliff face was expected to hold little water and the lack of soil cover was thought to provide too little of the essential nutrients that plants need to grow and develop. This idea was reinforced when studies demonstrated that the cliff face trees were genetically identical to the cedar trees growing a few metres away that had a "normal" growth form. To test this hypothesis, Larson's group designed a very challenging experiment (Figure 36.1). They watered a subset of small trees on the cliff

Flashon Studio/Shutterstock

◀ **Trimming roots is essential in manicured bonsai**

face with a dilute nutrient solution. In effect, they fertilized the small trees. Contrary to their initial hypothesis, fertilization did not increase the growth rate of the small trees. Apparently the trees were already receiving adequate amounts of water and nutrients. Subsequent experiments have demonstrated that the size of the trees is limited by their ability to produce roots that can penetrate the rock and soil of the cliff face. Thus, rather than exhibiting a dwarf phenotype due to nutrient deprivation, it may be the small root structure that keeps both the cedars of the Niagara Escarpment and bonsai trees small.

CONCEPT 36.1

Adaptations for acquiring resources were key steps in the evolution of vascular plants

EVOLUTION Land plants typically inhabit two worlds—above ground, where their shoot systems acquire sunlight and CO_2, and below ground, where their root systems acquire water and minerals. Without adaptations that allow acquisition of resources, plants could not have colonized land.

The algal ancestors of land plants absorbed water, minerals, and CO_2 directly from the water in which they lived. Transport in these algae was relatively simple because every cell was close to the source of these substances. The earliest land plants were nonvascular plants that grew photosynthetic shoots above the shallow fresh water in which they lived. These leafless shoots typically had waxy cuticles and few stomata, which allowed them to avoid excessive water loss while still permitting some exchange of CO_2 and O_2 for photosynthesis. The anchoring and absorbing functions of early land plants were assumed by the base of the stem or by threadlike rhizoids (see Figure 29.7).

As land plants evolved and increased in number, competition for light, water, and nutrients intensified. Taller plants with broad, flat appendages had an advantage in absorbing light. This increase in surface area, however, resulted in more evaporation and therefore a greater need for water. Larger shoots also required more anchorage. These needs favoured the production of multicellular, branching roots. Meanwhile, as greater shoot heights further separated the top of the photosynthetic shoot from the nonphotosynthetic parts below ground, natural selection favoured plants capable of efficient long-distance transport of water, minerals, and products of photosynthesis.

The evolution of vascular tissue consisting of xylem and phloem made possible the development of extensive root and shoot systems that carry out long-distance transport (see Figure 35.10). The xylem transports water and minerals from roots to shoots. The phloem transports products of photosynthesis from where they are made or stored to where they are needed. Figure 36.2 provides an overview of resource acquisition and transport in a vascular plant.

▼ Figure 36.2 **An overview of resource acquisition and transport in a vascular plant.**

CO$_2$ is taken up and O$_2$ released through the stomata of leaves and green stems.

Sugars are produced by photosynthesis in the leaves.

Transpiration, the loss of water from leaves (mostly through stomata), creates a force within leaves that pulls xylem sap upward.

Phloem sap can flow both ways between shoots and roots. It moves from sites of sugar production (usually leaves) or storage (usually roots) to sites of sugar use or storage.

Water and minerals are transported upward from roots to shoots as xylem sap.

Water and minerals in the soil are absorbed by roots.

Roots exchange gases with the air spaces of soil, taking in O$_2$ and discharging CO$_2$.

Because plant success depends on photosynthesis, evolution has resulted in many structural adaptations for efficiently acquiring light from the sun, CO_2 from the air, and water from the ground. Perhaps just as importantly, land plants must minimize the evaporative loss of water, particularly in environments where water is scarce. The adaptations of each species represent compromises between enhancing photosynthesis and minimizing water loss in the species' particular habitat. Later in the chapter, we discuss how plants enhance CO_2 uptake and minimize water loss by regulating stomatal pores. Here, we examine how the basic architecture of shoots and roots helps plants acquire resources such as water, minerals, and sunlight.

Shoot Architecture and Light Capture

Much of the diversity we see in plants is a reflection of differences in the branching patterns, dimensions, shapes, and orientations of the shoot's two components—stems and leaves. Shoot architecture typically facilitates light capture for photosynthesis.

Stems serve as supporting structures for leaves and as conduits for the transport of water and nutrients. The length of stems and their branching patterns are two architectural features affecting light capture. Plants that grow tall avoid shading from neighbouring plants. Most tall plants require thick stems, which enable greater vascular flow to and from the leaves and stronger mechanical support for them. Vines are an exception, relying on other objects (usually other plants) to support their stems. In woody plants, stems become thicker through secondary growth (see Figure 35.11).

Branching generally enables plants to harvest sunlight for photosynthesis more effectively. However, some species, such as the coconut palm, do not branch at all. Why is there so much variation in branching patterns? Plants have only a finite amount of energy to devote to shoot growth. If most of that energy goes into branching, there is less available for growing tall, and the risk of being shaded by taller plants increases. Conversely, if most of the energy goes into growing tall, the plants are not optimally harvesting sunlight. A variety of shoot architectures among species have evolved through natural selection optimizing the ability to absorb light in the ecological niche each species occupies.

Leaf size and structure account for much of the outward diversity in plant form. Leaves range in length from the minuscule 1.3-mm leaves of the pygmy weed (*Crassula erecta*), a native of dry, sandy regions in the western United States, to the 20-m leaves of the palm *Raphia regalis*, a native of African rain forests. These species represent extreme examples of a general correlation observed between water availability and leaf size. The largest leaves

are typically found in species from tropical rain forests, whereas the smallest are usually found in species from dry or very cold environments, where liquid water is scarce and evaporative loss from leaves is potentially more problematic.

The arrangement of leaves on a stem, known as **phyllotaxy**, is an architectural feature of immense importance in light capture. Phyllotaxy is genetically determined and programmed by the shoot apical meristem (see Figure 35.16) and is specific to each species (**Figure 36.3**). A species may have one leaf per node (alternate, or spiral, phyllotaxy), two leaves per node (opposite phyllotaxy), or more (whorled phyllotaxy). Most angiosperms have alternate phyllotaxy, with leaves arranged in an ascending spiral around the stem, each successive leaf emerging 137.5° from the site of the previous one. Why 137.5°? Mathematical analyses suggest that this angle minimizes shading of the lower leaves by those above. In environments where intense sunlight can harm leaves, the greater shading provided by oppositely arranged leaves may be advantageous.

Plant features that reduce self-shading increase light capture. A useful measurement in this regard is the *leaf area index*, the ratio of the total upper leaf surface of a single plant or an entire crop divided by the surface area of the land on which the plant or crop grows (**Figure 36.4**). Leaf area index values of up to 7 are common for many mature crops, and there is little agricultural benefit to leaf area indexes higher than this value. Adding more leaves increases shading of lower leaves to the point that they respire more than photosynthesize. When this happens, the nonproductive leaves or branches undergo programmed

▲ **Figure 36.3 Emerging phyllotaxy of Norway spruce.** This SEM, taken from above a shoot tip, shows the pattern of emergence of leaves. The leaves are numbered, with 1 being the youngest. (Some numbered leaves are not visible in the close-up.)

? *With your finger, trace the progression of leaf emergence, starting with leaf number 29. What is the pattern?*

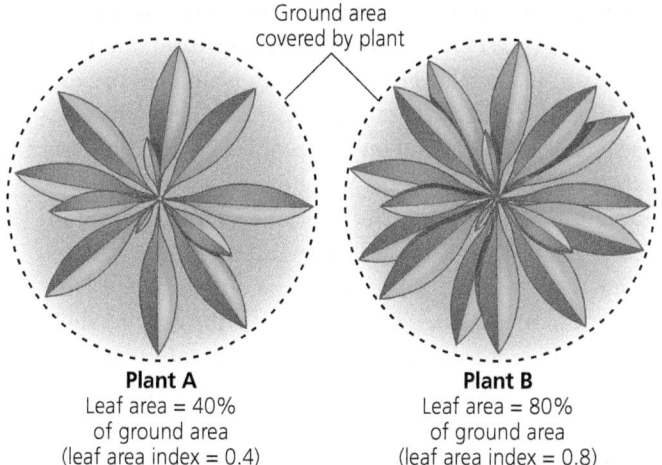

Ground area covered by plant

Plant A
Leaf area = 40%
of ground area
(leaf area index = 0.4)

Plant B
Leaf area = 80%
of ground area
(leaf area index = 0.8)

▲ Figure 36.4 **Leaf area index.** The leaf area index of a single plant is the ratio of the total area of the top surfaces of the leaves to the area of ground covered by the plant, as shown in this illustration of two plants viewed from the top. With many layers of leaves, a leaf area index value can easily exceed 1.

? *Would a higher leaf area index always increase the amount of photosynthesis? Explain.*

cell death and are eventually shed, a process called *self-pruning*.

Another factor affecting light capture is leaf orientation. Some plants have horizontally oriented leaves; others, such as grasses, have leaves that are vertically oriented. In low-light conditions, horizontal leaves capture sunlight much more effectively than vertical leaves. In grasslands or other sunny regions, however, horizontal orientation may expose upper leaves to overly intense light, injuring leaves and reducing photosynthesis. But if a plant's leaves are nearly vertical, light rays are essentially parallel to the leaf surfaces, so no leaf receives too much light, and light penetrates more deeply to the lower leaves.

Root Architecture and Acquisition of Water and Minerals

Just as carbon dioxide and sunlight are resources exploited by the shoot system, soil contains resources mined by the root system. Plants rapidly adjust the architecture and physiology of their roots to exploit patches of available nutrients in the soil. The roots of many plants, for example, respond to pockets of low nitrate availability in soils by extending straight through the pockets instead of branching within them. Conversely, when encountering a pocket rich in nitrate, a root will often branch extensively there. Root cells also respond to high soil nitrate levels by synthesizing more proteins involved in nitrate transport and assimilation. Thus, not only does the plant devote more of its mass to exploiting a nitrate-rich patch, the cells also absorb nitrate more efficiently.

Efficient absorption of limited nutrients is also enhanced by reduced competition within the root system of a plant. For example, cuttings from the stolons of buffalo grass (*Buchloe dactyloides*) develop fewer and shorter roots in the presence of cuttings from the same plant than they do in the presence of cuttings from another buffalo grass plant. Although the mechanism underlying this ability to distinguish self from nonself is unknown, avoiding competition between roots of the same plant for the same limited pool of resources certainly seems beneficial.

The evolution of mutualistic associations between roots and fungi called **mycorrhizae** was a critical step in the successful colonization of land by vascular plants, especially given the poorly developed soils available at that time. Mycorrhizal hyphae endow the fungus and plant roots with an enormous surface area for absorbing water and minerals, particularly phosphate. The role of mycorrhizae in plant nutrition will be examined more fully in Chapter 37.

Once acquired, resources must be transported to other parts of the plant that need them. In the next section, we examine the processes and pathways that enable resources such as water, minerals, and sugars to be transported throughout the plant.

CONCEPT CHECK 36.1

1. Why is long-distance transport important for vascular plants?

2. What architectural features influence self-shading?

3. Some plants can detect increased levels of light reflected from leaves of encroaching neighbours. This detection elicits stem elongation, production of erect leaves, and reduced lateral branching. How do these responses help the plant compete?

4. **WHAT IF?** If you prune a plant's shoot tips, what will be the immediate effect on the plant's branching and leaf area index?

5. **MAKE CONNECTIONS** Explain how fungal hyphae provide more surface area for nutrient absorption. (See Concept 31.1).

For suggested answers, see Appendix A.

CONCEPT **36.2**

Different mechanisms transport substances over short or long distances

Given the diversity of substances that move through plants and the great range of distances and barriers over which such substances must be transported, it is not surprising that plants employ a variety of transport processes. Before examining these processes, however, we will look at the two major pathways of transport: the apoplast and the symplast.

The Apoplast and Symplast: Transport Continuums

Plant tissues may be viewed as having two major compartments—the apoplast and the symplast. The

apoplast consists of everything external to the plasma membranes of living cells and includes cell walls, extracellular spaces, and the interior of dead cells such as vessel elements and tracheids (see Figure 35.10). The **symplast** consists of the entire mass of cytosol of all the living cells in a plant, as well as the plasmodesmata, the cytoplasmic channels that interconnect them.

The compartmental structure of plants provides three routes for transport within a plant tissue or organ: the apoplastic, symplastic, and transmembrane routes (Figure 36.5). In the *apoplastic route*, water and solutes (dissolved chemicals) move along the continuum of cell walls and extracellular spaces much like the way water moves through a sponge. In the *symplastic route*, water and solutes move along the continuum of cytosol. This route requires substances to cross a plasma membrane once, when they first enter the plant. After entering one cell, substances can move from cell to cell via plasmodesmata. In the *transmembrane route*, water and solutes move out of one cell, across the cell wall, and into the neighbouring cell, which may pass them to the next cell in the same way. The transmembrane route requires repeated crossings of plasma membranes as substances exit one cell and enter the next. These three routes are not mutually exclusive, and some substances may use more than one route to varying degrees.

Short-Distance Transport of Solutes across Plasma Membranes

In plants, as in any organism, the selective permeability of the plasma membrane controls the short-distance movement of substances into and out of cells (see Chapter 7). Both active and passive transport mechanisms occur in plants, and plant cell membranes are equipped with the same general types of pumps and transport proteins (channel proteins, carrier proteins, and cotransporters) that function in other cells. In this section, we focus on some ways that plants differ from animals in solute transport across plasma membranes.

Unlike animal cells, hydrogen ions (H^+) rather than sodium ions (Na^+) play the primary role in basic transport processes in plant cells. For example, in plant cells the membrane potential (the voltage across the membrane) is established mainly through the pumping of H^+ by proton pumps (Figure 36.6a), rather than the pumping of Na^+ by sodium-potassium pumps. Also, H^+ is most often cotransported in plants, whereas Na^+ is typically cotransported in animals. During cotransport, plant cells use the energy in the H^+ gradient and membrane potential to drive the active transport of many different solutes. For instance, cotransport with H^+ is responsible for absorption of neutral solutes, such as the sugar sucrose, by phloem cells and other plant cells. An H^+/sucrose cotransporter couples movement of sucrose against its concentration gradient with movement of H^+ down its electrochemical gradient (Figure 36.6b). Cotransport with H^+ also facilitates movement of ions, as in the uptake of nitrate (NO_3^-) by root cells (Figure 36.6c).

The membranes of plant cells also have ion channels that allow only certain ions to pass (Figure 36.6d). As in animal cells, most channels are gated, opening or closing in response to stimuli such as chemicals, pressure, or voltage. Later in this chapter, we discuss how K^+ ion channels in guard cells function in opening and closing stomata. Ion channels are also involved in producing electrical signals analogous to the action potentials of animals (see Chapter 48). However, these signals are 1000 times slower and employ Ca^{2+}-activated anion channels rather than the Na^+ ion channels used by animal cells.

Short-Distance Transport of Water across Plasma Membranes

The absorption or loss of water by a cell occurs by **osmosis**, the diffusion of free water—water that is not bound to solutes or surfaces—across a membrane (see Figure 7.11). The physical property that predicts the direction in which water will flow is called **water potential**, a quantity that includes the effects of solute concentration and physical pressure.

Free water moves from regions of higher water potential to regions of lower water potential if there is no barrier to its flow. The word *potential* in the term *water potential* refers to water's potential energy—water's capacity to perform work when it moves from a region of higher water potential to a region of lower water potential.

For example, if a plant cell or seed is immersed in a solution that has a higher water potential, water will move into the cell or seed, causing it to expand. The expansion of plant cells and seeds

The apoplast is the continuum of cell walls and extracellular spaces.

The symplast is the continuum of cytosol connected by plasmodesmata.

Cell wall

Cytosol

Apoplastic route

Symplastic route

Transmembrane route

Plasmodesma

Plasma membrane

Key

Apoplast

Symplast

▲ Figure 36.5 **Cell compartments and routes for short-distance transport.** Some substances may use more than one transport route.

(a) H⁺ and membrane potential. The plasma membranes of plant cells use ATP-dependent proton pumps to pump H⁺ out of the cell. These pumps contribute to the membrane potential and the establishment of a pH gradient across the membrane. These two forms of potential energy can drive the transport of solutes.

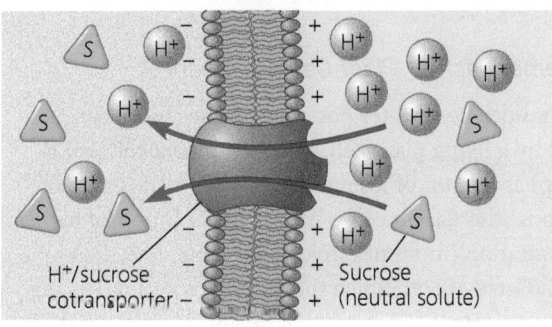

(b) H⁺ and cotransport of neutral solutes. Neutral solutes such as sugars can be loaded into plant cells by cotransport with H⁺ ions. H⁺/sucrose cotransporters, for example, play a key role in loading sugar into the phloem prior to sugar transport throughout the plant.

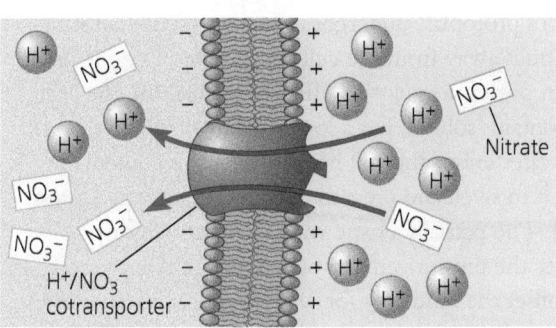

(c) H⁺ and cotransport of ions. Cotransport mechanisms involving H⁺ also participate in regulating ion fluxes into and out of cells. For example, H^+/NO_3^- cotransporters in the plasma membranes of root cells are important for the uptake of NO_3^- by plant roots.

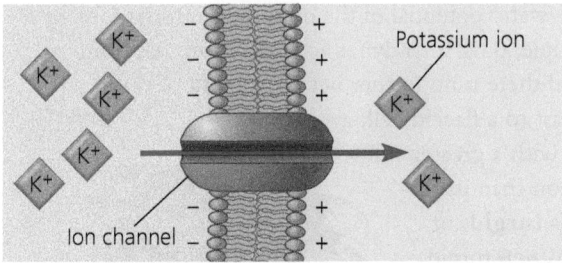

(d) Ion channels. Plant ion channels open and close in response to voltage, stretching of the membrane, and chemical factors. When open, ion channels allow specific ions to diffuse across membranes. For example, a K⁺ ion channel is involved in the release of K⁺ from guard cells when stomata close.

▲ Figure 36.6 **Solute transport across plant cell plasma membranes.**

? *Assume that a plant cell has all four of the plasma membrane transport proteins shown above. Assume also that you have specific inhibitors for each of the four transport proteins. Then predict what effect the individual application of each inhibitor would have on the cell's membrane potential.*

can be a powerful force: The expansion of cells in tree roots can break concrete sidewalks, and the swelling of wet grain seeds within the holds of damaged ships can produce catastrophic hull failure and sink the ships. Given the strong forces generated by swelling seeds, it is interesting to consider what causes water uptake by seeds. You can explore this question in the Scientific Skills Exercise by examining the effect of temperature.

Water potential is abbreviated by the Greek letter ψ (psi, pronounced "sigh"). Plant biologists measure ψ in a unit of pressure called a **megapascal** (abbreviated MPa).

By definition, the ψ of pure water in a container open to the atmosphere under standard conditions (at sea level and 20°C) is 0 MPa. One MPa is equal to about 10 times atmospheric pressure at sea level (101.3 kPa). The internal pressure of a living plant cell due to the osmotic uptake of water is approximately 0.5 MPa, about twice the air pressure inside an inflated car tire.

How Solutes and Pressure Affect Water Potential

Both solute concentration and physical pressure can affect water potential, as expressed in the *water potential equation*:

$$\psi = \psi_S + \psi_P$$

where ψ is the water potential, ψ_S is the solute potential (osmotic potential), and ψ_P is the pressure potential. The **solute potential** (ψ_S) of a solution is directly proportional to its molarity. Solute potential is also called *osmotic potential* because solutes affect the direction of osmosis. The solutes in plants are typically mineral ions and sugars. By definition, the ψ_S of pure water is 0. When solutes are added, they bind water molecules. As a result, there are fewer free water molecules, reducing the capacity of the water to move and do work. In this way, an increase in solutes has a negative effect on water potential, which is why the ψ_S of a solution is always expressed as a negative number. For example, a 0.1 M solution of a sugar has a ψ_S of −0.23 MPa. As the solute concentration increases, ψ_S becomes more negative.

Pressure potential (ψ_P) is the physical pressure on a solution. Unlike ψ_S, ψ_P can be positive or negative relative to atmospheric pressure. For example, when a solution is being withdrawn by a syringe, it is under negative pressure; when it is being expelled from a syringe, it is under positive pressure. The water in living cells is usually under positive pressure due to the osmotic uptake of water. Specifically, the **protoplast** (the living part of the cell, which also includes the plasma membrane) presses against the cell wall, creating what is known as **turgor pressure**. This pushing effect of

Calculating and Interpreting Temperature Coefficients

Does the Initial Uptake of Water by Seeds Depend on Temperature? One way to answer this question is to soak seeds in water at different temperatures and measure the rate of water uptake at each temperature. The data can be used to calculate the temperature coefficient, Q_{10}, the factor by which a physiological reaction (or process) rate increases when the temperature is raised by 10°C:

$$Q_{10} = \left(\frac{k_2}{k_1}\right)^{\frac{10}{t_2-t_1}}$$

where t_2 is the higher temperature (°C), t_1 is the lower temperature, k_2 is the reaction (or process) rate at t_2, and k_1 is the reaction (or process) rate at t_1. (If $t_2 - t_1 = 10$, as here, the math is simplified.)

Q_{10} values may be used to make inferences about the physiological process under investigation. Chemical (metabolic) processes involving large-scale protein shape changes are highly dependent on temperature and have higher Q_{10} values, closer to 2 or 3. In contrast, many, but not all, physical parameters are relatively independent of temperature and have Q_{10} values closer to 1. For example, the Q_{10} of the change in the viscosity of water is 1.2–1.3. In this exercise, you will calculate Q_{10} using data from radish seeds (*Raphanus sativum*) to assess whether the initial uptake of water by seeds is more likely to be a physical or a chemical process.

How the Experiment Was Done Samples of radish seeds were weighed and placed in water at four different temperatures. After 30 minutes, the seeds were removed, blotted dry, and reweighed. The researchers then calculated the percent increase in mass due to water uptake for each sample.

Data from the Experiment

Temperature	% Increase in Mass Due to Water Uptake After 30 Minutes
5°C	18.5
15°C	26.0
25°C	31.0
35°C	36.2

Interpret the Data

1. Based on the data, does the initial uptake of water by radish seeds vary with temperature? What is the relationship between temperature and water uptake?

2. (a) Using the data for 35°C and 25°C, calculate Q_{10} for water uptake by radish seeds. Repeat the calculation using the data for 25°C and 15°C and the data for 15°C and 5°C. (b) What is the average Q_{10}? (c) Do your results imply that the uptake of water by radish seeds is mainly a physical process or a chemical (metabolic) process? (d) Given that the Q_{10} for the change in the viscosity of water is 1.2–1.3, could the slight temperature dependence of water uptake by seeds be a reflection of the slight temperature dependence of the viscosity of water?

3. Besides temperature, what other independent variables could you alter to test whether radish seed swelling is essentially a physical process or a chemical process?

4. Would you expect plant growth to have a Q_{10} closer to 1 or 3? Why?

Data from J. D. Murphy and D. L. Noland, Temperature effects on seed imbibition and leakage mediated by viscosity and membranes, *Plant Physiology* 69:428–431 (1982). © Jane B Reece.

internal pressure, much like the air in an inflated tire, is critical for plant function because it helps maintain the stiffness of plant tissues and also serves as the driving force for cell elongation. Conversely, the water in the hollow nonliving xylem cells (tracheids and vessel elements) of a plant is often under a negative pressure potential (tension) of less than −2 MPa.

As you learn to apply the water potential equation, keep in mind the key point: *Water moves from regions of higher water potential to regions of lower water potential.*

Water Movement across Plant Cell Membranes

Now let's consider how water potential affects absorption and loss of water by a living plant cell. First, imagine a cell that is **flaccid** (limp) as a result of losing water. The cell has a ψ_P of 0 MPa. Suppose this flaccid cell is bathed in a solution of higher solute concentration (more negative solute potential) than the cell itself (**Figure 36.7a**). Since the external solution has the lower (more negative) water potential, water diffuses out of the cell. The cell's protoplast undergoes **plasmolysis**—that is, it shrinks and pulls away from the cell wall. If we place the same flaccid cell in pure water ($\psi = 0$ MPa) (**Figure 36.7b**), the cell, because it contains solutes, has a lower water potential than the water, and water enters the cell by osmosis. The contents of the cell begin to swell and press the plasma membrane against the cell wall. The partially elastic wall, exerting turgor pressure, confines the pressurized protoplast. When this pressure is enough to offset the tendency for water to enter because of the solutes in the cell, then ψ_P and ψ_S are equal, and $\psi = 0$. This matches the water potential of the extracellular environment—in this example, 0 MPa. A dynamic equilibrium has been reached, and there is no further net movement of water.

In contrast to a flaccid cell, a walled cell with a greater solute concentration than its surroundings is **turgid**, or very firm. When turgid cells in a nonwoody tissue push against each other, the tissue is stiffened. The effects of turgor loss are seen during **wilting**, when leaves and stems droop as a result of cells losing water.

Turgid

Wilted

Nigel Cattlin/Science Source

Aquaporins: Facilitating Diffusion of Water

A difference in water potential determines the *direction* of water movement across membranes, but how do water molecules actually cross the membranes? Water molecules are small enough

Initial flaccid cell:
$\psi_P = 0$
$\underline{\psi_S = -0.7}$
$\psi = -0.7$ MPa

Environment
0.4 *M* sucrose solution:
$\psi_P = 0$
$\underline{\psi_S = -0.9}$
$\psi = -0.9$ MPa

Final plasmolyzed cell
at osmotic equilibrium
with its surroundings:
$\psi_P = 0$
$\underline{\psi_S = -0.9}$
$\psi = -0.9$ MPa

(a) Initial conditions: cellular ψ > environmental ψ. The protoplast loses water, and the cell plasmolyzes. After plasmolysis is complete, the water potentials of the cell and its surroundings are the same.

Initial flaccid cell:
$\psi_P = 0$
$\underline{\psi_S = -0.7}$
$\psi = -0.7$ MPa

Environment
Pure water:
$\psi_P = 0$
$\underline{\psi_S = 0}$
$\psi = 0$ MPa

Final turgid cell
at osmotic equilibrium
with its surroundings:
$\psi_P = 0.7$
$\underline{\psi_S = -0.7}$
$\psi = 0$ MPa

(b) Initial conditions: cellular ψ < environmental ψ. There is a net uptake of water by osmosis, causing the cell to become turgid. When this tendency for water to enter is offset by the back pressure of the elastic wall, water potentials are equal for the cell and its surroundings. (The volume change of the cell is exaggerated in this diagram.)

▲ **Figure 36.7 Water relations in plant cells.** In these experiments, flaccid cells (cells in which the protoplast contacts the cell wall but lacks turgor pressure) are placed in two environments. Blue arrows indicate initial net water movement.

to diffuse across the phospholipid bilayer, even though the bilayer's interior is hydrophobic. However, their movement across biological membranes is too rapid to be explained by unaided diffusion. The transport of water molecules across membranes is facilitated by transport proteins called **aquaporins** (see Chapter 7). These selective channels affect the *rate* at which water moves osmotically across the membrane. Aquaporin channel proteins are highly dynamic: Their permeability is decreased by increases in cytosolic Ca^{2+} or decreases in cytosolic pH.

Long-Distance Transport: The Role of Bulk Flow

Diffusion is an effective transport mechanism over the spatial scales typically found at the cellular level. However, diffusion is much too slow to function in long-distance transport within a plant. Although diffusion from one end of a cell to the other takes just seconds, diffusion from the roots to the top of a giant redwood would take several centuries. Instead, long-distance transport occurs through **bulk flow**, the movement of liquid in response to a pressure gradient. The bulk flow of material always occurs from higher to lower pressure. Unlike osmosis, bulk flow is independent of solute concentration.

Long-distance bulk flow occurs within the tracheids and vessel elements of the xylem and within the sieve-tube elements of the phloem. The structures of these conducting cells facilitate bulk flow. As you saw in Figure 35.10, mature tracheids and vessel elements are dead cells and therefore have no cytoplasm, and the cytoplasm of sieve-tube elements is almost devoid of internal organelles. If you have ever dealt with a partially clogged drain, you know that

the volume of flow depends on the pipe's diameter. Clogs reduce the effective diameter of the drainpipe. Such experiences help us understand how the structures of plant cells specialized for bulk flow fit their function. Like the unplugging of a kitchen drain, the absence or reduction of cytoplasm in a plant's "plumbing" allows for efficient bulk flow through the xylem and phloem. Bulk flow is also enhanced by the perforation plates at the ends of vessel elements and the porous sieve plates connecting sieve-tube elements.

Diffusion, active transport, and bulk flow act in concert to transport resources throughout the whole plant. For example, bulk flow due to a pressure difference is the mechanism of long-distance transport of sugars in the phloem, but active transport of sugar at the cellular level maintains this pressure difference. In the next three sections, we examine in more detail the transport of water and minerals from roots to shoots, the control of evaporation, and the transport of sugars.

CONCEPT CHECK 36.2

1. If a plant cell immersed in distilled water has a ψ_S of −0.7 MPa and a ψ of 0 MPa, what is the cell's ψ_P? If you put it in an open beaker of solution that has a ψ of −0.4 MPa, what would be its ψ_P at equilibrium?

2. How would a reduction in the number of aquaporin channels affect a plant cell's ability to adjust to new osmotic conditions?

3. How would the long-distance transport of water be affected if tracheids and vessel elements were alive at maturity? Explain.

4. **WHAT IF?** What would happen if you put plant protoplasts in pure water? Explain.

For suggested answers, see Appendix A.

Transpiration drives the transport of water and minerals from roots to shoots via the xylem

Picture yourself struggling to carry a 19-L container of water weighing 19 kg up several flights of stairs. Imagine doing this 40 times a day. Now consider how a 70-m-tall Western Red Cedar tree (*Thuja plicata*) (the provincial tree of British Columbia) is able to move water from below ground level to the tips of its branches, despite having neither heart nor muscle. How do trees accomplish this feat? To answer this question, we'll follow each step in the journey of water and minerals from the tips of roots to leaves.

Absorption of Water and Minerals by Root Epidermal Cells

Although all living plant cells absorb nutrients across their plasma membranes, the root hair epidermal cells near the tips of roots are particularly important because most of the absorption of water and minerals occurs there. In this region, the epidermal cells are permeable to water, and many are differentiated into root hairs, modified cells that account for much of the absorption of water by roots (see Figure 35.3). The root hairs absorb the soil solution, which consists of water molecules and dissolved mineral ions that are not bound tightly to soil particles. The soil solution is drawn into the hydrophilic walls of epidermal cells and passes freely along the cell walls and the extracellular spaces into the root cortex. This flow enhances the exposure of the cells of the cortex to the soil solution, providing a much greater membrane surface area for absorption than the surface area of the epidermis alone. Although the soil solution usually has a low mineral concentration, active transport enables roots to accumulate essential minerals, such as K^+ and NO_3^-, to concentrations hundreds of times greater than in the soil.

Transport of Water and Minerals into the Xylem

Water and minerals that pass from the soil into the root cortex cannot be transported to the rest of the plant until they enter the xylem of the vascular cylinder, or stele. The **endodermis**, the innermost layer of cells in the root cortex, functions as a last checkpoint for the selective passage of minerals from the cortex into the vascular cylinder (Figure 36.8). Minerals already in the symplast when they reach the endodermis continue through the plasmodesmata of endodermal cells and pass into the vascular cylinder. These minerals were already screened by the plasma membrane they had to cross to enter the symplast in the epidermis or cortex.

Minerals that reach the endodermis via the apoplast encounter a dead end that blocks their passage into the vascular cylinder. This barrier, located in the transverse and radial walls of each endodermal cell, is the **Casparian strip**, a belt made of suberin, a waxy material impervious to water and dissolved minerals (see Figure 36.8). Because of the Casparian strip, water and minerals cannot cross the endodermis and enter the vascular cylinder via the apoplast. Instead, water and minerals that are passively moving through the apoplast must cross the *selectively permeable* plasma membrane of an endodermal cell before they can enter the vascular cylinder. In this way, the endodermis transports needed minerals from the soil into the xylem and keeps many unneeded or toxic substances out. The endodermis also prevents solutes that have accumulated in the xylem from leaking back into the soil solution.

The last segment in the soil-to-xylem pathway is the passage of water and minerals into the tracheids and vessel elements of the xylem. These water-conducting cells lack protoplasts when mature and are therefore parts of the apoplast. Endodermal cells, as well as living cells within the vascular cylinder, discharge minerals from their protoplasts into their own cell walls. Both diffusion and active transport are involved in this transfer of solutes from symplast to apoplast, and the water and minerals are now free to enter the tracheids and vessel elements, where they are transported to the shoot system by bulk flow.

Bulk Flow Transport via the Xylem

Water and minerals from the soil enter the plant through the epidermis of roots, cross the root cortex, and pass into the vascular cylinder. From there the **xylem sap**, the water and dissolved minerals in the xylem, gets transported long distances by bulk flow to the veins that branch throughout each leaf. As noted earlier, bulk flow is much faster than diffusion or active transport. Peak velocities in the transport of xylem sap can range from 15 to 45 m/hr for trees with wide vessel elements. Stems and leaves depend on this efficient delivery system for their supply of water and minerals.

The process of transporting xylem sap involves the loss of an astonishing amount of water by **transpiration**, the loss of water vapour from leaves and other aerial parts of the plant. A single maize plant, for example, transpires 60 L of water during a growing season. A maize crop growing at a typical density of 60 000 plants per hectare transpires almost 4 million L of water per hectare every growing season. Unless the transpired water is replaced by water transported up from the roots, the leaves will wilt, and the plants will eventually die.

Xylem sap rises to heights of more than 120 m in the tallest trees. Is the sap mainly *pushed* upward from the roots, or is it mainly *pulled* upward? Let's evaluate the relative contributions of these two mechanisms.

▼ **Figure 36.8 Transport of water and minerals from root hairs to the xylem.**

? *How does the Casparian strip force water and minerals to pass through the plasma membranes of endodermal cells?*

1 Apoplastic route. Uptake of soil solution by the hydrophilic walls of root hairs provides access to the apoplast. Water and minerals can then diffuse into the cortex along this matrix of walls and extracellular spaces.

2 Symplastic route. Minerals and water that cross the plasma membranes of root hairs can enter the symplast.

3 Transmembrane route. As soil solution moves along the apoplast, some water and minerals are transported into the protoplasts of cells of the epidermis and cortex and then move inward via the symplast.

4 The endodermis: controlled entry to the vascular cylinder (stele). Within the transverse and radial walls of each endodermal cell is the Casparian strip, a belt of waxy material (purple band) that blocks the passage of water and dissolved minerals. Only minerals already in the symplast or entering that pathway by crossing the plasma membrane of an endodermal cell can detour around the Casparian strip and pass into the vascular cylinder (stele).

5 Transport in the xylem. Endodermal cells and also living cells within the vascular cylinder discharge water and minerals into their walls (apoplast). The xylem vessels then transport the water and minerals by bulk flow upward into the shoot system.

Pushing Xylem Sap: Root Pressure

At night, when there is almost no transpiration, root cells continue actively pumping mineral ions into the xylem of the vascular cylinder. Meanwhile, the Casparian strip of the endodermis prevents the ions from leaking back out into the cortex and soil. The resulting accumulation of minerals lowers the water potential within the vascular cylinder. Water flows in from the root cortex, generating **root pressure**, a push of xylem sap. The root pressure sometimes causes more water to enter the leaves than is transpired, resulting in **guttation**, the exudation of water droplets that can be seen in the morning on the tips or edges of some plant leaves (Figure 36.9). Guttation fluid should not be confused with dew, which is condensed atmospheric moisture.

In most plants, root pressure is a minor mechanism driving the ascent of xylem sap, pushing water only a few metres at most. The positive pressures produced are simply too weak to overcome the gravitational force of the water column in the xylem, particularly in tall plants. Many plants

do not generate any root pressure or do so only during part of the growing season. Even in plants that display guttation, root pressure cannot keep pace with transpiration after

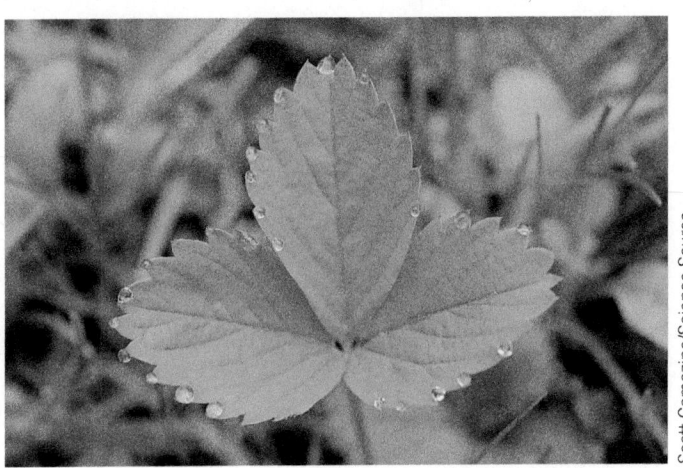

▲ **Figure 36.9 Guttation.** Root pressure is forcing excess water from this strawberry leaf.

sunrise. For the most part, xylem sap is not pushed from below by root pressure but is pulled up.

Pulling Xylem Sap: The Cohesion-Tension Hypothesis

As we have seen, root pressure, which depends on the active transport of solutes by plants, is only a minor force in the ascent of xylem sap. Far from depending on the metabolic activity of cells, most of the xylem sap that rises through a tree does not even require living cells to do so. As demonstrated by Eduard Strasburger in 1891, leafy stems with their lower end immersed in toxic solutions of copper sulphate or acid will readily draw these poisons up if the stem is cut below the surface of the liquid. As the toxic solutions ascend, they kill all living cells in their path, eventually arriving in the transpiring leaves and killing the leaf cells as well. Nevertheless, as Strasburger noted, the uptake of the toxic solutions and the loss of water from the dead leaves can continue for weeks.

In 1894, a few years after Strasburger's findings, two Irish scientists, John Joly and Henry Dixon, put forward a hypothesis that remains the leading explanation of the ascent of xylem sap. According to their **cohesion-tension hypothesis**, transpiration provides the pull for the ascent of xylem sap, and the cohesion of water molecules transmits this pull along the entire length of the xylem from shoots to roots. Hence, xylem sap is normally under negative pressure, or tension. Since transpiration is a "pulling" process, our exploration of the rise of xylem sap by the cohesion-tension mechanism begins not with the roots but with the leaves, where the driving force for transpirational pull begins.

Transpirational Pull Stomata on a leaf's surface lead to a maze of internal air spaces that expose the mesophyll cells to the CO_2 they need for photosynthesis. The air in these spaces is saturated with water vapour because it is in contact with the moist walls of the cells. On most days, the air outside the leaf is drier; that is, it has lower water potential than the air inside the leaf. Therefore, water vapour in the air spaces of a leaf diffuses down its water potential gradient and exits the leaf via the stomata. It is this loss of water vapour by diffusion and evaporation that we call transpiration.

But how does loss of water vapour from the leaf translate into a pulling force for upward movement of water through a plant? The negative pressure potential that causes water to move up through the xylem develops at the surface of mesophyll cell walls in the leaf (**Figure 36.10**). The cell wall acts like a very thin capillary network. Water adheres to the cellulose microfibrils and other hydrophilic components of the cell wall. As water evaporates from the water film that covers the cell walls of mesophyll cells, the air-water interface retreats farther into the cell wall. Because of the high surface tension of water, the curvature of the interface induces a tension, or negative pressure potential, in the water. As more water evaporates from the cell wall, the curvature of the air-water interface increases and the pressure of the water becomes more negative. Water molecules from the more hydrated parts of the leaf are then pulled toward this area, reducing the tension. These pulling forces are transferred to the xylem because each water molecule is cohesively bound to the next by hydrogen bonds. Thus, transpirational pull depends on several of the properties of water discussed in Chapter 3: adhesion, cohesion, and surface tension.

The role of negative pressure potential in transpiration is consistent with the water potential equation because negative

⑤ Water from the xylem is pulled into the surrounding cells and air spaces to replace the water that was lost.

④ The increased surface tension shown in step ③ pulls water from surrounding cells and air spaces.

③ The evaporation of the water film causes the air-water interface to retreat farther into the cell wall and to become more curved. This curvature increases the surface tension and the rate of transpiration.

② At first, the water vapour lost by transpiration is replaced by evaporation from the water film that coats mesophyll cells.

Cuticle
Upper epidermis
Xylem
Mesophyll
Air space
Lower epidermis
Cuticle
Stoma
Microfibrils in cell wall of mesophyll cell
Microfibril (cross section) — Water film — Air-water interface

① In transpiration, water vapour (shown as blue dots) diffuses from the moist air spaces of the leaf to the drier air outside via stomata.

◄ **Figure 36.10 Generation of transpirational pull.** Negative pressure (tension) at the air-water interface in the leaf is the basis of transpirational pull, which draws water out of the xylem.

pressure potential (tension) *lowers* water potential. Because water moves from areas of higher water potential to areas of lower water potential, the more negative pressure potential at the air-water interface causes water in xylem cells to be "pulled" into mesophyll cells, which lose water to the air spaces, the water diffusing out through stomata. In this way, the negative water potential of leaves provides the "pull" in transpirational pull. The transpirational pull on xylem sap is transmitted all the way from the leaves to the root tips and even into the soil solution (Figure 36.11).

One consequence of climate change is that there is an increasing amount of water vapour in the atmosphere (increased relative humidity), which decreases the air's water potential. With a smaller difference between the water potentials of the air spaces within the leaves and the atmosphere, transpirational pull, and therefore xylem sap transport, will diminish. As a result, there will be insufficient water delivered to meet the photosynthetic demands of the leaves. As you will learn in the next chapter, decreased xylem transport also produces deficiencies in essential nutrients required for the synthesis of biological molecules and growth.

Adhesion and Cohesion in the Ascent of Xylem Sap

Adhesion and cohesion facilitate the transport of water by bulk flow. Adhesion is the attractive force between water molecules and other polar substances. Because both water and cellulose are polar molecules capable of forming hydrogen bonds, there is a strong attraction between water molecules and the cellulose molecules in the xylem cell walls. Cohesion is the attractive force between molecules of the same substance. Water has an unusually high cohesive force due to the hydrogen bonds each water molecule can potentially make with other water molecules. It is estimated that water's cohesive force within the xylem gives it a tensile strength equivalent to that of a steel wire of similar diameter. The cohesion of water makes it possible to pull a column of xylem sap from above without the water molecules separating. Water molecules exiting the xylem in the leaf tug on adjacent water molecules, and this pull is relayed,

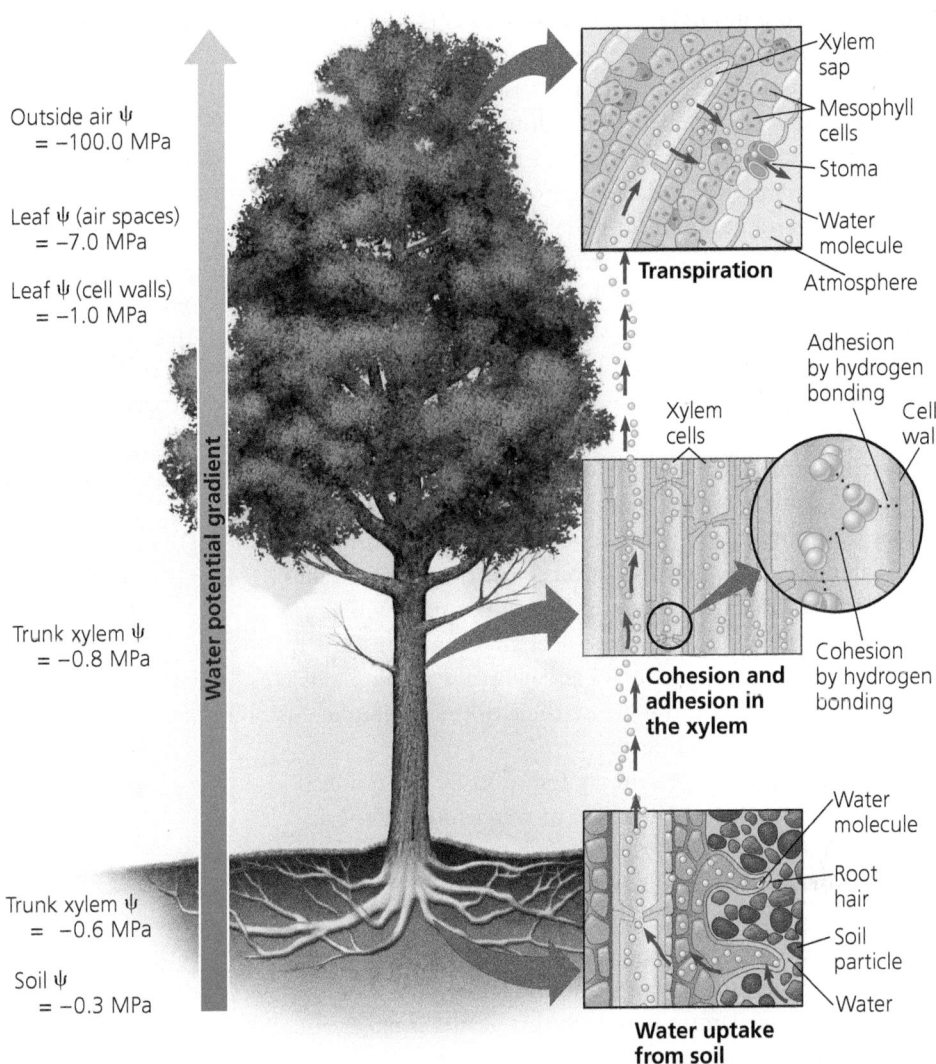

Outside air ψ = −100.0 MPa

Leaf ψ (air spaces) = −7.0 MPa

Leaf ψ (cell walls) = −1.0 MPa

Trunk xylem ψ = −0.8 MPa

Trunk xylem ψ = −0.6 MPa

Soil ψ = −0.3 MPa

Water potential gradient

Xylem sap
Mesophyll cells
Stoma
Water molecule
Transpiration
Atmosphere

Adhesion by hydrogen bonding
Cell wall

Xylem cells

Cohesion and adhesion in the xylem

Cohesion by hydrogen bonding

Water molecule
Root hair
Soil particle
Water

Water uptake from soil

▲ **Figure 36.11 Ascent of xylem sap.** Hydrogen bonding forms an unbroken chain of water molecules extending from leaves to the soil. The force driving the ascent of xylem sap is a gradient of water potential (ψ). For bulk flow over long distance, the ψ gradient is due mainly to a gradient of the pressure potential (ψ_P). Transpiration results in the ψ_P at the leaf end of the xylem being lower than the ψ_P at the root end. The ψ values shown at the left are a "snapshot." They may vary during daylight, but the direction of the ψ gradient remains the same.

ANIMATION *BioFlix* Visit the Study Area in **MasteringBiology** for the BioFlix® 3-D Animation on Water Transport in Plants.

molecule by molecule, down the entire column of water in the xylem. Meanwhile, the strong adhesion of water molecules (again by hydrogen bonds) to the hydrophilic walls of xylem cells helps offset the downward force of gravity.

The upward pull on the sap creates tension within the vessel elements and tracheids, which are like elastic pipes. Positive pressure causes an elastic pipe to swell, whereas tension pulls the walls of the pipe inward. On a warm day, a decrease in the diameter of a tree trunk can even be measured. As transpirational pull puts the vessel elements and tracheids under tension, their thick secondary walls prevent them from collapsing, much as wire rings maintain the shape of a vacuum-cleaner hose. The tension produced by transpirational pull lowers water potential in the root xylem to such an extent that water flows passively from the soil, across the root cortex, and into the vascular cylinder.

Transpirational pull can extend down to the roots only through an unbroken chain of water molecules. Cavitation, the formation of a water vapour pocket, breaks the chain. It is more common in wide vessel elements than in tracheids and can occur during drought stress or when xylem sap freezes in winter. The air bubbles resulting from cavitation expand and block water channels of the xylem—known as **hydraulic failure**. The rapid expansion of air bubbles produces clicking noises that can be heard by placing sensitive microphones at the surface of the stem.

During prolonged episodes of hydraulic failure, such as when a plant is under drought stress, water exiting the leaves via transpiration is not replenished, leaving the leaves desiccated and wilted. If conditions persist, entire branches or the whole organism may die. Climate change will alter weather patterns and exacerbate drought conditions in many areas around the globe. This will place many plants under drought stress and increase their risk of hydraulic failure, desiccation, and death.

The interruption of xylem sap transport by cavitation is not always permanent. The chain of water molecules can detour around the air bubbles through pits between adjacent tracheids or vessel elements (see Figure 35.10). Moreover, root pressure enables small plants to refill blocked vessel elements. Recent evidence suggests that cavitation may even be repaired when the xylem sap is under negative pressure, although the mechanism by which this occurs is uncertain. In addition, secondary growth adds a layer of new xylem each year. Only the youngest, outermost secondary xylem layers transport water. Although the older secondary xylem no longer transport water, it does provide support for the tree (see Figure 35.22).

Xylem Sap Ascent by Bulk Flow: *A Review*

The cohesion-tension mechanism that transports xylem sap against gravity is an excellent example of how physical principles apply to biological processes. In the long-distance transport of water from roots to leaves by bulk flow, the movement of fluid is driven by a water potential difference at opposite ends of xylem tissue. The water potential difference is created at the leaf end of the xylem by the evaporation of water from leaf cells. Evaporation lowers the water potential at the air-water interface, thereby generating the negative pressure (tension) that pulls water through the xylem.

Bulk flow in the xylem differs from diffusion in some key ways. First, bulk flow is driven by differences in pressure potential (ψ_P); solute potential (ψ_S) is not a factor. Therefore, the water potential gradient within the xylem

is essentially a pressure gradient. Also, the flow does not occur across plasma membranes of living cells, but instead within hollow, dead cells. Furthermore, it moves the entire solution together—not just water or solutes—and at much greater speed than diffusion.

The plant expends no energy to lift xylem sap by bulk flow. Instead, the absorption of sunlight drives most of transpiration by causing water to evaporate from the moist walls of mesophyll cells and by lowering the water potential in the air spaces within a leaf. Thus, the ascent of xylem sap, like the process of photosynthesis, is ultimately solar powered.

CONCEPT CHECK 36.3

1. What structural characteristics of xylem cells facilitate long-distance transport?
2. A horticulturalist notices that when *Zinnia* flowers are cut at dawn, a small drop of water collects at the surface of the stump. However, when the flowers are cut at noon, no drop is observed. Suggest an explanation.
3. A scientist adds a water-soluble inhibitor of photosynthesis to roots of a transpiring plant, but photosynthesis is not reduced. Why?
4. **WHAT IF?** Suppose an *Arabidopsis* mutant lacking functional aquaporin proteins has a root mass three times greater than that of wild-type plants. Suggest an explanation.
5. **MAKE CONNECTIONS** How are the Casparian strip and tight junctions functionally similar? See Figure 6.30.

For suggested answers, see Appendix A.

CONCEPT 36.4

The rate of transpiration is regulated by stomata

Leaves generally have large surface areas and high surface-to-volume ratios. The large surface area enhances light absorption for photosynthesis. The high surface-to-volume ratio aids in CO_2 absorption during photosynthesis as well as in the release of O_2, a by-product of photosynthesis. Upon diffusing through the stomata, CO_2 enters a honeycomb of air spaces formed by the spongy mesophyll cells (see Figure 35.18). Because of the irregular shapes of these cells, the leaf's internal surface area may be 10 to 30 times greater than the external surface area.

Although large surface areas and high surface-to-volume ratios increase the rate of photosynthesis, they also increase water loss by way of the stomata. Thus, a plant's tremendous requirement for water is largely a consequence of the shoot system's need for ample exchange of CO_2 and O_2 for photosynthesis. By opening and closing the stomata, guard cells help balance the plant's requirement to conserve water with its requirement for photosynthesis (Figure 36.12).

▲ Figure 36.12 **An open stoma (left) and closed stoma (LMs).**

Stomata: Major Pathways for Water Loss

About 95% of the water a plant loses escapes through stomata, although these pores account for only 1–2% of the external leaf surface. The waxy cuticle limits water loss through the remaining surface of the leaf. Each stoma is flanked by a pair of guard cells. Guard cells control the diameter of the stoma by changing shape, thereby widening or narrowing the gap between the guard cell pair. Under the same environmental conditions, the amount of water lost by a leaf depends largely on the number of stomata and the average size of their pores.

The stomatal density of a leaf, which may be as high as 20 000 per square centimetre, is under both genetic and environmental control. For example, as a result of evolution by natural selection, desert plants are genetically programmed to have lower stomatal densities than do marsh plants. Stomatal density, however, is a developmentally plastic feature of many plants. High light exposures and low CO_2 levels during leaf development lead to increased density in many species. By measuring the stomatal density of leaf fossils, scientists have gained insight into the levels of atmospheric CO_2 in past climates. A recent British survey found that stomatal density of many woodland species has decreased since 1927, when a similar survey was made. This observation is consistent with other findings that atmospheric CO_2 levels increased dramatically during the late 20th century.

Mechanisms of Stomatal Opening and Closing

When guard cells take in water from neighbouring cells by osmosis, they become more turgid. In most angiosperm species, the cell walls of guard cells are uneven in thickness, and the cellulose microfibrils are oriented in a direction that causes the guard cells to bow outward when turgid (Figure 36.13a). This bowing outward increases the size of the pore between the guard cells. When the cells lose

water and become flaccid, they become less bowed, and the pore closes.

The changes in turgor pressure in guard cells result primarily from the reversible absorption and loss of K^+. Stomata open when guard cells actively accumulate K^+ from neighbouring epidermal cells (Figure 36.13b). The flow of K^+ across the plasma membrane of the guard cell is coupled to the generation of a membrane potential by proton pumps (see Figure 36.6a). Stomatal opening correlates with active transport of H^+ out of the guard cell. The resulting voltage (membrane potential) drives K^+ into the cell through specific membrane channels. The absorption of K^+ causes the water potential to become more negative within the guard cells, and the cells become more turgid as water enters by osmosis. Because most of the K^+ and water are stored in the vacuole, the vacuolar membrane also plays a role in

Guard cells turgid/Stoma open   **Guard cells flaccid/Stoma closed**

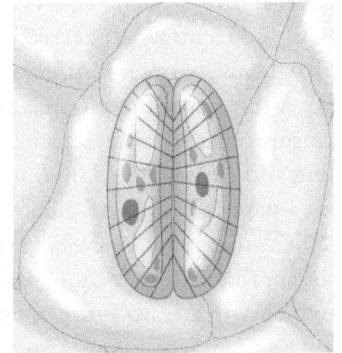

(a) Changes in guard cell shape and stomatal opening and closing (surface view). Guard cells of a typical angiosperm are illustrated in their turgid (stoma open) and flaccid (stoma closed) states. The radial orientation of cellulose microfibrils in the cell walls causes the guard cells to increase more in length than width when turgor increases. Since the two guard cells are tightly joined at their tips, they bow outward when turgid, causing the stomatal pore to open.

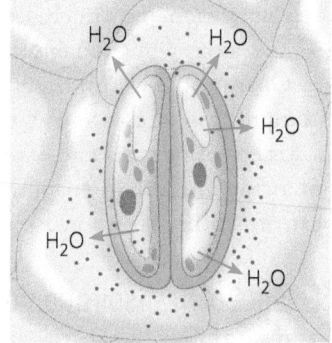

(b) Role of potassium in stomatal opening and closing. The transport of K^+ (potassium ions, symbolized here as red dots) across the plasma membrane and vacuolar membrane causes the turgor changes of guard cells. The uptake of anions, such as malate and chloride ions (not shown), also contributes to guard cell swelling.

▲ Figure 36.13 **Mechanisms of stomatal opening and closing.**

regulating guard cell dynamics. Stomatal closing results from a loss of K^+ from guard cells to neighbouring cells, which leads to an osmotic loss of water. Aquaporins also help regulate the osmotic swelling and shrinking of guard cells.

Stimuli for Stomatal Opening and Closing

In general, stomata are open during the day and mostly closed at night, preventing the plant from losing water under conditions when photosynthesis cannot occur. At least three cues contribute to stomatal opening at dawn: light, CO_2 depletion, and an internal "clock" in guard cells.

The light stimulates guard cells to accumulate K^+ and become turgid. This response is triggered by illumination of blue-light receptors in the plasma membrane of guard cells. Activation of these receptors stimulates the activity of proton pumps in the plasma membrane of the guard cells, in turn promoting absorption of K^+.

The stomata also open in response to depletion of CO_2 within the leaf's air spaces as a result of photosynthesis. As CO_2 concentrations decrease during the day, the stomata progressively open if sufficient water is supplied to the leaf.

A third cue, the internal "clock" in the guard cells, ensures that stomata continue their daily rhythm of opening and closing. This rhythm occurs even if a plant is kept in a dark location. All eukaryotic organisms have internal clocks that regulate cyclic processes. Cycles with intervals of approximately 24 hours are called **circadian rhythms**, which you'll learn more about in Chapter 39.

Environmental stresses, such as drought, high temperature, and wind, can cause stomata to close during the daytime. When the plant has a water deficiency, guard cells may lose turgor and close stomata. In addition, a hormone called **abscisic acid (ABA)**, produced in roots and leaves in response to water deficiency, signals guard cells to close stomata. This response reduces wilting but also restricts CO_2 absorption, thereby slowing photosynthesis. Since turgor is necessary for cell elongation, growth ceases throughout the plant. These are some reasons why droughts reduce crop yields.

Guard cells control the photosynthesis-transpiration compromise on a moment-to-moment basis by integrating a variety of internal and external stimuli. Even the passage of a cloud or a transient shaft of sunlight through a forest can affect the rate of transpiration.

Effects of Transpiration on Wilting and Leaf Temperature

As long as most stomata remain open, transpiration is greatest on a day that is sunny, warm, dry, and windy because these environmental factors increase evaporation. If transpiration cannot pull sufficient water to the leaves, the shoot becomes slightly wilted as cells lose turgor pressure.

Although plants respond to such mild drought stress by rapidly closing stomata, some evaporative water loss still occurs through the cuticle. Under prolonged drought conditions, leaves can become severely wilted and irreversibly injured.

Transpiration also results in evaporative cooling, which can lower a leaf's temperature by as much as 10°C compared with the surrounding air. This cooling prevents the leaf from reaching temperatures that could denature enzymes involved in photosynthesis and other metabolic processes.

Adaptations That Reduce Evaporative Water Loss

Water availability is a major determinant of plant productivity. The main reason water availability is tied to plant productivity is not related to photosynthesis's direct need for water as a substrate but rather because freely available water allows plants to keep stomata open and take up more CO_2. The problem of reducing water loss is especially acute for desert plants. Plants adapted to arid environments are called **xerophytes** (from the Greek *xero*, dry).

Many species of desert plants avoid drying out by completing their short life cycles during the brief rainy seasons. Rain comes infrequently in deserts, but when it arrives, the vegetation is transformed as dormant seeds of annual species quickly germinate and bloom, completing their life cycle before dry conditions return.

Other xerophytes have unusual physiological or morphological adaptations that enable them to withstand harsh desert conditions. The stems of many xerophytes are fleshy because they store water for use during long dry periods. Cacti have highly reduced leaves that resist excessive water loss; photosynthesis is carried out mainly in their stems. Another adaptation common in arid habitats is crassulacean acid metabolism (CAM), a specialized form of photosynthesis found in succulents of the family Crassulaceae and several other families (see Figure 10.21). Because the leaves of CAM plants take in CO_2 at night, the stomata can remain closed during the day, when evaporative stresses are greatest. Other examples of xerophytic adaptations are discussed in **Figure 36.14**.

CONCEPT CHECK 36.4

1. What are the stimuli that control the opening and closing of stomata?

2. The pathogenic fungus *Fusicoccum amygdali* secretes a toxin called fusicoccin that activates the plasma membrane proton pumps of plant cells and leads to uncontrolled water loss. Suggest a mechanism by which the activation of proton pumps could lead to severe wilting.

3. **WHAT IF?** If you buy cut flowers, why might the florist recommend cutting the stems underwater and then transferring the flowers to a vase while the cut ends are still wet?

4. **MAKE CONNECTIONS** Explain why the evaporation of water from leaves lowers their temperature. See p. 51 of Concept 3.2.

For suggested answers, see Appendix A.

► Ocotillo (*Fouquieria splendens*) is common in the southwestern region of the United States and northern Mexico. It is leafless during most of the year, thereby avoiding excessive water loss (right). Immediately after a heavy rainfall, it produces small leaves (below and inset). As the soil dries, the leaves quickly shrivel and die.

Mary Lane/Dreamstime

Nature Conservancy Tennessee Chapter Headquarters

Kate Shane/Southwest School of Botanical Medicine

► This is a close-up view of stems of old man cactus (*Cephalocereus senilis*), a Mexican desert plant. The long, white, hairlike bristles help reflect the sun.

▼ Oleander (*Nerium oleander*), shown in the inset, is commonly found in arid climates. Its leaves have a thick cuticle and multilayered epidermal tissue that reduce water loss. Stomata are recessed in cavities called "crypts," an adaptation that reduces the rate of transpiration by protecting the stomata from hot, dry wind. Trichomes help minimize transpiration by breaking up the flow of air, allowing the chamber of the crypt to have a higher humidity than the surrounding atmosphere (LM).

Cuticle   Upper epidermal tissue

Natalie Bronstein

Andrew de Lory/Dorling Kindersley, Ltd

100 μm

Trichomes ("hairs")   Crypt   Stoma   Lower epidermal tissue

Rob Tilley/Danita Delimont/Alamy

▲ Figure 36.14 **Some xerophytic adaptations.**

CONCEPT 36.5

Sugars are transported from sources to sinks via the phloem

You have read how water and minerals are absorbed by root epidermal cells, transported through the endodermis, released into the vessel elements and tracheids of the xylem, and carried to the tops of plants by the bulk flow driven by transpiration. However, transpiration cannot meet all the long-distance transport needs of the plant. The flow of water and minerals from soil to roots to leaves is largely in a direction opposite to the direction necessary for transporting sugars from mature leaves to lower parts of the plant, such as root tips that require large amounts of sugars for energy and growth. The transport of the products of photosynthesis, known as **translocation**, is carried out by another tissue, the phloem.

Movement from Sugar Sources to Sugar Sinks

In angiosperms, the specialized cells that are conduits for translocation are the sieve-tube elements. Arranged end to end, they form long sieve tubes (see Figure 35.10). Between these cells are sieve plates, structures that allow the flow of sap along the sieve tube.

Phloem sap, the aqueous solution that flows through sieve tubes, differs markedly from the xylem sap that is transported by tracheids and vessel elements. By far the most prevalent solute in phloem sap is sugar, typically sucrose in most species. The sucrose concentration may be as high as 30% by weight, giving the sap a syrupy thickness. Phloem sap may also contain amino acids, hormones, and minerals.

In contrast to the unidirectional transport of xylem sap from roots to leaves, phloem sap moves from sites of sugar production to sites of sugar use or storage (see Figure 36.2). A **sugar source** is a plant organ that is a net producer of sugar, by photosynthesis or by breakdown of starch. A **sugar sink** is an organ that is a net consumer or depository of sugar. Growing roots, buds, stems, and fruits are sugar sinks. Although expanding leaves are sugar sinks, mature leaves, if well illuminated, are sugar sources. A storage organ, such as a tuber or a bulb, may be a source or a sink, depending on the season. When stockpiling carbohydrates in the summer, it is a sugar sink. After breaking dormancy in the spring, it is a sugar source because its starch is broken down to sugar, which is carried to the growing shoot tips.

Sinks usually receive sugar from the nearest sugar sources. The upper leaves on a branch, for example, may export sugar to the growing shoot tip, whereas the lower leaves may export sugar to the roots. A growing fruit may monopolize the sugar sources that surround it. For each sieve tube, the direction of transport depends on the locations of the sugar source and sugar sink that are connected by that tube. Therefore, neighbouring sieve tubes may carry sap in opposite directions if they originate and end in different locations.

Sugar must be transported, or loaded, into sieve-tube elements before being exported to sugar sinks. In some species, it moves from mesophyll cells to sieve-tube elements via the symplast, passing through plasmodesmata. In other species, it moves by symplastic and apoplastic pathways. In maize leaves, for example, sucrose diffuses through the symplast from photosynthetic mesophyll cells into small veins. Much of it then moves into the apoplast and is accumulated by nearby sieve-tube elements, either directly or through companion cells (Figure 36.15a). In some plants, the walls of the companion cells feature many ingrowths, enhancing solute transfer between apoplast and symplast.

In many plants, sugar movement into the phloem requires active transport because sucrose is more concentrated in sieve-tube elements and companion cells than in mesophyll. Proton pumping and H$^+$/sucrose cotransport enable sucrose to be actively transported from mesophyll cells to sieve-tube elements or companion cells (Figure 36.15b).

Sucrose is unloaded at the sink end of a sieve tube. The process varies by species and organ. However, the concentration of free sugar in the sink is always lower than in the sieve tube because the unloaded sugar is consumed during growth and metabolism of the cells of the sink or converted to insoluble polymers such as starch. As a result of this sugar concentration gradient, sugar molecules move by facilitated diffusion from the phloem into the sink tissues, and water follows by osmosis.

Although the mechanism of phloem transport may be different among the gymnosperms, its primary function remains the same—the transport of sugars throughout the plant body. The elaborate burrows of the pine beetle and the blue stain fungus that grows within can greatly disrupt the phloem of their host trees (Figure 36.16). With loss of phloem function, sugar transport becomes severely compromised and the end result is typically death of the tree within 5 years of infection.

Bulk Flow by Positive Pressure: The Mechanism of Translocation in Angiosperms

Phloem sap flows from source to sink at rates as great as 1 m/hr, much faster than diffusion or cytoplasmic streaming. Researchers have concluded that phloem sap moves through the sieve tubes of angiosperms by bulk flow driven by positive pressure, known as *pressure flow* (Figure 36.17). In this system, sugars are loaded into the phloem sap by source cells ❶. This movement of solutes lowers the water potential of the phloem sap in the region, which causes water to enter from nearby cells and xylem. The resulting increase in water pressure forces phloem sap to move along the tubes ❷. Simultaneously, at the sink cells, sugars are unloaded ❸, which increases water potential and causes water to leave the phloem sap and enter neighbouring cells and xylem vessels. The xylem then recycles the water from sink to source ❹.

Key

Apoplast

Symplast

(a) Sucrose manufactured in mesophyll cells can travel via the symplast (blue arrows) to sieve-tube elements. In some species, sucrose exits the symplast near sieve tubes and travels through the apoplast (red arrow). It is then actively accumulated from the apoplast by sieve-tube elements and their companion cells.

(b) A chemiosmotic mechanism is responsible for the active transport of sucrose into companion cells and sieve-tube elements. Proton pumps generate an H$^+$ gradient, which drives sucrose accumulation with the help of a cotransport protein that couples sucrose transport to the diffusion of H$^+$ back into the cell.

▲ Figure 36.15 **Loading of sucrose into phloem.**

▲ Figure 36.16 **Beautiful and deadly.** The burrows produced by the mountain pine beetle can severely affect sugar transport in infected trees.

The pressure-flow hypothesis explains why phloem sap flows from source to sink, and experiments build a strong case for pressure flow as the mechanism of translocation in angiosperms (Figure 36.18). However, studies using electron microscopes suggest that in nonflowering vascular plants, the pores between phloem cells may be too small or obstructed to permit pressure flow.

Sinks vary in energy demands and capacity to unload sugars. Sometimes there are more sinks than can be supported by sources. In such cases, a plant might abort some flowers, seeds, or fruits—a phenomenon called *self-thinning*.

① Loading of sugar (green dots) into the sieve tube at the source reduces water potential inside the sieve-tube elements. This causes the tube to take up water by osmosis.

② This uptake of water generates a positive pressure that forces the sap to flow along the tube.

③ The pressure is relieved by the unloading of sugar and the consequent loss of water at the sink.

④ In leaf-to-root translocation, xylem recycles water from sink to source.

▲ Figure 36.17 **Bulk flow by positive pressure (pressure flow) in a sieve tube.**

▼ Figure 36.18 | **Inquiry**

Does phloem sap contain more sugar near sources than sinks?

Experiment The pressure-flow hypothesis predicts that phloem sap near sources should have a higher sugar content than phloem sap near sinks. To test this aspect of the hypothesis, researchers used aphids that feed on phloem sap. An aphid probes with a hypodermic-like mouthpart called a stylet that penetrates a sieve-tube element. As sieve-tube pressure forced out phloem sap into the stylets, the researchers separated the aphids from the stylets, which then acted as taps exuding sap for hours. Researchers measured the sugar concentration of sap from stylets at different points between a source and sink.

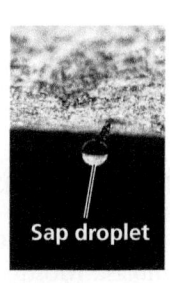

Aphid feeding

Stylet in sieve-tube element

Separated stylet exuding sap

Results The closer the stylet was to a sugar source, the higher its sugar concentration.

Conclusion The results of such experiments support the pressure-flow hypothesis, which predicts that sugar concentrations should be higher in sieve tubes closer to sugar sources.

Source: Based on S. Rogers and A. J. Peel, Some evidence for the existence of turgor pressure in the sieve tubes of willow (*Salix*), *Planta* 126:259–267 (1975). © Jane B Reece.

WHAT IF? *Spittlebugs are xylem sap feeders that use strong muscles to pump xylem sap through their guts. Could you isolate xylem sap from the excised stylets of spittlebugs?*

Removing sinks can also be a horticulturally useful practice. For example, since large apples command a much better price than small ones, growers sometimes remove flowers or young fruits so that their trees produce fewer but larger apples.

CONCEPT CHECK 36.5

1. Compare and contrast the forces that move phloem sap and xylem sap over long distances.

2. Identify plant organs that are sugar sources, organs that are sugar sinks, and organs that might be either. Explain.

3. Why can xylem transport water and minerals using dead cells, whereas phloem requires living cells?

4. **WHAT IF?** Apple growers in Japan sometimes make a nonlethal spiral slash around the bark of trees that are destined for removal after the growing season. This practice makes the apples sweeter. Why?

For suggested answers, see Appendix A.

CONCEPT 36.6

The symplast is highly dynamic

Although we have been discussing transport in mostly physical terms, almost like the flow of solutions through pipes, plant transport is a finely tuned process. That is, the transport needs of a plant cell typically change during its development. A leaf, for example, may begin as a sugar sink but spend most of its life as a sugar source. Also, environmental changes may trigger marked responses in plant transport processes. Water stress may activate signal transduction pathways that greatly alter the membrane transport proteins governing the overall transport of water and minerals. Because the symplast is living tissue, it is largely responsible for the dynamic changes in plant transport processes. We'll now look at some other examples: changes in plasmodesmata, chemical signalling, and electrical signalling.

Changes in Plasmodesmata

Plasmodesmata are highly dynamic components of the symplast. Mostly on the basis of static images from electron microscopy, biologists formerly thought of plasmodesmata as unchanging pore-like structures. Recently, however, new techniques have revealed that plasmodesmata are highly dynamic structures that can change in permeability and number. They can open or close rapidly in response to changes in turgor pressure, cytosolic Ca^{2+} levels, or cytosolic pH. Although some form during cytokinesis, they can also form much later. Moreover, loss of function is common during differentiation. For example, as a leaf matures from a sink to a source, its plasmodesmata either close or are eliminated, causing phloem unloading to cease.

Early studies by plant physiologists and pathologists came to differing conclusions regarding pore sizes of plasmodesmata. Physiologists injected fluorescent probes of different molecular sizes into cells and recorded whether the molecules passed into adjacent cells. Based on these observations, they concluded that the pore sizes were approximately 2.5 nm—too small for macromolecules such as proteins to pass. In contrast, pathologists provided electron micrographs showing evidence of the passage of virus particles with diameters of 10 nm or greater (Figure 36.19). One hypothesis to explain these discordant findings was that viruses dilate plasmodesmata.

Subsequently, it was learned that plant viruses produce *viral movement proteins* that cause plasmodesmata to dilate, enabling viral RNA to pass between cells. More recent evidence shows that plant cells themselves regulate

▲ **Figure 36.19 Virus particles moving cell to cell through a plasmodesma connecting turnip leaf cells (TEM).**

plasmodesmata as part of a communication network. Viruses subvert this network by mimicking the cell's regulators of plasmodesmata.

A high degree of cytosolic interconnectedness exists only within certain groups of cells and tissues, known as *symplastic domains*. Informational molecules, such as proteins and RNAs, coordinate development between cells within each symplastic domain. If symplastic communication is disrupted, development can be grossly affected.

Phloem: An Information Superhighway

In addition to transporting sugars, the phloem is a "superhighway" for the transport of macromolecules and viruses. This transport is systemic (throughout the body), affecting many or all of the plant's systems or organs. Macromolecules translocated through the phloem include proteins and various types of RNA that enter the sieve tubes through plasmodesmata. Although they are often likened to the gap junctions between animal cells, plasmodesmata are unique in their ability to traffic proteins and RNA.

Systemic communication through the phloem helps integrate the functions of the whole plant. One classic example is the delivery of a flower-inducing signal from leaves to vegetative meristems. Another is a defensive response to localized infection, in which signals travelling through the phloem activate defence genes in noninfected tissues.

Electrical Signalling in the Phloem

Rapid, long-distance electrical signalling through the phloem is another dynamic feature of the symplast. Electrical signalling has been studied extensively in plants that have rapid leaf movements, such as the sensitive plant (*Mimosa pudica*) and Venus flytrap (*Dionaea muscipula*). However, its role in other species is less clear. Some studies have revealed that a stimulus in one part of a plant can trigger an electrical signal in the phloem that affects another part, where it may elicit a change in gene transcription, respiration, photosynthesis, phloem unloading, or hormonal levels.

Thus, the phloem can serve a nerve-like function, allowing for swift electrical communication between widely separated organs.

The coordinated transport of materials and information is central to plant survival. Plants acquire only so many resources in the course of their lifetimes. Ultimately, the successful acquisition of resources and their optimal distribution are the most critical determinants of whether the plant will compete successfully.

CONCEPT CHECK 36.6

1. How do plasmodesmata differ from gap junctions?
2. Nerve-like signals in animals are thousands of times faster than their plant counterparts. Suggest a behavioural reason for the difference.
3. **WHAT IF?** Suppose plants were genetically modified to be unresponsive to viral movement proteins. Would this be a good way to prevent the spread of infection? Explain.

For suggested answers, see Appendix A.

36 Chapter Review

Go to MasteringBiology® for Assignments, the eText, and the Study Area with Animations, Activities, Vocab Self-Quiz, and Practice Tests.

SUMMARY OF KEY CONCEPTS

CONCEPT 36.1

Adaptations for acquiring resources were key steps in the evolution of vascular plants (pp. 829–831)

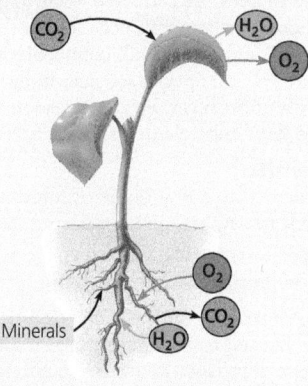

- Leaves typically function in gathering sunlight and CO_2. Stems serve as supporting structures for leaves and as conduits for the long-distance transport of water and nutrients. Roots mine the soil for water and minerals and anchor the whole plant. **Mycorrhizae** are mutualistic associations formed between roots and certain soil fungi that aid in the absorption of minerals and water.
- Natural selection has produced plant architectures that optimize resource acquisition in the ecological niche in which the plant species naturally exists.

? *How did the evolution of xylem and phloem contribute to the successful colonization of land by vascular plants?*

CONCEPT 36.2

Different mechanisms transport substances over short or long distances (pp. 831–835)

- The selective permeability of the plasma membrane controls the movement of substances into and out of cells. Both active and passive transport mechanisms occur in plants.
- Plant tissues have two major compartments: the **apoplast** (everything outside the cells' plasma membranes) and the **symplast** (the cytosol and connecting plasmodesmata).

- The direction of water movement depends on the **water potential**, a quantity incorporating solute concentration and physical pressure. The osmotic uptake of water by plant cells and the resulting internal pressure that builds up make plant cells **turgid**.
- Long-distance transport occurs through **bulk flow**, the movement of liquid in response to a pressure gradient. Bulk flow occurs within the tracheids and vessel elements of the xylem and within the sieve-tube elements of the phloem.

? *Is xylem sap usually pulled or pushed up the plant?*

CONCEPT 36.3

Transpiration drives the transport of water and minerals from roots to shoots via the xylem (pp. 836–840)

- Water and minerals from the soil enter the plant through the epidermis of roots, cross the root cortex, and then pass into the vascular cylinder by way of the selectively permeable cells of the **endodermis**. From the vascular cylinder, the **xylem sap** is transported long distances by bulk flow to the veins that branch throughout each leaf.
- The **cohesion-tension hypothesis** proposes that the movement of xylem sap is driven by a water potential difference created at the leaf end of the xylem by the evaporation of water from leaf cells. Evaporation lowers the water potential at the air-water interface, thereby generating the negative pressure that pulls water through the xylem.

? *Why is the ability of water molecules to form hydrogen bonds important for the movement of xylem sap?*

CONCEPT 36.4

The rate of transpiration is regulated by stomata (pp. 840–843)

- **Transpiration** is the loss of water vapour from plants. **Wilting** occurs when the water lost by transpiration is not replaced by absorption from roots.
- Stomata are the major pathway for water loss from plants. Guard cells widen or narrow the stomatal pores. When guard cells take up K^+, the pore widens. The opening and closing of stomata is controlled by light, CO_2, the drought hormone **abscisic acid**, and a **circadian rhythm**.
- Reduced leaves and CAM photosynthesis are examples of adaptations to arid environments.

? *Why are stomata necessary?*

CONCEPT 36.5

Sugars are transported from sources to sinks via the phloem (pp. 843–845)

- Mature leaves are the main **sugar sources**, although storage organs can be seasonal sources. Growing organs such as roots, stems, and fruits are the main **sugar sinks**.
- Phloem loading depends on the active transport of sucrose. Sucrose is cotransported with H^+, which diffuses down a gradient generated by proton pumps. Loading of sugar at the source and unloading at the sink maintain a pressure difference that keeps sap flowing through a sieve tube.

? *Why is phloem transport considered an active process?*

CONCEPT 36.6

The symplast is highly dynamic (pp. 846–847)

- Plasmodesmata can change in permeability and number. When dilated, they provide a passageway for the symplastic transport of proteins, RNAs, and other macromolecules over long distances. The phloem also conducts nerve-like electrical signals that help integrate whole-plant function.

? *By what mechanisms are symplastic communication regulated?*

TEST YOUR UNDERSTANDING

LEVEL 1: KNOWLEDGE/COMPREHENSION

1. The symplast transports all of the following *except*
   a. sugars.   c. DNA.
   b. mRNA.   d. viruses.

2. Which of the following is an adaptation that enhances the uptake of water and minerals by roots?
   a. mycorrhizae
   b. active uptake by vessel elements
   c. rhythmic contractions by cortical cells
   d. pumping through plasmodesmata

3. Which structure or compartment is part of the symplast?
   a. the interior of a vessel element
   b. the interior of a sieve tube
   c. the cell wall of a mesophyll cell
   d. an extracellular air space

4. Movement of phloem sap from a source to a sink
   a. occurs through the apoplast of sieve-tube elements.
   b. depends ultimately on the activity of proton pumps.
   c. depends on tension, or negative pressure potential.
   d. results mainly from diffusion.

LEVEL 2: APPLICATION/ANALYSIS

5. Photosynthesis ceases when leaves wilt, mainly because
   a. the chlorophyll in wilting leaves is degraded.
   b. stomata close, preventing CO_2 from entering the leaf.
   c. photolysis, the water-splitting step of photosynthesis, cannot occur when there is a water deficiency.
   d. accumulation of CO_2 in the leaf inhibits enzymes.

6. What would enhance water uptake by a plant cell?
   a. decreasing the ψ of the surrounding solution
   b. the loss of solutes from the cell
   c. increasing the ψ of the cytoplasm
   d. positive pressure on the surrounding solution

7. A plant cell with a ψ_S of -0.65 MPa maintains a constant volume when bathed in a solution that has a ψ_S of -0.30 MPa and is in an open container. The cell has a
   a. ψ_P of $+0.65$ MPa.   c. ψ_P of $+0.35$ MPa.
   b. ψ of -0.65 MPa.   d. ψ of 0 MPa.

8. Compared with a cell with few aquaporin proteins in its membrane, a cell containing many aquaporin proteins will
   a. have a faster rate of osmosis.
   b. have a lower water potential.
   c. have a higher water potential.
   d. accumulate water by active transport.

9. Which of the following would tend to increase transpiration?
   a. sunken stomata   c. higher stomatal density
   b. a thicker cuticle   d. spiny leaves

10. **DRAW IT** Trace the uptake of water and minerals from root hairs to the endodermis in a root, following a symplastic route and an apoplastic route. Label the routes on the diagram below.

LEVEL 3: SYNTHESIS/EVALUATION

11. **EVOLUTION CONNECTION**
    Large brown algae called kelps can grow as tall as 25 m. Kelps consist of a holdfast anchored to the ocean floor, blades that float at the surface and collect light, and a long stalk connecting the blades to the holdfast (see Figure 28.12). Specialized cells in the stalk, although nonvascular, can transport sugar. Suggest a reason why these structures analogous to sieve-tube elements might have evolved in kelps.

12. **SCIENTIFIC INQUIRY**
    Cotton plants wilt within a few hours of flooding their roots. The flooding leads to low-oxygen conditions, increases in cytosolic Ca^{2+}, and decreases in cytosolic pH. Suggest a hypothesis to explain how flooding leads to wilting.

13. **WRITE ABOUT A THEME: ORGANIZATION**
    Natural selection has led to changes in the architecture of plants that enable them to photosynthesize more efficiently in the ecological niches they occupy. In a short essay (100–150 words), explain how shoot architecture enhances photosynthesis.

14. **SYNTHESIZE YOUR KNOWLEDGE**

Catalin Petolea/Alamy

Imagine yourself as a water molecule in the soil solution of a forest. In a short essay (100–150 words), explain what pathways and what forces would be necessary to carry you to the leaves of these trees.

For selected answers, see Appendix A.

37

Soil and Plant Nutrition

Barthlott, Wilhlem

Elhardt, Noah

▲ Figure 37.1 **Does this plant have roots?**

KEY CONCEPTS

37.1 Soil contains a living, complex ecosystem

37.2 Plants require essential elements to complete their life cycle

37.3 Plant nutrition often involves relationships with other organisms

Bartosz Plachno

The Corkscrew Carnivore

The pale, root-like appendages of *Genlisea* (Figure 37.1), a herb that grows throughout African and Central and South American wetlands, are actually highly modified underground leaves adapted for trapping and digesting a variety of small soil inhabitants, including bacteria, algae, protozoa, nematodes, and copepods. But how do these trap-leaves work? Imagine twisting a narrow strip of paper to make a drinking straw. This is essentially the mechanism by which these corkscrew-shaped tubular leaves form. A narrow spiral slit runs along most of the trap-leaf's length; it is lined with curved hairs that allow microorganisms to enter the leaf tube but not exit. Once inside, prey find themselves travelling inexorably upward toward a small chamber lined with digestive glands that seal their fate. The inability of prey to backtrack is ensured by another set of curved hairs that allow only one-way passage (see micrograph at left). *Genlisea*'s carnivorous habit is a marvellous adaptation that enables the plant to supplement the meagre mineral rations available from the boggy, nutrient-poor soils in which it grows with minerals released from its digested prey.

As discussed in Chapter 36, plants obtain nutrients from both the atmosphere and the soil. Using sunlight as an energy source, they produce organic nutrients by reducing carbon dioxide to sugars through the process of photosynthesis.

They also take up water and various inorganic nutrients from the soil through their root systems. This chapter focuses on plant nutrition, the study of the minerals necessary for plant growth. After discussing the physical properties of soils and factors that govern soil quality, we'll explore why certain mineral nutrients are essential for plant function. Finally, we examine some nutritional adaptations that have evolved, often in relationships with other organisms.

CONCEPT 37.1

Soil contains a living, complex ecosystem

The upper layers of the soil, from which plants absorb nearly all of the water and minerals they require, contain a wide range of living organisms that interact with each other and with the physical environment. This complex ecosystem may take centuries to form but can be destroyed by human mismanagement in just a few years. To understand why soil must be conserved and why particular plants grow where they do, it is necessary to first consider the basic physical properties of soil: its texture and composition.

Soil Texture

The texture of soil depends on the sizes of its particles. Soil particles can range from coarse sand (0.02–2 mm in diameter) to silt (0.002–0.019 mm) to microscopic clay particles (less than 0.002 mm). These different-sized particles arise ultimately from the weathering of rock. Water freezing in the crevices of rocks causes mechanical fracturing, and weak acids in the soil break rocks down chemically. When organisms penetrate the rock, they accelerate breakdown by chemical and mechanical means. Plant roots, for example, secrete acids that dissolve the rock, and their growth in fissures leads to mechanical fracturing. The mineral particles released by weathering become mixed with living organisms and **humus**, the remains of dead organisms and other organic matter, forming **topsoil**. The topsoil and other distinct soil layers are called **soil horizons** (Figure 37.2). The topsoil, or A horizon, can range in depth from millimetres to metres. We focus mostly on the properties of topsoil because it is generally the most important soil layer for the growth of plants.

In the topsoil, plants are nourished by the soil solution, the water, and dissolved minerals in the pores between soil particles. The pores also contain air pockets. After a heavy rainfall, water drains away from the larger spaces in the soil, but smaller spaces retain water because water molecules are attracted to the negatively charged surfaces of clay and other soil particles.

The A horizon is the topsoil, a mixture of broken-down rock of various textures, living organisms, and decaying organic matter.

The B horizon contains much less organic matter than the A horizon and is less weathered.

The C horizon is composed mainly of partially broken-down rock. Some of the rock served as "parent" material for minerals that later helped form the upper horizons.

USDA Agricultural Research Service

▲ Figure 37.2 **Soil horizons.**

The topsoils that are the most fertile—supporting the most abundant growth—are **loams**, which are composed of roughly equal amounts of sand, silt, and clay. Loamy soils have enough small silt and clay particles to provide ample surface area for the adhesion and retention of minerals and water. Meanwhile, the large spaces between sand particles enable efficient diffusion of oxygen to the roots. Sandy soils generally don't retain enough water to support vigorous plant growth, and clayey soils tend to retain too much water. When soil does not drain adequately, the air is replaced by water, and the roots suffocate from lack of oxygen. Typically, the most fertile topsoils have pores that are about half water and half air, providing a good balance between aeration, drainage, and water storage capacity. The physical properties of soils can be adjusted by adding soil amendments, such as peat moss, compost, manure, or sand.

Topsoil Composition

A soil's composition encompasses its inorganic (mineral) and organic chemical components. The organic components include the many life-forms that inhabit the soil.

Inorganic Components

The surface charges of soil particles determine their ability to bind many nutrients. Most soil particles are negatively charged. Positively charged ions (cations)—such as potassium (K^+), calcium (Ca^{2+}), and magnesium (Mg^{2+})—adhere to these particles and are therefore not easily lost by *leaching*, the percolation of water through the soil. Roots, however, do not absorb mineral cations directly from soil particles; they absorb them from the soil solution. Mineral cations enter the soil solution by **cation exchange**, a process in which cations are displaced from soil particles by other cations, particularly H^+ (Figure 37.3). Therefore, a soil's capacity to exchange cations is determined by the number of cation adhesion sites and by the soil's pH. Soils with higher capacities generally have a larger reserve of mineral nutrients.

Negatively charged ions (anions)—such as the plant nutrients nitrate (NO_3^-), phosphate ($H_2PO_4^-$), and sulphate (SO_4^{2-})—do not bind to the negatively charged soil particles and are therefore easily lost from the soil. During heavy rain or overirrigation, they are leached into the groundwater, moving the nutrients into the lower soil horizons and away from the plant roots.

Organic Components

The major organic component of topsoil is humus, which consists of organic material produced by the decomposition of dead organisms, feces, fallen leaves, and other organic matter by bacteria and fungi. Humus prevents clay particles from packing together and forms a crumbly soil that retains water but is still porous enough to aerate roots adequately. Humus also increases the soil's capacity to exchange cations and serves as a reservoir of mineral nutrients that return gradually to the soil as microorganisms decompose the organic matter.

Topsoil is home to an astonishing number and variety of organisms. A teaspoon of topsoil has about 5 billion bacteria, which cohabit with fungi, algae, protists, insects, earthworms, nematodes, and plant roots. The activities of all these organisms affect the soil's physical and chemical properties. Earthworms, for example, consume organic matter and derive their nutrition from the bacteria and fungi growing on this material. They excrete wastes and move large amounts of material to the soil surface. In addition, they move organic matter into deeper layers of the soil. In effect, earthworms mix and clump the soil particles, allowing for better gaseous diffusion and retention of water. Plant roots also affect soil texture and composition. For example, by binding the soil, they reduce erosion, and by excreting acids, they lower soil pH.

Soil Conservation and Sustainable Agriculture

Ancient farmers recognized that yields from a particular plot of land decreased over the years. Moving to uncultivated areas, they observed the same pattern of reduced yields over time. Eventually, they realized that fertilization could make soil a renewable resource that enabled crops to be cultivated season after season at a fixed location. This sedentary agriculture facilitated a new way of life. Humans began to build permanent dwellings—the first villages. They also stored food for use between harvests, and food surpluses enabled some members of these early communities to specialize in nonfarming occupations. In short, soil management, by fertilization and other practices, helped prepare the way for modern societies.

Despite our agricultural knowledge, soil mismanagement remains a recurring problem. As populations grow and more food needs to be harvested on a given area of land, the soil can suffer from overuse, despite fertilization. Often year-to-year declines are small, but significant climate events can lead to catastrophic soil loss. An example of this occurred in the Canadian West during the early 20th century. Before the arrival of farmers, the Great Plains had been covered by hardy grasses with deep roots that held the soil in place despite recurring droughts and torrential rains. But planting wheat, an annual plant with a relatively shallow root system, and raising cattle left the soil exposed to erosion by fierce prairie winds. During World War I and immediately thereafter, the high price of wheat led many farmers to stop crop rotations. This further overtaxed their land. As a result, when a multi-year drought hit the centre of North America in the early 1930s the loose soil blew away in enormous dust storms (Figure 37.4). Huge quantities of fertile soil were blown away in "black blizzards," rendering millions of hectares of farmland useless. In one of the worst dust storms, clouds of dirt blew eastward as far as Chicago, where soil fell like snow. This was an ecological and human disaster that devastated the way of life on the Canadian Prairies and the

❸ H^+ ions in the soil solution neutralize the negative charge of soil particles, causing release of mineral cations into the soil solution.

❷ CO_2 reacts with H_2O to form H_2CO_3, which releases H^+ upon disassociation.

Soil particle

$H_2O + CO_2 \rightarrow H_2CO_3 \rightarrow HCO_3^- + H^+$

Root hair

❶ Roots acidify the soil solution by releasing CO_2 from respiration and pumping H^+ into the soil.

Cell wall

❹ Roots absorb the released cations.

▲ Figure 37.3 **Cation exchange in soil.**

❓ *Which are more likely to be leached from the soil by heavy rains—cations or anions? Explain.*

National Oceanic and Atmospheric Administration (NOAA)

▲ Figure 37.4 **During the drought of 1929 to 1938, the loss of agricultural crops and overgrazing led to weakening of the topsoil.** Winds were then able to blow the soil into drifts, like snow. This had a devastating effect on agriculture, particularly in Saskatchewan, where many farms did not recover until the 1950s.

Great Plains of the United States. Hundreds of thousands of people in the "Dust Bowl" region were forced to abandon their homes and land, a plight immortalized in John Steinbeck's novel *The Grapes of Wrath.*

Soil mismanagement continues to be a major problem to this day. More than 30% of the world's farmland has reduced productivity stemming from poor soil conditions such as chemical contamination, mineral deficiencies, acidity, salinity, and poor drainage. As the world's population continues to grow, the demand for food increases. Because soil quality is a major determinant of crop yield, the need to manage soil resources prudently has never been greater.

We'll now discuss how farmers irrigate and modify soil in order to maintain good crop yields. The goal is **sustainable agriculture**, a commitment embracing a variety of farming methods that are conservation-minded, environmentally safe, and profitable. We will also examine problems and solutions relating to soil degradation.

Irrigation

In areas that receive the high temperatures and long hours of sunlight required for some crop plants, water is often the limiting factor in plant growth. Since ancient times, farmers have watered their crops to increase yields—perhaps no technology has increased crop yield as much as irrigation. However, irrigation must be done carefully. Water used for irrigation is normally obtained from lakes and rivers. As a result, it contains dissolved minerals. When applied to fields in hot, dry areas, some of the water evaporates and leaves these minerals behind. If continued over a long period of time, this can significantly increase the amounts of certain minerals or salts in the soil. This makes it harder for the plants to take water from the soil, as we discussed in the

water relations section of Chapter 36. Irrigation can also be a huge drain on freshwater resources. Globally, about 75% of all freshwater use is devoted to agriculture. Many rivers in arid regions have been reduced to trickles by the diversion of water for irrigation. In Canada, a prime area of farmland that is greatly enhanced by irrigation is found in southwestern Alberta. This region is one of the hottest and driest in Canada, existing in the rain shadow of the Rocky Mountains. However, since the 1890s farmers have utilized the glacial runoff to water their crops. This area has some of the most technologically advanced irrigation systems in the world, taking water from the Oldman River and the St. Mary River system (Figure 37.5).

Many forms of irrigation, such as the flooding of fields, are wasteful because much of the water evaporates. To use water efficiently, farmers must understand

Design Pics Inc/Alamy

Google Inc.

▲ Figure 37.5 **Irrigation has transformed agriculture in southern Alberta, both in terms of what is grown and where.** The use of centre-pivot irrigation systems **(a)** leaves an undeniable mark on the landscape **(b)**.

the water-holding capacity of their soil, the water needs of their crops, and use the appropriate irrigation technology. Irrigation pivots (Figure 37.5a), used in western North America, pump water from a central point through a motorized arm that can be up to 400 m in length. They produce a very particular landscape (Figure 37.5b). Another popular technology is *drip irrigation*, the slow release of water to soil and plants from perforated plastic tubing placed directly at the root zone. Because drip irrigation requires less water and reduces salinization, it is used in many arid agricultural regions. In addition, it is critical for farmers to know when to use irrigation. State-of-the-art monitoring systems continuously track the soil moisture content to allow real-time evaluation of the water needs of everything from farmers' fields to golf courses. Watering only when needed can save both water and the energy needed to pump and spray the water onto fields.

Fertilization

In natural ecosystems, mineral nutrients are usually recycled by the excretion of animal wastes and the decomposition of humus. Agriculture, however, places an increased demand on soil nutrients. In addition, unlike a natural ecosystem, while the lettuce you eat, for example, contains minerals extracted from a farmer's field, the wastes that you excrete are deposited far from their original source. Over many harvests, the farmer's field will eventually become depleted of nutrients. Nutrient depletion is a major cause of global soil degradation. Farmers must reverse nutrient depletion by **fertilization**, the addition of mineral nutrients to the soil.

Today, most farmers in industrialized nations use fertilizers containing minerals that are either mined or prepared by energy-intensive processes. These fertilizers are usually enriched in nitrogen (N), phosphorus (P), and potassium (K)—the nutrients most commonly deficient in depleted soils. You may have seen fertilizers labelled with a three-number code, called the N-P-K ratio. A fertilizer marked "15-10-5," for instance, is 15% N (as ammonium or nitrate), 10% P (as phosphate), and 5% K (as the mineral potash). The remaining percentage (70% in this case) is inert filler. The filler helps avoid overfertilization and improves the ability to spread the fertilizer evenly.

Manure, fishmeal, and compost are called "organic" fertilizers because they are of biological origin and contain decomposing organic material. Before plants can use organic material, however, it must be decomposed into the inorganic nutrients that roots can absorb. Whether from organic fertilizer or a chemical factory, the minerals a plant extracts are in the same form. However, organic fertilizers release them gradually, whereas minerals in commercial fertilizers are immediately available but may not be retained by the soil for long. Minerals not absorbed by roots are often leached from the soil by rainwater or irrigation. To make matters worse, mineral runoff into lakes may lead to explosions in algal populations that can deplete oxygen levels and decimate fish populations, as is the case in Lake Winnipeg, Canada's "sickest" lake, and many others.

Adjusting Soil pH

Soil pH is an important factor that influences mineral availability by its effect on cation exchange and the chemical form of minerals. Depending on the soil pH, a particular mineral may be bound too tightly to clay particles or may be in a chemical form that the plant cannot absorb. Most plants prefer slightly acidic soil because the high H^+ concentrations can displace positively charged minerals from soil particles, making them more available for absorption. Adjusting soil pH for optimal crop growth is tricky because a change in H^+ concentration may make one mineral more available but another less available. At pH 8, for instance, plants can absorb calcium, but iron is almost unavailable. The soil pH should be matched to a crop's mineral needs. If the soil is too alkaline, adding sulphate will lower the pH. Soil that is too acidic can be adjusted by adding lime (calcium carbonate or calcium hydroxide).

When the soil pH dips to 5 or lower, toxic aluminum ions (Al^{3+}) become more soluble and are absorbed by roots, stunting root growth and preventing the uptake of calcium, a needed plant nutrient. Some plants can cope with high Al^{3+} levels by secreting organic anions that bind Al^{3+} and render it harmless. However, low soil pH and Al^{3+} toxicity continue to pose serious problems, especially in tropical regions, where the pressure of producing food for a growing population is often most acute.

Controlling Erosion

As happened most dramatically in the Dust Bowl, water and wind erosion can remove considerable amounts of topsoil. Erosion is a major cause of soil degradation because soil nutrients are carried away by wind and water. To limit erosion, farmers plant rows of trees as windbreaks, terrace hillside crops, and cultivate crops in a contour pattern (Figure 37.6). Crops such as alfalfa and wheat provide good ground cover and protect the soil better than maize and other crops that are usually planted in more widely spaced rows.

Erosion can also be reduced by a ploughing technique called **no-till agriculture**. In traditional ploughing, the entire field is tilled, or turned over. This practice helps control weeds but disrupts the meshwork of roots that holds the soil in place, leading to increased surface runoff and erosion. In no-till agriculture, special implements create narrow furrows for seeds and fertilizer. In this way, the field can be seeded with minimal disturbance to the soil, while also requiring less fertilizer.

▲ Figure 37.6 **Contour tillage.** These crops are planted in rows that go around, rather than up and down, the hills. Contour tillage helps slow water runoff and topsoil erosion after heavy rains.

Phytoremediation

Some land areas are unfit for cultivation because toxic heavy metals or organic pollutants have contaminated the soil or groundwater. Traditionally, soil remediation, the detoxification of contaminated soils, has focused on nonbiological technologies, such as removing and storing contaminated soil in landfills, but these techniques are very costly and often disrupt the landscape. **Phytoremediation** is a nondestructive biotechnology that harnesses the ability of some plants to extract soil pollutants and concentrate them in portions of the plant that can be easily removed for safe disposal. For example, alpine pennycress (*Thlaspi caerulescens*) can accumulate zinc in its shoots at concentrations 300 times higher than most plants can tolerate. The shoots can then be harvested and the contaminating zinc removed. Such plants show promise for cleaning up areas contaminated by smelters, mining operations, or nuclear testing. Phytoremediation is a type of bioremediation, which also includes the use of prokaryotes and protists to detoxify polluted sites (see Chapters 27 and 55).

We have discussed the importance of soil conservation for sustainable agriculture. Mineral nutrients contribute greatly to soil fertility, but which minerals are most important, and why do plants need them? These are the topics of the next section.

CONCEPT CHECK 37.1

1. Explain how the phrase "too much of a good thing" can apply to watering and fertilizing plants.
2. Some lawn mowers collect clippings for easy disposal. What is a drawback of this practice with respect to plant nutrition?
3. **WHAT IF?** How would adding clay to loamy soil affect the soil's capacity to exchange cations and retain water? Explain.
4. **MAKE CONNECTIONS** Note three ways in which the properties of water contribute to soil formation. See Concept 3.2.

For suggested answers, see Appendix A.

Plants require essential elements to complete their life cycle

Water, air, and soil minerals all contribute to plant growth. A plant's water content can be measured by comparing the mass before and after drying. Typically, 80–90% of a plant's fresh mass is water. Some 96% of the remaining dry mass consists of carbohydrates such as cellulose and starch that are produced by photosynthesis. Thus, the components of carbohydrates—carbon, oxygen, and hydrogen—are the most abundant elements in dried plant residue. Inorganic substances from the soil, although essential for plant survival, account for only about 4% of a plant's dry mass.

▼ Figure 37.7	**Research Method**

Hydroponic Culture

Application In hydroponic culture, plants are grown in mineral solutions without soil. One use of hydroponic culture is to identify essential elements in plants.

Technique Plant roots are bathed in aerated solutions of known mineral composition. Aerating the water provides the roots with oxygen for cellular respiration. (Note: The flasks would normally be opaque to prevent algal growth.) A mineral, such as potassium, can be omitted to test whether it is essential.

Control: Solution containing all minerals

Experimental: Solution without potassium

Results If the omitted mineral is essential, mineral deficiency symptoms occur, such as stunted growth and discoloured leaves. By definition, the plant would not be able to complete its life cycle. Deficiencies of different elements may have different symptoms, which can aid in diagnosing mineral deficiencies in soil.

The carbon and most of the oxygen atoms comprising about 90% of a plant's dry mass come from CO_2 assimilated from the air. As plants grow, they sequester CO_2, removing it from the atmosphere. Currently, many fast-growing species are being investigated as a potential means to mitigate the increasing CO_2 concentrations in our atmosphere. Changing weather patterns and rainfall may facilitate CO_2 sequestration in areas that will see increased rainfall, such as higher latitudes. However, in subtropical latitudes, where rainfall is expected to decline, photosynthesis will be limited by water availability despite a higher CO_2 concentration. Moreover, essential nutrients coming from the soil, comprising the remaining 10% of dry mass, will also be limited, further inhibiting plant growth and CO_2 sequestration.

Essential Elements

The inorganic substances in plants contain more than 50 chemical elements. In studying the chemical composition of plants, we must distinguish elements that are essential from those that are merely present in the plant. A chemical element is considered an **essential element** only if it is required for a plant to complete its life cycle and produce another generation.

To determine which chemical elements are essential, researchers use **hydroponic culture**, in which plants are grown in mineral solutions instead of soil (Figure 37.7). Such studies have helped identify 17 essential elements needed by all plants (Table 37.1). Hydroponic culture is also used on a small scale to grow some greenhouse crops.

Nine of the essential elements are called **macronutrients** because plants require them in relatively large amounts. Six of these are the major components of organic compounds forming a plant's structure: carbon, oxygen, hydrogen, nitrogen, phosphorus, and sulphur. The other three macronutrients are potassium, calcium, and magnesium. Of all the mineral nutrients, nitrogen contributes the most to plant growth and crop yields.

The remaining eight essential elements are called **micronutrients** because plants need them in only tiny quantities. They are chlorine, iron, manganese, boron, zinc, copper, nickel, and molybdenum. In some cases, sodium may be a ninth essential micronutrient: Plants that use the C_4 and CAM pathways of photosynthesis (see Chapter 10) require sodium ions to regenerate

Table 37.1 Essential Elements in Plants

Element	Form Primarily Absorbed by Plants	% Mass in Dry Tissue	Major Functions
Macronutrients			
Carbon	CO_2	45%	Major component of plant's organic compounds
Oxygen	CO_2	45%	Major component of plant's organic compounds
Hydrogen	H_2O	6%	Major component of plant's organic compounds
Nitrogen	NO_3^-, NH_4^+	1.5%	Component of nucleic acids, proteins, hormones, chlorophyll, coenzymes
Potassium	K^+	1.0%	Cofactor that functions in protein synthesis; major solute functioning in water balance; operation of stomata
Calcium	Ca^{2+}	0.5%	Important in formation and stability of cell walls and in maintenance of membrane structure and permeability; activates some enzymes; regulates many responses of cells to stimuli
Magnesium	Mg^{2+}	0.2%	Component of chlorophyll; cofactor and activator of many enzymes
Phosphorus	$H_2PO_4^-$, HPO_4^{2-}	0.2%	Component of nucleic acids, phospholipids, ATP, several coenzymes
Sulphur	SO_4^{2-}	0.1%	Component of proteins, coenzymes
Micronutrients			
Chlorine	Cl^-	0.01%	Required for water-splitting step of photosynthesis; functions in water balance
Iron	Fe^{3+}, Fe^{2+}	0.01%	Component of cytochromes; cofactor of some enzymes; cofactor in chlorophyll synthesis; needed for photosynthesis
Manganese	Mn^{2+}	0.005%	Active in formation of amino acids; activates some enzymes; required for water-splitting step of photosynthesis
Boron	$H_2BO_3^-$	0.002%	Cofactor in chlorophyll synthesis; may be involved in carbohydrate transport and nucleic acid synthesis; role in cell wall function
Zinc	Zn^{2+}	0.002%	Active in formation of chlorophyll; cofactor of some enzymes; needed for DNA transcription
Copper	Cu^+, Cu^{2+}	0.001%	Component of many redox and lignin-biosynthetic enzymes
Nickel	Ni^{2+}	0.001%	Cofactor for an enzyme functioning in nitrogen metabolism
Molybdenum	MoO_4^{2-}	0.0001%	Essential for mutualistic relationship with nitrogen-fixing bacteria; cofactor in nitrate reduction

MAKE CONNECTIONS *Explain why CO_2, rather than O_2, is the source of much of the dry mass oxygen in plants. See Concept 10.1*

phosphoenolpyruvate, which is the CO_2 acceptor in these two types of carbon fixation.

Micronutrients function in plants mainly as cofactors, nonprotein helpers in enzymatic reactions (see Chapter 8). Iron, for example, is a metallic component of cytochromes, the proteins in the electron transport chains of chloroplasts and mitochondria. It is because micronutrients generally play catalytic roles that plants need only tiny quantities. The requirement for molybdenum, for instance, is so modest that there is only one atom of this rare element for every 60 million atoms of hydrogen in dried plant material. Yet a deficiency of molybdenum or any other micronutrient can weaken or kill a plant.

Symptoms of Mineral Deficiency

The symptoms of a deficiency depend partly on the mineral's function as a nutrient. For example, a deficiency of magnesium, a component of chlorophyll, causes *chlorosis*, yellowing of the leaves. In some cases, the relationship between a mineral deficiency and its symptoms is less direct. For instance, iron deficiency can cause chlorosis even though chlorophyll contains no iron, because iron ions are required as a cofactor in one of the enzymatic steps of chlorophyll synthesis.

Mineral deficiency symptoms depend not only on the role of the nutrient but also on its mobility within the plant. If a nutrient moves about freely, symptoms appear first in older organs because young, growing tissues are a greater sink for nutrients that are in short supply. For example, magnesium is relatively mobile and is shunted preferentially to young leaves. Therefore, a plant deficient in magnesium first shows signs of chlorosis in its older leaves. The mechanism for preferential routing is the source-to-sink translocation in phloem, as minerals move along with sugars to the growing tissues (see Figure 36.18). In contrast, a deficiency of a mineral that is relatively immobile affects young parts of the plant first. Older tissues may have adequate amounts that they retain during periods of short supply. For example, iron does not move freely within a plant, and an iron deficiency causes yellowing of young leaves before any effect on older leaves is visible. The mineral requirements of a plant may also change with the time of the year and the age of the plant. Young seedlings, for example, rarely show mineral deficiency symptoms because their mineral requirements are met largely by minerals released from stored reserves in the seed itself.

Deficiencies of phosphorus, potassium, and especially nitrogen are most common. Micronutrient shortages are less common and tend to occur in certain geographic regions because of differences in soil composition. Symptoms of a mineral deficiency may vary between species but are often distinctive enough for a plant physiologist or farmer to diagnose (see the Scientific Skills Exercise). One way to confirm a diagnosis is to analyze the mineral content of the plant or soil. The amount of a micronutrient needed to correct a deficiency is usually quite small. For example, a zinc deficiency in fruit trees can usually be cured by hammering a few zinc nails into each tree trunk. Moderation is important because overdoses of many nutrients can be detrimental or toxic to plants. Too much nitrogen, for example, can lead to excessive vine growth in tomato plants at the expense of good fruit production.

Improving Plant Nutrition by Genetic Modification

In exploring plant nutrition so far, we have discussed how farmers use irrigation, fertilization, and other means to tailor the soil conditions to fit the needs of a crop. An opposite approach involves tailoring the plant by genetic engineering to better fit the soil conditions. Here we highlight a few examples of how genetic engineering is improving plant nutrition and fertilizer usage.

Resistance to Aluminum Toxicity

As previously discussed, aluminum in acidic soils damages roots and greatly reduces crop yields. The major mechanism of aluminum resistance is the secretion of organic acids (such as malic acid and citric acid) by roots. These acids bind to free aluminum ions and lower the levels of toxic aluminum in the soil. Scientists have altered tobacco and papaya plants by introducing a citrate synthase gene from a bacterium into the plants' genomes. The resulting overproduction of citric acid increased aluminum resistance.

Smart Plants

Agricultural researchers are developing ways to maintain crop yields while reducing fertilizer use. One approach is to genetically engineer "smart" plants that signal when a nutrient deficiency is imminent—but *before* damage has occurred. One type of smart plant takes advantage of a promoter (a DNA sequence indicating where the transcription of a gene starts) that more readily binds RNA polymerase (the transcription enzyme) when the phosphorus content of the plant's tissues begins to decline. This promoter is linked to a "reporter" gene that leads to production of a light blue pigment in the leaf cells (Figure 37.8). When leaves of these smart plants develop a blue tinge, the farmer knows it is time to add phosphate-containing fertilizer.

So far, you have learned that soil, to support vigorous plant growth, must have an adequate supply of mineral nutrients, sufficient aeration, good water-holding capacity, low salinity, and a pH near neutrality. It must also be free of toxic concentrations of minerals and other chemicals. These physical and

Making Observations

What Mineral Deficiency Is This Plant Exhibiting? Plant growers often diagnose deficiencies in their crops by examining changes to the foliage, such as chlorosis (yellowing), death of some leaves, discolouring, mottling, scorching, or changes in size or texture. In this exercise, you will diagnose a mineral deficiency by observing a plant's leaves and applying what you have learned about symptoms from the text and Table 37.1.

Data The data for this exercise comes from the photograph below of leaves on an orange tree exhibiting a mineral deficiency.

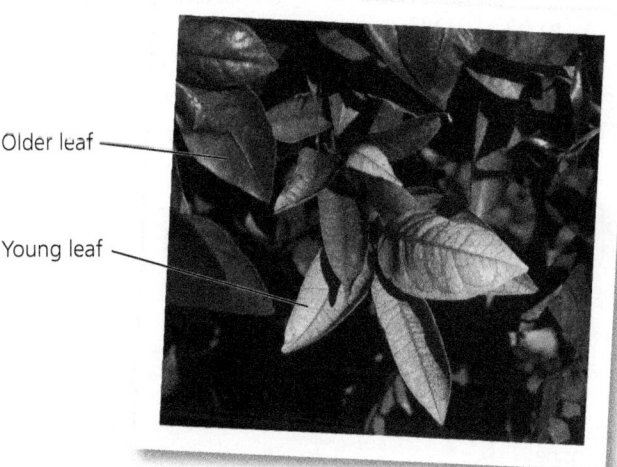

Older leaf

Young leaf

Nigel Cattlin/Science Source

Interpret the Data

1. How do the young leaves differ in appearance from the older leaves?
2. In three words, what is the most prominent mineral deficiency symptom seen in this photo? List the three nutrients whose deficiencies give rise to this symptom. Based on the symptom's location, which one of these three nutrients can be ruled out, and why? What does the location suggest about the other two nutrients?
3. How would your hypothesis about the cause of this deficiency be influenced if tests showed that the soil was low in humus?

Philip J. White

No phosphorus deficiency

Beginning phosphorus deficiency

Well-developed phosphorus deficiency

▲ **Figure 37.8 Deficiency warnings from "smart" plants.** Some plants have been genetically modified to signal an impending nutrient deficiency before irreparable damage occurs. For example, after laboratory treatments, the research plant *Arabidopsis* develops a blue colour in response to an imminent phosphate deficiency.

chemical features of soil, however, are just part of the story: We must also consider the living components of soil.

1. Are some essential elements more important than others? Explain.
2. **WHAT IF?** If an element increases the growth rate of a plant, can it be defined as an essential element?
3. **MAKE CONNECTIONS** Based on Figure 9.18, explain why ethanol accumulates in plant roots subjected to waterlogging.

For suggested answers, see Appendix A.

CONCEPT **37.3**

Plant nutrition often involves relationships with other organisms

To this point, we have portrayed plants as exploiters of soil resources. But plants and soil have a two-way relationship. Dead plants provide much of the energy needed by soil-dwelling microorganisms, while secretions from living roots support a wide variety of microbes in the near-root environment. Here we'll focus on some *mutualistic*—mutually beneficial—relationships between plants and soil bacteria or fungi. Then we'll look at some unusual plants that form nonmutualistic relationships with other plants or, in a few cases, with animals.

Bacteria and Plant Nutrition

A variety of mutualistic bacteria play roles in plant nutrition. **Rhizobacteria** live in the **rhizosphere**, the soil closely surrounding the plant's roots. **Endophytes** are nonpathogenic bacteria (or fungi) that live between cells within the plant itself but do not form deep, intimate associations with the cells or alter their morphology. Both endophytic bacteria and rhizobacteria depend on nutrients such as sugars, amino acids, and organic acids that are secreted by plant cells. In the case of the rhizosphere, up to 20% of a plant's photosynthetic production fuels the organisms in this miniature ecosystem. In turn, endophytic bacteria and rhizobacteria enhance plant growth by a variety of mechanisms. Some produce chemicals that stimulate plant growth. Others produce antibiotics that protect roots from disease. Still others absorb toxic metals or make nutrients more available to roots. Inoculation of seeds with plant-growth-promoting rhizobacteria can increase crop yield and reduce the need for fertilizers and pesticides.

Both the intercellular spaces occupied by endophytic bacteria and the rhizosphere associated with each plant root system contain a unique and complex cocktail of root secretions and microbial products that differ from those of the surrounding soil. A recent metagenomics study has revealed that the compositions of bacterial communities living endophytically and in the rhizosphere are not identical (Figure 37.9). A better understanding of the bacteria within and around roots could have profound agricultural benefits.

Bacteria in the Nitrogen Cycle

Plants have mutualistic relationships with several groups of bacteria that help make nitrogen more available. From a global perspective, no mineral nutrient is more limiting to plant growth than nitrogen, which is required in large amounts for synthesizing proteins and nucleic acids. Here we focus on processes leading directly to nitrogen assimilation by plants.

Unlike other soil minerals, ammonium ions (NH_4^+) and nitrate ions (NO_3^-)—the forms of nitrogen that plants can use—are not derived from the weathering of rocks. Although lightning produces small amounts of NO_3^- that get carried to the soil in rain, most soil nitrogen comes from the activity of bacteria (Figure 37.10).

The **nitrogen cycle**, also discussed in Figure 55.13, describes transformations of nitrogen and nitrogenous compounds in nature. When a plant or animal dies, or an animal expels waste, the initial form of nitrogen is organic. Decomposers convert the organic nitrogen within the remains back into ammonium (NH_4^+), a process called ammonification. Other sources of soil NH_4^+ are *nitrogen-fixing bacteria* that convert gaseous nitrogen (N_2) to NH_3, which then picks up another H^+ in the soil solution, forming NH_4^+.

In addition to NH_4^+, plants can also acquire nitrogen in the form of nitrate (NO_3^-). Soil NO_3^- is largely formed by a two-step process called *nitrification*, which consists of the oxidation of ammonia (NH_3) to nitrite (NO_2^-), followed by oxidation of NO_2^- to NO_3^-. Different types of *nitrifying bacteria* mediate each step. After the roots absorb NO_3^-, a plant enzyme reduces it back to NH_4^+, which other enzymes incorporate into amino acids and other organic compounds. Most plant species export

▼ Figure 37.9 | **Inquiry**

How variable are the compositions of bacterial communities inside and outside of roots?

Experiment The bacterial communities found within and immediately outside of root systems are known to improve plant growth. In order to devise agricultural strategies to increase the benefits of these bacterial communities, it is necessary to determine how complex they are and what factors affect their composition. A problem inherent in studying these bacterial communities is that a handful of soil contains as many as 10 000 types of bacteria, more than all the bacterial species that have been described. One cannot simply culture each species and use a taxonomic key to identify them; a molecular approach is needed.

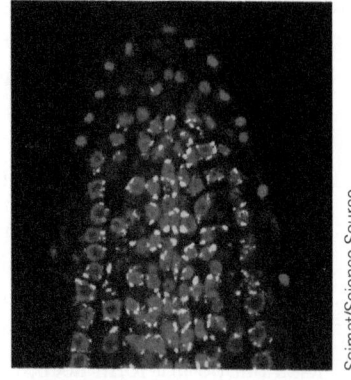

▲ Bacteria (green) on surface of root (fluorescent LM)

Scimat/Science Source

Scientists have estimated the number of bacterial "species" in various samples using a technique called metagenomics (see Concept 21.1). The bacterial community samples they studied differed in location (endophytic, rhizospheric, or outside the rhizosphere), soil type (clayey or porous), and the developmental stage of the root system with which they were associated (old or young). The DNA from each sample was purified, and the polymerase chain reaction (PCR) was used to amplify the DNA that codes for the 16S ribosomal RNA subunits. Many thousands of DNA sequence variations were found in each sample. The researchers then lumped the sequences that were more than 97% identical into "taxonomic units" or "species." (The word "species" is in quotation marks because "two organisms having a single gene that is more than 97% identical" is not explicit in any definition of species.) Having established the types of "species" in each community, the researchers constructed a tree diagram showing the percent of bacterial "species" that were found in common in each community.

Results This tree diagram breaks down the relatedness of bacterial communities into finer and finer levels of detail. The two explanatory labels give examples of how to interpret the diagram.

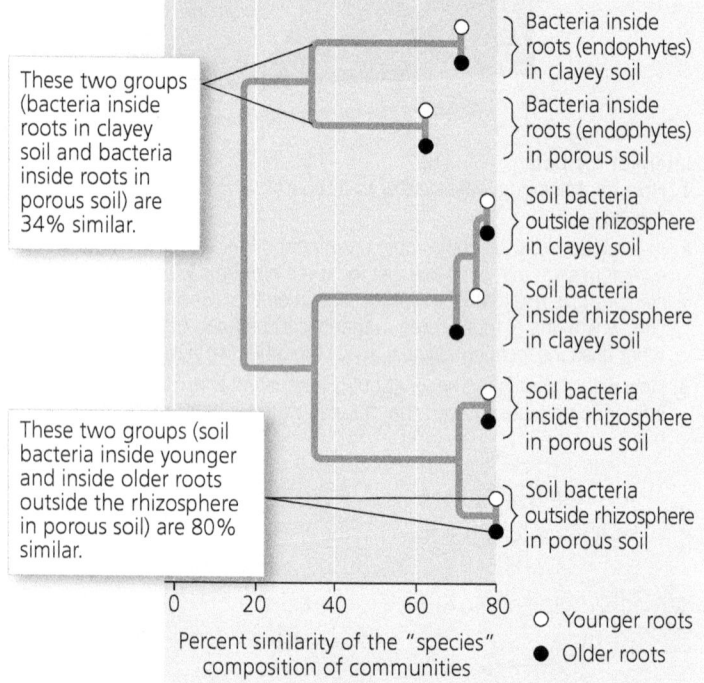

These two groups (bacteria inside roots in clayey soil and bacteria inside roots in porous soil) are 34% similar.

These two groups (soil bacteria inside younger and inside older roots outside the rhizosphere in porous soil) are 80% similar.

Bacteria inside roots (endophytes) in clayey soil

Bacteria inside roots (endophytes) in porous soil

Soil bacteria outside rhizosphere in clayey soil

Soil bacteria inside rhizosphere in clayey soil

Soil bacteria inside rhizosphere in porous soil

Soil bacteria outside rhizosphere in porous soil

0   20   40   60   80

Percent similarity of the "species" composition of communities

○ Younger roots
● Older roots

Conclusion The "species" composition of the bacterial communities varied markedly according to the location inside the root versus outside the root and according to soil type.

INTERPRET THE DATA *(a) Which of the three community locations was least like the other two? (b) Rank the three variables (community location, developmental stage of roots, and soil type) in terms of how strongly they affect the "species" composition of the bacterial communities.*

Data from D.S. Lundberg et al., Defining the core *Arabidopsis thaliana* root microbiome, *Nature* 488:86–94 (2012). © Jane B Reece.

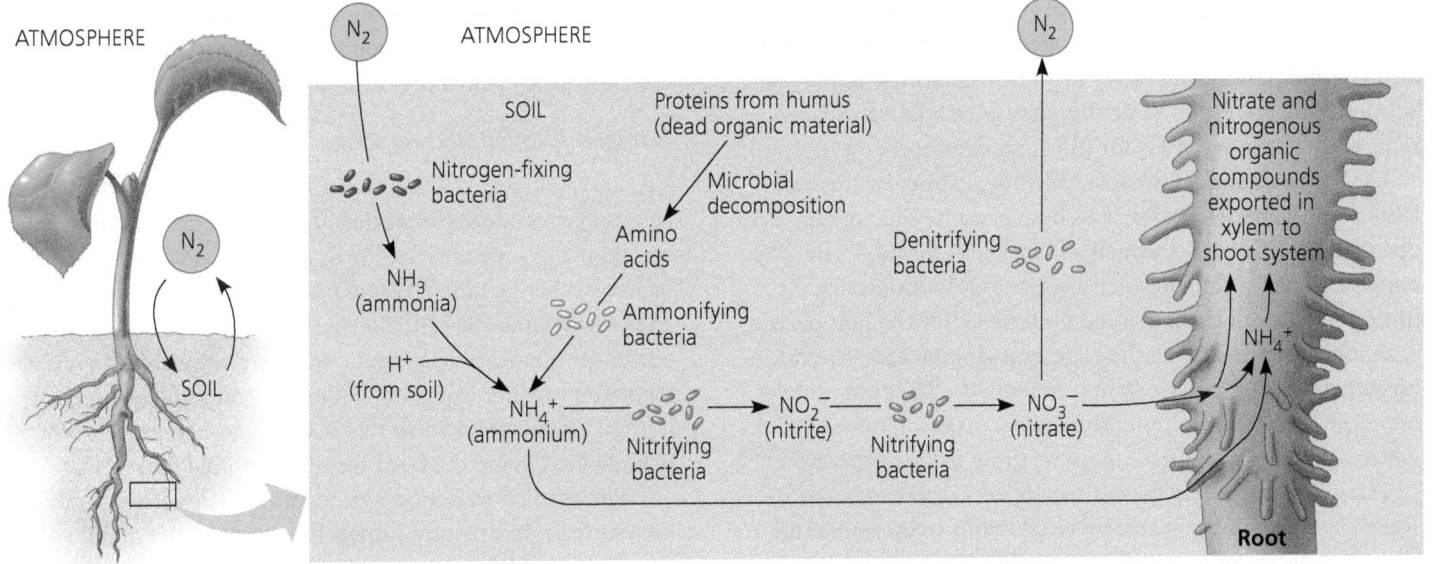

▲ **Figure 37.10 The roles of soil bacteria in the nitrogen nutrition of plants.** Ammonium is made available to plants by two types of soil bacteria: those that fix atmospheric N_2 (nitrogen-fixing bacteria) and those that decompose organic material (ammonifying bacteria). Although plants absorb some ammonium from the soil, they absorb mainly nitrate, which is produced from ammonium by nitrifying bacteria. Plants reduce nitrate back to ammonium before incorporating the nitrogen into organic compounds.

nitrogen from roots to shoots via the xylem as NO_3^- or organic compounds synthesized in the roots. Some soil nitrogen is lost, particularly in anaerobic soils, when denitrifying bacteria convert NO_3^- to N_2, which diffuses into the atmosphere.

Nitrogen-Fixing Bacteria: A Closer Look

Although Earth's atmosphere is 79% nitrogen, plants cannot use free gaseous nitrogen (N_2) because there is a triple bond between the two nitrogen atoms, making the molecule almost inert. For atmospheric N_2 to be of use to plants, it must be reduced to NH_3 by a process called **nitrogen fixation**. All N_2-fixing organisms are bacteria, and some that carry out this process are free-living (see Figure 37.10), whereas others are endophytic. Still others, particularly members of the genus *Rhizobium*, form intimate associations with the roots of legumes (such as peas, soybeans, alfalfa, and peanuts) and markedly alter their root structure. Although *Rhizobium* can be free-living in the soil, it cannot fix N_2 in its free state, nor can legume roots fix N_2 without the bacteria.

The multistep conversion of N_2 to NH_3 by nitrogen fixation can be summarized as follows:

$$N_2 + 8e^- + 8H^+ + 16ATP \rightarrow 2NH_3 + H_2 + 16\ ADP + 16\ \textcircled{P}_i$$

The reaction is driven by the enzyme complex *nitrogenase*. Because the process of nitrogen fixation requires eight ATP molecules for each NH_3 synthesized, nitrogen-fixing bacteria require a rich supply of carbohydrates from decaying material, root secretions, or (in the case of *Rhizobium*) the vascular tissue of roots.

The specialized mutualism between *Rhizobium* bacteria and legume roots involves dramatic changes in root structure. Along a legume's roots are swellings called **nodules**, composed of plant cells that have been "infected" by *Rhizobium* ("root living") bacteria (**Figure 37.11**). Inside each nodule, *Rhizobium* bacteria assume a form called **bacteroids**, which are contained within vesicles formed in the root cells. Legume-*Rhizobium* relationships generate more usable nitrogen for plants than all industrial fertilizers used today, and the mutualism provides the right amount of nitrogen at the right time at virtually no cost to the farmer.

The location of the bacteroids inside living, nonphotosynthetic cells is conducive to nitrogen fixation, which requires an anaerobic environment. Lignified external layers of root nodules also limit gas exchange. Some root nodules appear reddish because of a molecule called leghemoglobin (*leg*- for "legume"), an iron-containing protein that binds reversibly to oxygen (similar to the hemoglobin in human

American Chemical Society (ACS)

◀ **Figure 37.11 Root nodules on a legume.** The spherical structures along this soybean root system are nodules containing *Rhizobium* bacteria. The bacteria fix nitrogen and obtain photosynthetic products supplied by the plant.

? *How is the relationship between legume plants and* Rhizobium *bacteria mutualistic?*

Nodules

Roots

red blood cells). This protein is an oxygen "buffer," reducing the concentration of free oxygen and thereby providing an anaerobic environment for nitrogen fixation while regulating the oxygen supply for the intense cellular respiration required to produce ATP for nitrogen fixation.

Each legume species is associated with a particular strain of *Rhizobium*. **Figure 37.12** describes how a root nodule develops after bacteria enter through an "infection thread." The symbiotic relationship between a legume and nitrogen-fixing bacteria is mutualistic in that the bacteria supply the host plant with fixed nitrogen while the plant provides the bacteria with carbohydrates and other organic compounds. The root nodules use most of the ammonium produced to make amino acids, which are then transported up to the shoot through the xylem.

How does a legume species recognize a certain strain of *Rhizobium* among the many bacterial strains in the soil? And how does an encounter with that specific *Rhizobium* strain lead to development of a nodule? These two questions have led researchers to uncover a chemical dialogue between the bacteria and the root. Each partner responds to chemical signals from the other by expressing certain genes whose products contribute to nodule formation. By understanding the molecular biology underlying the formation of root nodules,

researchers hope to learn how to induce *Rhizobium* uptake and nodule formation in crop plants that do not normally form such nitrogen-fixing mutualistic relationships.

Nitrogen Fixation and Agriculture

The agricultural benefits of mutualistic nitrogen fixation underlie most types of **crop rotation**. In this practice, a nonlegume such as maize is planted one year, and the following year alfalfa or some other legume is planted to restore the concentration of fixed nitrogen in the soil. To ensure that the legume encounters its specific *Rhizobium* strain, the seeds are exposed to bacteria before sowing. Instead of being harvested, the legume crop is often ploughed under so that it will decompose as "green manure," reducing the need for manufactured fertilizers.

Many plant families besides legumes include species that benefit from mutualistic nitrogen fixation. For example, alder trees and certain tropical grasses host nitrogen-fixing actinomycete bacteria (see the gram-positive bacteria in Figure 27.16). Rice, a crop of great commercial importance, benefits indirectly from mutualistic nitrogen fixation. Rice farmers culture a free-floating aquatic fern, *Azolla*, which has mutualistic cyanobacteria that fix nitrogen. The growing rice eventually shades and kills the *Azolla*, and decomposition

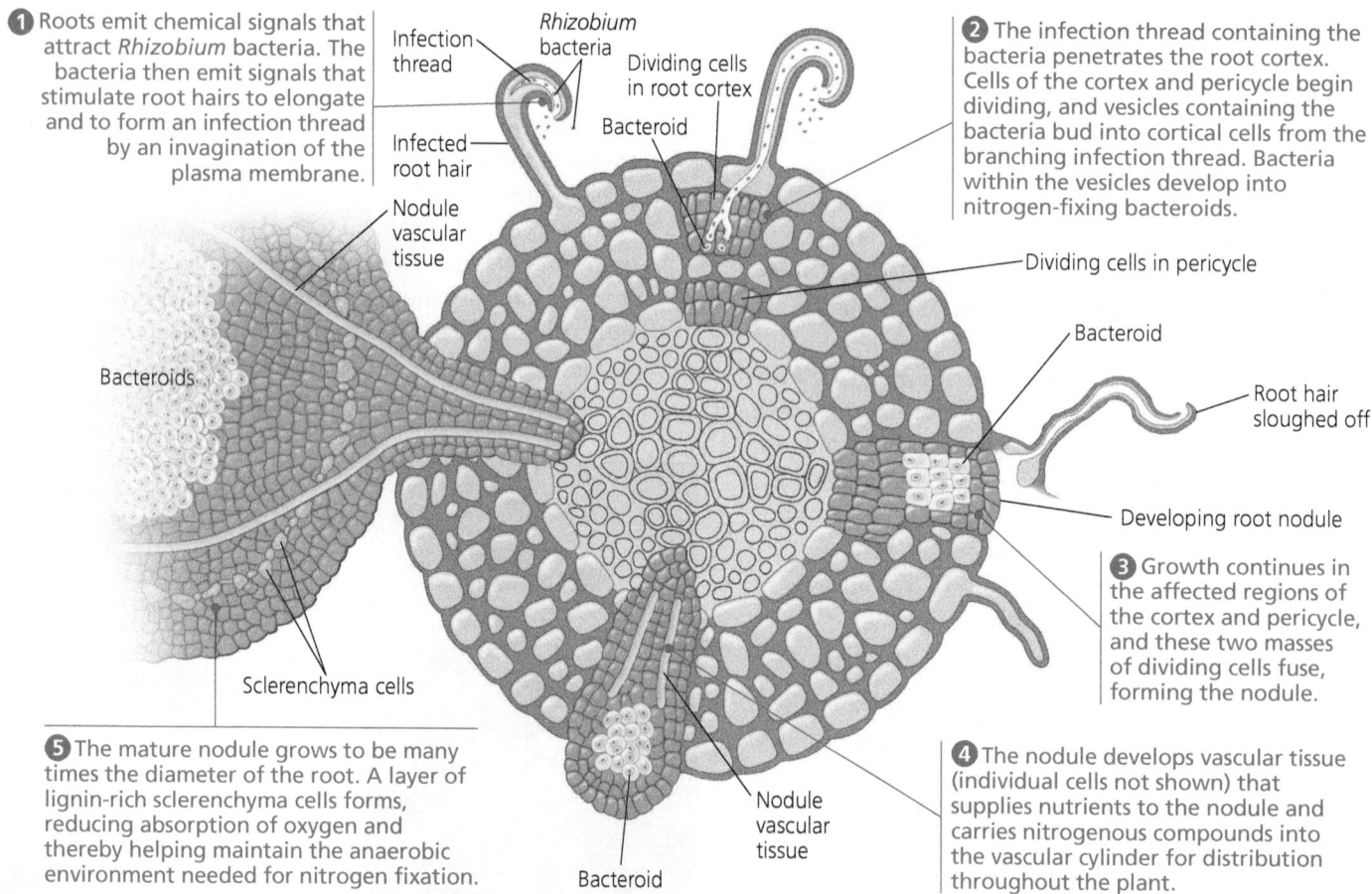

1 Roots emit chemical signals that attract *Rhizobium* bacteria. The bacteria then emit signals that stimulate root hairs to elongate and to form an infection thread by an invagination of the plasma membrane.

Rhizobium bacteria
Infection thread
Dividing cells in root cortex
Bacteroid
Infected root hair
Nodule vascular tissue
Bacteroids
Sclerenchyma cells

2 The infection thread containing the bacteria penetrates the root cortex. Cells of the cortex and pericycle begin dividing, and vesicles containing the bacteria bud into cortical cells from the branching infection thread. Bacteria within the vesicles develop into nitrogen-fixing bacteroids.

Dividing cells in pericycle
Bacteroid
Root hair sloughed off
Developing root nodule

3 Growth continues in the affected regions of the cortex and pericycle, and these two masses of dividing cells fuse, forming the nodule.

5 The mature nodule grows to be many times the diameter of the root. A layer of lignin-rich sclerenchyma cells forms, reducing absorption of oxygen and thereby helping maintain the anaerobic environment needed for nitrogen fixation.

Nodule vascular tissue
Bacteroid

4 The nodule develops vascular tissue (individual cells not shown) that supplies nutrients to the nodule and carries nitrogenous compounds into the vascular cylinder for distribution throughout the plant.

▲ Figure 37.12 **Development of a soybean root nodule.**

? *What plant tissue systems are modified by root nodule formation?*

of this nitrogen-rich organic material increases the paddy's fertility.

Fungi and Plant Nutrition

Certain species of soil fungi also form mutualistic relationships with roots and play a major role in plant nutrition.

When the earliest plants, which evolved from green algae, began to invade the land 400 to 500 million years ago, they encountered a harsh environment. Although the soil contained mineral nutrients, it lacked organic matter. Therefore, rain probably quickly leached away many of the soluble mineral nutrients. The barren land, however, was also a place of opportunities because there was very little competition, and light and carbon dioxide were readily available. Neither the early land plants nor early land fungi, which evolved from an aquatic protist, were fully equipped to exploit the terrestrial environment. The early plants lacked the ability to extract essential nutrients from the soil, while the fungi were unable to manufacture carbohydrates. Instead of the fungi becoming parasitic on the rhizoids of the evolving plants (roots or root hairs had not yet evolved), the two organisms formed mycorrhizal associations, a mutualistic symbiosis that allowed both of them to exploit the terrestrial environment. Fossil evidence supports the idea that mycorrhizal associations occurred in the earliest land plants. The small minority of extant angiosperms that are nonmycorrhizal probably lost this ability through gene loss.

The Two Main Types of Mycorrhizae

The major mutualistic symbioses of fungi and plants are classified as either ectomycorrhizae or arbuscular mycorrhizae (sometimes called endomycorrhizae). In **ectomycorrhizae**, the mycelium (mass of branching hyphae; see Chapter 31) forms a dense sheath, or mantle, over the surface of the root (Figure 37.13a). Fungal hyphae extend from the mantle into the soil, greatly increasing the surface area for water and mineral absorption. Hyphae also grow into the root cortex. These hyphae do not penetrate the root cells but form a network in the apoplast, or extracellular space, that facilitates nutrient exchange between the fungus and the plant. Compared with "uninfected" roots, ectomycorrhizae are generally thicker, shorter, and more branched. They typically do not form root hairs, which would be superfluous given the extensive surface area of the fungal mycelium. About 10% of plant families have species that form ectomycorrhizae, and the vast majority of these species are woody, including members of the pine, spruce, oak, walnut, birch, willow, and eucalyptus families.

In contrast, **arbuscular mycorrhizae** do not have a dense mantle ensheathing the root (Figure 37.13b).

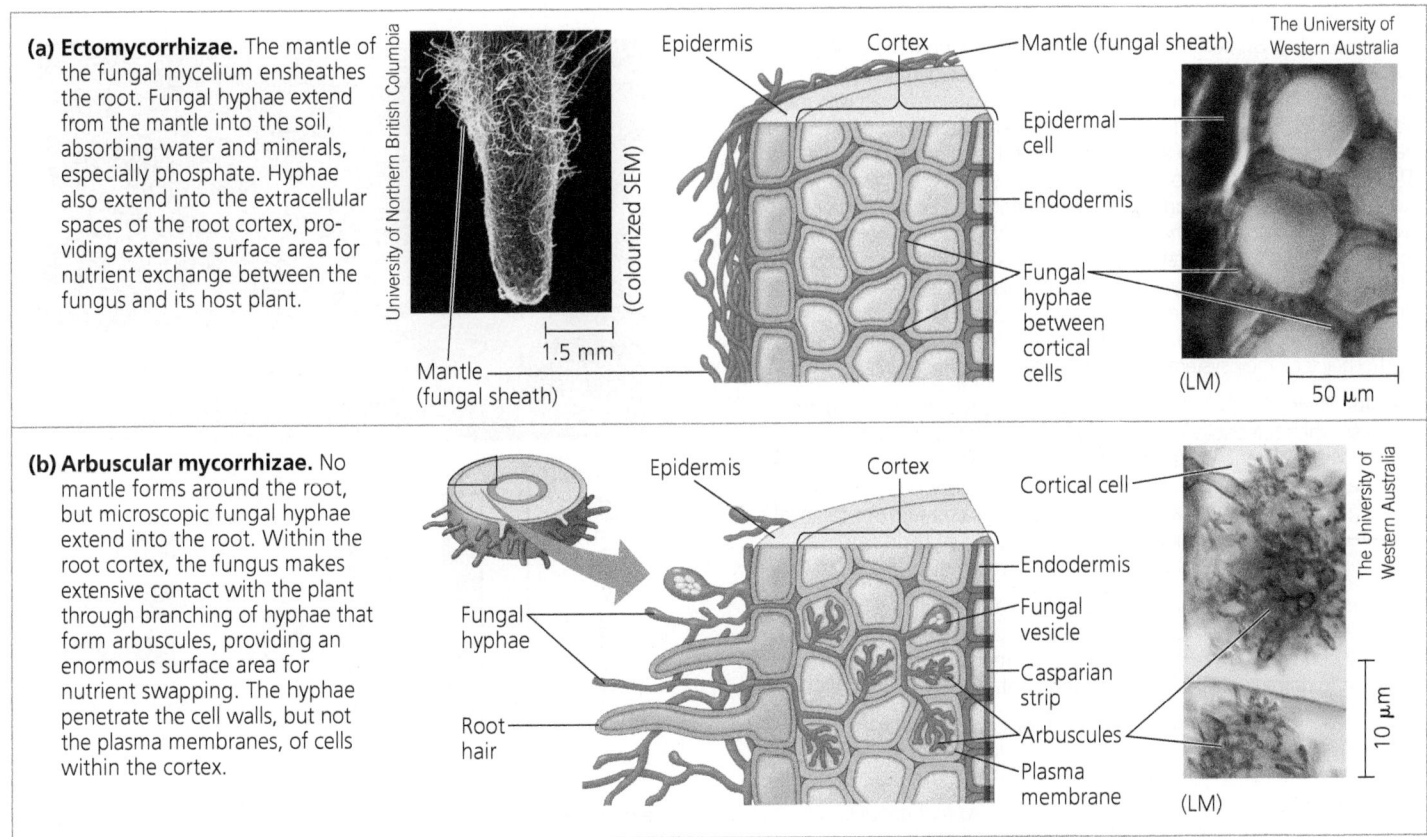

(a) Ectomycorrhizae. The mantle of the fungal mycelium ensheathes the root. Fungal hyphae extend from the mantle into the soil, absorbing water and minerals, especially phosphate. Hyphae also extend into the extracellular spaces of the root cortex, providing extensive surface area for nutrient exchange between the fungus and its host plant.

University of Northern British Columbia

(Colourized SEM)

1.5 mm

Mantle (fungal sheath)

Epidermis   Cortex   Mantle (fungal sheath)

The University of Western Australia

Epidermal cell

Endodermis

Fungal hyphae between cortical cells

(LM)   50 μm

(b) Arbuscular mycorrhizae. No mantle forms around the root, but microscopic fungal hyphae extend into the root. Within the root cortex, the fungus makes extensive contact with the plant through branching of hyphae that form arbuscules, providing an enormous surface area for nutrient swapping. The hyphae penetrate the cell walls, but not the plasma membranes, of cells within the cortex.

Fungal hyphae

Root hair

Epidermis   Cortex

Cortical cell

Endodermis

Fungal vesicle

Casparian strip

Arbuscules

Plasma membrane

The University of Western Australia

10 μm

(LM)

▲ Figure 37.13 **Mycorrhizae.**

Arbuscular mycorrhizae are much more common than ectomycorrhizae and are found in over 85% of plant species. Among those species are most crop plants, including grains and legumes.

To the unaided eye, arbuscular mycorrhizae look like "normal" roots with root hairs, but a microscope reveals the enormous extent of the mutualistic relationship. Arbuscular mycorrhizal associations start when microscopic soil hyphae respond to the presence of a root by growing toward it, establishing contact, and growing along its surface. The hyphae penetrate between epidermal cells and then enter the root cortex. These hyphae digest small patches of the cortical cell walls, but they do not actually pierce the plasma membrane and enter the cytoplasm. Instead, a hypha grows into a tube formed by invagination of the root cell's membrane. The process of invagination is analogous to poking a finger gently into a balloon without popping it; your finger is like the fungal hypha, and the balloon skin is like the root cell's membrane. After the fungal hyphae have penetrated in this way, some of them branch densely, forming structures called arbuscules ("little trees"), which are important sites of nutrient transfer between the fungus and the plant. Within the hyphae themselves, oval vesicles may form, possibly serving as food storage sites for the fungus.

Agricultural and Ecological Importance of Mycorrhizae

Roots can form mycorrhizal symbioses only if exposed to the appropriate species of fungus. In most ecosystems, these fungi are present in the soil, and seedlings develop mycorrhizae. But if seeds are collected in one environment and planted in foreign soil, the plants may show signs of malnutrition (particularly phosphorus deficiency), resulting from the absence of fungal partners. Treating seeds with spores of mycorrhizal fungi can sometimes help seedlings to form mycorrhizae and improve crop yield.

Interactions between the bacteria and fungi in the soil can alter how plants respond to stress. Researchers from the University of Waterloo have demonstrated that plants grow better on petroleum-contaminated soil when a mixture of bacteria and mycorrhizal fungi are added to the soil during seeding (Figure 37.14).

Epiphytes, Parasitic Plants, and Carnivorous Plants

Almost all plant species have mutualistic symbiotic relationships with soil fungi or bacteria or both. Some plant species, including epiphytes, parasites, and carnivores, have unusual adaptations that facilitate exploiting other organisms (Figure 37.15). A recent study suggests that such

---

▼ Figure 37.14 | **Inquiry**

Can soil bacteria make plants more resistant to a stressful environment?

Experiment Drs. Bruce Greenberg and Bernie Glick, from the Biology Department at the University of Waterloo, are interested in how plants and bacteria can work together to clean up areas contaminated with toxic waste or spills. Sites surrounding oil refineries are often contaminated with petroleum hydrocarbons to the point where plants cannot grow in the soil. These petroleum hydrocarbons can stay in the soil for many years and are extremely expensive to clean up. Using their combined expertise in plant biology and microbiology, the research groups of Drs. Greenberg and Glick found a mixture of soil bacteria that can diminish plant stress perception. Thus, in the lab, they can grow grasses with this soil-bacteria mixture in the presence of petroleum hydrocarbons, and the plants grow better than in the absence of the bacteria. However, can this technology be used in the field? They took their system to a refinery site near Sarnia, Ontario, to test it.

Results Their plantings of rye grass, barley, and fescue produced more biomass when the bacterial mixture was added to the soil. In the photo to the right, the plants on the right were treated with the rhizobacteria mixture while those on the left were not. Quantitatively, it can be seen in the graph to the right that soil from the sites treated with the bacterial mixture contained approximately 50% less petroleum hydrocarbons after five months compared to a 25% decrease in soil from untreated plots.

Conclusion The data support the concept that interactions between plants and microbes in the soil can help the plants survive in poor growing conditions. This experiment also demonstrated that plants can be used to help us clean up our environment.

Source: J. Gurska et al., Three-year field test of a plant growth promoting rhizobacteria enhanced phytoremediation system at a land farm for treatment of hydrocarbon waste. Environmental Science & Technology 43:4472–4479 (2009).

WHAT IF? *Similar research has demonstrated that nodulating bacteria added to barren or contaminated soil when planted with new seed can enhance biomass production. What role would the nodulating bacteria be expected to play?*

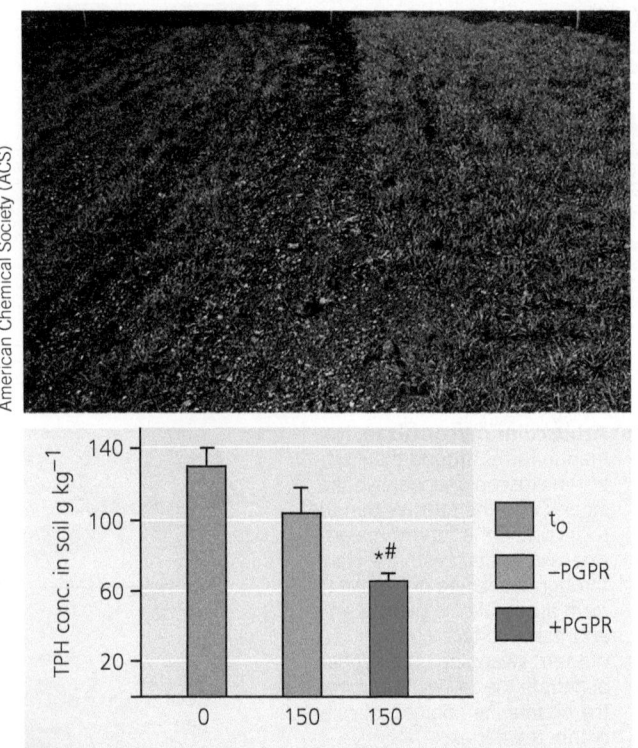

The graph above illustrates the amount of total petroleum hydrocarbons (TPH) in the soil before planting (t_0), and after growing grasses in the absence (−PGPR) or presence (+PGPR) of plant growth promoting rhizobacteria for 150 days.

Exploring **Unusual Nutritional Adaptations in Plants**

Epiphytes

An **epiphyte** (from the Greek *epi*, upon, and *phyton*, plant) is a plant that grows on another plant. Epiphytes produce and gather their own nutrients; they do not tap into their hosts for sustenance. Usually anchored to the branches or trunks of living trees, epiphytes absorb water and minerals from rain, mostly through leaves rather than roots. Some examples are staghorn ferns, bromeliads, and many orchids, including the vanilla plant.

▶ **Staghorn fern,** an epiphyte

David Wall/Alamy

Parasitic Plants

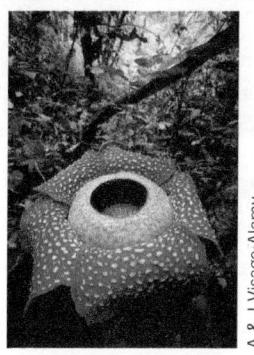

Unlike epiphytes, parasitic plants absorb water, minerals, and sometimes products of photosynthesis from their living hosts. Many species have roots that function as haustoria, nutrient-absorbing projections that tap into the host plant. Some parasitic species, such as mistletoe (genus *Phoradendron*), are photosynthetic and only steal water and minerals, whereas others, such as *Rafflesia arnoldiis* lack chlorophyll entirely and steal photosynthates from its host. Still others, such as Indian pipe (*Monotropa uniflora*), absorb nutrients from the hyphae of mycorrhizae associated with other plants.

Mantonature/Getty Images

◀ **Mistletoe,** a photosynthetic parasite

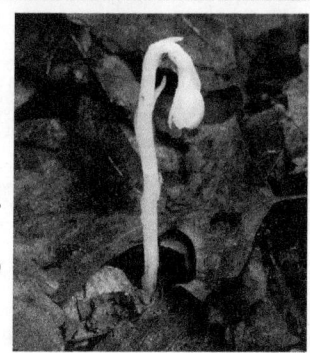

A & J Visage/Alamy

Martin Shields/Alamy

▲ ***Rafflesia*,** a nonphotosynthetic parasite

▲ **Indian pipe,** a nonphotosynthetic parasite of mycorrhizae

Carnivorous Plants

Carnivorous plants are photosynthetic but supplement their mineral diet by capturing insects and other small animals. They live in acid bogs and other habitats where soils are poor in nitrogen and other minerals. Pitcher plants such as *Nepenthes* and *Sarracenia* have water-filled funnels into which prey slip and drown, eventually to be digested by enzymes. Sundews (genus *Drosera*) exude a sticky fluid from tentacle-like glands on highly modified leaves. Stalked glands secrete sweet mucilage that attracts and ensnares insects, and they also release digestive enzymes. Other glands then absorb the nutrient "soup." The highly modified leaves of Venus flytrap (*Dionaea muscipula*) close quickly but partially when a prey hits two trigger hairs in rapid enough succession. Smaller insects can escape, but larger ones are trapped by the teeth lining the margins of the lobes. Excitation by the prey causes the trap to narrow more and digestive enzymes to be released.

Fritz Polking/FLPA/Corbis

▲ **Sundews**

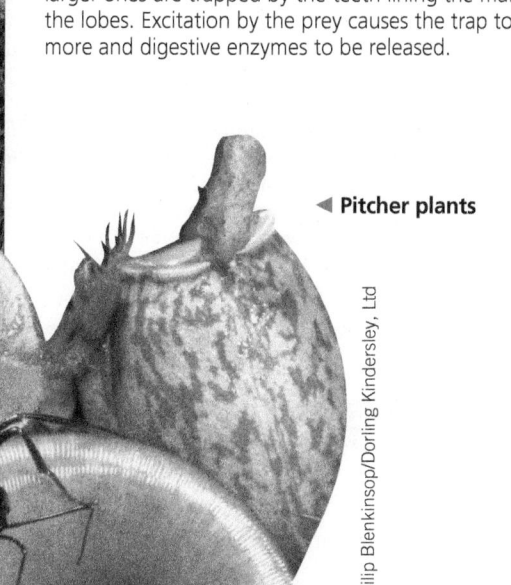

◀ **Pitcher plants**

Philip Blenkinsop/Dorling Kindersley, Ltd

Vera Kuttelvaserova/Fotolia

◀ **Venus flytrap**

863

behaviours may be more normal than once thought. Chan-yarat Paungfoo-Lonhienne and her colleagues at the University of Queensland in Australia have provided evidence that *Arabidopsis* and tomato can take up bacteria and yeast into their roots and digest them. This pioneering research suggests that carnivory by plants may not be an adaptation limited to only a handful of odd species such as *Genlisea* (see Figure 37.1), but that many plant species might engage in a limited amount of heterotrophy.

CONCEPT CHECK 37.3

1. Why is the study of the rhizosphere critical to understanding plant nutrition?
2. How do soil bacteria and mycorrhizae contribute to plant nutrition?
3. **MAKE CONNECTIONS** What is a general term used to describe the strategy of using photosynthesis and heterotrophy for nutrition (see Chapter 28)? What is a well-known example of a class of protists that uses this strategy?
4. **WHAT IF?** A peanut farmer finds that the older leaves of his plant are turning yellow following a long period of wet weather. Suggest a reason why.

For suggested answers, see Appendix A.

37 Chapter Review

Go to **MasteringBiology®** for Assignments, the eText, and the Study Area with Animations, Activities, Vocab Self-Quiz, and Practice Tests.

SUMMARY OF KEY CONCEPTS

CONCEPT 37.1

Soil contains a living, complex ecosystem (pp. 850–854)

- Soil particles of various sizes derived from the breakdown of rock are found in soil. Soil particle size affects the availability of water, oxygen, and minerals in the soil.
- A soil's composition refers to its inorganic and organic components. **Topsoil** is a complex ecosystem teeming with bacteria, fungi, protists, animals, and the roots of plants.
- Some agricultural practices can deplete the mineral content of soil, tax water reserves, and promote erosion. The goal of soil conservation is to minimize this damage.

? *How is soil a complex ecosystem?*

CONCEPT 37.2

Plants require essential elements to complete their life cycle (pp. 854–857)

- **Macronutrients**, elements required in relatively large amounts, include carbon, oxygen, hydrogen, nitrogen, and other major ingredients of organic compounds. **Micronutrients**, elements required in very small amounts, typically have catalytic functions as cofactors of enzymes.
- Deficiency of a mobile nutrient usually affects older organs more than younger ones; the reverse is true for nutrients that are less mobile within a plant. Macronutrient deficiencies are most common, particularly deficiencies of nitrogen, phosphorus, and potassium.
- Rather than tailoring the soil to match the plant, genetic engineers are tailoring the plant to match the soil.

? *Do plants need soil to grow? Explain.*

CONCEPT 37.3

Plant nutrition often involves relationships with other organisms (pp. 857–864)

- **Rhizobacteria** derive their energy from the **rhizosphere**, a microbe-enriched ecosystem intimately associated with roots. Plant

secretions support the energy needs of the rhizosphere. Some rhizobacteria produce antibiotics, whereas others make nutrients more available for plants. Most are free-living, but some live inside plants. Plants satisfy most of their huge needs for nitrogen from the bacterial decomposition of **humus** and the fixation of gaseous nitrogen.

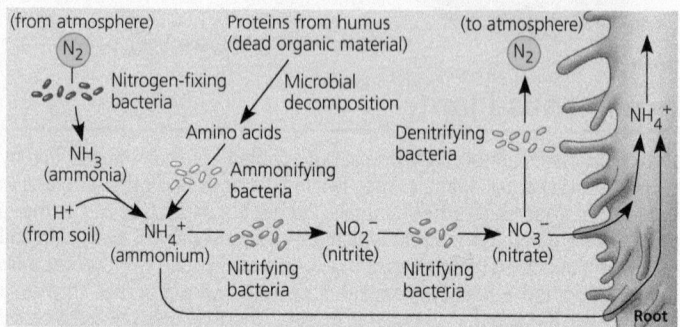

Nitrogen-fixing bacteria convert atmospheric N_2 to nitrogenous minerals that plants can absorb as a nitrogen source for organic synthesis. The most efficient mutualism between plants and nitrogen-fixing bacteria occurs in the nodules formed by *Rhizobium* bacteria growing in the roots of legumes. These bacteria obtain sugar from the plant and supply the plant with fixed nitrogen. In agriculture, legume crops are rotated with other crops to restore nitrogen to the soil.

- **Mycorrhizae** are mutualistic associations of fungi and roots. The fungal hyphae of mycorrhizae absorb water and minerals, which they supply to their plant hosts.
- **Epiphytes** grow on the surfaces of other plants but acquire water and minerals from rain. Parasitic plants absorb nutrients from host plants. Carnivorous plants supplement their mineral nutrition by digesting animals.

? *Do all plants gain their energy directly from photosynthesis? Explain.*

TEST YOUR UNDERSTANDING

LEVEL 1: KNOWLEDGE/COMPREHENSION

1. The inorganic nutrient most often lacking in crops is
   a. carbon.
   b. nitrogen.
   c. phosphorus.
   d. potassium.

2. Micronutrients are needed in very small amounts because
   a. most of them are mobile in the plant.
   b. most serve mainly as cofactors of enzymes.
   c. most are supplied in large enough quantities in seeds.
   d. they play only a minor role in the growth and health of the plant.

3. Mycorrhizae enhance plant nutrition mainly by
   a. absorbing water and minerals through the fungal hyphae.
   b. providing sugar to root cells, which have no chloroplasts.
   c. converting atmospheric nitrogen to ammonia.
   d. enabling the roots to parasitize neighbouring plants.

4. Epiphytes are
   a. fungi that attack plants.
   b. fungi that form mutualistic associations with roots.
   c. nonphotosynthetic parasitic plants.
   d. plants that grow on other plants.

5. Leghemoglobin is produced in some root nodules to
   a. transport oxygen from air in the soil to the root tissues.
   b. bind oxygen in the nodule to keep the area anaerobic.
   c. supply iron to the nitrogenase enzyme.
   d. feed the symbiotic bacteria.

LEVEL 2: APPLICATION/ANALYSIS

6. A mineral deficiency is likely to affect older leaves more than younger leaves if
   a. the mineral is a micronutrient.
   b. the mineral is very mobile within the plant.
   c. the mineral is required for chlorophyll synthesis.
   d. the mineral is a macronutrient.

7. The greatest difference in plant health between two groups of plants of the same species, one group with mycorrhizae and one group without mycorrhizae, would be found in an environment
   a. where nitrogen-fixing bacteria are abundant.
   b. that has soil with poor drainage.
   c. that has hot summers and cold winters.
   d. in which the soil is relatively deficient in mineral nutrients.

8. Two groups of tomatoes were grown under laboratory conditions, one with humus added to the soil and one a control without humus. The leaves of the plants grown without humus were yellowish (less green) compared with those of the plants grown in humus-enriched soil. The best explanation for this difference is that
   a. the healthy plants used the food in the decomposing leaves of the humus for energy to make chlorophyll.
   b. the humus made the soil more loosely packed, so water penetrated more easily to the roots.
   c. the humus contained minerals such as magnesium and iron, needed for the synthesis of chlorophyll.
   d. the heat released by the decomposing leaves of the humus caused more rapid growth and chlorophyll synthesis.

9. The specific relationship between a legume and its mutualistic *Rhizobium* strain probably depends on
   a. each legume having a chemical dialogue with a fungus.
   b. each *Rhizobium* strain having a form of nitrogenase that works only in the appropriate legume host.
   c. each legume being found where the soil has only the *Rhizobium* specific to that legume.
   d. specific recognition between the chemical signals and signal receptors of the *Rhizobium* strain and legume species.

10. **DRAW IT** Draw a simple sketch of cation exchange, showing a root hair, a soil particle with anions, and a hydrogen ion displacing a mineral cation.

LEVEL 3: SYNTHESIS/EVALUATION

11. **EVOLUTION CONNECTION**
    Imagine taking the plant out of the picture in Figure 37.10. Write a paragraph explaining how soil bacteria could sustain the recycling of nitrogen *before* land plants evolved.

12. **SCIENTIFIC INQUIRY**
    Acid precipitation has an abnormally high concentration of hydrogen ions (H^+). One effect of acid precipitation is to deplete the soil of nutrients such as calcium (Ca^{2+}), potassium (K^+), and magnesium (Mg^{2+}). Suggest a hypothesis to explain how acid precipitation washes these nutrients from the soil. How might you test your hypothesis?

13. **SCIENCE, TECHNOLOGY, AND SOCIETY**
    In many countries, irrigation is emptying reservoirs that are also used for human water consumption, recreational activities, and hydroelectric power. As reservoir levels decline, regulators must make difficult choices among watering crops, suppling electricity, and human water needs. Discuss the possible consequences of this trend. What can society and science do to help alleviate this growing problem?

14. **WRITE ABOUT A THEME: INTERACTIONS**
    The soil in which plants grow teems with organisms from every taxonomic kingdom. In a short essay (100–150 words), discuss examples of how the mutualistic interactions of plants with bacteria, fungi, and animals improve plant nutrition.

15. **SYNTHESIZE YOUR KNOWLEDGE**

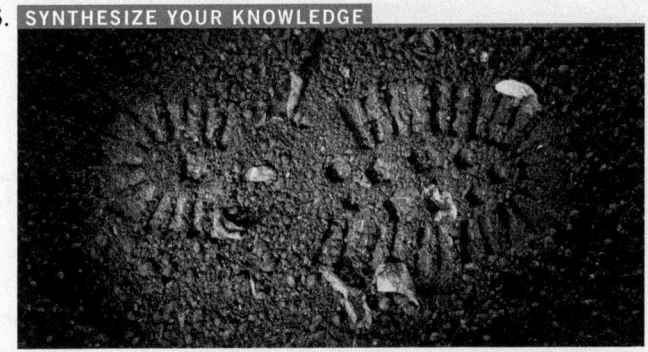

Wayne Forward/Mode Images/Alamy

Making a footprint in the soil seems like an insignificant event. In a short essay (100–150 words), explain how a footprint would affect the properties of the soil and how these changes would affect soil organisms and the emergence of seedlings.

For selected answers, see Appendix A.

38

Angiosperm Reproduction and Biotechnology

KEY CONCEPTS

38.1 Flowers, double fertilization, and fruits are unique features of the angiosperm life cycle

38.2 Flowering plants reproduce sexually, asexually, or both

38.3 People modify crops by breeding and genetic engineering

▲ **Figure 38.1 How did classical breeding techniques and modern molecular biotechnology change the face of Canadian agriculture?**

Canola (Canadian Oil Low Acid): A Canadian Invention

It is hard to believe that a crop plant so iconic to the Canadian Prairie landscape (Figure 38.1), whose oil is a staple of our diet, did not exist 50 years ago. While Canadian farmers grew "rapeseed" during the Second World War, its oil was used as a lubricant for steam engines. It was essentially inedible due to high levels of glucosinolates and erucic acid. In the years following the war, Canada imported almost all of its edible oil, and this was a market that Canada's agricultural leaders were very interested in exploiting. Starting in the early 1960s, Dr. R. Keith Downey, a researcher with the Canadian Ministry of Agriculture in Saskatoon, and Dr. Baldur Stefansson, a professor at the University of Manitoba in Winnipeg, worked toward breeding a new oil-seed plant that could be grown in Canada. Their classical breeding techniques involved crossing plants with desirable traits such as low glucosinolate levels. By techniques reminiscent of Mendel and his pea plants, pollen from one plant would be manually transferred to the pistils of other plants. Over the course of several generations, Downey and Stefansson obtained new domesticated varieties of the rapeseed plant *Brassica napus*, seen in Figure 38.1, which produced oils suitable for human consumption. These new strains were named Canola for Canadian Oil, Low Acid. In recognition of their work in the breeding of Canola strains, Drs. Downey and Stefansson were both made Officers of the Order of Canada and inducted into the Canadian Agricultural Hall of Fame.

While these plants originated due to traditional breeding techniques, in recent years researchers have begun to genetically modify canola using transgenic approaches. The most common alteration produced canola plants that are herbicide resistant. This allows farmers to spray broad spectrum herbicides on newly emerged fields for the control of weed species. This type of agricultural approach uses less fuel and increases yields by up to 10%. Using modern transgenic techniques, the herbicide resistance gene is only expressed in the vegetative tissues. As a result, there is no difference in the content or quality of the oil produced by the genetically modified plants.

Thus, through a combination of classical breeding and molecular biology, what were once inedible rapeseed plants are now an iconic staple of the Canadian landscape and diet. Today, over 10 million tonnes of canola seed are harvested in Canada each year, and Canada is the second-largest producer in the world, behind China. Canola is a great success story in Canadian agricultural research.

In Chapters 29 and 30, we approached plant reproduction from an evolutionary perspective, tracing the descent of land plants from algal ancestors. Here, we'll explore the reproductive biology of flowering plants in greater detail because they are the most important group of plants in most terrestrial ecosystems and in agriculture. After discussing the sexual and asexual reproduction of angiosperms, we'll examine the role of humans in genetically altering crop species, as well as the controversies surrounding modern plant biotechnology.

CONCEPT 38.1

Flowers, double fertilization, and fruits are unique features of the angiosperm life cycle

The life cycles of all plants are characterized by an alternation of generations, in which sporophytes (spore-producing plants) and gametophytes (gamete-producing plants) alternate producing each other. In the angiosperms, the sporophytes are the plants we see; they are much larger, more conspicuous, and longer-lived than the gametophytes. In exploring the life cycle of angiosperms, we'll pay especially close attention to three key derived traits of angiosperm reproduction that can be remembered as the "three Fs": *f*lowers, double *f*ertilization, and *f*ruits.

Flower Structure and Function

Flowers, the reproductive shoots of angiosperm sporophytes, are typically composed of four types of floral organs: **carpels**, **stamens**, **petals**, and **sepals** (Figure 38.2). When viewed from above, these organs take the form of concentric whorls. Carpels form the first (innermost) whorl, stamens the second, petals the third, and sepals the fourth (outermost) whorl. All are attached to a part of the stem called the **receptacle**.

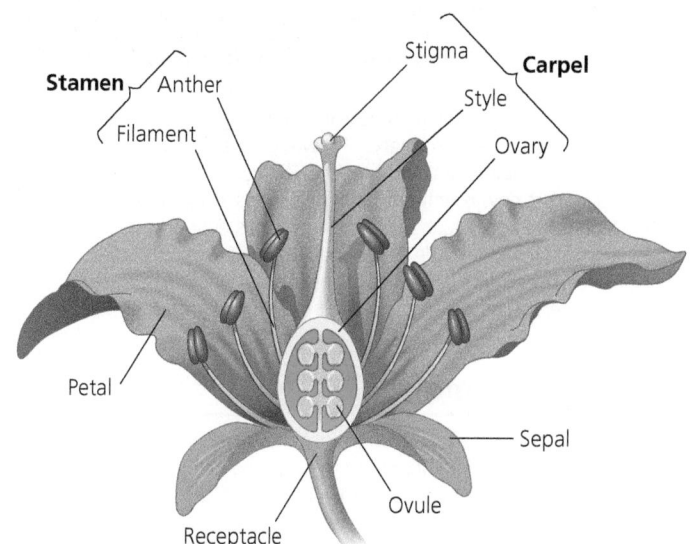

▲ Figure 38.2 **The structure of an idealized flower.**

Unlike vegetative shoots, flowers are determinate shoots; they cease growing after the flower and fruit are formed.

Carpels and stamens are reproductive organs; sepals and petals are sterile. A carpel has an **ovary** at its base and a long, slender neck called the **style**. At the top of the style is a sticky structure called the **stigma** that captures pollen. Within the ovary are one or more **ovules**, which become seeds if fertilized; the number of ovules depends on the species. The flower shown in Figure 38.2 has a single carpel, but many species have multiple carpels. In most species, two or more carpels are fused into a single structure; the result is an ovary with two or more chambers, each containing one or more ovules. The term **pistil** is sometimes used to refer to a single carpel or two or more fused carpels. A stamen consists of a stalk called the filament and a terminal structure called the **anther**; within the anther are chambers called microsporangia (pollen sacs) that produce pollen. Petals are typically more brightly coloured than sepals and advertise the flower to insects and other animal pollinators. Sepals, which enclose and protect unopened floral buds, usually resemble leaves more than the other floral organs do.

Complete flowers have all four basic floral organs (see Figure 38.2). Some species have **incomplete flowers**, lacking sepals, petals, stamens, or carpels. For example, most grass flowers lack petals. Some incomplete flowers are sterile, lacking functional stamens and carpels; others are *unisexual*, lacking either stamens or carpels. Flowers also vary in size, shape, colour, odour, organ arrangement, and time of opening. Some are borne singly, while others are arranged in showy clusters called **inflorescences**. For example, a sunflower's central disk consists of hundreds of tiny incomplete flowers, and what look like petals are actually sterile flowers (see Figure 1.3). Much of floral diversity represents adaptation to specific pollinators. Figure 38.3

Exploring Trends in the Evolution of Flowers

EVOLUTION Charles Darwin described the origin of flowering plants as an "abominable mystery." He was puzzled by their relatively sudden appearance and rapid diversification in the fossil record. Scientists now estimate that angiosperms arose about 140 million years ago. Much of their diversity has evolved through selective pressures that made flower-pollinator interactions more specific. However, there can be negative consequences associated with floral overspecialization if, for example, a pollinator goes

extinct. Also, there are selective pressures associated with preventing the plunder of nectar and floral parts by "robbers," animals that feed on a flower without transferring its pollen to other plants of the same species. Despite these varied and sometimes opposing selective pressures, four general trends can be seen in the evolution of flowers: bilateral symmetry, reduction in the number of floral parts, fusion of floral parts, and the location of ovaries inside receptacles.

Bilateral Symmetry

The flowers of musk mallow (*Malva moschata*) exhibit radial symmetry. That is, any imaginary line through the central axis divides the flower into two equal parts. In contrast, the "Bramley" orchid (*Disa watsonii*) is bilaterally symmetrical. That is, only a single imaginary line can divide the flower into equal halves. Flowers with bilateral symmetry orient insects such as bees in their approach to the flower, enabling the insects to find their way to the nectar and enhancing pollen transfer between insect and flower.

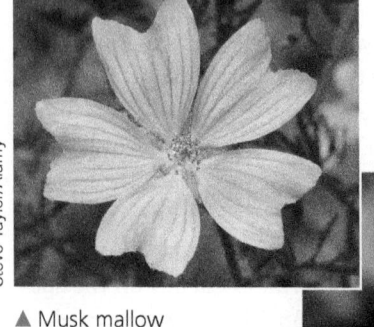

▲ Musk mallow
(radial symmetry)

▼ "Bramley" orchid
(bilateral symmetry)

Reduction in Number of Floral Parts

The flower of bloodroot (*Sanguinaria canadensis*) has many petals and stamens, with the exact number varying among individual flowers. In contrast, the flowers of drooping trillium (*Trillium flexipes*) have fewer floral parts and have a fixed number of them. Although a greater number of floral parts may attract pollinators, such a large display may also entice unwanted visitors, such as pollen or nectar "robbers."

▲ Bloodroot

▼ Drooping trillium

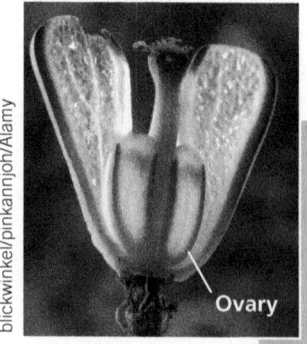

Fusion of Floral Parts

The petals of Star of Bethlehem (*Ornithogalum arabicum*) are unfused, whereas the petals of hedge bindweed (*Calystegia septium*) are fused together. The fusion of floral parts often increases the specificity of animal pollinators that visit the flower. For example, a long "floral tube" made from fused petals may allow only certain animal pollinators to reach the nectar.

▲ Star of Bethlehem

▼ Hedge bindweed

Ovaries Located Inside Receptacles

In the flowers of the stone plant (*Lithops* sp.), the ovary is situated above the receptacle. In contrast, the ovary of Japanese quince (*Chaenomeles japonica*) is embedded in the receptacle, providing the seeds with even greater protection during their development and later enhancing the dispersal of seeds by animals.

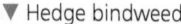

▼ Japanese quince
(longitudinal section)

Ovary

▲ Stone plant
(longitudinal section)

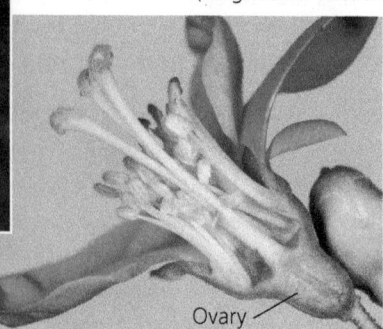

Ovary

Nigel Cattlin/Alamy Stock Photo

shows some examples of variations in floral structures that have evolved in some plants.

The Angiosperm Life Cycle: An Overview

Figure 30.12 shows the complete angiosperm life cycle, including gametophyte development, pollination, double fertilization, and seed development. Here, we'll revisit this life cycle, beginning with a closer examination of angiosperm gametophyte development (Figure 38.4).

Gametophyte Development

Over the course of seed plant evolution, gametophytes became reduced in size and wholly dependent on the sporophyte for nutrients (see Figure 30.2). The gametophytes of angiosperms are the most reduced of all plants, consisting of only a few cells: they are microscopic, and protective tissues obscure their development.

Development of Male Gametophytes in Pollen Grains As the stamens are produced, each anther develops four microsporangia, also called pollen sacs (Figure 38.4a). Within the microsporangia are many diploid cells called *microsporocytes,* or microspore mother cells ❶. Each microsporocyte undergoes meiosis, forming four haploid **microspores** ❷, each of which eventually gives rise to a haploid male gametophyte. Each microspore then undergoes unequal mitosis, producing a haploid male gametophyte consisting of only two cells: the small *generative cell,* which forms within the larger *tube cell* ❸. Together, these two cells *and* the spore wall constitute a **pollen grain**. The spore wall, which consists of material produced by both the microspore and the anther, usually exhibits an elaborate pattern unique to the species. During maturation of the male gametophyte, the generative cell passes into the tube cell: The tube cell now has a completely free-standing cell inside it.

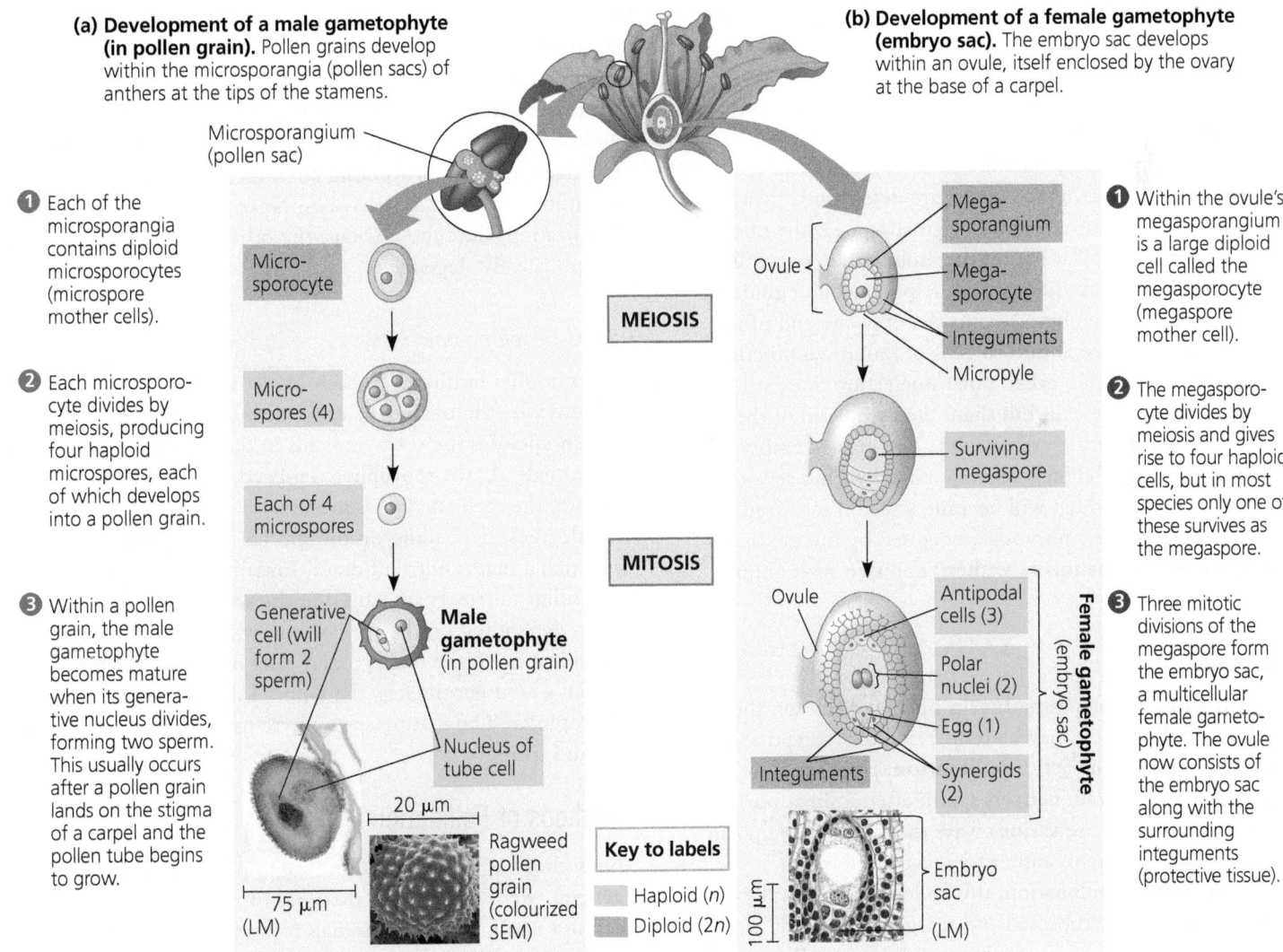

(a) Development of a male gametophyte (in pollen grain). Pollen grains develop within the microsporangia (pollen sacs) of anthers at the tips of the stamens.

Microsporangium (pollen sac)

❶ Each of the microsporangia contains diploid microsporocytes (microspore mother cells).

❷ Each microsporocyte divides by meiosis, producing four haploid microspores, each of which develops into a pollen grain.

❸ Within a pollen grain, the male gametophyte becomes mature when its generative nucleus divides, forming two sperm. This usually occurs after a pollen grain lands on the stigma of a carpel and the pollen tube begins to grow.

Microsporocyte

Microspores (4)

Each of 4 microspores

Generative cell (will form 2 sperm)

Male gametophyte (in pollen grain)

Nucleus of tube cell

75 μm (LM)

20 μm

Ragweed pollen grain (colourized SEM)

MEIOSIS

MITOSIS

Key to labels

Haploid (*n*)

Diploid (2*n*)

(b) Development of a female gametophyte (embryo sac). The embryo sac develops within an ovule, itself enclosed by the ovary at the base of a carpel.

Ovule

Megasporangium

Megasporocyte

Integuments

Micropyle

Surviving megaspore

Ovule

Antipodal cells (3)

Polar nuclei (2)

Egg (1)

Synergids (2)

Integuments

Female gametophyte (embryo sac)

Embryo sac

100 μm

(LM)

❶ Within the ovule's megasporangium is a large diploid cell called the megasporocyte (megaspore mother cell).

❷ The megasporocyte divides by meiosis and gives rise to four haploid cells, but in most species only one of these survives as the megaspore.

❸ Three mitotic divisions of the megaspore form the embryo sac, a multicellular female gametophyte. The ovule now consists of the embryo sac along with the surrounding integuments (protective tissue).

▲ Figure 38.4 **The development of male and female gametophytes in angiosperms.**

Climate change may have significant negative effects on the development of pollen grains and fertility of many plant species. High temperatures can induce programmed cell death in the cells of the anther that nurture microspore development. Without these cells, fewer microspores survive to complete their development into functional pollen grains.

Development of Female Gametophytes (Embryo Sacs) As a carpel develops, one or more ovules form deep within its ovary, its swollen base. A female gametophyte, also known as an **embryo sac**, develops inside each ovule ❶. The process of embryo sac formation occurs in a tissue called the megasporangium within each ovule. Two *integuments* (layers of protective sporophytic tissue that will develop into the seed coat) surround each megasporangium, except at a gap called the *micropyle*. Female gametophyte development begins when one cell in the megasporangium of each ovule, the *megasporocyte* (or megaspore mother cell), enlarges and undergoes meiosis, producing four haploid **megaspores** ❷. Only one megaspore survives; the others degenerate.

The nucleus of the surviving megaspore divides by mitosis three times without cytokinesis, resulting in one large cell with eight haploid nuclei. The multinucleate mass is then divided by membranes to form the embryo sac ❸. The cell fates of the nuclei are determined by a gradient of the hormone auxin originating near the micropyle. At the micropylar end of the embryo sac, two cells called synergids flank the egg and help attract and guide the pollen tube to the embryo sac. At the opposite end of the embryo sac are three antipodal cells of unknown function. The other two nuclei, called polar nuclei, are not partitioned into separate cells but share the cytoplasm of the large central cell of the embryo sac. The mature embryo sac thus consists of eight nuclei contained within seven cells. The ovule, which will become a seed if fertilized, now consists of the embryo sac, enclosed by the megasporangium (which eventually withers) and two surrounding integuments.

Pollination

After the microsporangium breaks open and releases the pollen, a pollen grain may be transferred to a receptive surface of a stigma—the act of **pollination**. Here we'll focus on how a pollen grain delivers sperm after pollination. Later we'll look at the various ways that a pollen grain can be transported from an anther to a stigma.

At the time of pollination, the pollen grain typically consists of only the tube cell and the generative cell. It then absorbs water and germinates by producing a **pollen tube**, a long cellular protuberance that delivers sperm to the female gametophyte. A pollen tube can grow very quickly, at rates of 1 cm/hr or faster. As the pollen tube elongates through the style, the nucleus of the generative cell divides by mitosis and produces two sperm, which remain inside the tube cell. The tube nucleus then leads the two sperm as the tip of the pollen tube grows toward the micropyle in response to chemical attractants produced by the synergids. The arrival of the pollen tube initiates the death of one of the two synergids, thereby providing a passageway into the embryo sac. The tube nucleus and the two sperm are then discharged from the pollen tube in the vicinity of the female gametophyte.

Double Fertilization

Fertilization, the fusion of gametes, occurs after the two sperm reach the female gametophyte. One sperm fertilizes the egg, forming the zygote. The other sperm combines with the two polar nuclei, forming a triploid (3n) nucleus in the centre of the large central cell of the female gametophyte. This cell will give rise to the **endosperm**, a food-storing tissue of the seed. The union of the two sperm cells with different nuclei of the female gametophyte is called **double fertilization**. Double fertilization ensures that endosperm develops only in ovules where the egg has been fertilized, thereby preventing angiosperms from squandering nutrients on infertile ovules. Near the time of double fertilization, the tube nucleus, the other synergid, and the antipodal cells degenerate.

Seed Development

After double fertilization, each ovule develops into a seed. Meanwhile, the ovary (typically) develops into a fruit, which encloses the seeds and aids in their dispersal by wind or animals. As the sporophyte embryo develops from the zygote, the seed stockpiles proteins, oils, and starch to varying degrees, depending on the species. This is why seeds are such a major nutrient drain. Initially, carbohydrates and other nutrients are stored in the seed's endosperm, but later, depending on the species, the swelling cotyledons (seed leaves) of the embryo may take over this function. When a seed germinates, the embryo develops into a new sporophyte. The mature sporophyte produces its own flowers and fruits.

Methods of Pollination

Now that we've examined the angiosperm life cycle in general, we'll explore the methods of pollination. Plants can use wind, water, or animals to transfer pollen from an anther to a stigma (Figure 38.5). In wind-pollinated species, including grasses and many trees, the release of enormous quantities of smaller-sized pollen compensates for the randomness of dispersal by the wind. At certain times of the year, the air is loaded with pollen grains, as anyone who suffers from pollen allergies can attest. Some species of aquatic plants rely on water to disperse pollen. Most angiosperm species, however, depend on insects, birds, or other animal pollinators to transfer pollen directly from one flower to another.

Coevolution of Flower and Pollinator

EVOLUTION The joint evolution of two interacting species, each in response to selection imposed by the other, is called **coevolution**. Many species of flowering plants have coevolved with specific pollinators. Natural selection favours individual plants or insects having slight deviations of structure that enhance the flower-pollinator mutualism. For example, some species have flower petals fused together, forming long, tube-like structures bearing nectaries tucked deep inside. Charles Darwin suggested that a race between flower and insect might lead to correspondences between the length of a floral tube and the length of an insect's proboscis, a straw-like mouthpart. Imagine an insect with a tongue long enough to drink the nectar of flowers without picking up pollen on its body. The resulting failure of these plants to fertilize others would render them less evolutionarily fit. Natural selection would then favour flowers with longer tubes. At the same time, an insect with a tongue that was too short for the tube wouldn't be able to use the nectar as a food source and therefore would be at a selective disadvantage compared

▼ Figure 38.5

Exploring Flower Pollination

Most angiosperm species rely on a living (biotic) or nonliving (abiotic) pollinating agent that can move pollen from the anther of a flower on one plant to the stigma of a flower on another plant. Approximately 80% of all angiosperm pollination is biotic, employing animal go-betweens. Among abiotically pollinated species, 98% rely on wind and 2% on water. (Some angiosperm species can self-pollinate, but such species are limited to inbreeding in nature.)

Abiotic Pollination by Wind

About 20% of all angiosperm species are wind-pollinated. Since their reproductive success does not depend on attracting pollinators, there has been no selective pressure favouring colourful or scented flowers. Accordingly, the flowers of wind-pollinated species, such as hazel (*Corylus avellana*), are often small, green, and inconspicuous, and they produce neither nectar nor scent.

◄ Hazel staminate flowers (stamens only) releasing clouds of pollen

Carola Schubbel/Fotolia

▲ Hazel carpellate flower (carpels only)

WILDLIFE GmbH/Alamy

Pollination by Bees

About 65% of all flowering plants require insects for pollination; the percentage is even greater for major crops. Bees are the most important insect pollinators and are attracted to bright colours, primarily yellow and blue. Many bee-pollinated flowers, such as the common dandelion (*Taraxacum vulgare*), have ultraviolet markings visible to bees called "nectar guides" that help insects locate the nectaries (nectar-producing glands) but are only visible to human eyes under ultraviolet light.

Rorslett Bjorn

▲ Common dandelion under normal light

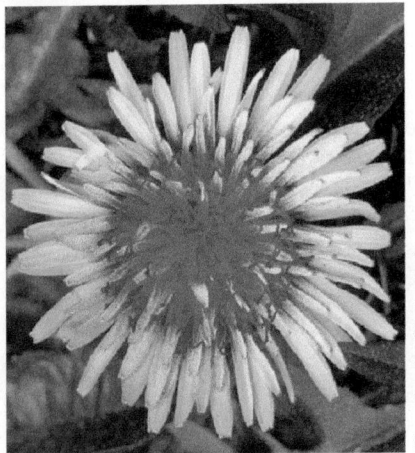

Bjorn Rorslett Photographer

▲ Common dandelion under ultraviolet light

Continued on next page

with long-tongued rivals. As a result, the shapes and sizes of flowers often show a close correspondence to the pollen-adhering parts of their animal pollinators. In fact, based on the length of a long, tubular flower that grows in Madagascar, Darwin predicted the existence of a pollinating moth with a 28-cm-long proboscis. Such a moth was discovered two decades after Darwin's death (Figure 38.6).

From Seed to Flowering Plant: A Closer Look

Let's look at how a seed develops into a flowering plant after pollination and fertilization. This process includes endosperm development, embryo development, seed dormancy, seed germination, seedling development, and flowering.

▼ Figure 38.5 (continued)

Exploring Flower Pollination

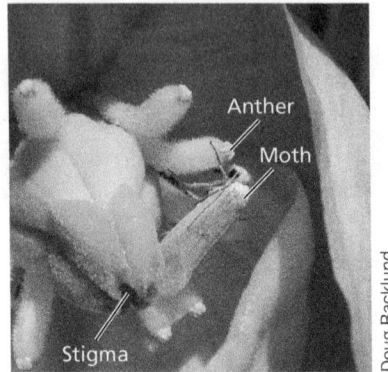

▲ Moth on yucca flower

Doug Backlund

▲ Blowfly on carrion flower

Florian Andronache/Shutterstock

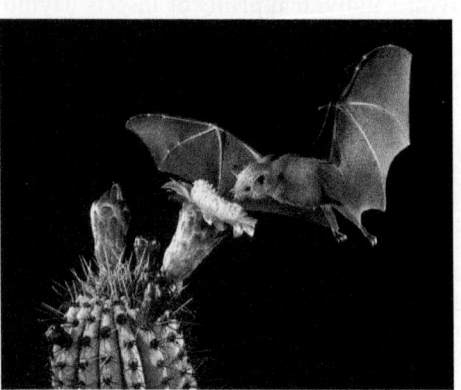

▲ Long-nosed bat feeding on cactus flower at night

Bat Conservation International

Pollination by Moths and Butterflies

Moths and butterflies detect odours, and the flowers they pollinate are often sweetly fragrant. Butterflies perceive many bright colours, but moth-pollinated flowers, like the yucca plant (shown here), are usually white or yellow, which stand out at night when moths are active.

Pollination by Flies

Many fly-pollinated flowers, including the carrion flowers (*Stapelia* sp.), are reddish and fleshy, with an odour like rotten meat to attract flies.

Pollination by Bats

Bat-pollinated flowers, like moth-pollinated flowers, are light-coloured and aromatic, attracting their nocturnal pollinators.

Pollination by Birds

Bird-pollinated flowers, such as columbine flowers, are usually large and bright red or yellow, but they have little odour. Since birds often do not have a well-developed sense of smell, there has been no selective pressure favouring scent production. However, the flowers produce the sugary solution called nectar that helps meet the high energy demands of the pollinating birds.

[?] *What are the benefits and dangers to a plant of having a highly specific animal pollinator?*

▶ Hummingbird drinking nectar of columbine flower

Rolf Nussbaumer/Nature Picture Library

Endosperm Development

Endosperm usually develops before the embryo does. After double fertilization, the triploid nucleus of the ovule's central cell divides, forming a multinucleate "supercell" that has a milky consistency. This liquid mass, the endosperm, becomes multicellular when cytokinesis partitions the cytoplasm by forming membranes between the nuclei. Eventually, these "naked" cells produce cell walls, and the endosperm becomes solid. Coconut "milk" and "meat" are examples of liquid and solid endosperm, respectively. The white fluffy part of popcorn is also endosperm.

As discussed in earlier chapters, plants under drought stress become dehydrated and nutrient deficient, and photosynthesis is reduced. Drought stress at the time of endosperm development often results in lower endosperm quantity and quality.

In grains and most other species of monocots, as well as many eudicots, the endosperm stores nutrients that can be used by the seedling after germination. In other eudicot seeds, the food reserves of the endosperm are completely exported to the cotyledons before the seed completes its development; consequently, the mature seed lacks endosperm.

Embryo Development

The first mitotic division of the zygote splits the fertilized egg into a basal cell and

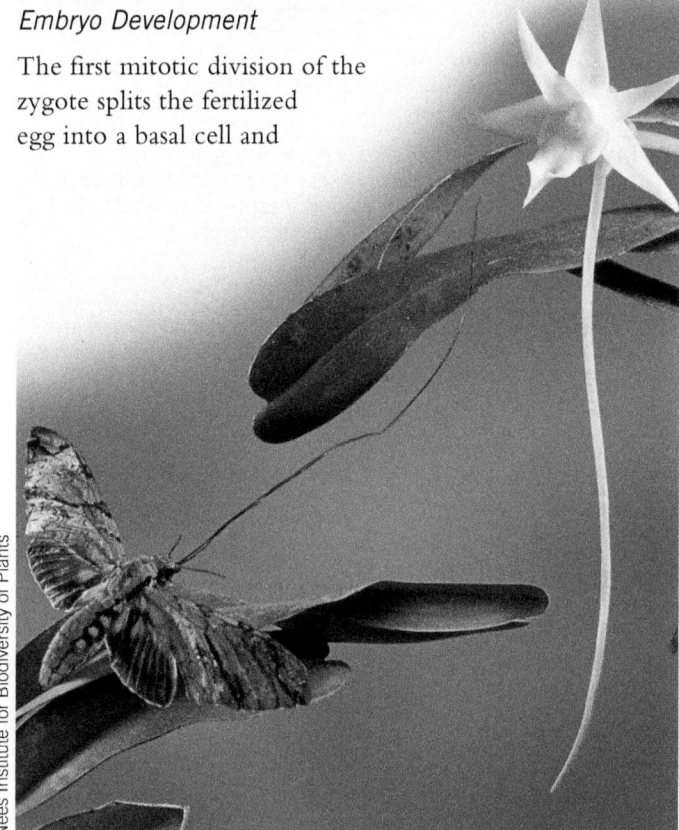

Nees Institute for Biodiversity of Plants

▲ Figure 38.6 **Coevolution of a flower and an insect pollinator.** The long floral tube of the Madagascar orchid *Angraecum sesquipedale* has coevolved with the 28-cm-long proboscis of its pollinator, the hawkmoth *Xanthopan morganii praedicta*. The moth is named in honour of Darwin's prediction of its existence.

a terminal cell (**Figure 38.7**). The terminal cell eventually gives rise to most of the embryo. The basal cell continues to divide, producing a thread of cells called the *suspensor*, which anchors the embryo to the parent plant. The suspensor helps in transferring nutrients to the embryo from the parent plant and, in some species of plants, from the endosperm. As the suspensor elongates, it pushes the embryo deeper into the nutritive and protective tissues. Meanwhile, the terminal cell divides several times and forms a spherical proembryo (early embryo) attached to the suspensor. The cotyledons begin to form as bumps on the proembryo.

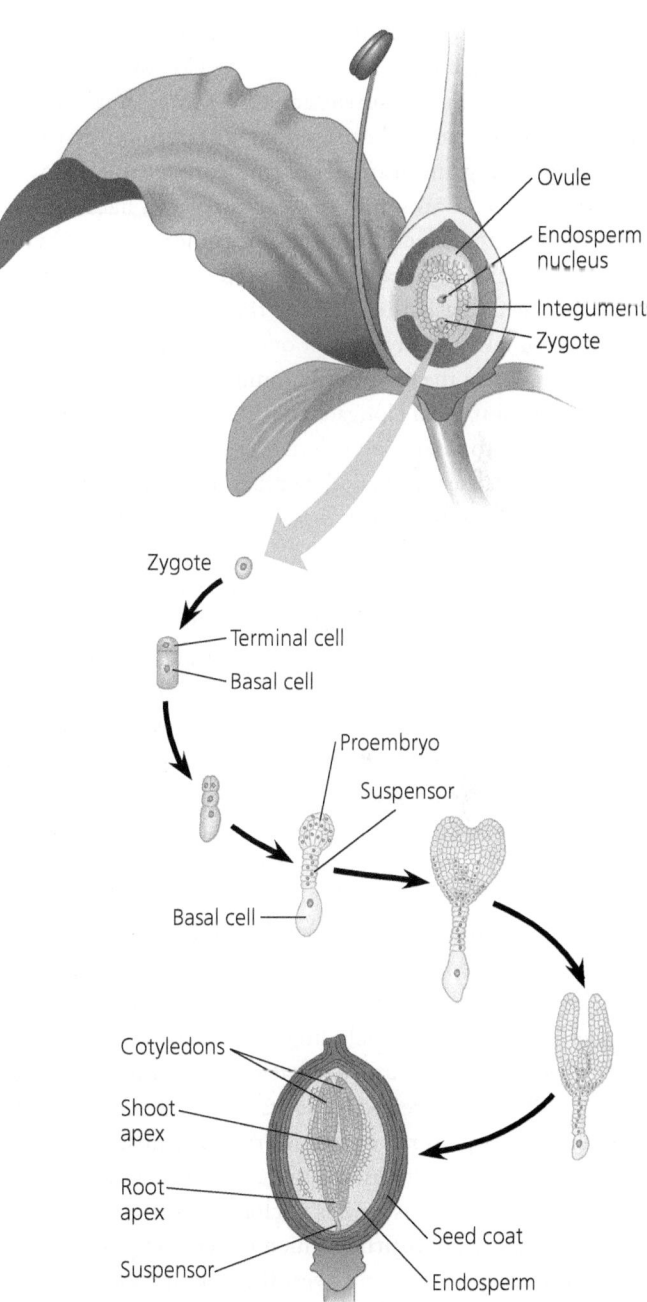

▲ Figure 38.7 **The development of a eudicot plant embryo.** By the time the ovule becomes a mature seed and the integuments harden and thicken into the seed coat, the zygote has given rise to an embryonic plant with rudimentary organs.

A eudicot, with its two cotyledons, is heart-shaped at this stage. Only one cotyledon develops in monocots.

Soon after the rudimentary cotyledons appear, the embryo elongates. Cradled between the two cotyledons is the embryonic shoot apex. At the opposite end of the embryo's axis, where the suspensor attaches, an embryonic root apex forms. After the seed germinates—indeed, for the rest of the plant's life—the apical meristems at the apices of shoots and roots sustain primary growth (see Figure 35.11).

Structure of the Mature Seed

During the last stages of its maturation, the seed dehydrates until its water content is only about 5–15% of its weight. The embryo, which is surrounded by a food supply (cotyledons, endosperm, or both), enters **dormancy**; that is, it stops growing and its metabolism nearly ceases. The embryo and its food supply are enclosed by a hard, protective **seed coat** formed from the integuments of the ovule. In some species, dormancy is imposed by the presence of an intact seed coat rather than by the embryo itself.

You can take a closer look at one type of eudicot seed by splitting open the seed of a common garden bean. The embryo consists of an elongated structure, the embryonic axis, attached to fleshy cotyledons (**Figure 38.8a**). Below where the cotyledons are attached, the embryonic axis is called the **hypocotyl** (from the Greek *hypo*, under). The hypocotyl terminates in the **radicle**, or embryonic root. The portion of the embryonic axis above where the cotyledons are attached and below the first pair of miniature leaves is the **epicotyl** (from the Greek *epi*, on, over). The epicotyl, young leaves, and shoot apical meristem are collectively called the *plumule*.

The cotyledons of the common garden bean are packed with starch before the seed germinates because they absorbed carbohydrates from the endosperm when the seed was developing. However, the seeds of some eudicot species, such as castor beans (*Ricinus communis*), retain their food supply in the endosperm and have very thin cotyledons (**Figure 38.8b**). The cotyledons absorb nutrients from the endosperm and transfer them to the rest of the embryo when the seed germinates.

The embryos of monocots possess only a single cotyledon (**Figure 38.8c**). Grasses, including maize and wheat, have a specialized cotyledon called a *scutellum* (from the Latin *scutella*, small shield, a reference to its shape). The scutellum, which has a large surface area, is pressed against the endosperm, from which it absorbs nutrients during germination. The embryo of a grass seed is enclosed within two protective sheaths: a **coleoptile**, which covers the young shoot, and a **coleorhiza**, which covers the young root. Both structures aid in soil penetration after germination.

Seed weights range from less than 1 µg for some orchids to 20 kg for coco-de-mer palms. Orchid seeds have almost no food reserves and must bond symbiotically with mycorrhizae

(a) Common garden bean, a eudicot with thick cotyledons. The fleshy cotyledons store food absorbed from the endosperm before the seed germinates.

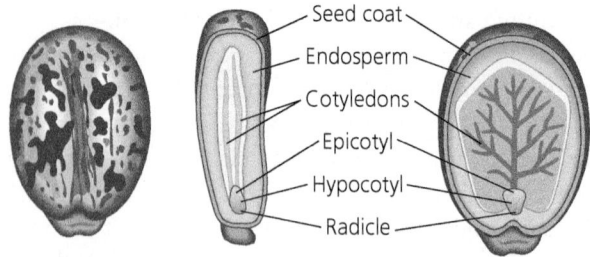

(b) Castor bean, a eudicot with thin cotyledons. The narrow, membranous cotyledons (shown in edge and flat views) absorb food from the endosperm when the seed germinates.

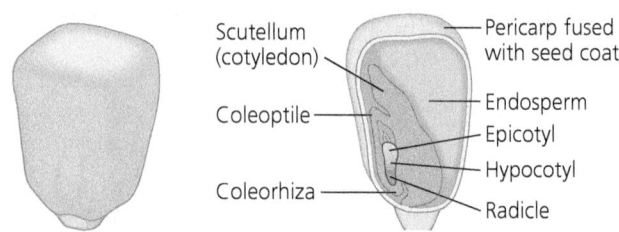

(c) Maize, a monocot. Like all monocots, maize has only one cotyledon. Maize and other grasses have a large cotyledon called a scutellum. The rudimentary shoot is sheathed in a structure called the coleoptile, and the coleorhiza covers the young root.

▲ **Figure 38.8 Seed structure.**

MAKE CONNECTIONS *In addition to cotyledon number, what are some others ways that the structures of monocots and eudicots differ? (See Figure 30.17.)*

prior to germination. Large, endosperm-rich palm seeds are an adaptation for seedling establishment on nutrient-poor beaches.

Seed Dormancy: An Adaptation for Tough Times

Environmental conditions required to break seed dormancy vary among species. Seeds of some species germinate as soon as they are in a suitable environment. Others remain dormant, even if sown in a favourable place, until a specific environmental cue causes them to break dormancy.

The requirement for specific cues to break seed dormancy increases the chances that germination will occur at a time and place most advantageous to the seedling. Seeds of many desert plants, for instance, germinate only after a substantial rainfall. If they were to germinate after a mild drizzle, the soil might soon become too dry to support the seedlings. Where natural fires are common, many seeds require intense heat or smoke to break dormancy; seedlings are therefore most abundant after fire has cleared away competing vegetation. Where winters are harsh, seeds may require extended exposure to cold. Seeds sown during summer or fall will then not germinate until the following spring, ensuring a long growth season before the next winter. Certain small seeds, such as those of some lettuce varieties, require light for germination and will break dormancy only if buried shallow enough for the seedlings to poke through the soil surface. Some seeds have coats that must be weakened by chemical attack as they pass through an animal's digestive tract and thus are usually carried a considerable distance before germinating from dropped feces.

The length of time a dormant seed remains viable and capable of germinating varies from a few days to decades or even longer, depending on the plant species and environmental conditions. The oldest carbon-14–dated seed that has grown into a viable plant was a 2000-year-old date palm seed recovered from excavations of Herod's palace in Israel. Most seeds are durable enough to last a year or two until conditions are favourable for germinating. Thus, the soil has a bank of ungerminated seeds that may have accumulated for several years. This is one reason vegetation reappears so rapidly after an environmental disruption such as fire.

Seed Germination and Seedling Development

Germination depends on **imbibition**, the uptake of water due to the low water potential of the dry seed. Imbibing water causes the seed to expand and rupture its coat and also triggers metabolic changes in the embryo that enable it to resume growth. Following hydration, enzymes begin digesting the storage materials of the endosperm or cotyledons, and the nutrients are transferred to the growing regions of the embryo.

The first organ to emerge from the germinating seed is the radicle, the embryonic root. The development of a root system anchors the seedling in the soil and supplies it with the water necessary for cell expansion. A ready supply of water is a prerequisite for the next step, the emergence of the shoot tip into the drier conditions found above ground. In garden beans and many other eudicots, a hook forms in the hypocotyl, and growth pushes the hook above ground (Figure 38.9a). In response to light, the hypocotyl straightens, the cotyledons separate, and the delicate epicotyl, now exposed, spreads its first true leaves (as distinct from the cotyledons, or seed leaves). These leaves expand, become green, and begin making food by photosynthesis. The cotyledons shrivel and fall away from the seedling, their food reserves having been exhausted by the germinating embryo.

Some monocots, such as maize and other grasses, use a different method for breaking ground when they germinate (Figure 38.9b). The coleoptile, the sheath enclosing and

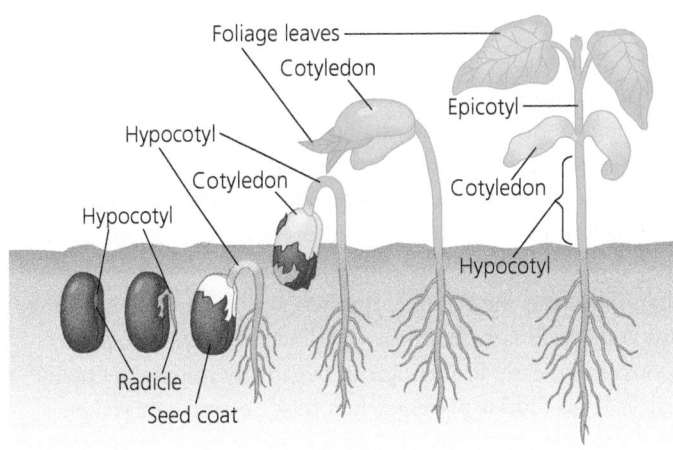

(a) Common garden bean. In common garden beans, straightening of a hook in the hypocotyl pulls the cotyledons from the soil.

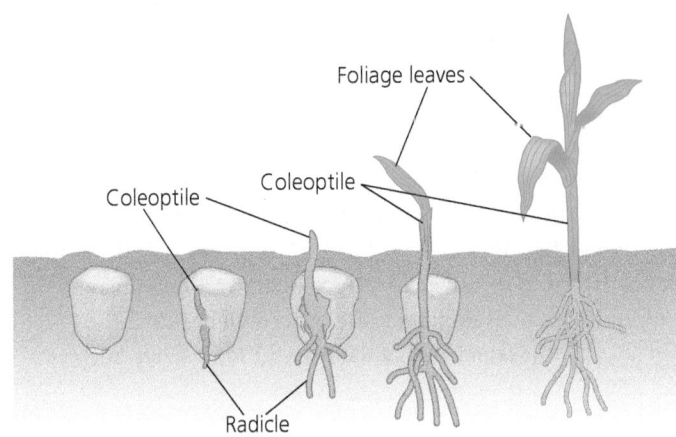

(b) Maize. In maize and other grasses, the shoot grows straight up through the tube of the coleoptile.

▲ **Figure 38.9 Two common types of seed germination.**

? *How do bean and maize seedlings protect their shoot systems as they push through the soil?*

protecting the embryonic shoot, pushes upward through the soil and into the air. The shoot tip then grows straight up through the tunnel provided by the tubular coleoptile and eventually breaks out through the coleoptile's tip.

Flowering

The flowers of a given plant species typically appear suddenly and simultaneously at a specific time of year. Such synchrony promotes outbreeding, the main advantage of sexual reproduction. Flower formation involves a developmental switch in the shoot apical meristem from a vegetative to a reproductive mode of growth. This transition into a *floral meristem* is triggered by a combination of environmental cues (such as day length and temperature) and internal signals, as you'll learn in Chapter 39. Once the transition to flowering has begun, the order of each organ's emergence from the floral meristem determines whether it will develop into a sepal, petal, stamen, or carpel (see Figure 35.35).

As the climate changes and temperatures rise, many areas experience spring-like weather much earlier. Earlier springs can allow plants and seeds to break their dormancy early, start growing sooner, and potentially set flowers early. Although it may seem like an advantage to have a longer growing season, early flowering may have significant consequences to a plant, especially if its pollinators are not present. Animal pollinators may rely on different environmental cues to wake or migrate than the plants they visit. If the two populations are not present and active simultaneously, pollination may not occur. Conversely, early flowering can negatively impact the pollinators if no food is present when they do arrive or waken.

Fruit Form and Function

Before a seed can germinate and develop into a mature plant, it must be deposited in suitable soil. Fruits play a key role in this process. A **fruit** is the mature ovary of a flower. While the seeds are developing from ovules, the flower develops into a fruit (**Figure 38.10**). The fruit protects the enclosed seeds and, when mature, aids in their dispersal by wind or animals. Fertilization triggers hormonal changes that cause the ovary to begin its transformation into a fruit. If a flower has not been pollinated, fruit typically does not develop, and the flower usually withers and falls away.

During fruit development, the ovary wall becomes the *pericarp*, the thickened wall of the fruit. In some fruits, such as

▲ Figure 38.10 **The flower-to-fruit transition** After flowers, such as those of the American pokeweed, are fertilized, stamens and petals fall off, stigmas and styles wither, and the ovary walls that house the developing seeds swell to form fruits. Developing seeds and fruits are major sinks for sugars and other carbohydrates.

soybean pods, the ovary wall dries out completely at maturity, whereas in other fruits, such as grapes, it remains fleshy. In still others, such as peaches, the inner part of the ovary becomes stony (the pit) while the outer parts stay fleshy. As the ovary grows, the other parts of the flower usually wither and are shed.

Fruits are classified into several types, depending on their developmental origin. Most fruits are derived from a single carpel or several fused carpels and are called **simple fruits** (**Figure 38.11a**). Some simple fruits are dry, such as a pea pod or a nut, whereas others are fleshy, such as a nectarine (see Figure 30.10). An **aggregate fruit** results from a single flower that has more than one separate carpel, each forming a small fruit (**Figure 38.11b**). These "fruitlets" are clustered

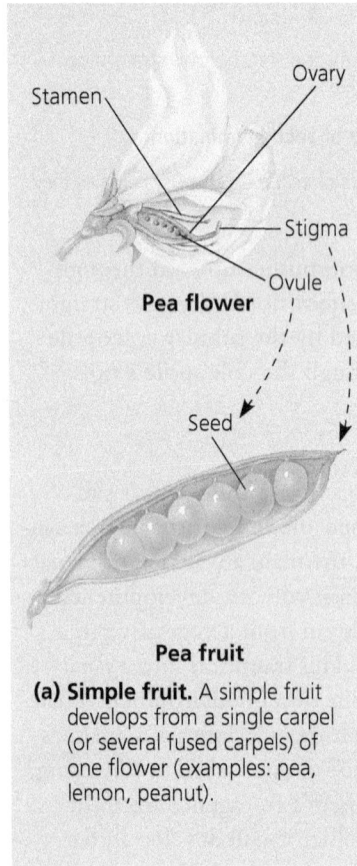

Pea flower

Pea fruit

(a) Simple fruit. A simple fruit develops from a single carpel (or several fused carpels) of one flower (examples: pea, lemon, peanut).

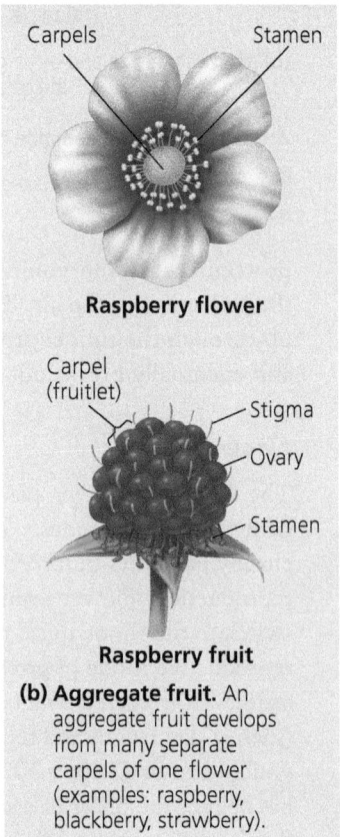

Raspberry flower

Raspberry fruit

(b) Aggregate fruit. An aggregate fruit develops from many separate carpels of one flower (examples: raspberry, blackberry, strawberry).

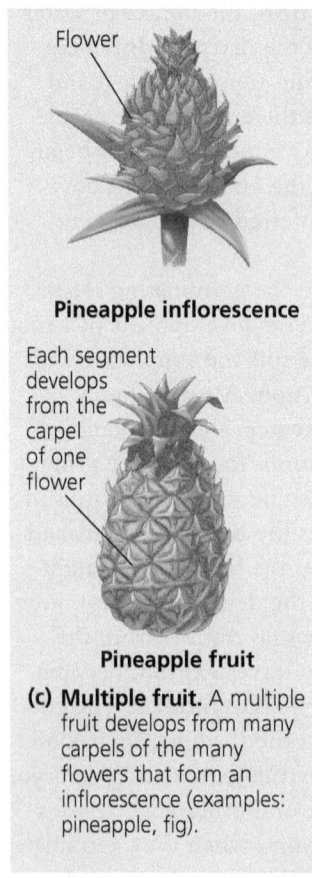

Pineapple inflorescence

Each segment develops from the carpel of one flower

Pineapple fruit

(c) Multiple fruit. A multiple fruit develops from many carpels of the many flowers that form an inflorescence (examples: pineapple, fig).

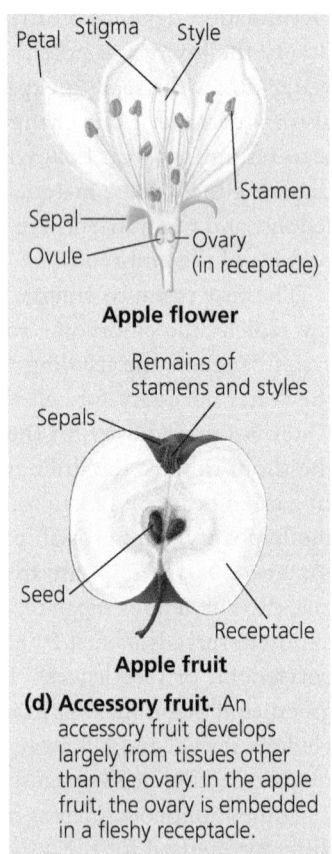

Apple flower

Apple fruit

(d) Accessory fruit. An accessory fruit develops largely from tissues other than the ovary. In the apple fruit, the ovary is embedded in a fleshy receptacle.

▲ Figure 38.11 **Developmental origin of fruits.**

together on a single receptacle, as in a raspberry. A **multiple fruit** develops from an inflorescence, a group of flowers tightly clustered together. When the walls of the many ovaries start to thicken, they fuse together and become incorporated into one fruit, as in a pineapple (Figure 38.11c).

In some angiosperms, other floral parts contribute to what we commonly call the fruit. Such fruits are called **accessory fruits**. In apple flowers, the ovary is embedded in the receptacle, and the fleshy part of this simple fruit is derived mainly from the enlarged receptacle; only the apple core develops from the ovary (Figure 38.11d). Another example is the strawberry, an aggregate fruit consisting of an enlarged receptacle studded with tiny, partially embedded fruits, each bearing a single seed.

A fruit usually ripens about the same time that its seeds complete their development. Whereas the ripening of a dry fruit, such as a soybean pod, involves the aging and drying out of fruit tissues, the process in a fleshy fruit is more elaborate. Complex interactions of hormones result in an edible fruit that entices animals that help disperse the seeds. The fruit's "pulp" becomes softer as a result of enzymes digesting components of the cell walls. The colour usually changes from green to another colour, such as red, orange, or yellow. The fruit becomes sweeter as organic acids or starch molecules are converted to sugar, which may reach a concentration of as much as 20% in a ripe fruit. Figure 38.12 on the next page examines some mechanisms of fruit dispersal in more detail.

In this section, you have learned about the unique features of sexual reproduction in angiosperms—flowers, fruits, and double fertilization. Next, we'll examine asexual reproduction.

CONCEPT CHECK 38.1

1. Distinguish between pollination and fertilization.
2. What is the benefit of seed dormancy?
3. **WHAT IF?** If flowers had shorter styles, pollen tubes would more easily reach the embryo sac. Suggest an explanation for why very long styles have evolved in most flowering plants.
4. **MAKE CONNECTIONS** Does the life cycle of animals have any structures analogous to plant gametophytes? Explain your answer. (See Figure 13.6.)

For suggested answers, see Appendix A.

CONCEPT 38.2

Flowering plants reproduce sexually, asexually, or both

Imagine chopping off your finger and watching it develop into an exact copy of you. If this could actually occur, it would be an example of **asexual reproduction**, in which offspring are derived from a single parent without fusion of egg and sperm. The result would be a clone, an asexually produced, genetically identical organism. Asexual reproduction is common in angiosperms, as well as in other

plants, and for some plant species it is the predominant mode of reproduction.

Mechanisms of Asexual Reproduction

Asexual reproduction in plants is typically an extension of the capacity for indeterminate growth. As described in Concept 35.2, plant growth can be sustained or renewed indefinitely by meristems, regions of undifferentiated, dividing cells. In addition, parenchyma cells throughout the plant can divide and differentiate into more specialized types of cells, enabling plants to regenerate lost parts. Detached vegetative fragments of some plants can develop into whole offspring; for example, pieces of a potato with an "eye" (vegetative bud) can each regenerate a whole plant. Such **fragmentation**, the separation of a parent plant into parts that develop into whole plants, is one of the most common modes of asexual reproduction. The adventitious plantlets on *Kalanchoë* leaves exemplify an unusual type of fragmentation (see Figure 35.7). In other cases, the root system of a single parent, such as an aspen tree, can give rise to many adventitious shoots that become separate shoot systems (Figure 38.13). One aspen clone in Utah named Pando has been estimated to be composed of 47 000 stems of genetically identical trees. Although it is likely that some of the root system connections have been severed, making some of the trees isolated from the rest of the clone, each tree still shares a common genome.

A different mechanism of asexual reproduction has evolved in dandelions and some other plants. These plants can sometimes produce seeds without pollination or fertilization. This asexual production of seeds is called **apomixis** (from the Greek words meaning "away from the act of mixing") because there is no joining or, indeed, production of sperm and egg. Instead, a diploid cell in the ovule gives rise to the embryo, and the ovules mature into seeds, which in the dandelion are dispersed by windblown fruits. Thus, these plants clone themselves by an asexual process but have the advantage of seed dispersal, usually associated with sexual reproduction. Introducing apomixis into hybrid crops is of great interest to plant breeders because apomixis would allow hybrid plants to pass on their desirable genomes intact to their offspring.

Advantages and Disadvantages of Asexual versus Sexual Reproduction

EVOLUTION An advantage of asexual reproduction is that there is no need for a pollinator. This may be beneficial in situations where plants of the same species are sparsely distributed and unlikely to be visited by the same pollinator. Asexual reproduction also allows the plant to pass on all of its genetic legacy intact to its progeny. In contrast, when reproducing sexually, a plant passes on only half of

Exploring Fruit and Seed Dispersal

A plant's life depends on finding fertile ground. But a seed that falls and sprouts beneath the parent plant will stand little chance of competing successfully for nutrients. To prosper, seeds must be widely dispersed. Plants use biotic dispersal agents as well as abiotic agents such as water and wind.

Dispersal by Water

▶ Some buoyant seeds and fruits can survive months or years at sea. In coconut, the seed embryo and fleshy white "meat" (endosperm) are within a hard layer (endocarp) surrounded by a thick and buoyant fibrous husk.

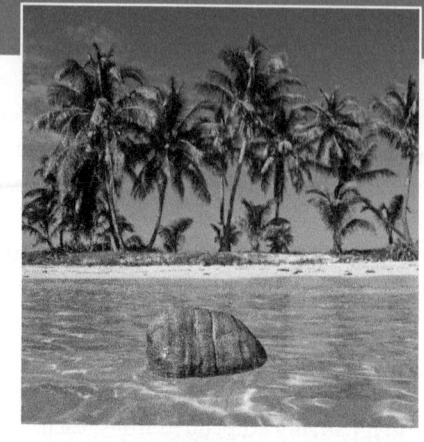

Kevin Schafer/Alamy

Dispersal by Wind

▶ The winged seed of the tropical Asian cllimbing gourd *Alsomitra macrocarpa* glides through the air of the rain forest in wide circles when released.

▼ The winged fruit of a maple spins like a helicopter blade, slowing descent and increasing the chance of being carried farther by horizontal winds.

Aquiya/Fotolia

Dandelion fruit

Steve Bloom Images/Alamy

Chrispo/Fotolia

▶ Tumbleweeds break off at the ground and tumble across the terrain, scattering their seeds.

Ann Cutting/Getty Images

▲ Some seeds and fruits are attached to umbrella-like "parachutes" that are made of intricately branched hairs and often produced in puffy clusters. These dandelion "seeds" (actually one-seeded fruits) are carried aloft by the slightest gust of wind.

Dispersal by Animals

◀ The sharp, tack-like spines on the fruits of puncture vine (*Tribulus terrestris*) can pierce bicycle tires and injure animals, including humans. When these painful "tacks" are removed and discarded, the seeds are dispersed.

California Department of Food and Agriculture's Plant Health and Pest Prevention Services

▶ Seeds in edible fruits are often dispersed in feces, such as the black bear feces shown here. Such dispersal may carry seeds far from the parent plant.

Kim A. Cabrera Photographer

Alan Williams/Alamy

◀ Some animals, such as squirrels, hoard seeds or fruits in underground caches. If the animal dies or forgets the cache's location, the buried seeds are well positioned to germinate.

▶ Ants are chemically attracted to seeds with "food bodies" rich in fatty acids, amino acids, and sugars. The ants carry the seed to their underground nest, where the food body (the lighter-coloured portion shown here) is removed and fed to larvae. Due to the seed's size, unwieldy shape, or hard coating, the remainder is usually left intact in the nest, where it germinates.

Guenard, Benoit

▲ Figure 38.13 **Asexual reproduction in aspen trees.** Some aspen groves, such as those shown here, consist of thousands of trees descended by asexual reproduction. Each grove of trees derives from the root system of one parent. Thus, the grove is a clone. Notice that genetic differences between groves descended from different parents result in different timing for the development of fall colour.

its alleles. If a plant is superbly suited to its environment, asexual reproduction can be advantageous. A vigorous plant can potentially clone many copies of itself, and if the environmental circumstances remain stable, these offspring will also be genetically well adapted to the same environmental conditions under which the parent flourished.

Generally, the progeny produced by asexual reproduction may be stronger than seedlings produced by sexual reproduction. For example, the adventitious stems of new aspen clones are being "fed" by the photosynthate produced by the parent plant. Thus, initial growth is quite rapid. The offspring usually arise from mature vegetative fragments from the parent plant, which is why asexual reproduction in plants is also known as **vegetative reproduction**. In contrast, seed germination is a precarious stage in a plant's life. The tough seed gives rise to a fragile seedling that may face exposure to predators, parasites, wind, and other hazards. In the wild, only a small fraction of seedlings survive to become parents themselves. Production of enormous numbers of seeds compensates for the odds against individual survival and gives natural selection ample genetic variations to screen. However, this is an expensive means of reproduction in terms of the resources consumed in flowering and fruiting.

Because sexual reproduction generates variation in offspring and populations, it can be advantageous in unstable environments where evolving pathogens and other fluctuating conditions affect survival and reproductive success. In contrast, the genotypic uniformity of asexually produced plants puts them at great risk of local extinction if there is a catastrophic environmental change, such as a new strain of disease. Moreover, seeds (which are almost always produced sexually) facilitate the dispersal of offspring to more distant locations. Finally, seed dormancy allows growth to be suspended until environmental conditions become more favourable. In the Scientific Skills Exercise, you can use data to determine which species of monkey flower are mainly asexual reproducers and which are mainly sexual reproducers.

Although sexual reproduction involving two genetically different plants has the benefit of producing the most genetically diverse offspring, some plants, such as garden peas, usually self-fertilize. This process, called "selfing," is a desirable attribute in some crop plants because it ensures that every ovule will develop into a seed, greatly increasing crop yields. However, one should keep in mind that "selfing" in crop plants, such as peas, is a domesticated trait that has been selected for over thousands of years by farmers seeking greater production from their crops. Thus, in many angiosperm species we find mechanisms that exist to make it difficult or impossible for a flower to fertilize itself, as we'll discuss next.

Mechanisms That Prevent Self-Fertilization

The various mechanisms that prevent self-fertilization contribute to genetic variety by ensuring that the sperm and egg come from different parents. In the case of **dioecious** species, plants cannot self-fertilize because different individuals have either staminate flowers (lacking carpels) or carpellate flowers (lacking stamens). In this case, the plants have evolved the genetic determination to be either "male" or "female" (Figure 38.14a). Other plants have flowers with functional stamens and carpels

(a) Some species, such as *Sagittaria latifolia* (common arrowhead), are dioecious, having plants that produce only staminate flowers (left) or carpellate flowers (right).

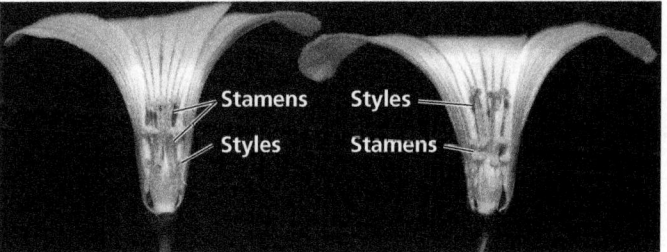

Thrum flower   Pin flower

(b) Some species, such as *Oxalis alpina* (alpine woodsorrel), produce two types of flowers on different individuals: "thrums," which have short styles and long stamens, and "pins," which have long styles and short stamens. An insect foraging for nectar would collect pollen on different parts of its body; thrum pollen would be deposited on pin stigmas, and vice versa.

▲ Figure 38.14 **Some floral adaptations that prevent self-fertilization.**

Using Positive and Negative Correlations to Interpret Data

Do Monkey Flower Species Differ in Allocating Their Energy to Sexual versus Asexual Reproduction? Over the course of its lifespan, a plant captures only a finite amount of resources and energy, which must be allocated to best meet the plant's individual requirements for maintenance, growth, defence, and reproduction. Researchers examined how five species of monkey flower (genus *Mimulus*) use their resources for sexual and asexual reproduction.

How the Experiment Was Done After growing specimens of each species in separate pots in the open, the researchers determined averages for nectar volume, nectar concentration, seeds produced per flower, and the number of times the plants were visited by broad-tailed hummingbirds (*Selasphorus platycercus*, shown on right). Using greenhouse-grown

Toby Bradshaw

specimens, they determined the average number of rooted branches per gram fresh shoot weight for each of the species. The phrase *rooted branches* refers to asexual reproduction through horizontal shoots that develop roots.

Data from the Experiment

Interpret the Data

1. A correlation is a way to describe the relationship between two variables. In a positive correlation, as the values of one of the variables increase, the values of the second variable also increase. In a negative correlation, as the values of one of the variables increase, the values of the second variable decrease. Or there may be no correlation between two variables. If researchers know how two variables are correlated, they can make a prediction about one variable based on what they know about the other variable. (a) Which variable(s) is/are positively correlated with the volume of nectar production in this genus? (b) Which is/are negatively correlated? (c) Which show(s) no clear relationship?

2. (a) Which *Mimulus* species would you categorize as mainly asexual reproducers? Why? (b) Which species would you categorize as mainly sexual reproducers? Why?

3. (a) Which species would probably fare better in response to a pathogen that infects all *Mimulus* species? (b) Which species would fare better if a pathogen caused hummingbird populations to dwindle?

Adaptation of Table 1 from "Trade-offs between Sexual and Asexual Reproduction in the Genus Mimulus" by S. Sutherland and R. K. Vickery, Jr., from *Oecologia*, August 1, 1988, Volume 76(3): 332. Copyright © 1988 by Springer. Reprinted with permission of Springer Science+Business Media.

Species	Nectar Volume (µL)	Nectar Concentration (% wt of sucrose/ total wt)	Seeds per Flower	Visits per Flower	Rooted Branches per Gram Shoot Weight
M. rupestris	4.93	16.6	2.2	0.22	0.673
M. eastwoodiae	4.94	19.8	25	0.74	0.488
M. nelson	20.25	17.1	102.5	1.08	0.139
M. verbenaceus	38.96	16.9	155.1	1.26	0.091
M. cardinalis	50.00	19.9	283.7	1.75	0.069

that mature at different times or are structurally arranged in such a way that it is unlikely that an animal pollinator could transfer pollen from an anther to a stigma of the same flower (Figure 38.14b). However, the most common anti-selfing mechanism in flowering plants is **self-incompatibility**, the ability of a plant to reject its own pollen and sometimes the pollen of closely related individuals. If a pollen grain lands on a stigma of a flower on the same plant, a biochemical block prevents the pollen from completing its development and fertilizing an egg.

This plant response is analogous to the immune response of animals because both are based on the ability to distinguish the cells of "self" from those of "nonself." The key difference is that the animal immune system rejects nonself, as when the immune system mounts a defence against a pathogen or rejects a transplanted organ (see Chapter 43). In contrast, self-incompatibility in plants is a rejection of self.

Researchers are unravelling the molecular mechanisms involved in self-incompatibility. Recognition of "self" pollen is based on genes for self-incompatibility, called

S-genes. In the gene pool of a plant population, there can be dozens of alleles of an S-gene. If a pollen grain has an allele that matches an allele of the stigma on which it lands, the pollen tube either fails to germinate or its tube fails to grow through the style to the ovary. There are two types of self-incompatibility: gametophytic and sporophytic.

In gametophytic self-incompatibility, the S-allele in the pollen genome governs the blocking of fertilization. For example, an S_1 pollen grain from an S_1S_2 parental sporophyte cannot fertilize eggs of an S_1S_2 flower but can fertilize an S_2S_3 flower. An S_2 pollen grain cannot fertilize either flower. Self-recognition of this kind involves the enzymatic destruction of RNA within a pollen tube. RNA-hydrolyzing enzymes are produced by the style and enter the pollen tube. If the pollen tube is a "self" type, these enzymes destroy its RNA.

In sporophytic self-incompatibility, fertilization is blocked by S-allele gene products in tissues of the parental sporophyte that adhere to the pollen grain wall. For example, neither an S_1 nor S_2 pollen grain from an S_1S_2 parental sporophyte can fertilize eggs of an S_1S_2 flower or

S_2S_3 flower, due to the S_1S_2 parental tissue attached to the pollen wall. Sporophytic incompatibility involves a signal transduction pathway in epidermal cells of the stigma that prevents germination of the pollen grain.

Research on self-incompatibility may have agricultural applications. Breeders often hybridize different genetic strains of a crop to combine the best traits of the two strains and to counter the loss of vigour that can often result from excessive inbreeding. To prevent self-fertilization within the two strains, breeders must either laboriously remove the anthers from the parent plants that provide the seeds (as Mendel did) or use male-sterile strains of the crop plant, if they exist. If self-compatibility can be genetically engineered back into domesticated plant varieties, these limitations to commercial hybridization of crop seeds will be overcome.

Totipotency, Vegetative Reproduction, and Tissue Culture

In a multicellular organism, any cell that can divide and asexually generate a clone of the original organism is said to be **totipotent**. Totipotency is found to a high degree in many plants and is usually associated with meristematic tissues. In some plants, however, some cells can dedifferentiate and become meristematic. With the objective of improving crops and ornamental plants, humans have devised methods for asexual propagation of angiosperms. Most of these methods are based on the ability of plants to form adventitious roots or shoots.

Vegetative Propagation and Grafting

Vegetative reproduction occurs naturally in many plants, but it can often be facilitated or induced by humans, in which case it is called **vegetative propagation**. Most houseplants, woody ornamentals, and orchard trees are asexually reproduced from plant fragments called cuttings. In some cases, shoot cuttings are used. At the cut end of the shoot, a mass of dividing, undifferentiated totipotent cells called a **callus** forms, and adventitious roots develop from the callus. If the shoot fragment includes a node, then adventitious roots form without a callus stage. Some plants, including African violets, can be propagated from single leaves rather than stems. For other plants, cuttings are taken from specialized storage stems, such as potato tubers. The Bartlett pear and Red Delicious apple are examples of varieties that have been propagated asexually for over 150 years.

In a modification of vegetative reproduction from cuttings, a twig or bud from one plant can be grafted onto a plant of a closely related species or a different variety of the same species. This process can combine the best qualities of different species or varieties into one plant. The plant that provides the roots is called the **stock**; the twig grafted onto the stock is known as the **scion**. For example, scions from varieties of vines that produce superior wine grapes are grafted onto rootstocks of varieties that produce inferior grapes but are more resistant to certain soil pathogens. The genes of the scion determine the quality of the fruit. During grafting, a callus first forms between the adjoining cut ends of the scion and stock; cell differentiation then completes the functional unification of the grafted individuals.

Test-Tube Cloning and Related Techniques

Plant biologists can exploit the totipotency of plant cells and have adopted *in vitro* methods to clone novel plant varieties. They can grow whole plants by culturing small pieces of tissue from the parent plant on an artificial medium containing nutrients and hormones. The cells or tissues can come from any part of a plant, but successful regeneration varies depending on the plant part, species, and artificial medium. In some media, the cultured cells divide and form a callus of undifferentiated cells (Figure 38.15a). When the concentrations of hormones and nutrients are manipulated appropriately, a callus can sprout shoots and roots with fully differentiated cells (Figure 38.15b, c). The plantlets can then be transferred to soil, where they continue their growth. A single plant can be cloned into thousands of copies by dividing calluses as they grow. This method is now used for propagating orchids as well as a wide variety of trees and shrubs. Not only does this technique allow plant breeders to select and propagate plants with specific traits, it is a much faster way to produce large numbers of identical plants which they have difficulty replicating by sexual crossing.

Plant tissue culture is important in eliminating weakly pathogenic viruses from vegetatively propagated varieties. Although the presence of weak viruses may not be obvious, yield or quality may be substantially reduced as a result of infection. Strawberry plants, for example, are susceptible to more than

(a) (b) (c) Developing root

University of Liverpool School of Biological Sciences

▲ Figure 38.15 **Cloning a garlic plant. (a)** A root from a garlic clove gave rise to this callus culture, a mass of undifferentiated cells. **(b and c)** The differentiation of a callus into a plantlet depends on the nutrient levels and hormone concentrations in the artificial medium, as can be seen in these cultures grown for different lengths of time.

60 viruses, and typically the plants must be replaced each year because of viral infection. However, the distribution of viruses in a plant is not uniform, and the apical meristems are sometimes virus-free. Therefore, apical meristems can be excised and used to produce virus-free material for tissue culture.

Plant tissue culture also facilitates genetic engineering. Most techniques for the introduction of foreign genes into plants require small pieces of plant tissue or single plant cells as the starting material. The term **transgenic** is used to describe genetically modified (GM) organisms that have been engineered to express a gene from another species. Test-tube culture makes it possible to regenerate GM plants from a single plant cell into which the foreign DNA has been incorporated. The techniques of genetic engineering are discussed in more detail in Chapter 20.

▲ Figure 38.16 **Maize: a product of artificial selection.** Modern maize (bottom) was derived from teosinte (top). Teosinte kernels are tiny, and each row has a husk that must be removed to get at the kernel. The seeds are loose at maturity, allowing dispersal, which probably made harvesting difficult for early farmers. Neolithic farmers selected seeds from plants with larger cob and kernel size as well as the permanent attachment of seeds to the cob and the encasing of the entire cob by a tough husk.

CONCEPT CHECK 38.2

1. The seedless banana, the world's most popular fruit, is losing the battle against two fungal epidemics. Why do such epidemics generally pose a greater risk to asexually propagated crops?

2. Self-fertilization, or selfing, seems to have obvious disadvantages as a reproductive "strategy" in nature, and it has even been called an "evolutionary dead end." So it is surprising that about 20% of angiosperm species primarily rely on selfing. Suggest a reason why selfing might be advantageous and yet still be an evolutionary dead end.

3. **WHAT IF?** Potatoes (*Solanum tuberosum*) and tomatoes (*Solanum lycopersicum*) are fairly closely related species. If you managed to cross the two, would it be possible to have a hybrid that makes potato-like tubers and tomato-like fruits on the same plant?

For suggested answers, see Appendix A.

CONCEPT **38.3**

People modify crops by breeding and genetic engineering

Humans have intervened in the reproduction and genetic makeup of plants since the dawn of agriculture, and many plant species, including maize and canola, owe their existence to humans. Left on its own in nature, maize would soon become extinct for the simple reason that it cannot spread its seeds. Maize kernels are not only permanently attached to the central axis (the "cob") but also permanently protected by tough, overlapping leaf sheaths (the "husk") (Figure 38.16). These attributes arose by artificial selection by humans. (See Chapter 22 to review the basic concept of artificial selection.) Despite having no understanding of the scientific principles underlying plant breeding, Neolithic (late Stone Age) humans domesticated most of our crop species over a relatively short period about 10 000 years ago. Stone Age farmers selected for better crops by preferentially harvesting the largest seeds that did not fall off the plant. The

farmers then replanted some of their seeds the following year. Thus, farmers have been selecting mutant plants for thousands of years to help them produce more and better quality food. But genetic modification began long before humans started altering crops by artificial selection. For example, the wheat species we rely on for much of our food evolved by the natural hybridization between different species of grasses. Such hybridization is common in plants and has long been exploited by breeders to introduce genetic variation for artificial selection and crop improvement.

Plant Breeding

The art of recognizing valuable traits is as important in plant breeding today as it was for Neolithic man. Breeders scrutinize their fields carefully and travel to other countries searching for domesticated varieties or wild relatives with desirable traits. Such traits occasionally arise spontaneously through mutation, but the natural rate of mutation is too slow and unreliable to produce all the mutations that breeders would like to study. Breeders sometimes hasten mutations by treating large batches of seeds or seedlings with radiation or chemicals.

When a desirable trait is identified in a wild species, the wild species is crossed with a domesticated variety. Generally, those progeny that have inherited the desirable trait from the wild parent have also inherited many traits that are not desirable for agriculture, such as small fruits or low yields. The progeny that express the desired trait are again crossed with members of the domesticated species and their progeny examined for the desired trait. This process is continued until progeny with the desired wild trait resemble the original domesticated parent in their other agricultural attributes.

While most breeders cross-pollinate plants of a single species, some breeding methods rely on hybridization between two distant species of the same genus. Such crosses often result in the abortion of the hybrid seed during development. Very often the embryo begins to develop, but the endosperm does not. Hybrid embryos are sometimes rescued by surgically removing them from the ovule and culturing them *in vitro*.

Plant Biotechnology and Genetic Engineering

Plant biotechnology has two meanings. In the general sense, it refers to innovations in the use of plants (or substances obtained from plants) to make products of use to humans—an endeavour that began in prehistory. In a more specific sense, biotechnology refers to the use of GM organisms in agriculture and industry. Indeed, in the last two decades, genetic engineering has become such a powerful force that the terms *genetic engineering* and *biotechnology* have become synonymous in the media.

Unlike traditional plant breeders, modern plant biotechnologists, using techniques of genetic engineering, are not limited to the transfer of genes between closely related species or genera. For example, traditional breeding techniques could not be used to insert a desired gene from daffodil into rice because the many intermediate species between rice and daffodil and their common ancestor are extinct. In theory, if breeders had the intermediate species, over the course of several centuries they could probably introduce a daffodil gene into rice by traditional hybridization and breeding methods. With genetic engineering, however, such gene transfers can be done more quickly, more specifically, and without the need for intermediate species. The term **transgenic** is used to describe organisms that have been engineered to express a gene from another species (see Chapter 20).

Not all plant biotechnology centres around transgenic research. Farmers are turning to cutting-edge genomics to help protect Canada's most important crops. Dr. Mark Belmonte (interviewed at the start of this Unit) is actively exploring the production of defence proteins in canola (*Brassica napus*) in response to devastating fungal diseases that cost canola growers millions of dollars in crop loss each year. Using next-generation RNA sequencing technologies, several defence molecules that are critical to plant immunity have been identified. By going back to the plant and upregulating the expression of these molecules through genetic engineering, Dr. Belmonte hopes to improve canola's resistance to fungal infections by tapping into the its own genetic potential.

In the remainder of this chapter, we examine the prospects and controversies surrounding the use of GM crops. The advocates of plant biotechnology believe that the genetic engineering of crop plants is the key to overcoming some of the most pressing problems of the 21st century, including world hunger and fossil fuel dependency.

Reducing World Hunger and Malnutrition

Currently, 800 million people suffer from nutritional deficiencies, with 40 000 dying each day of malnutrition, half of them children. There is much disagreement about the causes of such hunger. Some argue that food shortages arise from inequities in distribution and that the dire poor simply cannot afford food. Others regard food shortages as evidence that the world is overpopulated—that the human species has exceeded the carrying capacity of the planet (see Chapter 53). Whatever the social and demographic causes of malnutrition, increasing food production is a humane objective. Because land and water are the most limiting resources, the best option is to increase yields on already existing farmland. Indeed, there is very little "extra" land that can be farmed, especially if the few remaining pockets of wilderness are to be preserved. Based on conservative estimates of population growth, farmers will have to produce 40% more grain per hectare to feed the human population in 2030. Plant biotechnology can help make these crop yields possible.

The commercial use of transgenic crops has been one of the most dramatic examples of rapid technology adoption in the history of agriculture. These crops include varieties and hybrids of cotton, maize, and potatoes that contain genes from the bacterium *Bacillus thuringiensis*. These "transgenes" encode a protein (*Bt* toxin) that is toxic to insect pests (Figure 38.17). The use of such plant varieties greatly reduces the need for chemical insecticides. The *Bt* toxin used in crops is produced in the plant as a harmless protoxin that only becomes toxic if activated by alkaline conditions, such as occur in the guts of insects. Because vertebrates have highly acidic stomachs, protoxin consumed by humans or farm animals is rendered harmless by denaturation.

Considerable progress has also been made in developing transgenic crops that tolerate certain herbicides. The cultivation of these plants may reduce production costs by enabling farmers to "weed" crops with herbicides that do not damage the transgenic crop plants, instead of using heavy tillage, which can cause soil erosion. Researchers are also engineering plants with enhanced resistance to disease. In one case, a transgenic papaya resistant to a ring spot virus was introduced into Hawaii, thereby saving its papaya industry.

The nutritional quality of plants is also being improved. For example, some 250 000 to 500 000 children go blind each year because of vitamin A deficiencies. More than half of these children die within a year of becoming blind. In

Non-*Bt* maize   *Bt* maize

Gary Munkvold

▲ **Figure 38.17 Non-*Bt* versus *Bt* maize.** Field trials reveal that non-*Bt* maize (left) is heavily damaged by insect feeding and *Fusarium* mould infection, whereas *Bt* maize (right) suffers little or no damage.

Figure 38.18 **Fighting world hunger with transgenic cassava (*Manihot esculenta*).** This starchy root crop is the primary food for 800 million of the world's poor, but it does not provide a balanced diet. Moreover, it must be processed to remove chemicals that release cyanide, a toxin. Transgenic cassava plants have been developed with greatly increased levels of iron and beta-carotene (a vitamin A precursor). Researchers have also created cassava plants with root masses twice the normal size that contain almost no cyanide-producing chemicals.

response to this crisis, genetic engineers have created "Golden Rice," a transgenic variety supplemented with two daffodil genes that enable it to produce grain containing beta-carotene, a precursor of vitamin A. Another target for improvement by genetic engineering is cassava, a staple for 800 million of the poorest people on our planet (Figure 38.18).

Reducing Fossil Fuel Dependency

Global sources of inexpensive fossil fuels, particularly oil, are rapidly being depleted. Moreover, most climatologists attribute global warming mainly to the rampant burning of fossil fuels, such as coal and oil, and the resulting release of the greenhouse gas CO_2. How can the world meet its energy demands in the 21st century in an economical and nonpolluting way? In certain localities, wind or solar power may become economically viable, but such alternative energy sources are unlikely to fill global energy demands completely. Many scientists predict that biomass from extremely fast-growing plants, such as switchgrass (*Panicum virgatum*) and poplar (*Populus trichocarpa*), could produce a sizable fraction of the world's energy needs in the not-too-distant future.

Under optimal conditions, poplars can grow 3–4 m each year (Figure 38.19), and switchgrass grows well under a wide variety of conditions found in regions where most types of agriculture are not economically viable. Scientists do not envisage the plant biomass being burned directly. Instead, the polymers in cell walls, such as cellulose and hemicellulose, which constitute the most abundant organic compounds on Earth, would be broken down into sugars by enzymatic reactions. These sugars, in turn, would be fermented into alcohol and distilled to yield liquid **biofuels**.

The use of biofuels from plant biomass would reduce the net emission of CO_2. Whereas burning fossil fuels increases atmospheric CO_2 concentrations, biofuel crops reabsorb, by photosynthesis, the CO_2 emitted when biofuels are burned, creating a cycle that is carbon neutral. Plant breeders are trying to genetically engineer faster-growing poplar trees that produce more readily convertible biomass.

▼ Figure 38.19 | **Impact**

Cellulosic Biofuels

Wood was one of the first biofuels used by humans. Today, researchers around the world are working to renew our use of wood as a source of bioenergy. Rather than burning wood for heat and cooking, the plan is to use microbes to degrade the carbohydrates and proteins in the cell wall prior to fermenting the biomass to yield ethanol. While energy is lost in this process, liquid ethanol is a much more flexible fuel than wood. A research group operating under the acronym POPCAN, headed by Drs. Carl Douglas and Shawn Mansfield at the University of British Columbia, is attempting to identify natural genetic variants of Black Poplar (*Populus trichocarpa*), which grow faster than normal poplar trees and produce wood that is more easily digested and fermented.

Why It Matters Providing sufficient green and renewable energy sources is going to be a great challenge for Canada and other developed countries. No one source is likely to solve the problem, so we need to explore many options. While the use of crop plants such as corn and soybean to produce ethanol and biodiesel seem like good possibilities, the use of dwindling high-quality farmland for energy production may limit our capacity to feed growing populations. Biomass crops such as poplar can be grown in less hospitable areas, with minimal fertilization or pest management. By examining the existing genetic diversity, researchers are hoping to find more productive trees, without the need for genetic engineering.

Further Reading B. Ellis, Commentary: Bringing trees into the fuel line, *New Phytologist* 194:13.

MAKE CONNECTIONS *Many different types of plants have been suggested as sources of cellulosic biofuel. Among those gaining attention are sugar cane, switch grass, corn stalks, and the aforementioned poplar. While each of these plants provides advantages in how it grows, where it grows, and the type of fermentable product each produces, each also has specific disadvantages. What set of characteristics would make a plant an ideal candidate for a cellulosic biofuel research program?*

Biofuel technology does have its critics. For example, ecologist David Pimentel of Cornell University and geoengineer Tad Patzek of the University of California, Berkeley, have estimated that more energy may be required to produce biofuels than would be produced from combustion of these products. Based on current models, this is definitely true for some biofuel sources. For example, the production of ethanol from the fermentation of corn is now widely accepted to require much greater input of carbon than it can sequester. This is due not only to the diesel fuel used to run the tractors and harvesters, but also the energy needed to produce the fertilizers and insecticides required to obtain high yields of corn. Biofuel advocates, in turn, have questioned the accuracy of the data underlying these estimates. Further research is needed to determine whether specific plants, especially genetically modified versions of those plants, can be effective biofuels. One of the greatest determinants will be the future cost of traditional fuels. For example, currently it is suggested that algal-based biodiesel costs $1.50 per litre to produce. If the price of traditional diesel rises far enough above this value, then biofuel production becomes increasingly viable from an economic point of view.

The Debate over Plant Biotechnology

Much of the debate about GM organisms (GMOs) in agriculture is political, social, economic, or ethical and therefore outside the scope of this book. But we *should* consider the biological concerns about GM crops. Some biologists, particularly ecologists, are concerned about the unknown risks associated with the release of GMOs into the environment. The debate centres on the extent to which GMOs could harm the environment or human health. Those who want to proceed more slowly with agricultural biotechnology (or end it) are concerned about the unstoppable nature of the "experiment." If a drug trial produces unanticipated harmful results, the trial is stopped. But we may not be able to stop the "trial" of introducing novel organisms into the biosphere.

Here we examine some criticisms that have been levelled by opponents of GMOs, including the alleged effects on human health and nontarget organisms and the potential for transgene escape.

Issues of Human Health

Many GMO opponents worry that genetic engineering may inadvertently transfer allergens, molecules to which some people are allergic, from a species that produces an allergen to a plant used for food. However, biotechnologists are already engaged in removing genes that encode allergenic proteins from soybeans and other crops. So far, there is no credible evidence that GM plants specifically designed for human consumption have adverse effects on human health. In fact, some GM foods are potentially healthier than non-GM foods. For example, *Bt* maize (the transgenic variety with the *Bt* toxin) contains 90% less of a cancer-causing and birth defect–causing fungal toxin than non-*Bt* maize. Called fumonisin, this toxin is highly resistant to degradation and has been found in alarmingly high concentrations in some batches of processed maize products, ranging from cornflakes to beer. Fumonisin is produced by a fungus (*Fusarium*) that infects insect-damaged maize. Because *Bt* maize generally suffers less insect damage than non-GM maize, it contains much less fumonisin.

Nevertheless, because of health concerns, GMO opponents lobby for the clear labelling of all foods containing products of GMOs. Some also argue for strict regulations against the mixing of GM foods with non-GM foods during food transport, storage, and processing. Biotechnology

advocates, however, note that similar demands were not made when "transgenic" crops produced by traditional plant-breeding techniques were put on the market. There are, for example, some commercially grown varieties of wheat derived by traditional plant-breeding techniques that contain entire chromosomes (and thousands of genes) from rye.

Possible Effects on Nontarget Organisms

Many ecologists are concerned that the growing of GM crops might have unforeseen effects on nontarget organisms. One laboratory study indicated that the larvae (caterpillars) of monarch butterflies responded adversely and even died after eating milkweed leaves (their preferred food) heavily dusted with pollen from transgenic *Bt* maize. This study has since been discredited, affording a good example of the self-correcting nature of science. As it turns out, when the original researchers shook the male maize inflorescences onto the milkweed leaves in the laboratory, the filaments of stamens, opened microsporangia, and other floral parts also rained onto the leaves. Subsequent research found that it was these other floral parts, *not* the pollen, that contained *Bt* toxin in high concentrations. Unlike pollen, these floral parts would not be carried by the wind to neighbouring milkweed plants when shed under natural field conditions. Only one *Bt* maize line, accounting for less than 2% of commercial *Bt* maize production (and now discontinued), produced pollen with high *Bt* toxin concentrations.

In considering the negative effects of *Bt* pollen on monarch butterflies, one must also weigh the effects of an alternative to the cultivation of *Bt* maize—the spraying of non-*Bt* maize with chemical pesticides. Recent studies have shown that such spraying is much more harmful to nearby monarch populations than is *Bt* maize production. Although the effects of *Bt* maize pollen on monarch butterfly larvae appear to be minor, the controversy has emphasized the need for accurate field testing of all GM crops and the importance of targeting gene expression to specific tissues to improve safety.

Addressing the Problem of Transgene Escape

Perhaps the most serious concern raised about GM crops is the possibility of the introduced genes escaping from a transgenic crop into related weeds through crop-to-weed hybridization. The fear is that the spontaneous hybridization between a crop engineered for herbicide resistance and a wild relative might give rise to a "superweed" that would have a selective advantage over other weeds in the wild and would be much more difficult to control in the field. Some crops *do* hybridize with weedy relatives, and crop-to-weed transgene escape is a possibility. Its likelihood depends on the ability of the crop and weed to hybridize and on how the transgenes affect the overall fitness of the hybrids. A desirable crop trait—a dwarf phenotype, for example—might be disadvantageous to a weed growing in the wild. In other instances, there are no weedy relatives nearby with which to hybridize; soybean, for example, has no wild relatives in Canada. However, canola, sorghum, and many other crops do hybridize readily with weeds.

Many different strategies are being pursued with the goal of preventing transgene escape. For example, if male sterility could be engineered into plants, these plants would still produce seeds and fruit if pollinated by nearby nontransgenic plants, but they would produce no viable pollen. A second approach involves genetically engineering apomixis into transgenic crops. When a seed is produced by apomixis, the embryo and endosperm develop without fertilization. The transfer of this trait to transgenic crops would therefore minimize the possibility of transgene escape via pollen because plants could be male-sterile without compromising seed or fruit production. A third approach is to engineer the transgene into the chloroplast DNA of the crop. Chloroplast DNA in many plant species is inherited strictly from the egg, so transgenes in the chloroplast cannot be transferred by pollen (see Chapter 15 to review maternal inheritance). A fourth approach for preventing transgene escape is to genetically engineer flowers that develop normally but fail to open. Consequently, self-pollination would occur, but pollen would be unlikely to escape from the flower. This solution would require modifications to flower design. Several floral genes have been identified that could be manipulated to this end.

The continuing debate about GMOs in agriculture exemplifies one of this textbook's recurring ideas: the relationship of science and technology to society. Technological advances almost always involve some risk of unintended outcomes. In plant biotechnology, zero risk is probably unattainable. Therefore, scientists and the public must assess on a case-by-case basis the possible benefits of transgenic products versus the risks that society is willing to take. The best scenario is for these discussions and decisions to be based on sound scientific information and rigorous testing rather than on reflexive fear or blind optimism.

CONCEPT CHECK 38.3

1. Compare traditional plant-breeding methods with genetic engineering.
2. Explain some benefits and risks of GM crops.
3. Why does *Bt* maize have less fumonisin than non-GM maize?
4. **WHAT IF?** In a few species, chloroplast genes are inherited only from sperm. How might this influence efforts to prevent transgene escape?

For suggested answers, see Appendix A.

---

38 Chapter Review

Go to **MasteringBiology**® for Assignments, the eText, and the Study Area with Animations, Activities, Vocab Self-Quiz, and Practice Tests.

SUMMARY OF KEY CONCEPTS

CONCEPT 38.1

Flowers, double fertilization, and fruits are unique features of the angiosperm life cycle (pp. 867–877)

- Angiosperm reproduction involves an alternation of generations between a multicellular diploid sporophyte generation and a multicellular haploid gametophyte generation. Flowers, produced by the sporophyte, function in sexual reproduction.
- The four floral organs are sepals, petals, stamens, and carpels. **Sepals** protect the floral bud. **Petals** help attract pollinators. **Stamens** bear anthers in which haploid **microspores** develop into **pollen grains** containing a male gametophyte. **Carpels** contain ovules (immature seeds) in their swollen bases. Within the ovules, **embryo sacs** (female gametophytes) develop from megaspores.
- **Pollination**, which precedes fertilization, is the placing of pollen on the stigma of a carpel. After pollination, the pollen tube

Tube nucleus

One sperm will fuse with the egg, forming a zygote (2*n*).

One sperm cell will fuse with the 2 polar nuclei, forming an endosperm nucleus (3*n*).

discharges two sperm into the female gametophyte. Two sperm are needed for **double fertilization**, a process in which one sperm fertilizes the egg, forming a zygote and eventually an embryo, while the other sperm combines with the polar nuclei, giving rise to food-storing endosperm.
- The **seed coat** encloses the embryo along with a food supply stocked in either the **endosperm** or the **cotyledons**. Seed **dormancy** ensures that seeds germinate only when conditions for seedling survival are optimal. The breaking of dormancy often requires environmental cues, such as temperature or lighting changes.
- The **fruit** protects the enclosed seeds and aids in wind dispersal or in the attraction of seed-dispersing animals.

? *What changes occur to the four types of floral parts as a flower changes into a fruit?*

CONCEPT 38.2

Flowering plants reproduce sexually, asexually, or both (pp. 877–882)

- **Asexual reproduction** enables successful plants to proliferate quickly. Sexual reproduction generates most of the genetic variation that makes evolutionary adaptation possible.
- Plants have evolved many mechanisms to avoid self-fertilization, including dioecy (male and female flowers on different individuals), nonsynchronous production of male and female parts within a single flower, and **self-incompatibility** reactions in which pollen grains that bear an allele identical to one in the female are rejected.

- Plants can be cloned from single cells, which can be genetically manipulated before being allowed to develop into a plant.

? *What are the advantages and disadvantages of asexual reproduction?*

CONCEPT 38.3

Humans modify crops by breeding and genetic engineering (pp. 882–886)

- Hybridization of different varieties and even species of plants is common in nature and has been used by breeders, ancient and modern, to introduce new genes into crops. After two plants are successfully hybridized, plant breeders select those progeny that have the desired traits.
- In genetic engineering, genes from unrelated organisms are incorporated into plants. Genetically modified (GM) plants have the potential of increasing the quality and quantity of food worldwide and may also become increasingly important as biofuels.
- Two important GM crops are Golden Rice, which provides more vitamin A, and *Bt* maize, which is insect resistant.
- There are concerns about the unknown risks of releasing GM organisms into the environment, but the potential benefits of transgenic crops need to be considered.

? *Give three examples of how genetic engineering has improved food quality or agricultural productivity.*

TEST YOUR UNDERSTANDING

LEVEL 1: KNOWLEDGE/COMPREHENSION

1. A seed develops from
   a. an ovum.
   b. an ovule.
   c. an ovary.
   d. an embryo.

2. A fruit is
   a. a mature ovary.
   b. a mature ovule.
   c. a seed plus its integuments.
   d. an enlarged embryo sac.

3. Double fertilization means that
   a. flowers must be pollinated twice to yield fruits and seeds.
   b. every egg must receive two sperm to produce an embryo.
   c. one sperm is needed to fertilize the egg, and a second sperm is needed to fertilize the polar nuclei.
   d. every sperm has two nuclei.

4. "Golden Rice"
   a. is resistant to various herbicides, making it practical to weed rice fields with those herbicides.
   b. includes bacterial genes that produce a toxin that reduces damage from insect pests.
   c. produces larger, golden grains that increase crop yields.
   d. contains transgenes that increase vitamin A content.

5. Which statement concerning grafting is correct?
   a. Stocks and scions refer to twigs of different species.
   b. Stocks provide root systems for grafting.
   c. Grafting creates new species.
   d. Stocks and scions must come from unrelated species.

LEVEL 2: APPLICATION/ANALYSIS

6. Some dioecious species have the XY genotype for male and XX for female. After double fertilization, what would be the genotypes of the embryos and endosperm nuclei?
   a. embryo XX/endosperm XX or embryo XY/endosperm XY
   b. embryo XX/endosperm XXX or embryo XY/endosperm XYY
   c. embryo XX/endosperm XXX or embryo XY/endosperm XXY
   d. embryo XY/endosperm XXX or embryo XX/endosperm XXY

7. A small flower with green petals is most likely
   a. bee-pollinated.
   b. bird-pollinated.
   c. bat-pollinated.
   d. wind-pollinated.

8. The black dots that cover strawberries are actually fruits. The fleshy and tasty portion of a strawberry derives from the receptacle of a flower with many separate carpels. Therefore, a strawberry is
   a. a simple fruit with many seeds.
   b. both a multiple fruit and an accessory fruit.
   c. both a simple fruit and an aggregate fruit.
   d. both an aggregate fruit and an accessory fruit.

9. **DRAW IT** Draw and label the parts of a flower.

LEVEL 3: SYNTHESIS/EVALUATION

10. **EVOLUTION CONNECTION**
    With respect to sexual reproduction, some plant species are fully self-fertile, others are fully self-incompatible, and some exhibit a "mixed strategy" with partial self-incompatibility. These reproductive strategies differ in their implications for evolutionary potential. How, for example, might a self-incompatible species fare as a small founder population or remnant population in a severe population bottleneck (see Chapter 23), as compared with a self-fertile species?

11. **SCIENTIFIC INQUIRY**
    Critics of GM foods have argued that foreign genes may disturb normal cellular functioning, causing unexpected and potentially harmful substances to appear inside cells. Toxic intermediary substances that normally occur in very small amounts may arise in larger amounts, or new substances may appear. The disruption may also lead to loss of substances that help maintain normal metabolism. If you were your nation's chief scientific advisor, how would you respond to these criticisms?

12. **SCIENCE, TECHNOLOGY, AND SOCIETY**
    Humans have engaged in genetic manipulation for millennia, producing plant and animal varieties through selective breeding and hybridization processes that significantly modify the genomes of organisms. Why do you think modern genetic engineering, which often entails introducing or modifying only one or a few genes, has met with so much public opposition? Should some forms of genetic engineering be of greater concern than others? Explain.

13. **WRITE ABOUT A THEME: ORGANIZATION**
    In a short essay (100–150 words), discuss how the ability of a flower to reproduce with other flowers of the same species is an emergent property that arises from its floral parts and their organization.

14. **SYNTHESIZE YOUR KNOWLEDGE**

Dartmouth Electron Microscope Facility

(a) What is a pollen grain? (b) How does it form? (c) What is its function, and how does it accomplish this function? (d) In an evolutionary context, why was pollen an important step in allowing seed plants to become the dominant plants?

For selected answers, see Appendix A.

39

Plant Responses to Internal and External Signals

KEY CONCEPTS

39.1 Signal transduction pathways link signal reception to response

39.2 Plant hormones help coordinate growth, development, and responses to stimuli

39.3 Responses to light are critical for plant success

39.4 Plants respond to a wide variety of stimuli other than light

39.5 Plants respond to attacks by herbivores and pathogens

Smith, Jason

▲ Figure 39.1 **A "vampire" plant?**

Stimuli and a Stationary Life

Slowly, the hunter slinks through the brush toward the shade, where its prey can best be found. It began its hunt with only a week of provisions. If it does not find food soon, it will perish. At long last, it detects a promising scent and steers toward the source. When it's within reach, it lassoes its quarry. Then it senses even better prey! It sets course for this new target, lassoes it, and taps into the vital juices of its nutritious victim.

The hunter is a parasitic, nonphotosynthetic flowering plant called dodder (*Cuscuta*). Upon germination, a dodder seedling, fuelled by nutrients stored during embryo development, searches for a host plant (**Figure 39.1**). If a host is not found within a week or so, the seedling dies. Dodder attacks by sending out tendrils that coil around the host, as seen in photo at the lower left. Within an hour, it either exploits the host or moves on. If it stays, it takes several days to tap into the host's phloem by means of feeding appendages called haustoria. Depending on how nutritious its host is, dodder grows more or fewer coils.

How does dodder locate its victims? Biologists have long known that it grows toward the shade (where better to find a stem?) but thought it just bumped into its victims. However, new studies reveal that chemicals released by a potential host plant attract dodder, causing it to rapidly set course in that direction.

Emilio Ereza/Alamy

◄ **Dodder entangling a host plant**

Dodder's behaviour is unusual, but photosynthetic plants also sense their environment, taking advantage of available sunlight and nutrient-rich patches in the soil. These behaviours involve signal transduction pathways similar to some pathways by which you interact with your environment. At the levels of signal reception and signal transduction, your cells are not that different from those of plants. As an animal, however, your responses to environmental stimuli are generally quite different from those of plants. Animals commonly respond by movement; plants respond by altering growth and development.

Plants must also adjust to changes in time, such as the passage of seasons, to compete successfully. In addition, they interact with a wide range of organisms. All of these physical and chemical interactions involve complex signal transduction pathways. In this chapter, we focus on understanding the internal chemicals (hormones) that regulate plant growth and development and how plants perceive and respond to their environments.

Signal transduction pathways link signal reception to response

Dodder plants receive specific signals from their environment and respond to them in ways that enhance survival and reproductive success, but dodder is not unique in this regard. Consider, for example, a forgotten potato in the back corner of a kitchen cupboard. This modified underground stem, or tuber, has sprouted shoots from its "eyes" (axillary buds). These shoots, however, scarcely resemble those of a typical plant. Instead of sturdy stems and broad green leaves, this plant has ghostly pale stems and unexpanded leaves, as well as short, stubby roots (Figure 39.2a). These morphological adaptations for growing in darkness, collectively referred to as **etiolation**, make sense if we consider that a young potato plant in nature usually encounters continuous darkness when sprouting underground. Under these circumstances, expanded leaves would be a hindrance to soil penetration and would be damaged as the shoots pushed through the soil. Because the leaves are unexpanded and underground, there is little evaporative loss of water and little requirement for an extensive root system to replace the water lost by transpiration. Moreover, the energy expended in producing green chlorophyll would be wasted because there is no light for photosynthesis. Instead, a potato plant growing in the dark allocates as much energy as possible to elongating its stems. This adaptation minimizes the energy required by the shoots to break ground, thus giving the shoot a better chance of reaching the light. The etiolation response is one example of how a plant's morphology and physiology are tuned to its surroundings by complex interactions between environmental and internal signals.

When a shoot reaches light, the plant undergoes profound changes, collectively called **de-etiolation** (informally known

Natalie Bronstein

(a) Before exposure to light. A dark-grown potato has tall, spindly stems and nonexpanded leaves—morphological adaptations that enable the shoots to penetrate the soil. The roots are short, but there is little need for water absorption because little water is lost by the shoots.

(b) After a week's exposure to natural daylight. The potato plant begins to resemble a typical plant with broad green leaves, short sturdy stems, and long roots. This transformation begins with the reception of light by the phytochrome and cryptochrome photoreceptors.

▲ **Figure 39.2 Light-induced de-etiolation (greening) of dark-grown potatoes.**

as greening). Stem elongation slows; leaves expand; roots elongate; and the shoot produces chlorophyll. In short, it begins to resemble a typical plant (Figure 39.2b). In this section, we will use this de-etiolation response as an example of how a plant cell's reception of a signal—in this case, light—is transduced into a response (greening). Along the way, we will explore how studies of mutants provide insights into the molecular details of the stages of cell signal processing: reception, transduction, and response (Figure 39.3).

As discussed in Chapter 11, a hormone or other kind of stimulus interacting with a specific receptor protein can trigger the sequential activation of relay proteins and also the production of second messengers that participate in the pathway. The signal is passed along, ultimately bringing about cellular responses. In this diagram, the receptor is on the surface of the target cell; in other cases, the stimulus interacts with receptors inside the cell.

▲ **Figure 39.3 Review of a general model for signal transduction pathways.**

Reception

Signals are first detected by receptors, proteins that undergo changes in shape in response to a specific stimulus. The receptor involved in de-etiolation is a type of *phytochrome*, a member of a class of photoreceptors that we'll discuss more fully later in the chapter. Unlike most receptors, which are built into the plasma membrane, the type of phytochrome that functions in de-etiolation is located in the cytoplasm. Researchers demonstrated the requirement for phytochrome in de-etiolation through studies of the tomato, a close relative of the potato. The *aurea* mutant of tomato, which has reduced levels of phytochrome, greens less than wild-type tomatoes when exposed to light. (*Aurea* is Latin for "gold." In the absence of chlorophyll, the yellow and orange accessory pigments called carotenoids are more obvious.) Researchers produced a normal de-etiolation response in individual *aurea* leaf cells by injecting phytochrome from other plants and then exposing the cells to light. Such experiments indicated that phytochrome functions in light detection during de-etiolation.

Transduction

Receptors can be sensitive to very weak environmental or chemical signals. Some de-etiolation responses are triggered by extremely low levels of light, in certain cases as little as the equivalent of a few seconds of moonlight. The transduction of these extremely weak signals involves **second messengers**—small molecules and ions in the cell that amplify the signal and transfer it from the receptor to other proteins that carry out the response (**Figure 39.4**). In Chapter 11, we discussed several kinds of second messengers (see Figures 11.12 and 11.14). Here, we examine the particular roles of two types of second messengers in de-etiolation: calcium ions (Ca^{2+}) and cyclic GMP (cGMP).

Changes in cytosolic Ca^{2+} levels play an important role in phytochrome signal transduction. The concentration of cytosolic Ca^{2+} is generally very low (about 10^{-7} *M*), but phytochrome activation leads to the opening of Ca^{2+} channels and a transient 100-fold increase in cytosolic Ca^{2+} levels. In response to light, phytochrome undergoes a change in shape

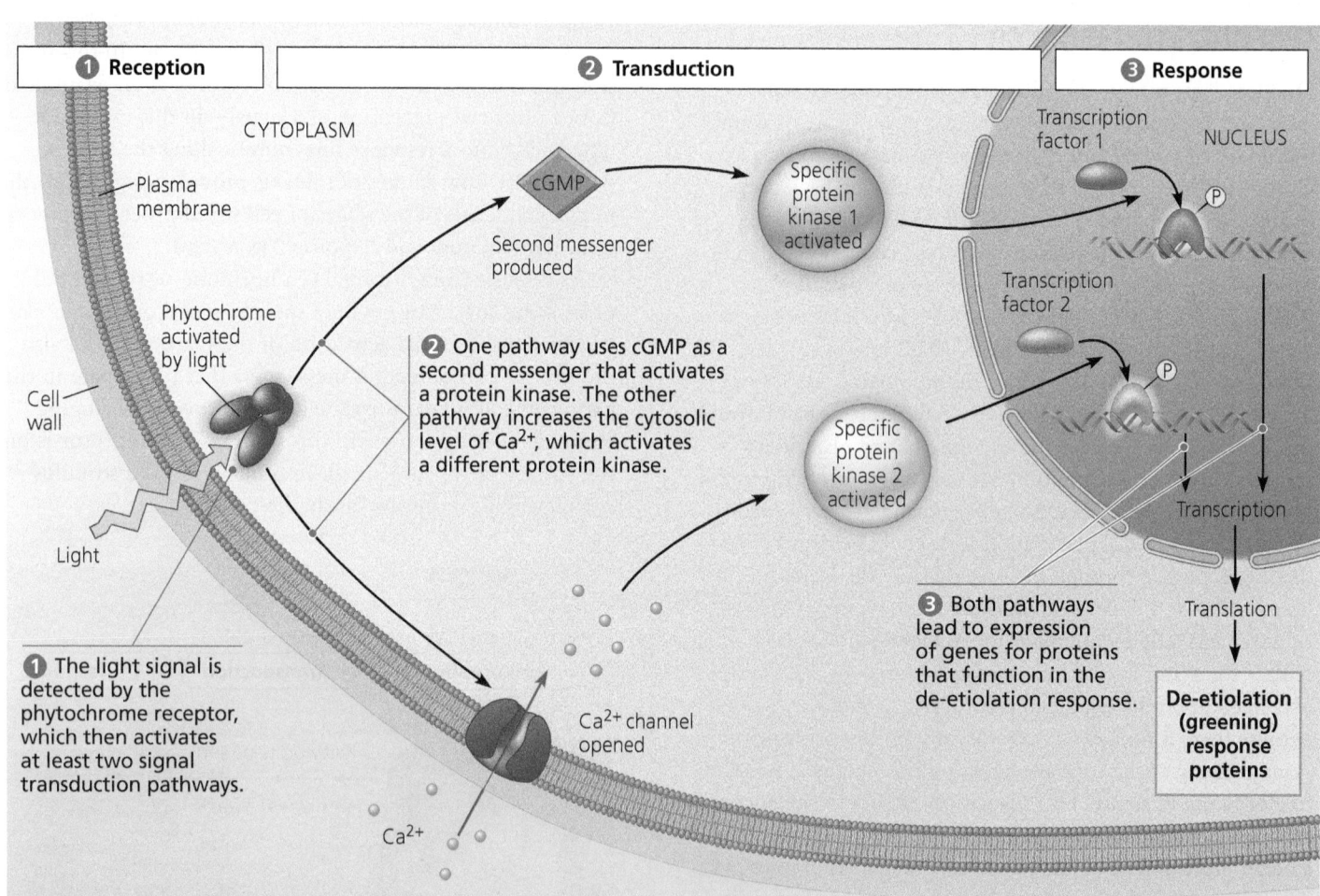

▲ **Figure 39.4** An example of signal transduction in plants: the role of phytochrome in the de-etiolation (greening) response.

MAKE CONNECTIONS *Which panel in Figure 11.17 best exemplifies the phytochrome-dependent signal transduction pathway during de-etiolation? Explain.*

that leads to the activation of guanylyl cyclase, an enzyme that produces the second messenger cyclic GMP. Both Ca^{2+} and cGMP must be produced for a complete de-etiolation response. The injection of cGMP into *aurea* tomato leaf cells, for example, induces only a partial de-etiolation response.

Response

Ultimately, second messengers regulate one or more cellular activities. In most cases, these responses involve the increased activity of particular enzymes. There are two main mechanisms by which a signalling pathway can enhance an enzymatic step in a biochemical pathway: post-translational modification and transcriptional regulation. Post-translational modification activates preexisting enzymes. Transcriptional regulation increases or decreases the synthesis of mRNA encoding a specific enzyme.

Post-Translational Modification of Preexisting Proteins

In most signal transduction pathways, preexisting proteins are modified by the phosphorylation of specific amino acids, which alters the protein's shape, hydrophobicity, and activity. Many second messengers, including cGMP and Ca^{2+}, activate protein kinases directly. Often, one protein kinase will phosphorylate another protein kinase, which then phosphorylates another, and so on (see Figure 11.10). Such kinase cascades may link initial stimuli to responses at the level of gene expression, usually via the phosphorylation of transcription factors. As we'll discuss, many signal transduction pathways ultimately regulate the synthesis of new proteins by turning specific genes on or off.

Signal transduction pathways must also have a means for turning off when the initial signal is no longer present, such as when a sprouting potato is put back into the cupboard. Protein phosphatases, which are enzymes that dephosphorylate specific proteins, are important in these "switch-off" processes. By removing the phosphate group added by the kinase, the phosphatase allows the protein shape to return to the "inactive" form. At any particular moment, a cell's functioning depends on the balance of activity of many types of protein kinases and protein phosphatases.

Transcriptional Regulation

As discussed in Chapter 18, the proteins we call *specific transcription factors* bind to specific regions of DNA and control the transcription of specific genes (see Figure 18.9). In the case of phytochrome-induced de-etiolation, several such transcription factors are activated by phosphorylation in response to the appropriate light conditions. The activation of some of these transcription factors depends on their phosphorylation by protein kinases activated by cGMP or Ca^{2+}.

The mechanism by which a signal promotes developmental changes may depend on transcription factors that are activators (which *increase* transcription of specific genes) or repressors (which *decrease* transcription) or both. For example, some *Arabidopsis* mutants, except for their pale colour, have a light-grown morphology when grown in the dark; they have expanded leaves and short, sturdy stems but are not green because the final step in chlorophyll production requires light directly. These mutants have defects in a repressor that normally inhibits the expression of other genes that are activated by light. When the repressor is eliminated by mutation, the pathway that is normally blocked proceeds. Thus, these mutants appear to have been grown in the light, except for their lack of chlorophyll.

De-Etiolation ("Greening") Proteins

What types of proteins are either activated by phosphorylation or newly transcribed during the de-etiolation process? Many are enzymes that function in photosynthesis directly; others are enzymes involved in supplying the chemical precursors necessary for chlorophyll production; still others affect the levels of plant hormones that regulate growth. For example, the levels of auxin and brassino steroids, hormones that enhance stem elongation, decrease following the activation of phytochrome. That decrease explains the slowing of stem elongation that accompanies de-etiolation.

We have discussed the signal transduction involved in the de-etiolation response of a potato plant in some detail to give you a sense of the complexity of biochemical changes that underlie this one process. Every plant hormone and every environmental stimulus triggers one or more signal transduction pathways of comparable complexity. As in the studies on the *aurea* mutant tomato, the isolation of mutants (a genetic approach) and techniques of molecular biology are helping researchers identify these various pathways. But this recent research builds on a long history of careful physiological and biochemical investigations into how plants work. As you will read in the next section, classic experiments provided the first clues that transported signalling molecules called hormones are internal regulators of plant growth.

CONCEPT CHECK 39.1

1. What are the morphological differences between dark- and light-grown plants? Explain how etiolation helps a seedling compete successfully.

2. Cycloheximide is a drug that inhibits protein synthesis. Predict what effect cycloheximide would have on de-etiolation.

3. **WHAT IF?** The sexual dysfunction drug Viagra inhibits an enzyme that breaks down cyclic GMP. If tomato leaf cells have a similar enzyme, how would applying Viagra to these cells affect the de-etiolation response of *aurea* mutant tomato leaves?

For suggested answers, see Appendix A.

Plant hormones help coordinate growth, development, and responses to stimuli

A **hormone**, in the original meaning of the term, is a signalling molecule that is produced in tiny amounts by one part of an organism's body and transported to other parts, where it binds to a specific receptor and triggers responses in target cells and tissues. In animals, hormones are usually transported through the circulatory system, a criterion often included in definitions of the term.

Many modern plant biologists, however, argue that the hormone concept, which originated from studies of animals, is too limiting to describe plant physiological processes. For example, plants don't have circulating blood to transport hormone-like signalling molecules. Moreover, some signalling molecules that are considered plant hormones act only locally. Finally, there are some signalling molecules in plants, such as glucose, that typically occur in plants at concentrations that are thousands of times greater than a typical hormone. Nevertheless, in a manner similar to a hormone, signalling molecules activate signal transduction pathways that greatly alter the functioning of plants. Thus, many plant biologists prefer the broader term *plant growth regulator* to describe organic compounds, either natural or synthetic, that modify or control one or more specific physiological processes within a plant. At this point in time, the terms *plant hormone* and *plant growth regulator* are used about equally, but for historical continuity we will use the term *plant hormone* and adhere to the criterion that plant hormones are active at very low concentrations.

Plant hormones are produced in very low concentrations, but a tiny amount of hormone can have a profound effect on plant growth and development. Virtually every aspect of plant growth and development is under hormonal control to some degree. Each hormone has multiple effects, depending on its site of action, its concentration, and the developmental stage of the plant. Conversely, multiple hormones can influence a single process. Plant hormone responses commonly depend on both the amounts of the hormones involved and their relative concentrations. It is often the interactions between different hormones, rather than hormones acting in isolation, that control growth and development. These interactions will become apparent in the following survey of hormone function.

A Survey of Plant Hormones

Table 39.1 previews the major types and actions of plant hormones, including auxin, cytokinins, gibberellins, abscisic acid, ethylene, brassinosteroids, jasmonates, and strigolactones.

Table 39.1	Overview of Plant Hormones	
Hormone	**Where Produced or Found in Plant**	**Major Functions**
Auxin (IAA)	Shoot apical meristems and young leaves are the primary sites of auxin synthesis. Root apical meristems also produce auxin, although the root depends on the shoot for much of its auxin. Developing seeds and fruits contain high levels of auxin, but it is unclear whether it is newly synthesized or transported from maternal tissues.	Stimulates stem elongation (low concentration only); promotes the formation of lateral and adventitious roots; regulates development of fruit; enhances apical dominance; functions in phototropism and gravitropism; promotes vascular differentiation; retards leaf abscission
Cytokinins	These are synthesized primarily in roots and transported to other organs, although there are many minor sites of production as well.	Regulate cell division in shoots and roots; modify apical dominance and promote lateral bud growth; promote movement of nutrients into sink tissues; stimulate seed germination; delay leaf senescence
Gibberellins (GA)	Meristems of apical buds and roots, young leaves, and developing seeds are the primary sites of production.	Stimulate stem elongation, pollen development, pollen tube growth, fruit growth, and seed development and germination; regulate sex determination and the transition from juvenile to adult phases
Abscisic acid (ABA)	Almost all plant cells have the ability to synthesize abscisic acid, and its presence has been detected in every major organ and living tissue; it may be transported in the phloem or xylem.	Inhibits growth; promotes stomatal closure during drought stress; promotes seed dormancy and inhibits early germination; promotes leaf senescence; promotes desiccation tolerance
Ethylene	This gaseous hormone can be produced by most parts of the plant. It is produced in high concentrations during senescence, leaf abscission, and the ripening of some types of fruits. Synthesis is also stimulated by wounding and stress.	Promotes ripening of many types of fruit, leaf abscission, and the triple response in seedlings (inhibition of stem elongation, promotion of lateral expansion, and horizontal growth); enhances the rate of senescence; promotes root and root hair formation; promotes flowering in the pineapple family
Brassinosteroids	These compounds are present in all plant tissues, although different intermediates predominate in different organs. Internally produced brassinosteroids act near the site of synthesis.	Promote cell expansion and cell division in shoots; promote root growth at low concentrations; inhibit root growth at high concentrations; promote xylem differentiation and inhibit phloem differentiation; promote seed germination and pollen tube elongation
Jasmonates	These are a small group of related molecules derived from the fatty acid linolenic acid. They are produced in several parts of the plant and travel in the phloem to other parts of the plant.	Regulate a wide variety of functions, including fruit ripening, floral development, pollen production, tendril coiling, root growth, seed germination, and nectar secretion; also produced in response to herbivory and pathogen invasion
Strigolactones	These carotenoid-derived hormones and extracellular signals are produced in roots in response to low phosphate conditions or high auxin flow from the shoot.	Promote seed germination, control of apical dominance, and the attraction of mycorrhizal fungi to the root

Auxin

The idea that chemical messengers exist in plants emerged from a series of classic experiments on how stems respond to light. As you know, the shoot of a houseplant on a windowsill grows toward light. Any growth response that results in plant organs curving toward or away from stimuli is called a **tropism** (from the Greek *tropos*, turn). The growth of a shoot toward light or away from it is called **phototropism**; the former is positive phototropism, and the latter is negative phototropism.

In natural ecosystems, where plants may be crowded, phototropism directs shoot growth toward the sunlight that powers photosynthesis. This response results from a differential growth of cells on opposite sides of the shoot; the cells on the darker side elongate faster than the cells on the brighter side.

Charles Darwin and his son Francis conducted some of the earliest experiments on phototropism in the late 1800s (Figure 39.5). They observed that a grass seedling ensheathed in its coleoptile (see Figure 38.9b) could bend toward light only if the tip of the coleoptile was present. If the tip was removed, the coleoptile did not curve. The seedling also failed to grow toward light if the tip was covered with an opaque cap, but neither a transparent cap over the tip nor an opaque shield placed below the coleoptile tip prevented the phototropic response. It was the tip of the coleoptile, the Darwins concluded, that was responsible for sensing light. However, they noted that the differential growth response that led to curvature of the coleoptile occurred some distance below the tip. The Darwins postulated that some signal was transmitted downward from the tip to the elongating region of the coleoptile. A few decades later, the Danish scientist Peter Boysen-Jensen demonstrated that the signal was a mobile chemical substance. He separated the tip from the remainder of the coleoptile by a cube of gelatin, which prevented cellular contact but allowed chemicals to pass through. These seedlings responded normally, bending toward light. However, if the tip was experimentally separated from the lower coleoptile by an impermeable barrier, such as the mineral mica, no phototropic response occurred.

Subsequent research showed that a chemical was released from coleoptile tips and could be collected by means of diffusion into agar blocks. Little cubes of agar containing this chemical could induce "phototropic-like" curvatures even in complete darkness if the agar cubes were placed off-centre atop the cut surface of decapitated coleoptiles. Coleoptiles curve toward light because of a higher concentration of this growth-promoting chemical on the darker side of the coleoptile. Since this chemical stimulated growth as it passed down the coleoptile, it was dubbed "auxin" (from the Greek *auxein*, to increase). Auxin was later purified, and its chemical structure determined to be indoleacetic acid (IAA). The term **auxin** is used for any chemical

▼ Figure 39.5 | **Inquiry**

What part of a grass coleoptile senses light, and how is the signal transmitted?

Experiment Based on their observations that seedlings bend toward light, in 1880, Charles and Francis Darwin removed and covered parts of grass coleoptiles to determine what part of the seedling senses light. In 1913, Peter Boysen-Jensen separated coleoptiles with different materials to determine how the signal for phototropism is transmitted.

Results

Darwin and Darwin: Phototropism occurs only when the tip is illuminated.

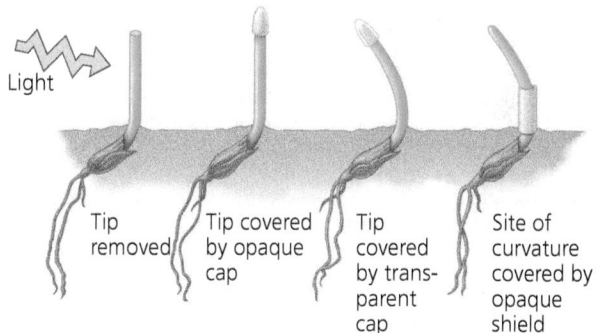

Boysen-Jensen: Phototropism occurs when the tip is separated by a permeable barrier but not an impermeable barrier.

Conclusion The Darwins' experiment suggested that only the tip of the coleoptile senses light. The phototropic bending, however, occurred at a distance from the site of light perception (the tip). Boysen-Jensen's results suggested that the signal for the bending is a light-activated mobile chemical.

Source: Based on C. R. Darwin, *The Power of Movement in Plants,* John Murray, London (1880). P. Boysen-Jensen, Concerning the performance of phototropic stimuli on the *Avena* coleoptile, *Berichte der Deutschen Botanischen Gesellschaft* (*Reports of the German Botanical Society*) 31:559–566 (1913). © Jane B Reece.

WHAT IF? *How could you experimentally determine which colours of light cause the most phototropic bending?*

substance that promotes elongation of coleoptiles, although auxins have multiple functions in flowering plants. The major natural auxin in plants is IAA, although several other compounds, including some synthetic ones, have auxin activity.

Auxin is produced predominantly in shoot tips and is transported from cell to cell down the stem at a rate of about 1 cm/hr. It moves only from tip to base, not in the reverse direction. This unidirectional transport of auxin is called *polar transport*. Polar transport is unrelated to gravity; experiments have shown that auxin travels upward when a stem or coleoptile segment is placed upside down. Rather, the polarity of auxin movement is attributable to the polar distribution of auxin transport protein in the cells. Concentrated at the basal end of a cell, the auxin transporters move the hormone out of the cell. The auxin can then enter the apical end of the neighbouring cell (**Figure 39.6**). Auxin has

▼ Figure 39.6 | **Inquiry**

What causes polar movement of auxin from shoot tip to base?

Experiment To investigate how auxin is transported unidirectionally, Leo Gälweiler and colleagues designed an experiment to identify the location of the auxin transport protein. They used a greenish yellow fluorescent molecule to label antibodies that bind to the auxin transport protein. Then they applied the antibodies to longitudinally sectioned *Arabidopsis* stems.

Results The light micrograph on the left shows that auxin transport proteins are not found in all stem tissues, but only in the xylem parenchyma. In the light micrograph on the right, a higher magnification reveals that these proteins are primarily localized at the basal ends of the cells.

Conclusion The results support the hypothesis that concentration of the auxin transport protein at the basal ends of cells mediates the polar transport of auxin.

Source: Based on L. Gälweiler et al., Regulation of polar auxin transport by AtPIN1 in *Arabidopsis* vascular tissue, *Science* 282:2226–2230 (1998). © Jane B Reece.

WHAT IF? *If auxin transport proteins were equally distributed at both ends of the cells, would polar auxin transport still be possible? Explain.*

a variety of effects, including stimulating cell elongation and regulating plant architecture.

The Role of Auxin in Cell Elongation One of auxin's chief functions is to stimulate elongation of cells within young developing shoots. As auxin from the shoot apex moves down to the region of cell elongation (see Figure 35.16), the hormone stimulates cell growth, probably by binding to a receptor in the plasma membrane. Auxin stimulates growth only over a certain concentration range, from about 10^{-8} to 10^{-4} M. At higher concentrations, auxin may inhibit cell elongation, probably by inducing production of ethylene, a hormone that generally hinders growth. We will return to this hormonal interaction when we discuss ethylene.

According to a model called the *acid growth hypothesis*, proton pumps play a major role in the growth response of cells to auxin. In a shoot's region of elongation, auxin stimulates the plasma membrane's proton (H^+) pumps. This pumping of H^+ increases the voltage across the membrane (membrane potential) and lowers the pH in the cell wall within minutes (**Figure 39.7**). Acidification of the wall activates enzymes called **expansins** that break the cross-links (hydrogen bonds) between cellulose microfibrils and other cell wall constituents, loosening the wall's fabric. (Expansins can even weaken the integrity of filter paper made of pure cellulose.) Increasing the membrane potential enhances ion uptake into the cell, which causes osmotic uptake of water and increased turgor. Increased turgor and a directionally weakened cell wall allow the cell to elongate in a specific direction.

Auxin also rapidly alters gene expression, causing cells in the region of elongation to produce new proteins within minutes. Some of these proteins are short-lived transcription factors that repress or activate the expression of other genes. For sustained growth after this initial spurt, cells must make more cytoplasm and wall material. Auxin also stimulates this sustained growth response.

Auxin's Role in Plant Development The polar transport of auxin is a central element controlling the spatial organization, or *pattern formation*, of the developing plant. Auxin is synthesized in shoot tips, and it carries integrated information about the development, size, and environment of individual branches. This flow of information controls branching patterns. A reduced flow of auxin from a branch, for example, indicates that the branch is not being sufficiently productive: New branches are needed elsewhere. Thus, lateral buds below the branch are released from dormancy and begin to grow.

Auxin transport also plays a key role in establishing *phyllotaxy* (see Figure 36.3), the arrangement of leaves on the stem. A leading model proposes that polar auxin transport in the shoot apex generates local peaks in auxin

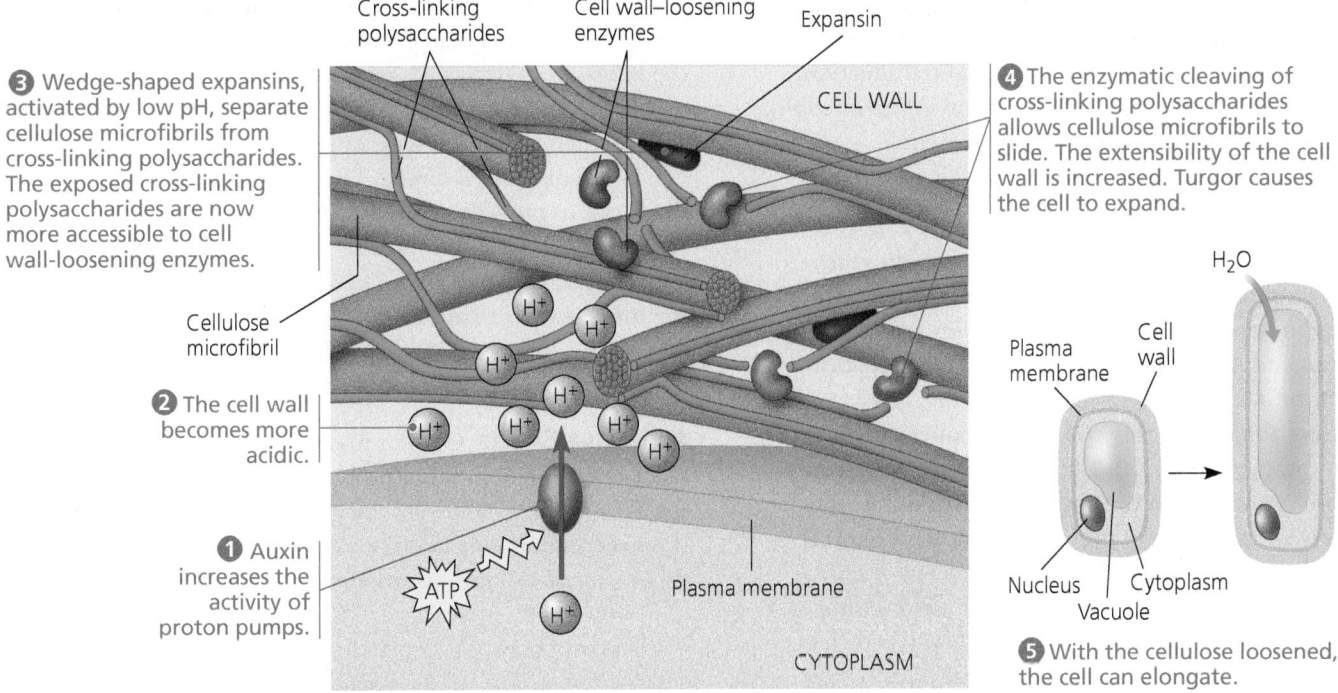

3 Wedge-shaped expansins, activated by low pH, separate cellulose microfibrils from cross-linking polysaccharides. The exposed cross-linking polysaccharides are now more accessible to cell wall-loosening enzymes.

Cross-linking polysaccharides

Cell wall–loosening enzymes

Expansin

CELL WALL

4 The enzymatic cleaving of cross-linking polysaccharides allows cellulose microfibrils to slide. The extensibility of the cell wall is increased. Turgor causes the cell to expand.

Cellulose microfibril

2 The cell wall becomes more acidic.

H^+

H^+ H^+ H^+ H^+ H^+ H^+ H^+

1 Auxin increases the activity of proton pumps.

ATP

H^+

Plasma membrane

CYTOPLASM

H_2O

Plasma membrane

Cell wall

Nucleus

Cytoplasm

Vacuole

5 With the cellulose loosened, the cell can elongate.

▲ Figure 39.7 **Cell elongation in response to auxin: the acid growth hypothesis.**

concentration that determine the site of leaf primordium formation and thereby the different phyllotaxies found in nature.

The polar transport of auxin from the leaf margin also directs the patterns of leaf veins. Inhibitors of polar auxin transport result in leaves that lack vascular continuity through the petiole and have broad, loosely organized main veins, an increased number of secondary veins, and a dense band of irregularly shaped vascular cells adjacent to the leaf margin.

The activity of the vascular cambium, the meristem that produces woody tissues, is also under the control of auxin transport. When a plant becomes dormant at the end of a growing season, there is a reduction in auxin transport capacity and the expression of genes encoding auxin transporters.

Auxin's effects on plant development are not limited to the familiar sporophyte plant that we see. Recent evidence suggests that the organization of the microscopic angiosperm female gametophytes is regulated by an auxin gradient.

Practical Uses for Auxins Auxins, both natural and synthetic, have many commercial applications. For example, the natural auxin indolebutyric acid (IBA) is used in the vegetative propagation of plants by cuttings. Treating a detached leaf or stem with powder containing IBA often causes adventitious roots to form near the cut surface.

Certain synthetic auxins, including 2,4-dichlorophenoxyacetic acid (2,4-D), are widely used as herbicides.

Monocots, such as maize and turfgrass, can rapidly inactivate such synthetic auxins. However, eudicots cannot and therefore die from hormonal overdose. Spraying cereal fields or turf with 2,4-D eliminates eudicot (broadleaf) weeds. These uses, and its relative safety to mammals, make 2,4-D the most widely employed herbicide in the world. In Canada, it is commonly found in lawn sprays and fertilizer mixes to kill dandelions.

Developing seeds produce auxin, which promotes fruit growth. In tomato plants grown in greenhouses, often fewer seeds are produced, resulting in poorly developed tomato fruits. However, spraying synthetic auxins on greenhouse-grown tomato vines induces normal fruit development, making the greenhouse-cultivated tomatoes commercially viable.

Cytokinins

Trial-and-error attempts to find chemical additives that would enhance the growth and development of plant cells in tissue culture led to the discovery of **cytokinins**. In the 1940s, researchers stimulated the growth of plant embryos in culture by adding coconut milk, the liquid endosperm of a coconut's giant seed. Subsequent researchers found that they could induce cultured tobacco cells to divide by adding degraded DNA samples. The active ingredients of both experimental additives turned out to be modified forms of adenine, a component of nucleic acids. These growth regulators were named cytokinins because they stimulate cytokinesis, or cell division. The most common natural cytokinin is zeatin, so named because it was discovered first in maize (*Zea mays*). Although much remains to be learned about cytokinin synthesis and signal transduction, the effects of cytokinins on cell division and differentiation, apical dominance, and aging are well documented.

Control of Cell Division and Differentiation Cytokinins are produced in actively growing tissues, particularly in roots, embryos, and fruits. Cytokinins produced in roots reach their target tissues by moving up the plant in the xylem sap. Acting in concert with auxin, cytokinins stimulate cell division and influence the pathway of differentiation. The effects of cytokinins on cells growing in tissue culture provide clues about how this class of hormones may function in an intact plant. When a piece of parenchyma tissue from a stem is cultured in the absence of cytokinins, the cells grow very large but do not divide. But if cytokinins are added along with auxin, the cells divide. Cytokinins alone have no effect. The ratio of cytokinins to auxin controls cell differentiation. When the concentrations of these two hormones are at certain levels, the mass of cells continues to grow, but it remains a cluster of undifferentiated cells called a callus (see Figure 38.15). If cytokinin levels increase, shoot buds develop from the callus. If auxin levels increase, roots form.

Control of Apical Dominance Cytokinins, auxin, and newly discovered plant hormones called strigolactones interact in the control of apical dominance, the ability of the apical bud to suppress the development of axillary buds (Figure 39.8a). Until recently, the leading hypothesis to explain the hormonal regulation of apical dominance—the direct inhibition hypothesis—proposed that auxin and cytokinins act antagonistically in regulating axillary bud growth. According to this view, auxin transported down the shoot from the apical bud directly inhibits axillary buds from growing, causing a shoot to lengthen at the expense of lateral branching. Meanwhile, cytokinins entering the shoot system from roots counter the action of auxin by signalling axillary buds to begin growing. Thus, the ratio of auxin and cytokinins was viewed as the critical factor in controlling axillary bud inhibition.

Many observations are consistent with the direct inhibition hypothesis. If the apical bud, the primary source of auxin, is removed, the inhibition of axillary buds is removed and the plant

becomes bushier (Figure 39.8b). Applying auxin to the cut surface of the decapitated shoot resuppresses the growth of the lateral buds (Figure 39.8c). Mutants that overproduce cytokinins or plants treated with cytokinins also tend to be bushier than normal. It now appears, however, that auxin's effects are partially indirect. The polar flow of auxin down the shoot triggers the synthesis of strigolactones, which repress bud growth. Moreover, another signal, perhaps an electrical one, appears to cause buds to begin growing much earlier than can be explained by disrupted auxin flow. Thus, the control of apical dominance is much more complicated than previously thought.

Anti-Aging Effects Cytokinins slow the aging of certain plant organs by inhibiting protein breakdown, stimulating RNA and protein synthesis, and mobilizing nutrients from surrounding tissues. If leaves removed from a plant are dipped in a cytokinin solution, they stay green much longer than otherwise. Cytokinins also slow the progress of **apoptosis**, a type of programmed cell death.

Gibberellins

In the early 1900s, farmers in Asia noticed that some rice seedlings in their paddies grew so tall and spindly that they toppled over before they could mature. In 1926, it was discovered that a fungus of the genus *Gibberella* causes this "foolish seedling disease." By the 1930s, it was determined that the fungus causes hyperelongation of rice stems by

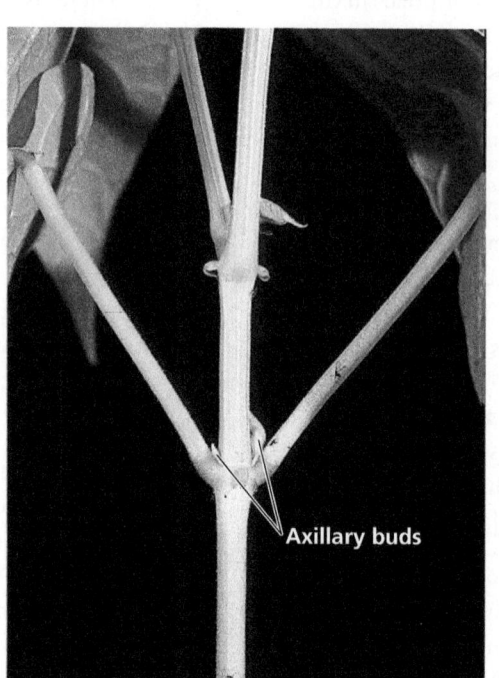

(a) Apical bud intact (not shown in photo)

(b) Apical bud removed

(c) Auxin added to decapitated stem

▲ Figure 39.8 **Apical dominance.** (a) The inhibition of growth of axillary buds, possibly influenced by auxin from the apical bud, favours elongation of the shoot's main axis. (b) Removal of the apical bud from the same plant enables lateral branches to grow. (c) Applying a gelatin capsule containing auxin to the stump prevents the lateral branches from growing.

secreting a chemical, which was given the name **gibberel-lin**. In the 1950s, researchers discovered that plants also produce gibberellins (GAs). Since that time, scientists have identified more than 100 different gibberellins that occur naturally in plants, although a much smaller number occur in each plant species. "Foolish rice" seedlings, it seems, suffer from too much gibberellin. Gibberellins have a variety of effects, such as stem elongation, fruit growth, and seed germination.

Stem Elongation The major sites of gibberellin production are young roots and leaves. Gibberellins are best known for stimulating stem and leaf growth by enhancing cell elongation *and* cell division. One hypothesis proposes that they activate enzymes that loosen cell walls, facilitating entry of expansin proteins. Thus, gibberellins act in concert with auxin to promote stem elongation.

The effects of gibberellins in enhancing stem elongation are evident when certain dwarf (mutant) varieties of plants are treated with gibberellins. For instance, some dwarf pea plants (including the variety Mendel studied; see Chapter 14) grow tall if treated with gibberellins. But there is often no response if the gibberellins are applied to wild-type plants. Apparently, these plants already produce an optimal dose of the hormone. The most dramatic example of gibberellin-induced stem elongation is *bolting*, rapid growth of the floral stalk (Figure 39.9a).

Fruit Growth In many plants, both auxin and gibberellins must be present for fruit to develop. The most important commercial application of gibberellins is in the spraying of Thompson seedless grapes (Figure 39.9b). The hormone makes the individual grapes grow larger, a trait valued by the consumer. The gibberellin sprays also make the internodes of the grape bunch elongate, allowing more space for the individual grapes. By enhancing air circulation between the grapes, this increase in space also makes it harder for yeasts and other microorganisms to infect the fruit.

Germination The embryo of a seed is a rich source of gibberellins. After water is imbibed, the release of gibberellins from the embryo signals the seed to break dormancy and germinate. Some seeds that normally require particular environmental conditions to germinate, such as exposure to light or low temperatures, break dormancy if they are treated with gibberellins. Gibberellins

Dr. Richard Amasino

Fred Jensen

(a) Some plants develop in a rosette form, low to the ground with very short internodes, as in the *Arabidopsis* plant shown at the left. As the plant switches to reproductive growth, a surge of gibberellins induces bolting: Internodes elongate rapidly, elevating floral buds that develop at stem tips (right).

(b) The Thompson seedless grape bunch on the left is from an untreated control vine. The bunch on the right is growing from a vine that was sprayed with gibberellin during fruit development.

▲ **Figure 39.9 Effects of gibberellins on stem elongation and fruit growth.**

support the growth of cereal seedlings by stimulating the synthesis of digestive enzymes such as α-amylase that mobilize stored nutrients (Figure 39.10).

Abscisic Acid

In the 1960s, one research group studying the chemical changes that precede bud dormancy and leaf abscission in deciduous trees and another team investigating chemical

❶ After a seed imbibes water, the embryo releases gibberellin (GA), which sends a signal to the aleurone, the thin outer layer of the endosperm.

❷ The aleurone responds to GA by synthesizing and secreting digestive enzymes that hydrolyze nutrients stored in the endosperm. One example is α-amylase, which hydrolyzes starch.

❸ Sugars and other nutrients absorbed from the endosperm by the scutellum (cotyledon) are consumed during growth of the embryo into a seedling.

Aleurone

Endosperm

Water

Scutellum (cotyledon)

GA

GA

α-amylase

Radicle

Sugar

▲ **Figure 39.10 Mobilization of nutrients by gibberellins during the germination of grain seeds such as barley.**

changes preceding abscission of cotton fruits isolated the same compound, **abscisic acid (ABA)**. Ironically, ABA is no longer thought to play a primary role in bud dormancy or leaf abscission, but it is very important in other functions. Unlike the growth-stimulating hormones we have discussed so far—auxin, cytokinins, gibberellins, and brassinosteroids—ABA *slows* growth. ABA often antagonizes the actions of growth hormones, and the ratio of ABA to one or more growth hormones determines the final physiological outcome. We will consider here two of ABA's many effects: seed dormancy and drought tolerance.

Seed Dormancy Seed dormancy increases the likelihood that seeds will germinate only when there are sufficient amounts of light, temperature, and moisture for the seedlings to survive (see Chapter 38). What prevents seeds dispersed in autumn from germinating immediately, only to die in the winter? What mechanisms ensure that such seeds do not germinate until spring? For that matter, what prevents seeds from germinating in the dark, moist interior of the fruit? The answer to these questions is ABA. The levels of ABA may increase 100-fold during seed maturation. The high levels of ABA in maturing seeds inhibit germination and induce the production of proteins that help the seeds withstand the extreme dehydration that accompanies maturation.

Many types of dormant seeds germinate when ABA is removed or inactivated. The seeds of some desert plants break dormancy only when heavy rains wash ABA out of them. Other seeds require light or prolonged exposure to cold to inactivate ABA. Often, the ratio of ABA to gibberellins determines whether seeds remain dormant or germinate, and adding ABA to seeds that are primed to germinate makes them dormant again. Inactivated ABA or low levels of ABA can lead to precocious (early) germination **(Figure 39.11)**. For example, a maize mutant with grains that germinate while still on the cob lacks a functional transcription factor required for ABA to induce expression of certain genes. Precocious germination of red mangrove seeds, due to low ABA levels, is actually an adaptation that helps the young seedlings to plant themselves like darts in the soft mud below the parent tree.

Drought Tolerance ABA plays a major role in drought signalling. When a plant begins to wilt, ABA accumulates in the leaves and causes stomata to close rapidly, reducing transpiration and preventing further water loss. By affecting second messengers such as calcium, ABA causes potassium channels in the plasma membrane of guard cells to open, leading to a massive loss of potassium ions from the cells. The accompanying osmotic loss of water reduces guard cell turgor and leads to closing of the stomatal pores (see Figure 36.13). In some cases, water shortage stresses the root system before the shoot system, and ABA transported from roots to leaves may function as an "early warning

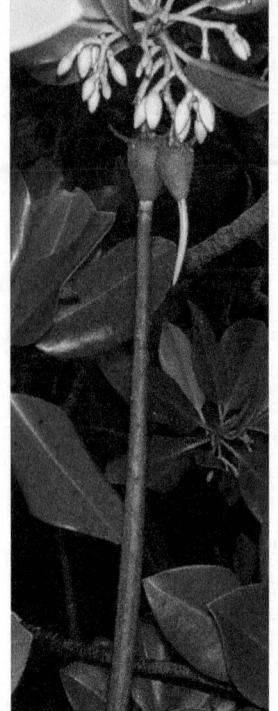

Red mangrove (*Rhizophora mangle*) seeds produce only low levels of ABA, and their seeds germinate while still on the tree. In this case, early germination is a useful adaptation. When released, the radicle of the dart-like seedling deeply penetrates the soft mudflats in which the mangroves grow.

Coleoptile

▲ Precocious germination in this maize mutant is caused by lack of a functional transcription factor required for ABA action.

▲ **Figure 39.11 Precocious germination of wild-type mangrove and mutant maize seeds.**

system." Many mutants that are especially prone to wilting are deficient in ABA production.

Ethylene

During the 1800s, when coal gas was used as fuel for streetlights, leakage from gas pipes caused nearby trees to drop leaves prematurely. In 1901, the gas **ethylene** was demonstrated to be the active factor in coal gas. But the idea that it is a plant hormone was not widely accepted until the advent of a technique called gas chromatography simplified its identification.

Plants produce ethylene in response to stresses such as drought, flooding, mechanical pressure, injury, and infection. Ethylene is also produced during fruit ripening and programmed cell death and in response to high concentrations of externally applied auxin. Indeed, many effects previously ascribed to auxin, such as inhibition of root elongation, may be due to auxin-induced ethylene production. We will focus here on four of ethylene's many effects: response to mechanical stress, senescence, leaf abscission, and fruit ripening.

The Triple Response to Mechanical Stress Imagine a pea seedling pushing upward through the soil, only to come up against a stone. As it pushes against the obstacle, the stress in its delicate tip induces the seedling to produce ethylene. The hormone then instigates a growth manoeuvre known as the **triple response** that enables the shoot to avoid the obstacle. The three parts of this response are a slowing of stem elongation, a thickening of the stem (which makes it stronger), and a curvature that causes the stem to start growing horizontally. As the effects of the initial ethylene pulse lessen, the stem resumes vertical growth. If it again contacts a barrier, another burst of ethylene is released, and horizontal growth resumes. However, if the upward touch detects no solid object, then ethylene production decreases, and the stem, now clear of the obstacle, resumes its normal upward growth. It is ethylene that induces the stem to grow horizontally rather than the physical obstruction itself; when ethylene is applied to normal seedlings growing free of physical impediments, they still undergo the triple response (Figure 39.12).

Studies of *Arabidopsis* mutants with abnormal triple responses are an example of how biologists identify a signal transduction pathway. Scientists isolated ethylene-insensitive (*ein*) mutants, which fail to undergo the triple response after exposure to ethylene (Figure 39.13a). Some types of *ein* mutants are insensitive to ethylene because they lack a functional ethylene receptor. Mutants of a different sort undergo the triple response even out of soil, in the air, where there are no physical obstacles. Some of these mutants have a regulatory defect that causes them to produce ethylene at rates 20 times normal. The phenotype of

ein mutant

ctr mutant

Kurt Stepnitz

Joseph J. Kieber

(a) *ein* mutant. An ethylene-insensitive (*ein*) mutant fails to undergo the triple response in the presence of ethylene.

(b) *ctr* mutant. A constitutive triple-response (*ctr*) mutant undergoes the triple response even in the absence of ethylene.

▲ **Figure 39.13** **Ethylene triple-response *Arabidopsis* mutants.**

such ethylene-overproducing (*eto*) mutants can be restored to wild-type by treating the seedlings with inhibitors of ethylene synthesis. Other mutants, called constitutive triple-response (*ctr*) mutants, undergo the triple response in air but do not respond to inhibitors of ethylene synthesis (Figure 39.13b). (Constitutive genes are genes that are continually expressed in all cells of an organism.) In *ctr* mutants, ethylene signal transduction is permanently turned on, even though ethylene is not present.

The affected gene in *ctr* mutants codes for a protein kinase. The fact that this mutation *activates* the ethylene response suggests that the normal kinase product of the wild-type allele is a *negative* regulator of ethylene signal transduction. Thus, binding of the hormone ethylene to the ethylene receptor normally leads to inactivation of the kinase; and the inactivation of this negative regulator allows synthesis of the proteins required for the triple response.

Senescence Consider the shedding of a leaf in autumn or the death of an annual after flowering. Or think about the final step in differentiation of a vessel element, when its living contents are destroyed, leaving a hollow tube behind. Such events involve **senescence**—the programmed death of certain cells or organs or the entire plant. Cells, organs, and plants genetically programmed to die on a schedule do not simply shut down cellular machinery and await death. Instead, at the molecular level, the onset of the programmed cell death called apoptosis is a very busy time in a cell's life, requiring new gene expression (see Concept 11.5). During apoptosis, newly formed enzymes break

Ethylene concentration (parts per million)

0.00   0.10   0.20   0.40   0.80

▲ **Figure 39.12** **The ethylene-induced triple response.** In response to ethylene, a gaseous plant hormone, germinating pea seedlings grown in the dark undergo the triple response—slowing of stem elongation, stem thickening, and horizontal stem growth. The response is greater with increased ethylene concentration.

down many chemical components, including chlorophyll, DNA, RNA, proteins, and membrane lipids. The plant salvages many of the breakdown products. A burst of ethylene is almost always associated with the apoptosis of cells during senescence.

Leaf Abscission The loss of leaves from deciduous trees helps prevent desiccation during seasonal periods of climatic stress that severely limit the availability of water to the roots. Before dying leaves abscise, many essential elements are salvaged from them and stored in stem parenchyma cells. These nutrients are recycled back to developing leaves the following spring. Autumn leaf colours are due to newly made red pigments as well as yellow and orange carotenoids (see Chapter 10) that were already present in the leaf and are rendered visible by the breakdown of the dark green chlorophyll in autumn.

When an autumn leaf falls, the breaking point is an abscission layer that develops near the base of the petiole (Figure 39.14). The small parenchyma cells of this layer have very thin walls, and there are no fibre cells around the vascular tissue. The abscission layer is further weakened when enzymes hydrolyze polysaccharides in the cell walls. Finally, the weight of the leaf, with the help of the wind, causes a separation within the abscission layer. Even before the leaf falls, a layer of cork forms a protective scar on the twig side of the abscission layer, preventing pathogens from invading the plant.

A change in the ratio of ethylene to auxin controls abscission. An aging leaf produces less and less auxin, rendering the cells of the abscission layer more sensitive to ethylene. As the influence of ethylene on the abscission layer prevails, the cells produce enzymes that digest the cellulose and other components of cell walls.

Fruit Ripening Immature fleshy fruits are generally tart, hard, and green—features that help protect the developing seeds from herbivores. After ripening, the mature fruits help *attract* animals that disperse the seeds (see Figures 30.10 and 30.11). In many cases, a burst of ethylene production in the fruit triggers the ripening process. The enzymatic breakdown of cell wall components softens the fruit, and the conversion of starches and acids to sugars makes the fruit sweet. The production of new scents and colours helps advertise ripeness to animals, which eat the fruits and disperse the seeds.

A chain reaction occurs during ripening: Ethylene triggers ripening, and ripening triggers more ethylene production. The result is a huge burst in ethylene production. Because ethylene is a gas, the signal to ripen spreads from fruit to fruit. If you pick or buy green fruit, you may be able to speed ripening by storing the fruit in a paper bag, allowing ethylene to accumulate. On a commercial scale, many kinds of fruits are ripened in huge storage containers in which ethylene levels are enhanced. In other cases, fruit producers take measures to slow ripening caused by natural ethylene. Apples, for instance, are stored in bins flushed with carbon dioxide. Circulating the air prevents ethylene from accumulating, and carbon dioxide inhibits synthesis of new ethylene. Stored in this way, apples picked in autumn can still be shipped to grocery stores the following summer.

Given the importance of ethylene in the postharvest physiology of fruits, the genetic engineering of ethylene signal transduction pathways has potential commercial applications. For example, by engineering a way to block the transcription of one of the genes required for ethylene synthesis, molecular biologists have created tomato fruits that ripen on demand. These fruits are picked while green and will not ripen unless ethylene gas is added. As such methods are refined, they will reduce spoilage of fruits and vegetables, a problem that ruins almost half the produce harvested in Canada. Due to the large size of our country, and the fact that many regions are not able to grow specific food crops, spoilage becomes an even greater problem due to the time required to transport crops from field to market.

More Recently Discovered Plant Hormones

Auxin, gibberellins, cytokinins, abscisic acid, and ethylene are often considered the five "classic" plant hormones. However, more recently discovered hormones have swelled the list of important plant growth regulators.

Brassinosteroids are steroids similar to cholesterol and the sex hormones of animals. They induce cell elongation and division in stem segments and seedlings at

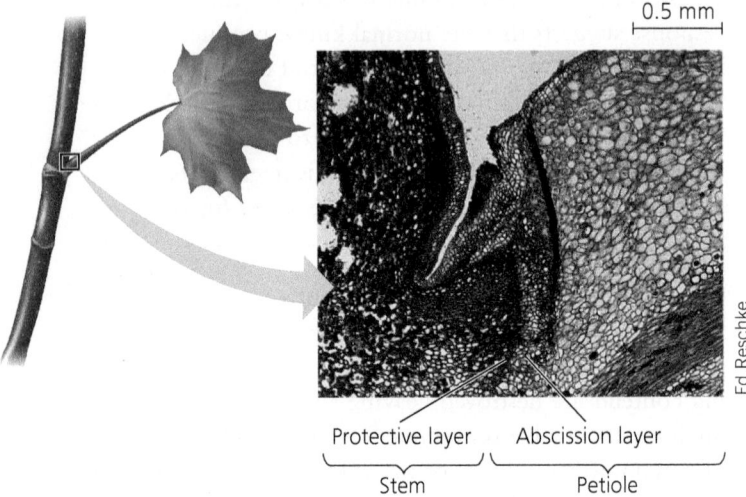

0.5 mm

Protective layer   Abscission layer

Stem   Petiole

Ed Reschke

▲ **Figure 39.14 Abscission of a maple leaf.** Abscission is controlled by a change in the ratio of ethylene to auxin. The abscission layer is seen in this longitudinal section as a vertical band at the base of the petiole. After the leaf falls, a protective layer of cork becomes the leaf scar that helps prevent pathogens from invading the plant (LM).

concentrations as low as 10^{-12} M. They also slow leaf abscission (leaf drop) and promote xylem differentiation. These effects are so qualitatively similar to those of auxin that it took years for plant physiologists to determine that brassinosteroids were not types of auxins.

The identification of brassinosteroids as plant hormones arose from studies of an *Arabidopsis* mutant that even when grown in the dark exhibited morphological features similar to plants grown in the light. The researchers discovered that the mutation affects a gene that normally codes for an enzyme similar to one involved in steroid synthesis in mammals. They also found that this brassinosteroid-deficient mutant could be restored to the wild-type phenotype by applying brassinosteroids.

Jasmonates, including *jasmonate* (JA) and *methyl jasmonate* (MeJA), are fatty acid–derived molecules that play important roles both in plant defence (see Concept 39.5) and, as discussed here, in plant development. Chemists first isolated MeJA as a key ingredient producing the enchanting fragrance of jasmine (*Jasminum grandiflorum*) flowers. Interest in jasmonates exploded when it was realized that jasmonates are produced by wounded plants and play a key role in controlling plant defences against herbivores and pathogens. In studying jasmonate signal transduction mutants as well as the effects of applying jasmonates to plants, it soon became apparent that jasmonates and their derivatives regulate a wide variety of physiological processes in plants, including nectar secretion, fruit ripening, pollen production, flowering time, seed germination, root growth, tuber formation, mycorrhizal symbioses, and tendril coiling. In controlling plant processes, jasmonates also engage in crosstalk with phytochrome and various hormones, including GA, IAA, and ethylene.

Strigolactones are xylem-mobile chemicals that stimulate seed germination, suppress adventitious root formation, help establish mycorrhizal associations, and (as noted earlier) help control apical dominance. Their recent discovery relates back to studies of their namesake, *Striga*, a colourfully named genus of rootless parasitic plants that penetrate the roots of other plants, diverting essential nutrients from them and stunting their growth. (In Romanian legend, Striga is a vampire-like creature that lives for thousands of years, only needing to feed every 25 years or so.) Also known as witchweed, *Striga* may be the greatest obstacle to food production in Africa, infesting about two-thirds of the area devoted to cereal crops. Each *Striga* plant produces tens of thousands of tiny seeds that can remain dormant in the soil for many years until a suitable host begins to grow. Thus, *Striga* cannot be eradicated by growing non-grain crops for several years. Strigolactones, exuded by the host roots, were first identified as the chemical signals that stimulate the germination of *Striga* seeds.

CONCEPT CHECK 39.2

1. Suggest a reason why cut flowers such as carnations are often treated with cytokinins prior to shipping.
2. Fusicoccin is a fungal toxin that stimulates the plasma membrane H^+ pumps of plant cells. How may it affect the growth of isolated stem sections?
3. **WHAT IF?** If a plant has the double mutation *ctr* and *ein*, what is its triple-response phenotype? Explain your answer.
4. **MAKE CONNECTIONS** What type of feedback process is exemplified by the production of ethylene during fruit ripening? Explain. (See Figure 1.12.)

For suggested answers, see Appendix A.

CONCEPT **39.3**

Responses to light are critical for plant success

Light is an especially important environmental factor in the lives of plants. In addition to being required for photosynthesis, light triggers many key events in plant growth and development. The effects of light on plant morphology are called **photomorphogenesis**. Light reception also allows plants to measure the passage of days and seasons.

Plants detect not only the presence of light but also its direction, intensity, and wavelength (colour). As you saw in Figure 10.10b for photosynthesis, a graph called an **action spectrum** depicts the relative effectiveness of different wavelengths of radiation in driving a particular process. Action spectra are useful in studying *any* process that depends on light. By comparing action spectra of various plant responses, researchers can determine which responses are mediated by the same photoreceptor (pigment). They also compare action spectra with absorption spectra of pigments; a close correspondence for a given pigment suggests that the pigment is the photoreceptor mediating the response. Action spectra reveal that red and blue light are the most important colours in regulating a plant's photomorphogenesis. These observations led researchers to two major classes of light receptors: **blue-light photoreceptors** and **phytochromes**, photoreceptors that absorb mostly red light.

Blue-Light Photoreceptors

Blue light initiates a variety of responses in plants, including phototropism, the light-induced opening of stomata (see Figure 36.12), and the light-induced slowing of hypocotyl elongation that occurs when a seedling breaks ground. The biochemical identity of the blue-light photoreceptor was so elusive that, in the 1970s, plant physiologists began to call this receptor "cryptochrome" (from the Greek *kryptos*, hidden, and *chrom*, pigment). In the 1990s, molecular biologists analyzing *Arabidopsis* mutants found that plants use as many as three different types of pigments to detect blue light. *Cryptochromes*, molecular relatives of DNA repair enzymes, are involved in the blue-light-induced inhibition of stem elongation that occurs, for example, when a seedling first emerges from the soil. *Phototropin* is a protein kinase involved in mediating blue light-mediated stomatal opening, chloroplast movements in response to light, and phototropic curvatures (Figure 39.15), such as those studied by the Darwins.

(a) This action spectrum illustrates that only light wavelengths below 500 nm (blue and violet light) induce curvature.

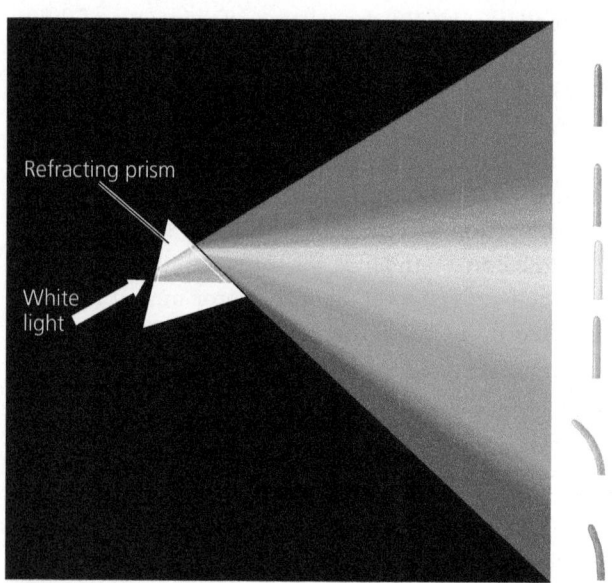

(b) When coleoptiles are exposed to light of various wavelengths as shown here, violet light induces slight curvature toward the light and blue light induces the most curvature. The other colours do not induce any curvature.

▲ **Figure 39.15 Action spectrum for blue-light-stimulated phototropism in maize coleoptiles.** Phototropic bending toward light is controlled by phototropin, a photoreceptor sensitive to blue and violet light, particularly blue light.

Source: Based on *Plantwatching: How plants remember, tell time, form relationships and more* by Malcolm Wilkins. Facts on File, 1988. © Jane B Reece.

Phytochromes as Photoreceptors

When introducing signal transduction in plants earlier in the chapter, we discussed the role of the plant pigments called phytochromes in the de-etiolation process. Phytochromes regulate many plant responses to light. Let's look at two more examples: seed germination and shade avoidance.

Phytochromes and Seed Germination

Studies of seed germination led to the discovery of phytochromes. Because of limited nutrient reserves, many types of seeds, especially small ones, germinate only when the light environment and other conditions are near optimal. Such seeds often remain dormant for years until light conditions change. For example, the death of a shading tree or the ploughing of a field may create a favourable light environment.

In the 1930s, scientists determined the action spectrum for light-induced germination of lettuce seeds. They exposed water-swollen seeds to a few minutes of monochromatic (single-coloured) light of various wavelengths and then stored the seeds in the dark. After two days, the researchers counted the number of seeds that had germinated under each light regimen. They found that red light of wavelength 660 nm increased the germination percentage of lettuce seeds maximally, whereas far-red light—that is, light of wavelengths near the upper edge of human visibility (730 nm)—*inhibited* germination compared with dark controls (Figure 39.16). What happens when the lettuce seeds are subjected to a flash of red light followed by a flash of far-red light or, conversely, to far-red light followed by red light? The *last* flash of light determines the seeds' response: The effects of red and far-red light are reversible.

The photoreceptors responsible for the opposing effects of red and far-red light are phytochromes. So far, researchers have identified five phytochromes in *Arabidopsis*, each with a slightly different polypeptide component. In most phytochromes, the light-absorbing portion is photoreversible, converting back and forth between two forms, depending on the colour of light to which it is exposed. In its red-absorbing form (P_r), a phytochrome absorbs red (R) light maximally and is converted to its far-red-absorbing form (P_{fr}); in its P_{fr} form, it absorbs far-red (FR) light and is converted to its P_r form (Figure 39.17). This $P_r \leftrightarrow P_{fr}$ interconversion is a switching mechanism that controls various light-induced events in the life of the plant. P_{fr} is the form of phytochrome that triggers many of a plant's developmental responses to light. For example, P_r in lettuce seeds exposed to red light is converted to P_{fr}, stimulating the cellular responses that lead to germination. When red-illuminated seeds are then exposed to far-red light, the P_{fr} is converted back to P_r, inhibiting the germination response.

Inquiry

How does the order of red and far-red illumination affect seed germination?

Experiment Scientists at the U.S. Department of Agriculture briefly exposed batches of lettuce seeds to red light or far-red light to test the effects on germination. After the light exposure, the seeds were placed in the dark, and the results were compared with control seeds that were not exposed to light.

Results The bar below each photo indicates the sequence of red light exposure, far-red light exposure, and darkness. The germination rate increased greatly in groups of seeds that were last exposed to red light (left). Germination was inhibited in groups of seeds that were last exposed to far-red light (right).

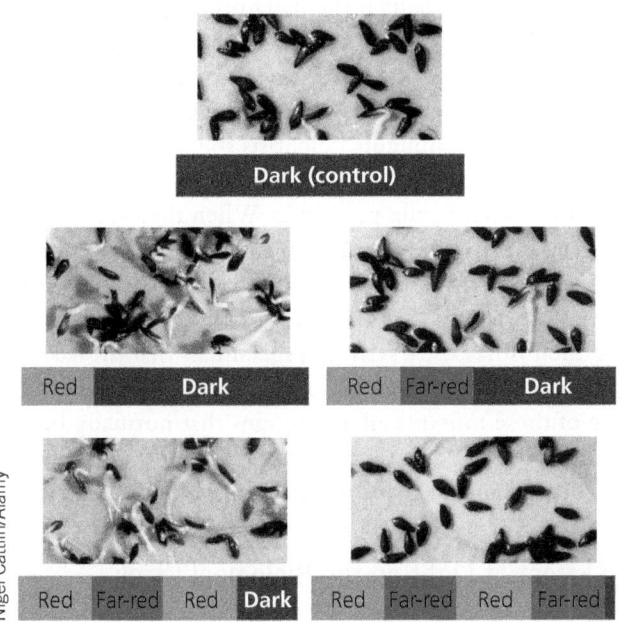

Conclusion Red light stimulates germination, and far-red light inhibits germination. The final light exposure is the determining factor. The effects of red and far-red light are reversible.

Source: Based on H. Borthwick et al., A reversible photoreaction controlling seed germination, *Proceedings of the National Academy of Sciences, USA* 38:662–666 (1952). © Jane B Reece.

WHAT IF? *Phytochrome responds faster to red light than to far-red. If the seeds had been placed in white light instead of the dark after their red and far-red light treatments, would the results have been different?*

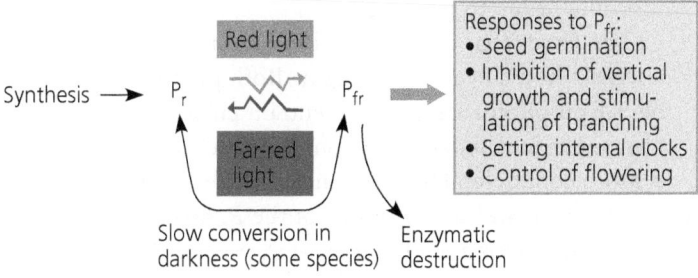

▲ **Figure 39.17 Phytochrome: a molecular switching mechanism.** Absorption of red light causes the P_r to change to the P_{fr}. Far-red light reverses this conversion. In most cases, it is the P_{fr} form of the pigment that switches on physiological and developmental responses in the plant.

How does phytochrome switching explain light-induced germination in nature? Plants synthesize phytochrome as P_r, and if seeds are kept in the dark, the pigment remains almost entirely in the P_r form, inhibiting germination (see Figure 39.17). Sunlight contains both red light and far-red light, but the conversion to P_{fr} is faster than the conversion to P_r. Therefore, the ratio of P_{fr} to P_r increases in the sunlight. When seeds are exposed to adequate sunlight, the production and accumulation of P_{fr} will trigger their germination.

Phytochromes and Shade Avoidance

The phytochrome system also provides the plant with information about the *quality* of light. Because sunlight includes both red and far-red radiation, during the day the $P_r \leftrightarrow P_{fr}$ interconversion reaches a dynamic equilibrium, with the ratio of the two phytochrome forms indicating the relative amounts of red and far-red light. This sensing mechanism enables plants to adapt to changes in light conditions. Consider, for example, the "shade avoidance" response of a tree that requires relatively high light intensity. If other trees in a forest shade this tree, the phytochrome ratio shifts in favour of P_r because the forest canopy screens out more red light than far-red light. This is because the chlorophyll pigments in the leaves of the canopy absorb red light and allow far-red light to pass. The shift in the ratio of red to far-red light induces the tree to allocate more of its resources to growing taller. In contrast, direct sunlight increases the proportion of P_{fr}, which stimulates branching and inhibits vertical growth.

In addition to helping plants detect light, phytochrome helps a plant keep track of the passage of days and seasons. To understand phytochrome's role in these timekeeping processes, we must first examine the nature of the plant's internal clock.

Biological Clocks and Circadian Rhythms

Many plant processes, such as transpiration and the synthesis of certain enzymes, undergo a daily oscillation. Some of these cyclic variations are responses to the changes in light levels, temperature, and relative humidity that accompany the 24-hour cycle of day and night. We can control these external factors by growing plants in growth chambers under rigidly maintained conditions of light, temperature, and humidity. But even under artificially constant conditions, many physiological processes in plants, such as the opening and closing of stomata and the production of photosynthetic enzymes, continue to oscillate with a frequency of about 24 hours. For example, many legumes lower their leaves in the evening and raise them in the morning (Figure 39.18). A bean plant continues these "sleep movements" even if kept in constant light or constant darkness;

Noon   10:00 PM

▲ **Figure 39.18 Sleep movements of a bean plant (*Phaseolus vulgaris*).** The movements are caused by reversible changes in the turgor pressure of cells on opposing sides of the pulvini, motor organs of the leaf.

the leaves are not simply responding to sunrise and sunset. Such cycles, with a frequency of about 24 hours and not directly controlled by any known environmental variable, are called **circadian rhythms** (from the Latin *circa*, approximately, and *dies*, day).

Recent research supports the idea that the molecular "gears" of the circadian clock really are internal and not a daily response to some subtle but pervasive environmental cycle, such as geomagnetism or cosmic radiation. Organisms, including plants and humans, continue their rhythms even when placed in deep mine shafts or when orbited in satellites, conditions that alter these subtle geophysical periodicities. However, daily signals from the environment can entrain (set) the circadian clock to a period of precisely 24 hours.

If an organism is kept in a constant environment, its circadian rhythms deviate from a 24-hour period (a period is the duration of one cycle). These free-running periods, as they are called, vary from about 21 to 27 hours, depending on the particular rhythmic response. The sleep movements of bean plants, for instance, have a period of 26 hours when the plants are kept in the free-running condition of constant darkness. Deviation of the free-running period from exactly 24 hours does not mean that biological clocks drift erratically. Free-running clocks are still keeping perfect time, but they are not synchronized with the outside world. To understand the mechanisms underlying circadian rhythms, we must distinguish between the clock and the rhythmic processes it controls. For example, the leaves of the bean plant in Figure 39.18 are the clock's "hands" but are not the essence of the clock itself. If bean leaves are restrained for several hours and then released, they will reestablish the position appropriate for the time of day. We can interfere with a biological rhythm, but the underlying clockwork continues to tick.

At the heart of the molecular mechanisms underlying circadian rhythms are oscillations in the transcription of certain genes. The monitoring of *Arabidopsis* over

a 24-hour cycle revealed that approximately 5% of its mRNAs undergo a circadian rhythm in synthesis. Some of these mRNAs are more abundant at dawn, others at dusk, and some in the middle of the day. Mathematical models propose that the 24-hour period arises from negative-feedback loops involving the transcription of a few central "clock genes." Some clock genes may encode transcription factors that inhibit, after a time delay, the transcription of the gene that encodes the transcription factor itself. Such negative-feedback loops, together with a time delay, are enough to produce oscillations.

Researchers have recently used a novel technique to identify clock mutants of *Arabidopsis*. One prominent circadian rhythm in plants is the daily production of certain photosynthesis-related proteins. Molecular biologists traced the source of this rhythm to the promoter that initiates the transcription of the genes for these photosynthesis proteins. To identify clock mutants, scientists spliced the gene for an enzyme responsible for the bioluminescence of fireflies, called luciferase, to the promoter. When the biological clock turned on the promoter in the *Arabidopsis* genome, it also turned on the production of luciferase. The plants began to glow with a circadian periodicity. Clock mutants were then isolated by selecting specimens that glowed for a longer or shorter time than normal. The genes altered in some of these mutants affect proteins that normally bind photoreceptors. Perhaps these particular mutations disrupt a light-dependent mechanism that sets the biological clock.

The Effect of Light on the Biological Clock

As we have discussed, the free-running period of the circadian rhythm of bean leaf movements is 26 hours. Consider a bean plant placed at dawn in a dark cabinet for 72 hours: Its leaves would not rise again until 2 hours after natural dawn on the second day, 4 hours after natural dawn on the third day, and so on. Shut off from environmental cues, the plant becomes desynchronized. Desynchronization happens to humans when we fly across several time zones; when we reach our destination, the clocks on the wall are not synchronized with our internal clocks. Most organisms are probably prone to jet lag.

The factor that entrains the biological clock to precisely 24 hours every day is light. Both phytochromes and blue-light photoreceptors can entrain circadian rhythms in plants, but our understanding of how phytochromes do this is more complete. The mechanism involves turning cellular responses on and off by means of the $P_r \leftrightarrow P_{fr}$ switch.

Consider again the photoreversible system in Figure 39.17. In darkness, the phytochrome ratio shifts gradually in favour of the P_r form, partly as a result of turnover in the overall phytochrome pool. The pigment is synthesized in the P_r form, and enzymes destroy more P_{fr} than P_r. In some

 UNIT SIX Plant Form and Function

plant species, P_{fr} present at sundown slowly converts to P_r. In darkness, there is no means for the P_r to be reconverted to P_{fr}, but upon illumination, the P_{fr} level suddenly increases again as P_r is rapidly converted. This increase in P_{fr} each day at dawn resets the biological clock: Bean leaves reach their most extreme night position 16 hours after dawn.

In nature, interactions between phytochrome and the biological clock enable plants to measure the passage of night and day. The relative lengths of night and day, however, change over the course of the year (except at the equator). Plants use this change to adjust activities in synchrony with the seasons.

Photoperiodism and Responses to Seasons

Imagine the consequences if a plant produced flowers when pollinators were not present or if a deciduous tree produced leaves in the middle of winter. Seasonal events are of critical importance in the life cycles of most plants. Seed germination, flowering, and the onset and breaking of bud dormancy are all stages that usually occur at specific times of the year. The environmental stimulus that plants use most often to detect the time of year is the photoperiod, the relative lengths of night and day. A physiological response to photoperiod, such as flowering, is called **photoperiodism**.

Photoperiodism and Control of Flowering

An early clue to how plants detect seasons came from a mutant variety of tobacco, Maryland Mammoth, which grew tall but failed to flower during summer. It finally bloomed in a greenhouse in December. After trying to induce earlier flowering by varying temperature, moisture, and mineral nutrition, researchers learned that the shortening days of winter stimulated this variety to flower. If the plants were kept in light-tight boxes so that lamps could manipulate "day" and "night," flowering occurred only if the day length were 14 hours or shorter. It did not flower during summer because, at Maryland's latitude, the summer days were too long.

The researchers called Maryland Mammoth a **short-day plant** because it apparently required a light period *shorter* than a critical length to flower. Chrysanthemums, poinsettias, and some soybean varieties are also short-day plants, which generally flower in late summer, fall, or winter. Another group of plants flower only when the light period is *longer* than a certain number of hours. These **long-day plants** generally flower in late spring or early summer. Spinach, for example, flowers when days are 14 hours or longer. Radishes, lettuce, irises, and many cereal varieties are also long-day plants. **Day-neutral plants**, such as tomatoes, rice, and dandelions, are unaffected by photoperiod and flower when they reach a certain stage of maturity, regardless of day length.

Critical Night Length In the 1940s, researchers learned that flowering and other responses to photoperiod are actually controlled by night length, not day length. Many of these scientists worked with cocklebur (*Xanthium strumarium*), a short-day plant that flowers only when days are 16 hours or shorter (and nights are at least 8 hours long). These researchers found that if the light portion of the photoperiod is broken by a brief exposure to darkness, flowering proceeds. However, if the dark part of the photoperiod is interrupted by even a few minutes of dim light, cocklebur will not flower, and this turned out to be true for other short-day plants as well (Figure 39.19a). Cocklebur is unresponsive to day length, but it requires at least 8 hours of continuous darkness to flower. Short-day plants are really long-night plants, but the older term is embedded firmly in the lexicon of plant physiology. Similarly, long-day plants are actually short-night plants. A long-day plant grown on photoperiods of long nights that would not normally induce flowering will flower if the period of continuous darkness is interrupted by a few minutes of light (Figure 39.19b). Notice that we distinguish long-day from short-day plants *not* by an absolute night length but by whether the critical night length sets a maximum (long-day plants) or minimum (short-day plants) number of hours of darkness required for flowering. In both cases, the actual number of hours in the critical night length is specific to each species of plant.

Red light is the most effective colour in interrupting the nighttime portion of the photoperiod. Action spectra and photoreversibility experiments show that phytochrome is the pigment that detects the red light (Figure 39.20). For example, if a flash of red (R) light during the dark period is followed by a flash of far-red (FR) light, then the plant detects no interruption of night length. As in the case of phytochrome-mediated seed germination, red/far-red photoreversibility occurs.

Plants detect night length very precisely; some short-day plants will not flower if night is even 1 minute shorter than the critical length. Some plant species always flower on the same day each year. It appears that plants use their biological clock, entrained by night length with the help of phytochrome, to tell the season of the year. The floriculture (flower-growing) industry applies this knowledge to produce flowers out of season. Chrysanthemums, for instance, are short-day plants that normally bloom in fall, but their blooming can be stalled until Mother's Day in May by punctuating each long night with a flash of light, thus turning one long night into two short nights.

Some plants bloom after a single exposure to the photoperiod required for flowering. Other species need several

(a) **Short-day (long-night) plant.** Flowers when night exceeds a critical dark period. A flash of light interrupting the dark period prevents flowering.

Light   Flash of light   Darkness

Critical dark period

(b) **Long-day (short-night) plant.** Flowers only if the night is shorter than a critical dark period. A brief flash of light artificially interrupts a long dark period, thereby inducing flowering.

Flash of light

▲ **Figure 39.19 Photoperiodic control of flowering.**

24 hours

R

R FR

R FR R

R FR R FR

Critical dark period

Short-day (long-night) plant   Long-day (short-night) plant

▲ **Figure 39.20 Reversible effects of red and far-red light on photoperiodic response.** A flash of red (R) light shortens the dark period. A subsequent flash of far-red (FR) light cancels the red flash's effect.

? *How would a single flash of full-spectrum light, given in the middle of the dark period, affect each plant?*

successive days of the appropriate photoperiod. Still others respond to a photoperiod only if they have been previously exposed to some other environmental stimulus, such as a period of cold. Winter wheat, for example, will not

flower unless it has been exposed to several weeks of temperatures below 10°C. The use of pretreatment with cold to induce flowering is called **vernalization** (from the Latin for "spring"). Several weeks after winter wheat is vernalized, a photoperiod with long days (short nights) induces flowering.

A Flowering Hormone?

Although flowers form from apical or axillary bud meristems, it is leaves that detect changes in photoperiod and produce signalling molecules that cue buds to develop as flowers. In many short-day and long-day plants, exposing just one leaf to the appropriate photoperiod is enough to induce flowering. Indeed, as long as one leaf is left on the plant, photo period is detected and floral buds are induced. If all leaves are removed, the plant is insensitive to photoperiod.

Classic experiments revealed that the floral stimulus could move across a graft from an induced plant to a noninduced plant and trigger flowering in the latter. Moreover, the flowering stimulus appears to be the same for short-day and long-day plants, despite the different photoperiodic conditions required for leaves to send this signal (Figure 39.21). The hypothetical signalling molecule for flowering, called **florigen**, remained unidentified for over 70 years as scientists focused on small hormone-like molecules. However, as discussed in Chapter 36, large macromolecules, such as mRNA and proteins, can move by the

Graft

Short-day plant   Long-day plant grafted to short-day plant   Long-day plant

▲ **Figure 39.21 Experimental evidence for a flowering hormone.** If grown individually under short-day conditions, a short-day plant will flower and a long-day plant will not. However, both will flower if grafted together and exposed to short days. This result indicates that a flower-inducing substance (florigen) is transmitted across grafts and induces flowering in both short-day and long-day plants.

WHAT IF? *If flowering were inhibited in both parts of the grafted plants, what would you conclude?*

symplastic route via plasmodesmata (see Figure 36.5) and regulate plant development. It now appears that florigen is a macromolecule. A gene called *FLOWERING LOCUS T* (*FT*) is activated in leaf cells during conditions favouring flowering, and the FT protein travels through the symplasm to the shoot apical meristem and initiates flowering.

Whatever combination of environmental cues (such as photoperiod or vernalization) and internal signalling molecules (such as the FT protein) is necessary for flowering, the outcome is the transition of a bud's meristem from a vegetative to a flowering state. This transition requires changes in the expression of genes that regulate pattern formation. Meristem identity genes that induce the bud to form a flower instead of a vegetative shoot must be switched on. Then the organ identity genes that specify the spatial organization of the floral organs—sepals, petals, stamens, and carpels—are activated in the correct regions of the meristem (see Figure 35.35).

CONCEPT CHECK 39.3

1. If an enzyme in field-grown soybean leaves is most active at noon and least active at midnight, is its activity under circadian regulation?

2. A guard absentmindedly turns on the lights in a greenhouse one night, but the plants still flower on schedule. Suggest two reasons why they were not affected by the interruption of darkness.

3. **WHAT IF?** If a plant flowers in a controlled chamber with a daily cycle of 10 hours of light and 14 hours of darkness, is it a short-day plant? Explain.

4. **MAKE CONNECTIONS** Plants detect the quality of their light environment by using blue-light photoreceptors and red-light-absorbing phytochromes. After reviewing Figure 10.10, suggest a reason why plants are so sensitive to these colours of light.

For suggested answers, see Appendix A.

CONCEPT 39.4

Plants respond to a wide variety of stimuli other than light

EVOLUTION Plants can neither migrate to a watering hole when water is scarce nor seek shelter from wind. A seed landing upside down in the soil cannot manoeuvre itself into an upright position. Plants are immobile, but mechanisms have evolved by natural selection that enable them to adjust to a wide range of environmental circumstances by developmental or physiological means. Light is so important in the life of a plant that we devoted the entire previous section to a plant's reception of and response to this one environmental factor. In this section, we examine responses to some of the other environmental stimuli that a plant commonly encounters.

Gravity

Because plants are solar-powered organisms, it is not surprising that mechanisms for growing toward sunlight have evolved. But what environmental cue does the shoot of a young seedling use to grow upward when it is completely underground and there is no light for it to detect? Similarly, what environmental factor prompts the young root to grow downward? The answer to both questions is gravity.

Place a plant on its side, and it adjusts its growth so that the shoot bends upward and the root curves downward. In their responses to gravity, or **gravitropism**, roots display positive gravitropism (Figure 39.22a) and shoots exhibit negative gravitropism. Gravitropism occurs as soon as a seed germinates, ensuring that the root grows into the soil and the shoot grows toward sunlight, regardless of how the seed is oriented when it lands.

Plants may detect gravity by the settling of **statoliths**, dense cytoplasmic components that settle under the influence of gravity to the lower portions of the cell. The statoliths of vascular plants are specialized plastids containing dense starch grains (Figure 39.22b). In roots, statoliths are located in certain cells of the root cap. According to one hypothesis, the aggregation of statoliths at the low points of these cells triggers a redistribution of calcium, which causes lateral transport of auxin within the root. The calcium and auxin accumulate on the lower side of the root's zone of elongation. At high concentration, auxin inhibits cell elongation, an effect that slows

Michael L. Evans

(a) Over the course of hours, a horizontally oriented primary root of maize bends gravitropically until its growing tip becomes vertically oriented (LMs).

(b) Within minutes after the root is placed horizontally, plastids called statoliths begin settling to the lowest sides of root cap cells. This settling may be the gravity-sensing mechanism that leads to redistribution of auxin and differing rates of elongation by cells on opposite sides of the root (LMs).

▲ Figure 39.22 **Positive gravitropism in roots: the statolith hypothesis.**

growth on the root's lower side. The more rapid elongation of cells on the upper side causes the root to curve as it grows. This tropism continues until the root grows straight down.

Falling statoliths, however, may not be necessary for gravitropism. For example, there are mutants of *Arabidopsis* and tobacco that lack statoliths but are still capable of gravitropism, though the response is slower than in wild-type plants. It could be that the entire cell helps the root sense gravity by mechanically pulling on proteins that tether the protoplast to the cell wall, stretching the proteins on the "up" side and compressing the proteins on the "down" side of the root cells. Dense organelles, in addition to starch granules, may also contribute by distorting the cytoskeleton as they are pulled by gravity. Statoliths, because of their density, may enhance gravitational sensing by a mechanism that simply works more slowly in their absence.

Mechanical Stimuli

Trees in windy environments usually have a shorter, stockier trunk than a tree of the same species growing in a more sheltered location. The advantage of this stunted morphology is that it enables the plant to hold its ground against strong gusts of wind. The term **thigmomorphogenesis** (from the Greek *thigma*, touch) refers to the changes in form that result from mechanical perturbation. Plants are very sensitive to mechanical stress: Even the act of measuring the length of a leaf with a ruler alters its subsequent growth. Rubbing the stems of a young plant a couple of times daily results in plants that are shorter than controls (Figure 39.23).

Some plant species have become, over the course of their evolution, "touch specialists." Acute responsiveness to mechanical stimuli is an integral part of these plants' "life strategies." Most vines and other climbing plants have

Elsevier Science Ltd.

▲ **Figure 39.23 Altering gene expression by touch in *Arabidopsis*.** The shorter plant on the left was rubbed twice a day. The untouched plant (right) grew much taller.

tendrils that coil rapidly around supports (see Figure 35.7). These grasping organs usually grow straight until they touch something; the contact stimulates a coiling response caused by differential growth of cells on opposite sides of the tendril. This directional growth in response to touch is called **thigmotropism**, and it allows the vine to take advantage of whatever mechanical supports it comes across as it climbs upward toward a forest canopy.

Other examples of touch specialists are plants that undergo rapid leaf movements in response to mechanical stimulation. For example, when the compound leaf of the sensitive plant *Mimosa pudica* is touched, it collapses and its leaflets fold together (Figure 39.24). This response, which takes only a second or two, results from a rapid loss of turgor in cells within pulvini, specialized motor organs located at the joints of the leaf. The motor cells suddenly become flaccid after stimulation because they lose potassium ions, causing water to leave the cells by osmosis. It takes about 10 minutes for the cells to regain their turgor and restore the "unstimulated" form of the leaf. The function of the sensitive plant's behaviour invites speculation. Perhaps by folding its leaves and reducing its surface area when jostled by strong winds, the plant conserves water. Or perhaps because the collapse of the leaves exposes thorns on the stem, the rapid response of the sensitive plant discourages herbivores.

A remarkable feature of rapid leaf movements is the mode of transmission of the stimulus through the plant. If one leaflet on a sensitive plant is touched, first that leaflet responds, then the adjacent leaflet responds, and so on, until all the leaflet pairs have folded together. From the point of stimulation, the signal that produces this response travels at a speed of about 1 cm/sec. An electrical impulse travelling at the same rate can be detected when electrodes are attached to the leaf. These impulses, called **action potentials**, resemble nerve impulses in animals, though the action potentials of plants are thousands of times slower. Action potentials have been discovered in many species of algae and plants and may be used as a form of internal communication. For example, in the Venus flytrap (*Dionaea muscipula*), action potentials are transmitted from sensory hairs in the trap to the cells that respond by closing the trap (see Figure 37.15). In the case of *Mimosa pudica*, more violent stimuli, such as touching a leaf with a hot needle, causes *all* the leaves and leaflets on a plant to droop, but this whole-plant response involves the spread of signalling molecules released from the injured area to other parts of the shoot.

Environmental Stresses

Certain factors in the environment may change severely enough to have a potentially adverse effect on a plant's survival, growth, and reproduction. Environmental stresses, such as flooding, drought, or extreme temperatures, can have a devastating impact on crop yields in agriculture. In natural

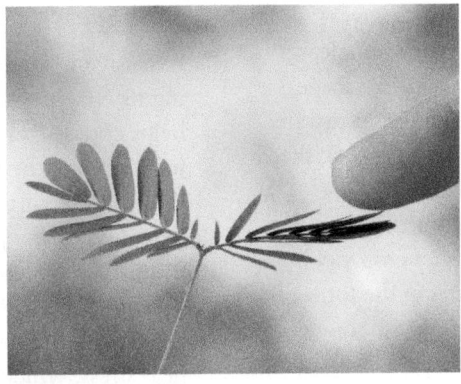

(a) Unstimulated state (leaflets spread apart)   **(b) Stimulated state (leaflets folded)**

Martin Shields/Science Source

Leaflets after stimulation

Pulvinus (motor organ)

Side of pulvinus with flaccid cells

Side of pulvinus with turgid cells

Vein

0.5 μm

John Wiley & Sons, Inc.

(c) Cross section of a leaflet pair in the stimulated state (LM). The pulvinus (motor organ) becomes curved when motor cells on one side of the pulvinus lose water and become flaccid while cells on the opposite side retain their turgor.

▲ Figure 39.24 **Rapid turgor movements by the sensitive plant (*Mimosa pudica*).**

ecosystems, plants that cannot tolerate an environmental stress will either succumb or be outcompeted by other plants, and they will become locally extinct. Thus, environmental stresses are an important factor in determining the geographic ranges of plants. Here we will consider some of the more common **abiotic** (non-living) stresses that plants encounter. In the last section of this chapter, we will examine the defensive responses of plants to common **biotic** (living) stresses, such as herbivores and pathogens.

Flooding

Too much water is also a problem for a plant. An overwatered houseplant may suffocate because the soil lacks the air spaces that provide oxygen for cellular respiration in the roots. Some plants are structurally adapted to very wet habitats. For example, the submerged roots of mangroves, which inhabit coastal

marshes, are continuous with aerial roots exposed to oxygen (see Figure 35.4). But how do less specialized plants cope with oxygen deprivation in waterlogged soils? Oxygen deprivation stimulates the production of ethylene, which causes some cells in the root cortex to undergo apoptosis. The destruction of these cells creates air tubes that function as "snorkels," providing oxygen to the submerged roots (Figure 39.25).

Drought

On a sunny, dry day, a plant may wilt because its water loss by transpiration exceeds the ability of the root system to absorb water from the soil. Prolonged drought, of course, will kill a plant, but plants have control systems that enable them to cope with less extreme water deficits. Chronic drought stress associated with climate change, however, is a new challenge for plants living in affected areas as discussed throughout this unit.

Many of a plant's responses to water deficit help the plant conserve water by reducing the rate of transpiration. Water deficit in a leaf causes guard cells to lose turgor, a simple control mechanism that slows transpiration by closing stomata (see Figure 36.13). Water deficit also stimulates increased synthesis and release of abscisic acid in the leaf; this hormone helps keep

Vascular cylinder

Air tubes

Epidermis

100 μm

100 μm

Malcolm C. Drew

(a) Control root (aerated).   **(b) Experimental root (nonaerated).**

▲ Figure 39.25 **A developmental response of maize roots to flooding and oxygen deprivation.** **(a)** A cross section of a control root grown in an aerated hydroponic medium. **(b)** A root grown in a nonaerated hydroponic medium. Ethylene-stimulated apoptosis (programmed cell death) creates the air tubes (SEMs).

stomata closed by acting on guard cell membranes. Leaves respond to water deficit in several other ways. For example, when the leaves of grasses wilt, they roll into a tubelike shape that reduces transpiration by exposing less leaf surface to dry air and wind. Other plants, such as ocotillo (see Figure 36.14), shed their leaves in response to seasonal drought. Although these leaf responses conserve water, they also reduce photosynthesis, which is one reason why a drought diminishes crop yield. Plants can even take advantage of early warnings in the form of chemical signals from wilting neighbours and prime themselves to respond more readily and intensely to impending drought stress (see the Scientific Skills Exercise).

Heat Stress

Excessive heat may harm or even kill a plant by denaturing its enzymes and disrupting its metabolism. Transpiration helps cool leaves by evaporative cooling. On a warm day, for example, the temperature of a leaf may be 3–10°C below the ambient air temperature. Hot, dry weather also tends to dehydrate many plants; the closing of stomata in response to this stress conserves water but then sacrifices evaporative cooling. This dilemma is one reason why very hot, dry days take a toll on most plants. As discussed throughout this unit, heat stress, which limits xylem sap flow and nutrient availability, can significantly reduce growth and seed development.

SCIENTIFIC SKILLS EXERCISE

Interpreting Experimental Results from a Bar Graph

Do Drought-Stressed Plants Communicate Their Condition to Their Neighbours? Researchers wanted to learn if plants can communicate drought-induced stress to neighbouring plants and, if so, whether they use above-ground or below-ground signals. In this exercise, you will interpret a bar graph concerning widths of stomatal openings to investigate whether drought-induced stress can be communicated from plant to plant.

How the Experiment Was Done Eleven potted pea plants (*Pisum sativum*) were placed equidistantly in a row. The root systems of plants 6–11 were connected to those of their immediate neighbours by tubes, which allowed chemicals to move from the roots of one plant to the roots of the next plant without moving through the soil. The root systems of plants 1–6 were not connected. Osmotic shock was inflicted on plant 6 using a highly concentrated solution of mannitol, a natural sugar commonly used to mimic drought stress in vascular plants.

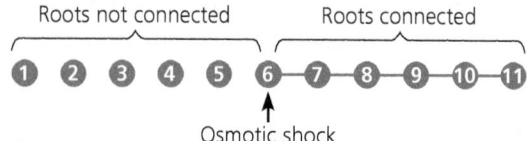

Fifteen minutes following the osmotic shock to plant 6, researchers measured the width of stomatal openings in leaves from all the plants. A control experiment was also done in which water was added to plant 6 instead of mannitol.

Data from the Experiment

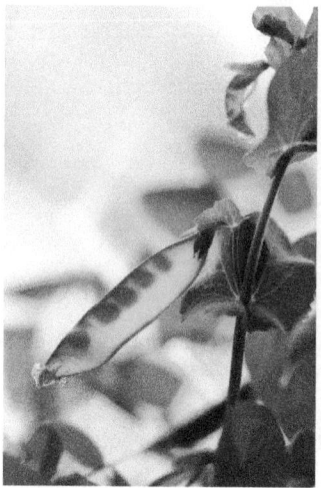

► Pea plant (*Pisum sativum*)

sarsmis/Fotolia

Interpret the Data

1. How do the widths of the stomatal openings of plants 6–8 and plants 9 and 10 compare with those of the other plants in the experiment? What does this indicate about the state of plants 6–8 and 9 and 10? (For information about reading graphs, see the Scientific Skills Review in Appendix E and in the Study Area in MasteringBiology.)

2. Do the data support the idea that plants can communicate their drought-stressed condition to their neighbours? If so, do the data indicate that the communication is via the shoot system or the root system? Make specific reference to the data in answering both questions.

3. Why was it necessary to make sure that chemicals could not move through the soil from one plant to the next?

4. When the experiment was run for 1 hour rather than 15 minutes, the results were about the same except that the stomatal openings of plants 9–11 were comparable to those of plants 6–8. Suggest a reason why.

5. Why was water added to plant 6 instead of mannitol in the control experiment? What do the results of the control experiment indicate?

Data from O. Falik et al., Rumor has it ... : Relay communication of stress cues in plants, *PLoS ONE* 6(11):e23625 (2011). © Jane B Reece.

Making a difficult situation even worse, high temperatures and drought often occur simultaneously in the changing climates of many regions with compounding effects.

Most plants have a backup response that enables them to survive heat stress. Above a certain temperature—about 40°C for most plants in temperate regions—plant cells begin synthesizing **heat-shock proteins**, which help protect other proteins from heat stress. This response also occurs in heat-stressed animals and microorganisms. Some heat-shock proteins are chaperone proteins (chaperonins), which function in unstressed cells as temporary scaffolds that help other proteins fold into their functional shapes (see Chapter 5). In their roles as heat-shock proteins, perhaps these molecules bind to other proteins and help prevent their denaturation.

Salt Stress

An excess of sodium chloride or other salts in the soil threatens plants for two reasons. First, by lowering the water potential of the soil solution, salt can cause a water deficit in plants even though the soil has plenty of water. As the water potential of the soil solution becomes more negative, the water potential gradient from soil to roots is lowered, thereby reducing water uptake (see Chapter 36). Another problem with saline soil is that sodium and certain other ions are toxic to plants when their concentrations are so high that they overwhelm the selective permeability capabilities of the root cell membranes. Many plants can respond to moderate soil salinity by producing solutes that are well tolerated at high concentrations: These mostly organic compounds keep the water potential of cells more negative than that of the soil solution without admitting toxic quantities of salt. However, most plants cannot survive salt stress for long. The exceptions are halophytes, salt-tolerant plants with adaptations such as salt glands that pump salts out across the leaf epidermis.

Cold Stress

One problem plants face when the temperature of the environment falls is a change in the fluidity of cell membranes. Recall from Chapter 7 that a biological membrane is a fluid mosaic, with proteins and lipids moving laterally in the plane of the membrane. When a membrane cools below a critical point, it loses its fluidity as the lipids become locked into crystalline structures. This alters solute transport across the membrane and also adversely affects the functions of membrane proteins. Plants respond to cold stress by altering the lipid composition of their membranes. For example, membrane lipids increase in their proportion of unsaturated fatty acids, which have shapes that help keep membranes fluid at lower temperatures by impeding crystal formation (see Figure 7.5a). Such membrane modification requires from several hours to days, which is one reason why unseasonably cold temperatures are generally more stressful to plants than the more gradual seasonal drop in air temperature.

Freezing is another type of cold stress. At subfreezing temperatures, ice forms in the cell walls and intercellular spaces of most plants. The cytosol generally does not freeze at the cooling rates encountered in nature because it contains more solutes than the very dilute solution found in the cell wall, and solutes lower the freezing point of a solution. The reduction in liquid water in the cell wall caused by ice formation lowers the extracellular water potential, causing water to leave the cytoplasm. The resulting increase in the concentration of ions in the cytoplasm is harmful and can lead to cell death. Whether the cell survives depends largely on how well it resists dehydration. In regions with cold winters, native plants are adapted to cope with freezing stress. For example, before the onset of winter, the cells of many frost-tolerant species increase cytoplasmic levels of specific solutes, such as sugars, that are well tolerated at high concentrations and that help reduce the loss of water from the cell during extracellular freezing. The unsaturation of membrane lipids also increases, thereby maintaining proper levels of membrane fluidity.

EVOLUTION Many organisms, including certain vertebrates, fungi, bacteria, and many species of plants, have special proteins that hinder ice crystals from growing, helping the organism escape freezing damage. First described in Arctic fish in the 1950s, these *antifreeze proteins* permit survival at temperatures below 0°C. Antifreeze proteins bind to small ice crystals and inhibit their growth or, in the case of plants, prevent the crystallization of ice. The five major classes of antifreeze proteins differ markedly in their amino acid sequences but have a similar three-dimensional structure, suggesting convergent evolution. Surprisingly, antifreeze proteins from winter rye are homologous to antifungal proteins called PR proteins that you'll learn about later in the chapter, but they are produced in response to cold temperatures and shorter days, not fungal pathogens. Progress is being made in increasing the freezing tolerance of crop plants by genetically engineering antifreeze protein genes into their genomes.

CONCEPT CHECK 39.4

1. Thermal images are photographs of the heat emitted by an object. Researchers have used thermal imaging of plants to isolate mutants that overproduce abscisic acid. Suggest a reason why these mutants are warmer than wild-type plants under conditions that are normally nonstressful.

2. A greenhouse worker finds that potted chrysanthemums nearest to the aisles are often shorter than those in the middle of the bench. Explain this "edge effect," a common problem in horticulture.

3. **WHAT IF?** If you removed the root cap from a root, would the root still respond to gravity? Explain.

For suggested answers, see Appendix A.

CONCEPT 39.5

Plants respond to attacks by herbivores and pathogens

Through natural selection, plants have evolved many types of interactions with other species in their communities. Some interspecific interactions are mutually beneficial, such as the associations of plants with mycorrhizal fungi (see Figure 37.13) or with pollinators (see Figure 38.5). Most of a plant's interactions with other organisms, however, do not benefit the plant. As primary producers, plants are at the base of most food webs and are subject to attack by a wide range of plant-eating (herbivorous) animals. A plant is also subject to infection by diverse viruses, bacteria, and fungi that can damage tissues or even kill the plant. Plants counter these threats with defence systems that deter herbivory and prevent infection or combat pathogens that infect the plant.

Defences against Herbivores

Herbivory—animals eating plants—is a stress that plants face in any ecosystem. Plants prevent excessive herbivory by using both physical defences, such as thorns and trichomes, and chemical defences, such as the production of distasteful or toxic compounds. For example, some plants produce an unusual amino acid called *canavanine*, named for one of its sources, the jackbean (*Canavalia ensiformis*). Canavanine resembles arginine, one of the 20 amino acids that organisms incorporate into their proteins. If an insect eats a plant containing canavanine, the molecule is incorporated into the insect's proteins in place of arginine. Because canavanine is different enough from arginine to adversely affect the shape and hence the function of the proteins, the insect dies.

Some plants even "recruit" predatory animals that help defend the plant against specific herbivores. Consider the insects called parasitoid wasps, which inject their eggs into caterpillars feeding on plants. The eggs hatch within the caterpillars, and the larvae eat through their organic containers from the inside out. The plant, which benefits from the destruction of the herbivorous caterpillars, has an active role in this drama. A leaf damaged by caterpillars releases volatile compounds that attract parasitoid wasps. The stimulus for this response is a combination of physical damage to the leaf caused by the chewing caterpillar and a specific compound in the caterpillar's saliva (**Figure 39.26**).

The volatile molecules a plant releases in response to herbivore damage can also function as an early warning system for nearby plants of the same species. For example, lima bean plants infested with spider mites release a cocktail

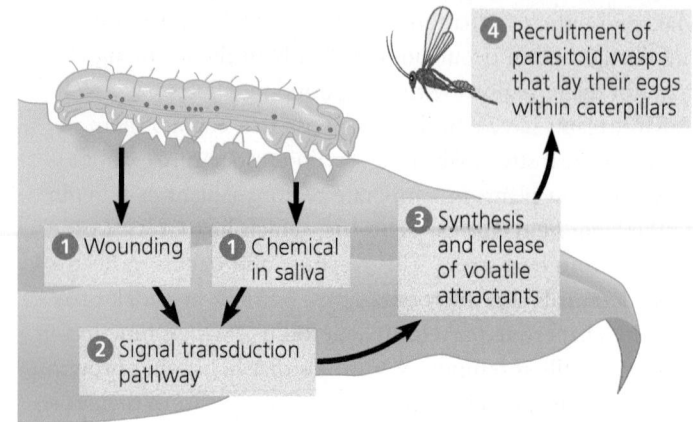

▲ Figure 39.26 **A maize leaf "recruiting" a parasitoid wasp as a defensive response to an armyworm caterpillar, an herbivore.**

of volatile chemicals, including methyljasmonic acid, that signals "news" of the attack to neighbouring, noninfested lima bean plants. In response to these volatile compounds, the neighbours instigate biochemical changes that make themselves less susceptible, including the release of volatile chemicals that attract another predatory mite species that feeds on spider mites. Researchers have even transgenically engineered *Arabidopsis* plants to produce two volatile chemicals that normally are not made by *Arabidopsis* but which have been found to attract carnivorous predatory mites in other plants. The predatory mites become attracted to the genetically modified *Arabidopsis*, a finding that could have implications for the genetic engineering of insect resistance in crop plants.

Defences against Pathogens

A plant's first line of defence against infection is the physical barrier presented by the epidermis and periderm of the plant body (see Figure 35.19). This first defence system, however, is not impenetrable. The mechanical wounding of leaves by herbivores, for example, opens up portals for invasion by pathogens. Even when plant tissues are intact, viruses, bacteria, and the spores and hyphae of fungi can still enter the plant through natural openings in the epidermis, such as stomata. Once the physical lines of defence are breached, a plant's next lines of defence are two types of immune responses.

Immune Responses of Plants

When a pathogen succeeds in invading a host plant, the plant mounts the first of two lines of immune defence, which ultimately results in a chemical attack that isolates the pathogen and prevents its spread from the site of infection. This first line of immune defence, called *PAMP-triggered immunity*, depends on the plant's ability to recognize **pathogen-associated molecular patterns** (**PAMPs**; formerly called elicitors), molecular sequences that are specific to certain pathogens. For example, bacterial flagellin, a major protein found in bacterial flagella, is a PAMP. Many soil bacteria, including some pathogenic varieties, get splashed onto the shoots of plants by raindrops. If these bacteria penetrate the plant, a specific amino-acid sequence within flagellin is perceived by a **Toll-like receptor**, a type of receptor that is also found in invertebrates and vertebrates and that plays a key role in the innate immune system (see Concept 43.1). The innate immune system is an evolutionarily old defence strategy and is the dominant immune system in plants, fungi, insects, and primitive multicellular organisms. Unlike vertebrates, plants do not have an adaptive immune system: Plants neither generate antibody or T cell responses nor possess mobile cells that detect and attack pathogens.

PAMP recognition in plants leads to a chain of signalling events that lead ultimately to the local production of broad spectrum, antimicrobial chemicals called *phytoalexins*, which are compounds having fungicidal and bactericidal properties. The plant cell wall is also toughened to hinder further progress of the pathogen during PAMP-triggered immunity. Similar but even stronger defences are initiated by a second plant immune system, as discussed in the next section.

EVOLUTION Over the course of evolution, plants and pathogens have engaged in an arms race. PAMP-triggered immunity can be overcome by the evolution of pathogens that can evade detection by the plant. The key to these pathogens' success is their ability to deliver **effectors**, pathogen-encoded proteins that cripple the host's innate immune system, directly into the plant cell. For example, several bacterial pathogens deliver effectors inside the plant cell that actively block the perception of flagellin. Thus, these effectors suppress PAMP-mediated immunity and allow the pathogen to redirect the host's metabolism to the pathogen's advantage.

The suppression of PAMP-triggered immunity by pathogen effectors led to the evolution of a second level of the plant immune defence system. Because there are thousands of effectors, this branch of the plant immune system is typically made up of hundreds of disease resistance (R) genes in a plant's genome. Each R protein can be activated by its specific effector, resulting in a suite of strong defence responses called effector-triggered immunity. This second type of immune defence involves signal transduction pathways that lead to the activation of an arsenal of defence responses, including a local defence called the hypersensitive response and a general defence called systemic acquired resistance. Local and systemic responses to pathogens require extensive genetic reprogramming and commitment of cellular resources. Therefore, a plant activates these defences only after detecting an invading pathogen.

The Hypersensitive Response

The **hypersensitive response** refers to the local cell and tissue death that occurs at and near the infection site. In some cases, the hypersensitive response restricts the spread of a pathogen, but in other cases it appears to be merely a consequence of the overall defence response. As indicated in **Figure 39.27**, the hypersensitive response is initiated as part of effector-triggered immunity. The hypersensitive response is part of a complex defence response that involves transcriptional activation of over 10% of the plant's genes that can encode enzymes that hydrolyze components in the cell walls of pathogens. Effector-triggered immunity also stimulates the formation of lignin and the cross-linking of molecules within the plant cell wall, responses that hinder the spread of the pathogen to other parts of the plant. We can see the result of a hypersensitive response as lesions on a leaf, as shown at the upper right in the figure. As "sick" as such a leaf appears, it will still survive, and its defensive response will help protect the rest of the plant.

The initial response of a mountain pine beetle-infected pine tree involves a hypersensitive reaction. By inducing cell death around the initial infection site, the pine tree minimizes the nutritional value of those tissues. In addition, jasmonate signals within the trees trigger the concentration of defensive chemicals at infection sites to increase from non-lethal to lethal levels.

Systemic Acquired Resistance

The hypersensitive response is localized and specific. However, as noted previously, pathogen invasions can also produce signalling molecules that "sound the alarm" of infection to the whole plant. The resulting **systemic acquired resistance** arises from the plant-wide expression of defence genes. It is nonspecific, providing protection against a diversity of pathogens that can last for days. The search for a signalling molecule that moves from the infection site to elicit systemic acquired resistance led to the identification of methylsalicylic acid as the most likely candidate. Methylsalicylic acid is produced around the infection site and carried by the phloem throughout the plant, where it is converted to **salicylic acid** in areas remote from the sites of infection. Salicylic acid activates a signal transduction pathway that poises the defence system to respond rapidly to another infection.

Concurrent to the hypersensitive response described above, pines also mount more a systemic immune response. Such a response involves the production of volatile chemicals to interfere with the beetles' reproduction. Trees are

4 Before they die, infected cells release the signalling molecule methylsalicylic acid.

3 In a hypersensitive response, plant cells produce anti-microbial molecules, seal off infected areas by modifying their walls, and then destroy themselves. This localized response produces lesions and protects other parts of an infected leaf.

2 The identification in step **1** triggers a signal transduction pathway.

1 Effector-mediated immunity is based on the binding of pathogen effector molecules to specific plant resistance (R) proteins.

Signal

3 Hypersensitive response

2 Signal transduction pathway

1

R protein

Pathogen

Effector protein

Hypersensitive response

Cornell University College of Agriculture and Life Sciences

Infected tobacco leaf with lesions

5 The signalling molecule is distributed to the rest of the plant.

6 In cells remote from the infection site, methylsalicylic acid is converted to salicylic acid, which initiates a signal transduction pathway.

7 Systemic acquired resistance is activated: the production of molecules that help protect the cell against a diversity of pathogens for several days.

5

Signal transduction pathway **6**

7 Acquired resistance

Systemic acquired resistance

▲ **Figure 39.27 Defence responses against an avirulent pathogen.** Plants can often prevent the systemic spread of infection by instigating a hypersensitive response. This response helps isolate the pathogen by producing lesions that form "rings of death" around the sites of infection.

initially infected by females who later try and attract mates through pheromones—chemical signals that are released into the environment and have effects on other individuals, usually of the same species. In attempts to prevent further colonization by male beetles, mating, and the rearing of offspring that feed on its tissues increasing disease severity, newly infected pines produce compounds such as resins to bind the females and block their burrows and mono-terpenes to mask the presence or inhibit the actions of the female's pheromones.

Plant disease epidemics, such as the potato blight (see Concept 28.6) that caused the Irish potato famine of the 1840s, can lead to incalculable human misery. Other dis-eases, such as chestnut blight and sudden oak death (see Concept 54.5), can dramatically alter community struc-tures. Another example, the pine beetle epidemic, has both significant ecological and economic impacts. Plant epidem-ics are often the result of infected plants or timber being inadvertently transported around the world. As global com-merce increases, such epidemics will become increasingly common. To prepare for such outbreaks, plant biologists are stockpiling the seeds of wild relatives of crop plants in special storage facilities. Scientists hope that undomesticated relatives may have genes that will be able to curb the next plant epidemic.

CONCEPT CHECK 39.5

1. What are some drawbacks of spraying fields with general-purpose insecticides?

2. Chewing insects mechanically damage plants and lessen the surface area of leaves for photosynthesis. In addition, these insects make plants more vulnerable to pathogen attack. Sug-gest a reason why.

3. Many fungal pathogens get their food by causing plant cells to become leaky, thereby releasing nutrients into the intercellular spaces. Would it benefit the fungus to kill the host plant in a way that results in all the nutrients leaking out?

4. **WHAT IF?** Suppose a scientist finds that a population of plants growing in a breezy location is more prone to herbivory by insects than a population of the same species growing in a sheltered area. Suggest a hypothesis to account for this observation.

For suggested answers, see Appendix A.

39 Chapter Review

SUMMARY OF KEY CONCEPTS

CONCEPT 39.1

Signal transduction pathways link signal reception to response (pp. 889–891)

? *What are two common ways by which signal transduction pathways enhance the activity of specific enzymes?*

CONCEPT 39.2

Plant hormones help coordinate growth, development, and responses to stimuli (pp. 892–901)

- Hormones control plant growth and development by affecting the division, elongation, and differentiation of cells. Some hormones also mediate the responses of plants to environmental stimuli.

Plant Hormone	Major Responses
Auxin	Regulates cell elongation; regulates branching and organ bending
Cytokinins	Stimulate plant cell division; promote later bud growth; slow organ death
Gibberellins	Promote stem elongation; help seeds break dormancy and use stored reserves
Brassinosteroids	Chemically similar to the sex hormones of animals; induce cell elongation and division
Strigolactones	Regulate apical dominance, seed germination, and mycorrhizal associations
Ethylene	Mediates fruit ripening

? *Is there any truth to the old adage, "One bad apple spoils the whole bunch?" Explain.*

CONCEPT 39.3

Responses to light are critical for plant success (pp. 901–907)

- **Blue-light photoreceptors** control hypocotyl elongation, stomatal opening, and phototropism.
- **Phytochromes** act like molecular "on-off" switches. Red light turns phytochrome "on," and far-red light turns it "off."

Phytochrome regulates shade avoidance and the germination of many seed types.

- Phytochrome conversion also provides information about the relative lengths of day and night (photoperiod) and hence the time of year. **Photoperiodism** regulates the time of flowering in many species. **Short-day plants** require a night longer than a critical length to flower. **Long-day plants** need a night length shorter than a critical period to flower.
- Many daily rhythms in plant behaviour are controlled by an internal circadian clock. Free-running circadian cycles are approximately 24 hours long but are entrained to exactly 24 hours by dawn and dusk effects on phytochrome form.

? *Why did plant physiologists propose the existence of a mobile molecule (florigen) that triggers flowering?*

CONCEPT 39.4

Plants respond to a wide variety of stimuli other than light (pp. 907–911)

- **Gravitropism** is the bending of an organ in response to gravity. Roots show positive gravitropism, and stems show negative gravitropism. **Statoliths**, starch-filled plastids, help plant roots to detect gravity.
- Plants are highly sensitive to touch. **Thigmotropism** is a growth response to touch. Rapid leaf movements involve transmission of electrical impulses called action potentials.
- Plants are sensitive to environmental stresses, including drought, flooding, high salinity, and extremes of temperature.

Environmental Stress	Major Response
Drought	ABA production, reducing water loss by closing stomata
Flooding	Production of ethylene, causing formation of air tubes that help roots survive oxygen deprivation
Salt	Avoiding osmotic water loss by producing solutes tolerated at high concentrations
Heat	Synthesis of heat-shock proteins, which reduce protein denaturation at high temperatures
Cold	Adjusting membrane fluidity; avoiding osmotic water loss; producing antifreeze proteins

? *Plants that have acclimated to drought stress are often more resistant to freezing stress as well. Suggest a reason why.*

CONCEPT 39.5

Plants respond to attacks by herbivores and pathogens (pp. 912–914)

- In addition to physical defences such as thorns and trichomes, plants produce distasteful or toxic chemicals, as well as attractants that recruit animals that destroy herbivores.

- The **hypersensitive response** seals off an infection and destroys both pathogen and host cells in the region. **Systemic acquired resistance** is a generalized defence response in organs distant from the infection site.

? *How do chewing insects make plants more susceptible to pathogens?*

TEST YOUR UNDERSTANDING

LEVEL 1: KNOWLEDGE/COMPREHENSION

1. The hormone that helps plants respond to drought is
   a. auxin.
   b. cytokinin.
   c. ethylene.
   d. abscisic acid.

2. Auxin enhances cell elongation in all of these ways *except*
   a. increased uptake of solutes.
   b. gene activation.
   c. acid-induced denaturation of cell wall proteins.
   d. cell wall loosening.

3. Charles and Francis Darwin discovered that
   a. auxin is responsible for phototropic curvature.
   b. light destroys auxin.
   c. light is perceived by the tips of coleoptiles.
   d. red light is most effective in shoot phototropism.

4. How may a plant respond to *severe* heat stress?
   a. by reorienting leaves to increase evaporative cooling
   b. by creating air tubes for ventilation
   c. by increasing the proportion of unsaturated fatty acids in cell membranes, reducing their fluidity
   d. by producing heat-shock proteins, which may protect the plant's proteins from denaturing

LEVEL 2: APPLICATION/ANALYSIS

5. The signalling molecule for flowering might be released earlier than usual in a long-day plant exposed to flashes of
   a. far-red light during the night.
   b. red light during the night.
   c. red light followed by far-red light during the night.
   d. far-red light during the day.

6. If a long-day plant has a critical night length of 9 hours, which 24-hour cycle would prevent flowering?
   a. 16 hours light/8 hours dark
   b. 14 hours light/10 hours dark
   c. 4 hours light/8 hours dark/4 hours light/8 hours dark
   d. 8 hours light/8 hours dark/light flash/8 hours dark

7. A plant mutant that shows normal gravitropic bending but does not store starch in its plastids would require a reevaluation of the role of _____ in gravitropism.
   a. auxin
   b. calcium
   c. statoliths
   d. differential growth

8. **DRAW IT** In the following table, indicate the response to each condition by drawing a straight seedling or one with the triple response.

	Control	Ethylene added	Ethylene synthesis inhibitor
Wild-type			
Ethylene insensitive (*ein*)			
Ethylene overproducing (*eto*)			
Constitutive triple response (*ctr*)			

LEVEL 3: SYNTHESIS/EVALUATION

9. **EVOLUTION CONNECTION**
   As a general rule, light-sensitive germination is more pronounced in small seeds compared with large seeds. Suggest a reason why.

10. **SCIENTIFIC INQUIRY**
    A plant biologist observed a peculiar pattern when a tropical shrub was attacked by caterpillars. After a caterpillar ate a leaf, it would skip over nearby leaves and attack a leaf some distance away. Simply removing a leaf did not deter caterpillars from eating nearby leaves. The biologist suspected that an insect-damaged leaf sent out a chemical that signalled nearby leaves. How could the researcher test this hypothesis?

11. **SCIENCE, TECHNOLOGY, AND SOCIETY**
    Describe how our knowledge about the control systems of plants is being applied to agriculture or horticulture.

12. **WRITE ABOUT A THEME: INTERACTIONS**
    In a short essay (100–150 words), summarize phytochrome's role in altering shoot growth for the enhancement of light capture.

13.
SYNTHESIZE YOUR KNOWLEDGE

This mule deer is grazing on the shoot tips of a shrub. Describe how this event will alter the physiology, biochemistry, structure, and health of the plant, and identify which hormones are involved in making these changes.

Gary Crabbe/Alamy

For selected answers, see Appendix A.

ANIMAL FORM AND FUNCTION

AN INTERVIEW WITH

Suzie Currie

Suzie Currie, originally from Cape Breton, did her Ph.D. at Queen's University, and was later the Charles and Katherine Darwin Research Fellow at Cambridge University. She is currently a Professor at Mount Allison University in New Brunswick. She has received research funding from numerous sources, including NSERC, the New Brunswick Innovation Foundation, and the Canadian Foundation for Innovation.

> " Embrace discovery, embrace the unknown, and don't be discouraged by what you don't know. "

How did you become interested in science?

I think it started when I was quite young because my dad was a biology teacher. I was always very interested in nature, and would start these clubs with my sister and friends when I was little—I now realize those were actually research experiments. I also had a very inspirational high school biology teacher, who really set the stage for what I did afterward in science.

What questions are you trying to answer right now in your research?

The overarching focus of my research is phenotypic plasticity. Specifically, I'm interested in the plasticity that aquatic animals possess around how they deal with environmental stress: changes in temperature, oxygen, and salinity.

We are studying this in three ways: (1) Shark nurseries—These are in an estuary environment with shallow water where sharks will come to pup. These areas usually have a high density of juveniles and are susceptible to wide variations in temperature, salinity, and oxygen. We've been using these nurseries as a model to understand how animals are coping with changing environments. (2) *Mangrove rivulus*—This is a little fish that is native to mangroves in Florida and Central America. It is interesting because it is an air-breathing fish, and is the only known vertebrate hermaphrodite. This fish is a wonderful

Courtesy of Suzie Currie

model in which to look at phenotypic plasticity because you can have individuals that are genetically identical, and you can see how the environment affects physiological responses. We have just established a colony of these fish here at Mount Allison, and we are using them to understand how behaviour and thermal history might influence responses to stress. (3) The Miramichi River—This is one of North America's most productive salmon rivers. The summer water temperatures have been very high in the last few years, potentially exceeding the thermal limits of Atlantic salmon. We have a lab facility that allows us to mimic the natural situation of this river, and we can look at the physiological and behavioural responses to relevant high-temperature fluctuations for salmon.

What is the key "take-home" message for students about your research?

Students should be aware that if we better understand physiological and cellular responses to stress, we can better understand the impact of environmental change on animals. Also—context is everything. To look at the inherent plasticity (or flexibility) that allows coping with changing environments, you have to consider the physiological state of an animal, its behavioural state, its diet, and its habitat. You can't look at one aspect in isolation. You have to think about an animal in its natural environment and consider how the environment influences the organism's function.

What is the relevance of your research for first-year students studying climate change?

Ocean temperatures are the highest they have been in 30 years, and climate change will cause changes in both temperature and salinity. Our research allows us to understand the limits that animals have in dealing with these changes.

What advice would you give to a biology student just starting out at university?

Embrace discovery, embrace the unknown, and don't be discouraged by what you don't know. In fact, celebrate what you don't know, constantly ask questions, and be inspired by the natural world around you.

What do you enjoy most about life as a scientist?

The sense of discovery and the excitement about the unknown. When you find something you are interested in and you ask a question, and then find that no one knows the answer. Science and biology are both about creativity. To be an excellent scientist you need to be a creative scientist.

Source: Interview with Suzie Currie. Used with permission from Suzie Currie.

Satirus/Shutterstock

MAKE CONNECTIONS

Life Challenges and Solutions

The physiological diversity of animals reflects the many ways they have evolved to overcome the challenges imposed by the environment. Despite the diversity, many common themes emerge when comparing distantly related animals.

Form and Function

Evolutionary pressures often lead to changes in both anatomy and physiology, and thus anatomical features (form) often reflect physiological properties (function). This relationship between form and function leads scientists to devise ways to understand both how a particular trait arises and how the trait influences function. For example, the collection of teeth in the jaw of a wolf reveals much about what the animal evolved to eat. In some cases, the relationship between form and function is less obvious. Can you predict the under-lying benefit of the large bill of the toucan? Glen Tattersall (Brock University) has shown that one function of the large toucan bill is to dissipate body heat.

Eduardo Rivero/Shutterstock

Jared Hobbs/All Canada Photos

Courtesy of Andrew Turko

Homeostasis and Signalling

The cell-signalling pathways you learned about in Chapter 11 are essential for homeostasis. Without hormones and other signalling factors, animals could not coordinate the physiological processes needed for survival. Signalling pathways allow a wood frog, *Rana sylvatica* (above right) to survive the physiological changes that occur in winter. Ken Storey (Carleton University) has studied how frogs use signal transduction pathways to coordinate the physiological changes needed to tolerate freezing during its overwintering period. Hormones also allow animals to coordinate the many tissues that are involved in sexual reproduc-tion. This is particularly challenging in animals that switch sex in their lifetime, or are simultaneously both male and female, as with the *Mangrove rivulus* (right) studied by Suzie Currie (see Unit 7 overview).

Sensing and Responding to the Environment

Animals possess an ability to detect environmental conditions and use physiology to meet the challenges imposed by the environment. Environmental sensing typically falls to the nervous system, which coordinates behavioural and physiological responses. This is typified by the animals that undergo long-distance migrations as part of their life history strategy. Monarch butterflies use information from the Sun and magnetic fields to

guide their multigenerational migrations (see Concept 50.3). Pacific salmon remodel the machinery of ion and water balance to prepare themselves for moving between fresh water and seawater (see Concept 44.1). In each of these examples, a successful migration requires coordination of digestion, locomotion, and reproduction.

Mark Conlin/Image Quest Marine

Evolution and Development

The nature of animal diversity is usually the product of evolution, development, and their interaction with the environment. Exploring how form and function evolve demands an understanding of the processes that occur in embryonic development (see Concept 47.2). There are evolutionary explanations for, or at least questions about, how populations and species differ, yet why so many aspects of physiology are highly conserved across animals.

Barrett & MacKay/Shutterstock

Researchers at UBC use stickle-backs as a model for studying how form and function evolve in different environments (see Concept 51.1). Populations of sticklebacks can become isolated in waterways and evolve in unexpected directions in relation to conditions such as water flow, food availability, and water quality. Many of these anatomical changes coincide with behavioural evolution.

MAKE CONNECTIONS *Like animals, plants have the need to extract molecules and fluids from the environment, and move them through the organism. What plant tissues and processes (Unit 6) are functionally analogous to the vertebrate circulatory, respiratory and digestive systems?*

40

Basic Principles of Animal Form and Function

KEY CONCEPTS

40.1 Animal form and function are correlated at all levels of organization

40.2 Feedback control maintains the internal environment in many animals

40.3 Homeostatic processes for thermoregulation involve form, function, and behaviour

40.4 Energy requirements are related to animal size, activity, and environment

National Geographic Image Collection/Alamy

▲ Figure 40.1 **How does a jackrabbit keep from overheating?**

Diverse Forms, Common Challenges

Jackrabbits live throughout the deserts of North America, from the badlands of Alberta to Mexico. The ears of the jackrabbit *(Lepus townsendii)* in **Figure 40.1** are thin and remarkably large. They provide this hare with an acute sense of hearing, a primary defence against predators. The ears also help the jackrabbit shed excess heat. Blood flowing through each ear's network of vessels transfers heat to the surrounding air. However, when the air is warmer than the jackrabbit, blood passing through the ears could absorb heat, raising body temperature to a dangerous level. How, then, does a big-eared jackrabbit survive in the midday desert heat? To answer this question, we need to look more closely at the biological form, or **anatomy**, of the animal.

Over the course of its life, this hare faces the same fundamental challenges as any other animal, whether hydra, hawk, or human. All animals must obtain oxygen and nutrients, escape predators and disease, and produce offspring. Given that they share these and other basic requirements, why do species vary so enormously in makeup, complexity, organization, and appearance? The answer is **adaptation:** Natural selection favours those variations in a population that increase relative fitness (see Chapter 23). The solutions to the challenges of survival vary among environments and species, but they frequently result in a close match of form and function.

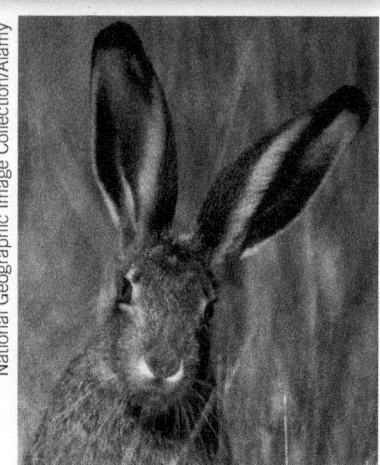

National Geographic Image Collection/Alamy

◀ **A White-tailed Jackrabbit (*Lepus townsendii*)**

920

Because form and function are correlated, examining anatomy often provides clues to **physiology**—biological function. Jackrabbits differ from other rabbits in possessing very large ears. The form of the ears, with their high surface area, is vital to their role as a heat exchanger. Jackrabbits can alter blood flow to their ears to regulate the amount of heat lost to the environment. For example, by increasing blood flow to the ears, they can shed internal heat to the environment.

In this chapter, we will begin our study of animal form and function by examining the levels of organization in the animal body and the systems for coordinating the activities of distinct body parts. Next, we will use the example of body temperature regulation to illustrate how animals control their internal environment. Finally, we will explore how anatomy and physiology relate to an animal's interactions with the environment and its management of energy use.

CONCEPT 40.1

Animal form and function are correlated at all levels of organization

An animal's size and shape are fundamental aspects of form that significantly affect the way the animal interacts with its environment. The body plan, or design, of an animal is the result of a pattern of development programmed by the genome, itself the product of hundreds of millions of years of evolution.

Evolution of Animal Size and Shape

EVOLUTION Many body plans have arisen during the course of evolution, but these variations fall within certain bounds. The range of animal forms is limited by the laws of physics and chemistry, which govern properties such as strength, diffusion, reactions, movement, and heat exchange.

As an example of how physical laws constrain evolution, let's consider how some properties of water limit the possible shapes for animals that are fast swimmers. Water is about a thousand times denser than air and also far more viscous. Therefore, any bump on an animal's body surface that causes drag impedes a swimmer more than it would a runner or flyer. Tuna and other fast ray-finned fishes can swim at speeds up to 80 km/hr. Sharks, penguins, dolphins, and seals are also fast swimmers. As is apparent in the examples in **Figure 40.2**, such animals share a streamlined body contour: a shape that is fusiform, meaning tapered on both ends. The similar shape found in these speedy vertebrates

is an example of convergent evolution (see Chapter 22). Natural selection often results in similar adaptations when diverse organisms face the same environmental challenge, such as overcoming drag during swimming.

Physical laws also influence animal body plans with regard to maximum size. As body dimensions increase, stronger skeletons are required to maintain adequate support. This limitation affects internal skeletons, such as those of vertebrates, as well as external skeletons, such as those of insects and other arthropods. In addition, as bodies increase in size, the muscles required for locomotion must represent an ever-larger fraction of the total body mass. At some point, mobility becomes limited. By considering the fraction of body mass in leg muscles and the effective force such muscles generate, scientists can estimate maximum running speed for a wide range of body plans. Such calculations indicate that the dinosaur *Tyrannosaurus rex*, which stood more than 6 m tall, probably could reach speeds of 30 km/hr, about as fast as the fastest humans can run.

Exchange with the Environment

Animals must exchange materials with their environment, and this requirement imposes limitations on their body plans (as it does for all multicellular organisms). Exchange occurs as substances dissolved in an aqueous solution move across the plasma membrane of each cell. The rates of exchange for nutrients, waste products, and gases are proportional to membrane surface area, whereas the amount of material that must be exchanged to sustain life is proportional to cell volume.

The opportunity for exchange depends on the organization of cells in the body. A single-celled organism, such as the amoeba in **Figure 40.3a**, has a sufficient membrane surface area in contact with its environment to carry out all necessary exchange. In contrast, animals are composed of many cells, each with its own plasma membrane across which exchange must occur. A multicellular organization therefore works only if every cell has access to a suitable aqueous environment, either inside or outside the animal's body.

Many animals with a simple internal organization have body plans that enable direct exchange between almost all their cells and the external environment. For example, a pond-dwelling hydra, which has a saclike body plan, has a body wall only two cell layers thick (**Figure 40.3b**). Because its gastrovascular cavity opens to the external environment, both the outer and inner layers of cells are constantly bathed by pond

Seal

Frank Greenaway/Getty Images

Penguin

Alamy Images

Tuna

Andre Seale/Image Quest Marine

▲ Figure 40.2 **Convergent evolution in fast swimmers.**

Mouth

Gastrovascular cavity

Exchange

Exchange

Exchange

0.1 mm

1 mm

(a) An amoeba, a single-celled organism

(b) A hydra, an animal with two layers of cells

water. Another common body plan that maximizes exposure to the surrounding medium is a flat shape. Consider, for instance, a parasitic tapeworm, which can reach several metres in length (see Figure 33.12). A thin, flat shape places most cells of the worm in direct contact with its particular environment—the nutrient-rich intestinal fluid of a vertebrate host.

Our bodies and those of most other animals are composed of compact masses of cells, with an internal organization much more complex than that of a hydra or a tapeworm. For such a body plan, increasing the cell number decreases the ratio of outer surface area to total volume. As an extreme comparison, the ratio of outer surface area to volume for a whale is hundreds of thousands of times smaller than that for a water flea. Nevertheless, every cell in the whale must be bathed in fluid and have access to oxygen, nutrients, and other resources. How is this accomplished?

In whales and most other animals, the evolutionary adaptations that enable sufficient exchange with the environment are specialized surfaces that are extensively branched or folded **(Figure 40.4)**. In almost all cases, these exchange surfaces lie within the body, an arrangement that protects their delicate tissues from abrasion or dehydration and allows for streamlined body contours. The branching or folding serves to greatly increase surface area: In humans, the internal exchange surfaces of the digestive, respiratory, and circulatory systems each have an area more than 25 times that of the skin.

Internal body fluids link exchange surfaces to body cells. The spaces between cells are filled with fluid, in many animals called **interstitial fluid** (from the Latin for "stand

▶ Figure 40.4 **Internal exchange surfaces of complex animals.** This diagram provides an overview of chemical exchange between an animal body and the environment. Most animals have surfaces that are specialized for exchanging chemicals with the surroundings. These exchange surfaces are usually internal but are connected to the environment via openings on the body surface (the mouth, for example). The exchange surfaces are finely branched or folded, giving them a very large area. The digestive, respiratory, and excretory systems all have such exchange surfaces. The circulatory system carries chemicals transported across these surfaces throughout the body.

? *In what sense are exchange surfaces such as the lining of the digestive system both internal and external?*

External environment

Food CO_2 O_2

Mouth

Animal body

Respiratory system

Blood

Heart

Nutrients

Circulatory system

Cells

Interstitial fluid

Digestive system

Excretory system

Anus

Unabsorbed matter (feces)

Metabolic waste products (nitrogenous waste)

250 μm

Susumu Nishinaga/Science Source

A microscopic view of the lung reveals that it is much more sponge-like than balloon-like. This construction provides an expansive wet surface for gas exchange with the environment (SEM).

50 μm

Susumu Nishinaga/Science Source

Within the kidney, blood is filtered across the surface of long, narrow blood vessels packed into ball-shaped structures (SEM).

100 μm

Eye of Science/Science Source

The lining of the small intestine has finger-like projections that expand the surface area for nutrient absorption (SEM).

between"). Complex body plans also include a circulatory fluid, such as blood. Exchange between the interstitial fluid and the circulatory fluid enables cells throughout the body to obtain nutrients and get rid of wastes (see Figure 40.4).

Despite the greater challenges of exchange with the environment, complex body plans have distinct benefits over simple ones. For example, an external skeleton can protect against predators, and sensory organs can provide detailed information on the animal's surroundings. Internal digestive organs can break down food gradually, controlling the release of stored energy. In addition, specialized filtration systems can adjust the composition of the internal fluid that bathes the animal's body cells. In this way, an animal can maintain a relatively stable internal environment while living in a changeable external environment. A complex body plan is especially advantageous for animals living on land, where the external environment may be highly variable.

Hierarchical Organization of Body Plans

Cells form a functional animal body through their emergent properties. Recall from Chapter 1 that emergent properties arise by way of successive levels of structural and functional organization. Cells are organized into **tissues**, groups of cells with a similar appearance and a common function. Different types of tissues are further organized into functional units called **organs**. (The simplest animals, such as sponges, lack organs or even true tissues.) Groups of organs that work together provide an additional level of organization and coordination and make up an **organ system** (Table 40.1). The skin, for example, is an organ of the integumentary system, which protects against infection and helps regulate body temperature.

Many organs contain tissues with distinct physiological roles. In some cases, the roles are different enough that we consider the organ to belong to more than one organ system. The pancreas, for instance, produces enzymes critical to the function of the digestive system and also regulates the level of sugar in the blood as a vital part of the endocrine system.

Just as viewing the body's organization from the "bottom up" (from cells to organ systems) reveals emergent properties, a "top-down" view of the hierarchy reveals the multilayered basis of specialization, and the need for regulation. Consider the human digestive system: the mouth, pharynx, esophagus, stomach, small and large intestines, accessory organs, and anus. Each organ has specific roles in digestion. One function of the stomach, for example, is to initiate the breakdown of proteins. This process requires a churning motion powered by stomach muscles, as well as digestive juices secreted by the stomach lining. Producing digestive juices, in turn, requires highly specialized cell types: One cell type secretes a protein-digesting enzyme, a second generates concentrated hydrochloric acid, and a third produces mucus, which protects the stomach lining.

The specialized and complex organ systems of animals are built from a limited set of cell and tissue types. For example, lungs and blood vessels have distinct functions but are lined by tissues that are of the same basic type and that therefore share many properties.

There are four main types of animal tissues: epithelial, connective, muscle, and nervous. Figure 40.5 explores the structure and function of each type. In later chapters, we'll discuss how the tissues described here contribute to the functions of particular organ systems.

Table 40.1	Organ Systems in Mammals	
Organ System	**Main Components**	**Main Functions**
Digestive	Mouth, pharynx, esophagus, stomach, intestines, liver, pancreas, anus	Food processing (ingestion, digestion, absorption, elimination)
Circulatory	Heart, blood vessels, blood	Internal distribution of materials
Respiratory	Lungs, trachea, other breathing tubes	Gas exchange (uptake of oxygen; disposal of carbon dioxide)
Immune and lymphatic	Bone marrow, lymph nodes, thymus, spleen, lymph vessels, white blood cells	Body defence (fighting infections and cancer)
Excretory	Kidneys, ureters, urinary bladder, urethra	Disposal of metabolic wastes; regulation of osmotic balance of blood
Endocrine	Pituitary, thyroid, pancreas, adrenal, and other hormone-secreting glands	Coordination of body activities (such as digestion and metabolism)
Reproductive	Ovaries or testes and associated organs	Reproduction
Nervous	Brain, spinal cord, nerves, sensory organs	Coordination of body activities; detection of stimuli and formulation of responses to them
Integumentary	Skin and its derivatives (such as hair, claws, skin glands)	Protection against mechanical injury, infection, dehydration; thermoregulation
Skeletal	Skeleton (bones, tendons, ligaments, cartilage)	Body support, protection of internal organs, movement
Muscular	Skeletal muscles	Locomotion and other movement

Exploring Structure and Function in Animal Tissues

Epithelial Tissue

Occurring as sheets of cells, **epithelial tissues**, or **epithelia** (singular, *epithelium*), cover the outside of the body and line organs and cavities within the body. Because epithelial cells are closely packed, often with tight junctions (see Figure 6.30), they function as a barrier against mechanical injury, pathogens, and fluid loss. Epithelia also form active interfaces with the environment. For example, the epithelium that lines the nasal passages is crucial for olfaction, the sense of smell. Note how different cell shapes and arrangements correlate with distinct functions.

Stratified squamous epithelium

Apical surface

Basal surface

A stratified squamous epithelium is multilayered and regenerates rapidly. New cells formed by division near the basal lamina (see micrograph below) push outward, replacing cells that are sloughed off. This epithelium is commonly found on surfaces subject to abrasion, such as the outer skin and the linings of the mouth, anus, and vagina.

Cuboidal epithelium

Cuboidal epithelium, with dice-shaped cells specialized for secretion, makes up the epithelium of kidney tubules and many glands, including the thyroid gland and salivary glands.

Simple columnar epithelium

The large, brick-shaped cells of simple columnar epithelia are often found where secretion or active absorption is important. For example, a simple columnar epithelium lines the intestines, secreting digestive juices and absorbing nutrients.

Simple squamous epithelium

The single layer of platelike cells that form a simple squamous epithelium functions in the exchange of material by diffusion. This type of epithelium, which is thin and leaky, lines blood vessels and the air sacs of the lungs, where diffusion of nutrients and gases is critical.

Pseudostratified columnar epithelium

A pseudostratified epithelium consists of a single layer of cells varying in height. In many vertebrates, a pseudostratified epithelium of ciliated cells forms a mucous membrane that lines portions of the respiratory tract. The beating cilia sweep the film of mucus along the surface.

Lumen — Apical surface

Basal surface

10 μm

Steve Downing/Pearson Education

Polarity of epithelia

All epithelia are polarized, meaning that they have two different sides. The *apical* surface faces the lumen (cavity) or outside of the organ and is therefore exposed to fluid or air. Specialized projections often cover this surface. For example, the apical surface of the epithelium lining the small intestine is covered with microvilli, projections that increase the surface area available for absorbing nutrients. The opposite side of each epithelium is the *basal* surface.

Connective Tissue

Connective tissue, consisting of a sparse population of cells scattered through an extracellular matrix, holds many tissues and organs together and in place. The matrix generally consists of a web of fibres embedded in a liquid, jellylike, or solid foundation. Within the matrix are numerous cells called **fibroblasts**, which secrete fibre proteins, and **macrophages**, which engulf foreign particles and any cell debris by phagocytosis (see Chapter 6).

Connective tissue fibres are of three kinds: *Collagenous fibres* provide strength and flexibility, *reticular fibres* join connective tissue to adjacent tissues, and *elastic fibres* make tissues elastic. If you pinch a fold of tissue on the back of your hand, the collagenous and reticular fibres prevent the skin from being pulled far from the bone, whereas the elastic fibres restore the skin to its original shape when you release your grip. Different mixtures of fibres and foundation form the major types of connective tissue shown below.

Loose connective tissue

The most widespread connective tissue in the vertebrate body is *loose connective tissue,* which binds epithelia to underlying tissues and holds organs in place. Loose connective tissue gets its name from the loose weave of its fibres, which include all three types. It is found in the skin and throughout the body.

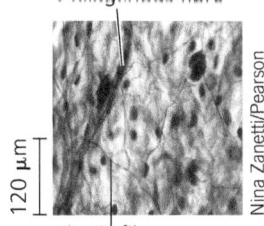

Collagenous fibre

Elastic fibre

120 µm

Nina Zanetti/Pearson Education

Fibrous connective tissue

Fibrous connective tissue is dense with collagenous fibres. It is found in **tendons**, which attach muscles to bones, and in **ligaments**, which connect bones at joints.

30 µm

Nuclei

Alamy Images

Bone

The skeleton of most vertebrates is made of **bone**, a mineralized connective tissue. Bone-forming cells called *osteoblasts* deposit a matrix of collagen. Calcium, magnesium, and phosphate ions combine into a hard mineral within the matrix. The microscopic structure of hard mammalian bone consists of repeating units called *osteons*. Each osteon has concentric layers of the mineralized matrix, which are deposited around a central canal containing blood vessels and nerves.

Central canal

700 µm

Osteon

Nina Zanetti/Pearson Education

Blood

Blood has a liquid extracellular matrix called plasma, which consists of water, salts, and dissolved proteins. Suspended in plasma are erythrocytes (red blood cells), leukocytes (white blood cells), and cell fragments called platelets. Red cells carry oxygen, white cells function in defence, and platelets aid in blood clotting.

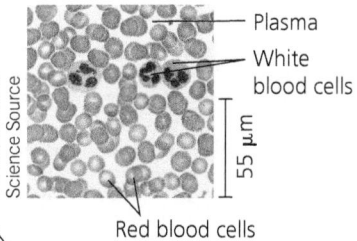

Plasma

White blood cells

55 µm

Red blood cells

Dr. Gopal Murti/Science Source

Adipose tissue

Adipose tissue is a specialized loose connective tissue that stores fat in adipose cells distributed throughout its matrix. Adipose tissue pads and insulates the body and stores fuel as fat molecules (see Figure 4.6). Each adipose cell contains a large fat droplet that swells when fat is stored and shrinks when the body uses that fat as fuel.

Fat droplets

150 µm

Nina Zanetti/Pearson Education

Cartilage

Cartilage contains collagenous fibres embedded in a rubbery protein-carbohydrate complex called chondroitin sulphate. Cells called *chondrocytes* secrete the collagen and chondroitin sulphate, which together make cartilage a strong yet flexible support material. The skeletons of many vertebrate embryos contain cartilage that is replaced by bone as the embryo matures. Cartilage remains in some locations, such as the disks that act as cushions between vertebrae.

Chondrocytes

100 µm

Chondroitin sulphate

Chuck Brown/Science Source

Continued on next page

Exploring Structure and Function in Animal Tissues

Muscle Tissue

The tissue responsible for nearly all types of body movement is **muscle tissue**. All muscle cells consist of filaments containing the proteins actin and myosin, which together enable muscles to contract. There are three types of muscle tissue in the vertebrate body: skeletal, smooth, and cardiac.

Skeletal muscle

Attached to bones by tendons, **skeletal muscle**, or *striated muscle,* is responsible for voluntary movements. Skeletal muscle consists of bundles of long cells called muscle fibres. During development, skeletal muscle fibres form by the fusion of many cells, resulting in multiple nuclei in each muscle cell or fibre. The arrangement of contractile units, or sarcomeres, along the fibres gives the cells a striped (striated) appearance. In adult mammals, building muscle increases the size but not the number of muscle fibres.

Smooth muscle

Smooth muscle, which lacks striations, is found in the walls of the digestive tract, urinary bladder, arteries, and other internal organs. The cells are spindle-shaped. Smooth muscles are responsible for involuntary body activities, such as churning of the stomach and constriction of arteries.

Cardiac muscle

Cardiac muscle forms the contractile wall of the heart. It is striated like skeletal muscle and has similar contractile properties. Unlike skeletal muscle, however, cardiac muscle has fibres that interconnect via intercalated disks, which relay signals from cell to cell and help synchronize heart contraction.

Nina Zanetti/Pearson Education

Nuclei

Muscle fibre

Sarcomere

100 μm

Ed Reschke/Photolibrary/Getty Images

Nucleus   Muscle fibres   25 μm

Ed Reschke/Getty Images

Nucleus   Intercalated disk   25 μm

Nervous Tissue

Nervous tissue functions in the receipt, processing, and transmission of information. Nervous tissue contains **neurons**, or nerve cells, which transmit nerve impulses, as well as support cells called **glial cells**, or simply **glia**. In many animals, a concentration of nervous tissue forms a brain, an information-processing centre.

Neurons

Neurons are the basic units of the nervous system. A neuron receives nerve impulses from other neurons via its cell body and multiple extensions called dendrites. Neurons transmit impulses to other neurons, muscles, or other cells via extensions called axons, which are often bundled together into nerves.

Neuron:
Dendrites
Cell body
Axon

40 μm

(Fluorescent LM)

Ulrich Gartner

Glia

The various types of glia help nourish, insulate, and replenish neurons, and in some cases, modulate neuron function.

Glia

15 μm

Axons of neurons

Blood vessel

(Confocal LM)

Thomas Deerinck

Coordination and Control

An animal's tissues, organs, and organ systems must act in concert with one another. For example, during long dives, the harbour seal in Figure 40.2 slows its heart rate, collapses its lungs, and lowers its body temperature while propelling itself forward with its hind flippers. Coordinating activity across an animal's body in this way requires communication between different locations in the body. What signals are used? How do the signals move within the body? There are two sets of answers to these questions, reflecting the two major systems, unique to animals, that control and coordinate responses to stimuli: the endocrine and nervous systems (Figure 40.6).

Signalling molecules, called **hormones**, are released from endocrine cells into the blood, where they travel throughout the body. In the nervous system, neurons use electrical signals to carry messages throughout the body. Most physiological processes in the body are regulated by both the endocrine and nervous systems.

The hormones of the endocrine system exert effects by binding to receptors located on target cells. Different hormones cause distinct effects, and only cells that have receptors for a particular hormone respond (Figure 40.6a). Depending on which cells have receptors for that hormone, the hormone may have an effect in just a single location or in sites throughout the body. For example, only cells of the thyroid gland have the receptor for thyroid-stimulating hormone (TSH). Upon binding TSH, thyroid cells release thyroid hormone. In contrast to TSH, receptors for thyroid hormone itself occur throughout the body.

Signalling with hormones can be very fast or very slow. When faced with a threat, your body immediately releases stores of the hormone epinephrine (also known as adrenaline), allowing you to respond quickly. However, it takes many seconds for TSH to be released into the bloodstream and carried throughout the body. The effects of hormones are often long-lasting, however, because hormones remain in the bloodstream for seconds, minutes, or even hours.

In the nervous system, signals are not broadcast throughout the entire body. Instead, each nerve impulse travels to specific target cells along dedicated communication lines consisting mainly of axons (Figure 40.6b). Unlike the endocrine system, the nervous system sends signals to specific nearby target cells. Four types of cells can receive nerve signals: other neurons, muscle cells, endocrine cells, and exocrine cells.

Communication in the nervous system usually involves both electrical and chemical signals. Electrical nerve impulses travel along axons, sometimes over long distances, as changes in voltage. But in many cases, passing information from one neuron to another involves very short-range chemical signals called neurotransmitters. Overall, neuronal signalling is extremely fast; nerve impulses take only a fraction of a second to reach the target and last only a fraction of a second.

Because the two major communication systems of the body differ in signal type, transmission, speed, and duration, they are specialized for different functions. The endocrine system is well suited for coordinating gradual changes that affect the entire body, such as growth and development, reproduction, metabolic processes, and digestion. The nervous system is well suited for directing immediate and rapid responses to the environment, especially in controlling fast locomotion and behaviour.

Although the functions of the endocrine and nervous systems are distinct, the two systems often work in close coordination. Both contribute to maintaining a stable internal environment, our next topic of discussion.

▼ Figure 40.6 **Signalling in the endocrine and nervous systems.**

(a) Signalling by hormones

STIMULUS

Endocrine cell

Hormone

Signal travels everywhere via the bloodstream.

Blood vessel

Response: Limited to cells that have the receptor for the signal.

(b) Signalling by neurons

STIMULUS

Cell body of neuron

Axon

Nerve impulse

Signal travels along axon to a specific location.

Nerve impulse

Axons

Response: Limited to cells that connect by specialized junctions to an axon that transmits an impulse.

1. What properties are shared by all types of epithelia?

2. In cool weather, jackrabbits sometimes flatten their ears against their body. What advantage and disadvantage do you think this body posture offers for survival?

3. **WHAT IF?** Suppose you are standing at the edge of a cliff and suddenly slip—you barely manage to keep your balance and avoid falling. As your heart races, you feel a burst of energy, due in part to a surge of blood into dilated (widened) vessels in your muscles and an upward spike in the level of glucose in your blood. Why might you expect that this "fight-or-flight" response requires both the nervous and endocrine systems?

For suggested answers, see Appendix A.

CONCEPT 40.2

Feedback control maintains the internal environment in many animals

Imagine that your body temperature soared every time you took a hot shower or drank a freshly brewed cup of coffee. Managing the state of the internal environment is a major challenge for the animal body. Faced with environmental fluctuations, animals manage their internal environment by either regulating or conforming.

Regulating and Conforming

An animal is said to be a **regulator** for a particular environmental variable if it uses internal mechanisms to control internal change in the face of external fluctuation. The otter in **Figure 40.7** is a regulator for temperature, keeping its body at a temperature that is largely independent of the water in which it swims. In contrast, an animal is a **conformer** for a particular variable if it allows its internal condition to change in accordance with external changes in the variable. The bass in Figure 40.7 conforms to the temperature of the lake it inhabits. As the water warms or cools, so does the body of the bass. Though conformers do not use physiology to control internal conditions, they may be able to

▶ Figure 40.7 **The relationship between body and environmental temperatures in an aquatic temperature regulator and an aquatic temperature conformer.** The river otter regulates its body temperature, keeping it stable across a wide range of environmental temperatures. The largemouth bass, meanwhile, allows its internal environment to conform to the water temperature.

avoid internal changes by living in a stable environment. For example, Antarctic fish live in waters that remain a nearly constant temperature, about −1.8°C.

An animal may regulate some internal conditions while allowing others to conform to the environment. For example, even though the bass conforms to the temperature of the surrounding water, it regulates the solute concentration in its blood and interstitial fluid; it is a thermoconformer but ionoregulator. You will learn more about ion regulation in Chapter 44.

Even animals that are considered to be regulators for a physiological system tolerate some variation. Most animals fall somewhere in the continuum between regulating and conforming.

Homeostasis

The steady body temperature of a river otter and the stable concentration of solutes in a freshwater bass are examples of **homeostasis**, which means "same state," referring to the maintenance of internal balance. In achieving homeostasis, animals maintain a relatively constant internal environment even when the external environment changes significantly.

Like many animals, humans exhibit homeostasis for a range of physical and chemical properties. For example, the human body maintains a fairly constant temperature of about 37°C and a pH of the blood and interstitial fluid within 0.1 pH unit of 7.4. The body also regulates the concentration of glucose in the bloodstream so that it remains predominantly in the range of 70–110 mg of glucose per 100 mL of blood.

Mechanisms of Homeostasis

Before exploring homeostasis in animals, let's first consider a

Jeffrey Lepore/Science Source

Neil McNicoll/Alamy Stock photo

[Graph: Body temperature (°C) on y-axis (0 to 40) vs Ambient (environmental) temperature (°C) on x-axis (0 to 40). River otter (temperature regulator) line stays flat near 39°C. Largemouth bass (temperature conformer) line increases linearly from about 2°C to about 34°C.]

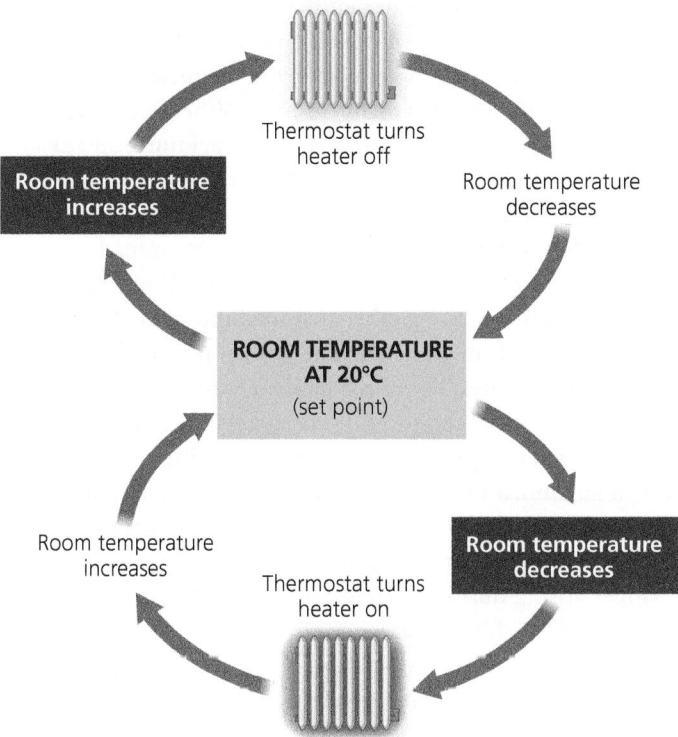

▲ **Figure 40.8 A nonliving example of temperature regulation: control of room temperature.** Regulating room temperature depends on a control centre (a thermostat) that detects temperature change and activates mechanisms that reverse that change.

WHAT IF? *Label at least one stimulus, response, and sensor/control centre in the above figure. How would adding an air conditioner to the system contribute to homeostasis?*

nonliving example: the regulation of room temperature (Figure 40.8). Let's assume you want to keep a room at 20°C, a comfortable temperature for normal activity. You adjust a control device—the thermostat—to 20°C and allow a thermometer in the thermostat to monitor temperature. If the room temperature falls below 20°C, the thermostat responds by turning on a heater. Heat is produced until the room reaches 20°C, at which point the thermostat switches off the heater. Whenever the temperature in the room again drifts below 20°C, the thermostat activates another heating cycle.

Like a home heating system, an animal achieves homeostasis by maintaining a variable, such as body temperature or solute concentration, at or near a particular value, or **set point**. Fluctuations in the variable above or below the set point serve as the **stimulus** detected by a receptor, or **sensor**. Upon receiving a signal from the sensor, a *control centre* generates output that triggers a **response**, a physiological activity that helps return the variable to the set point. In the home heating example, a drop in temperature below the set point acts as a stimulus, the thermostat serves as the sensor and control centre, and the heater produces the response.

Feedback Control in Homeostasis

Like the regulatory circuit shown in Figure 40.8, homeostasis in animals relies largely on **negative feedback**, a control mechanism that reduces the disturbance. For example, when you exercise vigorously, you produce heat, which increases your body temperature. Your nervous system detects this increase and triggers sweating. As you sweat, the evaporation of moisture from your skin cools your body, helping return your body temperature to its set point.

Homeostasis is a dynamic equilibrium, the interplay between external factors that tend to change the internal environment and internal control mechanisms that oppose such changes. Note that physiological responses to stimuli are not instantaneous, just as switching on a furnace does not immediately warm a room. As a result, homeostasis moderates but doesn't eliminate changes in the internal environment. Additional fluctuation occurs if a variable has a *normal range*—an upper and lower limit—rather than a single set point. This is equivalent to a heating system that begins producing heat when the room temperature drops to 19°C and stops heating when the temperature reaches 21°C. Regardless of whether there is a set point or a normal range, homeostasis is enhanced by adaptations that reduce fluctuations, such as insulation in the case of temperature and physiological buffers in the case of pH.

Unlike negative feedback, **positive feedback** is a control mechanism that amplifies rather than reduces the stimulus. Positive feedback loops in animals do not play a major role in homeostasis, but instead help drive processes to completion. During childbirth, for instance, the pressure of the baby's head against receptors near the opening of the mother's uterus stimulates the uterus to contract. These contractions result in greater pressure against the opening of the uterus, heightening the contractions and thereby causing even greater pressure, until the baby is born.

Alterations in Homeostasis

The set points and normal ranges for homeostasis can change under various circumstances. In fact, *regulated changes* in the internal environment are essential to normal body functions. Some regulated changes are associated with a particular stage in life, such as the radical shift in hormone balance that occurs during puberty. Other regulated changes are cyclic, such as the variation in hormone levels responsible for a woman's menstrual cycle (see Figure 46.13).

In all animals (and plants, too), certain cyclic alterations in metabolism reflect a **circadian rhythm**, a set of physiological changes that occur roughly every 24 hours. For example, your body temperature typically undergoes a cyclic rise and fall of more than 0.6°C in every 24-hour period. Remarkably, a biological clock maintains this rhythm even when variations in human activity, room temperature, and light levels are minimized (Figure 40.9a). A circadian rhythm is thus intrinsic to the body, although the biological clock is normally coordinated with the cycle of light and darkness in the environment (Figure 40.9b). For example, the hormone melatonin is secreted at night, and more is released during the longer nights of winter. External stimuli can reset the biological clock, but the effect is not immediate. That is why flying across several time zones results in jet lag, a mismatch between the circadian rhythm and local environment that persists until the clock fully resets.

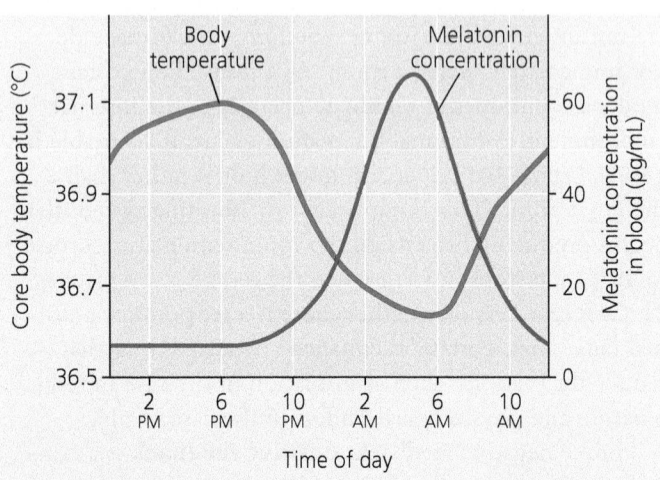

(a) Variation in core body temperature and melatonin concentration in blood. Researchers measured these two variables in resting but awake volunteers in an isolation chamber with constant temperature and low light. (Melatonin is a hormone that appears to be involved in sleep/wake cycles.)

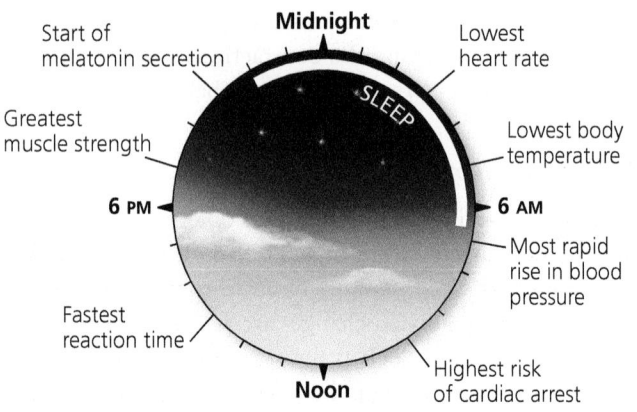

(b) The human circadian clock. Metabolic activities undergo daily cycles in response to the circadian clock. As illustrated for a typical individual who rises early in the morning, eats lunch around noon, and sleeps at night, changes in metabolism arise throughout the day and are repeated on a 24-hour cycle.

▲ Figure 40.9 **Human circadian rhythm.**

Animals are able to remodel their cells and tissues in response to environmental conditions. For example, temperature has a debilitating effect on biochemical processes and cellular structure for many animals. When faced with prolonged changes in environmental temperature, an animal may remodel proteins and lipids to compensate. The remodelling in response to a single environmental factor is known as **acclimation**. In most situations, animals are exposed to multiple changes simultaneously. Consider the situation when an elk or other mammal moves up into the mountains from sea level. The animal may experience colder temperatures, lower oxygen, and less food. Each of these factors could exert important effects on physiology and require a compensatory response in multiple systems. When an animal remodels itself in response to complex environmental changes, the process is called **acclimatization**. Note that acclimation and acclimatization are temporary changes arising during the lifetime of an individual animal. These changes should not be confused with *adaptation*, a process of change in a population brought about by natural selection acting over many generations (see Chapter 22).

CONCEPT CHECK 40.2

1. **MAKE CONNECTIONS** How does negative feedback in thermoregulation differ from feedback inhibition in an enzyme-catalyzed biosynthetic process (see Figure 8.21)?

2. If you were deciding where to put the thermostat in a house, what factors would govern your decision? How do these factors relate to the fact that many homeostatic control sensors in humans are located in the brain?

3. **MAKE CONNECTIONS** Like animals, cyanobacteria have a circadian rhythm. By analyzing the genes that maintain biological clocks, scientists were able to conclude that the 24-hour rhythms of humans and cyanobacteria reflect convergent evolution (see Concept 26.2). What evidence would have supported this conclusion? Explain.

For suggested answers, see Appendix A.

CONCEPT 40.3

Homeostatic processes for thermoregulation involve form, function, and behaviour

In this section, we will examine the regulation of body temperature as an example of how form and function work together in regulating an animal's internal environment. Later chapters in this unit will discuss other physiological systems involved in maintaining homeostasis.

Thermoregulation is the process by which animals maintain an internal temperature within a tolerable range. Thermoregulation is critical to survival because most biochemical and physiological processes are very sensitive to changes in body temperature. For every 10°C decrease in temperature, the rates of most enzyme-mediated reactions decrease two- to threefold. Increases in temperature speed up reactions but cause some proteins to become less active. For instance, the oxygen carrier molecule hemoglobin becomes less effective at binding oxygen as temperature increases. Membranes can also change fluidity, becoming increasingly fluid or rigid as temperatures rise or fall, respectively.

Each animal species has an optimal temperature range. Thermoregulation helps maintain body temperature within that optimal range, enabling cells to function effectively even as the external temperature fluctuates.

Endothermy and Ectothermy

Two thermal strategies are distinguished on the basis of the source of heat. **Endotherms** are animals that use internal metabolic processes as a major heat source. The body temperature of **ectotherms** is determined mainly by external conditions. Ectotherms also produce some heat in metabolism, but not enough to elevate temperature above that imposed by the environment. Likewise, endotherms can gain heat from the environment (think of a cat lying in a sunny window) but metabolic heat is most important in their thermoregulation.

Most birds and mammals are endotherms, as well as select species of reptiles, fish, and invertebrates. However, most animals on the planet are ectotherms.

Endotherms can maintain a stable body temperature even in the face of large fluctuations in the environmental temperature (Figure 40.10a). In a cold environment, an endotherm generates enough heat to keep its body substantially warmer than its surroundings. In a hot environment, endothermic vertebrates have mechanisms for cooling their bodies, enabling them to withstand heat loads that are intolerable for most ectotherms.

Because ectotherms do not use metabolism to generate heat, they generally need to consume much less food than endotherms of equivalent size—an advantage if food supplies are limited. Ectotherms also usually tolerate larger fluctuations in their internal temperature. Although ectotherms

do not generate enough heat for thermoregulation, many adjust body temperature by behavioural means, such as seeking out shade or basking in the sun (Figure 40.10b). Overall, ectothermy is an effective and successful strategy in most environments, as shown by the abundance and diversity of ectothermic animals.

Variation in Body Temperature

Animals can have either a variable or a constant body temperature. An animal whose body temperature varies with its environment is called a *poikilotherm* (from the Greek *poikilos*, varied). In contrast, a *homeotherm* has a relatively constant body temperature. For example, the largemouth bass is a poikilotherm, and the river otter is a homeotherm (see Figure 40.7).

From the descriptions of ectotherms and endotherms, it might seem that all ectotherms are poikilothermic and all endotherms are homeothermic. In fact, there is no fixed relationship between the source of heat and the stability of body temperature. For example, many ectothermic marine fishes and invertebrates inhabit waters with such stable temperatures that their body temperature varies less than that of endotherms such as humans and other mammals. Conversely, the body temperature of a few endotherms varies considerably. For example, bats and hummingbirds may periodically enter an inactive state in which they maintain a lower body temperature.

It is a common misconception that ectotherms are "cold-blooded" and endotherms are "warm-blooded." Ectotherms do not necessarily have low body temperatures. On the contrary, when sitting in the sun, many ectothermic lizards have higher body temperatures than mammals. Thus, the terms *cold-blooded* and *warm-blooded* are misleading and are avoided in scientific communication.

John Shaw/Science Source

(a) A walrus, an endotherm

▲ Figure 40.10 **Thermoregulation by internal or external sources of heat.** Endotherms obtain heat from their internal metabolism, whereas ectotherms rely on heat from their external environment.

Brian Lasenby/Shutterstock

(b) A turtle, an ectotherm

Balancing Heat Loss and Gain

Thermoregulation depends on an animal's ability to control the exchange of heat with its environment. Any organism, like any object, exchanges heat by four physical processes: radiation, evaporation, convection, and conduction. Figure 40.11 distinguishes these processes, which account for the flow of heat both within an organism and between an organism and its external environment. Note that heat is always transferred from an object of higher temperature to one of lower temperature.

The essence of thermoregulation is maintaining rates of heat gain that equal rates of heat loss. Animals do this through mechanisms that either reduce heat exchange overall or favour heat exchange in a particular direction. In mammals, several of these mechanisms involve the **integumentary system**, the outer covering of the body, consisting of the skin, hair, and nails (claws or hooves in some species).

Radiation is the emission of electromagnetic waves by all objects warmer than absolute zero. Here, a lizard absorbs heat radiating from the distant sun and radiates a smaller amount of energy to the surrounding air.

Evaporation is the removal of heat from the surface of a liquid that is losing some of its molecules as gas. Evaporation of water from a lizard's moist surfaces that are exposed to the environment has a strong cooling effect.

Convection is the transfer of heat by the movement of air or liquid past a surface, as when a breeze contributes to heat loss from a lizard's dry skin or when blood moves heat from the body core to the extremities.

Conduction is the direct transfer of thermal motion (heat) between molecules of objects in contact with each other, as when a lizard sits on a hot rock.

▲ Figure 40.11 **Heat exchange between an organism and its environment.**

Insulation

A major thermoregulatory adaptation in mammals and birds is insulation, which reduces the flow of heat between an animal and its environment. Sources of insulation include hair, feathers, and layers of fat formed by adipose tissue.

Many animals that rely on insulation to reduce overall heat exchange also adjust their insulating layers to help thermoregulate. Most land mammals and birds, for example, react to cold by raising their fur or feathers. This action traps a thicker layer of air, thereby increasing the insulating power of the fur or feather layer. To repel water that would reduce the insulating capacity of feathers or fur, some animals secrete oily substances, such as the oils that birds apply to their feathers during preening. Lacking feathers or fur, humans must rely primarily on fat for insulation.

Insulation is particularly important for marine mammals, such as whales and walruses. These animals swim in water colder than their body core, and many species spend at least part of the year in nearly freezing polar seas. The problem of thermoregulation is made worse by the fact that the transfer of heat to water occurs 50 to 100 times more rapidly than heat transfer to air. Just under their skin, marine mammals have a very thick layer of insulating fat called blubber. The insulation that blubber provides is so effective that marine mammals can maintain body core temperatures of about 36–38°C without requiring much more energy from food than land mammals of similar size.

Circulatory Adaptations

Circulatory systems provide a major route for heat flow between the interior and exterior of the body. Adaptations that regulate the extent of blood flow near the body surface or that trap heat within the body core play a significant role in thermoregulation.

In response to changes in the temperature of their surroundings, many animals alter the amount of blood (and hence heat) flowing between their body core and their skin. Nerve signals that relax the muscles of the vessel walls result in **vasodilation**, a widening of superficial blood vessels (those near the body surface). As a consequence of the increase in vessel diameter, blood flow in the skin increases. In endotherms, vasodilation usually warms the skin and increases the transfer of body heat to the environment by radiation, conduction, and convection (see Figure 40.11). The reverse process, **vasoconstriction**, reduces blood flow and heat transfer by decreasing the diameter of superficial vessels. It is vasoconstriction in blood vessels of the ear that allows the jackrabbit shown in Figure 40.1 to avoid overheating on hot desert days.

Like endotherms, some ectotherms control heat exchange by regulating blood flow. For example, when the marine iguana of the Galápagos Islands swims in the cold ocean, its superficial blood vessels undergo vasoconstriction. This process routes more blood to the central core of the iguana's body, conserving body heat.

In many birds and mammals, reducing heat loss from the body relies on **countercurrent exchange**, the transfer of heat (or solutes) between fluids that are flowing in opposite directions. In a countercurrent heat exchanger, arteries and veins are located adjacent to each other (Figure 40.12). As warm arterial blood moves from the body core to the extremities it transfers heat to the colder blood returning to the body core from the extremities. Because blood flows through the arteries and veins in opposite directions, heat is transferred along the entire length of the exchanger, maximizing the rate of heat exchange.

Certain sharks, bony fishes, and insects also use countercurrent heat exchange to warm parts of their bodies above ambient temperature. Although most sharks and bony fishes are ectotherms, countercurrent heat exchangers are found in some large, powerful swimmers, including great white sharks, bluefin tuna, and swordfish. By keeping the main swimming muscles several degrees warmer than tissues near the animal's surface, this adaptation enables the vigorous, sustained activity that is characteristic of these animals.

In controlling heat gain and loss, some species regulate the blood flow to the countercurrent exchanger. By allowing blood to pass through the heat exchanger or diverting it to other blood vessels, these animals are able to alter the rate of heat loss as needed. For example, insects flying in hot weather run the risk of overheating because of the large amount of heat produced by working flight muscles. In some species, the countercurrent mechanism can be "shut down," allowing muscle-produced heat to be lost from the thorax to the abdomen and then to the environment.

Cooling by Evaporative Heat Loss

Many mammals and birds live in places where thermoregulation requires cooling as well as warming. If the environmental temperature is above their body temperature, animals gain heat from the environment as well as from metabolism, and evaporation is the only way to keep body temperature from rising. Terrestrial animals lose water by evaporation from their skin and respiratory surfaces. Water absorbs considerable heat when it evaporates (see Chapter 3); this heat is carried away from the body surface with the water vapour.

Some animals have adaptations that can greatly augment the cooling effect of evaporation. Panting is important in

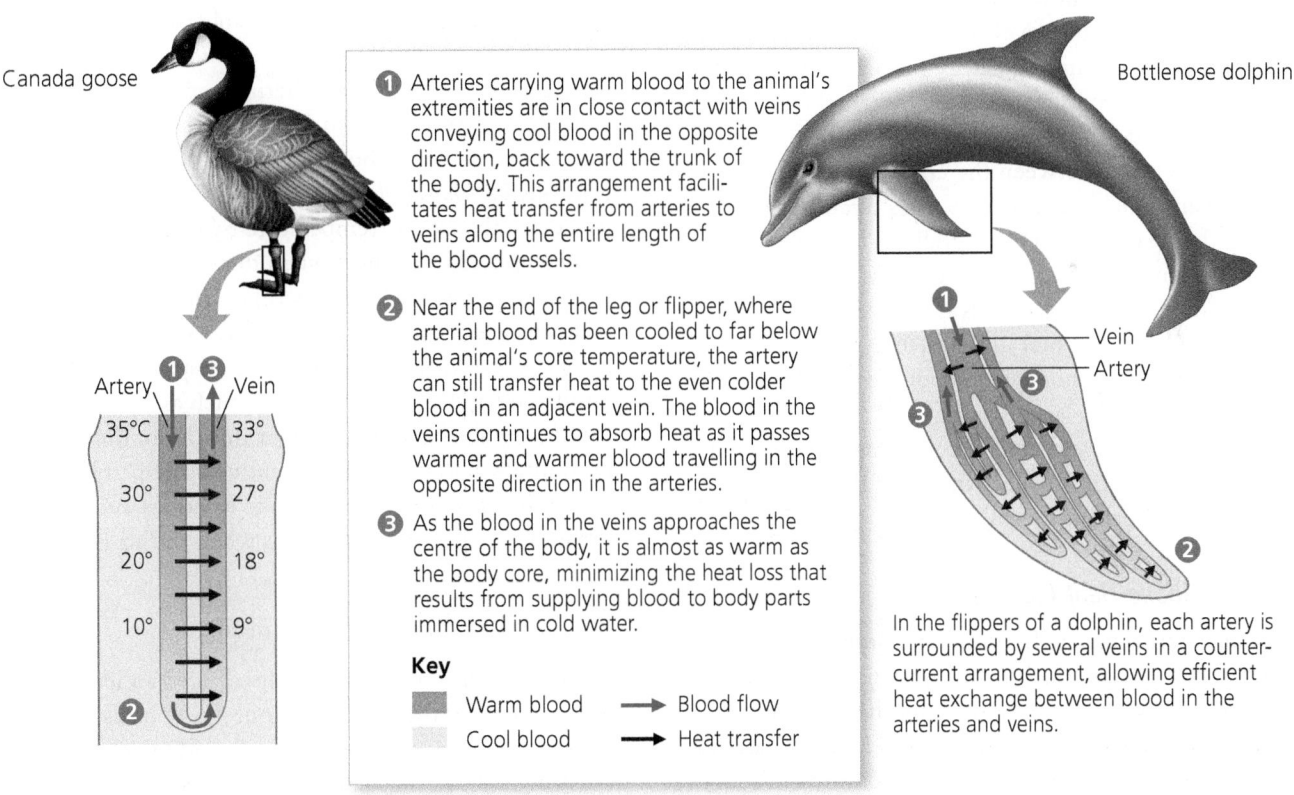

Canada goose

Bottlenose dolphin

1 Arteries carrying warm blood to the animal's extremities are in close contact with veins conveying cool blood in the opposite direction, back toward the trunk of the body. This arrangement facilitates heat transfer from arteries to veins along the entire length of the blood vessels.

2 Near the end of the leg or flipper, where arterial blood has been cooled to far below the animal's core temperature, the artery can still transfer heat to the even colder blood in an adjacent vein. The blood in the veins continues to absorb heat as it passes warmer and warmer blood travelling in the opposite direction in the arteries.

3 As the blood in the veins approaches the centre of the body, it is almost as warm as the body core, minimizing the heat loss that results from supplying blood to body parts immersed in cold water.

Artery Vein
35°C 33°
30° 27°
20° 18°
10° 9°

Key

Warm blood   → Blood flow
Cool blood   → Heat transfer

Vein
Artery

In the flippers of a dolphin, each artery is surrounded by several veins in a countercurrent arrangement, allowing efficient heat exchange between blood in the arteries and veins.

▲ Figure 40.12 **Countercurrent heat exchangers.** A countercurrent exchange system traps heat in the body core, thus reducing heat loss from the extremities, particularly when they are immersed in cold water or in contact with ice or snow. In essence, heat in the arterial blood emerging from the body core is transferred directly to the returning venous blood instead of being lost to the environment.

birds and many mammals. Some birds have a pouch richly supplied with blood vessels in the floor of the mouth; fluttering the pouch increases evaporation. Pigeons, for example, can use this adaptation to keep their body temperature close to 40°C in air temperatures as high as 60°C, as long as they have sufficient water. Sweating or bathing moistens the skin and enhances evaporative cooling. Many terrestrial mammals have sweat glands that are controlled by the nervous system.

Behavioural Responses

Both endotherms and ectotherms control body temperature through behavioural responses to changes in the environment. Many ectotherms maintain a nearly constant body temperature by engaging in relatively simple behaviours.

When cold, they seek warm places, orienting themselves toward heat sources and expanding the portion of their body surface exposed to the heat source. When hot, they bathe, move to cool areas, or turn in another direction, minimizing their absorption of heat from the sun. For example, a dragonfly's "obelisk" posture is an adaptation that minimizes the amount of body surface exposed to the sun and thus to heating (Figure 40.13).

Honeybees use a thermoregulatory mechanism that depends on social behaviour. In cold weather, they increase heat production and huddle together, thereby retaining heat. Individuals move between the cooler outer edges of the cluster and the warmer centre, thus circulating and distributing the heat. Even when huddling, honeybees must expend considerable energy to keep warm during long periods of cold weather. (This is the main function of storing large quantities of fuel in the hive in the form of honey.) In hot weather, honeybees cool the hive by transporting water to the hive and fanning with their wings, promoting evaporation and convection. Thus, a colony of honeybees uses many of the mechanisms of thermoregulation seen in individual organisms.

Adjusting Metabolic Heat Production

Because endotherms generally maintain a body temperature considerably higher than that of the environment, they must counteract continual heat loss. Endotherms can vary heat production—*thermogenesis*—to match changing rates of heat loss. Thermogenesis is increased by such muscle activity as moving or shivering. For example, shivering helps chickadees (genus *Poecile*), birds with a body mass of only 20 g, remain active and hold their body temperature nearly

▲ **Figure 40.13 Thermoregulatory behaviour in a dragonfly.** By orienting its body so that the narrow tip of its abdomen faces the sun, the dragonfly minimizes heating by solar radiation.

Robert Ganz

constant at 40°C in environmental temperatures as low as −40°C, as long as they have adequate food.

Some mammals possess brown adipose tissue (BAT), a tissue specialized to produce heat. The cells of BAT produce a protein, called thermogenin, that causes their abundant mitochondria to produce heat rather than ATP, a process known as **nonshivering thermogenesis**. Many small mammals, including infant humans, possess BAT in the region of the neck and shoulders where its metabolic activity keeps the body core warm. Until recently, it was thought that humans lose their BAT as they mature, but it is now known that adult humans possess BAT and produce more BAT in the cold, yet lose this capacity with age. Through shivering and nonshivering thermogenesis, mammals and birds in cold environments can increase their metabolic heat production by as much as five to ten times the levels that occur in warm conditions.

Some ectothermic animals are able to use metabolism to elevate body temperature. Because their thermoregulatory strategy is a mixture of ectothermy and endothermy, such animals are typically called *heterotherms*. When an ectotherm can elevate its whole body temperature for short periods, it is called a *temporal heterotherm*. Some large snakes are able to elevate their body temperature by coiling. They use this mechanism to retain heat when they are incubating eggs. *Spatial heterotherms* are ectothermic animals that are able to warm select tissues. The large sharks and tuna discussed earlier in this chapter are examples of spatial heterotherms. Similarly, large and active insects, such as bumblebees and moths, are able to heat the flight muscles of the thorax to be warmer than the environment or other parts of the body (Figure 40.14). By using metabolic reactions and shivering, these insects are able to fly even when the air is cold.

Acclimation and Acclimatization

Changes in environmental temperature can lead many animals to modify thermoregulation. Many birds and mammals respond to seasonal changes by adjusting their body covering to affect insulation. Wolves, for example, grow a thicker coat of fur in the winter and shed it in the summer. The main effect of changes in body covering may be linked to thermoregulation, but the environmental factor that

▲ Figure 40.14 **Preflight warm-up in the hawkmoth.** The hawkmoth (*Manduca sexta*) is one of many insect species that use a shivering-like mechanism for preflight warm-up of thoracic flight muscles. Warming up helps these muscles produce enough power to let the animal take off. Once the moth is airborne, flight muscle activity maintains a high thoracic temperature.

Source: Adaptation of figure 7 from "Thermoregulation in Endothermic Insects" by Bernd Heinrich from *Science,* August 1974, Volume 185(4153). Copyright © 1974 by AAAS. Reprinted with permission.

induces the seasonal acclimatization is not always temperature. Experimentally mimicking the seasonal changes in day length (photoperiod) is sufficient in many animals to trigger changes in thermoregulation.

Seasonal acclimatization in thermoregulation helps endotherms defend a warm body temperature, but with many ectotherms, seasonal changes in body temperature are largely unavoidable. The ectotherm responses to seasonal acclimatization or thermal acclimation allow them to preserve function despite changes in body temperature. The remodelling process can change the ability of the animal to survive at thermal extremes. For more than 50 years, researchers have been studying the mechanisms by which ectotherms remodel their cells and tissues in response to temperature (Figure 40.15).

Acclimatization in ectotherms often includes adjustments at the cellular level. Cells may produce variants of enzymes that have the same function but different optimal temperatures. Also, the proportions of saturated and unsaturated lipids in membranes may change; unsaturated lipids help keep membranes in a fluid state at lower temperatures (see Figure 7.5).

Some ectotherms that experience subzero body temperatures protect themselves by producing "antifreeze" compounds that prevent ice formation in their cells. In the Arctic Ocean and Southern (Antarctic) Ocean, these compounds enable certain fishes to survive in water as cold as −2°C, below the freezing point of unprotected body fluids (about −1°C).

▼ Figure 40.15 | **Inquiry**

How does thermal history affect thermal tolerance?

Experiment In the middle of last century, researchers from the Fisheries Research Board of Canada (now the Department of Fisheries and Oceans) began many studies exploring the influence of environmental factors on the physiology of commercially important fish and shellfish. Recognizing that the environmental tolerance of lobsters changed seasonally, Dr. D.W. McLeese reared groups of lobsters at three different temperatures (5, 15, and 25°C) for three weeks. He then exposed the animals to a range of normal water temperatures and determined their survival after two days.

Source: D.W. McLeese, Effects of temperature, salinity and oxygen on the survival of the American lobster, *Journal of the Fisheries Research Board of Canada* 13: 247-272 (1956). © Canadian Science Publishing or its licensors.

Results Increasing the acclimation temperature of lobsters increases the thermal tolerance. For example, a temperature of 27°C will kill a lobster acclimated to 5°C but will have no effect on lobsters acclimated at 15°C or 25°C.

Conclusion Over the three weeks of exposure, lobsters were able to remodel their physiology and anatomy in ways that made them better able to tolerate temperature extremes. In the many years since this early study, researchers have been able to better understand the control of the complex changes that contribute to sensitivity to temperature and other environmental conditions.

Source: Based on D. W. McLeese, Effects of temperature, salinity and oxygen on the survival of the American lobster, *Journal of the Fisheries Research Board of Canada* 13:247–272 (1956). © Jane B Reece.

WHAT IF? *What outcome might you predict if the experiment was designed to assess tolerance to low temperature? Other than temperature, what other environmental parameters change with the seasons in terrestrial and aquatic (freshwater and marine) environments?*

Physiological Thermostats and Fever

The regulation of body temperature in humans and other mammals is brought about by a complex system based on feedback mechanisms. The sensors for thermoregulation are concentrated in a brain region called the **hypothalamus**. A group of nerve cells in the hypothalamus functions as a thermostat, responding to body temperatures outside a

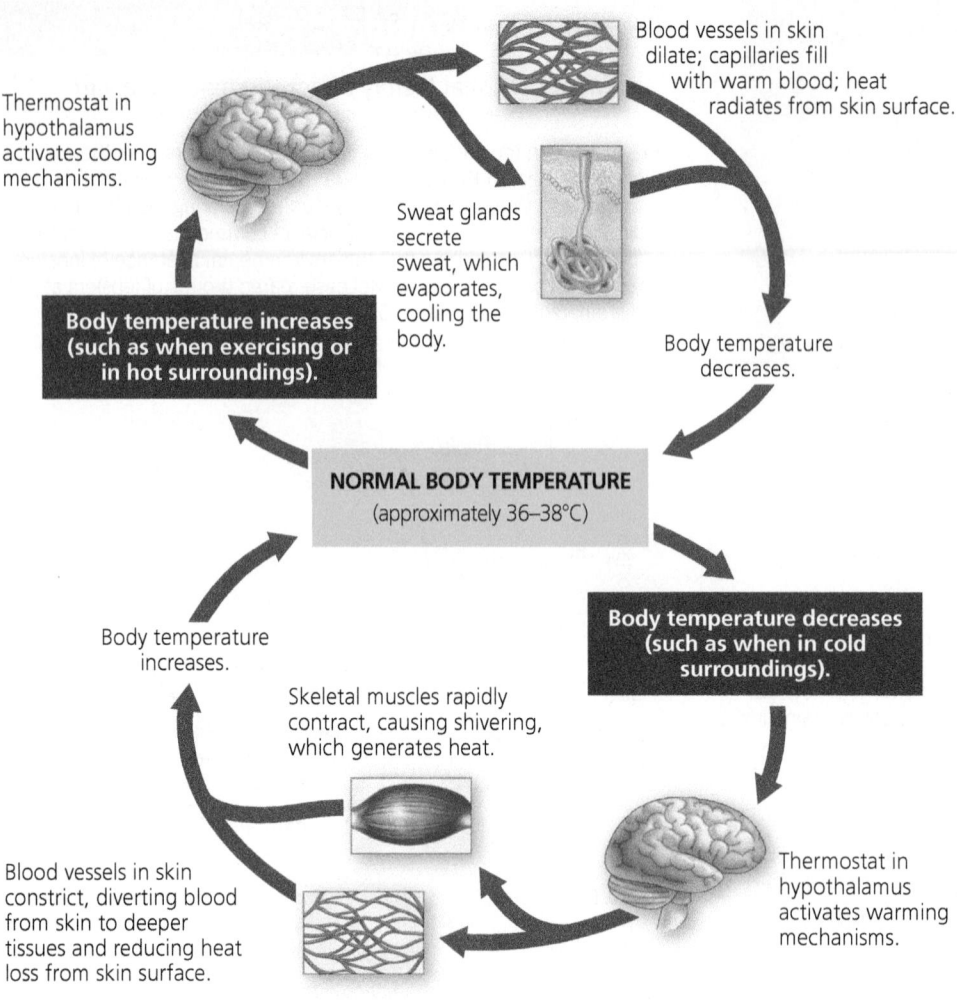

WHAT IF? *Suppose at the end of a hard run on a hot day you find that there are no drinks left in the cooler. If, out of desperation, you dunk your head into the cooler, how might the ice-cold water affect the rate at which your body temperature returns to normal?*

Thermostat in hypothalamus activates cooling mechanisms.

Blood vessels in skin dilate; capillaries fill with warm blood; heat radiates from skin surface.

Sweat glands secrete sweat, which evaporates, cooling the body.

Body temperature increases (such as when exercising or in hot surroundings).

Body temperature decreases.

NORMAL BODY TEMPERATURE (approximately 36–38°C)

Body temperature increases.

Body temperature decreases (such as when in cold surroundings).

Skeletal muscles rapidly contract, causing shivering, which generates heat.

Blood vessels in skin constrict, diverting blood from skin to deeper tissues and reducing heat loss from skin surface.

Thermostat in hypothalamus activates warming mechanisms.

normal range by activating mechanisms that promote heat loss or gain (Figure 40.16). Warm receptors signal the hypothalamic thermostat when temperatures increase; cold receptors signal when temperatures decrease. (Because the same blood vessel supplies the hypothalamus and ears, an ear thermometer records the temperature detected by the hypothalamic thermostat.) At body temperatures below the normal range, the thermostat inhibits heat loss mechanisms and activates heat-saving ones, such as vasoconstriction and the raising of fur, while stimulating heat-generating mechanisms (shivering and nonshivering thermogenesis). In response to elevated body temperature, the thermostat shuts down heat-retention mechanisms and promotes cooling the body by vasodilation, sweating, or panting.

In the course of certain bacterial and viral infections, mammals and birds develop fever, an elevated body temperature. A variety of experiments have shown that fever reflects an increase in the set point for the biological thermostat. For example, artificially raising the temperature of the hypothalamus in an infected animal reduces fever in the rest of the body!

Although only endotherms develop fever, lizards exhibit a related response. When infected with certain bacteria, the desert iguana (*Dipsosaurus dorsalis*) seeks a warmer environment and then maintains a body temperature that is elevated by 2–4°C. Similar observations in fishes, amphibians, and even cockroaches indicate that this response to certain infections is a common feature of many animal species.

Having explored thermoregulation in depth, we'll now consider some other energy-consuming processes and the different ways that animals allocate, use, and conserve energy.

CONCEPT CHECK 40.3

1. What mode of heat exchange is involved in "wind chill," when moving air feels colder than still air at the same temperature? Explain.
2. Flowers differ in how much sunlight they absorb. Why might this matter to a hummingbird seeking nectar on a cool morning?
3. Why does shivering accompany the onset of a fever?

For suggested answers, see Appendix A.

CONCEPT 40.4

Energy requirements are related to animal size, activity, and environment

One of the unifying themes of biology introduced in Chapter 1 is that life requires energy transfer and transformation. Like other organisms, animals use chemical energy for growth, repair, activity, and reproduction. The overall flow and transformation of energy in an animal—its **bioenergetics**—determines nutritional needs and is related to the animal's size, activity, and environment.

Energy Allocation and Use

As we have discussed in other chapters, organisms can be classified by how they obtain chemical energy. Most autotrophs, such as plants, use light energy to build energy-rich organic molecules and then use those organic molecules for fuel. Most heterotrophs, such as animals, must obtain their chemical energy from food, which contains organic molecules synthesized by other organisms.

Animals use chemical energy harvested from their food to fuel metabolism and activity (Figure 40.17). Food is hydrolyzed by enzymes (see Figure 5.2b), and nutrients are absorbed by cells. Most nutrient molecules are used to generate ATP. ATP produced by cellular respiration and fermentation powers cellular work, enabling cells, organs, and organ systems to perform the functions that keep an animal alive. Energy in the form of ATP is also used in biosynthesis, which is needed for body growth and repair, synthesis of storage material such as fat, and production of gametes. The production and use of ATP generates heat, which the animal eventually gives off to its surroundings.

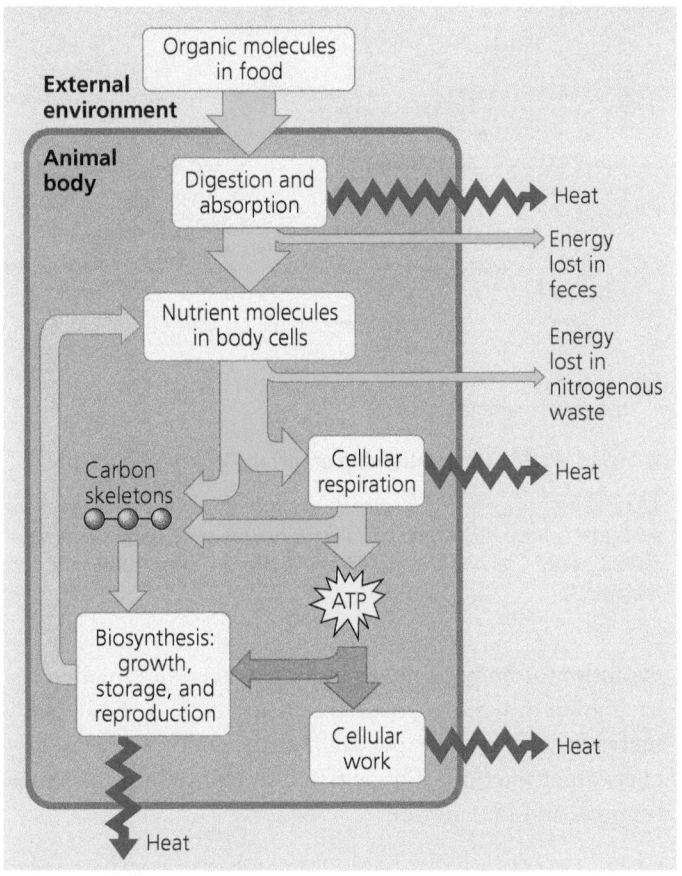

▲ Figure 40.17 **Bioenergetics of an animal: an overview.**

MAKE CONNECTIONS *Use the idea of energy coupling to explain why heat is produced in the absorption of nutrients, in cellular respiration, and in the synthesis of biopolymers (see Concept 8.3).*

Quantifying Energy Use

How much of the total energy an animal obtains from food does it need just to stay alive? How much energy must be expended to walk, run, swim, or fly from one place to another? What fraction of the energy intake is used for reproduction? Physiologists answer such questions by measuring the rate at which an animal uses chemical energy and how this rate changes in different circumstances.

The **metabolic rate** of an animal is the sum of all the energy used in biochemical reactions over a given time interval. Energy is measured in joules (J) and kilojoules (kJ), or in calories (cal) and kilocalories (kcal). (A kilocalorie equals 1000 calories, or 4184 joules. The unit Calorie, with a capital C, as used by many nutritionists, is actually a kilocalorie.)

Metabolic rate can be determined directly or indirectly. The amount of heat generated by metabolism can be measured using a calorimeter, which is a closed, insulated chamber equipped with a device that records an animal's heat loss. Metabolic rate can also be determined indirectly from the amount of oxygen consumed or rate of production of water or carbon dioxide produced in cellular respiration (Figure 40.18). To calculate metabolic rate over longer periods, researchers record the rate of food consumption, the energy content of the food (about 19–21 kJ per gram of protein or carbohydrate and about 38 kJ per gram of fat), and the chemical energy lost in waste products (feces and nitrogenous waste).

Minimum Metabolic Rate and Thermoregulation

Animals must maintain a minimum metabolic rate for basic functions such as cell maintenance, breathing, and heartbeat. Researchers measure this minimum metabolic rate differently for endotherms and ectotherms. The basal metabolic rate (BMR) is defined as the minimum metabolic rate of a nongrowing, unstressed endotherm at rest, with an empty digestive tract. **Basal metabolic rate (BMR)** is measured under a "comfortable" temperature range—a

▲ Figure 40.18 **Measuring the rate of oxygen consumption by a swimming shark.** A researcher monitors the drop in oxygen level in the recirculating water of a juvenile hammerhead's tank.

Jeff Rotman/Alamy

range that requires no generation or shedding of heat above the minimum. The minimum metabolic rate of ectotherms is called its **standard metabolic rate (SMR)**. It is determined at a specific temperature because changes in the environmental temperature alter body temperature and therefore metabolic rate. As with BMR in an endotherm, SMR in an ectotherm is determined when the animal is at rest, unfed, and unstressed.

Comparisons of minimum metabolic rates reveal that endothermy and ectothermy have different energy costs. The BMR for humans averages 7000–7500 kJ per day for adult males and 5500–6300 kJ per day for adult females. These BMRs are about equivalent to the rate of energy use by a 75-watt light bulb. In contrast, the SMR of an American alligator is only about 600 kJ per day at 37°C. Much of the 10-fold difference in metabolic rate between a human and an alligator at the same body temperature reflects the energetic costs of endothermy.

Influences on Metabolic Rate

Metabolic rate is affected by many factors besides whether the animal is an endotherm or an ectotherm. Some key factors are age, sex, size, activity, temperature, and nutrition. Here we'll examine the effects of size and activity.

Size and Metabolic Rate

Larger animals have more body mass and therefore require more chemical energy. Remarkably, the relationship between total metabolic rate and body mass is constant across a wide range of sizes and forms, as illustrated for various mammals in **Figure 40.19a**. In fact, for even more varied organisms ranging in size from bacteria to blue whales, metabolic rate remains roughly proportional to body mass to the three-quarter power ($m^{3/4}$). Scientists are still researching the basis of this relationship, which applies to ectotherms as well as endotherms.

The relationship of metabolic rate to size profoundly affects energy consumption by body cells and tissues. As shown in **Figure 40.19b**, the energy it takes to maintain each gram of body mass is inversely related to body size. Each gram of a mouse, for instance, requires about 20 times as many joules as a gram of an elephant, even though the whole elephant uses far more joules than the whole mouse. The smaller animal's higher metabolic rate per gram demands a higher rate of oxygen delivery. Correlated with its higher metabolic rate per gram, the smaller animal has a higher breathing rate, blood volume (relative to its size), and heart rate. Also, it must eat much more food per unit of body mass.

Bioenergetic considerations associated with body size provide a clear example of how trade-offs shape the

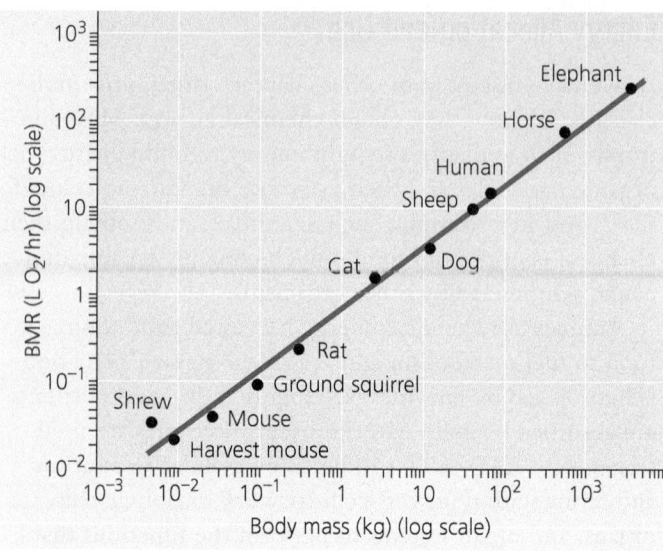

(a) Relationship of basal metabolic rate (BMR) to body size for various mammals. From shrew to elephant, size increases 1 millionfold.

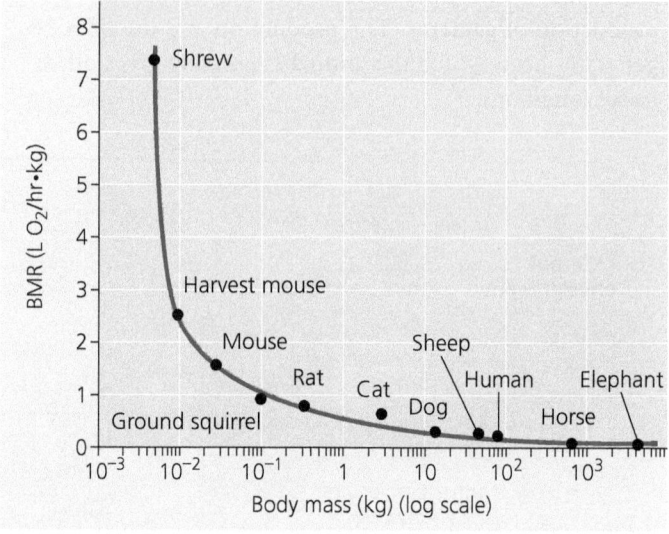

(b) Relationship of BMR per kilogram of body mass to body size for the same mammals as in (a).

▲ **Figure 40.19** **The relationship of metabolic rate to body size.**

INTERPRET THE DATA *Based on the graph in (a), one observer suggests that a group of 100 ground squirrels has the same basal metabolic rate as 1 dog. A second observer looking at the same graph disagrees. Who is correct?*

evolution of body plans. As body size becomes smaller, each gram of tissue increases in energy cost. As body size increases, energy costs per gram of tissue decrease, but an ever-larger fraction of body tissue is required for exchange, support, and locomotion.

Activity and Metabolic Rate

For both ectotherms and endotherms, activity greatly affects metabolic rate. Even a person reading quietly at a desk or an insect twitching its wings consumes energy beyond the BMR or SMR. Maximum metabolic rates (the highest rates of ATP use) occur during peak activity, such as lifting heavy weights, sprinting, or high-speed swimming. In general, the maximum metabolic rate an animal can sustain is inversely related to the duration of activity.

For most terrestrial animals, the average daily rate of energy consumption is 2 to 4 times BMR (for endotherms) or SMR (for ectotherms). Humans in most developed countries have an unusually low average daily metabolic rate of about 1.5 times BMR—an indication of their relatively sedentary lifestyles.

The fraction of an animal's energy "budget" that is devoted to activity depends on many factors, including its environment, behaviour, size, and thermoregulation. In the Scientific Skills Exercise, you'll interpret data on the annual energy budgets of three terrestrial vertebrates.

Torpor and Energy Conservation

Despite their many adaptations for homeostasis, animals may encounter conditions that severely challenge their abilities to balance their heat, energy, and materials budgets. For example, at certain times of the day or year, their surroundings may be extremely hot or cold, or food may be unavailable. **Torpor**, a physiological state of decreased activity and metabolism, is an adaptation that enables animals to save energy while avoiding difficult and dangerous conditions.

Many small mammals and birds exhibit a daily torpor that seems to be adapted to feeding patterns. For instance,

---

SCIENTIFIC SKILLS EXERCISE

Interpreting Pie Charts

How Do Energy Budgets Differ for Three Terrestrial Vertebrates? To explore bioenergetics in animal bodies, let's consider typical annual energy budgets for three terrestrial vertebrates that vary in size and thermoregulatory strategy: a 4-kg male Adélie penguin, a 25-g (0.025-kg) female deer mouse, and a 4-kg female ball python. The penguin is well insulated against his Antarctic environment but must expend energy in swimming to catch food, incubating eggs laid by his partner, and bringing food to his chicks. The tiny deer mouse lives in a temperate environment where food may be readily available, but her small size causes rapid loss of body heat. Unlike the penguin and mouse, the python is ectothermic and keeps growing throughout her life. She produces eggs but does not incubate them. In this exercise, we'll compare the energy expenditures of these animals for five important functions: basal (standard) metabolism, reproduction, thermoregulation, activity, and growth.

How the Data Were Obtained Energy budgets were calculated for each of the animals based on measurements from field and laboratory studies.

Data from the Experiments Pie charts are a good way to compare *relative* differences in a set of variables. In the pie charts here, the sizes of the wedges represent the relative annual energy expenditures for the functions shown in the key. The total annual expenditure for each animal is given below its pie chart.

Adélie penguin
4-kg male
340 000 kcal/yr

Deer mouse
0.025-kg female
4000 kcal/yr

Ball python
4-kg female
8000 kcal/yr

Key

◼ Basal (standard) metabolism   ◻ Activity

◼ Reproduction   ◼ Growth

◼ Thermoregulation

Interpret the Data

1. You can estimate the contribution of each wedge in a pie chart by remembering that the entire circle represents 100%, half is 50%, and so on. What percent of the mouse's energy budget goes to basal metabolism? What percent of the penguin's budget is for activity?

2. Without considering the sizes of the wedges, how do the three pie charts differ in which functions they include? Explain these differences.

3. Does the penguin or the mouse expend a greater proportion of its energy budget on thermoregulation? Why?

4. Now look at the *total* annual energy expenditures for each animal. How much more energy does the penguin expend each year compared to the similarly sized python?

5. Which animal expends the most kilocalories per year on thermoregulation?

6. If you monitored energy allocation in the penguin for just a few months instead of an entire year, you might find the growth category to be a significant part of the pie chart. Given that adult penguins don't grow from year to year, how would you explain this finding?

Based on M. A. Chappell et al., Energetics of foraging in breeding Adélie penguins, *Ecology* 74:2450–2461 (1993); M. A. Chappell et al., Voluntary running in deer mice: Speed, distance, energy costs, and temperature effects, *Journal of Experimental Biology* 207:3839–3854 (2004); T. M. Ellis and M. A. Chappell, Metabolism, temperature relations, maternal behavior, and reproductive energetics in the ball python (*Python regius*), *Journal of Comparative Physiology B* 157:393–402 (1987). © Jane B Reece.

▼ Figure 40.20   **Inquiry**

What happens to the circadian clock during hibernation?

Experiment To determine whether the 24-hour biological clock continues to run during hibernation, Paul Pévet and colleagues at the University of Louis Pasteur in Strasbourg, France, studied molecular components of the circadian clock in the European hamster (*Cricetus cricetus*). The researchers measured RNA levels for two clock genes—*Per2* and *Bmal1*—during normal activity (euthermia) and during hibernation in constant darkness. The RNA samples were obtained from the suprachiasmatic nuclei (SCN), a pair of structures in the mammalian brain that control circadian rhythms.

Results

Source: Adaptation of Figures 2b and 2c from The circadian clock stops ticking during deep hibernation in the European hamster by Florent G. Revel et al., from *Proceedings of the National Academy of Sciences USA,* August 2007, Volume 104(24). Copyright © 2007 by National Academy of Sciences. Reprinted with permission.

Conclusion Hibernation disrupted circadian variation in the hamster's clock gene RNA levels. Further experiments demonstrated that this disruption was not simply due to the dark environment during hibernation, since for nonhibernating animals RNA levels during a darkened daytime were the same as in daylight. The researchers concluded that the biological clock stops running in hibernating European hamsters and, perhaps, in other hibernators as well.

Source: Based on F. G. Revel et al., The circadian clock stops ticking during deep hibernation in the European hamster, *Proceedings of the National Academy of Sciences USA* 104:13816–13820 (2007). © Jane B Reece.

WHAT IF? *Suppose you discovered a new hamster gene and found that the levels of RNA for this gene were constant during hibernation. What could you conclude about the day and night RNA levels for this gene during euthermia?*

some bats feed at night and go into torpor in daylight. Chickadees and hummingbirds feed during the day and often go into torpor on cold nights; the body temperature of chickadees drops as much as 10°C at night, and the temperature of hummingbirds can fall 25°C or more. All endotherms that exhibit daily torpor are relatively small; when active, they have high metabolic rates and thus very high rates of energy consumption.

Hibernation is long-term torpor that is an adaptation to winter cold and food scarcity. When a mammal enters hibernation, its body temperature declines as its body's thermostat is turned down. The temperature reduction may be dramatic: Some hibernating mammals cool to as low as 1–2°C, and at least one, the Arctic ground squirrel (*Spermophilus parryii*), can enter a supercooled (unfrozen) state in which its body temperature dips below 0°C. Periodically, perhaps every two weeks or so, hibernating animals undergo arousal, raising their body temperature and becoming active briefly before resuming hibernation. Nevertheless, the energy savings from hibernation are huge: Metabolic rates during hibernation can be 20 times lower than if the animal attempted to maintain normal body temperatures of 36–38°C. As a result, hibernators such as the ground squirrel can survive through the winter on limited supplies of energy stored in the body tissues or as food cached in a burrow. Similarly, the slow metabolism and inactivity of *estivation*, or summer torpor, enables animals to survive long periods of high temperatures and scarce water supplies.

What happens to the circadian rhythm in hibernating animals? In the past, some researchers have reported detecting daily biological rhythms in hibernating animals. However, in some cases the animals were probably in a state of torpor, from which they could readily arouse, rather than "deep" hibernation. Recently, a group of researchers in France addressed this question in a different way, examining the machinery of the biological clock rather than the rhythms it controls (Figure 40.20). Working with the European hamster, they found that molecular components of the clock stopped oscillating during hibernation. These findings support the hypothesis that the circadian clock ceases operation during hibernation, at least in this species.

From discussing body shape to considering energy conservation, this chapter has focused on the whole animal. We surveyed common tissue types that make up organs and organ systems. We also investigated how body plans provide for exchange of materials with the environment, how some animals maintain a constant internal environment, and how size and activity affect metabolic rate. For much of the rest of this unit, we'll explore how specialized organs and organ systems enable animals to meet the basic challenges of life.

CONCEPT CHECK 40.4

1. If a mouse and a small lizard of the same mass (both at rest) were placed in experimental chambers under identical environmental conditions, which animal would consume oxygen at a higher rate? Explain.

2. Which animal must eat a larger proportion of its weight in food each day: a house cat or an African lion caged in a zoo? Explain.

3. **WHAT IF?** Suppose the animals at a zoo were resting comfortably and remained at rest while the nighttime air temperature dropped 10°C. What changes in minimum metabolic rate would you expect for an alligator and a lion?

For suggested answers, see Appendix A.

40 Chapter Review

Go to **MasteringBiology**® for Assignments, the eText, and the Study Area with Animations, Activities, Vocab Self-Quiz, and Practice Tests.

SUMMARY OF KEY CONCEPTS

CONCEPT 40.1

Animal form and function are correlated at all levels of organization (pp. 921–928)

- Physical laws constrain the evolution of an animal's size and shape. These constraints contribute to convergent evolution, the similar but independent adaptations of different species to a common environmental challenge.
- Each animal cell must have access to an aqueous environment. Simple two-layered sacs and flat shapes maximize exposure to the surrounding medium. More complex body plans have highly folded internal surfaces specialized for exchanging materials.
- In the hierarchical organization of animal bodies, groups of cells with a common structure and function make up **tissues**. Different tissues make up **organs**, which together make up **organ systems**. Animal tissues fall into four main groups, each with distinct functions. **Epithelial tissue** forms active interfaces with the environment on external and internal surfaces of the body. **Connective tissue** binds and supports other tissues. **Muscle tissue** contracts, moving the parts of the body. **Nervous tissue** transmits nerve impulses throughout the body.
- The endocrine and nervous systems are the two means of communication between different locations in the body. The endocrine system broadcasts signalling molecules called **hormones** everywhere via the bloodstream, but only certain cells are responsive to each hormone. The nervous system uses dedicated cellular circuits involving electrical and chemical signals to send information to specific locations.

? *For a large animal, what challenges would a spherical shape pose for carrying out exchange with the environment?*

CONCEPT 40.2

Feedback control maintains the internal environment in many animals (pp. 928–930)

- Faced with environmental fluctuations, animals *regulate* (control) certain internal variables while allowing other internal variables to *conform* to (correspond to) external changes. **Homeostasis** is the maintenance of a steady state despite internal and external changes.
- Homeostatic mechanisms are usually based on **negative feedback**, in which the **response** reduces the **stimulus**. In contrast, **positive feedback** involves amplification of a stimulus by the response and often brings about a change in state, such as the transition from pregnancy to childbirth.

- Regulated change in the internal environment is essential to normal function. **Circadian rhythms** are daily fluctuations in metabolism and behaviour tuned to the cycles of light and dark in the environment. Animals may remodel their physiology in response to environmental change. Such changes are **acclimation**, if in response to a single factor, such as temperature, or **acclimatization**, if in response to complex change, such as the transition to winter.

? *Is it accurate to define homeostasis as a constant internal environment? Explain.*

CONCEPT 40.3

Homeostatic processes for thermoregulation involve form, function, and behaviour (pp. 930–936)

- An animal maintains its internal temperature within a tolerable range by **thermoregulation**. **Endotherms** are warmed mostly by heat generated by metabolism. **Ectotherms** get most of their heat from external sources. Endothermy requires a greater expenditure of energy. Body temperature may vary with environmental temperature, as in *poikilotherms*, or be relatively constant, as in *homeotherms*.
- In thermoregulation, physiological and behavioural adjustments balance heat gain and loss, which occur through **radiation**, **evaporation**, **convection**, and **conduction**. Insulation and **countercurrent exchange** reduce heat loss, whereas panting, sweating, and bathing increase evaporation, cooling the body. Both ectotherms and endotherms adjust their rate of heat exchange with their surroundings by vasodilation or vasoconstriction and by behavioural responses.
- Many mammals and birds adjust their amount of body insulation in response to changes in environmental temperature. Ectotherms undergo a variety of changes at the cellular level to acclimatize to shifts in temperature.
- The **hypothalamus** acts as the thermostat in mammalian regulation of body temperature. Fever reflects a resetting of this thermostat to a higher set point in response to infection.

? *Given that humans thermoregulate, explain why your skin is cooler than your body core.*

CONCEPT 40.4

Energy requirements are related to animal size, activity, and environment (pp. 936–940)

- Animals obtain chemical energy from food, storing it for short-term use in ATP. The total amount of energy used in a unit of time defines an animal's **metabolic rate**. Metabolic rates are generally higher for endotherms than for ectotherms of the same size.
- Under similar conditions and for animals of the same size, the **basal metabolic rate** of endotherms is substantially higher than the **standard metabolic rate** of ectotherms. Minimum metabolic rate per gram is inversely related to body size among similar animals. Animals allocate energy for basal (or standard) metabolism, activity, homeostasis, growth, and reproduction.
- **Torpor**, a state of decreased activity and metabolism, conserves energy during environmental extremes. Animals may enter torpor during sleep periods (daily torpor), in winter (**hibernation**), or in summer (estivation).

? *Most hibernators are small. After reviewing Figure 40.19, suggest an explanation for this observation.*

LEVEL 1: KNOWLEDGE/COMPREHENSION

1. The body tissue that consists largely of material located outside of cells is
   a. epithelial tissue.
   b. connective tissue.
   c. muscle tissue.
   d. nervous tissue.

2. Which of the following would increase the rate of heat exchange between an animal and its environment?
   a. feathers or fur
   b. vasoconstriction
   c. wind blowing across the body surface
   d. countercurrent heat exchanger

3. Consider the energy budgets for a human, an elephant, a penguin, a mouse, and a snake. The _____ would have the highest total annual energy expenditure, and the _____ would have the highest energy expenditure per unit mass.
   a. elephant; mouse
   b. elephant; human
   c. mouse; snake
   d. penguin; mouse

LEVEL 2: APPLICATION/ANALYSIS

4. Compared with a smaller cell, a larger cell of the same shape has
   a. less surface area.
   b. less surface area per unit of volume.
   c. the same surface-to-volume ratio.
   d. a smaller cytoplasm-to-nucleus ratio.

5. An animal's inputs of energy and materials would exceed its outputs
   a. if the animal is an endotherm, which must always take in more energy because of its high metabolic rate.
   b. if it is actively foraging for food.
   c. if it is growing and increasing its mass.
   d. never; homeostasis makes these energy and material budgets always balance.

6. You are studying a large tropical reptile that has a high and relatively stable body temperature. How would you determine whether this animal is an endotherm or an ectotherm?
   a. You know from its high and stable body temperature that it must be an endotherm.
   b. You subject this reptile to various temperatures in the lab and find that its body temperature and metabolic rate change with the ambient temperature. You conclude that it is an ectotherm.
   c. You note that its environment has a high and stable temperature. Because its body temperature matches the environmental temperature, you conclude that it is an ectotherm.
   d. You measure the metabolic rate of the reptile, and because it is higher than that of a related species that lives in temperate forests, you conclude that this reptile is an endotherm and its relative is an ectotherm.

7. Which of the following animals uses the largest percentage of its energy budget for homeostatic regulation?
   a. a marine jelly (an invertebrate)
   b. a snake in a temperate forest
   c. a desert insect
   d. a desert bird

8. **DRAW IT** Draw a model of the control circuit(s) required for driving an automobile at a fairly constant speed over a hilly road. Indicate each feature that represents a sensor, stimulus, or response.

LEVEL 3: SYNTHESIS/EVALUATION

9. **EVOLUTION CONNECTION**
   In 1847, the German biologist Christian Bergmann noted that mammals and birds living at higher latitudes (farther from the equator) are on average larger and bulkier than related species found at lower latitudes. Suggest an evolutionary hypothesis to explain this observation.

10. **SCIENTIFIC INQUIRY**
    Eastern tent caterpillars (*Malacosoma americanum*) live in large groups in silk nests, or tents, which they build in trees. They are among the first insects to be active in early spring, when daily temperature fluctuates from freezing to very hot. Over the course of a day, they display striking differences in behaviour: Early in the morning, they rest in a tightly packed group on the tent's east-facing surface. In midafternoon, they are on its undersurface, each caterpillar hanging by a few of its legs. Propose a hypothesis to explain this behaviour. How could you test it?

11. **SCIENCE, TECHNOLOGY, AND SOCIETY**
    Medical researchers are investigating artificial substitutes for various human tissues. Why might artificial blood or skin be useful? What characteristics would these substitutes need in order to function well in the body? Why do real tissues work better? Why not use the real tissues if they work better? What other artificial tissues might be useful? What problems do you anticipate in developing and applying them?

12. **WRITE ABOUT A THEME: ENERGY AND MATTER** In a short essay (about 100–150 words) focusing on feedback control in thermoregulation, explain why shivering is likely during the onset of a fever.

13. **SYNTHESIZE YOUR KNOWLEDGE**

Oliver Wien/epa European Pressphoto Agency/Alamy Stock Photo

These macaques (*Macaca fuscata*) are partially immersed in a hot spring in a snowy region of Japan. What are some ways that form, function, and behaviour contribute to homeostasis for these animals?

For selected answers, see Appendix A.

41

Animal Nutrition

KEY CONCEPTS

41.1 An animal's diet must supply chemical energy, organic molecules, and essential nutrients

41.2 The main stages of food processing are ingestion, digestion, absorption, and elimination

41.3 Organs specialized for sequential stages of food processing form the mammalian digestive system

41.4 Evolutionary adaptations of vertebrate digestive systems correlate with diet

41.5 Feedback circuits regulate digestion, energy storage, and appetite

John Hyde/Alamy

▲ Figure 41.1 **How can you get fat on a vegetarian diet?**

The Need to Feed

Dinner time for most black bears (*Ursus americanus*), seen in **Figure 41.1**, consists of a varied diet predominated by berries and nuts. In fact, more than 85% of their diet is vegetarian, and in the summer it can be 100% vegetarian. The vegetable matter will be chewed into pieces, broken down in the bear's digestive tract by acid and enzymes, and the nutrients will be absorbed. Fruit contains a high amount of carbohydrate but is low in protein, so how can black bears get so big when plants are not an ideal food source? Bruce McLellan from the British Columbia Ministry of Forests and Range made a surprising discovery: Bears can rapidly gain fat and increase their mass very quickly on a fruit diet, but to meet their protein needs they break down muscle to liberate amino acids, and in doing so, lose muscle mass. **Nutrition** is the balance between nutrient intake and the needs of the body.

Almost all animals eat other organisms—dead or alive, piecemeal or whole. Unlike plants, animals must consume food. It is the source of both energy and the organic molecules used to assemble new molecules, cells, and tissues. The nature of the diet differs widely amongst animals. **Herbivores**, such as cattle, sea slugs, and termites, dine mainly on plants or algae. **Carnivores**, such as sharks, hawks, and spiders, mostly eat other animals. Bears and other **omnivores** (from the Latin *omni*, all) do not in fact eat everything, but they do regularly consume animals as well as plants or algae. We humans are typically omnivores, as are cockroaches and crows.

These strategies—herbivory, carnivory, and omnivory—distinguish feeding strategies based on the food animals most commonly eat. Keep in mind, however, that most animals are opportunistic feeders, eating foods outside their standard diet when their usual foods aren't available. For example, deer are herbivores, but in addition to feeding on grass and other plants, they occasionally eat insects, worms, or bird eggs. Note as well that microorganisms are an unavoidable "supplement" in every animal's diet.

Animals must eat. But to survive and reproduce, they must also balance their consumption, storage, and use of food. Bears, for example, store energy, largely in the form of body fat, in preparation for winter sleep. Eating too little food, too much food, or the wrong mixture of foods can endanger an animal's health. In this chapter, we will survey the nutritional requirements of animals, explore some of the diverse evolutionary adaptations for obtaining and processing food, and investigate the regulation of energy intake and expenditure.

CONCEPT 41.1

An animal's diet must supply chemical energy, organic molecules, and essential nutrients

Overall, an adequate diet must provide the chemical energy for cellular processes and building blocks for macromolecules.

The activities of cells, tissues, organs, and whole animals depend on sources of chemical energy in the diet. This energy is used to produce ATP, which powers processes ranging from DNA replication and cell division to vision and flight. To meet the continuous requirement for ATP, animals ingest and digest nutrients, including carbohydrates, proteins, and lipids, for use in cellular respiration and energy storage.

In addition to providing fuel for ATP production, an animal's diet must supply the raw materials needed for biosynthesis. Nucleic acids, carbohydrates, proteins, and lipids can be broken down, assimilated, and used as precursors to build the organic molecules an animal needs to grow, maintain itself, and reproduce.

Each animal has a suite of **essential nutrients**—molecules that the animal cannot produce and therefore must obtain from the diet. These nutrients include certain minerals and preassembled organic molecules. Some nutrients are essential for all animals, whereas others are needed only by certain species. For instance, ascorbic acid (vitamin C) is an essential nutrient for humans and other primates, guinea pigs, and some birds and snakes, but not for most other animals.

Essential Nutrients

There are four classes of essential nutrients: essential amino acids, essential fatty acids, vitamins, and minerals.

Essential Amino Acids

Animals require 20 amino acids to make proteins (see Figure 5.14). The majority of animal species have the enzymes to synthesize about half of these amino acids, as long as their diet includes sulphur and organic nitrogen. The remaining amino acids must be obtained from food in prefabricated form and are therefore called **essential amino acids**. Most animals, including adult humans, require eight amino acids in their diet (infants also need a ninth, histidine).

The proteins in animal products such as meat, eggs, and cheese are "complete," which means that they provide all the essential amino acids in their proper proportions. In contrast, most plant proteins are "incomplete," being deficient in one or more essential amino acids. For example, corn (maize) is deficient in tryptophan and lysine, and beans are deficient in methionine. However, vegetarians can easily obtain all of the essential amino acids by eating a varied diet of plant proteins.

Some animals have adaptations that help them through periods when their bodies demand extraordinary amounts of protein. In penguins, for example, muscle protein provides a source of amino acids for making new proteins when feathers are replaced after moulting.

Essential Fatty Acids

Animals produce the enzymes to synthesize most, but not all, of the fatty acids they need. The **essential fatty acids** are those that an animal cannot make, typically because they lack the ability to introduce specific types of double bonds. For example, humans require linoleic acid to make some membrane phospholipids. Because seeds, grains, and vegetables in the diets of humans and other animals generally furnish ample quantities of essential fatty acids, deficiencies in this class of nutrients are rare.

Nonessential fatty acids are also important dietary components because they are used to build cells. The fatty acids found in cell membranes and storage fats generally reflect those found in the diet. The profile of fatty acids in tissues, known as a *fatty acid signature*, can be used to determine what types of food an animal has consumed. Sarah Iverson (Dalhousie University) has pioneered the use of fatty acid analysis to determine what wild animals eat and their position in complex food webs (**Figure 41.2**).

▼ Figure 41.2 **Inquiry**

What do polar bears eat?

Experiment Sarah Iverson, of Dalhousie University, has developed methods to study food webs by characterizing the fatty acids found in animals and their diets. Teaming with polar bear researcher Ian Stirling (Canadian Wildlife Service), Dr. Iverson and her colleagues examined polar bear tissues from various locations around the Arctic. Polar bears can eat eight different marine mammal species, but the relative importance of the different species is unknown. They hypothesized that they could identify fatty acids that were indicative of specific prey species, and that these signature fatty acids would appear in the tissues of polar bears.

Results Walruses and bearded seals possessed two unusual fatty acids, 20:2Δ5,11 and 22:2Δ7,15 (Figure 41.2a). These signature fatty acids occurred in tissues of polar bears, and the levels varied between regions (Figure 41.2b). Also, males consistently had higher levels of these fatty acids than did females.

(a)

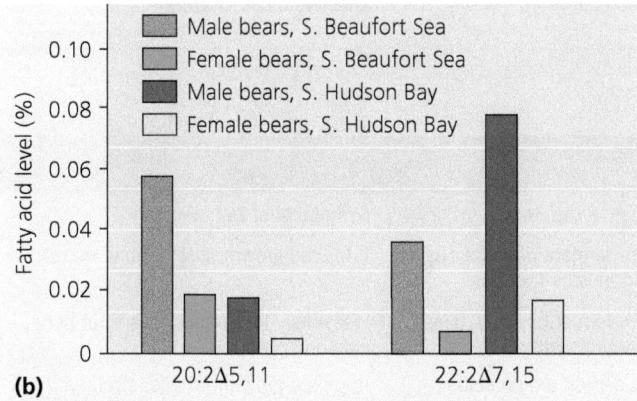

(b)

Conclusion Walruses and bearded seals possess unusual fatty acids in their tissues, which arise from a diet of marine molluscs. Polar bears consume bearded seals and walruses and retain signature fatty acids. Males eat more walruses and bearded seals than do females, but the importance to polar bear diets depends on the region.

Source: G. W. Thiemann, S. M. Budge, S. J. Iverson, and I. Stirling, Unusual fatty acid biomarkers reveal age- and sex-specific foraging in polar bears (*Ursus maritimus*), *Canadian Journal of Zoology* 85:505–517 (2007).

WHAT IF? *The main challenge of studying food webs in free-roaming animals is that you are never quite sure what happens when you aren't watching. What factors might complicate the conclusion that polar bears eat walruses and bearded seals? What might account for the differences between males and females? How would you test your hypotheses?*

Vitamins

Vitamins are organic molecules that have diverse functions and are required in the diet in very small amounts. As Nobel Prize winner Albert Szent-Györgyi pointed out, "A vitamin is a substance that makes you ill if you *don't* eat it." Vitamin B_2, for example, is converted in the body to FAD, a coenzyme used in many metabolic processes, including cellular respiration (see Figure 9.12). For humans, 13 vitamins have been identified. Depending on the vitamin, the required amount ranges from about 0.01 to 100 mg per day.

Vitamins are classified as water-soluble or fat-soluble (Table 41.1). The water-soluble vitamins include the B vitamins, which are compounds that generally function as coenzymes, and vitamin C, which is required for the production of connective tissue. Among the fat-soluble vitamins are vitamin A, which is incorporated into visual pigments of the eye, and vitamin K, which functions in blood clotting. Another is vitamin D, which aids in calcium absorption and bone formation. Our dietary requirement for vitamin D is variable because we synthesize this vitamin from other molecules when the skin is exposed to sunlight. The importance of vitamin D in the diet was identified in part through pioneering work of McGill graduate Dr. Charles Scriver. His studies on rickets in Quebec children led to a Canadian practice of supplementing milk with vitamin D, which has reduced the incidence of the disease from 1 in 200 to 1 in 20 000 children.

For people with poorly balanced diets, taking vitamin supplements that provide recommended daily levels is certainly reasonable. It is much less clear whether massive doses of vitamins confer any health benefits or are, in fact, safe. Moderate overdoses of water-soluble vitamins are probably harmless because excesses of these vitamins are excreted in urine. However, excesses of fat-soluble vitamins accumulate in the fat stores and can be released to the blood when the fat is metabolized, causing toxicity.

Minerals

Dietary **minerals** are inorganic nutrients, such as iron and sulphur, that are usually required in small amounts—from less than 1 mg to about 2500 mg per day. As shown in Table 41.2, minerals have diverse functions in animal physiology. Some are cofactors built into the structure of enzymes; magnesium, for example, is present in enzymes that split ATP. In contrast, sodium, potassium, and chloride are important in the functioning of nerves and in maintaining osmotic balance between cells and the surrounding body fluid. Vertebrates use one mineral—iodine—specifically to make thyroid hormones, which regulate metabolic rate. Vertebrates also require relatively large quantities of calcium and phosphorus for building and maintaining bone.

Table 41.1 Vitamin Requirements of Humans

Vitamin	Major Dietary Sources	Major Functions in the Body	Symptoms of Deficiency
Water-Soluble Vitamins			
B_1 (thiamine)	Pork, legumes, peanuts, whole grains	Coenzyme used in removing CO_2 from organic compounds	Beriberi (tingling, poor coordination, reduced heart function)
B_2 (riboflavin)	Dairy products, meats, enriched grains, vegetables	Component of coenzymes FAD and FMN	Skin lesions, such as cracks at corners of mouth
B_3 (niacin)	Nuts, meats, grains	Component of coenzymes NAD^+ and $NADP^+$	Skin and gastrointestinal lesions, delusions, confusion
B_5 (pantothenic acid)	Meats, dairy products, whole grains, fruits, vegetables	Component of coenzyme A	Fatigue, numbness, tingling of hands and feet
B_6 (pyridoxine)	Meats, vegetables, whole grains	Coenzyme used in amino acid metabolism	Irritability, convulsions, muscular twitching, anemia
B_7 (biotin)	Legumes, other vegetables, meats	Coenzyme in synthesis of fat, glycogen, and amino acids	Scaly skin inflammation, neuromuscular disorders
B_9 (folic acid)	Green vegetables, oranges, nuts, legumes, whole grains	Coenzyme in nucleic acid and amino acid metabolism	Anemia, birth defects
B_{12} (cobalamin)	Meats, eggs, dairy products	Production of nucleic acids and red blood cells	Anemia, numbness, loss of balance
C (ascorbic acid)	Citrus fruits, broccoli, tomatoes	Used in collagen synthesis; antioxidant	Scurvy (degeneration of skin and teeth), delayed wound healing
Fat-Soluble Vitamins			
A (retinol)	Dark green and orange vegetables and fruits, dairy products	Component of visual pigments; maintenance of epithelial tissues	Blindness, skin disorders, impaired immunity
D	Dairy products, egg yolk	Aids in absorption and use of calcium and phosphorus	Rickets (bone deformities) in children, bone softening in adults
E (tocopherol)	Vegetable oils, nuts, seeds	Antioxidant; helps prevent damage to cell membranes	Nervous system degeneration
K (phylloquinone)	Green vegetables, tea; also made by colon bacteria	Important in blood clotting	Defective blood clotting

Table 41.2 Mineral Requirements of Humans*

	Mineral	Major Dietary Sources	Major Functions in the Body	Symptoms of Deficiency
Greater than 200 mg per day required	Calcium (Ca)	Dairy products, dark green vegetables, legumes	Bone and tooth formation, blood clotting, nerve and muscle function	Impaired growth, loss of bone mass
	Phosphorus (P)	Dairy products, meats, grains	Bone and tooth formation, acid–base balance, nucleotide synthesis	Weakness, loss of minerals from bone, calcium loss
	Sulphur (S)	Proteins from many sources	Component of certain amino acids	Impaired growth, fatigue, swelling
	Potassium (K)	Meats, dairy products, many fruits and vegetables, grains	Acid–base balance, water balance, nerve function	Muscular weakness, paralysis, nausea, heart failure
	Chlorine (Cl)	Table salt	Acid–base balance, formation of gastric juice, nerve function, osmotic balance	Muscle cramps, reduced appetite
	Sodium (Na)	Table salt	Acid–base balance, water balance, nerve function	Muscle cramps, reduced appetite
	Magnesium (Mg)	Whole grains, green leafy vegetables	Enzyme cofactor; ATP bioenergetics	Nervous system disturbances
	Iron (Fe)	Meats, eggs, legumes, whole grains, green leafy vegetables	Component of hemoglobin and of electron carriers; enzyme cofactor	Iron-deficiency anemia, weakness, impaired immunity
	Fluorine (F)	Drinking water, tea, seafood	Maintenance of tooth structure	Higher frequency of tooth decay
	Iodine (I)	Seafood, iodized salt	Component of thyroid hormones	Goiter (enlarged thyroid gland)

*Additional minerals required in trace amounts are chromium (Cr), cobalt (Co), copper (Cu), manganese (Mn), molybdenum (Mo), selenium (Se), and zinc (Zn). All of these minerals, as well as those in the table, are harmful when consumed in excess.

Ingesting large amounts of some minerals can upset homeostatic balance and impair health. For example, excess intake of salt (sodium chloride) can contribute to high blood pressure. The recommended sodium uptake for Canadians between 19 and 30 years of age is 1.5 g/day. The typical Canadian male consumes more than 4 g of sodium per day; although women typically consume less sodium (2.8 g per day), consumption in either sex is well above recommended levels. The main culprit is not the salt you add to a meal but rather the sodium hidden in processed foods. Excessive consumption of iron can also endanger health: Liver damage due to iron overload affects as much as 10% of the human population in some regions of Africa where the water supply is especially iron-rich.

Dietary Deficiencies

Malnutrion (literally, poor nutrition) is when the diet has either too much or too little of critical nutrients. Most commonly, malnutrition is due to *undernutrition*, a shortage of an essential nutrient or caloric intake.

Deficiencies in Essential Nutrients

Insufficient intake of essential nutrients can cause deformities, disease, and even death. For example, cattle, deer, and other herbivores may develop dangerously fragile bones if they graze on plants growing in soil that lacks phosphorus. Some grazing animals obtain otherwise missing nutrients by consuming concentrated sources of salt or other minerals (Figure 41.3). Among carnivores, spiders have been found to adjust for dietary deficiencies by switching to prey that restores nutritional balance.

Like other animals, humans sometimes suffer from diets lacking in essential nutrients. A diet that provides insufficient amounts of one or more essential amino acids causes protein deficiency, the most

▲ **Figure 41.3 Obtaining essential nutrients.** A juvenile chamois (*Rupicapra rupicapra*), a herbivore, licks exposed salts and minerals in its rocky alpine habitat. This behaviour is common among herbivores living where soils and plants provide insufficient amounts of essential nutrients, such as sodium, calcium, phosphorus, and iron.

common type of malnutrition among humans. For example, protein deficiency may arise if a child's diet shifts from consisting of breast milk to consisting solely of foods that provide almost all of their calories in the form of starch and other carbohydrates. Such children, if they survive infancy, often have impaired physical and mental development.

Among populations subsisting on simple rice diets, individuals are often afflicted with vitamin A deficiency, which can cause blindness or death. To overcome this problem, scientists have engineered a strain of rice to synthesize beta-carotene, the orange-coloured pigment that is abundant in carrots. Once absorbed into the body, beta-carotene is converted to vitamin A. The potential benefit of this "Golden Rice" (see Chapter 38) is enormous because 1–2 million young children worldwide die every year from vitamin A deficiency.

Deficiencies in Energy Intake

When an animal does not consume adequate energy, a series of events unfold: The body uses up stored carbohydrates and fat and then begins breaking down its own proteins for fuel; muscles begin to decrease in size; and the brain may become protein-deficient. If energy intake remains less than energy expenditures, the animal will eventually die. Even if a seriously undernourished animal survives, some of the damage may be irreversible.

Human undernutrition is most common when drought, war, or another crisis severely disrupts the food supply. In sub-Saharan Africa, where the AIDS epidemic has crippled both rural and urban communities, approximately 200 million children and adults cannot obtain enough food.

Sometimes undernutrition occurs within well-fed human populations as a result of eating disorders. For example, anorexia nervosa leads individuals, usually female, to starve themselves compulsively.

Assessing Nutritional Needs

Determining the ideal diet for the human population is an important but difficult problem for scientists. There are many regional and cultural differences in nutritional requirements between human populations, some of which relate to genetic background. Aboriginal communities in Canada have a high prevalence of obesity and type 2 diabetes, arising when people are linked to a transition from subsistence on traditional foods to a greater reliance on processed foods. As objects of study, people present many challenges. Unlike laboratory animals, humans are genetically diverse. They also live in settings far more varied than the stable and uniform environment that scientists use to facilitate comparisons in laboratory experiments. Ethical concerns present an additional barrier. For example, it is not acceptable to investigate the nutritional needs of children in a way that might harm a child's growth or development.

The methods used to study human nutrition have changed dramatically over time. To avoid harming others, several of the researchers who discovered vitamins a century ago used themselves as subject animals. Today, researchers typically rely on the study of genetic defects that disrupt food uptake, storage, or use. For example, a genetic disorder called hemochromatosis causes iron build-up in the absence of any abnormal iron consumption or exposure. Fortunately, this common disorder is remarkably easy to treat: Drawing blood regularly removes enough iron from the body to restore homeostasis. By studying the defective genes that can cause the disease, scientists have learned a great deal about the regulation of iron absorption.

Many insights into human nutrition have come from *epidemiology*, the study of human health and disease at the population level. In the 1970s, for instance, researchers discovered that children born to women of low socioeconomic status were more likely to have neural tube defects, which occur when tissue fails to enclose the developing brain and spinal cord (see Chapter 47). In the 1980s, researchers discovered that supplementing diets with folic acid (vitamin B$_9$) greatly reduced the prevalence of neural tube defects. Policies were adopted that required folic acid be added into many foods, and now healthcare workers encourage pregnant women to supplement their diet with folic acid. Thus, at a time when microsurgery and sophisticated diagnostic imaging dominate the headlines, a simple dietary change such as folic acid supplementation or consumption of Golden Rice may be among the greatest contributors to human health.

CONCEPT CHECK 41.1

1. All 20 amino acids are needed to make animal proteins. Why aren't they all essential to animal diets?

2. MAKE CONNECTIONS Review the discussion of enzymes in metabolic reactions in Concept 8.4. Then explain why vitamins are required in very small amounts in the diet.

3. WHAT IF? If a zoo animal eating ample food shows signs of malnutrition, how might a researcher determine which nutrient is lacking in its diet?

For suggested answers, see Appendix A.

CONCEPT 41.2

The main stages of food processing are ingestion, digestion, absorption, and elimination

In this section, we turn from nutritional requirements to the mechanisms by which animals process food. Food processing can be divided into four distinct stages: ingestion, digestion, absorption, and elimination (Figure 41.4). The first

▲ Figure 41.4 **The four stages of food processing.**

stage, **ingestion**, is the act of eating or feeding. Figure 41.5 surveys and classifies the principal feeding mechanisms that have evolved in animals. Given the variation in food sources among animal species, it is not surprising that strategies for extracting resources from food also differ widely. We will focus, however, on the shared processes, pausing periodically to consider some adaptations to particular diets or environments.

In **digestion**, the second stage of food processing, food is broken down into molecules small enough for the body to absorb. Mechanical digestion, such as chewing, typically precedes chemical digestion. Mechanical digestion breaks food into smaller pieces, increasing the surface area available for chemical processes. Chemical digestion is necessary because animals cannot directly use the proteins, carbohydrates, nucleic acids, fats, and phospholipids in food. One problem is that these molecules are too large to pass through membranes and enter the cells of the animal. In addition, the large molecules in food are not all identical to those the animal needs for its particular tissues and functions. When large molecules in food are broken down into their components, however, the animal can use these smaller molecules to assemble the large molecules it needs. For example, although fruit flies and humans have very different diets, both convert proteins in their food to the same 20 amino acids from which they assemble all of the proteins specific for their species.

Recall from Chapter 5 that a cell makes a macromolecule by linking together smaller components; it does so by removing a molecule of water for each new covalent bond formed. Chemical digestion by enzymes reverses

Exploring Four Main Feeding Mechanisms of Animals

Suspension Feeders and Filter Feeders

Baleen

Hervey Bay Whale Watch

Many aquatic animals are **suspension feeders,** which eat small organisms or food particles suspended in the water. For example, clams and oysters feed on tiny morsels of food in the water that passes over their gills; cilia sweep the food particles to the animal's mouth in a film of mucus. **Filter feeders** such as the humpback whale shown above move water through a filtering structure to obtain food. Attached to the whale's upper jaw are comb-like plates called baleen, which strain small invertebrates and fish from enormous volumes of water.

Substrate Feeders

Substrate feeders are animals that live in or on their food source. This leaf miner caterpillar, the larva of a moth, is eating through the soft tissue of an oak leaf, leaving a dark trail of feces in its wake. Some other substrate feeders include maggots (fly larvae), which burrow into animal carcasses.

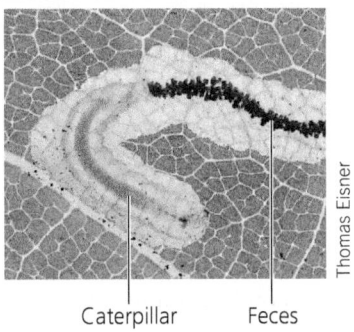

Thomas Eisner

Caterpillar   Feces

Fluid Feeders

Fluid feeders suck nutrient-rich fluid from a living host. This mosquito has pierced the skin of its human host with hollow, needle-like mouth parts and is consuming a blood meal (colourized SEM). Similarly, aphids are fluid feeders that tap the phloem sap of plants. In contrast to such parasites, some fluid feeders actually benefit their hosts. For example, hummingbirds and bees move pollen between flowers as they fluid-feed on nectar.

Scanpix Sweden AB

Bulk Feeders

Most animals, including humans, are **bulk feeders,** which eat relatively large pieces of food. Their adaptations include tentacles, pincers, claws, poisonous fangs, jaws, and teeth that kill their prey or tear off pieces of meat or vegetation. In this amazing scene, a rock python is beginning to ingest a gazelle it has captured and killed. Snakes cannot chew their food into pieces and must swallow it whole—even if the prey is much bigger than the diameter of the snake. They can do so because the lower jaw is loosely hinged to the skull by an elastic ligament that permits the mouth and throat to open very wide. After swallowing its prey, which may take more than an hour, the python will spend two weeks or more digesting its meal.

Gunter Ziesler/Getty Images

this process by breaking bonds with the addition of water (see Figure 5.2). *Hydrolysis*, literally splitting with water, is mediated by enzymes that are specialized to attack different macromolecules. Polysaccharides and disaccharides are split into simple sugars; proteins are broken down into amino acids; and nucleic acids are cleaved into nucleotides and their components. Enzymatic hydrolysis also releases fatty acids and other components from fats and phospholipids.

The last two stages of food processing occur after the food is digested. In the third stage, **absorption**, the animal's cells take up (absorb) small molecules such as amino acids and simple sugars. **Elimination** completes the process as undigested material passes out of the digestive system.

Digestive Compartments

In our overview of food processing, we have seen that digestive enzymes hydrolyze the same biological materials (such as proteins, fats, and carbohydrates) that make up the bodies of the animals themselves. How, then, are animals able to digest food without digesting their own cells and tissues? The evolutionary adaptation found across a wide range of animal species is the processing of food within specialized compartments. Such compartments can be intracellular, in the form of food vacuoles, or extracellular, as in digestive organs and systems.

Intracellular Digestion

Food vacuoles—cellular organelles in which hydrolytic enzymes break down food—are the simplest digestive compartments. The hydrolysis of food inside vacuoles, called *intracellular digestion*, begins after a cell engulfs solid food by phagocytosis or liquid food by pinocytosis (see Figure 7.19). Newly formed food vacuoles fuse with lysosomes, organelles containing hydrolytic enzymes. This fusion of organelles brings food in contact with the enzymes, allowing digestion to occur safely within a compartment enclosed by a protective membrane. A few animals, such as sponges, digest their food entirely by this intracellular mechanism (see Figure 33.4).

Extracellular Digestion

In most animal species, hydrolysis of food begins with *extracellular digestion*, the breakdown of food in compartments that are continuous with the outside of the animal's body. Having one or more extracellular compartments for digestion enables an animal to devour much larger pieces of food than can be ingested by phagocytosis.

Many animals with relatively simple body plans have a digestive compartment with a single opening (Figure 41.6).

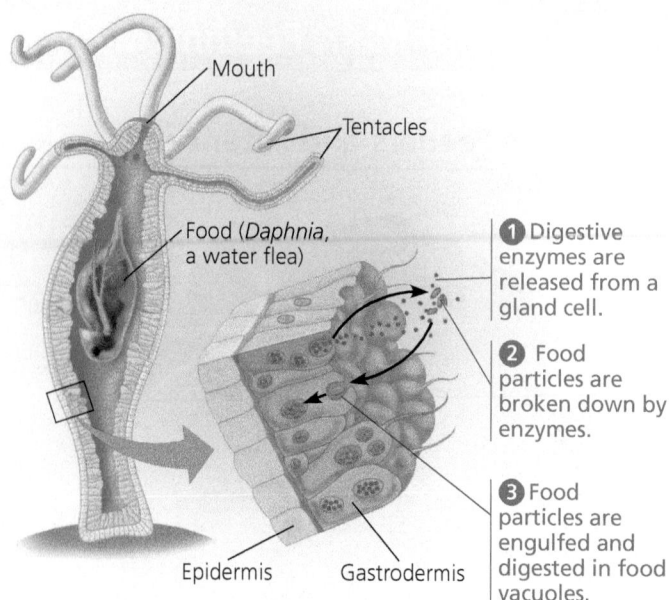

▲ Figure 41.6 **Digestion in a hydra.** Digestion begins in the gastrovascular cavity and is completed intracellularly after small food particles are engulfed by specialized cells of the gastrodermis.

This pouch, called a **gastrovascular cavity**, functions in digestion as well as in the distribution of nutrients throughout the body (hence the *vascular* part of the term). The carnivorous cnidarians called hydras provide a good example of how a gastrovascular cavity works. A hydra uses its tentacles to stuff captured prey through its mouth into its gastrovascular cavity. Specialized gland cells of the hydra's gastrodermis, the tissue layer that lines the cavity, then secrete digestive enzymes that break the soft tissues of the prey into tiny pieces. Other cells of the gastrodermis engulf these food particles, and most of the hydrolysis of macromolecules occurs intracellularly, as in sponges. After a hydra has digested its meal, undigested materials that remain in the gastrovascular cavity, such as exoskeletons of small crustaceans, are eliminated through the same opening by which food entered. Many flatworms also have a gastrovascular cavity with a single opening (see Figure 33.10).

In contrast with cnidarians and flatworms, most animals have a digestive tube extending between two openings, a mouth and an anus (Figure 41.7). Such a tube is called a *complete digestive tract* or, more commonly, an **alimentary canal**. Because food moves along the alimentary canal in a single direction, the tube can be organized into specialized compartments that carry out digestion and nutrient absorption in a stepwise fashion. An animal with an alimentary canal can ingest food while earlier meals are still being digested, a feat that is likely to be difficult or inefficient for animals with gastrovascular cavities. In the next section, we'll explore the spatial and functional organization of an alimentary canal.

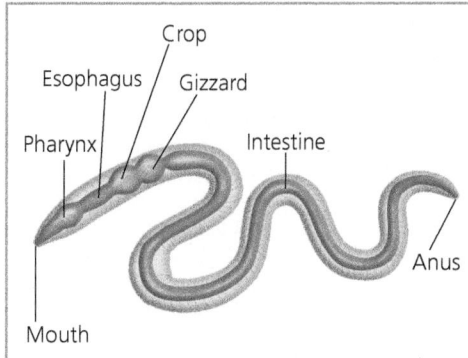

(a) **Earthworm.** The alimentary canal of an earthworm includes a muscular pharynx that sucks food in through the mouth. Food passes through the esophagus and is stored and moistened in the crop. Mechanical digestion occurs in the muscular gizzard, which pulverizes food with the aid of small bits of sand and gravel. Further digestion and absorption occur in the intestine.

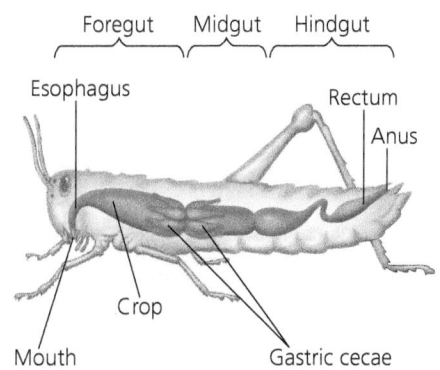

(b) **Grasshopper.** A grasshopper has several digestive chambers grouped into three main regions: a foregut, with an esophagus and crop; a midgut; and a hindgut. Food is moistened and stored in the crop, but most digestion occurs in the midgut. Pouches called gastric cecae (singular, *ceca*) extend from the beginning of the midgut and function in digestion and absorption.

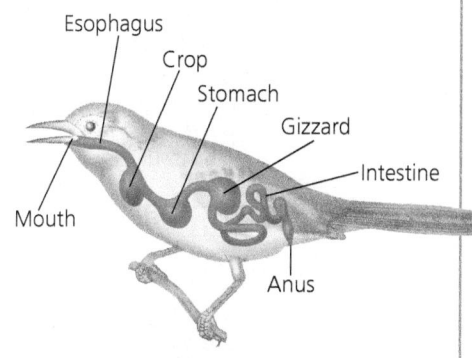

(c) **Bird.** Many birds have a crop for storing food and a stomach and gizzard for mechanically digesting it. Chemical digestion and absorption of nutrients occur in the intestine.

▲ Figure 41.7 **Variation in alimentary canals.**

CONCEPT CHECK 41.2

1. Distinguish the overall structure of a gastrovascular cavity from that of an alimentary canal.

2. In what sense are nutrients from a recently ingested meal not really "inside" your body prior to the absorption stage of food processing?

3. **WHAT IF?** Thinking in broad terms, what similarities can you identify between digestion in an animal body and the breakdown of gasoline in an automobile? (You don't have to know about auto mechanics.)

For suggested answers, see Appendix A.

CONCEPT 41.3

Organs specialized for sequential stages of food processing form the mammalian digestive system

Because most animals, including mammals, have an alimentary canal, we can use the mammalian digestive system as a representative example of the general principles of food processing. In mammals, the digestive system consists of the alimentary canal and various accessory glands that secrete digestive juices through ducts into the canal (**Figure 41.8**). The accessory glands of the mammalian digestive system are three pairs of salivary glands, the pancreas, the liver, and the gallbladder.

Food is pushed along the alimentary canal by **peristalsis**, alternating waves of contraction and relaxation in the smooth muscles lining the canal. At some of the junctions between specialized compartments, the muscular layer forms ringlike valves called **sphincters**. Acting like drawstrings to close off the alimentary canal, sphincters regulate the passage of material between compartments.

Using the human digestive system as a model, let's now follow a meal through the alimentary canal. As we do so, we'll examine in more detail what happens to the food in each digestive compartment along the way.

The Oral Cavity, Pharynx, and Esophagus

Ingestion and the initial steps of digestion occur in the mouth, or **oral cavity**. Mechanical digestion begins as teeth of various shapes cut, mash, and grind food, making the food easier to swallow and increasing its surface area. Meanwhile, the presence of food stimulates a nervous reflex that causes the **salivary glands** to deliver saliva through ducts to the oral cavity. Saliva may also be released before food enters the mouth, triggered by a learned association between eating and the time of day, a cooking odour, or another stimulus.

Saliva initiates chemical digestion while also protecting the oral cavity. The enzyme **salivary amylase** hydrolyzes starch (a glucose polymer from plants) and glycogen (a glucose polymer from animals) into smaller polysaccharides and the disaccharide maltose. Much of the protective effect of saliva is provided by **mucus**, which is a viscous mixture of water, salts, cells, and slippery glycoproteins (carbohydrate-protein complexes) called mucins. Mucus in saliva protects the lining of the mouth from abrasion and

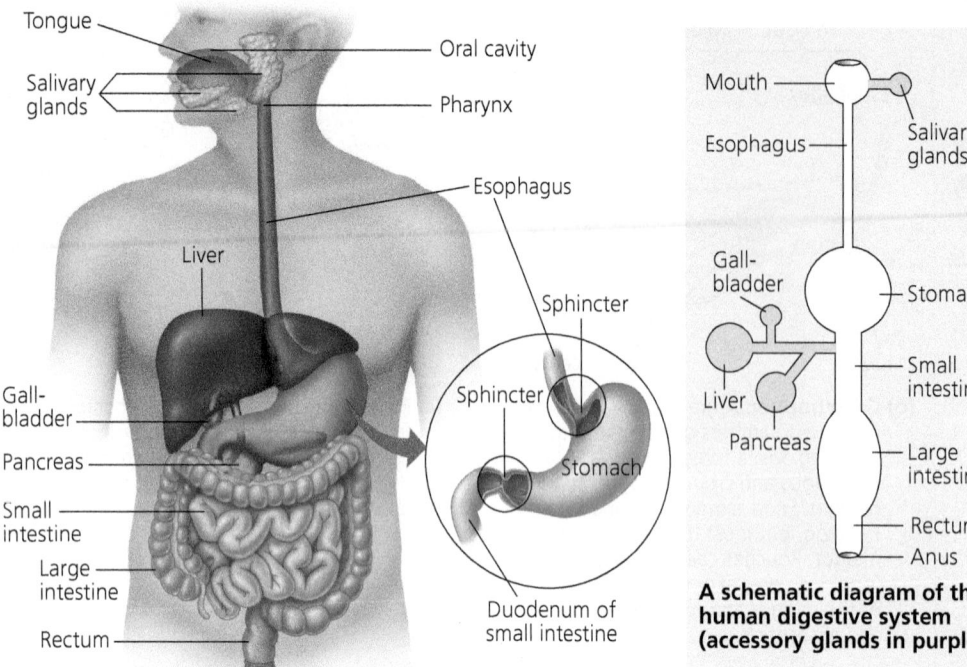

Tongue
Oral cavity
Salivary glands
Pharynx
Esophagus
Liver
Sphincter
Gall-bladder
Sphincter
Pancreas
Small intestine
Stomach
Large intestine
Rectum
Duodenum of small intestine
Anus

Source: *Human Anatomy and Physiology*, 8th edition, by Elaine N. Marieb and Katja Hoehn. Copyright © 2010 by Pearson Education. Reprinted and electronically reproduced by permission of Pearson Education, Inc., Upper Saddle River, New Jersey.

Mouth
Esophagus
Salivary glands
Gall-bladder
Stomach
Liver
Small intestine
Pancreas
Large intestine
Rectum
Anus

A schematic diagram of the human digestive system (accessory glands in purple)

Source: Figure adapted from *Human Physiology*, 3rd edition, by R. A. Rhodes. Copyright © 1996 by Brooks/Cole, a part of Cengage Learning, Inc. Reprinted with permission. www.cengage.com/permissions.

◄ **Figure 41.8 The human digestive system.** After food is chewed and swallowed, it takes 5–10 seconds for it to pass down the esophagus and into the stomach, where it spends 2–6 hours being partially digested. Final digestion and nutrient absorption occur in the small intestine over a period of 5–6 hours. In 12–24 hours, any undigested material passes through the large intestine, and feces are expelled through the anus.

lubricates food for easier swallowing. Additional components of saliva include buffers, which help prevent tooth decay by neutralizing acid, and antimicrobial agents (such as lysozyme; see Figure 5.16), which protect against bacteria that enter the mouth with food.

Much as a doorman screens and assists people entering a building, the tongue aids digestive processes by evaluating ingested material and then enabling its further passage. When food arrives at the oral cavity, the tongue plays a critical role in distinguishing which foods should be processed further. (See Chapter 50 for a discussion of the sense of taste.) After food is deemed acceptable and chewing commences, tongue movements manipulate the food, helping shape it into a ball called a **bolus**. During swallowing,

the tongue provides further help, pushing the bolus to the back of the oral cavity and into the pharynx.

The **pharynx**, or throat region, opens to two passageways: the trachea (windpipe) and the esophagus (Figure 41.9). The trachea leads to the lungs (see Figure 42.23), whereas the **esophagus** connects to the stomach. Once food enters the esophagus, peristaltic contractions of smooth muscle move each bolus to the stomach.

Swallowing must be carefully choreographed to keep food and liquids from entering the trachea and causing choking, a blockage of the trachea. The resulting lack of airflow into the lungs can be fatal if the material is not dislodged by vigorous coughing, a series of back slaps, or a forced upward thrust of the diaphragm (the Heimlich manoeuvre).

▶ **Figure 41.9 Intersection of the human airway and digestive tract.** In humans, the pharynx connects to the trachea and the esophagus. **(a)** At most times, a contracted sphincter seals off the esophagus while the trachea remains open. **(b)** When a food bolus arrives at the pharynx, the swallowing reflex is triggered. Movement of the larynx, the upper part of the airway, tips a flap of tissue called the epiglottis down, preventing food from entering the trachea. At the same time, the esophageal sphincter relaxes, allowing the bolus to pass into the esophagus. The trachea then reopens, and peristaltic contractions of the esophagus move the bolus to the stomach.

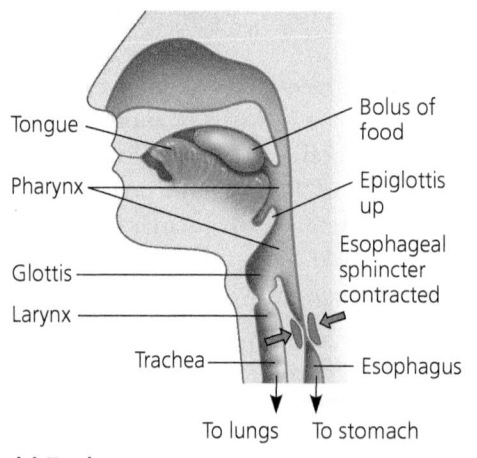

Tongue
Pharynx
Glottis
Larynx
Bolus of food
Epiglottis up
Esophageal sphincter contracted
Trachea
Esophagus

To lungs   To stomach

(a) Trachea open

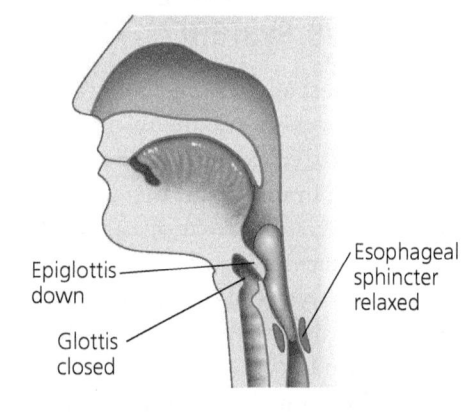

Epiglottis down
Glottis closed
Esophageal sphincter relaxed

(b) Esophagus open

Digestion in the Stomach

The **stomach**, which is located just below the diaphragm, stores food and begins digestion of proteins. With accordion-like folds and a very elastic wall, this organ can stretch to accommodate about 2 L of food and fluid. The stomach secretes a digestive fluid called **gastric juice** and mixes this secretion with the food through a churning action. This mixture of ingested food and digestive juice is called **chyme**.

Chemical Digestion in the Stomach

Two components of gastric juice carry out chemical digestion. One is hydrochloric acid (HCl), which disrupts the extracellular matrix that binds cells together in meat and plant material. The concentration of HCl is so high that the pH of gastric juice is about 2, acidic enough to dissolve iron nails (and to kill most bacteria). This low pH denatures (unfolds) proteins in food, increasing exposure of their peptide bonds. The exposed bonds are attacked by the second component of gastric juice—a **protease**, or protein-digesting enzyme, called **pepsin**. Unlike most enzymes, pepsin works best in a strongly acidic environment. By breaking peptide bonds, it cleaves proteins into smaller polypeptides. Further digestion to individual amino acids occurs in the small intestine.

Why doesn't gastric juice destroy the stomach cells from the inside? The answer is that the ingredients of gastric juice are kept inactive until they are released into the lumen (cavity) of the stomach. The components of gastric juice are produced by cells in the gastric glands of the stomach (**Figure 41.10**). *Parietal cells* secrete hydrogen and chloride ions. Using an ATP-driven pump, the parietal cells expel hydrogen ions into the lumen. The movement of hydrogen ions out of the parietal cell draws chloride out of the cell through specific membrane channels. Though they arrive in the lumen by different routes, the secretion of hydrogen and chloride ions is chemically equivalent to secreting hydrochloric acid (HCl). Meanwhile, *chief cells* release pepsin into the lumen in an inactive form called **pepsinogen**. When exposed to the low pH of the stomach, pepsinogen unfolds and activates itself into pepsin by clipping off a small portion of the molecule, which exposes its active site. Through these processes, both HCl and pepsin form in the lumen of the stomach, not within the cells of the gastric glands.

After a small amount of pepsinogen converts itself to pepsin, pepsin itself helps activate the remaining pepsinogen. Pepsin, like HCl, can clip pepsinogen to expose the enzyme's active site. This generates more pepsin, which activates more pepsinogen, forming more active enzyme. This series of events is an example of positive feedback, which amplifies the effect of an initially small input.

When HCl and pepsin form within the stomach lumen, why aren't the cells that line the stomach damaged? Actually, these cells are vulnerable to gastric juice as well as to acid-tolerant pathogens in food or water. However, the stomach lining protects against self-digestion by secreting mucus. In addition, cell division adds a new epithelial layer every three days, replacing cells eroded by digestive juices. Despite these defences, damaged areas

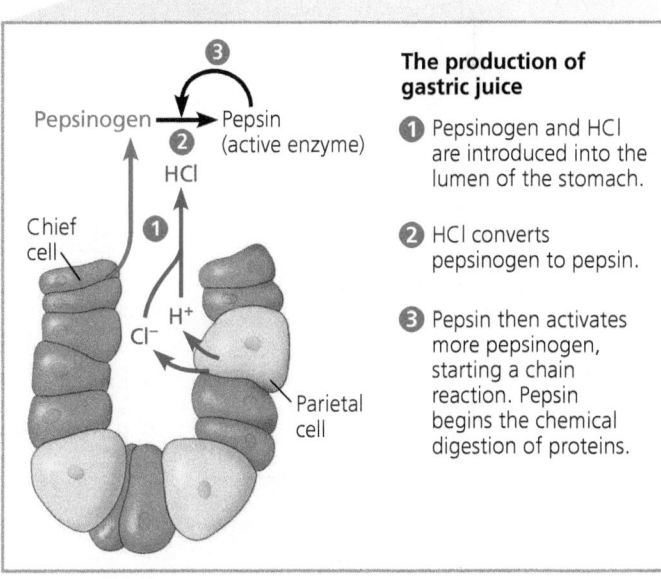

Interior surface of stomach. The interior surface of the stomach wall is highly folded and dotted with pits leading into tubular gastric glands.

Gastric gland. The gastric glands have three types of cells that secrete different components of the gastric juice: mucous cells, chief cells, and parietal cells.

Mucous cells secrete mucus, which lubricates and protects the cells lining the stomach.

Chief cells secrete pepsinogen, an inactive form of the digestive enzyme pepsin.

Parietal cells produce the components of hydrochloric acid (HCl).

Stomach

Epithelium

The production of gastric juice

1. Pepsinogen and HCl are introduced into the lumen of the stomach.

2. HCl converts pepsinogen to pepsin.

3. Pepsin then activates more pepsinogen, starting a chain reaction. Pepsin begins the chemical digestion of proteins.

Pepsinogen → Pepsin (active enzyme)

HCl

Chief cell

H^+

Cl^-

Parietal cell

▲ Figure 41.10 **The stomach and its secretions.** The magnified area shows the base of the gastric pits where acid and pepsinogen are secreted.

of the stomach lining called gastric ulcers may appear. For decades, scientists thought they were caused by psychological stress and resulting excess acid secretion. In 1982, however, Australian researchers Barry Marshall and Robin Warren reported that infection by the acid-tolerant bacterium *Helicobacter pylori* causes ulcers. They also demonstrated that an antibiotic treatment could cure most gastric ulcers. For these findings, they were awarded the Nobel Prize in 2005.

Stomach Dynamics

Chemical digestion by gastric juice is facilitated by the churning action of the stomach. This coordinated series of muscle contractions and relaxations mixes your stomach contents about every 20 seconds. As a result of mixing and enzyme action, what begins as a recently swallowed meal becomes the acidic, nutrient-rich broth known as chyme. Most of the time, the stomach is closed off at both ends (see Figure 41.8). The sphincter between the esophagus

and the stomach normally opens only when a bolus arrives. Occasionally, however, a person experiences acid reflux, a backflow of chyme from the stomach into the lower end of the esophagus. The resulting irritation of the esophagus is commonly called "heartburn."

The contents of the stomach typically pass into the small intestine within 2–6 hours after a meal. The sphincter located where the stomach opens to the small intestine helps regulate passage into the small intestine, allowing only one squirt of chyme at a time.

Digestion in the Small Intestine

Although chemical digestion of some nutrients begins in the oral cavity or stomach, most enzymatic hydrolysis of the macromolecules from food occurs in the **small intestine (Figure 41.11).** Over 6 m long in humans, the small intestine is the alimentary canal's longest compartment. Its name refers to its small diameter compared with that of the large intestine. The first 25 cm or so of the small

▼ Figure 41.11 **Chemical digestion in the human digestive system.**

? *Pepsin is resistant to the denaturing effect of the low pH environment of the stomach. Thinking about the different digestive processes that occur in the small intestine, describe an adaptation shared by the digestive enzymes in that compartment.*

intestine forms the **duodenum**. It is here that chyme from the stomach mixes with digestive juices from the pancreas, liver, and gallbladder, as well as from gland cells of the intestinal wall itself. As you will see in Concept 41.5, hormones released by the stomach and duodenum control the digestive secretions into the alimentary canal.

Pancreatic Secretions

The **pancreas** aids chemical digestion by producing an alkaline solution rich in bicarbonate as well as several enzymes. The bicarbonate neutralizes the acidity of chyme. Among the pancreatic enzymes are trypsin and chymotrypsin, proteases secreted into the duodenum in inactive forms (see Figure 41.11). In a chain reaction similar to activation of pepsin, they are activated when safely located in the lumen within the duodenum.

Bile Production by the Liver

Digestion of fats and other lipids begins in the small intestine and relies on the production of **bile**, a mixture of substances that is made in the **liver**. Bile contains bile salts, which act as emulsifiers (detergents) that aid in digestion and absorption of lipids. Bile is stored and concentrated in the **gallbladder**.

Bile production is integral to one of the other vital functions of the liver: the destruction of red blood cells that are no longer fully functional. In producing bile, the liver incorporates some pigments that are by-products of red blood cell disassembly. These bile pigments are then eliminated from the body with the feces. In some liver or blood disorders, bile pigments accumulate in the skin, resulting in a characteristic yellowing called jaundice.

Secretions of the Small Intestine

The epithelial lining of the duodenum is the source of several digestive enzymes (see Figure 41.11). Some are secreted into the lumen of the duodenum, whereas others are bound to the surface of epithelial cells.

While enzymatic hydrolysis proceeds, peristalsis moves the mixture of chyme and digestive juices along the small intestine. Most digestion is completed in the duodenum. The remaining regions of the small intestine, called the *jejunum* and *ileum*, function mainly in the absorption of nutrients and water.

Absorption in the Small Intestine

To reach body tissues, nutrients in the lumen must first cross the lining of the alimentary canal. Most of this absorption occurs across the highly folded surface of the small intestine, as illustrated in Figure 41.12. Large folds in the lining encircle the intestine and are studded with finger-like projections called **villi**. In turn, each epithelial cell of a villus has on its apical surface many microscopic projections, or **microvilli**, that are exposed to the intestinal lumen. The many side-by-side microvilli give cells of the intestinal epithelium a brush-like appearance—reflected in the name *brush border*. Together, the folds, villi, and microvilli of the small intestine have a surface area of 300 m^2,

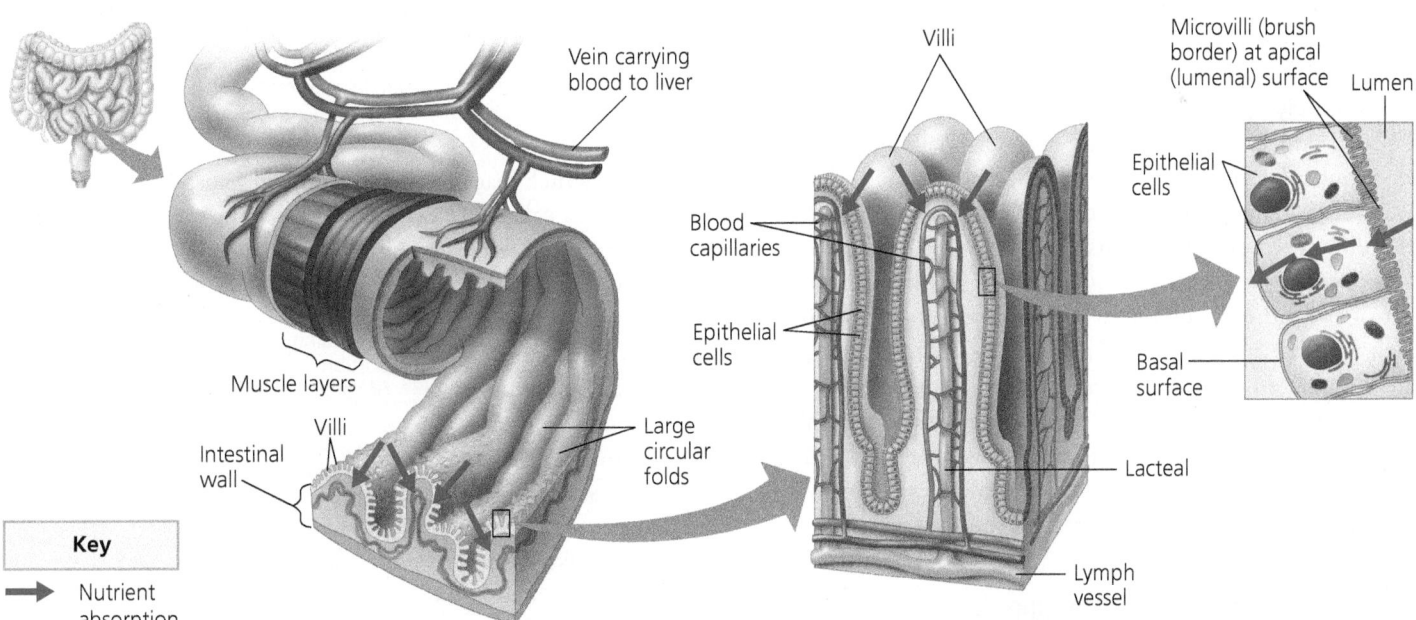

▲ Figure 41.12 **Nutrient absorption in the small intestine.**

? *Tapeworms sometimes infect humans, anchoring themselves to the wall of the small intestine. Based on how digestion is compartmentalized along the mammalian alimentary canal, what digestive functions would you expect these parasites to have?*

ANIMATION *BioFlix* Visit the Study Area in **MasteringBiology** for the Bioflix® 3-D Animation on Membrane Transport.

roughly the size of a tennis court. This enormous surface area is an evolutionary adaptation that greatly increases the rate of nutrient absorption.

Depending on the nutrient, transport across the epithelial cells can be passive or active (see Chapter 7). The sugar fructose, for example, moves by facilitated diffusion down its concentration gradient from the lumen of the small intestine into the epithelial cells. From there, fructose exits the basal surface and is absorbed into microscopic blood vessels, or capillaries, at the core of each villus. Other nutrients, including amino acids, small peptides, vitamins, and most glucose molecules, are pumped against concentration gradients by the epithelial cells of the villus. This active transport allows much more absorption of nutrients than would be possible with passive diffusion alone.

The capillaries and veins that carry nutrient-rich blood away from the villi all converge into the **hepatic portal vein**, a blood vessel that leads directly to the liver. From the liver, blood travels to the heart and then to other tissues and organs. This arrangement serves two major functions. First, it allows the liver to regulate the distribution of nutrients to the rest of the body. Because the liver can interconvert many organic molecules, blood that leaves the liver may have a very different nutrient balance than the blood that entered via the hepatic portal vein. Second, the arrangement allows the liver to remove toxic substances before the blood circulates broadly. The liver is the primary site for the detoxification of many organic molecules, including drugs, that are foreign to the body.

Although many nutrients leave the intestine through the bloodstream, some products of fat (triglyceride) digestion take a different path. As shown in **Figure 41.13**, hydrolysis of fats by lipase in the small intestine generates fatty acids and monoglycerides (glycerol joined to a single fatty acid). These products are absorbed by epithelial cells and recombined into triglycerides. They are then coated with phospholipids, cholesterol, and proteins, forming water-soluble globules called **chylomicrons**.

In exiting the intestine, chylomicrons are first transported out of an epithelial cell into a **lacteal**, a vessel at the core of each villus (see Figures 41.12 and 41.13). Lacteals are part of the vertebrate lymphatic system, which is a network of vessels that are filled with a clear fluid called lymph. Starting at the lacteals, lymph containing the chylomicrons passes into the larger vessels of the lymphatic system and eventually into large veins that return the blood to the heart.

Absorption in the Large Intestine

The alimentary canal ends with the **large intestine**, which includes the colon, cecum, and rectum. The small intestine connects to the large intestine at a T-shaped junction (Figure 41.14). One arm of the T is the 1.5-m-long

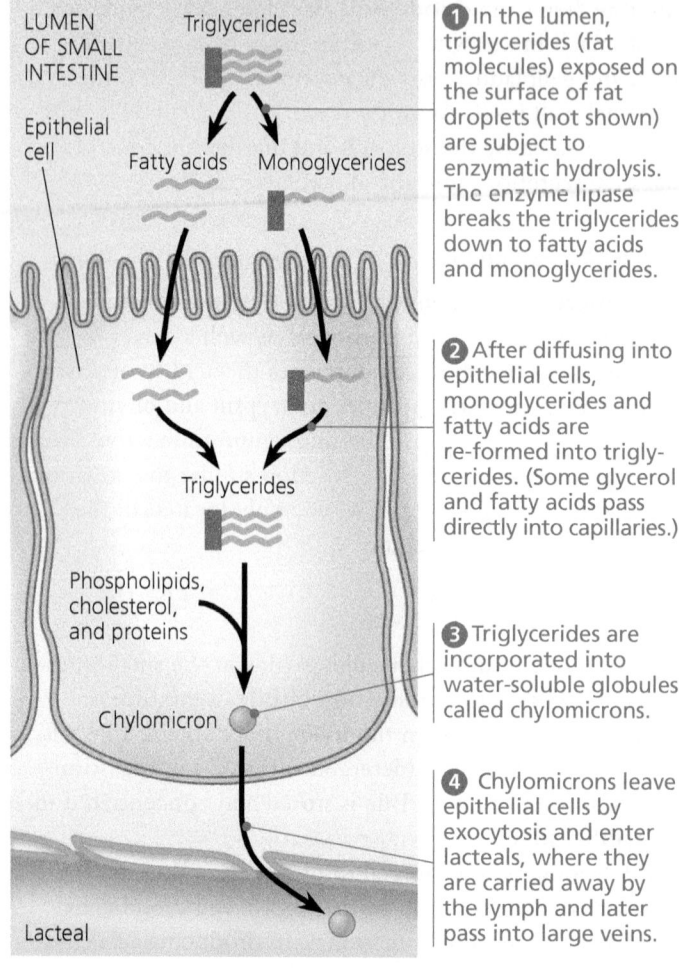

❶ In the lumen, triglycerides (fat molecules) exposed on the surface of fat droplets (not shown) are subject to enzymatic hydrolysis. The enzyme lipase breaks the triglycerides down to fatty acids and monoglycerides.

❷ After diffusing into epithelial cells, monoglycerides and fatty acids are re-formed into triglycerides. (Some glycerol and fatty acids pass directly into capillaries.)

❸ Triglycerides are incorporated into water-soluble globules called chylomicrons.

❹ Chylomicrons leave epithelial cells by exocytosis and enter lacteals, where they are carried away by the lymph and later pass into large veins.

▲ **Figure 41.13 Absorption of fats.** Because fats are insoluble in water, adaptations are needed to digest and absorb them. Bile salts (not shown) break up large fat droplets and maintain a small droplet size in the intestinal lumen, exposing more of the fat at the surface for enzymatic hydrolysis. The fatty acids and monoglycerides released by hydrolysis can diffuse into epithelial cells, where fats are reassembled and incorporated into water-soluble chylomicrons that enter the lymphatic system.

colon, which leads to the rectum and anus. The other arm is a pouch called the **cecum**. The cecum is important for fermenting ingested material, especially in animals that eat large amounts of plant material. Compared with many other mammals, humans have a small cecum. The **appendix**, a finger-like extension of the human cecum, has a minor and dispensable role in immunity.

A major function of the colon is to recover water that has entered

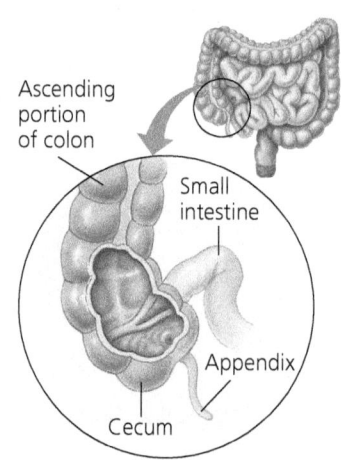

▲ **Figure 41.14 Junction of the small and large intestines.**

the alimentary canal as the solvent of digestive juices. About 7 L of fluid is secreted into the lumen of the alimentary canal each day, and about 90% of that is reabsorbed in the small intestine and colon. There is no mechanism for active transport of water. Instead, water is reabsorbed by osmosis when Na^+ and other ions are pumped out of the lumen of the colon.

The **feces**, the wastes of the digestive system, become increasingly solid as they are moved along the colon by peristalsis. It takes approximately 12–24 hours for material to travel the length of the colon. If the lining of the colon is irritated—by a viral or bacterial infection, for instance—less water than normal may be reabsorbed, resulting in diarrhea. The opposite problem, constipation, occurs when the feces move along the colon too slowly. An excess of water is reabsorbed, and therefore the feces become compacted.

A rich community of mostly harmless bacteria lives on unabsorbed organic material in the human colon, contributing approximately one-third of the dry weight of feces. One inhabitant, *Escherichia coli*, is so common in the human digestive system that its presence in lakes and streams is a useful indicator of contamination by untreated sewage. As by-products of their metabolism, many colon bacteria generate gases, including methane and hydrogen sulphide, which has an offensive odour. These gases and ingested air are expelled through the anus. Some bacteria produce vitamins, such as vitamin K, biotin, and folic acid, that supplement our dietary intake when absorbed into the blood.

Besides bacteria, feces contain undigested material, including cellulose fibre. Although it has no caloric value to humans, fibre helps move food along the alimentary canal.

The terminal portion of the large intestine is the **rectum**, where feces are stored until they can be eliminated. Between the rectum and the anus are two sphincters, the inner one being involuntary and the outer one being voluntary. Periodically, strong contractions of the colon create an urge to defecate. Because filling of the stomach triggers a reflex that increases the rate of contractions in the colon, the urge to defecate often follows a meal.

We have followed a meal from one opening (the mouth) of the alimentary canal to the other (the anus). Next we'll see how some digestive adaptations may have evolved.

CONCEPT 41.4

Evolutionary adaptations of vertebrate digestive systems correlate with diet

EVOLUTION The digestive systems of mammals and other vertebrates are variations on a common plan, but there are many intriguing adaptations, often associated with the animal's diet. To highlight how form fits function, we'll examine a few of them.

Dental Adaptations

Dentition, an animal's assortment of teeth, is one example of structural variation reflecting diet (Figure 41.15). The evolutionary adaptation of teeth for processing different

▼ Figure 41.15 **Dentition and diet.**

Carnivore	Herbivore	Omnivore
		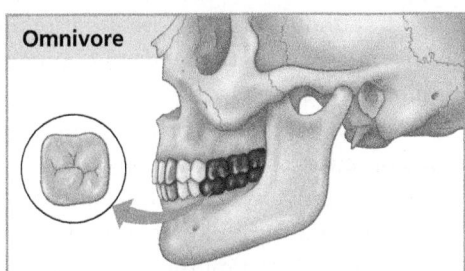
Carnivores, such as members of the dog and cat families, generally have large, pointed incisors and canines that can be used to kill prey and rip or cut away pieces of flesh. The jagged premolars and molars crush and shred food.	Herbivores, such as horses and deer, usually have premolars and molars with broad, ridged surfaces that grind tough plant material. The incisors and canines are generally modified for biting off pieces of vegetation. In some herbivores, canines are absent.	As omnivores, humans are adapted to eating both plants and meat. Adults have 32 teeth. From front to back along either side of the mouth are four bladelike incisors for biting, a pair of pointed canines for tearing, four premolars for grinding, and six molars for crushing (see inset, top view).

Key ▬ Incisors   ▬ Canines   ▬ Premolars   ▬ Molars

kinds of food is one of the major reasons mammals have been so successful. Nonmammalian vertebrates generally have less specialized dentition, but there are interesting exceptions. For example, poisonous snakes, such as rattlesnakes, have fangs, modified teeth that inject venom into prey. Some fangs are hollow, like syringes, whereas others drip the poison along grooves on the surfaces of the teeth.

Stomach and Intestinal Adaptations

Large, expandable stomachs are common in carnivorous vertebrates, which may go for a long time between meals and must eat as much as they can when they do catch prey. A 200-kg African lion can consume 40 kg of meat in one meal!

The length of the vertebrate digestive system is also correlated with diet. In general, herbivores and omnivores have longer alimentary canals relative to their body size than do carnivores. Vegetation is more difficult to digest than meat because it contains cell walls. A longer digestive tract furnishes more time for digestion and more surface area for the absorption of nutrients. As an example, consider the koala and coyote in Figure 41.16. Although these two mammals are about the same size, the koala's intestines are much longer, enhancing the processing of fibrous, protein-poor eucalyptus leaves from which the koala obtains virtually all its food and water.

Mutualistic Adaptations

Some digestive adaptations involve mutualistic symbiosis. An estimated 10–100 trillion bacteria live in the human digestive system. The coexistence of humans and many of these bacteria involves mutualistic symbiosis, a mutually beneficial interaction between two species (see Concept 54.1). For example, some intestinal bacteria produce vitamins, such as vitamin K, biotin, and folic acid, which supplement our dietary intake when absorbed into the blood. Intestinal bacteria also regulate the development of the intestinal epithelium and the function of the innate immune system.

Recently, we have greatly expanded our knowledge of the collection of bacteria, called the microbiome, in the human digestive system. To identify these bacteria, both beneficial and harmful, scientists are using a DNA sequencing approach based on the polymerase chain reaction (see Figure 20.8). They have found more than 400 bacterial species in the human digestive tract, a far greater number than had been identified through approaches relying on laboratory culture and characterization.

One recent microbiome study provided an important clue as to why the bacterium *H. pylori* disrupts stomach

▲ Figure 41.16 **The alimentary canals of a carnivore (coyote) and herbivore (koala).** The koala's alimentary canal is specialized for digesting eucalyptus leaves. Extensive chewing chops the leaves into tiny pieces, increasing exposure to digestive juices. In the long cecum and the upper portion of the colon, symbiotic bacteria convert the shredded leaves to a more nutritious diet.

health, leading to ulcers. After collecting stomach tissue from uninfected and *H. pylori*-infected adults, researchers identified all the bacterial species in each sample. What they found was remarkable: *H. pylori* infection led to a near complete elimination from the stomach of all other bacterial species (Figure 41.17). Such studies on differences in the microbiome as a result of particular diseases holds promise for the development of new and more effective therapies.

Mutualistic Adaptations in Herbivores

Mutualistic symbiosis is particularly important in herbivores. Much of the chemical energy in herbivore diets comes from the cellulose of plant cell walls, but animals do not produce enzymes that hydrolyze cellulose. Instead, many vertebrates (as well as termites, whose wooden diets consist largely of cellulose) host large populations of mutualistic bacteria and protists in fermentation chambers in their alimentary canals. These microorganisms have enzymes that can digest cellulose to simple sugars and other compounds that the animal can absorb. In many cases, the microorganisms also use the sugars from digested cellulose in the production of a variety of

▲ Figure 41.17 **The stomach microbiome.** By copying and sequencing bacterial DNA in samples obtained from human stomachs, researchers characterized the bacterial community that makes up the stomach microbiome. In samples from individuals infected with *Helicobacter pylori,* more than 95% of the sequences were from that species, which belongs to the phylum Proteobacteria. The stomach microbiome in uninfected individuals was much more diverse.

H. pylori

Juergen Berger/Science Source

▲ Giant tubeworm.

Peter Batson/Image Quest Marine

The most elaborate adaptations for an herbivorous diet have evolved in the animals called **ruminants**, the cud-chewing animals that include deer, sheep, and cattle (Figure 41.18).

Although we have focused our discussion on vertebrates, adaptations related to digestion are also widespread among other animals. Some of the most remarkable examples are the giant tubeworms (over 3 m long) that live at pressures as high as 260 atmospheres around deep-sea hydrothermal vents (see Figure 52.14). These worms have no mouth or digestive system. Instead, they obtain all of their energy and nutrients from mutualistic bacteria that live within their bodies. The bacteria carry out chemoautotrophy (see Concept 27.3) using the carbon dioxide, oxygen, hydrogen sulphide, and nitrate available at the vents. Thus, for invertebrates and vertebrates alike, mutualistic symbiosis has evolved as an adaptation that expands the sources of nutrition available to animals. Having examined how animals

nutrients essential to the animal, such as vitamins and amino acids.

In horses, koalas, and elephants, mutualistic microorganisms are housed in a large cecum. In contrast, the hoatzin, an herbivorous bird found in South American rain forests, hosts microorganisms in a large, muscular crop (an esophageal pouch; see Figure 41.7). Hard ridges in the wall of the crop grind plant leaves into small fragments, and the microorganisms break down cellulose.

In rabbits and some rodents, mutualistic bacteria live in the large intestine as well as in the cecum. Since most nutrients are absorbed in the small intestine, nourishing by-products of fermentation by bacteria in the large intestine are initially lost with the feces. Rabbits and rodents recover these nutrients by coprophagy (from the Greek, meaning "dung eating"), feeding on some of their feces and then passing the food through the alimentary canal a second time. The familiar rabbit "pellets," which are not reingested, are the feces eliminated after food has passed through the digestive tract twice.

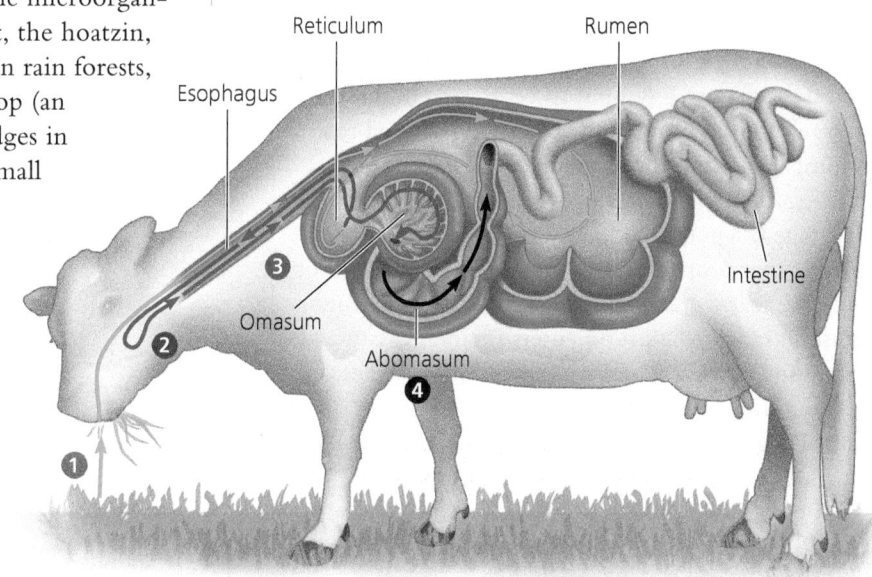

▲ Figure 41.18 **Ruminant digestion.** The stomach of a cow, a ruminant, has four chambers. ❶ Chewed food first enters the rumen and reticulum, where mutualistic microorganisms digest cellulose in the plant material. ❷ Periodically, the cow regurgitates and rechews "cud" from the reticulum, further breaking down fibres and thereby enhancing microbial action. ❸ The reswallowed cud passes to the omasum, where some water is removed. ❹ It then passes to the abomasum for digestion by the cow's enzymes. In this way, the cow obtains significant nutrients from both the grass and the mutualistic microorganisms, which maintain a stable population in the rumen.

optimize their extraction of nutrients from food, we'll next turn to the challenge of balancing the use of these nutrients.

CONCEPT CHECK 41.4

1. What are two advantages of a longer alimentary canal for processing plant material that is difficult to digest?

2. What features of a mammal's digestive system make it an attractive habitat for mutualistic microorganisms?

3. **WHAT IF?** "Lactose-intolerant" people have a shortage of lactase, the enzyme that breaks down lactose in milk. As a result, they sometimes develop cramps, bloating, or diarrhea after consuming dairy products. Suppose such a person ate yogurt containing bacteria that produce lactase. Why would eating yogurt likely provide at best only temporary relief of the symptoms?

For suggested answers, see Appendix A.

CONCEPT 41.5

Feedback circuits regulate digestion, energy storage, and appetite

Having examined the processes that enable an animal to obtain nutrients, we will finish our discussion of nutrition by considering how these processes are matched to circumstance and need.

Regulation of Digestion

Many animals go for long intervals between meals and do not need their digestive systems to be active continuously. Instead, each step in processing is activated as food reaches a new compartment in the alimentary canal. The arrival of food triggers the secretion of substances that promote the next stage of chemical digestion, as well as muscular contractions that propel food farther along the canal. For example, you learned earlier that nervous reflexes stimulate the release of saliva when food enters the oral cavity and orchestrate swallowing when a bolus of food reaches the pharynx. Similarly, the arrival of food in the stomach triggers churning and the release of gastric juices. A branch of the nervous system called the *enteric division*, which is dedicated to the digestive organs, regulates these events as well as peristalsis in the small and large intestines.

The endocrine system also plays a critical role in controlling digestion. As described in **Figure 41.19**, a series of hormones released by the stomach and duodenum help ensure that digestive secretions are present only when needed. Like all hormones, they are transported through the bloodstream. This is true even for the hormone gastrin, whose target (the stomach) is the same organ that secretes it.

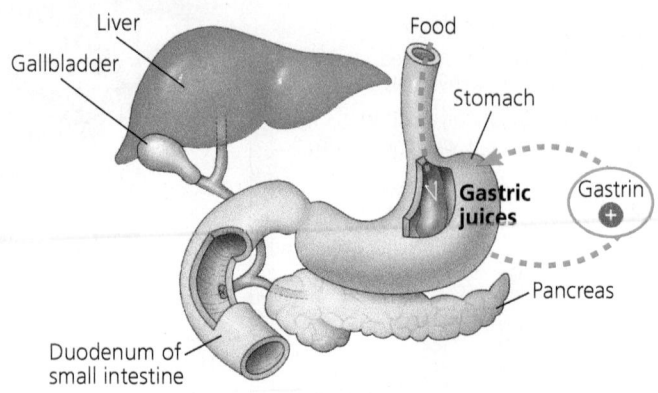

1 As food arrives at the stomach, it stretches the stomach walls, triggering release of the hormone *gastrin*. Gastrin circulates via the bloodstream back to the stomach, where it stimulates production of gastric juices.

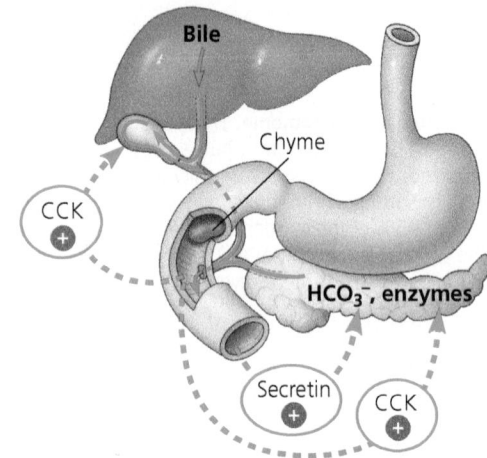

2 Chyme—an acidic mixture of partially digested food—eventually passes from the stomach to the duodenum. The duodenum responds to amino acids or fatty acids in the chyme by releasing the digestive hormones cholecystokinin and secretin. *Cholecystokinin (CCK)* stimulates the release of digestive enzymes from the pancreas and of bile from the gallbladder. *Secretin* stimulates the pancreas to release bicarbonate (HCO_3^-), which neutralizes chyme.

3 If the chyme is rich in fats, the high levels of secretin and CCK released act on the stomach to inhibit peristalsis and secretion of gastric juices, thereby slowing digestion.

Key Stimulation   Inhibition

▲ Figure 41.19 **Hormonal control of digestion.**

Regulation of Energy Storage

As discussed in Chapter 40, when an animal takes in more energy-rich molecules than it needs for metabolism and activity, it stores the excess energy. In concluding our overview of nutrition, we'll examine some ways in which animals manage their energy allocation.

In humans, the first sites used for energy storage are liver and muscle cells. In these cells, excess energy from the diet is stored in glycogen, a polymer made up of many glucose units (see Figure 5.6b). Once glycogen depots are full, any additional excess energy is usually stored in fat in adipose cells.

When fewer calories are taken in than are expended—perhaps because of sustained heavy exercise or lack of food—the human body generally expends liver glycogen first and then draws on muscle glycogen and fat. Fats are especially rich in energy; oxidizing a gram of fat liberates about twice the energy liberated from a gram of carbohydrate or protein. For this reason, adipose tissue provides the most space-efficient way for the body to store large amounts of energy. Most healthy people have enough stored fat to sustain them through several weeks without food.

Glucose Homeostasis

The synthesis and breakdown of glycogen is central not only to energy storage, but also to maintaining metabolic balance through glucose homeostasis. Tissues throughout the body rely on the generation of ATP by oxidation of glucose to fuel cellular processes (see Chapter 9). The pancreatic hormones insulin and glucagon maintain glucose homeostasis by tightly regulating the synthesis and breakdown of glycogen.

The liver is a key site for glucose homeostasis (Figure 41.20). When insulin levels rise after a carbohydrate-rich meal, glucose entering the liver in the hepatic portal vein is used to synthesize glycogen. Between meals, when blood in the hepatic portal vein has a much lower glucose concentration, glucagon stimulates the liver to break down glycogen, releasing glucose into the blood. Through the combined action of insulin and glucagon, blood exiting the liver has a glucose concentration of 70–110 mg per 100 mL at nearly all times.

We will return to the mechanism of glucose homeostasis (and explore the consequences when it fails) in our discussion of the endocrine system in Chapter 45.

Regulation of Appetite and Consumption

Overnourishment, the consumption of more calories than the body needs for normal metabolism, causes obesity, the excessive accumulation of fat. Obesity, in turn, contributes to a number of health problems, including the most common type of diabetes (type 2), cancer of the colon and breast, and cardiovascular disease that can lead to heart attacks and strokes. Canadian public health researchers

Insulin enhances the transport of glucose into body cells and stimulates the liver to store glucose as glycogen.

Beta cells of the pancreas secrete the hormone insulin into the blood.

Blood glucose level rises (such as after eating).

Blood glucose level falls.

NORMAL BLOOD GLUCOSE
(70–110 mg glucose/ 100 mL)

Blood glucose level rises.

Blood glucose level falls (such as after fasting).

Glucagon promotes the breakdown of glycogen in the liver and the release of glucose into the blood.

Alpha cells of the pancreas secrete the hormone glucagon into the blood.

◀ Figure 41.20 Homeostatic regulation of cellular fuel. After a meal is digested, glucose and other monomers are absorbed into the blood from the digestive tract. The human body regulates the use and storage of glucose, a major cellular fuel.

MAKE CONNECTIONS *What form of feedback control does each of these regulatory circuits reflect (see Concept 40.2)?*

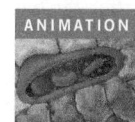
ANIMATION *BioFlix* Visit the Study Area in **MasteringBiology** for the BioFlix® 3-D Animation on Homeostasis: Regulating Blood Sugar.

suggest that, between 1985 and 2000, 57 000 Canadians died as a result of being overweight or obese. Obesity increases the risk of mortality for an individual by about 36%.

Researchers have discovered several homeostatic mechanisms that operate as feedback circuits controlling the storage and metabolism of fat. A network of neurons relays and integrates information from the digestive system to regulate secretion of hormones that regulate long-term and short-term appetite. The target for these hormones is a "satiety centre" in the brain (Figure 41.21). For example, ghrelin, a hormone secreted by the stomach wall, triggers feelings of hunger before meals. In contrast, both insulin and PYY, a hormone secreted by the small intestine after meals, suppress appetite. **Leptin**, a hormone produced by adipose (fat) tissue, also suppresses appetite and appears to play a major role in regulating body fat levels. In the Scientific Skills Exercise, you'll interpret data from an experiment studying genes that affect leptin production and function in mice.

Obtaining food, digesting it, and absorbing nutrients are part of the larger story of how animals fuel their activities. Provisioning the body also involves distributing nutrients (circulation), and using nutrients for metabolism requires exchanging respiratory gases with the environment. These processes and the adaptations that facilitate them are the focus of Chapter 42.

Obesity and Evolution

EVOLUTION The relationship between fat storage and evolutionary adaptation in animals is sometimes complex. Consider the plump offspring of the seabirds called petrels (Figure 41.22). Their parents must fly long distances to find food. Most of the food that they bring to their chicks is very rich in lipids. The fact that fat has about twice as much energy per gram as other fuels minimizes the number of foraging trips. However, growing petrels need lots of protein for building new tissues, and there is relatively little in their oily diet. To get all the protein they need, young petrels must consume many more calories than they burn in metabolism, and consequently they become obese. Their fat deposits nevertheless help them survive periods when their parents cannot find enough food. When food is plentiful, chicks at the end of the growth period weigh much more than their parents. The youngsters must then fast for several days to lose enough weight to be capable of flight.

Widespread obesity in humans is a recent phenomenon, and researchers have speculated that the origins may be linked to our evolutionary past. Our ancestors on

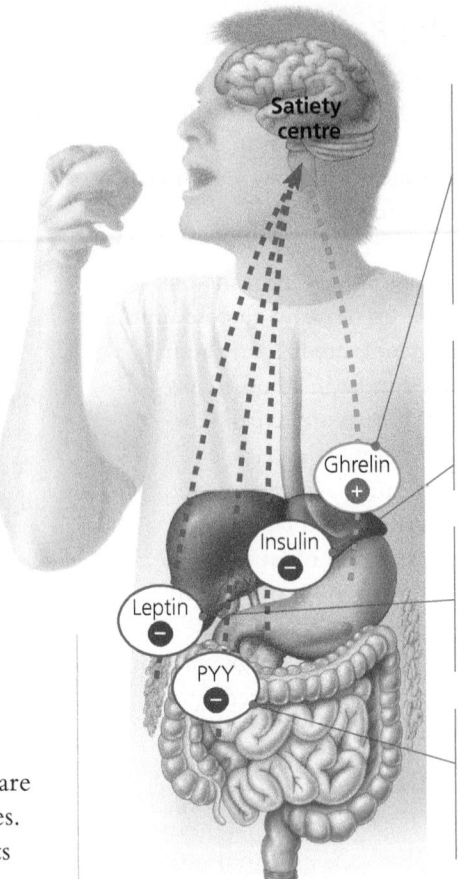

Secreted by the stomach wall, ghrelin is one of the signals that triggers feelings of hunger as mealtimes approach. In dieters who lose weight, ghrelin levels increase, which may be one reason it's so hard to stay on a diet.

A rise in blood sugar level after a meal stimulates the pancreas to secrete insulin. In addition to its other functions, insulin suppresses appetite by acting on the brain.

Produced by adipose (fat) tissue, leptin suppresses appetite. When the amount of body fat decreases, leptin levels fall, and appetite increases.

The hormone PYY, secreted by the small intestine after meals, acts as an appetite suppressant that counters the appetite stimulant ghrelin.

© 2003 AAAS

▲ **Figure 41.21 A few of the appetite-regulating hormones.** Secreted by various organs and tissues, the hormones reach the brain via the bloodstream. These signals act on a region of the brain that in turn controls the "satiety centre," which generates the nervous impulses that make us feel either hungry or satiated ("full"). The hormone ghrelin is an appetite stimulant; the other three hormones shown here are appetite suppressants.

Source: Adaptation of illustration "Appetite Controllers" from "Cellular Warriors at the Battle of the Bulge" by Kathleen Sutliff and Jean Marx, from *Science*, February 2003, Volume 299(5608). Copyright © 2003 by AAAS.

▲ **Figure 41.22 A plump petrel.** Too heavy to fly, the petrel chick (right) will have to lose weight before it can fly. In the meantime, its stored fat provides energy during times when its parents fail to bring enough food.

Interpreting Data from Experiments with Genetic Mutants

What Are the Roles of the *ob* and *db* Genes in Appetite Regulation? A mutation that disrupts a physiological process is often used to study the normal function of the mutated gene. Ideally, researchers use a standard set of conditions and compare animals that differ genetically only in whether a particular gene is mutant (nonfunctional) or wild-type (normal). In this way, a difference in phenotype, the physiological property being measured, can be attributed to a difference in genotype, the presence or absence of the mutation. To study the role of specific genes in regulating appetite, researchers used laboratory animals with known mutations in those genes.

Mice in which recessive mutations inactivate both copies of either the *ob* gene (ob^-/ob^-) or the *db* gene (db^-/db^-) eat voraciously and grow much more massive than wild-type mice. In the photograph below, the mouse on the right is wild-type (ob^+/ob^+), whereas the obese mouse on the left has an inactivating mutation in both copies of the *ob* gene (ob^-/ob^-).

Jackson Laboratory

One hypothesis for the normal role of the *ob* and *db* genes is that they participate in a hormone pathway that suppresses appetite when caloric intake is sufficient. Before setting out to isolate the potential hormone, researchers explored this hypothesis genetically.

How the Experiment Was Done The researchers measured the mass of young subject mice of various genotypes and surgically linked the circulatory system of each one to that of another mouse. This procedure ensured that any factor circulating in the bloodstream of either mouse would be transferred to the other in the pair. After eight weeks, they again measured the mass of each subject mouse.

Data from the Experiment

	Genotype Pairing (red type indicates mutant genes)		Average Change in Body Mass of Subject (g)
	Subject	Paired with	
(a)	ob^+/ob^+, db^+/db^+	ob^+/ob^+, db^+/db^+	8.3
(b)	ob^-/ob^-, db^+/db^+	ob^-/ob^-, db^+/db^+	38.7
(c)	ob^-/ob^-, db^+/db^+	ob^+/ob^+, db^+/db^+	8.2
(d)	ob^-/ob^-, db^+/db^+	ob^+/ob^+, db^-/db^-	−14.9*

* Due to pronounced weight loss and weakening, subjects in this pairing were remeasured after less than eight weeks.

Interpret the Data

1. First, practise reading the genotype information given in the data table. For example, pairing (a) joined two mice that each had the wild-type version of both genes. Describe the two mice in pairing (b), pairing (c), and pairing (d). Explain how each pairing contributed to the experimental design.

2. Compare the results observed for pairing (a) and pairing (b) in terms of phenotype. If the results had been identical for these two pairings, what would that outcome have implied about the experimental design?

3. Compare the results observed for pairing (c) to those observed for pairing (b). Based on these results, does the ob^+ gene product appear to promote or suppress appetite? Explain your answer.

4. Describe the results observed for pairing (d). Note how these results differ from those for pairing (b). Suggest a hypothesis to explain this difference. How could you test your hypothesis using the kinds of mice in this study?

Data from D. L. Coleman, Effects of parabiosis of obese mice with diabetes and normal mice, *Diabetologia* 9:294–298 (1973).

---

the African savannah were hunter-gatherers who probably survived mainly on seeds and other plant products, a diet only occasionally supplemented by hunting game or scavenging meat from animals killed by other predators. In such a feast-or-famine existence, natural selection may have favoured those individuals with a physiology that enabled them to store energy as fat on those rare occasions when such treats were available. Almost 50 years ago, James Neel proposed his *thrifty gene hypothesis*, suggesting that the genes promoting fat storage in ancestral populations may be detrimental in modern civilizations. Though the hypothesis is appealing, there remains no definitive evidence that the current epidemic in obesity is simply an evolutionary vestige of less nutritious times.

In the next chapter, we'll see that obtaining food, digesting it, and absorbing nutrients are parts of a larger story. Provisioning the body also involves distributing nutrients (circulation), and using nutrients for metabolism requires exchanging respiratory gases with the environment.

CONCEPT CHECK 41.5

1. Explain how people can become obese even if their intake of dietary fat is relatively low compared with carbohydrate intake.

2. **WHAT IF?** Suppose you were studying two groups of obese people with genetic abnormalities in the leptin pathway. In one group, the leptin levels are abnormally high; in the other group, they are abnormally low. How would each group's leptin levels change if both groups were placed on a low-calorie diet for an extended period? Explain.

3. **WHAT IF?** An insulinoma is a cancerous mass of pancreatic beta cells that secrete insulin but do not respond to feedback mechanisms. How you would expect an insulinoma to affect blood glucose levels and liver activity?

For suggested answers, see Appendix A.

41 Chapter Review

Go to **MasteringBiology**® for Assignments, the eText, and the Study Area with Animations, Activities, Vocab Self-Quiz, and Practice Tests.

SUMMARY OF KEY CONCEPTS

- Animals have diverse diets. **Herbivores** mainly eat plants; **carnivores** mainly eat other animals; and **omnivores** eat both. Animals must balance consumption, storage, and use of food.

CONCEPT 41.1

An animal's diet must supply chemical energy, organic molecules, and essential nutrients (pp. 944–948)

- Food provides animals with energy for ATP production, carbon skeletons for biosynthesis, and **essential nutrients**—nutrients that must be supplied in preassembled form. Essential nutrients include certain amino acids and fatty acids that animals cannot synthesize; **vitamins**, which are organic molecules; and **minerals**, which are inorganic substances.
- Animals can suffer from two types of malnutrition: an inadequate intake of essential nutrients and a deficiency in sources of chemical energy. Studies of genetic defects and of disease at the population level help researchers determine human dietary requirements.

  ? *Propose a reason why the diet of many mammals doesn't need to include vitamin C, a substance that is important for collagen synthesis.*

CONCEPT 41.2

The main stages of food processing are ingestion, digestion, absorption, and elimination (pp. 948–951)

Stages of food processing

1. **INGESTION** (eating)

2. **DIGESTION** (enzymatic breakdown of large molecules)

3. **ABSORPTION** (uptake of nutrients by cells)

4. **ELIMINATION** (passage of undigested materials out of the body in feces)

Undigested material

- Animals differ in the ways they obtain and ingest food. Many animals are **bulk feeders**, eating large pieces of food.
- Compartmentalization is necessary to avoid self-digestion. In intracellular digestion, food particles are engulfed by endocytosis and digested within food vacuoles that have fused with lysosomes. In extracellular digestion, which is used by most animals, enzymatic hydrolysis occurs outside cells in a **gastrovascular cavity** or **alimentary canal**.

  ? *Propose an artificial diet that would eliminate the need for one of the first three steps in food processing.*

CONCEPT 41.3

Organs specialized for sequential stages of food processing form the mammalian digestive system (pp. 951–957)

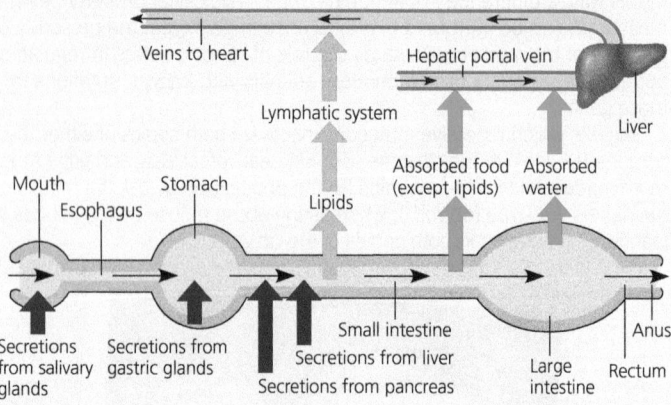

Veins to heart · Hepatic portal vein · Liver

Lymphatic system

Mouth · Esophagus · Stomach · Lipids · Absorbed food (except lipids) · Absorbed water

Secretions from salivary glands · Secretions from gastric glands · Secretions from liver · Secretions from pancreas · Small intestine · Large intestine · Rectum · Anus

  ? *What structural feature of the small intestine makes it better suited for absorption of nutrients than the stomach?*

CONCEPT 41.4

Evolutionary adaptations of vertebrate digestive systems correlate with diet (pp. 957–960)

- Vertebrate digestive systems display many evolutionary adaptations associated with diet. For example, dentition, which is the assortment of teeth, generally correlates with diet. In addition, herbivores usually have longer alimentary canals than carnivores, reflecting the longer time needed to digest vegetation. Many herbivores, including cows, also have fermentation chambers where microorganisms digest cellulose, a form of mutualism.

  ? *How does our anatomy indicate that our ancestors were not vegetarians?*

CONCEPT 41.5

Feedback circuits regulate digestion, energy storage, and appetite (pp. 960–963)

- Nutrition is regulated at multiple levels. Food in the alimentary canal triggers nervous and hormonal responses that control the secretion of digestive juices and that promote the movement of ingested material through the canal. The availability of glucose for energy production is regulated by the hormones insulin and glucagon, which control the synthesis and breakdown of glycogen.
- Vertebrates store excess calories in glycogen (in liver and muscle cells) and in fat (in adipose cells). These energy stores can be tapped when an animal expends more calories than it consumes. If, however, an animal consumes more calories than it needs for normal metabolism, the resulting overnourishment can lead to the serious health problem of obesity.
- Several hormones, including **leptin** and insulin, regulate appetite by affecting the brain's satiety centre.

  ? *Explain why your stomach might make growling noises when you skip a meal.*

TEST YOUR UNDERSTANDING

LEVEL 1: KNOWLEDGE/COMPREHENSION

1. Fat digestion yields fatty acids and glycerol, whereas protein digestion yields amino acids. Both digestive processes
   a. occur inside cells in most animals.
   b. add a water molecule to break bonds.
   c. require a low pH resulting from HCl production.
   d. consume ATP.

2. The mammalian trachea and esophagus both connect to the
   a. large intestine.   c. pharynx.
   b. stomach.   d. rectum.

3. Which of the following organs is *incorrectly* paired with its function?
   a. stomach—protein digestion
   b. large intestine—bile production
   c. small intestine—nutrient absorption
   d. pancreas—enzyme production

4. Which of the following is *not* a major activity of the stomach?
   a. mechanical digestion
   b. HCl secretion
   c. nutrient absorption
   d. enzyme secretion

LEVEL 2: APPLICATION/ANALYSIS

5. After surgical removal of an infected gallbladder, a person must be especially careful to restrict dietary intake of
   a. starch.   c. sugar.
   b. protein.   d. fat.

6. If you were to jog 1 km a few hours after lunch, which stored fuel would you probably tap?
   a. muscle proteins
   b. muscle and liver glycogen
   c. fat stored in the liver
   d. fat stored in adipose tissue

LEVEL 3: SYNTHESIS/EVALUATION

7. **DRAW IT** Make a flowchart of the events that occur after partially digested food leaves the stomach. Use the following terms: bicarbonate secretion, circulation, decrease in acidity, secretin secretion, increase in acidity, signal detection. Next to each term, indicate the compartment(s) involved. You may use a term more than once.

8. **EVOLUTION CONNECTION**
   The human esophagus and trachea share a passage leading from the mouth and nasal passages, which can cause problems. After reviewing vertebrate evolution in Chapter 34, explain the evolutionary basis for this "imperfect" anatomy.

9. **SCIENTIFIC INQUIRY**
   In human populations of northern European origin, the disorder called hemochromatosis causes excess iron uptake from food and affects 1 in 200 adults. Men are 10 times as likely as women to suffer from iron overload. Devise a hypothesis for the difference in the disease between the two sexes.

10. **WRITE ABOUT A THEME: ORGANIZATION**
    Hair is largely made up of the protein keratin. In a short essay (100–150 words), explain why a shampoo containing protein is not effective in replacing the protein in damaged hair.

11. **SYNTHESIZE YOUR KNOWLEDGE**

Jack Moskovita

Hummingbirds are well adapted to obtain sugary nectar from flowers, but they use some of the energy obtained from nectar when they forage for insects and spiders. Explain why this foraging is necessary.

For selected answers, see Appendix A.

42

Circulation and Gas Exchange

KEY CONCEPTS

42.1 Circulatory systems link exchange surfaces with cells throughout the body

42.2 Coordinated cycles of heart contraction drive double circulation in mammals

42.3 Patterns of blood pressure and flow reflect the structure and arrangement of blood vessels

42.4 Blood components function in exchange, transport, and defence

42.5 Gas exchange occurs across specialized respiratory surfaces

42.6 Breathing ventilates the lungs

42.7 Adaptations for gas exchange include pigments that bind and transport gases

Gary Meszaros/Science Source

▲ Figure 42.1 **How does a feathery fringe help this animal survive?**

Trading Places

The animal in **Figure 42.1** may look like a creature from a science fiction film, but it's actually a mudpuppy, a salamander native to shallow ponds in North America. The feathery, red appendages jutting out from the head of this adult are gills. Although many amphibians possess gills in the larval stage, mudpuppies are unusual in relying on gills throughout their adult life.

The exchange of substances between an animal and its surroundings ultimately occurs at the cellular level. The resources that animal cells require, such as nutrients and oxygen (O_2), enter the cytoplasm by crossing the plasma membrane. Metabolic by-products, such as carbon dioxide (CO_2), exit the cell by crossing the same membrane. In unicellular organisms, exchange occurs directly with the external environment. For most multicellular organisms, however, direct transfer of materials between every cell and the environment is not possible. Instead, these organisms rely on specialized systems that carry out exchange with the environment and that transport materials between sites of exchange and the rest of the body.

The reddish colour and branching structure of the mudpuppy's gills reflect the intimate association between exchange and transport. Tiny blood vessels lie just beneath the surface of each filament in the gills. Across this surface, there is a net diffusion of O_2 from the surrounding water into the blood and of CO_2 from the blood into the water. The short distances involved allow diffusion to be rapid. Pumping of the heart propels the oxygen-rich blood from the gill filaments to all other tissues of the body. There, more short-range exchange occurs, involving nutrients and O_2 as well as CO_2 and other wastes.

Because internal transport and gas exchange are functionally related in most animals, we will examine both circulatory and respiratory systems in this chapter. We will explore the remarkable variation in form and organization of these systems by considering examples from a number of species. We will also highlight the roles of circulatory and respiratory systems in maintaining homeostasis under a range of physiological and environmental conditions.

CONCEPT 42.1

Circulatory systems link exchange surfaces with cells throughout the body

The molecular trade that an animal carries out with its environment—gaining O_2 and nutrients while shedding CO_2 and other waste products—must ultimately involve every cell in the body. As you learned in Chapter 7, small, nonpolar molecules such as O_2 and CO_2 can move between cells and their immediate surroundings by diffusion. But diffusion is very slow for distances of more than a few millimetres. That's because the time it takes for a substance to diffuse from one place to another is proportional to the *square* of the distance. For example, if it takes 1 second for a given quantity of glucose to diffuse 100 μm, it will take 100 seconds for the same quantity to diffuse 1 mm and almost 3 hours to diffuse 1 cm! This relationship between diffusion time and distance places a substantial constraint on the body plan of any animal.

Given that diffusion is rapid only over very small distances, how does each cell of an animal exchange molecules with the environment? Natural selection has resulted in two general solutions to this problem. The first solution is a body size and shape that keep many or all cells in direct contact with the environment. Each cell can thus exchange materials directly with the surrounding medium. This type of body plan is found only in certain invertebrates, including cnidarians and flatworms. The second solution, found in all other animals, is a circulatory system that moves fluid between each cell's immediate surroundings and the tissues where exchange with the environment occurs.

Gastrovascular Cavities

Let's begin by looking at animals with body shapes that permit them to live without a distinct circulatory system.

In hydras, jellies, and other cnidarians, a central gastrovascular cavity functions in the distribution of substances throughout the body and in digestion (see Figure 41.6). An opening at one end connects the cavity to the surrounding water. In a hydra, thin branches of the gastrovascular cavity extend into the animal's tentacles. In jellies and some other cnidarians, the gastrovascular cavity has a much more elaborate branching pattern (Figure 42.2a).

In animals with a gastrovascular cavity, fluid bathes both the inner and outer tissue layers, facilitating exchange of gases and cellular waste. Only the cells lining the cavity have direct access to nutrients released by digestion.

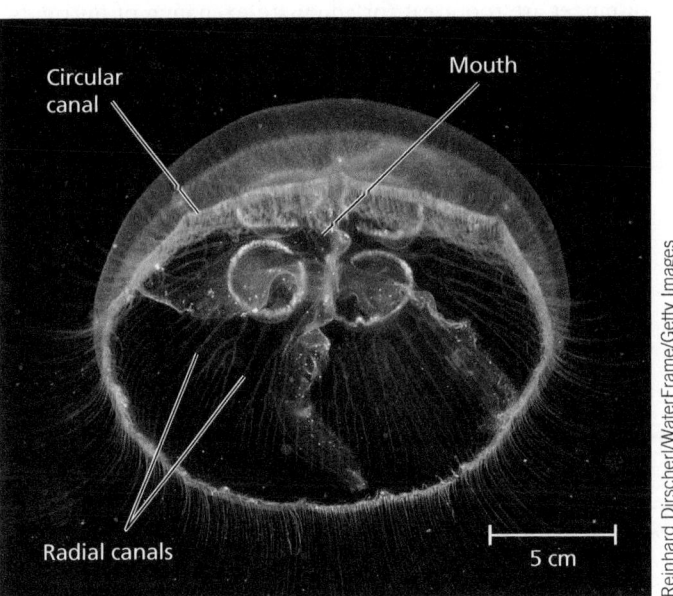

(a) **The moon jelly *Aurelia*, a cnidarian.** The jelly is viewed here from its underside (oral surface). The mouth leads to an elaborate gastrovascular cavity that consists of radial canals leading to and from a circular canal. Ciliated cells lining the canals circulate fluid within the cavity.

(b) **The planarian *Dugesia*, a flatworm.** The mouth and pharynx on the ventral side lead to the highly branched gastrovascular cavity, stained dark red in this specimen (LM).

▲ Figure 42.2 **Internal transport in gastrovascular cavities.**

WHAT IF? *Suppose a gastrovascular cavity were open at two ends, with fluid entering one end and leaving the other. How would this affect the gastrovascular cavity's functions in gas exchange and digestion?*

However, because the body wall is a mere two cells thick, nutrients need diffuse only a short distance to reach the cells of the outer tissue layer.

Planarians and most other flatworms also survive without a circulatory system. Their combination of a gastrovascular cavity and a flat body is well suited for exchange with the environment (Figure 42.2b). A flat body optimizes diffusional exchange by increasing surface area and minimizing diffusion distances.

Evolutionary Variation in Circulatory Systems

EVOLUTION   For animals with many cell layers, diffusion distances are too great for adequate exchange of nutrients and wastes by a gastrovascular cavity. In these organisms, a circulatory system minimizes the distances that substances must diffuse to enter or leave a cell.

General Properties of Circulatory Systems

A circulatory system has three basic components: a circulatory fluid, a set of interconnecting vessels, and a muscular pump, the **heart**. The heart powers circulation by using metabolic energy to elevate the hydrostatic pressure of the circulatory fluid, which then flows through the vessels and back to the heart.

By transporting fluid throughout the body, the circulatory system functionally connects the aqueous environment of the body cells to the organs that exchange gases, absorb nutrients, and dispose of wastes. In mammals, for example, O_2 from inhaled air diffuses across only two layers of cells in the lungs before reaching the blood. The circulatory system, powered by the heart, then carries the oxygen-rich blood to all parts of the body. As the blood streams throughout the body tissues in tiny blood vessels, O_2 in the blood diffuses only a short distance before entering the fluid that directly bathes the cells.

Several basic types of circulatory systems have arisen during evolution, each representing adaptations to constraints imposed by anatomy and environment. Circulatory systems are either open or closed, vary with regard to the number of circuits in the body, and rely on pumps that differ in structure and organization. We'll examine each of these variations and their physiological consequences in turn.

Open and Closed Circulatory Systems

Arthropods and most molluscs have an **open circulatory system**, in which the circulatory fluid bathes the organs directly (Figure 42.3a). In these animals, the circulatory fluid, called **hemolymph**, is also the *interstitial fluid* that bathes body cells. Contraction of one or more hearts pumps the hemolymph through the circulatory vessels into

▼ Figure 42.3 **Open and closed circulatory systems.**

(a) An open circulatory system

In an open circulatory system, such as that of a grasshopper, hemolymph surrounding body tissues also acts as the circulatory fluid.

(b) A closed circulatory system

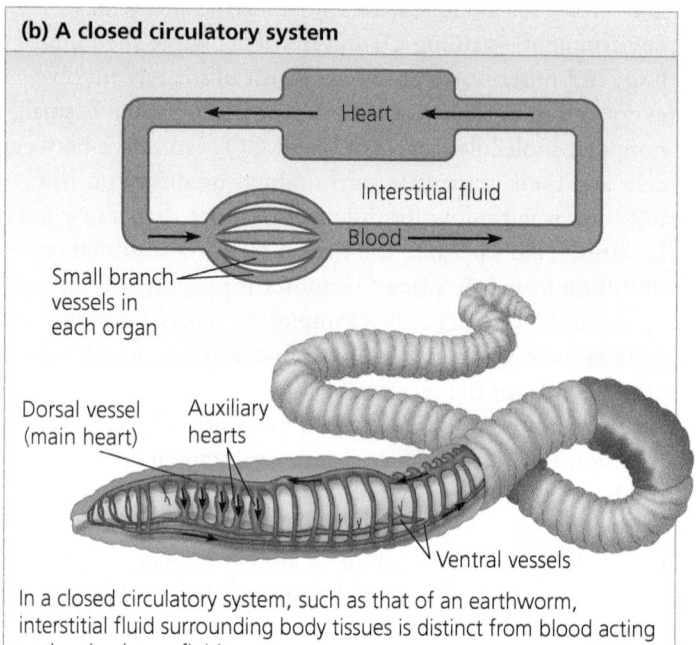

In a closed circulatory system, such as that of an earthworm, interstitial fluid surrounding body tissues is distinct from blood acting as the circulatory fluid.

interconnected sinuses, spaces surrounding the organs. Within the sinuses, chemical exchange occurs between the hemolymph and body cells. Relaxation of the heart draws hemolymph back in through pores, which are equipped with valves that close when the heart contracts. Body movements help circulate the hemolymph by periodically squeezing the sinuses. The open circulatory system of larger crustaceans, such as lobsters and crabs, includes a more extensive system of vessels as well as an accessory pump.

In a **closed circulatory system**, a circulatory fluid called **blood** is confined to vessels and is distinct from the interstitial fluid (Figure 42.3b). One or more hearts pump blood into large vessels that branch into smaller ones that infiltrate the organs. Chemical exchange occurs between the blood and the interstitial fluid, as well as between the interstitial fluid and body cells. Annelids (including earthworms), cephalopods (including squids and octopuses), and all vertebrates have closed circulatory systems.

The fact that both open and closed circulatory systems are widespread among animals suggests that there are advantages to each system. The lower hydrostatic pressures associated with open circulatory systems make them less costly than closed systems in terms of energy expenditure. In some invertebrates, open circulatory systems serve additional functions. For example, spiders use the hydrostatic pressure generated by their open circulatory system to extend their legs.

The benefits of closed circulatory systems include relatively high blood pressures, which enable the effective delivery of O_2 and nutrients to the cells of larger and more active animals. Among the molluscs, for instance, closed circulatory systems are found in the largest and most active species, the squids and octopuses. Closed systems are also particularly well suited to regulating the distribution of blood to different organs, as you'll learn later in this chapter. In examining closed circulatory systems in more detail, we will focus on the vertebrates.

Evolution of Vertebrate Circulatory Systems

The closed circulatory system of humans and other vertebrates is often called the **cardiovascular system**. Blood circulates to and from the heart through an amazingly extensive network of vessels: The total length of blood vessels in an average human adult is twice Earth's circumference at the equator!

Arteries, veins, and capillaries are the three main types of **blood vessels**. Within each type, blood flows in only one direction. **Arteries** carry blood away from the heart to organs throughout the body. Within organs, arteries branch into smaller arteries, or **arterioles**, that convey blood to the capillaries. **Capillaries** are microscopic vessels with very thin, porous walls. Networks of these vessels, called **capillary beds**, infiltrate every tissue, passing within a few cell diameters of every cell in the body. Across the thin walls of capillaries, chemicals, including dissolved gases, are exchanged by diffusion between the blood and the interstitial fluid around the tissue cells. At their "downstream" end, capillaries converge into small veins, or **venules** that converge into **veins**, the vessels that carry blood back to the heart.

Arteries and veins are distinguished by the *direction* in which they carry blood, not by the O_2 content or other characteristics of the blood they contain. Arteries carry blood from the heart *toward* capillaries, and veins return blood to the heart *from* capillaries. The only exceptions are the portal veins, which carry blood between pairs of capillary beds. The hepatic portal vein, for example, carries blood from capillary beds in the digestive system to capillary beds in the liver (see Chapter 41). From the liver, blood passes into the hepatic veins, which conduct blood toward the heart.

The hearts of all vertebrates contain two or more muscular chambers. The chambers that receive blood entering the heart are called **atria** (singular, *atrium*). The chambers responsible for pumping blood out of the heart are called **ventricles**. The number of chambers and the extent to which they are separated from one another differ substantially among groups of vertebrates, as we will discuss next.

Single Circulation in Fishes

In the most ancient vertebrates (jawless, bony, and cartilaginous fishes), the heart consists of two chambers: an atrium and a ventricle. The blood passes though the heart once in each complete circuit, an arrangement called **single circulation** (Figure 42.4a). Blood collects in the atrium, then enters the ventricle. Contraction of the ventricle pumps blood to the arteries that lead to the gills. In the capillaries of the gills, O_2 diffuses into the blood as CO_2 leaves the blood. From the gills, the blood travels to the rest of the body, releasing O_2 before returning to the heart. This single circuit in fish has two main disadvantages. First, by passing through the gill capillaries, blood pressure drops as blood is delivered to the rest of the body, reducing the efficiency of circulation. Second, the heart is forced to rely upon deoxygenated blood for its own metabolic needs. Though less efficient than the other vertebrate systems, it works well enough in these animals, which generally have relatively low metabolic demands. Other vertebrates evolved a **double circulation**, where the blood moving between the heart and the rest of the body (the **systemic circuit**) is separated from the blood that travels between the heart and the respiratory surface (the **pulmonary circuit**).

Incomplete Separation of Systemic and Pulmonary Circuits in Amphibians and Reptiles

Frogs and other amphibians have a heart with three chambers: two atria and one ventricle (Figure 42.4b). The right atrium collects blood from the body, and the left atrium collects blood from respiratory surfaces. These animals respire through lungs and skin, so this circuit is called a **pulmocutaneous circuit**. Both atria empty into the single ventricle, but the marvel of the amphibian heart is that a ridge within the ventricle separates blood arriving from the

Bony fishes, rays, and sharks have a single circuit of blood flow and a single circulatory pump—a heart with two chambers.

Amphibians, reptiles, and mammals have two circuits of blood flow and two pumps fused into a multi-chambered heart. Note that circulatory systems are depicted as if the animal is facing you: The right side of the heart is shown on the left, and vice versa.

Artery

Heart:
Atrium (A)
Ventricle (V)

Vein

Gill capillaries

Body capillaries

Key
- Oxygen-rich blood
- Oxygen-poor blood

(a) **Fish circulation.** Fish have a single circuit of blood moving through a two-chambered heart. Note that the fish heart receives only deoxygenated blood.

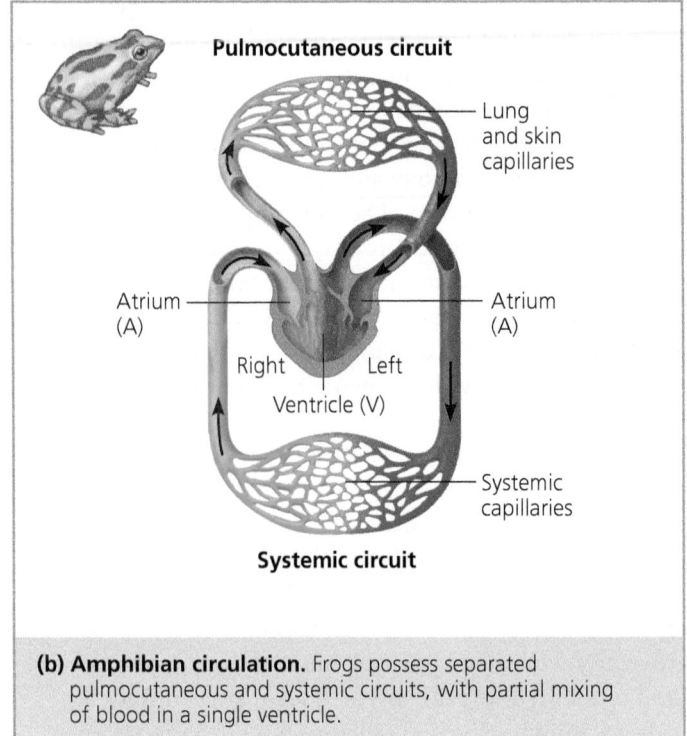

Pulmocutaneous circuit

Lung and skin capillaries

Atrium (A)

Atrium (A)

Right   Left
Ventricle (V)

Systemic capillaries

Systemic circuit

(b) **Amphibian circulation.** Frogs possess separated pulmocutaneous and systemic circuits, with partial mixing of blood in a single ventricle.

Pulmonary circuit

Lung capillaries

Right systemic aorta

Left systemic aorta

A   A
V   V
Right   Left

Incomplete septum

Systemic capillaries

Systemic circuit

(c) **Reptile circulation.** Lizards, turtles, and snakes have a septum that partially separates the single ventricle into two chambers, reducing mixing of pulmonary and systemic blood.

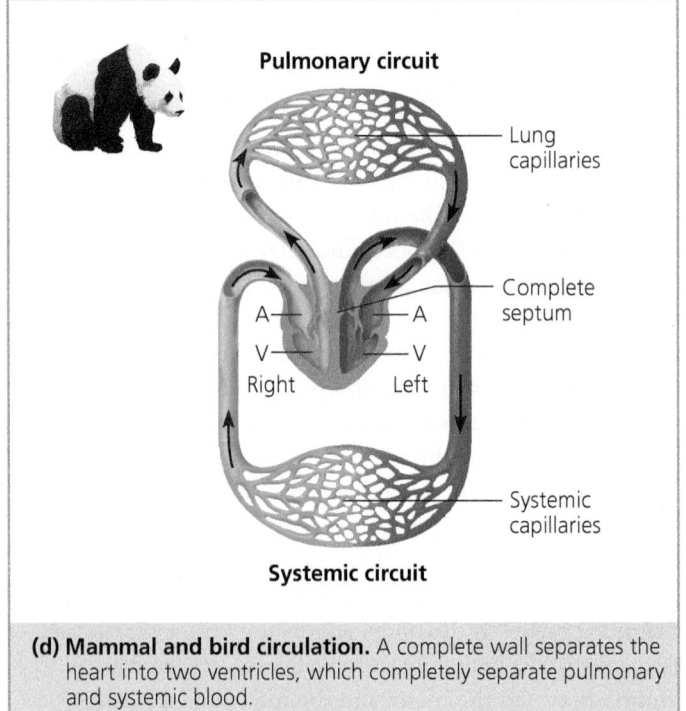

Pulmonary circuit

Lung capillaries

A   A
V   V
Right   Left

Complete septum

Systemic capillaries

Systemic circuit

(d) **Mammal and bird circulation.** A complete wall separates the heart into two ventricles, which completely separate pulmonary and systemic blood.

two atria. When the ventricle contracts, the oxygen-rich blood from the left atrium is sent via the systemic circuit to the rest of the body and oxygen-depleted blood from the right atrium is sent to the respiratory surface for oxygenation. Frogs can adjust the pulmocutaneous circuit, shunting blood to the skin when underwater, or to the lungs when breathing air.

Whereas the amphibian ventricle has a simple ridge to guide blood flows, reptiles have evolved a wall, or septum, within the single ventricle that better separates pulmonary and system blood (Figure 42.4c). In most reptiles (turtles, snakes, and lizards) the septum is incomplete, permitting some mixing of the blood flows within the ventricle. Crocodilians have evolved a complete septum, more efficiently separating the two circuits. Like amphibians, reptiles can control the relative amount of blood flowing to the lungs and the body, though the mechanisms differ among species.

Four-Chambered Hearts of Mammals and Birds

In mammals and birds, there are two atria and two ventricles (Figure 42.4d). The left side of the heart receives and pumps only oxygen-rich blood, while the right side receives and pumps only oxygen-poor blood. In completely separating systemic and pulmonary circuits, traits such as blood pressure can be regulated independently in the two circuits. A powerful four-chambered heart arose independently in the distinct ancestors of mammals and birds and thus reflects convergent evolution (see Chapter 34).

Evolutionary Themes

The diversity in the circulatory arrangements depicted in Figure 42.4 reflects the big steps taken by different taxa through evolution. Some adaptations improve the separation of blood flowing through the systemic and respiratory circulation. For example, the ridge seen in the amphibian ventricle or the incomplete septum of the ventricle of non-crocodilian reptiles provide an ability to send oxygen-poor blood to the respiratory surface and oxygen-rich blood to the rest of the body. Other adaptations increase the flexibility within the circulation. When they are submerged, alligators and amphibians can divert blood away from the lungs as it is not required for gas exchange. The inherent efficiency of the heart is an important determinant of metabolic rate. The four-chambered hearts of birds and mammals are needed to maximize the blood flow needed to support metabolic rates associated with endothermy.

In each taxon, there are variations in cardiovascular physiology. For example, the subtle differences in circulatory physiology in populations of salmon has profound implications for survival in a changing environment (Figure 42.5).

▼ Figure 42.5 | **Inquiry**

Temperature adaptation in salmon

Experiment Salmon living in waters that are growing warmer with each passing summer at the south of their geographic range are amongst the species that are most vulnerable to global warming. Researchers from the University of British Columbia have spent years studying the West Coast salmon that live in different local rivers. In a recent study, Tony Farrell and his team hypothesized that circulatory and respiratory adaptations contributed to the variation seen between salmon populations in traits such as thermal tolerance and the ability to exercise.

Results Populations of salmon differ in their cardiovascular physiology in ways that reflect a match to migration conditions. Panel A shows differences in thermal sensitivity of aerobic scope. Weaver River is much colder than the others, and salmon from this population perform better at colder temperatures. Panel B shows heart mass to be larger in fish that travel fastest up river.

Conclusion Circulatory physiology is critical to the ability of adult salmon to swim fast and reach their spawning grounds under challenging environmental conditions. The life history of the salmon permits adaptations that allow some populations to better tolerate intense swimming or heat stress.

Source: E.J. Eliason, T.D. Clark, M.J. Hague, L.M. Hanson, Z.S. Gallagher, K.M. Jeffries, M.K. Gale, D.A. Patterson, S.G. Hinch, and A.P. Farrell, Differences in thermal tolerance among sockeye salmon populations, *Science* 332:109–112 (2011). © 2011 American Association for the Advancement of Science. Reprinted with permission.

WHAT IF? *Salmon return to their natal rivers to spawn. Would you expect to find the same types of physiological variation between salmon from different rivers if salmon were less faithful in returning to the rivers where they hatched?*

1. How is the flow of hemolymph through an open circulatory system similar to the flow of water through an outdoor fountain?

2. Each of the evolutionary variants in Figure 42.4 works well for the animals, given their activity levels and lifestyle. What are the advantages and disadvantages of each of the four patterns?

3. **WHAT IF?** The heart of a normally developing human fetus has a hole between the left and right atria. In some cases, this hole does not close completely before birth. If the hole weren't surgically corrected, how would it affect the O_2 content of the blood entering the systemic circuit?

For suggested answers, see Appendix A.

CONCEPT 42.2

Coordinated cycles of heart contraction drive double circulation in mammals

The timely delivery of O_2 to the body's organs is critical. Some brain cells, for example, die if their O_2 supply is interrupted for as little as a few minutes. How does the mammalian cardiovascular system meet the body's continuous but variable demand for O_2? To answer this question, we need to consider how the parts of the system are arranged and how each part functions.

Mammalian Circulation

Let's first examine the overall organization of the mammalian cardiovascular system, beginning with the pulmonary circuit. (The circled numbers refer to corresponding locations in **Figure 42.6**.) ❶ Contraction of the right ventricle pumps blood to the lungs via ❷ the pulmonary arteries. As the blood flows through ❸ capillary beds in the left and right lungs, it loads O_2 and unloads CO_2. Oxygen-rich blood returns from the lungs via the pulmonary veins to ❹ the left atrium of the heart. Next, the oxygen-rich blood flows into ❺ the heart's left ventricle, which pumps the oxygen-rich blood out to body tissues through the systemic circuit. Blood leaves the left ventricle via ❻ the aorta, which conveys blood to arteries leading throughout the body. The first branches leading from the aorta are the coronary arteries (not shown), which supply blood to the heart muscle itself. Then branches lead to ❼ capillary beds in the head and arms (forelimbs). The aorta then descends into the abdomen, supplying oxygen-rich blood to arteries leading to ❽ capillary beds in the abdominal organs and legs (hind limbs). Within the capillaries, there is a net diffusion of O_2 from the blood to the tissues and of CO_2 (produced by cellular respiration) into the blood. Capillaries rejoin, forming venules, which convey blood to veins. Oxygen-poor blood from the head, neck, and forelimbs is channelled into a

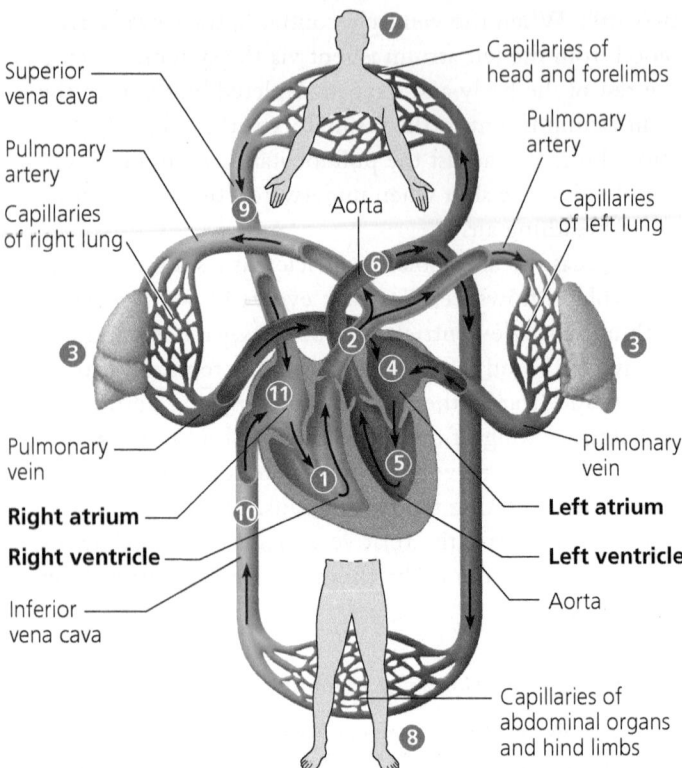

▲ Figure 42.6 **The mammalian cardiovascular system: an overview.** Note that the dual circuits operate simultaneously, not in the serial fashion that the numbering in the diagram suggests. The two ventricles pump almost in unison; while some blood is travelling in the pulmonary circuit, the rest of the blood is flowing in the systemic circuit.

large vein, ❾ the superior vena cava. Another large vein, ❿ the inferior vena cava, drains blood from the trunk and hind limbs. The two venae cavae empty their blood into ⓫ the right atrium, from which the oxygen-poor blood flows into the right ventricle.

The Mammalian Heart: *A Closer Look*

Using the human heart as an example, let's now take a closer look at how the mammalian heart works (**Figure 42.7**). Located behind the sternum (breastbone), the human heart is about the size of a clenched fist and consists mostly of cardiac muscle (see Figure 40.5). The two atria have relatively thin walls and serve as collection chambers for blood returning to the heart from the lungs or other body tissues. Much of the blood that enters the atria flows into the ventricles while all heart chambers are relaxed. The remainder is transferred by contraction of the atria before the ventricles begin to contract. The ventricles have thicker walls and contract much more forcefully than the atria—especially the left ventricle, which pumps blood to all body organs through the systemic circuit. Although the left ventricle contracts with greater force than the right ventricle, it pumps the same volume of blood as the right ventricle during each contraction.

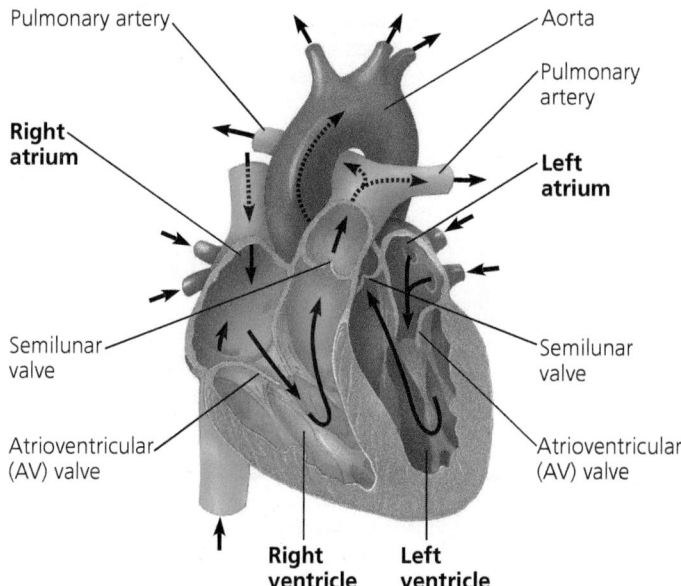

Figure 42.7 **The mammalian heart: a closer look.** Notice the locations of the valves, which prevent backflow of blood within the heart. Also notice how the atria and left and right ventricles differ in the thickness of their muscular walls.

The heart contracts and relaxes in a rhythmic cycle. When it contracts, it pumps blood; when it relaxes, its chambers fill with blood. One complete sequence of pumping and filling is referred to as the **cardiac cycle**. The contraction phase of the cycle is called **systole**, and the relaxation phase is called **diastole** (Figure 42.8).

The volume of blood each ventricle pumps per minute is the **cardiac output**. Two factors determine cardiac output: the rate of contraction, or **heart rate** (number of beats per minute), and the **stroke volume**, the amount of blood pumped by a ventricle in a single contraction. The average stroke volume in humans is about 70 mL. Multiplying this stroke volume by a resting heart rate of 72 beats per minute yields a cardiac output of 5 L/min—about equal to the total volume of blood in the human body. During heavy exercise, cardiac output increases as much as fivefold.

Four valves in the heart prevent backflow and keep blood moving in the correct direction (see Figures 42.7 and 42.8). Made of flaps of connective tissue, the valves open when pushed from one side and close when pushed from the other. An **atrioventricular (AV) valve** lies between each atrium and ventricle. The AV valves are anchored by strong fibres that prevent them from turning inside out. Pressure generated by the powerful contraction of the ventricles closes the AV valves, keeping blood from flowing back into the atria. **Semilunar valves** are located at the two exits of the heart: where the aorta leaves the left ventricle and where the pulmonary artery leaves the right ventricle. These valves are pushed open by the pressure

① **Atrial and ventricular diastole.** During a relaxation phase, blood returning from the large veins flows into the atria and then into the ventricles through the AV valves.

② **Atrial systole and ventricular diastole.** A brief period of atrial contraction then forces all blood remaining in the atria into the ventricles.

③ **Ventricular systole and atrial diastole.** During the remainder of the cycle, ventricular contraction pumps blood into the large arteries through the semilunar valves.

Figure 42.8 **The cardiac cycle.** For an adult human at rest with a heart rate of about 72 beats per minute, one complete cardiac cycle takes about 0.8 second. Note that during all but 0.1 second of the cardiac cycle, the atria are relaxed and are filling with blood returning via the veins.

generated during contraction of the ventricles. When the ventricles relax, blood pressure built up in the aorta closes the semilunar valves and prevents significant backflow.

You can follow the closing of the two sets of heart valves either with a stethoscope or by pressing your ear tightly against the chest of a friend (or a friendly dog). The sound pattern is "lub-dup, lub-dup, lub-dup." The first heart sound ("lub") is created by the recoil of blood against the closed AV valves. The second sound ("dup") is due to the vibrations caused by closing of the semilunar valves.

If blood squirts backward through a defective valve, it may produce an abnormal sound called a **heart murmur**. Some people are born with heart murmurs; in others, the valves may be damaged by infection (from rheumatic fever, for instance). When a valve defect is severe enough to endanger health, surgeons may implant a mechanical replacement valve. However, not all heart murmurs are caused by a defect, and most valve defects do not reduce the efficiency of blood flow enough to warrant surgery.

Maintaining the Heart's Rhythmic Beat

In vertebrates, the heartbeat originates in the heart itself. Some cardiac muscle cells are autorhythmic, meaning they contract and relax repeatedly without any signal from the nervous system. You can even see these rhythmic contractions in tissue that has been removed from the heart and placed in a dish in the laboratory! Because each of these cells has its own intrinsic contraction rhythm, how are their contractions coordinated in the intact heart? The answer lies in a group of autorhythmic cells located in the wall of the right atrium, near where the superior vena cava enters the heart. This cluster of cells is called the **sinoatrial (SA) node**, or *pacemaker*, and it sets the rate and timing at which all cardiac muscle cells contract. (In contrast to vertebrates, some arthropods have pacemakers located in the nervous system, outside the heart.)

The SA node produces electrical impulses much like those produced by nerve cells. Because cardiac muscle cells are electrically coupled through gap junctions (see Figure 6.30), impulses from the SA node spread rapidly within heart tissue. In addition, these impulses generate currents that are conducted to the skin via body fluids. In an **electrocardiogram** (**ECG** or, often, **EKG**, from the German spelling), these currents are recorded by electrodes placed on the skin. The resulting graph of current against time has a characteristic shape that represents the stages in the cardiac cycle (**Figure 42.9**).

Impulses from the SA node first spread rapidly through the walls of the atria, causing both atria to contract in unison. During atrial contraction, the impulses originating at the SA node reach other autorhythmic cells located in the wall between the left and right atria. These cells form a relay point called the **atrioventricular (AV) node**. Here the impulses are delayed for about 0.1 second before spreading to the heart apex. This delay allows the atria to empty completely before the ventricles contract. Then the signals from the AV node are conducted to the heart apex and throughout the ventricular walls by specialized structures called bundle branches and Purkinje fibres.

Physiological cues alter heart tempo by regulating the pacemaker function of the SA node. Two portions of the nervous system, the sympathetic and parasympathetic divisions, are largely responsible for this regulation. They function like the spurs and reins used in riding a horse: The

① Signals (yellow) from SA node spread through atria.

② Signals are delayed at AV node.

③ Bundle branches pass signals to heart apex.

④ Signals spread throughout ventricles.

SA node (pacemaker)

AV node

Bundle branches   Heart apex

Purkinje fibres

ECG

▲ **Figure 42.9 The control of heart rhythm.** The sequence of electrical events in the heart is shown at the top; red highlights specialized muscle cells involved in the electrical control of the rhythm. The corresponding components of an electrocardiogram (ECG) are highlighted at the bottom in yellow. In step 4, the portion of the ECG to the right of the "spike" represents electrical activity that reprimes the ventricles for the next round of contraction.

WHAT IF? *If a doctor gave you a copy of your ECG recording, how could you determine what your heart rate had been during the test?*

sympathetic division speeds up the pacemaker, and the parasympathetic division slows it down. For example, when you stand up and start walking, the sympathetic division increases your heart rate, an adaptation that enables your circulatory system to provide the additional O_2 needed by the muscles that are powering your activity. If you then sit down and relax, the parasympathetic division decreases your heart rate, an adaptation that conserves energy. Hormones secreted into the blood also influence the pacemaker. For instance, epinephrine, the "fight-or-flight" hormone secreted by the adrenal glands, causes the heart rate to increase. A third type of input that affects the pacemaker is body temperature. In your heart, an increase of only 1°C raises heart rate by about 10 beats per minute. This is the reason your heart beats faster when you have a fever.

Having examined the operation of the circulatory pump, we turn in the next section to the forces and structures that influence blood flow in the vessels of each circuit.

CONCEPT CHECK 42.2

1. Explain why blood in the pulmonary veins has a higher O_2 concentration than blood in the venae cavae, which are also veins.

2. Why is it important that the AV node delay the electrical impulse moving from the SA node and the atria to the ventricles?

3. **WHAT IF?** After exercising regularly for several months, you find that your resting heart rate decreases, but your cardiac output at rest is unchanged. What other change in the function of your heart at rest would you expect to find? Explain.

For suggested answers, see Appendix A.

Patterns of blood pressure and flow reflect the structure and arrangement of blood vessels

The vertebrate circulatory system enables blood to deliver oxygen and nutrients and remove wastes throughout the body. In doing so, the circulatory system relies on a branching network of vessels much like the plumbing system that delivers fresh water to a city and removes its wastes. In fact, the same physical principles that govern the operation of plumbing systems apply to the functioning of blood vessels.

Blood Vessel Structure and Function

Blood vessels contain a central lumen (cavity) lined with an **endothelium**, a single layer of flattened epithelial cells. The smooth surface of the endothelium minimizes resistance to the flow of blood. Surrounding the endothelium are layers of tissue that differ in capillaries, arteries, and veins, reflecting the specialized functions of these vessels.

Capillaries are the smallest blood vessels, having a diameter only slightly greater than that of a red blood cell (Figure 42.10). Capillaries also have very thin walls, which consist of just the endothelium and its basal lamina. This structural organization facilitates the exchange of substances between the blood in capillaries and the interstitial fluid.

The walls of arteries and veins have a more complex organization than those of capillaries. Both arteries and veins have two layers of tissue surrounding the endothelium: an outer layer of connective tissue containing elastic fibres, which allow the vessel to stretch and recoil, and a middle layer containing smooth muscle and more elastic fibres. However, the walls of arteries and veins also differ, reflecting distinct adaptations of these vessels to their particular functions in circulation.

The walls of arteries are thick and strong, accommodating blood pumped at high pressure by the heart. Arterial walls also have an elastic recoil that helps maintain blood pressure and flow to capillaries when the heart relaxes between contractions. Signals from the nervous system and hormones circulating in the blood act on the smooth muscle in arteries and arterioles, dilating or constricting these vessels and thus controlling blood flow to different parts of the body.

Because veins convey blood back to the heart at a lower pressure, they do not require thick walls. For a given blood vessel diameter, a vein has a wall only about a third as thick as that of an artery. Valves inside the veins maintain a unidirectional flow of blood despite the low blood pressure.

We consider next how blood vessel diameter, vessel number, and pressure influence the speed at which blood flows in different locations within the body.

Blood Flow Velocity

To understand how blood vessel diameter influences blood flow, consider how water flows through a thick hose connected to a faucet. When the faucet is turned on, water flows at the same velocity at each point along the hose. However, if a narrow nozzle is attached to the end of the hose, the water will exit the nozzle at a much greater velocity. Because water doesn't compress under pressure, the volume of water moving through the nozzle in a given time must be the same as the volume moving through the

▲ Figure 42.10 **The structure of blood vessels.**

rest of the hose. The cross-sectional area of the nozzle is smaller than that of the hose, so the water speeds up in the nozzle.

An analogous situation exists in the circulatory system, but blood *slows* as it moves from arteries to arterioles to the much narrower capillaries. Why? The reason is that the number of capillaries is enormous, roughly 7 billion in a human body. Each artery conveys blood to so many capillaries that the *total* cross-sectional area is much greater in capillary beds than in the arteries or any other part of the circulatory system (Figure 42.11). The result is a dramatic decrease in velocity from the arteries to the capillaries: Blood travels 500 times slower in the capillaries (about 0.1 cm/sec) than in the aorta (about 48 cm/sec).

The reduced velocity of blood flow in capillaries is essential to the function of the circulatory system. The exchange of substances between the blood and interstitial fluid occurs only in capillaries because only capillaries have walls thin enough to permit this transfer. Diffusion,

however, is not instantaneous. The slower flow of blood through capillaries is thus necessary to provide time for exchange to occur. After passing through the capillaries, the blood speeds up as it enters the venules and veins, which have smaller *total* cross-sectional areas than the capillaries.

Blood Pressure

Blood, like all fluids, flows from areas of higher pressure to areas of lower pressure. Contraction of a heart ventricle generates blood pressure, which exerts a force in all directions. The force directed lengthwise in an artery causes the blood to flow away from the heart, the site of highest pressure. The force exerted against the elastic wall of an artery stretches the wall, and the recoil of arterial walls plays a critical role in maintaining blood pressure, and hence blood flow, throughout the cardiac cycle. Once the blood enters the millions of tiny arterioles and capillaries, the narrow diameter of these vessels generates substantial resistance to flow. This resistance dissipates much of the pressure generated by the pumping heart by the time the blood enters the veins.

Changes in Blood Pressure during the Cardiac Cycle

Arterial blood pressure is highest when the heart contracts during ventricular systole. The pressure at this time is called **systolic pressure** (see Figure 42.11). The spikes in blood pressure caused by the powerful contractions of the ventricles stretch the arteries. By placing your fingers on the inside of your wrist, you can feel a **pulse**—the rhythmic bulging of the artery walls with each heartbeat. The surge of pressure is partly due to the narrow openings of arterioles impeding the exit of blood from the arteries. Thus, when the heart contracts, blood enters the arteries faster than it can leave, and the vessels stretch from the rise in pressure.

During diastole, the elastic walls of the arteries snap back. As a consequence, there is a lower but still substantial blood pressure when the ventricles are relaxed (**diastolic pressure**). Before enough blood has flowed into the arterioles to completely relieve pressure in the arteries, the heart contracts again. Because the arteries remain pressurized throughout the cardiac cycle (see Figure 42.11), blood continuously flows into arterioles and capillaries.

Regulation of Blood Pressure

Changes in arterial blood pressure are not limited to the oscillation during each cardiac cycle. Blood pressure also fluctuates on a longer time scale in response to signals that change the state of smooth muscles in arteriole walls. For

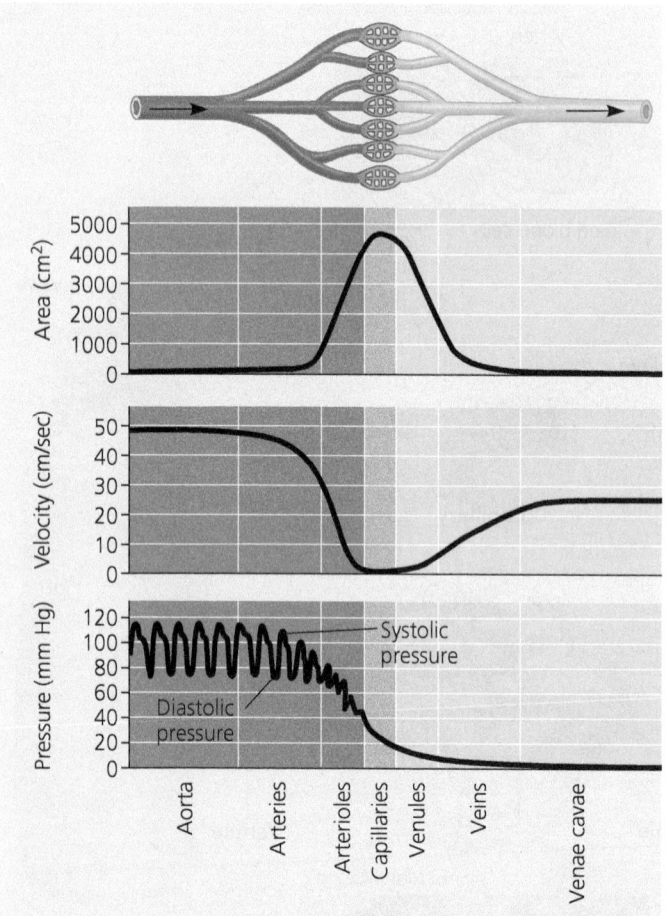

▲ Figure 42.11 **The interrelationship of cross-sectional area of blood vessels, blood flow velocity, and blood pressure.** Owing to an increase in total cross-sectional area, blood flow velocity decreases markedly in the arterioles and is lowest in the capillaries. Blood pressure, the main force driving blood from the heart to the capillaries, is highest in the aorta and other arteries.

example, physical or emotional stress can trigger nervous and hormonal responses that cause smooth muscles in arteriole walls to contract. When that happens, the arterioles narrow, a process called **vasoconstriction**. Narrowing of the arterioles increases blood pressure upstream in the arteries. When the smooth muscles relax, the arterioles undergo **vasodilation**, an increase in diameter that causes blood pressure in the arteries to fall.

Researchers have identified a gas, nitric oxide (NO), as a major inducer of vasodilation and a peptide, endothelin, as the most potent inducer of vasoconstriction. Both NO and endothelin are signalling molecules produced in blood vessels in response to cues from the nervous and endocrine systems. Each kind of molecule binds to a specific receptor, activating a signal transduction pathway that alters smooth muscle contraction and thus changes blood vessel diameter.

Vasoconstriction and vasodilation are often coupled to changes in cardiac output that also affect blood pressure. This coordination of regulatory mechanisms maintains adequate blood flow as the body's demands on the circulatory system change. During heavy exercise, for example, the arterioles in working muscles dilate, causing a greater flow of oxygen-rich blood to the muscles. By itself, this increased flow to the muscles would cause a drop in blood pressure (and therefore blood flow) in the body as a whole. However, cardiac output increases at the same time, maintaining blood pressure and supporting the necessary increase in blood flow.

Blood Pressure and Gravity

Blood pressure is generally measured for an artery in the arm at the same height as the heart (Figure 42.12). For a healthy 20-year-old human at rest, arterial blood pressure in the systemic circuit is typically about 120 millimetres of mercury (mm Hg) at systole and 70 mm Hg at diastole, expressed as 120/70. (Arterial blood pressure in the pulmonary circuit is six to ten times lower.)

Gravity has a significant effect on blood pressure. When you are standing, for example, your head is roughly 0.35 m higher than your chest, and the arterial blood pressure in your brain is about 27 mm Hg less than that near your heart. If the blood pressure in your brain is too low to

provide adequate blood flow, you will likely faint. By causing your body to collapse to the ground, fainting effectively places your head at the level of your heart, quickly increasing blood flow to your brain.

The challenge of pumping blood against gravity is particularly great for animals with very long necks. A giraffe, for example, requires a systolic pressure of more than 250 mm Hg near the heart to get blood to its head. When a giraffe lowers its head to drink, one-way valves and sinuses, along with feedback mechanisms that reduce cardiac output, prevent this high pressure from damaging its brain. We can calculate that a dinosaur with a neck nearly 10 m long would have required even greater systolic pressure—nearly 760 mm Hg—to pump blood to its brain when its head was fully raised. However, calculations based on anatomy and inferred metabolic rate suggest that dinosaurs did not have a heart powerful enough to generate such high pressure. Based on this evidence as well as studies of neck bone structure, some biologists have concluded that the long-necked dinosaurs fed close to the ground rather than on high foliage.

Gravity is also a consideration for blood flow in veins, especially those in the legs. Although blood pressure in veins is relatively low, several mechanisms assist the return

❶ A sphygmomanometer, an inflatable cuff attached to a pressure gauge, measures blood pressure in an artery. The cuff is inflated until the pressure closes the artery, so that no blood flows past the cuff. When this occurs, the pressure exerted by the cuff exceeds the pressure in the artery.

❷ The cuff is allowed to deflate gradually. When the pressure exerted by the cuff falls just below that in the artery, blood pulses into the forearm, generating sounds that can be heard with the stethoscope. The pressure measured at this point is the systolic pressure (120 mm Hg in this example).

❸ The cuff is allowed to deflate further, just until the blood flows freely through the artery and the sounds below the cuff disappear. The pressure at this point is the diastolic pressure (70 mm Hg in this example).

▲ Figure 42.12 **Measurement of blood pressure.** Blood pressure is recorded as two numbers separated by a slash. The first number is the systolic pressure; the second is the diastolic pressure.

of venous blood to the heart. First, rhythmic contractions of smooth muscles in the walls of venules and veins aid in the movement of the blood. Second, and more important, the contraction of skeletal muscles during exercise squeezes blood through the veins toward the heart (Figure 42.13). Third, the change in pressure within the thoracic (chest) cavity during inhalation causes the venae cavae and other large veins near the heart to expand and fill with blood.

In rare instances, runners and other athletes can suffer heart failure if they stop vigorous exercise abruptly. When the leg muscles suddenly cease contracting and relaxing, less blood returns to the heart, which continues to beat rapidly. If the heart is weak or damaged, this inadequate blood flow may cause the heart to malfunction. To reduce the risk of stressing the heart excessively, athletes are encouraged to follow hard exercise with moderate activity, such as walking, to "cool down" until their heart rate approaches its resting level.

Capillary Function

At any given time, only about 5–10% of the body's capillaries have blood flowing through them. However, each tissue has many capillaries, so every part of the body is supplied with blood at all times. Capillaries in the brain, heart, kidneys, and liver are usually filled to capacity, but at many other sites the blood supply varies over time as blood is diverted from one destination to another. For example, blood flow to the skin is regulated to help control body temperature, and blood supply to the digestive tract increases after a meal. During strenuous exercise, blood is diverted from the digestive tract and supplied more generously to skeletal muscles and skin. This is one reason why exercising heavily immediately after eating a big meal may cause indigestion.

Given that capillaries lack smooth muscle, how is blood flow in capillary beds altered? There are two mechanisms, both of which rely on signals that regulate the flow into capillaries. One mechanism involves contraction of the smooth muscle in the wall of an arteriole, which reduces the vessel's diameter and decreases blood flow to the adjoining capillary beds. When the smooth muscle relaxes, the arterioles dilate, allowing blood to enter the capillaries. The other mechanism for altering flow, shown in Figure 42.14, involves the action of *precapillary sphincters*, rings of smooth muscle located at the entrance to capillary beds. The signals that regulate blood flow include nerve impulses, hormones travelling throughout the bloodstream, and chemicals produced locally. For example, the chemical histamine released by cells at a wound site causes smooth muscle relaxation, dilating blood vessels, and increasing blood flow. The dilated vessels also give disease-fighting white blood cells greater access to invading microorganisms.

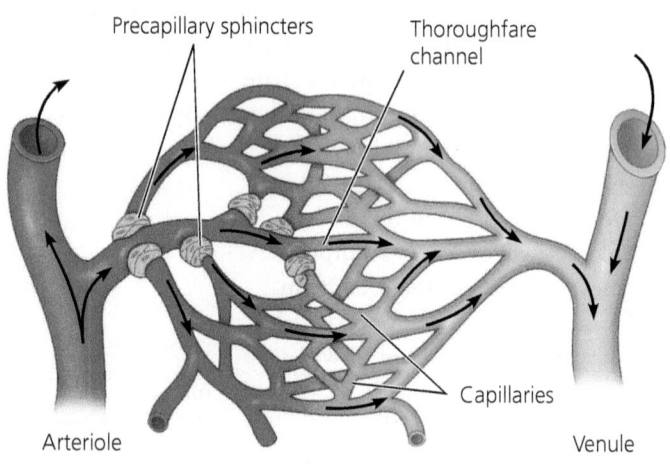

(a) Sphincters relaxed

(b) Sphincters contracted

▲ Figure 42.14 **Blood flow in capillary beds.** Precapillary sphincters regulate the passage of blood into capillary beds. Some blood flows directly from arterioles to venules through a short circuit called an anastomosis, which is always open.

▶ Figure 42.13 **Blood flow in veins.** Skeletal muscle contraction squeezes and constricts veins. Flaps of tissue within the veins act as one-way valves that keep blood moving only toward the heart. If you sit or stand too long, the lack of muscular activity may cause your feet to swell as blood pools in your veins.

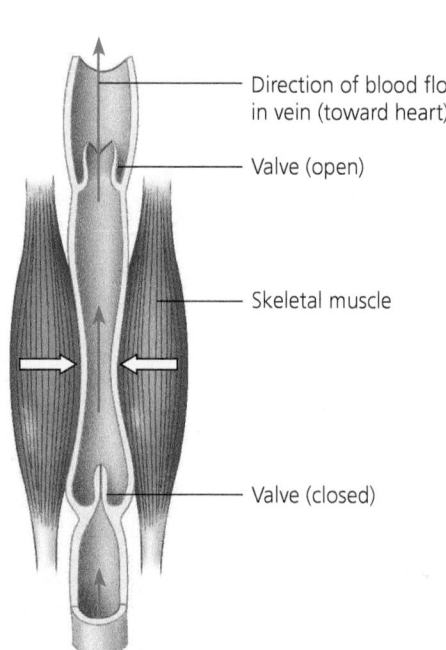

Direction of blood flow in vein (toward heart)

Valve (open)

Skeletal muscle

Valve (closed)

As you have read, the critical exchange of substances between the blood and interstitial fluid takes place across the endothelial cells that comprise the thin walls of the capillaries. Some substances are carried across the endothelium in vesicles that form on one side by endocytosis and release their contents on the opposite side by exocytosis. Small molecules, such as O_2 and CO_2, simply diffuse across the endothelial cells or, in some tissues, through microscopic pores in the capillary wall. These openings also provide the route for transport of small solutes such as sugars, salts, and urea, as well as for bulk flow of fluid into tissues driven by blood pressure within the capillary.

Two opposing forces control the movement of fluid between the capillaries and the surrounding tissues: Blood pressure tends to drive fluid out of the capillaries, and the presence of blood proteins tends to pull fluid back (Figure 42.15). Many blood proteins (and all blood cells) are too large to pass readily through the endothelium, and they remain in the capillaries. These dissolved proteins are responsible for much of the blood's *osmotic pressure* (the pressure produced by the difference in solute concentration across a membrane). The difference in osmotic pressure between the blood and the interstitial fluid opposes fluid movement out of the capillaries. On average, blood pressure is greater than the opposing forces, leading to a net loss of fluid from capillaries. The net loss is generally greatest at the arterial end of these vessels, where blood pressure is highest.

Fluid Return by the Lymphatic System

Each day, the adult human body loses approximately 4–8 L of fluid from capillaries to the surrounding tissues. There is also some leakage of blood proteins, even though the capillary wall is not very permeable to large molecules. The lost fluid and proteins return to the blood via the **lymphatic**

system, which includes a network of tiny vessels intermingled among capillaries of the cardiovascular system.

After entering the lymphatic system by diffusion, the fluid lost by capillaries is called **lymph**; its composition is about the same as that of interstitial fluid. The lymphatic system drains into large veins of the circulatory system at the base of the neck (see Figure 43.7). As you read in Chapter 41, this joining of the lymphatic and circulatory systems functions in the transfer of lipids from the small intestine to the blood.

The movement of lymph from peripheral tissues to the heart relies on much the same mechanisms that assist blood flow in veins. Lymph vessels, like veins, have valves that prevent the backflow of fluid. Rhythmic contractions of the vessel walls help draw fluid into the small lymphatic vessels. In addition, skeletal muscle contractions play a role in moving lymph.

Disorders that interfere with the lymphatic system highlight its role in maintaining proper fluid distribution in the body. Disruptions in the movement of lymph often cause edema, swelling resulting from the excessive accumulation of fluid in tissues. Severe blockage of lymph flow causes limbs or other body parts to swell to enormous proportions. For example, a condition known as elephantiasis arises when certain parasitic worms can lodge in the lymph vessels, blocking uptake of fluids from the extremities.

Along a lymph vessel are organs called **lymph nodes** (Figure 42.16). By filtering the lymph and by housing cells that attack viruses and bacteria, lymph nodes play an important role in the body's defence. Inside each lymph node is a honeycomb of connective tissue with spaces filled by white blood cells. When the body is fighting an infection, these cells multiply rapidly, and the lymph nodes become swollen and tender (which is why your doctor may check for swollen lymph nodes in your neck, armpits, or groin when you feel sick). Because lymph nodes have filtering and surveillance functions, doctors may examine the lymph nodes of cancer patients to detect the spread of diseased cells.

In recent years, evidence has surfaced demonstrating that the lymphatic system also plays a role in harmful immune responses, such as those responsible for

▲ **Figure 42.15 Fluid exchange between capillaries and the interstitial fluid.** This diagram shows a hypothetical capillary in which blood pressure exceeds osmotic pressure throughout the entire length of the capillary. In other capillaries, blood pressure may be lower than osmotic pressure along all or part of the capillary.

INTERSTITIAL FLUID
Net fluid movement out
Body cell
Blood pressure
Osmotic pressure
Arterial end of capillary
Direction of blood flow
Venous end of capillary

Biophoto Associates/Science Source

Lymph nodes

▶ **Figure 42.16 Human lymph nodes and vessels.** In this colourised X-ray image of the groin, lymph nodes and vessels (yellow) are visible next to the upper thigh bone (femur).

asthma. Because of these and other findings, the lymphatic system, largely ignored until the 1990s, has become a very active and promising area of biomedical research.

CONCEPT CHECK 42.3

1. Why does blood flow more slowly through capillaries than it flows through other vessels?

2. What short-term changes in cardiovascular function might best enable skeletal muscles to help an animal escape from a dangerous situation?

3. **WHAT IF?** If you had additional hearts distributed throughout your body, what would be one likely advantage and one likely disadvantage?

For suggested answers, see Appendix A.

CONCEPT 42.4

Blood components function in exchange, transport, and defence

As we discussed earlier, the fluid transported by an open circulatory system is continuous with the fluid that surrounds all of the body cells and therefore has the same composition. In contrast, the fluid in a closed circulatory system can be much more highly specialized, as is the case for the blood of vertebrates.

Blood Composition and Function

Vertebrate blood is a tissue consisting of cells suspended in a liquid called **plasma**. Dissolved in the plasma are ions and proteins that, together with the blood cells, function in osmotic regulation, transport, and defence. Separating the components of blood using a centrifuge reveals that cellular elements (cells and cell fragments) occupy about 45% of the volume of blood (**Figure 42.17**). The remainder is plasma.

Plasma

Among the many solutes in plasma are inorganic salts in the form of dissolved ions, sometimes referred to as blood electrolytes (see Figure 42.17). Although plasma is about 90% water, the dissolved salts are an essential component of the blood. Some of these ions buffer the blood, which in humans normally has a pH of 7.4. Salts are also important in maintaining the osmotic balance of the blood. In addition, the concentration of ions in plasma directly affects the composition of the interstitial fluid, where many of these ions have a vital role in muscle and nerve activity. To serve all of these functions, plasma electrolytes must be kept within narrow concentration ranges, a homeostatic function we will explore in Chapter 44.

Plasma 55%	
Constituent	**Major functions**
Water	Solvent for carrying other substances
Ions (blood electrolytes) Sodium Potassium Calcium Magnesium Chloride Bicarbonate	Osmotic balance, pH buffering, and regulation of membrane permeability
Plasma proteins Albumin	Osmotic balance, pH buffering
Fibrinogen	Clotting
Immunoglobulins (antibodies)	Defence
Substances transported by blood Nutrients (such as glucose, fatty acids, vitamins) Waste products of metabolism Respiratory gases (O_2 and CO_2) Hormones	

Separated blood elements

Cellular elements 45%		
Cell type	**Number** per μL (mm^3) of blood	**Functions**
Leukocytes (white blood cells) Basophils Lymphocytes Eosinophils Neutrophils Monocytes	5000–10 000	Defence and immunity
Platelets	250 000–400 000	Blood clotting
Erythrocytes (red blood cells)	5–6 million	Transport of O_2 and some CO_2

▲ Figure 42.17 **The composition of mammalian blood.**

Plasma proteins act as buffers against pH changes, help maintain the osmotic balance between blood and interstitial fluid, and contribute to the blood's viscosity (thickness). Particular plasma proteins have additional functions. The immunoglobulins, or antibodies, help combat viruses and other foreign agents that invade the body (see Chapter 43). Others are escorts for lipids, which are insoluble in water and can travel in blood only when bound to proteins. A third group of plasma proteins are clotting factors that help plug leaks when blood vessels are injured. (The term *serum* refers to blood plasma from which these clotting factors have been removed.)

Plasma also contains a wide variety of other substances in transit from one part of the body to another, including nutrients, metabolic wastes, respiratory gases, and hormones. Plasma has a much higher protein concentration than interstitial fluid, although the two fluids are otherwise similar. (Capillary walls, remember, are not very permeable to proteins.)

Cellular Elements

Blood contains two classes of cells: red blood cells, which transport O_2, and white blood cells, which function in defence (see Figure 42.17). Also suspended in blood plasma are **platelets**, fragments of cells that are involved in the clotting process.

Erythrocytes Red blood cells, or **erythrocytes**, are by far the most numerous blood cells. Each microlitre (μL, or mm^3) of human blood contains 5–6 million red cells, and there are about 25 trillion of these cells in the body's 5 L of blood. Their main function is O_2 transport, and their structure is closely related to this function. Human erythrocytes are small disks (7–8 μm in diameter) that are biconcave—thinner in the centre than at the edges. This shape increases surface area, enhancing the rate of diffusion of O_2 across their plasma membranes. Mature mammalian erythrocytes lack nuclei. This unusual characteristic leaves more space in these tiny cells for **hemoglobin**, the iron-containing protein that transports O_2 (see Figure 5.18). Mammalian erythrocytes also lack mitochondria and generate their ATP exclusively by anaerobic metabolism.

Despite its small size, an erythrocyte contains about 250 million molecules of hemoglobin. Because each molecule of hemoglobin binds up to four molecules of O_2, one erythrocyte can transport about a billion O_2 molecules. As erythrocytes pass through the capillary beds of lungs, gills, or other respiratory organs, O_2 diffuses into the erythrocytes and binds to hemoglobin. In the systemic capillaries, O_2 dissociates from hemoglobin and diffuses into body cells.

In **sickle-cell disease**, an abnormal form of hemoglobin (Hb^S) polymerizes into aggregates. Because the concentration of hemoglobin in erythrocytes is so high, these aggregates are large enough to distort the erythrocyte into an elongated, curved shape that resembles a sickle. As you learned in Chapter 5, this abnormality results from an alteration in the amino acid sequence of hemoglobin at a single position (see Figure 5.19).

Sickle-cell disease significantly impairs the function of the circulatory system. Sickled cells often lodge in arterioles and capillaries, preventing delivery of O_2 and nutrients and removal of CO_2 and wastes. Blood vessel blockage and resulting organ swelling often result in severe pain. In addition, sickled cells frequently rupture, reducing the number of red blood cells available for transporting O_2. The average life span of a sickled erythrocyte is only 20 days—one-sixth that of a normal erythrocyte. The rate of erythrocyte loss outstrips the replacement capacity of the bone marrow. Short-term therapy includes replacement of erythrocytes by blood transfusion; long-term treatments are generally aimed at inhibiting aggregation of Hb^S.

Leukocytes The blood contains five major types of white blood cells, or **leukocytes**. Their function is to fight infections. Some are phagocytic, engulfing and digesting microorganisms as well as debris from the body's own dead cells. As we will see in Chapter 43, other leukocytes, called lymphocytes, develop into specialized B cells and T cells that mount immune responses against foreign substances. Normally, 1 μL of human blood contains about 5000–10 000 leukocytes; their numbers increase temporarily whenever the body is fighting an infection. Unlike erythrocytes, leukocytes are also found outside the circulatory system, patrolling both interstitial fluid and the lymphatic system.

Platelets Platelets are pinched-off cytoplasmic fragments of specialized bone marrow cells. They are about 2–3 μm in diameter and have no nuclei. Platelets serve both structural and molecular functions in blood clotting.

Blood Clotting

The occasional cut or scrape is not life-threatening because blood components seal the broken blood vessels. A break in a blood vessel wall exposes proteins that attract platelets and initiate coagulation, the conversion of liquid components of blood to a solid clot. The coagulant, or sealant, circulates in an inactive form called *fibrinogen*. In response to a broken blood vessel, platelets release clotting factors that trigger reactions leading to the formation of *thrombin*, an enzyme that converts fibrinogen to *fibrin*. Newly formed fibrin aggregates into threads that form the framework of the clot. Thrombin also activates a factor that catalyzes the formation of more thrombin, driving clotting to completion through positive feedback (see Chapter 40). The steps in the production of a blood clot are diagrammed in **Figure 42.18**. Any genetic mutation that blocks a step in the clotting process can cause hemophilia,

① The clotting process begins when the endothelium of a vessel is damaged, exposing connective tissue in the vessel wall to blood. Platelets adhere to collagen fibres in the connective tissue and release a substance that makes nearby platelets sticky.

② The platelets form a plug that provides immediate protection against blood loss.

③ Unless the break is very small, this plug is reinforced by a fibrin clot.

Eye of Science/Science Source

— Collagen fibres

Platelet

Platelet plug

Fibrin clot

Red blood cells caught in threads of fibrin

5 μm

Clotting factors from:
→ Platelets
→ Damaged cells
→ Plasma (factors include calcium, vitamin K)

Enzymatic cascade

Prothrombin → Thrombin ⊕

Fibrinogen → Fibrin

Fibrin clot formation
Clotting factors released from the clumped platelets or damaged cells mix with clotting factors in the plasma, forming an enzymatic cascade that converts a plasma protein called prothrombin to its active form, thrombin. Thrombin itself is an enzyme that catalyzes the final step of the clotting process, the conversion of fibrinogen to fibrin. The threads of fibrin become interwoven into a clot (see colourized SEM above).

▲ Figure 42.18 **Blood clotting.**

a disease characterized by excessive bleeding and bruising from even minor cuts and bumps (see Chapter 15).

Anticlotting factors in the blood normally prevent spontaneous clotting in the absence of injury. Sometimes, however, clots form within a blood vessel, blocking the flow of blood. Such a clot is called a **thrombus**. We will explore how a thrombus forms and the danger that it poses later in this chapter.

Stem Cells and the Replacement of Cellular Elements

Erythrocytes, leukocytes, and platelets all develop from a common source: multipotent **stem cells** that are dedicated to replenishing the body's blood cell populations (**Figure 42.19**). The stem cells that produce blood cells are located in the red marrow of bones, particularly the ribs, vertebrae, sternum, and pelvis. Multipotent stem cells are so named because they have the ability to form multiple types of cells—in this case, the myeloid and lymphoid cell lineages. When a stem cell divides, one daughter cell remains a stem cell while the other takes on a specialized function.

Stem cells (in bone marrow)

Lymphoid stem cells

Myeloid stem cells

B cells   T cells

Lymphocytes

Erythrocytes

Neutrophils

Basophils

Monocytes

Platelets

Eosinophils

▲ Figure 42.19 **Differentiation of blood cells.** Some of the multipotent stem cells differentiate into lymphoid stem cells, which then develop into B cells and T cells, two types of lymphocytes that function in immunity (see Chapter 43). All other blood cells and platelets arise from myeloid stem cells.

Throughout a person's life, erythrocytes, leukocytes, and platelets arising from stem cell divisions replace the worn-out cellular elements of blood. Erythrocytes, for example, circulate for only 120 days on average before being replaced; the old cells are consumed by phagocytic cells in the liver and spleen. The production of new erythrocytes involves recycling of materials, such as the use of iron scavenged from old erythrocytes in new hemoglobin molecules.

A negative-feedback mechanism, sensitive to the amount of O_2 reaching the body's tissues via the blood, controls erythrocyte production. If the tissues do not receive enough O_2, the kidneys synthesize and secrete a hormone called **erythropoietin (EPO)** that stimulates erythrocyte production. If the blood is delivering more O_2 than the tissues can use, the level of EPO falls and erythrocyte production slows. Physicians use synthetic EPO to treat people with health problems such as *anemia*, a condition of lower-than-normal erythrocyte or hemoglobin levels that lowers the oxygen-carrying capacity of the blood. Some athletes inject themselves with EPO to increase their erythrocyte levels, although this practice, a form of blood doping, has been banned by the International Olympic Committee and other sports organizations. In recent years, a number of well-known athletes have tested positive for EPO-related drugs and have forfeited both their records and their right to participate in future competitions.

Cardiovascular Disease

More than one-third of all human deaths in Canada are caused by cardiovascular diseases—disorders of the heart and blood vessels. Cardiovascular diseases range from a minor disturbance of vein or heart valve function to a life-threatening disruption of blood flow to the heart or brain.

Cholesterol metabolism plays a central role in cardiovascular disease. As you learned in Chapter 7, the presence of this steroid in animal cell membranes helps maintain normal membrane fluidity. Cholesterol travels in blood plasma mainly in particles that consist of thousands of cholesterol molecules and other lipids bound to a protein. One type of particle—**low-density lipoprotein (LDL)**—delivers cholesterol to cells for membrane production. Another type—**high-density lipoprotein (HDL)**—scavenges excess cholesterol for return to the liver. Individuals with a high ratio of LDL to HDL are at substantially increased risk for heart disease.

Another factor in cardiovascular disease is *inflammation*, the body's reaction to injury. As you will learn in the next chapter, tissue damage leads to recruitment of two types of circulating immune cells, macrophages and leukocytes. Signals released by these cells trigger a flow of fluid out of blood vessels at the site of injury, resulting in the tissue swelling characteristic of inflammation (see Figure 43.8). Although inflammation is often a normal and healthy response to injury, it can significantly disrupt circulatory function, as explained in the next section.

Atherosclerosis, Heart Attacks, and Stroke

Circulating cholesterol and inflammation can act together to produce a cardiovascular disease called **atherosclerosis**, the hardening of the arteries by accumulation of fatty deposits (Figure 42.20). Healthy arteries have a smooth inner lining that reduces resistance to blood flow. Damage or infection can roughen the lining and lead to inflammation. Leukocytes are attracted to the damaged lining and begin to take up lipids, including cholesterol. A fatty deposit, called a plaque, grows steadily, incorporating fibrous connective tissue and additional cholesterol. As the plaque grows, the walls of the artery become thick and stiff, and the obstruction of the artery increases.

The result of untreated atherosclerosis is often a heart attack or a stroke. A **heart attack**, also called a *myocardial infarction*, is the damage or death of cardiac muscle tissue resulting from blockage of one or more coronary arteries, which supply oxygen-rich blood to the heart muscle. Because the coronary arteries are small in diameter, they are especially vulnerable to obstruction. Such blockage can destroy cardiac muscle quickly because the constantly beating heart muscle cannot survive long without O_2. If the heart stops beating, the victim may nevertheless survive if a heartbeat is restored by cardiopulmonary resuscitation (CPR) or some other emergency procedure within a few minutes of the attack. A **stroke** is the death of nervous tissue in the brain due to a lack of O_2. Strokes usually result from rupture or blockage of arteries in the head. The effects of a stroke and the individual's chance of survival depend on the extent and location of the damaged brain tissue. Rapid administration of a clot-dissolving drug may reduce the effects of a stroke or heart attack.

Although atherosclerosis often isn't detected until critical blood flow is disrupted, there can be warning signs. Partial blockage of the coronary arteries may cause occasional chest pain, a condition known as angina pectoris. The pain is most likely to be felt when the heart is labouring hard during physical or emotional stress, and it signals that part of the heart is not receiving enough O_2. An obstructed coronary artery may be treated surgically, either by inserting a metal mesh tube called a stent to expand the artery or by transplanting a healthy blood vessel from the chest or a limb to bypass the blockage.

① Lipoproteins such as LDL enter the lining of the artery and aggregate, leading to engulfment by immune cells called *macrophages*. Uptake of these lipoproteins by macrophages leads to the generation of lipid-rich *foam cells*.

② Secretion of extracellular matrix components increases lipoprotein aggregation. T lymphocytes enter the growing *plaque*, causing chronic inflammation. Smooth muscle cells from the lining of the artery also enter the plaque.

③ Smooth muscle cells form a fibrous cap separating the plaque from the blood. Within the plaque, foam cells die, releasing cellular debris and cholesterol. If the plaque ruptures, a blood clot can form within the artery.

④ Alternately, if the plaque continues to grow but does not rupture, the artery becomes increasingly obstructed.

▲ **Figure 42.20 Atherosclerosis.** In atherosclerosis, thickening of an arterial wall by plaque formation can restrict blood flow through the artery. Fragments of ruptured plaque can travel via the bloodstream and become lodged in other arteries. If those arteries supply the heart or brain, the resulting obstruction could cause a heart attack or stroke, respectively.

Risk Factors and Treatment of Cardiovascular Disease

Although the tendency to develop particular cardiovascular diseases is inherited, it is also strongly influenced by lifestyle. Smoking and consumption of certain processed vegetable oils called *trans fats* (see Chapter 5) increase the ratio of LDL to HDL, raising the risk of cardiovascular disease. In contrast, exercise decreases the LDL/HDL ratio.

There has been considerable progress in the last decade in preventing cardiovascular disease. For many individuals at high risk, treatment with drugs called statins can lower LDL levels and thereby reduce the risk of heart attacks In the Scientific Skills Exercise, you can interpret the effect of a genetic mutation on blood LDL levels.

The recognition that inflammation plays a central role in atherosclerosis and thrombus formation is also changing the treatment of cardiovascular disease. For example, aspirin, which inhibits the inflammatory response, has been found to help prevent the recurrence of heart attacks and stroke. Researchers have also focused on C-reactive protein (CRP), which is produced by the liver and found in the blood during episodes of acute inflammation. Like a high level of LDL cholesterol, the presence of significant amounts of CRP in blood is a useful risk indicator for cardiovascular disease.

Hypertension (high blood pressure) is yet another contributor to heart attack and stroke as well as other health problems. According to one hypothesis, chronic high blood pressure damages the endothelium that lines the arteries, promoting plaque formation. The usual definition of hypertension in adults is a systolic pressure above 140 mm Hg or a diastolic pressure above 90 mm Hg. Fortunately, hypertension is simple to diagnose and can usually be controlled by dietary changes, exercise, medication, or a combination of these approaches. Though the SI unit for pressure is the Pascal, medical practitioners have retained the use of mm Hg, the traditional measure of blood pressure.

CONCEPT CHECK 42.4

1. Explain why a physician might order a white cell count for a patient with symptoms of an infection.

2. Clots in arteries can cause heart attacks and strokes. Why, then, does it make sense to treat hemophiliacs by introducing clotting factors into their blood?

3. **WHAT IF?** Nitroglycerin (the key ingredient in dynamite) is sometimes prescribed for heart disease patients. Within the body, the nitroglycerin is converted to nitric oxide. Why would you expect nitroglycerin to relieve chest pain in these patients?

4. **MAKE CONNECTIONS** The allele that encodes Hb^S is codominant with the allele encoding normal hemoglobin (Hb) (see Concept 14.4). What can you deduce about the properties of Hb and Hb^S with regard to aggregate formation and sickling?

5. **MAKE CONNECTIONS** How do stem cells from the bone marrow of an adult differ from embryonic stem cells (see Concept 20.3)?

For suggested answers, see Appendix A.

Making and Interpreting Histograms

Does Inactivating the PCSK9 Enzyme Lower LDL Levels? Researchers interested in genetic factors affecting susceptibility to cardiovascular disease examined the DNA of 15 000 individuals. They found that 3% of the individuals had a mutation that inactivates one copy of the gene for PCSK9, a liver enzyme. Because mutations that *increase* the activity of PCSK9 are known to *increase* levels of LDL cholesterol in the blood, the researchers hypothesized that *inactivating* mutations in this gene would *lower* LDL levels. In this exercise, you will interpret the results of an experiment they carried out to test this hypothesis.

How the Experiment Was Done Researchers measured LDL cholesterol levels in blood plasma from 85 individuals with one copy of the *PCSK9* gene inactivated (the study group) and from 3278 individuals with two functional copies of the gene (the control group).

Data from the Experiment The plasma LDL cholesterol levels for the control group and study group are shown in the table at the bottom.

Interpret the Data

1. Graphing often facilitates data interpretation. For this exercise, graph the data in each row of the table as a *histogram* (a type of bar graph). Label the *y*-axis as *Percent of Individuals* and the *x*-axis as *Plasma LDL Cholesterol (mg/dl)*. Divide the *x*-axis into 12 equal divisions, one for each range of values (0–25, 26–50, etc.). Moving along the *x*-axis, draw a series of twelve vertical bars, with the height of each bar indicating the percentage of samples that fall into the specified range. Note that some bars will be of zero height, such as for a plasma LDL cholesterol level in the 0–25 mg/dL (milligram/decilitre) range. Add the percentages for the relevant bars to calculate the percentage of individuals in the study and control groups that had an LDL cholesterol level of 100 mg/dL or less.

cassis/Fotolia

(For additional information about histograms, see the Scientific Skills Review in Appendix E and the Study Area in MasteringBiology.)

2. Comparing the two histograms you drew, do you find support for the researchers' hypothesis? Explain.

3. What if, instead of graphing the data, you had compared the range of concentrations for plasma LDL cholesterol (low to high) in the control and study groups? How would the conclusions you could draw have differed?

4. Propose an explanation for the fact that the two histograms overlap as much as they do.

5. Consider two individuals with a plasma LDL cholesterol level of 160 mg/dL, one from the study group and one from the control group. What do you predict regarding their relative risk of developing cardiovascular disease? Explain how you arrived at your prediction. What role did the histograms play in helping you make your prediction?

Data from J. C. Cohen et al., Sequence variations in *PCSK9*, low LDL, and protection against coronary heart disease, *New England Journal of Medicine* 354:1264–1272 (2006). © Jane B Reece.

Plasma LDL Cholesterol (milligrams/decilitre)

	0–25	26–50	51–75	76–100	101–125	126–150	151–175	176–200	201–225	226–250	251–275	276–300
Control Group	0%	1%	4%	13%	23%	23%	18%	10%	5%	2%	1%	0%
Study Group	0%	4%	31%	23%	21%	13%	2%	1%	2%	0%	2%	0%

CONCEPT 42.5

Gas exchange occurs across specialized respiratory surfaces

In the remainder of this chapter, we will focus on the process of **gas exchange**. Although this process is often called respiratory exchange or respiration, it should not be confused with the energy transformations of cellular respiration. Gas exchange is the uptake of molecular O_2 from the environment and the discharge of CO_2 to the environment.

Partial Pressure Gradients in Gas Exchange

To understand the driving forces for gas exchange, we must calculate **partial pressure**, which is simply the pressure exerted by a particular gas in a mixture of gases. To do so, we need to know the pressure that the mixture exerts and the fraction of the mixture represented by a particular gas. Let's consider O_2 as an example. At sea level, the atmosphere exerts a downward force equal to that of a column of mercury (Hg) 760 mm high. Therefore, atmospheric pressure at sea level is 760 mm Hg. Since the atmosphere is 21% O_2 by volume, the partial pressure of O_2 is 0.21×760, or about 160 mm Hg. This value is called the *partial pressure* of O_2 (abbreviated P_{O_2}) because it is the part of atmospheric pressure contributed by O_2. The partial pressure of CO_2 (abbreviated P_{CO_2}) is much less, only 0.29 mm Hg at sea level.

Partial pressures also apply to gases dissolved in a liquid, such as water. When water is exposed to air, an equilibrium is reached in which the partial pressure of each gas in the water equals the partial pressure of that gas in the air. Thus, water exposed to air at sea level has a P_{O_2} of 160 mm Hg, the same as in the atmosphere. However, the *concentrations* of O_2 in the air and water differ substantially because O_2 is much less soluble in water than in air (**Table 42.1**).

Table 42.1	Comparing Air and Water as Respiratory Media		
	Air (Sea Level)	Water (20°C)	Air to Water Ratio
O_2 Partial Pressure	160 mm	160 mm	1 : 1
O_2 Concentration	210 ml/L	7 ml/L	30 : 1
Density	0.0013 kg/L	1 kg/L	1 : 770
Viscosity	0.02 cP	1 cP	1 : 50

Respiratory Media

The conditions for gas exchange vary considerably, depending on whether the respiratory medium—the source of O_2—is air or water. As already noted, O_2 is plentiful in air, making up about 21% of Earth's atmosphere by volume. Compared to water, air is much less dense and less viscous, so it is easier to move and to force through small passageways. As a result, breathing air is relatively easy and need not be particularly efficient. Humans, for example, extract only about 25% of the O_2 in inhaled air.

Gas exchange with water as the respiratory medium is much more demanding. The amount of O_2 dissolved in a given volume of water varies but is always less than in an equivalent volume of air: Water in many marine and freshwater habitats contains only 4–8 mL of dissolved O_2 per litre, a concentration roughly 30 times less than in air. The warmer and saltier the water is, the less dissolved O_2 it can hold. Water's lower O_2 content, greater density, and greater viscosity mean that aquatic animals such as fishes and lobsters must expend considerable energy to carry out gas exchange. In the context of these challenges, adaptations have evolved that enable most aquatic animals to be very efficient in gas exchange. Many of these adaptations involve the organization of the surfaces dedicated to exchange.

Respiratory Surfaces

Specialization for gas exchange is apparent in the structure of the respiratory surface, the part of an animal's body where gas exchange occurs. Like all living cells, the cells that carry out gas exchange have a plasma membrane that must be in contact with an aqueous solution. Respiratory surfaces are therefore always moist.

The movement of O_2 and CO_2 across moist respiratory surfaces takes place entirely by diffusion. The rate of diffusion is proportional to the surface area across which it occurs and inversely proportional to the square of the distance through which molecules must move. In other words, gas exchange is fast when the area for diffusion is large and the path for diffusion is short. As a result, respiratory surfaces tend to be large and thin.

In some relatively simple animals, such as sponges, cnidarians, and flatworms, every cell in the body is close enough to the external environment that gases can diffuse quickly between all cells and the environment. In many animals, however, the bulk of the body's cells lack immediate access to the environment. The respiratory surface in these animals is a thin, moist epithelium that constitutes a respiratory organ.

The skin serves as a respiratory organ in some animals, including earthworms and some amphibians. Just below the skin, a dense network of capillaries facilitates the exchange of gases between the circulatory system and the environment. Because the respiratory surface must remain moist, earthworms and many other skin-breathers can survive for extended periods only in damp places.

The general body surface of most animals lacks sufficient area to exchange gases for the whole organism. The evolutionary solution to this limitation is a respiratory organ that is extensively folded or branched, thereby enlarging the available surface area for gas exchange. Gills, tracheae, and lungs are three such organs.

Gills in Aquatic Animals

Gills are outfoldings of the body surface that are suspended in the water. As illustrated in Figure 42.21, the distribution of gills over the body can vary considerably. Regardless of their distribution, gills often have a total surface area much greater than that of the rest of the body's exterior.

Movement of the respiratory medium over the respiratory surface, a process called **ventilation**, maintains the partial pressure gradients of O_2 and CO_2 across the gill that are necessary for gas exchange. To promote ventilation, most gill-bearing animals either move their gills through the water or move water over their gills. For example, crayfish and lobsters have paddle-like appendages that drive a current of water over the gills, whereas mussels and clams move water with cilia. Octopuses and squids ventilate their gills by taking in and ejecting water, with the side benefit of locomotion by jet propulsion. Fishes use the motion of swimming or coordinated movements of the mouth and gill covers to ventilate their gills. In both cases, a current of water enters the mouth, passes through slits in the pharynx, flows over the gills, and then exits the body (Figure 42.22).

The arrangement of capillaries in a fish gill allows for **countercurrent exchange**, the exchange of a substance or heat between two fluids flowing in opposite directions. In a fish gill, this process maximizes gas exchange efficiency. Because blood flows in the direction opposite to that of water passing over the gills, at each point in its travel blood is less saturated with O_2 than the water it meets (see Figure 42.22). As blood enters a gill capillary, it encounters water that is completing its passage through the gill. Depleted of much of its dissolved O_2, this water nevertheless has a higher P_{O_2} than the incoming blood, and

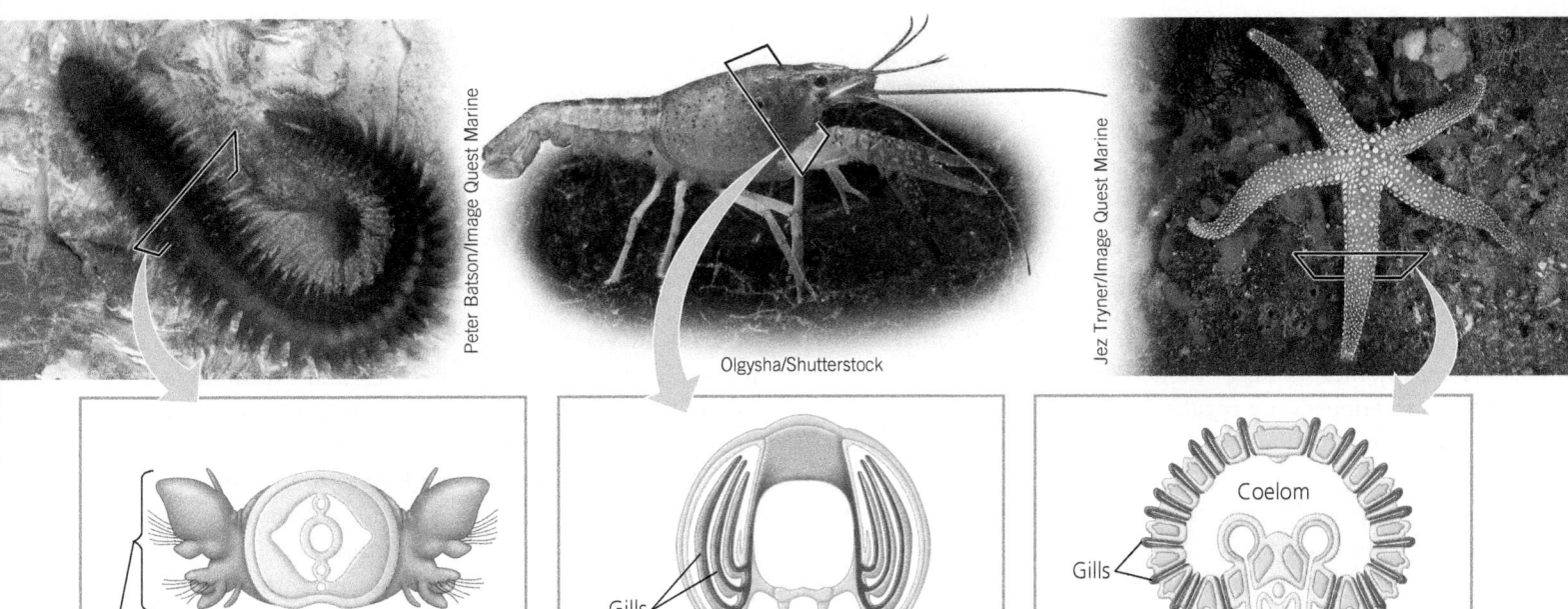

(a) Marine worm. Many polychaetes (marine worms of the phylum Annelida) have a pair of flattened appendages called parapodia on each body segment. The parapodia serve as gills and also function in crawling and swimming.

(b) Crayfish. Crayfish and other crustaceans have long, feathery gills covered by the exoskeleton. Specialized body appendages drive water over the gill surfaces.

(c) Sea star. The gills of a sea star are simple tubular projections of the skin. The hollow core of each gill is an extension of the coelom (body cavity). Gas exchange occurs by diffusion across the gill surfaces, and fluid in the coelom circulates in and out of the gills, aiding gas transport. The tube feet surfaces also function in gas exchange.

▲ **Figure 42.21 Diversity in the structure of gills, external body surfaces that function in gas exchange.**

▲ **Figure 42.22 The structure and function of fish gills.** A fish continuously pumps water through its mouth and over gill arches, using coordinated movements of the jaws and operculum (gill cover) for this ventilation. (A swimming fish can simply open its mouth and let water flow past its gills.) Each gill arch has two rows of gill filaments, composed of flattened plates called lamellae. Blood flowing through capillaries within the lamellae picks up O_2 from the water. Notice that the countercurrent flow of water and blood maintains a partial pressure gradient down which O_2 diffuses from the water into the blood over the entire length of a capillary.

Gill arch

Water flow

Operculum

Blood vessels

Gill arch

Gill filaments

O_2-poor blood

O_2-rich blood

Lamella

Water flow between lamellae

Blood flow through capillaries in lamella

Countercurrent exchange

P_{O_2} (mm Hg) in water

150 120 90 60 30

Net diffusion of O_2 from water to blood

140 110 80 50 20

P_{O_2} (mm Hg) in blood

O_2 transfer takes place. As the blood continues its passage, its P_{O_2} steadily increases, but so does that of the water it encounters, since each successive position in the blood's travel corresponds to an earlier position in the water's passage over the gills. Thus, a partial pressure gradient favouring the diffusion of O_2 from water to blood exists along the entire length of the capillary.

Countercurrent exchange mechanisms are remarkably efficient. In the fish gill, more than 80% of the O_2 dissolved in the water is removed as it passes over the respiratory surface. In other settings, countercurrent exchange contributes to temperature regulation (see Chapter 40) and to the functioning of the mammalian kidney, as we will see in Chapter 44.

Gills are generally unsuitable for an animal living on land. An expansive surface of wet membrane exposed directly to air currents in the environment would lose too much water by evaporation. Furthermore, the gills would collapse as their fine filaments, no longer supported by water, stuck together. In most terrestrial animals, respiratory surfaces are enclosed within the body, exposed to the atmosphere only through narrow tubes.

Tracheal Systems in Insects

Although the most familiar respiratory structure among terrestrial animals is the lung, the most common is actually the **tracheal system** of insects. Made up of air tubes that branch throughout the body, this system is one variation on the theme of an internal respiratory surface. The largest tubes, called tracheae, open to the outside (Figure 42.23a). The finest branches extend close to the surface of nearly every cell, where gas is exchanged by diffusion across the moist epithelium that lines the tips of the tracheal branches (Figure 42.23b). Because the tracheal system brings air within a very short distance of virtually every body cell in an insect, it can transport O_2 and CO_2 without the participation of the animal's open circulatory system.

For small insects, diffusion through the tracheae brings in enough O_2 and removes enough CO_2 to support cellular respiration. Larger insects meet their higher energy demands by ventilating their tracheal systems with rhythmic body movements that compress and expand the air tubes like bellows. For example, consider an insect in flight, which has a very high metabolic rate, consuming 10 to 200 times more O_2 than it does at rest. In many flying insects, alternating contraction and relaxation of the flight muscles pumps air rapidly through the tracheal system. The flight muscle cells are packed with mitochondria that support the high metabolic rate, and the tracheal tubes supply these ATP-generating organelles with ample O_2 (Figure 42.23c). Thus, adaptations of tracheal systems are directly related to bioenergetics.

Lungs

Unlike tracheal systems, which branch throughout the insect body, **lungs** are localized respiratory organs. Representing an infolding of the body surface, they are typically subdivided into numerous pockets. Because the respiratory surface of a lung is not in direct contact with all other parts of the body, the gap must be bridged by the circulatory system, which transports gases between the lungs and the rest of the body. Lungs have evolved in organisms with

Tracheoles   Mitochondria   Muscle fibre

Peng Chai

2.5 μm

(a) The respiratory system of an insect consists of branched internal tubes. The largest tubes, called tracheae, connect to external openings spaced along the insect's body surface. Air sacs formed from enlarged portions of the tracheae are found near organs that require a large supply of oxygen.

(b) Rings of chitin keep the tracheae open, allowing air to enter and pass into smaller tubes called tracheoles. The branched tracheoles deliver air directly to cells throughout the body. Tracheoles have closed ends filled with fluid (blue-grey). When the animal is active and using more O_2, most of the fluid is withdrawn into the body. This increases the surface area of air-filled tracheoles in contact with cells.

(c) The TEM above shows cross sections of tracheoles in a tiny piece of insect flight muscle. Each of the numerous mitochondria in the muscle cells lies within about 5 μm of a tracheole.

▲ Figure 42.23 **Tracheal systems.**

open circulatory systems, such as spiders and land snails, as well as in vertebrates, which possess closed circulatory systems.

Among vertebrates that lack gills, the use of lungs for gas exchange varies. Amphibian lungs, when present, are relatively small and lack an extensive surface for exchange. Amphibians instead rely heavily on diffusion across other body surfaces, such as the skin, to carry out gas exchange. In contrast, most reptiles (including all birds) and all mammals depend entirely on lungs for gas exchange. Turtles are an exception; they supplement lung breathing with gas exchange across moist epithelial surfaces continuous with their mouth or anus. Lungs and air breathing have evolved in a few aquatic vertebrates (including lungfishes) as adaptations to living in oxygen-poor water or to spending part of their time exposed to air (for instance, when the water level of a pond recedes).

Mammalian Respiratory Systems: A Closer Look

In mammals, a system of branching ducts conveys air to the lungs, which are located in the thoracic cavity (Figure 42.24). Air enters through the nostrils and is then filtered by hairs, warmed, humidified, and sampled for odours as it flows through a maze of spaces in the nasal cavity. The nasal cavity leads to the pharynx, an intersection where the paths for air and food cross. When food is swallowed, the **larynx** (the upper part of the respiratory tract) moves upward and tips the epiglottis over the glottis (the opening of the **trachea**, or windpipe). This allows food to go down the esophagus to the stomach (see Figure 41.9). The rest of the time, the glottis is open, enabling breathing.

From the larynx, air passes into the trachea. Cartilage reinforcing the walls of both the larynx and the trachea keeps this part of the airway open. Within the larynx of most mammals, exhaled air rushes by a pair of elastic bands of muscle called *vocal folds*, or, in humans, *vocal cords*. Sounds are produced when muscles in the larynx are tensed, stretching the cords so they vibrate. High-pitched sounds result from tightly stretched cords vibrating rapidly; low-pitched sounds come from less tense cords vibrating slowly.

The trachea branches into two **bronchi** (singular, *bronchus*), one leading to each lung. Within the lung, the bronchi branch repeatedly into finer and finer tubes called **bronchioles**. The entire system of air ducts has the

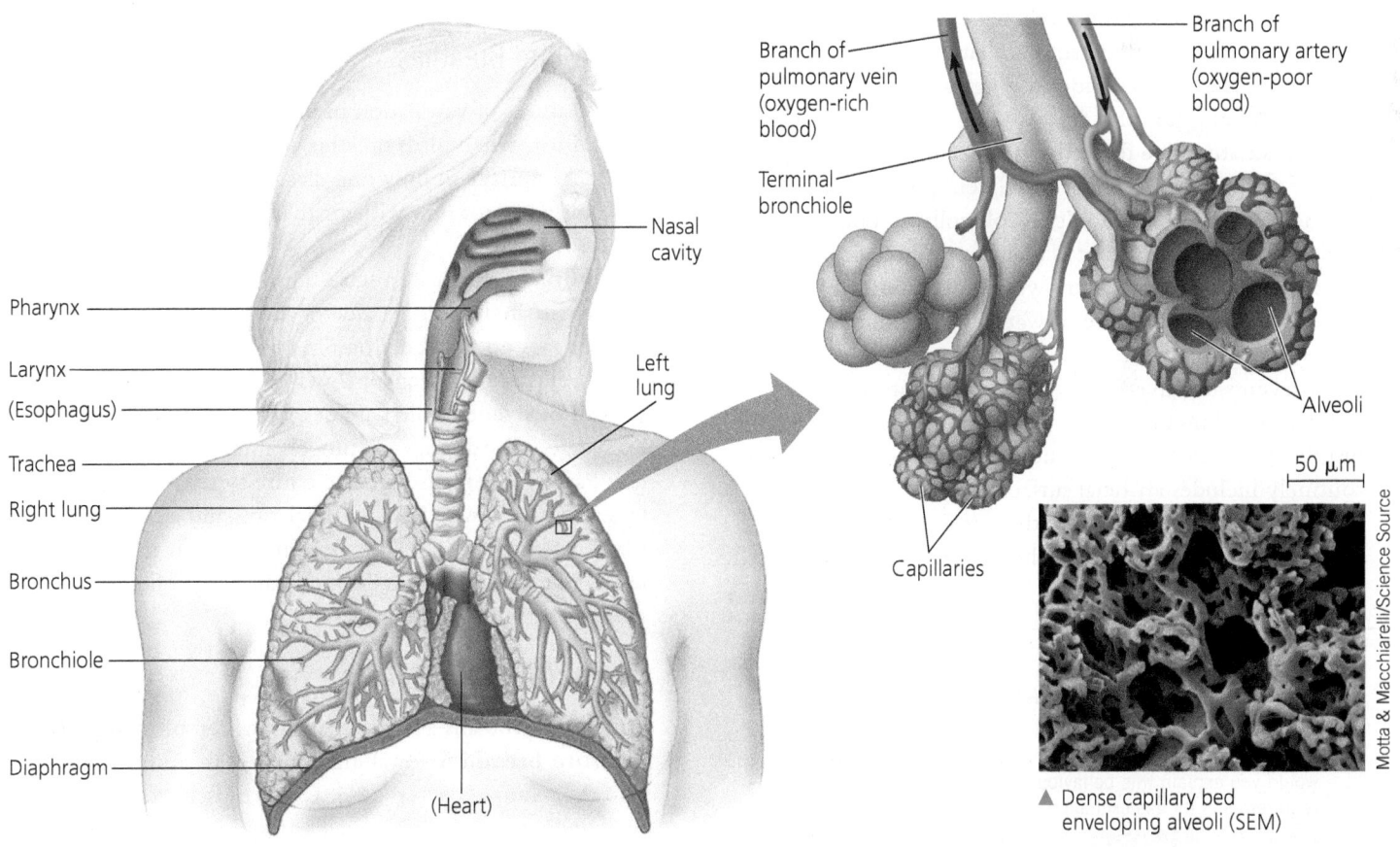

▲ Figure 42.24 **The mammalian respiratory system.** From the nasal cavity and pharynx, inhaled air passes through the larynx, trachea, and bronchi to the bronchioles, which end in microscopic alveoli lined by a thin, moist epithelium. Branches of the pulmonary arteries convey oxygen-poor blood to the alveoli; branches of the pulmonary veins transport oxygen-rich blood from the alveoli back to the heart.

appearance of an inverted tree, the trunk being the trachea. The epithelium lining the major branches of this respiratory tree is covered by cilia and a thin film of mucus. The mucus traps dust, pollen, and other particulate contaminants, and the beating cilia move the mucus upward to the pharynx, where it can be swallowed into the esophagus. This process, sometimes referred to as the "mucus escalator," plays a crucial role in cleansing the respiratory system.

Gas exchange in mammals occurs in **alveoli** (singular, *alveolus*; see Figure 42.24), air sacs clustered at the tips of the tiniest bronchioles. Human lungs contain millions of alveoli, which together have a surface area of about 100 m^2, 50 times that of the skin. Oxygen in the air entering the alveoli dissolves in the moist film lining their inner surfaces and rapidly diffuses across the epithelium into a web of capillaries that surrounds each alveolus. Net diffusion of carbon dioxide occurs in the opposite direction, from the capillaries across the epithelium of the alveolus and into the air space.

Lacking cilia or significant air currents to remove particles from their surface, alveoli are highly susceptible to contamination. White blood cells patrol alveoli, engulfing foreign particles. However, if too much particulate matter reaches the alveoli, the defences can be overwhelmed, leading to inflammation and irreversible damage. For example, particulates from cigarette smoke that enter alveoli can cause a permanent reduction in lung capacity.

The film of liquid that lines alveoli is subject to surface tension, an attractive force that acts to minimize the surface area of a liquid (see Chapter 3). Given their tiny diameter (about 0.25 mm), why don't alveoli collapse under high surface tension? The secret is that the surfaces of the alveoli are covered by a material known as **surfactant**, for surface-active agent. This mixture of water, phospholipid, and protein coats the inner surface of the lung, creating a force that prevents the alveoli from collapsing onto themselves. Premature babies often have poorly developed lungs with insufficient surfactant. Treatment of premature babies now routinely includes artificial surfactants.

Having surveyed the route that air follows when we breathe, we will turn next to the process of breathing itself.

CONCEPT CHECK 42.5

1. Why is the position of lung tissues *within* the body an advantage for terrestrial animals?
2. After a heavy rain, earthworms come to the surface. How would you explain this behaviour in terms of an earthworm's requirements for gas exchange?
3. **MAKE CONNECTIONS** Describe how countercurrent exchange can facilitate both thermoregulation (see Concept 40.3) and respiration.

For suggested answers, see Appendix A.

Breathing ventilates the lungs

Like fishes, terrestrial vertebrates rely on ventilation to maintain high O_2 and low CO_2 concentrations at the gas exchange surface. The process that ventilates lungs is **breathing**, the alternating inhalation and exhalation of air. A variety of mechanisms for moving air in and out of lungs have evolved, as we will see by considering breathing in amphibians, mammals, and birds.

How an Amphibian Breathes

An amphibian such as a frog ventilates its lungs by **positive pressure breathing**, inflating the lungs with forced airflow. During the first stage of inhalation, muscles lower the floor of an amphibian's oral cavity, drawing in air through its nostrils. Next, with the nostrils and mouth closed, the floor of the oral cavity rises, forcing air down the trachea. During exhalation, air is forced back out by the elastic recoil of the lungs and by compression of the muscular body wall. When male frogs puff themselves up in aggressive or courtship displays, they disrupt this breathing cycle, taking in air several times without allowing any release.

How a Bird Breathes

Two features of ventilation in birds make it highly efficient. First, when birds breathe, they pass air over the gas exchange surface in only one direction. Second, incoming fresh air does not mix with air that has already carried out gas exchange.

To bring fresh air to their lungs, birds use eight or nine air sacs situated on either side of the lungs (**Figure 42.25**). The air sacs do not function directly in gas exchange but act as bellows that keep air flowing through the lungs. Instead of alveoli, which are dead ends, the sites of gas exchange in bird lungs are tiny channels called parabronchi. Passage of air through the entire system—lungs and air sacs—requires two cycles of inhalation and exhalation. In some passageways, the direction in which air moves alternates, but within the parabronchi, air always flows in the same direction (see Figure 42.25).

How a Mammal Breathes

Unlike amphibians and birds, mammals employ **negative pressure breathing**—pulling, rather than pushing, air into their lungs (**Figure 42.26**). Using muscle contraction to actively expand the thoracic cavity, mammals lower air pressure in their lungs below that of the air outside their body. Because gas flows from a region of higher pressure to a region of lower pressure, air rushes through the nostrils and mouth and down the breathing tubes to the alveoli.

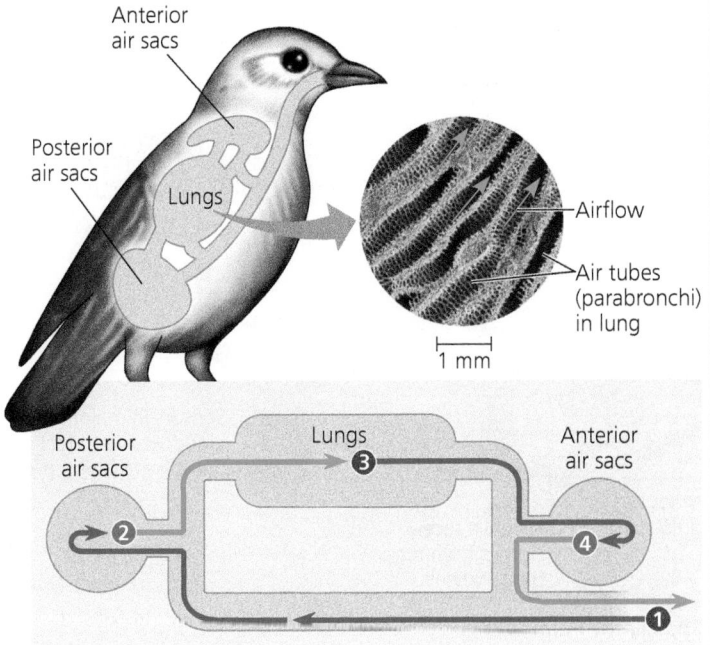

Two cycles of inhalation and exhalation are required to pass one breath through the system:

❶ First inhalation: Air fills the posterior air sacs.

❷ First exhalation: Posterior air sacs contract, pushing air into lungs.

❸ Second inhalation: Air passes through lungs and fills anterior air sacs.

❹ Second exhalation: As anterior air sacs contract, air that entered body at first inhalation is pushed out of body.

▲ **Figure 42.25 The avian respiratory system.** This diagram traces a breath of air through the respiratory system of a bird. As shown, two cycles of inhalation and exhalation are required for the air to pass all the way through the system and out of the bird.

❶ INHALATION: Diaphragm contracts (moves down).

❷ EXHALATION: Diaphragm relaxes (moves up).

▲ **Figure 42.26 Negative pressure breathing.** A mammal breathes by changing the air pressure within its lungs relative to the pressure of the outside atmosphere.

WHAT IF? *The walls of alveoli contain elastic fibres that allow the alveoli to expand and contract with each breath. If alveoli lost their elasticity, how would that affect gas exchange in the lungs?*

During exhalation, the muscles controlling the thoracic cavity relax, and the volume of the cavity is reduced. The increased air pressure in the alveoli forces air up the breathing tubes and out of the body. Thus, inhalation is always active and requires work, whereas exhalation is usually passive.

Expanding the thoracic cavity during inhalation involves the animal's rib muscles and the **diaphragm**, a sheet of skeletal muscle that forms the bottom wall of the cavity. Contracting the rib muscles expands the rib cage, the front wall of the thoracic cavity, by pulling the ribs upward and the sternum outward. At the same time, the diaphragm contracts, expanding the thoracic cavity downward. The effect of the descending diaphragm is similar to that of a plunger being drawn out of a syringe.

Within the thoracic cavity, a double membrane surrounds the lungs. The inner layer of this membrane adheres to the outside of the lungs, and the outer layer adheres to the wall of the thoracic cavity. A thin space filled with fluid separates the two layers. Surface tension in the fluid causes the two layers to stick together like two plates of glass separated by a film of water: The layers can slide smoothly past each other, but they cannot be pulled apart easily. Consequently, the volume of the thoracic cavity and the volume of the lungs change in unison.

Depending on activity level, additional muscles may be recruited to aid breathing. The rib muscles and diaphragm are sufficient to change lung volume when a mammal is at rest. During exercise, other muscles of the neck, back, and chest increase the volume of the thoracic cavity by raising the rib cage. In kangaroos and some other species, locomotion causes a rhythmic movement of organs in the abdomen, including the stomach and liver. The result is a piston-like pumping motion that pushes and pulls on the diaphragm, further increasing the volume of air moved in and out of the lungs.

The volume of air inhaled and exhaled with each breath is called **tidal volume**. It averages about 500 mL in resting humans. The tidal volume during maximal inhalation and exhalation is the **vital capacity**, which is about 3.4 L and 4.8 L for university-age women and men, respectively. The air that remains after a forced exhalation is called the **residual volume**. As we age, our lungs lose their resilience, and residual volume increases at the expense of vital capacity.

Because the lungs in mammals do not completely empty with each breath, and because inhalation occurs through the same airways as exhalation, each inhalation mixes fresh air with oxygen-depleted residual air. As a result, the maximum P_{O_2} in alveoli is always considerably less than in the atmosphere. The maximum P_{O_2} in lungs is also less for mammals than for birds, which renew the air in their lungs with every exhalation. This is one reason mammals function less well than birds at high altitude. For example, humans have great difficulty obtaining enough O_2 when climbing Earth's highest peaks, such as Mount Everest (8850 m) in the Himalayas. However, bar-headed geese and several other bird species easily fly over the Himalayas during their migrations.

Control of Breathing in Humans

Although you can voluntarily hold your breath or breathe faster and deeper, most of the time your breathing is regulated by involuntary mechanisms. These control mechanisms ensure that gas exchange is coordinated with blood circulation and with metabolic demand.

The neurons mainly responsible for regulating breathing are in the medulla oblongata, near the base of the brain (Figure 42.27). Neural circuits in the medulla form a pair of *breathing control centres* that establishes the breathing rhythm. When you breathe deeply, a negative-feedback mechanism prevents the lungs from overexpanding: During inhalation, sensors that detect stretching of the lung tissue send nerve impulses to the control circuits in the medulla, inhibiting further inhalation.

In regulating breathing, the medulla uses the pH of the surrounding tissue fluid as an indicator of blood CO_2 concentration. The reason pH can be used in this way is that blood CO_2 is the main determinant of the pH of *cerebrospinal fluid*, the fluid surrounding the brain and spinal cord. Carbon dioxide diffuses from the blood to the cerebrospinal fluid, where it reacts with water and forms carbonic acid (H_2CO_3). The H_2CO_3 can then dissociate into a bicarbonate ion (HCO_3^-) and a hydrogen ion (H^+):

$$CO_2 + H_2O \rightleftharpoons H_2CO_3 \rightleftharpoons HCO_3^- + H^+$$

Increased metabolic activity, such as occurs during exercise, lowers pH by increasing the concentration of CO_2 in the blood. Sensors in blood vessels and the medulla detect this pH change. In response, the medulla's control circuits increase the depth and rate of breathing. Both remain high until the excess CO_2 is eliminated in exhaled air and pH returns to a normal value.

The blood O_2 level usually has little effect on the breathing control centres. However, when the O_2 level drops very low (at high altitudes, for instance), O_2 sensors in the aorta and the carotid arteries in the neck send signals to the breathing control centres, which respond by increasing the breathing rate.

The pons, a part of the brain next to the medulla, also regulates breathing, although its exact role remains an open question. The pons may act in the regulatory circuit with the medulla or modulate the output of that circuit.

Breathing control is effective only if ventilation is matched to blood flow through alveolar capillaries. During exercise, for instance, such coordination couples an increased breathing rate, which enhances O_2 uptake and CO_2 removal, with an increase in cardiac output.

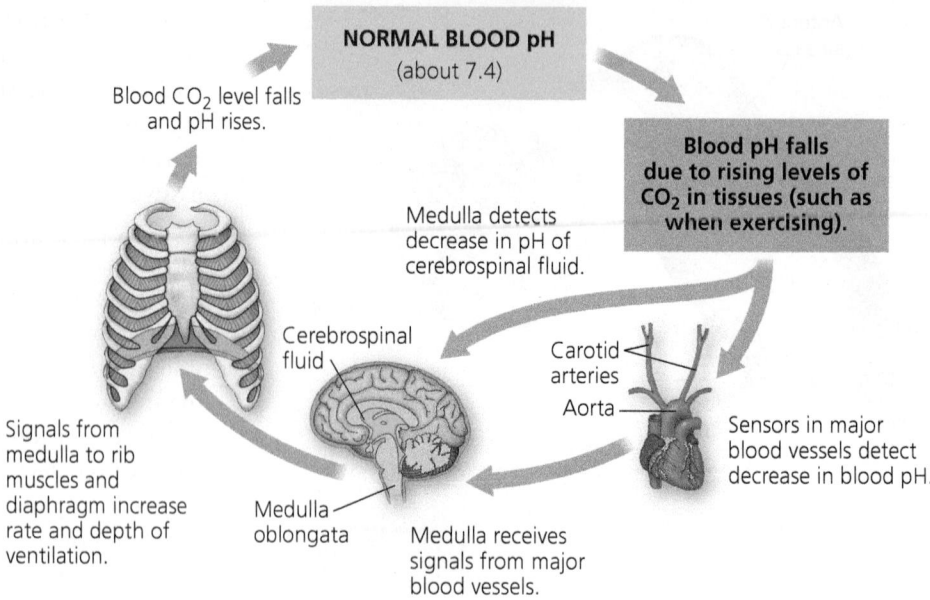

▲ Figure 42.27 **Homeostatic control of breathing.**

WHAT IF? *Suppose a person began breathing very rapidly while resting. Describe the effect on blood CO_2 levels and the steps by which the negative feedback circuit in this figure would restore homeostasis.*

The figure labels read:

NORMAL BLOOD pH (about 7.4)

Blood CO_2 level falls and pH rises.

Blood pH falls due to rising levels of CO_2 in tissues (such as when exercising).

Medulla detects decrease in pH of cerebrospinal fluid.

Cerebrospinal fluid

Carotid arteries

Aorta

Sensors in major blood vessels detect decrease in blood pH.

Signals from medulla to rib muscles and diaphragm increase rate and depth of ventilation.

Medulla oblongata

Medulla receives signals from major blood vessels.

CONCEPT CHECK 42.6

1. How does an increase in the CO_2 concentration in the blood affect the pH of cerebrospinal fluid?

2. A drop in blood pH causes an increase in heart rate. What is the function of this control mechanism?

3. **WHAT IF?** If an injury tore a small hole in the membranes surrounding your lungs, what would you expect to happen to lung function?

For suggested answers, see Appendix A.

CONCEPT 42.7

Adaptations for gas exchange include pigments that bind and transport gases

The high metabolic demands of many animals necessitate the exchange of large quantities of O_2 and CO_2. Here we'll examine how blood molecules called respiratory pigments facilitate this exchange through their interaction with O_2 and CO_2. We will also investigate physiological adaptations that enable animals to be active under conditions of high metabolic load or very limiting P_{O_2}. As a basis for exploring these topics, let's summarize the basic gas exchange circuit in humans.

Coordination of Circulation and Gas Exchange

The partial pressures of O_2 and CO_2 in the blood vary at different points in the circulatory system, as shown in **Figure 42.28**. Blood flowing through the alveolar capillaries has a lower P_{O_2} and a higher P_{CO_2} than the air in the alveoli. As a result, CO_2 diffuses down its partial pressure gradient from the blood to the air in the alveoli. Meanwhile, O_2 in the air dissolves in the fluid that coats the alveolar epithelium and diffuses into the blood. By the time the blood leaves the lungs in the pulmonary veins, its P_{O_2} has been raised and its P_{CO_2} has been lowered. After returning to the heart, this blood is pumped through the systemic circuit.

In the tissue capillaries, gradients of partial pressure favour the diffusion of O_2 out of the blood and CO_2 into the blood. These gradients exist because cellular respiration in the mitochondria of cells near each capillary removes O_2 from and adds CO_2 to the surrounding interstitial fluid. After the blood unloads O_2 and loads CO_2, it is returned to the heart and pumped to the lungs again.

Although this description faithfully characterizes the driving forces for gas exchange in different tissues, it omits the critical role of the specialized carrier proteins we will discuss next.

Respiratory Pigments

The low solubility of O_2 in water (and thus in blood) poses a problem for animals that rely on the circulatory system to deliver O_2. For example, a person requires almost 2 L of O_2 per minute during intense exercise, and all of it must be carried in the blood from the lungs to the active tissues. At normal body temperature and air pressure, however, only 4.5 mL of O_2 can dissolve into a litre of blood in the lungs. Even if 80% of the dissolved O_2 were delivered to the tissues (an unrealistically high percentage), the heart would still need to pump 555 L of blood per minute!

In fact, animals transport most of their O_2 bound to proteins called **respiratory pigments**. Respiratory pigments circulate with the blood or hemolymph and are often contained within specialized cells. The pigments greatly increase the amount of O_2 that can be carried in the

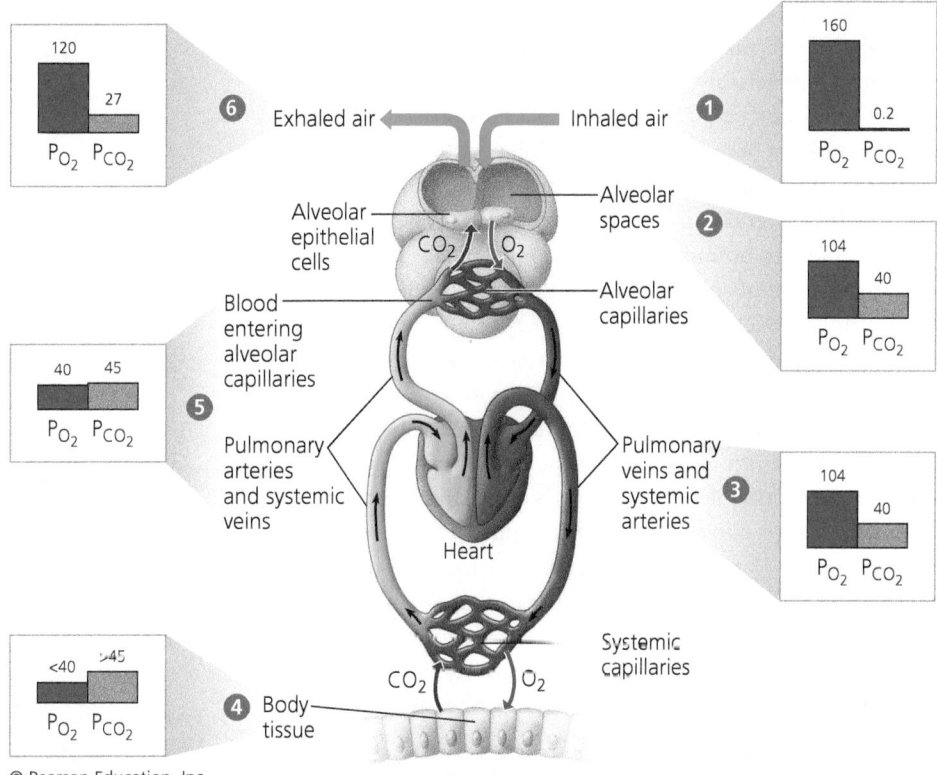

© Pearson Education, Inc.

▲ Figure 42.28 **Loading and unloading of respiratory gases.**

Source: Figure adapted from *Human Anatomy and Physiology*, 8th edition, by Elaine N. Marieb and Katja Hoehn. Copyright © 2010 by Pearson Education, Inc. Adapted and electronically reproduced by permission of Pearson Education, Inc., Upper Saddle River, New Jersey.

WHAT IF? *If you consciously forced more air out of your lungs each time you exhaled, how would that affect the values shown in the figure?*

circulatory fluid (to about 200 mL of O_2 per litre in mammalian blood). In our example of an exercising human with an O_2 delivery rate of 80%, the presence of a respiratory pigment reduces the cardiac output necessary for O_2 transport to a manageable 12.5 L of blood per minute.

A variety of respiratory pigments have evolved among the animal taxa. With a few exceptions, these molecules have a distinctive colour (hence the term *pigment*) and consist of a protein bound to a metal. One example is the blue pigment *hemocyanin*, which has copper as its oxygen-binding component and is found in arthropods and many molluscs. The respiratory pigment of almost all vertebrates and many invertebrates is hemoglobin. In vertebrates, it is contained in the erythrocytes.

Hemoglobin

Vertebrate hemoglobin consists of four subunits (polypeptide chains), each with a cofactor called a heme group that has an iron atom at its centre. Each iron atom binds one molecule

Hemoglobin

of O_2; hence, a single hemoglobin molecule can carry four molecules of O_2. Like all respiratory pigments, hemoglobin binds O_2 reversibly, loading O_2 in the lungs or gills and unloading it in other parts of the body. This process depends on cooperativity between the hemoglobin subunits (see pp. 171–172). When O_2 binds to one subunit, the others change shape slightly, increasing their affinity for O_2. When four O_2 molecules are bound and one subunit unloads its O_2, the other three subunits more readily unload O_2, as an associated shape change lowers their affinity for O_2.

Cooperativity in O_2 binding and release is evident in the dissociation curve for hemoglobin (Figure 42.29a). Over the range of P_{O_2} where the dissociation curve has a steep slope, even a slight change in P_{O_2} causes hemoglobin to load or unload a substantial amount of O_2. Notice that the steep part of the curve corresponds to the range of P_{O_2} found in body tissues. When cells in a particular location begin working harder—during exercise, for instance—P_{O_2} dips in their vicinity as the O_2 is consumed in cellular respiration. Because of the effect of subunit cooperativity, a slight drop in P_{O_2} causes a relatively large increase in the amount of O_2 the blood unloads.

The production of CO_2 during cellular respiration promotes the unloading of O_2 by hemoglobin in active tissues. As we have seen, CO_2 reacts with water, forming carbonic acid, which lowers the pH of its surroundings. Low pH, in turn, decreases the affinity of hemoglobin for O_2, an effect called the **Bohr shift** (Figure 42.29b). Thus, where CO_2 production is greater, hemoglobin releases more O_2, which can then be used to support more cellular respiration.

Changes in oxygen affinity are central to the ability of animals to regulate O_2 delivery. Like low pH, high temperature causes a reduction in the O_2 affinity, favouring unloading. This is helpful under exercise conditions where active muscles warm the blood as it passes through muscle capillary beds. Red blood cells are also able to change the levels of cytoplasmic metabolites as a mechanism to change O_2 affinity of Hb. For example, increases in the level of 2,3-bisphosphoglycerate, produced in glycolysis (see Chapter 9), can also favour O_2 unloading.

Most of the regulation of Hb in humans is focused on the response to changing internal conditions, such as exercise. Other animals have a much greater need to use these same regulators to control oxygen transport in response to environmental changes. Animals that survive at low oxygen levels often possess Hb that is much better able to extract O_2 from an oxygen-poor environment. Temperature is another factor that can have a dramatic effect on an animal's ability to control oxygen levels. Figure 42.30 describes a study where researchers reconstructed Hb from an extinct woolly mammoth to see if the molecular evolution of Hb played a role in the ability of this animal to survive the intense cold.

(a) P_{O_2} and hemoglobin dissociation at pH 7.4. The curve shows the relative amounts of O_2 bound to hemoglobin exposed to solutions with different P_{O_2}. At a P_{O_2} of 100 mm Hg, typical in the lungs, hemoglobin is about 98% saturated with O_2. At a P_{O_2} of 40 mm Hg, common in the vicinity of tissues at rest, hemoglobin is about 70% saturated. Hemoglobin can release additional O_2 to metabolically very active tissues, such as muscle tissue during exercise.

(b) pH and hemoglobin dissociation. Because hydrogen ions affect the shape of hemoglobin, a drop in pH shifts the O_2 dissociation curve toward the right (the Bohr shift). At a given P_{O_2}, say 40 mm Hg, hemoglobin gives up more O_2 at pH 7.2 than at pH 7.4, the normal pH of human blood. The pH decreases in very active tissues because the CO_2 produced by cellular respiration reacts with water, forming carbonic acid. Hemoglobin then releases more O_2, which supports the increased cellular respiration in the active tissues.

▲ Figure 42.29 **Dissociation curves for hemoglobin at 37°C.**

Carbon Dioxide Transport

Only about 7% of the CO_2 released by respiring cells is transported in solution in blood plasma. The rest diffuses from plasma into erythrocytes and reacts with

Inquiry

Mammoth hemoglobin is less sensitive to changes in temperature

Experiment Kevin Campbell (University of Manitoba) has studied how the structure and function of hemoglobin (Hb) has evolved in animals that live in diverse environments. In a series of studies, he and a team of international colleagues explored the oxygen-binding properties of Hb "resurrected" from the extinct woolly mammoth (*Mammuthus primigenius*). The Hb genes were cloned from mammoth tissues and transfected into bacteria to produce the recombinant protein. The oxygen binding properties of the recombinant Hb from mammoth were compared with Hb from other mammals, including the Asian elephant (*Elephas maximus*).

Results Both elephants and mammoth experience a left shift in the Hb:oxygen dissociation curve, reflecting an increased affinity for oxygen in the cold. However, the shift is less pronounced in the mammoth, suggesting that their Hb is inherently less sensitive to temperature.

Conclusion This Hb trait, in combination with morphological and physiological adaptations to reduce heat loss, may have helped the mammoth survive the intense cold of the Pleistocene Ice Ages.

Source: Based on K. L. Campbell et al., Substitutions in woolly mammoth hemoglobin confer biochemical properties adaptive for cold tolerance, *Nature Genetics* 42:536–540 (2010). R. E. Weber and K. L. Campbell, Temperature dependence of haemoglobin–oxygen affinity in heterothermic vertebrates: Mechanisms and biological significance, *Acta Physiologica* (*Oxf*) 202:549–562 (2011). © Jane B Reece.

WHAT IF? *What properties of Hb would you expect to find if you studied extant (living) mammals that currently live in the high Arctic, such as musk ox?*

water (assisted by the enzyme carbonic anhydrase), forming H_2CO_3. The H_2CO_3 readily dissociates into H^+ and HCO_3^-. Most H^+ binds to hemoglobin and other proteins, minimizing change in blood pH. Most HCO_3^- diffuses out of the erythrocytes and is transported to the lungs in the plasma. The remaining HCO_3^-, representing about 5% of the CO_2, binds to hemoglobin and is transported in erythrocytes.

When blood flows through the lungs, the relative partial pressures of CO_2 favour the diffusion of CO_2 out of the blood. As CO_2 diffuses into alveoli, the amount of CO_2 in the blood decreases. This decrease shifts the chemical equilibrium in favour of the conversion of HCO_3^- to CO_2, enabling further net diffusion of CO_2 into alveoli. Overall, the P_{CO_2} gradient is sufficient to reduce P_{CO_2} by roughly 15% during passage of blood through the lungs.

Respiratory Adaptations of Diving Mammals

EVOLUTION Animals vary greatly in their ability to temporarily inhabit environments in which there is no access to their normal respiratory medium—for example, when an air-breathing mammal swims underwater. Whereas most humans, even well-trained divers, cannot hold their breath longer than 2 or 3 minutes or swim deeper than 20 m, the Weddell seal of Antarctica routinely plunges to 200–500 m and remains there for about 20 minutes (and sometimes for more than an hour). (Humans can remain submerged for comparable periods, but only with the aid of specialized gear and compressed air tanks.) Some whales and other species of seals make even more impressive dives. Elephant seals can reach depths of 1500 m—almost a mile—and stay submerged for as long as 2 hours! One elephant seal carrying a recording device spent 40 days at sea, diving almost continuously with no surface period longer than 6 minutes. What evolutionary adaptations enable these animals to perform such amazing feats?

One adaptation of diving mammals to prolonged stays underwater is an ability to store large amounts of O_2. Compared with humans, the Weddell seal can store about twice as much O_2 per kilogram of body mass. About 36% of our total O_2 is in our lungs, and 51% is in our blood. In contrast, the Weddell seal holds only about 5% of its O_2 in its relatively small lungs (and may exhale before diving, which reduces buoyancy), stockpiling 70% in the blood. And the seal has about twice the volume of blood per kilogram of body mass as a human. Diving mammals also have a high concentration of an oxygen-storing protein called **myoglobin** in their muscles. The Weddell seal can store about 25% of its O_2 in muscle, compared with only 13% in humans.

Diving mammals not only have a relatively large O_2 stockpile but also have adaptations that conserve O_2. They swim with little muscular effort and glide passively upward or downward by changing their buoyancy. Their heart rate and O_2

Doug Allan/Nature Picture Library

▲ **Weddell seal**

consumption rate decrease during a dive. At the same time, regulatory mechanisms route most blood to the brain, spinal cord, eyes, adrenal glands, and, in pregnant seals, the placenta. Blood supply to the muscles is restricted or, during the longest dives, shut off altogether. During dives of more than about 20 minutes, a Weddell seal's muscles deplete the O_2 stored in myoglobin and then derive their ATP from fermentation instead of respiration (see Chapter 9).

The unusual abilities of the Weddell seal and other air-breathing divers to power their bodies during long dives showcase two related themes in our study of organisms—the response to environmental challenges over the short term by physiological adjustments and over the long term as a result of natural selection.

CONCEPT CHECK 42.7

1. What determines whether O_2 and CO_2 diffuse into or out of the capillaries in the tissues and near the alveoli? Explain.
2. How does the Bohr shift help deliver O_2 to very active tissues?
3. **WHAT IF?** A doctor might give bicarbonate (HCO_3^-) to a patient who is breathing very rapidly. What assumption is the doctor making about the blood chemistry of the patient?

For suggested answers, see Appendix A.

42 Chapter Review

Go to **MasteringBiology**® for Assignments, the eText, and the Study Area with Animations, Activities, Vocab Self-Quiz, and Practice Tests.

SUMMARY OF KEY CONCEPTS

CONCEPT 42.1

Circulatory systems link exchange surfaces with cells throughout the body (pp. 967–972)

- In animals with simple body plans, gastrovascular cavities mediate exchange between the environment and cells that can be reached by diffusion. Because diffusion is slow over long distances, most complex animals have a circulatory system that moves fluid between cells and the organs that carry out exchange with the environment. Arthropods and most molluscs have an **open circulatory system**, in which **hemolymph** bathes organs directly. Vertebrates have a **closed circulatory system**, in which **blood** circulates in a closed network of pumps and vessels.
- The closed circulatory system of vertebrates consists of blood, **blood vessels**, and a two- to four-chambered **heart**. Blood pumped by a heart **ventricle** passes to **arteries** and then to **capillaries**, the sites of chemical exchange between blood and interstitial fluid. **Veins** return blood from capillaries to an **atrium**, which passes blood to a ventricle. Fishes, rays, and sharks have a single pump in their circulation. Air-breathing vertebrates have two pumps combined in a single heart. Variations in ventricle number and separation reflect adaptations to different environments and metabolic needs.

? *How does the flow of a fluid in a closed circulatory system differ from the movement of molecules between cells and their environment with regard to distance travelled, direction travelled, and driving force?*

CONCEPT 42.2

Coordinated cycles of heart contraction drive double circulation in mammals (pp. 972–974)

- The right ventricle pumps blood to the lungs, where it loads O_2 and unloads CO_2. Oxygen-rich blood from the lungs enters the heart at the left atrium and is pumped to the body tissues by the left ventricle. Blood returns to the heart through the right atrium.

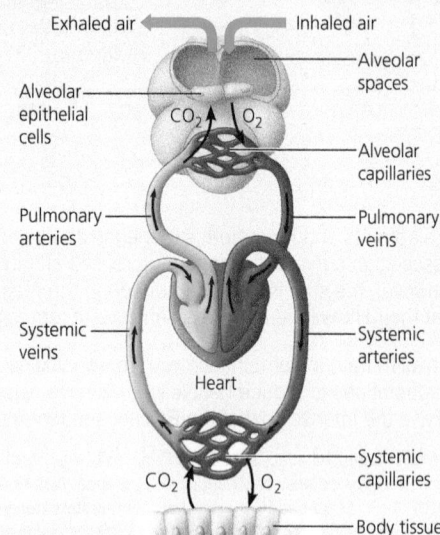

Source: Figure adapted from *Human Anatomy and Physiology*, 8th edition, by Elaine N. Marieb and Katja Hoehn. Copyright © 2010 by Pearson Education, Inc. Adapted and electronically reproduced by permission of Pearson Education, Inc., Upper Saddle River, New Jersey.

- The **cardiac cycle**, one complete sequence of the heart's pumping and filling, consists of a period of contraction, called **systole**, and a period of relaxation, called **diastole**. Heart function can be assessed by measuring the **pulse** (number of times the heart beats each minute) and **cardiac output** (volume of blood pumped by each ventricle per minute).
- The heartbeat originates with impulses at the **sinoatrial (SA) node** (pacemaker) of the right atrium. The impulses trigger contraction of both atria before passing to the **atrioventricular (AV) node**, where the impulses are temporarily delayed. They are then conducted along the bundle branches and Purkinje fibres, triggering contraction of the ventricles. The nervous system, hormones, and body temperature influence pacemaker activity.

? *What changes in cardiac function might you expect after surgical replacement of a defective heart valve?*

CONCEPT 42.3

Patterns of blood pressure and flow reflect the structure and arrangement of blood vessels (pp. 975–980)

- Blood vessels have structures well adapted to function. Capillaries have narrow diameters and thin walls that facilitate exchange. Arteries contain thick elastic walls that maintain blood pressure. Veins contain one-way valves that contribute to the return of blood to the heart.
- Physical laws governing the movement of fluids through pipes influence blood flow and blood pressure. The velocity of blood flow varies in the circulatory system, being lowest in the capillary beds as a result of their large total cross-sectional area. Blood pressure is altered by changes in cardiac output and by variable constriction of arterioles.
- Fluid leaks out of capillaries and is returned to blood by the **lymphatic system**. This system parallels the circulatory system in its extent and its mechanisms for fluid flow under low hydrostatic pressure. It also plays a vital role in defence against infection.

? *If you placed your forearm on your head, how, if at all, would the blood pressure in that arm change? Explain.*

CONCEPT 42.4

Blood components function in exchange, transport, and defence (pp. 980–985)

- Whole blood consists of cells and cell fragments (**platelets**) suspended in a liquid matrix called **plasma**. Plasma proteins influence blood pH, osmotic pressure, and viscosity, and they function in lipid transport, immunity (antibodies), and blood clotting (fibrinogen). Red blood cells, or **erythrocytes**, transport O_2. Five types of white blood cells, or **leukocytes**, function in defence against microbes and foreign substances in the blood. Platelets function in blood clotting, a cascade of reactions that converts plasma fibrinogen to fibrin.
- A variety of diseases impair function of the circulatory system. In **sickle-cell disease**, an aberrant form of **hemoglobin** disrupts erythrocyte shape and function, leading to blockage of small blood vessels and a decrease in the oxygen-carrying capacity of the blood. In cardiovascular disease, inflammation caused by damage to the lining of arteries enhances deposition of lipids and cells, resulting in the potential for life-threatening damage to the heart or brain.

? *In the absence of infection, what percentage of cells in human blood are leukocytes?*

CONCEPT 42.5

Gas exchange occurs across specialized respiratory surfaces (pp. 985–990)

- At all sites of **gas exchange**, a gas diffuses from where its **partial pressure** is higher to where it is lower. Air is more conducive to gas exchange than water because air has a higher O_2 content, lower density, and lower viscosity. Regardless of whether the respiratory medium is air or water, adequate diffusion of O_2 and CO_2 between the medium and an animal's cells requires large, moist respiratory surfaces.
- The structure and organization of respiratory surfaces differ among animal species. Gills are outfoldings of the body surface specialized for gas exchange in water. The effectiveness of gas exchange in some gills, including those of fishes, is increased by **ventilation** and **countercurrent exchange** between blood and water. Gas exchange in insects relies on a **tracheal system** consisting of

tiny, branching tubes that penetrate the body, bringing O_2 directly to cells. Spiders, land snails, and most terrestrial vertebrates have internal **lungs**. In mammals, air inhaled through the nostrils passes through the pharynx into the **trachea**, **bronchi**, **bronchioles**, and dead-end **alveoli**, where gas exchange occurs.

? *Why does altitude have almost no effect on an animal's ability to rid itself of CO_2 through gas exchange?*

CONCEPT 42.6

Breathing ventilates the lungs (pp. 990–992)

- **Breathing** mechanisms vary substantially among vertebrates. An amphibian ventilates its lungs by **positive pressure breathing**, which forces air down the trachea. Birds use a system of air sacs as bellows to keep air flowing through the lungs in one direction only. Every exhalation completely renews the air in the lungs. Mammals ventilate their lungs by **negative pressure breathing**, which pulls air into the lungs. Lung volume increases as the rib muscles and **diaphragm** contract. Incoming and outgoing air mix, decreasing the efficiency of ventilation.
- Control centres in the medulla oblongata and pons of the human brain regulate the rate and depth of breathing. Sensors detect the pH of cerebrospinal fluid (reflecting CO_2 concentration in the blood), and the medulla adjusts breathing rate and depth to match metabolic demands. Secondary control over breathing is exerted by sensors in the aorta and carotid arteries that monitor blood levels of O_2 as well as CO_2 (via blood pH).

? *How does tidal volume differ from the volume of fresh air that enters the body during inspiration?*

CONCEPT 42.7

Adaptations for gas exchange include pigments that bind and transport gases (pp. 992–996)

- In the lungs, gradients of partial pressure favour the diffusion of O_2 into the blood and CO_2 out of the blood. The opposite situation exists in the rest of the body. **Respiratory pigments** transport O_2, greatly increasing the amount of O_2 that blood or hemolymph can carry. Many arthropods and molluscs have copper-containing hemocyanin; vertebrates and a wide variety of invertebrates have hemoglobin. Hemoglobin also helps transport CO_2 and assists in buffering the blood.
- Evolutionary adaptations enable some animals to satisfy extraordinary O_2 demands. Deep-diving air-breathers stockpile O_2 in blood and other tissues and deplete it slowly.

? *In what way is the role of a respiratory pigment like that of an enzyme?*

TEST YOUR UNDERSTANDING

LEVEL 1: KNOWLEDGE/COMPREHENSION

1. Which of the following respiratory systems is not closely associated with a blood supply?
   a. the lungs of a vertebrate
   b. the gills of a fish
   c. the tracheal system of an insect
   d. the skin of an earthworm

2. Blood returning to the mammalian heart in a pulmonary vein drains first into the
   a. left atrium.
   b. right atrium.
   c. left ventricle.
   d. right ventricle.

3. Pulse is a direct measure of
   a. blood pressure.
   b. stroke volume.
   c. cardiac output.
   d. heart rate.

4. When you hold your breath, which of the following blood gas changes first leads to the urge to breathe?
   a. rising O_2
   b. falling O_2
   c. rising CO_2
   d. falling CO_2

5. One feature that amphibians and humans have in common is
   a. the number of heart chambers.
   b. a complete separation of circuits for circulation.
   c. the number of circuits for circulation.
   d. a low blood pressure in the systemic circuit.

LEVEL 2: APPLICATION/ANALYSIS

6. If a molecule of CO_2 released into the blood in your left toe is exhaled from your nose, it must pass through all of the following except
   a. the pulmonary vein.
   b. the trachea.
   c. the right atrium.
   d. the right ventricle.

7. Compared with the interstitial fluid that bathes active muscle cells, blood reaching these cells in arteries has a
   a. higher P_{O_2}.
   b. higher P_{CO_2}.
   c. greater bicarbonate concentration.
   d. lower pH.

LEVEL 3: SYNTHESIS/EVALUATION

8. **DRAW IT** Plot blood pressure against time for one cardiac cycle in humans, drawing separate lines for the pressure in the aorta, the left ventricle, and the right ventricle. Below the time axis, add a vertical arrow pointing to the time when you expect a peak in atrial blood pressure.

9. **EVOLUTION CONNECTION**
   One of the opponents of the movie monster Godzilla is Mothra, a giant mothlike creature with a wingspan of several dozen meters. The largest known insects were Paleozoic dragonflies with half-metre wingspans. Focusing on respiration and gas exchange, explain why giant insects are improbable.

10. **SCIENTIFIC INQUIRY**
    INTERPRET THE DATA
    The hemoglobin of a human fetus differs from adult hemoglobin. Compare the dissociation curves of the two hemoglobins in the graph at right. Propose a hypothesis to explain the benefit of this difference between these two hemoglobins.

11. **SCIENCE, TECHNOLOGY, AND SOCIETY**
    Hundreds of studies have linked smoking with cardiovascular and lung disease. According to most health authorities, smoking is the leading cause of preventable, premature death in the United States. Antismoking groups have proposed that cigarette advertising in all media be banned entirely. What are some arguments in favour of a total ban on cigarette advertising? What are arguments in opposition? Do you favour or oppose such a ban? Defend your position.

12. **WRITE ABOUT A THEME: INTERACTIONS**
    Some athletes prepare for competition at sea level by sleeping in a tent in which P_{O_2} is kept artificially low. When climbing very high peaks, some mountaineers breathe from bottles of pure O_2. In a short essay (100–150 words), relate these behaviours to the mechanism of O_2 transport in the human body and to our physiological interactions with our gaseous environment.

13. **SYNTHESIZE YOUR KNOWLEDGE**

Stefan Hetz/Newscom

The diving bell spider (*Argyroneta aquatica*) stores air under water in a net of silk. Explain why this adaptation could be more advantageous than having gills, taking into account differences in gas exchange media and gas exchange organs among animals.

For selected answers, see Appendix A.

43

The Immune System

KEY CONCEPTS

43.1 In innate immunity, recognition and response rely on traits common to groups of pathogens

43.2 In adaptive immunity, receptors provide pathogen-specific recognition

43.3 Adaptive immunity defends against infection of body fluids and body cells

43.4 Disruptions in immune system function can elicit or exacerbate disease

Biology Media/Science Source

▲ Figure 43.1 **How do an animal's immune cells recognize foreign cells?**

Recognition and Response

For a **pathogen**—a bacterium, fungus, virus, or other disease-causing agent—the internal environment of an animal is a nearly ideal habitat. The animal's body offers a ready source of nutrients, a protected setting for growth and reproduction, and a means of transport to new environments. From the perspective of a cold or flu virus, we are wonderful hosts. From our vantage point, things are not so ideal. Fortunately, adaptations have arisen over the course of evolution that protect animals against many pathogens.

Dedicated immune cells in the body fluids and tissues of most animals specifically interact with and destroy pathogens. As shown in **Figure 43.1** (a colourized scanning electron micrograph), an immune cell called a macrophage brown can engulf bacteria (green). Additional responses to infection take many forms, including proteins that punch holes in bacterial membranes or block viruses from entering body cells. These and other defences make up the **immune system**, which enables an animal to avoid or limit many infections. A foreign molecule or cell doesn't have to be pathogenic to elicit an immune response, but we'll focus here on the immune system's role in defending against pathogens.

Two types of molecular recognition provide the basis for the two types of immune defence found among animals: innate immunity, which is common to

Juergen Berger/Science Source

◀ **Lymphocyte**

all animals, and adaptive immunity, which is found only in vertebrates. Figure 43.2 summarizes these two types of immunity, highlighting fundamental similarities and differences.

All animals have **innate immunity**, a defence that is active immediately upon infection and is the same whether or not the pathogen has been encountered previously. Innate immunity includes an outer covering, such as a skin or shell, that provides a significant barrier to entry by microbes. Sealing off the entire body surface is impossible, however, because gas exchange, nutrition, and reproduction require openings to the environment. Chemical secretions that trap or kill microbes guard the body's entrances and exits, while the linings of the digestive tract, airway, and other exchange surfaces provide additional barriers to infection.

If a pathogen breaches barrier defences and enters the body, the problem of how to fend off attack changes substantially. Once the pathogen enters the body tissues, the options for attacking it must be more specific to avoid damaging host cells. The immune system is able to distinguish the animal's own molecules (self) from foreign molecules (nonself), the hallmark of the presence of potential pathogens or even abnormal cells. Detection of nonself is accomplished by *molecular recognition*, in which receptor molecules bind specifically to molecules from foreign cells or viruses.

In innate immunity, a small preset group of receptor proteins bind to molecules or structures that are

absent from animal bodies but common to a group of viruses, bacteria, or other microbes. Binding of an innate immune receptor to a foreign molecule activates internal defences, enabling responses to a very broad range of pathogens.

A different type of molecular recognition provides the basis for **adaptive immunity**, a defence found only in vertebrates. Animals with adaptive immunity produce a vast arsenal of receptors, each of which recognizes a feature typically found only on a particular part of a particular molecule in a particular pathogen. As a result, recognition and response in adaptive immunity occur with tremendous specificity.

The adaptive immune response, also known as the acquired immune response, is activated after the innate immune response and develops more slowly. The names *adaptive* and *acquired* reflect the fact that this immune response is enhanced by previous exposure to the infecting pathogen. Dr. Sam Kung from the University of Manitoba studies two of the cells that are essential in both the innate and adaptive immune responses. Dendritic cells provide crucial information to natural killer cells, as we will explore later in the chapter. Without the crucial communication between these two cells, autoimmune diseases and other errors of immune system can result. His lab is looking to genetically alter natural killer cells. By designing new receptors for natural killer cells, they can aim them, like pointing a weapon, and use them to kill cancer cells or virally infected cells. Kung's research on errors in the regulation of the immune system may result in the development of new therapeutics for immune disorders and improved vaccines.

In this chapter, you will learn how each type of immunity protects animals from disease. You will also examine how pathogens can avoid or overwhelm the immune system and how defects in the immune system can imperil an animal's health.

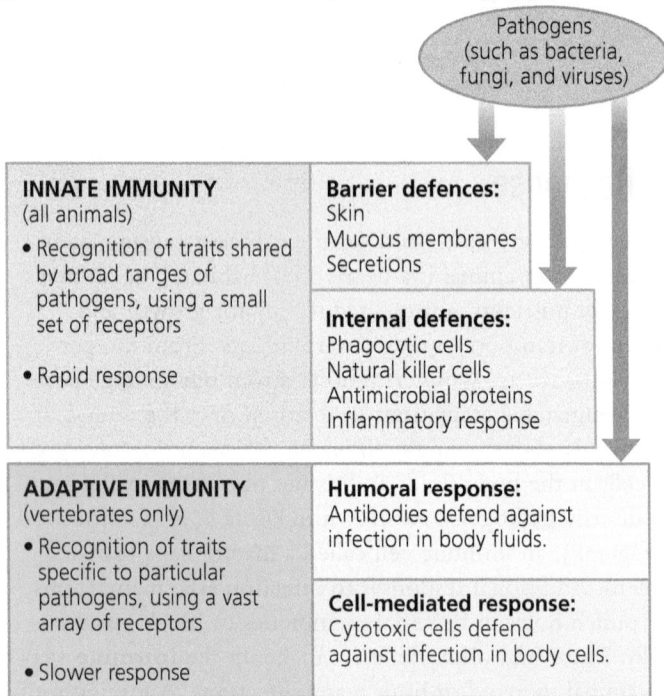

▲ Figure 43.2 **Overview of animal immunity.** Immune responses in animals can be divided into innate and adaptive immunity. Some components of innate immunity contribute to activation of adaptive immune defences.

CONCEPT 43.1

In innate immunity, recognition and response rely on traits common to groups of pathogens

Innate immunity is found in all animals (as well as in plants). In exploring innate immunity, we'll begin with invertebrates, which repel and fight infection using only innate immunity. We'll then turn to vertebrates, in which innate immunity serves both as an immediate defence against infection and as the foundation for adaptive immune defences.

Innate Immunity of Invertebrates

The great success of insects in terrestrial and freshwater habitats teeming with diverse microbes highlights the effectiveness of invertebrate innate immunity. In each of these environments, insects rely on their exoskeleton as a first line of defence against infection. Composed largely of the polysaccharide chitin, the exoskeleton provides an effective barrier defence against most pathogens. A chitin-based barrier is also present in the insect intestine, where it blocks infection by many pathogens ingested with food. **Lysozyme**, an enzyme that breaks down bacterial cell walls, further protects the insect digestive system.

Any pathogen that breaches an insect's barrier defences encounters a number of internal immune defences. Immune cells called *hemocytes* travel throughout the body in the hemolymph, the insect circulatory fluid. Some hemocytes carry out a defence called **phagocytosis**, the cellular ingestion and digestion of bacteria and other foreign substances (Figure 43.3). Other hemocytes trigger the production of chemicals that kill pathogens and help entrap large parasites, such as *Plasmodium*, the parasite of mosquitoes that causes malaria. In addition, encounters with pathogens in the hemolymph cause hemocytes and certain other cells

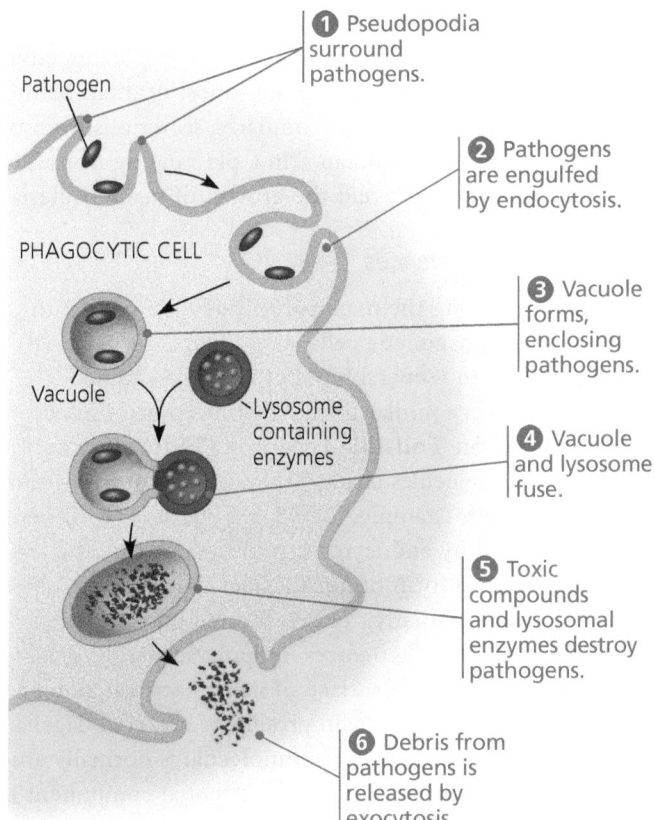

1 Pseudopodia surround pathogens.

Pathogen

2 Pathogens are engulfed by endocytosis.

PHAGOCYTIC CELL

3 Vacuole forms, enclosing pathogens.

Vacuole

Lysosome containing enzymes

4 Vacuole and lysosome fuse.

5 Toxic compounds and lysosomal enzymes destroy pathogens.

6 Debris from pathogens is released by exocytosis.

▲ **Figure 43.3 Phagocytosis.** This schematic depicts events in the ingestion and destruction of a microbe by a typical phagocytic cell.

► **Figure 43.4 An inducible innate immune response.** These fruit flies were engineered to express the green fluorescent protein (GFP) gene upon activation of the innate immune response. The fly on the top was injected with bacteria; the fly on the bottom was not. Only the infected fly activates antimicrobial peptide genes, produces GFP, and glows a bright green under fluorescent light.

Ferrandon, Dominique

to secrete *antimicrobial peptides*, which are short chains of amino acids. The antimicrobial peptides circulate throughout the body of the insect (Figure 43.4) and inactivate or kill fungi and bacteria by disrupting their plasma membranes.

Immune cells of insects bind to molecules found only in the outer layers of fungi or bacteria. Fungal cell walls contain certain unique polysaccharides, whereas bacterial cell walls have polymers containing combinations of sugars and amino acids not found in animal cells. Such macromolecules serve as identity tags in the process of pathogen recognition. Insect immune cells secrete specialized recognition proteins, each of which binds to a macromolecule characteristic of groups of bacteria or fungi.

Innate immune responses are distinct for different types of pathogens. For example, when the fungus *Neurospora crassa* infects a fruit fly, pieces of the fungal cell wall bind to a recognition protein. Together, the complex activates the protein Toll, a receptor on the surface of hemocytes. Signal transduction from the Toll receptor to the cell nucleus leads to synthesis of a set of antimicrobial peptides active against fungi. If the fly is instead infected by the bacterium *Micrococcus luteus*, a different recognition protein is activated, and the fly produces a different set of antimicrobial peptides effective against *M. luteus* and many related bacteria.

Because fruit flies secrete many distinct antimicrobial peptides in response to a single infection, it is difficult to study the activity of any one peptide. To get around this problem, Bruno Lemaitre and fellow researchers used modern genetic techniques to reprogram the fly immune system (Figure 43.5). They found that the synthesis of a single type of antimicrobial peptide in the fly's body could provide an effective immune defence. They also showed that particular antimicrobial peptides act against different kinds of pathogens.

Innate Immunity of Vertebrates

Among jawed vertebrates, innate immune defences coexist with the more recently evolved system of adaptive immunity. Because most of the recent discoveries regarding vertebrate innate immunity have come from studies of mice and humans, we'll focus here on mammals. We'll consider the innate defences that are similar to those found among

Can a single antimicrobial peptide protect fruit flies against infection?

Experiment In 2002, Bruno Lemaitre and colleagues in France devised a novel strategy to test the function of a single antimicrobial peptide. They began with a mutant fruit fly strain in which pathogens are recognized but the signalling that would normally trigger innate immune responses is blocked. As a result, the mutant flies do not make any antimicrobial peptides. The researchers then genetically engineered some of the mutant fruit flies to express significant amounts of a single antimicrobial peptide, either drosomycin or defensin. The scientists infected the various flies with the fungus *Neurospora crassa* and monitored survival over a five-day period. They repeated the procedure for infection by the bacterium *Micrococcus luteus*.

Results

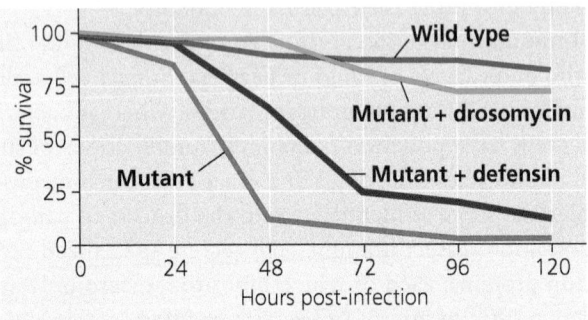

Fruit fly survival after infection by *N. crassa* fungi

Source: Adaptation of figure 4a from Constitutive Expression of a Single Antimicrobial Peptide Can Restore Wild-Type Resistance to Infection in Immunodeficient Drosophila Mutants by Phoebe Tzou et al., from *Proceedings of the National Academy of Sciences USA*, February 2002, Volume 99(4). Copyright © 2002 by National Academy of Sciences. Reprinted with permission.

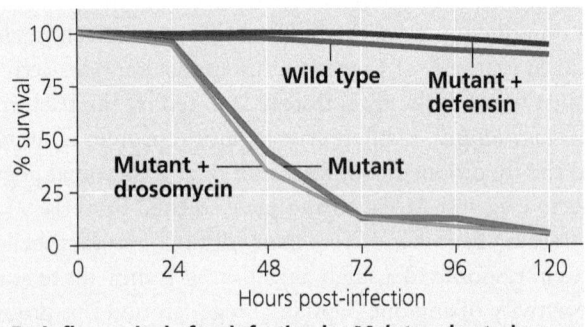

Fruit fly survival after infection by *M. luteus* bacteria

Source: Adaptation of figure 2a from Constitutive Expression of a Single Antimicrobial Peptide Can Restore Wild-Type Resistance to Infection in Immunodeficient Drosophila Mutants by Phoebe Tzou et al., from *Proceedings of the National Academy of Sciences USA*, February 2002, Volume 99(4). Copyright © 2002 by National Academy of Sciences. Reprinted with permission.

Conclusion Each of the two antimicrobial peptides provided a protective immune response. Furthermore, the different peptides defended against different pathogens. Drosomycin was effective against *N. crassa*, and defensin was effective against *M. luteus*.

Source: Based on P. Tzou, J. Reichhart, and B. Lemaitre, Constitutive expression of a single antimicrobial peptide can restore wild-type resistance to infection in immunodeficient *Drosophila* mutants, *Proceedings of the National Academy of Sciences USA* 99:2152–2157 (2002). © Jane B Reece.

WHAT IF? *Even if a particular antimicrobial peptide showed no beneficial effect in such an experiment, why might it still be beneficial to flies?*

invertebrates: barrier defences, phagocytosis, and antimicrobial peptides. We'll also examine some unique aspects of vertebrate innate immunity, such as natural killer cells, interferons, and the inflammatory response.

Barrier Defences

In mammals, the external epithelial surfaces of the body block the entry of many pathogens. The thickened outer body surface usually has protective barriers. More vulnerable are the internalized external surfaces, such as the lining of the digestive, respiratory, urinary, and reproductive tracts. These epithelial tissues are often called mucous membranes, or *mucosa*. Certain cells of the mucous membranes secrete **mucus**, a viscous fluid that enhances defences by trapping microbes and other particles. In the trachea, ciliated epithelial cells sweep mucus and any entrapped microbes upward, helping prevent infection of the lungs. Fluid secretions from the epithelial tissues, such as saliva, tears, and mucus, bathe the tissues, providing a washing action that also inhibits colonization by fungi and bacteria.

Beyond their physical role in inhibiting microbial entry, body secretions create an environment that is hostile to many pathogens. Lysozyme in tears, saliva, and mucosal secretions destroys the cell walls of susceptible bacteria as they enter the openings around the eyes or the upper respiratory tract. Microbes in food or water and those in swallowed mucus must also contend with the acidic environment of the stomach, which kills most of them before they can enter the intestines. Similarly, secretions from oil and sweat glands give human skin a pH ranging from 3 to 5, acidic enough to prevent the growth of many bacteria.

Cellular Innate Defences

Pathogens entering the mammalian body are subject to phagocytosis. Phagocytic cells detect fungal or bacterial components using several types of receptors, some of which are very similar to the Toll receptor of insects. Each mammalian **Toll-like receptor (TLR)** binds to fragments of molecules characteristic of a set of pathogens (Figure 43.6). For example, TLR3, on the inner surface of vesicles formed by endocytosis, is the sensor for double-stranded RNA, a form of nucleic acid characteristic of certain viruses. Similarly, TLR4, located on immune cell plasma membranes, recognizes lipopolysaccharide, a type of molecule found on the surface of many bacteria; and TLR5 recognizes flagellin, the main protein of bacterial flagella. In each case, the recognized macromolecule is normally absent from the vertebrate body and is an essential component of certain groups of pathogens.

After detecting invading pathogens, a phagocytic cell engulfs them, trapping them in a vacuole. The vacuole then fuses with a lysosome (see Figure 43.3), leading to destruction of the invaders in two ways. First, gases

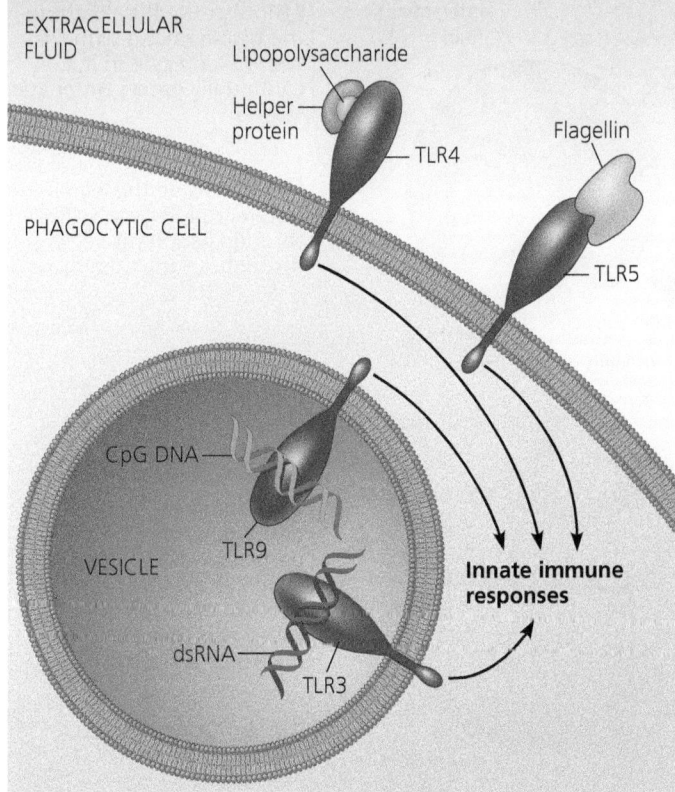

EXTRACELLULAR FLUID

Lipopolysaccharide

Helper protein

TLR4

Flagellin

TLR5

PHAGOCYTIC CELL

CpG DNA

TLR9

VESICLE

dsRNA

TLR3

Innate immune responses

▲ Figure 43.6 **TLR signalling.** Each mammalian Toll-like receptor (TLR) recognizes a molecular pattern characteristic of a group of pathogens. Lipopolysaccharide, flagellin, CpG DNA (DNA containing unmethylated CG sequences), and double-stranded (ds) RNA are all found in bacteria, fungi, or viruses, but not in animal cells. Together with other recognition and response factors, TLR proteins trigger internal innate immune defences.

? *Some TLR proteins are on the cell surface, whereas others are inside vesicles. Suggest a possible benefit of this distribution.*

produced in the lysosome poison the engulfed pathogens. Second, lysozyme and other enzymes in the lysosome degrade the components of the pathogens.

The two main types of phagocytic cells in the mammalian body are neutrophils and macrophages. **Neutrophils**, which circulate in the blood, are attracted by signals from infected tissues and then engulf and destroy the infecting pathogens. **Macrophages** ("big eaters"), like the one shown in Figure 43.1, are larger phagocytic cells. Some migrate throughout the body, whereas others accumulate in those organs and tissues where they are likely to encounter pathogens. For example, some macrophages are located in the spleen, where pathogens in the blood become trapped.

Two other types of phagocytic cells—dendritic cells and eosinophils—provide additional functions in innate defence. **Dendritic cells** mainly populate tissues, such as skin, that contact the environment. They stimulate adaptive immunity against pathogens they encounter and engulf, as we'll explore shortly. **Eosinophils**, often found beneath mucosal surfaces, have low phagocytic activity but

are important in defending against multicellular invaders, such as parasitic worms. Upon encountering such parasites, eosinophils discharge destructive enzymes.

Cellular innate defences in vertebrates also involve **natural killer cells**. These cells circulate through the body and detect the abnormal array of surface proteins characteristic of some virus-infected and cancerous cells. Natural killer cells do not engulf stricken cells. Instead, they release chemicals that lead to cell death, inhibiting further spread of the virus or cancer.

Many cellular innate defences in vertebrates involve the lymphatic system, a network that distributes the fluid called lymph throughout the body (Figure 43.7). Some macrophages reside in the structures called lymph nodes, where they engulf pathogens that have flowed from the interstitial fluid into the lymph. Dendritic cells reside outside the lymphatic system but migrate to the lymph nodes after interacting with pathogens. Within the lymph nodes, dendritic cells interact with other immune cells, stimulating adaptive immunity.

Antimicrobial Peptides and Proteins

In mammals, pathogen recognition triggers the production and release of a variety of peptides and proteins that attack pathogens or impede their reproduction. Some of these defence molecules function like the antimicrobial peptides of insects, damaging broad groups of pathogens by disrupting membrane integrity. Others, including the interferons and complement proteins, are unique to vertebrate immune systems.

Interferons are proteins that provide innate defence by interfering with viral infections. Virus-infected body cells secrete interferons, which induce nearby uninfected cells to produce substances that inhibit viral replication. In this way, interferons limit the cell-to-cell spread of viruses in the body, helping control viral infections such as colds and influenza. Some white blood cells secrete a different type of interferon that helps activate macrophages, enhancing their phagocytic ability. Pharmaceutical companies now use recombinant DNA technology to mass-produce interferons to help treat certain viral infections, such as hepatitis C.

The infection-fighting **complement system** consists of roughly 30 proteins in blood plasma. These proteins circulate in an inactive state and are activated by substances on the surface of many microbes. Activation results in a cascade of biochemical reactions that can lead to lysis (bursting) of invading cells. The complement system also functions in the inflammatory response, our next topic, as well as in the adaptive defences discussed later in the chapter.

Inflammatory Response

The pain and swelling that alert you to a splinter under your skin are the result of a local **inflammatory response**, the changes brought about by signalling molecules released

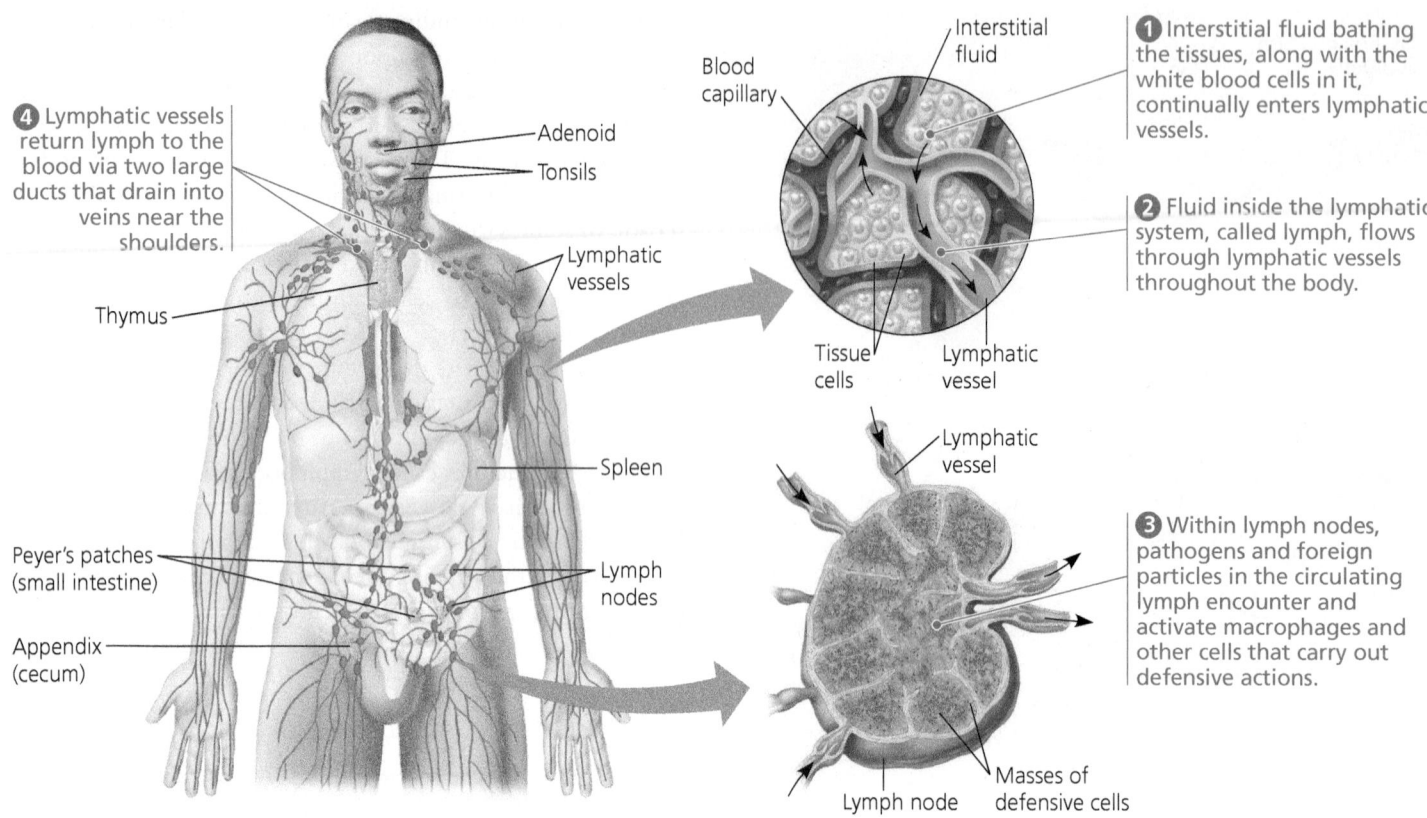

④ Lymphatic vessels return lymph to the blood via two large ducts that drain into veins near the shoulders.

Adenoid

Tonsils

Lymphatic vessels

Thymus

Spleen

Peyer's patches (small intestine)

Appendix (cecum)

Lymph nodes

Blood capillary

Interstitial fluid

❶ Interstitial fluid bathing the tissues, along with the white blood cells in it, continually enters lymphatic vessels.

❷ Fluid inside the lymphatic system, called lymph, flows through lymphatic vessels throughout the body.

Tissue cells

Lymphatic vessel

Lymphatic vessel

❸ Within lymph nodes, pathogens and foreign particles in the circulating lymph encounter and activate macrophages and other cells that carry out defensive actions.

Lymph node

Masses of defensive cells

▲ **Figure 43.7 The human lymphatic system.** The lymphatic system consists of lymphatic vessels (shown in green), through which lymph travels, and structures that trap foreign substances. These structures include lymph nodes (orange) and lymphoid organs (yellow): the adenoids, tonsils, spleen, Peyer's patches, and appendix. Steps 1–4 trace the flow of lymph and illustrate the critical role of lymph nodes in activating adaptive immunity. (Concept 42.3 describes the relationship between the lymphatic and circulatory systems.)

Source Figure adapted from *Human Anatomy and Physiology*, 8th edition, by Elaine N. Marieb and Katja Hoehn. Copyright © 2010 by Pearson Education, Inc. Adapted and electronically reproduced by permission of Pearson Education, Inc., Upper Saddle River, New Jersey.

upon injury or infection (Figure 43.8). One important inflammatory signalling molecule is **histamine**, which is stored in densely packed vesicles of **mast cells**, found in connective tissue. Histamine released at sites of damage triggers nearby blood vessels to dilate, permitting more blood flow to the region, and become more permeable, allowing proteins and cells to escape the vessel and enter the interstitial fluid surrounding cells. Activated macrophages and neutrophils discharge **cytokines**, signalling molecules that enhance an immune response. These cytokines promote blood flow to the site of injury or infection. The increase in local blood supply causes the redness and increased skin temperature typical of the inflammatory response (from the Latin *inflammare*, to set on fire). Blood-engorged capillaries leak fluid into neighbouring tissues, causing swelling.

During inflammation, cycles of signalling and response transform the site. Activated complement proteins promote further release of histamine, attracting more phagocytic cells that enter injured tissues (see Figure 43.8) and carry out additional phagocytosis. At the same time, enhanced blood flow to the site helps deliver antimicrobial peptides. The

result is an accumulation of *pus*, a fluid rich in white blood cells, dead pathogens, and debris from damaged tissue.

A minor injury or infection causes a local inflammatory response, but severe tissue damage or infection may lead to a response that is systemic (throughout the body). Cells in injured or infected tissue often secrete molecules that stimulate the release of additional neutrophils from the bone marrow. In a severe infection, such as meningitis or appendicitis, the number of white blood cells in the blood may increase several-fold within a few hours.

Another systemic inflammatory response is fever. In response to certain pathogens, substances released by activated macrophages cause the body's thermostat to reset to a higher temperature (see Chapter 40). The benefits of the resulting fever are still a subject of debate. One of several competing hypotheses is that an elevated body temperature may enhance phagocytosis and, by speeding up chemical reactions, accelerate tissue repair.

Certain bacterial infections can induce an overwhelming systemic inflammatory response, leading to a life-threatening condition called *septic shock*. Characterized by very high fever,

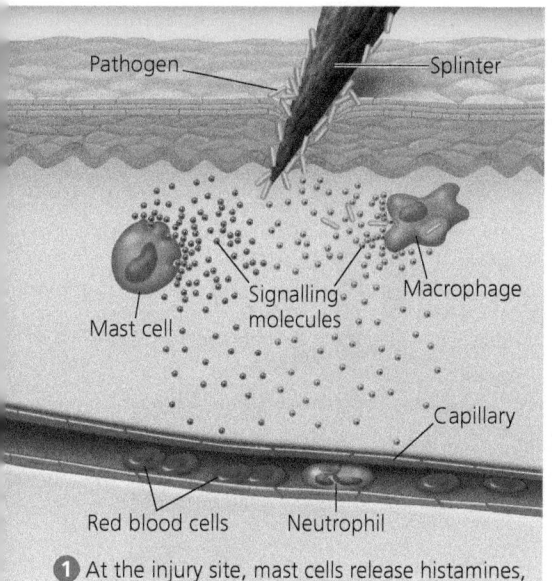

Pathogen — Splinter

Mast cell — Signalling molecules — Macrophage

Red blood cells — Neutrophil — Capillary

1 At the injury site, mast cells release histamines, and macrophages secrete cytokines. These signalling molecules cause nearby capillaries to dilate.

Movement of fluid

2 Capillaries widen and become more permeable, allowing fluid containing antimicrobial peptides to enter the tissue. Signals released by immune cells attract neutrophils.

Phagocytosis

3 Neutrophils digest pathogens and cell debris at the site, and the tissue heals.

▲ **Figure 43.8 Major events in a local inflammatory response.**

Source: Figure adapted from *Microbiology: An Introduction*, 11th edition, by Gerard J. Tortora, Berdell R. Funke, and Christine L. Case. Copyright © 2012 Pearson Education Inc. Adapted and electronically reproduced by permission of Pearson Education, Inc., Upper Saddle River, New Jersey.

low blood pressure, and poor blood flow through capillaries, septic shock occurs most often in the very old and the very young. Approximately 30 000 people in Canada are struck with sepsis each year, and about 30% of these cases are fatal.

Chronic (ongoing) inflammation can also threaten human health. For example, millions of individuals worldwide suffer from Crohn's disease and ulcerative colitis, often debilitating disorders in which an unregulated inflammatory response disrupts intestinal function.

Evasion of Innate Immunity by Pathogens

Adaptations have evolved in some pathogens that enable them to avoid destruction by phagocytic cells. For example, the outer capsule that surrounds certain bacteria interferes with molecular recognition and phagocytosis. One such bacterium, *Streptococcus pneumoniae*, played a critical role in the discovery that DNA can convey genetic information (see Figure 16.2). Other bacteria, after being engulfed by a host cell, resist breakdown within lysosomes. An example is the bacterium that causes tuberculosis (TB). Rather than being destroyed within host cells, this bacterium grows and reproduces, effectively hidden from the body's innate immune defences. These and other mechanisms that prevent destruction by the innate immune system make certain fungi and bacteria substantial pathogenic threats. Indeed, TB kills more than a million people a year worldwide. Countries that have largely obliterated TB, including Canada, are now threatened by the emergence of drug-resistant variants.

CONCEPT CHECK 43.1

1. Although pus is often seen simply as a sign of infection, it is also an indicator of immune defences in action. Explain.

2. **MAKE CONNECTIONS** How do the molecules that activate the vertebrate TLR signal transduction pathway differ from the ligands in most other pathways, such as those shown in Concept 11.2?

3. **WHAT IF?** Suppose humans were the major host for a bacterial species. What temperature would you predict would be optimal for growth of this species? Explain.

For suggested answers, see Appendix A.

CONCEPT **43.2**

In adaptive immunity, receptors provide pathogen-specific recognition

Vertebrates are unique in having adaptive immunity in addition to innate immunity. The adaptive response relies on T cells and B cells, which are types of white blood cells called **lymphocytes**. Like all blood cells, lymphocytes originate from stem cells in the bone marrow. Some lymphocytes migrate from the bone marrow to the **thymus**, an organ in the thoracic cavity

Antigen receptors

Mature B cell   **Mature T cell**

above the heart (see Figure 43.7). These lymphocytes mature into **T cells**. Lymphocytes that remain and mature in the bone marrow develop as **B cells**. (Lymphocytes of a third type remain in the blood and become the natural killer cells active in innate immunity.)

Any substance that elicits a response from a B cell or T cell is called an **antigen**. In adaptive immunity, recognition occurs when a B cell or T cell binds to an antigen, such as a bacterial or viral protein, via a protein called an **antigen receptor**. An antigen receptor is specific enough to bind to just one part of one molecule from a particular pathogen, such as a species of bacteria or strain of virus. Although the cells of the immune system produce millions of different antigen receptors, all of the antigen receptors made by a single B or T cell are identical. Infection by a virus, bacterium, or other pathogen triggers activation of B and T cells with antigen receptors specific for parts of that pathogen. B and T cells are shown here with only a few antigen receptors, but there are actually about 100 000 identical antigen receptors on the surface of a single B or T cell.

Antigens are usually foreign and are typically large molecules, either proteins or polysaccharides. Many antigens protrude from the surface of foreign cells or viruses. Other antigens, such as toxins secreted by bacteria, are released into the extracellular fluid.

The small, accessible portion of an antigen that binds to an antigen receptor is called an **epitope**. An example is a group of amino acids in a particular protein. A single antigen usually has several different epitopes, each binding a receptor with a different specificity. Because all antigen receptors produced by a single B cell or T cell are identical, they bind to the same epitope. Each B cell or T cell thus displays *specificity* for a particular epitope, enabling it to respond to any pathogen that produces molecules containing that same epitope.

The antigen receptors of B cells and T cells have similar components, but they encounter antigens in different ways. We'll consider the two processes in turn.

Antigen Recognition by B Cells and Antibodies

Each B cell antigen receptor is a Y-shaped molecule consisting of four polypeptide chains: two identical **heavy chains** and two identical **light chains**, with disulphide bridges linking the chains together (Figure 43.9). A transmembrane region near one end of each heavy chain anchors the receptor in the cell's plasma membrane. A short tail region at the end of the heavy chain extends into the cytoplasm.

The light and heavy chains each have a *constant (C) region*, where amino acid sequences vary little among the receptors on different B cells. The C region includes the cytoplasmic tail and transmembrane region of the heavy chain and all of the disulphide bridges. Within the two tips

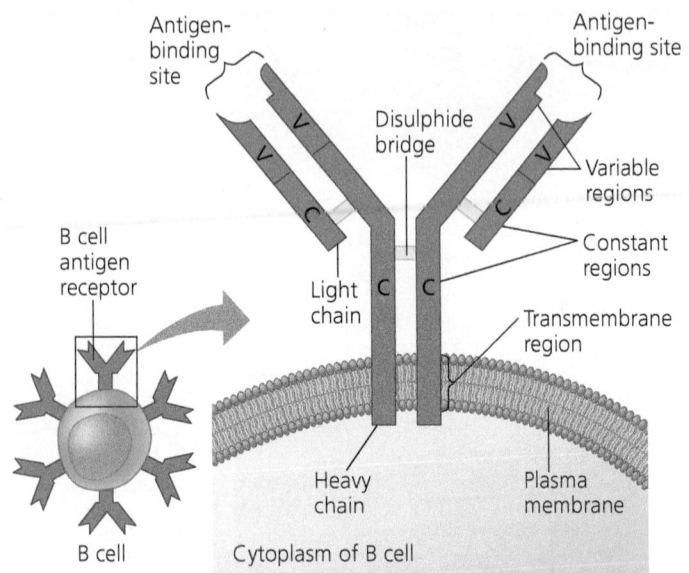

▲ Figure 43.9 **The structure of a B cell antigen receptor.**

of the Y shape, the light and heavy chains each have a *variable (V) region*, so named because its amino acid sequence varies extensively from one B cell to another. Together, parts of a heavy-chain V region and a light-chain V region form an asymmetrical binding site for an antigen. As shown in Figure 43.9, each B cell antigen receptor has two identical antigen-binding sites.

The binding of a B cell antigen receptor to an antigen is an early step in B cell activation, leading eventually to formation of cells that secrete a soluble form of the receptor (Figure 43.10a). This secreted protein is called an **antibody**, or **immunoglobulin (Ig)**. Antibodies have the same Y-shaped organization as B cell antigen receptors, but they are secreted rather than membrane bound. It is the antibodies, rather than the B cells themselves, that actually help defend against pathogens. Antibodies have distinct functions, as we'll see later.

The antigen-binding site of a membrane-bound receptor or antibody has a unique shape that provides a lock-and-key fit for a particular epitope. Many noncovalent bonds between an epitope and the binding surface provide a stable and specific interaction. Differences in the amino acid sequences of variable regions provide the variation in binding surfaces that enables this highly specific binding.

B cell antigen receptors and antibodies bind to intact antigens in the blood and lymph. As illustrated in Figure 43.10b for antibodies, they can bind to antigens on the surface of pathogens or free antigens in body fluids. The antigen receptors of T cells function quite differently, as we'll see next.

Antigen Recognition by T Cells

For a T cell, the antigen receptor consists of two different polypeptide chains, an α *chain* and a β *chain*, linked by a

(a) B cell antigen receptors and antibodies. An antigen receptor of a B cell binds to an epitope, a particular part of an antigen. Following binding, the B cell gives rise to cells that secrete a soluble form of the antigen receptor. This soluble receptor, called an antibody, is specific for the same epitope as the original B cell.

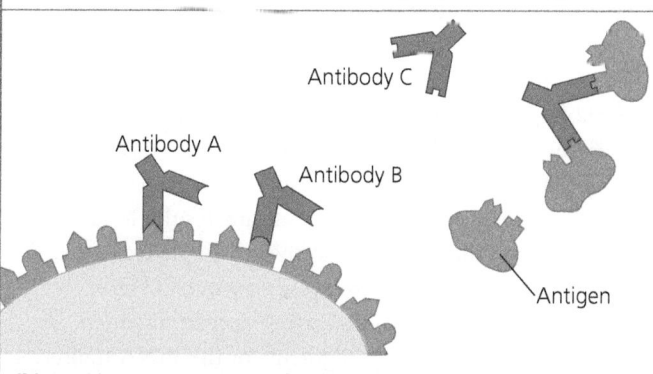

(b) Antigen receptor specificity. Different antibodies can recognize distinct epitopes on the same antigen. Furthermore, antibodies can recognize free antigens as well as antigens on a pathogen's surface.

▲ **Figure 43.10** Antigen recognition by B cells and antibodies.

MAKE CONNECTIONS *The interactions depicted here involve a highly specific binding between antigen and receptor, as shown in Figure 5.17. How is this similar to the enzyme-substrate interaction shown in Figure 8.15?*

disulphide bridge **(Figure 43.11)**. Near the base of the T cell antigen receptor (often called simply a T cell receptor) is a transmembrane region that anchors the molecule in the cell's plasma membrane. At the outer tip of the molecule, the variable (V) regions of α and β chains together form a single antigen-binding site. The remainder of the molecule is made up of the constant (C) regions. The discovery of the T cell receptor in 1984 by Canadian researcher Tak Wah Mak, at the University of Toronto, was essential to the understanding of the interaction of T cells and B cells.

Although T cell and B cell antigen receptors have many features in common, they function in fundamentally different ways. Whereas the antigen receptors of B cells bind to epitopes of intact antigens circulating in body fluids, those of T cells bind only to fragments of antigens that are displayed,

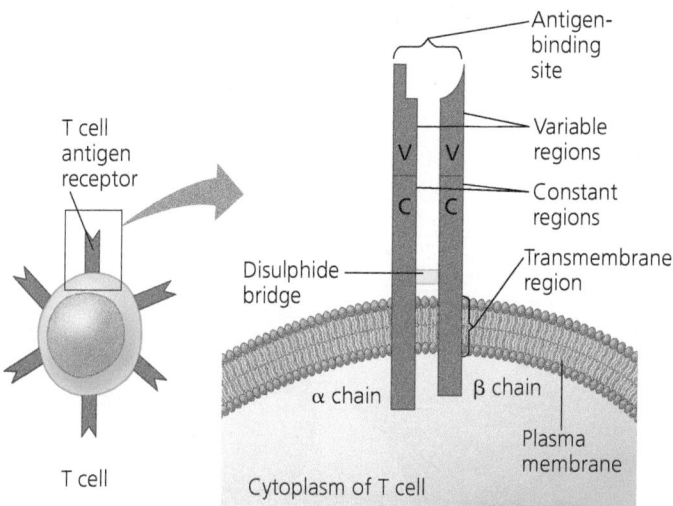

▲ **Figure 43.11** The structure of a T cell antigen receptor.

or *presented*, on the surface of host cells. The host protein that displays the antigen fragment on the cell surface is called an **MHC (major histocompatibility complex) molecule**.

Recognition of protein antigens by T cells begins when a pathogen or part of a pathogen either infects or is taken in by a host cell **(Figure 43.12a)**. Inside the host cell, enzymes in the cell cleave the antigen into smaller peptides. Each peptide, called an *antigen fragment*, then binds to an MHC molecule inside the cell. Movement of the MHC molecule and bound antigen fragment to the cell surface results in **antigen presentation**, the display of the antigen fragment in an exposed groove of the MHC protein. **Figure 43.12b** shows a close-up view of antigen presentation, which advertises the fact that a host cell contains a foreign substance. If the cell displaying an antigen fragment encounters a T cell with the right specificity, the antigen receptor on the T cell can bind to both the antigen fragment and the MHC molecule. This interaction of an MHC molecule, an antigen fragment, and an antigen receptor is necessary for a T cell to participate in an adaptive immune response, as we'll see later.

B Cell and T Cell Development

Now that you know how B cells and T cells recognize antigens, let's consider four major characteristics of adaptive immunity. First, there is an immense diversity of lymphocytes and receptors, enabling the immune system to detect pathogens never before encountered. Second, adaptive immunity normally has self-tolerance, the lack of reactivity against an animal's own molecules and cells. Third, cell proliferation triggered by activation greatly increases the number of B and T cells specific for an antigen. Fourth, there is a stronger and more rapid response to an antigen encountered previously, due to a feature known as *immunological memory*.

Receptor diversity and self-tolerance arise as a lymphocyte matures. Proliferation of cells and the formation of

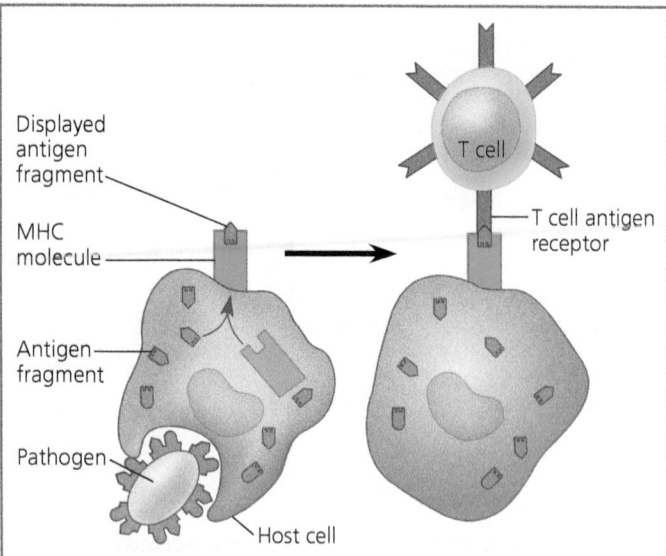

(a) Antigen recognition by a T cell. Inside the host cell, an antigen fragment from a pathogen binds to an MHC molecule and is brought up to the cell surface, where it is displayed. The combination of MHC molecule and antigen fragment is recognized by a T cell.

(b) A closer look at antigen presentation. As shown in this ribbon model, the top of the MHC molecule cradles an antigen fragment, like a bun holding a hot dog. An MHC molecule can display many different antigen fragments, but the antigen receptor of a T cell is specific for a single antigen fragment.

▲ Figure 43.12 **Antigen recognition by T cells.**

immunological memory occur later, after a mature lymphocyte encounters and binds to a specific antigen. We'll consider these four characteristics in the order in which they develop.

Generation of B Cell and T Cell Diversity

Each person makes more than 1 million different B cell antigen receptors and 10 million different T cell antigen receptors. Yet there are only about 20 000 protein-coding genes in the human genome. How, then, do we generate such remarkable diversity in antigen receptors? The answer lies in combinations. Think of selecting a car with a choice of three interior colours and six exterior colours. There are 18 (3 × 6) colour combinations to consider. Similarly, by combining variable elements, the immune system assembles many different receptors from a much smaller collection of parts.

To understand the origin of receptor diversity, let's consider an immunoglobulin (Ig) gene that encodes the light chain of both secreted antibodies (immunoglobulins) and membrane-bound B cell antigen receptors. Although we'll analyze only a single Ig light-chain gene, all B and T cell antigen receptor genes undergo very similar transformations.

The capacity to generate diversity is built into the structure of Ig genes. A receptor light chain is encoded by three gene segments: a variable (*V*) segment, a joining (*J*) segment, and a constant (*C*) segment. The *V* and *J* segments together encode the variable region of the receptor chain, while the *C* segment encodes the constant region. The light-chain gene contains a single *C* segment, 40 different *V* segments, and 5 different *J* segments. These alternative copies of the *V* and *J* segments are arranged within the gene in a series (Figure 43.13). Because a functional gene is built from one copy of each type of segment, the pieces can be combined in 200 different ways (40 *V* × 5 *J* × 1 *C*). The number of different heavy-chain combinations is even greater, resulting in even more diversity.

Assembling a functional Ig gene requires rearranging the DNA. Early in B cell development, an enzyme complex called *recombinase* links one light-chain *V* gene segment to one *J* gene segment. This recombination event eliminates the long stretch of DNA between the segments, forming a single exon that is part *V* and part *J*. Because there is only an intron between the *J* and *C* DNA segments, no further DNA rearrangement is required. Instead, the *J* and *C* segments of the RNA transcript will be joined when splicing removes the intervening RNA (see Figure 17.11 to review RNA splicing).

Recombinase acts randomly, linking any one of the 40 *V* gene segments to any one of the 5 *J* gene segments. Heavy-chain genes undergo a similar rearrangement. In any given cell, however, only one allele of a light-chain gene and one allele of a heavy-chain gene are rearranged. Furthermore, the rearrangements are permanent and are passed on to the daughter cells when the lymphocyte divides.

After both a light-chain and a heavy-chain gene have been rearranged, antigen receptors can be synthesized. The rearranged genes are transcribed, and the transcripts are processed for translation. Following translation, the light chain and heavy chain assemble together, forming an antigen receptor (see Figure 43.13). Each pair of randomly rearranged heavy and light chains results in a different antigen-binding site. For the total population of B cells in a human body, the number of such combinations has been calculated as 3.5×10^6. Furthermore, mutations introduced during *VJ* recombination add additional variation, making the number of possible antigen-binding specificities even greater.

Origin of Self-Tolerance

How does adaptive immunity distinguish self from nonself? Because antigen receptor genes are randomly rearranged,

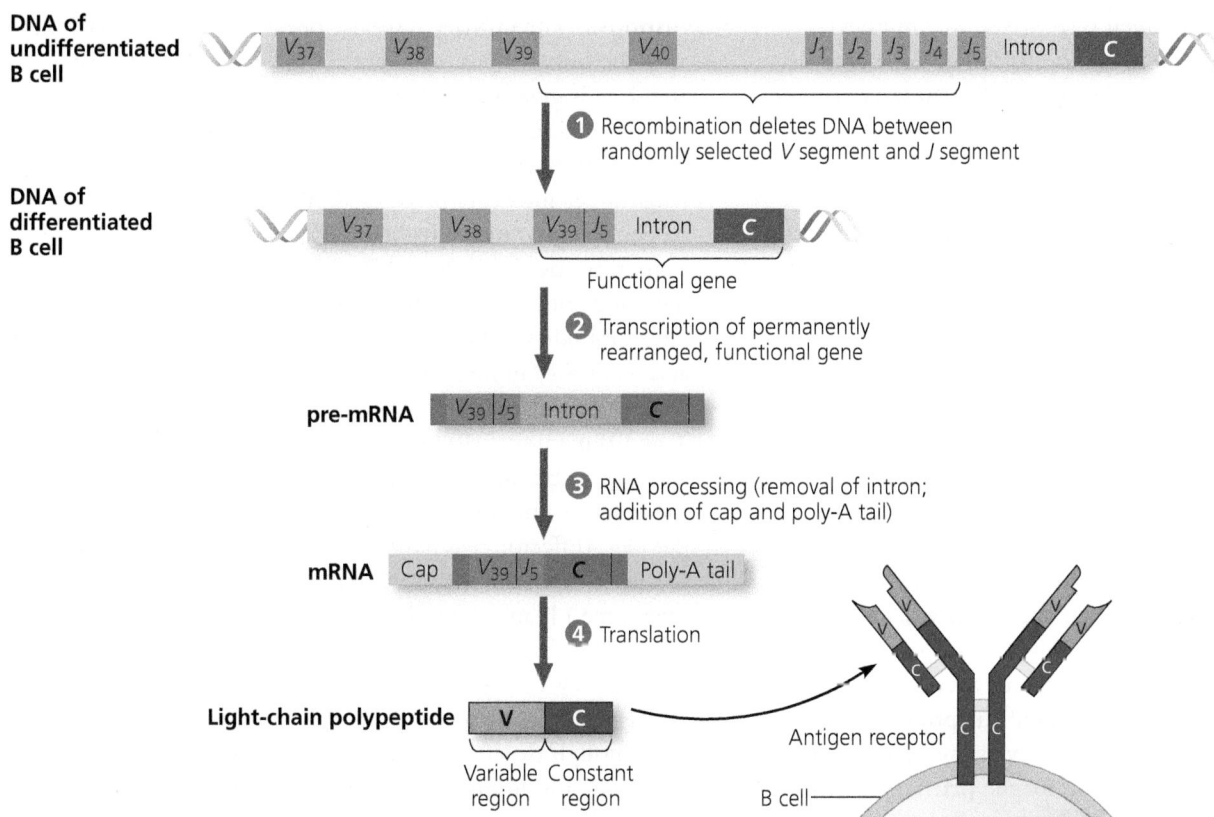

▲ Figure 43.13 **Immunoglobulin (antibody) gene rearrangement.** The joining of randomly selected *V* and *J* gene segments (V_{39} and J_5 in this example) results in a functional gene that encodes the light-chain polypeptide of a B cell antigen receptor. Transcription, splicing, and translation result in a light chain that combines with a polypeptide produced from an independently rearranged heavy-chain gene to form a functional receptor. Mature B cells (and T cells) are exceptions to the generalization that all nucleated cells in the body have exactly the same DNA.

MAKE CONNECTIONS *Both alternative splicing (see Figure 18.13) and joining of V and J segments by recombination generate diverse gene products from a limited set of gene segments. How do these processes differ?*

some immature lymphocytes produce receptors specific for epitopes on the organism's own molecules. If these self-reactive lymphocytes were not eliminated or inactivated, the immune system could not distinguish self from nonself and would attack body proteins, cells, and tissues. Instead, as lymphocytes mature in the bone marrow or thymus, their antigen receptors are tested for self-reactivity. Some B and T cells with receptors specific for the body's own molecules are destroyed by *apoptosis*, which is a programmed cell death (see Chapter 11). The remaining self-reactive lymphocytes are typically rendered nonfunctional, leaving only those that react to foreign molecules. Since the body normally lacks mature lymphocytes that can react against its own components, the immune system is said to exhibit *self-tolerance*.

Proliferation of B Cells and T Cells

Despite the enormous variety of antigen receptors, only a tiny fraction are specific for a given epitope. So how is adaptive immunity so effective? To begin with, an antigen is presented to a steady stream of lymphocytes in the lymph nodes (see Figure 43.7) until a match is made. A successful match then triggers changes in cell number and activity for the lymphocyte to which an antigen has bound.

The binding of an antigen receptor to an epitope initiates events that activate the lymphocyte. Once activated, a B cell or T cell undergoes multiple cell divisions. For each activated cell, the result of this proliferation is a clone, a population of cells that are identical to the original cell. Some cells from this clone become **effector cells**, short-lived cells that take effect immediately against the antigen and any pathogens producing that antigen. The effector forms of B cells are plasma cells, which secrete antibodies. The effector forms of T cells are helper T cells and cytotoxic T cells, whose roles we'll explore in Concept 43.3. The remaining cells in the clone become **memory cells**, long-lived cells that can give rise to effector cells if the same antigen is encountered later in the animal's life.

The proliferation of a B cell or T cell into a clone of cells occurs in response to a specific antigen and to immune cell signals. The process is called **clonal selection** because an encounter with an antigen selects which lymphocyte will divide to produce a clonal population of thousands of cells specific for a particular epitope. Cells that have antigen receptors specific for other antigens do not respond.

Figure 43.14 summarizes the process of clonal selection, using the example of B cells, which generate memory cells and plasma cells. When T cells undergo clonal selection, they generate memory T cells and effector T cells (cytotoxic T cells and helper T cells).

Immunological Memory

Immunological memory is responsible for the long-term protection that a prior infection or vaccination provides against many diseases, such as chickenpox. This type of protection was noted almost 2400 years ago by the Greek historian Thucydides. He observed that individuals who had recovered from the plague could safely care for those who were sick or dying, "for the same man was never attacked twice—never at least fatally."

Prior exposure to an antigen alters the speed, strength, and duration of the immune response. The production of effector cells from a clone of lymphocytes during the first exposure to an antigen is the basis for the **primary immune response**. The primary response peaks about 10–17 days after the initial exposure. During this time, selected B cells and T cells give rise to their effector forms. If an individual is exposed again to the same antigen, the response is faster (typically peaking only 2–7 days after exposure), of greater magnitude, and more prolonged. This is the **secondary immune response**, a hallmark of adaptive, or acquired, immunity. Because selected B cells give rise to antibody-secreting effector cells, measuring the concentrations of specific antibodies in blood over time distinguishes the primary and secondary immune responses (**Figure 43.15**).

The secondary immune response relies on the reservoir of T and B memory cells generated following initial exposure to an antigen. Because these cells are long-lived, they provide the basis for immunological memory, which can span many decades. (Effector cells have much shorter life spans, which is why the immune response diminishes after an infection is overcome.) If an antigen is encountered again, memory cells specific for that antigen enable the rapid formation of clones of thousands of effector cells also specific for that antigen, thus generating a greatly enhanced immune defence.

Although the processes for antigen recognition, clonal selection, and immunological memory are similar for B

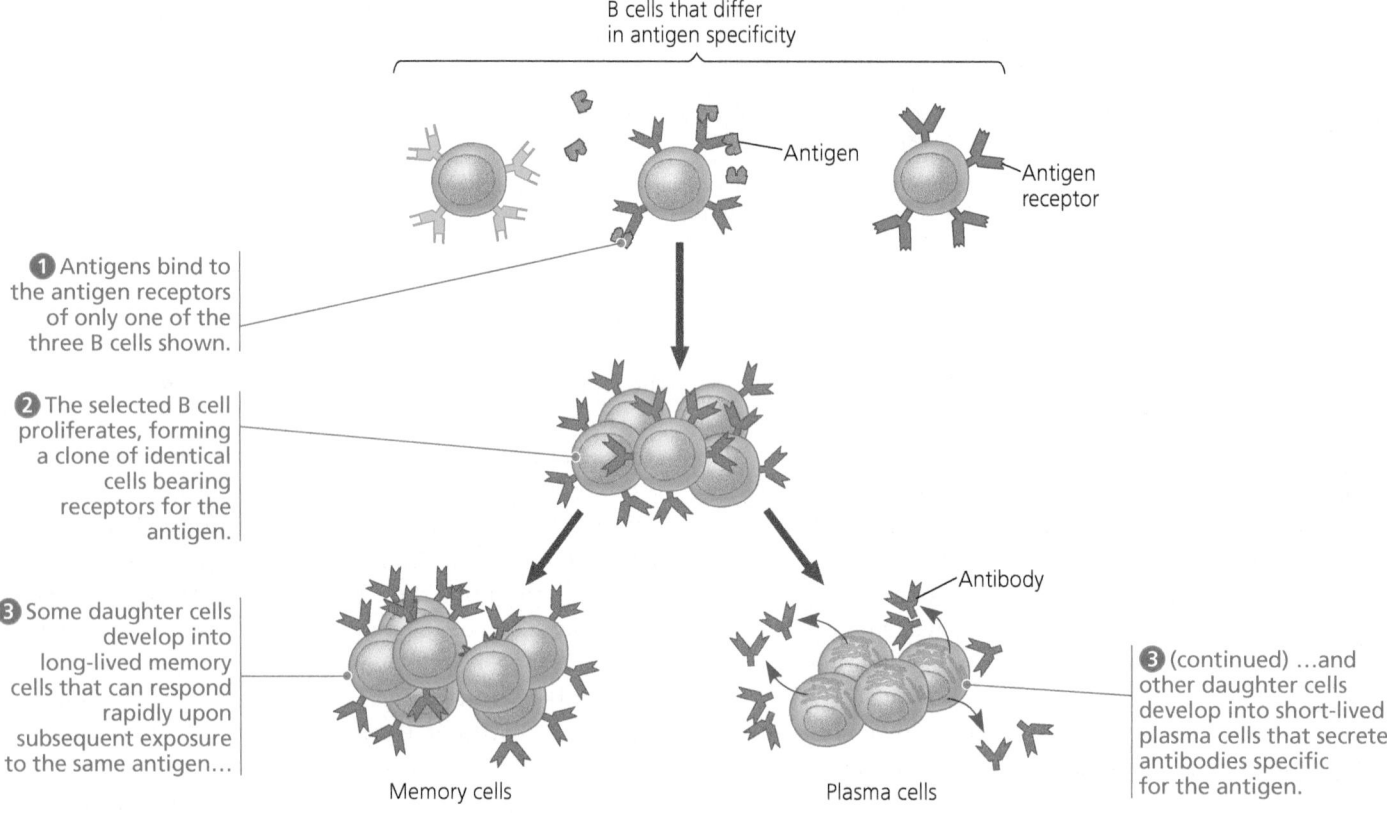

B cells that differ
in antigen specificity

Antigen

Antigen receptor

1 Antigens bind to the antigen receptors of only one of the three B cells shown.

2 The selected B cell proliferates, forming a clone of identical cells bearing receptors for the antigen.

3 Some daughter cells develop into long-lived memory cells that can respond rapidly upon subsequent exposure to the same antigen...

Antibody

3 (continued) ...and other daughter cells develop into short-lived plasma cells that secrete antibodies specific for the antigen.

Memory cells

Plasma cells

▲ **Figure 43.14 Clonal selection.** This figure illustrates clonal selection, using B cells as an example. In response to a specific antigen and to immune cell signals (not shown), one B cell divides and forms a clone of cells. The remaining B cells, which have antigen receptors specific for other antigens, do not respond. The clone of cells formed by the selected B cell gives rise to memory B cells and antibody-secreting plasma cells. T cells also undergo clonal selection, generating memory T cells and effector T cells (cytotoxic T cells and helper T cells).

Primary immune response to antigen A produces antibodies to A.

Secondary immune response to antigen A produces antibodies to A; **primary immune response** to antigen B produces antibodies to B.

Antibodies to A

Antibodies to B

Exposure to antigen A

Exposure to antigens A and B

Time (days)

▲ **Figure 43.15 The specificity of immunological memory.** Long-lived memory cells generated in the primary response to antigen A give rise to a heightened secondary response to the same antigen, but do not affect the primary response to a different antigen (B).

INTERPRET THE DATA *Assume that on average one out of every 10^5 B cells in the body is specific for antigen A on day 16 and that the number of B cells producing a specific antibody is proportional to the concentration of that antibody. What would you predict is the frequency of B cells specific for antigen A on day 36?*

cells and T cells, these two classes of lymphocytes fight infection in different ways and in different settings, as we'll explore next.

CONCEPT CHECK 43.2

1. **DRAW IT** Sketch a B cell antigen receptor. Label the *V* and *C* regions of the light and heavy chains. Label the antigen-binding sites, disulphide bridges, and transmembrane region. Where are these features located relative to the *V* and *C* regions?

2. Explain two advantages of having memory cells when a pathogen is encountered for a second time.

3. **WHAT IF?** If both copies of a light-chain gene and a heavy-chain gene recombined in each (diploid) B cell, how would this affect B cell development?

For suggested answers, see Appendix A.

CONCEPT 43.3

Adaptive immunity defends against infection of body fluids and body cells

Having considered how clones of lymphocytes arise, we now explore how these cells help fight infections and minimize damage by pathogens. The activities of B and T lymphocytes produce a humoral immune response and a cell-mediated immune response. The **humoral immune response** occurs in the blood and lymph, fluids that were long ago called body humours. In the humoral response, antibodies help neutralize or eliminate toxins and pathogens in the blood and lymph. In the **cell-mediated immune response**, specialized T cells destroy infected host cells. Both responses include a primary immune response and a secondary immune response, with memory cells enabling the secondary response. In addition to the lymphocytes (T cells and B cells), dendritic cells play an important role in adaptive immunity. Though they engulf bacteria and viruses as part of the innate immune response, these phagocytic cells break down the pathogen internally and export fragments of the invading cell to their own cell surface, where they act as antigens. An **antigen-presenting cell** thereby informs the adaptive immune system of the molecular nature of the pathogen it has encountered. For his work on dendritic cells, Canadian Ralph Steinman was awarded the 2011 Nobel Prize in Physiology or Medicine (**Figure 43.16**).

▼ Figure 43.16 | **Impact**

Discovery of Dendritic Cells

Ralph M. Steinman, born in Montreal in 1943, won the 2011 Nobel Prize in Physiology or Medicine, but unfortunately passed away only days before the announcement. After a B.Sc. at McGill (1963), Steinman entered Harvard Medical School, then joined Rockefeller Institute in 1970. Working much of his career at Rockefeller University, he was awarded the prize for the discovery of the dendritic cell and its role in adaptive immunity. After discovering dendritic cells with his collaborator, Z. A. Cohn, Steinman spent his career understanding their function and their role in immunity, as well as their implications for issues such as autoimmune disease, tumour biology, infections, tissue grafts, and transplants. The diverse functions of dendritic cells in innate and adaptive immunity is due to the fact that many distinct types of dendritic cells exist, specialized for different tasks and functional only in specific tissues.

Eye of Science/Science Source

Further Reading R. M. Steinman and J. Idoyaga, Features of the dendritic cell lineage, *Immunological Reviews* 234:5–17 (2010).

WHAT IF? *What would be the consequences if all the dendritic cells in your body lost their capacity to phagocytose pathogens?*

Helper T Cells: A Response to Nearly All Antigens

A type of T cell called a **helper T cell** triggers both the humoral and cell-mediated immune responses. Helper T cells themselves do not carry out those responses. Instead, signals from helper T cells initiate production of antibodies that neutralize pathogens and activate T cells that kill infected cells.

Two requirements must be met for a helper T cell to activate adaptive immune responses. First, a foreign molecule must be present that can bind specifically to the antigen receptor of the T cell. Second, this antigen must be displayed on the surface of an antigen-presenting cell. The antigen-presenting cell can be a dendritic cell, macrophage, or B cell.

When host cells are infected, they too display antigens on their surface. What then distinguishes an antigen-presenting cell? The answer lies in the existence of two classes of MHC molecules. Most body cells have only class I MHC molecules, but antigen-presenting cells have both class I and class II MHC molecules. The class II molecules provide a molecular signature by which an antigen-presenting cell is recognized.

A helper T cell and the antigen-presenting cell displaying its specific epitope have a complex interaction (Figure 43.17). The antigen receptors on the surface of the helper T cell bind to the antigen fragment and to the class II MHC molecule displaying that fragment on the antigen-presenting cell. At the same time, an accessory protein called CD4 on the helper T cell surface binds to the class II MHC molecule, helping keep the cells joined. As the two cells interact, signals in the form of cytokines are exchanged. For example, the cytokines secreted from a dendritic cell act in combination with the antigen to stimulate the helper T cell, causing it to produce its own set of cytokines. Also, extensive contact between the cell surfaces enables further information exchange.

The different types of antigen-presenting cells interact with helper T cells in distinct contexts. Antigen presentation by a dendritic cell or macrophage activates a helper T cell. The helper T cell then proliferates, forming a clone of activated helper T cells. The B cells present antigens to *already* activated helper T cells, which in turn activate the B cells themselves. Activated helper T cells also help stimulate cytotoxic T cells, as we'll discuss next.

Cytotoxic T Cells: A Response to Infected Cells

In the cell-mediated immune response, **cytotoxic T cells** are the effector cells. The term *cytotoxic* refers to their use of toxic gene products to kill infected cells. To become active, they require signalling molecules from helper T cells as well as interaction with a cell that presents an antigen. Once activated, cytotoxic T cells can eliminate cells that are infected by viruses or other intracellular pathogens.

Fragments of foreign proteins produced in infected host cells associate with class I MHC molecules and are displayed

① An antigen-presenting cell engulfs a pathogen, degrades it, and displays antigen fragments complexed with class II MHC molecules on the cell surface. A specific helper T cell binds to this complex via its antigen receptor and an accessory protein (called CD4).

② Binding of the helper T cell promotes secretion of cytokines by the antigen-presenting cell. These cytokines, along with cytokines from the helper T cell itself, activate the helper T cell and stimulate its proliferation.

③ Cell proliferation produces a clone of activated helper T cells. All cells in the clone have receptors for the same antigen fragment complex with the same antigen specificity. These cells secrete other cytokines, which help activate B cells and cytotoxic T cells.

▲ Figure 43.17 **The central role of helper T cells in humoral and cell-mediated immune responses.** In this example, a helper T cell responds to a dendritic cell displaying a microbial antigen.

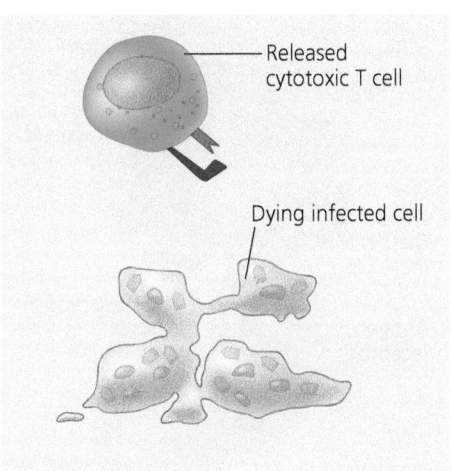

1 An activated cytotoxic T cell binds to a class I MHC–antigen fragment complex on an infected cell via its antigen receptor and an accessory protein (called CD8).

2 The T cell releases perforin molecules, which form pores in the infected cell membrane, and granzymes, enzymes that break down proteins. Granzymes enter the infected cell by endocytosis.

3 The granzymes initiate apoptosis within the infected cell, leading to fragmentation of the nucleus and cytoplasm and eventual cell death. The released cytotoxic T cell can attack other infected cells.

▲ **Figure 43.18 The killing action of cytotoxic T cells on an infected host cell.** An activated cytotoxic T cell releases molecules that make pores in an infected cell's membrane and enzymes that break down proteins, promoting the cell's death.

on the cell surface, where they can be recognized by cytotoxic T cells (**Figure 43.18**). As with helper T cells, cytotoxic T cells have an accessory protein that binds to the MHC molecule. This accessory protein, called CD8, helps keep the two cells in contact while the cytotoxic T cell is activated.

The targeted destruction of an infected host cell by a cytotoxic T cell involves the secretion of proteins that disrupt membrane integrity and trigger apoptosis (see Figure 43.18). The death of the infected cell not only deprives the pathogen of a place to reproduce, but also exposes cell contents to circulating antibodies, which mark them for disposal. After destroying an infected cell, the cytotoxic T cell can move on and kill other cells infected with the same pathogen.

B Cells and Antibodies: A Response to Extracellular Pathogens

The secretion of antibodies by clonally selected B cells is the hallmark of the humoral immune response. We'll explore how B cells become activated before investigating how antibodies function.

Activation of B Cells

Activation of the humoral immune response typically involves B cells and helper T cells as well as proteins on the surface of pathogens. As depicted in **Figure 43.19**, B cell activation by an antigen is aided by cytokines secreted from helper T cells that have encountered the same antigen. Stimulated by both an antigen and cytokines, the B

cell proliferates and differentiates into memory B cells and antibody-secreting effector cells called **plasma cells**.

The pathway for antigen processing and display in B cells differs from that in other antigen-presenting cells. A macrophage or dendritic cell can present fragments from a wide variety of protein antigens, whereas a B cell presents only the antigen to which it specifically binds. When an antigen first binds to receptors on the surface of a B cell, the cell takes in a few foreign molecules by receptor-mediated endocytosis (see Figure 7.19). The class II MHC protein of the B cell then presents an antigen fragment to a helper T cell. This direct cell-to-cell contact is usually critical to B cell activation (see step 2 in Figure 43.19).

B cell activation leads to a robust humoral immune response: An activated B cell gives rise to thousands of identical plasma cells. These plasma cells stop expressing a membrane-bound antigen receptor and begin producing and secreting antibodies (see step 3 in Figure 43.19). Each plasma cell secretes approximately 2000 antibodies every second of the cell's 4- to 5-day life span. Furthermore, most antigens recognized by B cells contain multiple epitopes. An exposure to a single antigen therefore normally activates a variety of B cells, with different plasma cells producing antibodies directed against different epitopes on the common antigen.

Antibody Function

Antibodies do not kill pathogens, but by binding to antigens, they mark pathogens in various ways for inactivation or destruction. In the simplest of these activities,

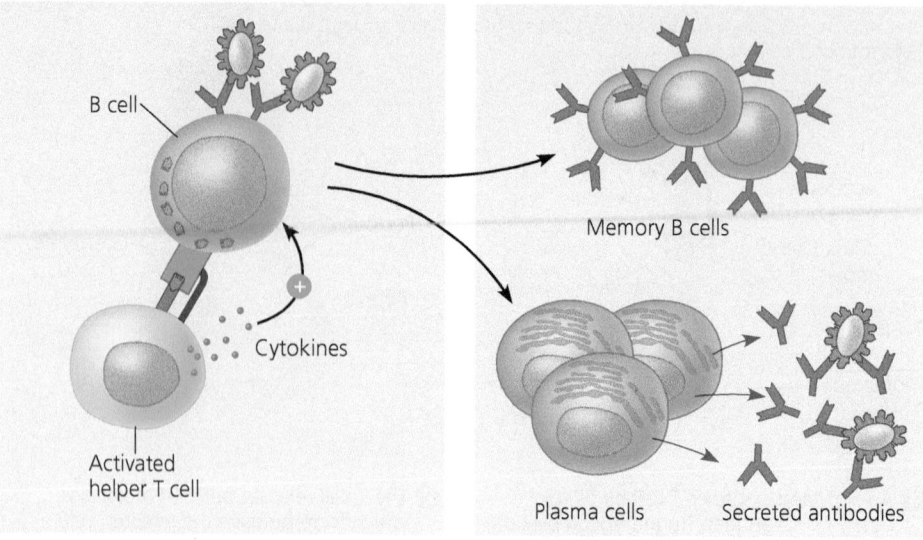

① After an antigen-presenting cell engulfs and degrades a pathogen, it displays an antigen fragment complexed with a class II MHC molecule. A helper T cell that recognizes the complex is activated with the aid of cytokines secreted from the antigen-presenting cell.

② When a B cell with receptors for the same epitope internalizes the antigen, it displays an antigen fragment on the cell surface in a complex with a class II MHC molecule. An activated helper T cell bearing receptors specific for the displayed fragment binds to and activates the B cell.

③ The activated B cell proliferates and differentiates into memory B cells and antibody-secreting plasma cells. The secreted antibodies are specific for the same antigen that initiated the response.

▲ **Figure 43.19 Activation of a B cell in the humoral immune response.** Most protein antigens require activated helper T cells to trigger a humoral response. A macrophage (shown here) or a dendritic cell can activate a helper T cell, which in turn can activate a B cell to give rise to antibody-secreting plasma cells.

? *What function do cell-surface antigen receptors play for memory B cells?*

neutralization, antibodies bind to viral surface proteins (Figure 43.20a). The bound antibodies prevent infection of a host cell, thus neutralizing the virus. Similarly, antibodies sometimes bind to toxins released in body fluids, preventing the toxins from entering body cells. In another process, called *opsonization*, antibodies bound to antigens on bacteria present a readily recognized structure for macrophages or neutrophils and therefore increase phagocytosis (Figure 43.20b). Because each antibody has two antigen-binding sites, antibodies sometimes also facilitate phagocytosis by linking bacterial cells, virus particles, or other foreign substances into aggregates.

Antibodies sometimes work together with the proteins of the complement system to dispose of pathogens. (The name *complement* reflects the fact that these proteins increase the effectiveness of antibody-directed attacks on bacteria.) Binding of a complement protein to an antigen-antibody complex on a foreign cell (or an enveloped virus) triggers a cascade in which each protein of the complement system activates the next protein. Ultimately, activated complement proteins generate a *membrane attack complex* that forms a pore in the membrane of the foreign cell. Ions and water rush into the cell, causing it to swell and lyse (Figure 43.20c). Whether activated as part of innate defences or as part of adaptive defences, this cascade of complement protein

activity results in the lysis of foreign cells and produces factors that promote inflammation or stimulate phagocytosis.

When antibodies facilitate phagocytosis (see Figure 43.20b), they also help fine-tune the humoral immune response. Recall that phagocytosis enables macrophages and dendritic cells to present antigens to and stimulate helper T cells, which in turn stimulate the very B cells whose antibodies contribute to phagocytosis. This positive feedback between innate and adaptive immunity contributes to a coordinated, effective response to infection.

Although antibodies are the cornerstone of the response in body fluids, there is also a mechanism by which they can bring about the death of infected body cells. When a virus uses a cell's biosynthetic machinery to produce viral proteins, these viral products can appear on the cell surface. If antibodies specific for epitopes on these viral proteins bind to the exposed proteins, the presence of bound antibody at the cell surface can recruit a natural killer cell. The natural killer cell then releases proteins that cause the infected cell to undergo apoptosis.

B cells can express five types, or classes, of immunoglobulin (IgA, IgD, IgE, IgG, and IgM). For a given B cell, each *class* has an identical antigen-binding specificity, but a distinct heavy-chain *C* region. The B cell antigen receptor,

(a) Neutralization

Antibody

Virus

Antibodies bound to antigens on the surface of a virus neutralize it by blocking its ability to bind to a host cell.

(b) Opsonization

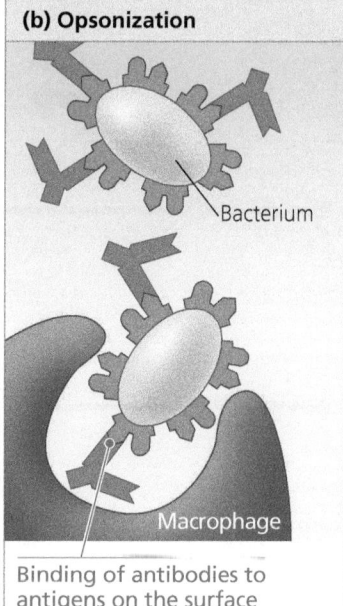

Bacterium

Macrophage

Binding of antibodies to antigens on the surface of bacteria promotes phagocytosis by macrophages and neutrophils.

(c) Activation of complement system and pore formation

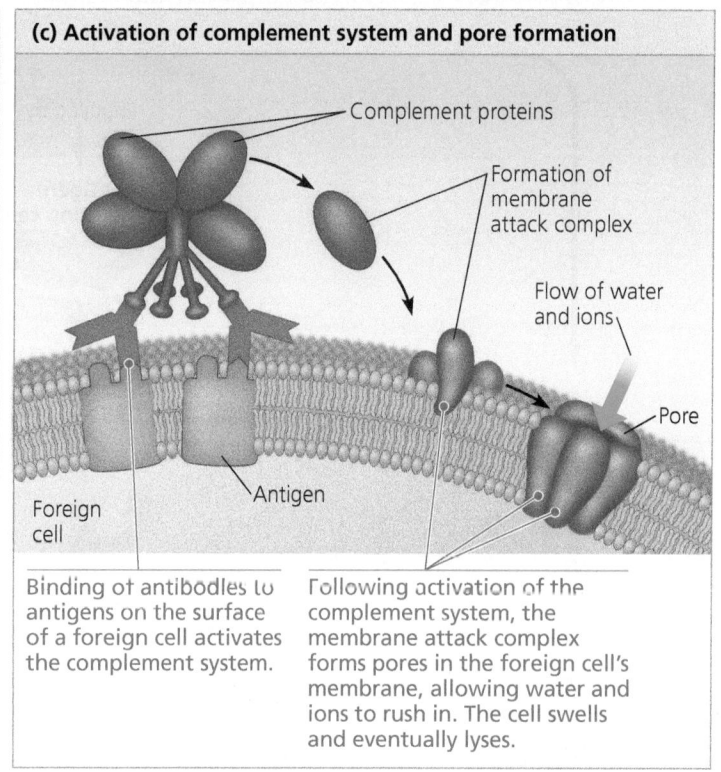

Complement proteins

Formation of membrane attack complex

Flow of water and ions

Pore

Foreign cell

Antigen

Binding of antibodies to antigens on the surface of a foreign cell activates the complement system.

Following activation of the complement system, the membrane attack complex forms pores in the foreign cell's membrane, allowing water and ions to rush in. The cell swells and eventually lyses.

known as IgD, is membrane bound. The other four classes consist of soluble antibodies, including those found in blood, tears, saliva, and breast milk.

Summary of the Humoral and Cell-Mediated Immune Responses

As noted earlier, both the humoral and cell-mediated responses can include primary and secondary immune responses. Memory cells of each type—helper T cell, B cell, and cytotoxic T cell—enable the secondary response. For example, when body fluids are reinfected by a pathogen encountered previously, memory B cells and memory helper T cells initiate a secondary humoral response. Figure 43.21 reviews the events that initiate humoral and cell-mediated immune responses, highlights the central role of the helper T cell, and serves as a helpful summary of adaptive immunity.

Active and Passive Immunization

Our discussion of adaptive immunity has to this point focused on **active immunity**, the defences that arise when a pathogen infects the body and prompts a primary or secondary immune response. In contrast, a different type of immunity results when the IgG antibodies in the blood of a pregnant female cross the placenta to her fetus. The transferred antibodies can immediately react with any pathogens for which they are specific. This protection is called **passive immunity** because the antibodies in the recipient (in this case, the fetus) are produced by another individual (the mother). IgA antibodies present in breast milk provide additional passive immunity to the infant's digestive tract while the infant's immune system develops. Because passive immunity does not involve the recipient's B and T cells, it persists only as long as the transferred antibodies last (a few weeks to a few months).

Both active immunity and passive immunity can be induced artificially. Active immunity can develop from the introduction of antigens into the body through **immunization**. In 1796, Edward Jenner noted that milkmaids who had cowpox, a mild disease usually seen only in cows, did not contract smallpox, a far more dangerous disease. In the first documented immunization (or **vaccination**, from the Latin *vacca,* cow), Jenner used the cowpox virus to induce adaptive immunity against the closely related smallpox virus. Today, many sources of antigen are used to make vaccines, including inactivated bacterial toxins, killed pathogens, parts of pathogens, weakened pathogens that generally do not cause illness, and even genes encoding microbial proteins. There is also a growing use of vaccines to promote the ability of immune cells to detect cancers by targeting tumour-specific proteins. Because all of these agents induce a primary immune response and immunological memory, an encounter with the pathogen from which

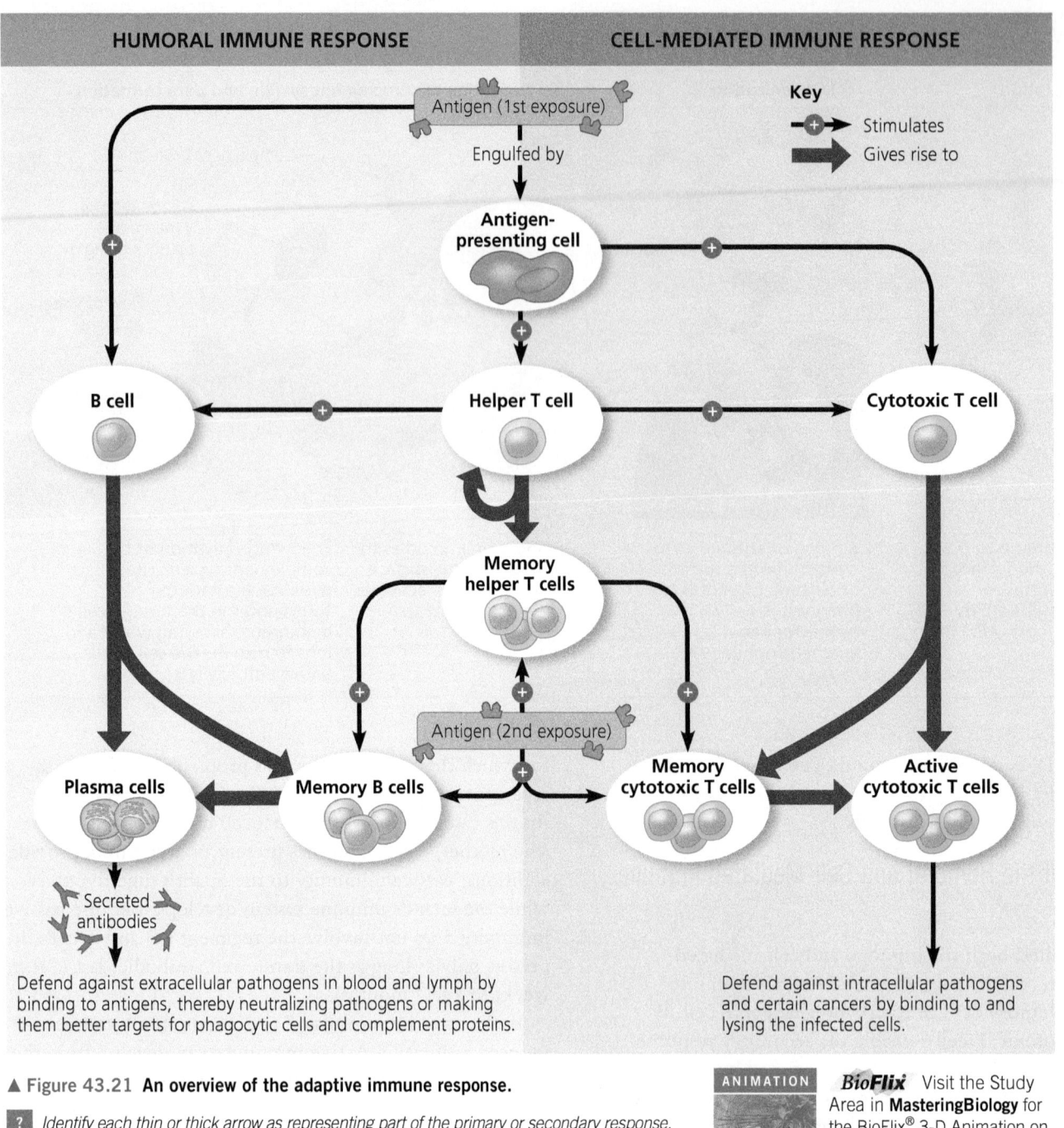

HUMORAL IMMUNE RESPONSE

CELL-MEDIATED IMMUNE RESPONSE

Antigen (1st exposure)

Key

+→ Stimulates

⇒ Gives rise to

Engulfed by

Antigen-presenting cell

B cell

Helper T cell

Cytotoxic T cell

Memory helper T cells

Antigen (2nd exposure)

Plasma cells

Memory B cells

Memory cytotoxic T cells

Active cytotoxic T cells

Secreted antibodies

Defend against extracellular pathogens in blood and lymph by binding to antigens, thereby neutralizing pathogens or making them better targets for phagocytic cells and complement proteins.

Defend against intracellular pathogens and certain cancers by binding to and lysing the infected cells.

▲ Figure 43.21 **An overview of the adaptive immune response.**

? *Identify each thin or thick arrow as representing part of the primary or secondary response.*

ANIMATION *BioFlix* Visit the Study Area in **MasteringBiology** for the BioFlix® 3-D Animation on Immunology.

the vaccine was derived triggers a rapid and strong secondary immune response (see Figure 43.15).

Vaccination programs have been successful against many infectious diseases that once killed or incapacitated large numbers of people. A worldwide vaccination campaign led to eradication of smallpox in the late 1970s. In industrialized nations, routine active immunization of infants and children has dramatically reduced the incidence of sometimes devastating diseases, such as polio, measles, and whooping cough. Unfortunately, not all pathogens are easily managed by vaccination. Furthermore, some

vaccines are not readily available in impoverished areas of the globe.

Misinformation about vaccine safety and disease risk has led some parents to refuse to immunize their children with available, effective vaccines. The consequence has been a substantial and growing public health problem. Consider measles as just one example. Side effects of immunization are remarkably rare: Fewer than one in a million children suffers a significant allergic reaction to the measles vaccine. The disease, however, is quite dangerous: Roughly one out of every 1000 patients develop *encephalitis*, an inflammation of the brain. Worldwide, measles affects more than 1 million people annually. Measles vaccinations are routine in most of the developed world, but in many countries the immunization rate has declined in recent years. From 2002 to 2007, there were an average of 11 cases in Canada each year; since then, the average has increased almost eight-fold. Deaths from measles in Canada remain uncommon, but can be expected to become more frequent as the rate of vaccinations declines.

In artificial passive immunization, antibodies from an immune animal are injected into a nonimmune animal. For example, humans bitten by venomous snakes are sometimes treated with antivenin, antibodies from sheep or horses that have been immunized against the venom of one or more species of venomous snakes. When injected immediately after a snakebite, the antibodies in antivenin can inactivate toxins in the venom before the toxins do massive damage.

Antibodies as Tools

The power of antibody specificity and antigen–antibody binding has been harnessed in research, diagnosis, and therapy. Some antibody tools are *polyclonal*: They are the products of many different clones of plasma cells, each specific for a different epitope (**Figure 43.22**). Antibodies that an animal produces after exposure to a microbial antigen are polyclonal. In contrast, other antibody tools are *monoclonal*: They are prepared from a single clone of B cells grown in culture. The **monoclonal antibodies** produced by such a culture are identical and specific for the same epitope on an antigen.

Monoclonal antibodies have provided the basis for many recent advances in medical diagnosis and treatment. For example, home pregnancy test kits use monoclonal antibodies to detect human chorionic gonadotropin (hCG). Because hCG is produced as soon as an embryo implants

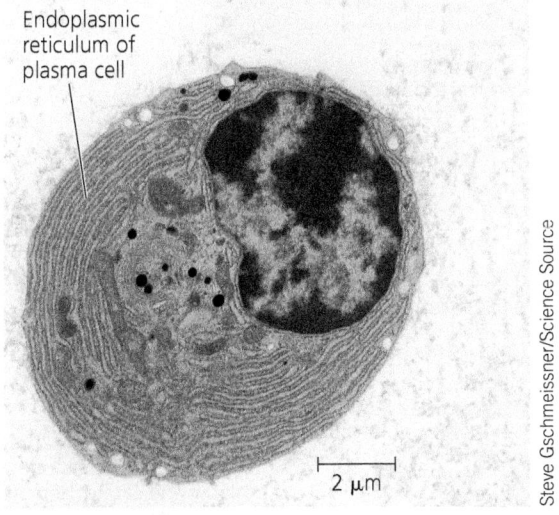

Endoplasmic reticulum of plasma cell

2 μm

Steve Gschmeissner/Science Source

▲ **Figure 43.22 A plasma cell.** A plasma cell contains abundant endoplasmic reticulum, a common feature of cells dedicated to making proteins for secretion (TEM).

in the uterus (see Chapter 46), the presence of this hormone in a woman's urine is a reliable indicator for a very early stage of pregnancy. Monoclonal antibodies are also produced in large amounts and injected as a therapy for a number of human diseases, including certain cancers.

Immune Rejection

Like pathogens, cells from another person can be recognized as foreign and attacked by immune defences. For example, skin transplanted from one person to a genetically nonidentical person will look healthy for a week or so but will then be destroyed (rejected) by the recipient's immune response. Keep in mind that the body's rejection of transplanted tissues or organs or of an incompatible blood transfusion is the expected reaction of a healthy immune system exposed to foreign antigens. (It remains a largely unanswered question why a pregnant woman does not reject her fetus as nonself tissue.)

Blood Groups

To avoid a blood transfusion being recognized as foreign by the recipient's immune system, the ABO blood groups of the donor and recipient must be taken into account. As discussed in Chapter 14, red blood cells are designated as type A if they have the type A carbohydrate on their surface. Similarly, the type B carbohydrate is found on type B red blood cells; both A and B carbohydrates are found on type AB red blood cells; and neither carbohydrate is found on type O red blood cells (see Figure 14.11).

To understand how ABO blood groups affect transfusions, let's consider the immune response of someone with type A blood. Early in development, cells producing antibodies for normal "self" proteins are destroyed, leaving those antibodies that target only nonself proteins. A person with A type cells has antibodies against the B type carbohydrate, so can only receive blood from those who lack the B type antigen (A or O types). They can only donate blood to those lack A type antigens (A or AB types). As O type possesses neither antigen, they can donate blood to anyone. As AB type has both antigens (and lacks antibodies to both antigens), they can receive blood from people of any blood type. If someone receives blood from an incompatible donor, that person's antibodies would cause an immediate and devastating reaction. The transfused red blood cells undergo lysis, which can lead to chills, fever, shock, and kidney malfunction.

Tissue and Organ Transplants

In the case of tissue and organ transplants, or grafts, MHC molecules stimulate the immune response that leads to rejection. Each vertebrate species has many alleles for each MHC gene, enabling presentation of antigen fragments that vary in shape and net electrical charge. This diversity of MHC molecules almost guarantees that no two people, except identical twins, will have exactly the same set. Thus, in the vast majority of graft and transplant recipients, some MHC molecules on the donated tissue are foreign to the recipient. To minimize rejection, physicians use donor tissue bearing MHC molecules that match those of the recipient as closely as possible. In addition, the recipient takes medicines that suppress immune responses (but as a result leave the recipient more susceptible to infections).

Transplants of bone marrow from one person to another can also cause an immune reaction, but for a different reason. Bone marrow transplants are used to treat leukemia and other cancers as well as various hematological (blood cell) diseases. Prior to receiving transplanted bone marrow, the recipient is typically treated with radiation to eliminate his or her own bone marrow cells, thus destroying the source of abnormal cells. This treatment effectively obliterates the recipient's immune system, leaving little chance of graft rejection. However, lymphocytes in the donated marrow may react against the recipient. This *graft versus host reaction* is limited if the MHC molecules of the donor and recipient are well matched. Bone marrow donor programs continually seek volunteers because the great variability of MHC molecules makes a diverse pool of donors essential.

CONCEPT CHECK 43.3

1. If a child were born without a thymus, what cells and functions would be deficient? Explain.

2. Treatment of antibodies with a particular protease clips the heavy chains in half, releasing the two arms of the Y-shaped molecule. How might the antibodies continue to function?

3. **WHAT IF?** Suppose that a snake handler bitten by a particular venomous snake species was treated with antivenin. Why might the same treatment for a second such bite have different results?

For suggested answers, see Appendix A.

CONCEPT 43.4

Disruptions in immune system function can elicit or exacerbate disease

Although adaptive immunity offers significant protection against a wide range of pathogens, it is not fail-safe. In this last section of the chapter, we'll first examine the problems that arise when adaptive immunity is blocked or misregulated. We'll then turn to some of the evolutionary adaptations of pathogens that diminish the effectiveness of host immune responses.

Exaggerated, Self-Directed, and Diminished Immune Responses

The highly regulated interplay among lymphocytes, other body cells, and foreign substances generates an immune response that provides extraordinary protection against many pathogens. For example, recent studies have shown that vertebrates possess a type of T cell that suppresses immune response. These regulatory T cells (Treg) are thought to be important in preventing the immune system from attacking self cells. When allergic, autoimmune, or immunodeficiency disorders disrupt this delicate balance, the effects are frequently severe and sometimes life-threatening.

Allergies

Allergies are exaggerated (hypersensitive) responses to certain antigens called **allergens**. The most common allergies involve antibodies of the IgE class. Hay fever, for instance, occurs when plasma cells secrete IgE antibodies specific for antigens on the surface of pollen grains (Figure 43.23). Some IgE antibodies attach by their base to mast cells in connective tissues. Pollen grains that enter the body later attach to the antigen-binding sites of these IgE antibodies. This attachment links adjacent IgE molecules, inducing the mast cell to release histamine and other inflammatory chemicals from granules (vesicles). Acting on a variety of cell types, these signals bring about the typical allergy symptoms: sneezing, runny nose, teary eyes, and smooth muscle contractions that can result in breathing difficulty. Drugs called antihistamines diminish allergy symptoms (and inflammation) by blocking receptors for histamine. An acute allergic response sometimes leads to *anaphylactic shock*, a

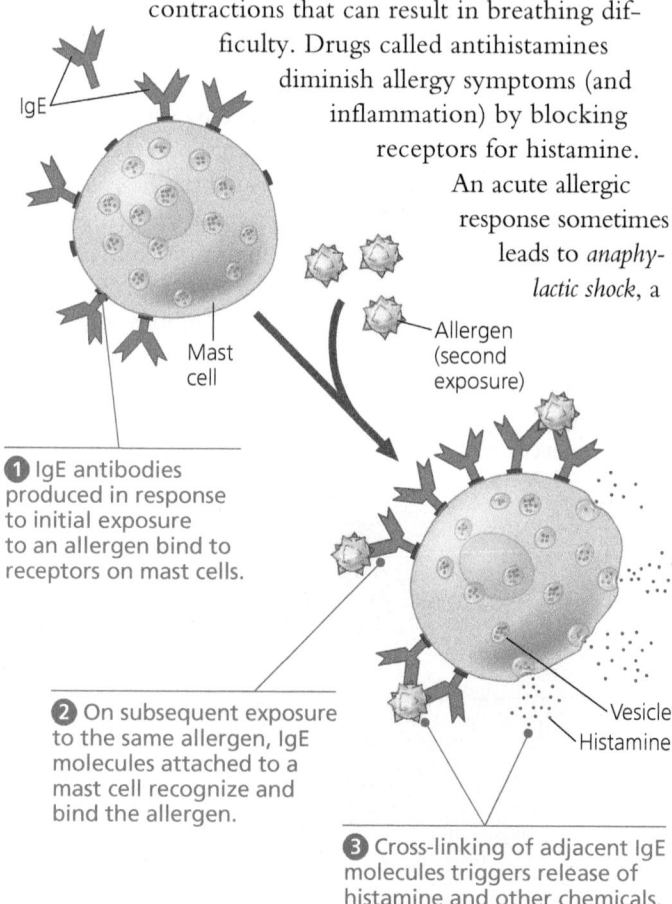

1 IgE antibodies produced in response to initial exposure to an allergen bind to receptors on mast cells.

IgE

Mast cell

Allergen (second exposure)

2 On subsequent exposure to the same allergen, IgE molecules attached to a mast cell recognize and bind the allergen.

Vesicle

Histamine

3 Cross-linking of adjacent IgE molecules triggers release of histamine and other chemicals, leading to allergy symptoms.

▲ Figure 43.23 **Mast cells, IgE, and the allergic response.** In this example, pollen grains act as the allergen.

whole-body, life-threatening reaction that can occur within seconds of exposure to an allergen. Anaphylactic shock develops when widespread release of mast cell contents triggers abrupt dilation of peripheral blood vessels, causing a precipitous drop in blood pressure, as well as constriction of bronchioles. Death may occur within minutes due to lack of blood flow and the inability to breathe. Allergic responses to bee venom or penicillin can lead to anaphylactic shock in people who are extremely allergic to these substances. Likewise, people very allergic to peanuts, fish, or shellfish can die from ingesting only tiny amounts of these allergens, which trigger reactions through interactions with mast cells on the surface of the digestive tract. People with severe hypersensitivities often carry syringes containing the hormone epinephrine, which counteracts this allergic response.

Autoimmune Diseases

In some people, the immune system is active against particular molecules of the body, causing an **autoimmune disease**. Such a loss of self-tolerance has many forms. In *systemic lupus erythematosus*, commonly called *lupus*, the immune system generates antibodies against histones and DNA released by the normal breakdown of body cells. These self-reactive antibodies cause skin rashes, fever, arthritis, and kidney dysfunction. Another autoimmune disease, *rheumatoid arthritis*, leads to damage and painful inflammation of the cartilage and bone of joints (Figure 43.24). In *type 1 diabetes mellitus*, the insulin-producing beta cells of the pancreas are the targets of autoimmune cytotoxic T cells. The most common chronic neurological disorder in developed countries is the autoimmune disease *multiple sclerosis*. In this disease, T cells infiltrate the central nervous system. The result is destruction of the myelin sheath that surrounds parts of many neurons (see Figure 48.12), leading to muscle paralysis through a disruption in neuron function.

Heredity, gender, and environment all influence susceptibility to autoimmune disorders. For example, members of certain families show an increased susceptibility to particular autoimmune disorders. In addition, many autoimmune diseases afflict females more often than males. Women are two to three times more likely than men to suffer from multiple sclerosis and rheumatoid arthritis and nine times more likely to develop lupus. The cause of this sex bias, as well as the rise in autoimmune disease frequency in industrialized countries, is an area

▲ Figure 43.24 **X-ray of hands deformed by rheumatoid arthritis.**

of active research and debate. Clearly, much remains to be learned about these often devastating disorders.

Exertion, Stress, and the Immune System

Many forms of exertion and stress influence immune system function. Consider, for example, susceptibility to the common cold and other infections of the upper respiratory tract. Moderate exercise improves immune system function and significantly reduces the risk of these infections. In contrast, exercise to the point of exhaustion leads to more frequent infections and to more severe symptoms. Studies of marathon runners support the conclusion that exercise intensity is the critical variable. On average, such runners get sick less often than their more sedentary peers during training, a time of moderate exertion, but have a marked increase in illness in the period immediately following the gruelling race itself. Similarly, psychological stress has been shown to disrupt immune system regulation by altering the interplay of the hormonal, nervous, and immune systems (see Figure 45.23) Recent research also confirms that rest is important for immunity: Adults who averaged fewer than 7 hours of sleep a night got sick three times as often when exposed to a cold virus as individuals who averaged at least 8 hours of sleep.

Immunodeficiency Diseases

A disorder in which an immune system response to antigens is defective or absent is called an **immunodeficiency**. An *inborn immunodeficiency* results from a genetic or developmental defect in the immune system. An *acquired immunodeficiency* develops later in life following exposure to chemical or biological agents. Whatever its cause and nature, an immunodeficiency can lead to frequent and recurrent infections and increased susceptibility to certain cancers.

Inborn immunodeficiencies result from defects in the development of various immune system cells or defects in the production of specific proteins, such as antibodies or the proteins of the complement system. Depending on the specific genetic defect, either innate or adaptive defences—or both—may be impaired. In severe combined immunodeficiency (SCID), functional lymphocytes are rare or absent. Lacking an adaptive immune response, SCID patients are susceptible to infections, such as pneumonia and meningitis, that can cause death in infancy. Treatments include bone marrow and stem cell transplantation.

Exposure to certain agents can cause immunodeficiencies that develop later in life. Drugs used to fight autoimmune diseases or prevent transplant rejection suppress the immune system, leading to an immunodeficient state. Certain cancers also suppress the immune system, especially Hodgkin's disease, which damages the lymphatic system. Acquired immunodeficiencies range from temporary states that may arise from physiological stress to the devastating

acquired immunodeficiency syndrome (AIDS), which is caused by the human immunodeficiency virus (HIV). We will discuss AIDS further in the next section, which focuses on how pathogens escape the adaptive immune response.

Evolutionary Adaptations of Pathogens That Underlie Immune System Avoidance

EVOLUTION Just as immune systems that ward off pathogens have evolved in animals, mechanisms that thwart immune responses have evolved in pathogens. Using human pathogens as examples, we'll examine some common mechanisms: antigenic variation, latency, and direct attack on the immune system.

Antigenic Variation

One mechanism for escaping the body's defences is for a pathogen to alter how it appears to the immune system. Immunological memory is a record of the foreign epitopes an animal has encountered. If the pathogen that expressed those epitopes no longer does so, it can reinfect or remain in a host without triggering the rapid and robust response that memory cells provide. Such changes in epitope expression, which are called *antigenic variation*, are regular events for some viruses and parasites. The parasite that causes sleeping sickness (trypanosomiasis) provides an extreme example, periodically switching at random among 1000 different versions of the protein found over its entire surface. In the Scientific Skills Exercise, you'll interpret data on this form of antigenic variation and the body's response.

Antigenic variation is the major reason the influenza, or "flu," virus remains a major public health problem. As it replicates in one human host after another, the human influenza virus mutates. Because any change that lessens recognition by the immune system provides a selective advantage, the virus steadily accumulates such alterations. These changes in the surface proteins of the influenza virus are the reason that a new flu vaccine must be manufactured and distributed each year. Of much greater danger, however, is the fact that the human virus occasionally exchanges genes with influenza viruses that infect domesticated animals, such as pigs or chickens. When this occurs, influenza can take on such a radically different appearance that none of the memory cells in the human population recognize the new strain. Such an event led to the influenza outbreak of 1918–1919, which killed more than 50 000 Canadians. Worldwide more than 20 million people died, a greater number than had died in World War I.

In 2009, an influenza virus called H1N1 appeared that contained a novel combination of genes from flu viruses that normally circulate in pigs, birds, and humans. The rapid spread of this flu across the human population caused a *pandemic*, an outbreak of worldwide proportions. Fortunately, a rapidly developed H1N1 vaccine soon provided public health officials with an excellent means of slowing the spread of this virus and reducing the impact of the outbreak.

Latency

After infecting a host, some viruses enter a largely inactive state called *latency*. Because such dormant viruses cease making most viral proteins and typically produce no free virus particles, they do not trigger an adaptive immune response. Nevertheless, the viral genome persists in the nuclei of infected cells, either as a separate small DNA molecule or as a copy integrated into the host genome. Latency typically persists until conditions arise that are favourable for viral transmission or unfavourable for host survival, such as when the host is infected by another pathogen. Such circumstances trigger the synthesis and release of virus particles that can infect new hosts.

Herpes simplex viruses, which establish themselves in human sensory neurons, provide a good example of latency. The type 1 virus causes most oral herpes infections, whereas the type 2 virus is responsible for most cases of genital herpes. Because sensory neurons express relatively few MHC I molecules, the infected cells are inefficient at presenting viral antigens to circulating lymphocytes. Stimuli such as fever, emotional stress, or menstruation reactivate the virus to reproduce and infect surrounding epithelial tissues. Activation of the type 1 virus can result in blisters around the mouth that are inaccurately called "cold" sores. The type 2 virus can cause genital sores, but people infected with either type 1 or type 2 virus often lack any apparent symptoms. Infections of the type 2 virus, which is sexually transmitted, pose a serious threat to the babies of infected mothers and can increase transmission of HIV, the virus that causes AIDS.

Attack on the Immune System: HIV

The **human immunodeficiency virus (HIV)**, the pathogen that causes AIDS, both escapes and attacks the adaptive immune response. Once introduced into the body, HIV infects helper T cells with high efficiency. To infect these cells, the virus binds specifically to the CD4 accessory protein (see Figure 43.17). However, HIV also infects some cell types that have low levels of CD4, such as macrophages and brain cells. In the cell, the HIV RNA genome is reverse-transcribed, and the product DNA is integrated into the host cell's genome (see Figure 19.10). In this form, the viral genome can direct production of new virus particles.

Although the body responds to HIV with an immune response sufficient to eliminate most viral infections, some HIV invariably escapes. One reason HIV persists is antigenic variation. The virus mutates at a very high rate during replication. Altered proteins on the surface of some mutated viruses reduce interaction with antibodies and cytotoxic T cells. Such viruses survive, proliferate, and mutate

Comparing Two Variables on a Common x-Axis

How Does the Immune System Respond to a Changing Pathogen? Natural selection favours parasites that are able to maintain a low-level infection in a host for a long time. *Trypanosoma*, the unicellular parasite that causes sleeping sickness, is one example. The glycoproteins covering a trypanosome's surface are encoded by a gene that is duplicated more than a thousand times in the organism's genome. Each copy is slightly different. By periodically switching among these genes, the trypanosome can display a series of surface glycoproteins with different molecular structures. In this exercise, you will interpret two data sets to explore hypotheses about the benefits of the trypanosome's evershifting surface glycoproteins and the host's immune response.

Eye of Science/ Science Source

Part A: Data from a Study of Parasite Levels This study measured the abundance of parasites in the blood of one human patient during the first few weeks of a chronic infection.

Day	Number of Parasites (in millions) per mL of Blood
4	0.1
6	0.3
8	1.2
10	0.2
12	0.2
14	0.9
16	0.6
18	0.1
20	0.7
22	1.2
24	0.2

Part A: Interpret the Data

1. Plot the data in the above table as a line graph. Which column is the independent variable, and which is the dependent variable? Put the independent variable on the *x*-axis. (For additional information about graphs, see the Scientific Skills Review in Appendix E and the Study Area in MasteringBiology.)

2. Visually displaying data in a graph can help make patterns in the data more noticeable. Describe any patterns revealed by your graph.

3. Assume that a drop in parasite abundance reflects an effective immune response by the host. Formulate a hypothesis to explain the pattern you described in question 2.

Part B: Data from a Study of Antibody Levels Many decades after scientists first observed the pattern of *Trypanosoma* abundance over the course of infection, researchers identified antibodies specific to different forms of the parasite's surface glycoprotein. The table below lists the relative abundance of two such antibodies during the early period of chronic infection, using an index ranging from 0 (absent) to 1.

Day	Antibody Specific to Glycoprotein Variant A	Antibody Specific to Glycoprotein Variant B
4	0	0
6	0	0
8	0.2	0
10	0.5	0
12	1	0
14	1	0.1
16	1	0.3
18	1	0.9
20	1	1
22	1	1
24	1	1

Part B: Interpret the Data

4. Note that these data were collected over the same period of infection (days 4–24) as the parasite abundance data you graphed in part A. Therefore, you can incorporate these new data into your first graph, using the same *x*-axis. However, since the antibody level data are measured in a different way than the parasite abundance data, add a second set of *y*-axis labels on the right side of your graph. Then, using different colours or sets of symbols, add the data for the two antibody types. Labelling the *y*-axis two different ways enables you to compare how two dependent variables change relative to a shared independent variable.

5. Describe any patterns you observe by comparing the two data sets over the same period. Do these patterns support your hypothesis from part A? Do they prove that hypothesis? Explain.

6. Scientists can now also distinguish the abundance of trypanosomes recognized specifically by antibodies type A and type B. How would incorporating such information change your graph?

Data from L. J. Morrison et al., Probabilistic order in antigenic variation of *Trypanosoma brucei*, *International Journal for Parasitology* 35:961-972 (2005) and L. J. Morrison et al., Antigenic variation in the African trypanosome: Molecular mechanisms and phenotypic complexity, *Cellular Microbiology* 1:1724–1734 (2009). © Jane B Reece.

further. The virus thus evolves within the body. The continued presence of HIV is also helped by latency. When the viral DNA integrates into the chromosome of a host cell but does not produce new virus proteins or particles, it is shielded from the immune system by the host cell. This inactive, or latent, viral DNA is also protected from antiviral agents currently used against HIV because they attack only actively replicating viruses.

Over time, an untreated HIV infection not only avoids the adaptive immune response but also abolishes it

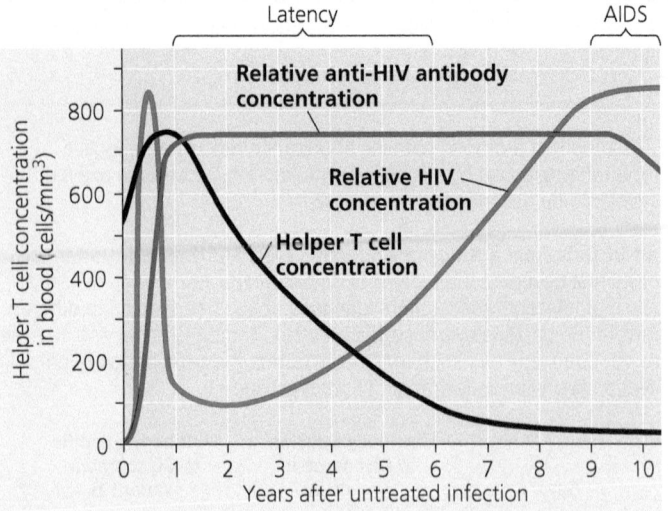

▲ Figure 43.25 **The progress of an untreated HIV infection.**

(Figure 43.25). Viral reproduction and cell death triggered by the virus lead to loss of helper T cells, impairing both humoral and cell-mediated immune responses. The result is a progression to AIDS, characterized by a susceptibility to infections and cancers that a healthy immune system would usually defeat. For example, *Pneumocystis carinii*, a common fungus that does not cause disease in healthy individuals, can result in severe pneumonia in people with AIDS. Likewise, the Kaposi's sarcoma herpesvirus causes a cancer among AIDS patients that is extremely rare in individuals not infected with HIV. Such opportunistic diseases, as well as nerve damage and body wasting, are the primary causes of death in AIDS patients, not the HIV virus itself.

At present, HIV infection cannot be cured, although certain drugs can slow HIV reproduction and the progression to AIDS. Unfortunately, mutations that occur in each round of viral reproduction can generate strains of HIV that are drug resistant. The impact of such viral drug resistance can be reduced by the use of a combination of drugs; viruses newly resistant to one drug can be defeated by another. However, the appearance of strains resistant to multiple drugs reduces the effectiveness of such multidrug "cocktails" in some patients. Frequent mutations in genes for HIV surface antigens also have hampered efforts to develop an effective vaccine. Worldwide, the AIDS epidemic continues to grow. In 2008, approximately 2 million people died of AIDS, and the disease is now the leading cause of death in Africa.

Transmission of HIV requires the transfer of virus particles or infected cells from person to person via body fluids such as semen, blood, or breast milk. Unprotected sex (that is, without a condom) and transmission via HIV-contaminated needles (typically among intravenous drug users) account for the vast majority of HIV infections. The virus can enter the body through the mucosal linings of the vagina, vulva,

penis, or rectum during intercourse or via the mouth during oral sex. The likelihood of transmission is increased by factors that may damage these linings, especially other sexually transmitted infections that cause ulcers or inflammation.

People infected with HIV can transmit the disease in the first few weeks of infection, *before* they express HIV-specific antibodies that can be detected in a blood test (see Figure 43.25). Currently, 10–50% of all new HIV infections appear to be caused by recently infected individuals.

Cancer and Immunity

When adaptive immunity is inactivated, the frequency of certain cancers increases dramatically. For example, the risk of developing Kaposi's sarcoma is 20 000 times greater for untreated AIDS patients than for healthy people. This observation was unanticipated. If the immune system recognizes only nonself, it should fail to recognize the uncontrolled growth of self cells that is the hallmark of cancer. It turns out, however, that viruses are involved in about 15–20% of all human cancers. Because the immune system can recognize viral proteins as foreign, it can act as a defence against viruses that can cause cancer and against cancer cells that harbour viruses.

Scientists have identified six viruses that can cause cancer in humans. The Kaposi's sarcoma herpesvirus is one such virus. Hepatitis B virus, which can trigger liver cancer, is another. A vaccine directed against hepatitis B virus that was introduced in 1986 was demonstrated to be the first vaccine to help prevent a specific human cancer. Rapid progress on virus-induced cancers continues. In 2006, the release of a vaccine against cervical cancer, specifically human papillomavirus (HPV), marked a major victory against cervical cancer, a disease that afflicts more than half a million women worldwide every year.

▲ Human papillomavirus

CONCEPT CHECK 43.4

1. In myasthenia gravis, antibodies bind to and block certain receptors on muscle cells, preventing muscle contraction. Is this disease best classified as an immunodeficiency disease, an autoimmune disease, or an allergic reaction? Explain.

2. People with herpes simplex type 1 viruses often get mouth sores when they have a cold or similar infection. How might this location benefit the virus?

3. **WHAT IF?** How would a macrophage deficiency likely affect a person's innate and adaptive defences?

For suggested answers, see Appendix A.

43 Chapter Review

Go to **MasteringBiology**® for Assignments, the eText, and the Study Area with Animations, Activities, Vocab Self-Quiz, and Practice Tests.

SUMMARY OF KEY CONCEPTS

CONCEPT 43.1

In innate immunity, recognition and response rely on traits common to groups of pathogens (pp. 1000–1005)

- In both invertebrates and vertebrates, **innate immunity** is mediated by physical and chemical barriers as well as cell-based defences. Activation of innate immune responses relies on recognition proteins specific for broad classes of **pathogens**. In insects, pathogens that penetrate barrier defences are ingested by cells in the hemolymph that also release antimicrobial peptides.
- In vertebrates, intact skin and mucous membranes form barriers to pathogens. Mucus produced by membrane cells, the low pH of the skin and stomach, and degradation by **lysozyme** also deter pathogens. Microbes that penetrate barrier defences are ingested by phagocytic cells, including **macrophages** and **dendritic cells**. Additional cellular defences include **natural killer cells**, which can induce the death of virus-infected cells. **Complement system** proteins, **interferons**, and other antimicrobial peptides also act against pathogens. In the **inflammatory response**, **histamine** and other chemicals released from cells at the injury site promote changes in blood vessels that allow fluid, more phagocytic cells, and antimicrobial peptides to enter tissues.
- Pathogens sometimes evade innate immune defences. For example, some bacteria have an outer capsule that prevents recognition, while others are resistant to breakdown within lysosomes.

? *In what ways does innate immunity protect the mammalian digestive tract?*

CONCEPT 43.2

In adaptive immunity, receptors provide pathogen-specific recognition (pp. 1005–1011)

- **Adaptive immunity** relies on **lymphocytes** that arise from stem cells in the bone marrow and complete their maturation in the bone marrow (**B cells**) or in the **thymus** (**T cells**). Lymphocytes have cell-surface **antigen receptors** for foreign molecules. All receptor proteins on a single B or T cell are the same, but there are millions of B and T cells in the body that differ in the foreign molecules that their receptors recognize. Upon infection, B and T cells specific for the pathogen are activated. Some T cells help other lymphocytes; others kill infected host cells. B cells called **plasma cells** produce soluble receptor proteins called **antibodies**, which bind to foreign molecules and cells. The activated lymphocytes called **memory cells** defend against future infections by the same pathogen.

- Recognition of foreign molecules involves the binding of variable regions of receptors to an **epitope**, a small region of an antigen. B cells and antibodies recognize epitopes on the surface of antigens circulating in the blood or lymph. T cells recognize protein epitopes in small antigen fragments (peptides) that are presented on the surface of host cells, complexed with cell-surface proteins called **MHC (major histocompatibility complex) molecules**.

- The four major characteristics of B and T cell development are the generation of cell diversity, self-tolerance, proliferation, and immunological memory.

The following figure uses B cells to illustrate clonal selection:

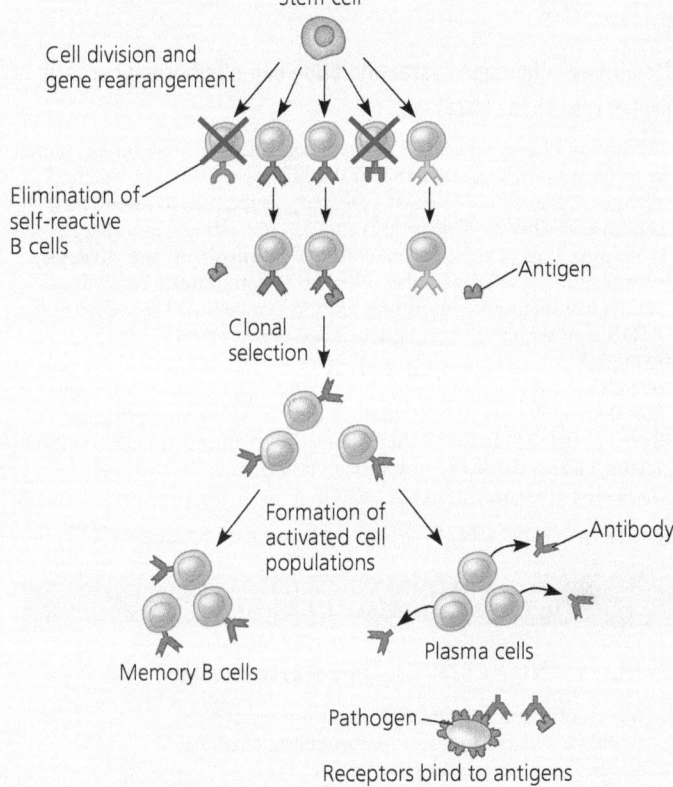

? *Why is the adaptive immune response to an initial infection slower than the innate response?*

CONCEPT 43.3

Adaptive immunity defends against infection of body fluids and body cells (pp. 1011–1018)

- **Helper T cells** interact with antigen fragments displayed by class II MHC molecules on the surface of dendritic cells, macrophages, and B cells (**antigen-presenting cells**). Activated helper T cells secrete **cytokines** that stimulate other lymphocytes as part of the response to nearly all antigens. **Cytotoxic T cells** bind to a complex of an antigen fragment and a class I MHC molecule on infected host cells. In the **cell-mediated immune response**, activated cytotoxic T cells secrete proteins that initiate destruction of infected cells. All T cells have an accessory protein that enhances binding to MHC–antigen fragment complexes.

  In the **humoral immune response**, B cell antigen receptors and antibodies bind to extracellular foreign substances in blood and lymph. The binding of antibodies helps eliminate antigens by phagocytosis and complement-mediated lysis. The five major antibody classes differ in distribution and function.

- **Active immunity** develops in response to infection or to **immunization** with a nonpathogenic form or part of a pathogen. Active immunity includes a response to and immunological memory for that pathogen. **Passive immunity**, which provides immediate, short-term protection, is conferred naturally when IgG crosses the placenta from mother to fetus or when IgA passes from mother to infant in breast milk. It also can be conferred artificially by injecting antibodies into a nonimmune person.

- Tissues or cells transferred from one person to another are subject to immune rejection. In tissue grafts and organ transplants, MHC molecules stimulate rejection. Lymphocytes in bone marrow transplants may cause a graft versus host reaction.

? *Is immunological memory after a natural infection fundamentally different from immunological memory after vaccination? Explain.*

CONCEPT 43.4

Disruptions in immune system function can elicit or exacerbate disease (pp. 1018–1022)

- Disruption of normal immune system regulation or function can result in an exaggerated, self-directed, or diminished response. In localized allergies, IgE attached to **mast cells** induces the cells to release histamine and other mediators that cause vascular changes and allergic symptoms. Loss of self-tolerance can lead to **autoimmune diseases**, such as multiple sclerosis. Inborn **immunodeficiencies** result from defects that interfere with innate, humoral, or cell-mediated defences. **AIDS** is an acquired immunodeficiency caused by HIV.

- Antigenic variation, latency, and direct assault on the immune system allow some pathogens to thwart immune responses. HIV infection destroys helper T cells, leaving the patient prone to disease. Immune defence against cancer appears to primarily involve action against viruses that can cause cancer, as well as against cancer cells that harbour viruses.

? *Is being infected with HIV the same as having AIDS? Explain.*

TEST YOUR UNDERSTANDING

LEVEL 1: KNOWLEDGE/COMPREHENSION

1. Which of these is *not* part of insect immunity?
   a. enzyme activation of microbe-killing chemicals
   b. activation of natural killer cells
   c. phagocytosis by hemocytes
   d. production of antimicrobial peptides

2. An epitope associates with which part of an antigen receptor or antibody?
   a. the tail
   b. the heavy-chain constant regions only
   c. variable regions of a heavy chain and light chain combined
   d. the light-chain constant regions only

3. Which statement best describes the difference in responses of effector B cells (plasma cells) and cytotoxic T cells?
   a. B cells confer active immunity; cytotoxic T cells confer passive immunity.
   b. B cells kill pathogens directly; cytotoxic T cells kill host cells.
   c. B cells secrete antibodies against a pathogen; cytotoxic T cells kill pathogen-infected host cells.
   d. B cells carry out the cell-mediated response; cytotoxic T cells carry out the humoral response.

LEVEL 2: APPLICATION/ANALYSIS

4. Which of the following statements is *not* true?
   a. An antibody has more than one antigen-binding site.
   b. An antigen can have different epitopes.
   c. A pathogen makes more than one antigen.
   d. A lymphocyte has receptors for multiple different antigens.

5. Which of the following should be the same in identical twins?
   a. the set of antibodies produced
   b. the set of MHC molecules produced
   c. the set of T cell antigen receptors produced
   d. the susceptibility to a particular virus

LEVEL 3: SYNTHESIS/EVALUATION

6. Vaccination increases the number of
   a. different receptors that recognize a pathogen.
   b. lymphocytes with receptors that can bind to the pathogen.
   c. epitopes that the immune system can recognize.
   d. macrophages specific for a pathogen.

7. Which of the following would *not* help a virus avoid triggering an adaptive immune response?
   a. having frequent mutations in genes for surface proteins
   b. infecting cells that produce very few MHC molecules
   c. producing proteins very similar to those of other viruses
   d. infecting and killing helper T cells

8. **DRAW IT** Consider a pencil-shaped protein with two epitopes, Y (the "eraser" end) and Z (the "point" end). They are recognized by antibodies A1 and A2, respectively. Draw and label a picture showing the antibodies linking proteins into a complex that could trigger endocytosis by a macrophage.

9. **MAKE CONNECTIONS** Contrast Lamarck's idea for the inheritance of acquired characteristics, discussed in Concept 22.1, with the clonal selection of lymphocytes.

10. **EVOLUTION CONNECTION** Describe one invertebrate defence mechanism and discuss how it is an evolutionary adaptation retained in vertebrates.

11. **SCIENTIFIC INQUIRY** The presence of bacterial lipopolysaccharide (LPS) in the blood is a major cause of septic shock. Suppose you have available purified LPS and several strains of mice, each with a mutation that inactivates a particular TLR gene. How might you use these mice to test the feasibility of treating septic shock with a drug that blocks TLR signalling?

12. **WRITE ABOUT A THEME: INFORMATION** Among all nucleated body cells, only B and T cells lose DNA during their development and maturation. In a short essay (100–150 words), discuss the relationship between this loss and the theme of DNA as heritable biological information, focusing on similarities between cellular and organismal generations.

13. **SYNTHESIZE YOUR KNOWLEDGE**

Tatan YUFLANA/AP Images

This photo shows a child receiving an oral vaccine against polio, a disease caused by a virus that infects neurons. Given that the body cannot readily replace most neurons, why is it important that a polio vaccine stimulate not only a cell-mediated response but also a humoral response?

For selected answers, see Appendix A.

44

Osmoregulation and Excretion

KEY CONCEPTS

44.1 Osmoregulation balances the uptake and loss of water and solutes

44.2 An animal's nitrogenous wastes reflect its phylogeny and habitat

44.3 Diverse excretory systems are variations on a tubular theme

44.4 The nephron is organized for stepwise processing of blood filtrate

44.5 Hormonal circuits link kidney function, water balance, and blood pressure

▲ Figure 44.1 **How does a puffin drink salt water without ill effect?**

A Balancing Act

Seabirds, such as the puffin, *Fratercula arctica* (Figure 44.1), spend most of their lives living near the ocean, eating marine organisms, and drinking seawater. Birds and reptiles have evolved unique adaptations that permit them to tolerate a high-salt diet and maintain the osmolarity of the fluids in a range similar to your own. In addition, ions that are abundant in seawater, such as sodium and calcium, must be eliminated to maintain their internal levels within a range that permits normal function of muscles, neurons, and other cells of the body. Homeostasis thus requires **osmoregulation**, the general term for the processes by which animals control solute concentrations and balance water gain and loss.

A number of strategies for water and solute control have arisen during evolution, reflecting the varied and often severe osmoregulatory challenges presented by an animal's surroundings. The arid environment of a desert, for instance, can quickly deplete an animal of body water. Despite a quite different environment, marine animals also face potential dehydration. The success of animals in an ocean environment depends critically on conserving water and, for marine birds and fishes, eliminating excess salts. In contrast, freshwater animals live in an environment that threatens to flood and dilute their body fluids. These organisms survive by conserving solutes and absorbing salts from their surroundings.

In safeguarding their internal fluid environment, animals must also deal with a hazardous metabolite produced by the dismantling of proteins and nucleic acids. Breakdown of *nitrogenous* (nitrogen-containing) molecules produces ammonia, a very toxic compound. Several different mechanisms have evolved for **excretion**, the process that rids the body of nitrogenous metabolites and other metabolic waste products. Because systems for excretion and osmoregulation are structurally and functionally linked in many animals, we will consider both of these processes in this chapter.

CONCEPT 44.1

Osmoregulation balances the uptake and loss of water and solutes

Just as thermoregulation depends on balancing heat loss and gain (see Chapter 40), regulating the chemical composition of body fluids depends on balancing the uptake and loss of water and solutes. If water uptake is excessive, animal cells swell and burst; if water loss is substantial, they shrivel and die. Ultimately, the driving force for the movement of both water and solutes—in animals as in all other organisms—is a concentration gradient of one or more solutes across the plasma membrane.

Osmosis and Osmolarity

Water enters and leaves cells by osmosis. Recall from Chapter 7 that **osmosis** is the diffusion of water across a selectively permeable membrane. It occurs whenever two solutions separated by the membrane differ in osmotic pressure, or **osmolarity** (total solute concentration expressed as molarity, that is, moles of solute per litre of solution). The unit of measurement for osmolarity used in this chapter is milliosmoles per litre (mOsm/L). The osmolarity of mammalian blood is about 300 mOsm/L, whereas that of seawater is about 1000 mOsm/L.

Two solutions with the same osmolarity are said to be isoosmotic. If a selectively permeable membrane separates the solutions, water molecules will continually cross the membrane at equal rates in both directions. Thus, there is no *net* movement of water by osmosis between isoosmotic solutions. When two solutions differ in osmolarity, the one with the greater concentration of solutes is said to be *hyperosmotic*, and the more dilute solution is said to be *hypoosmotic* (**Figure 44.2**). Water flows by osmosis from a hypoosmotic solution to a hyperosmotic one.*

---

*In this chapter, we use the terms *isoosmotic, hypoosmotic,* and *hyperosmotic,* which refer specifically to osmolarity, instead of isotonic, hypotonic, and hypertonic. The latter set of terms applies to the response of animal cells—whether they swell or shrink—in solutions of known solute concentrations.

▲ Figure 44.2 **Solute concentration and osmosis.**

MAKE CONNECTIONS *Review types of membrane proteins and their functions in Concepts 7.1 and 7.2. Which membrane proteins allow water, but not solutes, to diffuse across a lipid bilayer?*

Osmotic Challenges

An animal can maintain water balance in two ways. One is to be an **osmoconformer**: to be isoosmotic with its surroundings. The second is to be an **osmoregulator**: to control internal osmolarity independent of that of its environment.

All osmoconformers are marine animals. Because an osmoconformer's internal osmolarity is the same as that of its environment, there is no tendency to gain or lose water. Many osmoconformers live in parts of the ocean where external osmolarity is nearly constant, enabling them to maintain a nearly constant internal osmolarity. Some marine environments, such as tide pools and estuaries, can experience changes in osmolarity. Osmoconformers living in such regions also endure the changes in internal osmolarity imposed on them by the environment.

Osmoregulators are found in terrestrial and aquatic environments, both freshwater and marine. The ability to defend a near-constant internal osmolarity allows these animals to survive changes in external osmolarity. Osmoregulators in fresh water must cope with inflow of water from the environment, whereas osmoregulators in salt water must resist loss of water from their tissues.

Much of this discussion has focused on the movement of water as a result of osmotic gradients. Whether an osmoregulator or an osmoconformer, changes in internal osmolarity are achieved by moving ions into or out of tissues. Water movement is a consequence of active transport of ions. Thus, ion regulation and osmoregulation are integrated processes.

Most animals, whether osmoconformers or osmoregulators, cannot tolerate substantial changes in external osmolarity and are said to be *stenohaline* (from the Greek *stenos,* narrow, and *halos,* salt). In contrast, *euryhaline* animals (from the Greek *eurys,* broad) can survive large fluctuations in external osmolarity. Euryhaline osmoconformers include many barnacles and mussels, which are continually covered and uncovered by ocean tides; examples of euryhaline osmoregulators are the striped bass and the various species of salmon.

Next we'll examine some adaptations for osmoregulation that have evolved in marine, freshwater, and terrestrial animals.

Marine Animals

Most marine invertebrates are osmoconformers. Their osmolarity is the same as that of seawater. They therefore face no substantial challenges in water balance. However, because these animals differ considerably from seawater in the concentrations of *specific* solutes, they must actively transport these solutes to maintain homeostasis. For example, although the concentration of magnesium ions (Mg^{2+}) in seawater is 50 mmol/L, homeostatic mechanisms in the Atlantic lobster (*Homarus americanus*) result in a Mg^{2+} concentration of less than 9 mmol/L in this animal's hemolymph (circulatory fluid).

Many marine vertebrates and some marine invertebrates are osmoregulators. For most of these animals, the ocean is a strongly dehydrating environment. For example, marine fishes, such as the cod in **Figure 44.3a**, constantly lose water by osmosis. Such fishes balance the water loss by drinking large amounts of seawater. In ridding themselves of salts, they make use of both their gills and kidneys. In the gills, specialized *chloride cells* actively transport chloride ions (Cl^-) out and allow sodium ions (Na^+) to follow passively. In the kidneys, excess calcium (Ca^{2+}), magnesium (Mg^{2+}), and sulphate (SO_4^{2-}) ions are excreted with the loss of only small amounts of water.

A distinct osmoregulatory strategy evolved in marine sharks and most other chondrichthyans (cartilaginous animals; see Chapter 34). Like "bony fishes" (as we'll refer collectively to ray-finned and lobe-finned fishes in this chapter), sharks have an internal salt concentration much lower than that of seawater. Thus, salt tends to diffuse into their bodies from the water, especially across their gills. Unlike bony fishes, however, marine sharks are not hypoosmotic to seawater. The explanation is that shark tissue contains high concentrations of urea, a nitrogenous waste product of protein and nucleic acid metabolism (see Figure 44.7). A shark's body fluids also contain trimethylamine oxide (TMAO), an organic molecule that protects proteins from damage by urea. Together, the salts, urea, TMAO, and other compounds maintained in the body fluids of sharks result in an osmolarity very close to that of seawater. For this reason, sharks are often considered osmoconformers. However, because the solute concentration in their body fluids is actually somewhat higher than 1000 mOsm/L, water slowly *enters* the shark's body by osmosis and in food (sharks do not drink). This small influx of water is disposed of in urine produced by the shark's kidneys. The urine also removes some of the salt that diffuses into the shark's body; the rest is lost in feces or is secreted from a specialized gland.

Freshwater Animals

The osmoregulatory problems of freshwater animals are the opposite of those of marine animals. The body fluids of freshwater animals must be hyperosmotic because animal cells cannot tolerate salt concentrations as low as that of lake or river water. Having internal fluids with an osmolarity higher than that of their surroundings, freshwater animals face the problem of gaining water by osmosis and losing salts by diffusion. Many freshwater animals, including bony fishes, solve the problem of water balance by drinking almost no water and excreting large amounts of very

(a) Osmoregulation in a marine fish

Gain of water and salt ions from food

Excretion of salt ions from gills

Osmotic water **loss** through gills and other parts of body surface

SALT WATER

Gain of water and salt ions from drinking seawater

Excretion of salt ions and small amounts of water in scanty urine from kidneys

Key

⇨ Water

➡ Salt

(b) Osmoregulation in a freshwater fish

Gain of water and some ions in food

Uptake of salt ions by gills

Osmotic water **gain** through gills and other parts of body surface

FRESH WATER

Excretion of salt ions and large amounts of water in dilute urine from kidneys

▲ Figure 44.3 **Osmoregulation in marine and freshwater bony fishes: a comparison.**

dilute urine. At the same time, salts lost by diffusion and in the urine are replenished by eating. Freshwater fishes, such as the perch in Figure 44.3b, also replenish salts by uptake across the gills. Chloride cells in the gills of the fish actively transport Cl⁻ into the body, and Na⁺ follows.

Animals That Move between Fresh Water and Seawater

Salmon and eels are examples of types of *diadromous* fishes, spending part of their life in fresh water and part in seawater. The American eel, *Anguilla rostrata*, breeds in the Sargasso Sea, with juveniles migrating into freshwater rivers of North America, including the St. Lawrence River. Salmon, such as sockeye (Figure 44.4) live their adult life in seawater, returning to fresh water to breed. These migrations require a reorganization of the osmoregulatory systems. Young salmon control ion and water balance like any other freshwater fishes, but when they mature and are ready for migration, there is a remarkable reorganization of osmoregulatory apparatus. The physiological and anatomical remodelling, known as *smoltification*, prepares the fish to enter seawater. Once in seawater, the salmon undergoes the final steps of acclimatization, enabling the fish to maintain homeostasis in seawater.

Many of the fishes that live in seawater have the ability to move into fresh water for short periods. Unlike diadromous fishes, which remodel their physiology, these euryhaline animals are able to resist disruption of their internal ion and water homeostasis.

Animals That Live in Temporary Waters

Extreme dehydration, or *desiccation*, is fatal for most animals. However, a few aquatic invertebrates that live in temporary ponds and in films of water around soil particles can lose almost all their body water and survive. These animals enter a dormant state when their habitats dry up,

▲ Figure 44.4 **Sockeye salmon (*Oncorhynchus nerka*), euryhaline osmoregulators.**

Mark Conlin/Image Quest Marine

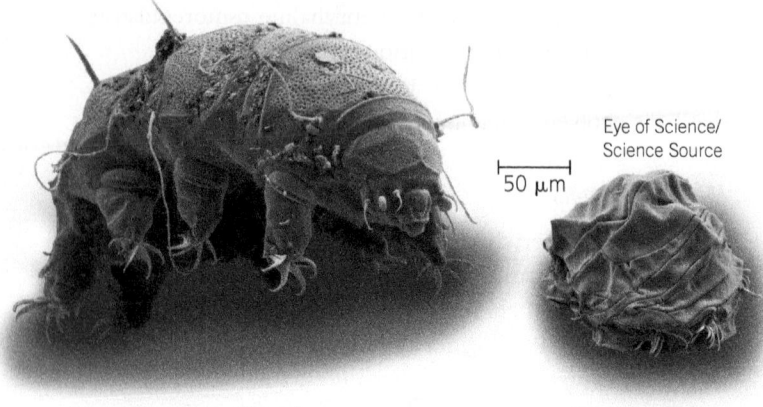

Eye of Science/ Science Source

50 μm

(a) **Hydrated tardigrade**

(b) **Dehydrated tardigrade**

▲ Figure 44.5 **Anhydrobiosis.** SEM images of tardigrades (water bears), which inhabit temporary ponds as well as droplets of water in soil and on moist plants.

an adaptation called **anhydrobiosis** ("life without water"). Among the most striking examples are the tardigrades, or water bears (Figure 44.5). Less than 1 mm long, these tiny invertebrates are found in marine, freshwater, and moist terrestrial environments. In their active, hydrated state, they contain about 85% water by weight, but they can dehydrate to less than 2% water and survive in an inactive state, dry as dust, for a decade or more. Just add water, and within hours the rehydrated tardigrades are moving about and feeding.

Anhydrobiosis requires adaptations that keep cell membranes intact. Researchers are just beginning to learn how tardigrades survive drying out, but studies of anhydrobiotic roundworms (phylum Nematoda; see Chapter 33) show that desiccated individuals contain large amounts of sugars. In particular, a disaccharide called trehalose seems to protect the cells by replacing the water that is normally associated with proteins and membrane lipids. Many insects that survive freezing in the winter also use trehalose as a membrane protectant, as do some plants resistant to desiccation.

Land Animals

The threat of dehydration is a major regulatory problem for many terrestrial plants and animals. Adaptations that reduce water loss are key to survival on land. Much as a waxy cuticle contributes to the success of land plants, the body coverings of most terrestrial animals help prevent dehydration. Examples are the waxy layers of insect exoskeletons, the shells of land snails, and the layers of dead, keratinized skin cells covering most terrestrial vertebrates, including humans. Many terrestrial animals, especially desert-dwellers, are nocturnal, which reduces evaporative water loss because of the lower temperature and higher humidity of night air.

Despite these and other adaptations, most terrestrial animals lose water through many routes: in urine and feces, across their skin, and from the surfaces of gas exchange organs. Land animals maintain water balance by drinking and eating moist foods and by producing water metabolically through cellular respiration.

A number of desert animals are well-enough adapted for minimizing water loss that they can survive for long periods of time without drinking. Camels, for example, can lose 25% of their body water and survive. (In contrast, a human who loses half this amount of body water will die from heart failure.)

Although most reptiles, birds, and mammals are terrestrial, many have evolved in aquatic environments, facing similar challenges as marine and freshwater fish. Semi-aquatic mammals, for example, muskrats and beavers, spend enough time in water that they have adaptations that permit them to excrete large volumes of water to maintain osmotic balance. In the Scientific Skills Exercise, you can examine how different mammals regulated water excretion to maintain osmotic balance.

Energetics of Osmoregulation

Maintaining an osmolarity difference between an animal's body and its external environment carries an energy cost. Because diffusion tends to equalize concentrations in a system, osmoregulators must expend energy to maintain the osmotic gradients that cause water to move in or out. They do so by using active transport to manipulate solute concentrations in their body fluids.

The energy cost of osmoregulation depends on how different an animal's osmolarity is from its surroundings, how easily water and solutes can move across the animal's surface, and how much work is required to pump solutes across the membrane. Osmoregulation accounts for 5% or more of the resting metabolic rate of many freshwater and marine bony fishes. For brine shrimp, small crustaceans that live in extremely salty lakes, the gradient between internal and external osmolarity is very large, and the cost of osmoregulation is correspondingly high—as much as 30% of the resting metabolic rate.

The energy cost to an animal of maintaining water and salt balance is minimized by having body fluids that are adapted to the salinity of the animal's habitat. Thus, the body fluids of most animals that live in fresh water (which has an osmolarity of 0.5–15 mOsm/L) have lower solute concentrations than the body fluids of their closest relatives that live in seawater (1000 mOsm/L). For instance, whereas marine molluscs have body fluids with solute concentrations of approximately 1000 mOsm/L, some freshwater molluscs maintain the osmolarity of their body fluids at just 40 mOsm/L. In each case, minimizing the osmotic difference between body fluids and the surrounding environment decreases the energy the animal expends for osmoregulation.

Transport Epithelia in Osmoregulation

The ultimate function of osmoregulation is to control solute concentrations in cells, but most animals do this indirectly by managing the solute content of an internal body fluid that bathes the cells. In insects and other animals with an open circulatory system, the fluid surrounding cells is hemolymph. In vertebrates and other animals with a closed circulatory system, the cells are bathed in an interstitial fluid that contains a mixture of solutes controlled indirectly by the blood. Maintaining the composition of such fluids depends on structures ranging from individual cells that regulate solute movement to complex organs such as the vertebrate kidney.

In most animals, osmoregulation and metabolic waste disposal rely on **transport epithelia**—one or more layers of epithelial cells specialized for moving particular solutes in controlled amounts in specific directions. Transport epithelia are typically arranged into complex networks with extensive surface areas (Figure 44.6). Some transport epithelia face the outside environment directly, while others line channels connected to the outside by an opening on the body surface.

The transport epithelium that enables marine birds to survive on seawater remained undiscovered for many years. To explore this question, researchers gave captive marine birds only seawater to drink. Although very little salt appeared in the birds' urine, fluid dripping from the tip of their beaks was a concentrated solution of salt (NaCl). The source of this solution was a pair of nasal salt glands (Figure 44.6). Salt glands, which are also found in sea turtles and marine iguanas, use active transport of ions to secrete a fluid much saltier than the ocean. Even though drinking seawater brings in a lot of salt, the salt gland enables these marine vertebrates to achieve a net gain of water. By contrast, humans who drink a given volume of seawater must use a greater volume of water to excrete the salt load, with the result that they become dehydrated.

Transport epithelia that function in maintaining water balance also often function in disposal of metabolic wastes. We will see examples of this coordinated function in our upcoming consideration of earthworm and insect excretory systems as well as the vertebrate kidney.

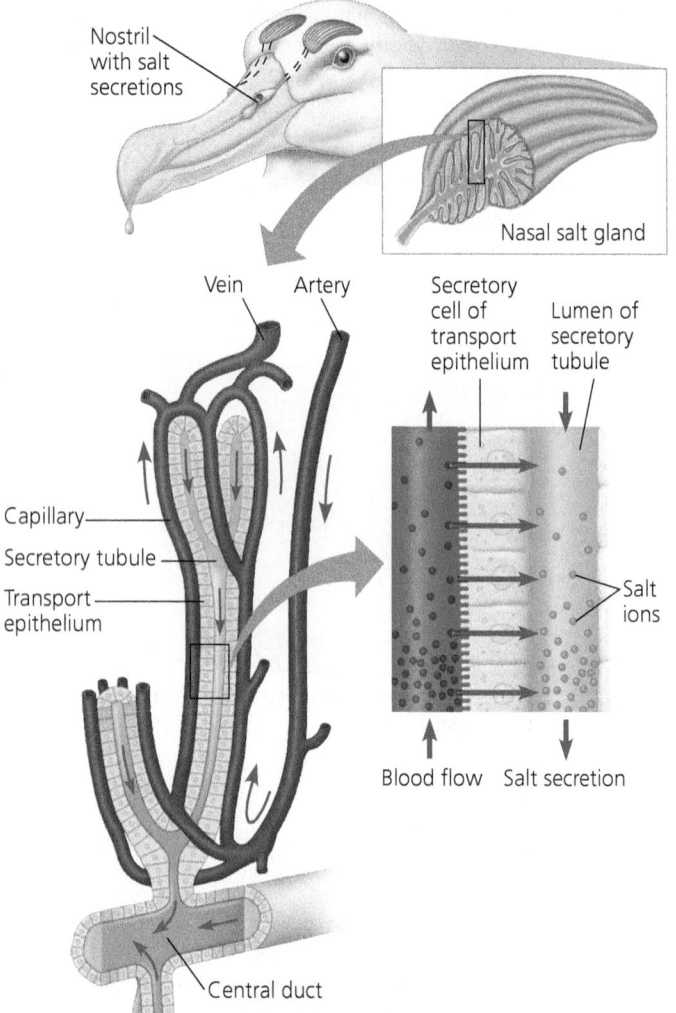

▲ **Figure 44.6 Salt secretion in the nasal glands of a marine bird.** Salt is transported from the blood into secretory tubules, which drain into central ducts leading to the nostrils.

Nostril with salt secretions

Nasal salt gland

Vein   Artery

Secretory cell of transport epithelium

Lumen of secretory tubule

Capillary

Secretory tubule

Transport epithelium

Salt ions

Blood flow   Salt secretion

Central duct

CONCEPT 44.2

An animal's nitrogenous wastes reflect its phylogeny and habitat

Because most metabolic wastes must be dissolved in water to be excreted from the body, the type and quantity of an animal's waste products may have a large impact on its water balance. In this regard, some of the most significant waste products are the nitrogenous breakdown products of proteins and nucleic acids (Figure 44.7). When proteins and nucleic acids are broken apart for energy or converted to carbohydrates or fats, enzymes remove nitrogen in the form of **ammonia** (NH_3). Ammonia is very toxic, in part because its ion, ammonium (NH_4^+), interferes with diverse biochemical processes, including pH balance, electrochemical gradients, exocytosis, and enzyme function.

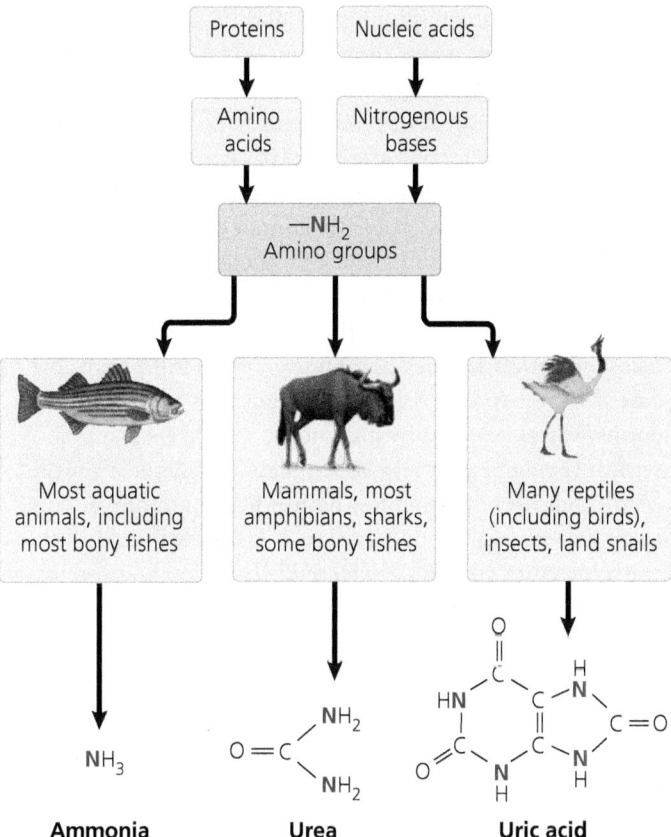

▲ Figure 44.7 **Forms of nitrogenous waste.**

Source: Figure adapted from *Zoology*, 1st edition, by Lawrence G. Mitchell. Copyright © 1988 by Pearson Education Inc. Adapted and electronically reproduced by permission of Pearson Education, Inc., Upper Saddle River, New Jersey.

Nervous tissue is particularly sensitive to ammonia toxicity. Although some animals excrete ammonia directly, many species expend energy to convert it to less toxic compounds prior to excretion, primarily urea or uric acid.

Forms of Nitrogenous Waste

The three main forms of nitrogenous waste—ammonia, urea, and uric acid—differ in their toxicity and energetic costs of production. Animals produce one type as their main nitrogenous waste, though most animals are capable of producing the other forms. The terms *ammoniotelism*, *ureotelism*, and *uricotelism* are used to define physiological strategies where the dominant excretory product is ammonia, urea, or uric acid (respectively).

Ammonia

Because ammonia can be tolerated only at very low concentrations, animals that excrete nitrogenous wastes as ammonia need access to lots of water. Therefore, ammonia excretion is most common in aquatic species. Being highly soluble, ammonia molecules easily pass through membranes and are readily lost by diffusion to the surrounding water. In many invertebrates, ammonia release occurs across the whole body surface. In fishes, most of the ammonia is lost as NH_4^+ across

the epithelium of the gills; their kidneys excrete only minor amounts of nitrogenous waste. However, many fishes retain the ability to produce urea, and given the right circumstances can switch their main nitrogenous waste product (**Figure 44.8**).

Urea

Although ammonia excretion works well in many aquatic species, it is much less suitable for land animals. Ammonia is so toxic that it can be transported and excreted only in large volumes of very dilute solutions. As a result, most

▼ Figure 44.8 **Inquiry**

Fishes living in alkaline lakes switch from ammonia to urea as their nitrogenous waste

Experiment Ammonia (NH_3) crosses cell membranes as a dissolved gas, then quickly accepts a proton to become ammonium (NH_4^+). When fishes excrete ammonia, this conversion is critical because it reduces the level of NH_3 immediately outside the gill, maintaining a driving force for diffusion of ammonia out of the animal. Since protons are critical for this transport process, Dave Randall (University of British Columbia) asked what might be different in fishes that live in waters with low concentrations of protons (high pH). He and his colleagues travelled to Lake Magadi, Kenya, to study how native populations of tilapia manage nitrogen excretion in this alkaline lake (pH 10), in comparison to fishes living at more neutral pH (Sagana River).

Results Lake Magadi tilapia excrete their nitrogenous waste almost exclusively as urea, whereas a related species living in waters with more neutral pH excrete primarily ammonia. The difference in total nitrogen excretion (much higher in Lake Magadi tilapia) is likely due to diet.

Conclusion These studies were among the first to show that fishes were capable of excreting urea as nitrogenous waste. Subsequent studies have shown that many species are capable of producing urea at certain life stages and under challenging environmental conditions.

Source: Based on D. J. Randall, C. M. Wood, S. F. Perry, H. Bergman, G. M. Maloiy, T. P. Mommsen, and P. A. Wright, Urea excretion as a strategy for survival in a fish living in a very alkaline environment, *Nature* 337:165–166 (1989). © Jane B Reece.

WHAT IF? *What would you expect to happen if Lake Magadi tilapia invaded surrounding lakes with more neutral pH? Consider the responses of the Lake Magadi transplants as well as the indigenous fishes, both in the short term (weeks to months) and long term (generations).*

terrestrial animals and many marine species (principally those that tend to lose water to their environment by osmosis) simply do not have access to sufficient water to routinely excrete ammonia. Instead, mammals, most adult amphibians, sharks, and some marine bony fishes and turtles mainly excrete a different nitrogenous waste, **urea**. Produced in the vertebrate liver, urea is the product of a metabolic cycle that combines ammonia with carbon dioxide.

The main advantage of urea is its very low toxicity. Animals can transport urea in the circulatory system and store it safely at high concentrations. Furthermore, much less water is lost when a given quantity of nitrogen is excreted in a concentrated solution of urea rather than a dilute solution of ammonia.

The main disadvantage of urea is its energy cost: Animals must expend energy to produce urea from ammonia. From a bioenergetic standpoint, we would predict that animals that spend part of their lives in water and part on land would switch between excreting ammonia (thereby saving energy) and excreting urea (reducing excretory water loss). Indeed, many amphibians excrete mainly ammonia when they are aquatic tadpoles and switch largely to urea excretion when they become land-dwelling adults.

Uric Acid

Insects, land snails, and many reptiles, including birds, excrete **uric acid** as their primary nitrogenous waste. (Bird droppings, or *guano*, are a mixture of white uric acid and brown feces.) Uric acid is relatively nontoxic and does not readily dissolve in water. It therefore can be excreted as a semisolid paste with very little water loss. This is a great advantage for animals with little access to water, but there is a cost: Uric acid is even more energetically expensive to produce than urea, requiring considerable ATP for synthesis from ammonia.

While not primarily uric acid producers, humans and some other animals generate a small amount of uric acid as a product of purine breakdown. Diseases that alter this process reflect the problems that can arise when a metabolic product is insoluble. For example, a genetic defect in purine metabolism predisposes Dalmatian dogs to form uric acid stones in their bladder. In humans, adult males are particularly susceptible to *gout*, a painful joint inflammation caused by deposits of uric acid crystals. Meals containing purine-rich animal tissues can increase the inflammation. Some dinosaurs appear to have been similarly affected: Fossilized bones of *Tyrannosaurus rex* exhibit joint damage characteristic of gout.

The Influence of Evolution and Environment on Nitrogenous Wastes

EVOLUTION   In general, the kind of nitrogenous wastes an animal excretes depends on both the species'

evolutionary history (phylogeny) and its habitat, especially the availability of water. For example, terrestrial turtles (which often live in dry areas) excrete mainly uric acid, whereas aquatic turtles excrete both urea and ammonia. Another factor affecting the primary type of nitrogenous waste produced by a particular group of animals is the immediate environment of the animal egg. For example, soluble wastes can diffuse out of a shell-less amphibian egg or be carried away from a mammalian embryo by the mother's blood. However, the shelled eggs produced by birds and other reptiles (see Figure 34.26) are permeable to gases but not to liquids, which means that soluble nitrogenous wastes released by an embryo would be trapped within the egg and could accumulate to dangerous levels. (Although urea is much less harmful than ammonia, it is toxic at very high concentrations.) Using uric acid as a waste product conveys a selective advantage because it precipitates out of solution and can be stored within the egg as a harmless solid left behind when the animal hatches.

Regardless of the type of nitrogenous waste, the amount produced is coupled to the animal's energy budget. Endotherms, which use energy at high rates, eat more food and produce more nitrogenous waste than ectotherms. The amount of nitrogenous waste is also linked to diet. Predators, which derive much of their energy from protein, excrete more nitrogen than animals that rely mainly on lipids or carbohydrates as energy sources.

Having surveyed the forms of nitrogenous waste and their interrelationship with evolutionary lineage, habitat, and energy consumption, we will turn next to the processes and systems animals use to excrete these and other wastes.

CONCEPT CHECK 44.2

1. What advantage does uric acid offer as a nitrogenous waste in arid environments?

2. **WHAT IF?** Suppose a bird and a human both have gout. Why might reducing purine in their diets help the human much more than the bird?

For suggested answers, see Appendix A.

CONCEPT 44.3

Diverse excretory systems are variations on a tubular theme

Whether an animal lives on land, in salt water, or in fresh water, water balance depends on the regulation of solute movement between internal fluids and the external environment. Much of this movement is handled by excretory systems. These systems are central to homeostasis because they dispose of metabolic wastes and control body fluid composition. Before we describe particular excretory systems, let's consider a generalized version of the process of excretion.

Excretory Processes

Animals across a wide range of species produce a fluid waste called urine through the basic steps shown in **Figure 44.9**. In the first step, body fluid (blood, coelomic fluid, or hemolymph) is brought in contact with the selectively permeable barrier that acts as a biological filter. In most cases, hydrostatic pressure (blood pressure in many animals) drives a process of **filtration**. Cells, as well as proteins and other large molecules, encounter the filter but cannot penetrate it and remain in the body fluid. In contrast, water and small solutes such as salts, sugars, amino acids, and nitrogenous wastes cross the filter, forming a solution called the **filtrate**.

The filtrate is converted to a waste fluid by the specific transport of materials into or out of the filtrate. The process of selective **reabsorption** recovers useful molecules and water from the filtrate and returns them to the body fluids. Valuable solutes—including glucose, certain salts, vitamins, hormones, and amino acids—are reabsorbed by active transport. Nonessential solutes and wastes are left in the filtrate or are added to it by selective **secretion**, which also

occurs by active transport. The pumping of various solutes adjusts the osmotic movement of water into or out of the filtrate. In the last step—excretion—the processed filtrate containing nitrogenous wastes is released from the body as urine.

Survey of Excretory Systems

The systems that perform the basic excretory functions vary widely among animal groups. However, they are generally built on a complex network of tubules that provide a large surface area for the exchange of water and solutes, including nitrogenous wastes. We'll examine the excretory systems of flatworms, earthworms, insects, and vertebrates as examples of evolutionary variations on tubule networks.

Protonephridia

Flatworms (phylum Platyhelminthes) have excretory systems called **protonephridia** (singular, *protonephridium*), which form a network of dead-end tubules (**Figure 44.10**). The tubules, which are connected to external openings, branch throughout the flatworm's body, which lacks a coelom or body cavity. Cellular units called flame bulbs cap the branches of each protonephridium. Consisting of a tubule cell and a cap cell, each flame bulb has a tuft of cilia projecting into the tubule. During filtration, the beating

1 Filtration. The excretory tubule collects a filtrate from the blood. Water and solutes are forced by blood pressure across the selectively permeable membranes of a cluster of capillaries and into the excretory tubule.

2 Reabsorption. The transport epithelium reclaims valuable substances from the filtrate and returns them to the body fluids.

3 Secretion. Other substances, such as toxins and excess ions, are extracted from body fluids and added to the contents of the excretory tubule.

4 Excretion. The altered filtrate (urine) leaves the system and the body.

Capillary

Filtrate

Excretory tubule

Urine

▲ **Figure 44.9 Key steps of excretory system function: an overview.** Most excretory systems produce a filtrate by pressure-filtering body fluids and then modifying the filtrate's contents. This diagram is modelled after the vertebrate excretory system.

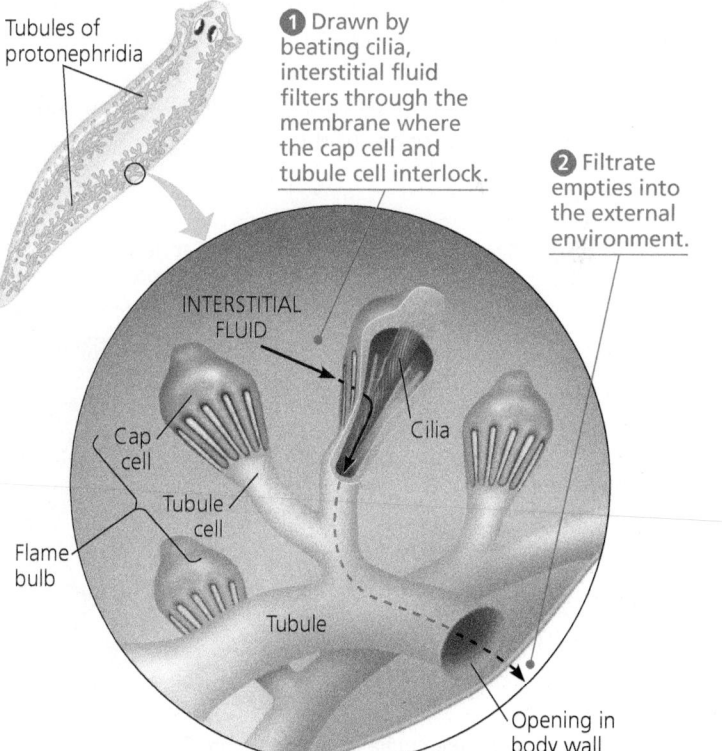

Tubules of protonephridia

1 Drawn by beating cilia, interstitial fluid filters through the membrane where the cap cell and tubule cell interlock.

2 Filtrate empties into the external environment.

INTERSTITIAL FLUID

Cap cell

Cilia

Tubule cell

Flame bulb

Tubule

Opening in body wall

▲ **Figure 44.10 Protonephridia: the flame bulb system of a planarian.** Protonephridia are branching internal tubules that function mainly in osmoregulation.

of the cilia draws water and solutes from the interstitial fluid through the flame bulb, releasing filtrate into the tubule network. (The moving cilia resemble a flickering flame, hence the name *flame bulb*.) The processed filtrate then moves outward through the tubules and empties as urine into the external environment. The urine excreted by freshwater flatworms has a low solute concentration, helping to balance the osmotic uptake of water from the environment.

Protonephridia are also found in rotifers, some annelids, mollusc larvae, and lancelets (see Figure 34.4). Among these animals the function of the protonephridia varies. In the freshwater flatworms, protonephridia serve chiefly in osmoregulation. Most metabolic wastes diffuse out of the animal across the body surface or are excreted into the gastrovascular cavity and eliminated through the mouth (see Figure 33.10). However, in some parasitic flatworms, which are isoosmotic to the surrounding fluids of their host organisms, the main function of protonephridia is the disposal of nitrogenous wastes. Natural selection has thus adapted protonephridia to different tasks in different environments.

Metanephridia

Most annelids, such as earthworms, have **metanephridia** (singular, *metanephridium*), excretory organs that collect fluid directly from the coelom (**Figure 44.11**). Each segment of a worm has a pair of metanephridia, which are immersed in coelomic fluid and enveloped by a capillary network. A ciliated funnel surrounds the internal opening. As the cilia beat, fluid is drawn into a collecting tubule, which includes a storage bladder that opens to the outside.

The metanephridia of an earthworm have both excretory and osmoregulatory functions. As urine moves along the tubule, the transport epithelium bordering the lumen reabsorbs most solutes and returns them to the blood in the capillaries. Nitrogenous wastes remain in the tubule and are excreted to the outside. Earthworms inhabit damp soil and usually experience a net uptake of water by osmosis through their skin. Their metanephridia balance the water influx by producing urine that is dilute (hypoosmotic to body fluids).

Malpighian Tubules

Insects and other terrestrial arthropods have organs called **Malpighian tubules** that remove nitrogenous wastes and that also function in osmoregulation (**Figure 44.12**). The Malpighian tubules extend from dead-end tips immersed in hemolymph (circulatory fluid) to openings into the digestive tract. The filtration step common to other excretory systems is absent. Instead, the transport epithelium that lines the tubules secretes certain solutes, including nitrogenous wastes, from the hemolymph into the lumen of the tubule. Water follows the solutes into the tubule by osmosis, and the fluid then passes into the rectum. There, most solutes are pumped back into the hemolymph, and water reabsorption by osmosis follows. The nitrogenous wastes—mainly insoluble uric acid—are eliminated as nearly dry matter along with the feces. Capable of conserving water very effectively, the insect excretory system is a key adaptation contributing to these animals' tremendous success on land.

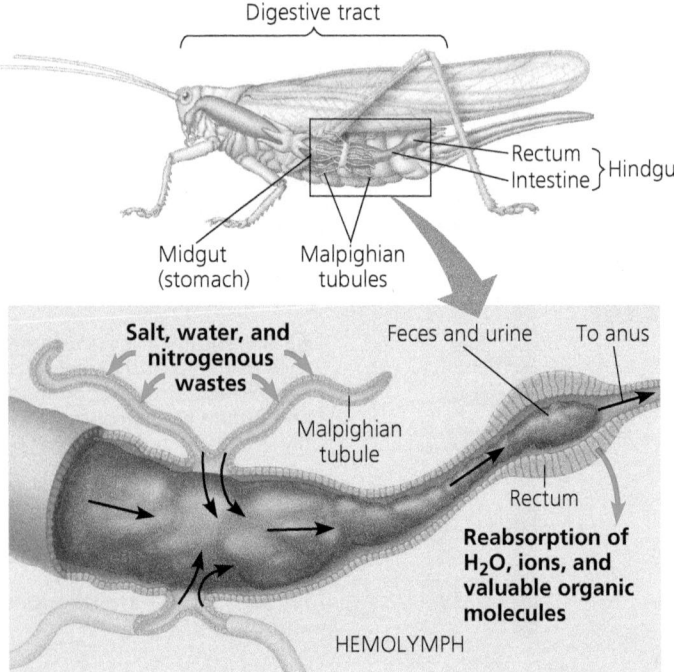

▲ **Figure 44.12 Malpighian tubules of insects.** Malpighian tubules are outpocketings of the digestive tract that remove nitrogenous wastes and function in osmoregulation.

▲ **Figure 44.11 Metanephridia of an earthworm.** Each segment of the worm contains a pair of metanephridia, which collect coelomic fluid from the adjacent anterior segment. The region highlighted in yellow illustrates the organization of one metanephridium of a pair; the other would be behind it.

Some terrestrial insects have an additional adaptation for water balance: The rectal end of their gut enables water uptake from the air. Although some species absorb water from air only when it is very humid, others, such as fleas (genus *Xenopsylla*), can capture water from the atmosphere when relative humidity is as low as 50%.

Kidneys

In vertebrates and some other chordates, a specialized organ called the kidney functions in both osmoregulation and excretion. Like the excretory organs of most animal phyla, kidneys consist of tubules. The numerous tubules of these compact organs are arranged in a highly organized manner and are closely associated with a network of capillaries. The vertebrate excretory system also includes ducts and other structures that carry urine from the tubules out of the kidney and, eventually, the body.

Vertebrate kidneys are typically nonsegmented. However, hagfishes, which are invertebrate chordates, have kidneys with segmentally arranged excretory tubules. This suggests that the excretory structures of vertebrate ancestors also may have been segmented.

Because kidney organization is integral to kidney function, we begin with **Figure 44.13** on the next two pages, an exploration of the anatomy of the mammalian kidney and associated structures. Familiarizing yourself with the terms and diagrams in this figure will provide you with a solid foundation for learning about filtrate processing in the kidney, our focus in the next concept.

CONCEPT CHECK 44.3

1. Compare and contrast the different ways that metabolic waste products enter the excretory systems of flatworms, earthworms, and insects.

2. What is the function of the filtration step in excretory systems?

3. **WHAT IF?** Kidney failure is often treated by hemodialysis, in which blood diverted out of the body is filtered and then allowed to flow on one side of a semipermeable membrane. Fluid called dialysate flows in the opposite direction on the other side of the membrane. In replacing the reabsorption and secretion of solutes in a functional kidney, the makeup of the starting dialysate is critical. What initial solute composition would work well?

For suggested answers, see Appendix A.

CONCEPT 44.4

The nephron is organized for stepwise processing of blood filtrate

We'll continue our exploration of the nephron with a discussion of filtrate processing. We will then focus on how tubules, capillaries, and surrounding tissue function together.

The porous capillaries and specialized cells of a Bowman's capsule are permeable to water and small solutes, but not blood cells or large molecules, such as plasma proteins. Thus, the filtrate produced in the capsule contains water, salts, glucose, amino acids, vitamins, nitrogenous wastes, and other small molecules. Because such molecules pass freely between glomerular capillaries and Bowman's capsule, the concentrations of these substances in the initial filtrate are the same as those in blood plasma.

From Blood Filtrate to Urine: *A Closer Look*

In this section, we will follow filtrate along its path in the nephron and collecting duct, examining how each region contributes to the stepwise processing of filtrate into urine. The circled numbers correspond to the numbers in **Figure 44.14** on page 1038.

1 Proximal tubule. Reabsorption in the proximal tubule is critical for the recapture of ions, water, and valuable nutrients from the huge volume of initial filtrate. NaCl (salt) in the filtrate diffuses into the cells of the transport epithelium, where Na^+ is actively transported into the interstitial fluid. This transfer of positive charge out of the tubule drives the passive transport of Cl^-, as well as the movement of more Na^+ from the lumen into the cells of the tubule wall by facilitated diffusion and cotransport mechanisms (see Figures 7.14 and 7.18).

As salt moves from the filtrate to the interstitial fluid, water follows by osmosis. The salt and water then diffuse from the interstitial fluid into the peritubular capillaries. Glucose, amino acids, potassium ions (K^+), and other essential substances are also actively or passively transported from the filtrate to the interstitial fluid and then into the peritubular capillaries.

Processing of filtrate in the proximal tubule helps maintain a relatively constant pH in body fluids. Cells of the transport epithelium secrete H^+ into the lumen of the tubule but also synthesize and secrete ammonia, which acts as a buffer to trap H^+ in the form of ammonium ions (NH_4^+). The more acidic the filtrate, the more ammonia the cells produce and secrete, and a mammal's urine usually contains some ammonia from this source (even though most nitrogenous waste is excreted as urea). The proximal tubules also reabsorb about 90% of the buffer bicarbonate (HCO_3^-) from the filtrate, contributing further to pH balance in body fluids.

As the filtrate passes through the proximal tubule, materials to be excreted become concentrated. Many wastes leave the body fluids during the nonselective filtration process and remain in the filtrate while water and salts are reabsorbed. Urea, for example, is reabsorbed at a much lower rate than are salt and water. Some other toxic materials are actively secreted into filtrate from surrounding tissues. For

Exploring The Mammalian Excretory System

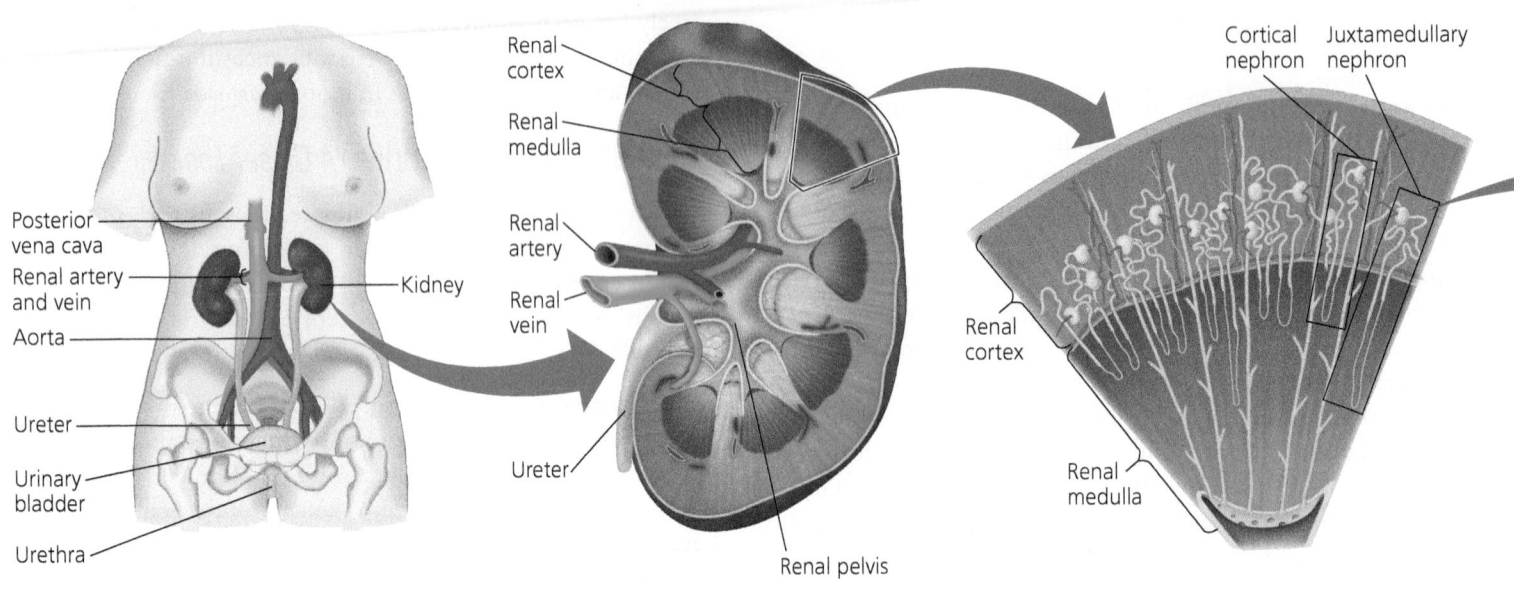

Excretory Organs

In humans, the excretory system consists of a pair of **kidneys**, bean-shaped organs about 10 cm in length, as well as organs for transporting and storing urine. Urine produced by each kidney exits through a duct called the **ureter**; the two ureters drain into a common sac called the **urinary bladder**. During urination, urine is expelled from the bladder through a tube called the **urethra**, which empties to the outside near the vagina in females and through the penis in males. Sphincter muscles near the junction of the urethra and bladder regulate urination.

Kidney Structure

Each kidney has an outer **renal cortex** and an inner **renal medulla**. Both regions are supplied with blood by a renal artery and drained by a renal vein. Within the cortex and medulla lie tightly packed excretory tubules and associated blood vessels. The excretory tubules carry and process a filtrate produced from the blood entering the kidney. Nearly all of the fluid in the filtrate is reabsorbed into the surrounding blood vessels and exits the kidney in the renal vein. The remaining fluid leaves the excretory tubules as urine is collected in the inner **renal pelvis** and exits the kidney via the ureter.

Nephron Types

Weaving back and forth across the renal cortex and medulla are the **nephrons**, the functional units of the vertebrate kidney. Of the roughly 1 million nephrons in a human kidney, 85% are **cortical nephrons**, which reach only a short distance into the medulla. The remainder, the **juxtamedullary nephrons**, extend deep into the medulla. Juxtamedullary nephrons are essential for production of urine that is hyperosmotic to body fluids, a key adaptation for water conservation in mammals.

---

example, drugs and toxins that have been processed in the liver pass from the peritubular capillaries into the interstitial fluid. These molecules then enter the proximal tubule, where they are actively secreted from the transport epithelium into the lumen.

❷ **Descending limb of the loop of Henle.** Reabsorption of water continues as the filtrate moves into the descending limb of the loop of Henle. Here numerous water channels formed by **aquaporin** proteins make the transport epithelium freely permeable to water. In contrast, there are almost no channels for salt and other small solutes, resulting in very low permeability for these substances.

For water to move out of the tubule by osmosis, the interstitial fluid bathing the tubule must be hyperosmotic to the filtrate. This condition is met along the entire length of the descending limb, because the osmolarity of the interstitial fluid increases progressively from the outer cortex to the inner medulla of the kidney. As a result, the filtrate loses water—and therefore its solute concentration increases—all along its journey down the descending limb.

❸ **Ascending limb of the loop of Henle.** The filtrate reaches the tip of the loop and then travels within the ascending limb as it returns to the cortex. Unlike the descending limb, the ascending limb has a transport epithelium studded with ion channels, but not water channels. Indeed, this membrane is impermeable to water. Impermeability to water is very rare among biological membranes and is critical to the function of the ascending limb.

The ascending limb has two specialized regions: a thin segment near the loop tip and a thick segment adjacent to the distal tubule. As filtrate ascends in the thin segment,

Nephron Organization

Afferent arteriole from renal artery

Glomerulus

Bowman's capsule

Proximal tubule

Distal tubule

Peritubular capillaries

Efferent arteriole from glomerulus

Branch of renal vein

Descending limb

Vasa recta

Loop of Henle

Collecting duct

Ascending limb

Source: Figure adapted from *Human Anatomy and Physiology*, 8th edition, by Elaine N. Marieb and Katja Hoehn. Copyright © 2010 by Pearson Education, Inc. Adapted and electronically reproduced by permission of Pearson Education, Inc., Upper Saddle River, New Jersey.

Each nephron consists of a single long tubule as well as a ball of capillaries called the **glomerulus**. The blind end of the tubule forms a cup-shaped swelling, called **Bowman's capsule**, which surrounds the glomerulus. Filtrate is formed when blood pressure forces fluid from the blood in the glomerulus into the lumen of Bowman's capsule. Processing occurs as the filtrate passes through three major regions of the nephron: the **proximal tubule**, the **loop of Henle** (a hairpin turn with a descending limb and an ascending limb), and the **distal tubule**. A **collecting duct** receives processed filtrate from many nephrons and transports it to the renal pelvis.

Each nephron is supplied with blood by an *afferent arteriole*, an offshoot of the renal artery that branches and forms the capillaries of the glomerulus. The capillaries converge as they leave the glomerulus, forming an *efferent arteriole*. Branches of this vessel form the **peritubular capillaries**, which surround the proximal and distal tubules. Other branches extend downward and form the **vasa recta**, hairpin-shaped capillaries that serve the renal medulla, including the long loop of Henle of juxtamedullary nephrons.

Steve Gschmeissner/Science Source

▶ In this SEM of densely packed blood vessels from a human kidney, arterioles and peritubular capillaries appear pink; the glomeruli appear yellow.

200 μm

NaCl, which became concentrated in the descending limb, diffuses out of the permeable tubule into the interstitial fluid. This movement of NaCl out of the tubule helps maintain the osmolarity of the interstitial fluid in the medulla. In the thick segment of the ascending limb, the movement of NaCl out of the filtrate continues. Here, however, the epithelium actively transports NaCl into the interstitial fluid. As a result of losing salt but not water, the filtrate becomes progressively more dilute as it moves up to the cortex in the ascending limb of the loop.

❹ **Distal tubule.** The distal tubule plays a key role in regulating the K^+ and NaCl concentration of body fluids. This regulation involves variation in the amount of K^+ secreted into the filtrate as well as the amount of NaCl reabsorbed from the filtrate. Like the proximal tubule, the distal tubule

contributes to pH regulation by the controlled secretion of H^+ and reabsorption of HCO_3^-.

❺ **Collecting duct.** The collecting duct carries the filtrate through the medulla to the renal pelvis. The transport epithelium of the nephron and collecting duct processes the filtrate, forming the urine. One of this epithelium's most important tasks is reabsorption of solutes and water. Under normal conditions, approximately 1600 L of blood flows through a pair of human kidneys each day, about 300 times the total volume of blood in the body. From this enormous traffic of blood, the nephrons and collecting ducts process about 180 L of initial filtrate. Of this, about 99% of the water and nearly all of the sugars, amino acids, vitamins, and other organic nutrients are reabsorbed into the blood, leaving only about 1.5 L of urine to be transported to the bladder.

▲ Figure 44.14 The nephron and collecting duct: regional functions of the transport epithelium. The numbered regions in this diagram are keyed to the circled numbers in the text discussion of kidney function.

Source: Figure adapted from *Human Anatomy and Physiology*, 8th edition, by Elaine N. Marieb and Katja Hoehn. Copyright © 2010 by Pearson Education, Inc. Adapted and electronically reproduced by permission of Pearson Education, Inc., Upper Saddle River, New Jersey.

? *Some cells lining tubules in the kidney synthesize organic solutes to maintain normal cell volume. Where in the kidney would you find these cells? Explain.*

As filtrate passes along the transport epithelium of the collecting duct, hormonal control of permeability and transport determines the extent to which the urine becomes concentrated.

When the kidneys are conserving water, aquaporin channels in the collecting duct allow water molecules to cross the epithelium. At the same time, the epithelium remains impermeable to salt and, in the renal cortex, to urea. As the collecting duct traverses the gradient of osmolarity in the kidney, the filtrate becomes increasingly concentrated, losing more and more water by osmosis to the hyperosmotic interstitial fluid. In the inner medulla, the duct becomes permeable to urea. Because of the high urea concentration in the filtrate at this point, some urea diffuses out of the duct and into the interstitial fluid. Along with NaCl, this urea contributes to the high osmolarity of the interstitial fluid in the medulla. The net result is urine that is hyperosmotic to the general body fluids.

In producing dilute rather than concentrated urine, the kidney actively reabsorbs salts without allowing water to follow by osmosis. At these times, the epithelium lacks water channels, and NaCl is actively transported out of filtrate. As we will see shortly, the state of the collecting duct epithelium is controlled by hormones that together maintain homeostasis for osmolarity, blood pressure, and blood volume.

Solute Gradients and Water Conservation

The mammalian kidney's ability to conserve water is a key terrestrial adaptation. In humans, the osmolarity of blood is about 300 mOsm/L, but the kidney can excrete urine up to four times as concentrated—about 1200 mOsm/L. Some mammals can do even better: Australian hopping mice, small marsupials that live in dry desert regions, can produce urine with an osmolarity of 9300 mOsm/L, 25 times as concentrated as the animal's blood.

In a mammalian kidney, the production of hyperosmotic urine is possible only because considerable energy is expended for the active transport of solutes against concentration gradients. The nephrons—particularly the loops of

Henle—can be thought of as energy-consuming machines that produce an osmolarity gradient suitable for extracting water from the filtrate in the collecting duct. The two primary solutes affecting osmolarity are NaCl, which is deposited in the renal medulla by the loop of Henle, and urea, which passes across the epithelium of the collecting duct in the inner medulla.

The Two-Solute Model

To better understand the physiology of the mammalian kidney as a water-conserving organ, let's retrace the flow of filtrate through the excretory tubule. This time, let's focus on how the juxtamedullary nephrons maintain an osmolarity gradient in the tissues that surround the loop of Henle and how they use that gradient to excrete a hyperosmotic urine (Figure 44.15). Filtrate passing from Bowman's capsule to the proximal tubule has an osmolarity of about 300 mOsm/L, the same as blood. A large amount of water *and* salt is reabsorbed from the filtrate as it flows through the proximal tubule in the renal cortex. As a result, the filtrate's volume decreases substantially, but its osmolarity remains about the same.

As the filtrate flows from cortex to medulla in the descending limb of the loop of Henle, water leaves the tubule by osmosis. Solutes, including NaCl, become more concentrated, increasing the osmolarity of the filtrate. The highest osmolarity (about 1200 mOsm/L) occurs at the tip of the loop of Henle. This maximizes the diffusion of salt out of the tubule as the filtrate rounds the curve and enters the ascending limb, which is permeable to salt but not to water. NaCl diffusing from the ascending limb helps maintain a high osmolarity in the interstitial fluid of the renal medulla.

Notice that the loop of Henle has several qualities of a countercurrent system, such as the mechanisms that maximize oxygen absorption by fish gills (see Figure 42.21) or reduce heat loss in endotherms (see Figure 40.12). In those cases, the countercurrent mechanisms involve passive movement along either an oxygen concentration gradient or a heat gradient. In contrast, the countercurrent system involving the loop of Henle expends energy to actively transport NaCl from the filtrate in the upper part of the ascending limb of the loop. Such countercurrent systems, which expend energy to create concentration gradients, are called **countercurrent multiplier systems**. The countercurrent multiplier system involving the loop of Henle maintains a high salt concentration in the interior of the kidney, enabling the kidney to form concentrated urine.

▶ Figure 44.15 **How the human kidney concentrates urine: the two-solute model.** Two solutes contribute to the osmolarity of the interstitial fluid: NaCl (used as shorthand here to refer collectively to Na$^+$ and Cl$^-$) and urea. The loop of Henle maintains the interstitial gradient of NaCl, which increases continuously in concentration from the cortex to the inner medulla. Urea diffuses into the interstitial fluid of the medulla from the collecting duct (most of the urea in the filtrate remains in the collecting duct and is excreted). The filtrate makes three trips between the cortex and medulla: first down, then up, and then down again in the collecting duct. As the filtrate flows in the collecting duct past interstitial fluid of increasing osmolarity, more water moves out of the duct by osmosis. The loss of water concentrates the solutes, including urea, that will be excreted in the urine.

WHAT IF? *The drug furosemide blocks the cotransporters for Na$^+$ and Cl$^-$ in the ascending limb of the loop of Henle. What effect would you expect this drug to have on urine volume?*

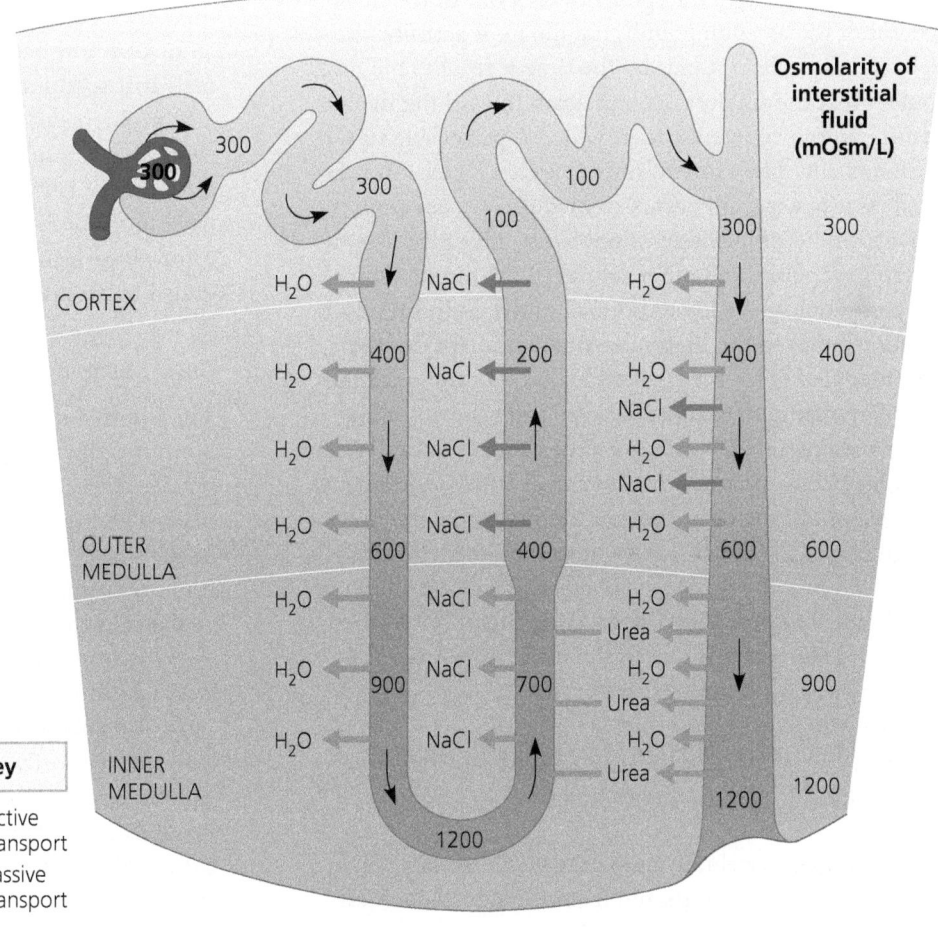

Key
→ Active transport
→ Passive transport

What prevents the capillaries of the vasa recta from dissipating the gradient by carrying away the high concentration of NaCl in the medulla's interstitial fluid? As shown in Figure 44.13, the descending and ascending vessels of the vasa recta carry blood in opposite directions through the kidney's osmolarity gradient. As the descending vessel conveys blood toward the inner medulla, water is lost from the blood and NaCl is gained by diffusion. These fluxes are reversed as blood flows back toward the cortex in the ascending vessel, with water reentering the blood and salt diffusing out. Thus, the vasa recta can supply the kidney with nutrients and other important substances carried by the blood without interfering with the osmolarity gradient in the inner and outer medulla.

The countercurrent-like characteristics of the loop of Henle and the vasa recta help to generate the steep osmotic gradient between the medulla and cortex. However, diffusion will eventually eliminate any osmotic gradient within animal tissue unless gradient formation is supported by an expenditure of energy. In the kidney, this expenditure largely occurs in the thick segment of the ascending limb of the loop of Henle, where NaCl is actively transported out of the tubule. Even with the benefits of countercurrent exchange, this process—along with other renal active transport systems—consumes considerable ATP. Thus, for its size, the kidney has one of the highest metabolic rates of any organ.

As a result of active transport of NaCl out of the thick segment of the ascending limb, the filtrate is actually hypoosmotic to body fluids by the time it reaches the distal tubule. Next the filtrate descends again toward the medulla, this time in the collecting duct, which is permeable to water but not to salt. Therefore, osmosis extracts water from the filtrate as it passes from cortex to medulla and encounters interstitial fluid of increasing osmolarity. This process concentrates salt, urea, and other solutes in the filtrate. Some urea passes out of the lower portion of the collecting duct and contributes to the high interstitial osmolarity of the inner medulla. (This urea is recycled by diffusion into the loop of Henle, but continual leakage from the collecting duct maintains a high interstitial urea concentration.) When the kidney concentrates urine maximally, the urine reaches 1200 mOsm/L, the osmolarity of the interstitial fluid in the inner medulla. Although *isoosmotic* to the inner medulla's interstitial fluid, the urine is *hyperosmotic* to blood and interstitial fluid elsewhere in the body. This high osmolarity allows the solutes remaining in the urine to be excreted from the body with minimal water loss.

Adaptations of the Vertebrate Kidney to Diverse Environments

EVOLUTION Vertebrate animals occupy habitats ranging from rain forests to deserts and from some of the saltiest bodies of water to the nearly pure waters of high mountain lakes. Variations in nephron structure and function equip the kidneys of different vertebrates for osmoregulation in their various habitats. The adaptations of the vertebrate kidney are made apparent by comparing species that inhabit a wide range of environments or by comparing the responses of different vertebrate groups to similar environmental conditions.

Mammals

The juxtamedullary nephron, with its urine-concentrating features, is a key adaptation to terrestrial life, enabling mammals to get rid of salts and nitrogenous wastes without squandering water. As we have seen, the remarkable ability of the mammalian kidney to produce hyperosmotic urine depends on the precise arrangement of the tubules and collecting ducts in the renal cortex and medulla. In this respect, the kidney is one of the clearest examples of how natural selection links the function of an organ to its structure.

Mammals that excrete the most hyperosmotic urine, such as Australian hopping mice, North American kangaroo rats, and other desert mammals, have loops of Henle that extend deep into the medulla. Long loops maintain steep osmotic gradients in the kidney, resulting in urine becoming very concentrated as it passes from cortex to medulla in the collecting ducts.

In contrast, beavers, muskrats, and other aquatic mammals that spend much of their time in fresh water and rarely face problems of dehydration have nephrons with relatively short loops, resulting in a much lower ability to concentrate urine. Terrestrial mammals living in moist conditions have loops of Henle of intermediate length and the capacity to produce urine intermediate in concentration to that produced by freshwater and desert mammals.

Case Study: Kidney Function in the Vampire Bat

The South American vampire bat shown in Figure 44.16 illustrates the versatility of the mammalian kidney. This species feeds at night on the blood of large birds and mammals. The bat uses its sharp teeth to make a small incision in the prey's skin and then laps up blood from the wound (the prey animal is typically not seriously harmed). Anticoagulants in the bat's saliva prevent the blood from clotting.

A vampire bat often searches for hours and flies long distances to locate a suitable victim. When it does find prey, it drinks as much blood as it can, which could make it too heavy to fly. As it feeds, however, the bat's kidneys excrete large volumes of dilute urine, up to 24% of body mass per hour. Having lost enough weight to take off, the bat can fly back to its roost in a cave or hollow tree, where it spends the day.

▲ Figure 44.16 A vampire bat (*Desmodus rotundas*), a mammal with a unique excretory situation.

In the roost, the bat faces a different regulatory problem. Most of the nutrition it derives from blood comes in the form of protein. Digesting proteins generates large quantities of urea, but roosting bats lack access to the drinking water necessary to dilute it. Instead, their kidneys shift to producing small quantities of highly concentrated urine (up to 4600 mOsm/L), an adjustment that disposes of the urea load while conserving as much water as possible. The vampire bat's ability to alternate rapidly between producing large amounts of dilute urine and small amounts of very hyperosmotic urine is an essential part of its adaptation to an unusual food source.

Birds and Other Reptiles

Most birds, including the puffin (see Figure 44.1) and the roadrunner (Figure 44.17), live in environments that are dehydrating. Like mammals, birds have kidneys with juxtamedullary nephrons that specialize in conserving water. However, the nephrons of birds have loops of Henle that extend less far into the medulla than those of mammals. Thus, bird kidneys

▲ Figure 44.17 The roadrunner (*Geococcyx californianus*), an animal well adapted to its dry environment.

cannot concentrate urine to the high osmolarities achieved by mammalian kidneys. Although birds can produce hyperosmotic urine, their main water conservation adaptation is having uric acid as the nitrogen waste molecule. Since uric acid can be excreted as a paste, it reduces urine volume.

The kidneys of other reptiles, which have only cortical nephrons, produce urine that is isoosmotic or hypoosmotic to body fluids. However, the epithelium of the chamber from which urine and feces leave the body (the cloaca) helps conserve fluid by reabsorbing water from these wastes. Also like birds, most other reptiles excrete their nitrogenous wastes as uric acid.

Freshwater Fishes and Amphibians

Freshwater fishes are hyperosmotic to their surroundings, so they must excrete excess water continuously. In contrast to mammals and birds, freshwater fishes produce large volumes of very dilute urine. Their kidneys, which contain many nephrons, produce filtrate at a high rate. Freshwater fishes conserve salts by reabsorbing ions from the filtrate in their distal tubules, leaving water behind.

Amphibian kidneys function much like those of freshwater fishes. When in fresh water, the kidneys of frogs excrete dilute urine while the skin accumulates certain salts from the water by active transport. On land, where dehydration is the most pressing problem of osmoregulation, frogs conserve body fluid by reabsorbing water across the epithelium of the urinary bladder.

Marine Bony Fishes

The tissues of marine bony fishes gain excess salts from their surroundings and lose water. These environmental challenges are opposite to those faced by their freshwater relatives. Compared with freshwater fishes, marine fishes have fewer and smaller nephrons, and their nephrons lack a distal tubule. In addition, their kidneys have small glomeruli or lack glomeruli entirely. In keeping with these features, filtration rates are low and very little urine is excreted.

The main function of kidneys in marine bony fishes is to get rid of divalent ions (those with a charge of 2+ or 2−) such as calcium (Ca^{2+}), magnesium (Mg^{2+}), and sulphate (SO_4^{2-}). Marine fishes take in divalent ions by incessantly drinking seawater. They rid themselves of these ions by secreting them into the proximal tubules of the nephrons and excreting them in urine. Secretion by the gills maintains proper levels of monovalent ions (charge of 1+ or 1−) such as Na^+ and Cl^-.

The generation of ion gradients and the movement of ions across membranes is central to salt and water balance in marine bony fishes. These events, however, are by no means unique to these organisms nor to homeostasis. As illustrated by the examples in Figure 44.18, osmoregulation by chloride cells is but one of many diverse physiological processes that are driven by the movement of ions across a membrane.

MAKE CONNECTIONS

Ion Movement and Gradients

The transport of ions across the plasma membrane of a cell is a fundamental activity of all animals, and indeed of all living things. By generating ion gradients, ion transport provides the potential energy that powers processes ranging from an organism's regulation of salts and gases in internal fluids to its perception of and locomotion through its environment.

Information Processing

In neurons, the opening and closing of channels selective for sodium or other ions underlies the transmission of information as nerve impulses. These signals enable nervous systems to receive and process input and to direct appropriate output, such as this leap of a frog capturing prey. See Concept 48.3.

Osmoregulation

In marine bony fishes, ion gradients drive secretion of salt (NaCl), a process essential to avoid dehydration. Within gills, the pumps, cotransporters, and channels of specialized chloride cells function together to drive salt from the blood across the gill epithelium and into the surrounding salt water. See Concept 44.1.

Locomotion

A gradient of H^+ ions powers the bacterial flagellum. An electron transport chain generates this gradient, establishing a higher concentration of H^+ outside the bacterial cell. Protons reentering the cell provide a force that causes the flagellar motor to rotate. The rotating motor turns the curved hook, causing the attached filament to propel the cell. See Concepts 9.4 and 27.1.

Gas Exchange

Ion gradients provide the basis for the opening of plant stomata by surrounding guard cells. Active transport of H^+ out of a guard cell generates a voltage (membrane potential) that drives inward movement of K^+ ions. This uptake of K^+ by guard cells triggers an osmotic influx of water that changes cell shape, bowing the guard cells outward and thereby opening the stoma. See Concept 36.4.

MAKE CONNECTIONS *Explain why the set of forces driving ion movement across the plasma membrane of a cell are described as an electrochemical (electrical and chemical) gradient* (see Concept 7.4).

ANIMATION *BioFlix* Visit the Study Area in **MasteringBiology** for the BioFlix 3-D Animation on Membrane Transport (Chapter 7). BioFlix Tutorials can also be assigned in MasteringBiology.

CONCEPT CHECK 44.4

1. What do the number and length of nephrons in a fish's kidney indicate about the fish's habitat? How do they correlate with urine production?

2. Many medications make the epithelium of the collecting duct less permeable to water. How would taking such a drug affect kidney output?

3. **WHAT IF?** If blood pressure in the afferent arteriole leading to a glomerulus decreased, how would the rate of blood filtration within Bowman's capsule be affected? Explain.

For suggested answers, see Appendix A.

CONCEPT 44.5

Hormonal circuits link kidney function, water balance, and blood pressure

In mammals, both the volume and osmolarity of urine are adjusted according to an animal's water and salt balance and its rate of urea production. In situations of high salt intake and low water availability, a mammal can excrete urea and salt in small volumes of hyperosmotic urine with minimal water loss. If salt is scarce and fluid intake is high, the kidney can instead get rid of the excess water with little salt loss by producing large volumes of hypoosmotic urine. At such times, the urine can be as dilute as 70 mOsm/L, compared with an osmolarity of 300 mOsm/L for human blood.

Antidiuretic Hormone

A combination of nervous and hormonal controls manages the osmoregulatory function of the mammalian kidney. One key hormone in this regulatory circuitry is **antidiuretic hormone (ADH)**, also called *vasopressin*. ADH is produced in the hypothalamus of the brain and stored in the posterior pituitary gland, located just below the hypothalamus. Osmo-receptor cells in the hypothalamus monitor the osmolarity of blood and regulate release of ADH from the posterior pituitary.

To understand the role of ADH, let's consider what occurs when blood osmolarity rises, such as after eating salty food or losing water through sweating (Figure 44.19). In response to an increase in osmolarity above the set point of 300 mOsm/L, more ADH is released into the bloodstream. When ADH reaches the kidney, its main targets are the collecting ducts. There, ADH brings about changes that make the epithelium more permeable to water. The resulting increase in water reabsorption concentrates urine, reduces urine volume, and lowers blood

osmolarity back toward the set point. (Only the gain of additional water in food and drink can fully restore osmolarity to 300 mOsm/L.) As the osmolarity of the blood subsides, a negative-feedback mechanism reduces the activity of osmoreceptor cells in the hypothalamus, and ADH secretion is reduced (not shown in figure).

A reduction in blood osmolarity below the set point has the opposite set of effects. For example, intake of a large volume of water leads to a decrease in ADH secretion to a very low level. The resulting decrease in permeability of the collecting ducts reduces water reabsorption, resulting in discharge of large volumes of dilute urine. (Diuresis refers to increased urination, and ADH is called *anti*diuretic hormone because it opposes this state.)

ADH influences water uptake in the kidney's collecting ducts by regulating the water-selective channels formed by aquaporins. Binding of ADH to receptor molecules leads to a temporary increase in the number of aquaporin proteins in the membranes of collecting duct cells (Figure 44.20). Additional channels recapture more water, reducing urine volume.

Blood osmolarity, ADH release, and water reabsorption in the kidney are normally linked in a feedback circuit that contributes to homeostasis. Anything that disrupts this circuit can interfere with water balance. For example, alcohol inhibits ADH release, leading to excessive urinary water loss and dehydration (which may cause some of the symptoms of a hangover).

Mutations that prevent ADH production or that inactivate the ADH receptor gene block the increase in channel number and thus the ADH response. The resulting disorder

▲ Figure 44.19 **Regulation of fluid retention in the kidney by antidiuretic hormone (ADH).**

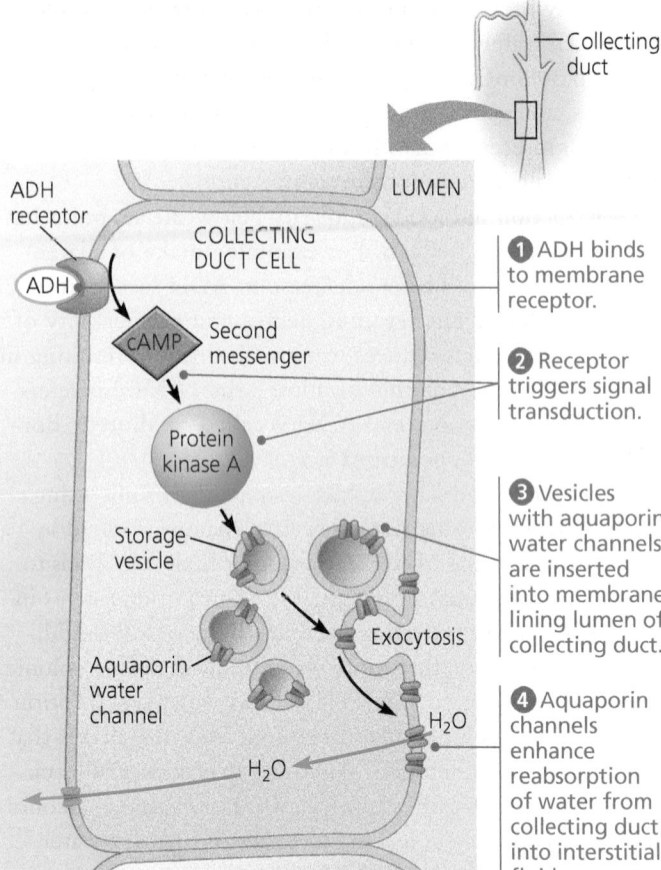

1 ADH binds to membrane receptor.

2 Receptor triggers signal transduction.

3 Vesicles with aquaporin water channels are inserted into membrane lining lumen of collecting duct.

4 Aquaporin channels enhance reabsorption of water from collecting duct into interstitial fluid.

▲ Figure 44.20 **ADH response pathway in the collecting duct.**

can cause severe dehydration and solute imbalance due to production of urine that is abnormally large in volume and very dilute. These symptoms give the condition its name: *diabetes insipidus* (from the Greek for "to pass through" and "having no flavour"). Could mutations in an aquaporin gene have a similar effect? **Figure 44.21** describes an experimental approach that addressed this question.

The Renin-Angiotensin-Aldosterone System

A second regulatory mechanism that helps maintain homeostasis by acting on the kidney is the **renin-angiotensin-aldosterone system (RAAS)**. The RAAS involves the **juxtaglomerular apparatus (JGA)**, a specialized tissue consisting of cells of and around the afferent arteriole that supplies blood to the glomerulus (**Figure 44.22**). When blood pressure or blood volume in the afferent arteriole drops (for instance, as a result of dehydration), the JGA releases the enzyme renin. Renin initiates a sequence of chemical reactions that cleave a plasma protein called angiotensinogen, ultimately yielding a peptide called **angiotensin II**.

Functioning as a hormone, angiotensin II raises blood pressure by constricting arterioles, which decreases blood flow to many capillaries, including those of the kidney. Angiotensin II also stimulates the adrenal glands to release a hormone called

---

▼ Figure 44.21 | **Inquiry**

Can aquaporin mutations cause diabetes?

Experiment Researchers studied a diabetes insipidus patient with a normal ADH receptor gene but two mutant alleles (A and B) of the aquaporin-2 gene. The resulting changes are shown below in an alignment of protein sequences that includes other species.

Source of Aquaporin-2 Gene Sequence	Amino Acids 183–191* in Encoded Protein	Amino Acids 212–220* in Encoded Protein
Frog (*Xenopus laevis*)	MNPARSFAP	GIFASLIYN
Lizard (*Anolis carolinensis*)	MNPARSFGP	AVVASLLYN
Chicken (*Gallus gallus*)	MNPARSFAP	AAAASIIYN
Human (*Homo sapiens*)	MNPARSLAP	AILGSLLYN
Conserved residues	MNPARSxxP	xxxxSxxYN
Patient's gene: allele A	MNPACSLAP	AILGSLLYN
Patient's gene: allele B	MNPARSLAP	AILGPLLYN

*The numbering is based on the human aquaporin-2 protein sequence.

Each mutation changed the protein sequence at a highly conserved position. To test the hypothesis that the changes affect function, researchers used frog oocytes, cells that will express foreign messenger RNA and can be readily collected from adult female frogs.

1 Messenger RNA transcribed from wild-type and mutant aquaporin genes is injected into frog oocytes, where it directs the synthesis of aquaporin proteins.

2 The oocytes are transferred from a 200-mOsm/L to a 10-mOsm/L solution. The rate of oocyte swelling is measured as an indicator of water permeability.

Wild type · Allele A · Allele B · H₂O (control)

Oocyte

10-mOsm/L solution

Results

Source of Injected mRNA	Rate of Swelling (μm/sec)
Human wild type	196
Patient's allele A	17
Patient's allele B	18
None	20

Conclusion Because each mutation inactivates aquaporin as a water channel, the patient's disorder can be attributed to these mutations.

Source: Based on P. M. Deen et al., Requirement of human renal water channel aquaporin-2 for vasopressin-dependent concentration in urine, *Science* 264:5155 (1994). © Jane B Reece.

WHAT IF? *If you measured ADH levels in patients with ADH receptor mutations and in patients with aquaporin mutations, what would you expect to find, compared with wild-type subjects?*

More Na+ and H2O are reabsorbed in distal tubules, increasing blood volume.

Aldosterone

Adrenal gland

Arterioles constrict, increasing blood pressure.

NORMAL BLOOD PRESSURE AND VOLUME

Angiotensin II

ACE

Angiotensin I

Angiotensinogen

Renin

Liver

Blood pressure or blood volume drops (for example, due to dehydration or blood loss).

Distal tubule

JGA releases renin.

Sensors in JGA detect decrease in pressure or volume.

Juxtaglomerular apparatus (JGA)

▲ Figure 44.22 Regulation of blood volume and blood pressure by the renin-angiotensin-aldosterone system (RAAS).

aldosterone. This hormone acts on the nephrons' distal tubules and collecting duct, making them reabsorb more Na^+ and water, thus increasing blood volume and pressure.

Because angiotensin II acts in several ways that increase blood pressure, drugs that block angiotensin II production are widely used to treat hypertension (chronic high blood pressure). Many of these drugs are specific inhibitors of angiotensin converting enzyme (ACE), which catalyzes the second step in the production of angiotensin II. As shown in Figure 44.22, renin released from the JGA acts on angiotensinogen (in the blood), forming angiotensin I. ACE in vascular endothelium, particularly in the lungs, then splits off two amino acids from angiotensin I, forming active angiotensin II. Blocking ACE activity with drugs prevents angiotensin II production and often lowers blood pressure into the normal range.

Homeostatic Regulation of the Kidney

The renin-angiotensin-aldosterone system operates as part of a complex feedback circuit that results in homeostasis. A drop in blood pressure and blood volume triggers renin release from the JGA. In turn, the rise in blood pressure and volume resulting from the various actions of angiotensin II and aldosterone reduces the release of renin.

The functions of ADH and the RAAS may seem to be redundant, but this is not the case. Both increase water reabsorption in the kidney, but they counter different osmoregulatory problems. The release of ADH is a response to an increase in blood osmolarity, as when the body is dehydrated

from excessive water loss or inadequate water intake. However, a situation that causes an excessive loss of both salt and body fluids—a major wound, for example, or severe diarrhea—will reduce blood volume *without* increasing osmolarity. This will not affect ADH release, but the RAAS will respond to the drop in blood volume and pressure by increasing water and Na^+ reabsorption. Thus, ADH and the RAAS are partners in homeostasis. ADH alone would lower blood Na^+ concentration by stimulating water reabsorption in the kidney, but the RAAS helps maintain the osmolarity of body fluids at the set point by stimulating Na^+ reabsorption.

Another hormone, **atrial natriuretic peptide (ANP)**, opposes the RAAS. The walls of the atria of the heart release ANP in response to an increase in blood volume and pressure. ANP inhibits the release of renin from the JGA, inhibits NaCl reabsorption by the collecting ducts, and reduces aldosterone release from the adrenal glands. These actions lower blood volume and pressure. Thus, ADH, the RAAS, and ANP provide an elaborate system of checks and balances that regulate the kidney's ability to control the osmolarity, salt concentration, volume, and pressure of blood. The precise regulatory role of ANP is an area of active research.

In all animals, diverse tissues and organs work continuously to maintain ion and water balance and produce and excrete nitrogenous wastes. The details that we have reviewed in this chapter only hint at the great complexity of the neural and hormonal mechanisms involved in regulating these homeostatic processes.

CONCEPT CHECK 44.5

1. How does alcohol affect regulation of water balance in the body?

2. Why could it be dangerous to drink a very large amount of water in a short period of time?

3. **WHAT IF?** Conn's syndrome is a condition caused by tumours of the adrenal cortex that secrete high amounts of aldosterone in an unregulated manner. What would you expect to be the major symptom of this disorder?

4. **MAKE CONNECTIONS** Compare the activity of renin and ACE in the renin-angiotensin-aldosterone system with that of the protein kinases in a phosphorylation cascade, such as the one shown in Figure 11.10. How are the roles of these enzymes similar and different in the two regulated response pathways?

For suggested answers, see Appendix A.

44 Chapter Review

Go to **MasteringBiology**® for Assignments, the eText, and the
Study Area with Animations, Activities, Vocab Self-Quiz, and Practice Tests.

SUMMARY OF KEY CONCEPTS

CONCEPT 44.1

Osmoregulation balances the uptake and loss of water and solutes (pp. 1026–1030)

- Cells balance water gain and loss through **osmoregulation**, a process based on the controlled movement of solutes between internal fluids and the external environment and on the movement of water, which follows by osmosis. **Osmoconformers** are isoosmotic with their marine environment and do not regulate their **osmolarity**. In contrast, **osmoregulators** control water uptake and loss in a hypoosmotic or hyperosmotic environment, respectively. Water-conserving excretory organs help terrestrial animals to avoid desiccation. Animals that live in temporary waters may be **anhydrobiotic** for one stage of life.

Animal	Inflow/Outflow	Urine
Freshwater fish. Lives in water less concentrated than body fluids; fish tends to gain water, lose salt	Does not drink water. Salt in, H₂O in (active transport by gills). Salt out	▶ Large volume of urine ▶ Urine is less concentrated than body fluids
Marine bony fish. Lives in water more concentrated than body fluids; fish tends to lose water, gain salt	Drinks water. Salt in, H₂O out. Salt out (active transport by gills)	▶ Small volume of urine ▶ Urine is slightly less concentrated than body fluids
Terrestrial vertebrate. Terrestrial environment; tends to lose body water to air	Drinks water. Salt in (by mouth). H₂O and salt out	▶ Moderate volume of urine ▶ Urine is more concentrated than body fluids

Source: Adapted from *Life: An Introduction to Biology*, 3rd edition, by William Samson Beck. Copyright © 1991 by Pearson Education, Inc. Adapted and electronically reproduced by permission of Pearson Education, Inc., Upper Saddle River, New Jersey.

- **Transport epithelia** contain specialized epithelial cells that regulate the solute movements required for waste disposal and for tempering changes in body fluids.

? *Under what environmental conditions does water move into a cell by osmosis?*

CONCEPT 44.2

An animal's nitrogenous wastes reflect its phylogeny and habitat (pp. 1030–1032)

- Protein and nucleic acid metabolism generates **ammonia**. Most aquatic animals excrete ammonia. Mammals and most adult amphibians convert ammonia to the less toxic **urea**, which is excreted with a minimal loss of water. Insects and many reptiles, including birds, convert ammonia to **uric acid**, a mostly insoluble waste excreted in a paste-like urine.
- The kind of nitrogenous waste excreted depends on an animal's evolutionary history and habitat. The amount of nitrogenous waste produced is coupled to the animal's energy budget and amount of dietary protein.

DRAW IT *Construct a table summarizing the three major types of nitrogenous wastes and their relative toxicity, energy content, and associated water loss during excretion.*

CONCEPT 44.3

Diverse excretory systems are variations on a tubular theme (pp. 1032–1035)

- Most excretory systems carry out **filtration, reabsorption, secretion**, and **excretion**. The **protonephridia** of the flatworm flame bulb excrete a dilute **filtrate**. An earthworm has pairs of open-ended **metanephridia** in each segment that produce urine. In insects, **Malpighian tubules** function in osmoregulation and removal of nitrogenous wastes. **Kidneys** function in both excretion and osmoregulation in vertebrates.
- Excretory tubules (consisting of **nephrons** and **collecting ducts**) and blood vessels pack the mammalian kidney. Blood pressure forces fluid from blood in the **glomerulus** into the lumen of **Bowman's capsule**. Following reabsorption and secretion, filtrate flows into a collecting duct. The **ureter** conveys urine from the **renal pelvis** to the **urinary bladder**.

? *Given that a typical excretory system selectively absorbs and secretes materials, what function does filtration serve?*

CONCEPT 44.4

The nephron is organized for stepwise processing of blood filtrate (pp. 1035–1043)

- Within the nephron, selective secretion and reabsorption in the **proximal tubule** alter filtrate volume and composition. The *descending limb* of the **loop of Henle** is permeable to water but not salt; water moves by osmosis into the interstitial fluid. The *ascending limb* is permeable to salt but not water; as the filtrate ascends, salt leaves by diffusion and by active transport. The **distal tubule** and collecting duct regulate K⁺ and NaCl levels in body fluids. The collecting duct can respond to hormonal signals to reabsorb more water.
- In a mammalian kidney, a **countercurrent multiplier system** involving the loop of Henle maintains the gradient of salt concentration in the kidney interior. In response to hormonal signals, urine can be concentrated in the collecting duct. Urea, which leaves the collecting duct within the inner medulla, contributes to the osmotic gradient of the kidney.

- Natural selection has shaped the form and function of nephrons in various vertebrates to the osmoregulatory challenges of the animals' habitats. For example, desert mammals, which excrete the most hyperosmotic urine, have loops of Henle that extend deep into the **renal medulla**, whereas mammals in moist habitats have shorter loops and excrete more dilute urine.

? How do cortical and juxtamedullary nephrons differ with respect to reabsorbing nutrients and concentrating urine?

CONCEPT 44.5

Hormonal circuits link kidney function, water balance, and blood pressure (pp. 1043–1045)

- The posterior pituitary gland releases **antidiuretic hormone (ADH)** when blood osmolarity rises above a set point, such as when water intake is inadequate. ADH increases permeability to water in collecting ducts through an increase in the number of epithelial water channels. When blood pressure or blood volume in the afferent arteriole drops, the **juxtaglomerular apparatus (JGA)** releases renin. **Angiotensin II** formed in response to renin constricts arterioles and triggers release of the hormone **aldosterone**, raising blood pressure and reducing the release of renin. This **renin-angiotensin-aldosterone system (RAAS)** has functions that overlap with those of ADH and are opposed by **atrial natriuretic peptide (ANP)**.

? Why can only some patients with diabetes insipidus be treated effectively with ADH?

TEST YOUR UNDERSTANDING

LEVEL 1: KNOWLEDGE/COMPREHENSION

1. *Unlike* an earthworm's metanephridia, a mammalian nephron
   a. is intimately associated with a capillary network.
   b. forms urine by changing fluid composition inside a tubule.
   c. functions in both osmoregulation and excretion.
   d. receives filtrate from blood instead of coelomic fluid.

2. Which process in the nephron is *least* selective?
   a. filtration
   b. reabsorption
   c. active transport
   d. secretion

3. Which of the following animals generally has the lowest volume of urine production?
   a. a vampire bat
   b. a salmon in fresh water
   c. a marine bony fish
   d. a freshwater bony fish

LEVEL 2: APPLICATION/ANALYSIS

4. The high osmolarity of the renal medulla is maintained by all of the following *except*
   a. diffusion of salt from the thin segment of the ascending limb of the loop of Henle.
   b. active transport of salt from the thick segment of the ascending limb.
   c. the spatial arrangement of juxtamedullary nephrons.
   d. diffusion of salt from the descending limb of the loop of Henle.

5. Natural selection should favour the highest proportion of juxtamedullary nephrons in which of the following species?
   a. a river otter
   b. a mouse species living in a tropical rain forest
   c. a mouse species living in a temperate broadleaf forest
   d. a mouse species living in a desert

6. African lungfish, which are often found in small, stagnant pools of fresh water, produce urea as a nitrogenous waste. What is the advantage of this adaptation?
   a. Urea takes less energy to synthesize than ammonia.
   b. Small, stagnant pools do not provide enough water to dilute the toxic ammonia.
   c. The highly toxic urea makes the pool uninhabitable to potential competitors.
   d. Urea forms an insoluble precipitate.

LEVEL 3: SYNTHESIS/EVALUATION

7. **DRAW IT** Using Figure 44.3 as an example, sketch the exchange of salt (NaCl) and water between a shark and its marine environment.

8. **EVOLUTION CONNECTION**
   Merriam's kangaroo rats (*Dipodomys merriami*) live in North American habitats ranging from moist, cool woodlands to hot deserts. Assuming that natural selection has resulted in differences in water conservation between *D. merriami* populations, propose a hypothesis concerning the relative rates of evaporative water loss by populations that live in moist versus dry environments. Using a humidity sensor to detect evaporative water loss by kangaroo rats, how could you test your hypothesis?

9. **SCIENTIFIC INQUIRY**
   You are exploring kidney function in kangaroo rats. You measure urine volume and osmolarity, as well as the amount of chloride (Cl^-) and urea in the urine. If the water source provided to the animals were switched from tap water to a 2% NaCl solution, what change in urine osmolarity would you expect? How would you determine if this change was more likely due to a change in the excretion of Cl^- or urea?

10. **WRITE ABOUT A THEME: ORGANIZATION**
    In a short essay (100–150 words), compare how membrane structures in the loop of Henle and collecting duct of the mammalian kidney enable water to be recovered from filtrate in the process of osmoregulation.

11. **SYNTHESIZE YOUR KNOWLEDGE**

Steven A. Wasserman

The marine iguana (*Amblyrhynchus cristatus*), which spends long periods under water feeding on seaweed, relies on both salt glands and kidneys for homeostasis of its internal fluids. Describe how these organs together meet the particular osmoregulatory challenges of this animal's environment.

For selected answers, see Appendix A.

45

Hormones and the Endocrine System

KEY CONCEPTS

45.1 Hormones and other signalling molecules bind to target receptors, triggering specific response pathways

45.2 Feedback regulation and antagonistic hormone pairs are common in endocrine systems

45.3 Vertebrate hormones regulate homeostasis, development, and behaviour

StevenRussellSmithPhotos/Shutterstock

▲ Figure 45.1 **What signals triggered the metamorphosis of a caterpillar into this butterfly?**

The Body's Long-Distance Regulators

To say that a butterfly, such as the red-spotted Purple butterfly (*Limenitis arthemis*) common in Eastern Canada (**Figure 45.1**), was once a caterpillar is only partly true. The adult cells that form the butterfly begin growing in the embryo. Within the larval caterpillar, they are nourished as islands of tissues that will eventually become the eyes, wings, brain, and other structures of the butterfly. Once the plump, crawling caterpillar becomes a stationary pupa, the adult cells take over. They complete their program of development, while many larval tissues undergo programmed cell death. The end result is a butterfly, a delicate, free-flying adult that bears little resemblance to the larval and pupal forms from which it arose.

What brings about such a complete change of body form, or *metamorphosis*? The answer for this and many other biological processes is a type of molecule called a **hormone** (from the Greek *horman*, to excite).

In animals, hormones are secreted into the extracellular fluid, circulate in the hemolymph or blood, and communicate regulatory messages throughout the body. In the case of the caterpillar, hormones regulate the growth of adult tissues and the death of larval cells, and ensure that all of the steps of metamorphosis throughout the body occur at the correct time.

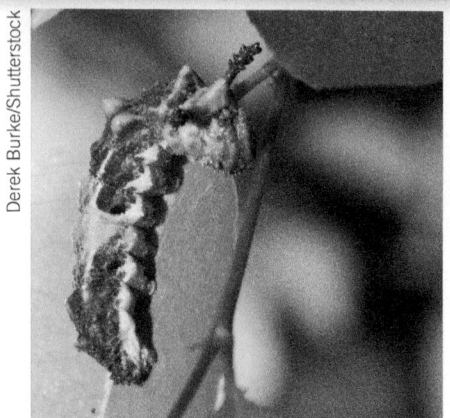

Derek Burke/Shutterstock

◀ Pupating caterpillar

Each hormone has specific receptors in the body. Although a given hormone can reach all cells of the body, only some cells have receptors for that hormone. A hormone elicits a response—such as a change in metabolism—only from specific *target cells*, those that have the matching receptor. Cells lacking a receptor for that particular hormone are unaffected.

Chemical signalling by hormones is the function of the **endocrine system**, one of the two basic systems of communication and regulation throughout the body. Hormones secreted by endocrine cells regulate reproduction, development, energy metabolism, growth, and behaviour. The other major communication and control system is the **nervous system**, a network of specialized cells—neurons—that transmit signals along dedicated pathways. These signals in turn regulate neurons, muscle cells, and endocrine cells. Because signalling by neurons can regulate the release of hormones, the nervous and endocrine systems often overlap in function.

Many hormones work together to regulate a system; for example, blood pressure is affected by a variety of hormones. epinephrine, norepinephrine, and aldosterone, as we will explore later in this chapter. About 23% of adult Canadians have high blood pressure, termed *hypertension*. Hypertension is the major risk factor for heart disease and stroke, the number two killer of Canadian adults. Often termed the silent killer, many people are unaware that they have hypertension. But in 1980, Dr. Adolfo de Bold and coworkers at the University of Ottawa discovered a new hormone, atrial natriuretic factor (ANP), produced by cells in the atria of the heart. A small protein hormone, it works to lower blood pressure by making the kidneys excrete sodium in urine. Blood volume decreases because of osmosis, and this lowers blood pressure. The discovery of ANP has fuelled a new field of research, and ANP itself has been used as a therapeutic drug to treat hypertension. Dr. Bold is currently working on developing a longer-lasting ANP analogue to treat heart failure.

In this chapter, we'll begin with an overview of the different types of chemical signalling in animals and the ways in which the activities of the endocrine and nervous systems are coordinated. We will then explore how hormones regulate target cells, how hormone secretion is regulated, and how hormones help maintain homeostasis. We'll conclude by examining the role of hormones in regulating growth, development, and reproduction, topics we'll return to in Chapters 46 and 47.

CONCEPT 45.1

Hormones and other signalling molecules bind to target receptors, triggering specific response pathways

Endocrine signalling is just one of several ways information is transmitted between animal cells. Let's consider the similarities and differences in these various chemical processes.

Intercellular Communication

The ways in which chemical signals are transmitted between animal cells are often classified by two criteria: the type of secreting cell and the route taken by the signal in reaching its target.

Endocrine Signalling

As illustrated in **Figure 45.2a**, hormones secreted into extracellular fluids by endocrine cells reach distant target cells via the bloodstream (or hemolymph). Endocrine signalling maintains homeostasis, mediates responses to environmental stimuli, and regulates growth and development. For example, hormones coordinate the body's responses to stress, dehydration, and low blood glucose levels. They also trigger behavioural and physical changes underlying sexual maturity and reproduction.

Paracrine and Autocrine Signalling

Many types of cells produce and secrete **local regulators**, molecules that act over short distances and reach their target cells solely by diffusion. Cytokines, for example, are local regulators that enable communication between immune cells (see Figures 43.17 and 43.19). Depending on the target cell, signalling by local regulators can be either paracrine or autocrine. In **paracrine** signalling (from the Greek *para*, to one side of), the secreting cell affects nearby cells (**Figure 45.2b**). In **autocrine** signalling (from the Greek *auto*, self), the secreting cell affects itself (**Figure 45.2c**). As we will discuss later in this chapter, paracrine and autocrine signalling play roles in many physiological processes, including blood pressure regulation, nervous system function, and reproduction.

Synaptic and Neuroendocrine Signalling

Secreted molecules are crucial for two types of signalling by neurons. In *synaptic signalling*, neurons secrete molecules called **neurotransmitters** that diffuse a very short distance to bind to receptors on the target cells (**Figure 45.2d**). The synapse is the space between the neuron and its target cell. This type of signalling could be considered a type of paracrine signalling if the target cell were a muscle, or autocrine if the target were another neuron. Neurotransmitters are central to sensation, memory, cognition, and movement, as we will explore in Chapters 48–50.

In *neuroendocrine signalling*, specialized neurons called neurosecretory cells secrete molecules that diffuse from nerve cell endings into the bloodstream (**Figure 45.2e**). These molecules, which travel through the bloodstream to target cells, are a class of hormone called **neurohormones**. One example is antidiuretic hormone, also known as vasopressin, a hormone essential to kidney function and water balance (see Chapter 44).

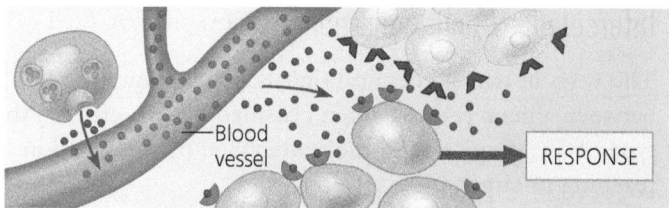

(a) In **endocrine signalling**, secreted molecules diffuse into the blood-stream and trigger responses in target cells anywhere in the body.

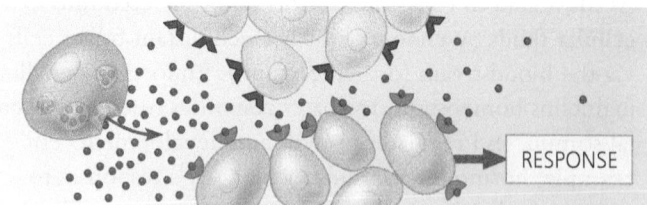

(b) In **paracrine signalling**, secreted molecules diffuse locally and trigger a response in neighbouring cells.

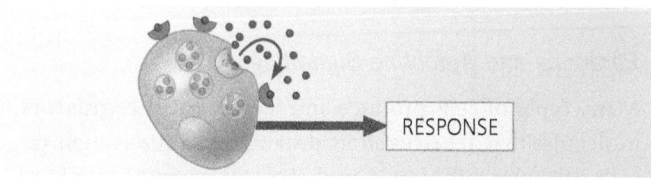

(c) In **autocrine signalling**, secreted molecules diffuse locally and trigger a response in the cells that secrete them.

(d) In **synaptic signalling**, neurotransmitters diffuse across synapses and trigger responses in cells of target tissues (neurons, muscles, or glands).

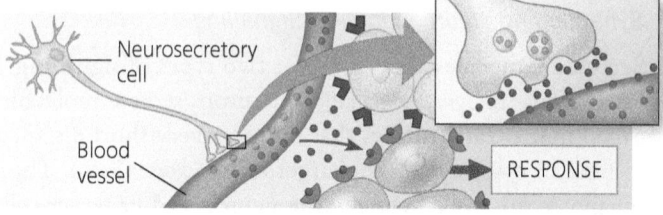

(e) In **neuroendocrine signalling**, neurohormones diffuse into the bloodstream and trigger responses in target cells anywhere in the body.

▲ Figure 45.2 **Intercellular communication by secreted molecules.** In each type of signalling, secreted molecules (•) bind to a specific receptor protein (◡) expressed by target cells. Some receptors are located inside cells, but for simplicity here, all are drawn on the cell surface.

Signalling by Pheromones

Not all secreted signalling molecules act within the body. Members of the same animal species sometimes communicate via **pheromones**, chemicals that are released into the external environment.

◀ Figure 45.3 **Signalling by pheromones.** A female luna moth (*Actias luna*) secretes pheromones to attract males, which use their elaborate antennae (shown here) to detect pheromone trails to the female.

Pheromones serve a wide range of functions that include defining territories, warning of predators, and attracting potential mates. The luna moth, Canada's largest moth species, relies on pheromones for mating (Figure 45.3). Forestry managers employ pheromone traps to assess the density of insects such as the emerald ash borer (*Agrilus planipennis*) and spruce budworm (*Choristoneura fumiferana*). Synthetic pheromones mimic the signals of females, luring these insects into traps searching for a mate.

Chemical Classes of Intercellular Signalling Factors

A vast array of chemicals is used by animals in communication between cells. The properties of the chemical, particularly its solubility (Figure 45.4), is important because it governs many aspects of the signalling pathway. Water-soluble (hydrophilic) or polar factors readily dissolve in body fluids but cannot pass through the lipid-rich plasma membranes of cells. In contrast, lipid-soluble (hydrophobic) or nonpolar hormones cannot dissolve in body fluids, but are able to freely pass through cell membranes. These solubility properties have a profound influence on the way the hormones are produced and stored, exit cells, travel through the blood, and affect their target tissues.

Gaseous Signalling Factors

Many cells produce gases that have local signalling effects. In recent years, several gases, products of metabolism, have been shown to play roles in regulating signalling pathways. Their small size and lack of charge allows them to diffuse freely in both lipid and water. Each of these gases is highly reactive, and because of this chemical reactivity, they do not travel far from sites of production.

Carbon monoxide (CO) and hydrogen sulphide (H_2S) regulate many pathways related to oxidative metabolism.

Water-soluble (hydrophilic)	Lipid-soluble (hydrophobic)
Polypeptides	**Steroids**
Insulin	Cortisol

Amines

Epinephrine

Thyroxine

▲ Figure 45.4 **Hormones differ in structure and solubility.**

MAKE CONNECTIONS *The biosynthesis of epinephrine involves breaking just one carbon-carbon bond in the amino acid tyrosine (see Figure 5.14). Which bond is it?*

Perhaps the best-known gaseous regulator is **nitric oxide (NO)**. It functions in the body as both a local regulator and a neurotransmitter. When the level of oxygen in the blood falls, endothelial cells in blood vessel walls synthesize and release NO. After diffusing into the surrounding smooth muscle cells, NO activates an enzyme that relaxes the cells. The result is vasodilation, which increases blood flow to tissues.

In human males, NO's ability to promote vasodilation enables sexual function by increasing blood flow into the penis, producing an erection. The drug Viagra (sildenafil citrate), a treatment for male erectile dysfunction, sustains an erection by prolonging activity of the NO response pathway.

Protein and Amine Signalling Factors

Many of the most familiar hormones are proteins, encoded by genes that are transcribed and translated in response to the need for the hormone. Insulin, for example, is a protein that is produced as a long, inactive polypeptide. It is stored within the beta-cells of the pancreas in this inactive form, or prohormone, then cleaved and secreted using vesicles when needed to reduce blood glucose levels. Other proteins that act as signalling factors include glucagon and

the various cytokines and **growth factors** that are used to regulate the cell cycle (see Chapter 13). Many types of cells grow, divide, and develop normally only when growth factors are present in their extracellular environment.

Amine hormones are signalling factors produced from amino acids. Glutamate and its derivative GABA are neuronal signalling factors. Catecholamines, such as epinephrine, are produced from tyrosine. Like peptide hormones, they are stored preformed within vesicles and released on demand. Thyroid hormones, such as thyroxine, are produced from tryptophan. Unlike the other amino acid derivatives discussed, thyroid hormones are hydrophobic and cannot be stored in membranous vesicles.

Lipid Signalling Factors

The main types of cell signalling factors that are lipid in nature are related to fatty acids and steroids. Unlike protein hormones, which can vary in structure among species, lipid hormones are chemicals with specific structures. They are all hydrophobic in nature.

Prostaglandins are modified fatty acids that are produced by many cell types and influence diverse physiological systems. In the immune response, they promote fever and inflammation, which is why many drugs that alleviate pain work by inhibiting prostaglandin synthesis or signalling. Prostaglandins help regulate the aggregation of platelets, one step in the formation of blood clots. They also regulate the smooth muscle of the uterus. Prostaglandins in semen induce contractions that help sperm reach the egg. At the onset of childbirth, prostaglandins produced by the placenta help induce labour.

Many hormones are derived from cholesterol or its precursors. Steroids have a central role in many physiological processes of vertebrates. Glucocorticoids regulate metabolism, mineralocorticoids govern ion and water balance, and sex steroids control reproductive biology and development.

Cellular Response Pathways

Focusing on hormones, consider how the solubility of a signalling factor creates constraints on how the hormone is produced, secreted, transported, and sensed by the target tissue (Figure 45.5). At the point of synthesis, the ability of a hydrophobic hormone to pass membranes means it can't be stored in vesicles, whereas hydrophilic hormone factors can be stored preformed within storage vesicles. To be secreted from the cell, a hydrophobic hormone simply diffuses out of the cell, whereas the hydrophilic hormone must be actively secreted. Within the blood, hydrophilic hormones readily dissolve, but insoluble hydrophobic hormones need carrier proteins. At the target tissue, hydrophobic hormones can diffuse into the cell, binding intracellular receptors. Hydrophilic hormones can't get into cells: Their receptors are on the cell membrane.

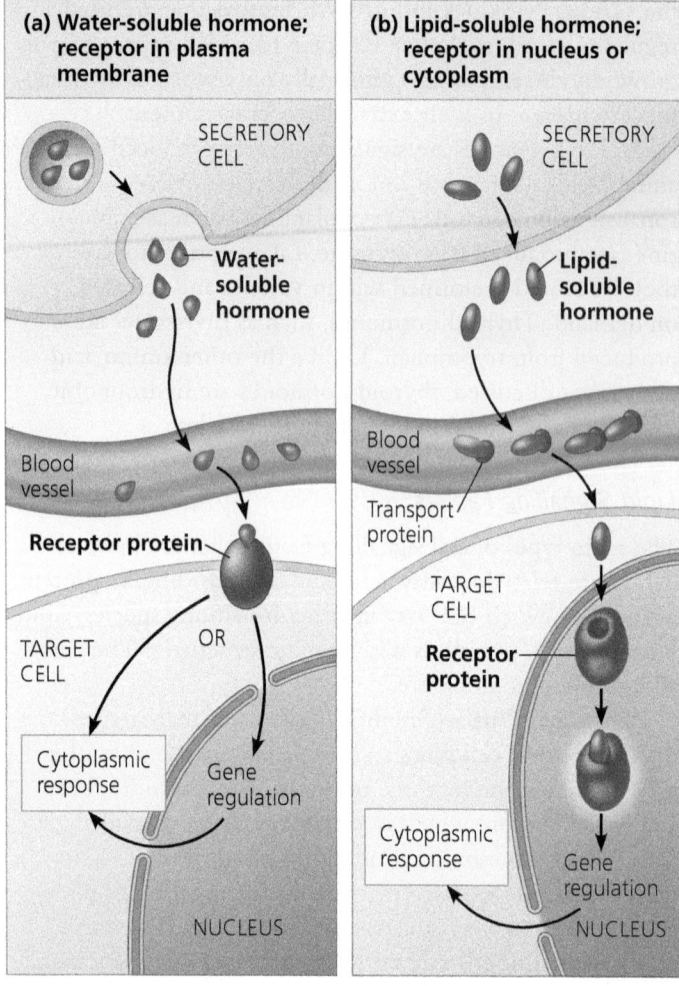

(a) Water-soluble hormone; receptor in plasma membrane

SECRETORY CELL

Water-soluble hormone

Blood vessel

Receptor protein

TARGET CELL

OR

Cytoplasmic response

Gene regulation

NUCLEUS

(b) Lipid-soluble hormone; receptor in nucleus or cytoplasm

SECRETORY CELL

Lipid-soluble hormone

Blood vessel

Transport protein

TARGET CELL

Receptor protein

Cytoplasmic response

Gene regulation

NUCLEUS

▲ **Figure 45.5 Receptor location varies with hormone type. (a)** A water-soluble hormone binds to a signal receptor protein on the surface of a target cell. This interaction triggers events that lead to either a change in cytoplasmic function or a change in gene transcription in the nucleus. **(b)** A lipid-soluble hormone penetrates the target cell's plasma membrane and binds to an intracellular signal receptor, either in the cytoplasm or in the nucleus (shown here). The hormone-receptor complex acts as a transcription factor, typically activating gene expression.

? *Suppose you were studying a cell's response to a particular hormone, and you observed that the cell continued to respond to the hormone even when treated with a chemical that blocks transcription. What could you surmise about the hormone and its receptor?*

To follow the distinct cellular responses to water-soluble and lipid-soluble hormones, we'll examine the two response pathways in turn.

Pathway for Water-Soluble Hormones

The binding of a water-soluble hormone to a signal receptor protein triggers events at the plasma membrane that result in a cellular response. The response may be the activation of an enzyme, a change in the uptake or secretion of specific molecules, or a rearrangement of the cytoskeleton. In addition, some cell-surface receptors cause proteins in the cytoplasm to move into the nucleus and alter transcription of specific genes.

The series of changes in cellular proteins that converts the extracellular chemical signal to a specific intracellular response is called **signal transduction**. As described in Chapter 11, a signal transduction pathway typically involves multiple steps, each involving specific molecular interactions.

To explore the role of signal transduction in hormone signalling, consider one response to short-term stress. When you find yourself in a stressful situation, perhaps running to catch a bus, your adrenal glands secrete **epinephrine**, a hormone also called *adrenaline*. When epinephrine reaches the liver, it binds to a G protein-coupled receptor in the plasma membrane of target cells, as discussed in Chapter 11 and reviewed in **Figure 45.6**. The binding of hormone to receptor triggers a cascade of events involving synthesis of cyclic AMP (cAMP) as a short-lived *second messenger*. Activation of protein kinase A by cAMP leads to activation of an enzyme required for glycogen breakdown and inactivation of an enzyme necessary for glycogen synthesis. The net result is that the liver releases glucose into the bloodstream, providing the fuel you need to chase the departing bus.

Pathway for Lipid-Soluble Hormones

Intracellular receptors for lipid-soluble hormones perform the entire task of transducing a signal within a target cell. The hormone activates the receptor, which then directly triggers the cell's response. In most cases, the response to a lipid-soluble hormone is a change in gene expression.

Steroid hormone receptors are located in the cytosol prior to binding to a hormone. When a steroid hormone binds to its cytosolic receptor, a hormone-receptor complex forms, which moves into the nucleus. There, the receptor

EXTRACELLULAR FLUID

Hormone (epinephrine)

G protein

Adenylyl cyclase

GTP

ATP

G protein-coupled receptor

cAMP

Second messenger

Inhibition of glycogen synthesis

Promotion of glycogen breakdown

Protein kinase A

CYTOPLASM

▲ **Figure 45.6 Cell-surface hormone receptors trigger signal transduction.**

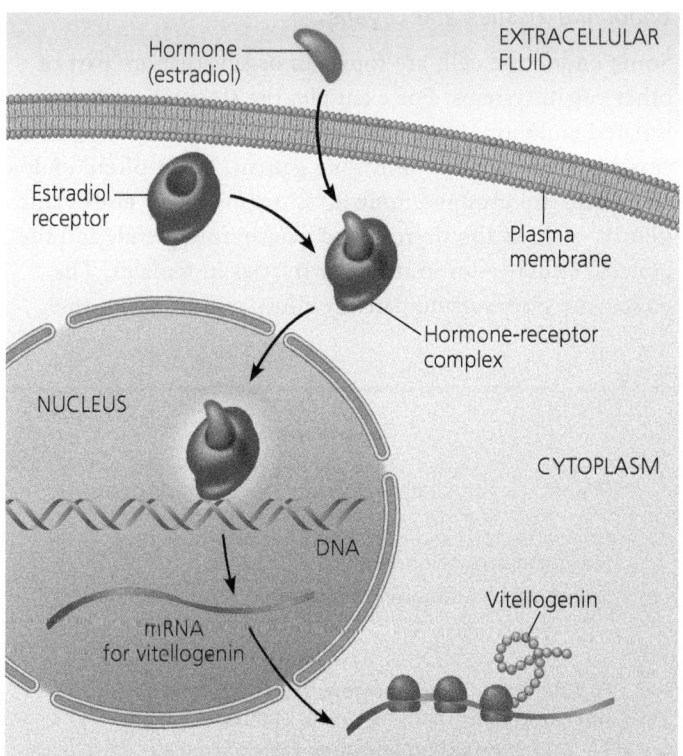

▲ Figure 45.7 **Steroid hormone receptors directly regulate gene expression.**

There is now substantial evidence that estrogens and some other lipid-soluble hormones sometimes trigger responses through mechanisms that don't involve their receptors, acting at the cell surface or elsewhere within cells. How and when these responses arise are currently the subjects of active study.

Multiple Effects of Hormones

Many hormones elicit more than one type of response in the body. The effects brought about by a particular hormone can vary if target cells differ in the molecules that receive or produce the response to that hormone. Consider the effects of epinephrine in mediating the body's response to short-term stress (Figure 45.8). Epinephrine simultaneously triggers glycogen breakdown in the liver, increased blood flow to major skeletal muscles, and decreased blood flow to the digestive tract. These varied effects enhance the rapid reactions of the body in emergencies.

Tissues vary in their response to epinephrine because they vary in their receptors or in their signal transduction pathways. Target cell recognition of epinephrine involves

portion of the complex alters transcription of particular genes by interacting with a specific response element in the DNA (see Figure 18.9). Consider, for example, estrogens, steroid hormones necessary for female reproductive function in vertebrates. In female birds and frogs, estradiol, a form of estrogen, has a specific receptor in liver cells. Binding of estradiol to this receptor activates transcription of the gene for the protein vitellogenin (Figure 45.7). Following translation of the messenger RNA, vitellogenin is secreted and transported in the blood to the reproductive system, where it is used to produce egg yolk.

In contrast to steroid hormone receptors, the thyroid hormone receptor attaches to its target genes in the absence of hormone, repressing transcription. Once thyroxine enters the cell, it travels into the nucleus to bind its receptor. Once the receptor binds the hormone, it releases the element and permits transcription to occur. In other words, the hormone relieves the repression exerted by the receptor in the absence of hormone.

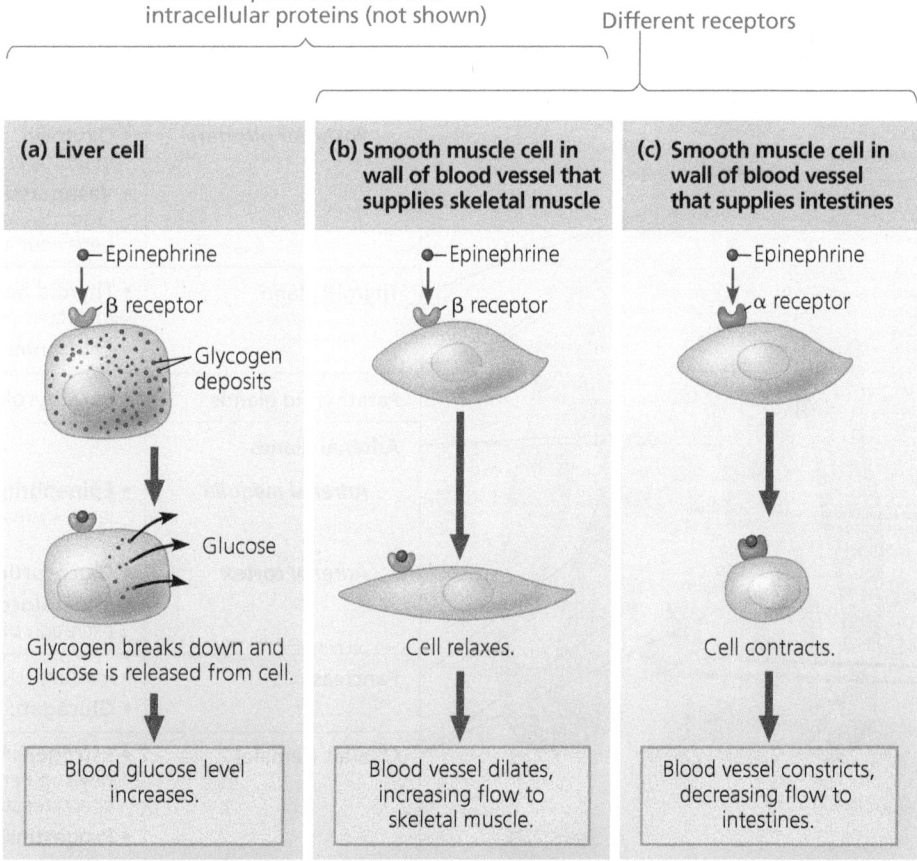

▲ Figure 45.8 **One hormone, different effects.** Epinephrine, the primary "fight-or-flight" hormone, produces different responses in different target cells. Target cells with the same receptor exhibit different responses if they have different signal transduction pathways and/or effector proteins; compare **(a)** with **(b)**. Responses of target cells may also differ if they have different receptors for the hormone; compare **(b)** with **(c)**.

G protein-coupled receptors. Liver cells have a β-type epinephrine receptor that activates the enzyme protein kinase A, which in turn regulates enzymes in glycogen metabolism (Figure 45.8a). In blood vessels supplying skeletal muscle, the same kinase activated by the same epinephrine receptor inactivates a muscle-specific enzyme. The result is smooth muscle relaxation and hence increased blood flow (Figure 45.8b). In contrast, intestinal blood vessels have an α-type epinephrine receptor (Figure 45.8c). Rather than activate protein kinase A, the α receptor triggers a distinct signalling pathway involving a different G protein and different enzymes. The result is smooth muscle contraction and restricted blood flow to the intestines.

Lipid-soluble hormones often exert different effects on different target cells as well. For example, the estrogen that stimulates a bird's liver to synthesize the yolk protein vitellogenin also stimulates its reproductive system to synthesize proteins that form the egg white.

Endocrine Tissues and Organs

Some endocrine cells are found in organs that are part of other organ systems. For example, the stomach contains isolated endocrine cells that help regulate digestive processes by secreting the hormone gastrin. More often, endocrine cells are grouped in ductless organs called **endocrine glands**, such as the thyroid and parathyroid glands and the gonads, either testes in males or ovaries in females. The endocrine glands of humans are illustrated in **Figure 45.9**.

▲ Figure 45.9 **Major human endocrine glands.**

Endocrine gland	Hormones
Pineal gland	• **Melatonin:** Participates in regulation of biological rhythms.
Hypothalamus	• **Hormones released from posterior pituitary (oxytocin and vasopressin)** • **Releasing and inhibiting hormones:** Regulate anterior pituitary
Pituitary gland *Anterior pituitary*	• **Follicle-stimulating hormone (FSH)** and **luteinizing hormone (LH):** Stimulate ovaries and testes • **Thyroid-stimulating hormone (TSH):** Stimulates thyroid gland • **Adrenocorticotropic hormone (ACTH):** Stimulates adrenal cortex • **Prolactin:** Stimulates mammary gland cells • **Growth hormone (GH):** Stimulates growth and metabolic functions
Posterior pituitary	• **Oxytocin:** Stimulates contraction of smooth muscle cells in uterus and mammary glands • **Vasopressin:** (also called **antidiuretic hormone, ADH**): Promotes retention of water by kidneys; influences social behaviour and bonding
Thyroid gland	• **Thyroid hormone (T_3 and T_4):** Stimulates and maintains metabolic processes • **Calcitonin:** Lowers blood calcium level
Parathyroid glands	• **Parathyroid hormone (PTH):** Raises blood calcium level
Adrenal glands *Adrenal medulla*	• **Epinephrine** and **norepinephrine:** Raise blood glucose level; increase metabolic activities; constrict certain blood vessels
Adrenal cortex	• **Glucocorticoids:** Raise blood glucose level • **Mineralocorticoids:** Promote reabsorption of Na^+ and excretion of K^+ in kidneys
Pancreas	• **Insulin:** Lowers blood glucose level • **Glucagon:** Raises blood glucose level
Ovaries (female)	• **Estrogens*:** Stimulate uterine lining growth; promote development and maintenance of female secondary sex characteristics • **Progestins*:** Promote uterine lining growth
Testes (male)	• **Androgens*:** Support sperm formation; promote development and maintenance of male secondary sex characteristics

*Found in both males and females, but with a major role in one sex

This overview of endocrine glands and the hormones that they produce will serve as a useful point of reference as you move through the chapter.

Note that endocrine glands secrete hormones directly into the surrounding fluid. In contrast, *exocrine glands*, such as salivary glands, have ducts that carry secreted substances onto body surfaces or into body cavities. This distinction is reflected in the glands' names: The Greek *endo* (within) and *exo* (out of) refer to secretion into or out of body fluids, while *crine* (from the Greek word meaning "separate") refers to movement away from the secreting cell. In the case of the pancreas, endocrine and exocrine tissues are found in the same gland: Ductless tissues secrete hormones, whereas tissues with ducts secrete enzymes and bicarbonate.

CONCEPT CHECK 45.1

1. How do response mechanisms in target cells differ for water-soluble and lipid-soluble hormones?

2. In what way does one activity described for prostaglandins resemble that of a pheromone?

3. **MAKE CONNECTIONS** How is the action of epinephrine on blood flow to muscles in the fight-or-flight response similar to the action of the plant hormone auxin in apical dominance (see Concept 39.2)?

For suggested answers, see Appendix A.

CONCEPT 45.2

Feedback regulation and antagonistic hormone pairs are common in endocrine systems

So far, we have explored forms of intercellular signalling as well as hormone structure, recognition, and response. We turn now to considering how regulatory pathways that control hormone secretion are organized.

Simple Hormone Pathways

In examining the regulation of hormone secretion, we begin with two basic types of organization—simple endocrine and simple neuroendocrine pathways. In a *simple endocrine pathway*, endocrine cells respond directly to an internal or environmental stimulus by secreting a particular hormone (Figure 45.10). The hormone travels in the bloodstream to target cells, where it interacts with its specific receptors. Signal transduction within target cells brings about a physiological response.

In the example of a simple endocrine pathway shown in Figure 45.10, the stimulus is the release of the acidic contents of the stomach into the duodenum (the first part of the small intestine). Low pH in the duodenum stimulates

▲ Figure 45.10 **A simple endocrine pathway.** Endocrine cells respond to a change in some internal or external variable—the stimulus—by secreting hormone molecules that trigger a specific response by target cells. In the case of secretin signalling, the simple endocrine pathway is self-limiting because the response to secretin (bicarbonate release) reduces the stimulus (low pH) through negative feedback.

certain endocrine cells there, called S cells, to secrete the hormone *secretin*. Secretin enters the bloodstream and travels to the **pancreas**, a gland located behind the stomach (see Figure 45.9). Exocrine cells in the pancreas then release bicarbonate into ducts leading to the duodenum, where it raises the pH.

In a *simple neuroendocrine pathway*, the stimulus is received by a sensory neuron, which stimulates a neurosecretory cell (Figure 45.11). The neurosecretory cell then secretes a neurohormone, which diffuses into the bloodstream and travels to target cells. Such a pathway regulates milk release during nursing in mammals. Suckling by an infant stimulates sensory neurons in the nipples, generating signals in the nervous system that reach the hypothalamus. Nerve impulses from the hypothalamus then trigger the release of the neurohormone **oxytocin** from the posterior pituitary gland. In response to circulating oxytocin, the mammary glands secrete milk.

Feedback Regulation

A feedback loop linking the response back to the initial stimulus is characteristic of control pathways. For many

Simple neuroendocrine pathway	Example: oxytocin signalling
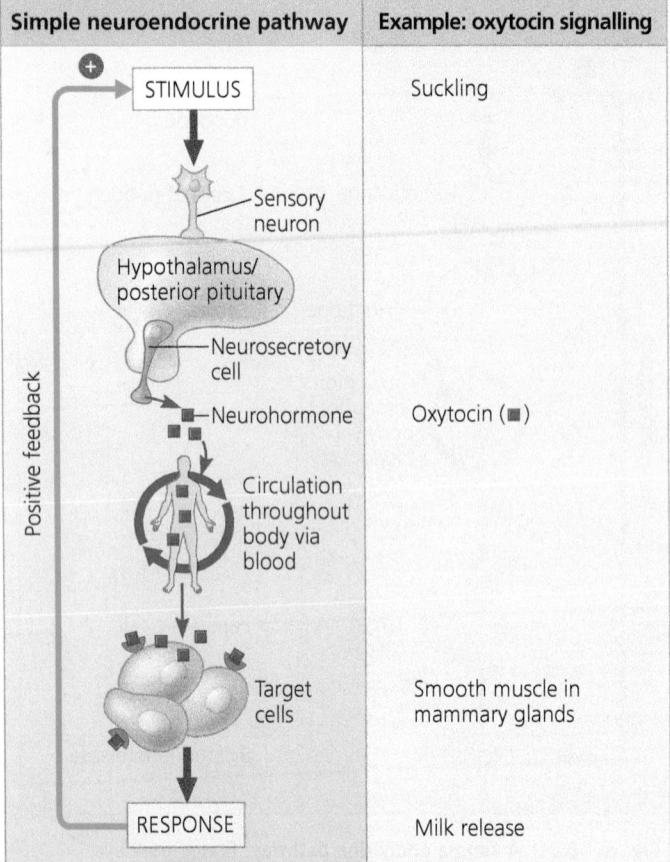

▲ **Figure 45.11 A simple neuroendocrine pathway.** Sensory neurons respond to a stimulus by sending nerve impulses to a neurosecretory cell, triggering secretion of a neurohormone. Upon reaching its target cells via the bloodstream, the neurohormone binds to its receptor, triggering signal transduction that results in a specific response. In the neuroendocrine pathway for oxytocin signalling, the response increases the stimulus, forming a positive-feedback loop that amplifies signalling in the pathway.

hormones, the response pathway involves **negative feedback**, a loop in which the response reduces the initial stimulus. In the case of secretin signalling (see Figure 45.10), the release of bicarbonate by the pancreas increases pH in the intestine, eliminating the stimulus and thereby shutting off the pathway. By decreasing or abolishing hormone signalling, negative-feedback regulation prevents excessive pathway activity.

Whereas negative feedback dampens a stimulus, **positive feedback** reinforces a stimulus, leading to an even greater response. Consider, for instance, the oxytocin pathway outlined in Figure 45.11. In response to the circulating oxytocin, the mammary glands secrete milk. Milk released in response to the oxytocin leads to more suckling and therefore more stimulation. Activation of the pathway is sustained until the baby stops suckling. Positive feedback regulates a second function of oxytocin. When mammals give birth, muscle contraction triggers release of oxytocin, which induces uterine muscles to contract more strongly.

While positive feedback amplifies both stimulus and response, negative feedback helps restore a preexisting state. It is not surprising, therefore, that hormone pathways involved in homeostasis typically involve negative rather than positive feedback. In fact, some homeostatic control systems rely on pairs of negatively regulated hormone pathways, each counterbalancing the other.

Control of Blood Glucose By Antagonistic Hormones

Two antagonistic (opposing) hormones, insulin and glucagon, regulate the concentration of glucose in the blood (Figure 45.12). Each of these hormones operates in a simple endocrine pathway regulated by negative feedback. When blood glucose rises above the normal range, release of **insulin** triggers uptake of glucose from the blood into body cells, decreasing the blood glucose concentration. When blood glucose drops below the normal range, the release of **glucagon** promotes the release of glucose into the blood from energy stores, such as liver glycogen, increasing the blood glucose concentration. Because insulin and glucagon have opposing effects, the combined activity of these two hormones tightly controls the concentration of glucose in the blood.

Glucagon and insulin are produced in the pancreas. Scattered throughout this organ are clusters of endocrine cells called pancreatic islets. Each pancreatic islet has *alpha cells*, which make glucagon, and *beta cells*, which make insulin. Like all hormones, insulin and glucagon are secreted into the interstitial fluid and enter the circulatory system.

Target Tissues for Insulin and Glucagon

Insulin lowers blood glucose levels by stimulating nearly all body cells outside the brain to take up glucose from the blood. (Brain cells can take up glucose without insulin, so the brain almost always has access to circulating fuel.) Insulin also decreases blood glucose by slowing glycogen breakdown in the liver and inhibiting the conversion of glycerol (from fats) and amino acids to glucose. Insulin was one of the first hormones to be produced and tested for therapeutic purposes (Figure 45.13).

Glucagon influences blood glucose levels mainly through its effects on target cells in the liver. The liver, skeletal muscles, and adipose tissues store large amounts of fuel. The liver and muscles store sugar as glycogen, whereas cells in adipose tissue convert sugars to fats. When the blood glucose level decreases to a level at or below the normal range (70–110 mg/100 mL), a primary effect of glucagon is to signal liver cells to increase glycogen hydrolysis, convert amino acids and glycerol to glucose, and release glucose into the bloodstream. The net result is a return of the blood glucose level to the normal range.

The antagonistic effects of glucagon and insulin are vital to managing fuel storage and consumption by body

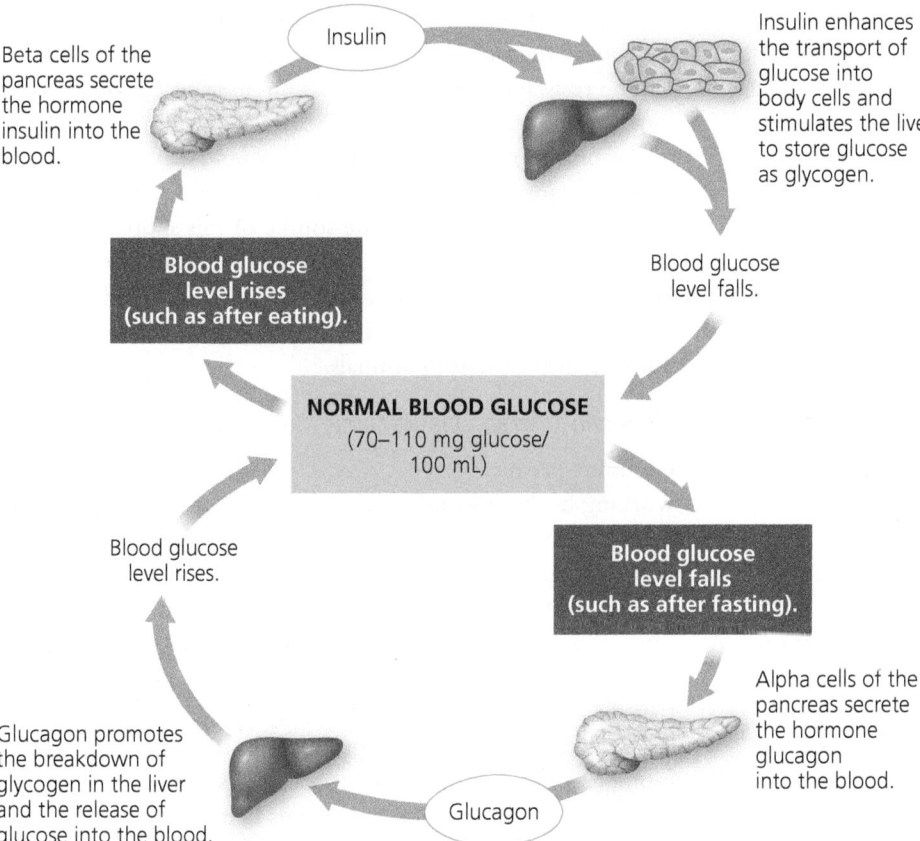

Beta cells of the pancreas secrete the hormone insulin into the blood.

Insulin

Insulin enhances the transport of glucose into body cells and stimulates the liver to store glucose as glycogen.

Blood glucose level rises (such as after eating).

Blood glucose level falls.

NORMAL BLOOD GLUCOSE
(70–110 mg glucose/ 100 mL)

Blood glucose level rises.

Blood glucose level falls (such as after fasting).

Glucagon promotes the breakdown of glycogen in the liver and the release of glucose into the blood.

Glucagon

Alpha cells of the pancreas secrete the hormone glucagon into the blood.

◄ **Figure 45.12 Maintenance of glucose homeostasis by insulin and glucagon.** The antagonistic effects of insulin and glucagon help keep blood glucose levels in the normal range.

ANIMATION **BioFlix** Visit the Study Area in **MasteringBiology** for the BioFlix® 3-D Animation on Homeostasis: Regulating Blood Sugar.

cells. For both hormones, as we've mentioned, the liver is a critical target. Recall from Chapter 41 that nutrients absorbed by blood vessels of the small intestine are transported directly to the liver by the hepatic portal vein. Within the liver, glucagon and insulin regulate nutrient processing in ways that support glucose homeostasis. However, glucose homeostasis also relies on responses to glucagon and insulin elsewhere in the body as well as responses to other hormones—growth hormone and glucocorticoids—discussed later in this chapter.

In discussing the role of insulin and glucagon in glucose homeostasis, we have focused exclusively on a healthy metabolic state. However, a number of disorders can disrupt glucose homeostasis with potentially serious consequences, especially for the heart, blood vessels, eyes, and kidneys. We'll discuss the best known and most prevalent of these disorders—diabetes mellitus—next.

Diabetes Mellitus

The disease **diabetes mellitus** is caused by a defect in insulin signalling, either an inability to produce enough insulin or a decreased response to insulin in target tissues. Blood glucose levels rise, but cells are unable to take up enough glucose to meet metabolic needs. Instead, fat becomes the main substrate for cellular respiration. In severe cases, acidic metabolites formed during fat breakdown accumulate in the blood, threatening life by lowering blood pH and depleting sodium and potassium ions from the body.

In people with diabetes mellitus, the level of glucose in the blood may exceed the capacity of the kidneys to reabsorb this nutrient. Glucose that remains in the kidney filtrate is excreted. For this reason, the presence of sugar in urine is one test for this disorder. As glucose is concentrated in the urine, more water is excreted along with it, resulting in excessive volumes of urine. *Diabetes* (from the Greek *diabainein*, to pass through) refers to this copious urination; and *mellitus* (from the Greek *meli*, honey) refers to the presence of sugar in urine.

▼ Figure 45.13 | **Impact**

Discovery and Use of Purified Insulin

By the early 1920s, scientists knew that the pancreas produced a hormone, insulin, that helped control blood glucose levels. Canadian researchers based at the University of Toronto, Frederick G. Banting and J.J.R. Macleod, were the first to purify insulin and use it on patients. Previous efforts to purify the hormone from the pancreas were thwarted by trypsin, a protease produced by exocrine cells of the pancreas. By selectively killing the trypsin-secreting cells, Banting was able to stop the degradation of insulin, enabling its purification. Within months of obtaining pure hormone, they began injecting children and adults, reversing the debilitating effects of diabetes. For their work, Banting and Macleod were awarded the 1923 Nobel Prize in Physiology or Medicine. Each recognized the role of colleagues by sharing their prize money: Banting with his research assistant C. Best; Macleod with J. Collip, a biochemist who helped perfect the insulin purification process.

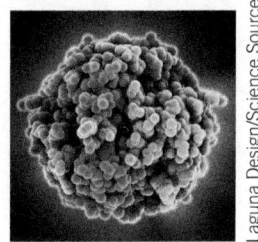

Laguna Design/Science Source

Why It Matters Insulin purified from the pancreas was the only source of the hormone for more than 50 years. The first recombinant insulin was produced in the late 1970s. Insulin injections remain the only treatment for type 1 diabetes.

Further Reading A. K. Steck and M. J. Rewers, Genetics of type I diabetes, *Clinical Chemistry* 57:176–185 (2011).

WHAT IF? *Insulin purified from some mammals does not work as well as human insulin in treatment of type 1 diabetes in humans. Why might this be the case?*

There are two main types of diabetes mellitus. Each is marked by high blood glucose, but with very different causes. *Type 1 diabetes*, or insulin-dependent diabetes, is an autoimmune disorder in which the immune system destroys the beta cells of the pancreas. Type 1 diabetes, which usually appears during childhood, destroys the person's ability to produce insulin. Treatment consists of insulin, typically injected several times daily. In the past, insulin was extracted from animal pancreases, but now human insulin can be obtained from genetically engineered bacteria, a relatively inexpensive source (see Figure 20.5). Stem cell research may someday provide a cure for type 1 diabetes by generating replacement beta cells that restore insulin production by the pancreas.

Type 2 diabetes, or non-insulin-dependent diabetes, is characterized by a failure of target cells to respond normally to insulin. Insulin is produced, but target cells fail to take up glucose from the blood, and blood glucose levels remain elevated. Although heredity can play a role in type 2 diabetes, excess body weight and lack of exercise significantly increase the risk. This form of diabetes generally appears after age 40, but even children who are overweight and sedentary can develop the disease. More than 90% of people with diabetes have type 2. Many can control their blood glucose levels with regular exercise and a healthy diet; some require medications.

The resistance to insulin signalling in type 2 diabetes is sometimes due to a genetic defect in the insulin receptor or the insulin response pathway. In many cases, however, events in target cells suppress activity of an otherwise functional response pathway. One source of this suppression appears to be inflammatory signals generated by the innate immune system (see Chapter 43). How obesity and inactivity relate to this suppression is being studied in both humans and laboratory animals.

Hormone Interactions Regulate Complex Processes

Complex processes are regulated by layers of hormones working both antagonistically and synergistically. As an example, we'll explore the life cycle of the butterfly, a process highlighted earlier in the chapter.

A butterfly larva grows in stages. Because its exoskeleton cannot stretch, the larva must periodically moult, shedding the old exoskeleton and secreting a new one. The signals that direct moulting originate in the brain (Figure 45.14). There, neurosecretory cells produce prothoracicotropic hormone (PTTH), a polypeptide neurohormone. In response to PTTH, a pair of endocrine glands behind the brain

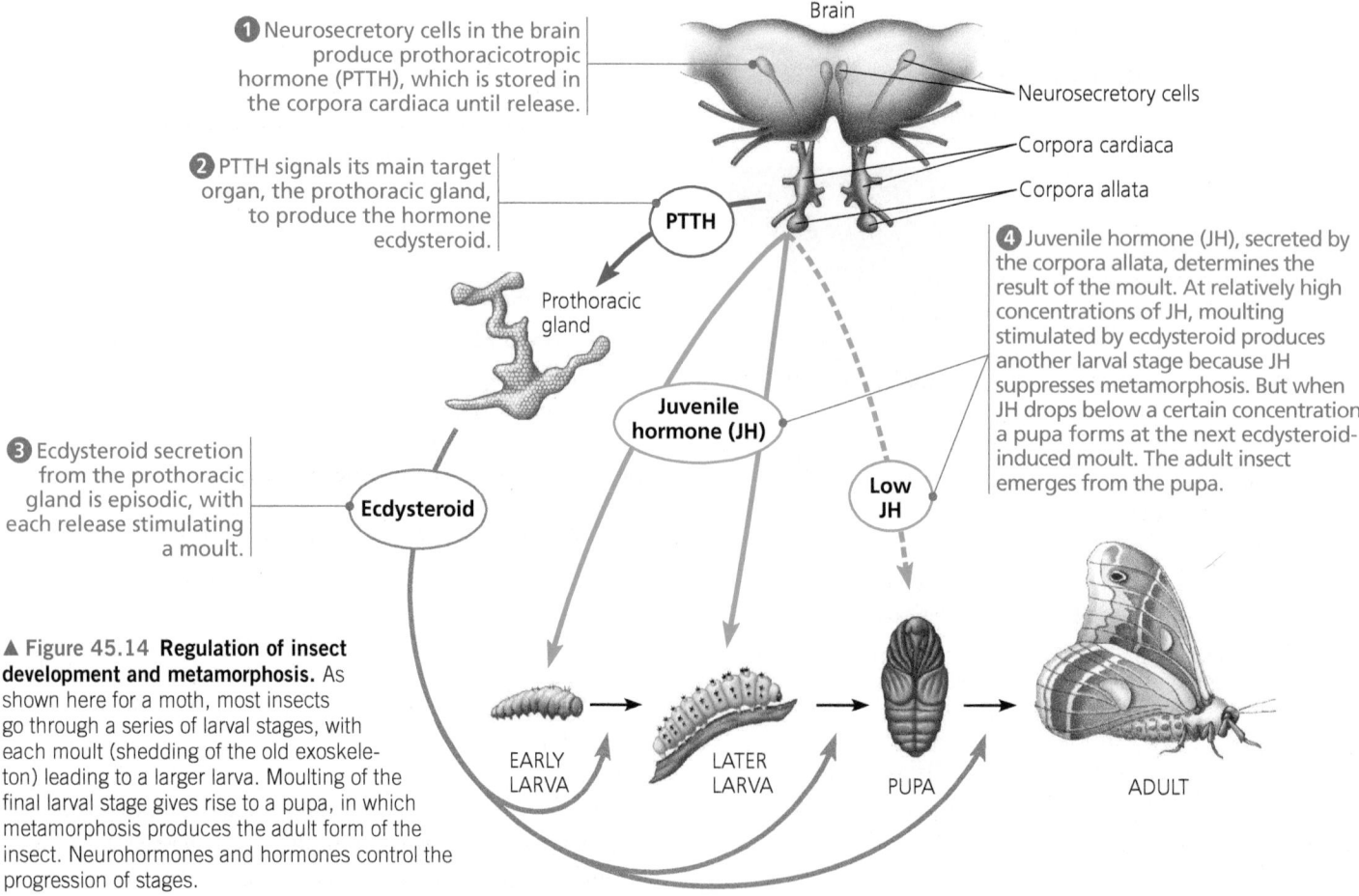

1 Neurosecretory cells in the brain produce prothoracicotropic hormone (PTTH), which is stored in the corpora cardiaca until release.

2 PTTH signals its main target organ, the prothoracic gland, to produce the hormone ecdysteroid.

3 Ecdysteroid secretion from the prothoracic gland is episodic, with each release stimulating a moult.

4 Juvenile hormone (JH), secreted by the corpora allata, determines the result of the moult. At relatively high concentrations of JH, moulting stimulated by ecdysteroid produces another larval stage because JH suppresses metamorphosis. But when JH drops below a certain concentration, a pupa forms at the next ecdysteroid-induced moult. The adult insect emerges from the pupa.

Brain

Neurosecretory cells
Corpora cardiaca
Corpora allata

PTTH

Prothoracic gland

Juvenile hormone (JH)

Low JH

Ecdysteroid

EARLY LARVA   LATER LARVA   PUPA   ADULT

▲ Figure 45.14 **Regulation of insect development and metamorphosis.** As shown here for a moth, most insects go through a series of larval stages, with each moult (shedding of the old exoskeleton) leading to a larger larva. Moulting of the final larval stage gives rise to a pupa, in which metamorphosis produces the adult form of the insect. Neurohormones and hormones control the progression of stages.

release the steroid-like hormone **ecdysteroid**. Ecdysteroid triggers each successive moult, as well as the metamorphosis of larva into butter-fly during the final moult.

Given that ecdysteroid triggers both moulting and metamorphosis, what deter-mines when metamorphosis takes place? The answer is a third molecule, juvenile hormone, secreted by another pair of endocrine glands behind the brain. As its name suggests, one of the many functions of juvenile hormone is to maintain larval (juvenile) characteristics. Juvenile hormone modulates the activity of ecdysteroid. As long as the level of juvenile hormone is high, ecdysteroid stimulates larval moulting. When the juvenile hormone level drops, ecdys-teroid-induced moulting instead produces the pupal form, within which metamorphosis occurs.

Knowledge of endocrine signalling in insects has impor-tant applications for agricultural pest control. For example, synthetic chemicals that can bind to the ecdysteroid recep-tor cause insect larvae to moult prematurely and die.

Evolution of Hormone Function

EVOLUTION Many of the hormones discussed in this chapter are found throughout vertebrates, but the role played may differ between animals. Thyroid hormone, for example, regulates metabolism, but in frogs it also controls metamorphosis of the larva into an adult (Figure 45.15).

Another example of a hormone that has evolved dif-ferent functions is prolactin. In mammals, it stimulates mammary gland growth and milk synthesis. It regulates fat metabolism and reproduction in birds, delays metamorpho-sis in amphibians, and controls salt and water balance in freshwater fishes.

Melanocyte-stimulating hormone (MSH) is another example of a hormone with distinct functions in different evolutionary lineages. In amphibians, fishes, and reptiles, MSH regulates skin colour by controlling pigment distribu-tion in skin cells called melanocytes. In mammals, MSH functions in hunger and metabolism in addition to colour-ation. The specialized action of MSH that has evolved in the mammalian brain may prove to be of particular medical importance. Many patients with late-stage cancer, AIDS, tuberculosis, and certain aging disorders suffer from a dev-astating wasting condition called cachexia. Characterized by weight loss, muscle atrophy, and loss of appetite, cachexia is only poorly responsive to existing therapies. However, it turns out that activation of one brain receptor for MSH stimulates metabolism of fat and severely decreases appe-tite, changes also seen in cachexia. This fact led scientists

Anup Photoshot Holdings Ltd/Alamy

▲ **Tadpole**

▲ **Adult frog** — Jurgen & Christine Sohns/Frank Lane Picture Agency Limited

◀ **Figure 45.15 Specialized role of a hor-mone in frog metamorphosis.** The hormone thyroxine is responsible for the resorption of the tadpole's tail as the frog develops into its adult form.

to hypothesize that activation of this MSH receptor causes cachexia. To test this idea, they studied mice with muta-tions that cause cancerous tumours to develop, triggering cachexia. When the mice were treated with drugs that inhibit the brain MSH receptor, tumours occurred, but not cachexia! Whether such drugs can be used to treat cachexia in humans is an area of active study.

CONCEPT CHECK 45.2

1. In a glucose tolerance test, periodic measurements of blood glu-cose level are taken after a person drinks a glucose-rich solution. In a healthy individual, blood glucose rises moderately at first but falls to near normal within 2–3 hours. Predict the results of this test in a person with diabetes mellitus. Explain your answer.

2. If a hormone pathway provides a transient response to a stimu-lus, how would shortening the stimulus duration affect the need for negative feedback?

3. **WHAT IF?** Consider a diabetes patient who has a family history of type 2 diabetes but is active and not obese. To iden-tify genes that might be defective in the patient, which genes would you examine first?

For suggested answers, see Appendix A.

CONCEPT **45.3**

Vertebrate hormones regulate homeostasis, development, and behaviour

In the remainder of the chapter, we'll survey the vari-ous hormonal systems that regulate important pathways of metabolism, development, growth, and reproduction, focusing on vertebrates.

The Hypothalamus-Pituitary Axis

In vertebrates, the **hypothalamus** plays a central role in inte-grating the endocrine and nervous systems. One of several

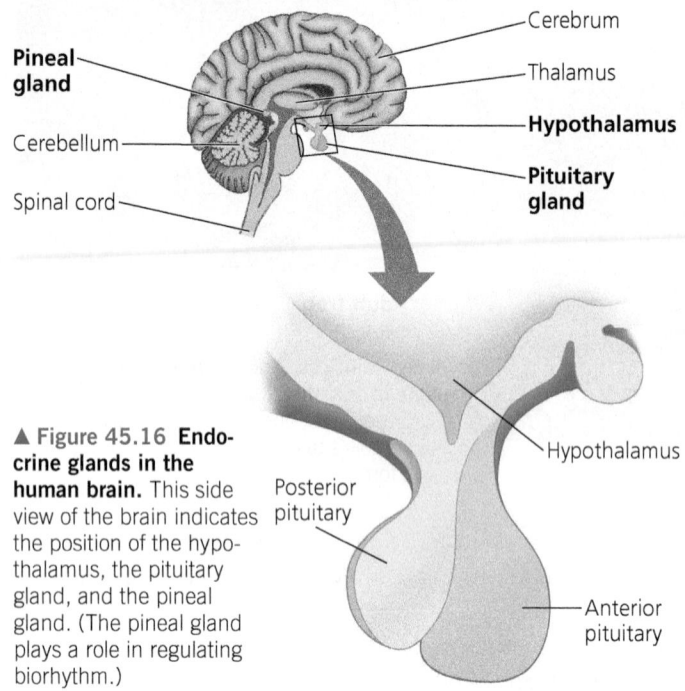

▲ Figure 45.16 **Endocrine glands in the human brain.** This side view of the brain indicates the position of the hypothalamus, the pituitary gland, and the pineal gland. (The pineal gland plays a role in regulating biorhythm.)

endocrine glands located in the brain (Figure 45.16), the hypothalamus receives information from nerves throughout the body, including the brain. In response, the hypothalamus initiates endocrine signalling appropriate to environmental conditions. In many vertebrates, for example, nerve signals from the brain pass sensory information to the hypothalamus about seasonal changes. The hypothalamus, in turn, regulates the release of reproductive hormones required during the breeding season.

Signals from the hypothalamus travel to the **pituitary gland**, a gland located at its base (see Figure 45.16). Roughly the size and shape of a lima bean, the pituitary has discrete posterior and anterior parts, or lobes, that secrete different sets of hormones.

The **posterior pituitary** is an extension of the hypothalamus. Hypothalamic axons that reach into the posterior pituitary secrete neurohormones synthesized in the hypothalamus. In contrast, the **anterior pituitary** is an endocrine gland that synthesizes and secretes hormones in response to signals from the hypothalamus. Many anterior pituitary hormones act as **tropic hormones**, meaning that they regulate the function of other endocrine cells or glands.

Posterior Pituitary Hormones

Neurosecretory cells of the hypothalamus synthesize the two posterior pituitary hormones: oxytocin and antidiuretic hormone. After travelling to the posterior pituitary within the long axons of the neurosecretory cells, the hormones are stored in pituitary cells, to be released in response to nerve impulses transmitted by the hypothalamus (Figure 45.17).

▲ Figure 45.17 **Production and release of posterior pituitary hormones.** The posterior pituitary gland is an extension of the hypothalamus. Certain neurosecretory cells in the hypothalamus make antidiuretic hormone (ADH) and oxytocin, which are transported to the posterior pituitary, where they are stored. Nerve signals from the brain trigger release of these neurohormones.

As discussed in Concept 45.2 (see Figure 45.11), oxytocin regulates milk secretion by the mammary glands and also contractions of the uterus during birthing. In addition, oxytocin has targets in the brain, where it influences behaviours related to maternal care, pair bonding, and sexual activity.

Like oxytocin, **antidiuretic hormone (ADH)**, or *vasopressin*, regulates both physiology and behaviour. As you read in Chapter 44, ADH is one of several hormones that regulate kidney function. In particular, ADH increases water retention in the kidneys, thus decreasing urine volume. The net result is to help maintain blood osmolarity within a normal range. ADH also plays an important role in social behaviour, as detailed in Chapter 51.

Anterior Pituitary Hormones

Endocrine signals generated by the hypothalamus regulate hormone secretion by the anterior pituitary (Figure 45.18). Each hypothalamic hormone is either a *releasing hormone* or an *inhibiting hormone*, reflecting its role in promoting or inhibiting release of one or more specific hormones by the anterior pituitary. *Prolactin-releasing hormone*, for example, is a hypothalamic hormone that stimulates the anterior pituitary to secrete **prolactin**, which has activities that include stimulating milk production. Every anterior pituitary hormone is controlled by at least one releasing hormone. Some, such as prolactin, have both a releasing hormone and an inhibiting hormone.

▶ Figure 45.18 **Production and release of anterior pituitary hormones.** The release of hormones synthesized in the anterior pituitary gland is controlled by hypothalamic releasing and inhibiting hormones. The hypothalamic hormones are secreted by neurosecretory cells and enter a capillary network within the hypothalamus. These capillaries drain into portal vessels that connect with a second capillary network in the anterior pituitary.

Neurosecretory cells of the hypothalamus

Portal vessels

Hypothalamic releasing and inhibiting hormones

Endocrine cells of the anterior pituitary

Anterior pituitary hormones

Posterior pituitary

HORMONE	FSH and LH	TSH	ACTH	Prolactin	MSH	GH
TARGET	Testes or ovaries	Thyroid	Adrenal cortex	Mammary glands	Melanocytes	Liver, bones, other tissues

Tropic effects only   **Nontropic effects only**   **Tropic and nontropic effects**

The hypothalamic releasing and inhibiting hormones are secreted near capillaries at the base of the hypothalamus. The capillaries drain into short blood vessels, called portal vessels, which subdivide into a second capillary bed within the anterior pituitary. In this way, the releasing and inhibiting hormones have direct access to the gland they control.

Thyroid Hormone Regulation

In humans and other mammals, thyroid hormone regulates bioenergetics; helps maintain normal blood pressure, heart rate, and muscle tone; and regulates digestive and reproductive functions. If the level of thyroid hormone in the blood drops, the hypothalamus responds by initiating a hormone cascade pathway (**Figure 45.19**). The hypothalamus secretes thyrotropin-releasing hormone (TRH), causing the anterior pituitary to secrete a tropic hormone known as either thyroid-stimulating hormone (TSH) or thyrotropin. TSH stimulates release of thyroid hormone by the **thyroid gland**, an organ in the neck consisting of two lobes on the ventral surface of the trachea. As thyroid hormone accumulates, it increases metabolic rate, while also initiating negative feedback that prevents its overproduction.

Disorders of Thyroid Function and Regulation

Disruption of thyroid hormone production and regulation can result in serious disorders. Hypothyroidism, the

secretion of too little thyroid hormone, can cause weight gain, lethargy, and intolerance to cold in adults. In contrast, excessive secretion of thyroid hormone, known as hyperthyroidism, can lead to high body temperature, profuse sweating, weight loss, irritability, and high blood pressure.

The most common form of hyperthyroidism is Graves' disease. Protruding eyes, caused by fluid accumulation behind the eyes, are a typical symptom. In this autoimmune disorder, the body produces antibodies that bind to and activate the receptor for TSH. The result is sustained thyroid hormone production.

Malnutrition can also alter thyroid hormone production. The specific link between diet and thyroid hormone synthesis reflects the chemical nature of thyroid hormone. The term *thyroid hormone* actually refers to a pair of very similar hormones derived from the amino acid tyrosine. **Triiodothyronine (T_3)** contains three iodine atoms, whereas tetraiodothyronine, or **thyroxine (T_4)**, contains four iodine atoms (see Figure 45.4). In mammals, the same receptor binds both hormones. The thyroid gland secretes mainly T_4, but target cells convert most of it to T_3 by removing one iodine atom.

Although iodine is readily obtained from seafood or iodized salt, people in many parts of the world suffer from inadequate iodine in their diet. Without sufficient iodine, the thyroid gland cannot synthesize adequate amounts of T_3 and T_4, and the resulting low blood levels of T_3 and T_4

STIMULUS

1 Thyroid hormone levels drop below the normal range.

Sensory neuron

Negative feedback

Hypothalamus

−

Neurosecretory cell

TRH

2 The hypothalamus secretes thyrotropin-releasing hormone (TRH●) into the blood. Portal vessels carry TRH to the anterior pituitary.

−

3 TRH causes the anterior pituitary to secrete thyroid-stimulating hormone (TSH, also known as thyrotropin ▲) into the circulatory system.

Anterior pituitary

▲ TSH

Circulation throughout body via blood

4 TSH stimulates endocrine cells in the thyroid gland to secrete thyroid hormone (T_3 and T_4 ■) into the circulatory system.

Thyroid gland

Thyroid hormone

Circulation throughout body via blood

5 Thyroid hormone levels increase in the blood and body tissues, returning to the normal range. Thyroid hormone acts on target cells throughout the body to control bioenergetics; help maintain normal blood pressure, heart rate, and muscle tone; and regulate digestive and reproductive functions.

RESPONSE

6 Thyroid hormone blocks TRH release from the hypothalamus and TSH release from the anterior pituitary, forming a negative-feedback loop that prevents overproduction of thyroid hormone.

▲ **Figure 45.19 Regulation of thyroid hormone secretion: a hormone cascade pathway.**

cannot exert the usual negative feedback on the hypothalamus and anterior pituitary (see Figure 45.18). As a consequence, the pituitary continues to secrete TSH. Elevated TSH levels cause an enlargement of the thyroid gland resulting in goiter, a characteristic swelling of the neck.

Humans and other vertebrates require thyroid hormones for the normal functioning of bone-forming cells, as well as for the branching of nerve cells during embryonic development of the brain. In humans, congenital hypothyroidism, an inherited condition of thyroid deficiency, results in markedly retarded skeletal growth and poor mental development. These defects can often be avoided, at least partially, if treatment with thyroid hormones begins early in life. Iodine deficiency in childhood causes the same defects, but it is fully preventable if iodized salt is used in food preparation.

The fact that iodine in the body is dedicated to the production of thyroid hormone provides a novel diagnostic tool for disorders of thyroid function: Radioactive forms of iodine enable specific imaging of the thyroid gland (Figure 45.20).

Growth Hormone

Growth hormone (GH), which is secreted by the anterior pituitary, stimulates growth through both tropic and nontropic effects. A major target, the liver, responds to GH by releasing *insulin-like growth factors* (*IGFs*), which circulate in the blood and directly stimulate bone and cartilage growth. (IGFs also appear to play a key role in aging in many animal species.) In the absence of GH, the skeleton of an immature animal stops growing. GH also exerts diverse metabolic effects that tend to raise blood glucose levels, thus opposing the effects of insulin.

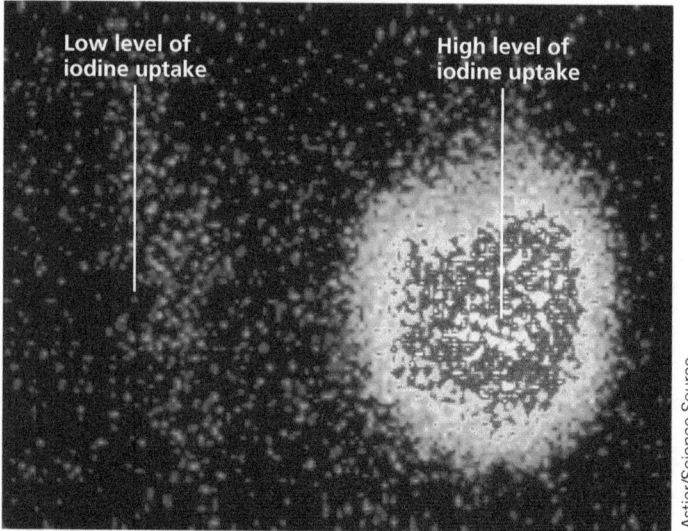

Low level of iodine uptake

High level of iodine uptake

Astier/Science Source

▲ **Figure 45.20 Thyroid scan.** Radioactive iodine enables doctors to identify abnormal patterns of iodine uptake that could indicate a thyroid disorder.

Parathyroid Hormone and Vitamin D: Control of Blood Calcium

Because calcium ions (Ca^{2+}) are essential to the normal functioning of all cells, homeostatic control of blood calcium level is critical. If the blood Ca^{2+} level falls substantially, skeletal muscles begin to contract convulsively, a potentially fatal condition called tetany. If the blood Ca^{2+} level rises substantially, precipitates of calcium phosphate can form in body tissues, leading to widespread organ damage.

In mammals, the **parathyroid glands**, a set of four small structures embedded in the posterior surface of the thyroid (see Figure 45.9), play a major role in blood Ca^{2+} regulation. When blood Ca^{2+} falls below a set point of about 10 mg/100 mL, these glands release **parathyroid hormone (PTH)**.

PTH raises the level of blood Ca^{2+} by direct and indirect effects (Figure 45.22). In bone, PTH causes the mineralized matrix to decompose and release Ca^{2+} into the blood. In the kidneys, PTH directly stimulates reabsorption of Ca^{2+} through the renal tubules. PTH also has an indirect effect on the kidneys, promoting the conversion of vitamin D to an active hormone. An inactive form of vitamin D, a steroid-derived molecule, is obtained from food or synthesized in the skin when exposed to sunlight. Vitamin D activation begins in the liver and is completed in the kidneys, the process stimulated by PTH. The active form of vitamin D acts directly on the intestines, stimulating the uptake of Ca^{2+} from food and thus augmenting the effect of PTH. As blood Ca^{2+} rises, a negative-feedback loop inhibits further release of PTH from the parathyroid glands (not shown in figure).

▲ Figure 45.21 **Effect of growth hormone overproduction.** Shown here surrounded by his family, Robert Wadlow grew to a height of 2.7 m (8 feet 11 inches) by age 22, making him the tallest man in history. His height was due to excess secretion of growth hormone by his pituitary gland.

Abnormal production of GH in humans can result in several disorders, depending on when the problem occurs and whether it involves hypersecretion (too much) or hyposecretion (too little). Hypersecretion of GH during childhood can lead to gigantism, in which the person grows unusually tall—as tall as 2.4 m—though body proportions remain relatively normal (Figure 45.21). Excessive GH production in adulthood stimulates bony growth in the few tissues that are still responsive to the hormone. Because remaining target cells are predominantly in the face, hands, and feet, the result is an overgrowth of the extremities called acromegaly (from the Greek *acros*, extreme, and *mega*, large).

Hyposecretion of GH in childhood retards long-bone growth and can lead to pituitary dwarfism. Individuals with this disorder are for the most part properly proportioned but generally reach a height of only about 1.2 m. If diagnosed before puberty, pituitary dwarfism can be treated successfully with human GH (also called HGH). Since the mid-1980s, scientists have used recombinant DNA technology to produce HGH in bacteria (see Chapter 20). Treatment with this genetically engineered HGH is now fairly routine for affected children.

NORMAL BLOOD Ca²⁺ LEVEL (about 10 mg/100 mL)

Blood Ca^{2+} level rises.

Blood Ca^{2+} level falls (such as when diet provides less calcium than is excreted in urine).

Active vitamin D increases Ca^{2+} uptake in intestines.

PTH stimulates Ca^{2+} uptake in kidneys and promotes activation of vitamin D by kidney.

PTH stimulates Ca^{2+} release from bones.

PTH

Parathyroid glands release PTH.

▲ Figure 45.22 **The roles of parathyroid hormone (PTH) in regulating blood calcium levels in mammals.**

The thyroid gland can also contribute to calcium homeostasis. If blood Ca^{2+} rises above the set point, the thyroid gland releases **calcitonin**, a hormone that inhibits bone resorption and enhances Ca^{2+} release by the kidney. In fishes, rodents, and some other animals, calcitonin is required for Ca^{2+} homeostasis. In humans, however, it is apparently needed only during the extensive bone growth of childhood.

Adrenal Hormones: Response to Stress

The **adrenal glands** of vertebrates are associated with the kidneys (the *renal* organs). In mammals, each adrenal gland is actually made up of two glands with different cell types, functions, and embryonic origins: the *adrenal cortex*, the outer portion, and the *adrenal medulla*, the central portion. The adrenal cortex consists of true endocrine cells, whereas the secretory cells of the adrenal medulla derive from neural tissue during embryonic development. Thus, like the pituitary gland, each adrenal gland is a fused endocrine and neuroendocrine gland.

Catecholamines from the Adrenal Medulla

Imagine that while walking in the woods at night you hear a growling noise nearby. "A bear?" you wonder. Your heart beats faster, your breath quickens, your muscles tense, and your thoughts speed up. These and other rapid responses to perceived danger compose the "fight-or-flight," or acute stress, response. This coordinated set of physiological changes is triggered by two hormones of the adrenal medulla, **norepinephrine** (also known as noradrenaline) and epinephrine (adrenaline). Both are **catecholamines**, a class of amine hormones synthesized from the amino acid tyrosine.

The adrenal medulla secretes epinephrine and norepinephrine in response to stress—whether extreme pleasure or life-threatening danger. A major activity of these hormones is to increase the amount of chemical energy available for immediate use. Both epinephrine and norepinephrine increase the rate of glycogen breakdown in the liver and skeletal muscles, promote glucose release by liver cells, and stimulate the release of fatty acids from fat cells. The released glucose and fatty acids circulate in the blood and can be used by body cells as fuel.

In addition to increasing the availability of energy sources, norepinephrine and epinephrine exert profound effects on the cardiovascular and respiratory systems. For example, they increase both the heart rate and stroke volume and dilate the bronchioles in the lungs, actions that raise the rate of oxygen delivery to body cells. For this reason, doctors may prescribe epinephrine as a heart stimulant or to open the airways during an asthma attack. The catecholamines also alter blood flow, causing constriction of some blood vessels and dilation of others (see Figure 45.8). The overall effect is to shunt blood away from the skin, digestive organs, and kidneys, while increasing the blood supply to the heart, brain, and skeletal muscles. Epinephrine generally has a stronger effect on heart and metabolic rates, while the primary role of norepinephrine is in modulating blood pressure.

Nerve signals carried from the brain via involuntary (autonomic) neurons regulate secretion by the adrenal medulla. In response to a stressful stimulus, nerve impulses travel to the adrenal medulla, where they trigger the release of catecholamines from neurosecretory cells (**Figure 45.23a**). Acting on target tissues, epinephrine and norepinephrine each function in a simple neurohormone pathway. As you will read in Chapter 48, epinephrine and norepinephrine also function as neurotransmitters.

Steroid Hormones from the Adrenal Cortex

Hormones from the adrenal cortex also function in the body's response to stress. But in contrast to the adrenal medulla, which reacts to nervous input, the adrenal cortex responds to endocrine signals. Stressful stimuli cause the hypothalamus to secrete a releasing hormone that stimulates the anterior pituitary to release the tropic hormone ACTH. When ACTH reaches the adrenal cortex via the bloodstream, it stimulates the endocrine cells to synthesize and secrete a family of steroids called **corticosteroids** (**Figure 45.23b**). The two main types of corticosteroids in humans are glucocorticoids and mineralocorticoids.

As reflected in their name, **glucocorticoids** have a primary effect on glucose metabolism. Augmenting the fuel-mobilizing effects of glucagon from the pancreas, glucocorticoids promote glucose synthesis from noncarbohydrate sources, such as proteins, making more glucose available as fuel. Glucocorticoids, such as cortisol (see Figure 45.4), act on skeletal muscle, causing the breakdown of muscle proteins. The resulting amino acids are transported to the liver and kidneys, where they are converted to glucose and released into the blood. The synthesis of glucose from muscle proteins provides circulating fuel when the body requires more glucose than the liver can mobilize from its glycogen stores.

When glucocorticoids are introduced into the body at levels above those normally present, they suppress certain components of the body's immune system. Because of this anti-inflammatory effect, glucocorticoids are sometimes used to treat inflammatory diseases such as arthritis. However, long-term use can have serious side effects, reflecting the potent activity of glucocorticoids on metabolism. For these reasons, nonsteroidal anti-inflammatory drugs (NSAIDs), such as aspirin or ibuprofen, generally are preferred for treating chronic inflammatory conditions.

Mineralocorticoids, named for their effects on mineral metabolism, act principally in maintaining salt and water balance. For example, the mineralocorticoid *aldosterone*

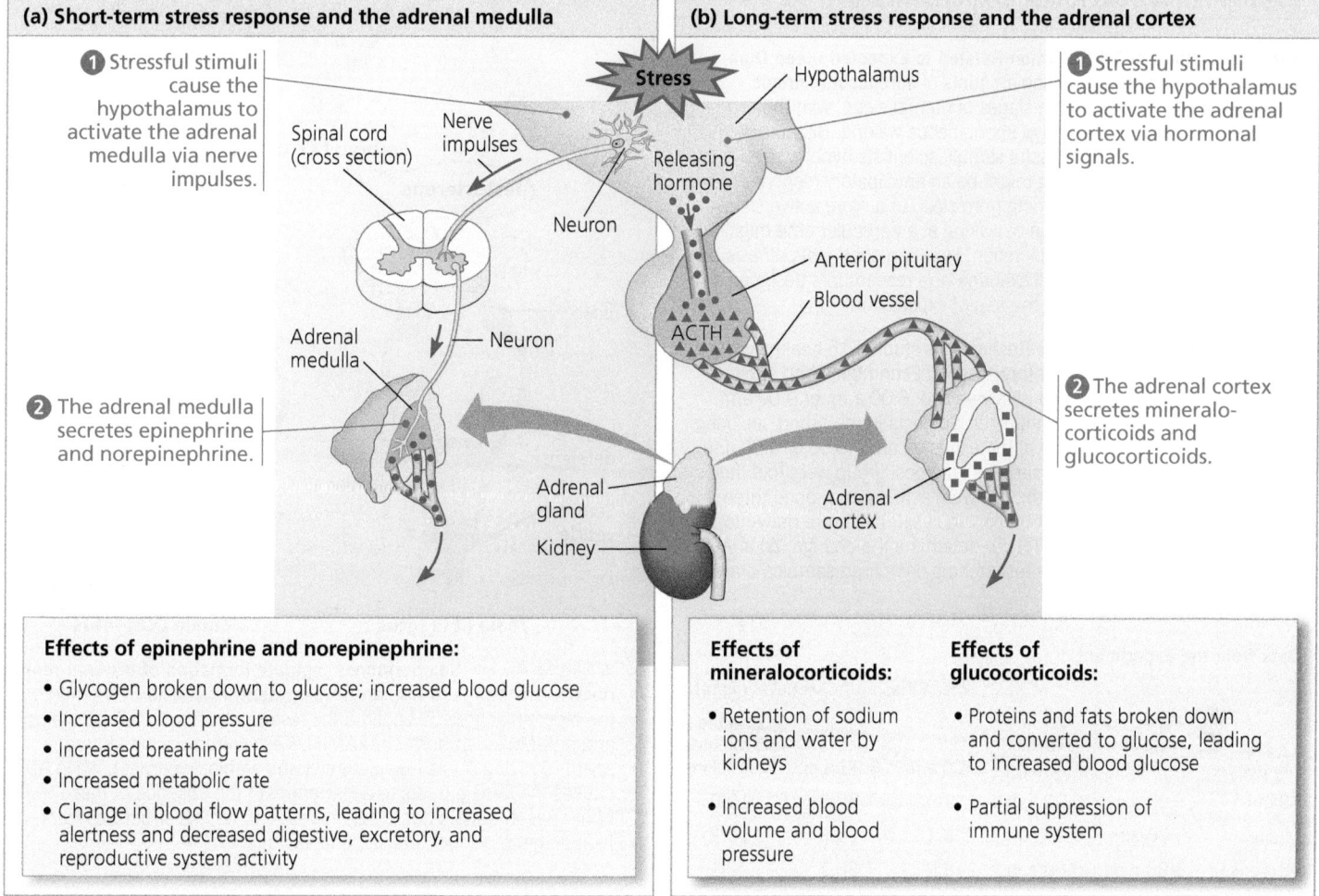

▼ Figure 45.23 **Stress and the adrenal gland.**

(a) Short-term stress response and the adrenal medulla

❶ Stressful stimuli cause the hypothalamus to activate the adrenal medulla via nerve impulses.

Spinal cord (cross section)

Nerve impulses

Neuron

Adrenal medulla

Neuron

❷ The adrenal medulla secretes epinephrine and norepinephrine.

Effects of epinephrine and norepinephrine:

- Glycogen broken down to glucose; increased blood glucose
- Increased blood pressure
- Increased breathing rate
- Increased metabolic rate
- Change in blood flow patterns, leading to increased alertness and decreased digestive, excretory, and reproductive system activity

(b) Long-term stress response and the adrenal cortex

Stress

Hypothalamus

Releasing hormone

Anterior pituitary

Blood vessel

ACTH

❶ Stressful stimuli cause the hypothalamus to activate the adrenal cortex via hormonal signals.

❷ The adrenal cortex secretes mineralo-corticoids and glucocorticoids.

Adrenal gland

Kidney

Adrenal cortex

Effects of mineralocorticoids:

- Retention of sodium ions and water by kidneys
- Increased blood volume and blood pressure

Effects of glucocorticoids:

- Proteins and fats broken down and converted to glucose, leading to increased blood glucose
- Partial suppression of immune system

functions in ion and water homeostasis of the blood (see Figure 44.23). Aldosterone also functions in the body's response to severe stress.

Glucocorticoids and mineralocorticoids not only mediate stress responses, but also participate in homeostatic regulation of metabolism. In the Scientific Skills Exercise, you can explore an experiment investigating changes in ACTH secretion as humans awaken from sleep.

Sex Hormones

Sex hormones affect growth, development, reproductive cycles, and sexual behaviour. Whereas the adrenal glands secrete small quantities of these hormones, the testes of males and ovaries of females are their principal sources. The gonads produce and secrete three major categories of steroid hormones: androgens, estrogens, and progestins. All three types are found in both males and females but in significantly different proportions.

The testes primarily synthesize **androgens**, the main one being **testosterone**. In humans, testosterone first functions before birth, promoting development of male

reproductive structures (Figure 45.24). Androgens play a major role again at puberty, when they are responsible for the development of male secondary sex characteristics. High concentrations of androgen lead to a low voice and male patterns of hair growth, as well as increases in muscle and bone mass. The muscle-building, or anabolic, action of testosterone and related steroids has enticed some athletes to take them as supplements, despite prohibitions against their use in nearly all sports. Use of anabolic steroids, while effective in increasing muscle mass, can cause severe acne outbreaks and liver damage, as well as significant decreases in sperm count and testicular size.

Estrogens, of which the most important is **estradiol**, are responsible for the maintenance of the female reproductive system and for the development of female secondary sex characteristics. In mammals, **progestins**, which include **progesterone**, are primarily involved in preparing and maintaining tissues of the uterus required to support the growth and development of an embryo.

Estrogens and other gonadal sex hormones are components of hormone cascade pathways. Synthesis of these

Designing a Controlled Experiment

How Is Nighttime ACTH Secretion Related to Expected Sleep Duration? Humans secrete increasing amounts of **adrenocorticotropic hormone (ACTH)** during the late stages of normal sleep, with the peak secretion occurring at the time of spontaneous waking. Because ACTH is released In response to stressful stimuli, scientists hypothesized that ACTH secretion prior to waking might be an anticipatory response to the stress associated with transitioning from sleep to a more active state. If so, an individual's expectation of waking at a particular time might influence the timing of ACTH secretion. How can such a hypothesis be tested? In this exercise, you will examine how researchers designed a controlled experiment to study the role of expectation.

How the Experiment Was Done Researchers studied 15 healthy volunteers in their mid-twenties over three nights. Each night each subject was told when he or she would be awakened: 6:00 a.m. or 9:00 a.m. The subjects went to sleep at midnight. Subjects in the "short" or "long" protocol group were awakened at the expected time (6:00 or 9:00 a.m., respectively). Subjects in the "surprise" protocol group were told they would be awakened at 9:00 a.m., but were actually awakened three hours early, at 6:00 a.m. At set times, blood samples were drawn to determine plasma levels of ACTH. To determine the change (Δ) in ACTH concentration post-waking, the researchers compared samples drawn at waking and 30 minutes later.

Data from the Experiment

Sleep Protocol	Expected Wake Time	Actual Wake Time	Mean Plasma ACTH Level (pg/mL)		
			1:00 a.m.	6:00 a.m.	Δ in the 30 Minutes Post-waking
Short	6:00 a.m.	6:00 a.m.	9.9	37.3	10.6
Long	9:00 a.m.	9:00 a.m.	8.1	26.5	12.2
Surprise	9:00 a.m.	6:00 a.m.	8.0	25.5	22.1

Interpret the Data

1. Describe the role of the "surprise" protocol in the experimental design.
2. Each subject was given a different protocol on each of the three nights, and the order of the protocols was varied among the subjects that so that one-third had each protocol each night. What factors were the researchers attempting to control for with this approach?
3. For subjects in the short protocol, what was the mean ACTH level at waking? Using the data in the last two columns, calculate the mean level 30 minutes later. Was the rate of change faster or slower in that 30-minute period than during the interval from 1:00 to 6:00 a.m.?
4. How does the change in ACTH levels between 1:00 and 6:00 a.m. for the surprise protocol compare to that for the short and long protocols? Does this result support the hypothesis being tested? Explain.
5. Using the data in the last two columns, calculate the mean ACTH concentration 30 minutes post-waking for the surprise protocol and compare to your answer for question 3. What do your results suggest about a person's physiological response immediately after waking?
6. What are some variables that weren't controlled for in this experiment that could be explored in a follow-up study?

Data from J. Born et al., Timing the end of nocturnal sleep, *Nature* 397:29-30 (1999). © Jane B. Reece.

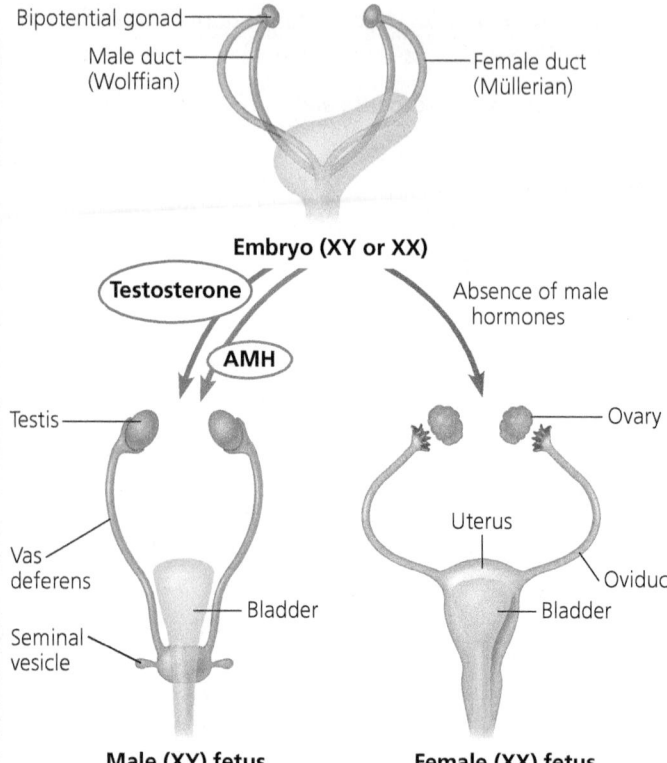

▲ **Figure 45.24 Sex hormones regulate formation of internal reproductive structures in human development.** In a male (XY) embryo, the bipotential gonads become the testes, which secrete testosterone and anti-Müllerian hormone (AMH). Testosterone directs formation of sperm-carrying ducts (vas deferens and seminal vesicles), while AMH causes the female ducts to degenerate. In the absence of these testis hormones, the male ducts degenerate and female structures form, including the oviduct, uterus, and vagina.

hormones is controlled by gonadotropins (FSH and LH) from the anterior pituitary gland (see Figure 45.18). FSH and LH secretion is in turn controlled by GnRH (gonadotropin-releasing hormone), a releasing hormone from the hypothalamus. We will examine the feedback relationships that regulate gonadal steroid secretion in detail in Chapter 46.

Endocrine Disruptors

Between 1938 and 1971, some pregnant women at risk for complications were prescribed a synthetic estrogen called diethylstilbestrol (DES). What was not known until 1971 was that exposure to DES can alter reproductive system development in the fetus. Collectively, daughters of women who took DES are more frequently afflicted with certain reproductive abnormalities, including a form of vaginal and cervical cancer, structural changes in the reproductive organs, and increased risk of miscarriage (spontaneous abortion). DES is now recognized as an *endocrine disruptor*, a foreign molecule that interrupts the normal function of a hormone pathway.

In recent years, it has been hypothesized that molecules in the environment also act as endocrine disruptors. Some estrogen-like molecules, such as those present in soybeans and other edible plant products, have been suggested to lower breast cancer risk. Others, such as bisphenol A, a chemical used in making some plastics, have been studied for potential interference with normal reproduction and development. Sorting out such effects has proved quite difficult, however, in part because enzymes in the liver change the properties of any such molecules entering the body through the digestive system.

Melatonin and Biorhythms

We conclude our discussion of the vertebrate endocrine system with the **pineal gland**, a small mass of tissue near the centre of the mammalian brain (see Figure 45.16). The pineal gland is a primary source of the hormone **melatonin**, a modified amino acid.

Melatonin regulates functions related to light and to seasons marked by changes in day length. Although melatonin affects skin pigmentation in many vertebrates, its primary functions relate to biological rhythms associated with reproduction and with daily activity levels. Melatonin is secreted at night, and the amount released depends on the length of the night. In winter, for example, when days are short and nights are long, more melatonin is secreted. There is also good evidence that nightly increases in the levels of melatonin play a significant role in promoting sleep.

The release of melatonin by the pineal gland is controlled by a group of neurons in the hypothalamus called the suprachiasmatic nucleus (SCN). The SCN functions as a biological clock and receives input from specialized light-sensitive neurons in the retina of the eye. Although the SCN regulates melatonin production during the 24-hour light/dark cycle, melatonin also influences SCN activity. We will consider biological rhythms further in Chapter 49, where we analyze experiments on SCN function.

In the next chapter, we will look at reproduction in both vertebrates and invertebrates. There we will see that the endocrine system is central not only to the survival of the individual, but also to the propagation of the species.

CONCEPT CHECK 45.3

1. How does the fact that two adrenal hormones act as neurotransmitters relate to the developmental origin of the adrenal gland?
2. How would a decrease in the number of corticosteroid receptors in the hypothalamus affect levels of corticosteroids in the blood?
3. **WHAT IF?** Suppose you receive an injection of cortisone, a glucocorticoid, in an inflamed joint. What aspects of glucocorticoid activity would you be exploiting? If a glucocorticoid pill were also effective at treating the inflammation, why would it still be preferable to introduce the drug locally?

For suggested answers, see Appendix A.

---

45 Chapter Review

Go to **MasteringBiology**® for Assignments, the eText, and the Study Area with Animations, Activities, Vocab Self-Quiz, and Practice Tests.

SUMMARY OF KEY CONCEPTS

CONCEPT 45.1

Hormones and other signalling molecules bind to target receptors, triggering specific response pathways (pp. 1049–1055)

- The forms of communication between animal cells differ in the type of secreting cell and the route taken by the signal to its target. **Endocrine** signals, or **hormones**, are secreted into extracellular fluids by endocrine cells or ductless glands and reach target cells via circulatory fluids. **Paracrine** signals act on neighbouring cells, whereas **autocrine** signals act on the cell that secreted it. **Neurotransmitters** also act locally, but **neurohormones** can act throughout the body. **Pheromones** are released into the environment for communication between animals of the same species.
- Distinct cellular responses are associated with water-soluble and lipid-soluble hormones. Polypeptide hormones and most amine hormones are water-soluble and bind to receptors embedded in the plasma membrane. Binding of water-soluble hormones to cell-surface receptors triggers intracellular **signal transduction**, leading to specific responses in the cytoplasm or changes in gene expression. In contrast, steroid and thyroid hormones are lipid-soluble and readily enter target cells. There they bind to specific protein receptors in the cytosol or nucleus. These complexes of a lipid-soluble hormone and its receptor act in the nucleus to regulate transcription of specific genes. The same hormone may have different effects on target cells that have different receptors for the hormone or different signal transduction pathways.
- **Local regulators**, which carry out paracrine and autocrine signalling, include cytokines and **growth factors** (proteins/peptides), **nitric oxide** (a gas), and **prostaglandins** (modified fatty acids).

? *Predict what would happen if you injected a water-soluble hormone directly into the cytosol of a target cell.*

Feedback regulation and antagonistic hormone pairs are common in endocrine systems (pp. 1055–1059)

- Hormone pathways may be regulated by **negative feedback**, which dampens the stimulus, or **positive feedback**, which amplifies the stimulus and drives the response to completion. Negative-feedback pathways sometimes occur in antagonistic pairs, such as the maintainance of glucose homeostasis by **glucagon** (from alpha cells of the **pancreas**) and **insulin** (from beta cells of the pancreas). Insulin reduces blood glucose levels by promoting cellular uptake of glucose, glycogen formation in the liver, protein synthesis, and fat storage. The disorder **diabetes mellitus**, which is marked by elevated blood glucose levels, results from inadequate production of insulin (type 1) or loss of responsiveness of target cells to insulin (type 2).

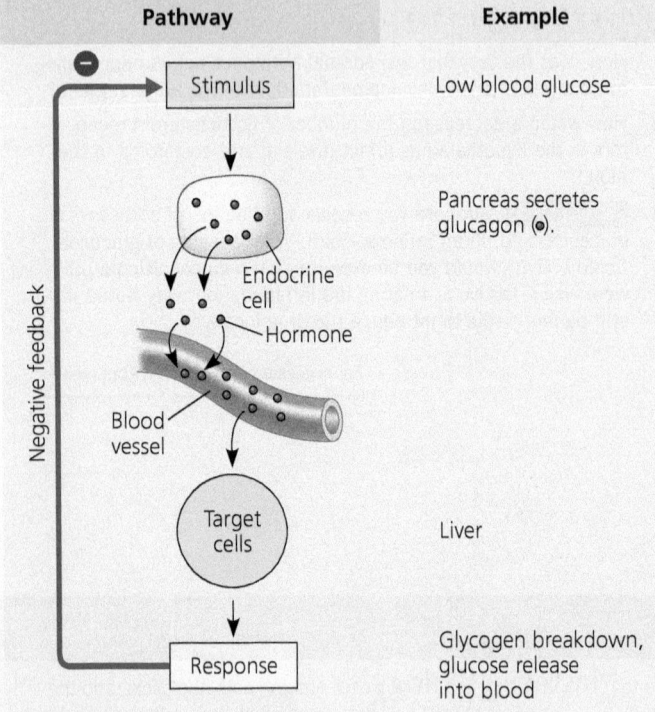

Pathway	Example
Stimulus	Low blood glucose
	Pancreas secretes glucagon (●).
Endocrine cell / Hormone / Blood vessel	
Target cells	Liver
Response	Glycogen breakdown, glucose release into blood

(Negative feedback)

- In insects, moulting and development are controlled by PTTH; **ecdysteroid**, whose release is triggered by PTTH; and juvenile hormone. Coordination of signals from the nervous and endocrine systems and modulation of one hormone activity by another bring about the precise series of developmental stages that lead to an adult form.

? *Would taking a drug that blocks the action of glucagon lessen the symptoms of diabetes or make them worse? Explain.*

CONCEPT 45.3

Vertebrate hormones regulate homeostasis, development, and behaviour (pp. 1059–1067)

- Some neurosecretory cells in the **hypothalamus** produce hormones secreted by the posterior pituitary. Other hypothalamic cells produce hormones that are transported by portal vessels to the anterior pituitary, where they stimulate or inhibit the release of particular hormones.
- The two hormones released from the **posterior pituitary** act directly on nonendocrine tissues. **Oxytocin** induces uterine contractions and

release of milk from mammary glands, and **antidiuretic hormone** (ADH) enhances water reabsorption in the kidneys.

- Often, **anterior pituitary** hormones act in a cascade. In the case of thyrotropin, or thyroid-stimulating hormone (TSH), TSH secretion is regulated by thyrotropin-releasing hormone (TRH). TSH in turn induces the **thyroid gland** to secrete **thyroid hormone**, a combination of the iodine-containing hormones T_3 and T_4. Thyroid hormone stimulates metabolism and influences development and maturation.
- Hormones sometimes acquire distinct roles in different species over the course of evolution. **Prolactin** stimulates milk production in mammals but has diverse effects in different vertebrates. **Melanocyte-stimulating hormone** (MSH) influences skin pigmentation in some vertebrates and fat metabolism in mammals.
- Although prolactin and MSH act on nonendocrine targets, most anterior pituitary hormones are tropic, acting on endocrine tissues or glands to regulate hormone secretion.
- **Growth hormone** (GH) promotes growth directly, has diverse metabolic effects, and stimulates the production of growth factors by other tissues.
- **Parathyroid hormone** (PTH), secreted by the **parathyroid glands**, causes bone to release Ca^{2+} into the blood and stimulates reabsorption of Ca^{2+} in the kidneys. PTH also stimulates the kidneys to activate vitamin D, which promotes intestinal uptake of Ca^{2+} from food. **Calcitonin**, secreted by the thyroid, has the opposite effects in bones and kidneys as PTH. Calcitonin is important for calcium homeostasis in adults of some vertebrates, but not humans.
- In response to stress, neurosecretory cells in the adrenal medulla release **epinephrine** and **norepinephrine**, which mediate various fight-or-flight responses. The adrenal cortex releases **glucocorticoids**, such as cortisol, which influence glucose metabolism and the immune system, as well as **mineralocorticoids**, primarily aldosterone, which help regulate salt and water balance.
- Although the adrenal cortex produces small amounts of sex hormones, the gonads—testes and ovaries—produce most of the body's sex hormones. All three types—**androgens, estrogens**, and **progestins**—are produced in males and females, but in different proportions.
- The **pineal gland**, located within the brain, secretes **melatonin**, which functions in biological rhythms related to reproduction and sleep. Release of melatonin is controlled by the SCN, the region of the brain that functions as a biological clock.

? *ADH and epinephrine act as hormones when released into the bloodstream and as neurotransmitters when released in synapses between neurons. What is similar about the endocrine glands that produce these two molecules?*

TEST YOUR UNDERSTANDING

LEVEL 1: KNOWLEDGE/COMPREHENSION

1. Which of the following is *not* an accurate statement?
   a. Hormones are chemical messengers that travel to target cells through the circulatory system.
   b. Hormones often regulate homeostasis through antagonistic functions.
   c. Hormones of the same chemical class usually have the same function.
   d. Hormones are secreted by specialized cells usually located in endocrine glands.

2. The hypothalamus
   a. synthesizes all of the hormones produced by the pituitary gland.
   b. influences the function of only one lobe of the pituitary gland.
   c. produces only inhibitory hormones.
   d. regulates both reproduction and body temperature.

3. Growth factors are local regulators that
   a. are produced by the anterior pituitary.
   b. are modified fatty acids that stimulate bone and cartilage growth.
   c. are found on the surface of cancer cells and stimulate abnormal cell division.
   d. bind to cell-surface receptors and stimulate growth and development of target cells.

4. Which hormone is *incorrectly* paired with its action?
   a. oxytocin—stimulates uterine contractions during childbirth
   b. thyroxine—stimulates metabolic processes
   c. insulin—stimulates glycogen breakdown in the liver
   d. ACTH—stimulates the release of glucocorticoids by the adrenal cortex

LEVEL 2: APPLICATION/ANALYSIS

5. Steroid and peptide hormones typically have in common
   a. the building blocks from which they are synthesized.
   b. their solubility in cell membranes.
   c. their requirement for travel through the bloodstream.
   d. the location of their receptors.

6. Which of the following is the most likely explanation for hypothyroidism in a patient whose iodine level is normal?
   a. greater production of T_3 than of T_4
   b. hyposecretion of TSH
   c. hypersecretion of TSH
   d. hypersecretion of MSH

7. Shortly after ingesting a big plate of carbohydrate-rich pasta, you measure your blood's hormone levels. What results would you expect, compared to before the meal?
   a. high insulin, low glucagon
   b. low insulin, low glucagon
   c. high insulin, high glucagon
   d. low insulin, high glucagon

8. The relationship between the insect hormones ecdysteroid and PTTH is an example of
   a. an interaction of the endocrine and nervous systems.
   b. homeostasis achieved by positive feedback.
   c. how peptide-derived hormones have more widespread effects than steroid hormones.
   d. homeostasis maintained by antagonistic hormones.

9. **DRAW IT** In mammals, milk production by mammary glands is controlled by prolactin and prolactin-releasing hormone. Draw a simple sketch of this pathway, including glands and tissues, hormones, routes for hormone movement, and effects.

LEVEL 3: SYNTHESIS/EVALUATION

10. **EVOLUTION CONNECTION**
    The intracellular receptors used by all the steroid and thyroid hormones are similar enough in structure that they are all considered members of one "superfamily" of proteins. Propose a hypothesis for how the genes encoding these receptors may have evolved. (*Hint*: See Figure 21.13.) How could you test your hypothesis using DNA sequence data?

11. **SCIENTIFIC INQUIRY**
    INTERPRET THE DATA Chronically high levels of glucocorticoids can result in obesity, muscle weakness, and depression, a combination of symptoms called Cushing's syndrome. Excessive activity of either the pituitary or the adrenal gland can be the cause. To determine which gland has abnormal activity in a particular patient, doctors use the drug dexamethasone, a synthetic glucocorticoid that blocks ACTH release. Based on the graph, which gland is affected in patient X?

12. **WRITE ABOUT A THEME: INTERACTIONS**
    In a short essay (100–150 words), use specific examples to discuss the role of hormones in an animal's responses to changes in its environment.

13. **SYNTHESIZE YOUR KNOWLEDGE**

Courtesy of Eric W. Roubos, Radboud University, Nymegen

The frog on the left was injected with MSH, causing a change in skin colour within minutes due to a rapid redistribution of pigment granules in specialized skin cells. Using what you know about neuroendocrine signalling, explain how a frog could use MSH to match its skin colouration to that of its surroundings.

For selected answers, see Appendix A.

46

Animal Reproduction

KEY CONCEPTS

46.1 Both asexual and sexual reproduction occur in the animal kingdom

46.2 Fertilization depends on mechanisms that bring together sperm and eggs of the same species

46.3 Reproductive organs produce and transport gametes

46.4 The interplay of tropic and sex hormones regulates mammalian reproduction

46.5 In placental mammals, an embryo develops fully within the mother's uterus

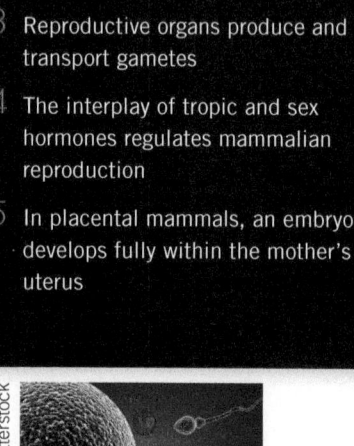

Alamy

▲ Figure 46.1 **How can each of these slugs be both male and female?**

Pairing Up for Sexual Reproduction

The banana slugs (*Ariolimax* sp.) in **Figure 46.1** are mating. Each has male and female genitalia, which protrude from each animal and wrap around the other during copulation. Sperm will be transferred and will fertilize eggs. After copulation, they each chew off the other's penis, then go their separate ways to release fertilized eggs. A few weeks later, sexual reproduction will be complete. New individuals will hatch, but which parent is the mother? The answer is simple yet probably unexpected: both. In fact, each banana slug produces eggs *and* sperm.

As humans, we tend to think of reproduction in terms of the mating of males and females and the fusion of a sperm and egg. Animal reproduction, however, takes many forms. In some species, individuals change their sex during their lifetime; in other species, such as slugs, an individual is both male and female. There are animals that can fertilize their own eggs, as well as others that can reproduce without any form of sex. For certain species, such as honeybees, only a few individuals within a large population reproduce.

Individual animals may die, but a population persists through reproduction of its members. In this chapter, we will compare the diverse reproductive mechanisms that have evolved in the animal kingdom. We will then examine details of mammalian reproduction, with emphasis on the well-studied example of

videodoctor/Shutterstock

humans. We will focus on the physiology of reproduction mostly from the parents' perspective, deferring the details of embryonic development until the next chapter.

CONCEPT 46.1

Both asexual and sexual reproduction occur in the animal kingdom

There are two modes of animal reproduction—sexual and asexual. In **sexual reproduction**, the fusion of haploid gametes forms a diploid cell, the **zygote**. The animal that develops from a zygote can in turn give rise to gametes by meiosis (see Figure 13.8). The female gamete, the **egg**, is a large, nonmotile cell. The male gamete, the **sperm**, is generally a much smaller, motile cell. **Asexual reproduction** is the generation of new individuals without the fusion of egg and sperm. In most asexual animals, reproduction relies entirely on mitotic cell division.

For the vast majority of animals, reproduction is primarily or exclusively sexual. However, there are species that have a primarily asexual mode of reproduction, including a few all-female species for which reproduction is exclusively asexual. These include the microscopic bdelloid rotifer (see p. 737), as well as certain species of whiptail lizard (*Aspidoscelis*), which we will discuss shortly.

Mechanisms of Asexual Reproduction

Several modes of asexual reproduction involve breaking a single parent into two or more pieces, each of which matures into an individual that is a genetic clone of the parent. These forms of asexual reproduction are distinguished by the number and size of fragments. In **fission**, an animal breaks into two similarly sized individuals. The sea anemone in **Figure 46.2** is reproducing by fission. In

budding, a large parent produces outgrowths that enlarge and eventually separate from the main body. In stony corals, for example, buds form and remain attached to the parent. The eventual result is a colony more than 1 m across, consisting of thousands of connected individuals. Some invertebrates undergo **fragmentation**, whereby an individual may disintegrate into many small pieces, each of which regenerates into a fully functional individual. For example, certain annelid worms can fragment, with each piece regenerating a complete worm in less than a week. Numerous sponges, cnidarians, and tunicates also reproduce by fragmentation and regeneration.

Another form of asexual reproduction uses the reproductive tract of the female. **Parthenogenesis** is asexual reproduction in which an egg develops without being fertilized by a sperm. Among invertebrates, parthenogenesis occurs in certain species of bees, wasps, and ants. The progeny can be either haploid or diploid. If haploid, the offspring develop into adults that produce eggs or sperm without meiosis. In the case of honeybees, males (drones) are fertile haploid adults that arise by parthenogenesis. (In contrast, female honeybees, including both the sterile workers and the fertile queens, are diploid adults that develop from fertilized eggs.) Among vertebrates, parthenogenesis has been observed in about one in every thousand species. Zookeepers have discovered parthenogenesis in the Komodo dragon and in a species of hammerhead shark. In both cases, females had been kept completely isolated from males of their species but nevertheless produced offspring.

Sexual Reproduction: An Evolutionary Enigma

EVOLUTION Sex must enhance reproductive success or survival because it would otherwise rapidly disappear. To see why, consider an animal population in which half the females reproduce sexually and half reproduce asexually (**Figure 46.3**). We'll assume that the number of offspring per female is a

▲ **Figure 46.2 Asexual reproduction of a sea anemone (*Anthopleura elegantissima*).** Aggregations of anemones can arise where individuals divide by fission, populating a region with genetically identical clones.

Peter Scoones/Science Source

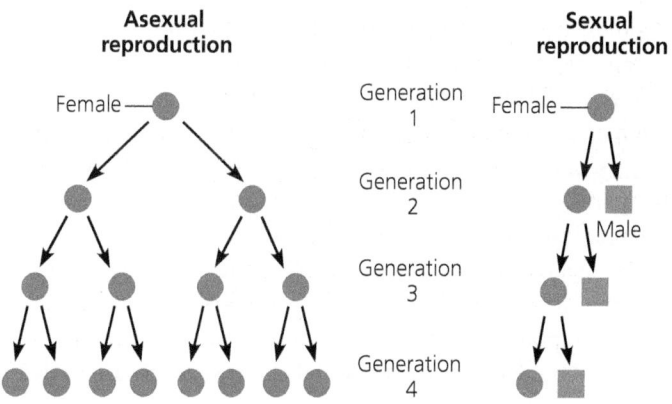

▲ **Figure 46.3 The "reproductive handicap" of sex.** These diagrams contrast the reproductive output of females (orange spheres) over four generations for asexual versus sexual reproduction, assuming two surviving offspring per female. The asexual population rapidly outgrows the sexual one.

constant, two in this case. The two offspring of an asexual female will both be daughters that will each give birth to two more reproductive daughters. In contrast, half of a sexual female's offspring will be male. The number of sexual offspring will remain the same at each generation, because both a male and a female are required to reproduce. Thus, the asexual condition will increase in frequency at each generation. Yet despite this "twofold cost," sex is maintained even in animal species that can also reproduce asexually.

What advantage does sex provide? The answer remains elusive. Most hypotheses focus on the unique combinations of parental genes formed during meiotic recombination and fertilization. By producing offspring of varied genotypes, sexual reproduction may enhance the reproductive success of parents when environmental factors, such as pathogens, change relatively rapidly. In contrast, asexual reproduction is expected to be most advantageous in stable, favourable environments because it perpetuates successful genotypes faithfully and precisely.

There are a number of reasons why the unique gene combinations formed during sexual reproduction might be advantageous. One is that beneficial gene combinations arising through recombination might speed up adaptation. Although this idea appears straightforward, the theoretical advantage is significant only when the rate of beneficial mutations is high and population size is small. Another idea is that the shuffling of genes during sexual reproduction might allow a population to rid itself of sets of harmful genes more readily. Experiments to test these and other hypotheses are ongoing in many laboratories.

Reproductive Cycles

Most animals exhibit cycles in reproductive activity, often related to changing seasons. In this way, animals conserve resources, reproducing only when sufficient energy sources or stores are available and when environmental conditions favour the survival of offspring. For example, ewes (female sheep) have a reproductive cycle lasting 15–17 days. **Ovulation**, the release of mature eggs, occurs at the midpoint of each cycle. A ewe's cycle generally occurs only during fall and early winter, and the length of any resulting pregnancy is 5 months. Thus, most lambs are born in the early spring, when their chances of survival are optimal. Reproductive cycles are controlled by hormones, which in turn are regulated by environmental cues. Common environmental cues are changes in day length, seasonal temperature, rainfall, and lunar cycles. Because seasonal temperature is often an important cue for reproduction, climate change can decrease reproductive success. Global climate changes are likely to have important consequences for species that live in the North, such as caribou, polar bears, and seals (Figure 46.4).

Reproductive cycles are also found among animals that can reproduce both sexually and asexually. Consider, for

▼ Figure 46.4

Impact

Global Warming and Arctic Mammals

Increases in average temperatures have profound effects on Arctic aquatic and terrestrial ecosystems, particularly on the reproductive biology of large Arctic mammals.

In spring, caribou (*Ranger tarandus*) migrate to calving grounds to eat sprouting green plants, give birth, and care for their new calves (inset). Because caribou reproduction is linked to photoperiod, whereas plant growth depends on temperature, the warmer springs have created a mismatch between caribou and its food. By the time the caribou give birth, the plants have become less digestible and nutritious. The loss in food quality has contributed to the 75% decline in caribou offspring.

Chris Wallace/Pearson Education, Inc.

Polar bear (*Ursus maritimus*) reproduction depends critically on sea ice. The availability of ice allows the bears to hunt marine mammals, storing energy that can be used to support embryonic growth and lactation. In recent times, the ice pack has been breaking up about 1 week earlier each decade. This means bears spend less time on ice fattening, and more time on land starving. Mathematical models suggest that, if the warming trend continues, polar bears could face drastic declines in the number of successful pregnancies and the mean litter size. Apart from physiology, the reduced ice increases human-bear interactions, which can also influence bear populations.

Many seal species delay the embryonic development by preventing the embryo from implanting in the uterus. In harbour seals, *Phoca vitulina*, this embryonic diapause extends the total gestation period to 11 months between mating (June) and birth (May). Recent studies on harbour seals suggest that the average birth date has been almost 1 day earlier per year since 1975. Whether this is due to a change in the length of the embryonic diapause is not yet clear, but it does suggest that seals may be able to alter how environmental conditions impinge upon reproductive strategies.

Why It Matters Animals living in the Arctic can survive this harsh world only through adaptations that match physiology to environmental conditions. Rapid global warming may outpace their capacity to cope as individuals or survive as populations.

Further Reading P. K. Molnar, A. E. Derocher, T. Klanjscek, and M. A. Lewis, Predicting climate change impacts on polar bear litter size, *Nature Communnications* 2:186l, DOI: 10.1038/ncomms1183 (2011). P. J. H. Reijnders, S. M. J. M. Brasseur, and E. H. W. G. Meesters, Earlier pupping in harbour seals, *Phoca vitulina*, *Biological Letters* 6:854–857 (2010).

WHAT IF? *What factors other than a shorter embryonic diapause might contribute to the shorter total gestation time of harbour seals?*

instance, the water flea (genus *Daphnia*). A *Daphnia* female can produce eggs of two types. One type of egg requires fertilization to develop, but the other type does not and develops instead by parthenogenesis. Asexual reproduction occurs when environmental conditions are favourable, whereas sexual reproduction occurs during times of environmental stress. As a result, the switch between sexual and asexual reproduction is roughly linked to season.

Some species of whiptail lizards in the genus *Aspidoscelis* exhibit a very different type of reproductive cycle: Reproduction is exclusively asexual, and there are no males. Nevertheless, these lizards have courtship and mating behaviours that are typical of sexual species of the same genus. During the breeding season, one female of each mating pair mimics a male (Figure 46.5a). Each member of the pair alternates roles two or three times during the season. An individual adopts female behaviour prior to ovulation, when the level of the female sex hormone estradiol is high, then switches to male-like behaviour after ovulation, when the level of progesterone is highest (Figure 46.5b). Ovulation is more likely to occur if the individual is mounted during the critical time of the hormone cycle; isolated lizards lay fewer eggs than those that go through the motions of sex. These observations support the hypothesis that these parthenogenetic lizards evolved from species having two sexes and still require certain sexual stimuli for maximum reproductive success.

Variation in Patterns of Sexual Reproduction

For many animals, finding a partner for sexual reproduction can be challenging. Adaptations that arose during the evolution of some species meet this challenge in a novel way—by blurring the strict distinction between male and female. One such adaptation arose among sessile (stationary) animals, such as barnacles; burrowing animals, such as clams; and some parasites, including tapeworms. Lacking locomotion, these animals have a very limited opportunity to find a mate. An evolutionary solution to this problem is **hermaphroditism**, in which each individual has both male and female reproductive systems (the term *hermaphrodite* merges the names Hermes and Aphrodite, a Greek god and goddess). Because each hermaphrodite reproduces as both a male and a female, *any* two individuals can mate. Each animal donates and receives sperm during mating, as the banana slugs in Figure 46.1 are doing. In some species, hermaphrodites are also capable of self-fertilization, allowing a form of sexual reproduction that doesn't require any partner.

The bluehead wrasse (*Thalassoma bifasciatum*), a coral reef fish, is a well-studied example of a quite different variation in sexual reproduction. These wrasses live in harems, each consisting of a single male and several females. When the lone male dies, the opportunity for sexual reproduction would appear lost. Instead, a female wrasse undergoes sex

(a) Both lizards in this photograph are *A. uniparens* females. The one on top is playing the role of a male. Every two or three weeks during the breeding season, individuals switch sex roles.

(b) The sexual behaviour of *A. uniparens* is correlated with the cycle of ovulation mediated by sex hormones. As the blood level of estradiol rises, the ovaries grow, and the lizard behaves as a female. After ovulation, the estradiol level drops abruptly, and the progesterone level rises; these hormone levels correlate with male-like behaviour.

▲ **Figure 46.5 Sexual behaviour in parthenogenetic lizards.** The desert-grassland whiptail lizard (*Aspidoscelis uniparens*) is an all-female species. These reptiles reproduce by parthenogenesis, the development of an unfertilized egg. Nevertheless, ovulation is stimulated by mating behaviour.

INTERPRET THE DATA *If you plotted hormone levels for the lizard shown in grey, how would your graph differ from the graph in (b)?*

reversal, a change in sex. Within a week, the transformed individual is producing sperm instead of eggs. Scientists have observed that it is the largest (and usually oldest) female in the harem that undergoes sex reversal. What advantage did this offer in the evolution of this wrasse? Because it is the male that defends a harem against intruders, a larger size may be more important for males than females in ensuring successful reproduction.

Certain oyster species also undergo sex reversal. In this case, individuals reproduce as males and then later as females, when their size is greatest. Since the number of gametes produced generally increases with size much more for females than for males, sex reversal in this direction maximizes gamete production. The result is enhanced reproductive success: Because oysters are sedentary animals and release their gametes into the surrounding water rather than mating directly, releasing more gametes tends to result in more offspring.

CONCEPT 46.2

Fertilization depends on mechanisms that bring together sperm and eggs of the same species

The union of sperm and egg—**fertilization**—can be either external or internal. In species with **external fertilization**, the female releases eggs into the environment, where the male then fertilizes them. Other species have **internal fertilization**: Sperm are deposited in or near the female reproductive tract, and fertilization occurs within the tract. (We'll discuss the cellular and molecular details of fertilization in Chapter 47.)

A moist habitat is almost always required for external fertilization, both to prevent the gametes from drying out and to allow the sperm to swim to the eggs. Many aquatic invertebrates simply shed their eggs and sperm into the surroundings, and fertilization occurs without the parents making physical contact. However, timing is crucial to ensure that mature sperm and eggs encounter one another.

Among some species with external fertilization, individuals clustered in the same area release their gametes into the water at the same time, a process known as *spawning*. In some cases, chemical signals that one individual generates in releasing gametes trigger others to release gametes. In other cases, environmental cues, such as temperature or day length, cause a whole population to release gametes at one time. For example, the palolo worm, native to coral reefs of the South Pacific, times its spawning to both the season and the lunar cycle. In spring, when the moon is in its last quarter, palolo worms break in half, releasing tail segments engorged with sperm or eggs. These packets rise to the ocean surface and burst in such vast numbers that the sea appears milky with gametes. The sperm quickly fertilize the floating eggs, and within hours, the palolo's once-a-year reproductive frenzy is complete.

When external fertilization is not synchronous across a population, individuals may exhibit specific mating behaviours leading to the fertilization of the eggs of one female by one male (Figure 46.6). Such "courtship" behaviour has two important benefits: It allows mate choice (see Chapter 23) and, by triggering the release of both sperm and eggs, increases the probability of successful fertilization.

Internal fertilization is an adaptation that enables sperm to reach an egg efficiently, even when the environment is dry. It typically requires cooperative behaviour that leads to copulation, as well as sophisticated and compatible reproductive systems. The male copulatory organ delivers sperm, and the female reproductive tract often has receptacles for storage and delivery of sperm to mature eggs.

No matter how fertilization occurs, the mating animals may make use of *pheromones*, chemicals released by one organism that can influence the physiology and behaviour of other individuals of the same species. Pheromones are small volatile or water-soluble molecules that disperse into the environment and, like hormones, are active in tiny amounts (see Chapter 45). Many pheromones function as mate attractants, enabling some female insects to be detected by males from as far away as a mile. (We will discuss mating behaviour and pheromones further in Chapter 51.)

Ensuring the Survival of Offspring

Comparing internal and external fertilization across many species reveals that internal fertilization is typically associated with the production of fewer gametes but the survival of a higher

▲ Figure 46.6 **External fertilization.** Many species of amphibians reproduce by external fertilization. In most of these species, behavioural adaptations ensure that a male is present when the female releases eggs. Here, a female frog (on bottom) has released a mass of eggs in response to being clasped by a male. The male released sperm (not visible) at the same time, and external fertilization has already occurred in the water.

Andy Sands/Nature Picture Library

fraction of zygotes. Better zygote survival is due in part to the fact that eggs fertilized internally are sheltered from potential predators. However, internal fertilization is also more often associated with mechanisms that provide greater protection of the embryos and parental care of the young. For example, the internally fertilized eggs of many species of terrestrial animals exhibit adaptations that protect against water loss and physical damage during their external development. In the case of birds and other reptiles, as well as monotremes (egg-laying mammals), the zygotes consist of eggs with calcium- and protein-containing shells and several internal membranes (see Figure 34.26). In contrast, the fertilized eggs of fishes and amphibians have only a gelatinous coat and lack internal membranes.

Rather than secreting a protective eggshell, some animals retain the embryo for a portion of its development within the female's reproductive tract. Embryos of marsupial mammals, such as kangaroos and opossums, spend only a short period in the uterus; the embryos then crawl out and complete fetal development attached to a mammary gland in the mother's pouch. However, embryos of eutherian (placental) mammals, such as humans, remain in the uterus throughout fetal development. There they are nourished by the mother's blood supply through a temporary organ, the placenta. The embryos of some fishes and sharks also complete development internally, although typically the embryo and mother in such species lack a connection dedicated to nutrient exchange.

When a baby eagle hatches out of an egg or when a human is born, the newborn is not yet capable of independent existence. Instead, adult birds feed their young and mammals nurse their offspring. Parental care is in fact much more widespread than you might suspect. For example, there are many invertebrates that provide parental care (Figure 46.7).

Gamete Production and Delivery

Sexual reproduction in animals relies on sets of cells that are precursors for eggs and sperm. A group of cells dedicated to this purpose is often established very early in the formation of the embryo and remains in an inactive state while the body plan develops. Cycles of growth and mitosis then increase, or *amplify*, the number of cells available for making eggs or sperm.

◀ Figure 46.7 **Parental care in an invertebrate.** Compared with many other insects, giant water bugs of the genus *Belostoma* produce relatively few offspring, but offer much greater parental protection. Following internal fertilization, the female glues her fertilized eggs to the back of the male (shown here). The male carries them for days, frequently fanning water over them to keep the eggs moist, aerated, and free of parasites.

In producing gametes from the amplified precursor cells and making them available for fertilization, animals employ a variety of reproductive systems. The simplest systems do not even include discrete **gonads**, the organs that produce gametes in most animals. The palolo and most other polychaete worms (phylum Annelida) have separate sexes but do not have distinct gonads; rather, the eggs and sperm develop from undifferentiated cells lining the coelom (body cavity). As the gametes mature, they are released from the body wall and fill the coelom. Depending on the species, mature gametes may be shed through the excretory opening, or the swelling mass of eggs may split a portion of the body open, spilling the eggs into the environment.

More elaborate reproductive systems include sets of accessory tubes and glands that carry, nourish, and protect the gametes and sometimes the developing embryos. Most insect species, for example, have separate sexes with complex reproductive systems (Figure 46.8). In the males, sperm develop in a pair of testes and are passed along a coiled duct to two seminal vesicles for storage. During mating, sperm are ejaculated into the female reproductive system. There, eggs develop in a pair of ovaries and are conveyed through ducts to the uterus. Eggs are fertilized in the uterus and then expelled for development outside the body. In many insect species, the female reproductive system includes one or more **spermathecae** (singular, *spermatheca*), sacs in which sperm may be stored for extended periods, a year or more in some species. Because the female releases male gametes from the spermatheca only in response to the appropriate stimuli, fertilization occurs under conditions likely to be well suited to embryonic development. Even more complex reproductive systems can be found in some animals whose body plans are otherwise fairly simple, such as parasitic flatworms.

Vertebrate reproductive systems are quite similar, but there are some important variations. In many nonmammalian vertebrates, the digestive, excretory, and reproductive systems have a common opening to the outside, the **cloaca**, a structure that was probably also present in the ancestors of all vertebrates. In contrast, mammals generally lack a cloaca and have a separate opening for the digestive tract. In addition, most female mammals have separate openings for the excretory and reproductive systems. Among most vertebrates, the uterus is partly or completely divided into two chambers. However, in humans and other mammals that produce only one or a few young at a time, as well as in birds and many snakes, the uterus is a single structure. Male reproductive systems differ mainly in the copulatory organs. Most fish simply release sperm into the environment without the aid of a copulatory organ, but some use modified pelvic fins that fold together to produce a channel for sperm transfer. Most reptiles simply empty their cloaca to release sperm; however, many reptiles have penis-like structures that insert into the female reproductive tract.

Although fertilization involves the union of a single egg and sperm, animals often mate with more than one member of the

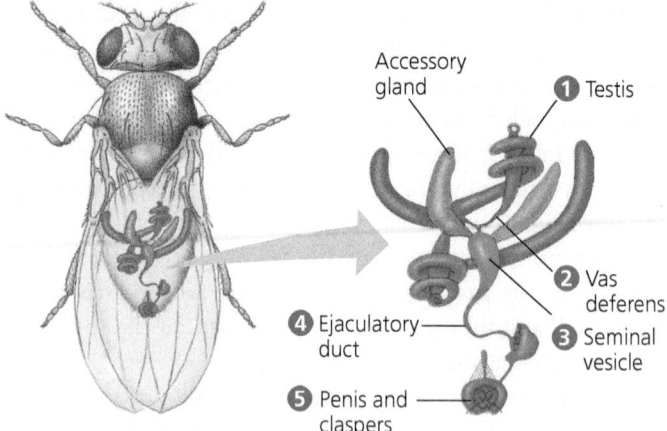

(a) **Male fruit fly.** Sperm form in the testes, pass through the sperm ducts (vas deferens), and are stored in the seminal vesicles. The male ejaculates sperm along with fluid from the accessory glands. (Males of some species of insects and other arthropods have appendages called claspers that grasp the female during copulation.)

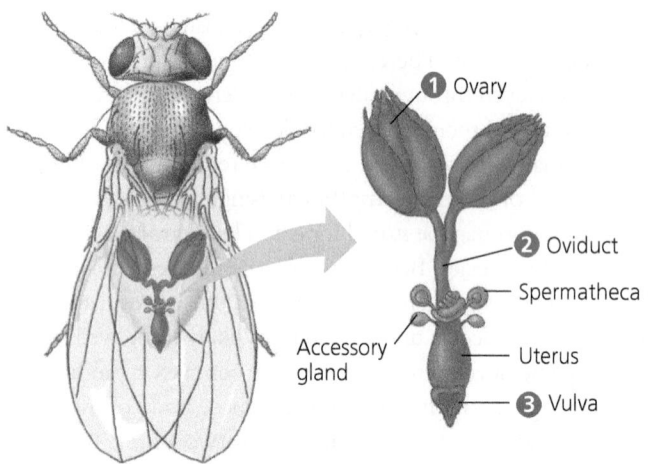

(b) **Female fruit fly.** Eggs develop in the ovaries and then travel through the oviducts to the uterus. After mating, sperm are stored in the spermathecae, which are connected to the uterus by short ducts. The female uses a stored sperm to fertilize each egg as it enters the uterus before she passes the egg out through the vulva.

▲ Figure 46.8 **Insect reproductive anatomy.** Circled numbers indicate sequences of sperm and egg movement.

other sex. Indeed, monogamy, the sustained sexual partnership of two individuals, is relatively rare among animals, including most mammals. Mechanisms have evolved, however, that enhance the reproductive success of a male with a particular female and diminish the chance of that female mating successfully with another partner. For example, some male insects transfer secretions that make a female less receptive to courtship, thereby reducing the likelihood of her mating again.

Can females also influence the relative reproductive success of their mates? This question intrigued two scientific collaborators working in Europe. Studying female fruit flies that copulated with one male and then another, the researchers traced the fate of sperm transferred in the first mating. As

▼ Figure 46.9 | **Inquiry**

Why is sperm usage biased when female fruit flies mate twice?

Experiment When a female fruit fly mates twice, 80% of the offspring result from the second mating. Scientists had postulated that ejaculate from the second mating displaces stored sperm. To test this hypothesis, Rhonda Snook, at the University of Sheffield, and David Hosken, at the University of Zurich, used mutant males with altered reproductive systems. "No-ejaculate" males mate, but do not transfer sperm or fluid to females. "No-sperm" males mate and ejaculate, but make no sperm. The researchers allowed females to mate with wild-type males and then mate with wild-type males, no-sperm males, or no-ejaculate males. As a control, some females were mated only once. The scientists then dissected each female under a microscope and recorded whether sperm were absent from the spermatheca, the major sperm storage organ.

Results

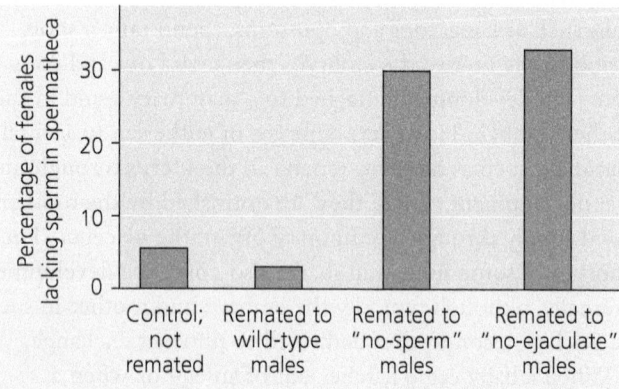

Conclusion Because remating reduces sperm storage when no sperm or fluids are transferred, the hypothesis that ejaculate from a second mating displaces stored sperm is incorrect. Instead, it appears that females sometimes get rid of stored sperm in response to remating. This might represent a way for females to replace stored sperm, possibly of diminished fitness, with fresh sperm.

Source: Adaptation of Figure 2 from "Sperm Death and Dumping in Drosophila" by Rhonda R. Snook and David J. Hosken, from *Nature*, April 29, 2004, Volume 428(6986). Copyright © 2004 by Macmillan Publishers Ltd. Reprinted with permission.

WHAT IF? *Suppose males in the first mating had a mutant allele for the dominant trait of smaller eyes. What fraction of the females would produce some offspring with smaller eyes?*

shown in **Figure 46.9**, they found that female fruit flies play a major role in determining the reproductive outcome of multiple matings. Nevertheless, the processes by which gametes and individuals compete during reproduction are only partly understood and remain a vibrant research area.

CONCEPT CHECK 46.2

1. How does internal fertilization facilitate life on land?
2. What mechanisms have evolved in animals with (a) external fertilization and (b) internal fertilization that help ensure that offspring survive to adulthood?
3. What are the shared and distinct functions of the uterus of an insect and the ovary of a flowering plant?

For suggested answers, see Appendix A.

Reproductive organs produce and transport gametes

Having surveyed some of the general features of animal reproduction, we will focus the rest of the chapter on humans, beginning with the anatomy of the reproductive system in each sex.

Female Reproductive Anatomy

The female's external reproductive structures are the clitoris and two sets of labia, which surround the clitoris and vaginal opening. The internal organs are the gonads, which produce both eggs and reproductive hormones, and a system of ducts and chambers, which receive and carry gametes and house the embryo and fetus (Figure 46.10).

Ovaries

The female gonads are a pair of ovaries that flank the uterus and are held in place in the abdominal cavity by ligaments. The outer layer of each ovary is packed with **follicles**, each consisting of an **oocyte**, a partially developed egg, surrounded by a group of support cells. The surrounding cells nourish and protect the oocyte during much of the formation and development of an egg. Although at birth the ovaries together contain about 1–2 million follicles, only about 500 follicles fully mature between puberty and menopause. During a typical 4-week menstrual cycle, one follicle matures and expels its egg, a process called ovulation. Prior to ovulation, cells of the follicle produce the primary female sex hormone, estradiol (a type of estrogen). After ovulation, the residual follicular tissue grows within the ovary, forming a mass called the **corpus luteum** ("yellow body"). The corpus luteum secretes additional estradiol, as well as progesterone, a hormone that helps maintain the uterine lining during pregnancy. If the egg cell is not fertilized, the corpus luteum degenerates, and a new follicle matures during the next cycle.

Oviducts and Uterus

An **oviduct**, or fallopian tube, extends from the uterus toward each ovary. The dimensions of this tube vary along its length, with the inside diameter near the uterus being as narrow as a human hair. At ovulation, the egg is released into the abdominal cavity near the funnel-like opening of the oviduct. Cilia on the epithelial lining of the duct help collect the egg by drawing fluid from the body cavity into the oviduct. Together with wavelike contractions of the oviduct, the cilia convey the egg down the duct to the **uterus**, also known as the womb. The uterus is a thick, muscular organ that can expand during pregnancy to accommodate a 4-kg fetus. The inner lining of the uterus, the **endometrium**, is richly supplied with blood vessels. The neck of the uterus, called the **cervix**, opens into the vagina.

Vagina and Vulva

The **vagina** is a muscular but elastic chamber that is the site for insertion of the penis and deposition of sperm during copulation. The vagina, which also serves as the birth canal through which a baby is born, opens to the outside at the **vulva**, the collective term for the external female genitalia.

▲ Figure 46.10 **Reproductive anatomy of the human female.** Some nonreproductive structures are labelled in parentheses for orientation purposes.

A pair of thick, fatty ridges, the **labia majora**, encloses and protects the rest of the vulva. The vaginal opening and the separate opening of the urethra are located within a cavity bordered by a pair of slender skin folds, the **labia minora**. A thin piece of tissue called the **hymen** partly covers the vaginal opening in humans at birth and usually until sexual intercourse or vigorous physical activity ruptures it. Located at the top of the labia minora, the **clitoris** consists of erectile tissue supporting a rounded **glans**, or head, covered by a small hood of skin, the **prepuce**. During sexual arousal, the clitoris, vagina, and labia minora all engorge with blood and enlarge. Richly supplied with nerve endings, the clitoris is one of the most sensitive points of sexual stimulation. Sexual arousal also induces the vestibular glands near the vaginal opening to secrete lubricating mucus, thereby facilitating intercourse.

Mammary Glands

The **mammary glands** are present in both sexes, but they normally produce milk only in females. Though not part of the reproductive system, the female mammary glands are important to reproduction. Within the glands, small sacs of epithelial tissue secrete milk, which drains into a series of ducts that open at the nipple. The breasts contain connective and fatty (adipose) tissue in addition to the mammary glands. Because the low level of estradiol in males limits the development of the fat deposits, male breasts usually remain small.

Male Reproductive Anatomy

The human male's external reproductive organs are the scrotum and penis. The internal reproductive organs consist of gonads that produce both sperm and reproductive hormones, accessory glands that secrete products essential to sperm movement, and ducts that carry the sperm and glandular secretions (**Figure 46.11**).

Testes

The male gonads, or **testes** (singular, *testis*), produce sperm in highly coiled tubes called **seminiferous tubules**. The **Leydig cells**, scattered in connective tissue between the tubules, produce testosterone and other androgens (see Chapter 45).

Most mammals produce sperm properly only when the testes are cooler than normal body temperature. In humans and many other mammals, the **scrotum**, a

fold of the body wall, maintains testis temperature about 2°C below that of the rest of the body. The testes develop in the abdominal cavity and descend into the scrotum just before birth (a testis within a scrotum is a *testicle*). In many rodents, the testes are drawn back into the cavity between breeding seasons, interrupting sperm maturation. Some mammals whose body temperature is low enough to allow sperm maturation—such as whales and elephants—retain the testes in the abdominal cavity.

Ducts

From the seminiferous tubules of a testis, the sperm pass into the coiled duct of an **epididymis**. In humans, it takes three weeks for sperm to pass through this 6-m-long duct. During this passage through the epididymis, the sperm complete

▲ Figure 46.11 **Reproductive anatomy of the human male.** Some nonreproductive structures are labelled in parentheses for orientation purposes.

maturation and become motile, although they acquire the ability to fertilize an egg only upon exposure to the chemical environment of the female reproductive system. During **ejaculation**, the sperm are propelled from each epididymis through a muscular duct, the **vas deferens**. Each vas deferens (one from each epididymis) extends around and behind the urinary bladder, where it joins a duct from the seminal vesicle, forming a short **ejaculatory duct**. The ejaculatory ducts open into the **urethra**, the outlet tube for both the excretory system and the reproductive system. The urethra runs through the penis and opens to the outside at the tip of the penis.

Accessory Glands

Three sets of accessory glands—the seminal vesicles, the prostate gland, and the bulbourethral glands—produce secretions that combine with sperm to form **semen**, the fluid that is ejaculated. Two **seminal vesicles** contribute about 60% of the volume of semen. The fluid from the seminal vesicles is thick, yellowish, and alkaline. It contains mucus, the sugar fructose (which provides most of the sperm's energy), a coagulating enzyme, ascorbic acid, and local regulators called prostaglandins (see Chapter 45).

The **prostate gland** secretes its products directly into the urethra through several small ducts. This fluid is thin and milky; it contains anticoagulant enzymes and citrate (a sperm nutrient). The prostate gland is the source of some of the most common medical problems of men over age 40. Benign (noncancerous) enlargement of the prostate occurs in more than half of all men in this age group and in almost all men over 70. In addition, prostate cancer, which most often afflicts men 65 and older, is one of the most common human cancers.

The *bulbourethral glands* are a pair of small glands along the urethra below the prostate. Before ejaculation, they secrete clear mucus that neutralizes any acidic urine remaining in the urethra. Bulbourethral fluid also carries some sperm released before ejaculation, which is one reason for the high failure rate of the withdrawal method of birth control (coitus interruptus).

Penis

The human **penis** contains the urethra, as well as three cylinders of spongy erectile tissue. During sexual arousal, the erectile tissue, which is derived from modified veins and capillaries, fills with blood from the arteries. As this tissue fills, the increasing pressure seals off the veins that drain the penis, causing it to engorge with blood. The resulting erection enables the penis to be inserted into the vagina. Alcohol consumption, certain drugs, emotional issues, and aging all can cause a temporary inability to achieve an erection (erectile dysfunction). For individuals with long-term erectile dysfunction, drugs such as Viagra promote the vasodilating action of the local regulator nitric oxide (NO; see Chapter 45);

the resulting relaxation of smooth muscles in the blood vessels of the penis enhances blood flow into the erectile tissues. Although all mammals rely on penile erection for mating, the penis of rodents, raccoons, walruses, whales, and several other mammals also contains a bone, the baculum, which probably further stiffens the penis for mating.

The main shaft of the penis is covered by relatively thick skin. The head, or glans, of the penis has a much thinner covering and is consequently more sensitive to stimulation. The human glans is covered by a fold of skin called the prepuce, or foreskin, which is removed if a male is circumcised.

Gametogenesis

Many of the differences in reproductive anatomy between males and females reflect the distinct structures and functions of the two types of gametes. Sperm are small and motile and must pass from the male to the female. In contrast, eggs, which provide the initial food stores for the embryo, are typically much larger and carry out their function within the female reproductive system. There they must mature in synchrony with the tissues that will support the embryo. Reflecting these differences, egg development and sperm development involve different patterns of meiotic division. We will highlight these differences as we explore **gametogenesis**, the production of gametes.

Spermatogenesis, the formation and development of sperm, is continuous and prolific in adult males. To produce hundreds of millions of sperm each day, cell division and maturation occur throughout the seminiferous tubules coiled within the two testes. For a single sperm, the process takes about seven weeks from start to finish.

Oogenesis, the development of mature oocytes (eggs), is a prolonged process in the human female. Immature eggs form in the ovary of the female embryo but do not complete their development until years, and often decades, later.

Spermatogenesis differs from oogenesis in three significant ways:

- Only in spermatogenesis do all four products of meiosis develop into mature gametes. In oogenesis, cytokinesis during meiosis is unequal, with almost all the cytoplasm segregated to a single daughter cell. This large cell is destined to become the egg; the other products of meiosis, smaller cells called polar bodies, degenerate.
- Spermatogenesis occurs throughout adolescence and adulthood. During oogenesis in human females, mitotic divisions are thought to be complete before birth, and the production of mature gametes ceases at about age 50.
- Spermatogenesis produces mature sperm from precursor cells in a continuous sequence, whereas oogenesis has long interruptions. **Figure 46.12**, on the next two pages, compares and contrasts the steps and organization of spermatogenesis and oogenesis in humans.

Exploring Human Gametogenesis

Spermatogenesis

These drawings correlate the mitotic and meiotic divisions in sperm development with the microscopic structure of seminiferous tubules. The initial or *primordial* germ cells of the embryonic testes divide and differentiate into stem cells that divide mitotically to form **spermatogonia**, which in turn generate spermatocytes, also by mitosis. Each spermatocyte gives rise to four spermatids through meiotic cell divisions that reduce the chromosome number from diploid ($2n = 46$ in humans) to haploid ($n = 23$). Spermatids undergo extensive changes in cell shape and organization in differentiating into sperm. Within the seminiferous tubules, there is a concentric organization of the steps of spermatogenesis. Stem cells are situated near the outer

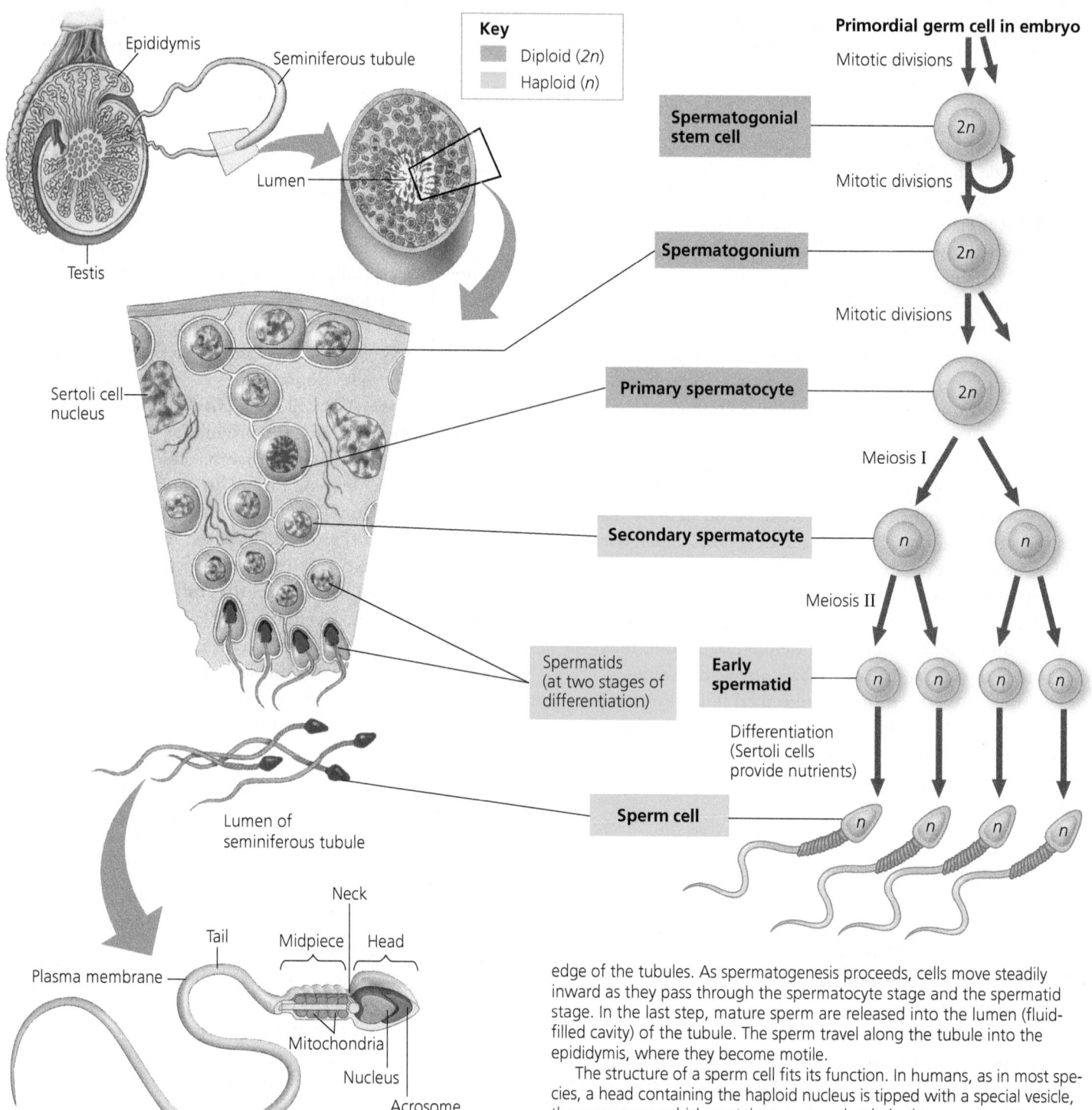

Key
- Diploid ($2n$)
- Haploid (n)

Epididymis
Seminiferous tubule
Lumen
Testis
Sertoli cell nucleus
Spermatids (at two stages of differentiation)
Lumen of seminiferous tubule
Plasma membrane
Tail
Midpiece
Neck
Head
Mitochondria
Nucleus
Acrosome

Primordial germ cell in embryo
Mitotic divisions
Spermatogonial stem cell — $2n$
Mitotic divisions
Spermatogonium — $2n$
Mitotic divisions
Primary spermatocyte — $2n$
Meiosis I
Secondary spermatocyte — n n
Meiosis II
Early spermatid — n n n n
Differentiation (Sertoli cells provide nutrients)
Sperm cell — n n n n

edge of the tubules. As spermatogenesis proceeds, cells move steadily inward as they pass through the spermatocyte stage and the spermatid stage. In the last step, mature sperm are released into the lumen (fluid-filled cavity) of the tubule. The sperm travel along the tubule into the epididymis, where they become motile.

The structure of a sperm cell fits its function. In humans, as in most species, a head containing the haploid nucleus is tipped with a special vesicle, the **acrosome**, which contains enzymes that help the sperm penetrate an egg. Behind the head, the sperm cell contains large numbers of mitochondria (or one large mitochondrion in some species) that provide ATP for movement of the tail, which is a flagellum.

Oogenesis

Oogenesis begins in the female embryo with the production of **oogonia** from primordial germ cells. The oogonia divide by mitosis to form cells that begin meiosis, but stop the process at prophase I before birth. These developmentally arrested cells, called **primary oocytes**, each reside within a small follicle, a cavity lined with protective cells. Beginning at puberty, follicle-stimulating hormone (FSH) periodically stimulates a small group of follicles to resume growth and development. Typically, only one follicle fully matures each month, with its primary oocyte completing meiosis I. The second meiotic division begins, but stops at metaphase.

Thus arrested in meiosis II, the **secondary oocyte** is released at ovulation, when its follicle breaks open. Only if a sperm penetrates the oocyte does meiosis II resume. (In other animal species, the sperm may enter the oocyte at the same stage, earlier, or later.) Each of the two meiotic divisions involves unequal cytokinesis, with the smaller cells becoming polar bodies that eventually degenerate (the first polar body may or may not divide again).

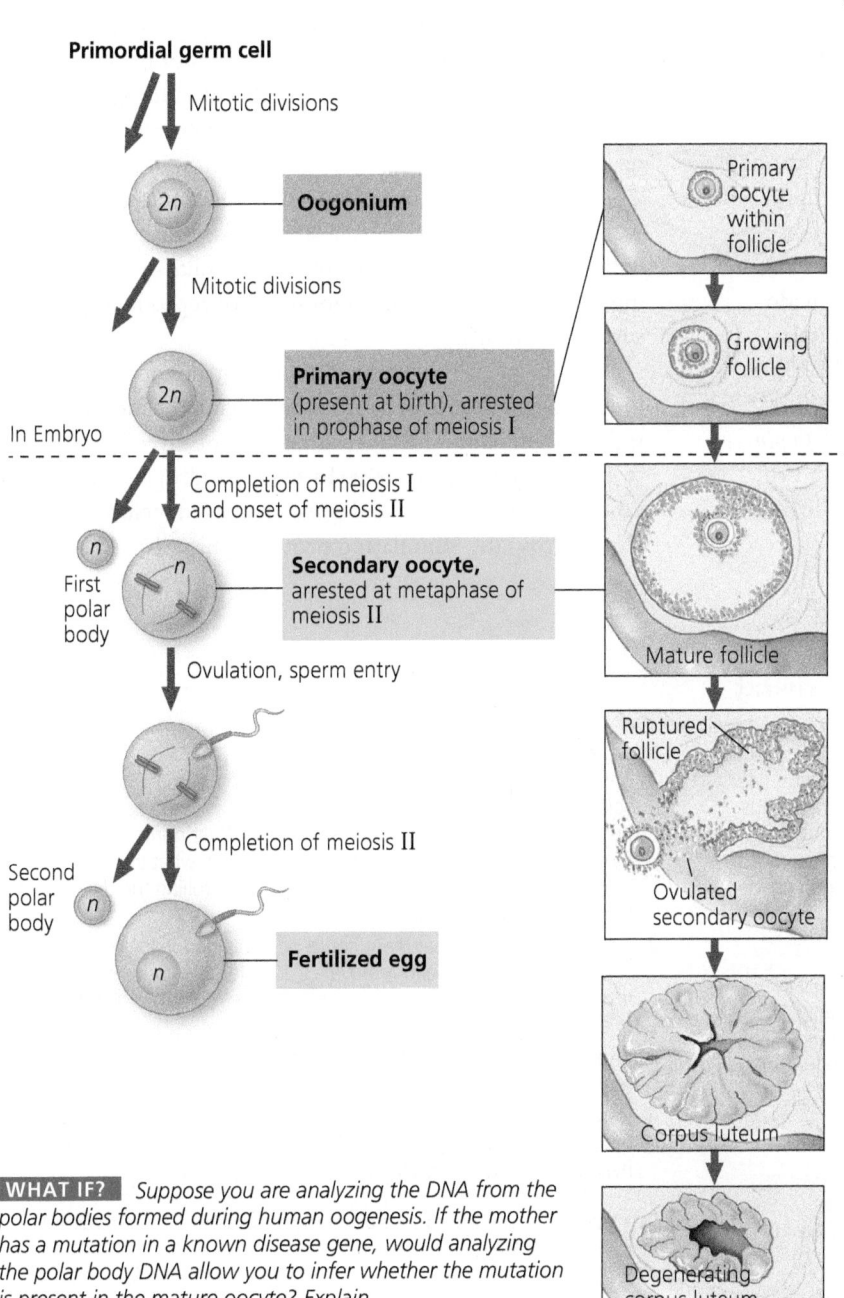

Thus, the functional product of complete oogenesis is a single mature egg already containing a sperm head; fertilization is defined strictly as the fusion of the haploid nuclei of the sperm and secondary oocyte, although we often use it loosely to mean the entry of the sperm head into the egg.

The ruptured follicle left behind after ovulation develops into the corpus luteum. If the released oocyte is not fertilized and does not complete oogenesis, the corpus luteum degenerates.

To the best of our current knowledge, women are born with all the primary oocytes they will ever have. It is worth noting, however, that a similar conclusion regarding most other mammals was overturned by the discovery in 2004 of multiplying oogonia in the ovaries of adult mice that develop into oocytes. If the same turned out to be true of humans, it might be that the marked decline in fertility that occurs as women age results from both a depletion of oogonia and the degeneration of aging oocytes.

WHAT IF? *Suppose you are analyzing the DNA from the polar bodies formed during human oogenesis. If the mother has a mutation in a known disease gene, would analyzing the polar body DNA allow you to infer whether the mutation is present in the mature oocyte? Explain.*

1. Why might using a hot tub frequently make it harder for a couple to conceive a child?

2. Oogenesis is often described as the production of a haploid egg by meiosis; but in some animals, including humans, this is not an entirely accurate description. Explain.

3. **WHAT IF?** If each vas deferens in a male was surgically sealed off, what changes would you expect in sexual response and ejaculate composition?

For suggested answers, see Appendix A.

CONCEPT 46.4

The interplay of tropic and sex hormones regulates mammalian reproduction

In both male and female humans, the coordinated actions of hormones from the hypothalamus, anterior pituitary, and gonads govern reproduction. The hypothalamus secretes gonadotropin-releasing hormone (GnRH), which then directs the anterior pituitary to secrete the gonadotropins, follicle-stimulating hormone (FSH) and luteinizing hormone (LH) (see Figure 45.18). FSH and LH are tropic hormones, meaning that they regulate the activity of endocrine cells or glands. They are called *gonadotropins* because they act on the male and female gonads, and they support gametogenesis, in part by stimulating sex hormone production.

The main sex hormones are steroid hormones. They consist of androgens (principally testosterone), estrogens (principally estradiol), and progesterone. Males and females differ in their blood concentrations of particular hormones. Testosterone levels are roughly 10 times higher in males than in females. In contrast, estradiol levels are about ten times higher in females than in males; females also produce more progesterone. The gonads are the major source of sex hormones, with much smaller amounts being produced by the adrenal glands.

Like gonadotropins, sex hormones regulate gametogenesis both directly and indirectly, but they have other actions as well.

In many vertebrates, androgens are responsible for male vocalizations, such as the territorial songs of birds and the mating calls of frogs. In human embryos, androgens promote the appearance of the primary sex characteristics of males, the structures directly involved in reproduction. These include the seminal vesicles and associated ducts, as well as external reproductive structures. In the Scientific Skills Exercise, you can interpret the results of an experiment investigating the development of reproductive structures in mammals.

At puberty, sex hormones in both males and females induce formation of secondary sex characteristics, the physical and behavioural features that are not directly related to the reproductive system. In males, androgens cause the voice to deepen, facial and pubic hair to develop, and muscles to grow (by stimulating protein synthesis). Androgens

SCIENTIFIC SKILLS EXERCISE

Making Inferences and Designing an Experiment

What Role Do Hormones Play in Making a Mammal Male or Female? In non-egg-laying mammals, females have two X chromosomes, whereas males have one X chromosome and one Y chromosome. In the 1940s, French physiologist Alfred Jost wondered whether development of mammalian embryos as female or male in accord with their chromosome set requires instructions in the form of hormones produced by the gonads. In this exercise, you will interpret the results of an experiment that Jost performed to answer this question.

How the Experiment Was Done Working with rabbit embryos still in the mother's uterus at a stage before sex differences are observable, Jost surgically removed the portion of each embryo that would form the ovaries or testes. When the baby rabbits were born, he made note of their chromosomal sex and whether their genital structures were male or female.

Data from the Experiment

Chromosome Set	Appearance of Genitalia	
	No Surgery	Embryonic Gonad Removed
XY (male)	Male	Female
XX (female)	Female	Female

Interpret the Data

1. This experiment is an example of a research approach in which scientists infer how something works normally based on what happens when the normal process is blocked. What normal process was blocked in Jost's experiment? From the results, what inference can you make about the role of the gonads in controlling the development of mammalian genitalia?

2. The data in Jost's experiment could be explained if some aspect of the surgery other than gonad removal caused female genitalia to develop. If you were to repeat Jost's experiment, how might you test the validity of such an explanation?

3. What result would Jost have obtained if female development also required a signal from the gonad?

4. Design another experiment to determine whether the signal that controls male development is a hormone. Make sure to identify your hypothesis, prediction, data collection plan, and controls.

Data from A. Jost, Recherches sur la differenciation sexuelle de l'embryon de lapin (Studies on the sexual differentiation of the rabbit embryo), *Archives d'Anatomie Microscopique et de Morphologie Experimentale* 36:271–316 (1947).

also promote specific sexual behaviours and sex drive, as well as an increase in general aggressiveness. Estrogens similarly have multiple effects in females. At puberty, estradiol stimulates breast and pubic hair development. Estradiol also influences female sexual behaviours, induces fat deposition in the breasts and hips, increases water retention, and alters calcium metabolism.

Hormonal Control of Female Reproductive Cycles

Upon reaching sexual maturity, human males carry out gametogenesis continuously, whereas human females produce gametes in cycles. Ovulation occurs only after the endometrium (lining of the uterus) has started to thicken and develop a rich blood supply, preparing the uterus for the possible implantation of an embryo. If pregnancy does not occur, the uterine lining is sloughed off, and another cycle begins. The cyclic shedding of the blood-rich endometrium from the uterus, a process that occurs in a flow through the cervix and vagina, is called **menstruation**.

There are two closely linked reproductive cycles in human females. Changes in the uterus define the **menstrual cycle**, also called the **uterine cycle**. Menstrual cycles average 28 days (although cycles vary, ranging from about 20 to 40 days). The cyclic events in the ovaries define the **ovarian cycle**. Hormone activity links the two cycles to one another, synchronizing ovarian follicle growth and ovulation with the establishment of a uterine lining that can support embryonic development. Let's examine the reproductive cycle of the human female (Figure 46.13).

The Ovarian Cycle

The reproductive cycle begins with ❶ the release from the hypothalamus of GnRH, which stimulates the anterior pituitary to ❷ secrete small amounts of FSH and LH. ❸ Follicle-stimulating hormone (as its name implies) stimulates follicle growth, aided by LH, and

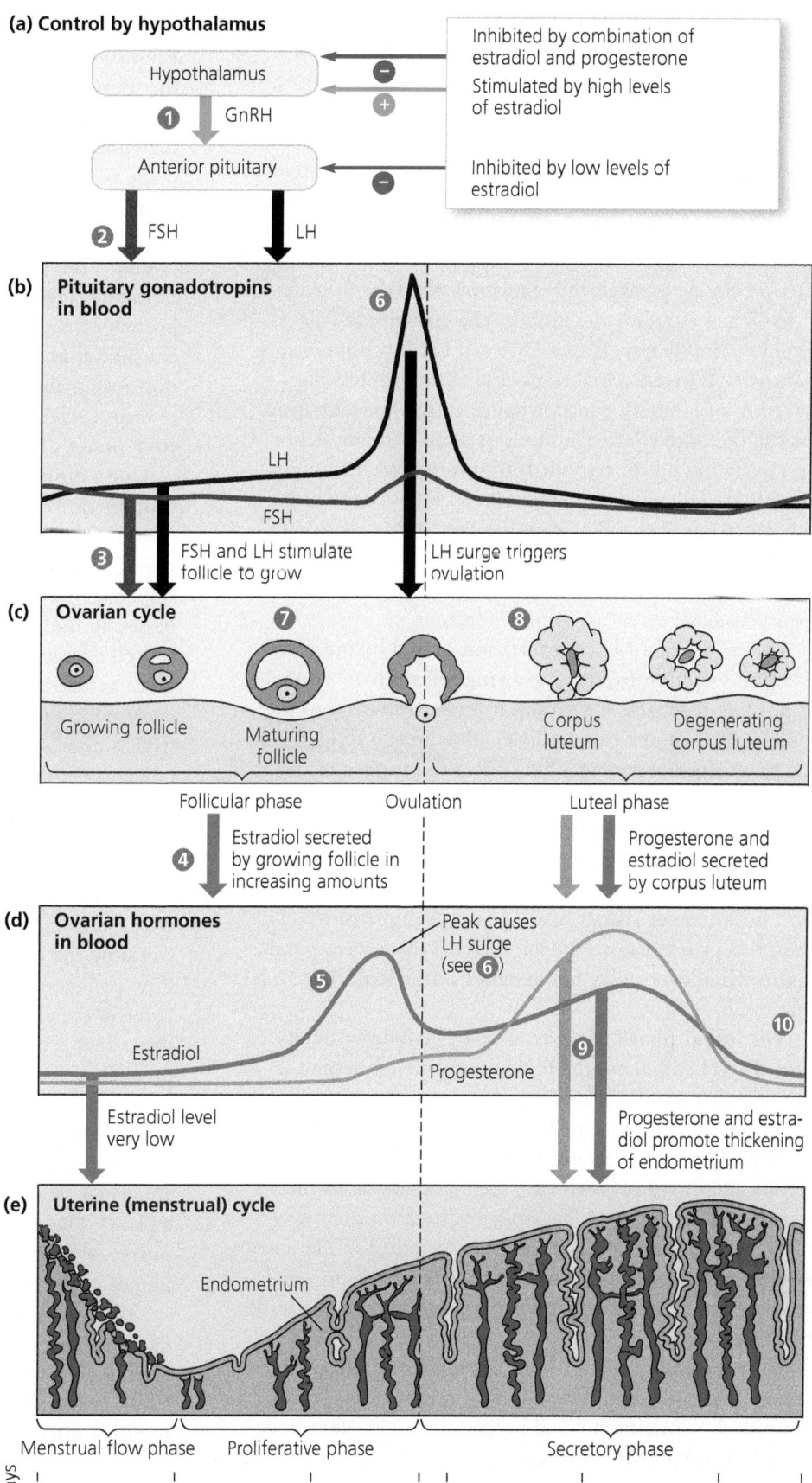

▲ Figure 46.13 **The reproductive cycle of the human female.** This figure shows how **(c)** the ovarian cycle and **(e)** the uterine (menstrual) cycle are regulated by changing hormone levels in the blood, depicted in parts **(a)**, **(b)**, and **(d)**. The time scale at the bottom of the figure applies to parts **(b)–(e)**.

④ the cells of the growing follicles start to make estradiol. There is a slow rise in estradiol secreted during most of the **follicular phase**, the part of the ovarian cycle during which follicles grow and oocytes mature. (Several follicles begin to grow with each cycle, but usually only one matures; the others disintegrate.) The low levels of estradiol inhibit secretion of the pituitary hormones, keeping the levels of FSH and LH relatively low. During this portion of the cycle, regulation of the hormones controlling reproduction closely parallels the regulation observed in males.

⑤ When estradiol secretion by the growing follicle begins to rise steeply, ⑥ the FSH and LH levels increase markedly. Whereas a low level of estradiol inhibits the secretion of pituitary gonadotropins, a high concentration has the opposite effect: It stimulates gonadotropin secretion by acting on the hypothalamus to increase its output of GnRH. The effect is greater for LH because the high concentration of estradiol increases the GnRH sensitivity of LH-releasing cells in the pituitary. In addition, follicles respond more strongly to LH at this stage because more of their cells have receptors for this hormone.

The increase in LH concentration caused by increased estradiol secretion from the growing follicle is an example of positive feedback. The result is final maturation of the follicle. ⑦ The maturing follicle, containing a fluid-filled cavity, enlarges, forming a bulge near the surface of the ovary. The follicular phase ends at ovulation, about a day after the LH surge. In response to the peak in LH levels, the follicle and adjacent wall of the ovary rupture, releasing the secondary oocyte. There is sometimes a distinctive pain in the lower abdomen at or near the time of ovulation; this pain is felt on the left or right side, corresponding to whichever ovary has matured a follicle during that cycle.

The **luteal phase** of the ovarian cycle follows ovulation. ⑧ LH stimulates the follicular tissue left behind in the ovary to transform into a corpus luteum, a glandular structure. Under continued stimulation by LH, the corpus luteum secretes progesterone and estradiol. As progesterone and estradiol levels rise, the combination of these steroid hormones exerts negative feedback on the hypothalamus and pituitary, reducing the secretion of LH and FSH to very low levels. This negative feedback prevents another egg from maturing when a pregnancy may already be under way.

Near the end of the luteal phase, low gonadotropin levels cause the corpus luteum to disintegrate, triggering a sharp decline in estradiol and progesterone concentrations. The decreasing levels of ovarian steroid hormones liberate the hypothalamus and pituitary from the negative-feedback effect of these hormones. The pituitary can then begin to secrete enough FSH to stimulate the growth of new follicles in the ovary, initiating the next ovarian cycle.

The Uterine (Menstrual) Cycle

Prior to ovulation, ovarian steroid hormones stimulate the uterus to prepare for support of an embryo. Estradiol secreted in increasing amounts by growing follicles signals the endometrium to thicken. In this way, the follicular phase of the ovarian cycle is coordinated with the **proliferative phase** of the uterine cycle. After ovulation, ⑨ estradiol and progesterone secreted by the corpus luteum stimulate continued development and maintenance of the uterine lining, including enlargement of arteries and growth of endometrial glands. These glands secrete a nutrient fluid that can sustain an early embryo even before it implants in the uterine lining. Thus, the luteal phase of the ovarian cycle is coordinated with what is called the **secretory phase** of the uterine cycle.

Upon disintegration of the corpus luteum, the rapid drop ⑩ in ovarian hormone levels causes arteries in the endometrium to constrict. Deprived of its circulation, much of the uterine lining disintegrates, and the uterus, in response to prostaglandin secretion, contracts. Small blood vessels in the endometrium constrict, releasing blood that is shed along with endometrial tissue and fluid. The result is menstruation—the **menstrual flow phase** of the uterine cycle. During menstruation, which usually persists for a few days, a new group of ovarian follicles begin to grow. By convention, the first day of menstruation is designated day 1 of the new uterine (and ovarian) cycle.

Overall, the hormonal cycles in females coordinate egg maturation and release with changes in the uterus, the organ that must accommodate an embryo if the egg cell is fertilized. If an embryo has not implanted in the endometrium by the end of the secretory phase, a new menstrual flow commences, marking the start of the next cycle. Later in the chapter, you will learn about override mechanisms that prevent disintegration of the endometrium in pregnancy.

About 7% of women of reproductive age suffer from **endometriosis**, a disorder in which some cells of the uterine lining migrate to an abdominal location that is abnormal, or **ectopic** (from the Greek *ektopos*, away from a place). Having migrated to a location such as an oviduct, ovary, or large intestine, the ectopic tissue responds to hormones in the bloodstream. Like the uterine endometrium, the ectopic tissue swells and breaks down each ovarian cycle, resulting in pelvic pain and bleeding into the abdomen. Researchers have not yet determined why endometriosis occurs, but hormonal therapy or surgery can be used to lessen discomfort.

Menopause

After about 500 cycles, a woman undergoes **menopause**, the cessation of ovulation and menstruation. Menopause usually occurs between the ages of 46 and 54. During this interval, the ovaries lose their responsiveness to FSH and LH, resulting in a decline in estradiol production.

Menopause is an unusual phenomenon. In most other species, females and males retain their reproductive capacity throughout life. Is there an evolutionary explanation for menopause? One intriguing hypothesis proposes that during early human evolution, undergoing menopause after bearing several children allowed a mother to provide better care for her children and grandchildren, thereby increasing the survival of individuals who share much of her genetic makeup.

Menstrual versus Estrous Cycles

In all female mammals, the endometrium thickens before ovulation, but only humans and some other primates have menstrual cycles. Other mammals have **estrous cycles**, in which, in the absence of a pregnancy, the uterus reabsorbs the endometrium and no extensive fluid flow occurs. Whereas human females may engage in sexual activity throughout the menstrual cycle, mammals with estrous cycles usually copulate only during the period surrounding ovulation. This period, called estrus (from the Latin *oestrus*, frenzy, passion), is the only time the female is receptive to mating. It is often called "heat," and the female's temperature does increase slightly.

The length and frequency of estrous cycles vary widely among mammals. Bears and wolves have one estrous cycle per year; elephants have several. Rats have estrous cycles throughout the year, each lasting only 5 days.

Hormonal Control of the Male Reproductive System

In males, the FSH and LH secreted in response to GnRH are both required for normal spermatogenesis. Each acts on a distinct type of cell in the testis (Figure 46.14). FSH promotes the activity of Sertoli cells. Within the seminiferous tubules, these cells nourish developing sperm (see Figure 46.12). LH regulates Leydig cells, located in the interstitial space between the seminiferous tubules. In response to LH, Leydig cells secrete testosterone and other androgens, which promote spermatogenesis in the tubules. Both androgen secretion and spermatogenesis occur continuously from puberty onward.

Two negative-feedback mechanisms control sex hormone production in males (see Figure 46.14). Testosterone regulates blood levels of GnRH, FSH, and LH through inhibitory effects on the hypothalamus and anterior pituitary. In addition, **inhibin**, a hormone that in males is produced by Sertoli cells, acts on the anterior pituitary gland to reduce FSH secretion. Together, these negative-feedback circuits maintain androgen production at optimal levels.

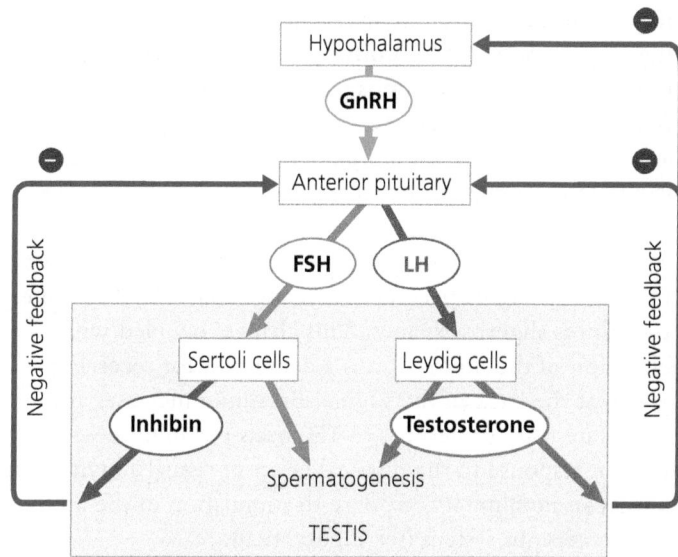

▲ Figure 46.14 **Hormonal control of the testes.** Gonadotropin-releasing hormone (GnRH) from the hypothalamus stimulates the anterior pituitary to secrete follicle-stimulating hormone (FSH) and luteinizing hormone (LH). FSH acts on Sertoli cells, which nourish developing sperm. LH acts on Leydig cells, which produce androgens, chiefly testosterone. Negative feedback by testosterone on the hypothalamus and anterior pituitary regulates blood levels of GnRH, LH, and FSH. FSH secretion is also subject to negative feedback by a hormone called inhibin, secreted by Sertoli cells.

Human Sexual Response

Whereas there is a wealth of information regarding the hormonal regulation of human oogenesis and spermatogenesis, comparable data regarding sexual desire and responses are scanty. Testosterone, prolactin, and oxytocin each appear to influence sexual function in males and females, but their precise roles have yet to be defined. Instead, the study of human sexual response has largely focused on the physiological changes associated with sexual activity.

As mentioned earlier, many animals exhibit elaborate mating behaviours. The arousal of sexual interest in humans is particularly complex, involving a variety of psychological as well as physical factors. Reproductive structures in the male and female that are quite different in appearance often serve similar functions, reflecting their shared developmental origin. For example, the same embryonic tissues give rise to the glans of the penis and the clitoris, the scrotum and the labia majora, and the skin on the penis and the labia minora.

The general pattern of human sexual response is similar in males and females. Two types of physiological reactions predominate in both sexes: **vasocongestion**, the filling of a tissue with blood, and **myotonia**, increased muscle tension. Both skeletal and smooth muscle may show sustained or rhythmic contractions, including those associated with orgasm.

The sexual response cycle can be divided into four phases: excitement, plateau, orgasm, and resolution. An important function of the excitement phase is to prepare the vagina and penis for **coitus** (sexual intercourse). During this phase, vasocongestion is particularly evident in erection of the penis and clitoris; enlargement of the testicles, labia, and breasts; and vaginal lubrication. Myotonia may occur, resulting in nipple erection or tension of the arms and legs.

In the plateau phase, these responses continue as a result of direct stimulation of the genitalia. In females, the outer third of the vagina becomes vasocongested, while the inner two-thirds slightly expands. This change, coupled with the elevation of the uterus, forms a depression for receiving sperm at the back of the vagina. Breathing increases and heart rate rises, sometimes to 150 beats per minute—not only in response to the physical effort of sexual activity, but also as an involuntary response to stimulation of the autonomic nervous system (see Figure 49.9).

Orgasm is characterized by rhythmic, involuntary contractions of the reproductive structures in both sexes. Male orgasm has two stages. The first, emission, occurs when the glands and ducts of the reproductive tract contract, forcing semen into the urethra. Expulsion, or ejaculation, occurs when the urethra contracts and the semen is expelled. During female orgasm, the uterus and outer vagina contract, but the inner two-thirds of the vagina does not. Orgasm is the shortest phase of the sexual response cycle, usually lasting only a few seconds. In both sexes, contractions occur at about 0.8-second intervals and may also involve the anal sphincter and several abdominal muscles.

The resolution phase completes the cycle and reverses the responses of the earlier stages. Vasocongested organs return to their normal size and colour, and muscles relax. Most of the changes of resolution are completed within 5 minutes, but some may take as long as an hour. Following orgasm, the male typically enters a refractory period, lasting anywhere from a few minutes to hours, during which erection and orgasm cannot be achieved. Females do not have a refractory period, making possible multiple orgasms within a short period of time.

CONCEPT CHECK 46.4

1. FSH and LH get their names from events of the female reproductive cycle, but they also function in males. How are their functions in females and males similar?

2. How does an estrous cycle differ from a menstrual cycle, and in what animals are the two types of cycles found?

3. **WHAT IF?** If a human female begins taking estradiol and progesterone immediately after the start of a new menstrual cycle, how will ovulation be affected? Explain.

4. **MAKE CONNECTIONS** A coordination of developmental events is characteristic of the reproductive cycles of a human female and an enveloped RNA virus (see Figure 19.9). What is the nature of the coordination in each of these cycles?

For suggested answers, see Appendix A.

In placental mammals, an embryo develops fully within the mother's uterus

Having surveyed the ovarian and uterine cycles of human females, we turn now to reproduction itself, beginning with the events that transform an egg into a developing embryo.

Conception, Embryonic Development, and Birth

During human copulation, 2–5 mL of semen is transferred, with hundreds of millions of sperm. When first ejaculated, the semen coagulates, which likely keeps the ejaculate in place until sperm reach the cervix. Soon after, anticoagulants liquefy the semen, and the sperm swim through the uterus and oviducts. Fertilization—also called **conception** in humans—occurs when a sperm fuses with an egg (mature oocyte) in an oviduct (Figure 46.15).

The zygote begins a series of cell divisions called **cleavage** about 24 hours after fertilization and after an additional 4 days produces a **blastocyst**, a sphere of cells surrounding a central cavity. A few days later, the embryo implants into the endometrium of the uterus. The condition of carrying one or more embryos in the uterus is called **pregnancy**, or **gestation**. Human pregnancy averages 266 days (38 weeks) from fertilization of the egg, or 40 weeks from the start of the last menstrual cycle. In comparison, gestation averages 21 days in many rodents, 270 days in cows, and more than 600 days in elephants. The roughly nine months of human gestation are divided into three **trimesters** of equal length.

First Trimester

During the first trimester, the implanted embryo secretes hormones that signal its presence and regulate the mother's reproductive system. One embryonic hormone, **human chorionic gonadotropin** (hCG), acts like pituitary LH in maintaining secretion of progesterone and estrogens by the corpus luteum through the first few months of pregnancy. Some hCG passes from the maternal blood to the urine, where it can be detected by most common early pregnancy tests.

Not all embryos are capable of completing development. Many spontaneously stop developing as a result of chromosomal or developmental abnormalities. Much less often, a fertilized egg lodges in an oviduct (fallopian tube), resulting in a tubal, or ectopic, pregnancy. Such pregnancies cannot be sustained and may rupture the oviduct, resulting in serious internal bleeding. The risk of ectopic pregnancy increases if the oviduct is scarred by bacterial infections arising during childbirth, by medical procedures, or by a sexually transmitted infection (STI).

During its first 2–4 weeks of development, the embryo obtains nutrients directly from the endometrium. Meanwhile, the outer layer of the blastocyst, called the **trophoblast**, grows outward and mingles with the endometrium, eventually helping

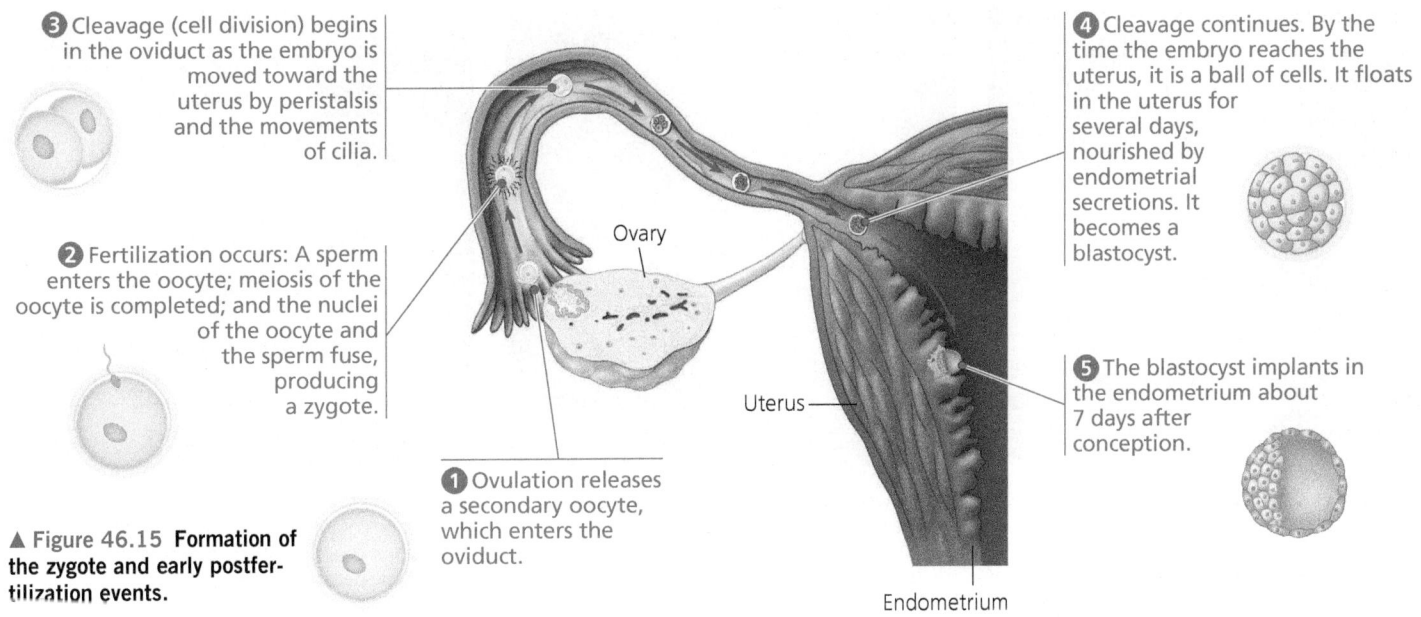

❸ Cleavage (cell division) begins in the oviduct as the embryo is moved toward the uterus by peristalsis and the movements of cilia.

❷ Fertilization occurs: A sperm enters the oocyte; meiosis of the oocyte is completed; and the nuclei of the oocyte and the sperm fuse, producing a zygote.

❹ Cleavage continues. By the time the embryo reaches the uterus, it is a ball of cells. It floats in the uterus for several days, nourished by endometrial secretions. It becomes a blastocyst.

Ovary

❺ The blastocyst implants in the endometrium about 7 days after conception.

Uterus

❶ Ovulation releases a secondary oocyte, which enters the oviduct.

▲ **Figure 46.15 Formation of the zygote and early postfertilization events.**

Endometrium

Placenta

Maternal arteries
Maternal veins

Maternal portion of placenta

Umbilical cord

Chorionic villus, containing fetal capillaries

Fetal portion of placenta (chorion)

Maternal blood pool

Umbilical arteries
Umbilical vein

Uterus

Fetal arteriole   Fetal venule

Umbilical cord

▲ **Figure 46.16 Placental circulation.** From the fourth week of development until birth, the placenta, a combination of maternal and embryonic tissues, transports nutrients, respiratory gases, and wastes between the embryo or fetus and the mother. Maternal blood enters the placenta in arteries, flows through blood pools in the endometrium, and leaves via veins. Embryonic or fetal blood, which remains in vessels, enters the placenta through arteries and passes through capillaries in finger-like chorionic villi, where oxygen and nutrients are acquired. As indicated in the drawing, the fetal (or embryonic) capillaries and villi project into the maternal portion of the placenta. Fetal blood leaves the placenta through veins leading back to the fetus. Materials are exchanged by diffusion, active transport, and selective absorption between the fetal capillary bed and the maternal blood pools. In this diagram, note that the umbilical veins are shown in red. This is to show that the venous blood vessel returning to the fetal heart is oxygenated. Likewise, the umbilical artery is shown in blue because it is lower in oxygen.

? *In a rare genetic disorder, the absence of a particular enzyme leads to increased testosterone production. When the fetus has this disorder, the mother develops a male-like pattern of body hair during the pregnancy. Explain.*

Source: Figure adapted from *Human Anatomy and Physiology*, 8th edition, by Elaine N. Marieb and Katja Hoehn. Copyright © 2010 by Pearson Education, Inc. Adapted and electronically reproduced by permission of Pearson Education, Inc., Upper Saddle River, New Jersey.

form the **placenta**. This disk-shaped organ, containing both embryonic and maternal blood vessels, can weigh close to 1 kg. Material diffusing between the maternal and embryonic circulatory systems supplies nutrients, provides immune protection,

exchanges respiratory gases, and disposes of metabolic wastes for the embryo. Blood from the embryo travels to the placenta through the arteries of the umbilical cord and returns via the umbilical vein (**Figure 46.16**).

(a) **5 weeks.** Limb buds, eyes, the heart, the liver, and rudiments of all other organs have started to develop in the embryo, which is only about 1 cm long.

(b) **14 weeks.** Growth and development of the offspring, now called a fetus, continue during the second trimester. This fetus is about 6 cm long.

(c) **20 weeks.** Growth to nearly 20 cm in length requires adoption of the fetal position (head at knees) due to the limited space available.

▲ **Figure 46.17 Human fetal development.**

Occasionally, an embryo splits during the first month of development, resulting in identical, or *monozygotic* (one-egg), twins. Fraternal, or *dizygotic*, twins arise in a very different way: Two follicles mature in a single cycle, followed by independent fertilization and implantation of two genetically distinct embryos.

The first trimester is the main period of **organogenesis**, the development of the body organs (Figure 46.17a). During organogenesis, the embryo is particularly susceptible to damage, such as from radiation or drugs, that can lead to birth defects. At 8 weeks, all the major structures of the adult are present in rudimentary form, and the embryo is called a **fetus**. The heart begins beating by the 4th week; a heartbeat can be detected at 8–10 weeks. At the end of the first trimester, the fetus, although well differentiated, is only 5 cm long.

Meanwhile, high levels of progesterone bring about rapid changes in the mother: Mucus in the cervix forms a plug that protects against infection, the maternal part of the placenta grows, the breasts and uterus get larger, and both ovulation and menstrual cycling stop. About three-fourths of all pregnant women experience nausea, misleadingly called "morning sickness," during the first trimester.

Second Trimester

During the second trimester, the fetus grows to about 30 cm in length and is very active (Figure 46.17b and c). The mother may feel fetal movements as early as one month into the second trimester; fetal activity is typically visible through the abdominal wall one to two months later. Hormone levels stabilize as hCG declines; the corpus luteum deteriorates; and the placenta completely takes over the production of progesterone, the hormone that maintains the pregnancy.

Third Trimester

During the final trimester, the fetus grows to about 3–4 kg in weight and 50 cm in length. Fetal activity may decrease as the fetus fills the available space. As the fetus grows and the uterus expands around it, the mother's abdominal organs become compressed and displaced, leading to frequent urination and digestive blockages.

Childbirth begins with **labour**, a series of strong, rhythmic uterine contractions that push the fetus and placenta out of the body. Recent studies suggest that labour begins when the fully developed fetus produces hormones and certain lung proteins that initiate an inflammatory response (see Chapter 43) in the mother. However, further study is needed to determine if inflammation does in fact trigger labour.

Once labour begins, a complex interplay of local regulators (prostaglandins) and hormones (chiefly estradiol and oxytocin) induces and regulates further contractions of the uterus (Figure 46.18). The action of oxytocin forms a positive-feedback loop (see Chapter 45), with uterine contractions stimulating secretion of oxytocin, which in turn stimulates further contractions.

Labour is typically described as having three stages (Figure 46.19). The first stage is the thinning and opening up (dilation) of the cervix. The second stage is the expulsion, or delivery, of the baby. Continuous strong contractions force the fetus out of the uterus and through the vagina. The final stage of labour is delivery of the placenta.

One aspect of postnatal care unique to mammals is **lactation**, the production of mother's milk. In response to suckling by the newborn, as well as changes in estradiol levels after birth, the hypothalamus signals the anterior pituitary to secrete prolactin, which stimulates the

▲ Figure 46.18 **Positive feedback in labour.**

> [?] *Predict the effect of a single dose of oxytocin on a pregnant woman at the end of 39 weeks gestation.*

mammary glands to produce milk. Suckling also stimulates the secretion of oxytocin from the posterior pituitary, which triggers release of milk from the mammary glands (see Figure 45.11).

Maternal Immune Tolerance of the Embryo and Fetus

Pregnancy is an immunological puzzle. Half of the embryo's genes are inherited from the father; thus, many of the chemical markers present on the surface of the embryo are foreign to the mother. Why, then, does the mother not reject the embryo as a foreign body, as she would a tissue or organ graft from another person? One intriguing clue comes from the relationship between certain autoimmune disorders and pregnancy. For example, the symptoms of rheumatoid arthritis, an autoimmune disease of the joints, become less severe during pregnancy. Thus, the overall regulation of the immune system appears to be altered by the reproductive process. Sorting out these changes and how they might protect the developing fetus is an active area of research for immunologists.

Contraception and Abortion

Contraception, the deliberate prevention of pregnancy, can be achieved in a number of ways. Some contraceptive methods prevent gamete development or release from female or male gonads; others prevent fertilization by keeping sperm and egg apart; and still others prevent implantation of an embryo. For complete information on contraceptive methods, you should consult a health-care provider. The following brief introduction to the biology of the most common methods and the corresponding

❶ Dilation of the cervix

❷ Expulsion: delivery of the infant

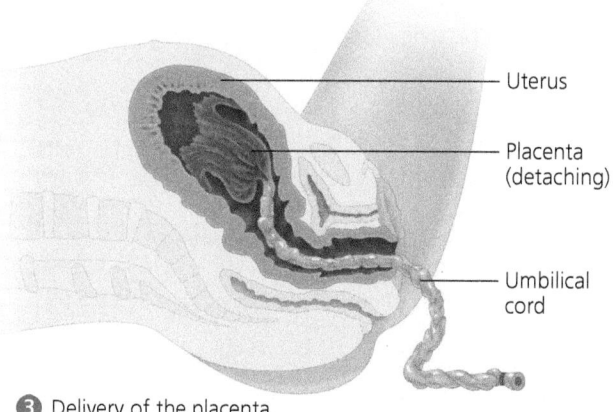

❸ Delivery of the placenta

▲ Figure 46.19 **The three stages of labour.**

diagram in **Figure 46.20** make no pretence of being a contraception manual.

Fertilization can be prevented by abstinence from sexual intercourse or by any of several barriers that keep live sperm from contacting the egg. Temporary abstinence, often called the **rhythm method** of birth control or **natural family planning**, depends on refraining from intercourse when conception is most likely. Because the egg can survive in the oviduct for 24–48 hours and sperm for up to 5 days, a couple practising temporary abstinence should not

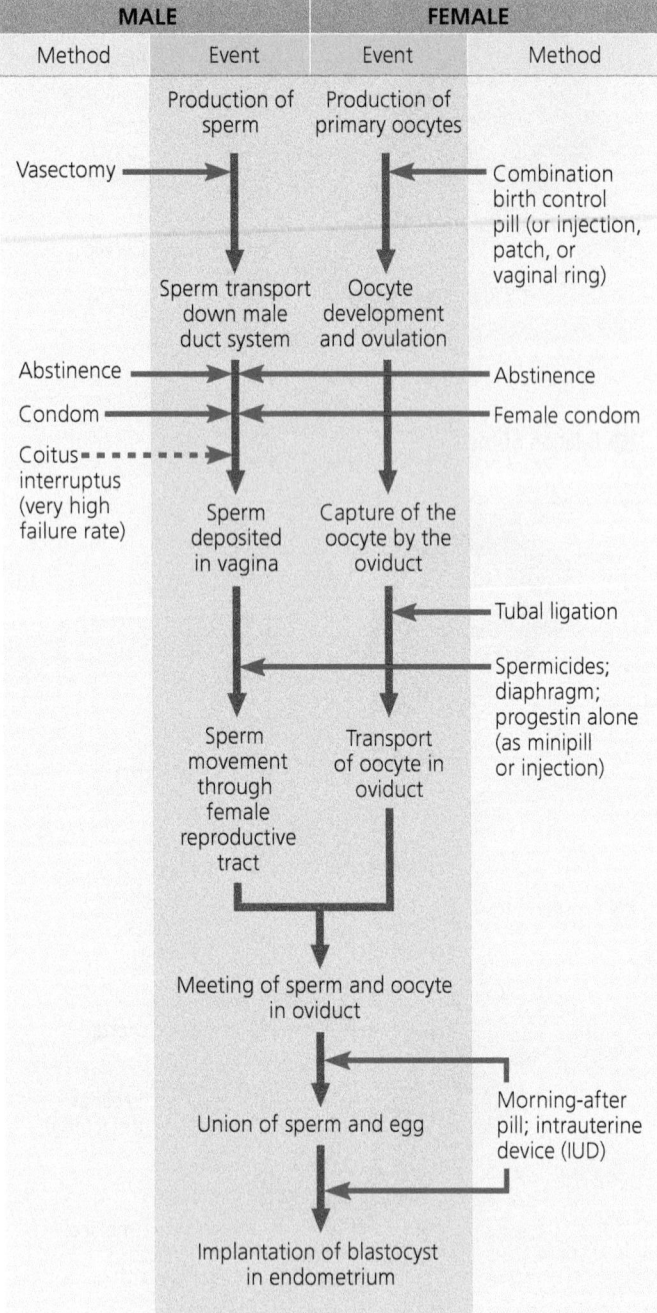

MALE		FEMALE	
Method	Event	Event	Method

Production of sperm → Production of primary oocytes

Vasectomy → Sperm transport down male duct system

Combination birth control pill (or injection, patch, or vaginal ring) → Oocyte development and ovulation

Abstinence → | ← Abstinence

Condom → | ← Female condom

Coitus interruptus (very high failure rate) ⤑ Sperm deposited in vagina

Capture of the oocyte by the oviduct

Tubal ligation →

Spermicides; diaphragm; progestin alone (as minipill or injection) →

Sperm movement through female reproductive tract

Transport of oocyte in oviduct

Meeting of sperm and oocyte in oviduct

Union of sperm and egg ← Morning-after pill; intrauterine device (IUD)

Implantation of blastocyst in endometrium

▲ Figure 46.20 **Mechanisms of several contraceptive methods.** Red arrows indicate where these methods, devices, or products interfere with events from the production of sperm and primary oocytes to an implanted, developing embryo.

engage in intercourse for a number of days before and after ovulation. The most effective methods for determining the time of ovulation combine several indicators, including changes in cervical mucus and body temperature during the menstrual cycle. Thus, natural family planning requires that the couple be knowledgeable about these physiological signs. Note that a pregnancy rate of 10–20% is typically reported for couples practising natural family planning. (Pregnancy rate is the average number of women who

become pregnant during a year for every 100 women using a particular pregnancy prevention method, expressed as a percentage.) Some couples use ovulation-timing methods to *increase* the probability of conception.

As a method of preventing fertilization, *coitus interruptus*, or withdrawal (removal of the penis from the vagina before ejaculation), is unreliable. Sperm from a previous ejaculate may be transferred in secretions that precede ejaculation. Furthermore, a split-second lapse in timing or willpower can result in tens of millions of sperm being transferred before withdrawal.

The several barrier methods of contraception that block the sperm from meeting the egg have pregnancy rates of less than 10%. The **condom** is a thin, latex rubber or natural membrane sheath that fits over the penis to collect the semen. For sexually active individuals, latex condoms are the only contraceptives that are highly effective in preventing the spread of sexually transmitted infection, including AIDS. (This protection is, however, not absolute.) Another common barrier device is the **diaphragm**, a dome-shaped rubber cap inserted into the upper portion of the vagina before intercourse. Both of these devices have lower pregnancy rates when used in conjunction with a spermicidal (sperm-killing) foam or jelly. Other barrier devices include the vaginal pouch, or "female condom."

Except for complete abstinence from sexual intercourse, the most effective means of birth control are sterilization, intrauterine devices (IUDs), and hormonal contraceptives. Sterilization (discussed later) is almost 100% effective. The IUD has a pregnancy rate of 1% or less and is used by about 2% of women who employ birth control in Canada. Placed in the uterus by a doctor, the IUD interferes with fertilization and implantation. Hormonal contraceptives, most often in the form of **birth control pills**, also have pregnancy rates of 1% or less.

The most commonly prescribed birth control pills are a combination of a synthetic estrogen and a synthetic progestin (progesterone-like hormone). This combination mimics negative feedback in the ovarian cycle, stopping the release of GnRH by the hypothalamus and thus of FSH and LH by the pituitary. The prevention of LH release blocks ovulation. In addition, the inhibition of FSH secretion by the low dose of estrogens in the pills prevents follicles from developing. A similar combination of hormones is also available as an injection, as a ring inserted into the vagina, and as a skin patch. Combination birth control pills can also be used in high doses as "morning-after" pills. Taken within 3 days after unprotected intercourse, they prevent fertilization or implantation with an effectiveness of about 75%.

A different type of hormone-based contraceptive contains only progestin. Progestin causes thickening of a woman's cervical mucus so that it blocks sperm from entering the uterus. Progestin also decreases the frequency of ovulation and causes changes in the endometrium that may interfere with implantation if fertilization occurs. Progestin can be administered as injections that last for three months or as a tablet ("minipill") taken daily. Pregnancy rates for women using progestin treatment are very low.

Hormone-based contraceptives have both beneficial and harmful side effects. For women taking a combination pill, cardiovascular problems are the most serious concern. Women who regularly smoke cigarettes face a three to ten times greater risk of dying from cardiovascular disease if they also use oral contraceptives. Among nonsmokers, birth control pills slightly raise a woman's risk of abnormal blood clotting, high blood pressure, heart attack, and stroke. Although oral contraceptives increase the risk for these cardiovascular disorders, they eliminate the dangers of pregnancy; women on birth control pills have mortality rates about one-half those of pregnant women. Also, the pill decreases the risk of ovarian and endometrial cancers.

One elusive research goal has been a reversible chemical contraceptive for men. Recent strategies have focused on hormone combinations that suppress gonadotropin release and thereby block spermatogenesis. Testosterone included in such combinations has two desirable effects: inhibiting reproductive functions of the hypothalamus and pituitary and maintaining secondary sex characteristics. Although there have been some promising results, hormonal male contraceptives are still in the testing stage.

Sterilization is the permanent prevention of gamete production or release. **Tubal ligation** in women usually involves sealing shut or tying off (ligating) a section of each oviduct to prevent eggs from travelling into the uterus. Similarly, **vasectomy** in men is the cutting and tying off of each vas deferens to prevent sperm from entering the urethra. Both male and female sterilization procedures are relatively safe and free from harmful effects. Sex hormone secretion and sexual function are unaffected by both procedures, with no change in menstrual cycles in females or ejaculate volume in males. Although tubal ligation or vasectomy are considered permanent, both procedures can in many cases be reversed by microsurgery.

The termination of a pregnancy in progress is called **abortion**. Spontaneous abortion, or *miscarriage*, is very common; it occurs in as many as one-third of all pregnancies, often before the woman is even aware she is pregnant. In addition, each year about 65 000 women in Canada choose to have an abortion in a hospital or clinic.

A drug called mifepristone, or RU486, can terminate a pregnancy nonsurgically within the first 7 weeks. RU486 blocks progesterone receptors in the uterus, thus preventing progesterone from maintaining the pregnancy. It is taken with a small amount of prostaglandin to induce uterine contractions.

The diversity in hormonal interventions that are effective in birth control are possible because of the vital role hormones play in coordinating the complex processes associated with gamete production and reproduction. An unexpected consequence of widespread use of birth control hormones arises when the hormones leave the female body in the urine. The estrogen makes its way to sewage treatment plants and, depending on the number of women taking birth control pills, elevates estrogen levels in the sewage and eventually in the waterways through sewage effluent. Working at the Ontario Experimental Lakes Area, Karen Kidd from the University of New Brunswick at St. John, showed that even low levels of estrogen in aquatic ecosystems can disrupt the normal reproductive biology of fish. Exposure to estrogen feminized male fish, causing them to display female traits such as production of egg proteins, and impaired testes development and sperm production.

Modern Reproductive Technologies

Recent scientific and technological advances have made it possible to address many reproductive problems, including genetic diseases and infertility.

Detecting Disorders during Pregnancy

Many genetic diseases and developmental problems can now be diagnosed while the fetus is in the uterus. Ultrasound imaging, which generates images using sound frequencies above the normal hearing range, is commonly used to analyze the fetus's size and condition. Amniocentesis and chorionic villus sampling are techniques in which a needle is used to obtain fetal cells from fluid or tissue surrounding the embryo; these cells then provide the basis for genetic analysis (see Figure 14.20). An alternative technique for obtaining fetal tissue relies on the fact that a few fetal blood cells leak across the placenta into the mother's bloodstream. A blood sample from the mother yields fetal cells that can be identified with specific antibodies (which bind to proteins on the surface of fetal cells) and then tested for genetic disorders.

Diagnosing genetic diseases in a fetus poses ethical questions. To date, almost all detectable disorders remain untreatable in the uterus, and many cannot be corrected even after birth. Parents may be faced with difficult decisions about whether to terminate a pregnancy or to raise a child who may have profound defects and a short life expectancy. These are complex issues that demand careful, informed thought and competent genetic counselling.

Treating Infertility

Infertility—an inability to conceive offspring—is quite common, affecting about one in ten couples worldwide. The causes of infertility are varied, and the likelihood of a reproductive defect is nearly the same for men and women.

For women, however, the risk of reproductive difficulties, as well as genetic abnormalities of the fetus, increases steadily past age 35. Evidence suggests that the prolonged period of time oocytes spend in meiosis is largely responsible for this increased risk.

Among preventable causes of infertility, STIs are the most significant. In women 15–24 years old, the rates of infection have been increasing since 1997. The actual number of women infected with the chlamydia or gonorrhea bacterium is considerably higher because most women with these infections have no symptoms and are therefore unaware of their infection. Up to 40% of women who remain untreated for chlamydia or gonorrhea develop an inflammatory disorder that can lead to infertility or to potentially fatal complications during pregnancy.

Some forms of infertility are treatable. Hormone therapy can sometimes increase sperm or egg production, and surgery can often correct ducts that formed improperly or have become blocked. In some cases, doctors recommend *in vitro* **fertilization (IVF)**, which involves combining oocytes and sperm in the laboratory. Fertilized eggs are incubated until they have formed at least eight cells and are then transferred to the woman's uterus for implantation. If mature sperm are defective or low in number, a whole sperm or a spermatid nucleus is injected directly into an oocyte (Figure 46.21). Though costly, IVF procedures have enabled more than a million couples to conceive children.

By whatever means fertilization occurs, a developmental program follows that transforms the single-celled zygote into a multicellular organism. The mechanisms of this

Phanie/SuperStock

▲ Figure 46.21 *In vitro* **fertilization (IVF).** In this form of IVF, a technician holds the egg in place with a pipette (left) and uses a very fine needle to inject one sperm into the egg cytoplasm (colourized LM).

remarkable program of development in humans and other animals are the subject of Chapter 47.

CONCEPT CHECK 46.5

1. Why does testing for hCG (human chorionic gonadotropin) work as a pregnancy test early in pregnancy but not late in pregnancy? What is the function of hCG in pregnancy?

2. In what ways are tubal ligation and vasectomy similar?

3. **WHAT IF?** If a sperm nucleus is injected into an oocyte, what steps of gametogenesis and conception are bypassed?

For suggested answers, see Appendix A.

46 Chapter Review

Go to **MasteringBiology®** for Assignments, the eText, and the Study Area with Animations, Activities, Vocab Self-Quiz, and Practice Tests.

SUMMARY OF KEY CONCEPTS

CONCEPT 46.1

Both asexual and sexual reproduction occur in the animal kingdom (pp. 1071–1074)

- Animals reproduce either asexually or sexually. **Sexual reproduction** requires the fusion of male and female gametes, forming a diploid **zygote**. **Asexual reproduction** is the production of offspring without gamete fusion. Fission, budding, fragmentation with regeneration, and **parthenogenesis** are mechanisms of asexual reproduction in various invertebrates. Facilitating selection for or against sets of genes may explain why sexual reproduction is widespread among animal species.

- Although most animals reproduce exclusively sexually or asexually, some alternate between the two. Variations on these two modes are made possible through parthenogenesis, **hermaphroditism**,

and sex reversal. Hormones and environmental cues control reproductive cycles.

? *Would a pair of haploid offspring produced by parthenogenesis be genetically identical?*

CONCEPT 46.2

Fertilization depends on mechanisms that bring together sperm and eggs of the same species (pp. 1074–1076)

- **Fertilization** can occur externally or internally with regard to the mother's body. In either case, fertilization requires coordinated timing, which may be mediated by environmental cues, pheromones, or courtship behaviours. Internal fertilization is typically often associated both with relatively fewer offspring and with greater protection of offspring by the parents. Systems for gamete production and delivery range from undifferentiated cells in the body cavity to complex **gonads** with accessory tubes and glands that carry and protect gametes and embryos. Although sexual reproduction involves a partnership, it also provides an opportunity for competition between individuals and between gametes.

? *Identify which of the following are unique to mammals: a female uterus and a male vas deferens, extended internal development, parental care of newborns.*

CONCEPT 46.3

Reproductive organs produce and transport gametes (pp. 1077–1082)

- The reproductive system of the human female consists principally of the **labia** and the **glans** of the **clitoris** externally and the **vagina**, **uterus**, **oviducts**, and **ovaries** internally. **Eggs** are produced in the ovaries and upon fertilization develop in the uterus. In human males, **sperm** are produced in **testes**, which are suspended outside the body in the **scrotum**. Ducts connect the testes to internal accessory glands and to the **penis**.

- **Gametogenesis**, or gamete production, consists of **oogenesis** in females and **spermatogenesis** in males. Meiosis generates one large egg in oogenesis, but four sperm in spermatogenesis. In humans, sperm develop continuously, whereas oocyte maturation is discontinuous and cyclic.

Human gametogenesis

Spermatogenesis   Oogenesis

Primary spermatocyte   Primary oocyte

Polar body

Secondary spermatocytes   Secondary oocyte

Spermatids

Sperm

Polar body

Fertilized egg

? *How does the difference in size and cellular contents between sperm and eggs relate to their specific functions in reproduction?*

CONCEPT 46.4

The interplay of tropic and sex hormones regulates mammalian reproduction (pp. 1082–1086)

- In mammals, GnRH from the hypothalamus regulates the release of two hormones, FSH and LH, from the anterior pituitary. In males,

FSH and LH control the secretion of androgens (chiefly testosterone) and sperm production. In females, cyclic secretion of FSH and LH orchestrates the ovarian and uterine cycles via estrogens and progesterone. The developing follicle and the corpus luteum also secrete hormones, which help coordinate the uterine and ovarian cycles through positive and negative feedback.

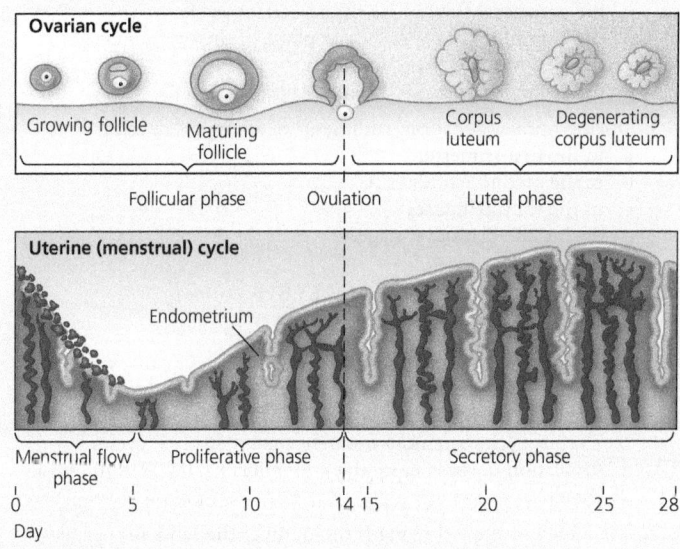

- In **estrous cycles**, the lining of the endometrium is reabsorbed, and sexual receptivity is limited to a heat period. Reproductive structures with a shared origin in development underlie many features of human sexual arousal and orgasm common to males and females.

? *Why do anabolic steroids lead to reduced sperm count?*

CONCEPT 46.5

In placental mammals, an embryo develops fully within the mother's uterus (pp. 1086–1092)

- After fertilization and the completion of meiosis in the oviduct, the zygote undergoes cleavage and develops into a blastocyst before implantation in the endometrium. All major organs start developing by eight weeks. A pregnant woman's acceptance of her "foreign" offspring likely reflects partial suppression of the maternal immune response.

- Contraceptive methods may prevent release of mature gametes from the gonads, fertilization, or implantation of the embryo. Reproductive technologies can assist infertile couples by hormonal methods or *in vitro* fertilization and can also help detect problems before birth.

? *What route would oxygen in the mother's blood follow to arrive at a body cell of the fetus?*

TEST YOUR UNDERSTANDING

LEVEL 1: KNOWLEDGE/COMPREHENSION

1. Which of the following characterizes parthenogenesis?
   a. An individual may change its sex during its lifetime.
   b. Specialized groups of cells grow into new individuals.
   c. An organism is first a male and then a female.
   d. An egg develops without being fertilized.

2. In male mammals, excretory and reproductive systems share
   a. the testes.   c. the seminal vesicle.
   b. the urethra.   d. the prostate.

3. Which of the following is *not* properly paired?
   a. seminiferous tubule—cervix
   b. vas deferens—oviduct
   c. testosterone—estradiol
   d. scrotum—labia majora

4. Peaks of LH and FSH production occur during
   a. the menstrual flow phase of the uterine cycle.
   b. the beginning of the follicular phase of the ovarian cycle.
   c. the period just before ovulation.
   d. the secretory phase of the menstrual cycle.

5. During human gestation, rudiments of all organs develop
   a. in the first trimester.
   b. in the second trimester.
   c. in the third trimester.
   d. during the blastocyst stage.

LEVEL 2: APPLICATION/ANALYSIS

6. Which of the following is a true statement?
   a. All mammals have menstrual cycles.
   b. The endometrial lining is shed in menstrual cycles but reabsorbed in estrous cycles.
   c. Estrous cycles are more frequent than menstrual cycles.
   d. Ovulation occurs before the endometrium thickens in estrous cycles.

7. For which of the following is the number the same in spermatogenesis and oogenesis?
   a. interruptions in meiotic divisions
   b. functional gametes produced by meiosis
   c. meiotic divisions required to produce each gamete
   d. different cell types produced by meiosis

8. Which statement about human reproduction is false?
   a. Fertilization occurs in the oviduct.
   b. Spermatogenesis and oogenesis require different temperatures.
   c. An oocyte completes meiosis after a sperm penetrates it.
   d. The earliest stages of spermatogenesis occur closest to the lumen of the seminiferous tubules.

LEVEL 3: SYNTHESIS/EVALUATION

9. **DRAW IT** In human spermatogenesis, mitosis of a stem cell gives rise to one cell that remains a stem cell and one cell that becomes a spermatogonium. (a) Draw four rounds of mitosis for a stem cell, and label the daughter cells. (b) For one spermatogonium, draw the cells it would produce from one round of mitosis followed by meiosis. Label the cells, and label mitosis and meiosis. (c) What would happen if stem cells divided like spermatogonia?

10. **EVOLUTION CONNECTION**
    Hermaphroditism is often found in animals that are fixed to a surface. Motile species are less often hermaphroditic. Why?

11. **SCIENTIFIC INQUIRY**
    You discover a new egg-laying worm species. You dissect four adults and find both oocytes and sperm in each. Cells outside the gonad contain five chromosome pairs. Lacking genetic variants, how would you determine whether the worms can self-fertilize?

12. **WRITE ABOUT A THEME: ENERGY AND MATTER**
    In reproducing, animals transfer energy to their offspring. In a short essay (100–150 words), discuss how distinct investments of energy by females contribute to the reproductive success of a frog, a chicken, and a human.

13. **SYNTHESIZE YOUR KNOWLEDGE**

Dave THOMPSON/AP Images

A female Komodo dragon (*Varanus komodoensis*) kept in isolation in a zoo had progeny. Each of the offspring had two identical copies of every gene in its genome. However, the offspring were not identical to one another. Based on your understanding of parthenogenesis and meiosis, generate a hypothesis to explain these observations.

For selected answers, see Appendix A.

47

Animal Development

| 1 mm

▲ Figure 47.1 **How did a single cell develop into this intricately detailed embryo?**

KEY CONCEPTS

47.1 Fertilization and cleavage initiate embryonic development

47.2 Morphogenesis in animals involves specific changes in cell shape, position, and survival

47.3 Cytoplasmic determinants and inductive signals contribute to cell fate specification

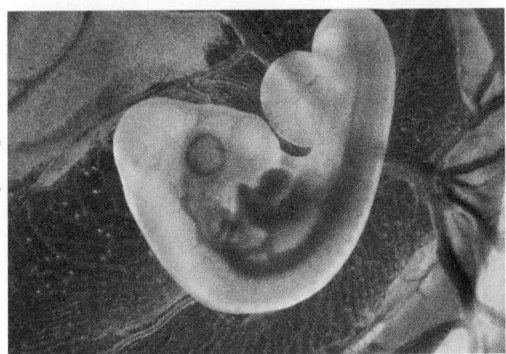

A Body-Building Plan

The 7-week-old human embryo in **Figure 47.1** has already achieved a remarkable number of milestones in its development. Its heart—the red spot in the centre—is beating, and a digestive tract traverses the length of its body. Its brain is forming (at the upper left in the photo), while the blocks of tissue that will give rise to the vertebrae are lined up along its back.

Development occurs at many points in the life cycle of an animal (**Figure 47.2**). In a frog, for example, a major developmental period is metamorphosis, when the larva (tadpole) is transformed into an adult. Other developmental events in the adult gonads produce sperm and eggs (gametes). In this chapter, our focus is on embryonic development.

By combining molecular genetics with classical embryology, developmental biologists have learned a great deal about the transformation of a fertilized egg into an adult. As an embryo develops, specific patterns of gene expression direct cells to adopt distinct fates. Although animals display widely differing body plans, they share many basic mechanisms of development and use a common set of regulatory genes. For example, the gene that specifies heart location in a human embryo (such as the one in Figure 47.1) has a close counterpart with a nearly identical function in the fruit fly, *Drosophila*. (Noting that the fly

1095

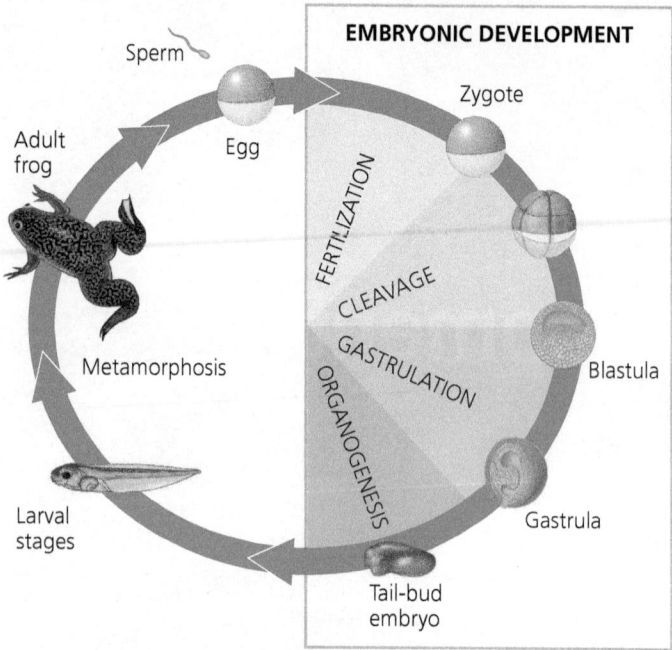

EMBRYONIC DEVELOPMENT

Sperm

Adult frog

Egg

Zygote

FERTILIZATION

CLEAVAGE

GASTRULATION

ORGANOGENESIS

Blastula

Metamorphosis

Larval stages

Tail-bud embryo

Gastrula

▲ Figure 47.2 **Developmental events in the life cycle of a frog.**

heart fails to develop when this gene is defective, researchers named the *Drosophila* gene *tinman*, after the similarly affected character from *The Wizard of Oz*.)

In studying development, biologists frequently make use of **model organisms**, species chosen for the ease with which they can be studied in the laboratory. *Drosophila* is a useful model organism: Its life cycle is short, and mutants can be readily identified and studied (see Chapters 15 and 18). In this chapter, we will concentrate on four other model organisms: the sea urchin, the frog, the chick, and the nematode (roundworm). We will also explore some aspects of human embryonic development. Even though humans are not model organisms, we are, of course, intensely interested in our own species.

Across a range of animal species, embryonic development involves common stages that occur in a set order. The animal is considered an embryo throughout this process, but specialized terms are used to identify discrete stages of embryonic development (Figure 47.2). Upon fertilization, the fusion of sperm and egg, the single-celled zygote is formed. The zygote then enters the cleavage phase: The cell undergoes multiple rounds of cell division, transforming the zygote into a hollow ball of cells known as the blastula. During the next stages, the animal develops from a nondescript ball of cells through steps that change its shape and organization into something more recognizable as an animal. Collectively, these steps are known as morphogenesis (the beginning of shape). First, the blastula folds in on itself, rearranging into a three-layered embryo, the gastrula, in a process called gastrulation. During organogenesis, the last major stage of embryonic development,

local changes in cell shape and large-scale changes in cell location generate the rudimentary organs from which adult structures grow.

Our exploration of embryonic development will begin with a description of the basic stages common to most animals. We will then look at some of the cellular mechanisms that generate body form. Finally, we will consider how a cell becomes committed to a particular specialized role.

CONCEPT 47.1

Fertilization and cleavage initiate embryonic development

With the preceding overview of embryonic development in mind, let's take a closer look at the events surrounding **fertilization**, the formation of a diploid zygote from a haploid egg and sperm.

Fertilization

Molecules and events at the egg surface play a crucial role in each step of fertilization. First, sperm dissolve or penetrate any protective layer surrounding the egg to reach the plasma membrane. Next, molecules on the sperm surface bind to receptors on the egg surface, helping ensure that a sperm of the same species fertilizes the egg. Finally, changes at the surface of the egg prevent *polyspermy*, the entry of multiple sperm nuclei into the egg. If polyspermy were to occur, the resulting abnormal number of chromosomes in the embryo would be lethal.

The cell surface events that take place during fertilization have been studied most extensively in sea urchins (members of the phylum Echinodermata; see Figure 33.47). Sea urchin gametes are easy to collect, and fertilization is external. As a result, researchers can observe fertilization and subsequent events simply by combining eggs and sperm in seawater in the laboratory. Furthermore, fertilization in sea urchins provides a good general model for the same process in vertebrates.

The Acrosomal Reaction

When sea urchins release their gametes into the water, the jelly coat that surrounds the egg exudes soluble molecules that attract the sperm, which swim toward the egg. As soon as the head of a sea urchin sperm contacts the jelly coat of a sea urchin egg, molecules in the jelly coat trigger the **acrosomal reaction** in the sperm (Figure 47.3). This reaction begins with the discharge of hydrolytic enzymes from the **acrosome**, a specialized vesicle at the tip of the sperm. These enzymes partially digest the jelly coat, enabling a sperm structure called the *acrosomal process* to elongate and penetrate the coat. Protein molecules on the tip of the extended acrosomal process bind to specific receptor

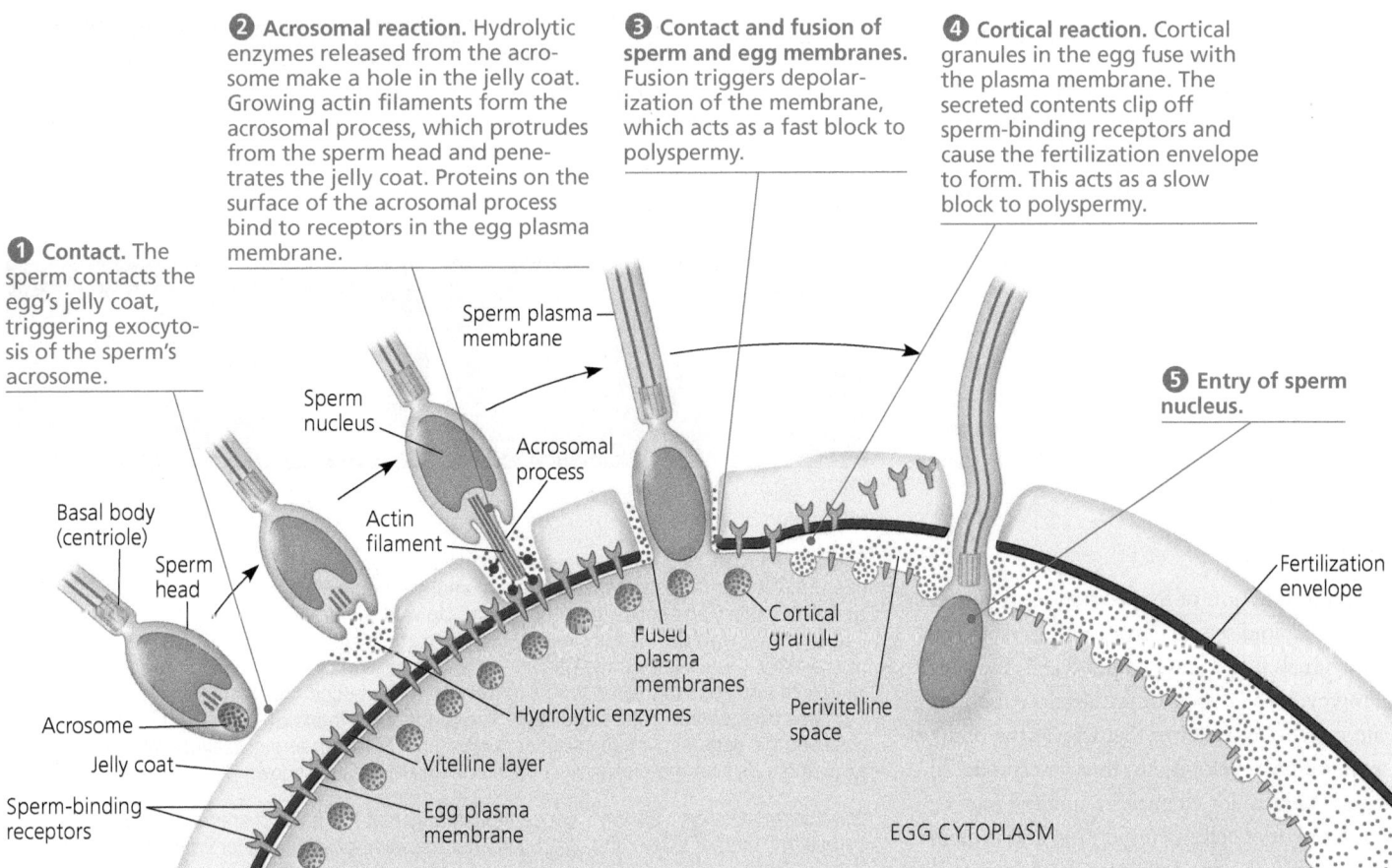

❷ Acrosomal reaction. Hydrolytic enzymes released from the acrosome make a hole in the jelly coat. Growing actin filaments form the acrosomal process, which protrudes from the sperm head and penetrates the jelly coat. Proteins on the surface of the acrosomal process bind to receptors in the egg plasma membrane.

❸ Contact and fusion of sperm and egg membranes. Fusion triggers depolarization of the membrane, which acts as a fast block to polyspermy.

❹ Cortical reaction. Cortical granules in the egg fuse with the plasma membrane. The secreted contents clip off sperm-binding receptors and cause the fertilization envelope to form. This acts as a slow block to polyspermy.

❶ Contact. The sperm contacts the egg's jelly coat, triggering exocytosis of the sperm's acrosome.

❺ Entry of sperm nucleus.

Sperm plasma membrane

Sperm nucleus

Acrosomal process

Basal body (centriole)

Actin filament

Sperm head

Fertilization envelope

Acrosome

Cortical granule

Fused plasma membranes

Hydrolytic enzymes

Perivitelline space

Jelly coat

Vitelline layer

Sperm-binding receptors

Egg plasma membrane

EGG CYTOPLASM

▲ Figure 47.3 **The acrosomal and cortical reactions during sea urchin fertilization.** The events following contact of a single sperm and egg ensure that the nucleus of only one sperm enters the egg cytoplasm.

The icon above is a simplified drawing of an adult sea urchin. Throughout the chapter, this and other icons of an adult frog, chicken, nematode, and human indicate the animals whose embryos are featured in certain figures.

proteins that jut out from the egg plasma membrane. This "lock-and-key" recognition is especially important for sea urchins and other species with external fertilization because the surrounding water may contain gametes of other species.

Contact between the tip of the acrosomal process and the receptors on the egg leads to the fusion of the sperm and egg plasma membranes. The sperm nucleus then enters the egg cytoplasm as ion channels open in the egg's plasma membrane. Sodium ions diffuse into the egg and cause *depolarization*, a decrease in the membrane potential (see Chapter 7). The depolarization occurs within about 1–3 seconds after a sperm binds to an egg. By preventing additional sperm from fusing with the egg's plasma membrane, this depolarization acts as a **fast block to polyspermy**.

The Cortical Reaction

Membrane depolarization lasts for only a minute or so. A longer-lasting block to polyspermy is established by vesicles that lie just beneath the egg plasma membrane, in the rim

of cytoplasm known as the *cortex*. Within seconds after a sperm binds to the egg, these vesicles, called cortical granules, fuse with the egg plasma membrane (see Figure 47.3, ❹). The contents of the cortical granules are released into the space between the plasma membrane and the surrounding *vitelline layer*, a structure formed by the extracellular matrix of the egg. Enzymes and other macromolecules from the granules trigger a cortical reaction, which lifts the vitelline layer away from the egg and hardens the layer into a protective fertilization envelope. Additional enzymes clip off and release the external portions of the remaining receptor proteins, along with any attached sperm. Together, the fertilization envelope and other changes in the egg's surface impede the entry of additional sperm nuclei and thus act as a longer-term **slow block to polyspermy**.

Formation of the fertilization envelope requires a high concentration of calcium ions (Ca^{2+}) in the egg. Does a change in the Ca^{2+} concentration trigger the cortical reaction? To answer this question, researchers at the University of California,

Berkeley, used a calcium-sensitive dye to assess the amount and distribution of Ca^{2+} in the egg during fertilization. As described in **Figure 47.4**, they found that Ca^{2+} spread across the egg in a wave that correlated with the appearance of the fertilization envelope. Further studies demonstrated that release of Ca^{2+} into the cytosol from the endoplasmic reticulum is controlled by a signal transduction pathway activated by sperm binding. The resulting increase in Ca^{2+} levels causes cortical granules to fuse with the plasma membrane. Although understood in greatest detail in sea urchins, the cortical reaction triggered by Ca^{2+} also occurs in vertebrates such as fishes and mammals.

Egg Activation

A major function of fertilization is the combining of haploid sets of chromosomes from two individuals into a single diploid cell, the zygote. However, the events of fertilization also initiate metabolic reactions that trigger the onset of embryonic development, thus "activating" the egg. There is, for example, a marked increase in the rates of cellular respiration and protein synthesis in the egg following fertilization.

What triggers egg activation? Studies show that injecting Ca^{2+} into an unfertilized egg activates egg metabolism in many species, despite the absence of sperm. Researchers therefore conclude that the rise in Ca^{2+} concentration that causes the cortical reaction also causes egg activation. Further experiments have revealed that artificial activation is possible even if the nucleus has been removed from the egg. This finding indicates that egg activation requires only the proteins and mRNAs already present in the egg cytoplasm.

About 20 minutes after the sperm nucleus enters the sea urchin egg, the sperm and egg nuclei fuse. DNA synthesis begins, and the first cell division occurs after about 90 minutes, marking the end of the fertilization stage.

Fertilization in other species shares many features with the process in sea urchins. However, the timing of events differs, as does the stage of meiosis the egg has reached by the time it is fertilized. Sea urchin eggs have already completed meiosis when they are released from the female. In other species, eggs are arrested at a specific stage of meiosis and do not complete the meiotic divisions until fertilization occurs. Human eggs, for example, are arrested at metaphase of meiosis II prior to fertilization (see Figure 46.12).

▼ Figure 47.4 | **Inquiry**

Does the distribution of Ca^{2+} in an egg correlate with formation of the fertilization envelope?

Experiment During fertilization, fusion of cortical granules with the egg plasma membrane causes the fertilization envelope to rise and spread around the egg from the point of sperm binding.

   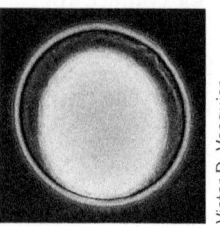

10 sec after fertilization	25 sec	35 sec	1 min

500 μm

Victor D. Vacquier

Calcium ion (Ca^{2+}) signalling is involved in fusion of vesicles with the plasma membrane during neurotransmitter release, insulin secretion, and plant pollen tube formation. Rick Steinhardt, Gerald Schatten, and colleagues, then at the University of California at Berkeley, hypothesized that an increase in Ca^{2+} levels similarly triggers cortical granule fusion. To test this hypothesis, they tracked the release of free Ca^{2+} in sea urchin eggs after sperm binding to see if it correlated with formation of the fertilization envelope. A fluorescent dye that glows when it binds free Ca^{2+} was injected into unfertilized eggs. The researchers then added sea urchin sperm and observed the eggs with a fluorescence microscope. Schatten and colleagues later repeated the experiment using a more sensitive dye, producing the results shown here.

Results A rise in cytosolic Ca^{2+} concentration began at the point of sperm entry and spread in a wave to the other side of the egg. Soon after the wave passed, the fertilization envelope rose.

Point of sperm nucleus entry

Spreading wave of Ca^{2+}

1 sec before fertilization	10 sec after fertilization	20 sec	30 sec

500 μm

Leah Kauffman

Conclusion The researchers concluded that Ca^{2+} release is correlated with the cortical reaction and formation of the fertilization envelope, supporting their hypothesis that an increase in Ca^{2+} levels triggers cortical granule fusion.

Source: Based on R. Steinhardt et al., Intracellular calcium release at fertilization in the sea urchin egg, *Developmental Biology* 58:185–197 (1977); M. Hafner et al., Wave of free calcium at fertilization in the sea urchin egg visualized with Fura-2, *Cell Motility and the Cytoskeleton* 9:271–277 (1988). © Jane B Reece.

(MB) See the related Experimental Inquiry Tutorial in MasteringBiology.

WHAT IF? *Suppose you were given a chemical compound that could enter the egg and bind to Ca^{2+}, blocking its function. How would you use this compound to further test the hypothesis that a rise in Ca^{2+} levels triggers cortical granule fusion?*

Fertilization in Mammals

Unlike sea urchins and most other marine invertebrates, terrestrial animals, including mammals, fertilize eggs internally. Secretions in the mammalian female reproductive tract not only provide a moist environment for the sperm, but also bring about changes in sperm motility and structure. Only after these changes occur do sperm have the capacity to fertilize an egg. In humans, this process of *capacitation* occurs during the first 6 hours after the sperm enter the female reproductive tract.

Support cells of the developing follicle surround the mammalian egg and remain with it during and after ovulation (see Figure 46.12). A sperm must travel through this layer of follicle cells before it reaches the **zona pellucida**, the extracellular matrix of the egg. Within the zona pellucida is a component that functions as a receptor for sperm. Binding of a sperm to this receptor induces an acrosomal reaction, facilitating sperm passage through the zona pellucida to the egg. This binding also exposes a protein on the sperm that binds with the egg plasma membrane. At this point, the two cells fuse (Figure 47.5).

As in sea urchin fertilization, sperm binding triggers changes within the mammalian egg that lead to a cortical reaction, the release of enzymes from cortical granules to the outside of the cell. These enzymes catalyze changes in the zona pellucida, which then functions as the slow block to polyspermy. (No fast block to polyspermy has been identified in mammals.)

After the egg and sperm membranes fuse, the whole sperm is taken into the egg. Once the envelopes of both haploid nuclei have dispersed, the sperm and egg chromosomes are organized onto a single mitotic spindle. Only after the first division is there a true diploid nucleus with a nuclear membrane.

Overall, fertilization is much slower in mammals than in sea urchins: The first cell division occurs 12–36 hours after sperm binding in mammals, compared with about 90 minutes in sea urchins. This cell division marks the end of fertilization and the beginning of the next stage, cleavage.

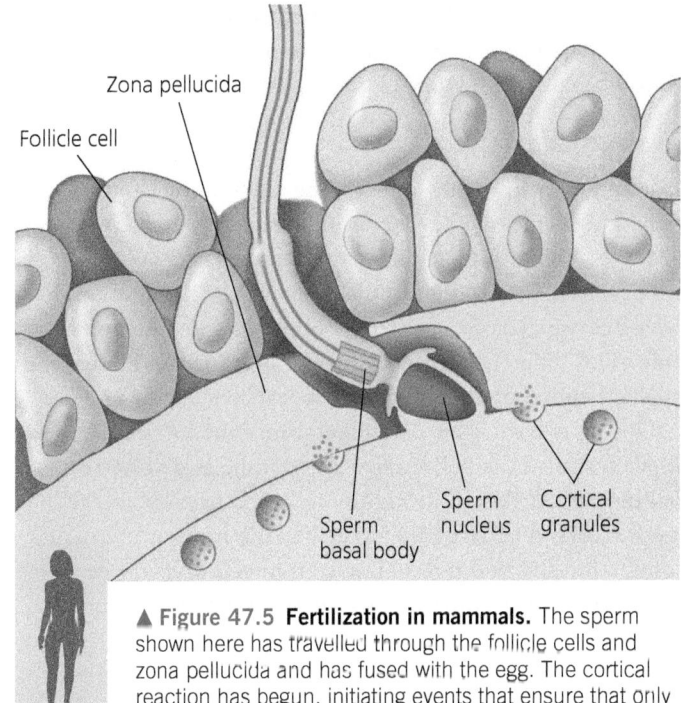

▲ **Figure 47.5 Fertilization in mammals.** The sperm shown here has travelled through the follicle cells and zona pellucida and has fused with the egg. The cortical reaction has begun, initiating events that ensure that only one sperm nucleus enters the egg.

Cleavage

Once fertilization is complete, many animal species undergo a succession of rapid cell divisions that characterize the **cleavage** stage of early development. During cleavage, the cell cycle consists primarily of the S (DNA synthesis) and M (mitosis) phases. Cells essentially skip the G_1 and G_2 (gap) phases, and little or no protein synthesis occurs (see Figure 12.6 for a review of the cell cycle). As a result, cleavage partitions the cytoplasm of the large fertilized egg into many smaller cells called **blastomeres**, as shown in Figure 47.6.

50 μm

George von Dassow

(a) Fertilized egg. Shown here is the zygote shortly before the first cleavage division, surrounded by the fertilization envelope.

(b) Four-cell stage. Remnants of the mitotic spindle can be seen between the two pairs of cells that have just completed the second cleavage division.

(c) Early blastula. After further cleavage divisions, the embryo is a multicellular ball that is still surrounded by the fertilization envelope. The blastocoel has begun to form in the centre.

(d) Later blastula. A single layer of cells surrounds a large blastocoel. Although not visible here, the fertilization envelope is still present; the embryo will soon hatch from it and begin swimming.

▲ **Figure 47.6 Cleavage in an echinoderm embryo.** Cleavage is a series of mitotic cell divisions that transform the fertilized egg into a blastula, a hollow ball composed of cells called blastomeres. These light micrographs show the cleavage stages of a sand dollar embryo, which are virtually identical to those of a sea urchin.

The first five to seven cleavage divisions produce a hollow ball of cells, the **blastula**, surrounding a fluid-filled cavity called the **blastocoel** (see Figure 47.6).

Cleavage Patterns

In frogs and many other animals, the distribution of **yolk** (stored nutrients) is a key factor influencing the pattern of cleavage. Yolk is often concentrated toward one pole of the egg, called the **vegetal pole**. The yolk concentration decreases significantly toward the opposite pole, the **animal pole**. This difference in yolk distribution results in animal and vegetal hemispheres that differ in appearance (**Figure 47.7**).

During cell division, an indentation called a *cleavage furrow* forms in the cell surface as cytokinesis divides the cell in half. As shown in Figure 47.7, the first two cleavage furrows in the frog lie parallel to the line (or meridian) connecting the two poles. The second cell division begins before the first is complete, so the second cleavage furrow further divides the animal hemisphere while the first furrow is dividing the yolky cytoplasm of the vegetal hemisphere. Nevertheless, the first two divisions eventually produce four blastomeres of equal size, each extending from the animal pole to the vegetal pole.

During the third division of the frog egg, the asymmetric distribution of yolk in the embryo affects the relative size of cells produced in the two hemispheres. This division is equatorial (perpendicular to the line connecting the poles) and produces an eight-celled embryo. However, as each of the four blastomeres begins this division, the high concentration of yolk around the vegetal pole displaces the mitotic apparatus toward the animal pole. Consequently, the cleavage furrow is also displaced from the egg equator toward the animal pole, yielding smaller blastomeres in the animal hemisphere than in the vegetal hemisphere. The displacing effect of the yolk persists in the subsequent divisions that produce a blastula. In frogs, these unequal cell divisions cause the blastocoel to form entirely in the animal hemisphere (see Figure 47.7).

Although yolk affects where division occurs in the eggs of frogs and other amphibians, the cleavage furrow still passes entirely through the egg. Cleavage in amphibian development is thus said to be **holoblastic** (from the Greek *holos*, complete). Holoblastic cleavage is also seen in many other groups of animals, including echinoderms, mammals, and annelids. The orientation of the cleavage furrows varies within these groups, resulting in blastulas that vary considerably in appearance. In those animals whose eggs contain relatively little yolk, the blastocoel forms centrally and the blastomeres are often of similar size, particularly during the first few divisions (see Figure 47.6). This is the case for

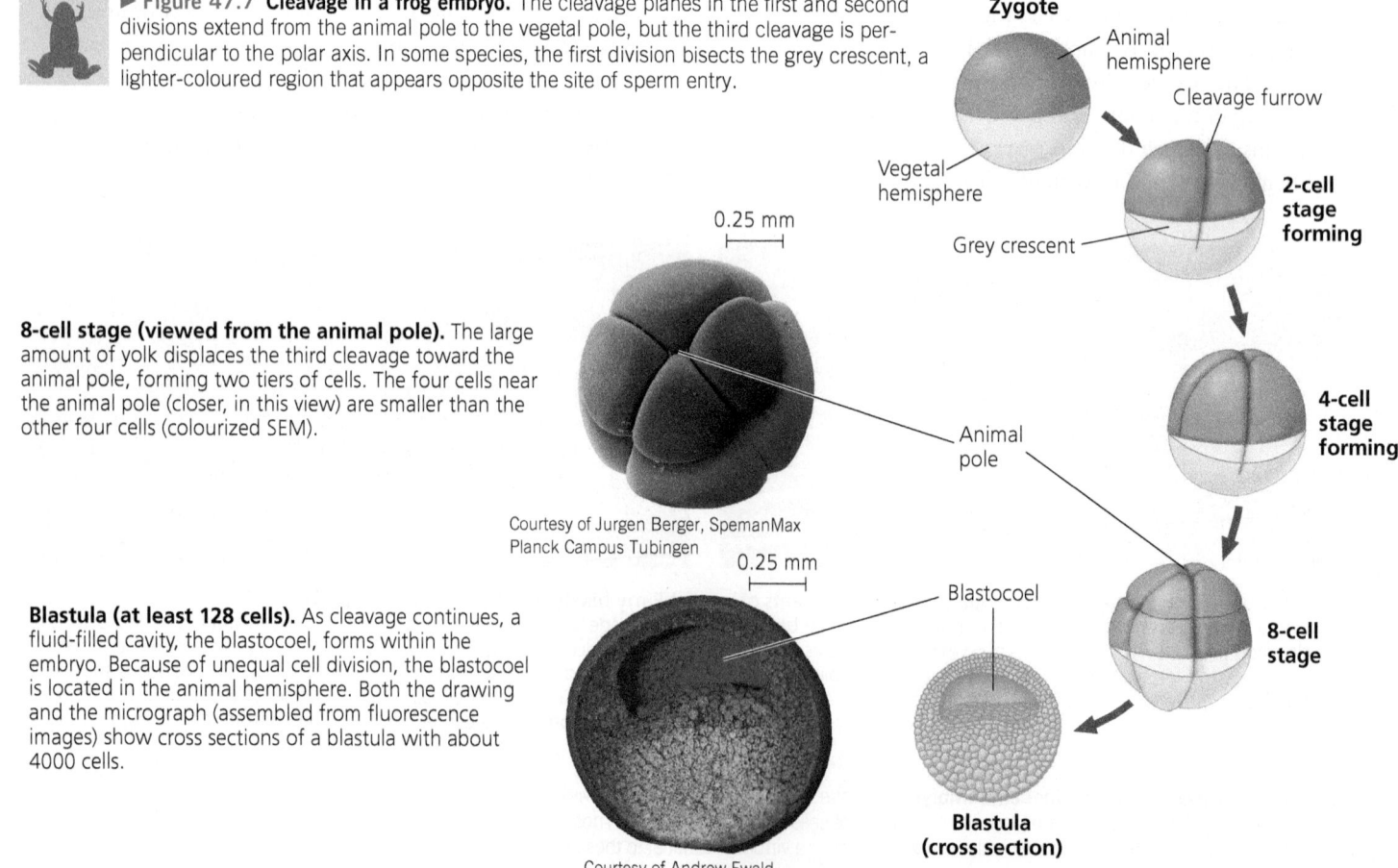

▶ Figure 47.7 **Cleavage in a frog embryo.** The cleavage planes in the first and second divisions extend from the animal pole to the vegetal pole, but the third cleavage is perpendicular to the polar axis. In some species, the first division bisects the grey crescent, a lighter-coloured region that appears opposite the site of sperm entry.

8-cell stage (viewed from the animal pole). The large amount of yolk displaces the third cleavage toward the animal pole, forming two tiers of cells. The four cells near the animal pole (closer, in this view) are smaller than the other four cells (colourized SEM).

0.25 mm

Courtesy of Jurgen Berger, SpemanMax Planck Campus Tubingen

Blastula (at least 128 cells). As cleavage continues, a fluid-filled cavity, the blastocoel, forms within the embryo. Because of unequal cell division, the blastocoel is located in the animal hemisphere. Both the drawing and the micrograph (assembled from fluorescence images) show cross sections of a blastula with about 4000 cells.

0.25 mm

Courtesy of Andrew Ewald, Johns Hopkins Medical School

Zygote

Animal hemisphere

Cleavage furrow

Vegetal hemisphere

Grey crescent

2-cell stage forming

4-cell stage forming

Animal pole

Blastocoel

8-cell stage

Blastula (cross section)

humans, whose embryos complete three divisions in the first 3 days after fertilization.

Yolk is most plentiful and has its most pronounced effect on cleavage in the eggs of birds, other reptiles, many fishes, and insects. In these animals, the volume of yolk is so great that cleavage furrows cannot pass through it, and only the region of the egg lacking yolk undergoes cleavage. This incomplete cleavage of a yolk-rich egg is said to be **meroblastic** (from the Greek *meros*, partial).

In birds, the part of the egg commonly called the yolk is actually the entire egg cell, swollen with yolk nutrients. Cell divisions are limited to a small whitish area at the animal pole. These divisions produce a cap of cells that sort into upper and lower layers. The cavity between these two layers is the avian version of the blastocoel.

In the eggs of *Drosophila* and most other insects, the sperm and egg nuclei fuse *within* a mass of yolk. Multiple rounds of mitosis occur without cytokinesis. In other words, no cell membranes form around the early nuclei. The first several hundred nuclei spread throughout the yolk and later migrate to the outer edge of the embryo. After several more rounds of mitosis, a plasma membrane forms around each nucleus, and the embryo, now the equivalent of a blastula, consists of a single layer of about 6000 cells surrounding a mass of yolk (see Figure 18.22).

Regulation of Cleavage

The single nucleus in a newly fertilized egg has too little DNA to produce the amount of messenger RNA required to meet the cell's need for new proteins. Instead, initial development is carried out by RNA and proteins deposited in the egg during oogenesis. After cleavage, the egg cytoplasm has been divided among the many blastomeres, each with its own nucleus. Because each blastomere is much smaller than the entire egg, its nucleus can make enough RNA to program the cell's metabolism and further development.

Given that the number of cleavage divisions varies among animals, what mechanism determines the end of the cleavage stage? The Scientific Skills Exercise explores one of the landmark studies that addressed this question.

SCIENTIFIC SKILLS EXERCISE

Interpreting a Change in Slope

What Causes the End of Cleavage in a Frog Embryo? During cleavage in a frog embryo, as in many other animals, the cell cycle consists mainly of the S (DNA synthesis) and M (mitosis) phases, and there are no G_1 and G_2 phases. However, after the 12th cell division, G_1 and G_2 phases appear, and the cells grow, producing proteins and cytoplasmic organelles. These and other changes in activity mark the end of cleavage. But what triggers the change in the cell cycle?

How the Experiments Were Done Researchers tested the hypothesis that a mechanism for counting cell divisions determines when cleavage ends. They allowed frog embryos to take up radioactively labelled nucleosides, in one experiment labelling thymidine to measure DNA synthesis and in another experiment labelling uridine to measure RNA synthesis. They then repeated these two experiments in the presence of a toxin that prevents cell division by blocking cleavage furrow formation and cytokinesis.

Data from the Experiments

	Nucleic Acid Synthesis (on scale of 0–100)										
DNA Toxin added	35	48	54	71	83	85	88	87	100	96	
DNA No toxin	10	24	28	31	47	49	49	53	55	55	55
RNA Toxin added			0		6		25	27			33
RNA No toxin			0		3		14	22			27
Time Point (every 35 min)	1	2	3	4	5	6	7	8	9	10	11

Interpret the Data

1. How were the researchers able to independently measure DNA synthesis and RNA synthesis?

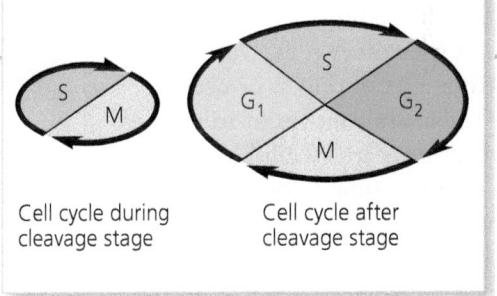

Cell cycle during cleavage stage   Cell cycle after cleavage stage

2. Use the data in the table to create a graph showing DNA synthesis and RNA synthesis with and without the toxin that prevents cell division. Note that time point 5 corresponds to cell division 12. For the DNA data, draw a straight line to represent the general trend for time points 1–5 and another straight line for time points 5 and later. For RNA, connect each data point with the next. Describe the changes in synthesis that occur at the end of cleavage.

3. The researchers hypothesized that the toxin increases diffusion of thymidine into the embryos. Explain their logic.

4. Do the data support the hypothesis that the timing of the end of cleavage depends on counting cell divisions? Explain.

5. In a separate experiment, researchers disrupted the block to polyspermy, generating embryos with 7 to 10 sperm nuclei. At the end of cleavage, these embryos had the same nucleus-to-cytoplasm ratio as the wild-type embryos, but cleavage ended at the 10th cell division rather than the 12th cell division. What do these results indicate about the timing of the end of cleavage?

Data from J. Newport and M. Kirschner, A major developmental transition in early *Xenopus* embryos: I. Characterization and timing of cellular changes at the midblastula stage, *Cell* 30:675–686 (1982).

CONCEPT 47.2

Morphogenesis in animals involves specific changes in cell shape, position, and survival

After cleavage, the rate of cell division slows considerably as the normal cell cycle is restored. Cells become specialized, they move within the embryo, and alter their relationships with other cells. During **gastrulation**, a set of cells at or near the surface of the blastula moves to an interior location, cell layers are established, and a primitive digestive tube is formed. Further transformation occurs during **organogenesis**, the formation of organs. **Morphogenesis** is a general term that usually includes all of the steps that reorganize cells into the final body plan, including gastrulation and organogenesis. We will discuss these two stages in turn, focusing in each case on the development of a few model organisms.

Gastrulation

Gastrulation is a dramatic reorganization of the hollow blastula into a two-layered or three-layered embryo called a **gastrula**. The cell layers produced by gastrulation are collectively called the embryonic **germ layers** (from the Latin *germen*, to sprout or germinate). In the late gastrula, **ectoderm** forms the outer layer and **endoderm** lines the embryonic digestive compartment or tract. In cnidarians and a few other radially symmetrical animals,

only these two germ layers form during gastrulation. Such animals are called diploblasts (see Chapter 32). In contrast, animals with bilateral symmetry are triploblasts, having a third germ layer, the **mesoderm**, between the ectoderm and the endoderm.

Gastrulation in Sea Urchins

Gastrulation in the sea urchin begins at the vegetal pole of the blastula (**Figure 47.8**). There, cells called *mesenchyme*

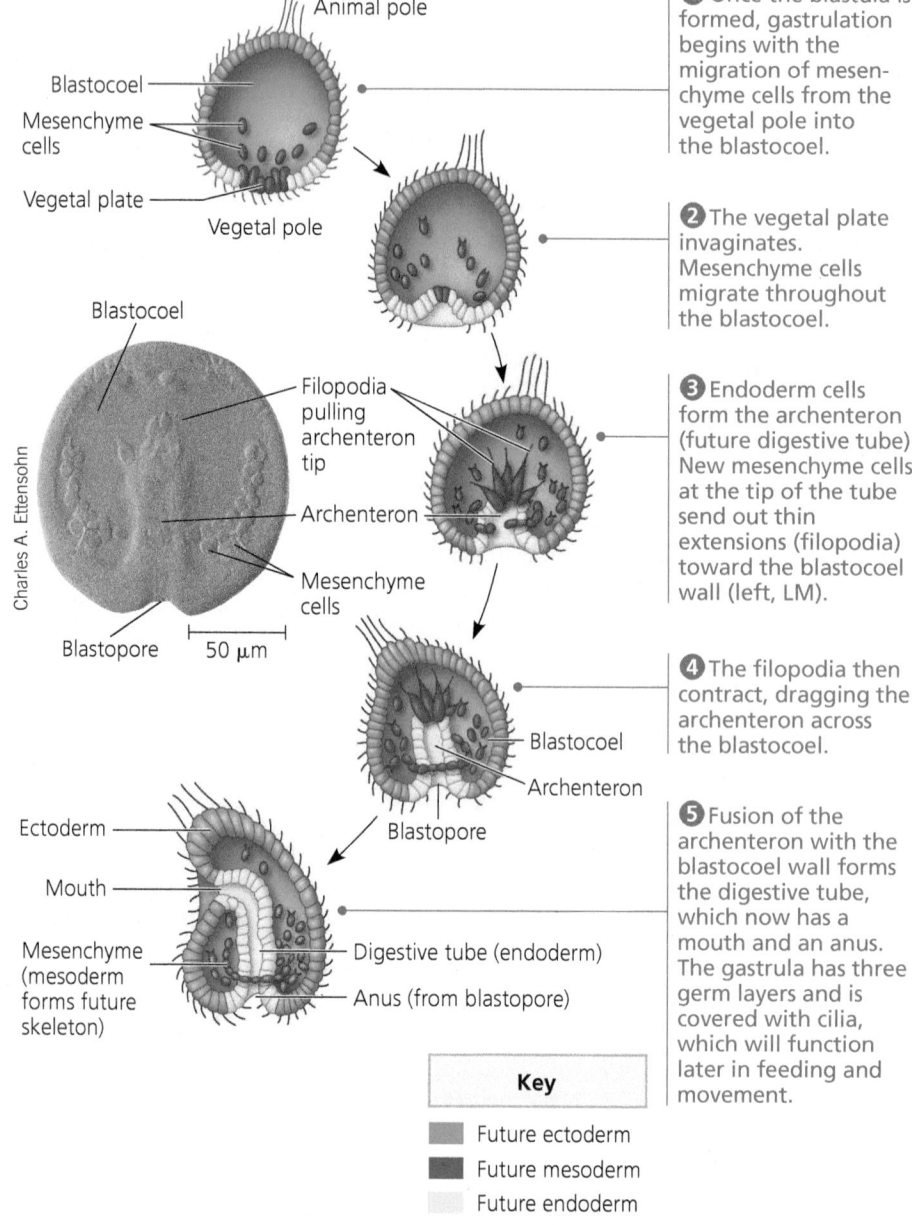

Charles A. Ettensohn

1 Once the blastula is formed, gastrulation begins with the migration of mesenchyme cells from the vegetal pole into the blastocoel.

2 The vegetal plate invaginates. Mesenchyme cells migrate throughout the blastocoel.

3 Endoderm cells form the archenteron (future digestive tube). New mesenchyme cells at the tip of the tube send out thin extensions (filopodia) toward the blastocoel wall (left, LM).

4 The filopodia then contract, dragging the archenteron across the blastocoel.

5 Fusion of the archenteron with the blastocoel wall forms the digestive tube, which now has a mouth and an anus. The gastrula has three germ layers and is covered with cilia, which will function later in feeding and movement.

Key	
	Future ectoderm
	Future mesoderm
	Future endoderm

▲ **Figure 47.8 Gastrulation in a sea urchin embryo.** The movement of cells during gastrulation forms an embryo with a primitive digestive tube and three germ layers. Some of the mesodermal mesenchyme cells that migrate inward (step **1**) will eventually secrete calcium carbonate and form a simple internal skeleton. Embryos in steps **1**–**3** are viewed from the front, those in **4** and **5** from the side.

ECTODERM (outer layer of embryo)	MESODERM (middle layer of embryo)	ENDODERM (inner layer of embryo)
• Epidermis of skin and its derivatives (including sweat glands, hair follicles) • Nervous and sensory systems • Pituitary gland, adrenal medulla • Jaws and teeth • Germ cells	• Skeletal and muscular systems • Circulatory and lymphatic systems • Excretory and reproductive systems (except germ cells) • Dermis of skin • Adrenal cortex	• Epithelial lining of digestive tract and associated organs (liver, pancreas) • Epithelial lining of respiratory, excretory, and reproductive tracts and ducts • Thymus, thyroid, and parathyroid glands

▲ Figure 47.9 Major derivatives of the three embryonic germ layers in vertebrates.

cells individually detach from the blastocoel wall and enter the blastocoel. The remaining cells near the vegetal pole flatten slightly and cause that end of the embryo to buckle inward as a result of cell shape changes we will discuss later. This process—the infolding of a sheet of cells into the embryo—is called *invagination*. Extensive rearrangement of cells transforms the shallow depression into a deeper, narrower, blind-ended tube called the **archenteron**. The open end of the archenteron, which will become the anus, is called the **blastopore**. A second opening, which will become the mouth, forms when the opposite end of the archenteron touches the inside of the ectoderm and the two layers fuse, producing a rudimentary digestive tube.

As you learned in Chapter 32, animals can be categorized by whether the mouth develops from the first opening that forms in the embryo (protostomes) or the second (deuterostomes). Sea urchins and other echinoderms are deuterostomes, as are chordates like ourselves and other vertebrates.

Upon completing gastrulation, sea urchin embryos develop into ciliated larvae that drift in ocean surface waters as zooplankton, feeding on bacteria and unicellular algae. Eventually, each larva metamorphoses into the adult form of the sea urchin, which takes up residence on the ocean floor.

Gastrulation in Frogs

Each germ layer contributes to a distinct set of structures in the adult animal (Figure 47.9). Some organs and many organ systems of the adult derive from more than one germ layer. For example, the adrenal gland has both ectodermal and mesoderm tissue, and many other endocrine glands contain endodermal tissue.

Frog and other bilaterally symmetrical animals have a dorsal (top) side and a ventral (bottom) side, a left side and a right side, and an anterior (front) end and a posterior (back) end. As shown in Figure 47.10, frog gastrulation begins when a group of cells on the dorsal side of the blastula begins to invaginate. This process forms a crease along the region where the grey crescent formed (see Figure 47.7). It may help to think of this crease as the site where two thin lips are pressed together. The part above the crease becomes the dorsal side of the blastopore, called the **dorsal lip**.

As the blastopore is forming, a sheet of cells begins to spread out of the animal hemisphere. Some of these cells roll over the edge of the lip into the interior of the embryo, a process called *involution*. Once inside the embryo, these cells move away from the blastopore toward the animal pole and become organized into layers of endoderm and mesoderm, with the endoderm on the inside. Cells continue to spread over the gastrula surface, shifting and shrinking the blastopore. In the interior of the embryo, an archenteron forms and grows as the blastocoel shrinks and eventually disappears.

At the end of gastrulation, the cells remaining on the surface make up the ectoderm, the tube of endoderm is the innermost layer, and the mesoderm lies between them. As in the sea urchin, the frog's anus develops from the blastopore, and the mouth eventually breaks through at the opposite end of the archenteron.

Gastrulation in Chicks

The starting point for gastrulation in chicks is an embryo consisting of a layer of cells, the *blastoderm*, divided into upper and lower layers—the *epiblast* and *hypoblast*—lying atop a yolk mass. All the cells that will form the embryo come from the epiblast. During gastrulation, some epiblast cells move toward the midline of the blastoderm, detach, and move inward toward the yolk (Figure 47.11). The pileup of cells moving inward at the blastoderm's midline produces a thickening called the **primitive streak**. Although the hypoblast contributes no cells to the embryo, it is required for normal development and seems to help direct the formation of the primitive streak before the onset of gastrulation. The hypoblast cells later segregate from the endoderm and eventually form part of the sac that surrounds the yolk and also part of the stalk that connects the yolk mass to the embryo.

Gastrulation in Humans

Unlike the large, yolky eggs of many vertebrates, human eggs are quite small, storing little in the way of food reserves. Fertilization takes place in the oviduct, and the earliest stages of development occur while the embryo completes its journey down the oviduct to the uterus

① Gastrulation begins when cells on the dorsal side invaginate to form a small indented crease, the blastopore. The part above the crease is called the dorsal lip. As the blastopore is forming, a sheet of cells begins to spread out of the animal hemisphere, rolls inward over the dorsal lip (involution), and moves into the interior (shown by the dashed arrow). In the interior, these cells will form endoderm and mesoderm, with the endodermal layer on the inside. Meanwhile, cells at the animal pole change shape and begin spreading over the outer surface.

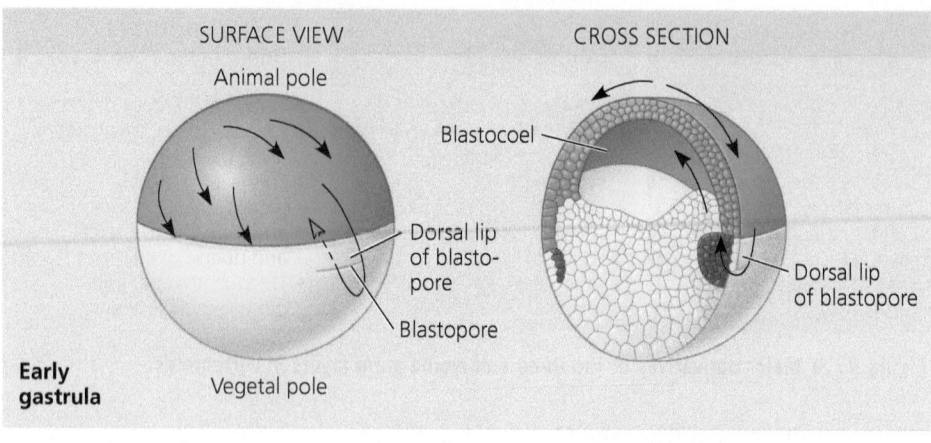

② The blastopore extends around both sides of the embryo as more cells invaginate. When the ends meet, the blastopore forms a circle that becomes smaller as ectoderm spreads downward over the surface. Internally, continued involution expands the endoderm and mesoderm, and the archenteron forms and grows as the blastocoel shrinks and eventually disappears.

③ Late in gastrulation, the cells remaining on the surface make up the ectoderm. The endoderm is the innermost layer, and the mesoderm lies between the ectoderm and endoderm. The circular blastopore surrounds a plug of yolk-filled cells.

Key	
	Future ectoderm
	Future mesoderm
	Future endoderm

▲ **Figure 47.10 Gastrulation in a frog embryo.** In the frog blastula, the blastocoel is displaced toward the animal pole and is surrounded by a wall several cells thick.

(see Figure 46.15). **Figure 47.12** depicts development of the human embryo starting about 6 days after fertilization. The description follows the numbered stages in the figure.

① At the end of cleavage, the embryo has more than 100 cells arranged around a central cavity and has travelled down the oviduct to the uterus. At this stage of development, the embryo is called a **blastocyst**, the mammalian version of a blastula. Clustered at one end of the blastocyst cavity is a group of cells called the **inner cell mass**, which will develop into the embryo proper. It is the cells of the very early blastocyst stage that are the source of embryonic stem cell lines.

② The **trophoblast**, the outer epithelium of the blastocyst, does not contribute to the embryo itself but instead supports embryo growth in a number of ways. It initiates implantation by secreting enzymes that break down molecules of the endometrium, the lining of the uterus. This allows the blastocyst to invade the endometrium. As the trophoblast thickens through cell division, it extends finger-like projections into the surrounding maternal tissue. Invasion by the trophoblast leads to erosion of capillaries in the endometrium, causing blood to spill out and bathe trophoblast tissues. Around the time of implantation, the inner cell mass of the blastocyst forms a flat disk with an upper layer of

▲ Figure 47.11 **Gastrulation in a chick embryo.** This is a cross section of a gastrulating embryo, looking toward the anterior end.

cells, the *epiblast*, and a lower layer, the *hypoblast*. As in birds, the human embryo develops almost entirely from epiblast cells.

❸ Following implantation, the trophoblast continues to expand into the endometrium, and four new membranes appear: allantois, amnion, chorion, and yolk sac. Although these **extraembryonic membranes** are formed by the embryo, they enclose specialized structures located outside the embryo. As implantation is completed, gastrulation begins. Cells move inward from the epiblast through a primitive streak and form mesoderm and endoderm, just as in the chick (see Figure 47.11).

❹ By the end of gastrulation, the embryonic germ layers have formed. Extraembryonic mesoderm and the four extraembryonic membranes now surround the embryo. As development proceeds, the invading trophoblast, cells from the epiblast, and adjacent endometrial tissue will all contribute to formation of the placenta. This vital organ mediates exchange of nutrients, gases, and nitrogenous wastes between the embryo and the mother (see Figure 46.16).

A great deal has been learned about gastrulation from studies on non-human mammals, where genetic manipulations are possible. For example, Janet Rossant at the University of Toronto explores the cellular mechanisms that determine the fate of the undifferentiated cells of the blastula **(Figure 47.13).** Using transgenic mice, she and her colleagues knock out specific genes to explore each gene's role in controlling development of the embryo. For example,

❶ Blastocyst reaches uterus.

❷ Blastocyst implants (7 days after fertilization).

❸ Extraembryonic membranes start to form (10–11 days), and gastrulation begins (13 days).

❹ Gastrulation has produced a three-layered embryo with four extraembryonic membranes.

▲ Figure 47.12 **Four stages in the early embryonic development of a human.** The names of the tissues that develop into the embryo proper are printed in blue.

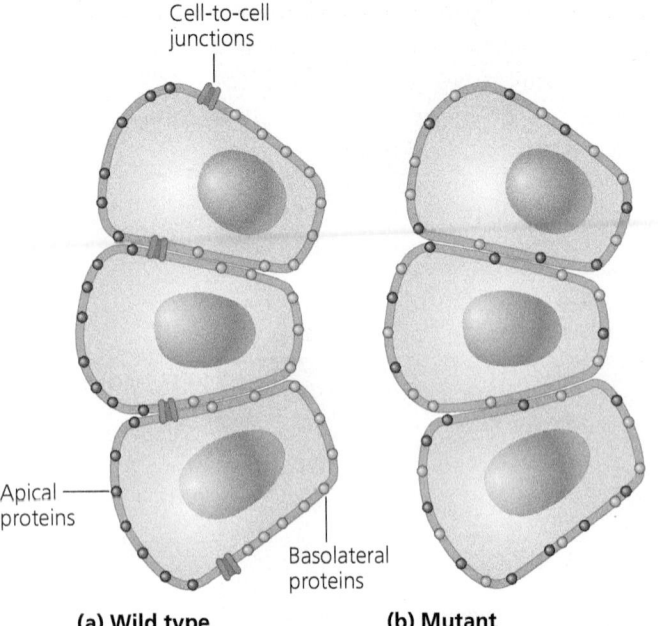

Cell-to-cell junctions

Apical proteins

Basolateral proteins

(a) Wild type   (b) Mutant

▲ **Figure 47.13 Tight junctions and cell polarity.** In addition to their role in cell-to-cell adhesion, tight junctions limit movement of cell membrane proteins between the apical and basolateral regions of the cell. The resulting differences between the regions, known as polarity, have important consequences in many cell types. **(a)** In embryogenesis of normal mice (wild type), polarity of the cells of the blastula means that daughter cells are produced with different suites of proteins, such as E-cadherin. These differences affect where the daughter cells migrate and facilitate the formation of the specialized regions of the blastocyst, such as the trophoblast and inner cell mass. **(b)** Mutant mice lacking E-cadherin are unable to form tight junctions. The loss of polarity impairs the normal cell determination and migration of the daughter cells and alters embryonic development.

Source: Modified from R. O. Stephenson, Y. Yamanaka, and J. Rossant, Disorganized epithelial polarity and excess trophectoderm cell fate in preimplantation embryos lacking E-cadherin, *Development and Stem Cells* 137:3383–3391 (2010). © Jane B Reece.

disrupting the gene for a protein that connects blastula cells together prevents the individual cells from properly recognizing which end of the cell faces outward (apical) and which faces inward (basolateral). Without such mechanisms, the cells of the blastula do not properly differentiate into the inner cell mass and trophoblast. Such studies on model organisms allow greater understanding of mechanisms shared by all mammals; however, there are many differences in patterns of embryogenesis between species. Thus, many researchers continue to study early human development in the lab, using *in vitro* fertilization.

Extraembryonic Membranes of Amniotes

EVOLUTION   One of the main differences between gastrulation seen in mammals and other vertebrates is the role of extraembryonic membranes. These are cells originating from the embryo that become tissues that are independent of the embryo but support its development. Fish and amphibians lack extraembryonic membranes and the

embryos develop directly in the water. Such a dependency on water for embryonic development was alleviated with the evolution of extraembryonic membranes in early reptiles (see Figure 34.26). In combination with the hard-shelled egg and resources (albumin and yolk) produced by the mother, the membranes within the egg produced by the embryo allowed the fertilized egg to be more self-contained. The chorion separates the embryo from the albumin and plays a role in gas exchange. The allantois forms a sac that collects metabolic waste formed during development. The yolk sac confines the yolk and mediates the transfer of nutrients to the embryo. The amnion holds fluid that acts as a cushion, protecting the embryo during development.

The organisms derived from ancient reptiles—modern reptiles (including birds) and mammals—are called **amniotes** because in each lineage the amnion plays a similar role. In fact, all of the extraembryonic membranes exist in amniotes, although they are barely recognizable in most mammals. Although monotremes, such as the platypus and echidna, have retained the reptilian trait of shelled eggs, in other mammals the embryo experiences early development within the uterus.

For the most part, the extraembryonic membranes of mammals play roles similar to those seen in reptiles. The chorion is the site of gas exchange, and the fluid within the amnion physically protects the developing embryo. (This amniotic fluid is released from the vagina when a pregnant woman's "water breaks" just before childbirth.) The allantois, which disposes of wastes in the reptilian egg, is incorporated into the umbilical cord in mammals. There it forms blood vessels that transport oxygen and nutrients from the placenta to the embryo and rid the embryo of carbon dioxide and nitrogenous wastes. The fourth extraembryonic membrane, the yolk sac, encloses yolk in the eggs of reptiles. In mammals it is a site of early formation of blood cells, which later migrate into the embryo proper. Thus, although the extraembryonic membranes of their egg-laying ancestors were conserved in mammals in the course of evolution, modifications appeared that were adapted to development within the uterus of the mother.

After gastrulation is complete and any extraembryonic membranes are formed, the next stage of embryonic development begins: organ formation.

Organogenesis

During organogenesis, regions of the three embryonic germ layers develop into the rudiments of organs. Whereas gastrulation involves mass movements of cells, organogenesis involves more localized changes. To illustrate the basic principles of this process, we'll focus on *neurulation*, the first steps in the formation of the brain and spinal cord in vertebrates.

Neurulation begins as cells from the dorsal mesoderm come together to form the **notochord**, the rod that extends along the dorsal side of the chordate embryo, seen in **Figure 47.14a** for the frog. Signalling molecules secreted by these mesodermal cells and other tissues induce the ectoderm above the notochord to become the *neural plate*. Next, the cells of the neural plate change shape, curving the neural plate inward. In this way, the neural plate rolls itself into the **neural tube**, which runs along the anterior-posterior axis of the embryo **(Figure 47.14b)**. The neural tube will become the brain in the head and the spinal cord along the rest of the body.

In vertebrate embryos, two sets of cells develop near the neural tube and then migrate elsewhere in the body. The first set is a band of cells called the **neural crest**, which develops along the borders where the neural tube pinches off from the ectoderm. Neural crest cells subsequently migrate to many parts of the embryo, forming a variety of tissues that include peripheral nerves as well as parts of the teeth and skull bones. The second set of migratory cells is formed when groups of cells located in strips of mesoderm lateral to the notochord separate into blocks called **somites** **(Figure 47.14c)**. The somites are arranged serially on both sides along the length of the notochord. Parts of the somites dissociate into mesenchyme cells, which migrate individually to new locations.

Somites play a major role in organizing the segmented structure of the vertebrate body. One of the major functions of the mesenchyme cells that leave the somites is formation of the vertebrae. Although the notochord disappears before birth, parts of the notochord persist as the inner portions of the vertebral disks in adults. (These are

(a) Neural plate formation. By this stage, the notochord has developed from dorsal mesoderm, and the dorsal ectoderm has thickened, forming the neural plate, in response to signals from other embryonic tissues. The neural folds are the two ridges that form the lateral edges of the neural plate. These folds are visible in the LM of a whole embryo.

(b) Neural tube formation. Infolding and pinching off of the neural plate generates the neural tube. Note the neural crest cells, which will migrate and give rise to numerous structures.

(c) Somites. The SEM is a side view of the whole embryo at the tail-bud stage. Part of the ectoderm has been removed to reveal the somites, blocks of tissue that will give rise to segmental structures such as vertebrae. The drawing shows a similar-stage embryo after formation of the neural tube, as if the embryo in the SEM were cut and viewed in cross section. By this time, the lateral mesoderm has begun to separate into two tissue layers that line the coelom, or body cavity. The somites, formed from mesoderm, flank the notochord.

▲ Figure 47.14 **Neurulation in a frog embryo.**

the disks that can herniate or rupture, causing back pain.) Somite cells that become mesenchymal later form the muscles associated with the vertebral column and the ribs. Through these processes, serially repeating structures of the embryo (somites) form repeated structures in the adult. Chordates can thus be described as segmented animals, although the segmentation becomes less obvious later in development. Lateral to the somites, the mesoderm splits into two layers that form the lining of the body cavity, or coelom (see Figure 32.9).

Early organogenesis in other vertebrates is quite similar to that in the frog. In the chick, for example, the borders of the blastoderm fold downward and come together, pinching the embryo into a three-layered tube joined under the middle of the body to the yolk **(Figure 47.15a)**. By the time the chick embryo is 3 days old, rudiments of the major organs, including the brain, eyes, and heart, are readily apparent **(Figure 47.15b)**.

In humans, an error in neural tube formation results in *spina bifida*, the most common disabling birth defect. In spina bifida, a portion of the neural tube fails to develop or close properly, leaving an opening in the spinal column and causing nerve damage. Although the opening can be surgically repaired shortly after birth, the nerve damage is permanent, resulting in varying degrees of leg paralysis.

Organogenesis is somewhat different in invertebrates, which is not surprising, given that their body plans diverge significantly from those of vertebrates. The underlying mechanisms, however, involve many of the same cellular activities: cell migration, cell signalling between different tissues, and cell shape changes generating new organs. In insects, for example, tissues of the nervous system form when ectoderm along the anterior-posterior axis rolls into a tube inside the embryo, similar to the vertebrate neural tube. Interestingly, the tube is on the ventral side of the insect embryo rather than the dorsal side, where it is in vertebrates. In spite of the different locations, the molecular signalling pathways that bring about the events in the two groups are very similar, underscoring their ancient shared evolutionary history.

As we have seen in our consideration of gastrulation and organogenesis, changes in cell shape and location are essential to early development. We will turn now to an exploration of how these changes take place.

Cellular Mechanisms in Morphogenesis

Morphogenesis, beginning with gastrulation and organogenesis, depends upon controlling the location and shape of individual cells and changing the relationships between cells in a tissue. These changes are controlled at the cellular level and rely on processes introduced in Chapter 6. We'll begin with the roles of the microtubules and microfilaments that make up the cytoskeleton (see Table 6.1).

Changes in Cell Shape

Reorganization of the cytoskeleton is a major force in changing cell shape during development. As an example, we can return to the topic of neurulation. At the onset of neural tube formation, microtubules oriented from dorsal to ventral in a sheet of ectodermal cells help lengthen the cells along that axis (Figure 47.16). At the dorsal end of each cell is a bundle of actin filaments (microfilaments) oriented crosswise. These actin filaments contract, giving the cells a

▶ **Figure 47.15 Organogenesis in a chick embryo.**

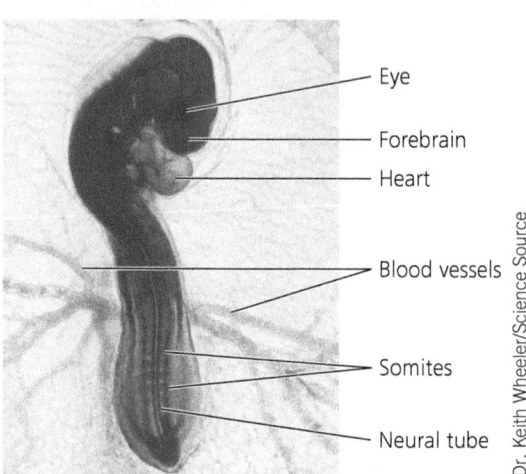

(a) Early organogenesis. The archenteron forms when lateral folds pinch the embryo away from the yolk. The embryo remains open to the yolk, attached by the yolk stalk, about midway along its length, as shown in this cross section. The notochord, neural tube, and somites subsequently develop much as they do in the frog. The germ layers lateral to the embryo itself form extraembryonic membranes.

(b) Late organogenesis. Rudiments of most major organs have already formed in this chick embryo, which is 3 days old and about 2–3 mm long. The extraembryonic membranes eventually are supplied by blood vessels extending from the embryo; several major blood vessels are seen here (LM).

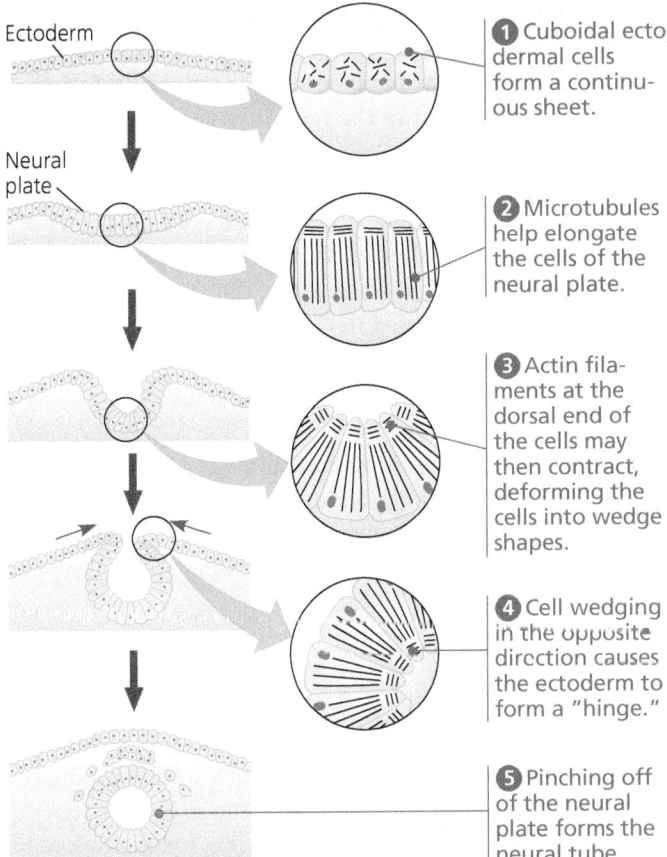

① Cuboidal ectodermal cells form a continuous sheet.

② Microtubules help elongate the cells of the neural plate.

③ Actin filaments at the dorsal end of the cells may then contract, deforming the cells into wedge shapes.

④ Cell wedging in the opposite direction causes the ectoderm to form a "hinge."

⑤ Pinching off of the neural plate forms the neural tube.

Ectoderm

Neural plate

▲ Figure 47.16 **Change in cell shape during morphogenesis.** Reorganization of the cytoskeleton is associated with morphogenetic changes in embryonic tissues, as shown here for the formation of the neural tube in vertebrates.

wedge shape that bends the ectoderm layer inward. Similar changes in cell shape occur at the hinge regions where the neural tube is pinching off from the ectoderm. However, the generation of wedge-shaped cells is not limited to neurulation or even to vertebrates. In *Drosophila* gastrulation, for instance, the formation of wedge-shaped cells along the ventral surface is responsible for invagination of a tube of cells that form the mesoderm.

The cytoskeleton directs a different type of morphogenetic movement in promoting elongation of the archenteron in the sea urchin embryo (see Figure 47.8). In this case, cytoskeletal changes direct **convergent extension**, a rearrangement of the cells of a tissue layer that causes the sheet to become narrower (converge) while it becomes longer (extends). It is as if a crowd of people waiting to enter a theatre for a concert began to form a single-file

▶ Figure 47.17 **Convergent extension of a sheet of cells.** In this simplified diagram, the cells elongate in a particular direction and crawl between each other (convergence) as the sheet becomes longer and narrower (extension).

Source: Adaptation from figure 1.9 and Box 8c from *Principles of Development,* 4th edition, by Lewis Wolpert. Copyright © 2011 by Oxford University Press. Reprinted with permission.

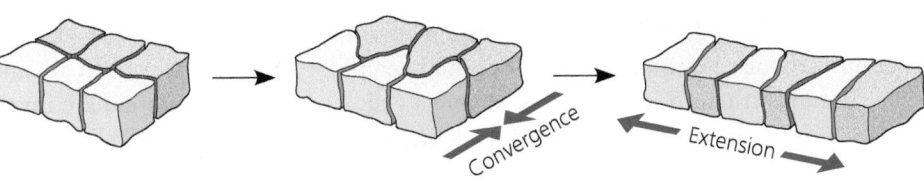

Convergence

Extension

line; the line would become much longer as it narrowed. In the embryo, the cells elongate, with their ends pointing in the direction they will move, and they wedge between each other into fewer columns of cells (**Figure 47.17**). Convergent extension is also important in other developmental settings, such as involution in the frog gastrula. There, convergent extension changes the gastrulating embryo from a spherical shape to the rounded rectangular shape seen in Figure 47.14c.

Cell Migration

The cytoskeleton is responsible not only for cell shape changes but also for cell migration. Movement of cells within an embryo are directed by signalling factors called morphogens. These factors are secreted by cells, creating concentration gradients that a migrating cell follows to guide it toward its final destination within the embryo.

During organogenesis in vertebrates, cells from the neural crest and from somites migrate to locations throughout the embryo. Cells "crawl" within the embryo by using cytoskeletal fibres to extend and retract cellular protrusions. This type of motility is akin to the amoeboid movement described in Figure 6.26b. Transmembrane glycoproteins called *cell adhesion molecules* play a key role in cell migration by promoting interaction between pairs of cells.

Cell migration also involves the *extracellular matrix (ECM)*, the meshwork of secreted glycoproteins and other macromolecules lying outside the plasma membranes of cells (see Figure 6.28). The ECM helps to guide cells in many types of movements, such as migration of individual cells and shape changes of cell sheets. Cells that line migration pathways regulate movement of migrating cells by secreting specific molecules into the ECM.

Programmed Cell Death

Just as certain cells of the embryo are programmed to change shape or location, others are programmed to die. A type of *programmed cell death* called **apoptosis** is in fact a common feature of animal development. At various times in development, individual cells, sets of cells, or whole tissues cease to develop and are engulfed by neighbouring cells. In some cases, a structure functions in a larval or other immature form of the organism and then is eliminated during later development. One familiar example is provided by the cells in the tail of a tadpole, which undergo apoptosis during frog metamorphosis (see Figure 45.15).

Apoptosis can also occur when cells compete with one another for survival. For instance, many more neurons are produced during development of the vertebrate nervous system than exist in the adult. In general, neurons survive if they make functional connections with other neurons and die if they do not.

Some cells that undergo apoptosis don't seem to have any function in the developing embryo. Why do such cells form? The answer can be found by considering the evolution of amphibians, birds, and mammals. When these groups began to diverge during evolution, the developmental program for making a vertebrate body was already in place. The differences in present-day body forms arose through modification of that common developmental program (which is why the early embryos of all vertebrates look so similar). As these groups evolved, many structures produced by the ancestral program that no longer offered a selective advantage were targeted for cell death. For example, the shared developmental program generates webbing between the embryonic digits, but in many birds and mammals the webbing is eliminated by apoptosis (see Figure 11.21).

As you have seen, cell behaviour and the molecular mechanisms underlying it are crucial to the morphogenesis of the embryo. In the next section, you'll learn that a shared set of cellular and genetic processes ensure that the various types of cells end up in the right places in each embryo.

CONCEPT CHECK 47.2

1. In the frog embryo, convergent extension elongates the notochord. Explain how the words *convergent* and *extension* apply to this process.

2. **WHAT IF?** Predict what would happen if, just before neural tube formation, you treated embryos with a drug that blocks the function of microfilaments.

3. **MAKE CONNECTIONS** Unlike some other types of birth defects, neural tube defects are largely preventable. Explain (see Concept 41.1).

For suggested answers, see Appendix A.

CONCEPT 47.3

Cytoplasmic determinants and inductive signals contribute to cell fate specification

During embryonic development, cells arise by division, take up particular locations in the body, and become specialized in structure and function. Where a cell resides, how it appears, and what it does define its fate

in development. Developmental biologists use the terms **determination** to refer to the process by which a cell or group of cells becomes committed to a particular fate and **differentiation** to refer to the resulting specialization in structure and function.

Every diploid cell formed during an animal's development has the same genome. With the exception of certain mature immune cells, the collection of genes present is the same throughout the cell's life. How, then, do cells acquire different fates? As discussed in Concept 18.4, particular tissues, and often cells within a tissue, differ from one another by expressing distinct sets of genes from their shared genome.

A major focus of developmental biology is to uncover the mechanisms that direct the differences in gene expression underlying developmental fates. As one step toward this goal, scientists often seek to trace tissues and cell types back to their origins in the early embryo.

Fate Mapping

One way to trace the ancestry of embryonic cells is direct observation through the microscope. Such studies produced the first **fate maps**, diagrams showing the structures arising from each region of an embryo. In the 1920s, German embryologist Walther Vogt used this approach to determine where groups of cells from the blastula end up in the gastrula (Figure 47.18a). Later researchers developed techniques that allowed them to mark an individual blastomere during cleavage and then follow the marker as it was distributed to all the mitotic descendants of that cell (Figure 47.18b).

A much more comprehensive approach to fate mapping has been carried out on the soil-dwelling nematode *Caenorhabditis elegans*. This roundworm is about 1 mm long, has a simple, transparent body with only a few types of cells, and develops into a mature adult hermaphrodite in only 3½ days in the laboratory. These attributes allowed Sydney Brenner, Robert Horvitz, and John Sulston to determine the complete cell lineage of *C. elegans*. They found that every adult hermaphrodite has exactly 959 somatic cells, which arise from the fertilized egg in virtually the same way for every individual. Careful microscopic observations of worms at all stages of development, coupled with experiments in which particular cells or groups of cells were destroyed by a laser beam or through mutations, resulted in the cell lineage diagram shown in Figure 47.19.

As an example of a particular cell fate, we'll consider *germ cells*, the specialized cells that give rise to eggs or sperm. In all animals studied, complexes of RNA and protein are involved in the specification of germ cell fate. In *C. elegans*, such complexes, called *P granules*, persist

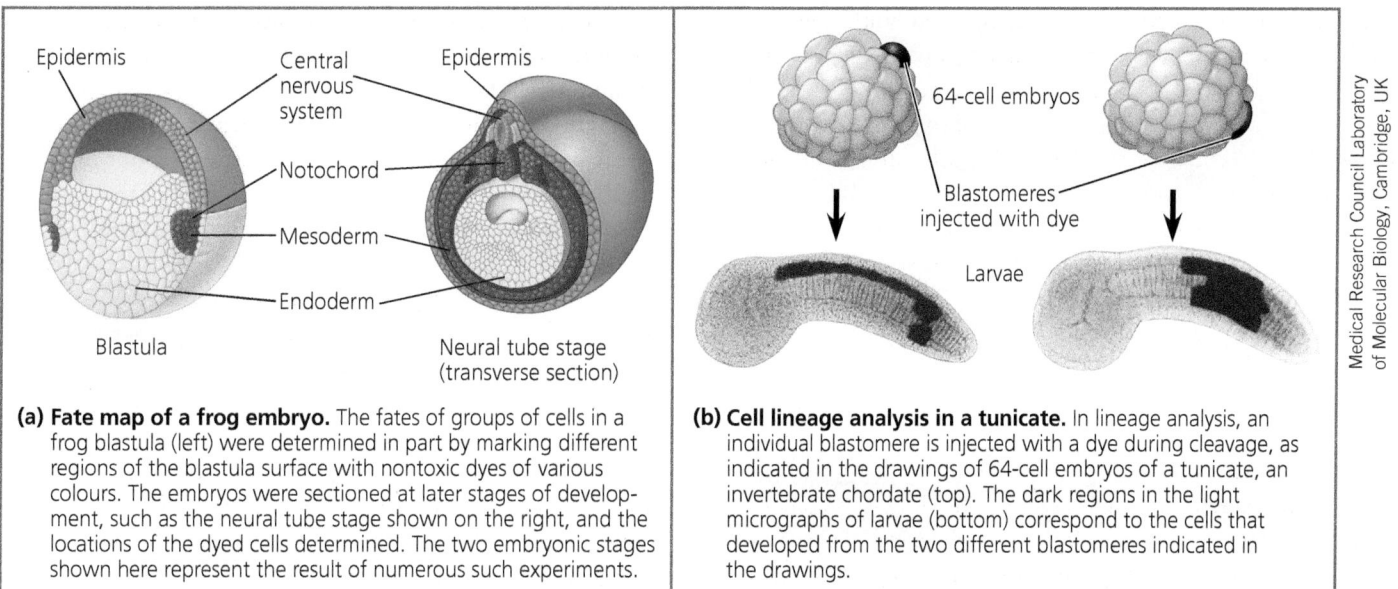

(a) **Fate map of a frog embryo.** The fates of groups of cells in a frog blastula (left) were determined in part by marking different regions of the blastula surface with nontoxic dyes of various colours. The embryos were sectioned at later stages of development, such as the neural tube stage shown on the right, and the locations of the dyed cells determined. The two embryonic stages shown here represent the result of numerous such experiments.

(b) **Cell lineage analysis in a tunicate.** In lineage analysis, an individual blastomere is injected with a dye during cleavage, as indicated in the drawings of 64-cell embryos of a tunicate, an invertebrate chordate (top). The dark regions in the light micrographs of larvae (bottom) correspond to the cells that developed from the two different blastomeres indicated in the drawings.

▲ Figure 47.18 **Fate mapping for two chordates.**

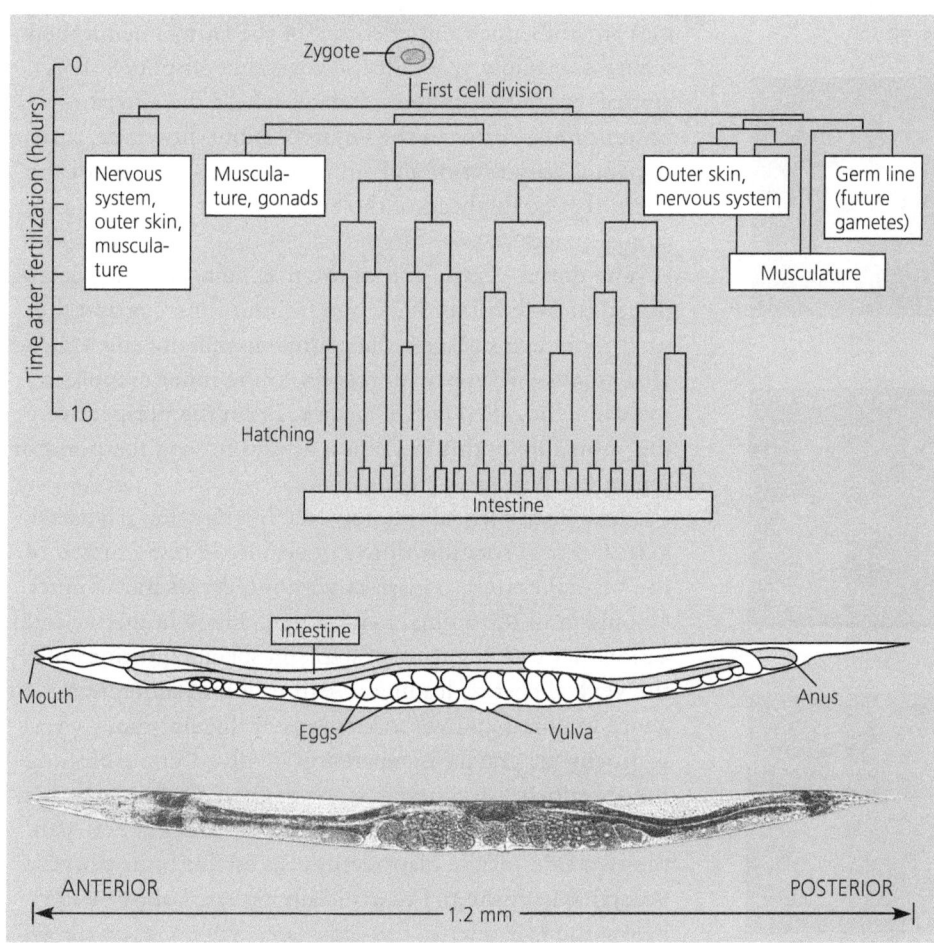

▲ Figure 47.19 **Cell lineage in *Caenorhabditis elegans*.** The *C. elegans* embryo is transparent, making it possible for researchers to trace the lineage of every cell, from the zygote to the adult worm (LM). The diagram shows a detailed lineage only for the intestine, which is derived exclusively from one of the first four cells formed from the zygote. The eggs will be fertilized internally and released through the vulva.

Source: Based on Adaptation of figure 21.17 from *Molecular Biology of the Cell,* 4th edition, by Bruce Alberts et al. Copyright © 2002 by Garland Science/Taylor & Francis LLC.

throughout development and can be detected in the germ cells of the adult gonad (Figure 47.20).

Tracing the position of the P granules provides a dramatic illustration of cell fate specification during development. The P granules are distributed throughout the newly fertilized egg but move to the posterior end of the zygote before the first cleavage division (Figure 47.21 ❶ and ❷). As a result, only the posterior of the two cells formed by the first division contains P granules (Figure 47.21 ❸). The P granules continue to be asymmetrically partitioned during subsequent divisions (Figure 47.21 ❹). Thus, the P granules act as cytoplasmic determinants (see Concept 18.4), fixing germ cell fate at the earliest stage of *C. elegans* development.

Fate mapping in *C. elegans* paved the way for major discoveries about programmed cell death. Lineage analysis demonstrated that exactly 131 cells die during normal *C. elegans* development. In the 1980s, researchers found that a mutation inactivating a single gene allows all 131 cells to live. Further research revealed that this gene is part of a pathway that controls and carries out apoptosis in a wide range of animals, including humans. In

100 μm

▲ Figure 47.20 **Determination of germ cell fate in *C. elegans*.** Labelling with an antibody specific for a *C. elegans* P granule protein (green) reveals the specific incorporation of P granules into the cells of the adult worm that will produce sperm or eggs.

20 μm

❶ Newly fertilized egg

❷ Zygote prior to first division

❸ Two-cell embryo

❹ Four-cell embryo

▲ Figure 47.21 **Partitioning of P granules during *C. elegans* development.** The differential interference contrast micrographs (left) highlight the boundaries of nuclei and cells through the first two cell divisions. The immunofluorescence micrographs (right) show identically staged embryos stained with a labelling antibody specific for a P granule protein.

2002, Brenner, Horvitz, and Sulston shared a Nobel Prize for their use of the *C. elegans* fate map in studies of programmed cell death and organogenesis.

Having established fate maps for early development, scientists were positioned to answer questions about underlying mechanisms, such as how the basic axes of the embryo are established, a process known as axis formation.

Axis Formation

A body plan with bilateral symmetry is found across a range of animals, including nematodes, echinoderms, and vertebrates (see Chapter 32). As shown for a frog tadpole in **Figure 47.22a**, this body plan exhibits asymmetry along the dorsal-ventral and anterior-posterior axes. The right-left axis is largely symmetrical, as the two sides are roughly mirror images of each other. These three body axes are established early in development.

The anterior-posterior axis of the frog embryo is determined during oogenesis. Asymmetry is apparent in the formation of two distinct hemispheres: Dark melanin granules are embedded in the cortex of the animal hemisphere, whereas a yellow yolk fills the vegetal hemisphere. This animal-vegetal asymmetry dictates where the anterior-posterior axis forms in the embryo. Note, however, that the anterior-posterior and animal-vegetal axes are not the same; that is, the head of the embryo does not form at the animal pole.

The dorsal-ventral axis of the frog embryo is not determined until fertilization. Upon fusion of the egg and the sperm, the egg surface—the plasma membrane and associated cortex—rotates with respect to the inner cytoplasm, a movement called *cortical rotation*. From the perspective of the animal pole, this rotation is always toward the point of sperm entry (**Figure 47.22b**).

How does cortical rotation establish the dorsal-ventral axis? Cortical rotation allows molecules in one portion of the vegetal cortex to interact with molecules in the inner cytoplasm of the animal hemisphere. These inductive interactions activate regulatory factors in specific portions of the vegetal cortex, leading to expression of different sets of genes in dorsal and ventral regions of the embryo.

In chicks, gravity is apparently involved in establishing the anterior-posterior axis as the egg travels down the hen's oviduct before being laid. Later, pH differences between the two sides of the blastoderm cells establish the dorsal-ventral axis. If the pH is artificially reversed above and below the blastoderm, the cells' fates will be reversed: The side facing the egg white will become the ventral part of the embryo, whereas the side facing the yolk will become the dorsal part.

In mammals, no polarity is obvious until after cleavage. However, the results of recent experiments suggest that the orientation of the egg and sperm nuclei before they

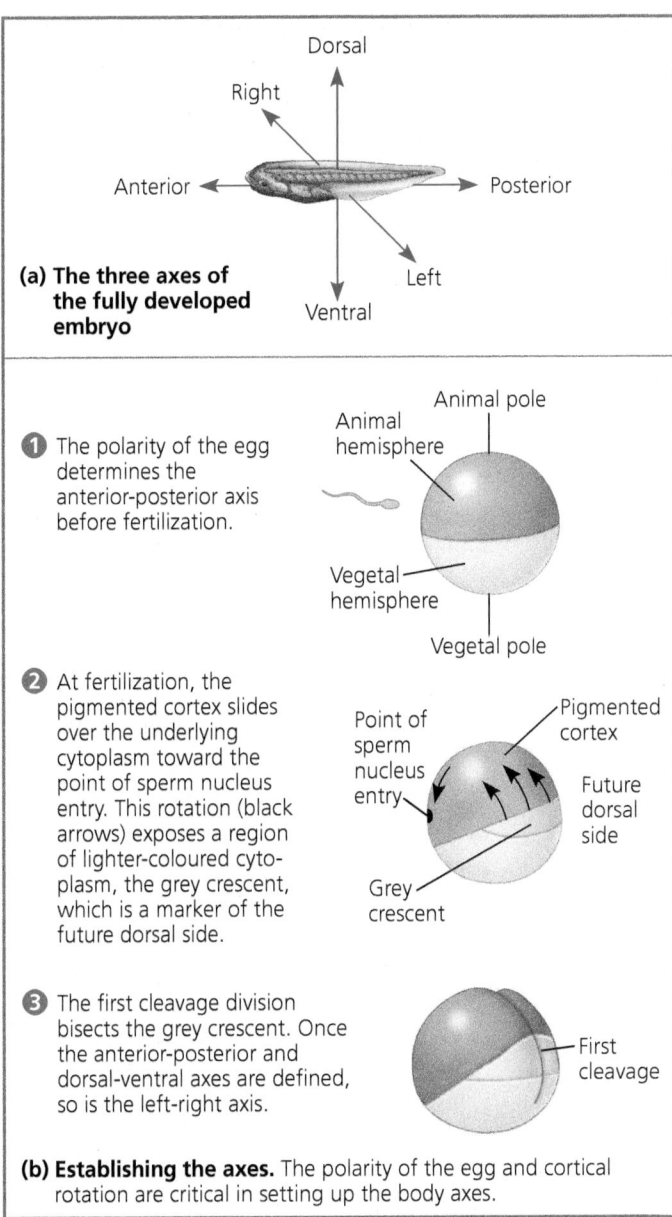

(a) The three axes of the fully developed embryo

Dorsal

Right

Anterior

Posterior

Left

Ventral

❶ The polarity of the egg determines the anterior-posterior axis before fertilization.

Animal pole

Animal hemisphere

Vegetal hemisphere

Vegetal pole

❷ At fertilization, the pigmented cortex slides over the underlying cytoplasm toward the point of sperm nucleus entry. This rotation (black arrows) exposes a region of lighter-coloured cytoplasm, the grey crescent, which is a marker of the future dorsal side.

Point of sperm nucleus entry

Pigmented cortex

Future dorsal side

Grey crescent

❸ The first cleavage division bisects the grey crescent. Once the anterior-posterior and dorsal-ventral axes are defined, so is the left-right axis.

First cleavage

(b) Establishing the axes. The polarity of the egg and cortical rotation are critical in setting up the body axes.

▲ **Figure 47.22 The body axes and their establishment in an amphibian.** All three axes are established before the zygote begins to undergo cleavage.

WHAT IF? *To study axis establishment, researchers can block cortical rotation or force it to occur in a specific direction. One such study resulted in a two-headed embryo because the "back" developed on both sides. What do you think the researchers did to obtain such an embryo?*

fuse influences the location of the first cleavage plane and thus may play a role in establishing the embryonic axes. In insects, morphogen gradients establish both the anterior-posterior and dorsal-ventral axes (see Chapter 18).

Once the anterior-posterior and dorsal-ventral axes are established, the position of the left-right axis is fixed. Nevertheless, specific molecular mechanisms must establish which side is left and which is right. In vertebrates, there are marked left-right differences in the location of internal organs as well as in the organization and structure of the

heart and brain. Recent research has revealed that cilia are involved in setting up this left-right asymmetry. We will discuss this and other developmental roles of cilia at the end of this chapter.

Restricting Developmental Potential

Earlier we described determination in terms of commitment to a particular cell fate. Is cell fate commitment immediately irreversible, or is there a period of time during which cell fate can be modified? The German zoologist Hans Spemann addressed this question in 1938. By manipulating embryos to perturb normal development and then examining cell fate after the manipulation, he was able to assay a cell's *developmental potential*, the range of structures to which it can give rise (Figure 47.23). Spemann found that the fates of embryonic cells are affected by both the distribution of determinants and the pattern of cleavage relative to this distribution. Furthermore, the work of Spemann and others demonstrated that the first two blastomeres of the frog embryo are **totipotent**, meaning that they can each develop into all the different cell types of that species.

In mammals, embryonic cells remain totipotent through the eight-cell stage, much longer than in many other animals. Recent work, however, indicates that the very early cells (even the first two) are not actually equivalent in a normal embryo. Rather, their totipotency when isolated likely means that the cells can regulate their fate in response to their embryonic environment. Once the 16-cell stage is reached, mammalian cells are determined to form the trophoblast or the inner cell mass. Although the cells have a limited developmental potential from this point onward, their nuclei remain totipotent, as demonstrated in cloning experiments.

As you learned in Chapter 46, identical (monozygotic) twins can develop when embryonic cells become separated. If the separation occurs before the trophoblast and inner cell mass become differentiated, two embryos grow, each with its own chorion and amnion. This is the case for about a third of identical twins. For the rest, the two embryos that develop share a chorion and, in very rare cases where separation is particularly late, an amnion as well.

Regardless of how uniform or varied early embryonic cells are in a particular species, the progressive restriction of developmental potential is a general feature of development in all animals. In general, the tissue-specific fates of cells are fixed in a late gastrula, but not always so in an early gastrula. For example, if the dorsal ectoderm of an early amphibian gastrula is experimentally replaced with ectoderm from some other location in the same gastrula, the transplanted tissue forms a neural plate. But if the same experiment is performed on a late-stage gastrula, the transplanted ectoderm does not respond to its new environment and does not form a neural plate.

Inquiry

How does distribution of the grey crescent affect the developmental potential of the first two daughter cells?

Experiment Hans Spemann, at the University of Freiburg-im-Breisgau, in Germany, carried out the following experiment in 1938 to test whether substances were located asymmetrically in the grey crescent.

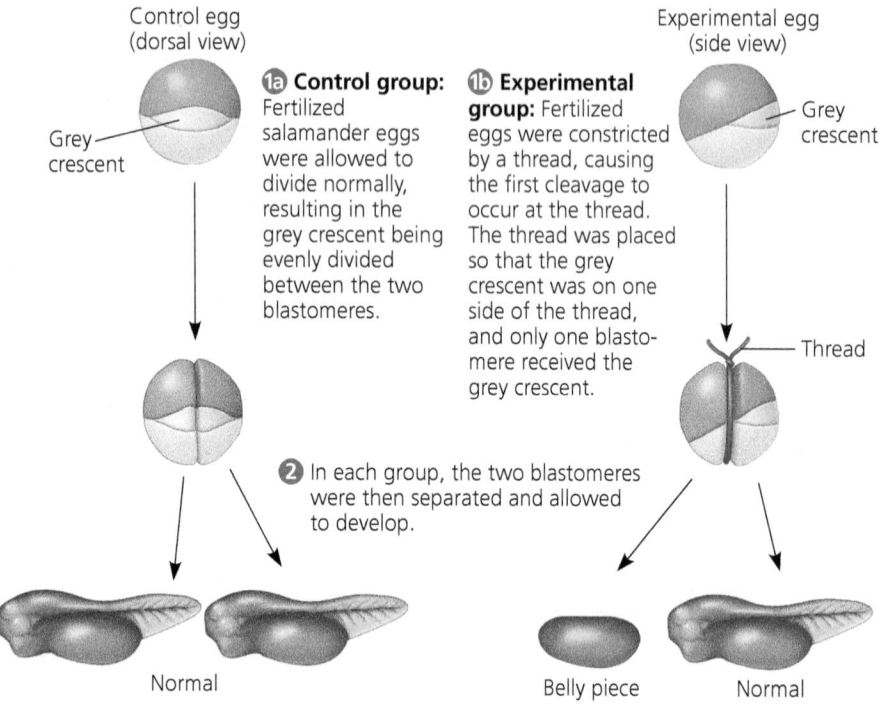

1a Control group: Fertilized salamander eggs were allowed to divide normally, resulting in the grey crescent being evenly divided between the two blastomeres.

1b Experimental group: Fertilized eggs were constricted by a thread, causing the first cleavage to occur at the thread. The thread was placed so that the grey crescent was on one side of the thread, and only one blastomere received the grey crescent.

2 In each group, the two blastomeres were then separated and allowed to develop.

Control egg (dorsal view) — Grey crescent

Experimental egg (side view) — Grey crescent — Thread

Normal   Belly piece   Normal

Results Blastomeres that received half or all of the material in the grey crescent developed into normal embryos, but a blastomere that received none of the grey crescent gave rise to an abnormal embryo without dorsal structures. Spemann called it a "belly piece."

Conclusion The developmental potential of the two blastomeres normally formed during the first cleavage division depends on their acquisition of cytoplasmic determinants localized in the grey crescent.

Source: Based on H. Spemann, *Embryonic Development and Induction*, Yale University Press, New Haven, CT (1938). © Jane B Reece.

WHAT IF? *In a similar experiment 40 years earlier, embryologist Wilhelm Roux allowed the first cleavage to occur and then used a needle to kill just one blastomere. The embryo that developed from the remaining blastomere (plus remnants of the dead cell) was abnormal, resembling a half-embryo. Propose a hypothesis to explain why Roux's result differed from the control result in Spemann's experiment.*

Cell Fate Determination and Pattern Formation by Inductive Signals

As embryonic cells acquire distinct fates, the cells begin to influence each other's fates by induction. At the molecular level, the response to an inductive signal is usually to switch on a set of genes that make the receiving cells differentiate into a specific tissue. Here we will examine two examples of induction, an essential process in the development of many tissues in most animals.

The "Organizer" of Spemann and Mangold

Before his studies of totipotency in the fertilized frog egg, Spemann had investigated cell fate determination during gastrulation. In these experiments, he and his student Hilde Mangold transplanted tissues between early gastrulas. In their most famous such experiment, summarized in **Figure 47.24**, they made a remarkable discovery. Not only did a transplanted dorsal lip of the blastopore continue to be a blastopore lip, but it also triggered gastrulation of the surrounding tissue. They concluded that the dorsal lip of the blastopore in the early gastrula functions as an "organizer" of the embryo's body plan, inducing changes in surrounding tissue that direct formation of the notochord, the neural tube, and other organs.

Nearly a century later, developmental biologists are still actively studying the basis of induction by *Spemann's organizer*. An important clue has come from studies of a growth factor called bone morphogenetic protein 4 (BMP-4). (Bone morphogenetic proteins, a family of related proteins with a variety of developmental roles, derive their name from members of the family that are important in bone formation.) One major function of the cells of the organizer seems to be to *inactivate* BMP-4 on the dorsal side of the embryo. Inactivation of BMP-4 allows cells on the dorsal side to make dorsal structures, such as the notochord and neural tube. Proteins related to BMP-4 and its inhibitors are also found in other animals, including invertebrates such as the fruit fly, where they also regulate the dorsal-ventral axis.

Formation of the Vertebrate Limb

Inductive signals play a major role in **pattern formation**, the development of an animal's spatial organization, the arrangement of organs and tissues in their characteristic places in three-dimensional space. The molecular cues that control pattern formation, called **positional information**, tell a cell where it is with respect to the animal's body axes and help to determine how the cell and its descendants will respond to molecular signalling.

In Chapter 18, we discussed pattern formation in the development of *Drosophila*. For the study of pattern formation in vertebrates, a classic model system has been limb development in the chick. The wings and legs of chicks, like

Inquiry

Can the dorsal lip of the blastopore induce cells in another part of the amphibian embryo to change their developmental fate?

Experiment In 1924, Hans Spemann and Hilde Mangold, at the University of Freiburg-im-Breisgau, in Germany, transplanted a piece of the dorsal lip from a pigmented newt gastrula to the ventral side of a nonpigmented newt gastrula to investigate the inductive ability of the dorsal lip. Cross sections of the gastrulas are shown here.

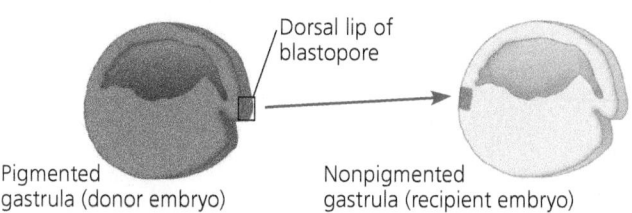

Pigmented gastrula (donor embryo) → Nonpigmented gastrula (recipient embryo)

Results The recipient embryo formed a second notochord and neural tube in the region of the transplant, and eventually most of a second embryo developed. Examination of the interior of the double embryo revealed that the secondary structures were formed partly, but not wholly, from recipient tissue.

Primary embryo → Secondary (induced) embryo

Primary structures:
— Neural tube
— Notochord

Secondary structures:
— Notochord (pigmented cells)
— Neural tube (mostly nonpigmented cells)

Conclusion The transplanted dorsal lip was able to induce cells in a different region of the recipient to form structures different from their normal fate. In effect, the transplanted dorsal lip "organized" the later development of an entire extra embryo.

Source: Top figure, Adaptation from figure 1.9 and Box 8c from Principles of Development, 4th edition, by Lewis Wolpert. Copyright © 2011 by Oxford University Press. Reprinted with permission; Bottom figure, Adaptation of Figure 15.12 from Developmental Biology by Scott F. Gilbert. Copyright © 1997 by Sinauer Associates, Inc. Reprinted with permission.

WHAT IF? *Because the transplanted dorsal lip caused the recipient tissue to become something it would not otherwise have become, a signal of some sort must have passed from the dorsal lip. If you identified a protein candidate for the signalling molecule, how could you test whether it actually functions in signalling?*

---

all vertebrate limbs, begin as limb buds, bumps of mesodermal tissue covered by a layer of ectoderm (**Figure 47.25a**). Each component of a chick limb, such as a specific bone or muscle, develops with a precise location and orientation

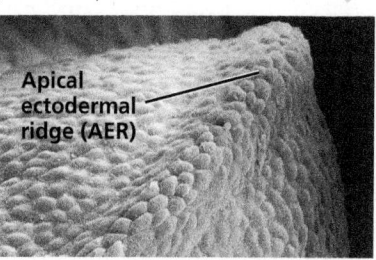

(a) Organizer regions. Vertebrate limbs develop from protrusions called limb buds, each consisting of mesoderm cells covered by a layer of ectoderm. Two regions in each limb bud, the apical ectodermal ridge (AER, shown in this SEM) and the zone of polarizing activity (ZPA), play key roles as organizers in limb pattern formation.

Apical ectodermal ridge (AER)

Kathryn W. Tosney, University of Michigan

(b) Wing of chick embryo. As the bud develops into a limb, a specific pattern of tissues emerges. In the chick wing, for example, the digits are always present in the arrangement shown here. Pattern formation requires each embryonic cell to receive some kind of positional information indicating location along the three axes of the limb. The AER and ZPA secrete molecules that help provide this information. (Numbers are assigned to the digits based on a convention established for vertebrate limbs. The chicken wing has only four digits; the first digit points backward and is not shown in the diagram.)

▲ Figure 47.25 **Vertebrate limb development.**

relative to three axes: the proximal-distal axis (the "shoulder-to-fingertip" axis), the anterior-posterior axis (the "thumb-to-little finger" axis), and the dorsal-ventral axis (the "knuckle-to-palm" axis). The embryonic cells within a limb bud respond to positional information indicating location along these three axes (**Figure 47.25b**).

Two regions in a limb bud have profound effects on the limb's development. These regions are present in all vertebrate limb buds, including those that will develop into forelimbs (such as wings or arms) and those destined to become hind limbs. The cells of these regions secrete proteins that provide key positional information to the other cells of the bud.

One region regulating limb-bud development is the **apical ectodermal ridge (AER)**, a thickened area of ectoderm at the tip of the bud (see Figure 47.25a). Removing the AER blocks outgrowth of the limb along the proximal-distal axis. The cells of the AER secrete several protein signals in the fibroblast growth factor (FGF) family that promote limb-bud outgrowth. If the AER is surgically removed and beads soaked with FGF are put in its place, a nearly normal limb will develop. In 2006, researchers identified an FGF-secreting AER that appears to be responsible for building a shark's unpaired (median) fins. This finding suggests that the specific function of the AER predated the appearance of paired limbs in the vertebrate lineage.

The second major limb-bud regulatory region is the **zone of polarizing activity (ZPA)**, a block of mesodermal tissue located underneath the ectoderm where the posterior aspect of the bud is attached to the body (see Figure 47.25a). The ZPA is necessary for proper pattern formation along the anterior-posterior axis of the limb. Cells nearest the ZPA give rise to the posterior structures, such as the most posterior of the chick's three digits (positioned like our little finger); cells farthest from the ZPA form anterior structures, including the most anterior digit (like our thumb).

The tissue transplantation experiment outlined in Figure 47.26 supports the hypothesis that the inductive signal produced by the ZPA conveys positional information indicating "posterior." Indeed, researchers have discovered that the cells of the ZPA secrete a growth factor called Sonic hedgehog. (Sonic hedgehog gets its name from two sources: its similarity to a *Drosophila* protein called Hedgehog, which is involved in segmentation of the fly embryo, and a video game character.) If cells genetically engineered to produce large amounts of Sonic hedgehog are implanted in the anterior region of a normal limb bud, a mirror-image limb results—just as if a ZPA had been grafted there. Studies of the mouse version of Sonic hedgehog suggest that extra toes in mice—and perhaps also in humans—can result when this protein is produced in part of the limb bud where it is normally absent. Sonic hedgehog and other similar Hedgehog proteins function in many developmental settings and organisms, including pattern formation in *Drosophila* and regulation of cell fate and number in the vertebrate nervous system.

Signalling by Sonic hedgehog plays a vital role in limb-bud development, but what determines whether a limb bud develops into a forelimb or a hind limb? It turns out that the cells receiving the Hedgehog signals from the

Inquiry

What role does the zone of polarizing activity (ZPA) play in limb pattern formation in vertebrates?

Experiment In 1985, Dennis Summerbell and Lawrence Honig, then at the National Institute for Medical Research in Mill Hill, near London, U.K., were eager to investigate the nature of the zone of polarizing activity. They transplanted ZPA tissue from a donor chick embryo under the ectoderm in the anterior margin of a limb bud in another chick (the host).

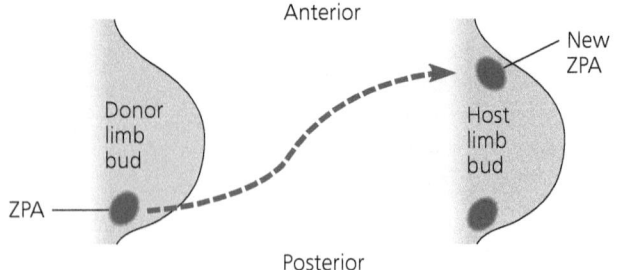

Results The host limb bud developed extra digits from host tissue in a mirror-image arrangement to the normal digits, which also formed (compare with Figure 47.25b, which shows a normal chick wing).

Conclusion The mirror-image duplication observed in this experiment suggests that ZPA cells secrete a signal that diffuses from its source and conveys positional information indicating "posterior." As the distance from the ZPA increases, the signal concentration decreases, and hence more anterior digits develop.

Source: Based on L. S. Honig and D. Summerbell, Maps of strength of positional signalling activity in the developing chick wing bud, *Journal of Embryology and Experimental Morphology* 87:163–174 (1985). © Jane B Reece.

WHAT IF? *Suppose you learned that the ZPA forms after the AER, leading you to develop the hypothesis that the AER is necessary for formation of the ZPA. Given what you know about molecules expressed in the AER and ZPA (see the text), how could you test your hypothesis?*

AER and ZPA respond according to their developmental histories. Before the AER or ZPA issues its signals, earlier developmental signalling sets up specific spatial patterns of *Hox* gene expression (see Figure 21.20). Differences in *Hox* gene expression cause cells of the forelimb and hind limb buds—and cells in different parts of each limb bud—to react differently to the same positional cues.

Hedgehog, FGF, and BMP-4 are examples of a much larger set of signalling molecules that govern cell fates in animals. Having mapped out many of the basic functions of these molecules in embryonic development, researchers are now addressing their role in organogenesis, focusing in particular on the development of the brain.

Cilia and Cell Fate?

For many years, developmental biologists largely ignored the cellular organelles known as cilia. That is no longer the case. There is now good experimental evidence that ciliary function is essential for proper specification of cell fate in the human embryo.

Like other mammals, humans have stationary and motile cilia (see Figure 6.24). Stationary primary cilia, or *monocilia*, exist as a single projection on the surface of nearly all cells. Motile cilia are found on cells that propel fluid over their surface, such as the epithelial cells of airways, and on sperm (in the form of flagella that propel sperm movement). Both stationary and motile cilia play vital roles in development.

In 2003, geneticists discovered that certain mutations disrupting development of the mouse nervous system affect genes that function in the assembly of monocilia. Other researchers found that mutations responsible for a severe kidney disease in mice alter a gene important for the transport of materials up and down monocilia. Mutations that block the function of monocilia have also been linked to cystic kidney disease in humans.

Given that monocilia are stationary, how do they function in development? The answer is that each acts as an antenna on the cell surface, receiving signals from multiple signalling proteins, including Sonic hedgehog. When the monocilia are defective, signalling is disrupted.

Research on the role of motile cilia in development grew from the observation that certain individuals share a particular set of medical conditions, later named Kartagener's syndrome. Such individuals are prone to infections of the nasal sinuses and bronchi. Males with Kartagener's syndrome also produce immotile sperm. But the most intriguing feature of this syndrome is *situs inversus*, a reversal of the normal left-right asymmetry of the organs in the chest and abdomen (Figure 47.27). For example, in situs inversus, the heart is on the right side rather than the left. (About one in 10 000 individuals have situs inversus, which causes no significant medical problems by itself.)

The conditions associated with Kartagener's syndrome all result from a defect that makes cilia immotile. Without motility, sperm tails cannot beat and airway cells cannot sweep mucus and microbes out of the airway. But what causes situs inversus in these individuals? The current model proposes that ciliary motion in a particular part of the embryo

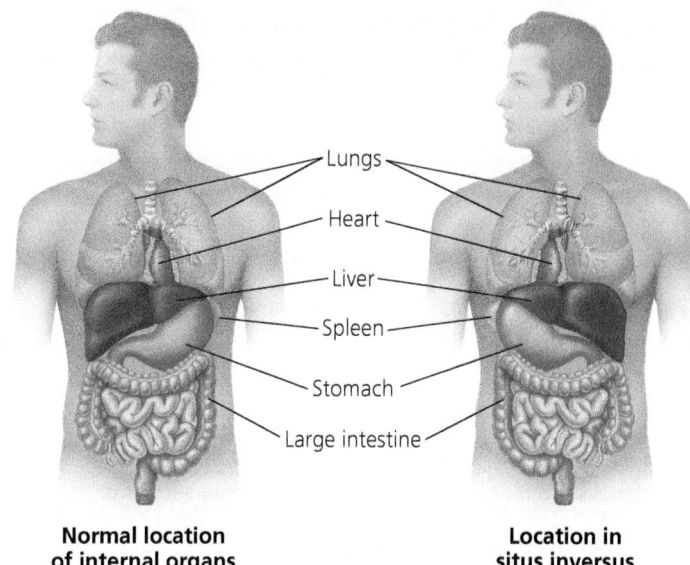

Normal location of internal organs	Location in situs inversus

▲ Figure 47.27 **Situs inversus, a reversal of normal left-right asymmetry in the chest and abdomen.**

Source. Figure adapted from *Human Anatomy and Physiology*, 8th edition, by Elaine N. Marieb and Katja Hoehn. Copyright © 2010 by Pearson Education, Inc. Adapted and electronically reproduced by permission of Pearson Education, Inc., Upper Saddle River, New Jersey.

is essential for normal development. Evidence indicates that movement of the cilia generates a leftward fluid flow, breaking the symmetry between left and right sides. Without that flow, asymmetry along the left-right axis arises randomly, and half of the affected embryos develop situs inversus.

If we step back from the specification of particular cell fates to consider development as a whole, we see a sequence of events marked by cycles of signalling and differentiation. Initial cell asymmetries allow different types of cells to influence each other, resulting in the expression of specific sets of genes. The products of these genes then direct cells to differentiate into specific types. Through pattern formation and morphogenesis, differentiated cells ultimately produce a complex arrangement of tissues and organs, each functioning in its appropriate location and in coordination with other cells, tissues, and organs throughout the organism.

CONCEPT CHECK 47.3

1. How do axis formation and pattern formation differ?

2. **MAKE CONNECTIONS** How does a morphogen gradient differ from cytoplasmic determinants and inductive interactions with regard to the set of cells it affects (see Concept 18.4)?

3. **WHAT IF?** If the ventral cells of an early frog gastrula are experimentally induced to express large amounts of a protein that inhibits BMP-4, could a second embryo develop? Explain.

4. **WHAT IF?** If you removed the ZPA from a limb bud and then placed a bead soaked in Sonic hedgehog in the middle of the limb bud, what would be the most likely result?

For suggested answers, see Appendix A.

47 Chapter Review

Go to **MasteringBiology®** for Assignments, the eText, and the Study Area with Animations, Activities, Vocab Self-Quiz, and Practice Tests.

SUMMARY OF KEY CONCEPTS

CONCEPT 47.1

Fertilization and cleavage initiate embryonic development (pp. 1096–1102)

- **Fertilization** brings together the nuclei of sperm and egg, forming a diploid zygote, and activates the egg, initiating embryonic development. The **acrosomal reaction**, which is triggered when the sperm meets the egg, releases hydrolytic enzymes that digest material surrounding the egg. Gamete contact and/or fusion depolarizes the egg cell membrane and sets up a **fast block to polyspermy** in many animals. Sperm-egg fusion also initiates the cortical reaction.

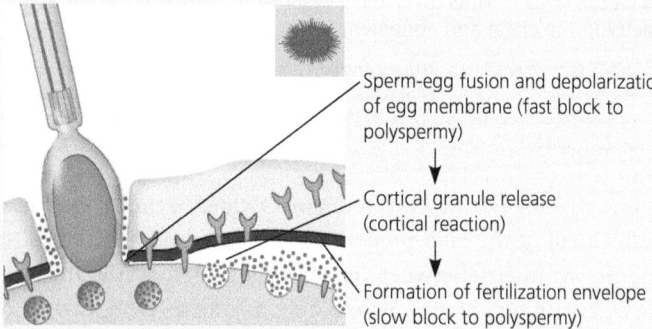

Sperm-egg fusion and depolarization of egg membrane (fast block to polyspermy)

↓

Cortical granule release (cortical reaction)

↓

Formation of fertilization envelope (slow block to polyspermy)

In mammalian fertilization, the cortical reaction modifies the zona pellucida as a **slow block to polyspermy**.

- Fertilization is followed by **cleavage**, a period of rapid cell division without growth, which results in the production of a large number of cells called **blastomeres**. In many species, cleavage creates a multicellular ball called the **blastula**, which contains a fluid-filled cavity, the **blastocoel**. **Holoblastic** cleavage (division of the entire egg) occurs in species whose eggs have little or moderate amounts of **yolk** (as in sea urchins, frogs, and mammals). **Meroblastic** cleavage (incomplete division of the egg) occurs in species with yolk-rich eggs (as in birds and other reptiles)

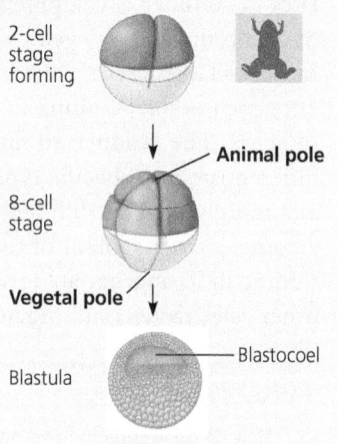

2-cell stage forming

Animal pole

8-cell stage

Vegetal pole

Blastula

Blastocoel

? *What cell-surface barrier prevents fertilization of an egg by a sperm of a different species?*

CONCEPT 47.2

Morphogenesis in animals involves specific changes in cell shape, position, and survival (pp. 1102–1110)

- **Gastrulation** converts the blastula to a **gastrula**, which has a primitive digestive cavity and three **germ layers**: ectoderm (blue), mesoderm (red), and endoderm (yellow).

- Mammalian eggs are small, store few nutrients, exhibit holoblastic cleavage, and show no obvious polarity. However, gastrulation and organogenesis in mammals resemble the processes in birds and other reptiles. After fertilization and early cleavage in the oviduct, the **blastocyst** implants in the uterus. The **trophoblast** initiates formation of the fetal portion of the placenta, and the embryo proper develops from a single layer of cells, the epiblast, within the blastocyst.

- The embryos of birds, other reptiles, and mammals develop within a fluid-filled sac that is contained within a shell or the uterus. In these organisms, the three germ layers give rise not only to embryonic tissue but also to the four **extraembryonic membranes**: the amnion, chorion, yolk sac, and allantois.

- The organs of the animal body develop from specific portions of the three embryonic germ layers. Early events in **organogenesis** in vertebrates include neurulation: formation of the **notochord** by cells of the dorsal mesoderm and development of the **neural tube** from infolding of the ectodermal neural plate.

Neural tube
Notochord
Coelom

Neural tube
Notochord
Coelom

- Cytoskeletal rearrangements are responsible for changes in the shape of cells that underlie cell movements in gastrulation and organogenesis, including invaginations and **convergent extension**. The cytoskeleton is also involved in cell migration, which relies on cell adhesion molecules and the extracellular matrix to help cells reach specific destinations.

? *How does the neural tube form? How do neural crest cells arise?*

CONCEPT 47.3

Cytoplasmic determinants and inductive signals contribute to cell fate specification (pp. 1110–1117)

- Experimentally derived **fate maps** of embryos show that specific regions of the zygote or blastula develop into specific parts of older embryos. The complete cell lineage has been worked out for *C. elegans*. Mechanisms for establishing cellular asymmetries include morphogen gradients, localized determinants, and inductive interactions. As embryonic development proceeds, the developmental potential of cells becomes progressively more limited in all species.

- Cells in a developing embryo receive and respond to **positional information** that varies with location. This information is often in the form of signalling molecules secreted by cells in specific regions of the embryo, such as the dorsal lip of the blastopore in the amphibian gastrula and the **apical ectodermal ridge** and **zone of polarizing activity** of the vertebrate limb bud. The signalling molecules influence gene expression in the cells that receive them, leading to **differentiation** and the development of particular structures.

? *Suppose you found two classes of mouse mutations, one that affected limb development only and one that affected both limb and kidney development. Which class would be more likely to alter the function of monocilia? Explain.*

TEST YOUR UNDERSTANDING

LEVEL 1: KNOWLEDGE/COMPREHENSION

1. The cortical reaction of sea urchin eggs functions directly in
   a. the formation of a fertilization envelope.
   b. the production of a fast block to polyspermy.
   c. the generation of an electrical impulse by the egg.
   d. the fusion of egg and sperm nuclei.

2. Which of the following is common to the development of both birds and mammals?
   a. holoblastic cleavage
   b. epiblast and hypoblast
   c. trophoblast
   d. grey crescent

3. The archenteron develops into
   a. the mesoderm.
   b. the endoderm.
   c. the placenta.
   d. the lumen of the digestive tract.

4. What structural adaptation in chickens allows them to lay their eggs in arid environments rather than in water?
   a. extraembryonic membranes
   b. yolk
   c. cleavage
   d. gastrulation

LEVEL 2: APPLICATION/ANALYSIS

5. In an egg cell treated with EDTA, a chemical that binds calcium and magnesium ions,
   a. the acrosomal reaction would be blocked.
   b. the fusion of sperm and egg nuclei would be blocked.
   c. the fast block to polyspermy would not occur.
   d. the fertilization envelope would not form.

6. In humans, identical twins are possible because
   a. extraembryonic cells interact with the zygote nucleus.
   b. convergent extension occurs.
   c. early blastomeres can form a complete embryo if isolated.
   d. the grey crescent divides the dorsal-ventral axis into new cells.

7. Cells transplanted from the neural tube of a frog embryo to the ventral part of another embryo develop into nervous system tissues. This result indicates that the transplanted cells were
   a. totipotent.
   b. determined.
   c. differentiated.
   d. mesenchymal.

8. **DRAW IT** Fill in the blanks in the figure below, and draw arrows showing the movement of ectoderm, mesoderm, and endoderm.

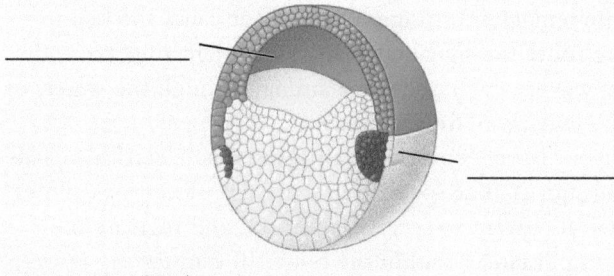

Species: _____

Stage: _____

LEVEL 3: SYNTHESIS/EVALUATION

9. **EVOLUTION CONNECTION**
   Evolution in insects and vertebrates has involved the repeated duplication of body segments, followed by fusion of some segments and specialization of their structure and function. What parts of vertebrate anatomy reflect the vertebrate segmentation pattern?

10. **SCIENTIFIC INQUIRY**
    The "snout" of a frog tadpole bears a sucker. A salamander tadpole has a mustache-shaped structure called a balancer in the same area. Suppose that you perform an experiment in which you transplant ectoderm from the side of a young salamander embryo to the snout of a frog embryo. The tadpole that develops has a balancer. When you transplant ectoderm from the side of a slightly older salamander embryo to the snout of a frog embryo, the frog tadpole ends up with a patch of salamander skin on its snout. Suggest a hypothesis to explain these results in terms of developmental mechanisms. How might you test your hypothesis?

11. **SCIENCE, TECHNOLOGY, AND SOCIETY**
    Many scientists think that fetal tissue transplants offer great potential for treating Parkinson's disease, epilepsy, diabetes, Alzheimer's disease, and spinal cord injuries. Why might tissues from a fetus be particularly useful for replacing diseased or damaged cells in patients with such conditions? Some people would allow only tissues from miscarriages to be used in fetal transplant research. However, most researchers prefer to use tissues from surgically aborted fetuses. Why? Explain your position on this controversial issue.

12. **WRITE ABOUT A THEME: ORGANIZATION**
    In a short essay (100–150 words), describe how the emergent properties of the cells of the gastrula direct embryonic development.

13. **SYNTHESIZE YOUR KNOWLEDGE**

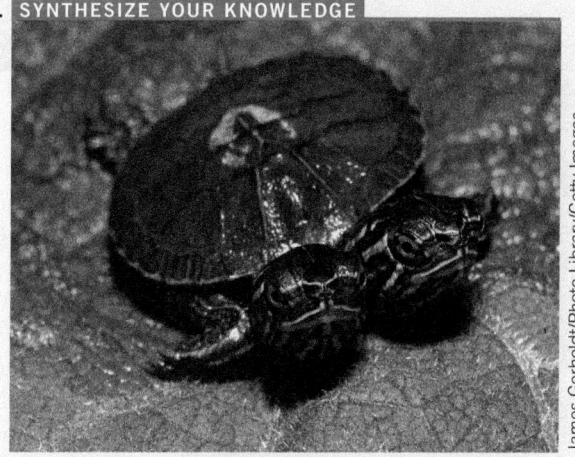

James Gerholdt/Photo Library/Getty Images

Occasionally, two-headed animals are born, such as this turtle. Thinking about the occurrence of identical twins and the property of totipotency, explain how this might occur.

For selected answers, see Appendix A.

48

Neurons, Synapses, and Signalling

KEY CONCEPTS

48.1 Neuron organization and structure reflect function in information transfer

48.2 Ion gradients and ion channels establish the resting membrane potential of a neuron

48.3 Action potentials are the signals conducted by axons

48.4 Neurons communicate with other cells at synapses

Alexander Semenov/Science Source

▲ Figure 48.1 **What makes this jellyfish such a deadly predator?**

Lines of Communication

Jellyfish, such as *Aglantha digitale* (Figure 48.1), move through the ocean using pulses of their umbrella-shaped body, or bell. Members of the phylum Cnidaria, these organisms are amongst the simplest of animals, lacking true tissues. Nonetheless, a jellyfish is able to coordinate the movement of its bell and tentacles. Dr. Gerry Mackie and his colleagues at the University of Victoria have studied the mechanisms these animals use to control their body movements. The giant ring axon is a collection of **neurons** that receives information from the tentacles and the edge of the bell. Depending on the stimulus, the giant ring axon may send signals to the tentacles to trigger a twitch, or cause the bell to contract. Depending on the route the signal takes from the giant ring axon, the bell may contract in a slow wave, which glides the animal through the water, or a rapid pulse, propelling the jelly away from a predator.

Communication by neurons largely consists of long-distance electrical signals and short-distance chemical signals. The specialized structure of neurons allows them to use pulses of electrical current to receive, transmit, and regulate the flow of information over long distances within the body. In transferring information from one cell to another, neurons often rely on chemical signals that act over very short distances.

vitstudio/Shutterstock

◄ Neuron and synapse

Neurons transmit sensory information, control heart rate, coordinate hand and eye movement, record memories, generate dreams, and much more. All of this information is transmitted within neurons as an electrical signal. The identity of the type of information being transmitted is encoded by the connections made by the active neuron. Interpreting signals in the nervous system therefore involves sorting a complex set of neuronal paths and connections. In more complex animals, this higher-order processing is carried out largely in groups of neurons organized into a **brain** or into simpler clusters called **ganglia**.

In this chapter, we examine the structure of a neuron and explore the molecules and physical principles that govern signalling by neurons. In Chapter 49, we will look at the organization of nervous systems and at higher-order information processing in vertebrates. In Chapter 50, we will investigate systems that detect environmental stimuli and systems that carry out the body's responses to those stimuli. Finally, in Chapter 51, we will consider how these nervous system functions are integrated into the activities and interactions that make up animal behaviour.

Neuron organization and structure reflect function in information transfer

Our starting point for exploring the nervous system is the neuron, a cell type exemplifying the close fit of form and function that often arises over the course of evolution.

Neuron Structure and Function

The ability of a neuron to receive and transmit information is based on a highly specialized cellular organization (**Figure 48.2**). Most of a neuron's organelles, including its nucleus, are located in the **cell body**. A typical neuron has numerous highly branched extensions called **dendrites** (from the Greek *dendron*, tree). Together with the cell body, the dendrites *receive* signals from other neurons. A neuron also has a single **axon**, an extension that *transmits* signals to other cells. Axons are often much longer than dendrites, and some, such as those that reach from the spinal cord of a giraffe to the muscle cells in its feet, are over a metre long. The cone-shaped base of an axon, the *axon hillock*, is typically where signals that travel down the axon are generated. Near its other end, an axon usually divides into many branches.

Each branched end of an axon transmits information to another cell. The space between the end of the axon, the *axon terminal*, and the target cell is called a **synapse** (see Figure 48.2). At most synapses, chemical messengers called **neurotransmitters** pass information from the transmitting neuron to the receiving cell. In describing a synapse, we refer to the transmitting neuron as the *presynaptic cell* and the neuron, muscle, or gland cell that receives the signal as the *postsynaptic cell*.

The neurons of vertebrates and most invertebrates require supporting cells called **glial cells**, or **glia** (from a Greek word meaning "glue") (**Figure 48.3**). Glia nourish neurons, insulate the axons of neurons, and regulate the extracellular fluid surrounding neurons. Overall,

▲ Figure 48.2 **Neuron structure and organization.** Arrows illustrate the flow of signals into, along, between, and out of neurons.

80 μm

Glia   Cell bodies of neurons

▲ **Figure 48.3 Glia in the mammalian brain.** This micrograph (a fluorescently labelled laser confocal image) shows a region of the rat brain packed with glia and interneurons. The DNA in each cell is labelled dark blue. The glia are labelled red and the dendrites of interneurons are labelled green.

glia outnumber neurons in the mammalian brain 10- to 50-fold. We will examine the functions of specific glia later in this chapter and in Chapter 49.

Introduction to Information Processing

Information processing by a nervous system occurs in three stages: sensory input, integration, and output. Consider what happens when you see a threat and respond by running (**Figure 48.4**). Neurons in the visual system sense the threat. The information is sent to the brain, which sends a signal to the body to initiate an appropriate response.

In all but the simplest animals, specialized populations of neurons handle each stage of information processing.

▲ **Figure 48.4 Summary of information processing.**

- **Sensory neurons** transmit information about external stimuli such as light, touch, or smell, or internal conditions such as blood pressure or muscle tension.
- Neurons in the brain or ganglia integrate (analyze and interpret) the sensory input, taking into account the immediate context and the animal's experience. The vast majority of neurons in the brain are **interneurons**, which form the local circuits connecting neurons in the brain.
- Neurons that extend out of the processing centres trigger output in the form of muscle or gland activity. For example, **motor neurons** transmit signals to muscle cells, causing them to contract.
- When bundled together, the axons of neurons form **nerves**.

In many animals, the neurons that carry out integration are organized in the **central nervous system (CNS)**. The neurons that carry information into and out of the CNS constitute the **peripheral nervous system (PNS)**.

Depending on its role in information processing, the shape of a neuron can vary from simple to quite complex (**Figure 48.5**). Neurons that transmit information to many target cells do so through highly branched axons. Similarly, neurons that have highly branched dendrites can receive input through tens of thousands of synapses in some interneurons.

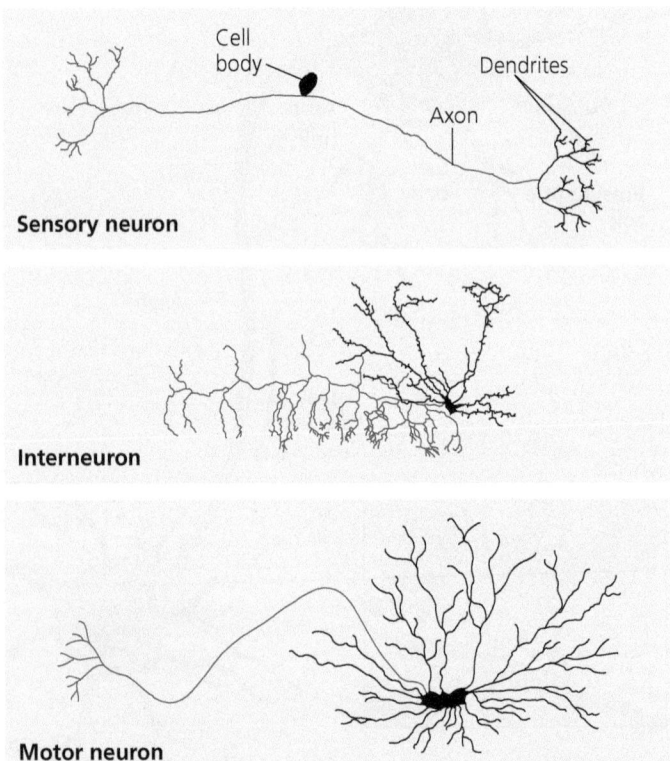

▲ **Figure 48.5 Structural diversity of neurons.** In these drawings of neurons, cell bodies and dendrites are black and axons are red.

1. Describe the basic pathway of information flow through neurons that causes you to turn your head when someone calls your name.

2. WHAT IF? How might increased branching of an axon help coordinate responses to signals communicated by the nervous system?

3. MAKE CONNECTIONS Consider how communication occurs in a colony of bacteria (see Figure 11.3). In what general ways is that communication similar to and different from transmission of a nerve impulse by a neuron?

4. MAKE CONNECTIONS Under what conditions would synaptic signalling be considered autocrine signalling? Under what conditions would it be considered paracrine signalling?

For suggested answers, see Appendix A.

CONCEPT 48.2

Ion gradients and ion channels establish the resting membrane potential of a neuron

As you read in Chapter 7, specific ions are unequally distributed between the interior of cells and the fluid that surrounds them. For example, animal cells have a high concentration of potassium ions (K^+) inside the cell and a high concentration of sodium ions (Na^+) outside the cell (Table 48.1). As a result of ion gradients and ion channels, minor differences in charge do exist, and when these interact across the thin cell membrane, they create a source of electrical potential energy. This charge difference, or voltage, is called the **membrane potential**. The membrane potential of an inactive neuron—one that is not sending a signal—is its **resting membrane potential** and is typically between −60 and −80 mV (millivolts).

Inputs from other neurons or specific stimuli cause changes in the neuron's membrane potential, which act as signals, transmitting and processing information. Rapid changes in membrane potential are what enable us to see a flower, read a book, or climb a tree. Thus, to understand how neurons function, we first need to examine how chemical and electrical forces form, maintain, and alter membrane potentials.

Table 48.1 Ion Concentrations Inside and Outside of Mammalian Neurons

Ion	Intracellular Concentration (mM)	Extracellular Concentration (mM)
Potassium (K^+)	140	5
Sodium (Na^+)	15	150
Chloride (Cl^-)	10	120
Large anions (A^-) inside cell, such as proteins	100	(not applicable)

The Resting Membrane Potential

Any solution, such as the cytoplasm, is *electroneutral*, meaning that there are an equal number of positive ions (cations) and negative ions (anions). When solutions are separated by a membrane, minor differences in the relative abundance of cations and anions can arise as ions move across the membrane. In cells, the cell membrane is thin enough that the charges on either side of the membrane can interact, giving rise to membrane potential. By convention, the membrane potential is expressed relative to the outside of a cell. Thus, a membrane potential of −70 mV means that the inside of the cell membrane is more negative than the outside. Any membrane with a membrane potential different from zero is considered polarized. Changes in the membrane potential can occur when ions move across the membrane, moving through ion channels. Only a few ions need to move to have local effects on the membrane potential, and therefore no change in ion concentrations would be detected in the solutions inside or outside the cell. Ion movements may increase the membrane potential (*hyperpolarization*) or decrease it (*depolarization*). Ions, such as Na^+ and K^+, may be permitted to cross the membrane through ion channels; ions may be actively transported across the membrane by ion pumps (Figure 48.6).

In a cell, the membrane potential depends on both the gradients of ions across the membrane and the permeability of the membrane to ions. The resting membrane potential is determined by several factors. First, the cell cytoplasm has a high concentration of proteins and other macromolecules that possess a net negative charge and cannot move across the membrane. This has the effect of retaining or attracting cations that are able to move. Since K^+ is the most permeable of the cations, it accumulates in cells, drawn by the negative charge. The membrane potential of a cell also depends on the permeability of the membrane. If an ion cannot cross the membrane, then it cannot contribute to the membrane potential, even if the ion has a steep concentration gradient.

If a membrane is suddenly made permeable to an ion, the direction of ion movement depends on both the concentration gradient of the ion and the membrane potential. At rest, the membrane has very low permeability to Na^+. If Na^+ channels opened, Na^+ would flow into the cell, driven by both the chemical gradient (more Na^+ outside) and the electrical gradient (more negative inside). The inward movement of Na^+ would reduce the membrane potential, making the cell less negative (depolarization). Once enough Na^+ entered the cell, the cell would depolarize to the point where it would prevent further movement of Na^+. At this point, *equilibrium,* the chemical and electrical forces exactly counterbalance each other and there would be no net movement of Na^+ in either direction.

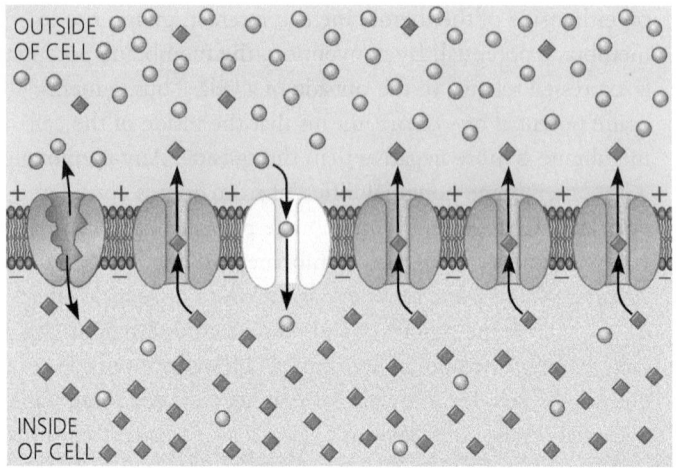

OUTSIDE OF CELL

INSIDE OF CELL

Key

 Na$^+$

K$^+$

 Sodium-potassium pump

 Potassium channel

 Sodium channel

▲ **Figure 48.6 Ion gradients and the membrane potential.** The sodium-potassium pump generates and maintains the ionic gradients of Na$^+$ and K$^+$ shown in Table 48.1. The pump uses ATP to actively transport Na$^+$ out of the cell and K$^+$ into the cell. Although there is a substantial concentration gradient of sodium across the membrane, very little net diffusion of Na$^+$ occurs because there are very few open sodium channels. In contrast, the large number of open potassium channels allows K$^+$ to move freely. There is a near balance between the chemical gradient, which favours K$^+$ movement outward, and the electrical gradient, which favours K$^+$ movement inward.

Much of neuron function depends upon regulation of ion channels, movements of ions, and the resulting impact on membrane potential. To understand how it all works together, we need to explore the relationship between membrane potential and concentration gradients in more quantitative terms.

Determining the Resting Membrane Potential

In the previous example, net ion movement stopped when the chemical potential energy driving Na$^+$ in one direction was equal to the membrane potential opposing its movement. The membrane potential at which equilibrium occurs is expressed as the **equilibrium potential** for the ion (E_{ion}).

The calculation of E_{ion} is used to predict the direction of ion movement under a given concentration gradient. For ion X, its E_x would be calculated using the Nernst equation:

$$E_x = 62\text{mV} \left(\log \frac{[\text{X}]_{outside}}{[\text{X}]_{inside}} \right)$$

The value of E_x, known as the Nernst potential, depends on the ion gradients and the permeability of ions (**Figure 48.7**). Consider a simple scenario where a chamber is divided into two compartments separated by a membrane. Addition of different amounts of salt to the two compartments creates chemical gradients across a membrane. The concentrations shown in Figure 48.7 are intended to mimic what is found in a typical mammalian neuron. When the system is set up with higher KCl inside, and the membrane is made permeable only to K$^+$, K$^+$ will move out, making the inside more negative. Movement will stop when the resulting electrical gradient reaches the Nernst potential for K$^+$ (E_K) of −90mV (**Figure 48.7a**). When the system is set up with higher NaCl outside, opening of Na$^+$ channels will allow some Na$^+$ to move inward, causing the inner compartment to become less negative. In this scenario, net Na$^+$ movement stops when the membrane potential reaches the Nernst potential for Na$^+$ (E_{Na}) of +62 mV (**Figure 48.7b**).

In this simple scenario, the membrane potential is a result of individual ions moving across the membrane, changing the membrane potential until the Nernst potential is reached at equilibrium. In real neurons, however, the situation is much more complex. The neuron deals with multiple concentration gradients and ion channels. In a living cell, the E_x values are used to predict what direction ions will move and the effects on the membrane potential, should individual ion channels open.

For a typical mammalian neuron, [K$^+$]$_{outside}$ = 5 mM, and [K$^+$]$_{inside}$ = 140 mM, giving E_K = −90 mV. If this neuron actually had a membrane potential of −90mV, and K channels were open, there would be no net movement of K. A typical membrane potential for a neuron is −60 to −80 mV, so when K channels open, K$^+$ would tend to move out of the cell. As positive charges leave the cell, the membrane becomes *hyperpolarized* relative to the resting state. Under these conditions, the outward force from the chemical gradient (more K$^+$ inside the cell) exceeds the inward electrical force (more negative inside). Movement of K$^+$ out of the cell would continue until the membrane potential hyperpolarized to −90 mV, the E_K.

The Na$^+$ concentrations for a typical neuron are about 150 mM outside the cell and 15 mM inside the cell. The E_{Na} is calculated as +62 mV. Thus, when Na channels open in a resting neuron, Na$^+$ enters the cell, *depolarizing* the membrane. The net movement of Na$^+$ would stop if the membrane potential reached +62 mV.

The membrane potential of a living cell is a product of the influences of all of the different ions that are permeable to the cell membrane. The resting membrane potential of a neuron is close to the E_K because K$^+$ is the most permeable of the ions. The membrane potential is not equal to E_K because other ions have low, but detectible, permeability. For example, a minor Na^+ leak tends to depolarize the cell. In many cells, the Cl^- gradients are such that E_{Cl} is also close to the resting potential, and any Cl^- permeability has little effect on the resting potential.

The ion channels that govern ion permeability of a cell membrane are regulated by the cell to change membrane potential. In addition to ion channels, cells are able to pump ions across the membrane by active transport. The sodium-potassium pump, also known as Na^+–K^+ ATPase, enables cells to create a Na^+ gradient, which is vital for neuronal function. The pump expels $3Na^+$ from the cell while bringing in $2K^+$, using the energy derived from hydrolysis of ATP. The unequal transport of Na^+ and K^+ does contribute to increasing the membrane potential, but the main function of this pump is to maintain a Na^+ gradient across the membrane. This electrochemical Na^+ gradient is a source of energy to drive other processes, such as transport (see Chapter 7). Neurons can induce changes in Na^+ permeability to rapidly depolarize the cell, the first step in an electrical event known as an action potential.

Under conditions that allow Na^+ to cross the membrane more readily, the membrane potential will move toward E_{Na} and away from E_K. Keep in mind that the extent of ion movement required to generate the resting potential is extremely small (about 10^{-12} mole/cm^2 of membrane), far less than would be required to alter the chemical concentration gradient. As we will see in the next section, this is precisely what happens during the generation of a nerve impulse.

(a) Membrane selectively permeable to K⁺

Nernst equation for K⁺ equilibrium potential at 37°C:

$$E_K = 62 \text{ mV} \left(\log \frac{5 \text{ m}M}{140 \text{ m}M} \right) = -90 \text{ mV}$$

(b) Membrane selectively permeable to Na⁺

Nernst equation for Na⁺ equilibrium potential at 37°C:

$$E_{Na} = 62 \text{ mV} \left(\log \frac{150 \text{ m}M}{15 \text{ m}M} \right) = +62 \text{ mV}$$

▲ Figure 48.7 Modelling a mammalian neuron. Each container is divided into inner and outer compartments with different concentrations of salts (KCl or NaCl). The compartments are separated by an artificial membrane. When ion channels open, cations (K⁺ or Na⁺) are able to cross, which changes the membrane electrical gradient, though does not significantly change the concentration gradients. (a) When K⁺ channels open, K⁺ moves from the inner to outer compartment, making the inside more negative. At equilibrium, the Nernst potential for K⁺ under these conditions is −90 mV. (b) When Na⁺ channels open, the concentration gradient drives Na⁺ into the inner compartment, making it less negative. At equilibrium, the Nernst potential for Na⁺ under these conditions is +62 mV.

WHAT IF? Adding channels specific for one type of ion to the membrane in (b) would alter the membrane potential. Which ion would pass through these channels, and in what direction would the membrane potential change?

CONCEPT CHECK 48.2

1. Under what circumstances could ions flow through ion channels from regions of low ion concentration to regions of high ion concentration?

2. **WHAT IF?** Suppose a cell's membrane potential shifts from −70 mV to −50 mV. What changes in the cell's permeability to K⁺ or Na⁺ could cause such a shift?

3. **WHAT IF?** Ouabain, a plant substance used in some cultures to poison hunting arrows, disables the sodium-potassium pump. What change in the resting membrane potential would you expect to see if you treated a neuron with ouabain? Explain.

4. **MAKE CONNECTIONS** Figure 7.10 illustrates diffusion by dye molecules. Could diffusion eliminate the concentration gradient of a dye that has a net charge? Explain.

For suggested answers, see Appendix A.

CONCEPT 48.3

Action potentials are the signals conducted by axons

The membrane potential of a neuron changes in response to a variety of stimuli. Using the technique of intracellular recording, researchers can record and graph these changes as a function of time (Figure 48.8). Changes in the membrane potential occur because neurons contain **gated ion channels**, ion channels that open or close in response to stimuli. *Voltage-gated* ion channels open with changes in the membrane potential; *ligand-gated* channels open in response to changes in the concentration of specific signalling molecules; *stretch-activated* ion channels open in response to changes in cell shape. Each of these types of gated ion channels play important roles in controlling membrane potential. The opening or closing of gated ion channels alters the membrane's permeability to particular ions, which in turn alters the membrane potential.

Hyperpolarization and Depolarization

To explore how the membrane potential changes, let's consider what happens when potassium channels that are

Research Method

Intracellular Recording

Application Electrophysiologists use intracellular recording to measure the membrane potential of neurons and other cells.

Technique A microelectrode is made from a glass capillary tube filled with an electrically conductive salt solution. One end of the tube tapers to an extremely fine tip (diameter < 1 μm). While looking through a microscope, the experimenter uses a micropositioner to insert the tip of the microelectrode into a cell. A voltage recorder (usually an oscilloscope or a computer-based system) measures the voltage between the microelectrode tip inside the cell and a reference electrode placed in the solution outside the cell.

closed in a resting neuron are stimulated to open. Opening these potassium channels increases the membrane's permeability to K^+. Net diffusion of K^+ out of the neuron increases, shifting the membrane potential toward

E_K (−90 mV at 37°C). This increase in the magnitude of the membrane potential, called a **hyperpolarization**, makes the inside of the membrane more negative (Figure 48.9a). In a resting neuron, hyperpolarization results from any stimulus that increases the outflow of positive ions or the inflow of negative ions.

Although opening potassium channels in a resting neuron causes hyperpolarization, opening some other types of ion channels has an opposite effect, making the inside of the membrane less negative (Figure 48.9b). A reduction in the magnitude of the membrane potential is called a **depolarization**. Depolarization in neurons often involves sodium channels. If a stimulus causes the voltage-gated sodium channels in a resting neuron to open, the membrane's permeability to Na^+ increases. Na^+ diffuses into the cell along its concentration gradient, causing a depolarization as the membrane potential shifts toward E_{Na} (+62 mV at 37°C).

Graded Potentials and Action Potentials

Sometimes, the response to hyperpolarization or depolarization is simply a shift in the membrane potential. This shift, called a **graded potential**, has a magnitude that varies with the strength of the stimulus, with a larger stimulus causing a greater change in the membrane potential. Graded potentials induce a small electrical current that leaks out of the neuron as it flows along the membrane. Graded

(a) Graded hyperpolarizations produced by two stimuli that increase membrane permeability to K^+. The larger stimulus produces a larger hyperpolarization.

(b) Graded depolarizations produced by two stimuli that increase membrane permeability to Na^+. The larger stimulus produces a larger depolarization.

(c) Action potential triggered by a depolarization that reaches the threshold.

▲ Figure 48.9 **Graded potentials and an action potential in a neuron.**

DRAW IT *Redraw the graph in part (c), extending the y-axis. Then label the positions of E_K and E_{Na}.*

potentials thus decay with distance from their source. Although graded potentials are not the nerve signals that travel along axons, they have a major effect on the generation of nerve signals.

If a depolarization shifts the membrane potential sufficiently, the result is a massive change in membrane voltage called an **action potential**. Unlike graded potentials, action potentials have a constant magnitude and can regenerate in adjacent regions of the membrane. Action potentials can therefore spread along axons, making them well suited for transmitting a signal over long distances.

Action potentials arise because some of the ion channels in neurons are **voltage-gated ion channels**, opening or closing when the membrane potential passes a particular level. If a depolarization opens voltage-gated sodium channels, the resulting flow of Na^+ into the neuron results in further depolarization. Because the sodium channels are voltage gated, an increased depolarization causes more sodium channels to open, leading to an even greater flow of current. The result is a process of *positive feedback* that triggers a very rapid opening of all voltage-gated sodium channels and the marked change in membrane potential that defines an action potential (Figure 48.9c).

Action potentials occur whenever a depolarization increases the membrane voltage to a particular value, called the **threshold**. For mammalian neurons, the threshold is a membrane potential of about −55 mV. Once initiated, the action potential has a magnitude that is independent of the strength of the triggering stimulus. Because action potentials occur fully or not at all, they represent an *all-or-none* response to stimuli. This all-or-none property reflects the fact that depolarization opens voltage-gated sodium channels, and the opening of sodium channels causes further depolarization. The positive-feedback loop of depolarization and channel opening triggers an action potential whenever the membrane potential reaches the threshold.

The discovery of how action potentials are generated dates to the 1940s and 1950s, with the work of British scientists Andrew Huxley and Alan Hodgkin. Because no techniques were available for studying electrical events in small cells, they took electrical recordings from the giant neurons of the squid. Their experiments led to a model, presented in the next section, that earned them a Nobel Prize in 1963.

Generation of Action Potentials: *A Closer Look*

The characteristic shape of the graph of an action potential (see Figure 48.9c) reflects the large change in membrane potential resulting from ion movement through voltage-gated sodium and potassium channels. Membrane depolarization opens both types of channels, but they respond independently and sequentially. Sodium channels open first, initiating the action potential. As the action potential

proceeds, the sodium channels become inactivated: A loop of the channel protein moves, blocking ion flow through the opening. Sodium channels remain inactivated until after the membrane returns to the resting membrane potential and the channels close. Potassium channels open more slowly than sodium channels, but remain open and functional until the end of the action potential.

To understand further how voltage-gated channels shape the action potential, we'll consider the process as a series of stages (Figure 48.10). ❶ When the membrane of the axon is at the resting membrane potential, most voltage-gated sodium channels are closed. Some potassium channels are open, but most voltage-gated potassium channels are closed. ❷ When a stimulus depolarizes the membrane, some gated sodium channels open, allowing more Na^+ to diffuse into the cell. The Na^+ inflow causes further depolarization, which opens still more gated sodium channels, allowing even more Na^+ to diffuse into the cell. ❸ Once the threshold is crossed, the positive-feedback cycle rapidly brings the membrane potential close to E_{Na}. This stage of the action potential is called the *rising phase*. ❹ Two events prevent the membrane potential from actually reaching E_{Na}: Voltage-gated sodium channels inactivate soon after opening, halting Na^+ inflow; and most voltage-gated potassium channels open, causing a rapid outflow of K^+. Both events quickly bring the membrane potential back toward E_K. This stage is called the *falling phase*. ❺ In the final phase of an action potential, called the *undershoot*, the membrane's permeability to K^+ is higher than at rest, so the membrane potential is closer to E_K than it is at the resting membrane potential. The gated potassium channels eventually close, and the membrane potential returns to the resting membrane potential.

The sodium channels remain inactivated during the falling phase and the early part of the undershoot. As a result, if a second depolarizing stimulus occurs during this period, it will be unable to trigger an action potential. The "downtime" when a second action potential cannot be initiated is called the **refractory period**. This interval sets a limit on the maximum frequency at which action potentials can be generated. As we will discuss shortly, the refractory period also ensures that all signals in an axon travel in one direction, from the cell body to the axon terminals.

Note that the refractory period is due to the inactivation of sodium channels, not to a change in the ion gradients across the plasma membrane. The flow of charged particles during an action potential involves far too few ions to change the concentration on either side of the membrane significantly.

For most neurons, the interval between the onset of an action potential and the end of the refractory period is only 1–2 milliseconds (msec). Because action potentials are so brief, a neuron can produce hundreds per second. Furthermore, the frequency with which a neuron generates action potentials varies in response to input. Such differences in action potential

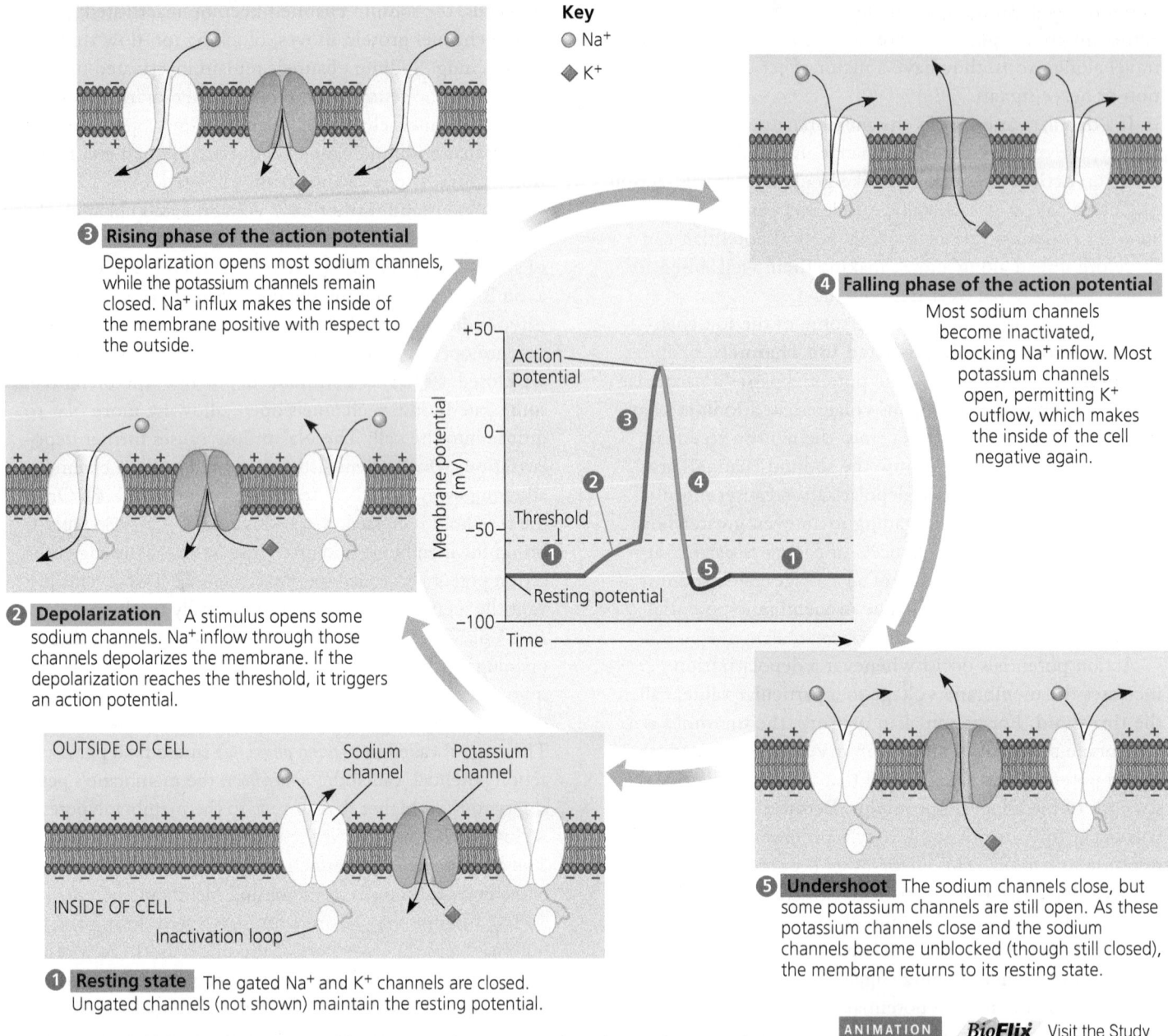

Key
○ Na+
◆ K+

③ Rising phase of the action potential
Depolarization opens most sodium channels, while the potassium channels remain closed. Na+ influx makes the inside of the membrane positive with respect to the outside.

④ Falling phase of the action potential
Most sodium channels become inactivated, blocking Na+ inflow. Most potassium channels open, permitting K+ outflow, which makes the inside of the cell negative again.

Action potential

③

②

④

Threshold

①

⑤

①

Resting potential

Time

② Depolarization A stimulus opens some sodium channels. Na+ inflow through those channels depolarizes the membrane. If the depolarization reaches the threshold, it triggers an action potential.

OUTSIDE OF CELL

Sodium channel   Potassium channel

INSIDE OF CELL

Inactivation loop

① Resting state The gated Na+ and K+ channels are closed. Ungated channels (not shown) maintain the resting potential.

⑤ Undershoot The sodium channels close, but some potassium channels are still open. As these potassium channels close and the sodium channels become unblocked (though still closed), the membrane returns to its resting state.

▲ Figure 48.10 **The role of voltage-gated ion channels in the generation of an action potential.** The circled numbers on the graph in the centre and the colours of the action potential phases correspond to the five diagrams showing voltage-gated sodium and potassium channels in a neuron's plasma membrane. (Ungated ion channels are not illustrated.)

ANIMATION   *BioFlix* Visit the Study Area in **MasteringBiology** for the BioFlix® 3-D Animation on How Neurons Work.

Source: Based on figure 6-2d from *Cellular Physiology of Nerve and Muscle,* 4th edition, by Gary G. Matthews. Wiley-Blackwell, 2003. © Jane B Reece.

frequency convey information about signal strength. In hearing, for example, louder sounds result in more frequent action potentials in neurons connecting the ear to the brain. Differences in the time interval between action potentials are in fact the only variable in transmission of information by an axon.

Gated ion channels and action potentials have a central role in all nervous system function. As a consequence, mutations in genes that encode ion channel proteins can cause disorders affecting the nerves, muscles, brain, or heart. The type of disorder depends largely on where in the body the gene for the ion channel protein is expressed. For example, mutations affecting voltage–gated sodium channels in skeletal muscle cells can cause myotonia, a periodic spasming of those muscles; and mutations affecting sodium channels in the brain can cause epilepsy, in which excessive synchronized firing of groups of nerve cells causes seizures.

Conduction of Action Potentials

At the site where an action potential is initiated (usually the axon hillock), Na+ inflow during the rising phase creates an electrical current that depolarizes the neighbouring region of the axon membrane (**Figure 48.11**). The depolarization in the neighbouring region is large enough to reach the threshold, causing the action potential to be reinitiated there. This process is repeated many times along the length of the axon. Because an action potential is an all-or-none

1 An action potential is generated as Na$^+$ flows inward across the membrane at one location.

2 The depolarization of the action potential spreads to the neighbouring region of the membrane, reinitiating the action potential there. To the left of this region, the membrane is repolarizing as K$^+$ flows outward.

3 The depolarization-repolarization process is repeated in the next region of the membrane. In this way, local currents of ions *across* the plasma membrane cause the action potential to be propagated *along* the length of the axon.

▲ **Figure 48.11 Conduction of an action potential.** This figure shows events at three successive times as an action potential passes from left to right. At each point along the axon, voltage-gated ion channels go through the sequence of changes in Figure 48.10. Membrane colours correspond to the action potential phases in Figure 48.10.

DRAW IT *For the axon segment shown, consider a point at the left end, a point in the middle, and a point at the right end. Draw a graph for each point showing the change in membrane potential over time at that point as a single nerve impulse moves from left to right across the segment.*

event, the magnitude and duration of the action potential remain constant at each position along the axon. The result is the movement of a nerve impulse from the axon hillock to the axon terminals, much like the cascade of events triggered by knocking over the first domino in a line.

An action potential that starts at the axon hillock moves along the axon only toward the axon terminals. Why? Immediately behind the travelling zone of depolarization caused by Na$^+$ inflow is a zone of repolarization caused by K$^+$ outflow. In the repolarized zone, the sodium channels remain inactivated. Consequently, the inward current that depolarizes the axon membrane *ahead* of the action potential cannot produce another action potential *behind* it. This prevents action potentials from travelling back toward the cell body.

Evolutionary Adaptations of Axon Structure

EVOLUTION Axon diameter is a major factor affecting the speed at which action potentials are conducted. One adaptation that increases conductance speed is an increased axon diameter. Resistance to electrical current flow is inversely proportional to the cross-sectional area of a conductor (such as a wire or an axon). In the same way that a large-diameter hose offers less resistance to the flow of water than does a narrow hose, a large-diameter axon provides less resistance to the current associated with an action potential than does a narrow axon.

In invertebrates, conduction speed varies from several centimetres per second in very narrow axons to about 30 m/sec in the giant axons of some arthropods and molluscs. These giant axons (up to 1 mm wide) function in rapid behavioural responses, such as the muscle contraction that propels a squid toward its prey.

Vertebrate axons have relatively narrow diameters but can still conduct action potentials at high speed. How is this possible? The evolutionary adaptation that enables fast conduction in vertebrate axons is electrical insulation, analogous to the plastic insulation that covers many electrical wires. Insulation causes the depolarizing current associated with an action potential to spread farther along the axon interior, bringing more distant regions to the threshold sooner.

The electrical insulation that surrounds vertebrate axons is called a **myelin sheath** (**Figure 48.12**). Myelin sheaths are produced by two types of glia—**oligodendrocytes** in the CNS and **Schwann cells** in the PNS. During development, these specialized glia wrap axons in many layers of membrane. The membranes forming these layers are mostly lipid, which is a poor conductor of electrical current.

In myelinated axons, voltage-gated sodium channels are restricted to gaps in the myelin sheath called **nodes of Ranvier** (see Figure 48.12). The extracellular fluid is in contact with the axon membrane only at the nodes. As a result, action potentials are not generated in the regions between the nodes. Rather, the inward current produced during the rising phase of the action potential at a node travels all the way to the next

Courtesy of Alan Peters

0.1 μm

▲ **Figure 48.12 Schwann cells and the myelin sheath.** In the PNS, glia called Schwann cells wrap themselves around axons, forming layers of myelin. Gaps between adjacent Schwann cells are called nodes of Ranvier. The transmission electron micrograph shows a cross section through a myelinated axon.

node, where it depolarizes the membrane and regenerates the action potential (Figure 48.13). Thus, the time-consuming process of opening and closing of ion channels occurs at only a limited number of positions along the axon. This mechanism for action potential propagation is called **saltatory conduction** (from the Latin *saltare*, to leap) because the action potential appears to jump along the axon from node to node.

The major selective advantage of myelination is its space efficiency. A myelinated axon 20 μm in diameter has a conduction speed faster than that of a squid giant axon with a diameter 40 times greater. Furthermore, more than 2000 of those myelinated axons can be packed into the space occupied by just one giant axon.

CONCEPT CHECK 48.3

1. How do action potentials and graded potentials differ?

2. In multiple sclerosis (from the Greek *skleros*, hard), myelin sheaths harden and deteriorate. How would this affect nervous system function?

3. **WHAT IF?** Suppose a mutation caused gated sodium channels to remain inactivated longer after an action potential. How would this affect the frequency at which action potentials could be generated? Explain.

For suggested answers, see Appendix A.

CONCEPT 48.4

Neurons communicate with other cells at synapses

In most cases, action potentials are not transmitted from neurons to other cells. However, information is transmitted, and this transmission occurs at the synaptic terminals, such as those shown in Figure 48.14. Some synapses, called *electrical synapses*, contain gap junctions (see Figure 6.30), which *do* allow electrical current to flow directly from one neuron to another. In both vertebrates and invertebrates, electrical synapses synchronize the activity of neurons responsible for certain rapid, unvarying behaviours. For example, electrical synapses associated with the giant axons of squids and lobsters facilitate the swift execution of escape responses. There are also many electrical synapses in the vertebrate brain.

The majority of synapses are *chemical synapses*, which involve the release of a chemical neurotransmitter by the presynaptic neuron. At each terminal, the presynaptic neuron synthesizes the neurotransmitter and packages it in multiple membrane-bounded compartments called *synaptic vesicles*. The arrival of an action potential at an axon terminal depolarizes the plasma membrane, opening

▶ **Figure 48.13 Saltatory conduction.** In a myelinated axon, the depolarizing current during an action potential at one node of Ranvier spreads along the interior of the axon to the next node (blue arrows), where voltage-gated sodium channels enable reinitiation. Thus, the action potential jumps from node to node as it travels along the axon (red arrows).

Postsynaptic neuron

Synaptic terminals of presynaptic neurons

5 μm

Edwin R. Lewis, Professor Emeritus, University of California-Berkeley

▲ Figure 48.14 **Synaptic terminals on the cell body of a post-synaptic neuron (colourized SEM).**

voltage-gated channels that allow Ca^{2+} to diffuse into the terminal (**Figure 48.15**). The resulting rise in Ca^{2+} concentration in the terminal causes some of the synaptic vesicles to fuse with the terminal membrane, releasing the neurotransmitter by exocytosis.

Once released, the neurotransmitter diffuses across the *synaptic cleft*, the gap that separates the presynaptic neuron from the postsynaptic cell. Diffusion time is very short because the gap is less than 50 nm across. Upon reaching the postsynaptic membrane, the neurotransmitter binds to and activates a specific receptor in the membrane.

Synaptic communication is essential to neuronal function. One of the main problems with neuronal damage is the inability of many neurons to reform synaptic connections lost when cells die from physical or chemical damage. In 1992, Naweed Syed from the University of Calgary began studies that examined how interneurons reform synaptic connections following damage (**Figure 48.16**).

Information transfer is much more readily modified at chemical synapses than at electrical synapses. A variety of factors can affect the amount of neurotransmitter that is released or the responsiveness of the postsynaptic cell. Such modifications underlie an animal's ability to alter its behaviour in response to change and form the basis for learning and memory, as you will learn in Chapter 49.

Presynaptic cell

Postsynaptic cell

Axon

Synaptic vesicle containing neurotransmitter

Synaptic cleft

Postsynaptic membrane

Presynaptic membrane

Ca^{2+}

Voltage-gated Ca^{2+} channel

Ligand-gated ion channels

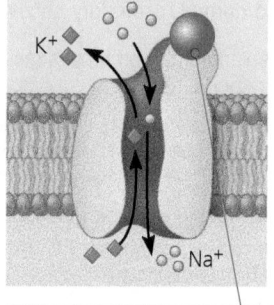

K^+

Na^+

❶ An action potential arrives, depolarizing the presynaptic membrane.

❷ The depolarization opens voltage-gated channels, triggering an influx of Ca^{2+}.

❸ The elevated Ca^{2+} concentration causes synaptic vesicles to fuse with the presynaptic membrane, releasing neurotransmitter into the synaptic cleft.

❹ The neurotransmitter binds to ligand-gated ion channels in the postsynaptic membrane. In this example, binding triggers opening, allowing Na^+ and K^+ to diffuse through.

▲ Figure 48.15 **A chemical synapse.** This figure illustrates the sequence of events that transmits a signal across a chemical synapse. In response to binding of neurotransmitter, ligand-gated ion channels in the postsynaptic membrane open (as shown here) or, less commonly, close. Synaptic transmission ends when the neurotransmitter diffuses out of the synaptic cleft, is taken up by the axon terminal or by another cell, or is degraded by an enzyme.

ANIMATION

BioFlix Visit the Study Area in **MasteringBiology** for the BioFlix® 3-D Animation on How Synapses Work.

WHAT IF? *If all the Ca^{2+} in the fluid surrounding a neuron were removed, how would this affect the transmission of information within and between neurons?*

Figure 48.16 — Inquiry

▼ Figure 48.16 | **Inquiry**

Can a damaged neuron reform synaptic connections?

Experiment One of the great challenges in neurobiology is in understanding what may be required to permit neuronal repair. Many cells of the nervous system are unable to be replaced, making it difficult in nature to undertake neuronal repair, and more difficult in a clinical setting to undertake surgical interventions that transplant healthy tissue into damaged nervous system tissue. In 1992, Naweed Syed and colleagues at the University of Calgary began studies exploring the ability of neurons to reform synaptic connections upon transplant using the freshwater snail *Lymnea stagnalis*. In their experiment, the specific interneuron controlling respiration, VD4, was destroyed in one animal then replaced with the VD4 neuron from a donor animal. They followed the anatomical and physiological recovery of the transplanted neuron, measuring respiratory behaviour as an index of repair of the neural circuit.

Results

Snails that had surgery but were left with their VD4 interneuron intact (sham) showed normal respiratory behaviour. Snails with the VD4 interneuron removed (−) showed no respiratory behaviour, but those who had their excised interneuron (+) replaced with a donor interneuron exhibited normal respiratory behaviour.

Conclusion The transplanted neuron repairs the damaged circuit and restores normal respiratory behaviour.

Source: Based on N. I. Syed, R. I. Ridgway, K. Lukowiak, and A. G. M. Bulloch, Transplantation and functional integration of an identified respiratory interneuron in *Lymnaea stagnalis*, *Neuron* 8:767–774 (1992). © Jane B Reece.

WHAT IF? *Suppose that only half of the snails with transplants showed a recovery in respiratory movements. What would you conclude about the ability to reform synaptic connections?*

Generation of Postsynaptic Potentials

At many chemical synapses, the receptor protein that binds and responds to neurotransmitters is a **ligand-gated ion channel**, often called an *ionotropic receptor*. These receptors are clustered in the membrane of the postsynaptic cell, directly opposite the axon terminal. Binding of the neurotransmitter (the receptor's ligand) to a particular part of the receptor opens the channel and allows specific ions to diffuse across the postsynaptic membrane. The result is a *postsynaptic potential*, a graded potential in the postsynaptic cell.

At some synapses, the ligand-gated ion channel is permeable to both K^+ and Na^+ (see Figure 48.15). When this channel opens, the membrane potential depolarizes toward a value roughly midway between E_K and E_{Na}. Because such a depolarization brings the membrane potential toward threshold, it is called an **excitatory postsynaptic potential (EPSP)**.

At other synapses, the ligand-gated ion channel is selectively permeable for only K^+ or Cl^-. When such a channel opens, the postsynaptic membrane hyperpolarizes. A hyperpolarization produced in this manner is an **inhibitory postsynaptic potential (IPSP)** because it moves the membrane potential further from threshold.

Summation of Postsynaptic Potentials

The postsynaptic cell may receive inputs from chemical synapses with hundreds or even thousands of axon terminals (Figure 48.15). The magnitude of the postsynaptic potential at any one synapse varies with a number of factors, including the amount of neurotransmitter released by the presynaptic neuron. As a graded potential, a postsynaptic potential becomes smaller with distance from the synapse. Therefore, by the time a single EPSP reaches the axon hillock, it is usually too small to trigger an action potential in a postsynaptic neuron (Figure 48.17a).

On some occasions, two EPSPs occur at a single synapse in such rapid succession that the postsynaptic neuron's membrane potential has not returned to the resting membrane potential before the arrival of the second EPSP. When that happens, the EPSPs add together, an effect called **temporal summation** (Figure 48.17b). Moreover, EPSPs produced nearly simultaneously by *different* synapses on the same postsynaptic neuron can also add together, an effect called **spatial summation** (Figure 48.17c). Through spatial and temporal summation, several EPSPs can combine to depolarize the membrane at the axon hillock to the threshold, causing the postsynaptic neuron to produce an action potential. Summation applies as well to IPSPs: Two or more IPSPs occurring nearly simultaneously at synapses in the same region or in rapid succession at the same synapse have a larger hyperpolarizing effect than a single IPSP. Through summation, an IPSP can also counter the effect of an EPSP (Figure 48.17d).

The interplay between multiple excitatory and inhibitory inputs is the essence of integration in the nervous system. The axon hillock is the neuron's integrating centre, the region where the membrane potential at any instant represents the summed effect of all EPSPs and IPSPs. Whenever the membrane potential at the axon hillock reaches the threshold, an action potential is generated and travels along the axon to its axon terminals. After the refractory period, the neuron may produce another action

▲ Figure 48.17 **Summation of postsynaptic potentials.** These graphs trace changes in the membrane potential at a postsynaptic neuron's axon hillock. The arrows indicate times when postsynaptic potentials occur at two excitatory synapses (E_1 and E_2, green in the diagrams above the graphs) and at one inhibitory synapse (I, red). Like most EPSPs, those produced at E_1 or E_2 do not reach the threshold at the axon hillock without summation.

potential, provided the membrane potential at the axon hillock once again reaches the threshold.

Modulated Signalling at Synapses

So far, we have focused on synapses where a neurotransmitter binds directly to an ion channel, causing the channel to open. However, there are also synapses in which the receptor for the neurotransmitter is *not* part of an ion channel. At these synapses, the neurotransmitter binds to a *metabotropic receptor*, so called because the resulting opening or closing of ion channels depends on one or more metabolic steps. Binding of a neurotransmitter to a metabotropic receptor activates a signal transduction pathway in the postsynaptic cell involving a second messenger (see Chapter 11). Compared with the postsynaptic potentials produced by ligand-gated channels, the effects of these second-messenger systems have a slower onset but last longer (minutes or even hours). Second messengers modulate the responsiveness of postsynaptic neurons to inputs in diverse ways, such as by altering the number of open potassium channels.

A variety of signal transduction pathways play a role in modulating synaptic transmission. One of the best-studied pathways involves cyclic AMP (cAMP) as a second messenger. For example, when the neurotransmitter norepinephrine binds to its metabotropic receptor, the neurotransmitter-receptor complex activates a G protein, which in turn activates adenylyl cyclase, the enzyme that converts ATP

to cAMP (see Figure 11.11). Cyclic AMP activates protein kinase A, which phosphorylates specific ion channel proteins in the postsynaptic membrane, causing them to open or close. Because of the amplifying effect of the signal transduction pathway, the binding of a neurotransmitter molecule to a metabotropic receptor can open or close many channels.

Neurotransmitters

Signalling at a synapse brings about a response that depends on both the neurotransmitter released from the presynaptic membrane and the receptor produced at the postsynaptic membrane. A single neurotransmitter may bind specifically to more than a dozen different receptors, including ionotropic and metabotropic types. Indeed, a particular neurotransmitter can excite postsynaptic cells expressing one receptor and inhibit postsynaptic cells expressing a different receptor.

How is neurotransmitter signalling terminated? Both receptor activation and postsynaptic response cease when neurotransmitter molecules are cleared from the synaptic cleft. The removal of neurotransmitters can occur by simple diffusion or by other mechanisms. For example, some neurotransmitters are inactivated by enzymatic hydrolysis (Figure 48.18a). Other neurotransmitters are recaptured into the presynaptic neuron (Figure 48.18b). Once this reuptake occurs, neurotransmitters are repackaged in synaptic vesicles or transferred to glia for metabolism or recycling to neurons.

(a) Enzymatic breakdown of neurotransmitter in the synaptic cleft

(b) Reuptake of neurotransmitter by presynaptic neuron

▲ Figure 48.18 **Two mechanisms of terminating neurotransmission.**

With these basic properties of neurotransmitters in mind, let's now examine some specific examples, beginning with **acetylcholine**, a common neurotransmitter in both invertebrates and vertebrates.

Acetylcholine

Acetylcholine is vital for nervous system functions that include muscle stimulation, memory formation, and learning. In vertebrates, there are two major classes of acetylcholine receptor. One type is a ligand-gated ion channel. We know the most about its function at the *neuromuscular junction*, the site where motor neurons synapse with skeletal muscle cells. When acetylcholine released by motor neurons binds this receptor, the ion channel opens, producing an EPSP. This excitatory activity is soon terminated by acetylcholinesterase, an enzyme in the synaptic cleft that hydrolyzes the neurotransmitter.

The acetylcholine receptor active at the neuromuscular junction is also found elsewhere in the PNS, as well as in the CNS. There this ionotropic receptor can bind nicotine, a chemical found in tobacco and tobacco smoke. Nicotine's effects as a physiological and psychological stimulant result from its binding to this receptor.

A metabotropic acetylcholine receptor is found at locations that include the vertebrate CNS and heart. In heart muscle, acetylcholine released by neurons activates a signal transduction pathway. The G proteins in the pathway inhibit adenylyl cyclase and open potassium channels in the muscle cell membrane. Both effects reduce the rate at which the heart pumps. Thus, the effect of acetylcholine in heart muscle is inhibitory rather than excitatory.

A number of natural and synthetic toxins disrupt neurotransmission by acetylcholine. For example, the nerve gas sarin inhibits acetylcholinesterase, causing a buildup of acetylcholine to levels that trigger paralysis and typically death. In contrast, certain bacteria produce a toxin that inhibits presynaptic release of acetylcholine. This toxin causes a rare but severe form of food poisoning called botulism. Untreated botulism is typically fatal because muscles required for breathing fail to contract when acetylcholine release is blocked. Today, the same botulinum toxin is commonly used in cosmetic procedures. Injections of the toxin, known by the trade name Botox, minimize wrinkles around the eyes or mouth by blocking transmission at synapses that control particular facial muscles.

Although acetylcholine has many roles, it is just one of more than 100 known neurotransmitters. As shown by the examples in Table 48.2, the rest fall into four classes: amino acids, biogenic amines, neuropeptides, and gases.

Table 48.2	Major Neurotransmitters
Neurotransmitter	**Structure**
Acetylcholine	$H_3C-\overset{\overset{O}{\|\|}}{C}-O-CH_2-CH_2-\overset{\overset{CH_3}{\|}}{\underset{\underset{CH_3}{\|}}{N^+}}-CH_3$
Amino Acids	
GABA (gamma-aminobutyric acid)	$H_2N-CH_2-CH_2-CH_2-COOH$
Glutamate	$H_2N-\overset{\overset{}{\underset{\underset{COOH}{\|}}{CH}}}{}-CH_2-CH_2-COOH$
Glycine	H_2N-CH_2-COOH
Biogenic Amines	
Norepinephrine	
Dopamine	
Serotonin	
Neuropeptides (a very diverse group, only two of which are shown)	
Substance P	Arg—Pro—Lys—Pro—Gln—Gln—Phe—Phe—Gly—Leu—Met
Met-enkephalin (an endorphin)	Tyr—Gly—Gly—Phe—Met
Gases	
Nitric oxide	$N=O$

Amino Acids

Amino acid neurotransmitters are active in the vertebrate CNS and PNS. In the CNS, the amino acid **glutamate** is the most common neurotransmitter. When glutamate binds to any of several types of ligand-gated ion channels, it has an excitatory effect on postsynaptic cells. Synapses at which glutamate is the neurotransmitter have a key role in the formation of long-term memory, as we will discuss in Chapter 49.

The amino acid **gamma-aminobutyric acid (GABA)** is the neurotransmitter at most inhibitory synapses in the brain. Binding of GABA to receptors in postsynaptic cells increases membrane permeability to Cl^-, resulting in an IPSP. The widely prescribed drug diazepam (Valium) reduces anxiety through binding to a site on a GABA receptor.

A third amino acid, glycine, acts at inhibitory synapses in parts of the CNS that lie outside of the brain. There, glycine binds to an ionotropic receptor that is inhibited by strychnine, a chemical often used as a rat poison.

Biogenic Amines

The neurotransmitters grouped as **biogenic amines** are synthesized from amino acids and include **norepinephrine**, which is made from tyrosine. Norepinephrine is an excitatory neurotransmitter in the autonomic nervous system, a branch of the PNS discussed in Chapter 49. Outside the nervous system, norepinephrine has distinct but related functions as a hormone, as does the related biogenic amine *epinephrine* (see Chapter 45).

The biogenic amines **dopamine**, made from tyrosine, and **serotonin**, made from tryptophan, are released at many sites in the brain and affect sleep, mood, attention, and learning. Some psychoactive drugs, including LSD and mescaline, apparently produce their hallucinatory effects by binding to brain receptors for these neurotransmitters.

Biogenic amines have a central role in a number of nervous system disorders and treatments (see Chapter 49). The degenerative illness Parkinson's disease is associated with a lack of dopamine in the brain. In addition, depression is often treated with drugs that increase the brain concentrations of biogenic amines. Prozac, for instance, enhances the effect of serotonin by inhibiting its reuptake after release.

Neuropeptides

Several **neuropeptides**, relatively short chains of amino acids, serve as neurotransmitters that operate via metabotropic receptors. Such peptides are typically produced by cleavage of much larger protein precursors. The neuropeptide *substance P* is a key excitatory neurotransmitter that mediates our perception of pain, while other neuropeptides, called **endorphins**, function as natural analgesics, decreasing pain perception.

Endorphins are produced in the brain during times of physical or emotional stress, such as childbirth. In addition to relieving pain, they decrease urine output, depress respiration, and produce euphoria, as well as other emotional effects. Because opiates bind to the same receptor proteins as endorphins, opiates mimic endorphins and produce many of the same physiological effects (see Figure 2.16). In the Scientific Skills Exercise, you can interpret data from an experiment designed to search for opiate receptors in the brain.

Gases

In common with many other types of cells, some neurons in vertebrates release dissolved gases, notably nitric oxide (NO), that act as local regulators. For example, during sexual arousal, certain neurons in human males release NO into the erectile tissue of the penis. In response, smooth muscle cells in the blood vessel walls of the erectile tissue relax, which causes the blood vessels to dilate and fill the spongy erectile tissue with blood, producing an erection. As you read in Chapter 45, the erectile dysfunction drug Viagra increases the ability to achieve and maintain an erection by inhibiting an enzyme that terminates the action of NO.

Unlike most neurotransmitters, NO is not stored in cytoplasmic vesicles but is instead synthesized on demand. NO diffuses into neighbouring target cells, produces a change, and is broken down—all within a few seconds. In many of its targets, including smooth muscle cells, NO works like many hormones, stimulating an enzyme to synthesize a second messenger that directly affects cellular metabolism.

Although inhaling air containing the gas carbon monoxide (CO) can be deadly, the vertebrate body produces small amounts of CO, some of which acts as a neurotransmitter. Carbon monoxide is generated by the enzyme hemeoxygenase, one form of which is found in certain populations of neurons in the brain and PNS. In the brain, CO regulates the release of hypothalamic hormones. In the PNS, it acts as an inhibitory neurotransmitter that hyperpolarizes the plasma membrane of intestinal smooth muscle cells.

In the next chapter, we will consider how the cellular and biochemical mechanisms we have discussed contribute to nervous system function on the system level.

CONCEPT CHECK 48.4

1. How is it possible for a particular neurotransmitter to produce opposite effects in different tissues?

2. Organophosphate pesticides work by inhibiting acetylcholinesterase, the enzyme that breaks down the neurotransmitter acetylcholine. Explain how these toxins would affect EPSPs produced by acetylcholine.

3. **MAKE CONNECTIONS** Name one or more membrane activities that occur both in fertilization of an egg and in neurotransmission across a synapse (see Figure 47.3).

For suggested answers, see Appendix A.

Interpreting Data Values Expressed in Scientific Notation

Does the Brain Have Specific Protein Receptors for Opiates? A team of researchers were looking for opiate receptors in the mammalian brain. Knowing that the drug naloxone blocks the analgesic effect of opiates, they hypothesized that naloxone acts by binding tightly to brain opiate receptors without activating them. In this exercise, you will interpret the results of an experiment that the researchers conducted to test their hypothesis.

How the Experiment Was Done The researchers added radioactive naloxone to a protein mixture prepared from rodent brains. If the mixture contained opiate receptors or other proteins that could bind naloxone, the radioactivity would stably associate with the mixture. To determine whether the binding was due to specific opiate receptors, they tested other drugs, opiate and non-opiate, for their ability to block naloxone binding.

① Radioactive naloxone and a test drug are incubated with a protein mixture.

Radioactive naloxone

Drug

② Proteins are trapped on a filter. Bound naloxone is detected by measuring radioactivity.

Data from the Experiment

Drug	Opiate	Lowest Concentration That Blocked Naloxone Binding
Morphine	Yes	6×10^{-9} M
Methadone	Yes	2×10^{-8} M
Levorphanol	Yes	2×10^{-9} M
Phenobarbital	No	No effect at 10^{-4} M
Atropine	No	No effect at 10^{-4} M
Serotonin	No	No effect at 10^{-4} M

Source: Data from "Opiate Receptor: Demonstration in Nervous Tissue" by Candace B. Pert and Solomon H. Snyder, from *Science*, March 1973, Volume 179(4077). © Jane B Reece.

Interpret the Data

1. The data above are expressed in scientific notation: a numerical factor times a power of 10. Remember that a negative power of 10 means a number less than 1. For example, 10^{-1} M (molar) can also be written as 0.1 M. Write the concentrations in the table above for morphine and atropine in this alternative format.

2. Compare the concentrations listed in the table for methadone and phenobarbital. Which concentration is higher? By how much?

3. Would phenobarbital, atropine, or serotonin have blocked naloxone binding at a concentration of 10^{-5} M? Explain why or why not.

4. Which drugs blocked naloxone binding in this experiment? What do these results indicate about the brain receptors for naloxone?

5. If researchers instead used tissue from intestinal muscles rather than brains, they found no naloxone binding. What does that suggest about opiate receptors in mammalian muscle?

Data from C. B. Pert and S. H. Snyder, Opiate receptor: Demonstration in nervous tissue, *Science* 179:1011–1014 (1973). © Jane B Reece.

---

48 Chapter Review

Go to **MasteringBiology®** for Assignments, the eText, and the Study Area with Animations, Activities, Vocab Self-Quiz, and Practice Tests.

SUMMARY OF KEY CONCEPTS

CONCEPT 48.1

Neuron organization and structure reflect function in information transfer (pp. 1121–1123)

- Most neurons have branched **dendrites** that receive signals from other neurons and an **axon** that transmits signals to other cells at **synapses**. Neurons rely on **glia** for functions that include nourishment, insulation, and regulation.

- A **central nervous system (CNS)** and a **peripheral nervous system (PNS)** process information in three stages: sensory input, integration, and motor output to effector cells.

? *How would severing an axon affect the flow of information in a neuron?*

CONCEPT 48.2

Ion gradients and ion channels establish the resting membrane potential of a neuron (pp. 1123–1125)

- Ionic gradients generate a voltage difference, or **membrane potential**, across the plasma membrane of cells. The concentration of Na^+ is higher outside than inside; the reverse is true for K^+. In resting neurons, the plasma membrane has many open potassium channels but few open sodium channels. Diffusion of ions, principally K^+, through channels generates a **resting membrane potential**, with the inside more negative than the outside.

? Suppose you placed an isolated neuron in a solution similar to extracellular fluid and later transferred the neuron to a solution lacking any sodium ions. What change would you expect in the resting potential?

CONCEPT 48.3

Action potentials are the signals conducted by axons (pp. 1125–1130)

- Neurons have **gated ion channels** that open or close in response to stimuli, leading to changes in the membrane potential. An increase in the magnitude of the membrane potential is a **hyperpolarization**; a decrease is a **depolarization**. Changes in membrane potential that vary continuously with the strength of a stimulus are known as **graded potentials**.
- An **action potential** is a brief, all-or-none depolarization of a neuron's plasma membrane. When a graded depolarization brings the membrane potential to the threshold, many **voltage-gated ion channels** open, triggering an inflow of Na^+ that rapidly brings the membrane potential to a positive value. A negative membrane potential is restored by the inactivation of sodium channels and by the opening of many voltage-gated potassium channels, which increases K^+ outflow. A **refractory period** follows, corresponding to the interval when the sodium channels are inactivated.

- A nerve impulse travels from the axon hillock to the axon terminals by propagation of a series of action potentials along the axon. The speed of conduction increases with the diameter of the axon and, in many vertebrate axons, with **myelination**. Action potentials in myelinated axons jump between the **nodes of Ranvier**, a process called **saltatory conduction**.

? In what ways do both positive and negative feedback contribute to the shape of an action potential?

CONCEPT 48.4

Neurons communicate with other cells at synapses (pp. 1130–1136)

- In an electrical **synapse**, electrical current flows directly from one cell to another. In a chemical synapse, depolarization causes synaptic vesicles to fuse with the terminal membrane and release **neurotransmitter** into the synaptic cleft.
- At many synapses, the neurotransmitter binds to **ligand-gated ion channels** in the postsynaptic membrane, producing an **excitatory** or **inhibitory postsynaptic potential (EPSP or IPSP)**. The neurotransmitter then diffuses out of the cleft, is taken up by surrounding cells, or is degraded by enzymes. **Temporal** and **spatial summation** at the axon hillock determines whether a neuron generates an action potential.
- Different receptors for the same neurotransmitter produce different effects. Some neurotransmitter receptors activate signal transduction pathways, which can produce long-lasting changes in postsynaptic cells. Major neurotransmitters include acetylcholine; the amino acids GABA, glutamate, and glycine; biogenic amines; neuropeptides; and gases such as NO.

? Why are many drugs used to treat nervous system diseases or affect brain function targeted to specific receptors rather than particular neurotransmitters?

TEST YOUR UNDERSTANDING

LEVEL 1: KNOWLEDGE/COMPREHENSION

1. What happens when a resting neuron's membrane depolarizes?
   a. There is a net diffusion of Na^+ out of the cell.
   b. The equilibrium potential for K^+ (E_K) becomes more positive.
   c. The neuron's membrane potential becomes more positive.
   d. The cell's inside is more negative than the outside.

2. A common feature of action potentials is that they
   a. cause the membrane to hyperpolarize and then depolarize.
   b. can undergo temporal and spatial summation.
   c. are triggered by a depolarization that reaches the threshold.
   d. move at the same speed along all axons.

3. Where are neurotransmitter receptors located?
   a. the nuclear membrane
   b. the nodes of Ranvier
   c. the postsynaptic membrane
   d. synaptic vesicle membranes

LEVEL 2: APPLICATION/ANALYSIS

4. Why are action potentials usually conducted in one direction?
   a. The nodes of Ranvier conduct potentials in one direction.
   b. The brief refractory period prevents reopening of voltage-gated Na^+ channels.
   c. The axon hillock has a higher membrane potential than the terminals of the axon.
   d. Ions can flow along the axon in only one direction.
   e. Voltage-gated channels for both Na^+ and K^+ open in only one direction.

5. Which of the following is a *direct* result of depolarizing the presynaptic membrane of an axon terminal?
   a. Voltage-gated calcium channels in the membrane open.
   b. Synaptic vesicles fuse with the membrane.
   c. The postsynaptic cell produces an action potential.
   d. Ligand-gated channels open, allowing neurotransmitters to enter the synaptic cleft.
   e. An EPSP or IPSP is generated in the postsynaptic cell.

6. Suppose a particular neurotransmitter causes an IPSP in postsynaptic cell X and an EPSP in postsynaptic cell Y. A likely explanation is that
   a. the threshold value in the postsynaptic membrane is different for cell X and cell Y.
   b. the axon of cell X is myelinated, but that of cell Y is not.
   c. only cell Y produces an enzyme that terminates the activity of the neurotransmitter.
   d. cells X and Y express different receptor molecules for this particular neurotransmitter.

LEVEL 3: SYNTHESIS/EVALUATION

7. **WHAT IF?** Ouabain, a plant substance used in some cultures to poison hunting arrows, disables the sodium-potassium pump. What change in the resting potential would you expect to see if you treated a neuron with ouabain? Explain.

8. **WHAT IF?** If a drug mimicked the activity of GABA in the CNS, what general effect on behaviour might you expect? Explain.

9. **DRAW IT** Suppose a researcher inserts a pair of electrodes at two different positions along the middle of an axon dissected out of a squid. By applying a depolarizing stimulus, the researcher brings the plasma membrane at both positions to threshold. Using the drawing below as a model, create one or more drawings that illustrate where each action potential would terminate.

Electrode

Squid axon

10. **EVOLUTION CONNECTION**
An action potential is an all-or-none event. This on/off signalling is an evolutionary adaptation of animals that must sense and act in a complex environment. It is possible to imagine a nervous system in which the action potentials are graded, with the amplitude depending on the size of the stimulus. What evolutionary advantage might on/off signalling have over a graded (continuously variable) kind of signalling?

11. **SCIENTIFIC INQUIRY**
From what you know about action potentials and synapses, propose two or three hypotheses for how various anesthetics might block pain.

12. **WRITE ABOUT A THEME: ORGANIZATION**
In a short essay (100–150 words), describe how the structure and electrical properties of vertebrate neurons reflect similarities and differences with other animal cells.

13. **SYNTHESIZE YOUR KNOWLEDGE**

B.A.E/Alamy Stock Photo

The rattlesnake alerts enemies to its presence with a rattle—a set of modified scales at the tip of its tail. Describe the distinct roles of gated ion channels in initiating and moving a signal along the nerve from the snake's head to its tail and then from that nerve to the muscle that shakes the rattle.

For selected answers, see Appendix A.

49

Nervous Systems

Image by Tamily Weissman, Harvard University. The Brainbow mouse was produced by J. Livet et al., Nature 450:56–62 (2007)

KEY CONCEPTS

49.1 Nervous systems consist of circuits of neurons and supporting cells

49.2 The vertebrate brain is regionally specialized

49.3 The cerebral cortex controls voluntary movement and cognitive functions

49.4 Changes in synaptic connections underlie memory and learning

49.5 Many nervous system disorders can be explained in molecular terms

▲ Figure 49.1 **How do scientists identify individual neurons in the brain?**

Command and Control Centre

What happens in your brain when you solve a math problem or listen to music? Until quite recently, scientists had little hope of answering that question. The human brain contains an estimated 10^{11} (100 billion) neurons. Interconnecting these brain cells are circuits more complex than those of even the most powerful supercomputers. Yet the circuitry of the brain has been largely hidden from view. That's no longer the case, thanks in part to several exciting new technologies.

One recent advance in exploring the brain relies on a method for expressing random combinations of coloured proteins in brain cells—such that each cell shows up in a different colour. The result is a "brainbow" like the one in **Figure 49.1**, which highlights neurons in the brain of a mouse. In this image, each neuron expresses one of more than 90 different colour combinations of four fluorescent proteins. Using the brainbow technology, neuroscientists hope to develop detailed maps of the connections that transfer information between particular regions of the brain.

Another advance has come in the rapid and easy detection of brain trauma and concussion. Brain trauma is common in a variety of team sports, as well as boxing and cycling. A study conducted in 1997 on Canadian Football League

◀ **Brain**

Soul wind/Shutterstock

players indicated that 44.8% of the players had likely suffered concussions during the season. Yet only 18.8% of them were aware that they had even suffered a concussion. The main problem is actually diagnosing a concussion or other head trauma. Individuals with head trauma may not lose consciousness at the time or their symptoms may not show up for hours or days. So, how does a coach or even a doctor know if an athlete has suffered a traumatic brain injury? Dr. Ryan D'Arcy, a neurologist at Dalhousie University in Halifax, may have an answer to that question. He has designed a mobile device called the Halifax Consciousness Scanner (HCS). A person suspected of a head trauma listens to a special sound recording while the HCS records his or her brain waves. The HCS rapidly determines the individual's level of consciousness and assigns a score to them. The HCS is now being tested in hospitals, and with over 500 000 Canadians competing annually in hockey, the number one team sport for concussions, the benefits of having an HCS at every hospital and eventually every sports event are clear.

In this chapter, we will discuss the organization and evolution of animal nervous systems, exploring how groups of neurons function in specialized circuits dedicated to specific tasks. First we'll focus on specialization in regions of the vertebrate brain. We will then turn to the ways in which brain activity makes information storage and organization possible. Finally, we'll consider several disorders of the nervous system that are the subject of intense research today.

CONCEPT 49.1

Nervous systems consist of circuits of neurons and supporting cells

The ability to sense and react originated billions of years ago with prokaryotes that could detect changes in their environment and respond in ways that enhanced their survival and reproductive success. For example, bacteria keep moving in a particular direction as long as they encounter increasing concentrations of a food source. Later in evolution, modification of simple recognition and response processes provided multicellular organisms with a mechanism for communication between cells of the body. By the time of the Cambrian explosion more than 500 million years ago (see Chapter 32), specialized systems of neurons had appeared, enabling animals to sense their surroundings and respond rapidly.

Hydras, jellies, and other cnidarians are the simplest animals with nervous systems. As you read in Chapters 33 and 41, these animals have radially symmetrical bodies organized around a central digestive compartment, the gastrovascular cavity. In most cnidarians, interconnected nerve cells form a diffuse **nerve net** (Figure 49.2a), which controls the contraction and expansion of the gastrovascular cavity. In more complex animals, the axons of multiple nerve cells are often bundled together, forming **nerves**. These fibrous structures channel and organize information flow along specific routes through the nervous system. For example, sea

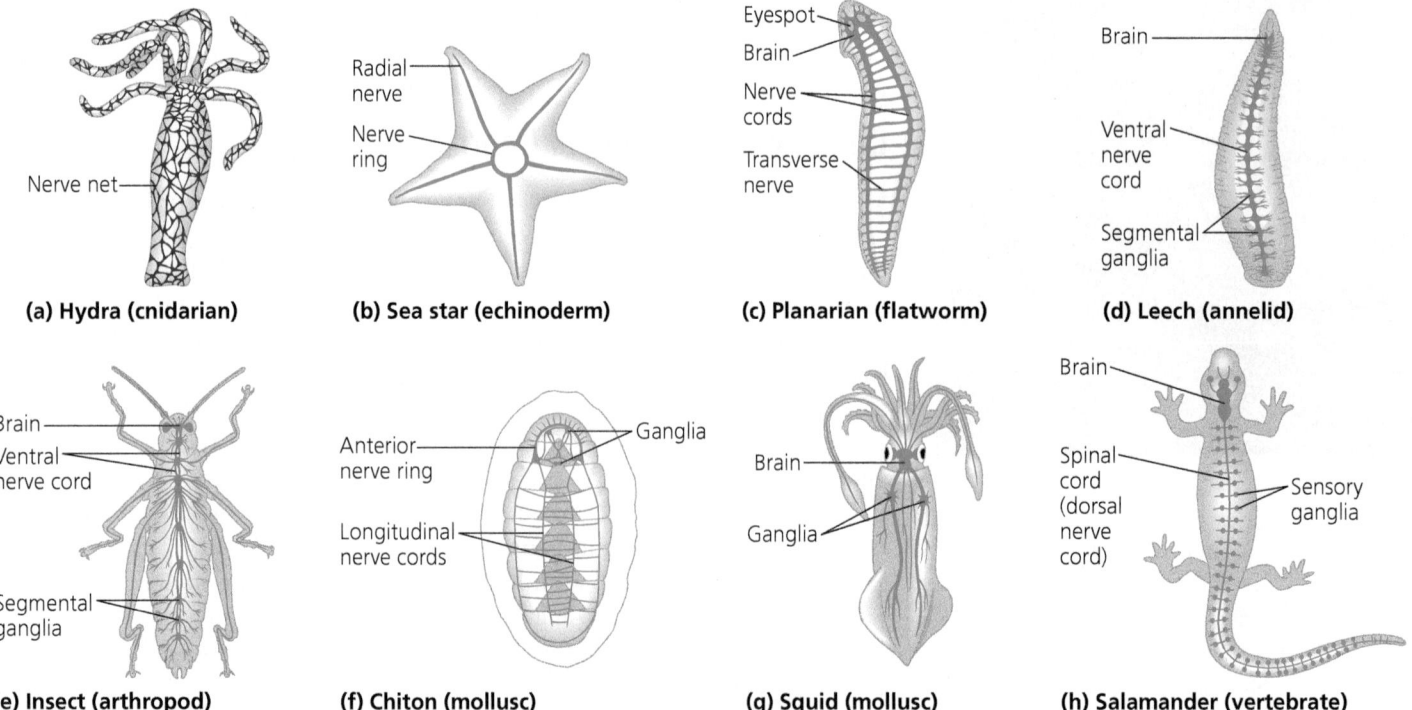

(a) Hydra (cnidarian)

(b) Sea star (echinoderm)

(c) Planarian (flatworm)

(d) Leech (annelid)

(e) Insect (arthropod)

(f) Chiton (mollusc)

(g) Squid (mollusc)

(h) Salamander (vertebrate)

▲ Figure 49.2 **Nervous system organization.** **(a)** A hydra contains individual neurons (purple) organized in a diffuse nerve net. **(b–h)** Animals with more sophisticated nervous systems contain groups of neurons (blue) organized into nerves and often ganglia and a brain.

stars have a set of radial nerves connecting to a central nerve ring (Figure 49.2b). Within each arm of a sea star, the radial nerve is linked to a nerve net from which it receives input and to which it sends signals controlling muscle contraction.

Animals that have elongated, bilaterally symmetrical bodies have even more specialized nervous systems. Such animals exhibit *cephalization*, an evolutionary trend toward a clustering of sensory neurons and interneurons at the anterior (front) end of the body. These anterior neurons communicate with cells elsewhere in the body, including neurons located in one or more nerve cords extending toward the posterior (rear) end.

As you learned in Concept 48.1, many animals organize their neurons into separate systems. The neurons of the *central nervous system (CNS)* integrate information and the neurons of the *peripheral nervous system (PNS)* carry information into and out of the CNS. In nonsegmented worms, such as the planarian shown in Figure 49.2c, a small brain and longitudinal nerve cords constitute the simplest clearly defined CNS. In some nonsegmented worms, the entire nervous system is constructed from only a small number of cells, as shown by studies of another nonsegmented worm, the nematode *Caenorhabditis elegans*. In this species, an adult worm (hermaphrodite) has exactly 302 neurons. More complex invertebrates, such as segmented worms (annelids; Figure 49.2d) and arthropods (Figure 49.2e), have many more

neurons. The behaviour of such invertebrates is regulated by more complicated brains and by ventral nerve cords containing **ganglia**, segmentally arranged clusters of neurons.

The nervous system organization often correlates with lifestyle. Among the molluscs, for example, sessile and slow-moving species, such as clams and chitons, have relatively simple sense organs and little or no cephalization (Figure 49.2f). In contrast, active predatory molluscs, such as octopuses and squids (Figure 49.2g), have the most sophisticated nervous systems of any invertebrates, rivalling those of some vertebrates. With their large, image-forming eyes and a brain containing millions of neurons, octopuses can learn to discriminate between visual patterns and to perform complex tasks.

In vertebrates (Figure 49.2h), the brain and the spinal cord form the CNS; nerves and ganglia are the key components of the PNS. Regional specialization is a hallmark of both systems, as we will see throughout the remainder of this chapter.

Glia

As discussed in Chapter 48, the nervous systems of vertebrates and most invertebrates include **glial cells**, or **glia**. Some examples of glia are the Schwann cells that produce the myelin sheaths surrounding axons in the PNS, and oligodendrocytes, their counterparts in the CNS. Figure 49.3

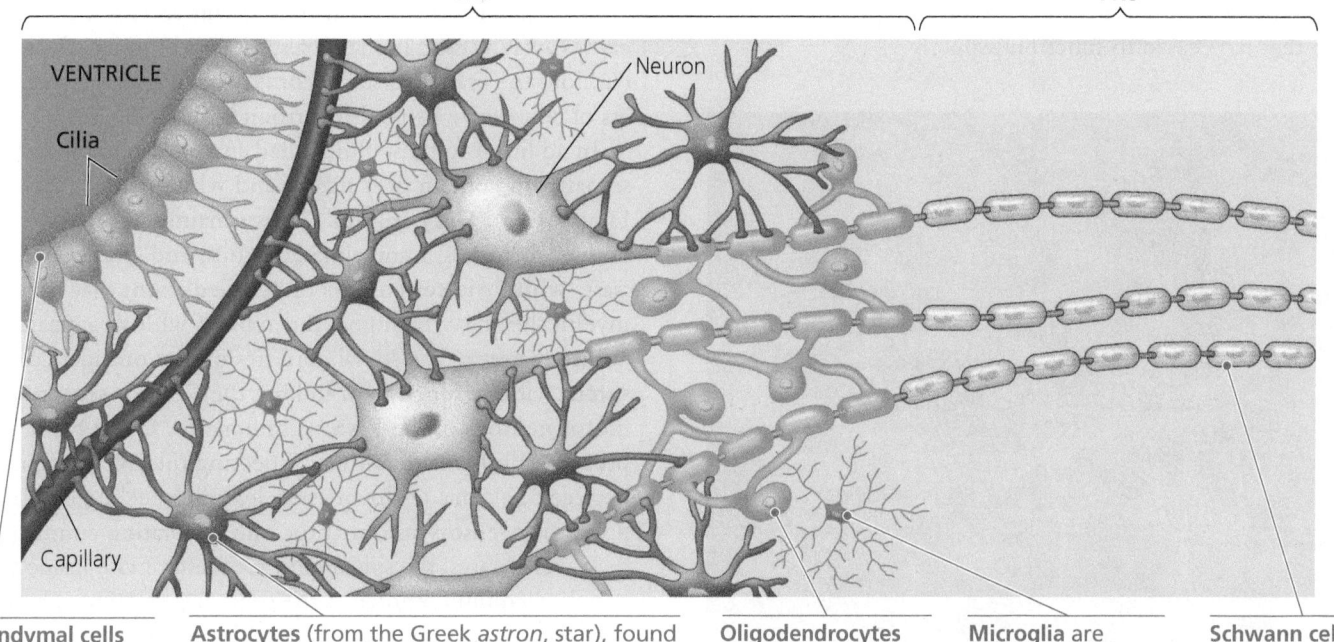

Ependymal cells line the ventricles of the brain (see Figure 49.5) and have cilia that promote circulation of the cerebrospinal fluid.

Astrocytes (from the Greek *astron*, star), found in the CNS, facilitate information transfer at synapses and in some instances release neurotransmitters. Astrocytes next to active neurons cause nearby blood vessels to dilate, increasing blood flow and enabling the neurons to obtain oxygen and glucose more quickly. Astrocytes also regulate extracellular concentrations of ions and neurotransmitters.

Oligodendrocytes myelinate axons in the CNS. Myelination greatly increases the conduction speed of action potentials.

Microglia are immune cells in the CNS that protect against pathogens.

Schwann cells myelinate axons in the PNS.

▲ Figure 49.3 **Glia in the vertebrate nervous system.**

illustrates the major types of glia in the adult nervous system and provides an overview of the ways in which they nourish, support, and regulate the functioning of neurons.

Glia also have an essential role in nervous system development. In embryos, cells called radial glia form tracks along which newly formed neurons migrate from the neural tube, the structure that gives rise to the CNS (see Figure 47.14). Later, astrocytes induce the formation of tight junctions in the endothelial cells that line the capillaries in the CNS. The result is the blood-brain barrier, which controls the extracellular environment of the CNS by restricting the entry of most substances from the blood. Some molecules, including hormones, cross the blood-brain barrier by passing through the endothelial cells. The barrier is incomplete in some regions, permitting the brain to detect blood-borne metabolites and proteins. We will discuss the significance of the incomplete blood-brain barrier later when considering how blood-borne metabolites and hormones affect brain function.

Both radial glia and astrocytes can act as stem cells, retaining the ability to divide indefinitely. While some of their progeny remain undifferentiated, others differentiate into specialized cells. Studies with mice reveal that stem cells in the brain give rise to neurons that mature, migrate to particular locations, and become incorporated into the circuitry of the adult nervous system (Figure 49.4). Researchers are now tackling the challenge of finding a way to use neural stem cells as a means of replacing brain tissue that has ceased to function properly.

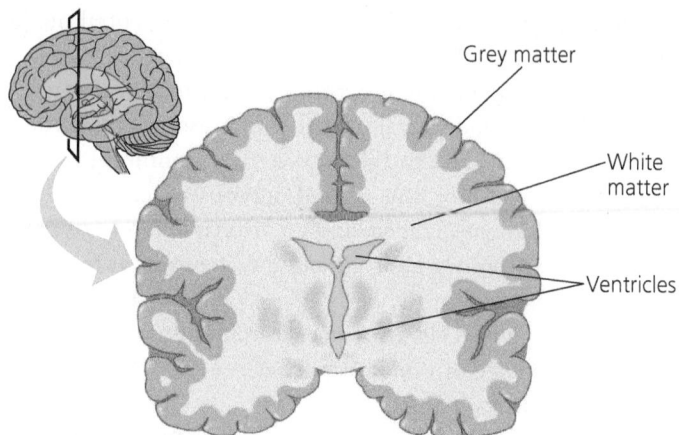

▲ Figure 49.5 **Ventricles, grey matter, and white matter.** Ventricles deep in the brain's interior contain cerebrospinal fluid. Most of the grey matter is on the surface of the brain, surrounding the white matter.

Organization of the Vertebrate Nervous System

During embryonic development in vertebrates, the central nervous system develops from the hollow dorsal neural tube—a hallmark of chordates (see Chapter 34). The cavity of the neural tube gives rise to the narrow **central canal** of the spinal cord as well as the **ventricles** of the brain (Figure 49.5). Both the canal and ventricles fill with **cerebrospinal fluid**, which is formed in the brain by filtration of arterial blood. The cerebrospinal fluid circulates slowly through the central canal and ventricles and then drains into the veins. This circulation supplies the brain with nutrients and hormones and carries away wastes. In mammals, the cerebrospinal fluid also cushions the brain and spinal cord by circulating between layers of connective tissue that surround the CNS.

In addition to these fluid-filled spaces, the brain and spinal cord contain grey matter and white matter (see Figure 49.5). **Grey matter** consists mainly of neuron cell bodies, dendrites, unmyelinated axons, and glia. In contrast, **white matter** consists of bundled axons that have myelin sheaths, which give the axons a whitish appearance. White matter in the spinal cord lies on the outside, consistent with its function in linking the CNS to sensory and motor neurons of the PNS. White matter in the brain is predominantly on the inside, reflecting the role of signalling between neurons of the brain in learning, feeling emotions, processing sensory information, and generating commands.

In vertebrates, the spinal cord runs lengthwise inside the vertebral column, known as the spine (Figure 49.6). The spinal cord conveys information to and from the brain and generates basic patterns of locomotion. It also acts independently of the brain as part of the simple nerve circuits that produce **reflexes**, the body's automatic responses to certain stimuli.

A reflex protects the body by triggering a rapid, involuntary response to a particular stimulus. If you put your hand on a hot burner, a reflex begins to pull your hand back well before the sensation of pain has been processed in

▲ Figure 49.4 **Newly born neurons in the brain of an adult mouse.** In this light micrograph, new neurons derived from adult stem cells are labelled with green fluorescent protein (GFP), and all neurons are labelled with a DNA-binding dye, coloured red in this image.

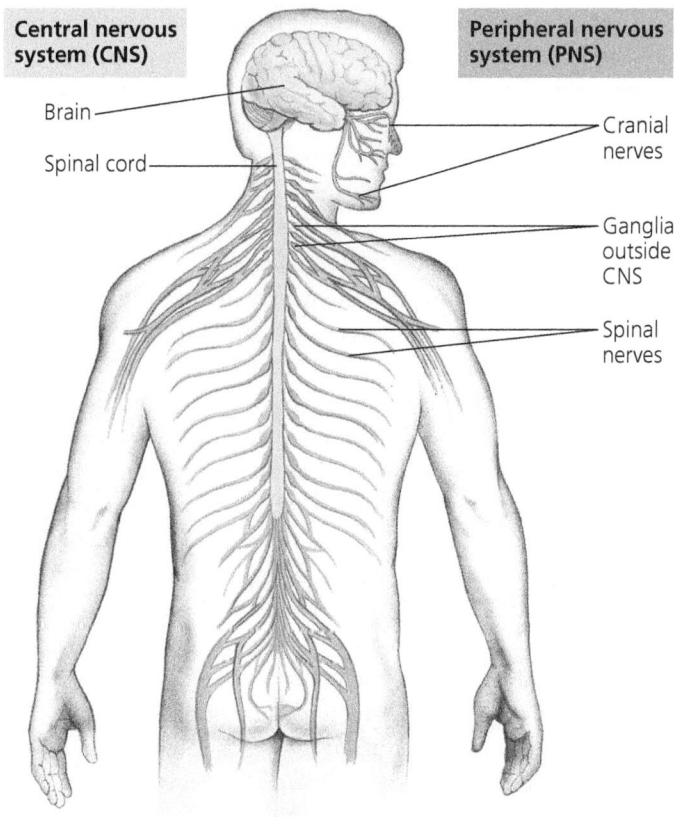

Central nervous system (CNS)

Brain
Spinal cord

Peripheral nervous system (PNS)

Cranial nerves
Ganglia outside CNS
Spinal nerves

▲ Figure 49.6 **The vertebrate nervous system.**

The central nervous system consists of the brain and spinal cord (yellow). Left-right pairs of cranial nerves, spinal nerves, and ganglia make up most of the peripheral nervous system (dark gold).

your brain. Similarly, if your knees buckle when you pick up a heavy object, the tension across your knees triggers a reflex that contracts the thigh muscles, helping you stay upright and support the load. During a physical exam, your doctor may trigger this knee-jerk reflex with a mallet to help assess nervous system function (Figure 49.7).

The Peripheral Nervous System

The PNS transmits information to and from the CNS and plays a large role in regulating an animal's movement and internal

▶ Figure 49.7 **The knee-jerk reflex.** Many neurons are involved in the reflex, but for simplicity, only a few neurons are shown.

MAKE CONNECTIONS *Using the nerve signals to the hamstring and quadriceps in this reflex as an example, propose a model for regulation of smooth muscle activity in the esophagus during the swallowing reflex (see Figure 41.9).*

environment (Figure 49.8). Sensory information reaches the CNS along PNS neurons designated as *afferent* (from the Latin, meaning "to carry toward"). Following information processing within the CNS, instructions then travel to muscles, glands, and endocrine cells along PNS neurons designated as *efferent* (from the Latin, meaning "to carry away"). Most nerves contain both afferent and efferent neurons. One exception is the olfactory nerve, which conveys only sensory information from the nose to the brain.

The PNS has two efferent components: the motor system and the autonomic nervous system (see Figure 49.8). The **motor system** consists of neurons that carry signals to skeletal muscles. Motor control can be voluntary, as when you raise your hand to ask a question, or involuntary, as in the knee-jerk reflex controlled by the spinal cord. In contrast, regulation of smooth and cardiac muscles by the **autonomic nervous system** is generally involuntary. The three divisions of the autonomic nervous system—sympathetic, parasympathetic, and enteric—together control the organs of the digestive, cardiovascular, excretory, and endocrine systems. For example, networks of neurons that form the **enteric division** of the autonomic nervous system are active in the digestive tract, pancreas, and gallbladder.

The sympathetic and parasympathetic divisions of the autonomic nervous system have largely antagonistic (opposite)

❶ The reflex is initiated artificially by tapping the tendon connected to the quadriceps muscle.

❷ Sensors detect a sudden stretch in the quadriceps, and **sensory neurons** convey the information to the spinal cord.

❸ In response to signals from the sensory neurons, **motor neurons** convey signals to the quadriceps, causing it to contract and jerking the lower leg forward.

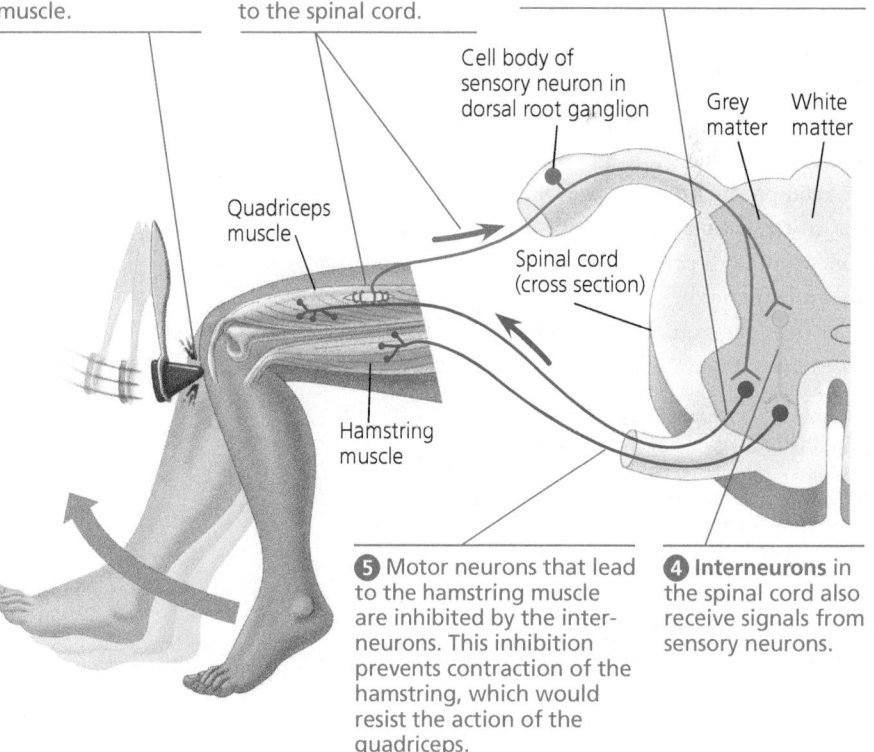

Cell body of sensory neuron in dorsal root ganglion

Grey matter   White matter

Quadriceps muscle

Spinal cord (cross section)

Hamstring muscle

❺ Motor neurons that lead to the hamstring muscle are inhibited by the interneurons. This inhibition prevents contraction of the hamstring, which would resist the action of the quadriceps.

❹ **Interneurons** in the spinal cord also receive signals from sensory neurons.

Key   ● Sensory neuron   ● Motor neuron   ● Interneuron

▲ **Figure 49.8 Functional hierarchy of the vertebrate peripheral nervous system.**

functions in regulating organ function (Figure 49.9). Activation of the **sympathetic division** corresponds to arousal and energy generation (the "fight-or-flight" response). For example, the heart beats faster, digestion is inhibited, the liver converts glycogen to glucose, and the adrenal medulla increases secretion of epinephrine (adrenaline). Activation of the **parasympathetic division** generally causes opposite responses that promote calming and a return to self-maintenance functions ("rest and digest"). Thus, heart rate decreases, digestion is enhanced, and glycogen production increases. However, in regulating reproductive activity, a function that is not homeostatic, the parasympathetic division complements rather than antagonizes the sympathetic division (see Figure 49.9).

▶ **Figure 49.9 The parasympathetic and sympathetic divisions of the autonomic nervous system.** Most pathways in each division involve two neurons. The axon of the first neuron extends from a cell body in the CNS to a set of PNS neurons whose cell bodies are clustered into a ganglion (plural, *ganglia*). The axons of these PNS neurons transmit instructions to internal organs, where they form synapses with smooth muscle, cardiac muscle, or gland cells.

Source: Human Anatomy and Physiology, 8th edition, by Elaine N. Marieb and Katja Hoehn. Copyright © 2010 by Pearson Education. Reprinted and electronically reproduced by permission of Pearson Education, Inc., Upper Saddle River, New Jersey.

The two divisions differ not only in overall function but also in organization and signals released. Parasympathetic nerves exit the CNS at the base of the brain or spinal cord and form synapses in ganglia near or within an internal organ (see Figure 49.9). In contrast, sympathetic nerves typically exit the CNS midway along the spinal cord and form synapses in ganglia located just outside of the spinal cord.

In both the sympathetic and parasympathetic divisions, the pathway for information flow frequently involves a preganglionic and a postganglionic neuron. The preganglionic neurons, those with cell bodies in the CNS, release acetylcholine as a neurotransmitter. In the case of the postganglionic neurons, those of the parasympathetic division release acetycholine, whereas their counterparts in the sympathetic division release norepinephrine. It is this difference in neurotransmitters that enables the sympathetic and parasympathetic divisions to bring about opposite effects in organs such as the lungs, heart, intestines, and bladder.

Homeostasis often relies on cooperation between the motor and autonomic nervous systems. In response to a drop in body temperature, for example, the hypothalamus signals the motor nerves to cause shivering, which increases heat production. At the same time, the hypothalamus signals the autonomic nervous system to constrict surface blood vessels, reducing heat loss.

1. Which division of the autonomic nervous system would likely be activated if a student learned that an exam she had forgotten about would start in 5 minutes? Explain your answer.

2. **WHAT IF?** Suppose a person had an accident that severed a small nerve required to move some of the fingers of the right hand. Would you also expect an effect on sensation from those fingers?

3. **MAKE CONNECTIONS** Most tissues regulated by the autonomic nervous system receive both sympathetic and parasympathetic input from postganglionic neurons. Responses are typically local. In contrast, the adrenal medulla receives input only from the sympathetic division and only from preganglionic neurons, yet responses are observed throughout the body. Explain why (see Figure 45.23).

For suggested answers, see Appendix A.

CONCEPT **49.2**

The vertebrate brain is regionally specialized

We turn now to the vertebrate brain, which has three major regions: the forebrain, midbrain, and hindbrain (shown here for a ray-finned fish):

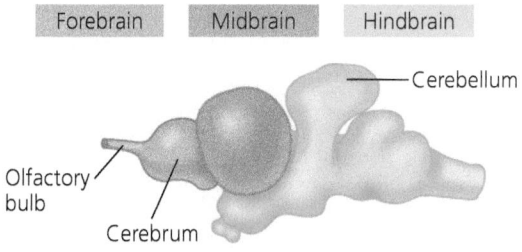

| Forebrain | Midbrain | Hindbrain |

- Cerebellum

Olfactory bulb

Cerebrum

Each region is specialized in function. The **forebrain**, which contains the *olfactory bulb* and *cerebrum*, has activities that include processing of olfactory input (smells), regulation of sleep, learning, and any complex processing. The **midbrain**, located centrally in the brain, coordinates routing of sensory input. The **hindbrain**, part of which forms the *cerebellum*, controls involuntary activities, such as blood circulation, and coordinates motor activities, such as locomotion.

Comparing vertebrates across a phylogenetic tree, we see that the relative sizes of particular brain regions vary (Figure 49.10). Furthermore, these size differences reflect differences in the importance of particular brain functions. Consider, for example, ray-finned fishes, which explore their environment using olfaction, vision, and a lateral line system that detects water currents, electrical stimuli, and body position. The olfactory bulb, which

detects scents in the water, is relatively large in these fishes. So is the midbrain, which processes input from the visual and lateral line systems. In contrast, the cerebrum, required for complex processing and learning, is relatively small. Evolution has thus resulted in a close match of structure to function, with the size of particular brain regions correlating with their importance for that species in nervous system function and, hence, species survival and reproduction.

The correlation between the size and function of brain regions can also be observed by considering the cerebellum. Free-swimming ray-finned fishes, such as the tuna, control movement in three dimensions in the open water and have a relatively large cerebellum. In comparison, the cerebellum is much smaller in species that don't swim actively.

If one compares birds and mammals with groups that diverged from the common vertebrate ancestor earlier in evolution, two trends are apparent. First, the forebrain of birds and mammals occupies a larger fraction of the brain than it does in amphibians, fishes, and other vertebrates. Second, birds and mammals have much larger brains relative to body size than do other groups. Indeed, the ratio of brain size to body weight is 10 times as large for birds and mammals as for their evolutionary ancestors. These differences in both overall brain size and the relative size of the forebrain reflect the greater capacity of birds and mammals for cognition and higher-order reasoning, traits we will return to later in this chapter.

In the case of humans, it is estimated that the brain contains 100 billion neurons. How are so many cells organized into circuits and networks that can perform highly sophisticated information processing, storage, and retrieval? In addressing this question, let's begin with **Figure 49.11**,

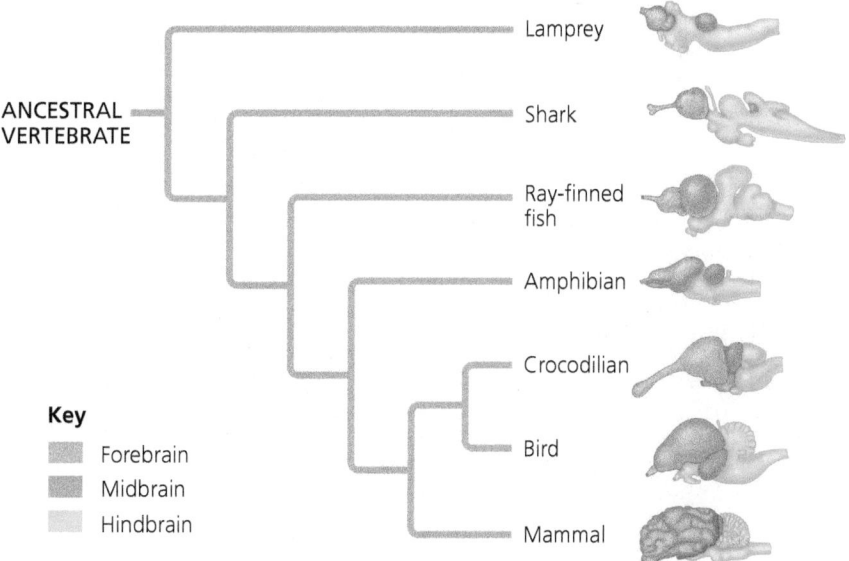

Lamprey

Shark

Ray-finned fish

Amphibian

Crocodilian

Bird

Mammal

ANCESTRAL VERTEBRATE

Key

Forebrain
Midbrain
Hindbrain

▲ **Figure 49.10 Vertebrate brain structure and evolution.** During evolution, differences arose in the relative size of the major structures common to vertebrate brains. As discussed in the text, size differences correlate with the importance of particular brain functions for particular vertebrate groups.

Exploring **The Organization of the Human Brain**

The brain is the most complex organ in the human body. Surrounded by the thick bones of the skull, the brain is divided into a set of distinctive structures, some of which are visible in the magnetic resonance image (MRI) of an adult's head shown at right. The diagram below traces the development of these structures in the embryo. Their major functions are explained on the facing page.

Larry Mulvehill/Corbis

Human Brain Development

As a human embryo develops, the neural tube forms three anterior bulges—the forebrain, midbrain, and hindbrain—that together produce the adult brain. The midbrain and portions of the hindbrain give rise to the **brainstem**, a stalk that joins with the spinal cord at the base of the brain. The rest of the hindbrain gives rise to the **cerebellum**, which lies behind the brainstem. The third anterior bulge, the forebrain, develops into the diencephalon, including the neuroendocrine tissues of the brain, and the telencephalon, which becomes the **cerebrum**. Rapid, expansive growth of the telencephalon during the second and third months causes the outer portion, or cortex, of the cerebrum to extend over and around much of the rest of the brain.

Embryonic brain regions

Brain structures in child and adult

Forebrain → Telencephalon → Cerebrum (includes cerebral cortex, white matter, basal nuclei)

Forebrain → Diencephalon → Diencephalon (thalamus, hypothalamus, epithalamus)

Midbrain → Mesencephalon → Midbrain (part of brainstem)

Hindbrain → Metencephalon → Pons (part of brainstem), cerebellum

Hindbrain → Myelencephalon → Medulla oblongata (part of brainstem)

Midbrain
Hindbrain
Forebrain

Embryo at 1 month

Mesencephalon
Metencephalon
Diencephalon
Myelencephalon
Spinal cord
Telencephalon

Embryo at 5 weeks

Cerebrum
Diencephalon
Midbrain
Pons
Medulla oblongata
Cerebellum
Spinal cord

Child

The Cerebrum

The cerebrum controls skeletal muscle contraction and is the centre for learning, emotion, memory, and perception. It is divided into right and left **cerebral hemispheres**. The **cerebral cortex** is vital for perception, voluntary movement, and learning. Like the rest of the cerebrum, the cerebral cortex is divided into right and left sides. The left side receives information from, and controls the movement of, the right side of the body, and vice versa. A thick band of axons known as the **corpus callosum** enables the right and left cerebral cortices to communicate. Deep within the white matter, clusters of neurons called *basal nuclei* serve as centres for planning and learning movement sequences. Damage to these sites during fetal development can result in cerebral palsy, a disorder resulting from a disruption in the transmission of motor commands to the muscles.

The Cerebellum

The cerebellum coordinates movement and balance and helps in learning and remembering motor skills. The cerebellum receives sensory information about the positions of the joints and the lengths of the muscles, as well as input from the auditory (hearing) and visual systems. It also monitors motor commands issued by the cerebrum. The cerebellum integrates this information as it carries out coordination and error checking during motor and perceptual functions. Hand-eye coordination is an example of cerebellar control; if the cerebellum is damaged, the eyes can follow a moving object, but they will not stop at the same place as the object. Hand movement toward the object will also be erratic.

Left cerebral hemisphere
Right cerebral hemisphere
Cerebral cortex
Corpus callosum
Basal nuclei
Cerebrum
Cerebellum

Adult brain viewed from the rear

The Diencephalon

The diencephalon gives rise to the thalamus, hypothalamus, and epithalamus. The **thalamus** is the main input centre for sensory information going to the cerebrum. Incoming information from all the senses is sorted in the thalamus and sent to the appropriate cerebral centres for further processing. The thalamus is formed by two masses, each roughly the size and shape of a walnut. A much smaller structure, the **hypothalamus**, contains the body's thermostat as well as the central biological clock. Through its control of the pituitary gland, the hypothalamus regulates hunger and thirst, plays a role in sexual and mating behaviours, and controls the fight-or-flight response. The hypothalamus is also the source of posterior pituitary hormones and of releasing hormones that act on the anterior pituitary (see Figures 45.16 and 45.18). The *epithalamus* includes the pineal gland, the source of melatonin. It also contains one of several clusters of capillaries that generate cerebrospinal fluid from blood.

Diencephalon
Thalamus
Pineal gland
Hypothalamus
Pituitary gland
Spinal cord

The Brainstem

The brainstem consists of the midbrain, the **pons**, and the **medulla oblongata** (commonly called the *medulla*). The midbrain receives and integrates several types of sensory information and sends it to specific regions of the forebrain. All sensory axons involved in hearing either terminate in the midbrain or pass through it on their way to the cerebrum. In addition, the midbrain coordinates visual reflexes, such as the peripheral vision reflex: The head turns toward an object approaching from the side without the brain having formed an image of the object.

A major function of the pons and medulla is to transfer information between the PNS and the midbrain and forebrain. The pons and medulla also help coordinate large-scale body movements, such as running and climbing. Most axons that carry instructions about these movements cross from one side of the CNS to the other in the medulla. As a result, the right side of the brain controls much of the movement of the left side of the body, and vice versa. An additional function of the medulla is the control of several automatic, homeostatic functions, including breathing, heart and blood vessel activity, swallowing, vomiting, and digestion. The pons also participates in some of these activities; for example, it regulates the breathing centres in the medulla.

Brainstem
Midbrain
Pons
Medulla oblongata

which explores the overall architecture of the human brain. You can use this figure to trace how brain structures arise during embryonic development; as a reference for their size, shape, and location in the adult brain; and as an introduction to their best-understood functions.

To learn more about how particular brain structure and brain organization overall relate to brain function in humans, we'll first consider activity cycles of the brain and the physiological basis of emotion. Then, in Concept 49.3, we'll shift our attention to regional specialization within the cerebrum.

Arousal and Sleep

If you've ever drifted off to sleep while listening to a lecture (or reading a book), you know that your attentiveness and mental alertness can change rapidly. Such transitions are regulated by the brainstem and cerebrum, which control arousal and sleep. Arousal is a state of awareness of the external world. Sleep is a state in which external stimuli are received but not consciously perceived.

Contrary to appearances, sleep is an active state, at least for the brain. By placing electrodes at multiple sites on the scalp, we can record patterns of electrical activity called brain waves in an electroencephalogram (EEG). These recordings reveal that brain wave frequencies change as the brain progresses through distinct stages of sleep.

Although sleep is essential for survival, we still know very little about its function. One hypothesis is that sleep and dreams are involved in consolidating learning and memory. This hypothesis is supported by the finding that test subjects who are kept awake for 36 hours have a reduced ability to remember when particular events occurred, even if they first "perk up" with caffeine. Other experiments show that regions of the brain that are activated during a learning task can become active again during sleep.

Arousal and sleep are controlled in part by the **reticular formation**, a diffuse network of neurons in the core of the brainstem (**Figure 49.12**). Acting as a sensory filter, the reticular formation determines which incoming information reaches the cerebrum. The more information the cerebrum receives, the more alert and aware a person is, although the brain often ignores certain stimuli while actively processing other inputs. Besides the diffuse reticular formation, there are also specific parts of the brainstem that regulate sleep and wakefulness: The pons and medulla contain centres that cause sleep when stimulated, and the midbrain has a centre that causes arousal.

All birds and mammals show characteristic sleep/wake cycles. Melatonin, a hormone produced by the pineal gland, appears to play an important role in these cycles. As you read in Chapter 45, peak melatonin secretion occurs at night.

Some animals display evolutionary adaptations that allow for substantial activity during sleep. Bottlenose dolphins, for example, swim while sleeping, rising to the surface to

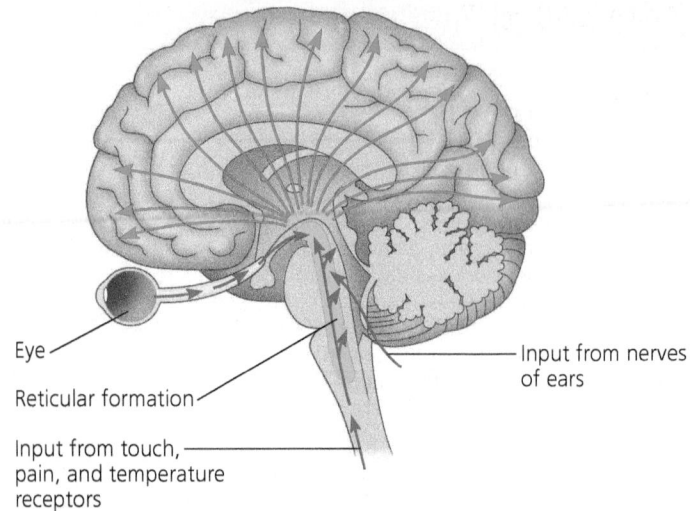

Eye

Reticular formation

Input from touch, pain, and temperature receptors

Input from nerves of ears

▲ Figure 49.12 **The reticular formation.** This system of neurons distributed throughout the core of the brainstem filters sensory input (blue arrows), blocking familiar and repetitive information that constantly enters the nervous system. It sends the filtered input to the cerebral cortex (green arrows).

breathe air on a regular basis. How do they manage this feat? A critical clue came from American physiologist John Lilly, who in 1964 observed that dolphins sleep with one eye open and one closed. As in humans and other mammals, the forebrain of dolphins is physically and functionally divided into two halves, the right and left hemispheres. Lilly suggested that a dolphin sleeping with one eye closed could mean that just one side of the brain was asleep. In 1977, Russian scientist Lev Mukhametov set out to test Lilly's hypothesis by collecting EEG recordings from each hemisphere of sleeping dolphins (**Figure 49.13**). Mukhametov's findings demonstrate that dolphins do in fact sleep with one brain hemisphere resting at a time.

Key

⋀⋀ Low-frequency waves characteristic of sleep

〰 High-frequency waves characteristic of wakefulness

Location	Time: 0 hours	Time: 1 hour
Left hemisphere	⋀⋀⋀⋀⋀	〰〰〰
Right hemisphere	〰〰〰	⋀⋀⋀⋀⋀

▲ Figure 49.13 **Dolphins can be asleep and awake at the same time.** EEG recordings were made separately for the two sides of a dolphin's brain. Low-frequency activity was recorded in one hemisphere while higher-frequency activity typical of being awake was recorded in the other hemisphere.

Source: Based on "Sleep in Marine Mammals" by L. M. Mukhametov, from Sleep Mechanisms, *edited by Alexander A. Borberly and J. L. Valatx. Springer, 1984.*

Biological Clock Regulation

Cycles of sleep and wakefulness are just one example of a circadian rhythm, a daily cycle of biological activity. Such cycles occur in organisms ranging from bacteria to fungi, plants, insects, birds, and humans. As in other organisms, circadian rhythms in mammals rely on a **biological clock**, a molecular mechanism that directs periodic gene expression and cellular activity. Although biological clocks are typically synchronized to the cycles of light and dark in the environment, they can maintain a roughly 24-hour cycle even in the absence of environmental cues (see Figure 40.9). For example, humans kept in a constant environment exhibit a cycle length of 24.2 hours, with very little variation among individuals.

What normally links an animal's biological clock to environmental cycles of light and dark? In mammals, circadian rhythms are coordinated by a group of neurons in the hypothalamus called the **suprachiasmatic nucleus**, or **SCN**. (Certain clusters of neurons in the CNS are referred to as "nuclei.") In response to transmission of sensory information by the eyes, the SCN acts as a pacemaker, synchronizing the biological clock in cells throughout the body to the natural cycles of day length. By surgically removing the SCN from laboratory animals and then observing their behaviour, scientists demonstrated that the SCN is required for circadian rhythms: Animals without an SCN lack rhythmicity in behaviours and in electrical activity of the brain. These experiments did not, however, reveal whether rhythms originate in the SCN or elsewhere. In 1990, researchers answered this question with the aid of a mutation that changes the circadian rhythm of hamsters, as discussed in the Scientific Skills Exercise. By transplanting brain tissue between normal and mutant hamsters, these

SCIENTIFIC SKILLS EXERCISE

Designing an Experiment Using Genetic Mutants

Does the SCN Control the Circadian Rhythm in Hamsters? By surgically removing the SCN from laboratory mammals, scientists demonstrated that the SCN is required for circadian rhythms. Those experiments did not, however, reveal whether circadian rhythms originate in the SCN. To answer this question, researchers performed an SCN transplant experiment on wild-type and mutant hamsters (*Mesocricetus auratus*). Whereas wild-type hamsters have a circadian cycle lasting about 24 hours in the absence of external cues, hamsters homozygous for the τ (tau) mutation have a cycle lasting only about 20 hours. In this exercise, you will evaluate the design of this experiment and propose additional experiments to gain further insight.

How the Experiment Was Done The researchers surgically removed the SCN from wild-type and τ hamsters. Several weeks later, each of these hamsters received a transplant of an SCN from a hamster of the opposite genotype. To determine the periodicity of rhythmic activity for the hamsters before the surgery and after the transplants, the researchers measured activity levels over a three-week period. They plotted the data collected for each day in the manner shown in Figure 40.9a and then calculated the circadian cycle period.

Data from the Experiment In 80% of the hamsters in which the SCN had been removed, transplanting an SCN from another hamster restored rhythmic activity. For hamsters in which an SCN transplant restored a circadian rhythm, the net effect of the two procedures (SCN removal and replacement) on the circadian cycle period is graphed at the upper right. Each red line connects the two data points for an individual hamster.

Interpret the Data

1. What was the variable manipulated in this study? Why did the researchers use more than one hamster for each procedure? What traits of the individual hamsters would likely have been held constant among the treatment groups?

2. For the wild-type hamsters that received τ SCN transplants, what would have been an appropriate experimental control?

3. What general trends does the graph reveal about the circadian cycle period of the transplant recipients? Do the trends differ for the

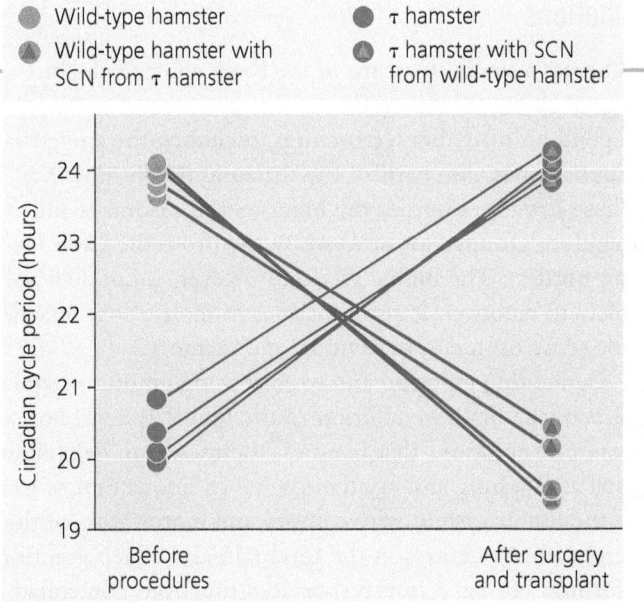

wild-type and τ recipients? Based on these data, what can you conclude about the role of the SCN in determining the period of the circadian rhythm?

4. In 20% of the hamsters, there was no restoration of rhythmic activity following the SCN transplant. What are some possible reasons for this finding? Do you think you can be confident of your conclusion about the role of the SCN based on data from 80% of the hamsters?

5. Suppose that researchers identified a mutant hamster that lacked rhythmic activity; that is, its circadian activity cycle had no regular pattern. Propose SCN transplant experiments using such a mutant along with (a) wild-type and (b) τ hamsters. Predict the results of those experiments in light of your conclusion in question 3.

Adaptation of Figure 2a from "Transplanted Suprachiasmatic Nucleus Determines Circadian Period" by Martin R. Ralph et al., from *Science*, February 1990, Volume 247(4945). Copyright © 1990 by AAAS. Reprinted with permission.

Hypothalamus
Thalamus

Olfactory
bulb

Amygdala   Hippocampus

▲ Figure 49.14 **The limbic system.**

scientists demonstrated that the SCN determines the circadian rhythm of the whole animal.

Emotions

Whereas a single structure in the brain controls the biological clock, the generation and experience of emotions depend on many brain structures, including the amygdala, hippocampus, and parts of the thalamus (Figure 49.14). These structures border the brainstem in mammals and are therefore grouped as the *limbic system* (from the Latin *limbus*, border). The limbic system, however, is not dedicated solely to emotion. It also functions in motivation, olfaction (the sense of smell), behaviour, and memory.

Generating emotion and experiencing emotion require parts of the brain in addition to the limbic system. For example, emotions that manifest themselves in behaviours such as laughing and crying involve an interaction of parts of the limbic system with sensory and motor areas of the cerebrum. Structures in the forebrain also attach emotional "feelings" to basic, survival-related functions controlled by the brainstem, including aggression, feeding, and sexuality.

Emotional experiences are often stored as memories that can be recalled by similar circumstances. In the case of fear, emotional memory is stored separately from the memory system that supports explicit recall of events. The brain structure with the most important role in storage of emotional memory is the **amygdala**, an almond-shaped mass of nuclei (clusters of neurons) located near the base of the cerebrum.

To study the function of the human amygdala, researchers sometimes present adult subjects with an image followed by an unpleasant experience, such as a mild electrical shock. After several trials, study participants experience *autonomic arousal*—as measured by increased heart rate or sweating—if they see the image again. Subjects with brain

damage confined to the amygdala can recall the image because their explicit memory is intact. However, they do not exhibit autonomic arousal, indicating that damage to the amygdala has resulted in a reduced capacity for emotional memory.

Functional Imaging of the Brain

Today, the amygdala and other brain structures are being probed and analyzed with functional imaging methods. The first widely used technique was positron-emission tomography (PET), in which injection of a radioactive glucose analogue enables a display of metabolic activity. Today, many studies rely on functional magnetic resonance imaging (fMRI). In fMRI, a subject lies with his or her head in the centre of a large, doughnut-shaped magnet. Brain activity in a region is detected by changes in the local oxygen concentration. By scanning the brain while the subject performs a task, such as forming a mental image of a person's face, researchers can correlate particular tasks with activity in specific brain areas.

In one experiment using fMRI, researchers mapped brain activity while subjects listened to music that they described as happy or sad (Figure 49.15). Listening to happy music led to increased activity in the nucleus accumbens, a brain structure important for the perception of pleasure. In contrast, subjects who heard sad music had increased activity in the amygdala.

The range of applications of fMRI includes monitoring recovery from stroke, mapping abnormalities in migraine headaches, and increasing the effectiveness of brain surgery. This technique has even been used to explore sex-based differences in the CNS, demonstrating, for instance, that cerebral blood flow is higher on average in women than in men.

Nucleus accumbens   Amygdala

Happy music   **Sad music**

▲ Figure 49.15 **Functional imaging in the working brain.** Functional magnetic resonance imaging (fMRI) was used to reveal brain activity associated with music that listeners described as happy or sad.

Source: From M. T. Mitterschiffthaler et al. A functional MRI study of happy and sad affective states induced by classical music. Hum Brain Mapp. 2007;28(11):1150–1162.

WHAT IF? *In the experiment that produced the images shown above, some regions of the brain were active under both conditions. What function might such regions carry out?*

1. When you wave your right hand, what part of your brain initiates the action?

2. People who are inebriated have difficulty touching their nose with their eyes closed. Which brain region does this observation indicate is one of those impaired by alcohol?

3. **WHAT IF?** Suppose you examine individuals with damage to the CNS that has resulted in either coma (a prolonged state of unconsciousness) or general paralysis (a loss of skeletal muscle function throughout the body). Relative to the position of the reticular formation, where would you predict the site of injury to lie in each group of patients? Explain.

For suggested answers, see Appendix A.

CONCEPT 49.3

The cerebral cortex controls voluntary movement and cognitive functions

We turn now to the cerebrum, the part of the brain essential for awareness of our surroundings, language, cognition, memory, and consciousness. As shown in Figure 49.11, the cerebrum is the largest structure in the human brain. Like the brain overall, it exhibits regional specialization. For the most part, cognitive functions reside in the cortex, the outer layer of the cerebrum. Within the cortex, sensory areas receive and process sensory information, association areas integrate the information, and motor areas transmit instructions to other parts of the body.

In discussing the location of particular functions in the cerebral cortex, neurobiologists often use four regions, or *lobes*, as physical landmarks. As shown in **Figure 49.16**, each side of the cerebral cortex has a frontal, temporal, occipital, and parietal lobe (each is named for a nearby bone of the skull).

Information Processing

Broadly speaking, there are two sources of sensory input to the human cerebral cortex. Some sensory input to the cerebral cortex comes from groups of receptors clustered in dedicated sensory organs, such as the eyes and nose. Other sensory input originates in individual receptors in the hands, scalp, and elsewhere in the body. These somatic sensory, or *somatosensory*, receptors (from the Greek *soma*, body) provide information about touch, pain, pressure, temperature, and the position of muscles and limbs.

Most sensory information coming into the cortex is directed via the thalamus to primary sensory areas within the cerebral lobes. Information received at the primary sensory areas is passed along to nearby association areas, which process particular features in the sensory input. In the occipital lobe, for instance, some groups of neurons in

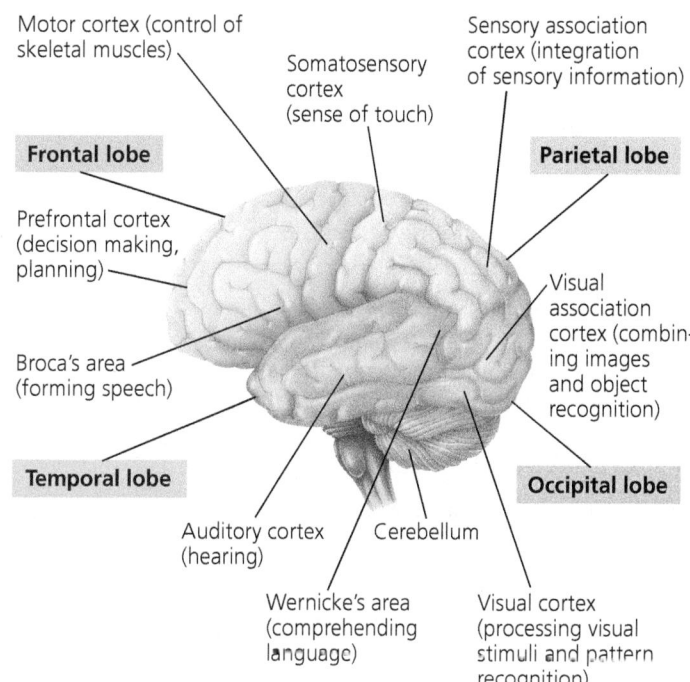

▲ Figure 49.16 **The human cerebral cortex.** Each side of the cerebral cortex is divided into four lobes, and each lobe has specialized functions, some of which are listed here. Some areas on the left side of the brain (shown here) have different functions from those on the right side (not shown).

the primary visual area are specifically sensitive to rays of light oriented in a particular direction. In the visual association area, information related to such features is combined in a region dedicated to recognizing complex images, such as faces.

Once processed, sensory information passes to the prefrontal cortex, which helps plan actions and movement. The cerebral cortex may then generate motor commands that cause particular behaviours—moving a limb or saying hello, for example. These commands consist of action potentials produced by neurons in the motor cortex, which lies at the rear of the frontal lobe (see Figure 49.16). The action potentials travel along axons to the brainstem and spinal cord, where they excite motor neurons, which in turn excite skeletal muscle cells.

In the somatosensory cortex and motor cortex, neurons are arranged according to the part of the body that generates the sensory input or receives the motor commands. Dr. Wilder Penfield, a neurosurgeon who founded the Montreal Neurological Institute in 1934, is credited with first depicting the responsibilities of regions of the brain using a homunculus. Like the version shown in **Figure 49.17**, a homunculus exaggerates anatomical features to illustrate the fraction of the brain controlling each body part. For example, neurons that process sensory information from the legs and feet lie in the region of the somatosensory cortex closest to the midline. Neurons that control muscles

▶ **Figure 49.17 Body part representation in the primary motor and primary somatosensory cortices.** In these cross-sectional maps of the cortices, the cortical surface area devoted to each body part is represented by the relative size of that part in the cartoons.

in the legs and feet are located in the corresponding region of the motor cortex. Notice in Figure 49.17 that the cortical surface area devoted to each body part is not proportional to the size of the part. Instead, surface area correlates with the extent of neuronal control needed (for the motor cortex) or with the number of sensory neurons that extend axons to that part (for the somatosensory cortex). Thus, the surface area of the motor cortex devoted to the face is much larger than that devoted to the trunk, reflecting the extensive involvement of facial muscles in communication.

Although our focus here is on humans, it is worth noting that the processing sites for sensory information vary among vertebrates. In ray-finned fishes, for example, the relatively large midbrain (see Figure 49.10) serves as the primary centre for processing and responding to visual stimuli. Such differences reflect a recognizable evolutionary trend: Following the vertebrate phylogenetic tree from lamprey to sharks, ray-finned fishes, amphibians, reptiles, and mammals, one observes a steadily increasing role for the forebrain in processing sensory information.

Language and Speech

The mapping of cognitive functions within the cortex began in the 1800s when physicians studied the effects of damage to particular regions of the cortex by injuries, strokes, or tumours. Pierre Broca conducted postmortem (after death) examinations of patients who had been able to understand language but unable to speak. He discovered that many had defects in a small region of the left frontal lobe, now known as *Broca's area*. Karl Wernicke found that damage to a posterior portion of the left temporal lobe, now called *Wernicke's area*, abolished the ability to comprehend speech but not the ability to speak. PET studies have now confirmed activity in Broca's area during speech generation and Wernicke's area when speech is heard (Figure 49.18).

Frontal Lobe Function

In 1848, a horrific workplace accident pointed to the role of the prefrontal cortex in temperament and decision making. Phineas Gage was working as the foreman of a railroad construction crew when an explosion drove a metre-long iron rod through his head. The rod, which was more than 3 cm in diameter at one end, entered his

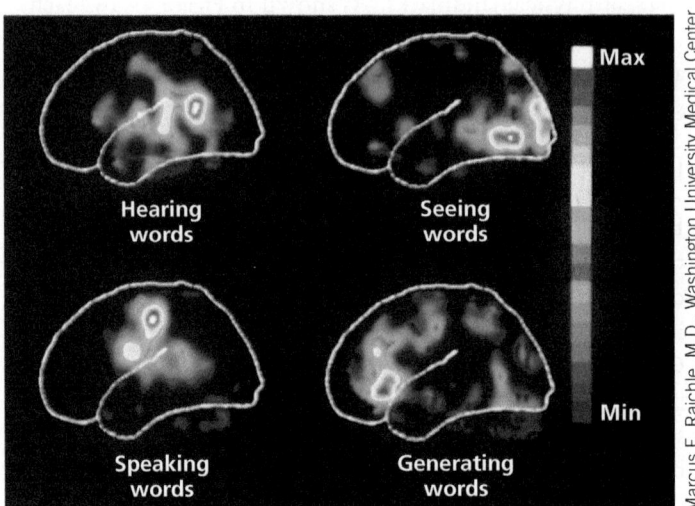

▲ **Figure 49.18 Mapping language areas in the cerebral cortex.** These PET images show regions with different activity levels in one person's brain during four activities, all related to speech. Increases in activity are seen in Wernicke's area when hearing words, Broca's area when speaking words, the visual cortex when seeing words, and the frontal lobe when generating words (without reading them).

skull just below his left eye and exited through the top of his head, damaging large portions of his frontal lobe. Astonishingly, Gage recovered. His personality, however, changed dramatically. He became emotionally detached, impatient, and erratic in his behaviour.

Although the connection between Gage's brain injury and his personality change is a subject of debate, some tumours that develop in the frontal lobe cause symptoms that are similar to those of Gage. Intellect and memory seem intact, but decision making is flawed and emotional responses are diminished. In the 20th century, the same problems were observed as a result of frontal lobotomy, a surgical procedure that severs the connection between the prefrontal cortex and the limbic system. Together, these observations provide evidence that the frontal lobes have a substantial influence on what are often called "executive functions."

Frontal lobotomy was once a common treatment for severe behavioural disorders but later was abandoned as a medical practice. Behavioural disorders are now typically treated with medications, as discussed later in this chapter.

Evolution of Cognition in Vertebrates

 In humans, the cerebral cortex accounts for about 80% of total brain mass and is highly convoluted (see Figure 49.11). The convolutions allow the cerebral cortex to have a large surface area and still fit inside the skull: Less than 5 mm thick, it has a surface area of approximately 1000 cm^2. The outermost part of the human cerebral cortex forms the *neocortex*, six parallel layers of neurons arranged tangential to the brain surface.

It was long thought that a highly convoluted neocortex was required for advanced *cognition*, the perception and reasoning that constitute knowledge. Primates and cetaceans (whales, dolphins, and porpoises) possess an extensively convoluted neocortex. However, birds lack such a structure and were thought to have much lower intellectual capacity. Experiments in recent years have refuted this idea. Western scrub jays (*Aphelocoma californica*) can remember the relative period of time that has passed after they stored and hid specific food items. New Caledonian crows (*Corvus moneduloides*) are highly skilled at making and using tools, an ability otherwise well documented only for humans and some other apes. African grey parrots (*Psittacus erithacus*) understand numerical and abstract concepts, distinguishing between "same" and "different" and grasping the idea of "none."

(a) Songbird brain

(b) Human brain

▲ Figure 49.19 **Comparison of regions for higher cognition in avian and human brains.** Although structurally different, the pallium of a songbird brain **(a)** and the cerebral cortex of the human brain **(b)** play similar roles in higher cognitive activities and make many similar connections with other brain structures.

Source: Adaptation of figure 1c from "Avian Brains and a New Understanding of Vertebrate Brain Evolution" by Erich D. Jarvis et al., from *Nature Reviews Neuroscience,* February 2005, Volume 6(2). Copyright © 2005 by Macmillan Publishers Ltd. Reprinted with permission.

The anatomical basis for sophisticated information processing in birds appears to be the grouping of nuclei within the *pallium*, the top or outer portion of the brain **(Figure 49.19)**. This arrangement is different from that in the human pallium—the cerebral cortex—which contains flat sheets of cells in six layers. Thus, there are two types of pallium, each of which supports complex and flexible brain function.

How did the differences between the bird pallium and human pallium arise during evolution? The current consensus is that the common ancestor of birds and mammals had a pallium in which neurons were organized into nuclei, as is still found in birds. Early in mammalian evolution, this nuclear (clustered) organization of neurons was transformed into a layered one. Connectivity was maintained during this transformation such that, for example, the thalamus relays sensory input relating to sights, sounds, and touch to the pallium in both birds and mammals.

Sophisticated information processing depends not only on the overall organization of a brain but also on the very small-scale changes that enable learning and encode memory. We'll turn to these changes in the context of humans in the next section.

1. How can studying individuals with damage to a particular brain region provide insight into the normal function of that region?

2. How do the functions of Broca's area and Wernicke's area each relate to the activity of the surrounding cortex?

3. **WHAT IF?** If a woman with a severed corpus callosum viewed a photograph of a familiar face, first in her left field of vision and then in her right field, why would she find it difficult to put a name to the face in either field?

For suggested answers, see Appendix A.

CONCEPT 49.4

Changes in synaptic connections underlie memory and learning

During embryonic development, regulated gene expression and signal transduction establish the overall structure of the nervous system (see Chapter 47). Two processes then dominate the remaining development and remodelling of the nervous system. The first is a competition among neurons for survival. Neurons compete for growth-supporting factors, which are produced in limited quantities by tissues that direct neuron growth. Cells that don't reach the proper locations fail to receive such factors and undergo programmed cell death. The competition is so severe that half of the neurons formed in the embryo are eliminated. The net effect is the preferential survival of neurons that are located properly within the nervous system.

Synapse elimination is the second major process that shapes the nervous system. A developing neuron forms numerous synapses—more than are required for its proper function. The activity of that neuron then stabilizes some synapses and destabilizes others. By the end of embryonic development, neurons on average have lost more than half of their initial synapses, leaving behind the connections that survive into adulthood.

Together, neuron death and synapse elimination set up the basic network of cells and connections within the nervous system required throughout life.

Neural Plasticity

Although the overall organization of the CNS is established during embryonic development, it can change after birth. This capacity for the nervous system to be remodelled, especially in response to its own activity, is called **neural plasticity**.

Much of the reshaping of the nervous system occurs at synapses. When the activity of a synapse correlates with that of other synapses, changes may occur that reinforce that synaptic connection. Conversely, when the activity of

(a) Connections between neurons are strengthened or weakened in response to activity. High-level activity at the synapse of the post-synaptic neuron with presynaptic neuron N_1 leads to recruitment of additional axon terminals from that neuron. Lack of activity at the synapse with presynaptic neuron N_2 leads to loss of functional connections with that neuron.

(b) If two synapses on the same postsynaptic cell are often active at the same time, the strength of the postsynaptic response may increase at both synapses.

▲ Figure 49.20 **Neural plasticity.** Synaptic connections can change over time, depending on the activity level at the synapse.

a synapse fails to correlate with that of other synapses, the synaptic connection sometimes becomes weaker. In this way, synapses belonging to circuits that link information in useful ways are maintained, whereas those that convey bits of information lacking any context may be lost.

Figure 49.20a illustrates how these processes can result in either the addition or loss of a synapse. If you think of signals in the nervous system as traffic on a highway, such changes are comparable to adding or removing an entrance ramp. The net effect is to increase signalling between particular pairs of neurons and decrease signalling between other pairs. As shown in Figure 49.20b, changes can also strengthen or weaken signalling at a synapse. In our traffic analogy, this would be equivalent to widening or narrowing an entrance ramp.

Research indicates that *autism*, a developmental disorder that first appears early in childhood, involves a disruption of activity-dependent remodelling at synapses. Children affected with autism display impaired communication and social interaction, as well as stereotyped and repetitive behaviours.

Although the underlying causes of autism are unknown, there is a strong genetic contribution to this and related disorders. Extensive research has ruled out a link to vaccine preservatives, once proposed as a potential risk factor.

Further understanding of the autism-associated disruption in synaptic plasticity may help efforts to better understand and treat this disorder.

Remodelling and refining of the nervous system occur in many contexts. For instance, soon after birth, the visual cortex of the mammalian brain undergoes reorganization in response to input from the optic nerve triggered by visual stimuli. Experiments have shown that this remodelling is a necessary step in the development of normal visual ability.

Remodelling of functional brain circuitry also occurs in diseases and injuries to the nervous system from which significant recovery is possible. One example is the treatment for a condition called phantom limb syndrome, in which a person feels pain or discomfort that seems to originate from an arm or leg that has been amputated. Having the patient view a reflection of the remaining limb in a mirrored box can reorganize the brain's neural connections in a way that eliminates the unpleasant feelings from the lost limb.

Memory and Learning

The formation of memories is another example of neural plasticity. Though we may not be aware of it, we are constantly checking what is happening against what just happened a few moments ago. We hold information for a time in **short-term memory** locations and then release it if it becomes irrelevant. If we wish to retain knowledge of a name, phone number, or other fact, the mechanisms of **long-term memory** are activated. If we later need to recall the name or number, we fetch it from long-term memory and return it to short-term memory.

Scientists have long wondered where in the brain short-term and long-term memories are located. We now know that both types of memory involve the storage of information in the cerebral cortex. One of the most influential studies of the anatomical basis of short-term memory came from Brenda Milner at McGill University's Montreal Neurological Institute (Figure 49.21). In short-term memory, this information is accessed via temporary links formed in the hippocampus. When memories are made long-term, the links in the hippocampus are replaced by more permanent connections within the cerebral cortex itself. Some of this consolidation of memory is thought to occur during sleep. Furthermore, the reactivation of the hippocampus that is required for memory consolidation likely forms the basis for at least some of our dreams.

According to our current understanding of memory, the hippocampus is essential for acquiring new long-term memories but not for maintaining them. This hypothesis readily explains the symptoms of some individuals who suffer damage to the hippocampus: They cannot form any new lasting memories but can freely recall events from

▼ Figure 49.21

Impact

What regions of the brain control short-term memory?

In the mid-1900s, it was common to subject patients with severe neurological disorders to surgeries that removed parts of the brain (lobotomy). One subject, identified as HM, had both sides of his medial temporal lobe removed as a treatment for uncontrollable seizures. The image below, based upon imaging work performed on HM's brain postmortem, shows the areas of the hippocampus removed in his lobotomy. The surgery removed regions on both sides, but a normal brain is shown on the right for reference.

Hippocampus

In 1957, the surgeon William Scoville and Brenda Milner, a neuroscientist from McGill University, examined HM to assess the impact of partial lobotomy on memory and intelligence. HM lost most of his hippocampus, parahippocampal gyrus, and amygdala without effect on his personality. Unexpectedly, HM showed a severe memory defect that left him unable to form any short-term memories. Though he could not recall what he did even 30 minutes earlier in his day, HM retained vivid memories of his life before 1953. HM was identified as Henry Molaison after he died in 2008.

Why It Matters Neurological disorders are amongst the most difficult diseases to detect and treat because of the sheer complexity of the human brain. Over the past century, clinicians have treated neurological disorders with electroshock, lobotomy, and wide ranges of pharmacological agents. HM's lobotomy achieved its main goal of reducing seizures, but the unexpected effects on memory created an opportunity to study the anatomical basis of memory. For more than 50 years, neuropsychologists studied Henry Molaison to better understand how these regions of the brain contributed to memory formation. He is widely held to be the most studied patient in the history of brain science.

Further Reading W. B. Scoville and B. Milner, Loss of recent memory after bilateral hippocampal lesions, *Journal of Neurology, Neurosurgery and Psychiatry* 20:11–21 (1957).

WHAT IF? *The surgery conducted on HM proceeded at his request in an effort to alleviate seizures. Subsequent studies proceeded with his "informed consent," a central pillar of research on humans. Discuss with your peers the factors that should be considered in doing research on humans who are unable to give informed consent because of neurological disorders that prevent them from understanding their situation.*

before their injury. In effect, their lack of normal hippo-campal function traps them in their past.

What evolutionary advantage might be offered by organizing short-term and long-term memories differently? Current thinking is that the delay in forming connections in the cerebral cortex allows long-term memories to be integrated gradually into the existing store of knowledge and experience, providing a basis for more meaningful associations. Consistent with this idea, the transfer of information from short-term to long-term memory is enhanced by the association of new data with data previously learned and stored in long-term memory. For example, it's easier to learn a new card game if you already have "card sense" from playing other card games.

Motor skills, such as walking, tying your shoes, or writing, are usually learned by repetition. You can perform these skills without consciously recalling the individual steps required to do these tasks correctly. Learning skills and procedures, such as those required to ride a bicycle, appears to involve cellular mechanisms very similar to those responsible for brain growth and development. In such cases, neurons actually make new connections. In contrast, memorizing phone numbers, facts, and places—which can be very rapid and may require only one exposure to the relevant item—may rely mainly on changes in the strength of existing neuronal connections. Next we will consider one way that such changes in strength can take place.

Long-Term Potentiation

In searching for the physiological basis of memory, researchers have concentrated their attention on processes that can alter a synaptic connection, making the flow of communication either more efficient or less efficient. We will focus here on **long-term potentiation (LTP)**, a lasting increase in the strength of synaptic transmission.

First characterized in tissue slices from the hippocampus, LTP involves a presynaptic neuron that releases the excitatory neurotransmitter glutamate. For LTP to occur, there must be a high-frequency series of action potentials in this presynaptic neuron. In addition, these action potentials must arrive at the axon terminal at the same time that the postsynaptic cell receives a depolarizing stimulus at another synapse.

LTP involves two types of glutamate receptors, each named for a molecule—NMDA or AMPA—that artificially activates that particular receptor. As shown in **Figure 49.22**, the set of receptors present on the postsynaptic membrane changes in response to an active synapse and a depolarizing stimulus. The result is LTP—a stable increase in the size of the postsynaptic potentials at the synapse. Because LTP can last for days or weeks in dissected tissue, it is thought to represent one of the fundamental processes by which memories are stored and learning takes place.

(a) Synapse prior to long-term potentiation (LTP). The NMDA glutamate receptors open in response to glutamate but are blocked by Mg^{2+}.

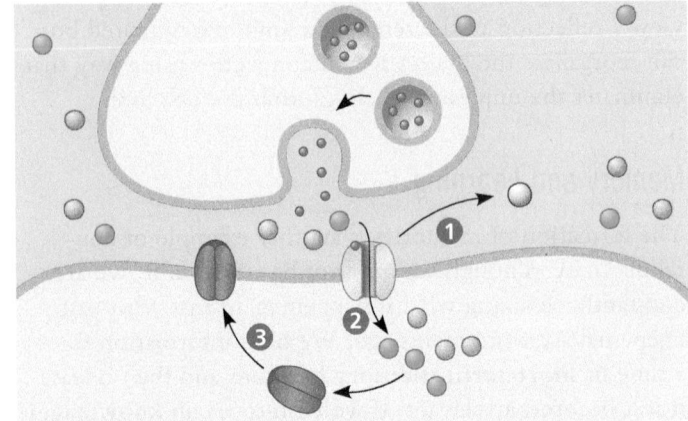

(b) Establishing LTP. Activity at nearby synapses (not shown) depolarizes the postsynaptic membrane, causing ❶ Mg^{2+} release from NMDA receptors. The unblocked receptors respond to glutamate by allowing ❷ an influx of Na^+ and Ca^{2+}. The Ca^{2+} influx triggers ❸ insertion of stored AMPA glutamate receptors into the postsynaptic membrane.

(c) Synapse exhibiting LTP. Glutamate release activates ❶ AMPA receptors that trigger ❷ depolarization. The depolarization unblocks ❸ NMDA receptors. Together, the AMPA and NMDA receptors trigger postsynaptic potentials strong enough to initiate ❹ action potentials without input from other synapses. Additional mechanisms (not shown) contribute to LTP, including receptor modification by protein kinases.

▲ **Figure 49.22 Long-term potentiation in the brain.**

1. Outline two mechanisms by which the flow of information between two neurons in adults can increase.

2. Individuals with localized brain damage have been very useful in the study of many brain functions. Why is this unlikely to be true for consciousness?

3. **WHAT IF?** Suppose that a person with damage to the hippocampus is unable to acquire new long-term memories. Why might the acquisition of short-term memories also be impaired?

For suggested answers, see Appendix A.

CONCEPT 49.5

Many nervous system disorders can be explained in molecular terms

Disorders of the nervous system, including schizophrenia, depression, drug addiction, Alzheimer's disease, and Parkinson's disease, are a major public health problem. Together, they result in more hospitalizations in Canada and the United States than do heart disease or cancer. Until recently, hospitalization was typically the only available treatment, and many affected individuals were institutionalized for the rest of their lives. Today, many disorders that alter mood or behaviour can be treated with medication, reducing average hospital stays for these disorders to only a few weeks. At the same time, societal attitudes are changing as awareness grows that nervous system disorders often result from chemical or anatomical changes in the brain. Many challenges remain, however, especially for Alzheimer's and other diseases that lead to nervous system degeneration.

Major research efforts are under way to identify genes that cause or contribute to disorders of the nervous system. Identifying such genes offers hope for identifying causes, predicting outcomes, and developing effective treatments. For most nervous system disorders, however, genetic contributions only partially account for which individuals are affected. The other significant contribution to disease comes from environmental factors. Unfortunately, environmental contributions are typically very difficult to identify.

To distinguish between genetic and environmental variables, scientists often carry out family studies. In such studies, researchers track how family members are related genetically, which individuals are affected, and which family members grew up in the same household. These studies are especially informative when one of the affected individuals has either an identical twin or an adopted sibling who is genetically unrelated. The results of family studies indicate that certain nervous system disorders, such as schizophrenia, have a very strong genetic component (Figure 49.23).

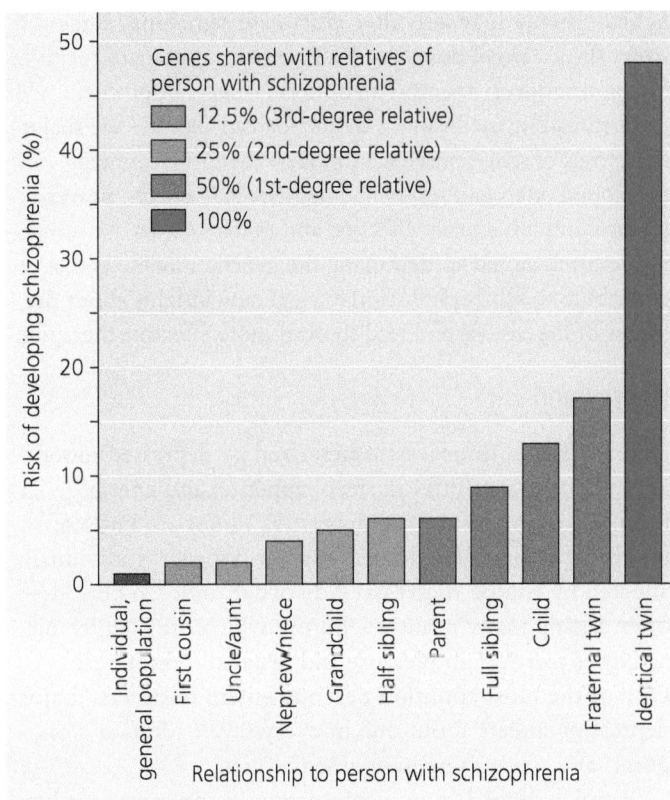

▲ Figure 49.23 **Genetic contribution to schizophrenia.** First cousins, uncles, and aunts of a person with schizophrenia have twice the risk of unrelated members of the population of developing the disease. The risks for closer relatives are many times greater.

Source: Adaptation of figure 10 from *Schizophrenia Genesis: The Origins of Madness* by Irving I. Gottesman. Copyright © 1991 by Irving I. Gottesman. Reprinted by permission of Worth Publishers.

INTERPRET THE DATA *What is the likelihood of a person developing schizophrenia if the disorder affects his or her fraternal twin? How would the likelihood change if DNA sequencing revealed that the twins shared the genetic variants that contribute to the disorder?*

Schizophrenia

About 1% of the world's population suffer from **schizophrenia**, a severe mental disturbance characterized by psychotic episodes in which patients have a distorted perception of reality. People with schizophrenia typically experience hallucinations (such as "voices" that only they can hear) and delusions (for example, the idea that others are plotting to harm them). Despite the commonly held notion, schizophrenia does not necessarily result in multiple personalities. Rather, the name *schizophrenia* (from the Greek *schizo*, split, and *phren*, mind) refers to the fragmentation of what are normally integrated brain functions.

Two lines of evidence suggest that schizophrenia affects neuronal pathways that use dopamine as a neurotransmitter. First, the drug amphetamine ("speed"), which stimulates dopamine release, can produce the same set of symptoms as schizophrenia. Second, many of the drugs that alleviate the symptoms of schizophrenia block dopamine receptors.

Schizophrenia may also alter glutamate signalling, since the street drug "angel dust," or PCP, blocks glutamate receptors and induces strong schizophrenia-like symptoms.

Fortunately, medications frequently can alleviate the major symptoms of schizophrenia. Although the first treatments developed often had substantial negative side effects, newer medications are equally effective and much safer to use. Ongoing research aimed at identifying the genetic mutations that contribute to schizophrenia may yield new insights about the causes of the disease and lead to even more effective therapies.

Depression

Depression is a disorder characterized by depressed mood, as well as abnormalities in sleep, appetite, and energy level. Two broad forms of depressive illness are known: major depressive disorder and bipolar disorder. Individuals affected by **major depressive disorder** undergo periods—often lasting many months—during which once enjoyable activities provide no pleasure and provoke no interest. One of the most common nervous system disorders, major depression affects about one in every seven adults at some point, and twice as many women as men.

Bipolar disorder, or manic-depressive disorder, involves swings of mood from high to low and affects about 1% of the world's population. The manic phase is characterized by high self-esteem, increased energy, a flow of ideas, overtalkativeness, and increased risk taking. In its milder forms, this phase is sometimes associated with great creativity, and some well-known artists, musicians, and literary figures (including Vincent Van Gogh, Robert Schumann, Virginia Woolf, and Ernest Hemingway, to name a few) have had very productive periods during manic phases. The depressive phase comes with lowered ability to feel pleasure, loss of motivation, sleep disturbances, and feelings of worthlessness. These symptoms can be so severe that affected individuals attempt suicide.

Major depressive and bipolar disorders are among the nervous system disorders for which available therapies are most effective. Many drugs used to treat depressive illness, including fluoxetine (Prozac), increase the activity of biogenic amines in the brain.

The Brain's Reward System and Drug Addiction

Drug addiction is a disorder characterized by compulsive consumption of a drug and loss of control in limiting intake. Addictive drugs include stimulants, such as cocaine and amphetamine, and sedatives, such as heroin. However, all of these drugs, as well as alcohol and nicotine, are addictive for the same reason: Each increases activity of the brain's reward system, neural circuitry that normally functions in pleasure, motivation, and learning.

In the absence of drug addiction, the reward system of the brain provides motivation for activities that enhance

▲ Figure 49.24 **Effects of addictive drugs on the reward system of the mammalian brain.** Addictive drugs alter the transmission of signals in the pathway formed by neurons of the ventral tegmental area (VTA).

MAKE CONNECTIONS *Based on what you learned in Concept 48.3, what effect would you expect if you depolarized the neurons in the VTA? Explain.*

survival and reproduction, such as eating in response to hunger, drinking when thirsty, and engaging in sexual activity when aroused. In addicted individuals, "wanting" is instead directed toward further drug consumption.

As shown in **Figure 49.24**, inputs to the reward system are received by neurons in a region near the base of the brain called the *ventral tegmental area (VTA)*. When activated, these neurons release dopamine from their axon terminals in specific regions of the cerebrum, including the *nucleus accumbens*.

Addictive drugs affect the reward system in several ways. First, each drug has an immediate and direct effect that enhances the activity of the dopamine pathway (see Figure 49.24). As addiction develops, there are also long-lasting changes in the reward circuitry. The result is a craving for the drug independent of any pleasure associated with consumption.

Laboratory animals have proved especially useful in teaching us how the brain's reward system works and how particular drugs affect its function. Rats, for example, will provide themselves with cocaine, heroin, or amphetamine when given a dispensing system linked to a lever in their cage. Furthermore, they exhibit addictive behaviour in such circumstances, continuing to self-administer the drug rather than seek food, even to the point of starvation.

As scientists expand their knowledge about the brain's reward system and the various forms of addiction, there is hope that the insights will lead to more effective prevention and treatment.

Alzheimer's Disease

Alzheimer's disease is a mental deterioration, or dementia, characterized by confusion and memory loss. Its incidence is age related, rising from about 10% at age 65 to about 35% at age 85. The disease is progressive, with patients gradually becoming less able to function and eventually needing to be dressed, bathed, and fed by others. Moreover, patients with Alzheimer's disease often lose their ability to recognize people, including their immediate family, and may treat them with suspicion and hostility.

Alzheimer's disease leads to the death of neurons in many areas of the brain, including the hippocampus and cerebral cortex. As a result, there is often massive shrinkage of brain tissue. Postmortem examination of the remaining brain tissue reveals two characteristic features—amyloid plaques and neurofibrillary tangles (**Figure 49.25**).

The plaques are aggregates of β-amyloid, an insoluble peptide that is cleaved from the extracellular portion of a membrane protein found in neurons. Membrane enzymes, called secretases, catalyze the cleavage, causing β-amyloid to accumulate in plaques outside the neurons. It is these plaques that appear to trigger the death of surrounding neurons.

The neurofibrillary tangles observed in Alzheimer's disease are primarily made up of the tau protein. (This protein is unrelated to the tau mutation that affects circadian rhythm in hamsters.) The tau protein normally helps assemble and maintain microtubules that transport nutrients along axons. In Alzheimer's disease, tau undergoes changes that cause it to bind to itself, resulting in neurofibrillary tangles.

Amyloid plaque   Neurofibrillary tangle   20 μm

▲ Figure 49.25 **Microscopic signs of Alzheimer's disease.** A hallmark of Alzheimer's disease is the presence in brain tissue of neurofibrillary tangles surrounding plaques made of β-amyloid (LM).

There is evidence that changes in tau are associated with the appearance of early-onset Alzheimer's disease, a much less common disorder that affects relatively young individuals.

There is currently no cure for Alzheimer's disease, but an enormous effort has led to the recent development of drugs that are partially effective in relieving some of the symptoms. Doctors are also beginning to use functional brain imaging to diagnose Alzheimer's disease in patients exhibiting early signs of dementia.

Parkinson's Disease

Symptoms of **Parkinson's disease**, a motor disorder, include muscle tremors, poor balance, a flexed posture, and a shuffling gait. Facial muscles become rigid, limiting the ability of patients to vary their expressions. Like Alzheimer's disease, Parkinson's disease is a progressive brain illness and is more common with advancing age. The incidence of Parkinson's disease is about 1% at age 65 and about 5% at age 85.

The symptoms of Parkinson's disease result from the death of neurons in the midbrain that normally release dopamine at synapses in the basal nuclei. As with Alzheimer's disease, protein aggregates accumulate. Most cases of Parkinson's disease lack an identifiable cause; however, a rare form of the disease that appears in relatively young adults has a clear genetic basis. Molecular studies of mutations linked to this early-onset Parkinson's disease reveal disruption of genes required for certain mitochondrial functions. Researchers are investigating whether mitochondrial defects also contribute to the more common and later-onset form of the disease.

At present there is no cure for Parkinson's disease. Approaches used to manage the symptoms include brain surgery, deep-brain stimulation, and drugs such as L-dopa, a molecule that can cross the blood-brain barrier and be converted to dopamine in the CNS. One potential cure is to implant dopamine-secreting neurons, either in the midbrain or in the basal nuclei. Laboratory studies of this strategy show promise: In rats with an experimentally induced condition that mimics Parkinson's disease, implanting dopamine-secreting neurons can lead to a recovery of motor control. Whether this regenerative approach can also work in humans is one of many important questions in modern brain research.

CONCEPT CHECK 49.5

1. Compare Alzheimer's disease and Parkinson's disease.

2. How is dopamine activity related to schizophrenia, drug addiction, and Parkinson's disease?

3. **WHAT IF?** If you could detect early-stage Alzheimer's disease, would you expect to see brain changes that were similar to, although less extensive than, those seen in patients who have died of this disease? Explain.

For suggested answers, see Appendix A.

49 Chapter Review

Go to **MasteringBiology**® for Assignments, the eText, and the Study Area with Animations, Activities, Vocab Self-Quiz, and Practice Tests.

SUMMARY OF KEY CONCEPTS

CONCEPT 49.1

Nervous systems consist of circuits of neurons and supporting cells (pp. 1140–1145)

- Invertebrate nervous systems range in complexity from simple **nerve nets** to highly centralized nervous systems having complicated brains and ventral nerve cords.

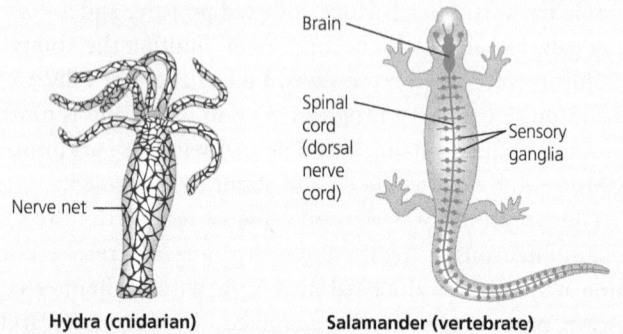

Hydra (cnidarian)   **Salamander (vertebrate)**

In vertebrates, the central nervous system (CNS), consisting of the brain and the spinal cord, integrates information, while the **nerves** of the peripheral nervous system (PNS) transmit sensory and motor signals between the CNS and the rest of the body. The simplest circuits in the vertebrate nervous system control **reflex** responses, in which sensory input is linked to motor output without involvement of the brain.

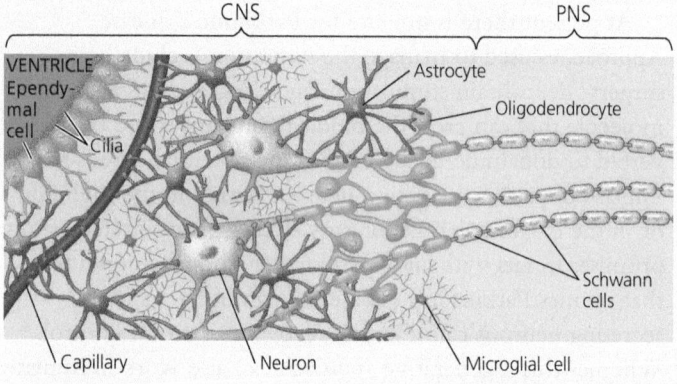

- Afferent neurons carry sensory signals to the CNS. Efferent neurons function in either the somatic nervous system, which transmits signals between the CNS and the periphery, or the **autonomic nervous system**, which regulates smooth and cardiac muscles. The **sympathetic** and **parasympathetic divisions** of the autonomic nervous system have antagonistic effects on a diverse set of target organs, while the **enteric division** controls the activity of many digestive organs.
- Vertebrate neurons are supported by several types of glia, including astrocytes, oligodendrocytes, Schwann cells, and ependymal cells.

[?] *How does the circuitry of a reflex facilitate a rapid response?*

CONCEPT 49.2

The vertebrate brain is regionally specialized (pp. 1145–1151)

- The cerebrum has two hemispheres, each of which consists of cortical **grey matter** overlying **white matter** and basal nuclei, which are important in planning and learning movements. The **pons** and **medulla oblongata** are relay stations for information travelling between the PNS and the cerebrum. The **cerebellum** helps coordinate motor, perceptual, and cognitive functions. It is also involved in learning and remembering motor skills. The **thalamus** is the main centre through which sensory and motor information passes to the **cerebrum**. The **hypothalamus** regulates homeostasis and basic survival behaviours. Within the hypothalamus, the **suprachiasmatic nucleus (SCN)** acts as the pacemaker for circadian rhythms. The **amygdala** plays a key role in recognizing and recalling a number of emotions.

[?] *What role do particular regions of the brain play in vision and responses to visual input?*

CONCEPT 49.3

The cerebral cortex controls voluntary movement and cognitive functions (pp. 1151–1154)

- Each side of the **cerebral cortex** has four lobes—frontal, temporal, occipital, and parietal—that contain primary sensory areas and association areas. Specific types of sensory input enter the primary sensory areas. Association areas integrate information from different sensory areas. Broca's area and Wernicke's area are essential for generating and understanding language. These functions are concentrated in the left **cerebral hemisphere**, as are math and logic operations.
- In the somatosensory cortex and the motor cortex, neurons are distributed according to the part of the body that generates sensory input or receives motor commands.
- Primates and cetaceans, which are capable of higher cognition, have an extensively convoluted neocortex, the outermost part of the cerebral cortex. In birds, a brain region called the pallium contains clustered nuclei that carry out functions similar to those performed by the cerebral cortex of mammals. Some birds can solve problems and understand abstractions in a manner indicative of higher cognition.

[?] *A patient has trouble with language and has paralysis on one side of the body. Which side would you expect to be paralyzed? Why?*

CONCEPT 49.4

Changes in synaptic connections underlie memory and learning (pp. 1154–1157)

- During development, more neurons and synapses form than will exist in the adult. The programmed death of neurons and elimination of synapses in embryos establish the basic structure of the nervous system. In the adult, reshaping of the nervous system can involve the loss or addition of synapses or the strengthening or weakening of signalling at synapses. This capacity for remodelling is termed **neural plasticity**. **Short-term memory** relies on temporary links in the hippocampus. In **long-term memory**, these temporary links are replaced by connections within the cerebral cortex.

> **?** *Learning multiple languages is typically easier earlier in childhood than later in life. How does this fit with our understanding of neural development?*

CONCEPT 49.5

Many nervous system disorders can be explained in molecular terms (pp. 1157–1159)

- **Schizophrenia**, which is characterized by hallucinations, delusions, and other symptoms, affects neuronal pathways that use dopamine as a neurotransmitter. Drugs that increase the activity of biogenic amines in the brain can be used to treat **bipolar disorder** and **major depressive disorder**. The compulsive drug use that characterizes addiction reflects altered activity of the brain's reward system, which normally provides motivation for actions that enhance survival or reproduction.
- **Alzheimer's disease** and **Parkinson's disease** are neurodegenerative and typically are age related. Alzheimer's disease is a dementia in which neurofibrillary tangles and amyloid plaques form in the brain. Parkinson's disease is a motor disorder caused by the death of dopamine-secreting neurons and is associated with the presence of protein aggregates.

> **?** *The fact that both amphetamines and PCP have effects similar to the symptoms of schizophrenia suggests a potentially complex basis for this disease. Explain.*

TEST YOUR UNDERSTANDING

LEVEL 1: KNOWLEDGE/COMPREHENSION

1. Wakefulness is regulated by the reticular formation, which is present in the
   a. basal nuclei.
   b. brainstem.
   c. limbic system.
   d. spinal cord.

2. Which of the following structures or regions is *incorrectly* paired with its function?
   a. limbic system—motor control of speech
   b. medulla oblongata—homeostatic control
   c. cerebellum—coordination of movement and balance
   d. amygdala—emotional memory

3. Patients with damage to Wernicke's area have difficulty
   a. coordinating limb movement.
   b. generating speech.
   c. recognizing faces.
   d. understanding language.

4. The cerebral cortex plays a major role in all of the following *except*
   a. short-term memory.   c. circadian rhythm.
   b. long-term memory.   d. breath holding.

LEVEL 2: APPLICATION/ANALYSIS

5. After suffering a stroke, a patient can see objects anywhere in front of him but pays attention only to objects in his right field of vision. When asked to describe these objects, he has difficulty judging their size and distance. What part of the brain was likely damaged by the stroke?
   a. the left frontal lobe
   b. the right frontal lobe
   c. the right parietal lobe
   d. the corpus callosum

6. Injury localized to the hypothalamus would most likely disrupt
   a. short-term memory.
   b. coordination during locomotion.
   c. executive functions, such as decision making.
   d. regulation of body temperature.

7. **DRAW IT** The reflex that pulls your hand away when you prick your finger on a sharp object relies on a simple neuronal circuit with two synapses in the spinal cord. (a) Using a circle to represent a cross section of the spinal cord, draw the circuit, labelling the types of neurons, the direction of information flow in each, and the locations of synapses. (b) Draw a simple diagram of the brain indicating where pain would eventually be perceived.

LEVEL 3: SYNTHESIS/EVALUATION

8. **EVOLUTION CONNECTION**
   Scientists often use measures of "higher-order thinking" to assess intelligence in other animals. For example, birds are judged to have sophisticated thought processes because they can use tools and make use of abstract concepts. What problems do you see in defining intelligence in these ways?

9. **SCIENTIFIC INQUIRY**
   Consider an individual who had been fluent in American Sign Language before suffering damage to the left cerebral hemisphere. After the injury, this person could still understand signs, but could not readily generate signs that represented his thoughts. What two hypotheses could explain this finding, and how might you distinguish between them?

10. **SCIENCE, TECHNOLOGY, AND SOCIETY**
    With increasingly sophisticated methods for scanning brain activity, scientists are rapidly developing the ability to detect an individual's particular emotions and thought processes from outside the body. What benefits and problems do you envision when such technology becomes readily available?

11. **WRITE ABOUT A THEME: INFORMATION**
    In a short essay (100–150 words), explain how specification of the adult nervous system by the genome is incomplete.

12. **SYNTHESIZE YOUR KNOWLEDGE**

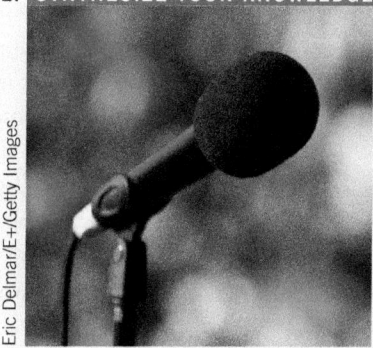

Eric Delmar/E+/Getty Images

Imagine you are standing at a microphone in front of a crowd. Checking your notes, you begin speaking. Using the information in this chapter, describe the series of events in particular regions of the brain that enabled you to say the very first word.

For selected answers, see Appendix A.

50

Sensory and Motor Mechanisms

KEY CONCEPTS

50.1 Sensory receptors transduce stimulus energy and transmit signals to the central nervous system

50.2 The mechanoreceptors responsible for hearing and equilibrium detect moving fluid or settling particles

50.3 Visual receptors in diverse animals depend on light-absorbing pigments

50.4 The senses of taste and smell rely on similar sets of sensory receptors

50.5 The physical interaction of protein filaments is required for muscle function

50.6 Skeletal systems transform muscle contraction into locomotion

Kenneth C. Catania/Vanderbilt University

▲ Figure 50.1 **Is a star-shaped nose merely decorative?**

Sensing and Acting

The face of the star-nosed mole (*Condulura cristata*) is, in a word, astounding (Figure 50.1). Eleven pairs of appendages protrude from its nose, forming a prominent pink star. Although they look a bit like fingers, these appendages are not used in grasping. Nor is the nose used to detect odours. Is the star, then, simply ornamental? No—it has a highly specialized function. Just below its surface lie 25 000 touch-sensitive receptors, more than are found in your whole hand.

Tunnelling beneath the wetlands of eastern North America, the virtually blind mole lives in almost total darkness. But as 100 000 neurons relay tactile information from its nose to its brain, the mole finds and captures food with remarkable rapidity: A star-nosed mole can detect and eat prey in as little as 120 milliseconds (msec).

Detecting and processing sensory information and generating motor responses provide the physiological basis for all animal behaviour. In this chapter, we will explore the processes of sensing and acting in both vertebrates and invertebrates. We will start with sensory processes that convey information about an animal's external and internal environment to its brain. We will then consider the structure and function of muscles and skeletons that carry out movements as instructed by the brain. Finally, we will investigate various mechanisms of animal movement. These topics will lead us naturally to our discussion of animal behaviour in Chapter 51.

CONCEPT 50.1

Sensory receptors transduce stimulus energy and transmit signals to the central nervous system

All sensory processes begin with stimuli, and all stimuli represent forms of energy. A sensory receptor converts stimulus energy to a change in membrane potential and thereby regulates the output of action potentials to the central nervous system (CNS). Activating a sensory receptor does not necessarily require a large amount of stimulus energy. Indeed, some sensory receptors can detect the smallest possible unit of stimulus; most light receptors, for example, can detect a single quantum (photon) of light.

When a stimulus is received and processed by the nervous system, a motor response may be generated. One of the simplest stimulus-response circuits is a reflex, such as the knee-jerk reflex shown in Figure 49.7. Many other behaviours rely on more elaborate processing that involves integration of sensory input. As an example, consider how the star-nosed mole forages for food in its tunnel environment (Figure 50.2). When the mole's nose contacts an object in its tunnel, touch receptors in the nose are activated. These receptors transmit sensory information about the object to the mole's brain. Circuits in the brain integrate the input and initiate one of two response pathways, depending on whether food was detected. Motor output commands

from the brain sent to skeletal muscles in the body cause the mole either to bite down with its teeth or to continue moving along the tunnel.

With this overview in mind, let's examine the general organization and activity of animal sensory systems.

Sensory Pathways

Sensory pathways have in common four basic functions: sensory reception, transduction, transmission, and perception.

Sensory Reception and Transduction

A sensory pathway begins with **sensory reception**, the detection of a stimulus by sensory cells. Some sensory cells are themselves specialized neurons, whereas others are non-neuronal cells that regulate neurons (Figure 50.3). Some exist singly; others are collected in sensory organs, such as the star-shaped nose of the mole in Figure 50.1.

The term **sensory receptor** is used to describe a sensory cell or organ, as well as the subcellular structure that interacts directly with stimuli. Many sensory receptors detect stimuli from outside the body, such as heat, light, pressure, and chemicals, but there are also receptors for stimuli from within the body, such as blood pressure and body position.

Although animals use a range of sensory receptors to detect widely varying stimuli, the effect in all cases is to open or close ion channels. Thus, for example, ion channels open or close when a substance outside the cell binds to a chemical

Sensory input	Integration	Motor output
Contact with an object activates touch receptors on the mole's nose, which transmit information to the brain along sensory nerves.	Circuits of neurons in the brain integrate the input and generate action potentials in motor neurons.	Muscles contract, causing the mole to bite down on food or move farther along the tunnel.

Mole forages along tunnel. → Food absent → Mole moves on. OR Food present → Mole bites.

▲ Figure 50.2 **A simple response pathway: foraging by a star-nosed mole.**

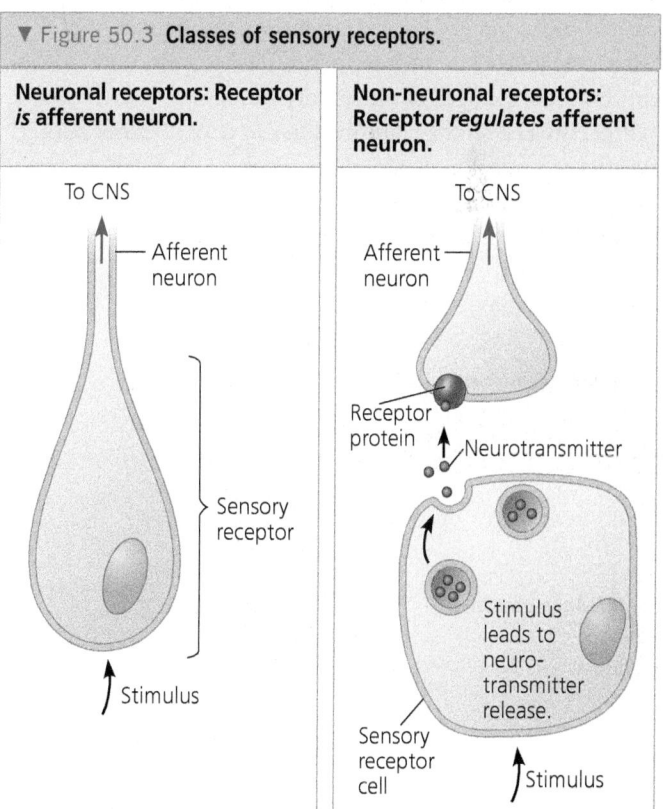

▼ Figure 50.3 **Classes of sensory receptors.**

Neuronal receptors: Receptor *is* afferent neuron.	Non-neuronal receptors: Receptor *regulates* afferent neuron.

To CNS — Afferent neuron — Sensory receptor — Stimulus

To CNS — Afferent neuron — Receptor protein — Neurotransmitter — Stimulus leads to neurotransmitter release. — Sensory receptor cell — Stimulus receptor in the plasma membrane. The resulting flow of ions across the membrane changes the membrane potential.

The conversion of a physical or chemical stimulus to a change in the membrane potential of a sensory receptor is called **sensory transduction**, and the change in membrane potential itself is known as a **receptor potential**. Receptor potentials are graded potentials; their magnitude varies with the strength of the stimulus.

Transmission

Sensory information travels through the nervous system as nerve impulses, or action potentials. For many sensory receptors, transducing the energy in a stimulus into a receptor potential initiates **transmission** of action potentials to the CNS.

Neurons that act directly as sensory receptors produce action potentials and have an axon that extends into the CNS. Non-neuronal sensory receptor cells form chemical synapses with sensory (afferent) neurons and typically respond to stimuli by increasing the rate at which the afferent neurons produce action potentials. (One exception is in the vertebrate visual system, discussed in Concept 50.3.)

The size of a receptor potential increases with the intensity of the stimulus. If the receptor is a sensory neuron, a larger receptor potential results in more frequent action potentials (Figure 50.4). If the receptor is not a sensory neuron, a larger receptor potential usually causes more neurotransmitter to be released.

Many sensory neurons spontaneously generate action potentials at a low rate. In these neurons, a stimulus does not switch the production of action potentials on or off, but it does change *how often* an action potential is produced. The frequency of action potentials of the sensory neuron informs the nervous system about the strength of the sensory stimulus.

Processing of sensory information can occur before, during, and after transmission of action potentials to the CNS. In many cases, the *integration* of sensory information begins as soon as the information is received. Receptor potentials produced by stimuli delivered to different parts of a sensory receptor cell are integrated through summation, as are postsynaptic potentials in sensory neurons that form synapses with multiple receptors (see Figure 48.15). As we will discuss shortly, sensory structures such as eyes also provide higher levels of integration, and the brain further processes all incoming signals.

Perception

When action potentials reach the brain via sensory neurons, circuits of neurons process this input, generating the **perception** of the stimuli. Perceptions—such as colours, smells, sounds, and tastes—are constructions formed in the brain and do not exist outside it. So, if a tree falls and no animal is present to hear it, is there a sound? The falling tree certainly produces pressure waves in the air, but if sound is defined as a perception, then there is none unless an animal senses the waves and its brain perceives them.

An action potential triggered by light striking the eye has the same properties as an action potential triggered by air vibrating in the ear. How, then, do we distinguish sights, sounds, and other stimuli? The answer lies in the connections that link sensory receptors to the brain. Action potentials from sensory receptors travel along neurons that are dedicated to a particular stimulus; these dedicated neurons synapse with particular neurons in the brain or spinal cord. As a result, the brain distinguishes sensory stimuli such as sight or sound solely by the path to the brain along which the action potentials have travelled.

Amplification and Adaptation

The transduction of stimuli by sensory receptors is subject to two types of modification—amplification and adaptation. **Amplification** refers to the strengthening of a sensory signal during transduction. The effect can be considerable. For example, an action potential conducted from the eye to the human brain has about 100 000 times as much energy as the few photons of light that triggered it.

Amplification that occurs in sensory receptor cells often requires signal transduction pathways involving second messengers. Because these pathways include enzyme-catalyzed reactions, they amplify signal strength through the formation of many product molecules by a single enzyme molecule. Amplification may also take place in accessory structures of a complex sense organ, as when the pressure associated with sound waves is enhanced by a factor of more than 20 before reaching receptors in the innermost part of the ear.

Upon continued stimulation, many receptors undergo a decrease in responsiveness termed **sensory adaptation** (not to be confused with the evolutionary term *adaptation*). Without sensory adaptation, you would be constantly aware of feeling every beat of your heart and every bit of clothing on your body. Adaptation also enables you to see, hear, and smell changes in the environment that vary widely in stimulus intensity.

▲ Figure 50.4 **Coding of stimulus intensity by a single sensory receptor.**

Types of Sensory Receptors

A sensory cell typically has a single type of receptor specific for a particular stimulus, such as light or cold. Often, distinct cells and receptors are responsible for particular qualities of a sensation, such as distinguishing red from blue. Before exploring these specializations, let's consider sensory receptor function at a more basic level. We can classify sensory receptors into five categories based on the nature of the stimuli they transduce: mechanoreceptors, chemoreceptors, electromagnetic receptors, thermoreceptors, and pain receptors.

Mechanoreceptors

Mechanoreceptors sense physical deformation caused by forms of mechanical energy such as pressure, touch, stretch, motion, and sound. Mechanoreceptors typically consist of ion channels that are linked to structures that extend outside the cell, such as "hairs" (cilia), as well as internal cell structures, such as the cytoskeleton. Bending or stretching of the external structure generates tension that alters the permeability of the ion channels. This change in ion permeability alters the membrane potential, resulting in a depolarization or hyperpolarization (see Chapter 48).

The familiar knee-jerk reflex (see Figure 49.7) is triggered by the vertebrate stretch receptor, a mechanoreceptor that detects muscle movement. Vertebrate stretch receptors are dendrites of sensory neurons that spiral around the middle of certain small skeletal muscle fibres. Groups of about 2 to 12 of these fibres, formed into a spindle shape and surrounded by connective tissue, are distributed throughout the muscle, parallel to other muscle fibres. When the muscle is stretched, the spindle fibres are stretched, depolarizing sensory neurons and triggering action potentials that are transmitted to the spinal cord.

The mammalian sense of touch also relies on mechanoreceptors that are the dendrites of sensory neurons. Touch receptors, such as those illustrated in Figure 50.4, are often embedded in layers of connective tissue. The structure of the connective tissue and the location of the receptors dramatically affect the type of mechanical energy (light touch, vibration, or strong pressure) that best stimulates them (Figure 50.5). Receptors that detect a light touch or vibration are close to the surface of the skin; they transduce very slight inputs of mechanical energy into receptor potentials. Receptors that respond to stronger pressure and vibrations are in deep skin layers.

Some animals use mechanoreceptors to literally get a feel for their environment. For example, cats as well as many rodents have extremely sensitive mechanoreceptors at the base of their whiskers. Because deflection of different whiskers triggers action potentials that reach different cells in the brain, an animal's whiskers provide detailed information about nearby objects.

▲ Figure 50.5 **Sensory receptors in human skin.** Most receptors in the dermis are encapsulated by connective tissue. Receptors in the epidermis are naked dendrites, as are hair movement receptors that wind around the base of hairs in the dermis.

Chemoreceptors

Chemoreceptors include both general receptors—those that transmit information about total solute concentration—and specific receptors—those that respond to individual kinds of molecules. Osmoreceptors in the mammalian brain, for example, detect changes in the total solute concentration of the blood and stimulate thirst when osmolarity increases (see Figure 44.19). Most animals also have receptors for specific molecules, including glucose, oxygen, carbon dioxide, and amino acids.

Two of the most sensitive and specific chemoreceptors known are found in the antennae of the male silkworm moth (Figure 50.6); they detect the two chemical components of the female moth sex pheromone. For pheromones and other molecules detected by chemoreceptors, the stimulus molecule binds to the specific receptor on the membrane of the sensory cell and initiates changes in ion permeability.

Electromagnetic Receptors

Electromagnetic receptors detect various forms of electromagnetic energy, such as visible light, electricity, and magnetism. For example, the platypus, a monotreme mammal (see Chapter 34), has electroreceptors on its bill that are thought to detect the electric field generated by the

R. A. Steinbrecht

CSIRO

▲ **Figure 50.6 Chemoreceptors in an insect.** The antennae of the male silkworm moth *Bombyx mori* are covered with sensory hairs, visible in the SEM enlargement. The hairs have chemoreceptors that are highly sensitive to the sex pheromone released by the female.

Michael Nolan/Robert Harding World Imagery

(a) Some migrating animals, such as these beluga whales, apparently sense Earth's magnetic field and use the information, along with other cues, for orientation.

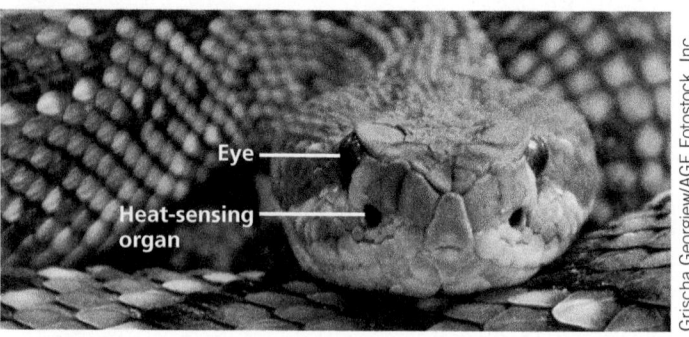

Grischa Georgiew/AGE Fotostock, Inc.

Eye

Heat-sensing organ

(b) This rattlesnake and other pit vipers have a pair of heat-sensing pit organs, one anterior to and just below each eye. These organs are sensitive enough to detect the infrared radiation emitted by a warm prey a metre away. The snake moves its head from side to side until the radiation is detected equally by the two pit organs, indicating that the prey is straight ahead.

▲ **Figure 50.7 Specialized electromagnetic receptors.**

muscles of crustaceans, frogs, small fish, and other prey. In a few cases, the animal detecting an electromagnetic stimulus is also its source: Some fishes generate electric currents and then use their electroreceptors to locate prey or other objects that disturb those currents.

Many animals appear to use Earth's magnetic field lines to orient themselves as they migrate (**Figure 50.7a**). The iron-containing mineral magnetite is found in many vertebrates (including salmon, pigeons, sea turtles, and humans), in bees, in some molluscs, and in certain protists and prokaryotes that orient to Earth's magnetic field. Once collected by sailors to make compasses for navigation, magnetite may be part of an orienting mechanism in many animals (see Chapter 51).

Thermoreceptors

Thermoreceptors detect heat and cold. For example, certain venomous snakes rely on thermoreceptors to detect the infrared radiation emitted by warm prey. These thermoreceptors are located in a pair of pit organs on the snake's head (**Figure 50.7b**). Human thermoreceptors, which are in the skin and in the anterior hypothalamus, send information to the body's thermostat in the posterior hypothalamus. Our understanding of thermoreception has increased substantially recently, thanks to scientists with an appreciation for fiery foods. Jalapeno and cayenne peppers taste "hot" because they contain a natural product called capsaicin. It turns out that exposing sensory neurons to capsaicin triggers an influx of calcium ions. When scientists

identified the receptor protein that binds capsaicin, they made a fascinating discovery: The receptor opens a calcium channel in response not only to capsaicin, but also to high temperatures (42°C or higher). In essence, spicy foods taste "hot" because they activate the same receptors as hot soup and coffee.

Mammals have a number of kinds of thermoreceptors, each specific for a particular temperature range. The capsaicin receptor and at least five other types of thermoreceptors belong to the TRP (transient receptor potential) family of ion channel proteins. Just as the TRP-type receptor specific for high temperature is sensitive to capsaicin, the receptor for temperatures below 28°C can be activated by menthol, a plant product that we perceive to have a "cool" flavour.

Pain Receptors

Extreme pressure or temperature, as well as certain chemicals, can damage animal tissues. To detect stimuli that reflect such noxious (or harmful) conditions, animals rely on **nociceptors** (from the Latin *nocere*, to hurt), also called **pain receptors**. By triggering defensive reactions, such as withdrawal from danger, the ability to detect dangerous signals and interpret them as pain serves an important function.

In humans, certain naked dendrites act as nociceptors by detecting noxious thermal, mechanical, or chemical stimuli. The capsaicin receptor is thus a thermoreceptor and also a nociceptor. Although nociceptor density is highest in skin, some pain receptors are associated with other organs.

Chemicals produced in an animal's body sometimes enhance the perception of pain. For example, damaged tissues produce prostaglandins, which act as local regulators of inflammation (see Chapter 45). Prostaglandins worsen pain by increasing nociceptor sensitivity to noxious stimuli. Aspirin and ibuprofen reduce pain by inhibiting the synthesis of prostaglandins.

Next we'll turn our focus to sensory systems, beginning with systems for maintaining balance and detecting sound.

CONCEPT CHECK 50.1

1. Which one of the five categories of sensory receptors is primarily dedicated to external stimuli?

2. Why can eating "hot" peppers cause a person to sweat?

3. **WHAT IF?** If you stimulated a sensory neuron electrically, how would that stimulation be perceived?

For suggested answers, see Appendix A.

CONCEPT 50.2

The mechanoreceptors responsible for hearing and equilibrium detect moving fluid or settling particles

Hearing and the perception of body equilibrium, or balance, are related in most animals. For both senses, mechanoreceptor cells produce receptor potentials when settling particles or moving fluid causes deflection of cell-surface structures.

Sensing of Gravity and Sound in Invertebrates

To sense gravity and maintain equilibrium, most invertebrates rely on mechanoreceptors located in organs called **statocysts** (Figure 50.8). In a typical statocyst, a layer of ciliated receptor cells surrounds a chamber that contains one or more **statoliths**, which are grains of sand or other dense granules. When statoliths settle to the low point in the chamber, they stimulate mechanoreceptors in that location. In experiments in which statoliths were replaced with metal shavings, researchers "tricked" crayfish into swimming upside down by using magnets to pull the shavings to the upper end of the statocysts located at the base of their antennae.

Many (perhaps most) insects have body hairs that vibrate in response to sound waves. Hairs of different stiffnesses and lengths vibrate at different frequencies. For example, fine hairs on the antennae of a male mosquito vibrate in a specific way in response to the hum produced by the beating wings

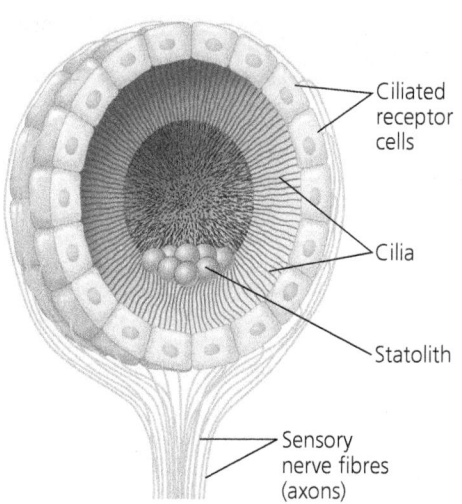

▶ Figure 50.8
The statocyst of an invertebrate. The settling of statoliths to the low point in the chamber bends cilia on receptor cells in that location, providing the brain with information about the orientation of the body with respect to gravity.

Ciliated receptor cells

Cilia

Statolith

Sensory nerve fibres (axons)

of flying females. The importance of this sensory system in the attraction of males to a potential mate can be demonstrated very simply: A tuning fork vibrating at the same frequency as that of a female's wings will itself attract males.

Many insects also detect sound by means of "ears" consisting of a tympanic membrane (eardrum) stretched over an internal air chamber (Figure 50.9). Sound waves vibrate the tympanic membrane, stimulating receptor cells attached to the inside of the membrane and resulting in nerve impulses that are transmitted to the brain. Cockroaches lack such a tympanic membrane, but instead have vibration-sensitive organs located in each leg. These organs can provide enough warning for the insect to avoid being crushed by a descending human foot.

Hearing and Equilibrium in Mammals

In mammals, as in most other terrestrial vertebrates, the sensory organs for hearing and equilibrium are closely associated. Figure 50.10 explores the structure and function of these organs in the human ear.

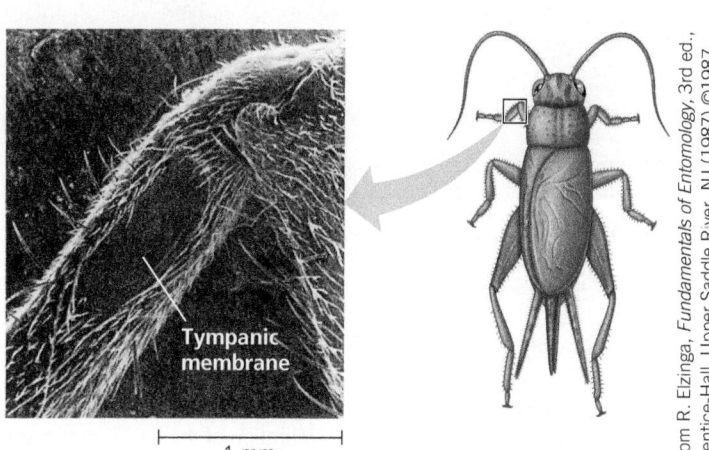

From R. Elzinga, *Fundamentals of Entomology*, 3rd ed., Prentice-Hall, Upper Saddle River, NJ (1987) ©1987

Tympanic membrane

1 mm

▲ Figure 50.9 **An insect's "ear"—on its leg.** The tympanic membrane, visible in this SEM of a cricket's front leg, vibrates in response to sound waves. The vibrations stimulate mechanoreceptors attached to the inside of the tympanic membrane.

Exploring The Structure of the Human Ear

1 Overview of Ear Structure

The **outer ear** consists of the external pinna and the auditory canal, which collect sound waves and channel them to the **tympanic membrane** (eardrum), which separates the outer ear from the middle ear. In the **middle ear**, three small bones—the malleus (hammer), incus (anvil), and stapes (stirrup)—transmit vibrations to the **oval window**, which is a membrane beneath the stapes. The middle ear also opens into the **Eustachian tube**, which connects to the pharynx and equalizes pressure between the middle ear and the atmosphere. The **inner ear** consists of fluid-filled chambers, including the **semicircular canals**, which function in equilibrium, and the coiled **cochlea** (from the Latin meaning "snail"), a bony chamber that is involved in hearing.

2 The Cochlea

The cochlea has two large canals—an upper vestibular canal and a lower tympanic canal—separated by a smaller cochlear duct. Both canals are filled with fluid.

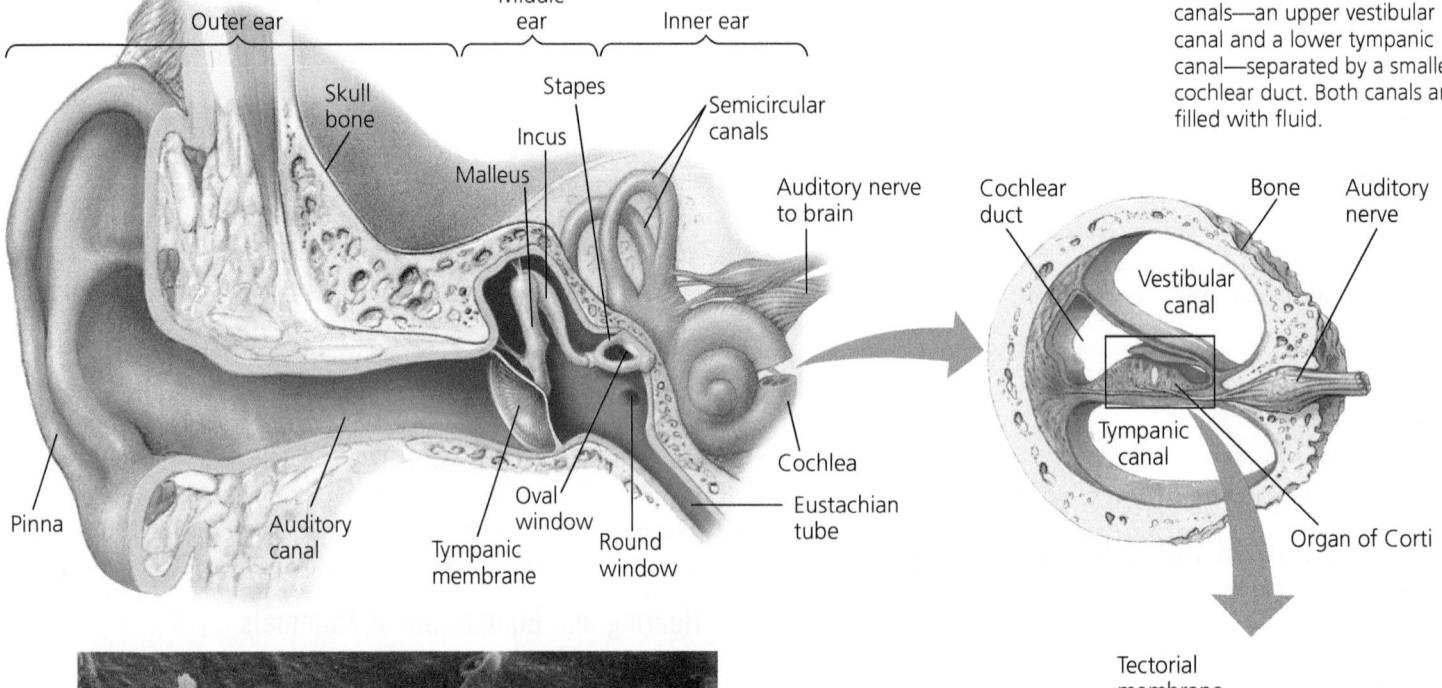

4 Hair Cell

Projecting from each hair cell is a bundle of rod-shaped "hairs," each containing a core of actin filaments. Vibration of the basilar membrane in response to sound raises and lowers the hair cells, bending the hairs against the surrounding fluid and the tectorial membrane. When the hairs within the bundle are displaced, mechanoreceptors are activated, changing the membrane potential of the hair cell.

▲ Bundled hairs projecting from a single mammalian hair cell (SEM). Two shorter rows of hairs lie behind the tall hairs in the foreground.

3 The Organ of Corti

The floor of the cochlear duct, the **basilar membrane**, bears the **organ of Corti**, which contains the mechanoreceptors of the ear, hair cells with hairs projecting into the cochlear duct. Many of the hairs are attached to the tectorial membrane, which hangs over the organ of Corti like an awning. Sound waves make the basilar membrane vibrate, which results in bending of the hairs and depolarization of the hair cells.

(a) No bending of hairs

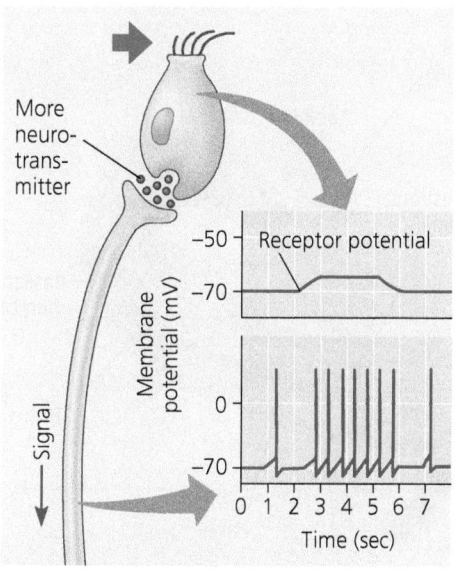

(b) Bending of hairs in one direction

(c) Bending of hairs in other direction

▲ Figure 50.11 **Sensory reception by hair cells.** Vertebrate hair cells required for hearing and balance have "hairs" formed into a bundle that bends when surrounding fluid moves. Each hair cell releases an excitatory neurotransmitter at a synapse with a sensory neuron, which conducts action potentials to the CNS. Bending of the bundle in one direction depolarizes the hair cell, causing it to release more neurotransmitter and increasing the frequency of action potentials in the sensory neuron. Bending in the other direction has the opposite effect.

Hearing

Vibrating objects, such as a plucked guitar string or the vocal cords of your instructor, create pressure waves in the surrounding air. In *hearing*, the ear transduces this mechanical stimulus (pressure waves) into nerve impulses that the brain perceives as sound. To hear music, speech, or other sounds in our environment, we rely on **hair cells**, sensory receptors with hair-like projections on the cell surface that detect motion. Before the vibration waves reach the hair cells, however, they are amplified and transformed by several accessory structures.

The first steps in hearing involve structures in the ear that convert the vibrations of moving air to pressure waves in fluid. Upon reaching the outer ear, moving air causes the tympanic membrane to vibrate. The three bones of the middle ear transmit the vibrations to the oval window, a membrane on the cochlea's surface. When one of those bones, the stapes, vibrates against the oval window, it creates pressure waves in the fluid (called perilymph) inside the cochlea.

Upon entering the vestibular canal, the pressure waves push down on the cochlear duct and basilar membrane. In response, the basilar membrane and attached hair cells vibrate up and down. The hairs projecting from the moving hair cells are deflected by the tectorial membrane, which lies immediately above in a fixed position (see Figure 50.10). With each vibration, the hairs bend first in one direction and then the other. Mechanoreceptors in the hair cells respond by opening or closing ion channels. As

shown in **Figure 50.11**, bending in one direction depolarizes hair cells, increasing neurotransmitter release and the frequency of action potentials directed to the brain along the auditory nerve. Bending the hairs in the other direction hyperpolarizes hair cells, reducing neurotransmitter release and the frequency of auditory nerve sensations.

What prevents pressure waves from reverberating within the ear and causing prolonged sensation? Once pressure waves travel through the vestibular canal, they pass around the apex (tip) of the cochlea. The waves then continue through the tympanic canal, dissipating as they strike the **round window** (Figure 50.12a). This damping of sound waves resets the apparatus for the next vibrations that arrive.

The ear conveys information to the brain about two important sound variables: volume and pitch. *Volume* (loudness) is determined by the amplitude, or height, of the sound wave. A large-amplitude sound wave causes more vigorous vibration of the basilar membrane, greater bending of the hairs on hair cells, and more action potentials in the sensory neurons. *Pitch* is a function of a sound wave's frequency, the number of vibrations per unit time. High-frequency waves produce high-pitched sounds, whereas low-frequency waves produce low-pitched sounds. Pitch is commonly expressed in cycles per second, or hertz (Hz). Healthy young humans can hear in the range of 20–20 000 Hz; dogs can hear sounds as high as 40 000 Hz; and bats can emit and hear clicking sounds at frequencies above 100 000 Hz, using this ability to locate objects.

(a) Vibrations of the stapes against the oval window produce pressure waves (black arrows) in the fluid (perilymph; blue) of the cochlea. (For purposes of illustration, the cochlea on the right is drawn partially uncoiled.) The waves travel to the apex via the vestibular canal and back toward the base via the tympanic canal. The energy in the waves causes the basilar membrane (pink) to vibrate, stimulating hair cells (not shown). Because the basilar membrane varies in stiffness along its length, each point along the membrane vibrates maximally in response to waves of a particular frequency.

(b) These graphs show the patterns of vibration along the basilar membrane for three different frequencies, high (top), medium (middle), and low (bottom). The higher the frequency, the closer the vibration to the oval window.

▲ **Figure 50.12 Transduction in the cochlea.**

Source: Human Anatomy and Physiology, 8th edition, by Elaine N. Marieb and Katja Hoehn. Copyright © 2010 by Pearson Education. Reprinted and electronically reproduced by permission of Pearson Education, Inc., Upper Saddle River, New Jersey.

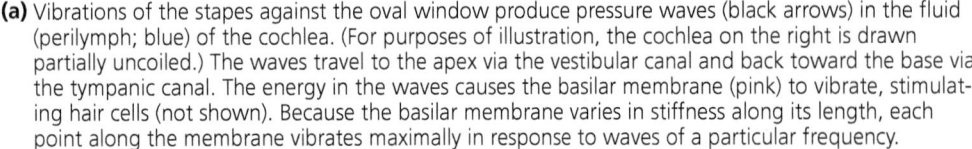

INTERPRET THE DATA *A musical chord consists of several notes, each formed by a sound wave of different frequency. When you hear a chord, where in your body are these notes combined?*

The cochlea can distinguish pitch because the basilar membrane is not uniform along its length: It is relatively narrow and stiff at the base of the cochlea near the oval window and wider and more flexible at the apex. Each region of the basilar membrane is tuned to a particular vibration frequency (**Figure 50.12b**). At any instant, the region of the membrane vibrating most vigorously triggers the highest frequency of action potentials in the neuronal pathway leading to the brain. There, within the cerebral cortex, the actual perception of pitch occurs. Axons in the auditory nerve project into auditory areas of the cerebral cortex according to the region of the basilar membrane in which the signal originated. When a particular site in our cortex is stimulated, we perceive the sound of a particular pitch.

Equilibrium

Several organs in the inner ear of humans and most other mammals detect body movement, position, and balance. Situated in a vestibule behind the oval window, the chambers called the **utricle** and **saccule** allow us to perceive position with respect to gravity or linear movement (**Figure 50.13**). Each of these chambers contains a sheet of hair cells that project into a gelatinous material. Embedded in this gel are many small calcium carbonate particles called otoliths ("ear stones"). When you tilt your head, the otoliths press on the hairs protruding into the gel. Through the hair cell receptors, this deflection of the hairs is transformed into a change in the output of sensory neurons, signalling the brain that your head is at an angle. The otoliths are also responsible for your ability to perceive acceleration, as, for example, when a stationary car in which you are sitting pulls forward. Because the utricle is oriented horizontally and the saccule is positioned vertically, you can detect motion in either the forward-and-back or up-and-down direction.

Three semicircular canals connected to the utricle detect turning of the head and other forms of angular acceleration (see Figure 50.11). Within each canal the hair cells form a single cluster, with the hairs projecting into a gelatinous cap called the cupula. Because the three canals are arranged in the three spatial planes, they can detect angular motion of the head in any direction. For example, if you turn your head to the left or right, the fluid within the horizontal canal pushes against the cupula, deflecting the hairs. The brain interprets the resulting changes in impulse production by the sensory neurons as turning of the head. If you spin in place, the fluid and canal eventually come to equilibrium and remain in that state until you stop. At that point, the moving fluid encounters a stationary cupula, triggering the false sensation of angular motion that we call dizziness.

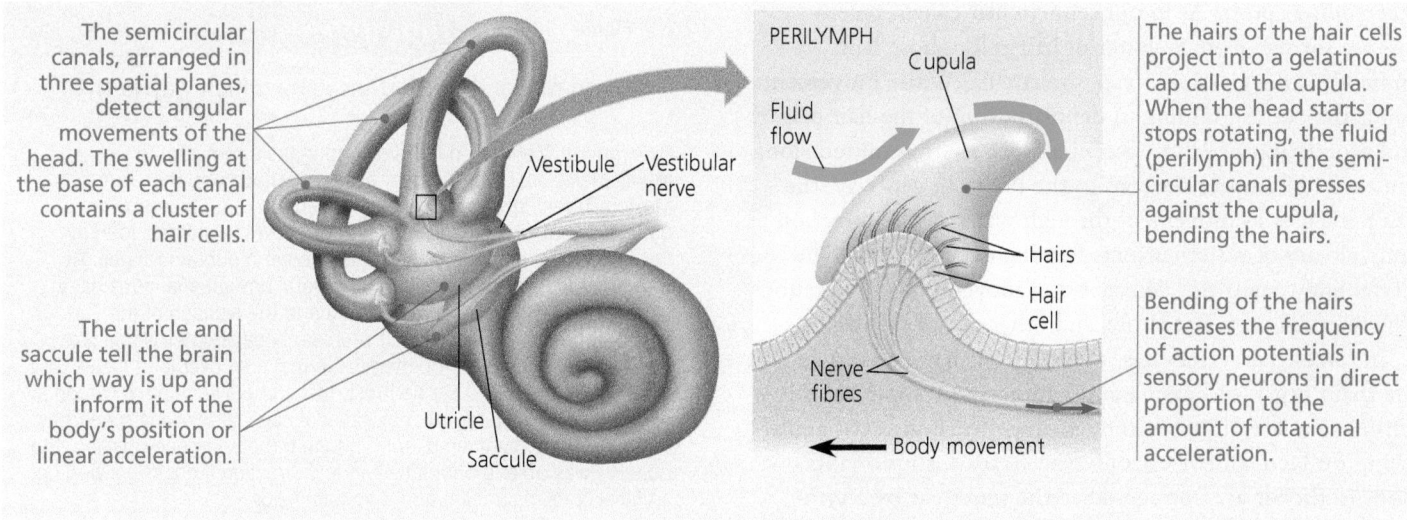

The semicircular canals, arranged in three spatial planes, detect angular movements of the head. The swelling at the base of each canal contains a cluster of hair cells.

Vestibule Vestibular nerve

Utricle

Saccule

The utricle and saccule tell the brain which way is up and inform it of the body's position or linear acceleration.

PERILYMPH

Cupula

Fluid flow

Hairs

Hair cell

Nerve fibres

Body movement

The hairs of the hair cells project into a gelatinous cap called the cupula. When the head starts or stops rotating, the fluid (perilymph) in the semi-circular canals presses against the cupula, bending the hairs.

Bending of the hairs increases the frequency of action potentials in sensory neurons in direct proportion to the amount of rotational acceleration.

▲ Figure 50.13 **Organs of equilibrium in the inner ear.**

Source: Human Anatomy and Physiology, 8th edition, by Elaine N. Marieb and Katja Hoehn. Copyright © 2010 by Pearson Education. Reprinted and electronically reproduced by permission of Pearson Education, Inc., Upper Saddle River, New Jersey.

Hearing and Equilibrium in Other Vertebrates

Unlike the mammalian hearing apparatus, the ear of a fish does not open to the outside of the body and has no eardrum or cochlea. The vibrations of the water caused by sound waves are conducted through the skeleton of the head to a pair of inner ears, setting otoliths in motion and stimulating hair cells. The fish's air-filled swim bladder (see Figure 34.16) also vibrates in response to sound. Some fishes, including catfishes and minnows, have a series of bones that conduct vibrations from the swim bladder to the inner ear.

As discussed in Chapter 34, most fishes and aquatic amphibians have a **lateral line system** along both sides of their body (Figure 50.14). The system contains mechanoreceptors that detect low-frequency waves by a mechanism similar to that of the mammalian inner ear. Water from the animal's surroundings enters the lateral line system through numerous pores and flows along a tube past the

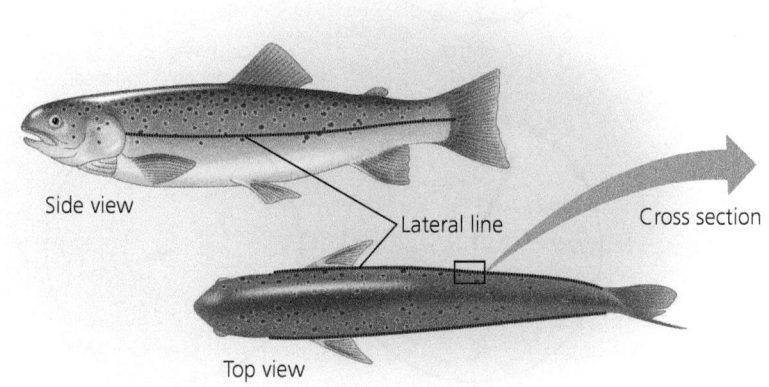

Side view

Lateral line

Top view

Cross section

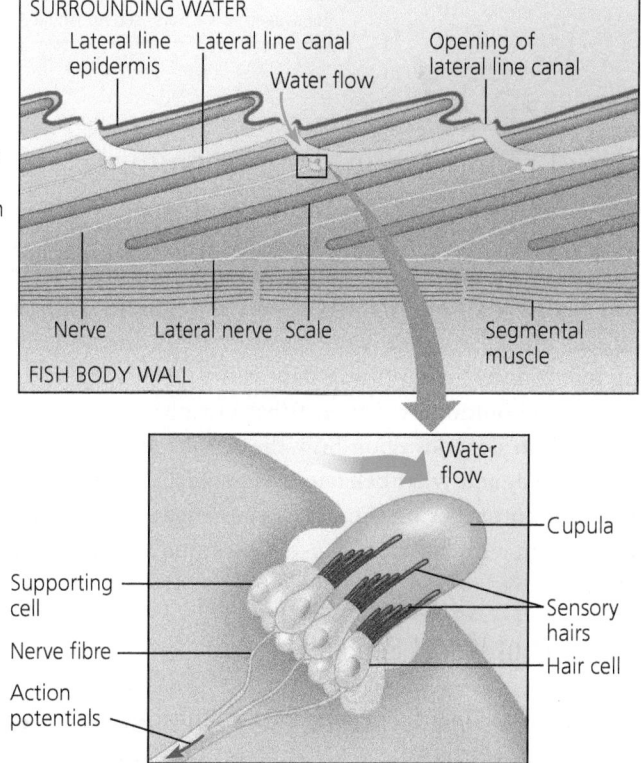

SURROUNDING WATER

Lateral line epidermis Lateral line canal Opening of lateral line canal

Water flow

Nerve Lateral nerve Scale Segmental muscle

FISH BODY WALL

Water flow

Cupula

Supporting cell

Nerve fibre

Action potentials

Sensory hairs

Hair cell

▲ Figure 50.14 **The lateral line system in a fish.** The sensory organs of the lateral line stretch from head to tail along each side of the fish. Water movement into and through the lateral line canals pushes on the gelatinous cupula, bending the hair cells within. In response, the hair cells generate receptor potentials, triggering action potentials that are conveyed to the brain. This information enables a fish to monitor water currents, any pressure waves produced by moving objects, and any low frequency sounds conducted through the water.

mechanoreceptors. As in our semicircular canals, receptors are formed from a cluster of hair cells whose hairs are embedded in a gelatinous cap, the cupula. Water movement bends the cupula, leading to depolarization of the hair cells and production of action potentials that are transmitted along the axons of sensory neurons to the brain. In this way, the fish perceives its movement through water or the direction and velocity of water currents flowing over its body. The lateral line system also detects water movements or vibrations generated by prey, predators, and other moving objects.

In terrestrial vertebrates, the inner ear has evolved as the main organ of hearing and equilibrium. Some amphibians have a lateral line system as juveniles, but not as adults living on land. In the ear of a frog or toad, sound vibrations in the air are conducted to the inner ear by a tympanic membrane on the body surface and a single middle ear bone. Like mammals, birds and other reptiles have a cochlea. However, as in amphibians, sound is conducted from the tympanic membrane to the inner ear of reptiles by a single bone (see Figure 34.37).

CONCEPT CHECK 50.2

1. How are statocysts adaptive for animals that burrow underground or live deep in the ocean?

2. **WHAT IF?** Suppose a series of pressure waves in your cochlea caused a vibration of the basilar membrane that moves gradually from the apex toward the base. How would your brain interpret this stimulus?

3. **WHAT IF?** If the stapes became fused to the other middle ear bones or to the oval window, how would this condition affect hearing? Explain.

For suggested answers, see Appendix A.

CONCEPT 50.3

Visual receptors in diverse animals depend on light-absorbing pigments

The ability to detect light has a central role in the interaction of nearly all animals with their environment. Although animals use a diverse set of organs for vision, the underlying mechanism for capturing light is the same, suggesting a common evolutionary origin. What organisms do with this information depends upon how the sensory information is processed, and what behaviour is evoked. For example, monarch butterflies use sunlight as a compass, helping them navigate on a remarkable long-distance, multigenerational migration (**Figure 50.15**).

Evolution of Visual Perception

EVOLUTION Light detectors in the animal kingdom range from simple clusters of cells that detect only the direction

▼ Figure 50.15 | **Inquiry**

How do monarch butterflies know which way to fly?

Experiment Monarch butterflies undertake a remarkable multigenerational journey from eastern Canada and the USA to Mexico. Tracking studies have identified the route taken by the butterflies but very little is known about how the animals identify the correct route across plains and through mountain ranges. As with other long-distance migrants, several navigational cues have been proposed including magnetism and the position of the sun. Experimentally this is a difficult problem because their small size makes it difficult to track butterflies in real time over long distances. Henrik Mouritsen and Barrie Frost, researchers working at Queen's University, investigated the navigational cues by allowing monarchs to fly while in a flight simulator. Though tethered in one position, the butterfly was able to orient itself in any direction it chose, relying on artificial cues of sunlight and magnetic fields.

Results Butterflies placed in the chamber typically flew in a southwest direction (panel A), which would have sent them on their normal flight path to Mexico if they were free. When researchers changed their circadian rhythm by manipulating sunrise and sunset times, the direction of flight shifted. When sunrise was advanced 6 hours, the monarchs flew southeast rather than southwest (panel B). When sunrise was delayed 6 hours, the monarchs flew northwest (panel C). When the light exposure was changed to approximate an overcast day, the butterflies flew in random directions (panel D).

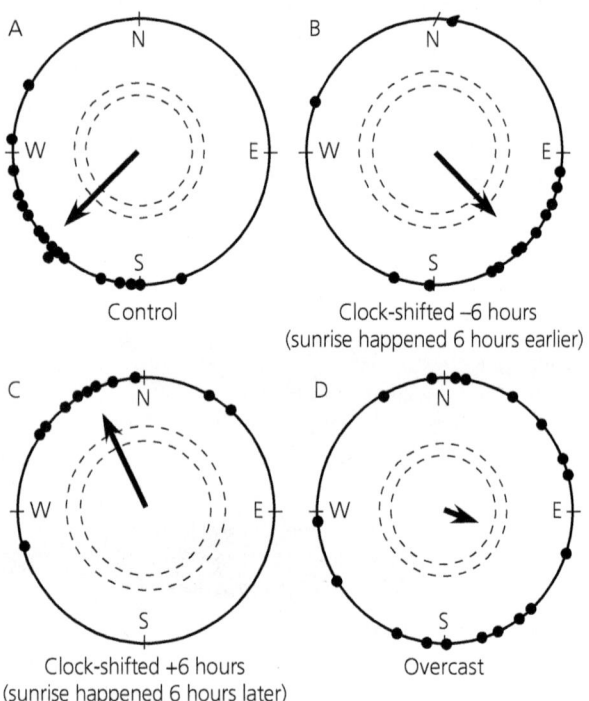

Control

Clock-shifted −6 hours
(sunrise happened 6 hours earlier)

Clock-shifted +6 hours
(sunrise happened 6 hours later)

Overcast

Conclusion Monarch butterflies choose their direction based on the direction of the sun at a given time of day, essentially using the sun as a compass.

Source: Figure 2 from Henrik Mouritsen and Barrie J. Frost, "Virtual Migration in Tethered Flying Monarch Butterflies Reveals Their Orientation Mechanisms" *Proceedings of the National Academy of Sciences of the United States of America,* Vol. 99, No. 15. © (2002) National Academy of Sciences, U.S.A. Used with permission.

WHAT IF? *What would happen if this experiment were performed at a university campus, rather than a remote field station?*

(a) The planarian's brain directs the body to turn until the sensations from the two ocelli are equal and minimal, causing the animal to move away from light.

(b) Whereas light striking the front of an ocellus excites the photoreceptors, light striking the back is blocked by the screening pigment. In this way, the ocelli indicate the direction of a light source, triggering the light avoidance behaviour.

▲ **Figure 50.16 Ocelli and orientation behaviour of a planarian.**

(a) The faceted eyes on the head of a fly form a repeating pattern visible in this photomicrograph.

2 mm

(b) The cornea and crystalline cone of each ommatidium together function as a lens that focuses light on the rhabdom, an organelle formed by and extending inward from a circle of photoreceptors. The rhabdom traps light, serving as the photosensitive part of the ommatidium. Information gathered from different intensities of light entering the many ommatidia from different angles is used to form a visual image.

▲ **Figure 50.17 Compound eyes.**

and intensity of light to complex organs that form images. These diverse light detectors all contain **photoreceptors**, cells that contain light-absorbing pigment molecules. Furthermore, the genes that specify where and when photoreceptors arise during embryonic development are shared among animals as diverse as flatworms, annelids, arthropods, and vertebrates. It is thus very probable that the genetic underpinnings of all photoreceptors were already present in the earliest bilaterian animals.

Light-Detecting Organs

Most invertebrates have some kind of light-detecting organ. One of the simplest is that of planarians (**Figure 50.16**). A pair of ocelli (singular, *ocellus*), which are sometimes called eyespots, are located in the head region. Photoreceptors in each ocellus receive light only through the opening where there are no pigmented cells. By comparing the rate of action potentials coming from the two ocelli, the planarian is able to move away from the light source until it reaches a shaded location, where a rock or other object is likely to hide the animal from predators.

Compound Eyes

Insects and crustaceans (phylum Arthropoda) have compound eyes, as do some polychaete worms (phylum Annelida). A **compound eye** consists of up to several thousand light detectors called **ommatidia** (the "facets" of the eye), each with its own light-focusing lens (**Figure 50.17**). Each ommatidium detects light from a tiny portion of the visual

field. A compound eye is very effective at detecting movement, an important adaptation for flying insects and small animals constantly threatened with predation. Whereas the human eye can distinguish only about 50 flashes of light per second, the compound eyes of some insects can detect flickering at six times that rate. (If they slipped into a movie theatre, these insects could easily resolve each frame of the film being projected as a separate still image.) Insects also have excellent colour vision, and some (including bees) can see into the ultraviolet (UV) range of the electromagnetic spectrum. Because UV light is invisible to humans, we miss seeing differences in the environment that bees and other insects detect. In studying animal behaviour, we cannot simply extrapolate our sensory world to other species; different animals have different sensitivities and different brain organizations.

Single-Lens Eyes

Among invertebrates, **single-lens eyes** are found in some jellies and polychaete worms, as well as in spiders and many molluscs. A single-lens eye works somewhat like a camera. The eye of an octopus or squid, for example, has a small opening, the **pupil**, through which light enters. Like a camera's adjustable aperture, the **iris** contracts or expands, changing the diameter of the pupil to let in more or less light. Behind the pupil, a single lens focuses light on a layer of photoreceptors. Similar to a camera's focusing action, muscles in an invertebrate's single-lens eye move the lens forward or backward, focusing on objects at different distances.

The eyes of all vertebrates have a single lens. In fishes, focusing is as in invertebrates, with the lens moving forward or backward. In other species, including mammals, focusing is achieved by changing the shape of the lens. We will learn about this mechanism, as well as explore visual

perception in much more detail, as we shift our attention to the vertebrate visual system.

The Vertebrate Visual System

The human eye will serve as our model of vision in vertebrates. As detailed in **Figure 50.18**, vision begins when photons of light enter the eye and strike the rods and cones. There the energy of each photon is captured by a shift in configuration of a single chemical bond in retinal.

Although light detection in the eye is the first stage in vision, remember that it is actually the brain that "sees."

▼ Figure 50.18

Exploring The Structure of the Human Eye

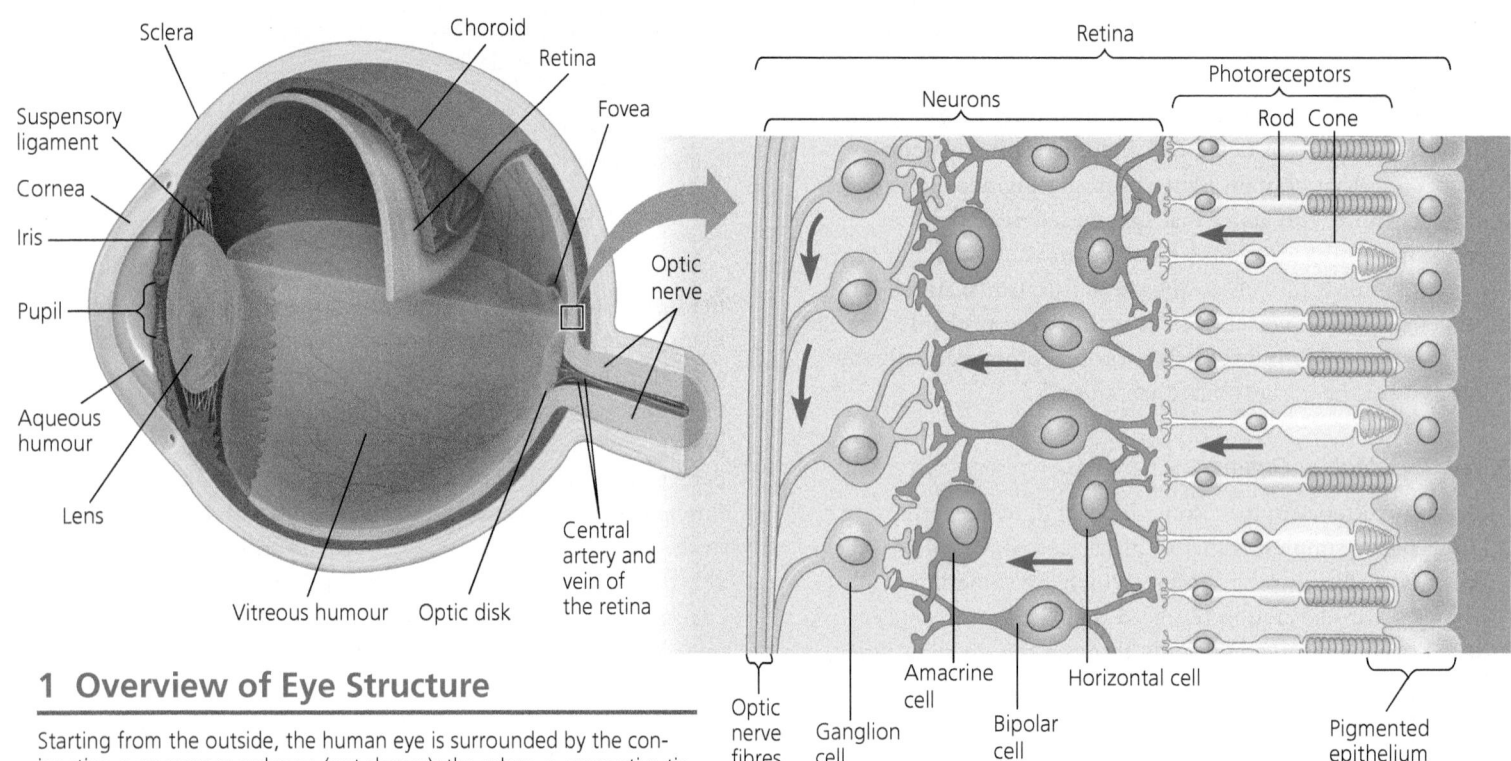

1 Overview of Eye Structure

Starting from the outside, the human eye is surrounded by the conjunctiva, a mucous membrane (not shown); the sclera, a connective tissue; and the choroid, a thin, pigmented layer. At the front, the sclera forms the transparent *cornea* and the choroid forms the coloured *iris*. By changing size, the iris regulates the amount of light entering the pupil, the hole in the centre of the iris. Just inside the choroid, the neurons and photoreceptors of the **retina** form the innermost layer of the eyeball. The optic nerve exits the eye at the optic disk.

The **lens**, a transparent disk of protein, divides the eye into two cavities. In front of the lens lies the *aqueous humour*, a clear watery substance. Blockage of ducts that drain this fluid can produce glaucoma, a condition in which increased pressure in the eye damages the optic nerve, causing vision loss. Behind the lens lies the jellylike *vitreous humour* (illustrated here in the lower portion of the eyeball).

2 The Retina

Light (coming from left in the above view) strikes the retina, passing through largely transparent layers of neurons before reaching the rods and cones, two types of photoreceptors that differ in shape and in function. The neurons of the retina then relay visual information captured by the photoreceptors to the optic nerve and brain along the pathways shown with red arrows. Each *bipolar cell* receives information from several rods or cones, and each *ganglion cell* gathers input from several bipolar cells. *Horizontal* and *amacrine cells* integrate information across the retina.

One region of the retina, the optic disk, lacks photoreceptors. As a result, this region forms a "blind spot" where light is not detected.

Source: Adaptation of figure 15.4(a) from *Human Anatomy and Physiology*, 8th edition, by Elaine N. Marieb and Katja Hoehn. Copyright © 2010 by Pearson Education, Inc. Adapted and electronically reproduced by permission of Pearson Education, Inc., Upper Saddle River, New Jersey.

Thus, to understand vision, we must examine how the capture of light by retinal changes the production of action potentials and then follow these signals to the visual centres of the brain, where images are perceived.

Sensory Transduction in the Eye

The transduction of visual information to the nervous system begins with the light-induced conversion of *cis*-retinal to *trans*-retinal. As shown in **Figure 50.19**, this conversion activates rhodopsin, which activates a G protein, which in turn activates an enzyme that can hydrolyze cyclic GMP.

In the dark, cyclic GMP in photoreceptor cells binds to sodium ion (Na^+) channels and keeps them open. When the G protein-dependent pathway is activated, cyclic GMP is broken down, Na^+ channels close, and the cell becomes hyperpolarized.

The signal transduction pathway in photoreceptor cells normally shuts off as enzymes convert retinal back to the *cis* form, returning rhodopsin to its inactive state. In very bright light, however, rhodopsin remains active, and the response in the rods becomes saturated. If the amount of light entering the eyes decreases abruptly, the rods do not

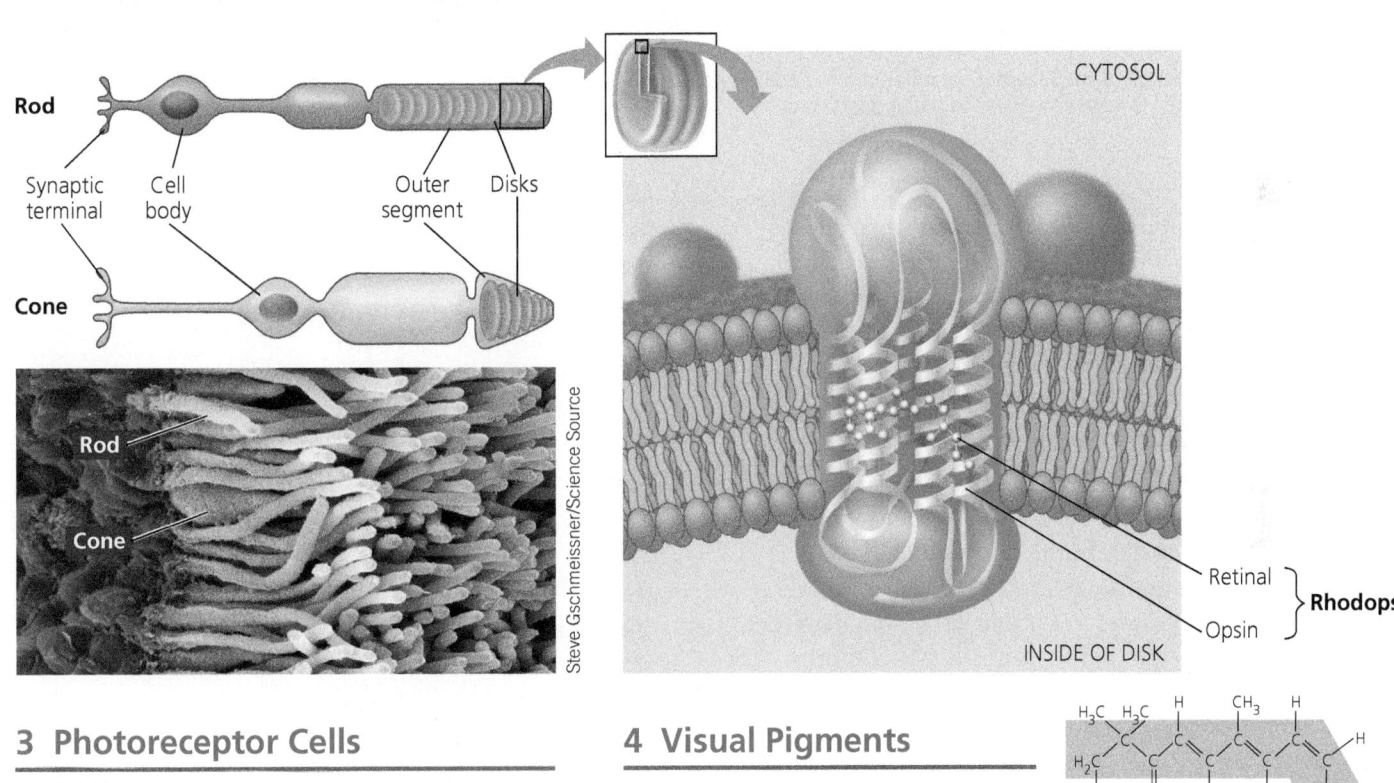

Steve Gschmeissner/Science Source

3 Photoreceptor Cells

Humans have two main types of photoreceptor cells: rods and cones. Within the outer segment of a rod or cone is a stack of membranous disks in which *visual pigments* are embedded. **Rods** are more sensitive to light but do not distinguish colours; they enable us to see at night, but only in black and white. **Cones** provide colour vision, but, being less sensitive, contribute very little to night vision. There are three types of cones. Each has a different sensitivity across the visible spectrum, providing an optimal response to red, green, or blue light.

In the colourized SEM shown above, cones (green), rods (light tan), and adjacent neurons (purple) are visible. The pigmented epithelium, which was removed in this preparation, would be to the right.

4 Visual Pigments

Vertebrate visual pigments consist of a light-absorbing molecule called **retinal** (a derivative of vitamin A) bound to a membrane protein called an **opsin**. Seven α helices of each opsin molecule span the disk membrane. The visual pigment of rods, shown here, is called **rhodopsin**.

Retinal exists as two isomers. Absorption of light shifts one bond in retinal from a *cis* to a *trans* arrangement, converting the molecule from an angled shape to a straight shape. This change in configuration destabilizes and activates the opsin protein to which retinal is bound.

▲ **Figure 50.19 Production of the receptor potential in a rod cell.** In rods (and cones), the receptor potential triggered by light is a hyperpolarization, not a depolarization.

① **Light** converts *cis*-retinal to *trans*-retinal, activating rhodopsin.

② **Active** rhodopsin in turn activates a G protein called transducin.

③ **Transducin** activates the enzyme phosphodiesterase.

④ **Activated phospho-diesterase** detaches cGMP from Na⁺ channels in the plasma membrane by hydrolyzing cGMP to GMP.

⑤ The Na⁺ channels close when cGMP detaches. The membrane's permeability to Na⁺ decreases, and the rod hyperpolarizes.

regain full responsiveness for several minutes. This is why you are temporarily blinded if you pass quickly from the bright sunshine into a movie theatre or other dark environment. (Because light activation changes the colour of rhodopsin from purple to yellow, rods in which the light response is saturated are often described as "bleached.")

Processing of Visual Information in the Retina

The processing of visual information begins in the retina itself, where both rods and cones form synapses with bipolar cells **(Figure 50.20)**. In the dark, rods and cones are depolarized and continually release the neurotransmitter glutamate at these synapses (see Table 48.2). Some bipolar cells depolarize in response to glutamate, whereas others hyperpolarize. Which of the two responses a bipolar cell exhibits depends on the type of glutamate receptor on its surface at the synapse. When light strikes the rods and cones, they hyperpolarize, shutting off their release of glutamate. In response, the bipolar cells that are depolarized by glutamate hyperpolarize, and those that are hyperpolarized by glutamate depolarize.

In addition to bipolar cells, information processing in the retina requires three other types of neurons—ganglion, horizontal, and amacrine cells (see Figure 50.18).

Signals from rods and cones can follow several different pathways in the retina. Some information passes directly from photoreceptors to bipolar cells to ganglion cells. In

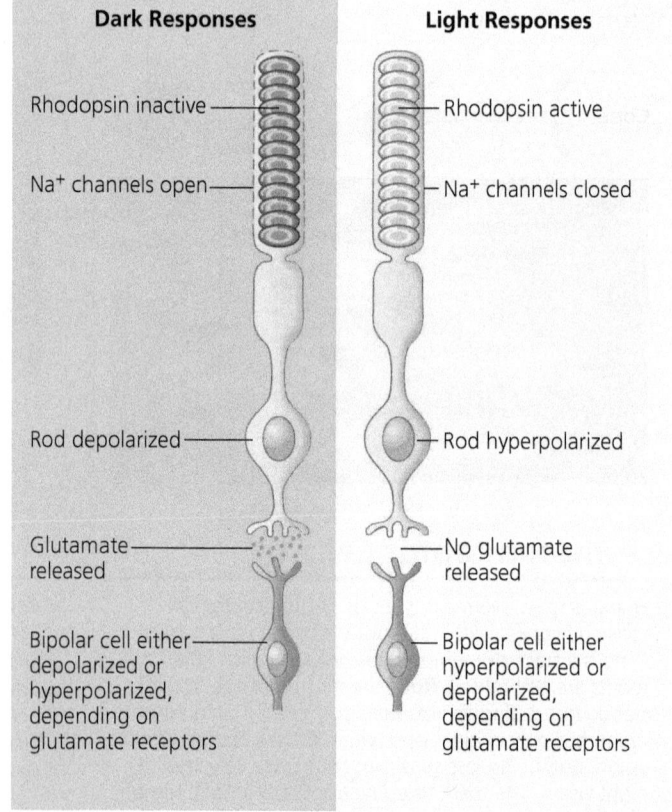

▲ **Figure 50.20 Synaptic activity of rod cells in light and dark.**

? *Like rods, cone cells are depolarized when rhodopsin is inactive. In the case of a cone, why might it be misleading to call this a dark response?*

other cases, horizontal cells carry signals from one rod or cone to other photoreceptors and to several bipolar cells. When an illuminated rod or cone stimulates a horizontal cell, the horizontal cell inhibits more distant photoreceptors and bipolar cells that are not illuminated. The result is that the region receiving light appears lighter and the dark surroundings even darker. This form of integration, called **lateral inhibition**, sharpens edges and enhances contrast in the image. Amacrine cells distribute some information from one bipolar cell to several ganglion cells. Lateral inhibition is repeated by the interactions of the amacrine cells with the ganglion cells and occurs at all levels of visual processing in the brain.

A single ganglion cell receives information from an array of rods and cones, each of which responds to light coming from a particular location. Together, the rods or cones that feed information to one ganglion cell define a *receptive field*—the part of the visual field to which the ganglion can respond. The fewer rods or cones that supply a single ganglion cell, the smaller the receptive field. A smaller receptive field results in a sharper image, because the information as to where light has struck the retina is more precise. The ganglion cells of the fovea have very small receptive fields, so visual acuity (sharpness) in the fovea is high.

Processing of Visual Information in the Brain

Axons of ganglion cells form the optic nerves that transmit sensations from the eyes to the brain (Figure 50.21). The two optic nerves meet at the **optic chiasm** near the centre of the base of the cerebral cortex. Axons in the optic nerves are routed at the optic chiasm such that sensations from the left visual field of both eyes are transmitted to the right side of the brain, and sensations from the right visual field are transmitted to the left side of the brain. (Note that each visual field, whether right or left, involves input from both eyes.)

Within the brain, most ganglion cell axons lead to the **lateral geniculate nuclei**, which have axons that reach the **primary visual cortex** in the cerebrum. Additional neurons carry the information to higher-order visual processing and integrating centres elsewhere in the cortex.

Point-by-point information in the visual field is projected along neurons onto the visual cortex. How does the cortex convert a complex set of action potentials representing two-dimensional images focused on the retina to three-dimensional perceptions of our surroundings? Researchers estimate that at least 30% of the cerebral cortex, comprising hundreds of millions of neurons in perhaps dozens of integrating centres, takes part in formulating what we actually "see." Determining how these centres integrate such components of our vision as colour, motion, depth, shape, and detail is the focus of much exciting research.

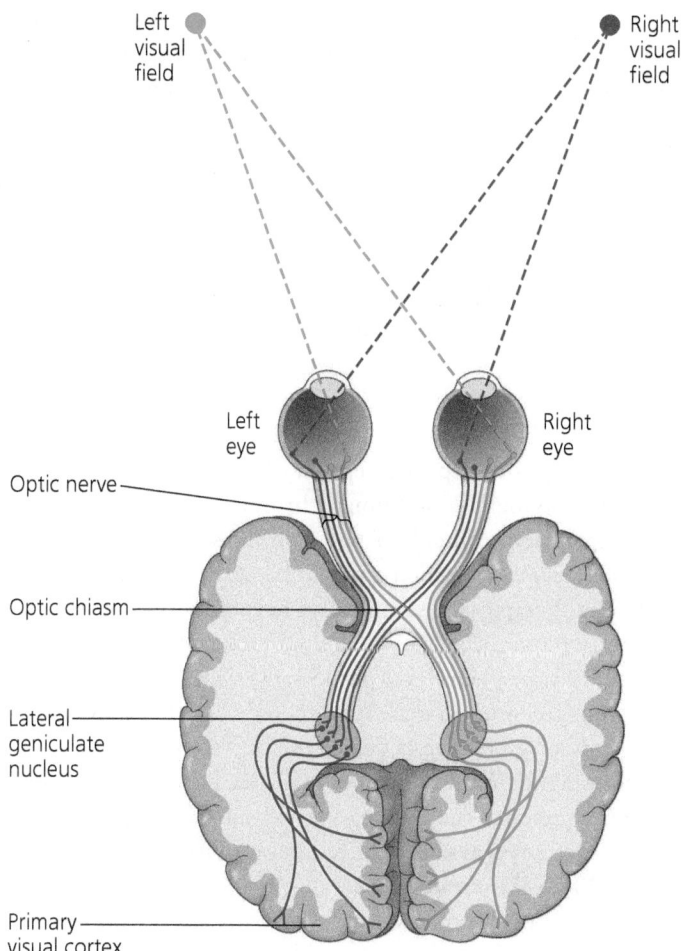

▲ Figure 50.21 **Neural pathways for vision.** Each optic nerve contains about a million axons that synapse with interneurons in the lateral geniculate nuclei. The nuclei relay sensations to the primary visual cortex, one of many brain centres that cooperate in constructing our visual perceptions.

Colour Vision

Among vertebrates, most fishes, amphibians, and reptiles, including birds, have very good colour vision. Humans and other primates also see colour well, but are among the minority of mammals with this ability. Many mammals are nocturnal, and having a high proportion of rods in the retina is an adaptation that gives these animals keen night vision. Cats, for instance, are usually most active at night; they have limited colour vision and probably see a pastel world during the day.

In humans, the perception of colour is based on three types of cones, each with a different visual pigment—red, green, or blue. The three visual pigments, called *photopsins*, are formed from the binding of retinal to three distinct opsin proteins. Slight differences in the opsin proteins are sufficient for each photopsin to absorb light optimally at a different wavelength. Although the visual pigments are designated as red, green, or blue, their absorption spectra in fact overlap. For this reason, the brain's perception of intermediate hues depends on the differential stimulation of two or more classes of cones. For example, when both red and green cones are stimulated, we may see yellow or orange, depending on which class is more strongly stimulated.

Abnormal colour vision typically results from alterations in the genes for one or more photopsin proteins. Because the human genes for the red and green pigments are located on the X chromosome, a single defective copy of either gene can disrupt colour vision in males (see Figure 15.7 to review the genetics of sex-linked traits). For this reason, colour blindness is more common in males than in females (5–8% of males, fewer than 1% of females) and nearly always disrupts perception of red or green (the gene for blue pigment is on human chromosome 7).

Experiments on colour vision in the squirrel monkey (*Saimiri sciureus*) enabled a recent breakthrough in the field of gene therapy. These monkeys have only two opsin genes, one sensitive to blue light and the other sensitive to either red or green light, depending on the allele. Because the red/green opsin gene is X-linked, all males have only the red- or green-sensitive version and are red-green colour-blind. When researchers injected a virus containing the gene for the missing version into the retina of adult male monkeys, evidence of full colour vision was apparent after 20 weeks (Figure 50.22).

The squirrel monkey gene therapy studies demonstrate that the neural circuits required to process visual information can be generated or activated even in adults, making it possible to treat a range of vision disorders. Indeed, gene therapy has been used to treat Leber's congenital amaurosis (LCA), an inherited retinal degenerative disease that causes severe loss of vision. After using gene therapy to restore vision in dogs and mice with LCA, researchers successfully treated the disease in humans by injecting the functional LCA gene in a viral vector (see Figure 20.24).

The Visual Field

The brain not only processes visual information, but also controls what information is captured. One important type of control is focusing, which, as noted earlier and illustrated in **Figure 50.23**, occurs by changing the shape of the lens. When you focus on a close object, your lens becomes almost spherical. When you view a distant object, your lens is flattened. By turning your head and pointing your eyes in a particular direction, your brain also determines what lies in your field of vision.

Although our peripheral vision allows us to see objects over a nearly 180° range, the distribution of photoreceptors across the eye limits both what we see and how well we see it. Overall, the human retina contains about 125 million rods and about 6 million cones. At the **fovea**, the centre of the visual field, there are no rods but a very high density of cones—about 150 000 cones per square millimetre. The ratio of rods to cones increases with distance from the fovea, with the peripheral regions having only rods.

From K. Mancuso et al., Gene therapy for red-green colour blindness in adult primates, *Nature* 461(7265):784–787 (2009). Photo: Neitz Laboratory.

▲ Figure 50.22 **Gene therapy for vision.** Once colour-blind, this adult male monkey treated with gene therapy demonstrates his ability to distinguish red from green.

MAKE CONNECTIONS *Red-green colour blindness is X-linked in squirrel monkeys and humans (see Figure 15.7). Why is the inheritance pattern in humans not apparent in squirrel monkeys?*

▼ Figure 50.23 **Focusing in the mammalian eye.** Ciliary muscles control the shape of the lens, which bends light and focuses it on the retina. The thicker the lens, the more sharply the light is bent.

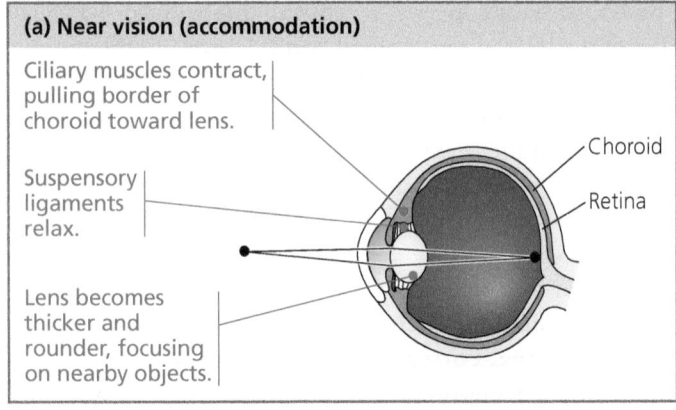

(a) Near vision (accommodation)

Ciliary muscles contract, pulling border of choroid toward lens.

Suspensory ligaments relax.

Lens becomes thicker and rounder, focusing on nearby objects.

Choroid

Retina

(b) Distance vision

Ciliary muscles relax, and border of choroid moves away from lens.

Suspensory ligaments pull against lens.

Lens becomes flatter, focusing on distant objects.

In daylight, you achieve your sharpest vision by looking directly at an object, such that light shines on the tightly packed cones in your fovea. At night, looking directly at a dimly lit object is ineffective, since the rods—the more sensitive light receptors—are found outside the fovea. Thus, for example, you see a dim star best by focusing on a point just to one side of it.

CONCEPT CHECK 50.3

1. Contrast the light-detecting organs of planarians and flies. How is each organ adaptive for the lifestyle of the animal?
2. In a condition called presbyopia, the eyes' lenses lose much of their elasticity and maintain a flat shape. Explain how this condition affects a person's vision.
3. **WHAT IF?** If you perceive an object floating across your field of view, how might you determine whether the image represents a real object rather than a disturbance in your eye or in a neural circuit of your brain?
4. **MAKE CONNECTIONS** Compare the function of retinal in the eye with that of the pigment chlorophyll in a plant photosystem (see Concept 10.2).

For suggested answers, see Appendix A.

CONCEPT 50.4

The senses of taste and smell rely on similar sets of sensory receptors

Many animals use their chemical senses to find mates (as when male silk moths respond to pheromones emitted by females), to recognize territory that has been marked by some chemical substance (as when dogs and cats sniff boundaries that have been staked out by their spraying neighbours), and to help navigate during migration (as when salmon use the unique scent of their streams of origin to return there for breeding). Animals such as ants and bees that live in large social groups rely extensively on chemical "conversation." In all animals, chemical senses are important in feeding behaviour. For example, a hydra retracts its tentacles toward its mouth when it detects the compound glutathione, which is released from prey captured by the tentacles.

The perceptions of **gustation** (taste) and **olfaction** (smell) both depend on chemoreceptors that detect specific chemicals in the environment. In the case of terrestrial animals, taste is the detection of chemicals called **tastants** that are present in a solution, and smell is the detection of **odorants** that are carried through the air, then dissolved in mucus. There is no distinction between taste and smell in aquatic animals.

The taste receptors of insects are located within sensory hairs located on the feet and in mouthparts. These animals use their sense of taste to select food. A tasting hair contains several chemoreceptors, each especially responsive to

a particular class of tastant, such as sugar or salt. Insects are also capable of smelling airborne odorants using olfactory hairs, usually located on their antennae (see Figure 50.6). The chemical DEET (N,N-diethyl-meta-toluamide), sold as an insect "repellant," actually protects against bites by blocking the olfactory receptor in mosquitoes that detects human scent.

Taste in Mammals

Humans and other mammals recognize five types of tastants. Four represent the familiar taste perceptions—sweet, sour, salty, and bitter. The fifth, called umami (Japanese for "delicious"), is elicited by the amino acid glutamate. Often used as a flavour enhancer, monosodium glutamate (MSG) occurs naturally in foods such as meat and aged cheese, imparting a quality sometimes described as savoury. Researchers have identified the receptor proteins for all of the tastes except salty.

For decades, many researchers assumed that a taste cell could have more than one type of receptor. An alternative idea is that each taste cell has a single receptor type, programming the cell to recognize only one of the five tastes. Which hypothesis is correct? In 2005, scientists at the University of California, San Diego, used a cloned bitter taste receptor to genetically reprogram gustation in a mouse (Figure 50.24). Based on these and other studies, the researchers concluded that an individual taste cell expresses a single receptor type and detects tastants representing only one of the five tastes.

The receptor cells for taste in mammals are modified epithelial cells organized into **taste buds**, which are scattered in several areas of the tongue and mouth (Figure 50.25). Most taste buds on the tongue are associated with nipple-shaped projections called papillae. Any region of the tongue with taste buds can detect any of the five types of taste. (The frequently reproduced "taste maps" of the tongue are thus not accurate.)

Taste receptors fall into two categories, each evolutionarily related to receptors for other senses. The sensation of sweet, umami, and bitter tastes requires a G protein-coupled receptor, or GPCR (see Figure 11.8). In humans, there are more than 30 different receptors for bitter taste, each able to recognize multiple bitter tastants. In contrast, humans have one type of sweet receptor and one type of umami receptor, each assembled from a different pair of GPCR proteins. Other GPCR proteins are critical for the sense of smell, as we will discuss shortly.

Unlike the other identified taste receptors, the receptor for sour tastants belongs to the TRP family (see p. 1166). Formed from a pair of TRP proteins, the sour receptor is similar to the capsaicin receptor and other thermoreceptor proteins. In taste buds, the TRP proteins of the sour receptor assemble into a channel in the plasma membrane of the taste cell. Binding of an acid or other sour-tasting substance

Inquiry

How do mammals detect different tastes?

Experiment To investigate the basis of mammalian taste perception, Ken Mueller, Nick Ryba, and Charles Zuker used a chemical called phenyl-β-D-glucopyranoside (PBDG). Humans find the taste of PBDG extremely bitter. Mice, however, appear to lack a receptor for PBDG. Whereas mice avoid drinking water containing other bitter tastants, they show no aversion to water that contains PBDG.

Using a molecular cloning strategy, Mueller generated mice that made the human PBDG receptor in cells that normally make either a sweet receptor or a bitter receptor. The mice were given a choice of two bottles, one filled with pure water and one filled with water containing PBDG at varying concentrations. The researchers then observed whether the mice had an attraction or an aversion to PBDG.

Results

Relative consumption = (Fluid intake from bottle containing PBDG ÷ Total fluid intake) × 100%

Conclusion The researchers found that the presence of a bitter receptor in sweet taste cells is sufficient to cause mice to be attracted to a bitter chemical. They concluded that the mammalian brain must therefore perceive sweet or bitter taste solely on the basis of which sensory neurons are activated.

Source: Adaptation of figure 4b from "The Receptors and Coding Logic for Bitter Taste" by Ken L. Muller et al., from *Nature*, March 10, 2005, Volume 434(7030). Copyright © 2005 by Macmillan Publishers Ltd. Reprinted with permission.

WHAT IF? *Suppose, instead of the PBDG receptor, the researchers had used a receptor specific for a sweetener that humans crave but mice ignore. How would the results of the experiment have differed?*

to the receptor triggers a change in the ion channel. Depolarization occurs, activating a sensory neuron.

Smell in Humans

In olfaction, unlike gustation, the sensory cells are neurons. Olfactory receptor cells line the upper portion of the nasal cavity and send impulses along their axons directly to the olfactory bulb of the brain (**Figure 50.26**). The receptive ends of the cells contain cilia that extend into the layer of mucus coating the nasal cavity. When an odorant diffuses into this region, it binds to a specific GPCR protein called an odorant receptor (OR) on the plasma membrane of the olfactory cilia. These events trigger signal transduction leading to the production of cyclic AMP. In olfactory

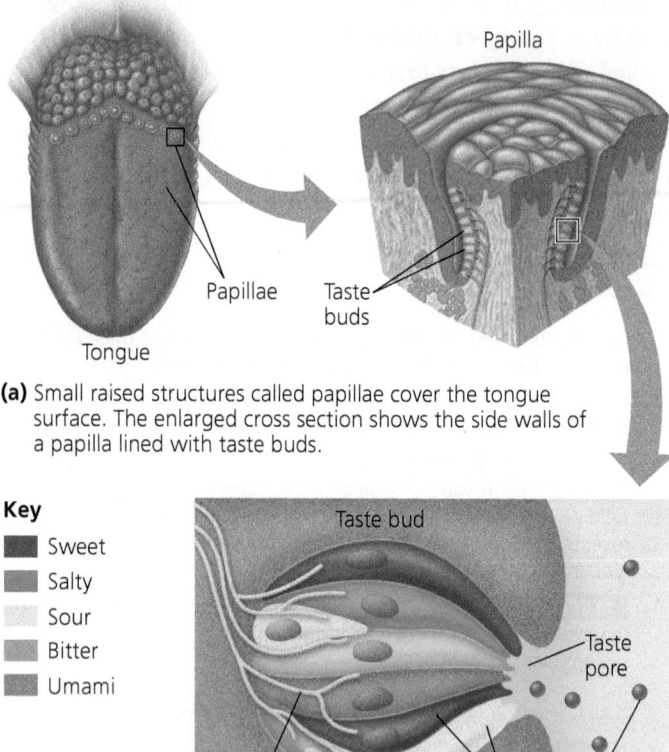

(a) Small raised structures called papillae cover the tongue surface. The enlarged cross section shows the side walls of a papilla lined with taste buds.

Key
- Sweet
- Salty
- Sour
- Bitter
- Umami

(b) Taste buds in all regions of the tongue contain sensory receptor cells specific for each of the five taste types.

▲ **Figure 50.25 Human taste receptors.**

Source: Adaptation of figure 15.23(a) from *Human Anatomy and Physiology*, 8th edition, by Elaine N. Marieb and Katja Hoehn. Copyright © 2010 by Pearson Education, Inc. Adapted and electronically reproduced by permission of Pearson Education, Inc., Upper Saddle River, New Jersey. Adaptation of figure 15.23(b) from *Human Anatomy and Physiology*, 8th edition, by Elaine N. Marieb and Katja Hoehn. Copyright © 2010 by Pearson Education, Inc. Adapted and electronically reproduced by permission of Pearson Education, Inc., Upper Saddle River, New Jersey.

cells, cyclic AMP opens channels in the plasma membrane that are permeable to both Na^+ and Ca^{2+}. The flow of these ions into the receptor cell leads to depolarization of the membrane, generating action potentials.

Humans can distinguish thousands of different odours, each caused by a structurally distinct odorant. This level of sensory discrimination requires many different ORs. In 1991, Richard Axel and Linda Buck, working at Columbia University, discovered a family of OR genes that alone represent more than 1% of all human genes. Each olfactory receptor cell appears to express one OR gene. Cells selective for different odorants are interspersed in the nasal cavity. Those cells that express the same OR gene transmit action potentials to the same small region of the olfactory bulb. In 2004, Axel and Buck shared a Nobel Prize for their studies of the gene family and receptors that function in olfaction.

Although the receptors and brain pathways for taste and smell are independent, the two senses do interact. Indeed,

▲ Figure 50.26 **Smell in humans.** Odorant molecules bind to specific receptor proteins in the plasma membrane of olfactory receptor cells, triggering action potentials.

WHAT IF? *If you spray an "air freshener" in a musty room, would you be affecting detection, transmission, or perception of the odorants responsible for the musty smell?*

much of the complex flavour humans experience when eating is due to our sense of smell. If the olfactory system is blocked, as occurs when you have a head cold, the perception of taste is sharply reduced.

CONCEPT CHECK 50.4

1. Explain why some taste receptor cells and all olfactory receptor cells use G protein-coupled receptors, yet only olfactory receptor cells produce action potentials.

2. Pathways involving G proteins provide an opportunity for an increase in signal strength in the course of signal transduction, a change referred to as amplification. How might this be beneficial in olfaction?

3. **WHAT IF?** If you discovered a mutation in mice that disrupted the ability to taste sweet, bitter, and umami, but not sour or salty, what might you predict about where this mutation acts in the signalling pathways used by these receptors?

For suggested answers, see Appendix A.

CONCEPT 50.5

The physical interaction of protein filaments is required for muscle function

Throughout our discussion of sensory mechanisms, we have seen how sensory inputs to the nervous system result in specific behaviours: the touch-guided foraging of a star-nosed mole, the upside-down swimming of a crayfish with manipulated statocysts, and the light-avoiding manoeuvres of planarians. Underlying the diverse forms of behaviour in animals are common fundamental mechanisms: Feeding, swimming, and crawling all require muscle activity in response to nervous system input.

Muscle cell function relies on actin filaments, similar in many respects to the microfilaments of the cytoskeleton. In muscle these filaments are called thin filaments. Recall from Chapter 6 that microfilaments function in cell motility by reorganizing within the cell; microfilaments lengthen and shorten, polymerize and depolymerize. In muscle cells, the thin filaments are arranged into a fixed array within the cell and do not change in length. Instead, within the muscle cell, thin filaments are pulled toward each other, causing the cell to change shape. These thin filament movements are driven by the motor protein myosin in a reaction that requires chemical energy in the form of ATP. To understand how these structures translate energy into muscle movement, we must analyze the structure of muscles and muscle fibres. We will begin by examining vertebrate skeletal muscle and then turn our attention to other types of muscle.

Vertebrate Skeletal Muscle

Vertebrate **skeletal muscle**, which moves bones and body, is characterized by a hierarchy of smaller and smaller units (**Figure 50.27**). Most skeletal muscles consist of a bundle of long fibres running parallel to the length of the muscle.

Muscle

Bundle of muscle fibres

Single muscle fibre (cell)

Plasma membrane

Myofibril

Nuclei

Z lines

Dr. H. E. Huxley

Sarcomere

TEM

0.5 μm

Thick filaments (myosin)

M line

Thin filaments (actin)

Z line

Z line

Sarcomere

▲ Figure 50.27 **The structure of skeletal muscle.**

Source: Figure adapted from *Human Anatomy and Physiology,* 8th edition, by Elaine N. Marieb and Katja Hoehn. Copyright © 2010 by Pearson Education, Inc. Adapted and electronically reproduced by permission of Pearson Education, Inc., Upper Saddle River, New Jersey.

Each fibre is a single cell. A muscle fibre, or cell, contains multiple nuclei, reflecting its formation by the fusion of many embryonic cells. Inside the fibre lies a bundle of smaller **myofibrils** arranged in parallel. The myofibrils, in turn, are composed of thin filaments and thick filaments. **Thin filaments** consist of two strands of actin and two strands of a regulatory protein (not shown here) coiled around one another. **Thick filaments** are staggered arrays of myosin molecules.

Skeletal muscle is also called **striated muscle** because the regular arrangement of the filaments creates a pattern of light and dark bands. Each repeating unit is a **sarcomere**, the basic contractile unit of the muscle. The borders of the sarcomere are lined up in adjacent myofibrils and contribute to the striations visible with a light microscope. Thin filaments are attached at the Z lines and project toward the centre of the sarcomere, while thick filaments are attached at the M lines centred in the sarcomere. In a muscle fibre at rest, thick and thin filaments only partially overlap. Near the edge of the sarcomere there are only thin filaments, whereas the zone in the centre contains only thick filaments. This arrangement is the key to how the sarcomere, and hence the whole muscle, contracts.

The Sliding-Filament Model of Muscle Contraction

We can explain much of what happens during the contraction of a whole muscle by focusing on the contraction of a single sarcomere (**Figure 50.28**). According to the **sliding-filament model**, neither thick nor thin filaments change in length when the sarcomere shortens. Instead, the thin and thick filaments slide past each other, increasing their overlap.

The longitudinal sliding of the filaments relies on the interaction of actin and myosin. Each myosin molecule has a long "tail" region and a globular "head" region. The tail adheres to the tails of other myosin molecules that form the thick filament. The head, which extends to the side, can bind ATP and hydrolyze it to ADP and inorganic phosphate. As shown in **Figure 50.29**, hydrolysis of ATP converts myosin to a high-energy form. This form of myosin binds to actin, forms a cross-bridge, and pulls the thin filament toward the centre of the sarcomere. The cross-bridge is broken when a new molecule of ATP binds to the myosin head.

Muscle contraction requires repeated cycles of binding, pulling, and release. In each cycle, the myosin head freed from a cross-bridge cleaves the newly bound ATP and binds again to actin. Because the thin filament moved toward the centre of the sarcomere in the previous cycle, the myosin head now attaches to a new binding site farther along the thin filament. Each of the approximately 350 heads of a thick filament forms and re-forms about five cross-bridges per second, driving filaments past each other.

Muscle Energy Production

The energy for muscle contraction is derived from hydrolysis of ATP; however, a typical muscle fibre at rest contains only enough ATP for a few contractions. To support repetitive contractions, the muscle cell must replenish the ATP pool. Many muscles possess an alternate form of energy equivalent to ATP: creatine phosphate. When ATP levels

► Figure 50.28 **The sliding-filament model of muscle contraction.** The drawings on the left show that the lengths of the thick (myosin) filaments (purple) and thin (actin) filaments (orange) remain the same as a muscle fibre contracts.

Relaxed muscle

Contracting muscle

Fully contracted muscle

Dr. H. E. Huxley

0.5 μm

Thick filament

Thin filaments

❶ Starting here, the myosin head is bound to ATP and is in its low-energy configuration.

Thin filament

ATP

Myosin head (low-energy configuration)

Thick filament

❷ The myosin head hydrolyzes ATP to ADP and phosphate (Ⓟ) and is in its high-energy configuration.

❺ Binding of a new molecule of ATP releases the myosin head from actin, and a new cycle begins.

ATP

Actin

Myosin-binding sites

ADP
Ⓟ

Myosin head (high-energy configuration)

Thin filament moves toward centre of sarcomere.

Myosin head (low-energy configuration)

ADP + Ⓟ$_i$

ADP
Ⓟ

Cross-bridge

❸ The myosin head binds to actin, forming a cross-bridge.

❹ Releasing ADP and inorganic phosphate (Ⓟ$_i$), myosin returns to its low-energy configuration, sliding the thin filament.

ANIMATION

BioFlix Visit the Study Area in **MasteringBiology** for the BioFlix® 3-D Animation on Muscle Contraction.

▲ Figure 50.29 **Myosin-actin interactions underlying muscle fibre contraction.**

? *When ATP binds, what prevents the filaments from sliding back into their original positions?*

decline, an enzyme can transfer a phosphate group from creatine phosphate to ADP to form ATP. The resting supply of creatine phosphate can sustain contractions for about 15 seconds. ATP stores are also replenished when carbon fuels are broken down. Mitochondria can produce ATP using the very efficient pathway of oxidative phosphorylation. Lipids, carbohydrates, and amino acids can be broken down to water and carbon dioxide, producing a continuous supply of ATP. Muscle cells can also use glycolysis to produce ATP from the fermentation of carbohydrates (see Chapter 9). Glycolysis is much faster than oxidative phosphorylation but it is much less efficient because the carbohydrate is only partially broken down, forming lactate. Using a typical muscle fibre's glycogen store, glycolysis can support about one minute of repetitive contractions, whereas oxidative phosphorylation can fuel contractions for very long periods. In some cases, muscles can use oxidative phosphorylation to support near-continuous contraction, such as in the back muscles that control posture.

The Role of Calcium and Regulatory Proteins

Calcium ions (Ca^{2+}) and proteins bound to actin play crucial roles in both muscle cell contraction and relaxation. **Tropomyosin**, a regulatory protein, and the **troponin complex**, a set of additional regulatory proteins, are bound to the actin strands of thin filaments. In a muscle fibre at rest, tropomyosin covers the myosin-binding sites along the thin filament, preventing actin and myosin from interacting (Figure 50.30a). When Ca^{2+} accumulates in the cytosol, it

(a) Myosin-binding sites blocked

(b) Myosin-binding sites exposed

▲ Figure 50.30 **The role of regulatory proteins and calcium in muscle fibre contraction.** Each thin filament consists of two strands of actin, tropomyosin, and multiple copies of the troponin complex.

binds to the troponin complex, causing tropomyosin bound along the actin strands to shift position and expose the myosin-binding sites on the thin filament (Figure 50.30b). Thus, when the Ca^{2+} concentration rises in the cytosol, the thin and thick filaments slide past each other, and the muscle fibre contracts. When the Ca^{2+} concentration falls, the binding sites are covered, and contraction stops.

Motor neurons cause muscle contraction by triggering the release of Ca^{2+} into the cytosol of muscle cells with which they form synapses. This regulation of Ca^{2+} concentration is a multistep process involving a network of membranes and compartments within the muscle cell. As you read the following description, refer to the overview and diagram in Figure 50.31.

The arrival of an action potential at the axon terminal of a motor neuron causes release of the neurotransmitter acetylcholine. Binding of acetylcholine to receptors on the muscle fibre leads to a depolarization, triggering an action potential. Within the muscle fibre, the action potential spreads deep into the interior, following infoldings of the plasma membrane called **transverse (T) tubules**. The T tubules make close contact with the **sarcoplasmic reticulum (SR)**, a specialized endoplasmic reticulum. As the action potential spreads along the T tubules, it triggers changes in the SR, opening Ca^{2+} channels. Calcium ions stored in the interior of the SR flow through these open channels into the cytosol and bind to the troponin complex, initiating contraction of the muscle fibre.

When motor neuron input stops, the muscle cell relaxes. As it relaxes, the filaments slide back to their starting position. During this phase, proteins in the cell reset the muscle for the next cycle of contraction. Relaxation begins as transport proteins in the SR pump Ca^{2+} in from the cytosol. When the Ca^{2+} concentration in the cytosol drops to a low level, the regulatory proteins bound to the thin filament shift back to their starting position, once again blocking the myosin-binding sites. At the same time, the Ca^{2+} pumped from the cytosol accumulates in the SR, providing the stores needed to respond to the next action potential.

Several diseases cause paralysis by interfering with the excitation of skeletal muscle fibres by motor neurons. In amyotrophic lateral sclerosis (ALS), also called Lou Gehrig's disease, motor neurons in the spinal cord and brainstem degenerate, and the muscle fibres with which they synapse atrophy. ALS is progressive and usually fatal within five years after symptoms appear; currently there is no cure or treatment. Myasthenia gravis is an autoimmune disease in which a person produces antibodies to the acetylcholine receptors on skeletal muscle fibres. As the number of these receptors decreases, synaptic transmission between motor neurons and muscle fibres declines. Fortunately, effective treatments are available for mysathenia gravis.

Exploring **The Regulation of Skeletal Muscle Contraction**

The electrical, chemical, and molecular events regulating skeletal muscle contraction are shown in a cutaway view of a muscle cell and in the enlarged diagram below. Action potentials (red arrows) triggered by the motor neuron sweep across the muscle fibre and into it along the transverse (T) tubules, initiating the movements of calcium (green dots) that regulate muscle activity.

Axon terminal

Axon of motor neuron

T tubule

Sarcoplasmic reticulum (SR)

Myofibril

Plasma membrane of muscle fibre

Mitochondrion

Ca^{2+} released from SR

Sarcomere

Axon terminal of motor neuron

ACh

1 Acetylcholine (ACh) released at axon terminal diffuses across synaptic cleft and binds to receptor proteins on muscle fibre's plasma membrane, triggering an action potential in muscle fibre.

Synaptic cleft

T tubule

Plasma membrane

2 Action potential is propagated along plasma membrane and down T tubules.

Sarcoplasmic reticulum (SR)

3 Action potential triggers Ca^{2+} release from SR.

Ca^{2+} pump

Ca^{2+}

ATP

CYTOSOL

4 Calcium ions bind to troponin in thin filament; myosin-binding sites exposed.

Ca^{2+}

7 Tropomyosin blockage of myosin-binding sites is restored; contraction ends, and muscle fibre relaxes.

6 Cytosolic Ca^{2+} is removed by active transport into SR after action potential ends.

5 Cycles of myosin cross-bridge formation and breakdown, coupled with ATP hydrolysis, slide thin filament toward centre of sarcomere.

Nervous Control of Muscle Tension

Whereas contraction of a single skeletal muscle fibre is a brief all-or-none twitch, contraction of a whole muscle, such as the biceps in your upper arm, is graded; you can voluntarily alter the extent and strength of its contraction. There are two basic mechanisms by which the nervous system produces graded contractions of whole muscles: (1) by varying the number of muscle fibres that contract and (2) by varying the rate at which muscle fibres are stimulated. Let's consider each mechanism in turn.

In vertebrates, each branched motor neuron may form synapses with many skeletal muscle fibres, although each fibre is controlled by only one motor neuron. For the whole muscle, there may be hundreds of motor neurons, each with its own pool of muscle fibres. A **motor unit** consists of a single motor neuron and all the muscle fibres it controls (Figure 50.32). When a motor neuron produces an action potential, all the muscle fibres in its motor unit contract as a group. The strength of the resulting contraction depends on how many muscle fibres the motor neuron controls.

In most muscles, the number of muscle fibres in different motor units ranges from a few to hundreds. The

nervous system can thus regulate the strength of contraction in a muscle by determining how many motor units are activated at a given instant and by selecting large or small motor units to activate. The force (tension) developed by a muscle progressively increases as more and more of the motor neurons controlling the muscle are activated, a process called *recruitment* of motor neurons. Depending on the number of motor neurons your brain recruits and the size of their motor units, you can lift a fork or something much heavier, like your biology textbook.

Some muscles, especially those that hold up the body and maintain posture, are almost always partially contracted. In such muscles, the nervous system may alternate activation among the motor units, reducing the length of time any one set of fibres is contracted. Prolonged contraction can result in muscle fatigue. Depletion of ATP, dissipation of ion gradients, loss of Ca^{2+}, homeostasis, and accumulation of end products, such as lactate and phosphate, have each been implicated as contributors to fatigue.

The nervous system regulates muscle contraction not only by controlling which motor units are activated, but also by varying the rate of muscle fibre stimulation. A single action potential produces a twitch lasting about 100 msec or less. If a second action potential arrives before the muscle fibre has completely relaxed, the two twitches add together, resulting in greater tension (Figure 50.33). Further **summation** occurs as the rate of stimulation increases. When the rate is so high that the muscle fibre cannot relax at all between stimuli, the twitches fuse into one smooth, sustained contraction called **tetanus**. Motor neurons usually deliver their action potentials in rapid-fire volleys, and the resulting summation of tension results in the smooth contraction typical of tetanus rather than the jerky actions

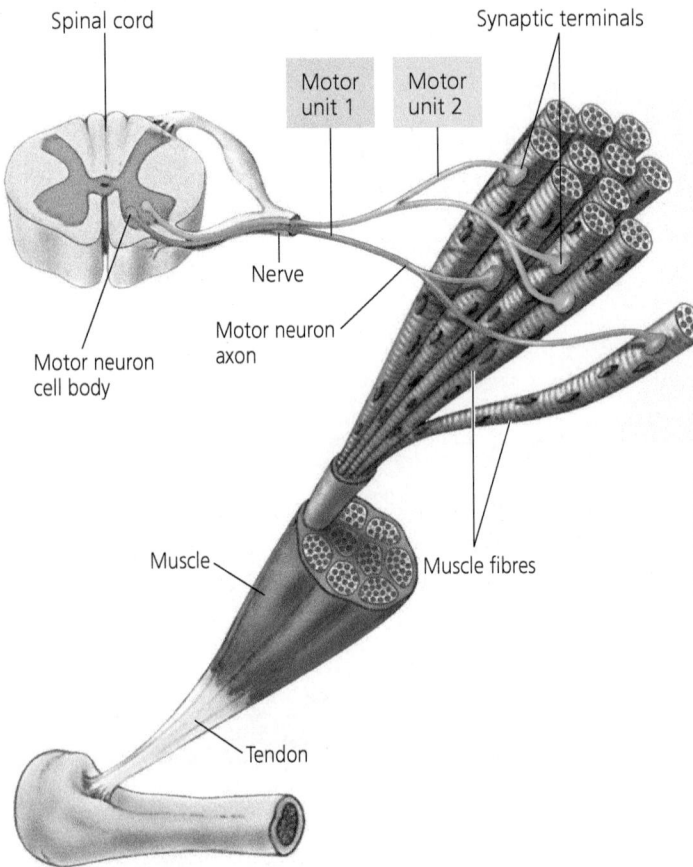

▲ Figure 50.32 **Motor units in a vertebrate skeletal muscle.** Each muscle fibre (cell) forms synapses with only one motor neuron, but each motor neuron typically synapses with many muscle fibres. A motor neuron and all the muscle fibres it controls constitute a motor unit.

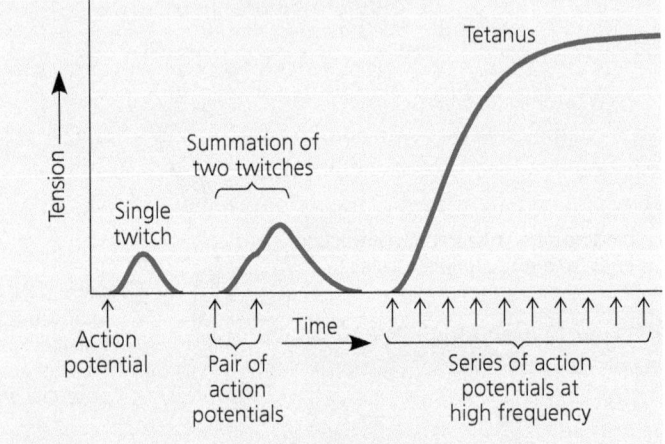

▲ Figure 50.33 **Summation of twitches.** This graph illustrates how the number of action potentials in a short period of time influences the tension developed in a muscle fibre.

? *How could the nervous system cause a skeletal muscle to produce the most forceful contraction it is capable of?*

of individual twitches. (Although a smooth, sustained contraction is part of normal muscle function, tetanus is also the name of a disease of uncontrolled muscle contraction caused by a bacterial toxin.)

The increase in tension during summation and tetanus occurs because skeletal muscle fibres are connected to bones via tendons and connective tissues. When a muscle fibre contracts, it stretches these elastic structures, which then transmit tension to the bones. In a single twitch, the muscle fibre begins to relax before the elastic structures are fully stretched. During summation, however, the high-frequency action potentials maintain an elevated concentration of Ca^{2+} in the muscle fibre's cytosol, prolonging cross-bridge cycling and causing greater stretching of the elastic structures. During tetanus, the elastic structures are fully stretched, and all of the tension generated by the muscle fibre is transmitted to the bones.

Types of Skeletal Muscle Fibres

Our discussion to this point has focused on the general properties of vertebrate skeletal muscles. There are, however, several distinct types of skeletal muscle fibres, each of which is adapted to a particular set of functions. Scientists typically classify these varied fibre types either by the source of ATP used to power muscle activity or by the speed of muscle contraction. We'll consider each of the two classification schemes.

Oxidative and Glycolytic Fibres Fibres that rely mostly on aerobic respiration are called oxidative fibres. Such fibres are specialized in ways that enable them to make use of a steady energy supply: They have many mitochondria, a rich blood supply, and a large amount of an oxygen-storing protein called **myoglobin**. A brownish-red pigment, myoglobin binds oxygen more tightly than does hemoglobin, enabling oxidative fibre to extract oxygen from the blood efficiently. In contrast to oxidative fibres, glycolytic fibres use glycolysis as their primary source of ATP. They have a larger diameter and less myoglobin than oxidative fibres and thus fatigue much more readily. These different fibre types are readily apparent in the muscle of poultry and fish: The dark meat is made up of oxidative fibres rich in myoglobin, and the light meat is composed of glycolytic fibres.

Fast-Twitch and Slow-Twitch Fibres Muscle fibres vary in the speed with which they contract: **Fast-twitch fibres** develop tension two to three times faster than **slow-twitch fibres**. Fast fibres enable brief, rapid, powerful contractions. Slow fibres, often found in muscles that maintain posture, can sustain long contractions. A slow fibre has less sarcoplasmic reticulum and pumps Ca^{2+} more slowly than a fast fibre. Because Ca^{2+} remains in the cytosol longer, a muscle twitch in a slow fibre lasts about five times as long as one in a fast fibre.

The difference in contraction speed between slow-twitch and fast-twitch fibres mainly reflects the rate at which their myosin heads hydrolyze ATP. However, there isn't a one-to-one relationship between contraction speed and ATP source. Whereas all slow-twitch fibres are oxidative, fast-twitch fibres can be either glycolytic or oxidative.

Most human skeletal muscles contain both fast- and slow-twitch fibres, although some muscles of the eye and hand are exclusively fast-twitch. In a muscle that has a mixture of fast and slow fibres, the relative proportions of each are genetically determined. However, if such a muscle is used repeatedly for activities requiring high endurance, some fast glycolytic fibres can develop into fast oxidative fibres. Because fast oxidative fibres fatigue more slowly than fast glycolytic fibres, the result will be a muscle that is more resistant to fatigue.

Some vertebrates have skeletal muscle fibres that twitch at rates far faster than any human muscle. For example, superfast muscles produce a rattlesnake's rattle and a dove's coo. The fastest of the vertebrate muscles, however, surround the gas-filled swim bladder inside the male toadfish (Figure 50.34). In producing its characteristic "boat whistle" mating call, the toadfish can contract and relax these muscles more than 200 times per second!

Other Types of Muscle

Although all muscles share the same fundamental mechanism of contraction—actin and myosin filaments sliding past each other—there are many different types of muscle. Vertebrates, for example, have cardiac muscle and smooth muscle in addition to skeletal muscle (see Figure 40.5).

Vertebrate **cardiac muscle** is found in only one part of the body: the heart. Like skeletal muscle, cardiac muscle is

▲ Figure 50.34 **Specialization of skeletal muscles.** The male toadfish (*Opsanus tau*) uses superfast muscles to produce its mating call.

striated. However, structural differences between skeletal and cardiac muscle fibres result in differences in their electrical and membrane properties. Whereas skeletal muscle fibres do not produce action potentials unless stimulated by a motor neuron, cardiac muscle cells have ion channels in their plasma membrane that cause rhythmic depolarizations, triggering action potentials without input from the nervous system. Action potentials of cardiac muscle cells last up to 20 times longer than those of the skeletal muscle fibres. Plasma membranes of adjacent cardiac muscle cells interlock at specialized regions called **intercalated disks**, where gap junctions (see Figure 6.30) provide direct electrical coupling between the cells. Thus, the action potential generated by specialized cells in one part of the heart spreads to all other cardiac muscle cells, causing the whole heart to contract. A long refractory period prevents summation and tetanus.

Smooth muscle in vertebrates is found mainly in the walls of hollow organs, such as blood vessels and organs of the digestive tract. Smooth muscle cells lack striations because their actin and myosin filaments are not regularly arrayed along the length of the cell. Instead, the thick filaments are scattered throughout the cytoplasm, and the thin filaments are attached to structures called dense bodies, some of which are tethered to the plasma membrane. There is less myosin than in striated muscle fibres, and the myosin is not associated with specific actin strands. Some smooth muscle cells contract only when stimulated by neurons of the autonomic nervous system. Others can generate action potentials without input from neurons—they are electrically coupled to one another. Smooth muscles contract and relax more slowly than striated muscles.

Although Ca^{2+} regulates smooth muscle contraction, the mechanism for regulation is different from that in skeletal and cardiac muscle. Smooth muscle cells have no troponin complex or T tubules, and their sarcoplasmic reticulum is not well developed. During an action potential, Ca^{2+} enters the cytosol mainly through the plasma membrane. Calcium ions cause contraction by binding to the protein calmodulin, which activates an enzyme that phosphorylates the myosin head, enabling cross-bridge activity.

Invertebrates have muscle cells similar to vertebrate skeletal and smooth muscle cells, and arthropod skeletal muscles are nearly identical to those of vertebrates. However, because the flight muscles of insects are capable of independent, rhythmic contraction, the wings of some insects can actually beat faster than action potentials can arrive from the central nervous system. Another interesting evolutionary adaptation has been discovered in the muscles that hold a clam's shell closed. The thick filaments in these muscles contain a protein called paramyosin that enables the muscles to remain contracted for as long as a month with only a low rate of energy consumption.

CONCEPT 50.6

Skeletal systems transform muscle contraction into locomotion

Converting muscle contraction to movement requires a skeleton—a rigid structure to which muscles can attach. An animal changes its rigidity, shape, or location by contracting muscles connecting two parts of its skeleton.

Because muscles exert force only during contraction, moving a body part back and forth typically requires two muscles attached to the same section of the skeleton. We can see such an arrangement of muscles in the upper portion of a human arm or grasshopper leg (Figure 50.35). Although we call such muscles an antagonistic pair, their function is

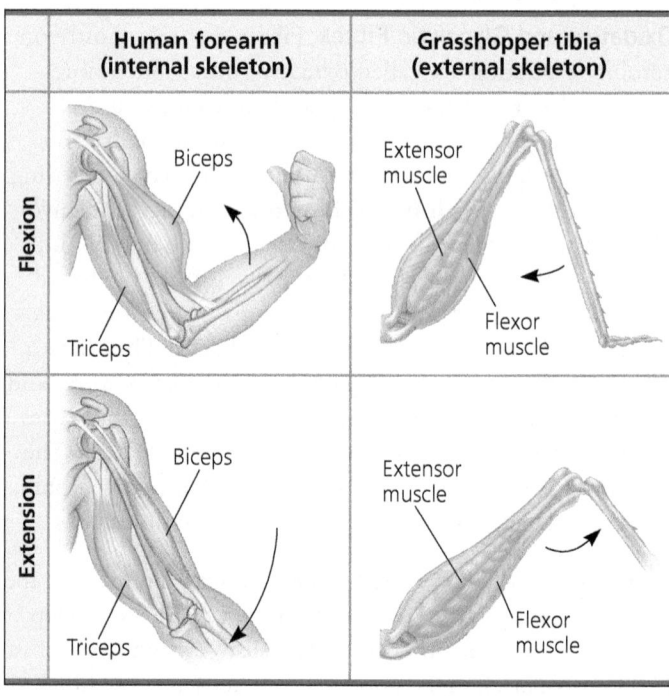

Key ▮ Contracting muscle ▯ Relaxing muscle

▲ Figure 50.35 **The interaction of muscles and skeletons in movement.** Back-and-forth movement of a body part is generally accomplished by antagonistic muscles. This arrangement works with either an internal skeleton, as in mammals, or an external skeleton, as in insects.

actually cooperative, coordinated by the nervous system. For example, when you extend your arm, motor neurons trigger your triceps muscle to contract while the absence of neuronal input allows your biceps to relax.

Vital for movement, the skeletons of animals also function in support and protection. Most land animals would collapse if they had no skeleton to support their mass. Even an animal living in water would be formless without a framework to maintain its shape. In many animals, a hard skeleton also protects soft tissues. For example, the vertebrate skull protects the brain, and the ribs of terrestrial vertebrates form a cage around the heart, lungs, and other internal organs.

Types of Skeletal Systems

Although we tend to think of skeletons only as interconnected sets of bones, skeletons come in many different forms. Hardened support structures can be external (as in exoskeletons), internal (as in endoskeletons), or even absent (as in fluid-based, or hydrostatic, skeletons).

Hydrostatic Skeletons

A **hydrostatic skeleton** consists of fluid held under pressure in a closed body compartment. This is the main type of skeleton in most cnidarians, flatworms, nematodes, and annelids (see Chapter 33). These animals control their form and movement by using muscles to change the shape of fluid-filled compartments. Among the cnidarians, for example, a hydra elongates by closing its mouth and using contractile cells in its body wall to constrict its central gastrovascular cavity. Because water cannot be compressed, decreasing the diameter of the cavity forces the cavity to become longer.

Worms use hydrostatic skeletons in diverse ways to move through their environment. In planarians and other flatworms, movement results mainly from muscles in the body wall exerting localized forces against the interstitial fluid. In nematodes (roundworms), longitudinal muscles contracting around the fluid-filled body cavity move the animal forward by undulations, or wavelike motions. In earthworms and many other annelids, circular and longitudinal muscles act together to change the shape of individual fluid-filled segments, which are divided by septa. These shape changes bring about **peristalsis**, a movement produced by rhythmic waves of muscle contractions passing from front to back **(Figure 50.36)**.

Hydrostatic skeletons are well suited for life in aquatic environments. On land, they provide support for crawling and burrowing and may cushion internal organs from shocks. However, a hydrostatic skeleton cannot support walking or running, in which an animal's body is held off the ground.

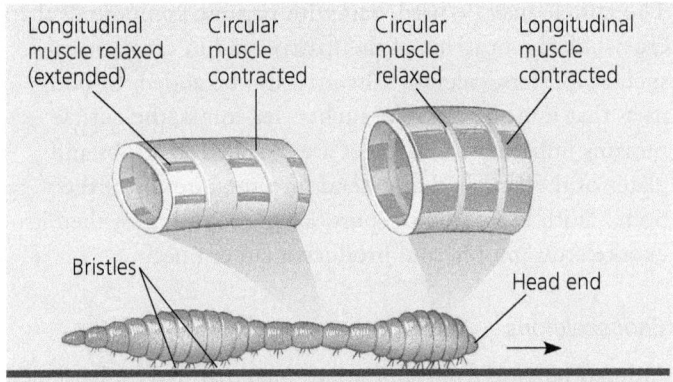

1 At the moment depicted, body segments at the earthworm's head end and just in front of the rear end are short and thick (longitudinal muscles contracted; circular muscles relaxed) and are anchored to the ground by bristles. The other segments are thin and elongated (circular muscles contracted; longitudinal muscles relaxed).

2 The head has moved forward because circular muscles in the head segments have contracted. Segments behind the head and at the rear are now thick and anchored, thus preventing the worm from slipping backward.

3 The head segments are thick again and anchored in their new positions. The rear segments have released their hold on the ground and have been pulled forward.

▲ **Figure 50.36 Crawling by peristalsis.** Contraction of the longitudinal muscles thickens and shortens the earthworm; contraction of the circular muscles constricts and elongates it.

Exoskeletons

The clam shell you find on a beach once served as an **exoskeleton**, a hard encasement deposited on an animal's surface. The shells of clams and most other molluscs are made of calcium carbonate secreted by the mantle, a sheet-like extension of the body wall (see Figure 33.15). Clams and other bivalves close their hinged shell using muscles attached to the inside of this exoskeleton. As the animal grows, it enlarges its shell by adding to the outer edge.

Insects and other arthropods have a jointed exoskeleton called a cuticle, a nonliving coat secreted by the epidermis. About 30–50% of the arthropod cuticle consists of **chitin**, a polysaccharide similar to cellulose (see Figure 5.8). Fibrils of chitin are embedded in a protein matrix, forming a composite material that combines strength and flexibility.

The cuticle may be hardened with organic compounds that cross-link the proteins of the matrix, and in crustaceans such as lobsters, calcium salts may also be added. In body parts that must be flexible, such as leg joints, the cuticle remains unhardened. Muscles are attached to knobs and plates of the cuticle that extend into the interior of the body. With each growth spurt, an arthropod must shed its exoskeleton (moult) and produce a larger one.

Endoskeletons

Animals ranging from sponges to mammals have a hardened internal skeleton, or **endoskeleton**, buried within their soft tissues. In sponges, the endoskeleton consists of hard needlelike structures of inorganic material (see Figure 33.4)

or fibres made of protein. Echinoderms' bodies are reinforced by ossicles, hard plates composed of magnesium carbonate and calcium carbonate crystals. Whereas the ossicles of sea urchins are tightly bound, the ossicles of sea stars are more loosely linked, allowing a sea star to change the shape of its arms.

Chordates have an endoskeleton consisting of cartilage, bone, or some combination of these materials (see Figure 40.5). The mammalian skeleton is built from more than 200 bones, some fused together and others connected at joints by ligaments that allow freedom of movement (**Figures 50.37** and **50.38**).

▼ Figure 50.38 **Types of joints.**

Ball-and-socket joint

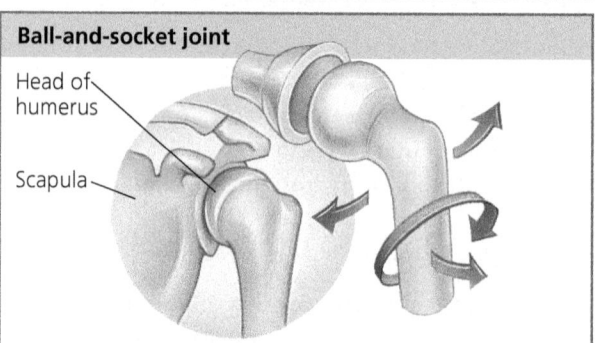

Ball-and-socket joints are found where the humerus contacts the shoulder girdle and where the femur contacts the pelvic girdle. These joints enable the arms and legs to rotate and move in several planes.

Hinge joint

Hinge joints, such as between the humerus and the head of the ulna, restrict movement to a single plane.

Pivot joint

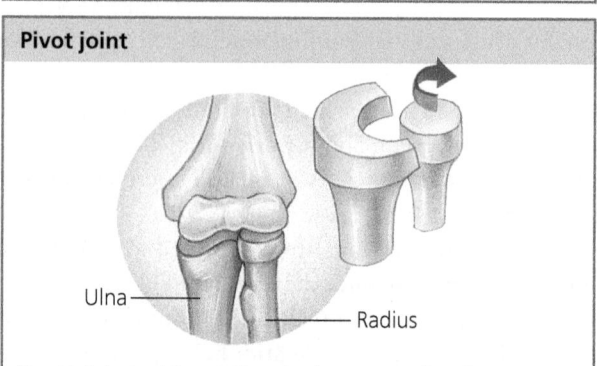

Pivot joints enable rotating the forearm at the elbow and turning the head from side to side.

Skull
Types of joints
Ball-and-socket joint
Shoulder girdle — Clavicle
Scapula
Sternum
Rib
Humerus
Vertebra
Hinge joint
Pivot joint
Radius
Ulna
Pelvic girdle
Carpals
Phalanges
Metacarpals
Femur
Patella
Tibia
Fibula
Tarsals
Metatarsals
Phalanges

▲ Figure 50.37 **Bones and joints of the human skeleton.**

Size and Scale of Skeletons

An exoskeleton needs to cover and protect an animal's body, but how thick does an endoskeleton need to be? We can begin to answer this question by applying ideas from civil engineering. For example, the weight of a building increases with the cube of its dimensions. However, the strength of a building support depends on its cross-sectional area, which only increases with the square of its diameter. We can thus predict that if we scaled up a mouse to the size of an elephant, the legs of the giant mouse would be too thin to support its weight. Indeed, large animals do have very different body proportions from those of small animals.

In applying the building analogy, we might also predict that the size of leg bones should be directly proportional to the strain imposed by body weight. However, our prediction would be inaccurate, in part because animal bodies are complex and nonrigid. In supporting body weight, it turns out that body posture—the position of the legs relative to the main body—is more important than leg size, at least in mammals and birds. Muscles and tendons (connective tissue that joins muscle to bone) hold the legs of large mammals relatively straight and positioned under the body and actually bear most of the load.

Types of Locomotion

Movement is a hallmark of animals. Even animals fixed to a surface move their body parts: Sponges use beating flagella to generate water currents that draw and trap small food particles, and sessile cnidarians wave tentacles that capture prey (see Chapter 33). Most animals, however, are mobile and spend a considerable portion of their time and energy actively searching for food, escaping from danger, and seeking mates. These activities involve **locomotion**, or active travel from place to place.

Friction and gravity tend to keep an animal stationary and thus oppose locomotion. To move, an animal must expend energy to overcome these two forces. As we will see next, the amount of energy required to oppose friction or gravity is often reduced by an animal body plan adapted for movement in a particular environment.

Locomotion on Land

On land, a walking, running, hopping, or crawling animal must be able to support itself and move against gravity, but air poses relatively little resistance, at least at moderate speeds. When a land animal walks, runs, or hops, its leg muscles expend energy both to propel it and to keep it from falling down. With each step, the animal's leg muscles must overcome inertia by accelerating a leg from a standing start. For moving on land, powerful muscles and strong skeletal support are more important than a streamlined shape.

Diverse adaptations for travelling on land have evolved in various vertebrates. For example, kangaroos have large, powerful muscles in their hind legs, suitable for locomotion by hopping (Figure 50.39). As a kangaroo lands after each leap, tendons in its hind legs momentarily store energy. The farther the animal hops, the more energy its tendons store. Analogous to the energy in a compressed spring, the energy stored in the tendons is available for the next jump and reduces the total amount of energy the animal must expend to travel. The legs of an insect, dog, or human also retain some energy during walking or running, although a considerably smaller share than those of a kangaroo.

Maintaining balance is another prerequisite for walking, running, or hopping. A kangaroo's large tail helps balance its body during leaps and also forms a stable tripod with its hind legs when the animal sits or moves slowly. Illustrating the same principle, a walking cat, dog, or horse keeps three feet on the ground. Bipedal animals, such as humans and birds, keep part of at least one foot on the ground when walking. When an animal runs, all four feet (or both feet for bipeds) may be off the ground briefly, but at running speeds it is momentum more than foot contact that keeps the body upright.

Crawling poses a very different situation. Because much of its body is in contact with the ground, a crawling animal must exert considerable effort to overcome friction. You have read how earthworms crawl by peristalsis. Many snakes crawl by undulating their entire body from side to side. Assisted by large, movable scales on its underside, a snake's body pushes against the ground, propelling the animal forward. Boa constrictors and pythons creep straight

▲ **Figure 50.39 Energy-efficient locomotion on land.** Members of the kangaroo family travel from place to place mainly by leaping on their large hind legs. Kinetic energy momentarily stored in tendons after each leap provides a boost for the next leap. In fact, a large kangaroo hopping at 30 km/hr uses no more energy per minute than it does at 6 km/hr. The large tail helps balance the kangaroo when it leaps as well as when it sits.

forward, driven by muscles that lift belly scales off the ground, tilt the scales forward, and then push them backward against the ground.

Swimming

Because most animals are reasonably buoyant in water, overcoming gravity is less of a problem for swimming animals than for species that move on land or through the air. On the other hand, water is a much denser and more viscous medium than air, and thus drag (friction) is a major problem for aquatic animals. A sleek, fusiform (torpedolike) shape is a common adaptation of fast swimmers (see Figure 40.2).

Although most animal phyla include species that swim, swimming occurs in diverse ways. For instance, many insects and four-legged vertebrates use their legs as oars to push against the water. Squids, scallops, and some cnidarians are jet-propelled, taking in water and squirting it out in bursts. Sharks and bony fishes swim by moving their body and tail from side to side, while whales and dolphins move by undulating their body and tail up and down.

Flying

Active flight (in contrast to gliding downward from a tree) has evolved in only a few animal groups: insects, reptiles (including birds), and, among the mammals, bats. One group of flying reptiles, the pterosaurs, died out millions of years ago, leaving birds and bats as the only flying vertebrates.

Gravity poses a major problem for a flying animal because its wings must develop enough lift to overcome gravity's downward force. The key to flight is wing shape. All wings are airfoils—structures whose shape alters air currents in a way that helps animals or airplanes stay aloft. As for the body to which the wings attach, a fusiform shape helps reduce drag in air as it does in water.

SCIENTIFIC SKILLS EXERCISE

Interpreting a Graph with Log Scales

What Are the Energy Costs of Locomotion? In the 1960s, animal physiologist Knut Schmidt-Nielsen, at Duke University, wondered whether general principles govern the energy costs of different forms of locomotion among diverse animal species. To answer this question, he drew on his own experiments as well as those of other researchers. In this exercise you will analyze the combined results of these studies and evaluate the rationale for plotting the experimental data on a graph with logarithmic scales.

How the Experiments Were Done Researchers measured the rate of oxygen consumption or carbon dioxide production in animals that ran on treadmills, swam in water flumes, or flew in wind tunnels. From these measurements, Schmidt-Nielsen calculated the amount of energy each animal used to transport a given amount of body mass over a given distance (calories/kilogram · metre). Recall that 1 calorie is the equivalent of 4.2 joules.

Data from the Experiments Schmidt-Nielsen plotted the cost of running, flying, and swimming versus body mass on a single graph with logarithmic (log) scales for the axes. He then drew a best-fit straight line through the data points for each form of locomotion. (On the graph below, the individual data points are not shown.)

Vance A. Tucker

Interpret the Data

1. The body masses of the animals used in these experiments ranged from about 0.001 g to 1 000 000 g, and their rates of energy use ranged from about 0.1 cal/kg m to 100 cal/kg m. If you were to plot these data on a graph with linear instead of log scales for the axes, how would you draw the axes so that all of the data would be visible? What is the advantage of using log scales for plotting data with a wide range of values? (For additional information about graphs, see the Scientific Skills Review in Appendix E and in the Study Area in MasteringBiology.)

2. Based on the graph, how much greater is the energy cost of flying for an animal that weighs 10^{-3} g than for an animal that weighs 1 g? For any given form of locomotion, which travels more efficiently, a larger animal or smaller animal?

3. The slopes of the flying and swimming lines are very similar. Based on your answer to question 2, if the energy cost of a 2-g swimming animal is 1.2 cal/kg m, what is the estimated energy cost of a 2-kg swimming animal?

4. Considering animals with a body mass of about 100 g, rank the three forms of locomotion from highest energy cost to lowest energy cost. Were these the results you expected, based on your own experience? What could explain the energy cost of running compared to that of flying or swimming?

5. Schmidt-Nielson calculated the swimming cost in a mallard duck and found that it was nearly 20 times as high as the swimming cost in a salmon of the same body mass. What could explain the greater swimming efficiency of salmon?

Adaptation of figure 4 from "Locomotion: Energy Cost of Swimming, Flying, and Running" by Knut Schmidt-Nielsen, from *Science*, July 1972, Volume 177(4045). Copyright © 1972 by AAAS. Reprinted with permission.

Flying animals are relatively light, with body masses ranging from less than a gram for some insects to about 20 kg for the largest flying birds. Many flying animals have structural adaptations that contribute to low body mass. Birds, for example, have no urinary bladder or teeth and have relatively large bones with air-filled regions that help lessen the bird's weight (see Chapter 34).

Flying, running, and swimming each impose different energetic demands on animals. In the Scientific Skills Exercise, you can interpret a graph that compares the relative energy costs of these three forms of locomotion.

CONCEPT CHECK 50.6

1. In what way are septa an important feature of the earthworm skeleton?

2. Contrast swimming and flying in terms of the main problems they pose and the adaptations that allow animals to overcome those problems.

3. **WHAT IF?** When using your arms to lower yourself into a chair, you bend your arms without using your biceps. Explain how this is possible. (*Hint*: Think about gravity as an antagonistic force.)

For suggested answers, see Appendix A.

50 Chapter Review

Go to **MasteringBiology®** for Assignments, the eText, and the Study Area with Animations, Activities, Vocab Self-Quiz, and Practice Tests.

SUMMARY OF KEY CONCEPTS

CONCEPT 50.1

Sensory receptors transduce stimulus energy and transmit signals to the central nervous system (pp. 1163–1167)

- **Sensory receptors** are usually specialized neurons or epithelial cells that detect external or internal stimuli. The detection of a stimulus by sensory cells precedes **sensory transduction**, the change in the membrane potential of a sensory receptor in response to a stimulus. The resulting receptor potential controls **transmission** of action potentials to the CNS, where sensory information is integrated to generate perceptions. The frequency of action potentials in an axon and the number of axons activated determine stimulus strength. The identity of the axon carrying the signal encodes the nature or quality of the stimulus. Signal transduction pathways in receptor cells often amplify the signal, which causes the receptor cell either to produce action potentials or to release neurotransmitter at a synapse with a sensory neuron.

- There are five basic types of sensory receptors. **Mechanoreceptors** respond to stimuli such as pressure, touch, stretch, motion, and sound. **Chemoreceptors** detect either total solute concentrations or specific molecules. **Electromagnetic receptors** detect different forms of electromagnetic radiation. Various types of **thermoreceptors** signal surface and core temperatures of the body. Pain is detected by a group of **nociceptors** that respond to excess heat, pressure, or specific classes of chemicals.

? *To simplify the classification of sensory receptors, why might it make sense to eliminate nociceptors as a distinct class?*

CONCEPT 50.2

The mechanoreceptors responsible for hearing and equilibrium detect moving fluid or settling particles (pp. 1167–1172)

- Most invertebrates sense their orientation with respect to gravity by means of **statocysts**. Specialized **hair cells** form the basis for hearing and balance in mammals and for detection of water movement

in fishes and aquatic amphibians. In mammals, the **tympanic membrane** (eardrum) transmits sound waves to three small bones of the middle ear, which transmit the waves through the oval window to the fluid in the coiled **cochlea** of the inner ear. Pressure waves in the fluid vibrate the **basilar membrane**, depolarizing hair cells and triggering action potentials that travel via the auditory nerve to the brain. Each region of the basilar membrane vibrates most vigorously at a particular frequency and leads to excitation of a specific auditory area of the cerebral cortex. Receptors in the inner ear function in balance and equilibrium.

? *What quality of sound determines the direction of displacement of a particular hair cell in the ear, and how is that quality encoded in signals sent to the brain?*

CONCEPT 50.3

The diverse visual receptors of animals depend on light-absorbing pigments (pp. 1172–1179)

- Invertebrates have varied light detectors, including simple light-sensitive eyespots, image-forming compound eyes, and single-lens eyes. In the vertebrate eye, a single lens is used to focus light on **photoreceptors** in the **retina**. Both **rods** and **cones** contain a pigment, **retinal**, bonded to a protein (opsin). Absorption of light by retinal triggers a signal transduction pathway that hyperpolarizes the photoreceptors, causing them to release less neurotransmitter. Synapses transmit information from photoreceptors to cells that integrate information and convey it to the brain along axons that form the optic nerve.

? *How does processing of sensory information sent to the vertebrate brain in vision differ from that in hearing or olfaction?*

CONCEPT 50.4

The senses of taste and smell rely on similar sets of sensory receptors (pp. 1179–1181)

- Both taste (**gustation**) and smell (**olfaction**) depend on the stimulation of chemoreceptors by small dissolved molecules that bind to proteins on the plasma membrane. In humans, sensory cells within taste buds express a single receptor type specific for one of the five taste perceptions—sweet, sour, salty, bitter, and umami (elicited by glutamate). Olfactory receptor cells line the upper part of the nasal cavity and extend axons to the olfactory bulb of the brain. More than 1000 genes code for membrane proteins that bind to specific classes of odorants, and each receptor cell appears to express only one of those genes.

? *Why do foods taste bland when you have a head cold?*

CONCEPT 50.5

The physical interaction of protein filaments is required for muscle function (pp. 1181–1188)

- The muscle cells (fibres) of vertebrate skeletal muscle contain myofibrils composed of **thin filaments** of (mostly) actin and **thick filaments** of myosin. Together with accessory proteins, these filaments are organized into repeating units called **sarcomeres**. Myosin heads, energized by the hydrolysis of ATP, bind to the thin filaments, forming cross-bridges, then release upon binding ATP anew. As this cycle repeats, the thick and thin filaments slide past each other, shortening the sarcomere and contracting the muscle fibre.

- Motor neurons release acetylcholine, triggering action potentials that penetrate the muscle fibre along the T tubules and stimulate the release of Ca^{2+} from the **sarcoplasmic reticulum**. When the Ca^{2+} binds the **troponin complex**, **tropomyosin** repositions on the thin filaments, exposing the myosin-binding sites on actin and thus initiating cross-bridge formation. A **motor unit** consists of a motor neuron and the muscle fibres it controls. Recruiting multiple motor units results in stronger contractions. A twitch results from a single action potential in a motor neuron. Skeletal muscle fibres can be slow-twitch or fast-twitch and oxidative or glycolytic.
- Cardiac muscle, found only in the heart, consists of striated cells that are electrically connected by **intercalated disks** and that can generate action potentials without input from neurons. In smooth muscles, contractions are slow and may be initiated by the muscles themselves or by stimulation from neurons in the autonomic nervous system.

? *What are two major functions of ATP hydrolysis in skeletal muscle activity?*

CONCEPT 50.6

Skeletal systems transform muscle contraction into locomotion (pp. 1188–1193)

- Skeletal muscles, often in antagonistic pairs, bring about movement by contracting and pulling against the skeleton. Skeletons may be **hydrostatic** and maintained by fluid pressure, as in worms; hardened into **exoskeletons**, as in insects; or in the form of **endoskeletons**, as in vertebrates.
- Each form of **locomotion**—swimming, movement on land, or flying—presents a particular challenge. For example, swimmers need to overcome friction, but face less of a challenge from gravity than do animals that move on land or fly. Animals specialized for swimming expend less energy per distance travelled than similarly sized animals specialized for flying or running. For any of the three major modes of locomotion, larger animals are more efficient than smaller ones.

? *Explain how microscopic and macroscopic anchoring of muscle filaments enables you to bend your elbow.*

TEST YOUR UNDERSTANDING

LEVEL 1: KNOWLEDGE/COMPREHENSION

1. Which of the following sensory receptors is *incorrectly* paired with its category?
   a. hair cell—mechanoreceptor
   b. muscle spindle—mechanoreceptor
   c. taste receptor—chemoreceptor
   d. olfactory receptor—electromagnetic receptor

2. The middle ear converts
   a. air pressure waves to fluid pressure waves.
   b. air pressure waves to nerve impulses.
   c. fluid pressure waves to nerve impulses.
   d. pressure waves to hair cell movements.

3. During the contraction of a vertebrate skeletal muscle fibre, calcium ions
   a. break cross-bridges by acting as a cofactor in the hydrolysis of ATP.
   b. bind with troponin, changing its shape so that the myosin-binding sites on actin are exposed.
   c. transmit action potentials from the motor neuron to the muscle fibre.
   d. spread action potentials through the T tubules.

LEVEL 2: APPLICATION/ANALYSIS

4. Which sensory distinction is *not* encoded by a difference in neuron identity?
   a. white and red
   b. red and green
   c. loud and faint
   d. salty and sweet

5. The transduction of sound waves into action potentials takes place
   a. within the tectorial membrane as it is stimulated by the hair cells.
   b. when hair cells are bent against the tectorial membrane, causing them to depolarize and release neurotransmitter that stimulates sensory neurons.
   c. as the basilar membrane vibrates at different frequencies in response to the varying volume of sounds.
   d. within the middle ear as the vibrations are amplified by the malleus, incus, and stapes.

LEVEL 3: SYNTHESIS/EVALUATION

6. Although some sharks close their eyes just before they bite, their bites are on target. Researchers have noted that sharks often misdirect their bites at metal objects and that they can find batteries buried under sand. This evidence suggests that sharks keep track of their prey during the split second before they bite in the same way that
   a. a rattlesnake finds a mouse in its burrow.
   b. a male silkworm moth locates a mate.
   c. a bat finds moths in the dark.
   d. a platypus locates its prey in a muddy river.

7. **DRAW IT** Based on the information in the text, fill in the following graph. Use one line for rods and another line for cones.

8. **EVOLUTION CONNECTION**
   In general, locomotion on land requires more energy than locomotion in water. By integrating what you have learned about animal form and function in Unit 7, discuss some of the evolutionary adaptations of mammals that support the high energy requirements for moving on land.

9. **SCIENTIFIC INQUIRY**
   Although skeletal muscles generally fatigue fairly rapidly, clam shell muscles have a protein called paramyosin that allows them to sustain contraction for up to a month. From your knowledge of the cellular mechanism of contraction, propose a hypothesis to explain how paramyosin might work. How would you test your hypothesis experimentally?

10. **WRITE ABOUT A THEME: ORGANIZATION**
    In a short essay (100–150 words), describe at least three ways in which the structure of the lens of the human eye is well adapted to its function in vision.

11. **SYNTHESIZE YOUR KNOWLEDGE**

Bloodhounds, which are adept at following a scent trail even days old, have 1000 times as many olfactory receptor cells as we have. How might this difference contribute to the tracking ability of these dogs? What differences in brain organization would you expect in comparing a bloodhound and a human?

For selected answers, see Appendix A.

51

Animal Behaviour

▲ **Figure 51.1 What prompts this ruffed grouse to make a drumming-like sound and display its feathers?**

KEY CONCEPTS

51.1 Discrete sensory inputs can stimulate both simple and complex behaviours

51.2 Learning establishes specific links between experience and behaviour

51.3 Selection for individual survival and reproductive success can explain most behaviours

51.4 Genetic analyses and the concept of inclusive fitness provide a basis for studying the evolution of behaviour

The How and Why of Animal Activity

For most of its life, the ruffed grouse (*Bonasa umbellus*) hides in the woods, using its cryptic colouration as camouflage (**Figure 51.1**). It moves quietly through the forest, picking away at seeds, vegetation, and insects on the forest floor. However, when mating season begins, the males become exhibitionists. They flap their wings noisily, creating a drum-like sound that can be heard at great distances. When females are attracted by the sound, the males give up their cryptic lives and proudly display their feathers. If a female accepts a male's advances, they mate; the male leaves and returns to a solitary life, while the female constructs a nest and lays 12 or more eggs over the next two weeks.

Animal behaviour, be it solitary or social, fixed or variable, is based on physiological systems and processes. An individual **behaviour** is an action carried out by muscles under control of the nervous system in response to a stimulus. Examples include an animal using its chest and throat muscles to produce a song, releasing a scent to mark its territory, or simply waving a claw as does the male fiddler crab to the left. Behaviour is an essential part of acquiring nutrients for digestion and finding a partner for sexual reproduction. Behaviour also contributes to homeostasis, as in honeybees huddling to conserve heat (see Chapter 40).

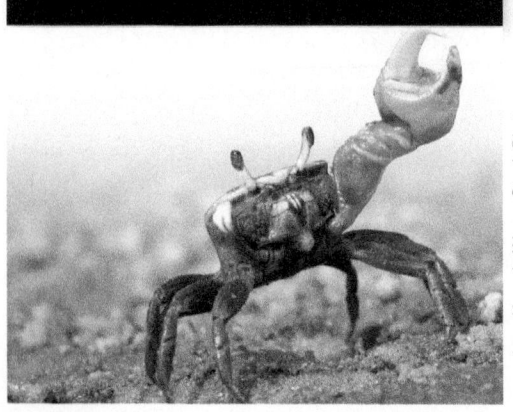

Ivan Kuzmin/Alamy Stock Photo

◄ **A male fiddler crab**

In short, all of animal physiology contributes to behaviour, and animal behaviour influences all of physiology.

Being essential for survival and reproduction, behaviour is subject to substantial natural selection over time. This evolutionary process of selection also affects anatomy because the recognition and communication that underlie many behaviours depend on body form and appearance.

In this chapter, we'll examine how behaviour is controlled, how it develops during an animal's life, and how it is influenced by genes and the environment. We'll also explore the ways in which behaviour evolves over many generations. In moving from our study of an animal's inner workings to its interactions with the outside world, we will also provide a transition to ecology, the focus of Unit Eight.

CONCEPT 51.1

Discrete sensory inputs can stimulate both simple and complex behaviours

What approach do biologists use to determine how behaviours arise and what functions they serve? Dutch scientist Niko Tinbergen, a pioneer in the study of animal behaviour, suggested that understanding any behaviour requires answering four questions, which can be summarized as follows:

1. What stimulus elicits the behaviour, and what physiological mechanisms mediate the response?
2. How does the animal's experience during growth and development influence the response?
3. How does the behaviour aid survival and reproduction?
4. What is the behaviour's evolutionary history?

Tinbergen's first two questions ask about *proximate causation*: "how" a behaviour occurs or is modified. The last two questions ask about *ultimate causation*: "why" a behaviour occurs in the context of natural selection.

Today, Tinbergen's questions and the associated ideas of causation underlie **behavioural ecology**, the study of the ecological and evolutionary basis for animal behaviour. As we explore this vibrant area of modern biological research, we will also review studies by Tinbergen and two other early researchers—Karl von Frisch and Konrad Lorenz—that earned the three scientists a Nobel Prize in 1973.

In addressing Tinbergen's first question, the nature of the stimuli that trigger behaviour, we'll begin with behavioural responses to well-defined stimuli, starting with an example from Tinbergen's own experiments.

Fixed Action Patterns

As part of his research, Tinbergen kept fish tanks containing three-spined sticklebacks (*Gasterosteus aculeatus*). Male sticklebacks, which have red bellies, attack other males that invade their nesting territories. Tinbergen noticed that his male sticklebacks

also behaved aggressively when a red truck passed in front of their tank. Inspired by this chance observation, he carried out experiments showing that the red colour of an intruder's underside is what provokes the attack behaviour. A male stickleback will not attack a fish lacking red colouration (note that female sticklebacks never have red bellies), but will attack even unrealistic models if they contain areas of red colour (Figure 51.2).

The territorial response of male sticklebacks is an example of a **fixed action pattern**, a sequence of unlearned acts directly linked to a simple stimulus. Fixed action patterns are essentially unchangeable and, once initiated, usually carried to completion. The trigger for the behaviour is an external cue called a **sign stimulus**, such as a red object prompting the male stickleback's aggressive behaviour.

Migration

Environmental stimuli not only trigger behaviours but also provide cues that animals use to carry out those behaviours.

(a) A male stickleback fish attacks other male sticklebacks that invade its nesting territory. The red belly of the intruding male (left) acts as the sign stimulus that instigates the aggressive behaviour.

(b) The realistic model at the top, without a red underside, produces no aggressive response in a male three-spined stickleback. The other models, with red undersides, produce strong responses.

▲ Figure 51.2 **Sign stimuli in a classic fixed action pattern.**

Source: Adaptation of figure 20 from *The Study of Instincts* by Nikolaas Tinbergen. Copyright © 1989 by Oxford University Press. Reprinted with permission. Adaptation of figures 65 and 66 in *Inleiding tot de Diersociologie*, by Nikolaas Tinbergen, © 1946. Reprinted by permission of E. Barendrecht-Tinbergen.

[?] *Suggest an explanation for why this behaviour evolved (its ultimate causation).*

For example, a wide variety of birds, fishes, and other animals use environmental cues to guide **migration**—a regular, long-distance change in location (Figure 51.3). Many migrating animals pass through environments they have not previously encountered. How, then, do they find their way in these foreign settings?

Some migrating animals track their position relative to the sun, even though the sun's position relative to Earth changes throughout the day. Animals can adjust for these changes by means of a *circadian clock*, an internal mechanism that maintains a 24-hour activity rhythm or cycle (see Chapter 49). For example, experiments have shown that migrating birds orient differently relative to the sun at distinct times of the day. Nocturnal animals can instead use the North Star, which has a constant position in the night sky.

Although the sun and stars can provide useful clues for navigation, these landmarks can be obscured by clouds. How do migrating animals overcome this problem? A simple experiment with homing pigeons provides one answer. On an overcast day, placing a small magnet on the head of a homing pigeon prevents it from returning efficiently to its roost. Researchers concluded that pigeons can sense their position relative to Earth's magnetic field and thereby navigate without solar or celestial cues. The way in which animals detect Earth's magnetic field remains a matter of debate. It is known that the heads of migrating birds (and fishes) contain bits of magnetite, a magnetic iron mineral. There is also evidence that cells in the pigeon's brainstem encode information about magnetic field direction, intensity, and polarity. The search continues for magnetoreceptors, which in migrating birds appear to be located in the eye, beak, and perhaps inner ear.

▲ Figure 51.3 **Migration.** Each spring, snow geese (*Chen caerulescens*) migrate from their wintering grounds, which may be as far south as Mexico, to their breeding grounds in Canada, Greenland, and Alaska. In the autumn, they return to their wintering grounds. More than 800 000 snow geese stop at Cap Tourmente on the north shore of the St. Lawrence River just east of Quebec City every autumn.

Susan Lee Powell/Pearson Education

Behavioural Rhythms

Although the circadian clock plays a small but significant role in navigation by some migrating species, it has a major role in the daily activity of all animals. As discussed in Chapters 40 and 49, the output of the clock is a circadian rhythm, a daily cycle of rest and activity with far-reaching effects on behavioural physiology. The clock is normally synchronized with the light and dark cycles of the environment but can maintain rhythmic activity under constant environmental conditions, such as during hibernation.

Some behaviours, such as migration and reproduction, reflect biological rhythms with a longer cycle, or period, than the circadian rhythm. Behavioural rhythms linked to the yearly cycle of seasons are called *circannual rhythms*. Although migration and reproduction typically correlate with food availability, these behaviours are not a direct response to changes in food intake. Instead, circannual rhythms, like circadian rhythms, are influenced by the periods of daylight and darkness in the environment. For example, studies with several bird species have shown that an artificial environment with extended daylight can induce out-of-season migratory behaviour.

In a classic study by William Rowan, from the University of Alberta, the impact of photoperiod was shown using crows that had been exposed to different light cycles. In 1931 Rowan released hundreds of crows and used a network of volunteers to follow their dispersal pattern. One group of crows was kept in cages that were illuminated at dusk and dawn to mimic the longer day length that is expected in summer. When released, this group migrated northward, heading toward their summer breeding grounds. The control group, exposed to a natural light cycle, ranged locally or headed south upon release.

Animal Signals and Communication

The feather display of the male ruffed grouse is an example of one animal generating the stimulus that guides the behaviour of another animal (the female grouse). A stimulus transmitted from one animal to another is called a **signal**. The transmission and reception of signals constitute animal **communication**, an essential element of interactions between individuals.

Forms of Animal Communication

Let's consider the courtship behaviour of *Drosophila melanogaster*, the fruit fly (Figure 51.4), as an introduction to the four common modes of animal communication: visual, chemical, tactile, and auditory.

Fruit fly courtship constitutes a *stimulus-response chain*, in which the response to each stimulus is itself the stimulus for the next behaviour. In the first step, a male identifies a

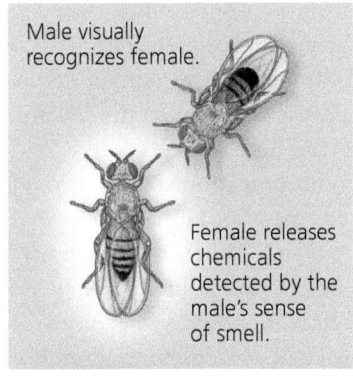

Male visually recognizes female.

Female releases chemicals detected by the male's sense of smell.

1 Orienting

Male taps female's abdomen with a foreleg.

2 Tapping

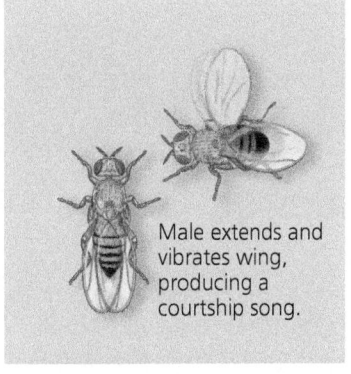

Male extends and vibrates wing, producing a courtship song.

3 "Singing"

◀ Figure 51.4 **Courtship behaviour of the fruit fly.** Fruit fly courtship involves a fixed set of behaviours that follow one another in a fixed order.

Source: Adaptation of figure 1 from "Drosophila: Genetics Meets Behavior" by Marla B. Sokolowski, from *Nature Reviews: Genetics*, November 2001, Volume 2(11). Copyright © 2001 by Macmillan Publishers Ltd. Reprinted with permission.

female of the same species and then orients his body toward hers. When the male sees and turns toward the female, he relies on *visual communication.*

In addition, the fly's sense of smell, or olfactory system, detects chemicals released into the air. Males may detect pheromones released from the female. However, females can detect odours emanating from the exoskeleton, or cuticle, of males. Howard Rundle, at Carleton University, has studied how both environmental exposure and genetic background influence the types of cuticle hydrocarbons released from flies, and how females use these odours in determining the male with which to mate. These are examples of *chemical communication,* the transmission and reception of signals in the form of specific molecules. Having recognized the female, the male approaches and taps the female with a foreleg (Figure 51.4**2**). This touching, or *tactile communication,* alerts the female to the male's presence. In the process, chemicals on her abdomen are transferred to the male, providing further chemical confirmation of her species identity. In the third stage of courtship (Figure 51.4**3**), the male extends and vibrates his wing, producing a specific courtship song. This singing, an example of *auditory communication,* informs the female that the male is of the same species. Only if all of these forms of communication are successful will a female allow the male to attempt copulation.

In general, the form of communication that evolves is closely related to an animal's lifestyle and environment. For example, visual displays are relatively ineffective in many mammals that live nocturnally (bats) or in environments with low light, such as tunnels (naked mole rats) or water (cetaceans). Instead, these species use olfactory and auditory signals, which work as well in the dark as in the light. In contrast, most birds are diurnal (active mainly in daytime) and communicate primarily by visual and auditory signals. Humans are also diurnal and, like birds, use primarily visual and auditory communication. We can thus detect and appreciate the songs and bright colours used by birds to communicate but miss many chemical cues on which other mammals base their behaviour.

The information content of animal communication varies considerably. One of the most remarkable examples is the symbolic language of the European honeybee (*Apis mellifera*), discovered in the early 1900s by Austrian researcher Karl von Frisch. Using glass-walled observation hives, he and his students spent several decades observing these bees. Methodical recordings of bee movements enabled von Frisch to decipher a "dance language" that returning foragers use to inform other bees about the distance and direction of travel to food sources.

A returning bee quickly becomes the centre of attention for other bees, called followers (**Figure 51.5a**). If the food source is close to the hive (less than 50 m away), the returning bee moves in tight circles while moving its abdomen from side to side (**Figure 51.5b**). This behaviour, called the "round dance," motivates the follower bees to leave the hive and search for nearby food.

When the food source is farther from the nest, the returning bee instead performs a "waggle dance." This dance, consisting of a half-circle swing in one direction, a straight run during which the bee waggles its abdomen, and a half-circle swing in the other direction, communicates to the follower bees both the direction and distance of the food source in relation to the hive. The angle of the straight run relative to the hive's vertical surface is the same as the horizontal angle of the food in relation to the sun. For example, if the returning bee runs at a 30° angle to the right of vertical, the follower bees leaving the hive fly 30° to the right of the horizontal direction of the sun. A dance with a longer straight run, and therefore more abdominal waggles per run, indicates a greater distance to the food source. As follower bees exit the hive, they fly almost directly to the area indicated by the waggle dance. By using flower odour and other clues, they locate the food source within this area.

Pheromones

Animals that communicate through odours or tastes emit chemical substances called **pheromones**. Pheromones are

(a) Worker bees cluster around a recently returned bee.

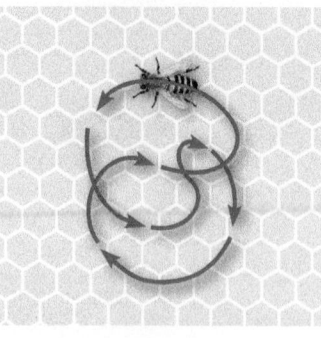

(b) The round dance indicates that food is near.

Beehive

Location **A**:
Food source is in same direction as sun.

Location **B**:
Food source is in direction opposite sun.

Location **C**:
Food source is 30° to right of sun.

(c) The waggle dance is performed when food is distant. The waggle dance resembles a figure eight. Distance is indicated by the number of abdominal waggles performed in the straight-run part of the dance. Direction is indicated by the angle (in relation to the vertical surface of the hive) of the straight run.

▲ **Figure 51.5 Honeybee dance language.** Honeybees returning to the hive communicate the location of food sources through the symbolic language of a dance.

especially common among mammals and insects and often relate to reproductive behaviour. For example, pheromones are the basis for the chemical communication when female fruit flies attract males during courtship (see Figure 51.4). Pheromones are not limited to short-distance signalling, however. Male spruce budworm moths have receptors that can detect the pheromone from a female moth from several kilometres away. After the moths are together, pheromones also trigger specific courtship behaviours.

In a honeybee colony, pheromones produced by the queen and her daughters, the workers, maintain the hive's

complex social order. One pheromone (once called the queen substance) has a particularly wide range of effects. It attracts workers to the queen, inhibits development of ovaries in workers, and attracts males (drones) to the queen during her mating flights out of the hive.

Another form of chemical communication is an alarm substance. When a fish is injured, specific skin cells release their chemical contents into the water. When other fish of the same species (conspecifics) detect this substance, they exhibit a fright response (**Figure 51.6**). They may become more vigilant, or form tightly packed aggregations. Though there are similarities with pheromones—they are released into the environment and signal conspecifics—alarm substances are not secreted, and are released only when the skin is damaged. Douglas Chivers at the University of Saskatchewan suggests that the cells that produce alarm substances originally evolved as part of the immune system.

As we have seen, the forms of animal communication used to convey information are quite diverse. So far in this chapter, we have explored the types of stimuli that elicit behaviours—the first part of Tinbergen's first question. The second part of that question—the physiological mechanisms that mediate responses—was the focus of Chapters 49 and 50. Stimuli activate sensory systems, are processed in the central nervous system, and result in motor outputs that

(a) Minnows are widely dispersed in an aquarium before an alarm substance is introduced.

(b) Within seconds of the alarm substance being introduced, minnows aggregate near the bottom of the aquarium and reduce their movement.

▲ **Figure 51.6 Minnows responding to the presence of an alarm substance.**

constitute behaviour. You may want to review those two chapters before proceeding to the next concept, which focuses on Tinbergen's second question—how experience influences behaviour.

CONCEPT 51.2

Learning establishes specific links between experience and behaviour

For many behaviours—such as a fixed action pattern, a courtship stimulus-response chain, and pheromone signalling—nearly all individuals in a population exhibit virtually the same behaviour, despite internal and environmental differences during development and throughout life. Behaviour that is developmentally fixed in this way is known as **innate behaviour**. In other cases, behaviour is variable, depending on experience.

Experience and Behaviour

Tinbergen's second question asks how an animal's experiences during growth and development influence the response to stimuli. How do researchers answer this question? One informative approach is a **cross-fostering study**, in which the young of one species are placed in the care of adults from another species. The extent to which the offspring's behaviour changes in such a situation provides one measure of how the social and physical environments influence behaviour.

Certain mouse species have behaviours well suited for cross-fostering studies. Male California mice (*Peromyscus californicus*) are highly aggressive toward other mice and provide extensive parental care. In contrast, male white-footed mice (*Peromyscus leucopus*) are less aggressive and engage in little parental care. When the pups of each species were placed in the nests of the other species, the cross-fostering altered some behaviours of both species (Table 51.1). For instance, male California mice raised by white-footed mice were less aggressive toward intruders. Thus, experience during development can strongly influence aggressive behaviour in these rodents.

One of the most important findings of the cross-fostering experiments with mice was that the influence of experience on behaviour can be passed on to progeny: When the cross-fostered California mice became parents, they spent less time retrieving offspring who wandered off than did California mice raised by their own species. Thus, experience during development can modify physiology in a way that alters parental behaviour, extending the influence of environment to a subsequent generation.

For humans, the influence of genetics and environment on behaviour can be explored by a **twin study**, in which researchers compare the behaviour of identical twins raised apart with the behaviour of those raised in the same household. Twin studies have been instrumental in studying human behavioural disorders, such as schizophrenia, anxiety disorders, and alcoholism. As discussed in Chapter 49, these investigations have revealed that both genetics and environment (nature *and* nurture) contribute significantly to the behaviours that characterize these disorders in humans.

Learning

One of the most powerful ways that environmental conditions can influence behaviour is through **learning**, the modification of behaviour based on specific experiences. The capacity for learning depends on nervous system organization established during development following instructions encoded in the genome. Learning itself involves the formation of memories by specific changes in neuronal connectivity (see Concept 49.4). Therefore, the essential challenge for research into learning is not to decide between nature (genes) and nurture (environment), but

Table 51.1	Influence of Cross-Fostering on Male Mice*		
Species	Aggression toward an Intruder	Aggression in Neutral Situation	Paternal Behaviour
California mice fostered by white-footed mice	Reduced	No difference	Reduced
White-footed mice fostered by California mice	No difference	Increased	No difference

*Comparisons are with mice raised by parents of their own species.

Imprinting

In some species, the ability of offspring to recognize and be recognized by a parent is essential for survival. In the young, this learning often takes the form of **imprinting**, the establishment of a long-lasting behavioural response to a particular individual or object. Imprinting can take place only during a specific time period in development, called the **sensitive period**. Among gulls, for instance, the sensitive period for a parent to bond with its young lasts one to two days. If bonding does not occur, the parent will not care for the infant, leading to death for the offspring and a decrease in reproductive success for the parent.

How do the young know on whom—or what—to imprint? Experiments with many species of waterfowl indicate that they have no innate recognition of "mother." Rather, they identify with the first object they encounter that has certain key characteristics. In the 1930s, the Austrian researcher Konrad Lorenz showed that the principal imprinting stimulus in graylag geese (*Anser anser*) is a nearby object that is moving away from the young. When incubator-hatched goslings spent their first few hours with Lorenz rather than with a goose, they imprinted on him and steadfastly followed him from then on (Figure 51.7a). In 1988, Canadians Bill Carrick (naturalist, cinematographer) and Bill Lishman (artist, inventor, pilot) were the first to use light aircraft to lead flying birds (Canada Geese, *Branta canadensis*) and in 1993 led geese on a fall migration from Ontario to Virginia. The feature film *Fly Away Home* is loosely based on Lishman's life and Operation Migration, the non-profit organization he co-founded.

Imprinting has become an important component of efforts to save endangered species, such as the whooping crane (*Grus americana*). Scientists have tried raising whooping cranes in captivity. They took whooping crane eggs from nests in Wood Buffalo National Park, NWT, to Gray's Lake National Wildlife Refuge in Idaho, to be hatched and raised by wild sandhill cranes (*Grus canadensis*). However, because the whooping cranes imprinted on their foster parents, none formed a *pair-bond* (strong attachment) with a whooping crane mate. To avoid such problems, captive breeding programs now isolate young cranes, exposing them to the sights and sounds of members of their own species.

Scientists have made further use of imprinting to teach cranes born in captivity to migrate along safe routes. Young whooping cranes are imprinted on humans in "crane suits" and then allowed to follow these "parents" as they fly ultralight aircraft along selected migration routes (Figure 51.7b). Importantly, these cranes still form mating pair-bonds with other whooping cranes, indicating that the

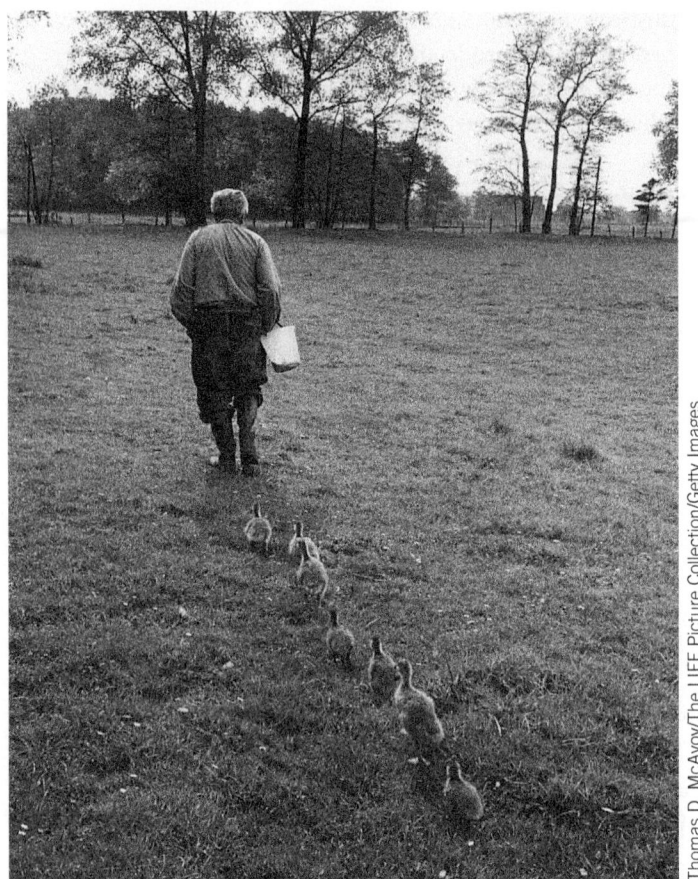

(a) These young greylag geese imprinted on zoologist Konrad Lorenz.

(b) A pilot wearing a crane suit and flying an ultralight plane acts as a surrogate parent to direct the migration of whooping cranes.

▲ Figure 51.7 **Imprinting.** Imprinting can be altered to (a) investigate animal behaviour or (b) direct animal behaviour.

WHAT IF? *Suppose the geese following Lorenz were bred to each other. How might their imprinting on Lorenz affect their offspring? Explain.*

crane costumes have the features required to direct "normal" imprinting.

Spatial Learning and Cognitive Maps

Every natural environment has spatial variation, as in locations of nest sites, hazards, food, and prospective mates.

Therefore, an organism's fitness may be enhanced by the capacity for **spatial learning**, the establishment of a memory that reflects the environment's spatial structure.

The idea of spatial learning intrigued Tinbergen while he was a graduate student in the Netherlands. At that time, he was studying the female digger wasp (*Philanthus triangulum*), which nests in small burrows dug into sand dunes. Tinbergen noticed that when a wasp left her nest to go hunting, she hid the entrance from potential intruders by covering it with sand. Upon her return, she flew directly to her hidden nest, despite the presence of hundreds of other burrows in the area. Tinbergen hypothesized that a wasp locates her nest by learning its position relative to visible landmarks, or location indicators. To test this hypothesis, he carried out an experiment in the wasps' natural habitat (Figure 51.8). By manipulating objects around nest entrances, he demonstrated that digger wasps engage in spatial learning. This experiment was so simple and informative that it could be summarized very concisely. In fact, at 32 pages, Tinbergen's Ph.D. thesis from 1932 is still the shortest ever approved at Leiden University.

In many animal species, spatial learning can be quite sophisticated. Some animals guide their activity by a **cognitive map**, a representation in the nervous system of the spatial relationships between objects in an animal's surroundings. Rather than relying solely on moving from landmark to landmark, animals using cognitive maps can navigate more flexibly and efficiently by relating landmark positions to one another.

One striking example of cognitive mapping is found in the grey jay (*Perisoreus canadensis*), studied for more than 40 years by park naturalist Dan Strickland in Ontario's Algonquin Park. Grey jays are corvids, the bird family that includes crows, ravens, and nutcrackers. These jays store food items in hundreds of holes and crevices in trees scattered over their year-round territory, which could be as big as 1.5 square kilometres. Then, when food is scarce, especially in the winter, they retrieve their caches, even finding enough stored food to begin breeding in February when snow is still thick on the ground. Field experiments show that grey jays have excellent short-term spatial memory but appear to use some simple rules to find long-stored food. Their close relative, the Clark's nutcracker (*Nucifraga columbiana*), stores up to 30 000 pine seeds in thousands of caches, often more than 20 kilometres apart. Researchers found that nutcrackers use an abstract geometric rule that tells them that seed caches are halfway between landmarks. Such rules are a fundamental property of cognitive maps, and serve to reduce the amount of detail that needs to be remembered to find a stored object. As we discussed in Chapter 49, corvids also display other forms of higher nervous system function.

▼ Figure 51.8 | Inquiry

Does a digger wasp use landmarks to find her nest?

Experiment A female digger wasp covers the entrance to her nest while foraging for food, but finds the correct wasp nest reliably upon her return 30 minutes or more later. Niko Tinbergen wanted to test the hypothesis that a wasp learns visual landmarks that mark her nest before she leaves on hunting trips. First, he marked one nest with a ring of pinecones while the wasp was in the burrow. After leaving the nest to forage, the wasp returned to the nest successfully.

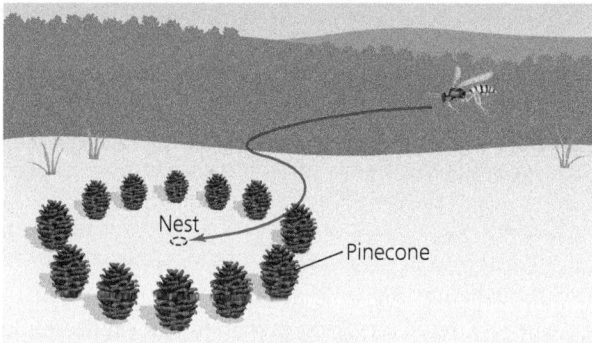

Source: Figure adapted from *Zoology,* 1st edition, by Lawrence G. Mitchell et al. Pearson Education Inc., 1988. © Jane B Reece.

Two days later, after the wasp had again left, Tinbergen shifted the ring of pinecones away from the nest. Then he waited to observe the wasp's behaviour.

Results When the wasp returned, she flew to the centre of the pinecone circle instead of to the nearby nest. Repeating the experiment with many wasps, Tinbergen obtained the same results.

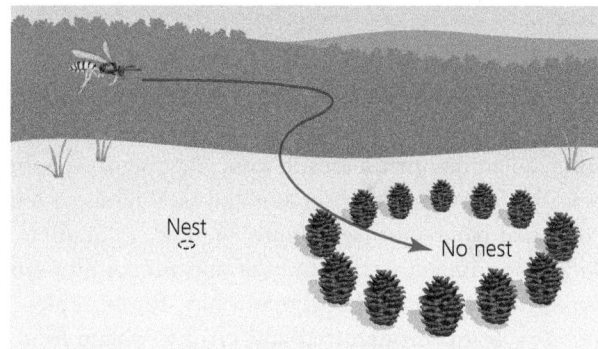

Conclusion The experiment supported the hypothesis that digger wasps use visual landmarks to keep track of their nests.

Source: Based on N. Tinbergen, *The Study of Instinct,* Clarendon Press, Oxford (1951). © Jane B Reece.

WHAT IF? *Suppose the digger wasp had returned to her original nest site, despite the pinecones having been moved. What alternative hypotheses might you propose regarding how the wasp finds her nest and why the pinecones didn't misdirect the wasp?*

Associative Learning

Learning often involves making associations between experiences. Consider, for example, a blue jay (*Cyanocitta cristata*) that ingests a brightly coloured monarch butterfly (*Danaus plexippus*). Substances that the monarch accumulates from milkweed plants cause the blue jay to vomit

▲ Figure 51.9 **Associative learning.** Having ingested and vomited a monarch butterfly, a blue jay has probably learned to avoid this species.

almost immediately (Figure 51.9). Following such experiences, blue jays avoid attacking monarchs and similar-looking butterflies. The ability to associate one environmental feature (such as a colour) with another (such as a foul taste) is called **associative learning**.

Associative learning is well suited to study in the laboratory. Such studies typically involve either classical conditioning or operant conditioning. In *classical conditioning*, an arbitrary stimulus becomes associated with a particular outcome. Russian physiologist Ivan Pavlov carried out early experiments in classical conditioning, demonstrating that if he always rang a bell just before feeding a dog, the dog would eventually salivate when the bell sounded, anticipating food. In *operant conditioning*, also called trial-and-error learning, an animal first learns to associate one of its behaviours with a reward or punishment and then tends to repeat or avoid that behaviour (see Figure 51.9). B. F. Skinner, an American pioneer in the study of operant conditioning, explored this process in the laboratory by, for example, having a rat learn through trial-and-error to obtain food by pressing a lever.

Studies reveal that animals can learn to link many pairs of features of their environment, but not all. For example, pigeons can learn to associate danger with a sound but not with a colour. However, they can learn to associate a colour with food. What does this mean? The development and organization of the pigeon's nervous system apparently restrict the associations that can be formed. Moreover, such restrictions are not limited to birds. Rats, for example, can learn to avoid illness-inducing foods on the basis of smells, but not on the basis of sights or sounds.

If we consider how behaviour evolves, the fact that some animals can't learn to make particular associations appears logical. The associations an animal can readily form typically reflect relationships likely to occur in nature.

Conversely, associations that can't be formed are those unlikely to be of selective advantage in a native environment. In the case of a rat's diet in the wild, for example, a harmful food is far more likely to have a certain odour than to be associated with a particular sound.

Cognition and Problem Solving

The most complex forms of learning involve **cognition**—the process of knowing that involves awareness, reasoning, recollection, and judgment. Although it was once argued that only primates and certain marine mammals have high-level thought processes, many other groups of animals, including insects, appear to exhibit cognition in controlled laboratory studies. For example, an experiment using Y-shaped mazes tested whether honeybees can distinguish between "same" and "different." One maze had different colours, and one had different black-and-white striped patterns, either vertical or horizontal bars. Two groups of honeybees were trained in the colour maze. Upon entering, a bee would see a sample colour and could then choose between an arm of the maze with the same colour or an arm with a different colour. Only one arm contained a food reward. The first group of bees were rewarded for flying into the arm with the *same* colour as the sample (Figure 51.10a); the second group were rewarded for choosing the arm with the *different* colour. Next, they were tested in the bar maze, which had no food reward. After encountering a sample black-and-white pattern of bars, a bee could choose between an arm with the same pattern or an arm with a different pattern. The bees in the first group most often chose the arm with the same pattern (Figure 51.10b), whereas those in the second group typically chose the arm with the different pattern.

The maze experiments provide strong experimental support for the hypothesis that honeybees can distinguish on the basis of "same" and "different." Remarkably, honeybees can also learn to distinguish between human faces.

The information-processing ability of a nervous system can also be revealed in **problem solving**, the cognitive activity of devising a method to proceed from one state to another in the face of real or apparent obstacles. For example, if a chimpanzee is placed in a room with several boxes on the floor and a banana hung high out of reach, the chimp can assess the situation and stack the boxes, enabling it to reach the food. Such problem-solving behaviour is highly developed in some mammals, especially primates and dolphins. Notable examples have also been observed in some bird species, especially corvids. In one study, ravens were confronted with food hanging from a branch by a string. After failing to grab the food in flight, one raven flew to the branch and alternately pulled up and stepped on the string until the food was within reach. A number of other ravens eventually arrived at similar solutions.

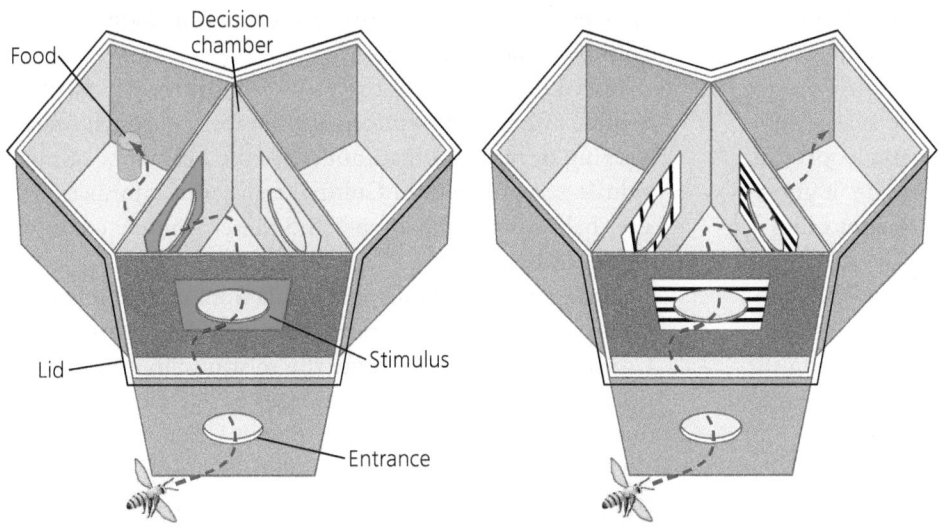

(a) Bees were trained in a colour maze. As shown here, one group was rewarded for choosing the same colour as the stimulus.

(b) Bees were tested in a pattern maze. If previously rewarded for choosing the same colour, bees most often chose lines oriented the same way as the stimulus.

▲ Figure 51.10 **A maze test of abstract thinking by honeybees.** These mazes are designed to test whether honeybees can distinguish "same" from "different."

Source: Adaptation of figure 3a from "Prospective and Retrospective Learning in Honeybees" by Martin Giurfa and Julie Bernard, from *International Journal of Comparative Psychology*, 2006, Volume 19(3). Copyright © 2006 by International Society for Comparative Psychology. Reprinted with permission.

Nevertheless, some ravens failed to solve the problem, indicating that problem-solving success in this species, as in others, varies with individual experience and abilities.

Development of Learned Behaviours

Most of the learned behaviours we have discussed develop over a relatively short time. Some behaviours develop more gradually. For example, some bird species learn songs in stages.

In the case of the white-crowned sparrow (*Zonotrichia leucophrys*), the first stage of song learning takes place early in life, when the fledgling sparrow first hears the song. If a fledgling is prevented from hearing real sparrows or recordings of sparrow songs during the first 50 days of its life, it fails to develop the adult song of its species. Although the young bird does not sing during the sensitive period, it memorizes the song of its species by listening to other white-crowned sparrows sing. During the sensitive period, fledglings chirp more in response to songs of their own species than to songs of other species. Thus, although young white-crowned sparrows learn the songs they will sing as adults, learning appears to be bounded by genetically controlled preferences.

The sensitive period when a white-crowned sparrow memorizes its species' song is followed by a second learning phase when the juvenile bird sings tentative notes called a subsong. The juvenile bird hears its own singing and compares it with the song memorized during the sensitive period. Once a sparrow's own song matches the one it

memorized, the song "crystallizes" as the final song, and the bird sings only this adult song for the rest of its life.

The song-learning process is quite different for canaries than for white-crowned sparrows. Canaries, for example, do not have a single sensitive period for song learning. A young canary begins with a subsong, but the full song does not crystallize in the same way as in white-crowned sparrows. Between breeding seasons, the song becomes flexible again, and an adult male may learn new song "syllables" each year, adding to the song it already sings.

Song learning is one of many examples of how animals learn from other members of their species. In finishing our exploration of learning, we'll look at several more examples that reflect the more general phenomenon of social learning.

Social Learning

Many animals learn to solve problems by observing the behaviour of other individuals. Young wild chimpanzees, for example, learn how to crack open oil palm nuts with two stones by copying experienced chimpanzees (Figure 51.11). This type of learning through observing others is called **social learning**.

Another example of how social learning can modify behaviour comes from studies of the vervet monkeys

▲ Figure 51.11 **A young chimpanzee learning to crack oil palm nuts by observing an experienced elder.**

(*Chlorocebus aethiops*) in Amboseli National Park, Kenya. Vervet monkeys, which are about the size of a domestic cat, produce a complex set of alarm calls. Amboseli vervets give distinct alarm calls for leopards, eagles, or snakes, all of which prey on vervets. When a vervet sees a leopard, it gives a loud barking sound; when it sees an eagle, it gives a short double-syllable cough; and the snake alarm call is a "chutter." Upon hearing a particular alarm call, other vervets in the group behave in an appropriate way: They run up a tree on hearing the alarm for a leopard (vervets are nimbler than leopards in the trees); look up on hearing the alarm for an eagle; and look down on hearing the alarm for a snake (Figure 51.12).

Infant vervet monkeys give alarm calls, but in a relatively undiscriminating way. For example, they give the "eagle" alarm on seeing any bird, including harmless birds such as bee-eaters. With age, the monkeys improve their accuracy. In fact, adult vervet monkeys give the eagle alarm only on seeing an eagle belonging to either of the two species that eat vervets. Infants probably learn how to give the right call by observing other members of the group and receiving social confirmation. For instance, if the infant gives the call on the right occasion—say, an eagle alarm when there is an eagle overhead—another member of the group will also give the eagle call. But if the infant gives the call when a bee-eater flies by, the adults in the group are silent. Thus, vervet monkeys have an initial, unlearned tendency to give calls upon seeing potentially threatening objects in the environment. Learning fine-tunes the call so that adult vervets give calls only

in response to genuine danger and can fine-tune the alarm calls of the next generation.

Social learning forms the roots of **culture**, which can be defined as a system of information transfer through social learning or teaching that influences the behaviour of individuals in a population. Cultural transfer of information can alter behavioural phenotypes and thereby influence the fitness of individuals.

Changes in behaviour that result from natural selection occur on a much longer time scale than does learning. In Concept 51.3, we'll examine the relationship between particular behaviours and the processes of selection related to survival and reproduction.

CONCEPT CHECK 51.2

1. How might associative learning explain why different species of distasteful or stinging insects have similar colours?

2. **WHAT IF?** How might you position and manipulate a few objects in a lab to test whether an animal can use a cognitive map to remember the location of a food source?

3. **MAKE CONNECTIONS** How can a learned behaviour contribute to speciation? (See Concept 24.1.)

For suggested answers, see Appendix A.

CONCEPT 51.3

Selection for individual survival and reproductive success can explain most behaviours

We turn now from the physiology of behaviour (how animals behave) to the benefits to a species from a particular behaviour (why animals behave the way they do). In particular, we will address Tinbergen's third question—how behaviour enhances survival and reproductive success in a population. We'll begin with an activity essential for both types of success: gathering food.

Foraging Behaviour

Because adequate nutrition is essential to an animal's survival and reproductive success, we should expect natural selection to refine behaviours that enhance the efficiency of feeding. Food-obtaining behaviour, or **foraging**, includes not only eating but also any activities an animal uses to search for, recognize, and capture food items.

Evolution of Foraging Behaviour

The fruit fly (*Drosophila melanogaster*) has provided an opportunity to examine how foraging behaviour might have evolved. Variation in a gene called *forager* (*for*) dictates

Richard Wrangham

Alissa Crandall/Corbis

▲ Figure 51.12 **Vervet monkeys learning correct use of alarm calls.** On seeing a python (foreground), vervet monkeys give a distinct "snake" alarm call (inset), and the members of the group stand upright and look down.

the food-search behaviour of fruit fly larvae. On average, larvae carrying the *for*^R ("Rover") allele travel nearly twice as far while feeding as do larvae with the *for*^s ("sitter") allele. Experiments have shown that the enzyme encoded by the *forager* locus is more active in *for*^R larvae than in *for*^s larvae and has properties typical of an enzyme in a signal transduction pathway (see Chapter 45).

Both the *for*^R and *for*^s alleles are present in natural populations. What circumstances might favour one or the other allele? The answer became apparent in experiments when flies were kept for many generations at either low or high population densities. The larvae from the two samples clearly diverged in behaviour, as measured by differences in average length of their foraging paths (Figure 51.13). Larvae maintained for many generations at a low density foraged over shorter distances than those kept at high density. Furthermore, genetic tests indicated that the *for*^s allele had increased in frequency in the low-density populations, whereas the *for*^R allele had increased in frequency in the high-density group. These changes make sense. At low population density, short-distance foraging yields sufficient food, while long-distance foraging would result in unnecessary energy expenditure. Under crowded conditions, however, long-distance foraging could enable larvae to move beyond areas of food depletion. In summary, there was an observable and interpretable evolutionary change in behaviour in the laboratory populations.

Optimal Foraging Model

To study the proximate and ultimate causation of diverse foraging strategies, biologists sometimes apply a type of cost-benefit analysis used in economics. This idea proposes that foraging behaviour is a compromise between the benefits of nutrition and the costs of obtaining food. These costs might include the energy expenditure of foraging as well as the risk of being eaten while foraging. According to this **optimal foraging model**, natural selection should favour a foraging behaviour that minimizes the costs of foraging and maximizes the benefits.

The Scientific Skills Exercise provides an example of how this model can be applied to animals in the wild.

Balancing Risk and Reward

One of the most significant potential costs to a forager is risk of predation. Maximizing energy gain and minimizing energy costs are of little benefit if the behaviour makes the forager a likely meal for a predator. It seems logical, therefore, that predation risk would influence foraging behaviour. Such appears to be the case for the mule deer (*Odocoileus hemionus*), which lives in the mountains of western North America. Researchers found that the food available for mule deer was fairly uniform across the

▲ **Figure 51.13 Evolution of foraging behaviour by laboratory populations of *Drosophila melanogaster*.** After 74 generations of living at low population density, *D. melanogaster* larvae (populations R1–R3) followed foraging paths significantly shorter than those of *D. melanogaster* larvae that had lived at high density (populations K1–K3).

Source: Adaptation of figure 2a from "Evolution of Foraging Behavior in Drosophila by Density Dependent Selection" by Maria B. Sokolowski et al., from *PNAS*, July 8, 1997, Volume 94(14). Copyright © 1997 by National Academy of Sciences, U.S.A. Reprinted with permission.

INTERPRET THE DATA *What alternative hypothesis is ruled out by having three R and K lines, rather than one of each?*

potential foraging areas, although somewhat lower in open, nonforested areas. In contrast, the risk of predation differed greatly; mountain lions (*Puma concolour*), the major predator, killed large numbers of mule deer at forest edges and only a small number in open areas and forest interiors.

How does mule deer foraging behaviour reflect the differences in predation risk in particular areas? Mule deer feed predominantly in open areas. Thus, it appears that mule deer foraging behaviour reflects the large variation in predation risk and not the smaller variation in food availability. This result underscores the point that behaviour typically reflects a compromise between competing selective pressures.

Mating Behaviour and Mate Choice

Just as foraging is crucial for individual survival, mating behaviour and mate choice play a major role in determining reproductive success. These behaviours include seeking or attracting mates, choosing among potential mates, competing for mates, and caring for offspring. Although we tend to think of mating simply as the union of a male and female, the mating relationship between males and females varies greatly from species to species, defining a number of distinct mating systems.

Mating Systems and Sexual Dimorphism

Mating systems vary with regard to both the length and number of relationships. In many animal species, mating is **promiscuous**, with no strong pair-bonds. In species in

Testing a Hypothesis with a Quantitative Model

Do Crows Display Optimal Foraging Behaviour? On islands off British Columbia, northwestern crows (*Corvus caurinus*) search rocky tide pools for sea snails called whelks. After spotting a whelk, the crow picks it up in its beak, flies upward, and drops the whelk onto the rocks. If the drop is successful, the shell breaks and the crow can dine on the whelk's soft parts. If not, the crow flies up and drops the whelk again and again until the shell breaks. What determines how high the crow flies? If energetic considerations dominated selection for the crow's foraging behaviour, the average drop height might reflect a trade-off between the cost of flying higher and the benefit of more frequent success. In this exercise you'll test how well this optimal foraging model predicts the average drop height observed in nature.

How the Experiments Were Done The height of drops made by crows in the wild was measured by referring to a marked pole erected nearby. In the test, the crow's behaviour was simulated using a device that dropped a whelk onto the rocks from a fixed platform. The average number of drops required to break whelks from various platform heights was recorded and averaged over many trials with the device. Combining the data for each platform height, total "flight" height was calculated by multiplying the height times the average number of drops required.

Data from the Experiment

Matt Goff

Interpret the Data

1. How does the average number of drops required to break open a whelk depend on platform height for a drop of 5 metres or less? For drops of more than 5 metres?

2. Total flight height can be considered to be a measure of the total energy required to break open a whelk. Why is this value lower for a platform set at 5 metres than for one at 2 or 15 metres?

3. Compare the drop height preferred by crows with the graph of total flight height for the platform drops. Are the data consistent with the hypothesis of optimal foraging? Explain.

4. In testing the optimal foraging model, it was assumed that changing the height of the drop only changed the total energy required. Do you think this is a realistic limitation, or might other factors than total energy be affected by height?

5. Researchers observed that the crows only gather and drop the largest whelks. What are some reasons crows might favour larger whelks?

6. It turned out that the probability of a whelk breaking was the same for a whelk dropped for the first time as for an unbroken whelk dropped several times previously. If the probability of breaking instead increased, what change might you predict in the crow's behaviour?

Data from R. Zach, Shell-dropping: Decision-making and optimal foraging in northwestern crows, *Behavior* 68:106–117 (1979). © Jane B Reece.

which the mates remain together for a longer period, the relationship may be **monogamous** (one male mating with one female) or **polygamous** (an individual of one sex mating with several of the other). Polygamous relationships most often involve a single male and many females, a system called *polygyny*, though some species exhibit *polyandry*, in which a single female mates with several males.

The extent to which males and females differ in appearance, a characteristic known as *sexual dimorphism*, typically varies with the type of mating system (**Figure 51.14**). Among monogamous species, males and females are often so much alike morphologically that they may be difficult or impossible to distinguish based on external characteristics. In contrast, polygynous species are generally dimorphic, with males being showier and often larger than females. Polyandrous species are also dimorphic, but the females are generally more ornamented and larger than the males.

(a) In monogamous species, such as these western gulls, males and females are difficult to distinguish using external characteristics only.

(b) Among polygynous species, such as elk, the male (right) is often highly ornamented.

(c) In polyandrous species, such as these red-necked phalaropes (*Phalaropus lobatus*), females (right) are generally more ornamented than males.

▲ Figure 51.14 **Relationship between mating system and male and female forms.**

Mating Systems and Parental Care

The needs of the young are an important factor constraining the evolution of mating systems. Most newly hatched birds, for instance, cannot care for themselves. Rather, they require a large, continuous food supply, a need that is difficult for a single parent to meet. In such cases, a male that stays with and helps a single mate may ultimately have more viable offspring than it would by going off to seek additional mates. This may explain why most birds are monogamous. In contrast, for birds with young that can feed and care for themselves almost immediately after hatching, the males derive less benefit from staying with their partner. Males of these species, such as pheasants and quail, can maximize their reproductive success by seeking other mates, and polygyny is relatively common in such birds. In the case of mammals, the lactating female is often the only food source for the young; males usually play no role in raising the young. In mammalian species where males protect the females and young, such as lions, a male or small group of males typically takes care of a harem of many females at the same time.

Another factor influencing mating behaviour and parental care is *certainty of paternity*. Young born to or eggs laid by a female definitely contain that female's genes. However, even within a normally monogamous relationship, a male other than the female's usual mate may have fathered that female's offspring. The certainty of paternity is relatively low in most species with internal fertilization because the acts of mating and birth (or mating and egg laying) are separated over time. This could explain why exclusively male parental care is rare in bird and mammal species. However, the males of many species with internal fertilization engage in behaviours that appear to increase their certainty of paternity. These behaviours include guarding females, removing any sperm from the female reproductive tract before copulation, and introducing large quantities of sperm that displace the sperm of other males.

Certainty of paternity is high when egg laying and mating occur together, as in external fertilization. This may explain why parental care in aquatic invertebrates, fishes, and amphibians, when it occurs at all, is at least as likely to be by males as by females (**Figure 51.15**; see also Figure 46.7). Among fishes and amphibians, parental care occurs in only 7% of species with internal fertilization but in 69% of species with external fertilization.

It is important to point out that certainty of paternity does not mean that animals are aware of those factors when they behave a certain way. Parental behaviour correlated with certainty of paternity exists because it has been reinforced over generations by natural selection. Nevertheless, the relationship between certainty of paternity and male parental care remains an area of active research, enlivened by controversy.

Figure 51.15 **Paternal care by a male jawfish.** The male jawfish, which lives in tropical marine environments, holds the eggs it has fertilized in its mouth, keeping them aerated and protecting them from egg predators until the young hatch.

James D Watt/Image Quest Marine

▶ Figure 51.17 **Appearance of zebra finches in nature.** The male zebra finch (left) is more patterned and colourful than the female zebra finch.

Cyril Laubscher/Dorling Kindersley , Ltd.

Sexual Selection and Mate Choice

Sexual dimorphism results from sexual selection, a form of natural selection in which differences in reproductive success among individuals are a consequence of differences in mating success (see Concept 23.4). Sexual selection can take the form of *intersexual selection*, in which members of one sex choose mates on the basis of characteristics of the other sex, such as courtship songs, or *intrasexual selection*, which involves competition between members of one sex for mates. Let's look at some experimental evidence for sexual selection.

Mate Choice by Females Mate preferences of females may play a central role in the evolution of male behaviour and anatomy through intersexual selection. As an example, let's consider the courtship behaviour of stalk-eyed flies. The eyes of these insects are at the tips of stalks, which

▲ Figure 51.16 **Male stalk-eyed flies.** Male eye span plays a role in mate selection by females and, as shown here, in ritualized contests between males. In such contests, two males face off, with the male whose eye span is smaller very often retreating without any combat taking place.

Gerald S. Wilkinson

are longer in males than in females (Figure 51.16). During courtship, a male approaches the female head-first. Researchers have shown that females are more likely to mate with males that have relatively long eye-stalks. Why would females favour this seemingly arbitrary trait? As discussed in Chapter 23,

ornaments such as long eyestalks in these flies and bright colouration in male birds correlate in general with the male's health and vitality. A female whose mate choice is a healthy male is likely to produce more offspring that survive to reproduce.

Mate choice can also be influenced by imprinting, as revealed by experiments carried out with zebra finches. Both male and female zebra finches normally lack any feather crest on their head (Figure 51.17). To explore whether parental appearance affects mate preference in offspring independent of any genetic influence, researchers provided zebra finches with artificial ornamentation. A 2.5-cm-long red feather was taped to the forehead feathers of either or both zebra finch parents when their chicks were 8 days old, approximately 2 days before they opened their eyes. A control group of zebra finches were raised by unadorned parents. When the chicks matured, they were presented with prospective mates that were either artificially ornamented with a red feather or non-ornamented (Figure 51.18). Males showed no preference. Females also showed no preference if they were raised by a male parent that was not ornamented. However, females raised by an ornamented male parent preferred ornamented males as their own mates. Thus, female finches apparently take cues from their fathers in choosing mates.

Mate-choice copying, a behaviour in which individuals in a population copy the mate choice of others, has been studied in the guppy *Poecilia reticulata*. When a female guppy chooses between males with no other females present, the female almost always chooses the male with more orange colouration. To explore if the behaviour of other females could influence this preference, an experiment was set up using both living females and artificial model females (Figure 51.19). If a female guppy observed the model "courting" a male with less extensive orange

Offspring

Offspring

Mate preference of female offspring: ornamented male

Mate preference of female offspring: none

▲ Figure 51.18 **Sexual selection influenced by imprinting.** Experiments demonstrated that female zebra finch chicks that had imprinted on artificially ornamented fathers preferred ornamented males as adult mates. For all experimental groups, male offspring showed no preference for either ornamented or non-ornamented female mates.

Source: Re-printed with the permission of Dr. Klaudia White.

female preference below a certain threshold of difference, in this case for male colour.

Mate-choice copying, a form of social learning, has also been observed in several other fish and bird species. What is the selective pressure for such a mechanism? One possibility is that a female that mates with males that are attractive to other females increases the probability that her male offspring will also be attractive and have high reproductive success.

Male Competition for Mates The previous examples show how female choice can select for one best type of male in a given situation, resulting in low variation among males. Male competition for mates also can reduce variation among males. Such competition may involve *agonistic behaviour*, an often-ritualized contest that determines which competitor gains access to a resource, such as food or mates (**Figure 51.20**). The outcomes of such contests are often determined by strength or size, but the consequences may nevertheless be psychological rather than physical (see Figure 51.16).

markings, she often copied the preference of the model female. That is, the female chose the male that had been presented in association with a model female rather than a more orange alternative. The exceptions were also informative. Mate-choice behaviour typically did not change when the difference in colouration was particularly large. Mate-choice copying can thus mask genetically controlled

Despite the potential for male competition to select for reduced variation, behavioural and morphological variation in males is extremely high in some vertebrate species, including species of fish and deer, as well as in a wide variety of invertebrates. In some species, sexual selection

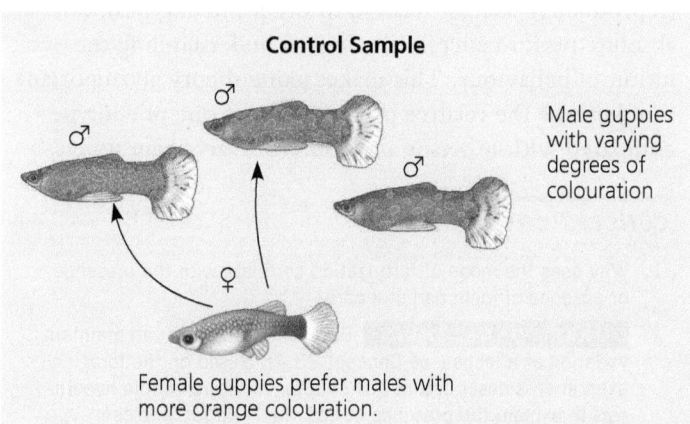

Control Sample

Male guppies with varying degrees of colouration

Female guppies prefer males with more orange colouration.

Experimental Sample

Female model in mock courtship with less orange male

Female guppies prefer males that are associated with another female.

▲ Figure 51.19 **Mate choice copying by female guppies (*Poecilia reticulata*).** In the absence of other females (control group), female guppies generally choose males with more orange colouration. However, when a female model is placed near one of the males (experimental group), female guppies often copy the apparent mate choice of the model, even if the male is less colourful than others. Guppy females ignored the mate choice of the model only if an alternative male had much more orange colouration.

Martin Harvey/Photolibrary/Getty Images

▲ **Figure 51.20 Agonistic interaction.** Male eastern grey kangaroos (*Macropus giganteus*) often "box" in contests that determine which male is most likely to mate with an available female. Typically, one male snorts loudly before striking the other around the head and throat with his forelimbs. Further snorting and cuffing, as well as grappling, often follow. If the male under attack does not retreat, the fight may escalate, with each male balancing on his tail while attempting to kick his rival with the sharp toenails of a hind leg.

has led to the evolution of alternative male mating behaviour and morphology. How do scientists analyze situations where more than one mating behaviour can result in successful reproduction? One approach relies on the rules that govern games.

Applying Game Theory

Often, the fitness of a particular behavioural phenotype is influenced by other behavioural phenotypes in the population. In studying such situations, behavioural ecologists use a range of tools, including game theory. Developed by American mathematician John Nash and others to model human economic behaviour, **game theory** evaluates alternative strategies in situations where the outcome depends on the strategies of all the individuals involved.

As an example of applying game theory to mating behaviour, let's consider the side-blotched lizard (*Uta stansburiana*) of California. Males can have orange, blue, or yellow throats (**Figure 51.21**). Each throat colour is associated with a different pattern of behaviour. Orange-throat males are the most aggressive and defend large territories that contain many females. Blue-throat males are also territorial but defend smaller territories and fewer females. Yellow-throats are nonterritorial males that mimic females and use

"sneaky" tactics to gain the chance to mate.

Evidence indicates that the mating success of each male lizard type is influenced by the relative abundance of the other types, an example of frequency-dependent selection. In one study population, the most frequent throat colouration

Erik Svensson

▲ **Figure 51.21 Male polymorphism in the side-blotched lizard (*Uta stansburiana*).** An orange-throat male, left; a blue-throat male, centre; a yellow-throat male, right.

changed over a period of several years from blue to orange to yellow and back to blue.

By comparing the competition between side-blotched lizard males to the children's game of rock–paper–scissors, scientists devised an explanation for the cycles of variation in the lizard population. In the game, paper defeats rock, rock defeats scissors, and scissors defeats paper. Each hand symbol thus wins one matchup but loses the other. Similarly, each type of male lizard has an advantage over one of the other two types. When blue-throats are abundant, they can defend the few females in their territories from the advances of the sneaky yellow-throat males. However, blue-throats cannot defend their territories against the hyperaggressive orange-throats. Once the orange-throats become the most abundant, the larger number of females in each territory provides the opportunity for the yellow-throats to have greater mating success. The yellow-throats become more frequent, but then give way to the blue-throats, whose tactic of guarding small territories once again allows them the most success.

Game theory provides a way to think about complex evolutionary problems in which relative performance (reproductive success relative to other phenotypes), not absolute performance, is the key to understanding the evolution of behaviour. This makes game theory an important tool because the relative performance of one phenotype compared with others is a measure of Darwinian fitness.

CONCEPT CHECK 51.3

1. Why does the mode of fertilization correlate with the presence or absence of male parental care?

2. **MAKE CONNECTIONS** Balancing selection can maintain variation at a locus (see Concept 23.4). Based on the foraging experiments described in this chapter, devise a simple hypothesis to explain the presence of both for^R and for^s alleles in natural fly populations.

3. **WHAT IF?** Suppose an infection in a side-blotched lizard population killed many more males than females. What would be the immediate effect on male competition for reproductive success?

For suggested answers, see Appendix A.

CONCEPT 51.4

Genetic analyses and the concept of inclusive fitness provide a basis for studying the evolution of behaviour

EVOLUTION We'll now explore issues related to the focus of Tinbergen's fourth question—the evolutionary history of behaviours. We will first look at examples that reveal the genetic underpinnings of behaviour. Next, we will examine the genetic variation underlying the evolution of particular behaviours. Finally, we will see how expanding the definition of fitness beyond individual survival can help explain "selfless" behaviour.

Genetic Basis of Behaviour

In exploring the behavioural basis of behaviour, we'll begin with the courtship behaviour of the male fruit fly, diagrammed in Figure 51.4. During courtship, the male fly carries out a complex series of actions in response to multiple sensory stimuli. Genetic studies have revealed that a single gene called *fru* controls this entire courtship ritual. If the *fru* gene is mutated to an inactive form, males do not court or mate with females. (The name *fru* is short for *fruitless*, reflecting the absence of offspring from the mutant males.) Normal male and female flies express distinct forms of the *fru* gene. When females are genetically manipulated to express the male form of *fru*, they court other females, performing the role normally played by the male. How can a single gene control so many behaviours and actions? Experiments carried out cooperatively in several laboratories demonstrated that *fru* is a master regulatory gene that directs the expression and activity of many genes with narrower functions. Together, genes that are controlled by the *fru* gene bring about sex-specific development of the fly nervous system. In effect, *fru* programs the fly for male courtship behaviour by overseeing a male-specific wiring of the central nervous system.

In many cases, differences in behaviour arise not from gene inactivation, but from variation in the activity or amount of a gene product. One striking example comes from the study of two related species of voles, which are small, mouse-like rodents. Male meadow voles (*Microtus pennsylvanicus*) are solitary and do not form lasting relationships with mates. Following mating, they pay little attention to their pups. In contrast, male prairie voles (*Microtus ochrogaster*) form a pair-bond with a single female after they mate (**Figure 51.22**). Male prairie voles hover over their young pups, licking them and carrying them, while acting aggressively toward intruders.

▲ **Figure 51.22 A pair of prairie voles (*Microtus ochrogaster*) huddling.** Male North American prairie voles associate closely with their mates, as shown here, and contribute substantially to the care of young.

Jennifer Jarvis

A peptide neurotransmitter is critical for the partnering and parental behaviour of male voles. Known as ADH or vasopressin (see Chapter 44), this peptide is released during mating and binds to a specific receptor in the central nervous system. When male prairie voles are given a drug that inhibits the brain receptor for vasopressin, they fail to form pair-bonds after mating.

The vasopressin receptor gene is much more highly expressed in the brain of prairie voles than in the brain of meadow voles. Testing the hypothesis that vasopressin receptor levels in the brain regulate postmating behaviour, researchers inserted the vasopressin receptor gene from prairie voles into meadow voles. The male meadow voles carrying this gene not only developed brains with higher levels of the vasopressin receptor but also showed many of the same mating behaviours as male prairie voles, such as pair-bonding. Thus, although many genes influence pair-bonding and parenting in voles, a change in vasopressin receptor levels is sufficient to alter the development of these behaviours.

Genetic Variation and the Evolution of Behaviour

Behavioural differences between closely related species, such as meadow and prairie voles, are common. Significant differences in behaviour can also be found *within* a species but are often less obvious. When behavioural variation between populations of a species corresponds to variation in environmental conditions, it may be evidence of past evolution.

Case Study: Variation in Prey Selection

An example of genetically based behavioural variation within a species involves prey selection by the western garter snake (*Thamnophis elegans*). The natural diet of this species differs widely across its range in California. Coastal populations feed predominantly on banana slugs (*Ariolimax californicus*) (Figure 51.23). Inland populations feed on frogs, leeches, and fish, but not on banana slugs. In fact, banana slugs are rare or absent in the inland habitats.

When researchers offered banana slugs to snakes from each wild population, most coastal snakes readily ate them, whereas inland snakes tended to refuse. To what extent does genetic variation contribute to a snake's fondness for banana slugs? To answer this question, researchers collected pregnant snakes from each wild population and housed them in separate cages in the laboratory. While still very young, the offspring were offered a small piece of banana slug on each of 10 days. More than 60% of the young snakes from coastal mothers ate banana slugs on 8 or more of the 10 days. In contrast, fewer than 20% of the young snakes from inland mothers ate a piece of banana slug even once. Perhaps not surprisingly, banana slugs thus appear to be a genetically acquired taste.

Patrick Gregory at the University of Victoria examined the feeding habits of three closely related species of garter snake living on Vancouver Island and found that banana slugs figured prominently in the diets of *T. elegans* and *T. ordinoides* but were not eaten at all by *T. sirtalis*, the common garter snake. On the other hand, *T. sirtalis* readily eats the extremely toxic rough-skinned newt (*Taricha*

▲ Figure 51.23 **Western garter snake from a coastal habitat eating a banana slug.** Experiments indicate that the preference of these snakes for banana slugs may be influenced mainly by genetics rather than by environment.

granulosa), an amphibian whose skin is so toxic that it has few natural predators. The newt's skin contains tetrodotoxin that paralyzes or kills most animals that eat it, except the common garter snake. These differences between species have presumably evolved in a similar fashion to the differences within populations of *T. elegans* when it comes to eating slugs.

How did a genetically determined difference in feeding preference come to match the snakes' habitats so well? It turns out that the coastal and inland populations also vary with respect to their ability to recognize and respond to odour molecules produced by banana slugs. Researchers hypothesize that when inland snakes colonized coastal habitats more than 10 000 years ago, some of them could recognize banana slugs by scent. Because these snakes took advantage of this food source, they had higher fitness than snakes in the population that ignored the slugs. Over hundreds or thousands of generations, the capacity to recognize the slugs as prey increased in frequency in the coastal population. The marked variation in behaviour observed today between the coastal and inland populations may be evidence of this past evolutionary change.

Case Study: Variation in Migratory Patterns

Another species suited to the study of behavioural variation is the blackcap (*Sylvia atricapilla*), a small migratory warbler. Blackcaps that breed in Germany generally migrate southwest to Spain and then south to Africa for the winter. In the 1950s, a few blackcaps began to spend their winters in Britain, and over time the population of blackcaps wintering in Britain grew to many thousands. Leg bands showed that some of these birds had migrated westward from central Germany. Why were there now two patterns of migration from Germany? To answer this question, researchers at the Max Planck Research centre in Radolfzell, Germany, devised a strategy to study migratory orientation in the laboratory (Figure 51.24). The results demonstrated that the two patterns of migration reflect genetic differences between the two populations.

The study of western European blackcaps indicated that the change in their migratory behaviour occurred both recently and rapidly. Before the year 1950, there were no known westward-migrating blackcaps in Germany. By the 1990s, westward migrants made up 7–11% of the blackcap populations of Germany. Once westward migration began, it persisted and increased in frequency, perhaps due to the widespread use of winter bird feeders in Britain, as well as shorter migration distances.

Altruism

We typically assume that behaviours are selfish; that is, they benefit the individual at the expense of others, especially

Figure 51.24 | Inquiry

Are differences in migratory orientation within a species genetically determined?

Experiment Peter Berthold and colleagues in southern Germany raised two sets of young birds for their study. One group consisted of the offspring of blackcaps captured while wintering in Britain and then bred in Germany in an outdoor cage. The other group consisted of young birds collected from nests near the laboratory and then raised in cages. In the autumn, Berthold's team placed the blackcaps captured in Britain and the young birds raised in cages in large, glass-covered funnel cages lined with carbon-coated paper for 1.5–2 hours. When the funnels were placed outside at night, the birds moved around, making marks on the paper that indicated the direction in which they were trying to "migrate."

Scratch marks

Source: Adaptations of photograph by Jonathan Blair from *Animal Behavior: An Evolutionary Approach,* 7th edition, by John Alcock. Copyright © 2002 by Sinauer Associates, Inc. Reprinted with permission.

Results The wintering adult birds captured in Britain and their laboratory-raised offspring both attempted to migrate to the west. In contrast, the young birds collected from nests in southern Germany attempted to migrate to the southwest.

Source: Adaptation of figure 1 from "Rapid Microevolution of Migratory Behaviour in a Wild Bird Species" by P. Berthold, et al., from *Nature,* December 1992, Volume 360(6405). Copyright © 1992 by Macmillan Publishers Ltd. Reprinted with permission.

Conclusion The young of the British blackcaps and the young birds from Germany (the control group) were raised under similar conditions but showed very different migratory orientations, indicating that migratory orientation has a genetic basis.

Source: Based on P. Berthold et al., Rapid microevolution of migratory behaviour in a wild bird species, *Nature* 360:668–690 (1992). © Jane B Reece

WHAT IF? *Suppose the birds had not shown a difference in orientation in these experiments. Could you conclude that the behaviour was not genetically based? Explain.*

competitors. For example, superior foraging ability by one individual may leave less food for others. The problem comes, however, with "unselfish" behaviours. How can such behaviours arise through natural selection? To answer this question, let's look more closely at some examples of unselfish behaviour and then consider how such behaviours might arise.

In discussing selflessness, we will use the term **altruism** to describe a behaviour that reduces an animal's individual fitness but increases the fitness of other individuals in the population. Richardson's ground squirrel (*Urocitellus richardsonii*), which lives on the short-grass prairies of southern Alberta and Saskatchewan, and the adjacent United States, is vulnerable to predators such as long-tailed weasels, badgers, hawks, and falcons. A squirrel that sees a predator approach often gives a high-pitched alarm call that alerts unaware individuals to retreat to their burrows. Note that for the squirrel that warns others, the conspicuous alarm behaviour increases the risk of being killed because it brings attention to the caller's location.

Another example of altruistic behaviour occurs in honeybee societies, in which the workers are sterile. The workers themselves never reproduce, but they labour on behalf of a single fertile queen. Furthermore, the workers sting intruders, a behaviour that helps defend the hive but results in the death of those workers.

Altruism is also observed in naked mole rats (*Heterocephalus glaber*), highly social rodents that live in underground chambers and tunnels in southern and northeastern Africa. The naked mole rat, which is almost hairless and nearly blind, lives in colonies of 75 to 250 or more individuals **(Figure 51.25)**. Each colony has only one reproducing female, the queen, who mates with one to three males, called kings. The rest of the colony consists of nonreproductive females and males who forage for underground roots and tubers and care for the queen, the kings, and new offspring. The nonreproductive individuals may sacrifice their own lives in trying to protect the

▲ **Figure 51.25 Naked mole rats, a species of colonial mammal that exhibits altruistic behaviour.** Pictured here is a queen nursing offspring while surrounded by other members of the colony.

Jennifer Jarvis

queen or kings from snakes or other predators that invade the colony.

Inclusive Fitness

How can a Richardson's ground squirrel, a worker honeybee, or a naked mole rat enhance its fitness by aiding members of the population that may be its closest competitors? How can altruistic behaviour be maintained by evolution if it does not enhance the survival and reproductive success of the self-sacrificing individuals?

The selection for altruistic behaviour is most readily apparent in the case of parents sacrificing for their offspring. When parents sacrifice their own well-being to produce and aid offspring, this actually increases the fitness of the parents because it maximizes their genetic representation in the population. However, individuals sometimes help others who are not their offspring.

Biologist William Hamilton proposed that an animal could increase its genetic representation in the next generation by "altruistically" helping close relatives other than its own offspring. Like parents and offspring, full siblings have half their genes in common. Therefore, selection might also favour helping siblings or helping one's parents produce more siblings. This idea led to Hamilton's idea of **inclusive fitness**, the total effect an individual has on proliferating its genes by producing its own offspring *and* by providing aid that enables other close relatives, who share many of those genes, to produce offspring.

Hamilton's Rule and Kin Selection

The power of Hamilton's hypothesis was that it provided a way to measure, or quantify, the effect of altruism on fitness. According to Hamilton, the three key variables in an act of altruism are the benefit to the recipient, the cost to the altruist, and the coefficient of relatedness. The benefit, B, is the average number of *extra* offspring that the beneficiary of an altruistic act produces. The cost, C, is how many *fewer* offspring the altruist produces. The **coefficient of relatedness**, r, equals the fraction of genes that, on average, are shared. Natural selection favours altruism when the benefit to the recipient multiplied by the coefficient of relatedness exceeds the cost to the altruist—in other words, when $rB > C$. This statement is called **Hamilton's rule**.

To better understand Hamilton's rule, let's apply it to a human population in which the average individual has two children. We'll imagine that a young man is close to drowning in heavy surf, and his sister risks her life to swim out and pull her sibling to safety. If the young man had drowned, his reproductive output would have been zero; but now, if we use the average, he can father two children. The benefit to the brother is thus two offspring ($B = 2$).

What about the risk taken by his sister? Let's say that the sister has a 25% chance of drowning in attempting to rescue her brother. We can then calculate the cost of the altruistic act to the sister as 0.25 times 2, the number of offspring she would be expected to have if she had stayed on shore ($C = 0.25 \times 2 = 0.5$). Finally, we note that a brother and sister share half their genes on average ($r = 0.5$). One way to see this is in terms of the segregation of homologous chromosomes that occurs during meiosis of gametes (Figure 51.26; see also Chapter 13).

We can now use our values of B, C, and r to evaluate whether natural selection would favour the altruistic act in our imaginary scenario. For the surf rescue, $rB = 0.5 \times 2 = 1$, whereas $C = 0.5$. Because rB is greater than C, Hamilton's rule is satisfied; thus, natural selection would favour this altruistic act of the sister attempting to save her brother. Averaging over many individuals and generations, any particular gene in a sister faced with this situation will be passed on to more offspring if she risks the rescue than if she does not. Furthermore, among genes propagated in this way may be some that contribute to altruistic behaviour. The natural selection that favours altruistic behaviour by enhancing reproductive success of relatives is called **kin selection**.

Kin selection weakens with hereditary distance. Siblings have an r of 0.5, but between an aunt and her niece, $r = 0.25$ (1/4), and between first cousins, $r = 0.125$ (1/8).

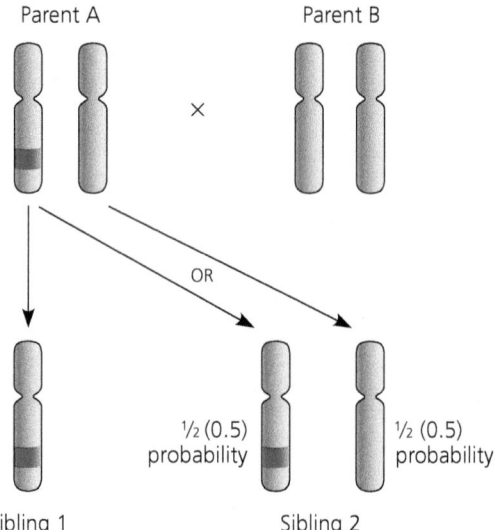

▲ Figure 51.26 **The coefficient of relatedness between siblings.** The red band indicates a particular allele (version of a gene) present on one chromosome, but not its homologue, in parent A. Sibling 1 has inherited the allele from parent A. There is a probability of ½ that sibling 2 will also inherit this allele from parent A. Any allele present on one chromosome of either parent will behave similarly. The coefficient of relatedness between the two siblings is thus ½, or 0.5.

WHAT IF? *The coefficient of relatedness of an individual to a full (nontwin) sibling or to either parent is the same, 0.5. Does this value also hold true in the cases of polyandry and polygamy?*

Notice that as the degree of relatedness decreases, the rB term in the Hamilton inequality also decreases. Would natural selection favour rescuing a cousin? Not unless the surf were less treacherous. For the original conditions, $rB = 0.125 \times 2 = 0.25$, which is only half the value of C (0.5). British geneticist J. B. S. Haldane appears to have anticipated these ideas when he jokingly stated that he would not lay down his life for one brother, but would do so for two brothers or eight cousins.

If kin selection explains altruism, then the examples of unselfish behaviour we observe among diverse animal species should involve close relatives. This is apparently the case, but often in complex ways. Like most mammals, female ground squirrels settle close to their site of birth, whereas males settle at distant sites (Figure 51.27). Since nearly all alarm calls are given by females, they are most likely aiding close relatives. In the case of worker bees, who are all sterile, anything they do to help the entire hive benefits the only permanent member who is reproductively active—the queen, who is their mother.

In the case of naked mole rats, DNA analyses have shown that all the individuals in a colony are closely related. Genetically, the queen appears to be a sibling, daughter, or mother of the kings, and the nonreproductive mole rats are the queen's direct descendants or her siblings. Therefore, when a nonreproductive individual enhances a queen's or king's chances of reproducing, the altruist increases the chance that some genes identical to its own will be passed to the next generation.

Reciprocal Altruism

Some animals occasionally behave altruistically toward others who are not relatives. A baboon may help an unrelated

S.J. Krasemann/Photolibrary/ Getty Images

▲ Figure 51.27 **Kin selection and altruism in Belding's ground squirrels.** This graph helps explain the male-female difference in altruistic behaviour of ground squirrels. Once weaned (pups are nursed for about one month), females are more likely than males to live near close relatives. Alarm calls that warn these relatives increase the inclusive fitness of the female altruist.

companion in a fight, or a wolf may offer food to another wolf even though they share no kinship. Such behaviour can be adaptive if the aided individual returns the favour in the future. This sort of exchange of aid, called **reciprocal altruism**, is commonly invoked to explain altruism that occurs between unrelated humans. Reciprocal altruism is rare in other animals; it is limited largely to species (such as chimpanzees) with social groups stable enough that individuals have many chances to exchange aid. It is generally thought to occur when individuals are likely to meet again and when there would be negative consequences associated with not returning favours to individuals who had been helpful in the past, a pattern of behaviour that behavioural ecologists refer to as "cheating."

Since cheating may benefit the cheater substantially, how could reciprocal altruism evolve? Game theory provides a possible answer in the form of a behavioural strategy called *tit for tat* devised in the early 1980s by Anatol Rapaport, then a professor of mathematics and psychology at the University of Toronto, in response to a contest on the evolution of cooperation. In the tit-for-tat strategy, an individual treats another in the same way it was treated the last time they met. Individuals adopting this behaviour are always altruistic, or cooperative, on the first encounter with another individual and will remain so as long as their altruism is reciprocated. When their cooperation is not reciprocated, however, individuals employing tit for tat will retaliate immediately but return to cooperative behaviour as soon as the other individual becomes cooperative. The tit-for-tat strategy has been used to explain the few apparently reciprocal altruistic interactions observed in animals—ranging from blood sharing between nonrelated vampire bats to social grooming in primates.

Evolution and Human Culture

Human culture is related to evolutionary theory in the discipline of **sociobiology**. The main premise of sociobiology is that certain behavioural characteristics exist because they are expressions of genes that have been perpetuated by natural selection. In his seminal 1975 book *Sociobiology: The New Synthesis*, E. O. Wilson speculated about the evolutionary basis of certain kinds of social behaviour. By including a few examples from human culture, he sparked a debate that remains heated today.

The spectrum of human social behaviours may be influenced by our genetic makeup, but this is very different from saying that genes are rigid determinants of behaviour. This distinction is at the core of the debate about evolutionary perspectives on human behaviour. Sceptics fear that evolutionary interpretations of human behaviour could be used to justify the status quo in human society, thus rationalizing current social injustices.

Evolutionary biologists argue that this is a gross oversimplification and misunderstanding of what the data tell us about human biology. Evolutionary explanations of human behaviour do not reduce us to robots stamped out of rigid genetic moulds. Just as individuals vary extensively in anatomical features, we should expect inherent variations in behaviour as well. Environment intervenes in the pathway from genotype to phenotype for physical traits and even more so for behavioural traits. And because of our capacity for learning and our versatility, human behaviour is probably more plastic than that of any other animal. Over our recent evolutionary history, we have built up a diversity of structured societies with governments, laws, cultural values, and religions that define what is acceptable behaviour and what is not, even when unacceptable behaviour might enhance an individual's Darwinian fitness. Perhaps it is our social and cultural institutions that make us distinct and that provide those qualities in which there is the least continuum between humans and other animals.

CONCEPT CHECK 51.4

1. Explain why geographic variation in garter snake prey choice might indicate that the behaviour evolved by natural selection.

2. **WHAT IF?** If an animal were unable to distinguish close from distant relatives, would the concept of inclusive fitness still be applicable? Explain.

3. **WHAT IF?** Suppose you applied Hamilton's logic to a situation in which one individual is past reproductive age. Could there still be a selection for an altruistic act?

For suggested answers, see Appendix A.

---

51 Chapter Review

Go to **MasteringBiology®** for Assignments, the eText, and the Study Area with Animations, Activities, Vocab Self-Quiz, and Practice Tests.

SUMMARY OF KEY CONCEPTS

CONCEPT 51.1

Discrete sensory inputs can stimulate both simple and complex behaviours (pp. 1197–1201)

- **Behaviour** is the sum of responses to external and internal stimuli and includes muscular as well as nonmuscular activity. Tinbergen developed a set of questions that highlight the complementary nature of two perspectives. Proximate, or "how," questions focus on the environmental stimuli, if any, that trigger a behaviour, as well as the genetic, physiological, and anatomical mechanisms underlying a behavioural act. Ultimate, or "why," questions address the evolutionary significance of a behaviour.

- A **fixed action pattern** is a largely invariant behaviour triggered by a simple cue known as a **sign stimulus**. Migratory movements involve navigation, which can be based on orientation relative to the sun, the stars, or Earth's magnetic field. Animal behaviour is sometimes synchronized to the daily, or circadian, cycle of light and dark in the environment or to environmental cues that cycle over the seasons.

- The transmission and reception of signals constitute animal **communication**. Animals use visual, auditory, chemical (usually olfactory), and tactile signals, sometimes as part of a stimulus-response chain that governs a complex behaviour. Chemical substances called pheromones transmit species-specific information through the environment in behaviours ranging from foraging to courtship.

? *How is migration based on circannual rhythms poorly suited for adaptation to global climate change?*

CONCEPT 51.2

Learning establishes specific links between experience and behaviour (pp. 1201–1206)

- **Cross-fostering studies** can be used to measure the influence of social environment and experience on behaviour.

- **Learning**, the modification of behaviour based on experience, can take many forms:

Imprinting

Forms of learning and problem solving

Spatial learning

Cognition

Associative learning

Social learning

? *How do imprinting in geese and song development in sparrows differ with regard to the resulting behaviour?*

CONCEPT 51.3

Selection for individual survival and reproductive success can explain most behaviours (pp. 1206–1212)

- An **optimal foraging model** is based on the idea that natural selection should favour foraging behaviour that minimizes the costs of foraging and maximizes the benefits.
- Sexual dimorphism correlates with the type of mating relationship between males and females. These include **monogamous** and **polygamous** mating systems. Variation in mating system and variation in the mode of fertilization affect certainty of paternity, which in turn has a significant influence on mating behaviour and parental care.
- **Game theory** provides a way of thinking about evolution in situations where the fitness of a particular behavioural phenotype is influenced by other behavioural phenotypes in the population.

? *In some spider species, the female eats the male immediately after copulation. How might you explain this behaviour from an evolutionary perspective?*

CONCEPT 51.4

Genetic analyses and the concept of inclusive fitness provide a basis for studying the evolution of behaviour (pp. 1213–1218)

- Genetic studies in insects have revealed the existence of master regulatory genes that control complex behaviours. Within the underlying hierarchy, multiple genes influence specific behaviours, such as a courtship song. Research with two species of voles has revealed that variation in a single gene can determine differences in complex behaviours involved in both mating and parenting.
- When behavioural variation within a species corresponds to variation in environmental conditions, it may be evidence of past evolution. Field and laboratory studies have documented the genetic basis for a change in migratory behaviour of certain birds and revealed behavioural differences in snakes that correlate with geographic variation in prey availability.
- On occasion, animals exhibit **altruism**. This behaviour can be explained by the concept of **inclusive fitness**, the total effect an individual has on proliferating its genes by producing its own offspring *and* by providing aid that enables close relatives to produce offspring. The **coefficient of relatedness** and **Hamilton's rule** provide a way of measuring the strength of the selective forces favouring altruism against the potential cost of the "selfless" behaviour. Kin selection favours altruistic behaviour by enhancing the reproductive success of relatives. Altruistic behaviour toward unrelated individuals can be adaptive if the aided individual returns the favour in the future, an exchange of aid called reciprocal altruism.

? *Suppose you studied the genetics of the lacewing courtship song, but not the effects of courtship mutations in flies or of variation in the vasopressin receptor gene of voles. What insight about the genetic basis of behaviour would you likely have missed?*

TEST YOUR UNDERSTANDING

LEVEL 1: KNOWLEDGE/COMPREHENSION

1. Which of the following is true of innate behaviours?
   a. Their expression is only weakly influenced by genes.
   b. They occur with or without environmental stimuli.
   c. They are expressed in most individuals in a population.
   d. They occur in invertebrates and some vertebrates but not mammals.

2. According to Hamilton's rule,
   a. natural selection does not favour altruistic behaviour that causes the death of the altruist.
   b. natural selection favours altruistic acts when the resulting benefit to the beneficiary, corrected for relatedness, exceeds the cost to the altruist.
   c. natural selection is more likely to favour altruistic behaviour that benefits an offspring than altruistic behaviour that benefits a sibling.
   d. the effects of kin selection are larger than the effects of direct natural selection on individuals.

3. Female spotted sandpipers aggressively court males and, after mating, leave the clutch of young for the male to incubate. This sequence may be repeated several times with different males until no available males remain, forcing the female to incubate her last clutch. Which of the following terms best describes this behaviour?
   a. polygyny
   b. polyandry
   c. promiscuity
   d. certainty of paternity

LEVEL 2: APPLICATION/ANALYSIS

4. A region of the canary forebrain shrinks during the nonbreeding season and enlarges when breeding season begins. This change is probably associated with the annual
   a. addition of new syllables to a canary's song repertoire.
   b. crystallization of subsong into adult songs.
   c. sensitive period in which canary parents imprint on new offspring.
   d. elimination of the memorized template for songs sung the previous year.

5. Although many chimpanzees live in environments containing oil palm nuts, members of only a few populations use stones to crack open the nuts. The likely explanation is that
   a. the behavioural difference is caused by genetic differences between populations.
   b. members of different populations have different nutritional requirements.
   c. the cultural tradition of using stones to crack nuts has arisen in only some populations.
   d. members of different populations differ in learning ability.

6. Which of the following is *not* required for a behavioural trait to evolve by natural selection?
   a. In each individual, the form of the behaviour is determined entirely by genes.
   b. The behaviour varies among individuals.
   c. An individual's reproductive success depends in part on how the behaviour is performed.
   d. Some component of the behaviour is genetically inherited.

LEVEL 3: SYNTHESIS/EVALUATION

7. **DRAW IT** You are considering two optimal foraging models for the behaviour of a mussel-feeding shorebird, the oystercatcher. In model A, the energetic reward increases solely with mussel size. In model B, you take into consideration that larger mussels are more difficult to open. Draw a graph of reward (energy benefit on a scale of 0–10) versus mussel length (scale of 0–70 mm) for each model. Assume that mussels under 10 mm

provide no benefit and are ignored by the birds. Also assume that mussels start becoming difficult to open when they reach 40 mm in length and impossible to open when 70 mm long. Considering the graphs you have drawn, how could you distinguish between the models by observation and measurement in the oystercatcher's habitat?

8. **EVOLUTION CONNECTION**
We often explain our behaviour in terms of subjective feelings, motives, or reasons, but evolutionary explanations are based on reproductive fitness. What is the relationship between the two kinds of explanation? For instance, is a human explanation for behaviour, such as "falling in love," incompatible with an evolutionary explanation?

9. **SCIENTIFIC INQUIRY**
Scientists studying scrub jays found that "helpers" often assist mated pairs of birds in raising their young. The helpers lack territories and mates of their own. Instead, they help the territory owners gather food for their offspring. Propose a hypothesis to explain what advantage there might be for the helpers to engage in this behaviour instead of seeking their own territories and mates. How would you test your hypothesis? If it is correct, what results would you expect your tests to yield?

10. **SCIENCE, TECHNOLOGY, AND SOCIETY**
Researchers are very interested in studying identical twins separated at birth and raised apart. So far, the data reveal that such twins frequently have similar personalities, mannerisms, habits, and interests. What general question do you think researchers hope to answer by studying such twins? Why do identical twins make good subjects for this research? What are the potential pitfalls of this research? What abuses might occur if the studies are not evaluated critically?

11. **WRITE ABOUT A THEME: INFORMATION**
Learning is defined as a change in behaviour based on experience. In a short essay (100–150 words), describe the role of heritable information in the acquisition of learning, using some examples from imprinting and associative learning.

12. **SYNTHESIZE YOUR KNOWLEDGE**

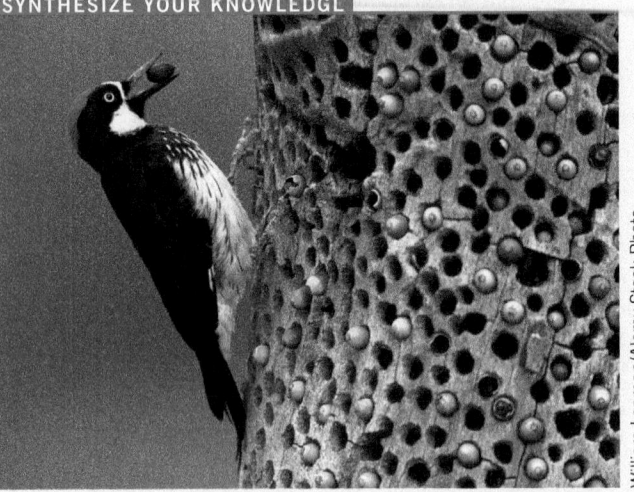

William Leaman/Alamy Stock Photo

Acorn woodpeckers (*Melanerpes formicivorus*) stash acorns in storage holes they drill in trees. When these woodpeckers breed, the offspring from previous years often help with parental duties. Activities of these nonbreeding helpers include incubating eggs and defending stashed acorns. What are some questions about the proximate and ultimate causation of these behaviours that a behavioural biologist might ask?

For selected answers, see Appendix A.

AN INTERVIEW WITH

Verena Tunnicliffe

Verena Tunnicliffe was born in Deep River, Ontario, did her undergraduate degree at McMaster University, and completed her Ph.D. at Yale University. She is currently a Professor at the University of Victoria and is a Canada Research Chair in Deep Ocean Research.

What questions are you trying to answer right now in your research?

After doing 35 years of research on the ocean, I have seen dramatic changes because of human impacts. Most of my research focuses on trying to develop good science behind conservation initiatives, trying to advise policy-making bodies, and working on issues that relate to deep sea and B.C. coastal conservation. We want to determine how we can manage the ocean in a way that people benefit and that the ecosystems can survive. We are looking at the impact of hypoxia (low oxygen) in the ocean, which is occurring due to climate change, and also looking at hydrothermal vents. Deep-sea mining will start in a couple of years, and hydrothermal vents are targeted for mining. We want to develop a full understanding of how hydrothermal vent ecosystems function in areas where people want to mine and determine which areas should be made into reserves.

> " I work on undersea volcanoes and I get to literally watch eruptions happen with the magma rolling out and toxic chemicals everywhere. You would think this is the last place on earth where you would find life, yet these spots are teeming with shrimp and fish. "

My grad student is working on a project with a giant mussel (*Bathymodiolus septemdierum*) that lives at hot vents throughout the Pacific Ocean and is one of the most widely distributed animals. It is only found at these hot vents, and yet we have no idea how it can get from one place to another. She is researching how that giant mussel reproduces and how it shares its genes with sites far away. We are focusing on that animal because it is abundant at sites that are targeted for mining, and we want to know how the population would keep going if its habitat were destroyed.

There is huge diversity that is completely unknown in the ocean. To date we have discovered almost 100 new species in my lab, but further diversity discovery remains important. The size of the deep sea is absolutely immense. Unanswered questions include: How does that ecosystem function? How do deep-sea communities connect to each other to maintain populations? If we do destroy part of the ecosystem through mining for ores and nodules or through fishing by trawling, how do we ensure that we protect the population integrity over large areas? These are questions that we need answers to when working in the international realm and trying to set guidelines for the high seas and protected areas.

What has surprised you most during your research?

I work on undersea volcanoes and I get to literally watch eruptions happen with the magma rolling out and toxic chemicals everywhere. You would think this is the last place on earth where you would find life, yet these spots are teeming with shrimp and fish. These little animals somehow know when an eruption is happening, and land on the volcanoes (some get fried in process), apparently targeting the food that is produced by bacteria there. It always amazes me that the limits to life are much more extreme than we think.

For a first-year student, what is the main "take-away" message from your research?

We have so many things left to learn on this planet. I work on the world's biggest ecosystem, and now that we are having international discussions about parks, conservation, and marine-protected areas, we find we know way too little. There is a huge opportunity for new research, not just science research, but understanding how humans interact with the oceans. There is so much that we need to understand.

What advice do you have for a student just starting out in introductory biology?

Follow your passion. Sometimes things will be tough, and the energy from your passion will help you get through it. Also, we really need science communicators, so think about your other talents (like photography or writing), and see how they might merge with the science that you are studying.

Source: Interview with Verena Tunnicliffe. Used with permission from Verena Tunnicliffe.

Science Source

MAKE CONNECTIONS

The Working Ecosystem

This Arctic tundra ecosystem teems with life in the short two-month growing season each summer. In ecosystems, organisms interact with each other and with the environment around them in diverse ways, including those illustrated here.

1 Caribou

2 Snow geese

Populations Are Dynamic (Chapter 53)

1 Populations change in size through births and deaths and through immigration and emigration. Caribou numbers rise and fall from year to year because changes in snowfall, food, and number of predators affect their birth and death rates. See Concept 53.1 and Figure 53.3.

2 Snow geese and many other species migrate to the Arctic each spring for the abundant food found there in summer. See Concept 51.1.

3 Birth and death rates influence the density of all populations. A warming climate will alter these rates, leading to higher densities of some species and lower densities of others. See Figure 53.18.

Arctic fox

3

4 Predation

Snow goose

Species Interact in Diverse Ways (Chapter 54)

4 Food webs describe the feeding interactions within a community. Arctic foxes, which are predators, kill and eat other animals, including snow goose chicks. Snow geese and caribou are animals that eat parts of plants or other primary producers, such as lichens. See Concept 54.1 and Figure 54.15.

5 In symbiosis, two or more species live in direct contact. For example, a lichen is a symbiosis between a fungus and an alga or cyanobacterium. See Concept 54.1 and Figures 31.22 and 31.23.

6 In competition, individuals seek to acquire the same limiting resources. For example, snow geese and caribou both eat cottongrass. See Concept 54.1.

Organisms Transfer Energy and Matter in Ecosystems (Chapter 55)

7 Primary producers convert the energy in sunlight to chemical energy through photosynthesis. Their growth is often limited by abiotic factors such as low temperatures and scarce soil nutrients. See Concept 55.2 and Figures 10.6 and 52.11.

8 Food chains are typically short in the tundra because primary production is low compared to other ecosystems. See Figure 54.14 and 54.15.

9 The transfer of energy from one trophic level to the next, from plants to herbivores or from herbivores to their predators, is usually less than 10%. See Figure 55.11.

10 Detritivores recycle chemical elements in dead organic matter back to primary producers. See Figures 55.3 and 55.4.

11 Chemical elements such as carbon and nitrogen move in cycles between the physical environment and organisms. See Figure 55.13.

Nitrogen cycle

N₂

11

Denitrification

Organisms   N fixation

Carbon cycle

CO₂

Cellular respiration

Photosynthesis

Secondary consumers (wolves)

8

9

Primary consumers (caribou)

Primary producers (plants and lichens)

Chemical elements

Detritivores (soil fungi and prokaryotes)

10

6 Competition

7

5 Symbiosis

Algal cell

Fungal hyphae   Lichen

52

An Introduction to Ecology and the Biosphere

▲ Figure 52.1 **Do songbirds bring Lyme disease to Canada?**

KEY CONCEPTS

52.1 Earth's climate varies by latitude and season and is changing rapidly

52.2 The structure and distribution of terrestrial biomes are controlled by climate and disturbance

52.3 Aquatic biomes are diverse and dynamic systems that cover most of Earth

52.4 Interactions between organisms and the environment limit the distribution of species

Discovering Ecology

In May of 1999, student volunteers helping with a survey of migrating songbirds on a coastal island near Nova Scotia got a surprise. While banding a warbler known as the common yellowthroat, *Geothlypis trichas* (Figure 52.1), a number of small ticks were seen under the bird's feathers. This was the first known arrival to the province of the blacklegged tick, *Ixodes scapularis*, a tick known to carry *Borrelia burgdorferi*, the bacterium that causes Lyme disease. Analysis showed that one of the ticks was indeed infected with *Borrelia*, and soon after, human cases of Lyme disease were detected in the province. Common yellowthroats overwinter in Central America and the southern United States, stopping to feed several times before reaching their breeding grounds in Canada. Could migratory songbirds be bringing Lyme disease north?

This discovery represented just one event in the spread of infected blacklegged ticks (photo lower left) into Canada. Lyme first emerged as a serious disease in the northeastern United States in the 1970s. Black-legged ticks (and *Borrelia*) were present in southern Ontario by the late 1980s, and are now established in every Canadian province. (A sister species, *Ixodes pacificus*, is found in British Columbia.) In most areas the ticks seem to be on a never-ending march

◀ **A blacklegged tick (*Ixodes scapularis*)**

into previously unoccupied territory. Why are ticks spreading north? Is a warming climate to blame? Where will they finally stop?

A central goal of the discipline of **ecology** (from the Greek *oikos*, home, and *logos*, study) is to discover how factors such as climate and interactions with other species influence the distribution and abundance of organisms. Ecological interactions occur at a hierarchy of scales that ecologists study, from single organisms to the globe **(Figure 52.2)**. Understanding what limits the distribution of the black-legged tick is of public health importance, as Lyme is a serious disease that can lead to debilitating joint pain and inflammation of the liver or meninges in humans. For other expansionist species such as the coyote, *Canis latrans,* we might be more interested in impacts on natural plant and animal communities (see Figure 52.17). Conservation concerns drive efforts to discover why the range occupied by the threatened wood turtle, *Glyptemys insculpta*, has been shrinking over the past decades (see Figure 52.15).

Ecology is a rigorous experimental science that requires a breadth of biological knowledge. Ecologists observe nature, generate hypotheses, manipulate environmental variables, and observe outcomes. In this chapter, we'll first consider how Earth's climate and other factors determine the location of major life zones on land and in the oceans. We'll then examine how ecologists investigate what controls the distribution of species. The next four chapters focus on population, community, ecosystem, and global ecology, as we explore how ecologists apply biological knowledge to predict the global consequences of human activities and to conserve Earth's biodiversity.

CONCEPT 52.1

Earth's climate varies by latitude and season and is changing rapidly

The most significant influence on the distribution of organisms on land and in the oceans is **climate**, the long-term, prevailing weather conditions in a given area. Four physical factors—temperature, precipitation, sunlight, and wind—are particularly important components of climate. In this section, we will describe climate patterns at two scales: **macroclimate**, patterns on the global, regional, and landscape level; and **microclimate**, very fine, localized patterns, such as those encountered by the community of organisms that live in the microhabitat beneath a fallen log. First let's examine Earth's macroclimate.

Global Climate Patterns

Global climate patterns are determined largely by the input of solar energy and Earth's movement in space. The

sun warms the atmosphere, land, and water. This warming establishes the temperature variations, cycles of air and water movement, and evaporation of water that cause dramatic latitudinal variations in climate. **Figure 52.3** on page 1227 summarizes Earth's climate patterns and how they are formed.

Regional and Local Effects on Climate

Climate patterns can be modified by many factors, including seasonal variation in climate, large bodies of water, and mountain ranges. We will examine each of these factors in more detail.

Seasonality

As described in **Figure 52.4** on page 1228, Earth's tilted axis of rotation and its annual passage around the sun cause strong seasonal cycles in middle to high latitudes. In addition to these global changes in day length, solar radiation, and temperature, the changing angle of the sun over the course of the year affects local environments. For example, the belts of wet and dry air on either side of the equator move slightly northward and southward with the changing angle of the sun, producing marked wet and dry seasons around 20° north and 20° south latitude, where many tropical deciduous forests grow. In addition, seasonal changes in wind patterns alter ocean currents, sometimes causing the upwelling of cold water from deep ocean layers. This nutrient-rich water stimulates the growth of phytoplankton and the organisms that feed on them. These upwelling zones make up only a few percent of ocean area but are responsible for more than a quarter of fish caught globally.

Bodies of Water

Ocean currents influence climate along the coasts of continents by heating or cooling overlying air masses that pass across the land. Coastal regions are also generally wetter than inland areas at the same latitude. The cool, misty climate produced by the cold California Current that flows southward along western North America supports a coniferous rain forest ecosystem along much of the continent's Pacific coast, from the Sitka spruce/western hemlock forests of the Haida Gwaii islands in northwestern British Columbia to the giant redwoods of northern California. High levels of precipitation and moderate temperatures make the coastal temperate rain forest one of the most productive ecosystems on the planet. In the Atlantic Ocean, the Labrador Current flows south from the coast of Greenland, cooling eastern Canada, while the Gulf Stream carries warm water from the equator to the western coasts of

Exploring The Scope of Ecological Research

Ecologists work at different levels of the biological hierarchy, from individual organisms to the planet. Here we present a sample research question for each level of the hierarchy.

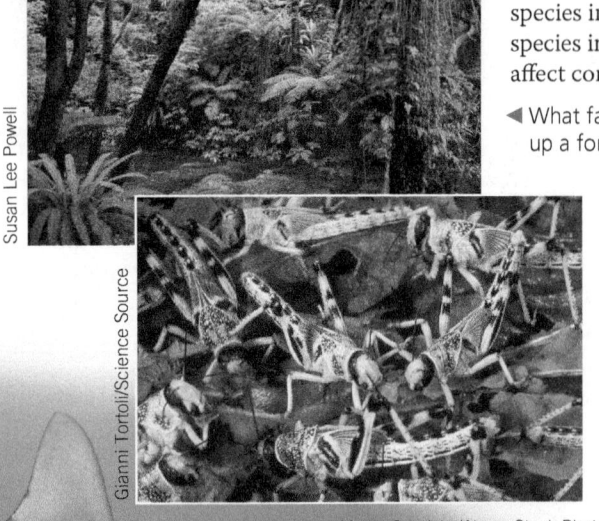

NASA

William D. Bachman/Science Source

B. Tharp/Science Source

Susan Lee Powell

Gianni Tortoli/Science Source

Martin Strmiska/Alamy Stock Photo

Global Ecology

The **biosphere** is the global ecosystem—the sum of all the planet's ecosystems and landscapes. **Global ecology** examines how the regional exchange of energy and materials influences the functioning and distribution of organisms across the biosphere.

◄ How does ocean circulation affect the global distribution of crustaceans?

Landscape Ecology

A **landscape** (or seascape) is a mosaic of connected eco-systems. Research in **landscape ecology** focuses on the factors controlling exchanges of energy, materials, and organisms across multiple ecosystems.

◄ To what extent do the trees lining a river serve as corridors of dispersal for animals?

Ecosystem Ecology

An **ecosystem** is the community of organisms in an area and the physical factors with which those organisms interact. **Ecosystem ecology** emphasizes energy flow and chemical cycling between organisms and the environment.

◄ What factors control photosynthetic productivity in a temperate grassland ecosystem?

Community Ecology

A **community** is a group of populations of different species in an area. **Community ecology** examines how species interactions, such as predation and competition, affect community structure and organization.

◄ What factors influence the diversity of species that make up a forest?

Population Ecology

A **population** is a group of individuals of the same species living in an area. **Population ecology** analyzes factors that affect population size and how and why it changes through time.

◄ What environmental factors affect the reproductive rate of locusts?

Organismal Ecology

Organismal ecology, which includes the subdisciplines of physiological, evolutionary, and behavioural ecology, is concerned with how an organism's structure, physiology, and behaviour meet the challenges posed by its environment.

◄ How do hammerhead sharks select a mate?

Exploring Global Climate Patterns

Latitudinal Variation in Sunlight Intensity

Earth's curved shape causes latitudinal variation in the intensity of sunlight. Because sunlight strikes the **tropics** (those regions that lie between 23.5° north latitude and 23.5° south latitude) most directly, more heat and light per unit of surface area are delivered there. At higher latitudes, sunlight strikes Earth at an oblique angle, and thus the light energy is more diffuse on Earth's surface.

Global Air Circulation and Precipitation Patterns

Intense solar radiation near the equator initiates a global pattern of air circulation and precipitation. High temperatures in the tropics evaporate water from Earth's surface and cause warm, wet air masses to rise and flow toward the poles. As the rising air masses cool, they release much of their water content, creating abundant precipitation in tropical regions. The high-altitude air masses, now dry, descend toward Earth around 30° north and south, absorbing moisture from the land and creating an arid climate conducive to the development of the deserts that are common at those latitudes. Some of the descending air then flows toward the poles. At latitudes around 60° north and south, the air masses again rise and release abundant precipitation (though less than in the tropics). Some of the cold, dry rising air then flows to the poles, where it descends and flows back toward the equator, absorbing moisture and creating the comparatively rainless and bitterly cold climates of the polar regions.

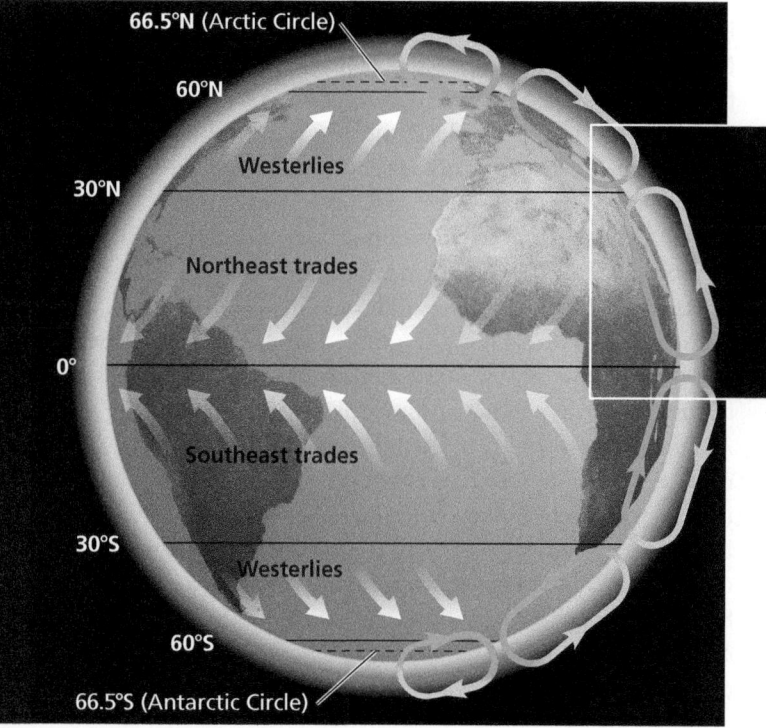

Air flowing close to Earth's surface creates predictable global wind patterns. As Earth rotates on its axis, land near the equator moves faster than that at the poles, deflecting the winds from the vertical paths shown above and creating the more easterly and westerly flows shown at left. Cooling trade winds blow from east to west in the tropics; prevailing westerlies blow from west to east in the temperate zones, defined as the regions between the Tropic of Cancer and the Arctic Circle and between the Tropic of Capricorn and the Antarctic Circle.

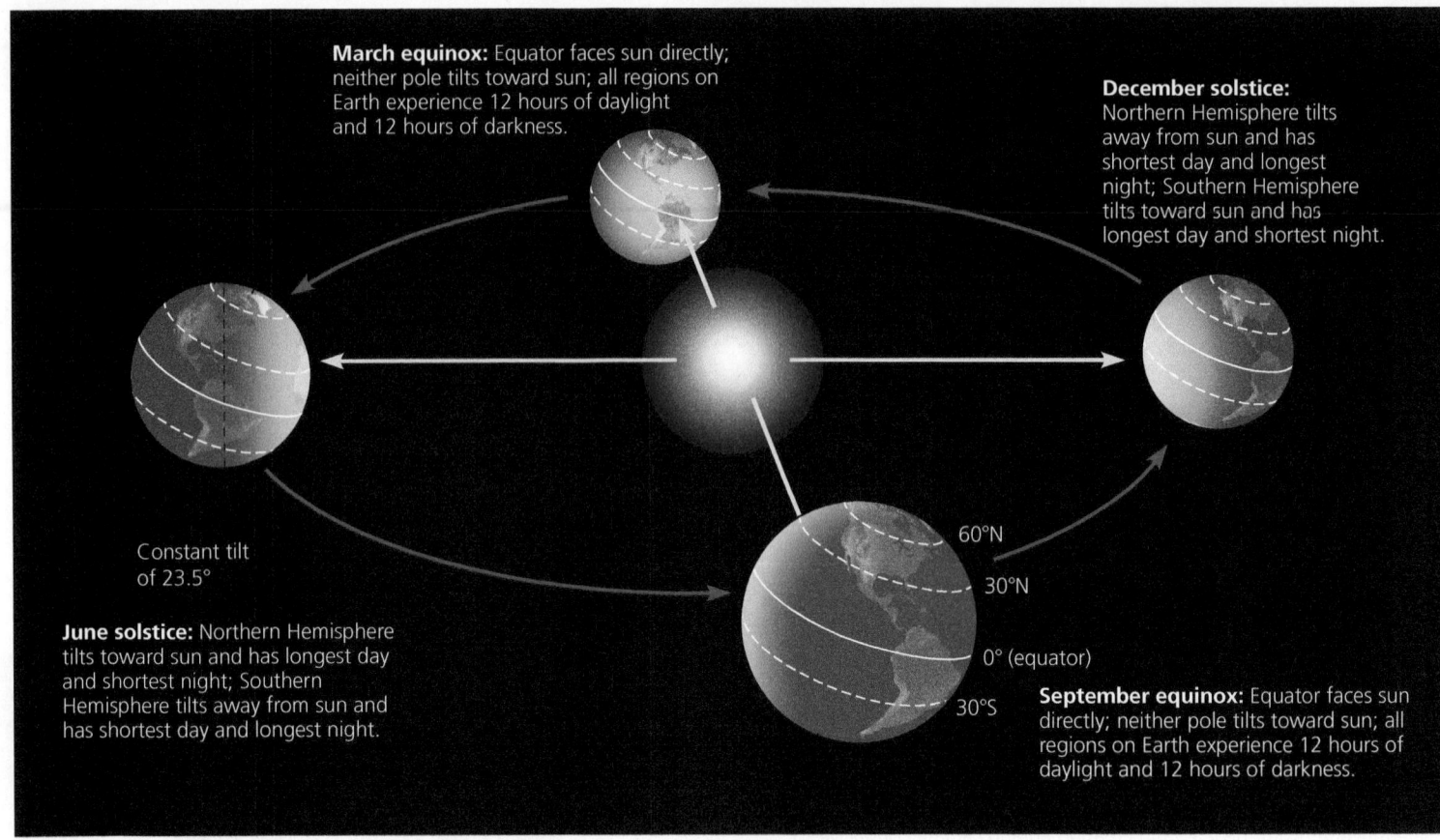

March equinox: Equator faces sun directly; neither pole tilts toward sun; all regions on Earth experience 12 hours of daylight and 12 hours of darkness.

December solstice: Northern Hemisphere tilts away from sun and has shortest day and longest night; Southern Hemisphere tilts toward sun and has longest day and shortest night.

Constant tilt of 23.5°

June solstice: Northern Hemisphere tilts toward sun and has longest day and shortest night; Southern Hemisphere tilts away from sun and has shortest day and longest night.

60°N
30°N
0° (equator)
30°S

September equinox: Equator faces sun directly; neither pole tilts toward sun; all regions on Earth experience 12 hours of daylight and 12 hours of darkness.

▲ **Figure 52.4 Seasonal variation in sunlight intensity.** Because Earth is tilted on its axis relative to its plane of orbit around the sun, the intensity of solar radiation varies seasonally. This variation is smallest in the tropics and increases toward the poles.

Europe (**Figure 52.5**). As a result, northwestern Europe has warmer winters than the Maritime provinces of Canada, which lie much further south.

Because of the high specific heat of water (see Chapter 3), oceans and large lakes tend to moderate the climate of nearby land. During a hot day, when land is warmer than the water, air over the land heats up and rises, drawing a cool breeze from the water across the land (**Figure 52.6**). In contrast, because temperatures drop more quickly over land than over water at night, air over the now warmer water rises, drawing cooler air from the land back out over the water and replacing it with warmer air from offshore. This local moderation of climate can be limited to the coast itself, however. In regions such as southern California and southwestern Australia, cool, dry ocean breezes in summer are warmed when they contact the land, absorbing moisture and creating a hot, arid climate just a few kilometres inland (see Figure 3.5). This climate pattern also occurs around the Mediterranean Sea, which gives it the name *Mediterranean climate*.

Mountains

Mountains also influence air flow over land. When warm, moist air approaches a mountain, the air rises and cools,

releasing moisture on the windward side of the peak (see Figure 52.6). On the leeward side, cooler, dry air descends, absorbing moisture and producing a "rain shadow." This leeward rain shadow determines where many deserts are found, including the Great Basin and the Mojave Desert of western North America, the Gobi Desert of Asia, and the small deserts found in the southwest corners of some Caribbean islands. The same mechanism produces the dry, warm chinook winds of southern Alberta that can melt snowpacks and raise winter temperatures from −20°C to +15°C over a few hours.

Mountains also affect the amount of sunlight reaching an area and thus the local temperature and rainfall. South-facing slopes in the Northern Hemisphere receive more sunlight than north-facing slopes and are therefore warmer and drier. These physical differences influence species distributions locally. In many mountains of western North America, spruce and other conifers grow on the cooler north-facing slopes, but shrubby, drought-resistant plants inhabit the south-facing slopes. In addition, every 1000-m increase in elevation produces an average temperature drop of approximately 6°C, equivalent to that produced by an 880-km increase in latitude. This is one reason that high-elevation communities at one latitude can be similar to those at lower elevations much farther from the equator.

▲ **Figure 52.5 Global circulation of surface water in the oceans.** Water is warmed at the equator and flows north and south toward the poles, where it cools. Note the similarities between the direction of water circulation in the gyres and the direction of the trade winds in Figure 52.3.

Microclimate

Many features in the environment influence microclimate by casting shade, altering evaporation from soil, or changing wind patterns. Forest trees often moderate the microclimate below them. Cleared areas therefore typically experience greater temperature extremes than the forest interior because of greater solar radiation and wind currents that arise from the rapid heating and cooling of open land. Within a forest, low-lying ground is usually wetter than higher ground and tends to be occupied by different tree species. A log or large stone can shelter organisms such as salamanders, worms, and insects, buffering them from the extremes of temperature and moisture. Every

▼ **Figure 52.6 How large bodies of water and mountains affect climate.** This figure illustrates what can happen on a hot summer day.

❷ Air that encounters mountains flows upward, cools at higher altitudes, and releases water as precipitation.

❶ Cool air flows inland from the water, moderating temperatures near the shore.

❸ Less moisture is left in the air reaching the leeward side, which therefore has little precipitation. This rain shadow can create a desert on the back side of the mountain range.

Leeward side of mountains

Mountain range

Ocean

environment on Earth is characterized by a mosaic of small-scale differences in **abiotic**, or nonliving, factors: the chemical and physical attributes, such as temperature, light, water, and nutrients, that influence the distribution and abundance of organisms. Later in this chapter, we will also examine how **biotic**, or living, factors—similarly influence the distribution and abundance of life on Earth.

Global Climate Change

Because climatic variables affect the geographic ranges of most plants and animals, any large-scale change in Earth's climate profoundly affects the biosphere. In fact, such a large-scale climate "experiment" is already under way, a topic we will examine in more detail in Chapter 56. The burning of fossil fuels and deforestation are increasing the concentrations of carbon dioxide and other greenhouse gases in the atmosphere. As a result, Earth has warmed an average of 0.8°C since 1900 and is projected to warm 1–6°C more by the year 2100.

One way to predict the possible effects of future climate change on geographic ranges is to look back at the changes that have occurred in temperate regions since the last ice age ended. Until about 16 000 years ago, continental glaciers covered much of North America and Eurasia. As the climate warmed and the glaciers retreated, tree distributions expanded northward. A detailed record of these changes is captured in fossil pollen deposited in lakes and ponds. If

---

▼ Figure 52.7 | **Inquiry**

Will the distribution of sugar maple "keep up" with global warming?

Sugar maple migrated north relatively quickly after the last ice age, its dispersal aided by its winged seeds. As the climate warms over the next 50 years, sugar maple is predicted to occupy much of northern Ontario and Quebec (see map below). Sugar maple is already advancing upslope in mountainous areas, but at a slower pace than predicted by temperature alone. Carissa Brown at Memorial University conducted experiments in southern Quebec to find out what was inhibiting upslope migration by sugar maple.

Experiment Brown buried pots containing soil *within* the range of sugar maple, at the *edge*, and 100 m *upslope* of its current range on Mont Mégantic. She then placed a known number of maple seeds on the soil and covered them with leaf litter. Half the pots were enclosed in cages (1 cm mesh) to exclude small mammals.

Source: Courtesy of *Canadian Geographic.*

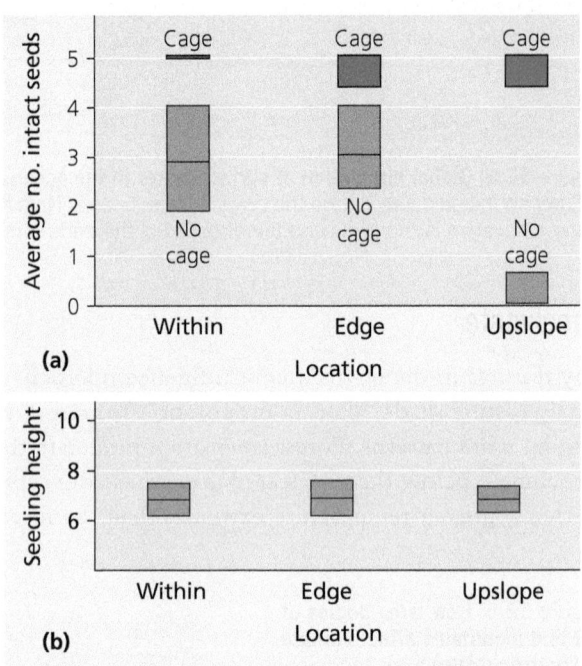

Results Seedlings grew to similar heights at all elevations (lower panel in graph above). Seed survival (no. intact seeds) was also about the same at all elevations if pots were caged (top graph, in blue). However, few seeds in uncaged pots survived in the upslope location, where the seeds were eaten by voles and mice. In the graph above, horizontal black lines are mean values and the boxes show the 25th and 75th percentiles.

Conclusion Seed predation, not just climate, currently limits the elevational distribution of sugar maple on Mont Mégantic. If biotic interactions are also important at the northern edge of its current range, sugar maple may not be able to migrate north as quickly as the climate warms.

Source: Based on C.D. Brown and M. Vellend, Non-climatic constraints on upper elevational plant range expansion under climate change. *Proceedings of the Royal Society B* 281:20141779. © Jane B Reece.

Randall Rosiere/Public Domain

▲ Sugar maple

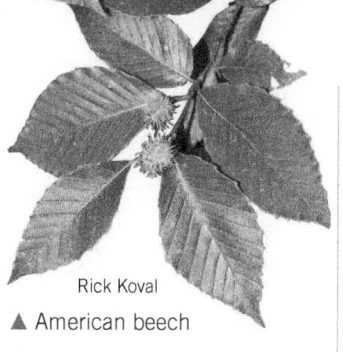

Rick Koval

▲ American beech

researchers can determine the climatic limits of current distributions of organisms, they can make predictions about how those distributions may change with continued climatic warming.

A big question is whether species will be able to shift their distributions quickly enough as the climate changes. Some plants may be limited by the ability of their seeds to disperse long distances. After the last ice age, sugar maple, (*Acer saccharum*), a species with winged seeds, expanded rapidly northward. In contrast, the northward range expansion of the American beech (*Fagus grandifolia*), whose seeds lack wings, was delayed for thousands of years. Even species that can disperse easily may not be able to keep up with current rates of climate change, however, if other factors inhibit their establishment in new habitat (Figure 52.7).

Changes in the distributions of species are already evident in many well-studied groups of terrestrial, marine, and freshwater organisms, consistent with the signature of a warmer world. In many places, tree line, the zone where northern coniferous forest grades into tundra, is advancing north and moving up mountain slopes. Some species of birds are breeding further north, and butterflies and moths have expanded their ranges to higher latitudes. Marine fish, including Atlantic cod (*Gadhus morhua*) and herring (*Clupea harengus*), also shift their distributions north and south in response to changes in sea temperature. As the Arctic Ocean warms, there may be increased opportunity for species to disperse between the Pacific and Atlantic Oceans. Scientists have reported that a Pacific diatom species, *Neodenticula seminae*, recently colonized the Atlantic Ocean for the first time in 800 000 years. As Arctic sea ice has receded in the past decade, the increased flow of water from the Pacific swept these diatoms around Canada and into the Atlantic, where they quickly became established. The observation that many species are on the move in the face of climate change illustrates the importance of climate in determining species distributions, a topic we will explore further in the next section.

CONCEPT 52.2

The structure and distribution of terrestrial biomes are controlled by climate and disturbance

Throughout this text, you have seen many examples of how climate and other factors influence where individual species are found on Earth (see Figure 30.7, for instance). We turn now to the role of climate in determining the nature and location of Earth's **biomes**, major life zones characterized by vegetation type (in terrestrial biomes) or by the physical environment (in aquatic biomes). We first examine the influence of climate on terrestrial biomes, surveying aquatic systems later in the chapter.

Climate and Terrestrial Biomes

Because of the latitudinal patterns of climate described in Figure 52.3, terrestrial biomes show strong latitudinal patterns (Figure 52.8). The importance of climate can be highlighted by plotting the annual mean temperature versus annual mean precipitation for the different terrestrial biomes (Figure 52.9). Notice, for instance, that the range of precipitation in northern coniferous and temperate forests is similar but that temperate forests are generally warmer. Grasslands are typically drier than either kind of forest, and deserts are drier still.

Factors other than mean temperature and precipitation also play a role in determining where biomes exist. For example, some areas in North America with a particular combination of temperature and precipitation support a temperate broadleaf forest, but other areas with similar values for these variables support a coniferous forest (see the

▲ Figure 52.8 **The distribution of major terrestrial biomes.** Although biomes are mapped here with sharp boundaries, biomes actually grade into one another, sometimes over large areas.

Tropical forest
Savanna
Desert
Chaparral
Temperate grassland
Temperate broadleaf forest
Northern coniferous forest
Tundra
High mountains
Polar ice

▲ Figure 52.9 **Annual climate (temperature and precipitation) regulates biome distribution in North America.** The areas plotted here encompass the ranges of annual mean temperature and precipitation in the biomes.

INTERPRET THE DATA *Some arctic tundra ecosystems receive as little rainfall as deserts but have much more dense vegetation. What climatic factor might account for this difference? Explain.*

overlap in Figure 52.9). How might we explain this variation? First, remember that the graph is based on annual *averages*. Often, however, the *pattern* of climatic variation is as important as the average climate. Some areas may receive regular precipitation throughout the year, whereas other areas may have distinct wet and dry seasons. A similar phenomenon may occur for temperature. In addition, other abiotic characteristics, such as the type of bedrock in an area, may greatly affect mineral nutrient availability and soil structure, which in turn affect the kind of vegetation that can grow.

General Features of Terrestrial Biomes

Most terrestrial biomes are named for major physical or climatic features and for their predominant vegetation. Temperate grasslands, for instance, are generally found in middle latitudes, where the climate is more moderate than in the tropics or polar regions, and are dominated by various grass species (see Figure 52.8). Each biome is also characterized by microorganisms, fungi, and animals adapted to that particular environment. Temperate grasslands are more likely than temperate forests to be populated by large grazing mammals and to have arbuscular mycorrhizal fungi (see Figure 37.13).

Although Figure 52.8 shows distinct boundaries between the biomes, terrestrial biomes usually grade into each other without sharp boundaries. The area of intergradation, called an **ecotone**, may be wide or narrow.

Vertical layering is an important feature of terrestrial biomes, and the shapes and sizes of plants largely define that layering. In many forests, the layers from top to bottom consist of the upper **canopy**, the low-tree layer, the shrub understory, the ground layer of herbaceous plants, the forest floor (litter layer), and the root layer. Nonforest biomes have similar, though usually less pronounced, layers. Grasslands have an herbaceous layer of grasses and forbs (small broadleaf plants), a litter layer, and a root layer. Layering of vegetation provides many different habitats for animals, which sometimes exist in well-defined feeding groups, from the insectivorous birds and bats that feed above canopies to the small mammals, numerous worms, and arthropods that search for food in the litter and root layers below.

The species composition of each kind of biome varies from one location to another. For instance, in the northern coniferous forest (taiga) of North America, red spruce is common in the east but does not occur in most other areas, where black spruce and white spruce are abundant. As Figure 52.10 shows, cacti living in deserts of North and South America appear very similar to plants called euphorbs found in African deserts. However, cacti and euphorbs belong to different evolutionary lineages, and their similarities are due to convergent evolution (see Concept 22.3).

Disturbance and Terrestrial Biomes

Biomes are dynamic, and disturbance rather than stability tends to be the rule. In ecological terms, **disturbance** is an event such as a storm, fire, or human activity that changes a community, removing organisms from it and altering resource availability. For instance, frequent fires can kill woody plants and keep a savanna from becoming the woodland that climate alone would support. Hurricanes and other storms create openings for new species in many tropical and temperate forests. Fires and outbreaks of pests, such as pine beetles and spruce budworms, produce gaps in northern coniferous forests that allow deciduous species, including aspen and birch, to grow. As a result of disturbances, biomes often exhibit extensive patchiness, with several different communities represented in a single area.

In many biomes, even the dominant plants depend on periodic disturbance. Natural wildfires are an integral component of grasslands, savannas, chaparral, and many coniferous forests. In North America, fires are no longer common across much of the Great Plains because tallgrass prairie ecosystems have been converted to agricultural fields that rarely burn. However, the lodgepole pine forests (*Pinus contorta latifolia*) that blanket much of the Rocky Mountains in Alberta and British Columbia are dependent on fire. Lodgepole pine produces cones that open only if exposed to high temperatures. Seeds are released after a stand of trees is destroyed by fire, and germinate and grow to form a new lodgepole pine forest. Decades of fire suppression altered this natural process in much of our forested land. In many areas, forest managers have begun to use programs of prescribed (controlled) fires to mimic the natural fire regime. Currently, another type of natural disturbance is affecting coniferous forests in Western Canada (see Concept 56.4). Mountain pine beetles (*Dendroctonus ponderosae*) are attacking and killing older trees, opening gaps in the forest that will likely be colonized by other species of plants and trees, increasing the diversity of the forest.

Figure 52.11 summarizes the major features of terrestrial biomes. As you read about the characteristics of each biome, remember that humans have altered much of Earth's surface, replacing natural communities with urban and agricultural ones. Natural grassland has been preserved in only a few places, such as the Grasslands National Park in southern Saskatchewan, for example, and little remains of the original temperate broadleaf forest in eastern North America.

CONCEPT CHECK 52.2

1. **INTERPRET THE DATA** Based on Figure 52.9, what mainly differentiates temperate grassland from temperate broadleaf forest?
2. Identify the natural biome in which you live, and summarize its abiotic and biotic characteristics. Do these reflect your actual surroundings? Explain.
3. **WHAT IF?** If global warming increases average temperatures on Earth by 4°C in this century, predict which biome is most likely to replace tundra in some locations as a result. Explain your answer.

For suggested answers, see Appendix A.

▼ Figure 52.10 **Convergent evolution in a cactus and a euphorb.** *Cereus peruvianus*, a cactus, is found in the Americas; *Euphorbia canariensis*, a euphorb, is native to the Canary Islands, off the northwest coast of Africa.

◄ *Cereus* sp.

Euphorbia ► *canariensis*

Krystyna Szulecka/Alamy

Exploring Terrestrial Biomes

Tropical Forest

Distribution Tropical forest occurs in equatorial and subequatorial regions.

Precipitation In **tropical rain forests**, rainfall is relatively constant, about 200–400 cm annually. In **tropical dry forests**, precipitation is highly seasonal, about 150–200 cm annually, with a six- to seven-month dry season.

Temperature High year-round, averaging 25–29°C with little seasonal variation.

Plants Tropical forests are vertically layered, and competition for light is intense. Layers in rain forests include trees that grow above a closed canopy, the canopy trees, one or two layers of subcanopy trees, and layers of shrubs and herbs (small, nonwoody plants). There are generally fewer layers in tropical dry forests. Broadleaf evergreen trees are dominant in tropical rain forests, whereas many tropical dry forest trees drop their leaves during the dry season. Epiphytes such as bromeliads and orchids generally cover tropical forest trees but are less abundant in dry forests. Thorny shrubs and succulent plants are common in some tropical dry forests.

Animals Earth's tropical forests are home to millions of species, including an estimated 6–8 million still undescribed species of insects, spiders, and other arthropods. In fact, animal diversity is higher in tropical forests than in any other terrestrial biome. The animals, including amphibians, birds and other reptiles, mammals, and arthropods, are adapted to the vertically layered environment and are often inconspicuous.

Human Impact Humans long ago established thriving communities in tropical forests. Rapid population growth leading to agriculture and development is now destroying many tropical forests.

Siepmann/Alamy

A tropical rain forest in Costa Rica

Desert

Distribution **Deserts** occur in bands near 30° north and south latitude or at other latitudes in the interior of continents (for instance, the Gobi Desert of north-central Asia).

Precipitation Precipitation is low and highly variable, generally less than 30 cm per year.

Henk Meijer/Alamy Stock Photo

Temperature Temperature is variable seasonally and daily. Maximum air temperature in hot deserts may exceed 50°C; minimum night temperature in some cold deserts may fall below −30°C.

Plants Desert landscapes are dominated by low, widely scattered vegetation; the proportion of bare ground is high compared with other terrestrial biomes. The plants include succulents such as cacti or euphorbs, deeply rooted shrubs, and herbs that grow during the infrequent moist periods. Desert plant adaptations include tolerance of heat and dessication, water storage, and reduced leaf surface area. Physical defences, such as spines, and chemical defences, such as toxins in the leaves of shrubs, are common. Many of the plants exhibit C_4 or CAM photosynthesis.

Animals Common desert animals include snakes and lizards, scorpions, ants, beetles, migratory and resident birds, and seed-eating rodents. Many species are nocturnal. Water conservation is a common adaptation, with some small mammal species surviving solely on metabolic water obtained by oxidizing food molecules in seeds.

Human Impact Long-distance transport of water and deep groundwater wells have allowed humans to maintain substantial populations in deserts. Urbanization and conversion to irrigated agriculture have reduced the natural biodiversity of some deserts.

Organ Pipe Cactus National Monument, Arizona

Savanna

Distribution **Savanna** occurs in equatorial and subequatorial regions.

Precipitation Seasonal rainfall averages 30–50 cm per year. The dry season can last up to eight or nine months.

Temperature The savanna is warm year-round, averaging 24–29°C, but with somewhat more seasonal variation than in tropical forests.

Plants The scattered trees found at different densities in the savanna often are thorny and have small leaves, an apparent adaptation to the relatively dry conditions. Fires are common in the dry season, and the dominant plant species are fire-adapted and tolerant of seasonal drought. Grasses and small nonwoody plants called forbs, which make up most of the ground cover, grow rapidly in response to seasonal rains and are tolerant of grazing by large mammals and other herbivores.

Animals Large plant-eating mammals, such as wildebeests and zebras, and predators, including lions and hyenas, are common inhabitants. However, the dominant herbivores are actually insects, especially termites. During seasonal droughts, grazing mammals often migrate to parts of the savanna with more forage and scattered watering holes.

Robert Harding/Alarry

A savanna in Kenya

Human Impact There is evidence that the earliest humans lived in savannas. Fires set by humans may help maintain this biome, though overly frequent fires reduce tree regeneration by killing the seedlings and saplings. Cattle ranching and overhunting have led to declines in large-mammal populations.

Chaparral

Distribution This biome occurs in midlatitude coastal regions on several continents, and its many names reflect its widespread distribution: **chaparral** in North America, *matorral* in Spain and Chile, *garigue* and *maquis* in southern France, and *fynbos* in South Africa.

The California Chaparral Institute

Precipitation Precipitation is highly seasonal, with rainy winters and dry summers. Annual precipitation generally falls within the range of 30–50 cm.

Temperature Fall, winter, and spring are cool, with average temperatures in the range of 10–12°C. Average summer temperature can reach 30°C, and daytime maximum temperature can exceed 40°C.

Plants Chaparral is dominated by shrubs and small trees, along with many kinds of grasses and herbs. Plant diversity is high, with many species confined to a specific, relatively small geographic area. Adaptations of the woody plants to drought include their tough evergreen leaves, which reduce water loss. Adaptations to fire are also prominent. Some of the shrubs produce seeds that will germinate only after a hot fire; food reserves stored in their fire-resistant roots enable them to resprout quickly and use nutrients released by the fire.

Animals Native mammals include browsers, such as deer and goats, that feed on twigs and buds of woody vegetation, and various species of small mammals. Chaparral areas also support many species of amphibians, birds and other reptiles, and insects.

Human Impact Chaparral areas have been heavily settled and reduced through conversion to agriculture and urbanization. Humans contribute to the fires that sweep across the chaparral.

An area of chaparral in California

Exploring Terrestrial Biomes

Temperate Grassland

Distribution The veldts of South Africa, the *puszta* of Hungary, the pampas of Argentina and Uruguay, the steppes of Russia, and the plains and prairies of central North America are examples of **temperate grasslands**.

Precipitation Precipitation is often highly seasonal, with relatively dry winters and wet summers. Annual precipitation generally averages between 30 and 100 cm. Periodic drought is common.

Temperature Winters are generally cold, with average temperatures falling below –10°C. Summers, with average temperatures often approaching 30°C, are hot.

Plants The dominant plants are grasses and forbs, which vary in height from a few centimetres to 2 m in tallgrass prairie. Many grassland plants have adaptations that help them survive periodic, protracted droughts and fire. For example, grasses can sprout quickly following fire. Grazing by large mammals helps prevent establishment of woody shrubs and trees.

Animals Native mammals include large grazers such as bison and wild horses. Temperate grasslands are also inhabited by a wide variety of burrowing mammals, such as prairie dogs in North America.

Hemis/Alamy Stock Photo

Grasslands National Park, Saskatchewan

Human Impact Deep, fertile soils make temperate grasslands ideal places for agriculture, especially for growing grains. As a consequence, most grassland in North America and much of Eurasia has been converted to farmland. In some drier grasslands, cattle and other grazers have turned parts of the biome into desert.

Northern Coniferous Forest

Distribution Extending in a broad band across northern North America and Eurasia to the edge of the arctic tundra, the **northern coniferous forest**, or *taiga*, is the largest terrestrial biome on Earth.

Precipitation Annual precipitation generally ranges from 30 to 70 cm, and periodic droughts are common. However, some coastal coniferous forests of the U.S. Pacific Northwest are temperate rain forests that may receive over 300 cm of annual precipitation.

Bent Nordeng/Shutterstock

Temperature Winters are usually cold; summers may be hot. Some areas of coniferous forest in Siberia typically range in temperature from –50°C in winter to over 20°C in summer.

Plants Northern coniferous forests are dominated by cone-bearing trees, such as pine, spruce, fir, and hemlock, some of which depend on fire to regenerate. The conical shape of many conifers prevents too much snow from accumulating and breaking their branches, and their needle- or scale-like leaves reduce water loss. The diversity of plants in the shrub and herb layers of these forests is lower than in temperate broadleaf forests.

Animals While many migratory birds nest in northern coniferous forests, other species reside there year-round. Mammals include large herbivores such as deer and moose, and their predators, wolves and bears. Periodically, outbreaks of herbivorous insects destroy vast tracts of forest.

Human Impact Although they have not been as heavily settled by human populations, northern coniferous forests are being logged at an alarming rate, and the old-growth stands of these trees may soon disappear.

A coniferous forest in Norway

Temperate Broadleaf Forest

Distribution **Temperate broadleaf forest** is found mainly at midlatitudes in the Northern Hemisphere, with smaller areas in Chile, South Africa, Australia, and New Zealand.

Precipitation Precipitation can average from about 70 to over 200 cm annually. Significant amounts fall during all seasons, including summer rain and, in some forests, winter snow.

Temperature Winter temperatures average 0°C. Summers, with temperatures up to 35°C, are hot and humid.

Plants A mature temperate broadleaf forest has distinct vertical layers, including a closed canopy, one or two strata of understory trees, a shrub layer, and an herb layer. There are few epiphytes. The dominant plants in the Northern Hemisphere are deciduous trees, which drop their leaves before winter, when low temperatures would reduce photosynthesis and make water uptake from frozen soil difficult. In Australia, evergreen eucalyptus trees dominate these forests.

Animals In the Northern Hemisphere, many mammals hibernate in winter, while many bird species migrate to warmer climates. Mammals, birds, and insects make use of all the vertical layers of the forest.

A temperate broadleaf forest in New Jersey

Human Impact Temperate broadleaf forest has been heavily settled on all continents. Logging and land clearing for agriculture and urban development cleared virtually all the original deciduous forests in North America. However, much agricultural land was abandoned as people moved to the cities over the past 150 years, and temperate forests are recovering in much of their former range.

Tundra

Distribution **Tundra** covers expansive areas of the Arctic, amounting to 20% of Earth's land surface. High winds and low temperatures produce similar plant communities, called *alpine tundra*, on very high mountaintops at all latitudes, including the tropics.

Precipitation Precipitation averages from 20 to 60 cm annually in arctic tundra but may exceed 100 cm in alpine tundra.

Temperature Winters are cold, with averages in some areas below −30°C. Summer temperatures generally average less than 10°C.

Plants The vegetation of tundra is mostly herbaceous, consisting of a mixture of mosses, grasses, and forbs, along with some dwarf shrubs and trees and lichens. A permanently frozen layer of soil called permafrost restricts the growth of plant roots.

Animals Large grazing musk oxen are resident, while caribou and reindeer are migratory. Predators include bears, wolves, and foxes. Many bird species migrate to the tundra for summer nesting.

Human Impact Tundra is sparsely settled but has become the focus of significant mineral and oil extraction in recent years.

Alpine tundra (fall foliage) in the Yukon Territory

CONCEPT 52.3

Aquatic biomes are diverse and dynamic systems that cover most of Earth

Unlike terrestrial biomes, aquatic biomes are characterized primarily by their physical environment. They also show far less latitudinal variation, with all types found across the globe. Ecologists distinguish between freshwater and marine biomes on the basis of physical and chemical differences. Marine biomes generally have salt concentrations that average 3%, whereas freshwater biomes are usually characterized by a salt concentration of less than 0.1%.

The oceans make up the largest marine biome, covering about 75% of Earth's surface. Because of their vast size, they greatly impact the biosphere. Water evaporated from the oceans provides most of the planet's rainfall, and ocean temperatures have a major effect on global climate and wind patterns (see Figure 52.3). Marine algae and photosynthetic bacteria also supply a substantial portion of the world's oxygen and consume large amounts of atmospheric carbon dioxide.

Freshwater biomes are closely linked to the soils and biotic components of the surrounding terrestrial biome. The particular characteristics of a freshwater biome are also influenced by the patterns and speed of water flow and the climate to which the biome is exposed.

Zonation in Aquatic Biomes

Many aquatic biomes are physically and chemically stratified (layered), vertically and horizontally, as illustrated for both a lake and a marine environment in **Figure 52.12**. Energy from sunlight is absorbed by the water itself and by photosynthetic organisms, so its intensity decreases rapidly with depth. Ecologists distinguish between the upper **photic zone**, where there is sufficient light for photosynthesis, and the lower **aphotic zone**, where little light penetrates. The photic and aphotic zones together make up the **pelagic zone**. Deep in the aphotic zone lies the **abyssal zone**, the part of the ocean 2000–6000 m below the surface. At the bottom of all aquatic biomes, deep or shallow, is the **benthic zone**. Made up of sand and organic and inorganic sediments, the benthic zone is occupied by communities of organisms collectively called the **benthos**. A major source of food for many benthic species is dead organic matter called **detritus**, which "rains" down from the productive surface waters of the photic zone.

Thermal energy from sunlight warms surface waters to whatever depth the sunlight penetrates, but the deeper waters remain quite cold. In the ocean and in most lakes, a narrow layer of abrupt temperature change called a **thermocline** separates the more uniformly warm upper layer from more uniformly cold deeper waters. Lakes tend to be particularly layered with respect to temperature, especially

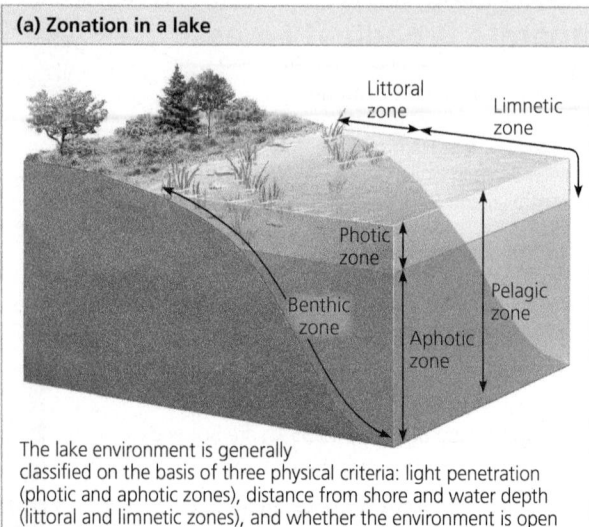

▼ Figure 52.12 **Zonation in aquatic environments.**

(a) Zonation in a lake

The lake environment is generally classified on the basis of three physical criteria: light penetration (photic and aphotic zones), distance from shore and water depth (littoral and limnetic zones), and whether the environment is open water (pelagic zone) or on the bottom (benthic zone).

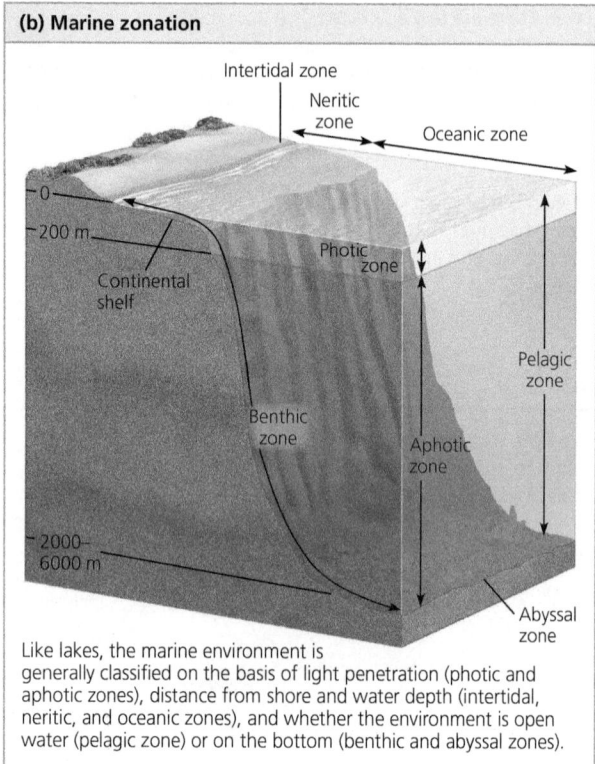

(b) Marine zonation

Like lakes, the marine environment is generally classified on the basis of light penetration (photic and aphotic zones), distance from shore and water depth (intertidal, neritic, and oceanic zones), and whether the environment is open water (pelagic zone) or on the bottom (benthic and abyssal zones).

during summer and winter, but many temperate lakes undergo a semiannual mixing of their waters as a result of changing temperature profiles (**Figure 52.13**). This **turnover**, as it is called, sends oxygenated water from a lake's surface to the bottom and brings nutrient-rich water from the bottom to the surface in both spring and autumn. Thermoclines are also important in the ocean. In tropical oceans, a strong shallow thermocline (25 to 200 m deep) tends to prevent deeper nutrient-rich water from reaching the surface. However, currents bring deep water to the surface in certain areas, a process known as upwelling. Upwelling areas

① In winter, the coldest water in the lake (0°C) lies just below the surface ice; water becomes progressively warmer at deeper levels of the lake, typically 4°C at the bottom.

② In spring, the surface water warms to 4°C and mixes with the layers below, eliminating thermal stratification. Spring winds help mix the water, bringing oxygen to the bottom and nutrients to the surface.

③ In summer, the lake regains a distinctive thermal profile, with warm surface water separated from cold bottom water by a narrow vertical zone of abrupt temperature change, called a thermocline.

④ In autumn, as surface water cools rapidly, it sinks beneath the underlying layers, remixing the water until the surface begins to freeze and the winter temperature profile is reestablished.

▲ Figure 52.13 **Seasonal turnover in lakes with winter ice cover.** Because of the seasonal turnover shown here, lake waters are well oxygenated at all depths in spring and autumn; in winter and summer, when the lake is stratified by temperature, oxygen concentrations are lower in deeper waters and higher near the surface of the lake.

tend to be very productive. For example, upwelling along the coast of Peru results in an ecosystem with abundant plankton and fish and is thus an important foraging location for marine mammals such as sperm whales.

In both freshwater and marine environments, communities are distributed according to water depth, degree of light penetration, distance from shore, and whether they are found in open water or near the bottom. Marine communities, in particular, illustrate the limitations on species distribution that result from these abiotic factors. Plankton and many fish species occur in the relatively shallow photic zone (see Figure 52.12b). Because water absorbs light so well and the ocean is so deep, most of the ocean volume is virtually devoid of light (the aphotic zone) and harbours relatively little life. **Figure 52.14** explores the main characteristics of Earth's major aquatic biomes.

CONCEPT CHECK 52.3

The first two questions refer to Figure 52.14.

1. Why are phytoplankton, and not benthic algae or rooted aquatic plants, the dominant photosynthetic organisms of the oceanic pelagic zone?

2. **MAKE CONNECTIONS** Many organisms living in estuaries experience freshwater and saltwater conditions each day with the rising and falling of tides. Based on what you learned in Concept 44.1, explain how these changing conditions challenge the survival of these organisms.

3. **WHAT IF?** Water leaving a reservoir behind a dam is often taken from deep layers of the reservoir. Would you expect fish found in a river below a dam in summer to be species that prefer colder or warmer water than fish found in an undammed river? Explain.

For suggested answers, see Appendix A.

CONCEPT **52.4**

Interactions between organisms and the environment limit the distribution of species

So far in this chapter we've examined Earth's climate and the characteristics of terrestrial and aquatic biomes. We've also introduced the range of biological levels at which ecologists work (see Figure 52.2). In this section we will examine how ecologists determine what factors control the distribution of species: *where* a species occurs and *why* it is not found elsewhere.

Species distributions are a consequence of both ecological and evolutionary interactions through time. The differential survival and reproduction of individuals that lead to evolution occur in *ecological time*, the minute-to-minute time frame of interactions between organisms and the environment. Through natural selection, organisms adapt to their environment over the time frame of many generations, in *evolutionary time*, and these adaptations can sometimes allow species to expand their ranges to occupy new types of habitats. One example of how events in ecological time have led to evolution is the selection for beak depth in Galápagos finches (see Figure 1.23). On the island of Daphne Major, finches with larger, deeper beaks were better able to survive during a drought because they could eat the large, hard seeds that were available. Finches with shallower beaks, which required smaller, softer seeds that were in short supply, were less likely to survive and reproduce. Because beak depth is hereditary in this species, the generation of finches born after the drought had beaks that were

Exploring Aquatic Biomes

Lakes

Physical Environment Standing bodies of water range from ponds a few square metres in area to lakes covering thousands of square kilometres. Light decreases with depth, creating stratification (see Figure 52.12a). Temperate lakes may have a seasonal thermocline (see Figure 52.13); tropical lowland lakes have a thermocline year-round.

Chemical Environment The salinity, oxygen concentration, and nutrient content differ greatly among lakes and can vary with season. Oligotrophic lakes are nutrient-poor and generally oxygen-rich; eutrophic lakes are nutrient-rich and often depleted of oxygen in the deepest zone in summer and if covered with ice in winter. The amount of decomposable organic matter in bottom sediments is low in oligotrophic lakes and high in eutrophic lakes; high rates of decomposition in deeper layers of eutrophic lakes cause periodic oxygen depletion.

Geologic Features Oligotrophic lakes may become more eutrophic over time as runoff adds sediments and nutrients. They tend to have less surface area relative to their depth than eutrophic lakes.

Photosynthetic Organisms Rooted and floating aquatic plants live in the **littoral zone**,

An oligotrophic lake in Jasper National Park, Alberta

Susan Lee Powell

the shallow, well-lit waters close to shore. Farther from shore, where water is too deep to support rooted aquatic plants, the **limnetic zone** is inhabited by a variety of phytoplankton, including cyanobacteria.

Heterotrophs In the limnetic zone, small drifting heterotrophs, or zooplankton, graze on the phytoplankton. The benthic zone is inhabited by assorted invertebrates whose species composition depends partly on oxygen levels. Fishes live in all zones, if sufficient oxygen is present.

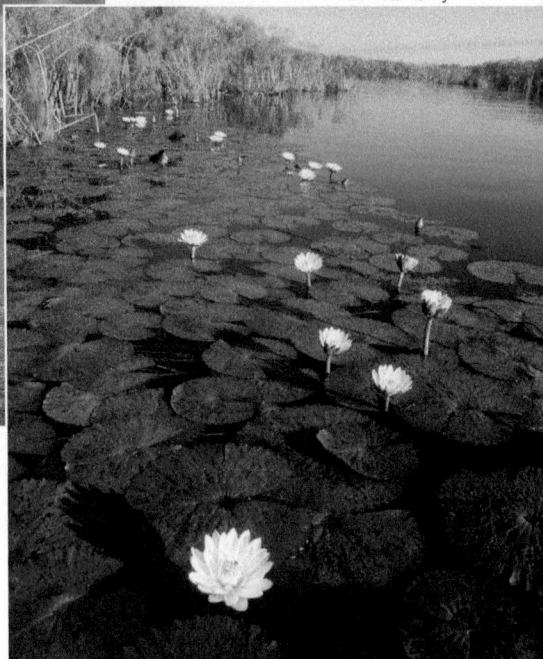

AfriPics/Alamy

A eutrophic lake in the Okavango Delta, Botswana

Human Impact Runoff from fertilized land and dumping of wastes lead to nutrient enrichment (eutrophication) which can produce algal blooms, oxygen depletion, and fish kills.

Wetlands

Physical Environment A **wetland** is a habitat that is inundated by water at least some of the time and that supports plants adapted to water-saturated soil. Some wetlands are inundated at all times, whereas others flood infrequently.

Chemical Enviroment Because of high organic production by plants and decomposition by microbes and other organisms, both the water and the soils are periodically low in dissolved oxygen. Wetlands have a high capacity to filter dissolved nutrients and chemical pollutants.

Geologic Features *Basin wetlands* develop in shallow basins, ranging from upland depressions to filled-in lakes and ponds. *Riverine wetlands* develop along shallow and periodically flooded banks of rivers and streams. *Fringe wetlands* occur along the coasts of large lakes and seas, where water flows back and forth because of rising lake levels or tidal action.

David Tipling/Nature Picture Library

Photosynthetic Organisms Wetlands are among the most productive biomes on Earth. Typical wetland plants include cattails, sedges, and sphagnum moss. A few tree species, such as tamarack and black spruce, have adaptations that allow them to grow in water-saturated soils.

Heterotrophs Wetlands are home to a communities of invertebrates, birds, and other organisms. Wetlands are home to communities of invertebrates, birds, and other organisms. Herbivores such as crustaceans, insects and muskrats, consume living algae and plants, Many aquatic insect larvae are detritivores that consume dead plant matter (detritus). Carnivores may include dragonflies, frogs, alligators, herons, and otters.

Human Impact Draining and filling have destroyed up to 90% of wetlands that formerly helped to purify water and reduce peak flooding.

A basin wetland in the United Kingdom

Streams and Rivers

Physical Environment The most prominent physical characteristic of streams and rivers is their current. Headwater streams are generally cold, clear, turbulent, and swift. Farther downstream, where numerous tributaries may have joined to form a river, the water is generally warmer and often more turbid because of suspended sediment.

Chemical Environment The underlying soil and rocks strongly influence the nutrient content and the pH (acidity) of streams and rivers. Headwaters are usually rich in oxygen. Downstream water may be oxygen-depleted where nutrients and organic material enter the river or stream as urban wastewater or agricultural runoff.

Geologic Features Headwater stream channels are often narrow, have a rocky bottom, and alternate between shallow sections and deeper pools. The downstream stretches of rivers are generally wide and meandering. River bottoms are often silty from sediments deposited over long periods of time.

Edmund Lowe Photography/Shutterstock

A small stream in the temperate rain forest of British Columbia

Photosynthetic Organisms Periphyton (diatoms and other algae attached to rocks) are usually important in smaller streams. Large rivers are often rich in phytoplankton.

Heterotrophs A great diversity of fishes and invertebrates inhabit unpolluted rivers and streams. In streams flowing through temperate or tropical forests, organic matter from terrestrial vegetation is the primary source of food for aquatic consumers.

Photononstop/Superstock

The Loire river (in France) far from its headwaters

Human Impact Municipal, agricultural, and industrial pollution degrade water quality and kill aquatic organisms. Damming and flood control impair the natural functioning of stream and river ecosystems and threaten migratory species such as salmon.

Estuaries

Physical Environment An **estuary** is a transition area between river and sea. Seawater flows up the estuary channel during a rising tide and flows back down during the falling tide. Often, higher-density seawater occupies the bottom of the channel and mixes little with the lower-density river water at the surface.

Chemical Environment Salinity varies spatially within estuaries, from nearly that of fresh water to that of seawater. Salinity also varies with the rise and fall of the tides. Nutrients from the river make estuaries, like wetlands, among the most productive biomes.

Byrne, Ted

Geologic Features Estuarine flow patterns combined with the sediments carried by river and tidal waters create a complex network of tidal channels, islands, natural levees, and mudflats.

Photosynthetic Organisms Saltmarsh grasses and algae, including phytoplankton, are the major producers in estuaries.

Heterotrophs Estuaries support an abundance of worms, oysters, crabs, and many fish species that humans consume. Many marine invertebrates and fishes use estuaries as a breeding ground or migrate through them to freshwater habitats upstream. Estuaries are also crucial feeding areas for waterfowl and some marine mammals.

Human Impact Filling, dredging, and pollution from upstream have disrupted estuaries worldwide. Some, such as the one shown in the photo to the left, have recently been protected by law.

Musquash Estuary, a Marine Protected Area in the Bay of Fundy, New Brunswick

Exploring Aquatic Biomes

Intertidal Zones

Physical Environment An **intertidal zone** is periodically submerged and exposed by the tides, twice daily on most marine shores. Upper zones experience longer exposures to air and greater variations in temperature and salinity. Changes in physical conditions from the upper to the lower intertidal zones limit the distributions of many organisms to particular strata.

Chemical Environment Oxygen and nutrient levels are generally high and are renewed with each turn of the tides.

Geologic Features The substrates of intertidal zones, which are generally either rocky or sandy, select for particular behaviour and anatomy among intertidal organisms. The configuration of bays or coastlines influences the magnitude of tides and the relative exposure of intertidal organisms to wave action.

Photosynthetic Organisms A high diversity and biomass of attached marine algae inhabit rocky intertidal zones, especially in the lower zone. Sandy intertidal zones exposed to vigorous wave action generally lack attached plants or algae, while sandy intertidal zones in protected bays or lagoons often support rich beds of seagrass and algae.

Heterotrophs Many of the animals in rocky intertidal environments, including the seastar and sea anemones shown in the photograph, have structural adaptations that enable them to attach to the hard substrate. The composition, density, and diversity of animals change markedly from the upper to the lower intertidal zones. Many of the animals in sandy or muddy intertidal zones, such as worms, clams, and predatory crustaceans, bury themselves and feed as the tides bring sources of food. Other common animals are sponges, mussels, barnacles, and small fishes.

Human Impact Oil pollution has disrupted many intertidal areas. The construction of rock walls and barriers to reduce erosion from waves and storm surges has disrupted this zone in some locations.

Keith Douglas/All Canada Photos

Rocky intertidal zone near Bamfield Marine Station on Vancouver Island

Oceanic Pelagic Zone

Physical Environment The **oceanic pelagic zone** is a vast realm of open blue water, constantly mixed by wind-driven oceanic currents. Because of higher water clarity, the photic zone extends to greater depths than in coastal marine waters.

Chemical Environment Oxygen levels are generally high. Nutrient concentrations are generally lower than in coastal waters. Because they are thermally stratified year-round, some tropical areas of the oceanic pelagic zone have lower nutrient concentrations than temperate oceans. Turnover between fall and spring renews nutrients in the photic zones of temperate and high-latitude ocean areas.

Geologic Features This biome covers approximately 70% of Earth's surface and has an average depth of nearly 4000 m. The deepest point in the ocean is more than 10 000 m beneath the surface.

Photosynthetic Organisms The dominant photosynthetic organisms are phytoplankton, including photosynthetic bacteria, that drift with the oceanic currents. Spring turnover renews nutrients in temperate oceans, producing a surge of phytoplankton growth. Because of the large extent of this biome, photosynthetic plankton account for about half of the photosynthetic activity on Earth.

Heterotrophs The most abundant heterotrophs in this biome are zooplankton. These protists, worms, copepods, shrimp-like krill, jellies, and small larvae of invertebrates and fishes graze on photosynthetic plankton. The oceanic pelagic zone also include free-swimming animals, such as large squids, fishes, sea turtles, and marine mammals.

Human Impact Overfishing has depleted fish stocks in all Earth's oceans, which have also been polluted by waste dumping.

Tatonka/Shutterstock

Open ocean near Iceland

Coral Reefs

Physical Environment **Coral reefs** are formed largely from the calcium carbonate skeletons of corals. Shallow reef-building corals live in the photic zone of relatively stable tropical marine environments with high water clarity, primarily on islands and along the edge of some continents. They are sensitive to temperatures below about 18–20°C and above 30°C. Deep-sea coral reefs, found between 200 and 1500 m deep, are less known than their shallow counterparts but harbor as much diversity as many shallow reefs do.

Chemical Environment Corals require high oxygen levels and are excluded by high inputs of fresh water and nutrients.

Geologic Features Corals require a solid substrate for attachment. A typical coral reef begins as a *fringing reef* on a young, high island, forming an offshore *barrier reef* later in the history of the island and becoming a *coral atoll* as the older island submerges.

A coral reef in the Red Sea

Photosynthetic Organisms Unicellular dinoflagellates live within the tissues of the corals, forming a mutualistic relationship that provides the corals with organic molecules. Diverse multicellular red and green algae growing on the reef also contribute substantial amounts of photosynthesis.

Heterotrophs Corals, a diverse group of cnidarians (see Chapter 33), are themselves the predominant animals on coral reefs. However, fish and invertebrate diversity is exceptionally high. Overall animal diversity on coral reefs rivals that of tropical forests.

Human Impact Collecting of coral skeletons and overfishing have reduced populations of corals and reef fishes. Global warming and pollution may be contributing to large-scale coral death. Development of coastal mangroves for aquaculture has also reduced spawning grounds for many species of reef fishes.

Marine Benthic Zone

Physical Environment The **marine benthic zone** consists of the seafloor below the surface waters of the coastal, or **neritic**, zone and the offshore pelagic zone (see Figure 52.12b). Except for shallow, near-coastal areas, the marine benthic zone receives no sunlight. Water temperature declines with depth, while pressure increases. As a result, organisms in the very deep benthic, or abyssal, zone are adapted to continuous cold (about 3°C) and very high water pressure.

Chemical Environment Except in areas of organic enrichment, oxygen is usually present at sufficient concentrations to support diverse animal life.

Geologic Features Soft sediments cover most of the benthic zone. However, there are areas of rocky substrate on reefs, submarine mountains, and new oceanic crust.

Autotrophs Photosynthetic organisms, mainly seaweeds and filamentous algae, are limited to shallow benthic areas with sufficient light to support them. Unique assemblages of organisms, such as those shown in the photo, are found near **deep-sea hydrothermal vents** on mid-ocean ridges. In these dark, hot environments, the food producers are chemoautotrophic prokaryotes (see Chapter 27) that obtain energy by oxidizing H_2S formed by a reaction of the hot water with dissolved sulphate (SO_4^{2-}).

Heterotrophs Neritic benthic communities include numerous invertebrates and fishes. Beyond the photic zone, most consumers depend entirely on organic matter raining down from above. Among the animals of the deep-sea hydrothermal vent communities are giant tube worms (pictured at left), some more than 1 m long. They are nourished by chemoautotrophic prokaryotes that live as symbionts within their bodies. Many other invertebrates, including arthropods and echinoderms, are also abundant around the hydrothermal vents.

Human Impact Overfishing has decimated important benthic fish populations, such as the cod of the Grand Banks off Newfoundland. Dumping of organic wastes has created oxygen-deprived benthic areas.

A deep-sea hydrothermal vent community

Bruce Corbett/Alamy

▲ **Figure 52.15 The northern range limit of the semi-aquatic wood turtle, *Glyptemys insculpta*, is set by an abiotic factor, temperature.** Arrows indicate how the wood turtle's range expanded north and west as the glaciers retreated.

Dispersal and Distribution

Ecologists must first consider the possibility that a species is absent from a region because it never had the chance to **disperse** there (Figure 52.16). Dispersal is the movement of individuals away from the area of origin or from centres of high population density. Biogeographers (Chapter 22) study the past and present distributions of species in the context of their evolutionary history. Knowing where and when species evolved often helps to explain current species distributions.

Ecologists are now using patterns of molecular genetic diversity (Chapter 23) to unravel the evolutionary past and historic dispersal routes of species such as the wood turtle. The wood turtle appears to have originated in the southeastern USA, a biodiversity hotspot for turtles. It survived the most recent glacial period in a relatively warm area south of its current distribution. As the climate warmed, **natural range expansion** occurred; wood turtles followed the warming temperatures north, eventually colonizing southern Quebec, New Brunswick, and Nova Scotia, and dispersing west to the Great Lakes area (Figure 52.15).

Two important dispersal barriers limit the wood turtle from expanding further. First, salty water prevents it from dispersing to Prince Edward Island or Newfoundland. Second, because of its dependence on streams, the wood turtle cannot cross the dry prairie grassland in the centre of North America to colonize western forests. A **species transplant experiment** could be used to determine if the *potential range* of wood turtles includes Europe or Western North America. If individuals transplanted to the new environment can both survive and reproduce, we can conclude that the potential range of the species is greater than its *actual range*, that is, the wood turtle *could* live in areas where it is not found.

deeper than those of previous generations. A population with large-beaked individuals will be more likely to persist on islands such as Daphne Major that experience severe droughts.

In seeking to explain species distributions, ecologists consider biotic or living factors—all the organisms that are part of the individual's environment—and abiotic or non-living factors—chemical and physical characteristics, such as temperature, light, water, and nutrients. **Figure 52.15** shows the current range of the wood turtle, *Glyptemys insculpta*, in orange. The wood turtle was once abundant in eastern North America, but its numbers have declined due to habitat loss and various mortality factors. It is now protected by law in Canada and in most of the U.S. states in which it occurs. The northern limit of the wood turtle's current range is in eastern Canada, and populations also occur just south of the Great Lakes. However, the species is completely absent from western North America. What historic, biotic, and abiotic factors produced this distribution?

In the following sections we will work our way through the series of questions posed in the flowchart in **Figure 52.16** to illustrate how an ecologist might arrive at an explanation for the current distribution of the wood turtle.

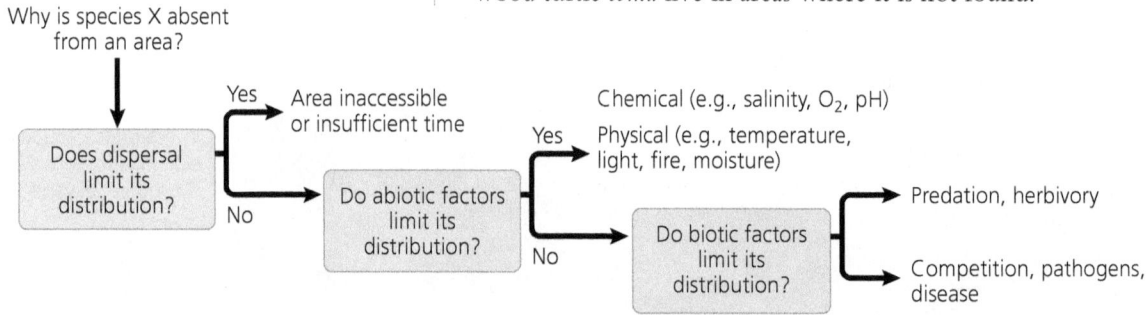

▲ **Figure 52.16 Factors that may limit geographic distributions of species.** As ecologists study the factors that limit the distribution of a species, they often consider a series of questions like the ones shown here.

[?] *How might the importance of various abiotic factors differ for aquatic and terrestrial ecosystems?*

Recent range expansion in many species is directly or indirectly linked to human range expansion and associated activities. For example, the coyote has greatly expanded its range over the past 100 years, in large part because it is adapted to open habitats and thrives in human-modified habitats such as agricultural landscapes and suburban developments (Figure 52.17).

Abiotic Factors

If the absence of a species is not due to dispersal limitation, abiotic factors such as temperature, water, salinity, sunlight, or soil may prevent it from living in the area (Figure 52.16). A species will not be found where physical or chemical conditions do not allow individuals to survive and reproduce. The range of abiotic conditions that does permit a species to persist is known as its *fundamental niche*, a concept we will discuss further in Chapter 54. Different abiotic factors limit different types of organisms. Low moisture levels prevent many species from inhabiting desert, chaparral, and grassland habitats. Photosynthetic organisms are often limited by the amount of sunlight. Only some plant species can live in the deep shade of a dense forest, for example, and aquatic plants cannot survive beneath the photic zone, the depth that light penetrates into water.

Salinity (salt content) and other chemical properties, such as pH, limit the distributions of many aquatic organisms. Different physiological adaptations allow organisms to regulate cellular salt content in salty versus fresh water (Concept 44.1), and thus only a few species have distributions that encompass both marine and freshwater habitats.

As you saw when we covered terrestrial biomes (Figure 52.11), temperature and moisture are the most important abiotic factors limiting the distribution of the major plant community types of the world. Temperature plays an important role for most organisms because of its effects on biological processes. Cells may rupture if the water they contain freezes, and the proteins of most organisms denature at temperatures above 45°C. In addition, few organisms can maintain an active metabolism at very low or very high temperatures, though extraordinary adaptations enable some, such as thermophilic prokaryotes (see Chapter 27), to live at extreme temperatures. Due to their evolutionary history, most organisms are adapted to (function best) within a specific range of environmental temperatures.

▼ Figure 52.17 | **Impact**

Range Expansion: The Adaptable Coyote

Over the past hundred years, the coyote (*Canis latrans*) has undergone a dramatic *range expansion*, spreading north, south, and east from the western grasslands of North America. Humans aided the spread through habitat change (clearing of forests for agriculture) and by hunting and poisoning a main competitor, the eastern wolf (*Canis lycaon*). As coyotes moved north and eastward through Ontario and Quebec, they hybridized with wolves, producing a larger Eastern coyote, or "coy-wolf," which has since colonized Atlantic Canada and parts of the northeastern United States. In many areas, the coy-wolf behaves much like a wolf, inhabiting forests as well as open habitat and preferring white-tailed deer over small mammals. The Eastern wolf was extirpated in eastern forests decades ago, and we may expect a reorganization of these ecosystems as the ecological niche of top predator is reoccupied, this time by a coyote-wolf hybrid.

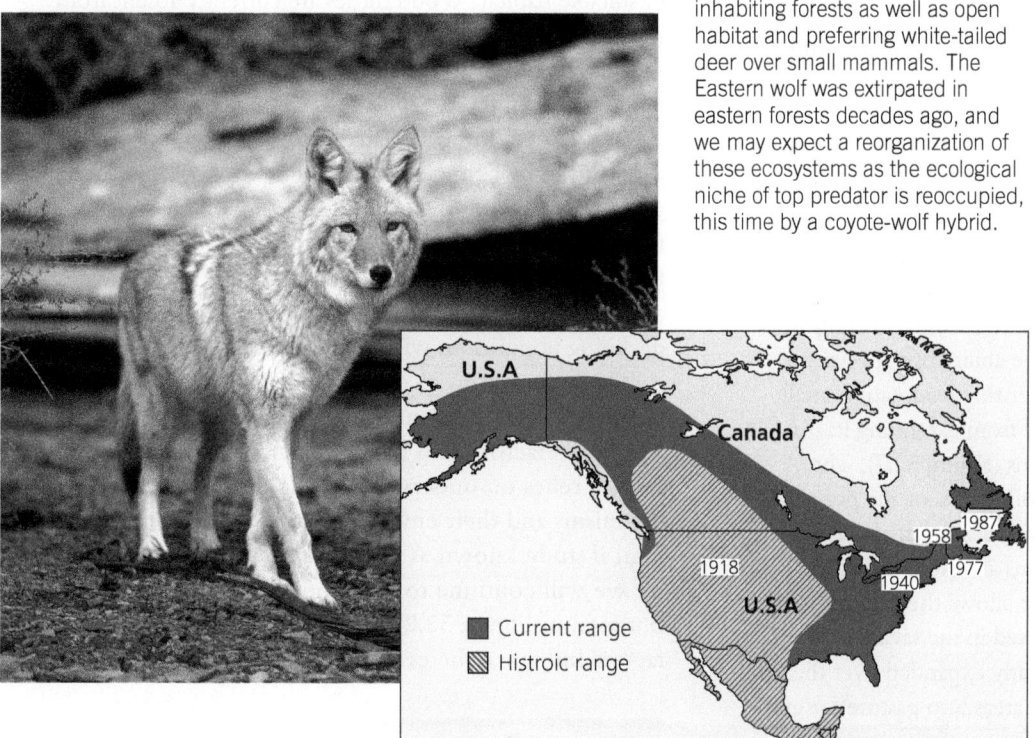

Hans Reinhard/Science Source

U.S.A

Canada

1958 1987
1918 1977
1940
U.S.A

■ Current range
▨ Histroic range

Why It Matters When coyotes first colonize a region, the focus is often on direct human-coyote interactions; after all, the Eastern coyote is a large predator. However indirect effects may also be important. White-tailed deer numbers often decline when coyotes establish in a region. This tends to please suburban gardeners, but to displease sports hunters. Reducing deer may also influence the distribution and spread of Lyme disease–carrying black-legged ticks. Other species may benefit. For example, if coyotes reduce the abundance of smaller predators such as raccoons, songbird numbers may increase.

Further Reading M. E. Gompper, Top carnivores in the suburbs? Ecological and conservation issues raised by colonization of north-eastern North America by coyotes, *BioScience* 52:185–190 (2002).

MAKE CONNECTIONS *When two species meet, a hybrid zone is often created (Concept 24.3). Over time, reproductive barriers between species may become stronger or, as seen with the coyote and the eastern wolf, species may begin to fuse. Should the coy-wolf be considered a new species?*

Temperature sets the northern limit for many Northern Hemisphere species (southern limit in the Southern Hemisphere). Organisms that live in the north have evolved various adaptations to cope with cold. Ectotherms, organisms whose temperature varies with the environment (Chapter 40), must find a way to avoid freezing in winter. Wood turtles (Figure 52.15) live in temperate forests near streams, and their use of water allows them to survive Canadian winters. The turtles spend the entire winter submerged in slow-moving streams (often under the ice) and thus keep their body temperature above the freezing point. Other behavioural adaptations allow wood turtles to obtain and conserve heat in the short northern summer. Body temperature is elevated by basking in the sun before moving about to forage for terrestrial plants, fungi, and invertebrates. The northern boundary of the wood turtle's range is ultimately set by cool summer temperatures rather than cold winters. Since embryo development depends on ambient temperature, turtle eggs require a minimum number of "heat units" (hours above a minimum temperature) to hatch. Wood turtles lay their eggs in sunny locations to maximize development rate. However, where summers are too cool and short, the eggs do not accumulate sufficient energy to hatch, and wood turtle populations cannot persist.

Biotic Factors

If abiotic factors do not explain why a species is absent from a region, the ecologist next asks if biotic factors—other species—are responsible (Figure 52.16). Negative interactions with predators (organisms that kill their prey) or herbivores (organisms that eat plants or algae) can restrict the ability of a species to survive and reproduce. We saw earlier that seed-eating small mammals are preventing sugar maple from extending its distribution upslope as the climate warms (Figure 52.7). The absence of food resources or plant pollinators, or the presence of pathogens, parasites, or competing species, can also act as biotic limiting factors. Today, humans are often the biotic factor that limits species distributions or allows them to expand their ranges. The cattle egret originated in the savannas of Africa and Asia, and its range has greatly expanded over the past 150 years as humans converted large areas into pasture for grazing livestock (Figure 52.18). The cattle egret forages by walking behind hoofed mammals such as zebras, giraffes, or cattle, eating the insects that are disturbed by the grazer. The egret will also happily follow a tractor as it ploughs a field! Other striking cases of limitation due to biotic factors become obvious when humans accidentally or intentionally introduce exotic predators or pathogens into new areas, which sometimes eliminate native species. You will encounter examples of these impacts in Chapter 56, when we discuss conservation biology.

Humans are the most important biotic factor limiting the distribution of the wood turtle today. By converting temperate forest into agricultural or urban habitat throughout much of

▼ Figure 52.18 **The range of the cattle egret expanded along with the global cattle industry.** Cattle egrets arrived in South America in the 1870s, and then spread north, west and south.

■ Current range of the cattle egret.

the turtle's former range, we have greatly reduced the amount of suitable habitat. Wood turtles are currently absent from many places that they inhabited 200 years ago, and they occur today as small isolated populations throughout much of their range. Some of these populations are in danger of disappearing as well, and human-related mortality, such as crushing of adult turtles by farm machinery and road traffic and the capture of young turtles for the pet trade, are important contributing factors. In the Scientific Skills Exercise, you can interpret data from a study that investigated the impact of human recreational activities on wood turtle population numbers. The ecology of declining populations will also be discussed in Chapter 56.

Throughout this chapter, you have seen how the distributions of biomes and organisms depend on abiotic and biotic factors, and how explaining the distribution of species relies on understanding the interactions between organisms and their environment. This is the field of ecological study known as *organismal ecology*. In the next chapter we will continue to work our way up the hierarchy outlined in Figure 52.2, focusing on how abiotic and biotic factors influence the ecology of *populations*.

CONCEPT CHECK 52.4

1. Give examples of human actions that could expand a species' distribution by changing its (a) dispersal or (b) biotic interactions.

2. **WHAT IF?** You suspect that deer are restricting the distribution of a tree species by preferentially eating the seedlings of the tree. How might you test this hypothesis?

3. **MAKE CONNECTIONS** Hawaiian silverswords underwent a remarkable adaptive radiation after their ancestor reached Hawaii, while the islands were still young (see Figure 25.23). Would you expect the cattle egret to undergo a similar adaptive radiation in the Americas (see Figure 52.18)? Explain.

For suggested answers, see Appendix A.

Making and Interpreting Line and Scatterplot Graphs

Can Wood Turtle Populations Coexist with Human Recreational Activities? When species distributions shrink, large populations often fragment into smaller populations, which may then decline to extinction. Throughout much of their range, wood turtles now occur mostly as small and isolated populations. A long-term study conducted in a 1000 ha protected watershed documented the fate of one of these populations. The area was originally closed to all recreation. In 1983 it was decided to allow people to enter to hike and fish, but only with the purchase of a permit.

How the Study Was Done Each year between 1974 and 1993, researchers intensively searched the forest and stream habitats for turtles. They aged, sexed, and then marked each newly encountered turtle by filing an identifying notch on the edge of the carapace.

Data from the Study The table below presents data on the number of adult female, adult male, and juvenile (< 12 years old) turtles in the population, and the number of hiking permits issued each year. In 1992 and 1993 no turtles were found.

Jay Ondreicka/Shutterstock

Interpret the Data

1. Make a line graph of the number of adult female, adult male, and juvenile turtles versus year. When did the decline in turtle abundance begin? Did adults or juveniles decline more rapidly?

2. Make a scatterplot of the *total* number of turtles versus number of hiking permits. (Decide which should be the independent variable.)

3. What does the scatterplot suggest about the relationship between human use of the wilderness area and the decline of wood turtles?

4. Humans may have caused the decline directly through removing turtles, handling the turtles, or by allowing their dogs to disturb the turtles. Alternatively, an increase in food waste (garbage cans, discarded fish) may have indirectly harmed the population by causing natural predation rates to rise. How might human food waste have led to more predation on turtle eggs and juveniles by predators such as raccoons and foxes?

5. This was a correlational study; that is, researchers measured and correlated two variables (turtle and permit numbers). They did not manipulate the variable of interest (human recreation) in a controlled experiment. In a correlational study one must carefully consider other factors that might have caused the observed impacts. The researchers found that there was no change in water quality or temperature that correlated with the decline of the turtles. Can you think of other factors unrelated to human recreation that could have contributed to the turtle decline?

Data from S. D Garber and J Burger, A 20-yr study documenting the relationship between turtle decline and human recreation, *Ecological Applications* 5:1151–1162 (1995). © Jane B Reece.

	Number of Turtles			
	Female	Male	Juvenile	Hiking Permits
1974	32	14	38	0
1975	34	7	41	0
1976	33	8	43	0
1977	34	8	44	0
1978	34	7	47	0
1979	35	7	52	0
1980	36	7	61	0
1981	37	7	61	0
1982	38	10	58	0
1983	37	15	50	16
1984	29	15	33	60
1985	28	15	25	128
1986	28	15	23	107
1987	24	14	19	197
1988	20	12	13	261
1989	15	11	10	304
1990	7	11	5	331
1991	4	8	2	359

52 Chapter Review

Go to **MasteringBiology**® for Assignments, the eText, and the Study Area with Animations, Activities, Vocab Self-Quiz, and Practice Tests.

SUMMARY OF KEY CONCEPTS

CONCEPT 52.1

Earth's climate varies by latitude and season and is changing rapidly (pp. 1225–1231)

- Global **climate** patterns are largely determined by the input of solar energy and Earth's revolution around the sun.
- The changing angle of the sun over the year, bodies of water, and mountains exert seasonal, regional, and local effects on **macroclimate**.
- Fine-scale differences in **abiotic** (nonliving) factors, such as sunlight and temperature, determine **microclimate**.
- Increasing greenhouse gas concentrations in the air are warming Earth and altering the distributions of many species. Some species will not be able to shift their ranges quickly enough to reach suitable habitat in the future.

? *Suppose global air circulation suddenly reversed, with most air ascending at 30° north and south latitude and descending at the equator. At what latitude would you most likely find deserts in this scenario?*

CONCEPT 52.2

The structure and distribution of terrestrial biomes are controlled by climate and disturbance (pp. 1231–1237)

- **Biomes** differ in average temperature and precipitation. **Ecotones** are transitional zones where two biomes intergrade.
- Terrestrial biomes are often named for major physical or climatic factors and for their predominant vegetation. Vertical layering is an important feature of terrestrial biomes.
- **Disturbance**, both natural and human-induced, influences the type of vegetation found in biomes. Humans have altered much of Earth's surface, replacing the natural terrestrial communities described and depicted in Figure 52.11 with urban and agricultural ones.

? *In what ways are disturbances important for savanna ecosystems and the plants in them?*

CONCEPT 52.3

Aquatic biomes are diverse and dynamic systems that cover most of Earth (pp. 1238–1239)

- Aquatic biomes are characterized primarily by their physical environment rather than by climate and are often layered with regard to light penetration, temperature, and community structure. Marine biomes have a higher salt concentration than freshwater biomes.
- In the ocean and in most lakes, an abrupt temperature change called a **thermocline** separates a more uniformly warm upper layer from more uniformly cold deeper waters.
- Many temperate lakes undergo a **turnover** or mixing of water in spring and fall that sends deep, nutrient-rich water to the surface and shallow, oxygen-rich water to deeper layers.

? *In which aquatic biomes might you find an aphotic zone?*

CONCEPT 52.4

Interactions between organisms and the environment limit the distribution of species (pp. 1239–1247)

- Ecologists want to know not only *where* species occur but also *why* those species occur where they do.

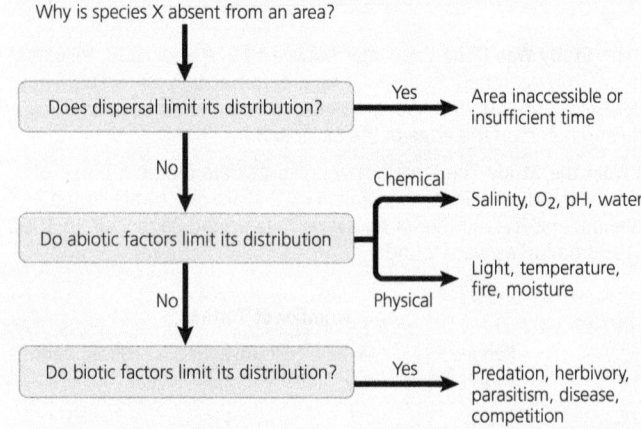

- The distribution of species may be limited by **dispersal** barriers or by time available for dispersal; by **abiotic** factors such as temperature, moisture or salinity; or by **biotic** factors (interactions with other organisms).

? *If you were an ecologist studying the chemical and physical limits to the distributions of species, how might you rearrange the flowchart preceding this question?*

TEST YOUR UNDERSTANDING

LEVEL 1: KNOWLEDGE/COMPREHENSION

1. Which of the following areas of study focuses on the exchange of energy, organisms, and materials between ecosystems?
   a. organismal ecology
   b. landscape ecology
   c. ecosystem ecology
   d. community ecology

2. Which lake zone would be absent in a very shallow lake?
   a. benthic zone
   b. aphotic zone
   c. pelagic zone
   d. littoral zone

3. Which of the following is true with respect to oligotrophic lakes and eutrophic lakes?
   a. Oligotrophic lakes are more subject to oxygen depletion.
   b. Rates of photosynthesis are lower in eutrophic lakes.
   c. Eutrophic lakes are richer in nutrients.
   d. Sediments in oligotrophic lakes contain larger amounts of decomposable organic matter.

LEVEL 2: APPLICATION/ANALYSIS

4. Which of the following is characteristic of most terrestrial biomes?
   a. a distribution predicted almost entirely by rock and soil patterns
   b. clear boundaries between adjacent biomes

c. vegetation demonstrating vertical layering
d. cold winter months

5. The oceans affect the biosphere in all of the following ways *except*
   a. producing a substantial amount of the biosphere's oxygen.
   b. removing carbon dioxide from the atmosphere.
   c. moderating the climate of terrestrial biomes.
   d. regulating the pH of freshwater biomes and terrestrial groundwater.

6. Which statement about dispersal is *false*?
   a. Dispersal is a common component of the life cycles of plants and animals.
   b. Colonization of devastated areas after floods or volcanic eruptions depends on dispersal.
   c. Dispersal occurs only on an evolutionary time scale.
   d. The ability to disperse can expand the geographic distribution of a species.

7. When climbing a mountain, we can observe transitions in biological communities that are analogous to the changes
   a. in biomes at different latitudes.
   b. in different depths in the ocean.
   c. in a community through different seasons.
   d. in an ecosystem as it evolves over time.

8. Suppose that the number of bird species is determined mainly by the number of vertical strata found in the environment. If so, in which of the following biomes would you find the greatest number of bird species?
   a. tropical rain forest
   b. savanna
   c. desert
   d. temperate broadleaf forest

LEVEL 3: SYNTHESIS/EVALUATION

9. **WHAT IF?** If the direction of Earth's rotation reversed, the most predictable effect would be
   a. a big change in the length of the year.
   b. winds blowing from west to east along the equator.
   c. a loss of seasonal variation at high latitudes.
   d. the elimination of ocean currents.

10. **INTERPRET THE DATA** After reading about the spread of Lyme disease into Canada, you want to test whether climate limits the distribution of the black-legged tick. You sample for ticks at eight sites by dragging a woollen blanket on the ground over a distance of 400 m, and then removing and counting all attached ticks. You obtain the weather records for each location and calculate the number of degree days (sum of daily temperature averages for all days > 0°C), a measure often correlated with insect growth. Make a graph that shows how black-legged tick abundance is related to climate (measured as degree days > 0°C). Then formulate a hypothesis that might explain the pattern you observe.

Site	Number of ticks	Degree days
1	10	2850
2	60	2960
3	80	3000
4	100	3080
5	130	3100
6	140	3140
7	145	3160
8	300	3400

11. **EVOLUTION CONNECTION**
    Discuss how the concept of time applies to ecological situations and evolutionary changes. Do ecological time and evolutionary time ever overlap? If so, what are some examples?

12. **SCIENTIFIC INQUIRY**
    Jens Clausen and colleagues at the Carnegie Institution of Washington studied how the size of yarrow plants (*Achillea lanulosa*) growing on the slopes of the Sierra Nevada varied with elevation. They found that plants from low elevations were generally taller than plants from high elevations, as shown in the diagram.

Source: J. Clausen et al., Experimental studies on the nature of species. III. Environmental responses of climatic races of *Achillea*, Carnegie Institution of Washington Publication No. 581 (1948).

13. **WRITE ABOUT A THEME: INTERACTIONS**
    Global warming is occurring rapidly in Arctic marine and terrestrial ecosystems, including tundra and northern coniferous forests. In such locations, reflective white snow and ice cover are melting quickly and extensively, uncovering darker-coloured ocean water, plants, and rocks. In a short essay (100–150 words), explain how this process might represent a positive-feedback loop (see Concept 40.2).

14. **SYNTHESIZE YOUR KNOWLEDGE**

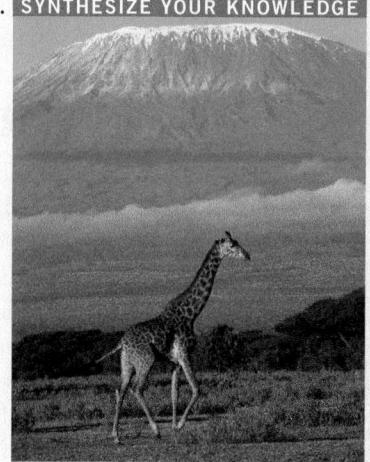

Daryl Balfour/Getty Images

If you were to hike up Mount Kilimanjaro in Tanzania, you would pass through several habitats, including savanna at the base, forest on the slopes, and alpine tundra near the top. Explain how such diverse habitats can be found at one location near the equator.

For selected answers, see Appendix A.

53

Population Ecology

▲ Figure 53.1 **What causes the number of sheep to fluctuate from year to year?**

KEY CONCEPTS

53.1 Dynamic biological processes influence population density, dispersion, and demographics

53.2 The exponential model describes population growth in an idealized, unlimited environment

53.3 The logistic model describes how a population grows more slowly as it nears its carrying capacity

53.4 Life history traits are products of natural selection

53.5 Many factors that regulate population growth are density dependent

53.6 The human population is no longer growing exponentially but is still increasing rapidly

Counting Sheep

Bighorn sheep (*Ovis canadensis*) graze the high alpine meadows of the Rocky Mountains in the summer, and move to lower elevations to feed in the winter (**Figure 53.1**). The physical environment can be harsh, and bighorns face threats from disease and natural predators, and from human hunters who value their large horns. In the 1960s, many bighorn sheep were dying of pneumonia (likely transmitted by domestic livestock), and wildlife biologists wanted to find ways to lower the risk of disease. A long-term monitoring study of a bighorn sheep population was begun at Ram Mountain in western Alberta.

The Ram Mountain bighorn population grew quickly at first, increasing from 100 sheep to more than 230 sheep. But numbers then dropped dramatically, and by 2005 only 40 sheep remained. Marco Festa-Bianchet, from the Université de Sherbrooke, has been studying the bighorns of Ram Mountain for the past 25 years, trying to explain these *fluctuations* in population size. He has discovered that bighorn numbers are influenced by competition for food and by predatory cougars. The study of how and why population size fluctuates over time is part of the field of **population ecology**, the study of populations in relation to their environment. Population ecology explores how biotic and abiotic factors influence the density, distribution, size, and age structure of populations.

◀ **Bighorn sheep** *(Ovis canadensis)*

Our earlier study of populations in Chapter 23 emphasized the relationship between population genetics—the structure and dynamics of gene pools—and evolution. Populations evolve as natural selection acts on heritable variations among individuals, changing the frequencies of alleles and traits over time. Evolution remains a central theme as we now view populations in the context of ecology.

In this chapter, we will first examine some of the structural and dynamic aspects of populations. We will then explore the tools and models ecologists use to analyze populations and the factors that regulate the abundance of organisms. Finally, we will apply these basic concepts as we examine recent trends in the size and makeup of the human population.

CONCEPT 53.1

Dynamic biological processes influence population density, dispersion, and demographics

A **population** is a group of individuals of a single species living in the same general area. Members of a population rely on the same resources, are influenced by similar environmental factors, and are likely to interact and breed with one another.

Populations are often described by their boundaries and size (the number of individuals living within those boundaries). Ecologists usually begin investigating a population by defining boundaries appropriate to the organism under study and to the questions being asked. A population's boundaries may be natural ones, as in the case of an island surrounded by water, or they may be arbitrarily defined by an investigator—for example, a specific pond in southern Ontario for a study of spotted salamanders.

Density and Dispersion

The **density** of a population is the number of individuals per unit area or volume: the number of oak trees per square kilometre in a temperate forest or the number of *Escherichia coli* bacteria per millilitre in a test tube. **Dispersion** is the pattern of spacing among individuals within the boundaries of the population.

Density: A Dynamic Perspective

In rare cases, population size and density can be determined by counting all individuals within the boundaries of the population. Researchers have tagged and counted all the bighorn sheep on Ram Mountain, for example. Large mammals that live in herds, such as buffalo or elephants, can sometimes be counted accurately from airplanes. In most cases, however, it is impractical or impossible to count all individuals in a population. Instead, ecologists use a variety of sampling techniques to estimate densities and total population sizes. For example, they might count the number of

oak trees in several randomly located 100×100 m plots, calculate the average density in the plots, and then extend the estimate to the population size in the entire area. Such estimates are most accurate when there are many sample plots and when the habitat is fairly homogeneous. In other cases, instead of counting single organisms, population ecologists estimate density from an indicator of population size, such as the number of nests, burrows, tracks, or fecal droppings. Ecologists also use the **mark-recapture method** to estimate the size of wildlife populations (Figure 53.2).

▼ Figure 53.2 | **Research Method**

Determining Population Size Using the Mark-Recapture Method

Application Ecologists often cannot count all the individuals in a population. In such cases, researchers may use the mark-recapture method to estimate population size. Andrew Gormley and his colleagues at the University of Otago applied this method to a population of endangered Hector's dolphins (*Cephalorhynchus hectori*) near Banks Peninsula, in New Zealand.

Hector's dolphins

Todd Pusser/Nature Picture Library

Technique Scientists typically begin by capturing a random sample of individuals in a population. They tag, or "mark," each individual and then release it. With some species, researchers can identify individuals without physically capturing them. For example, Gormley and colleagues identified 180 Hector's dolphins by photographing their distinctive dorsal fins from boats.

After waiting for the marked or otherwise identified individuals to mix back into the population, usually a few days or weeks, scientists capture or sample a second set of individuals. At Banks Peninsula, Gormley's team encountered 44 dolphins in their second sampling, 7 of which they had photographed before. The number of marked animals captured in the second sampling (x) divided by the total number of animals captured in the second sampling (n) should equal the number of individuals marked and released in the first sampling (s) divided by the estimated population size (N):

$$\frac{x}{n} = \frac{s}{N} \text{ or, solving for population size, } N = \frac{sn}{x}$$

The method assumes that marked and unmarked individuals have the same probability of being captured or sampled, that the marked organisms have mixed completely back into the population, and that no individuals are born, die, immigrate, or emigrate during the resampling interval.

Results Based on these initial data, the estimated population size of Hector's dolphins at Banks Peninsula would be $180 \times 44/7 = 1131$ individuals. Repeated sampling by Gormley and colleagues suggested a true population size closer to 1100.

Source: Based on A. M. Gormley et al., Capture-recapture estimates of Hector's dolphin abundance at Banks Peninsula, New Zealand, *Marine Mammal Science* 21:204–216 (2005). © Jane B Reece.

INTERPRET THE DATA *Suppose that none of the 44 dolphins encountered in the second sampling had been photographed before. Would you be able to solve the equation for N? What might you conclude about population size in this case?*

Births

Deaths

Births and immigration add individuals to a population.

Deaths and emigration remove individuals from a population.

Immigration

Emigration

▲ Figure 53.3 **Population dynamics.**

Source: Data from P.W Sherman and M.L. Morton, Demography of Belding's ground squirrel, *Ecology* 65:1617-1628 (1984) © Jane B Reece.

Density is not a static property but changes as individuals are added to or removed from a population (**Figure 53.3**). Additions occur through birth (which we define here to include all forms of reproduction) and **immigration**, the influx of new individuals from other areas. The factors that remove individuals from a population are death (mortality) and **emigration**, the movement of individuals out of a population and into other locations.

While birth and death rates influence the density of all populations, immigration and emigration also affect the density of many populations. Long-term studies of Belding's ground squirrels (*Spermophilus beldingi*) in the vicinity of Tioga Pass, in the Sierra Nevada of California, showed that some of the squirrels moved nearly 2 km from where

they were born. This long-distance movement made them immigrants to other populations. In fact, immigrants made up 1–8% of the males and 0.7–6% of the females in the study population. Although these percentages may seem small, such immigration is a meaningful biological exchange between populations over time.

Patterns of Dispersion

Within a population's geographic range, local densities may differ substantially, creating contrasting patterns of dispersion. Differences in local density are among the most important characteristics for a population ecologist to study, since they provide insight into the environmental associations and social interactions of individuals in the population.

The most common pattern of dispersion is *clumped*, in which individuals are aggregated in patches. Plants and fungi are often clumped where soil conditions and other environmental factors favour germination and growth. Mushrooms, for instance, may be clumped within and on top of a rotting log. Insects and salamanders may be clumped under the same log because of the higher humidity there. Clumping of animals may also be associated with mating behaviour. Mayflies, which survive only a day or two as mating adults, often swarm in great numbers, a behaviour that increases their chance of mating. Sea stars group together in tide pools, where food is readily available and where they can breed successfully (**Figure 53.4a**). Forming groups may also increase the effectiveness of predation or defence; for example, a wolf

▼ Figure 53.4 **Patterns of dispersion within a population's geographic range.**

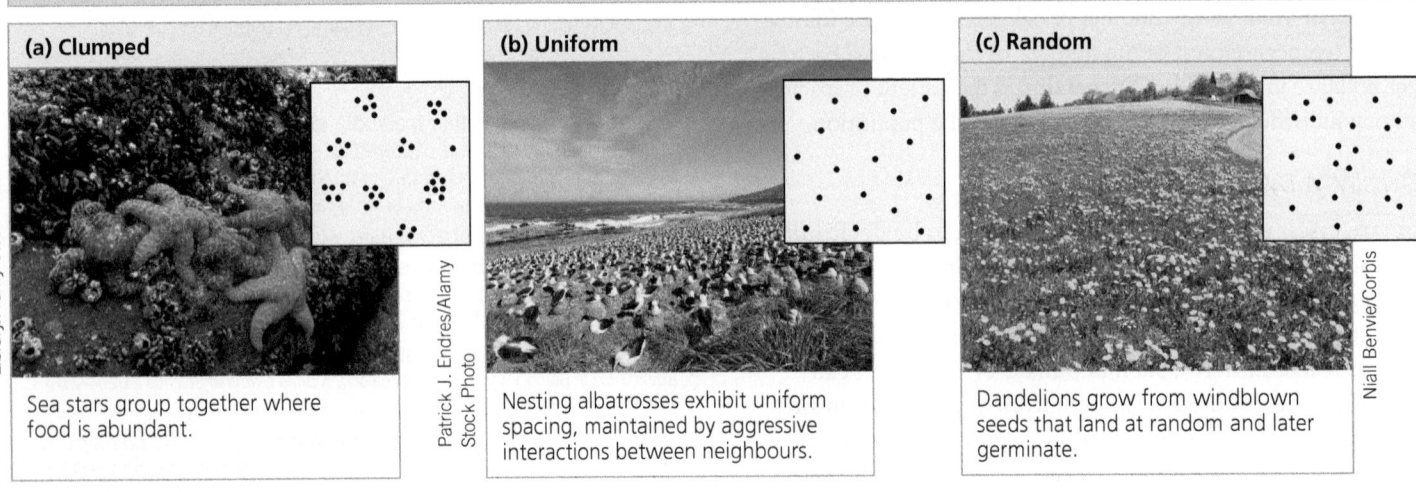

(a) Clumped

Sea stars group together where food is abundant.

(b) Uniform

Nesting albatrosses exhibit uniform spacing, maintained by aggressive interactions between neighbours.

(c) Random

Dandelions grow from windblown seeds that land at random and later germinate.

WHAT IF? *Patterns of dispersion can depend on scale. How might the albatross dispersion look from an airplane over the ocean?*

pack is more likely than a single wolf to subdue a moose, and a flock of birds is more likely than a single bird to warn of a potential attack.

A *uniform*, or evenly spaced, pattern of dispersion may result from direct interactions between individuals in the population. Some plants secrete chemicals that inhibit the germination and growth of nearby individuals that could compete for resources. Animals often exhibit uniform dispersion as a result of antagonistic social interactions, such as **territoriality**—the defence of a bounded physical space against encroachment by other individuals (**Figure 53.4b**). Uniform patterns are rarer than clumped patterns.

In *random* dispersion (unpredictable spacing), the position of each individual in a population is independent of other individuals. This pattern occurs in the absence of strong positive or negative interactions among individuals or where key physical or chemical factors are relatively constant across the study area. Plants established by windblown seeds, such as dandelions, may be randomly distributed in a fairly uniform habitat (**Figure 53.4c**). Random patterns are not as common in nature as one might expect; most populations show at least a tendency toward a clumped distribution.

Demographics

The factors that influence population density and dispersion patterns—ecological needs of

a species, structure of the environment, and interactions among individuals within the population—also influence other characteristics of populations. **Demography** is the study of the vital statistics of populations and how they change over time. Of particular interest to demographers are birth rates and death rates. A useful way to summarize some of the vital statistics of a population is to make a life table.

Life Tables

A life table summarizes the survival and reproduction rates of individuals in specific age-groups within a population. To construct a life table, researchers often follow the fate of a cohort, a group of individuals born at the same time, from their birth until all of the individuals are dead. The life table is built by calculating the proportion of the cohort that survives from one age-group to the next. It is also necessary to count the number of offspring produced by females in each age-group.

Demographers who study sexually reproducing species often ignore the males and concentrate on the females in a population since only females produce offspring. Using this approach, a population is viewed as females who give rise to new females. **Table 53.1** is a life table for a population of female Belding's ground squirrels (*Urocitellus beldingi*) living in the Sierra

Jill M. Mateo

Table 53.1	Life Table for Female Belding's Ground Squirrels (*Spermophilus beldingi*) at Tioga Pass, in the Sierra Nevada of California			
Age (years)	Number Alive at Start of Year	Proportion Alive at Start of Year*	Death Rate**	Average Number of Female Offspring per Female
0–1	653	1.000	0.614	0.0
1–2	252	0.386	0.496	1.1
2–3	127	0.197	0.472	1.9
3–4	67	0.106	0.478	2.2
4–5	35	0.054	0.457	2.6
5–6	19	0.029	0.526	2.1
6–7	9	0.014	0.444	1.7
7–8	5	0.008	0.200	1.9
8–9	4	0.006	0.750	1.9
9–10	1	0.002	1.00	1.6

Source: Data from P.W Sherman and M.L. Morton, Demography of Belding's ground squirrel, *Ecology* 65:1617-1628 (1984). © Jane B Reece.

*Indicates the proportion of the original cohort of 653 individuals that are still alive at the start of a time interval
**The death rate is the proportion of individuals alive at the start of a time interval that die during that time interval

Jennifer Dever

▲ Researchers working with a Belding's ground squirrel

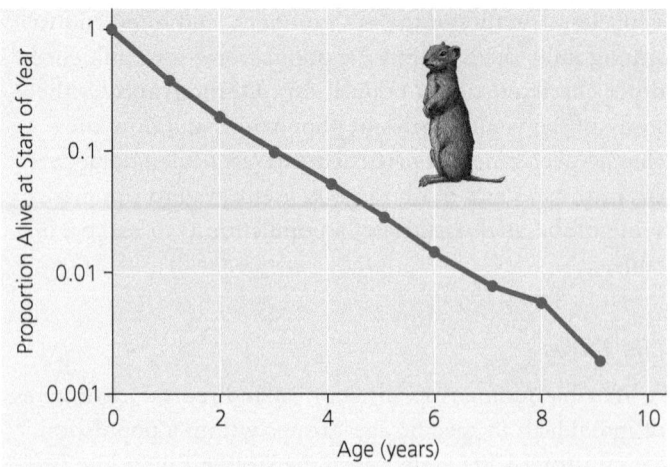

▲ **Figure 53.5 Survivorship curve for female Belding's ground squirrels.** A logarithmic scale is used for the *y*-axis.

Source: Adaptation of figure 1a from "Demography of Belding's Ground Squirrels" by Paul W. Sherman and Martin L. Morton, from *Ecology,* October 1984, Volume 65(5). Copyright © 1984 by Ecological Society of America. Reprinted with permission.

▲ **Figure 53.6 Idealized survivorship curves: Types I, II, and III.** The *y*-axis is logarithmic and the *x*-axis is on a relative scale, so that species with widely varying life spans can be presented together on the same graph.

Nevada mountains of California. In the next two sections, we'll look at the survival rates and the reproductive data contained in a life table.

Survivorship Curves

The survival data (proportion alive) in a life table can be represented as a **survivorship curve**, a plot of the proportion of individuals in a cohort still alive at each age. **Figure 53.5** shows the survivorship curve for female Belding's ground squirrels, using the data from Table 53.1. The survivorship curve plots the proportion of the cohort alive at the start of each age interval (third column of Table 53.1) versus age. The approximately straight line of the plot for the ground squirrels indicates a relatively constant rate of death. If you look at the fourth column in Table 53.1, you can see that the death rates are very similar from the age of 1 year to the age of about 7 years.

Figure 53.5 represents just one of many patterns of survivorship exhibited by natural populations. Survivorship curves are often classified into three general types **(Figure 53.6)**. A Type I curve is flat at the start, reflecting low death rates during early and middle life, and then drops steeply as death rates increase among older age-groups. Many large mammals, including humans, that produce few offspring but provide them with good care exhibit this kind of curve. In contrast, a Type III curve drops sharply at the start, reflecting very high death rates for the young, but flattens out as death rates decline for those few individuals that survive the early period of die-off. This type of curve is usually associated with organisms that produce very large numbers of offspring but provide

little or no care, such as long-lived plants, many fishes, and most marine invertebrates. An oyster, for example, may release millions of eggs, but most larvae hatched from fertilized eggs die from predation or other causes. Those few offspring that survive long enough to attach to a suitable substrate and begin growing a hard shell tend to survive for a relatively long time. Type II curves are intermediate, with a constant death rate over the organism's life span. This kind of survivorship occurs in Belding's ground squirrels (see Figure 53.5) and some other rodents, various invertebrates, some lizards, and some annual plants.

Many species fall somewhere between these basic types of survivorship or show more complex patterns. In birds, mortality is often high among the youngest individuals (as in a Type III curve) but fairly constant among adults (as in a Type II curve). Some invertebrates, such as crabs, may show a "stair-stepped" curve, with brief periods of increased mortality during moults, followed by periods of lower mortality when their protective exoskeleton is hard.

In populations not experiencing immigration or emigration, survivorship is one of the two key factors determining changes in population size. The other key factor determining population trends is reproductive rate.

Reproductive Rates

As mentioned above, demographers often ignore the males in sexually-reproducing populations, and view populations as females giving rise to new females. In most populations, reproductive output (average number of female offspring) varies with female age.

For Belding's ground squirrels, which begin to reproduce at age 1 year, reproductive output rises to a peak at 4 years of age and then falls off in older females (Table 53.1).

Reproductive rates vary tremendously among species. While bighorn sheep (Figure 53.1) produce one or two offspring each year, mussels and other invertebrates may release millions of eggs and sperm in a spawning cycle. However, a high reproductive rate will not lead to rapid population growth unless conditions are near ideal for the growth and survival of offspring, as you'll learn in the next section.

CONCEPT CHECK 53.1

1. **DRAW IT** Each female of a particular fish species produces millions of eggs per year. Draw and label the most likely survivorship curve for this species, and explain your choice.
2. **WHAT IF?** As noted in Figure 53.2, an important assumption of the mark-recapture method is that marked individuals have the same probability of being captured as unmarked individuals. Describe a situation where this assumption might not be valid, and explain how the estimate of population size would be affected.
3. **MAKE CONNECTIONS** A male stickleback fish attacks other males that invade its nesting territory (see Figure 51.2a). Predict the likely pattern of dispersion for male sticklebacks, and explain your reasoning.

For suggested answers, see Appendix A.

CONCEPT 53.2

The exponential model describes population growth in an idealized, unlimited environment

Populations of all species have the potential to expand greatly when resources are abundant. To appreciate the potential for population increase, consider a bacterium that can reproduce by fission every 20 minutes under ideal laboratory conditions. There would be 2 bacteria after 20 minutes, 4 after 40 minutes, and 8 after 60 minutes. If reproduction continued at this rate for a day and a half without mortality, there would be enough bacteria to form a layer 30 cm deep over the entire globe. Unlimited growth does not occur for long in nature, because individuals typically have access to fewer resources as a population grows. Nonetheless, ecologists study population growth in ideal, unlimited environments to reveal how fast populations are capable of growing and the conditions under which rapid growth might actually occur.

Change in Population Size

Imagine a population consisting of a few individuals living in an ideal, unlimited environment. Under these conditions, there are no external restrictions on the abilities of individuals to harvest energy, grow, and reproduce. The population will increase in size with every birth and with the immigration of individuals from other populations, and it will decrease in size with every death and with the emigration of individuals out of the population. We can thus define a change in population size during a fixed time interval with the following verbal equation:

$$\begin{matrix} \text{Change in} \\ \text{population} \\ \text{size} \end{matrix} = \text{Births} + \begin{matrix} \text{Immigrants} \\ \text{entering} \\ \text{population} \end{matrix} - \text{Deaths} - \begin{matrix} \text{Emigrants} \\ \text{leaving} \\ \text{population} \end{matrix}$$

For now, we will ignore the effects of immigration and emigration. We can use mathematical notation to express this simplified relationship more concisely. If N represents population size and t represents time, then ΔN is the change in population size and Δt is the time interval (appropriate to the life span or generation time of the species) over which we are evaluating population growth. (The Greek letter delta, Δ, indicates change, such as change in time.) Using B for the number of births in the population during the time interval and D for the number of deaths, we can rewrite the verbal equation:

$$\frac{\Delta N}{\Delta t} = B - D$$

Typically, population ecologists are most interested in changes in population size—the number of individuals that are added to or subtracted from a population during a given time interval, symbolized by R. Here, R represents the *difference* between the number of births (B) and the number of deaths (D) that occur in the time interval. Thus, $R = B - D$, and we can simplify our equation by writing:

$$\frac{\Delta N}{\Delta t} = R$$

Next, we can convert our model to one in which changes in population size are expressed on a per individual (per capita) basis. The *per capita* change in population size ($r_{\Delta t}$) represents the contribution that an average member of the population makes to the number of individuals added to or subtracted from the population during the time interval Δt. If, for example, a population of 1000 individuals increases by 16 individuals per year, then on a per capita basis, the annual change in population size is 16/1000, or 0.016. If we know the annual per capita change in population size, we can use the formula $R = r_{\Delta t} N$ to calculate how many individuals will be added to (or subtracted from) a population each year. For example, if $r_{\Delta t} = 0.016$ and the population size is 500,

$$R = r_{\Delta t} N = 0.016 \times 500 = 8 \text{ per year}$$

Since the number of individuals added to or subtracted from the population (R) can be expressed on a per capita basis as $R = r_{\Delta t} N$, we can revise our population growth equation to take this into account:

$$\frac{\Delta N}{\Delta t} = r_{\Delta t} N$$

Remember that our equation is for a specific time interval (often one year). However, many ecologists prefer to use differential calculus to express population growth as a rate of change *at each instant in time*:

$$\frac{dN}{dt} = rN$$

In this case, r represents the per capita change in population size that occurs at each instant in time (whereas $r_{\Delta t}$ represented the per capita change that occurred during the time interval Δt). If you have not yet studied calculus, don't be intimidated by the last equation; it is similar to the previous one, except that the time intervals Δt are very short and are expressed in the equation as dt. In fact, as Δt becomes shorter, $r_{\Delta t}$ and r become increasingly close to one another in value.

Exponential Growth

Earlier we described a population of bacteria whose members all have access to abundant food and other resources. Population increase under these conditions is called **exponential population growth**. The equation for exponential growth is the one presented at the end of the last section, namely:

$$\frac{dN}{dt} = rN$$

If the size of a population that is growing exponentially is plotted against time, a J-shaped curve results (Figure 53.7). Although the per capita rate of increase stays the same (and equals r) the *number* of individuals added to the population per unit of time gets larger and larger. For example, a population with a constant growth

▲ Figure 53.7 **Population growth predicted by the exponential model.** This graph compares growth in two populations with different values of r. Increasing the value of r from 0.5 to 1.0 increases the rate of rise in population size over time, as reflected by the relative slopes of the curves at any given population size.

rate of 2 will increase by 40 individuals (per unit time) when population size is 20 but will add 200 individuals when population size is 100. It is also clear from Figure 53.7 that a population with a higher rate of increase ($r = 1.0$) will grow faster than one with a lower rate of increase ($r = 0.5$).

The J-shaped curve of exponential growth is characteristic of some populations that are introduced into a new environment or whose numbers have been drastically reduced by a catastrophic event and are rebounding. For example, hunting by fur traders had driven sea otter populations extinct along most of the west coast of North America by the early 1900s. Sea otters were reintroduced to the coast of Vancouver Island, British Columbia in the early 1970s, and the population grew exponentially (Figure 53.8). The newly established population was able to expand so rapidly because its invertebrate food source was very abundant. Sea otters have continued to increase in numbers since 1995, but at a slower rate. As we will see in Chapter 54, the presence of the sea otter has large impacts on the rest of the coastal marine community.

CONCEPT CHECK 53.2

1. Explain why a constant rate of increase (r) for a population produces a growth graph that is J-shaped.

2. Where is exponential growth by a plant population more likely—in an area where a forest was destroyed by fire or in a mature, undisturbed forest? Why?

3. **WHAT IF?** In 2011, Canada had a population of about 34 million people. There were approximately 10 births and 8 deaths per 1000 people that year. What was the country's net population growth (ignoring immigration and emigration)? The net migration rate (immigration minus emigration) was 6 per 1000 people. What was the actual population growth?

For suggested answers, see Appendix A.

Design Pics Inc/Alamy stock Photo

▲ Figure 53.8 **Exponential growth in a sea otter population after individuals were transplanted to the west coast of Vancouver Island.**

CONCEPT 53.3

The logistic model describes how a population grows more slowly as it nears its carrying capacity

The exponential growth model assumes that resources are unlimited, which can only occur for relatively short periods of time in the real world. As population density increases, each individual has access to fewer resources. Ultimately, there is a limit to the number of individuals that can occupy a habitat. Ecologists define **carrying capacity**, symbolized by K, as the maximum population size that a particular environment can sustain. Carrying capacity varies over space and time with the abundance of limiting resources. Energy, shelter, refuge from predators, nutrient availability, water, and suitable nesting sites can all be limiting factors. For example, the carrying capacity for bats may be high in a habitat with abundant flying insects and roosting sites, but lower where there is abundant food but fewer suitable shelters.

Crowding and resource limitation can have a profound effect on population growth rate. If individuals cannot obtain sufficient resources to reproduce, the birth rate will decline. If they cannot consume enough energy to maintain themselves or if disease or parasitism increases with density, the death rate may increase. A decrease in per capita birth rate or an increase in per capita death rate results in a lower per capita rate of increase (r).

The Logistic Growth Model

We can modify our mathematical model to incorporate changes in growth rate as the population size nears the carrying capacity. In the **logistic population growth** model, the per capita population growth rate approaches zero as the carrying capacity is reached.

To construct the logistic model, we start with the exponential population growth model and add an expression that reduces the rate at which the population grows as N increases.

$$\frac{dN}{dt} = rN\frac{(K - N)}{K}$$

In the above equation, the maximum per capita rate of increase r is multiplied by the expression $(K - N)/K$, where K is the maximum sustainable population size (carrying capacity), $(K - N)$ is the number of additional individuals the environment can support, and $(K - N)/K$ is the fraction of K that is still available for population growth. When N is small compared to K, the term $(K - N)/K$ is close to 1, and the per capita population growth rate, $r(K - N)/K$, will be close to r, the intrinsic rate of increase. But when N is large and resources are limiting, then $(K - N)/K$ is close to 0, and the per capita population growth rate is also very small. When N equals K, the population stops growing. Table 53.2 shows calculations of population growth rate for a hypothetical population growing according to the logistic model, with $r = 1.0$ per individual per year. Notice that the overall population growth rate is highest, +375 individuals per year, when the population size is 750, or half the carrying capacity. At a population size of 750, the per capita rate of increase remains relatively high (one-half the maximum rate), but there are more reproducing individuals (N) in the population than at lower population sizes.

As shown in Figure 53.9, the logistic model of population growth produces a sigmoid (S-shaped) growth curve when N is plotted over time (the red line). New individuals are added to the population most rapidly at intermediate population sizes, when there is not only a breeding population of substantial size, but also lots of

Table 53.2	Logistic Growth of a Hypothetical Population (K = 1500)			
Population Size (N)	Intrinsic Rate of Increase (r)	$\dfrac{(K - N)}{K}$	Per Capita Population Growth Rate $r\dfrac{(K - N)}{K}$	Population Growth Rate* $rN\dfrac{(K - N)}{K}$
25	1.0	0.98	0.98	+25
100	1.0	0.93	0.93	+93
250	1.0	0.83	0.83	+208
500	1.0	0.67	0.67	+333
750	1.0	0.50	0.50	+375
1000	1.0	0.33	0.33	+333
1500	1.0	0.00	0.00	0

*Rounded to the nearest whole number.

available space and other resources in the environment. The population growth rate decreases dramatically as N approaches K.

Note that we haven't said anything yet about *why* the population growth rate decreases as N approaches K. For a population's growth rate to decrease, the birth rate must decrease, the death rate must increase, or both. Later in the chapter, we will consider some of the factors affecting these rates, including the presence of

▲ **Figure 53.9 Population growth predicted by the logistic model.** The rate of population growth decreases as population size (N) approaches the carrying capacity (K) of the environment. The red line shows logistic growth in a population where r = 1.0 and K = 1500 individuals. For comparison, the blue line illustrates a population continuing to grow exponentially with the same r.

disease, predation, and limited amounts of food and other resources. In the Scientific Skills Exercise, you can model what happens to a population if N becomes *greater* than K.

The Logistic Model and Real Populations

The growth of populations of small animals under conditions of limited resources sometimes fits an S-shaped curve fairly well (Figure 53.10a). However, the growth of most populations deviates from that predicted by the simple logistic model. See, for example, the growth of a laboratory population of water fleas (Figure 53.10b) or the growth of the bighorn sheep population on Ram Mountain after wildlife personnel stopped managing population size (Figure 53.10c). What causes these deviations?

Some of the assumptions built into the logistic model clearly do not apply to all populations. The logistic growth model assumes that populations can adjust *instantaneously* to increases in density, through lower birth rates or higher death rates. In reality, there is often a delay before the negative effects of an increasing population are realized. For example, females may use their energy reserves to continue reproducing after food is in short supply, or individuals may become weak and malnourished, but not die immediately when food becomes scarce. In either case, the population will overshoot its carrying capacity temporarily, as shown for the water fleas and sheep in Figure 53.10b and c. The population may then drop below its carrying capacity for a time until more offspring can be produced. Because few types of organisms adjust rapidly to higher densities, overshoots and undershoots are very common.

Another assumption of the logistic growth model is that the environment, biotic and abiotic, stays the same. If, for example, a change in weather reduces food supply, or a new predator enters the area, increasing mortality, the pattern of population growth will also change. In Figure 53.10c, the bighorn sheep population was driven to very low numbers in the 1990s when a few cougars learned to specialize on the sheep. (Cougars in western Canada usually feed on deer, moose, or elk.) Small sheep populations, such as the one on Ram Mountain, may even go extinct, and must then rely on immigrants from nearby bighorn populations to repopulate the area.

The logistic model provides a useful starting point for constructing more complex models that include more realistic assumptions such as delayed population responses and changing environments. The model is used in conservation biology to predict how rapidly a particular population might increase in numbers after it has been reduced to a small size and for estimating sustainable harvest rates

Using the Logistic Equation to Model Population Growth

What Happens to the Size of a Population When It Overshoots Its Carrying Capacity? In the logistic population growth model, the per capita rate of population increase approaches zero as the population size (N) approaches the carrying capacity (K). Under some conditions, however, a population in the laboratory or the field can overshoot K, at least temporarily. If food becomes limiting to a population, for instance, there may be a delay before reproduction declines, and N may briefly exceed K. In this exercise, you will use the logistic equation to model the growth of the hypothetical population in Table 53.2 when N > K.

▶ *Daphnia*

Interpret the Data

1. Assuming that r = 1.0 and K = 1500, calculate the population growth rate for four cases where population size (N) is greater than carrying capacity (K): N = 1510, 1600, 1750, and 2000 individuals. To do this, first write the equation for population growth rate given in Table 53.2. Plug in the values for each of the four cases, starting with N = 1510, and solve the equation for each one. Which population size has the highest growth rate?

2. If r is doubled, predict how the population growth rates will change for the four population sizes given in question 1. Now calculate the population growth rate for the same four cases, this time assuming that r = 2.0 (and with K still = 1500).

3. Now let's see how the growth of a real-world population of *Daphnia* corresponds to this model. At what times in Figure 53.10b is the *Daphnia* population changing in ways that correspond to the values you calculated? Hypothesize why the population drops below the carrying capacity briefly late in the experiment.

---

for fish and wildlife populations. Conservation biologists also use the model to estimate the critical size below which populations of certain organisms, such as the northern subspecies of the white rhinoceros (*Ceratotherium simum*), may become extinct (**Figure 53.11**).

CONCEPT CHECK 53.3

1. Explain why a population that fits the logistic growth model increases more rapidly at intermediate size than at relatively small and large sizes.

2. **WHAT IF?** Given the latitudinal differences in sunlight intensity (see Figure 52.3), how might you expect the carrying capacity of plant species found at the equator to compare with that of plant species found at high latitudes?

3. **MAKE CONNECTIONS** Many viruses are pathogens of animals and plants (see Concept 19.3). How might the presence of pathogens alter the carrying capacity of a population? Explain.

For suggested answers, see Appendix A.

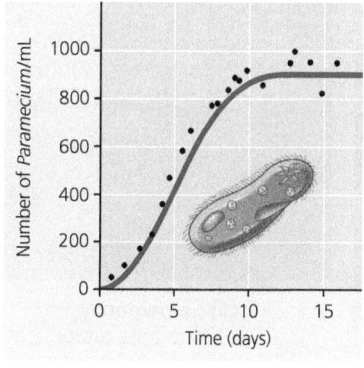

(a) A protist (*Paramecium aurelia*) population growing in the lab closely approximates logistic growth if the researcher maintains a constant environment.

(b) A water flea (*Daphnia*) population growing in the lab does not correspond as well to the logistic model. The population overshoots the carrying capacity of its environment before it settles down to an approximately stable population size.

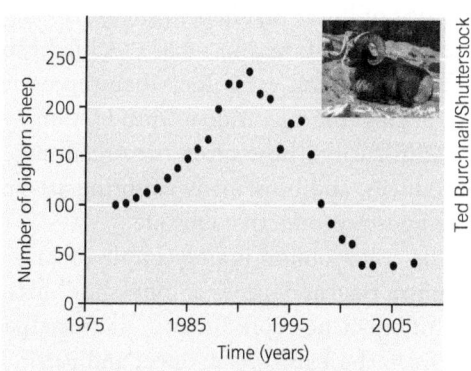

(c) The population of bighorn sheep on Ram Mountain grew after management ceased in the 1970s. Its pattern of growth deviated from that predicted by the logistic growth model.

▲ **Figure 53.10** **How well do these populations fit the logistic growth model?**

Photodisc/Getty Images

◀ **Figure 53.11 White rhinoceros mother and calf.** The two animals pictured here are members of the southern subspecies, which has a population of more than 10 000 individuals. The northern subspecies is critically endangered, with a population of fewer than 15 known individuals.

CONCEPT 53.4

Life history traits are products of natural selection

EVOLUTION Natural selection favours traits that improve an organism's chances of survival and reproductive success. In every species, there are trade-offs between survival and reproductive traits such as frequency of reproduction, number of offspring (number of seeds produced by plants; litter or clutch size for animals), and investment in parental care. The traits that affect an organism's schedule of reproduction and survival make up its **life history**. Life history traits of an organism are evolutionary outcomes reflected in its development, physiology, and behaviour.

Evolution and Life History Diversity

The fundamental idea that evolution accounts for the diversity of life is manifest in the broad range of life histories found in nature. A life history entails three main variables: when reproduction begins (the age at first reproduction or age at maturity), how often the organism reproduces, and how many offspring are produced per reproductive episode.

The coho salmon is an example of an organism that undergoes a "one-shot" pattern of big-bang reproduction, or **semelparity** (from the Latin *semel*, once, and *parere*, to beget). A coho hatches in the headwaters of a freshwater stream and then migrates to the Pacific Ocean, where it typically requires a few years to mature. If it survives, it eventually returns to the same stream to spawn, producing thousands of eggs in a single reproductive event before it dies. Semelparity also occurs in some plants, such as the agave, or "century plant" (Figure 53.12a). Agaves generally grow in arid climates with unpredictable rainfall and poor soils. An agave grows for years, accumulating nutrients in its tissues, until there is an unusually wet year. It then sends up a large flowering stalk, produces seeds, and dies. This life history is an adaptation to the agave's harsh desert environment.

The alternative to semelparity is **iteroparity** (from the Latin *iterare*, to repeat), or repeated reproduction. Some birds, such as the common eider (Figure 53.13) live up to 20 years, producing a few young each year.

▶ **Figure 53.12 Semelparity and iteroparity. (a)** An agave (*Agave americana*) is an example of semelparity, or big-bang reproduction. The leaves of the plant are visible at the base of the giant flowering stalk, which is produced only at the end of the agave's life. **(b)** Organisms that reproduce repeatedly, like humans, undergo iteroparity. Such organisms tend to have fewer, larger offspring and take better care of them.

Stone Nature Photography/Alamy Stock Photo

(a) Semelparity, one-time reproducer

ableimages/Alamy Stock Photo

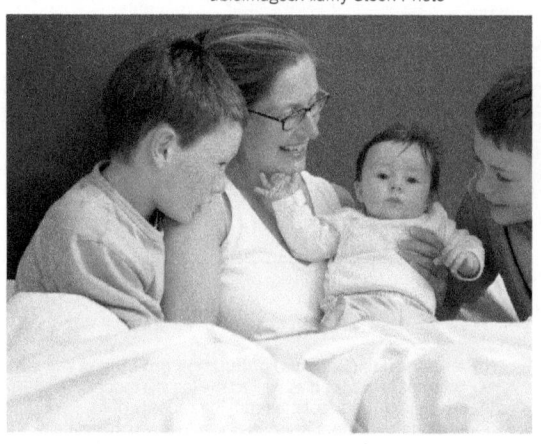

(b) Iteroparity, repeat reproducer

In iteroparity, organisms tend to produce relatively few but large offspring each time they reproduce, and they often provide for the offspring while the offspring are young (Figure 53.12b).

What factors contribute to the evolution of semelparity versus iteroparity? Two factors appear to be especially important: the survival rate of the offspring and the likelihood that the adult will survive to reproduce again. Semelparity is favoured in highly variable or unpredictable environments, where offspring and adult survival rates are low. Adults that are unlikely to survive to reproduce again put all their energy into one reproductive event, and usually produce many offspring to increase the probability that at least some will survive. Iteroparity is favoured in more dependable environments, where adults are likely to survive to breed again and where competition for resources may be intense. Relatively large, well-provisioned offspring usually have a better chance of surviving in highly competitive environments.

Nature abounds with life histories that are intermediate between the two extremes of semelparity and iteroparity. Oak trees and sea urchins, for example, can live a long time but repeatedly produce relatively large numbers of offspring.

"Trade-offs" and Life Histories

No organism could produce as many offspring as a semelparous species and provision them as well as an iteroparous species. There is a trade-off between reproduction and survival. Figure 53.13 describes a study of common eiders that nest on Arctic islands. The authors demonstrate that females are less likely to survive to the next breeding season if they produce many young.

Selective pressures influence the trade-off between the number and size of offspring. Plants and animals whose young are more likely to die often produce large numbers of relatively small offspring. Plants that colonize disturbed environments, for example, usually produce many small seeds, only a few of which may reach a suitable habitat. Small size may also increase the chance of seedling establishment by enabling the seeds to be carried longer distances to a broader range of habitats (Figure 53.14a). Animals that suffer high predation rates, such as quail, sardines, and mice, also tend to produce large numbers of offspring.

In other organisms, extra investment on the part of the parent greatly increases the offspring's chances of survival. Walnut and Brazil nut trees provision large seeds with nutrients that help the seedlings become established (Figure 53.14b). Primates generally bear only one or two offspring at a time; parental care and an extended period of learning in the first several years of life are very important to offspring fitness. Such provisioning and extra care can be especially important in habitats with high population densities.

Ecologists have attempted to connect differences in favoured traits at different population densities with the logistic growth model discussed in Concept 53.3. Selection for traits that are sensitive to population density and are favoured at high densities is known as **K-selection**, or density-dependent selection. In contrast, selection for traits that maximize reproductive success in

---

▼ **Figure 53.13** | **Inquiry**

Do common eiders "pay" for raising many offspring?

Experiment Sébastien Descamps and colleagues from Carleton University and the Université de Québec at Rimouski counted the number of eggs per nest (clutch size) for common eiders nesting on Southampton Island in Nunavut. Common eiders are long-lived iteroparous sea ducks that return to the same breeding site each year. The researchers then measured survival of the nesting female eiders (the proportion that returned to breed the following year), identifying individual birds by their leg bands. Because female eiders do not feed while incubating their eggs, they lose up to 40% of their body weight and become more susceptible to disease. The study was conducted during an outbreak of avian cholera, a contagious and deadly bacterial disease.

Results

Conclusion Female eiders that produced more offspring were much less likely to survive to breed again the next year, demonstrating that reproduction had a significant cost.

Source: Based on S. Descamps et al., Costs of reproduction in a long-lived bird: Large clutch size is associated with low survival in the presence of a highly virulent disease, *Biology Letters* 5:278–281 (2009). © Jane B Reece.

WHAT IF? *The researchers found a strong negative relationship between reproductive effort and survival during a disease outbreak. If disease is the main source of mortality for adult eiders, would you expect the same results in years with little disease?*

(a) Dandelions grow quickly and release a large number of tiny fruits, each containing a single seed. Producing numerous seeds ensures that at least some will grow into plants that eventually produce seeds themselves.

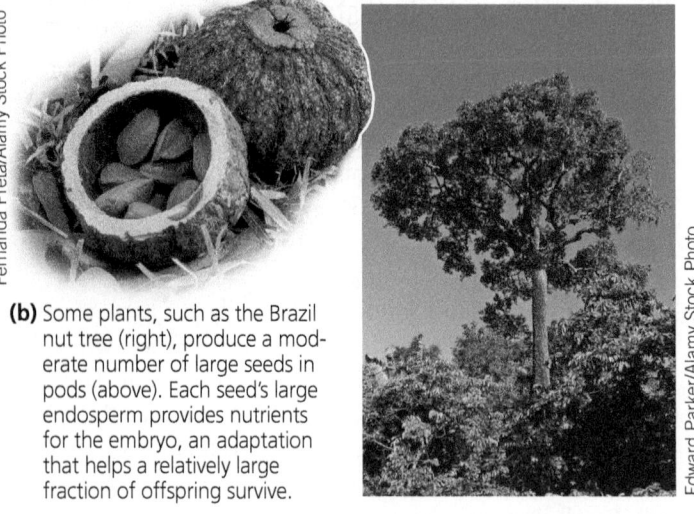

(b) Some plants, such as the Brazil nut tree (right), produce a moderate number of large seeds in pods (above). Each seed's large endosperm provides nutrients for the embryo, an adaptation that helps a relatively large fraction of offspring survive.

▲ Figure 53.14 **Variation in the size of seed crops in plants.**

uncrowded environments (low densities) is called **r-selection**, or density-independent selection. These names follow from the variables of the logistic equation. *K*-selection is said to operate in populations living at a density near the limit imposed by their resources (the carrying capacity, *K*), where competition among individuals is stronger. Mature trees growing in an old-growth forest are an example of *K*-selected organisms. In contrast, *r*-selection is said to maximize *r*, the per capita rate of increase, and occurs in environments in which population densities are well below carrying capacity or individuals face little competition. Such conditions are often found in disturbed habitats. Weeds growing in an abandoned agricultural field are an example of *r*-selected organisms.

The concepts of *K*- and *r*-selection represent two extremes in a range of actual life histories. The framework of *K*- and *r*-selection, grounded in the idea of carrying capacity, has helped ecologists to propose alternative hypotheses of life history evolution. They have also forced

ecologists to address the important question we alluded to earlier: *Why* does population growth rate decrease as population size approaches carrying capacity? Answering this question is the focus of the next section.

CONCEPT 53.5

Many factors that regulate population growth are density dependent

What environmental factors keep populations from growing indefinitely? To understand why a population stops growing, ecologists study how the rates of birth, death, immigration, and emigration change as population density rises. If immigration and emigration offset each other, then a population grows when the birth rate exceeds the death rate and declines when the death rate exceeds the birth rate.

A birth rate or death rate that does *not* change with population density is said to be **density independent**. For example, most of the mortality of dune fescue grass (*Vulpia fasciculata*) is caused by a physical factor, drought stress, which arises when the roots of the grass are uncovered by shifting sands. Drought is a density independent mortality factor because it kills about the same proportions of individuals regardless of population density. A death rate that increases with population density or a birth rate that falls with rising density is said to be **density dependent**. Researchers found that reproduction by dune fescue declines as population density increases, in part because water or nutrients become more scarce. Thus the key factors affecting birth rate in this population are density dependent, while death rate is largely density independent.

All environmental factors that affect birth and death rates influence population densities, whether they are density

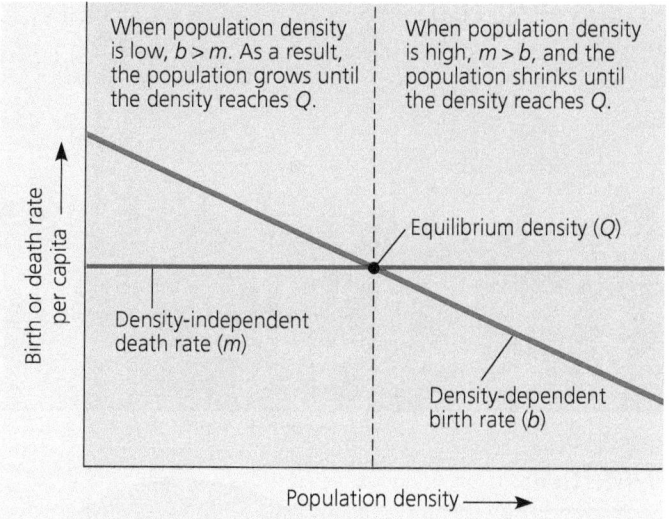

▲ **Figure 53.15 Determining equilibrium for population density.** This simple model considers only birth and death rates. (Immigration and emigration rates are assumed to be either zero or equal.) In this example, the birth rate changes with population density, while the death rate is constant. At the equilibrium density (Q), the birth and death rates are equal.

Source: Figure adapted from "Climate and Population Regulation: The Biogeographer's Dilemma" by J. T. Enright, from *Oecologia*, 1976, Volume 24(4), Springer. © Jane B Reece.

DRAW IT *Redraw this figure with a higher, but still density-independent death rate (m). Will the equilibrium density of the population be smaller or larger?*

dependent or density independent. **Figure 53.15** shows how the combination of density-dependent reproduction and density-independent mortality, such as that observed for dune fescue, determines the equilibrium density of the population.

But factors that cause density dependent birth or death rates can also *regulate* populations, providing negative feedback between increasing density and the rates of birth and death. Due to density dependence, populations grow when densities are low and decline when densities are high. For example, the mortality of bighorn lambs during their first winter is very high when population densities are high (**Figure 53.16**), causing population densities to fall. Lamb mortality increases as crowded ewes compete for food and are unable to provide as much milk for their offspring. The smaller lambs are then less likely to survive the winter. Competition and several other mechanisms of density-dependent population regulation are described in **Figure 53.17**.

These various examples of population regulation by negative feedback show how high densities can cause population growth rates to decline by affecting reproduction, growth, and survival. But though negative feedback helps explain why populations stop growing, it does not address why some populations fluctuate dramatically while others remain relatively stable. That is the topic we address next.

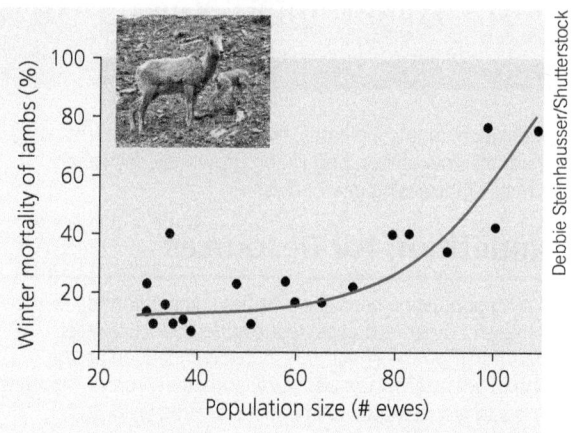

▲ **Figure 53.16 Mortality of lambs is higher when population densities are high.** The percent of bighorn lambs dying during their first winter on Ram Mountain, Alberta, rises dramatically as population size increases.

Population Dynamics

All populations show some fluctuation in size. Such population fluctuations from year to year, called **population dynamics**, are influenced by many factors and in turn affect other species. The study of population dynamics focuses on the biotic and abiotic factors that cause variation in population sizes.

Stability and Fluctuation

Populations of large mammals were once thought to remain relatively stable over time, but long-term studies have challenged that idea. For instance, the moose population on Isle Royale in Lake Superior has fluctuated substantially since around 1900. At that time, moose from the Ontario mainland 25 km away colonized the island by swimming to it or by walking across the lake when it was frozen over. Wolves, which rely on moose for most of their food, reached the island around 1950 by walking across the frozen lake. Over the past 50 years, the moose population experienced two major increases and collapses (**Figure 53.18**). The number of wolves has also fluctuated greatly, and the population is now at risk of extinction (three individuals were present in 2015). As ecologists study more species, they are finding that many populations exhibit large fluctuations in abundance.

Population Cycles: Scientific Inquiry

While many populations fluctuate at unpredictable intervals, others undergo regular boom-and-bust cycles. Some small herbivorous mammals, such as voles and lemmings, tend to have 3- to 4-year cycles, and some birds, such as ruffed grouse and ptarmigans, have 9- to 11-year cycles.

One striking example of population cycles is the roughly 10-year cycling of snowshoe hares (*Lepus americanus*) and lynx

Exploring Mechanisms of Density-Dependent Regulation

As population density increases, many density-dependent mechanisms slow or stop population growth by decreasing birth rates or increasing death rates.

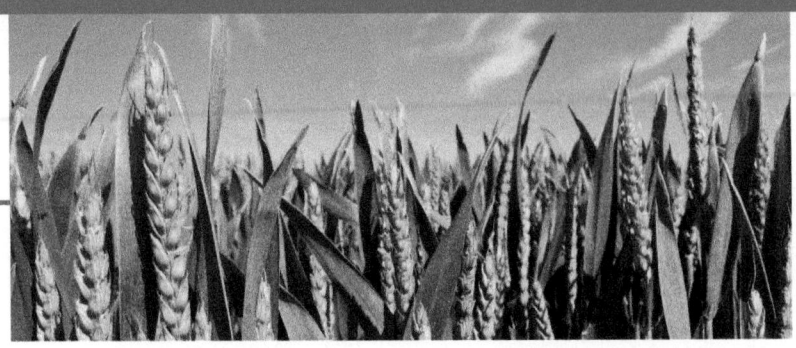

Competition for Resources

Increasing population density intensifies competition for nutrients and other resources, reducing reproductive rates. Farmers minimize the effect of resource competition on the growth of wheat (*Triticum aestivum*) and other crops by applying fertilizers to reduce nutrient limitations on crop yield.

jeka84/Shutterstock

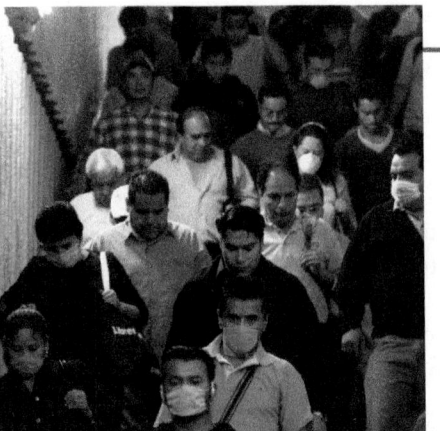

Reuters

Disease

If the transmission rate of a disease increases as a population becomes more crowded, then the disease's impact is density dependent. In humans, the respiratory diseases influenza (flu) and tuberculosis are spread through the air when an infected person sneezes or coughs. Both diseases strike a greater percentage of people in densely populated cities than in rural areas.

Predation

Predation can be an important cause of density-dependent mortality if a predator captures more food as the population density of the prey increases. As a prey population builds up, predators may also feed preferentially on that species. Population increases in the collared lemming (*Dicrostonyx groenlandicus*) lead to density-dependent predation by several predators, including the snowy owl (*Bubo scandiacus*).

Hellio & Van Ingen/NHPA/Photoshot, Ltd.

(*Lynx canadensis*) in the far northern forests of Canada and Alaska. Lynx are predators that specialize in preying on snowshoe hares, so lynx numbers might be expected to rise and fall with the numbers of hares, a pattern that occurs in much

▲ **Figure 53.18 Fluctuations in moose and wolf populations on Isle Royale, 1959–2010.**

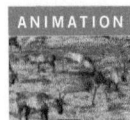

ANIMATION **_BioFlix_** Visit the Study Area in **MasteringBiology** for the BioFlix® 3-D Animation on Population Ecology.

of the northern forests of Canada (**Figure 53.19**). But why do hare numbers rise and fall in approximately 10-year cycles? Two main hypotheses have been proposed. According to the *food shortage hypothesis*, when hares become very abundant, they overexploit their winter food resources, and starvation causes a decline in abundance. The hare population recovers once the vegetation grows back. According to the *predation hypothesis*, the hare cycle is driven by the hare's interaction with its predators. Predators such as the lynx may overexploit the hare population, driving numbers very low. The predator population then also declines because there is not enough food, and this allows the hare population to recover.

Let's consider the evidence for the two hypotheses. If hare cycles are due to winter food shortage, then the cycles should stop if extra food is provided. If the cycles are due to predation, removing predators should stop the cycle. Researchers conducted such experiments in the Yukon for 20 years (or two hare cycles). They found that hare populations in the areas with extra food increased about threefold in density but continued to cycle in the same way as the unfed control populations. Therefore, food supplies alone do not cause the hare cycles shown in Figure 53.19, and we can reject the first hypothesis.

Gregory G. Dimijian/Science Source

Territoriality

Territoriality can limit population density when space becomes the resource for which individuals compete. Cheetahs (*Acinonyx jubatus*) use a chemical marker in urine to warn other cheetahs of their territorial boundaries. The presence of surplus, or nonbreeding, individuals is a good indication that territoriality is restricting population growth.

Intrinsic Factors

Intrinsic physiological factors can regulate population size. Reproductive rates of white-footed mice (*Peromyscus leucopus*) in a field enclosure can drop even when food and shelter are abundant. This drop in reproduction at high population density is associated with aggressive interactions and hormonal changes that delay sexual maturation and depress the immune system.

Nicholas Bergkessel, Jr./Science Source

Toxic Wastes

Andrew Syred/Science Source

Yeasts, such as the brewer's yeast *Saccharomyces cerevisiae*, are used to convert carbohydrates to ethanol in winemaking. The ethanol that accumulates in the wine is toxic to yeasts and contributes to density-dependent regulation of yeast population size. The alcohol content of wine is usually less than 13% because that is the maximum concentration of ethanol that most wine-producing yeast cells can tolerate.

5 μm

Joe McDonald/Corbis

▲ **Figure 53.19 Population cycles in the snowshoe hare and lynx at Kluane Lake, Yukon.**

? *What do you notice about the size of the four peaks? Why might they differ?*

What about predation? By attaching radio collars to some of the hares, the researchers discovered that almost 90% of hare deaths were due to predators, including lynx, coyotes, and raptors such as hawks and owls. In the areas where an electric fence kept out most predators, the collapse in survival that normally occurs in the decline phase of the cycle was nearly eliminated. Overexploitation by predators thus seems to be an essential part of snowshoe hare cycles; without predators, it is unlikely that hare populations would cycle in northern Canada.

The effects of predators on prey populations can be complex. In studies of the snowshoe hare it was found that hares caught by predators were usually more malnourished than the rest of the population. Predators can also have *indirect effects* on their prey, causing changes in their physiology and behaviour rather than directly killing them. In **Figure 53.20**, you can read about how stress from having predators around can cause snowshoe hares to produce smaller or even stillborn young.

Immigration, Emigration, and Metapopulations

So far, our discussion of population dynamics has focused mainly on the contributions of births and deaths. However, immigration and emigration also influence populations.

Inquiry

The sensitive snowshoe hare: Does stress from predators affect reproduction?

Experiment While studying the hare cycle in the Yukon, researchers observed that hares were producing fewer offspring when predator numbers were high. They wondered if stress due to the presence of so many predators were lowering reproduction. Michael Sheriff, then a graduate student at UBC, decided to test this hypothesis. He captured 26 pregnant hares and placed them in individual pens. For half the hares, he simulated predator stress by bringing a trained dog into the pens for 2 minutes per day. He collected the hare feces and measured the level of glucocorticoids, steroids released in response to stress. He compared the percentage of hares giving birth to live young, and the size of the offspring produced by stressed (green bars) and control (gold bars) hares.

Results

Conclusion Exposure to predators causes hares to produce higher levels of stress hormones. Stressed hares are less likely to give birth to live offspring, and if they do, their offspring are smaller. Predator stress thus contributes to the decline phase of the hare cycle.

Source: Based on Michael Sheriff et al., The sensitive hare: Sublethal effects of predator stress on reproduction in snowshoe hares, *Journal of Animal Ecology* 78:1249–1258 (2009). © Jane B Reece.

MAKE CONNECTIONS *Stress causes the release of the tropic hormone ACTH, which stimulates endocrine cells to produce corticosteroids (see page 1064, Chapter 45). Glucocorticoids are a type of corticosteroid that promotes glucose synthesis. Why might this affect fetal survival and the size of offspring produced by stressed hares?*

When a population becomes crowded and resource competition increases, individuals may begin to emigrate. If the rate of emigration increases with density, emigration can slow population growth in a manner similar to density-dependent birth or death rates (see Figure 53.15).

Immigration and emigration are particularly important when a number of local populations are linked, forming a **metapopulation**. Local populations within a metapopulation often occupy patches of suitable habitat in a sea of otherwise unsuitable habitat. Such patches vary in size, quality, and isolation from other patches, factors that influence how many individuals move among the populations. If one population becomes extinct, the patch it occupied may be recolonized by immigrants from another population.

Populations of the collared pika, a small social rodent found in talus or boulder fields in the northern Rocky Mountains (**Figure 53.21**), often form metapopulations. Pikas live in crevices among the loose talus rocks, where they have

NancyS/Shutterstock

▲ **Figure 53.21 Metapopulations of the collared pika (*Ochotona collaris*) are found in the talus slopes of the Rocky Mountains.** Only a fraction of suitable talus slope patches have a pika population at any point in time, because populations frequently go extinct. Since juvenile pikas wander to find open territories, they sometimes colonize unoccupied patches, restarting extinct populations.

shelter from predators, and forage in the surrounding alpine meadows. The alpine environment is harsh, and pika population sizes tend to be small. Populations thus occasionally go extinct and must be reestablished by individuals dispersing from other populations. Immigration can also rescue populations that are the verge of extinction, and help to maintain genetic diversity in very small populations.

The metapopulation concept is especially important in conservation biology. The habitats of organisms such as the collared pika are naturally small and patchy. However, many other species are now also found only in patches or networks of suitable habitat (parks, reserves) that are surrounded by human-modified habitat. Information on movement rates can help ecologists determine the optimal number, size, and location of conservation areas for species at risk. Conservation plans for species that occur as metapopulations often include appropriate habitat corridors that link populations and allow individuals to move between patches.

CONCEPT CHECK 53.5

1. Describe three attributes of habitat patches that could affect population density and rates of immigration and emigration.
2. **WHAT IF?** Suppose you were studying a species that has a population cycle of about 10 years. How long would you need to study the species to determine if its population size were declining? Explain.
3. **MAKE CONNECTIONS** Concept 40.2 describes negative feedback as a process that regulates biological systems. Explain how the density-dependent birth rate of dune fescue grass exemplifies negative feedback.

For suggested answers, see Appendix A.

CONCEPT 53.6

The human population is no longer growing exponentially but is still increasing rapidly

In the last few centuries, the human population has grown at an unprecedented rate, more like the reintroduced sea otter population of Vancouver Island (see Figure 53.8) than the fluctuating populations we considered in Concept 53.5. No population can grow indefinitely, however. In this section of the chapter, we'll apply the concepts of population dynamics to the specific case of the human population.

The Global Human Population

The human population has grown explosively over the last four centuries (Figure 53.22). Growth appeared slow until about 1650, at which time approximately 500 million people inhabited Earth. Our population doubled to 1 billion within the next two centuries, doubled again to 2 billion by 1930, and doubled still again by 1975 to more than 4 billion. The global population is now more than 7 billion people and is increasing by about 79 million each year. Currently the population grows by more than 1 million people each week, the equivalent of adding a city the size of Calgary or Edmonton. At this rate, it takes only about four years to add the equivalent of another United States to the world population. Population ecologists predict a population of 8.1–10.6 billion people on Earth by the year 2050.

Though the global population is still growing, the *rate* of growth did begin to slow during the 1960s (Figure 53.23). The annual rate of increase in the global population peaked at

▲ **Figure 53.22 Human population growth (data as of 2009).** The global human population has grown almost continuously throughout history, but it skyrocketed after the Industrial Revolution. Though it is not apparent at this scale, the rate of population growth has slowed in recent decades, mainly as a result of decreased birth rates throughout the world.

Source: Based on U.S. Census Bureau International Data Base. © Jane B Reece.

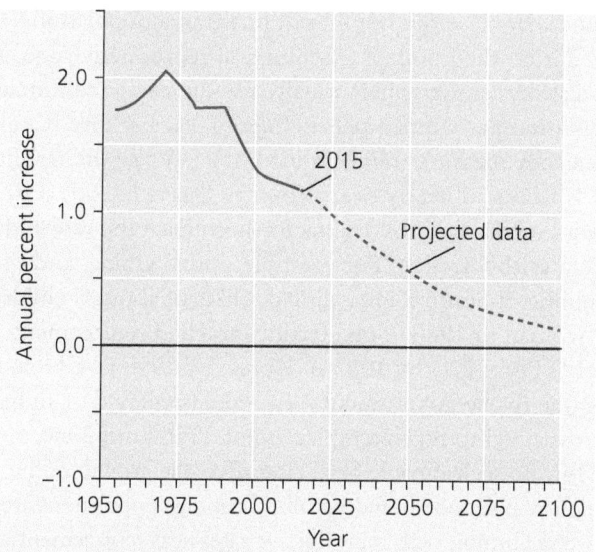

▲ **Figure 53.23 Annual percent increase in the global human population (data as of 2015).** Global growth rates are predicted to continue to decline. Projections by the Population Division of the United Nations suggest that we will mostly likely approach zero population growth by the year 2100.

2.2% in 1962; by 2014, it had declined to under 1.1%. Current models project a continued decline in the annual growth rate to roughly 0.5% by 2050, a rate that would still add 45 million more people per year if the population climbs to a projected 9 billion. The reduction in annual growth rate is the result of fundamental changes in population dynamics due to diseases, and to voluntary population control.

Regional Patterns of Population Change

We have described changes in the global population, but population dynamics vary widely from region to region. In a stable regional human population, birth rate equals death rate (disregarding the effects of immigration and emigration). Two possible configurations for a stable population are

Zero population growth = High birth rate − High death rate

or

Zero population growth = Low birth rate − Low death rate

The movement from high birth and death rates toward low birth and death rates, which tends to accompany industrialization and improved living conditions, is called the **demographic transition**. In Sweden, this transition took about 150 years, from 1810 to 1960, when birth rates finally approached death rates. In Mexico, where the human population is still growing, the transition is projected to take until at least 2050. Demographic transition is associated with an increase in the quality of health care and sanitation as well as improved access to education, especially for women.

After 1950, death rates declined rapidly in most developing countries, but birth rates declined in a more variable manner. Because the number of births in a population depends on the number of women of reproductive age, population demographers usually use the expected number of children per woman per lifetime (Total Fertility Rate) when they measure trends in birth rate. While the fertility rate is falling in nearly every country (**Figure 53.24**), economic, social, and political factors influence the rate and timing of the decline. For example, India, China, and the Republic of South Korea all had TFRs of about 6 children per woman in 1960. Total fertility reached replacement level (TFR = 2.1) by 1985 in Korea; by 1995 in China, in part due to the government's one-child policy, but India is not expected to reach a replacement TFR until 2030.

How do such variable birth rates affect the growth of the world's population? In industrialized nations, populations are near equilibrium, with reproductive rates near replacement level (total fertility rate = 2.1 children per female). In many industrialized countries, including Canada, Germany, Japan, and the United Kingdom, reproductive rates are in fact *below* replacement. These populations will eventually decline if there is no immigration and if the birth rate does not change. In fact, populations are already declining in many eastern and central European countries. Most of the current global population growth (1.1% per year) is concentrated in less industrialized countries, where about 80% of the world's people now live.

A unique feature of human population growth is our ability to control it with family planning and voluntary contraception. Social change and the rising educational and career aspirations of women in many cultures have resulted in smaller family sizes and a tendency to marry and have children at a later age. Both fewer offspring and delayed reproduction help decrease population growth rates, as societies move toward zero population growth with low birth rates and low death rates.

Age Structure

Another important demographic variable in present and future growth trends is a country's **age structure**, the relative number of individuals of each age in the population. Age structure is commonly graphed as "pyramids" like those in **Figure 53.25**. For countries such as Somalia, where birth and death rates are still high, the pyramid is bottom-heavy, skewed toward young individuals. Canada is beginning to show a spindle-shaped age structure, with fewer young people than middle-aged people (Figure 53.25). There is an obvious bulge (ages 50 to 59), that corresponds to the part of the "baby-boom" generation born after World War II, and a smaller "echo generation" (ages 20 to 35). Even though the current total fertility rate in Canada (about 1.6 children per female) is below replacement level, the population is expected to keep growing slowly due to immigration. The pyramid for Mexico indicates a country in transition. Mexico has a death rate comparable to that of Canada, and a declining but still moderately high birth rate.

Age-structure diagrams not only reflect a population's growth trends but can also illuminate social conditions. Based on the diagrams in Figure 53.25, we can predict, for instance, that education opportunities will continue to be a challenge for Somalia in the foreseeable future. In Canada, a decreasing proportion of younger working-age people will soon be supporting an increasing population of retired "boomers." This demographic feature is likely to put additional stress on universal healthcare and pension programs. Understanding age structures can help us plan for the future.

Infant Mortality and Life Expectancy

Globally, *infant mortality* has fallen, from an average of 148 deaths per 1000 live births in 1955 to a current average of only 34. Similarly, *life expectancy at birth*, the predicted average length of life at birth, is increasing. A child born in 1955 could expect to live 48 years, while a child born now can expect to live 71 years. However, these are global averages, and both infant mortality and life expectancy vary greatly across regions and countries. Infant mortality is still over 70 (per 1000 births) in Afghanistan but only 2 babies in 1000 die in Denmark or South Korea. Life expectancy at birth is 47 years for a person born in Botswana but 83 for someone born in Japan (87 for a Japanese woman). These differences reflect the enormous socio-economic differences that still remain across the globe.

Global Carrying Capacity

No ecological question is more important than the future size of the human population. The projected worldwide

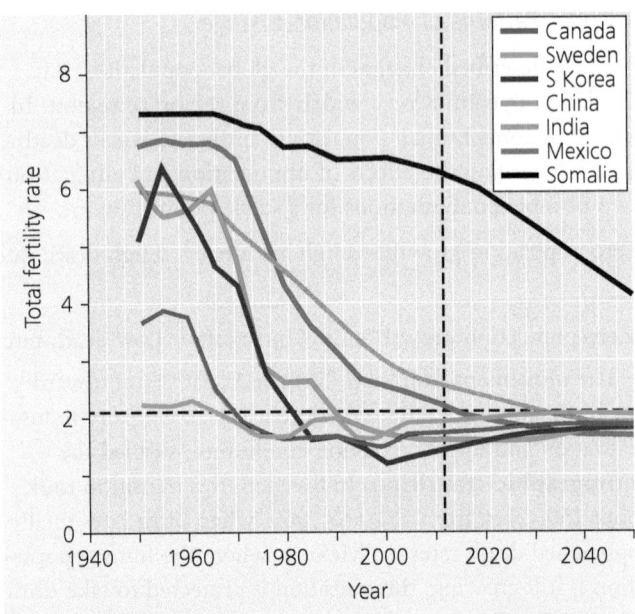

▲ **Figure 53.24 Decline in Total Fertility Rate (TFR) since the 1950s for a selection of countries.** Fertility is declining worldwide, and many countries are already at or below replacement TFR (= 2.1). Patterns of decline reflect economic development, health and education levels, and social policies.

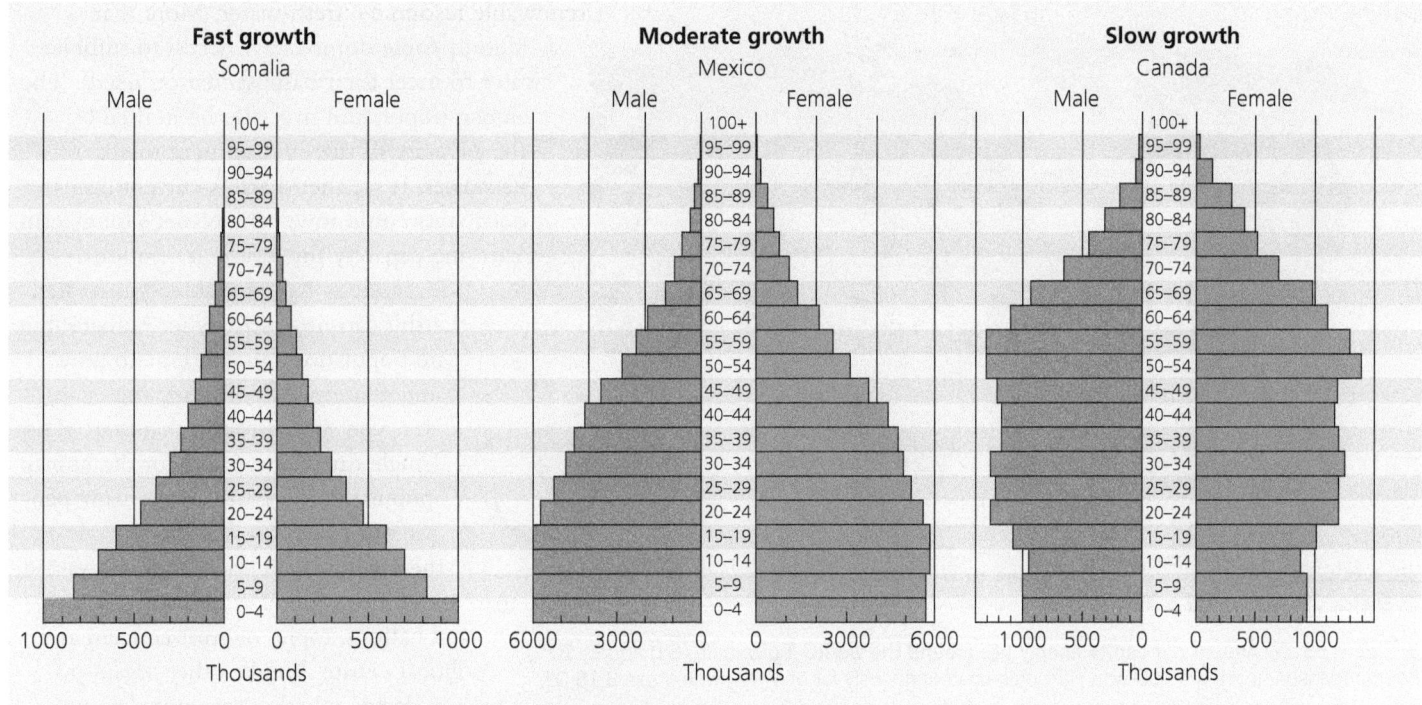

▲ Figure 53.25 Age-structure pyramids for the human population of three countries (data as of 2015). Annual growth rate (2010 to 2015) was 2.37% in Somalia, 1.37% in Mexico, and 1.04% in Canada.

population size depends on assumptions about future changes in birth and death rates. As we noted earlier, population ecologists project a global population of approximately 8.1–10.6 billion people in 2050. In other words, without some catastrophe, an estimated 1–4 billion people will be added to the population in the next four decades. But just how many humans can the biosphere support? Will the world be overpopulated in 2050? Is it *already* overpopulated?

Estimates of Carrying Capacity

For over three centuries, scientists have attempted to estimate the human carrying capacity of Earth. The first known estimate, 13.4 billion people, was made in 1679 by Anton van Leeuwenhoek, the discoverer of protists (see Chapter 28). Since then, estimates have varied from less than 1 billion to more than 1000 billion (1 trillion).

Carrying capacity is difficult to estimate, and scientists use different methods to produce their estimates. Some current researchers use curves like that produced by the logistic equation (see Figure 53.9) to predict the future maximum of the human population. Others generalize from existing "maximum" population density and multiply this number by the area of habitable land. Still others base their estimates on a single limiting factor, such as food, and consider variables such as the amount of available farmland, the average yield of crops, the prevalent diet—vegetarian or meat based—and the number of kilojoules needed per person per day.

Limits on Human Population Size

A more comprehensive approach to estimating the carrying capacity of Earth is to recognize that humans have multiple constraints: We need food, water, fuel, building materials, and other resources, such as clothing and transportation. The **ecological footprint** concept summarizes the aggregate land and water area required by each person, city, or nation to produce all the resources it consumes and to absorb all the waste it generates (Figure 53.26). One way to estimate the ecological footprint of the entire human population is to add up all the ecologically productive land on the planet and divide by the population. This calculation yields approximately 2 hectares (ha) per person. Reserving some land for parks and conservation means reducing this allotment to 1.7 ha per person—the benchmark for comparing actual ecological footprints. Anyone who consumes resources that require more than 1.7 ha to produce is said to be using an unsustainable share of Earth's resources. A typical ecological footprint for a person in Canada or the United States is about 10 ha.

Ecologists sometimes calculate ecological footprints using other currencies besides land area, such as energy use. Average energy use differs greatly for a person in developed and developing nations (Figure 53.26). A typical person in the United States, Canada, or Norway consumes roughly 30 times the energy that a person in central Africa does. Moreover, fossil fuels, such as oil, coal, and natural gas, are the source of 80% or more of the energy used in most developed nations.

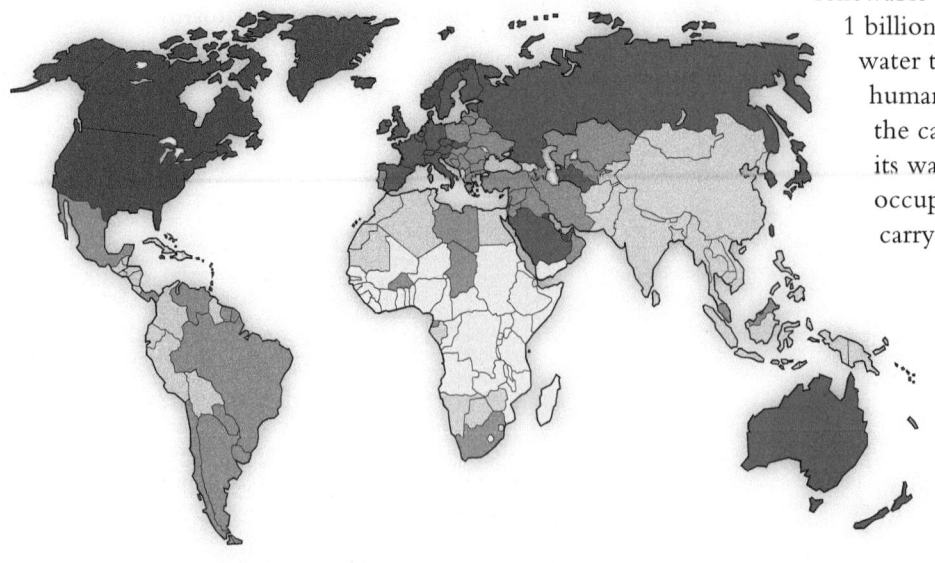

Energy use (GJ): ■ > 300 ■ 150–300 ■ 50–150 ░ 10–50 □ < 10

▲ **Figure 53.26 Annual per capita energy use around the world.** A gigajoule (GJ) equals 10^9 J. For comparison, leaving a 100-watt light bulb on continuously for one year would use 3.15 GJ.

Source: Adaptation of map from Vital Waste Graphics 2 by Emmanuelle Bournay and Claudia Heberlein. UNEP-GRID/Arendal, 2006. Used by permission.

As you will see in Chapter 56, this unsustainable reliance on fossil fuels is changing Earth's climate and increasing the amount of waste that each of us produces. Ultimately, the combination of resource use per person and population density determines our global ecological footprint.

We can only speculate about Earth's ultimate carrying capacity for the human population and about what factors will eventually limit our growth. Perhaps food will be the main limiting factor. Malnutrition and famine are common in some regions, but currently they result mainly from the unequal distribution of food rather than from inadequate production. So far, technological improvements in agriculture have allowed food supplies to keep up with global population growth.

The demands of many populations have already far exceeded the local and even regional supplies of one renewable resource—fresh water. More than 1 billion people do not have access to sufficient water to meet their basic sanitation needs. The human population may also be limited by the capacity of the environment to absorb its wastes. If so, then Earth's current human occupants could lower the planet's long-term carrying capacity for future generations.

Technology has undoubtedly increased Earth's carrying capacity for humans, but no population can continue to grow indefinitely. After reading this chapter, you should realize that there is no single carrying capacity for the human population on Earth. How many people our planet can sustain depends on the quality of life each of us enjoys and the distribution of wealth across people and nations, topics of great concern and political debate. Unlike other organisms, we can decide whether zero population growth will be attained through social changes based on human choices or, instead, through increased mortality due to resource limitation, plagues, war, and environmental degradation.

CONCEPT CHECK 53.6

1. How does a human population's age structure affect its growth rate?

2. How has the growth of Earth's human population changed in recent decades? In your answer, discuss growth rate and the number of people added each year.

3. **WHAT IF?** What choices can you make to influence your own ecological footprint?

For suggested answers, see Appendix A.

---

53 Chapter Review

Go to **MasteringBiology®** for Assignments, the eText, and the Study Area with Animations, Activities, Vocab Self-Quiz, and Practice Tests.

SUMMARY OF KEY CONCEPTS

CONCEPT 53.1

Dynamic biological processes influence population density, dispersion, and demographics (pp. 1251–1255)

- Population **density**—the number of individuals per unit area or volume—reflects the interplay of births, deaths, immigration, and emigration. Environmental and social factors influence the **dispersion** of individuals.

Patterns of dispersion

Clumped

Uniform

Random

- Populations increase from births and **immigration** and decrease from deaths and **emigration**. **Life tables**, **survivorship curves**, and **reproductive tables** summarize specific trends in **demography**.

  ? *Grey whales (Eschrichtius robustus) gather each winter near Baja California to give birth. How might such behaviour make it easier for ecologists to estimate birth and death rates for the species?*

CONCEPT 53.2

The exponential model describes population growth in an idealized, unlimited environment (pp. 1255–1257)

- If immigration and emigration are ignored, a population's growth rate (the per capita rate of increase) equals its birth rate minus its death rate.
- The **exponential growth** equation $dN/dt = rN$ represents a population's potential growth in an unlimited environment, where r is the maximum per capita rate of increase and N is the number of individuals in the population.

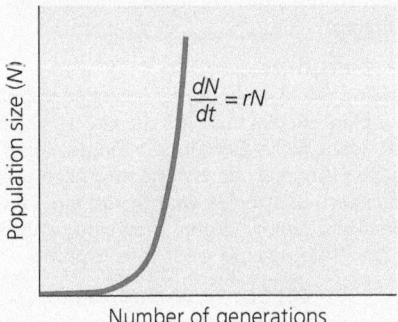

  ? *Suppose one population has an r that is twice as large as the r of another population. What is the maximum size that both populations will reach over time, based on the exponential model?*

CONCEPT 53.3

The logistic model describes how a population grows more slowly as it nears its carrying capacity (pp. 1257–1260)

- Exponential growth cannot be sustained for long in any population. A more realistic population model limits growth by incorporating **carrying capacity** (K), the maximum population size the environment can support.
- According to the **logistic growth** equation $dN/dt = rN(K - N)/K$, growth levels off as population size approaches the carrying capacity.

- The logistic model fits few real populations perfectly, but it is useful for estimating possible growth.

  ? *As an ecologist who manages a wildlife preserve, you want to increase the preserve's carrying capacity for a particular endangered species. How might you go about accomplishing this?*

CONCEPT 53.4

Life history traits are products of natural selection (pp. 1260–1262)

- **Life history** traits are evolutionary outcomes reflected in the development, physiology, and behaviour of organisms.
- Big-bang, or **semelparous**, organisms reproduce once and die. **Iteroparous** organisms produce offspring repeatedly.
- Life history traits such as brood size, age at maturity, and parental caregiving represent trade-offs between conflicting demands for time, energy, and nutrients. Two hypothetical life history patterns are *K*-selection, or density-dependent selection, and *r*-selection, or density-independent selection.

  ? *What two factors likely contribute to the evolution of semelparity versus iteroparity?*

CONCEPT 53.5

Many factors that regulate population growth are density dependent (pp. 1262–1266)

- In **density-dependent** population regulation, death rates rise and birth rates fall with increasing density. In **density-independent** population regulation, birth and death rates do not vary with density.
- Density-dependent changes in birth and death rates curb population increase through negative feedback and can eventually stabilize a population near its carrying capacity. Density-dependent limiting factors include intraspecific competition for limited food or space, increased predation, disease, stress due to crowding, and build-up of toxic substances.
- Because changing environmental conditions periodically disrupt them, all populations exhibit some size fluctuations. Many populations undergo regular boom-and-bust cycles that are influenced by complex interactions between biotic and abiotic factors. A **metapopulation** is a group of populations linked by immigration and emigration.

  ? *Give an example of one biotic and one abiotic factor that contribute to yearly fluctuations in the size of the human population.*

CONCEPT 53.6

The human population is no longer growing exponentially but is still increasing rapidly (pp. 1267–1270)

- Since about 1650, the global human population has grown exponentially, but within the last 50 years, the rate of growth has fallen by half. Differences in **age structure** show that while some nations' populations are growing rapidly, those of others are stable or declining in size. Infant mortality rates and life expectancy at birth differ markedly between countries.
- **Ecological footprint** is the aggregate land and water area needed to produce all the resources a person or group of people consume and to absorb all of their wastes. It is one measure of how close we are to the carrying capacity of Earth. With a world population of more than 7 billion people, we are already using many resources in an unsustainable manner.

  ? *How are humans different from other species in the ability to "choose" a carrying capacity for their environment?*

TEST YOUR UNDERSTANDING

LEVEL 1: KNOWLEDGE/COMPREHENSION

1. Population ecologists follow the fate of same-age cohorts to
   a. determine a population's carrying capacity.
   b. determine the birth rate and death rate of each group in a population.

c. determine if a population is regulated by density-dependent processes.

d. determine the factors that regulate the size of a population.

2. A population's carrying capacity
   a. may change as environmental conditions change.
   b. can be accurately calculated using the logistic growth model.
   c. increases as the per capita growth rate (r) decreases.
   d. can never be exceeded.

3. Scientific study of the population cycles of the snowshoe hare and its predator, the lynx, has revealed that
   a. predation is the dominant factor affecting prey population cycling.
   b. hares and lynx are so mutually dependent that each species cannot survive without the other.
   c. both hare and lynx populations are regulated mainly by abiotic factors.
   d. the hare population is r-selected and the lynx population is K-selected.

4. Analyzing ecological footprints reveals that
   a. Earth's carrying capacity would increase if per capita meat consumption increased.
   b. current demand by industrialized countries for resources is much smaller than the ecological footprint of those countries.
   c. it is not possible for technological improvements to increase Earth's carrying capacity for humans.
   d. the ecological footprint of the United States is large because per capita resource use is high.

5. Based on current growth rates, Earth's human population in 2020 will be closest to
   a. 2 million.   c. 7.5 billion.
   b. 4 billion.   d. 10.5 billion.

LEVEL 2: APPLICATION/ANALYSIS

6. The observation that members of a population are uniformly distributed suggests that
   a. resources are distributed unevenly.
   b. the members of the population are competing for access to a resource.
   c. the members of the population are neither attracted to nor repelled by one another.
   d. the density of the population is low.

7. According to the logistic growth equation

$$\frac{dN}{dt} = = rN\frac{(K - N)}{K}$$

   a. the number of individuals added per unit time is greatest when N is close to zero.
   b. the per capita growth rate (r) increases as N approaches K.
   c. population growth is zero when N equals K.
   d. the population grows exponentially when K is small.

8. Which pair of terms most accurately describes life history traits for a stable population of wolves?
   a. semelparous; r-selected
   b. semelparous; K-selected
   c. iteroparous; r-selected
   d. iteroparous; K-selected

9. During exponential growth, a population always
   a. has a constant, instantaneous per capita growth rate.
   b. quickly reaches its carrying capacity.
   c. cycles through time.
   d. loses some individuals to emigration.

10. Which of the following statements about human population in industrialized countries is incorrect?
    a. Life history is r-selected.
    b. Average family size is relatively small.
    c. The population has undergone the demographic transition.
    d. The survivorship curve is Type I.

LEVEL 3: SYNTHESIS/EVALUATION

11. **INTERPRET THE DATA** To estimate which age cohort in a population of females produces the most female offspring, you need information about the number of offspring produced per capita within that cohort and the number of individuals alive in the cohort. Make this estimate for Belding's ground squirrels by multiplying the number of females alive at the start of the year (column 2 in Table 53.1) by the average number of female offspring produced per female (column 5 in Table 53.1). Draw a bar graph with female age in years on the x-axis (0–1, 1–2, and so on) and total number of female offspring produced for each age cohort on the y-axis. Which cohort of female Belding's ground squirrels produces the most female young?

12. **EVOLUTION CONNECTION**
    Write a paragraph contrasting the conditions that favour the evolution of semelparous (one-time) reproduction versus iteroparous (repeated) reproduction.

13. **SCIENTIFIC INQUIRY**
    You are testing the hypothesis that increased population density of a particular plant species increases the rate at which a pathogenic fungus infects the plant. Because the fungus causes visible scars on the leaves, you can easily determine whether a plant is infected. Design an experiment to test your hypothesis. Describe your experimental and control groups, how you would collect data, and what results you would see if your hypothesis is correct.

14. **SCIENCE, TECHNOLOGY, AND SOCIETY**
    Many people regard the rapid population growth of less industrialized countries as our most serious environmental problem. Others think that the population growth in industrialized countries, though smaller, is actually a greater environmental threat. What problems result from population growth in (a) less industrialized countries and (b) industrialized nations? Which do you think is a greater threat, and why?

15. **WRITE ABOUT A THEME: INTERACTIONS**
    In a short essay (100–150 words), identify the factor or factors in Figure 53.17 that you think may ultimately be most important for density-dependent population regulation in humans, and explain your reasoning.

16. **SYNTHESIZE YOUR KNOWLEDGE**

Stringer/Reuters

Locusts (grasshoppers in the family Acrididae) undergo dramatic population outbreaks. Of the mechanisms of density-dependent regulation shown in Figure 53.17, choose the two that you think most apply to locust swarms, and explain why.

For selected answers, see Appendix A.

54
Community Ecology

KEY CONCEPTS

54.1 Community interactions are classified by whether they help, harm, or have no effect on the species involved

54.2 Diversity and trophic structure characterize biological communities

54.3 Disturbance influences species diversity and composition

54.4 Biogeographic factors affect community diversity

54.5 Pathogens alter community structure locally and globally

▲ Figure 54.1 **Why do kelp forest communities turn into urchin barrens?**

Dynamic Communities

An underwater "forest" occurs along the coasts of North America (**Figure 54.1**). Kelp stand anchored to the rocky bottom with their undulating blades reaching toward the water surface. Lobsters and crabs crawl on the bottom searching for clams, mussels, and worms. Wolffish dig in the bottom sediments for clams and worms, and attack passing sea urchins, crabs, and lobsters. The juveniles of large fish such as cod feed on zooplankton and hide from their predators among the kelp blades. Together, these species make up the *kelp forest community*. A **biological community** is a group of populations of different species that live close enough to interact.

Occasionally, these diverse and productive kelp forest communities disappear. Fronts of grazing sea urchins literally mow down the kelp, converting the habitat into an "urchin barrens" covered by low-lying crustose algae (Figure 54.1). Few species belonging to the original community survive in such a changed environment. What allows sea urchins to destroy kelp forest communities, and how does the kelp forest recover? As you will see, species interactions, including herbivory, predation, and disease, play critical roles.

In Chapter 53, you learned how individuals within a population can affect other individuals of the same species. This chapter will examine ecological

◀ **Atlantc Wolffish (*Anarhichas lupus*)**

interactions between populations of different species. While the most obvious species interactions in many communities are predation and herbivory, other less easily seen interactions, such as competition, parasitism, and mutualism, are often also very important. Ecologists define the boundaries of a particular community to fit their research questions. They might study the community of decomposers and other organisms living on a rotting log, the benthic community in Lake Superior, or the community of trees and shrubs in Banff National Park in Alberta.

We begin this chapter by exploring the kinds of interactions that occur between species in a community, such as the kelp and sea urchins in Figure 54.1. We'll then consider several of the factors that are most significant in structuring a community—in determining how many species there are, which particular species are present, and the relative abundance of these species. Finally, we will apply some of the principles of community ecology to the study of human disease.

CONCEPT 54.1

Community interactions are classified by whether they help, harm, or have no effect on the species involved

Some key relationships in the life of an organism are its interactions with individuals of other species in the community. These **interspecific interactions** include competition, predation, herbivory, symbiosis (including parasitism, mutualism, and commensalism), and facilitation. In this section, we will define and describe each of these interactions, recognizing that ecologists do not always agree on the precise boundaries of each type of interaction.

We will use the symbols + and − to indicate how each interspecific interaction affects the survival and reproduction of the two species engaged in the interaction. For example, predation is a +/− interaction, with a positive effect on the survival and reproduction of the predator population and a negative effect on that of the prey population. Mutualism is a +/+ interaction because the survival and reproduction of both species are increased in the presence of the other. A 0 indicates that a population is not affected by the interaction in any known way.

Species interactions influence the composition and dynamics of communities over two very different time frames. Species often decline or increase in abundance as interactions alter survival or reproductive rates—this is a relatively quick response that occurs in what we call ecological time. However, interactions can also influence the evolutionary trajectories of species within communities,

and the resulting changes in morphology, physiology, and behaviour can then alter interactions with other species. In this section, we will examine some of the ecological and evolutionary consequences of species interactions for communities.

Competition

Interspecific competition is a −/− interaction that occurs when individuals of different species compete for a resource that limits their growth and survival. Weeds growing in a garden compete with garden plants for soil nutrients and water. Grasshoppers and bison in the Great Plains compete for the grass they both eat. Lynx and foxes in the northern forests of Alaska and Canada compete for prey such as snowshoe hares. In contrast, some resources, such as oxygen, are rarely in short supply on land; thus, although most species use this resource, they do not usually compete for it.

Competitive Exclusion

What happens in a community when two species compete for limited resources? In 1934, Russian ecologist G. F. Gause studied this question using laboratory experiments with two closely related species of ciliated protists, *Paramecium aurelia* and *Paramecium caudatum*. He cultured the species under stable conditions, adding a constant amount of food each day. When Gause grew the two species separately, each population grew rapidly and then levelled off at the apparent carrying capacity of the culture (see Figure 53.10a for an illustration of the logistic growth of *P. aurelia*). But when Gause grew the two species together, *P. caudatum* became extinct in the culture. Gause inferred that *P. aurelia* had a competitive edge in obtaining food. He concluded that two species competing for the same limiting resources cannot coexist permanently in the same place. In the absence of disturbance, one species will use

Paramecium caudatum

25 μm

the resources more efficiently and reproduce more rapidly than the other. Even a slight reproductive advantage will eventually lead to local elimination of the inferior competitor, an outcome called **competitive exclusion**.

Ecological Niches

EVOLUTION The sum of a species' use of the biotic and abiotic resources in its environment is called its **ecological niche**. The niche of a species of tropical tree lizard, for instance, includes the temperature range it tolerates, the size of branches on which it perches, the time of day when it is active, and the sizes and kinds of insects it eats. Such factors define the species' niche, or ecological role—how it fits into an ecosystem.

We can use the niche concept to restate the principle of competitive exclusion: Two species cannot coexist permanently in a community if their niches are identical. However, ecologically similar species *can* coexist if one or more significant differences in their niches are present or arise through time. The differentiation of niches that enables similar species to coexist is called **resource partitioning** (Figure 54.2).

As a result of competition, a species' **fundamental niche**, which is the niche potentially occupied by that species, is often different from its **realized niche**, the portion of its fundamental niche that the species actually occupies. Ecologists can identify the fundamental niche of a species by testing the range of conditions in which it grows and reproduces in the absence of competitors. They can also test whether a potential competitor limits a species' realized niche by removing the competitor and seeing if the first species expands into the newly available niche space. The classic experiment depicted in **Figure 54.3** clearly showed that competition between two barnacle species kept one species from occupying part of its fundamental niche.

EVOLUTION Resource partitioning allows similar species to coexist in ecological communities. Each species uses only a portion of all the resources available. But how do these niche differences come about? Some partitioning

▲ Figure 54.2 **Resource partitioning among Dominican Republic lizards.** Seven species of *Anolis* lizards live in close proximity, and all feed on insects and other small arthropods. However, competition for food is reduced because each lizard species has a different preferred perch, thus occupying a distinct niche.

Source: Adaptation of figure 1 from "The Anoles of La Palma: Aspects of Their Ecological Relationships" by A. Stanley Rand and Ernest E. Williams, from *Breviora*, Volume 327: 1–19. Copyright © 1969 by Museum of Comparative Zoology, Harvard University. Reprinted with permission.

▼ Figure 54.3 | **Inquiry**

Can a species' niche be influenced by interspecific competition?

Experiment Ecologist Joseph Connell studied two barnacle species—*Chthamalus stellatus* and *Balanus balanoides*—that have a stratified distribution on rocks along the coast of Scotland. *Chthamalus* is usually found higher on the rocks than *Balanus*. To determine whether the distribution of *Chthamalus* is the result of interspecific competition with *Balanus*, Connell removed *Balanus* from the rocks at several sites.

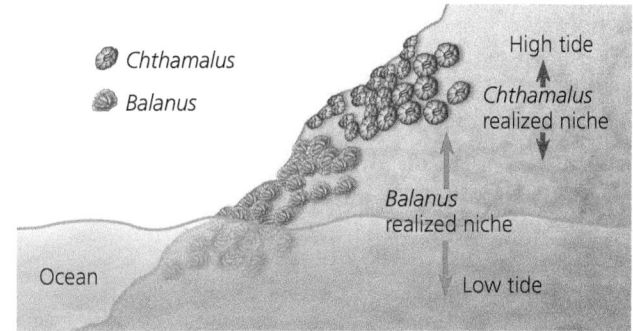

Results *Chthamalus* spread into the region formerly occupied by *Balanus*.

Conclusion Interspecific competition makes the realized niche of *Chthamalus* much smaller than its fundamental niche.

Source: Based on J. H. Connell, The influence of interspecific competition and other factors on the distribution of the barnacle *Chthamalus stellatus*, *Ecology* 42:710–723 (1961). © Jane B Reece.

(MB) See the related Experimental Inquiry Tutorial in MasteringBiology.

WHAT IF? *Other observations showed that* Balanus *cannot survive high on the rocks because it dries out during low tides. How would* Balanus's *realized niche compare with its fundamental niche?*

occurs due to current species interactions. For example, *Balanus* actively prevents *Chthamalus* from occupying space in the lower intertidal zone (Figure 54.3). But many of the differences among species are the result of natural selection and have evolved slowly over time. In the past, *Chthamalus* evolved physiological and morphological traits that allowed it to survive many hours of exposure to the air, and this adaptation now allows it to occupy the high intertidal niche. Similarly, lizard species that perch on shrubs and fence posts evolved long legs that allow them to jump to the ground to capture prey, while those that live on twigs evolved elongated bodies and short legs that allow them to creep along narrow branches (Figure 54.2).

Character Displacement

EVOLUTION Sometimes adaptations that allow species to partition resources are the consequence of competition that occurred in the past, called the "ghost of competition past." In Chapter 22, you saw how differences in beak size among the Galápagos finches led Charles Darwin to conclude that natural selection had produced the match between beak size and size of seed eaten. More recent studies have shown that where two species of finch are present on the same island, one has evolved a smaller beak and the other a larger beak. Since finches with different beak sizes eat different sizes of seeds, the evolution of greater differences reduces interspecific competition for resources. The evolution of differences in morphology and resource use as a result of competition is known as **character displacement**.

Another classic example of character displacement comes from populations of threespine sticklebacks, fishes that live in small lakes on the coastal islands of British Columbia. Some lakes have only one stickleback species, a generalist feeder that consumes benthic (lake bottom) invertebrates and zooplankton in the limnetic (surface) zone. However, in other lakes there are two species: a small limnetic species and a much larger benthic species (Figure 54.4). How did

this come about? Eric Taylor and colleagues from the University of British Columbia used molecular genetics to solve the puzzle. They discovered that marine sticklebacks, which feed mainly in the limnetic zone, first colonized the lakes 10 000 to 12 000 years ago. When sea level fell, the sticklebacks were trapped in the lakes, and became generalists, able to feed in the limnetic and the benthic zones. Then, about 2000 years later, sea level rose once more, allowing marine sticklebacks to again invade some of the lakes. In these lakes, competition between the early and late colonizers led to the evolution of greater differences in morphology and resource use. Over time, the early colonizers became deep-bodied benthic specialists, and the later colonizers remained in the limnetic zone. In lakes without a second invasion, sticklebacks remain generalists.

Predation

Predation refers to a +/− interaction between species in which one species, the predator, kills and eats the other, the prey. Though the term *predation* generally elicits such images as a lion attacking and eating an antelope, it applies to a wide range of interactions. An animal that kills a plant by eating the plant's tissues can also be considered a predator. Animals that consume seeds are often called seed predators.

Predators influence the communities in which they occur through their impacts on the abundance and dynamics of other species. In Chapter 53, for example, we saw that lynx predation can cause snowshoe hare populations to cycle from high to low densities in northern Canada. Later in this chapter, you will see that the impact of top predators on species abundance can extend to trophic levels below that of their prey through *trophic cascades*.

Understanding how predators influence ecological communities is hugely important, in part because human activities have disproportionately affected large predators, resulting in extinctions (for example, sabre-toothed tigers), extirpation (for example, wolves throughout much of North America), and population declines (for example, African lions, blacktip reef sharks). As a result, most ecological communities are very different today than they were in the past. There are now efforts worldwide, many successful, to reintroduce or to encourage the recovery of large predators. You will encounter examples in Chapters 55 and 56.

Historically, predators were targeted by people to protect human lives and livelihoods. Wolves are still culled in northern British Columbia and the Yukon to maintain higher numbers of moose and caribou for human hunters. Bears, coyotes, and cougars that harm humans or their pets are captured and sometimes euthanized. There have been calls to cull the grey seal population on the east coast to aid

Todd Hatfield

▲ **Figure 54.4 Character displacement in the threespine stickleback (*Gasterosterus* sp): indirect evidence of past competition.** The deep body of the larger benthic form is adapted for feeding on bottom invertebrates and the slender and smaller limnetic form is better adapted for feeding on zooplankton in the surface waters.

the recovery of the Atlantic cod fishery. Should we continue to "manage" or deliberately manipulate predator densities? Clearly there are social, economic, and ethical issues to consider, in addition to the potential ecological consequences. In the Scientific Skills Exercise you will examine a current controversy regarding a proposal to save threatened caribou populations in northern Alberta by lowering wolf numbers.

Because eating and avoiding being eaten are prerequisite to reproductive success, natural selection tends to refine predator and prey adaptations. Predators need effective means of finding, identifying, and capturing potential

prey. Rattlesnakes and other pit vipers find their prey with a pair of heat-sensing organs located between their eyes and nostrils (see Figure 50.7a). Owls have large eyes that help them see prey at night. Many predators have claws, fangs, or poison that help them catch and subdue their food.

Potential prey animals have behavioural, mechanical, and chemical adaptations that help them avoid being eaten. Common behavioural defences include hiding, fleeing, and forming herds or schools. Some birds use alarm calls to summon other individuals (of the same species), which then mob the predator. Mechanical and

---

SCIENTIFIC SKILLS EXERCISE

Graphing and Interpreting Experimental Data

Can Reducing Wolf Numbers Buy Time for Woodland Caribou in Northern Alberta? Populations of woodland caribou are declining precipitously across Canada, and nowhere is the situation more urgent than in northern Alberta. Without effective recovery strategies, some caribou populations are expected to disappear within 20 years.

We know that populations decline when mortality rate exceeds birth rate. And research shows that wolves are responsible for most caribou deaths in the region. But why is wolf predation is so high? After all, wolves and caribou have coexisted in the area for thousands of years.

The answer is that human activity has dramatically altered predator-prey relationships in these boreal communities. Forestry, agriculture, and construction associated with oil sands development have increased the amount of young forest and edge habitat at the expense of the mature forest favoured by caribou. High numbers of white-tailed deer and moose, which thrive in younger forests, have led to an estimated doubling of the wolf population. The result has been heavier predation on caribou. To make matters worse, roads, pipelines, and seismic corridors facilitate the movement of wolves, allowing them easier access to habitat that previously served as low-predator refuge areas for caribou.

Scientists have concluded that predator control may be necessary in the short term to prevent the extinction of the caribou populations in the region. An experimental wolf reduction was conducted to measure the impact on caribou survival and population growth rate. If effective, temporary wolf removals could be used to buy time for certain caribou herds, slowing or reversing declines, until longer-term solutions such as forest recovery can be implemented.

Menno Schaefer/Shutterstock

How the Experiment Was Done The ecologists chose to use a **BACI (Before-After-Control-Impact) design** for the experiment, in which response variables (for example, caribou survival rate) are measured in an experimental and in a control population, before and after the

manipulation. One caribou population was selected for wolf reduction, and another to serve as the control. Caribou survival and reproductive rates were monitored in both populations from 1999 to 2012. Beginning in 2005, wolf numbers were reduced by about half in one of the populations. Survival and reproductive rates were used to calculate per capita population growth rate (r) before and during wolf-removal for both caribou populations.

Table 1 Average female caribou survival rate and caribou population growth rate (r) in the wolf-removal and control populations, before and during wolf removals

	Average Adult Female Survival	
	Wolf-Removal	Control
Before	0.894	0.830
During	0.907	0.793
Population Growth Rate (r)		
	Wolf-Removal	Control
Before	−0.057	−0.096
During	−0.008	−0.148

Interpret the Data

1. Make a bar graph of the adult female survival data from Table 1.
2. What does the graph suggest about the effect of wolf removal on caribou survival in the experimental population? Did the control population show the same pattern?
3. Make a bar graph of the population growth rate data from Table 1.
4. What does the graph suggest about the effect of wolf removal on the growth rate of the experimental population? Did the control population show the same pattern?
5. Based on the observed population growth rate, would you expect the experimental population to grow if wolf reduction had been continued? Why or why not?
6. What do you think will happen to the experimental population after the experiment ends, and wolf reduction is no longer carried out?
7. Why does a BACI design include a control population?

Data from D. Hervieux, M. Hebblewhite, D. Stepnisky, M. Bacon, S. Boutin, Managing wolves (Canis lupus) to recover threatened woodland caribou (Rangifer tarandus caribou) in Alberta, Canadian Journal of Zoology 92:1029–1037 (2014). © Jane B Reece.

chemical defences protect species such as porcupines and skunks (**Figure 54.5a** and **b**). Some chemically defended animals such as the poison dart frog (**Figure 54.5c**) exhibit bright **aposematic** or warning colouration, which deters potential predators. Other species have **cryptic colouration**, or camouflage, which makes them difficult to see (**Figure 54.5d**).

Some prey species are protected by their resemblance to other species. In **Batesian mimicry**, a palatable or harmless species mimics an unpalatable or harmful one. The larva of the hawkmoth *Hemeroplanes ornatus* puffs up its head and thorax when disturbed, looking like the head of a small venomous snake (**Figure 54.5e**). In **Müllerian mimicry**,

two or more unpalatable species, such as the cuckoo bee and yellow jacket, resemble each other (**Figure 54.5f**). Presumably, predators learn more quickly to avoid such prey if they encounter them more often.

Some predators also use mimicry. The mimic octopus (*Thaumoctopus mimicus*) can take on the appearance and movement of more than a dozen marine animals, including crabs, sea stars, sea snakes, fish, and stingrays (**Figure 54.6**). It uses its mimicry to approach prey—for example, imitating a crab to approach another crab and eat it. It also uses its mimicry to scare predators. When attacked by a damselfish, the octopus quickly mimics a banded sea snake, a known predator of the damselfish.

(a) Mechanical defence

▶ Porcupine

Tony Heald/Nature Picture Library

(b) Chemical defence

▶ Skunk

geoffkuchera/Fotolia

(c) Aposematic colouration: warning colouration

◀ Poison dart frog

Dante Fenolio/Science Source

(d) Cryptic colouration: camouflage

▶ Canyon tree frog

Barry Mansell/Nature Picture Library

(e) Batesian mimicry: A harmless species mimics a harmful one

Robert Pickett/Papilio/Alamy Stock Photo

▲ Venomous green parrot snake

◀ Nonvenomous hawkmoth larva

Scott T. Smith/Corbis

(f) Müllerian mimicry: Two unpalatable species mimic each other

James K. Lindsey

▶ Yellow jacket

◀ Cuckoo bee

Edward S. Ross

▲ **Figure 54.5 Examples of defensive adaptation in animals.**

(a) Mimicking a sea snake

(b) Mimicking a flounder

(c) Mimicking a stingray

▲ **Figure 54.6 The mimic octopus. (a)** After hiding six of its tentacles in a hole in the seafloor, the octopus waves its other two tentacles to mimic a sea snake. **(b)** Flattening its body and arranging its arms to trail behind, the octopus mimics a flounder (a flat fish). **(c)** It can mimic a stingray by flattening most of its tentacles alongside its body while allowing one tentacle to extend behind.

Herbivory

Ecologists use the term **herbivory** to refer to a +/− interaction in which an organism eats parts of a plant or alga. While large mammalian herbivores, such as deer, moose, and elephants may be most familiar, most herbivores are actually invertebrates, such as grasshoppers and beetles. In the ocean, herbivores include snails, sea urchins, some tropical fishes, and certain mammals, including the manatee (Figure 54.7).

Like predators, herbivores can significantly influence the abundance of other species. Swarming desert locusts periodically destroy vegetation across large swaths of western Africa, causing severe economic harm to farmers in the herbivores' path. Sea urchins can transform a highly productive kelp bed community into unproductive barrens (see Figure 54.1). Other herbivores influence communities by altering the physical environment. Beavers convert forest-bordered streams into ponds and open meadows. Overgrazing by lesser snow geese (*Chen caerulescens caerulescens*) on their Hudson Bay breeding grounds has turned salt marsh habitat into bare mineral soil.

Herbivores have various specialized feeding adaptations. Many herbivorous insects have chemical sensors on their feet that enable them to distinguish between plants based

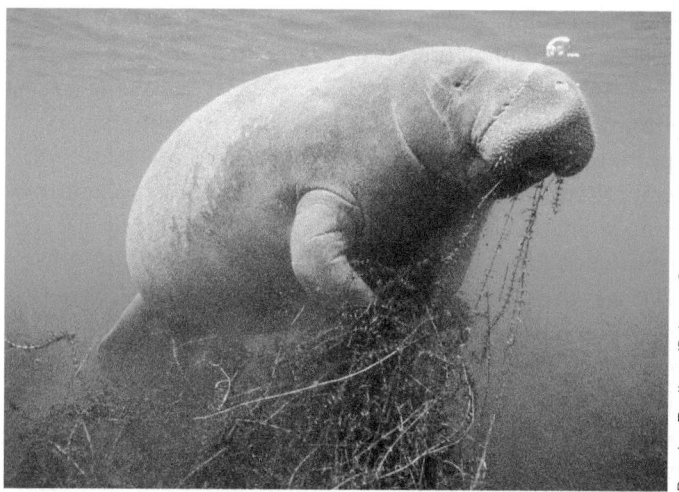

▲ **Figure 54.7 A West Indies manatee (*Trichechus manatus*) in Florida.** The animal in this photo is feeding on *Hydrilla*, an introduced species.

on their toxicity or nutritional value. Others have specialized teeth or digestive systems adapted for processing vegetation (see Chapter 41).

Since plants cannot run away to avoid being eaten, a plant's arsenal against herbivores often features chemical toxins or structures such as spines and thorns. The tropical vine *Strychnos* defends itself with the toxin *strychnine*, the tobacco plant uses *nicotine*, and many plant species use *tannins* to deter herbivores. Compounds that are not toxic to humans but may be distasteful to many herbivores are responsible for the familiar flavours of cinnamon, cloves, and peppermint. Certain plants produce chemicals that cause abnormal development in some insects that eat them.

Symbiosis

When individuals of two or more species live in direct and intimate contact with one another, their relationship is called **symbiosis**. In this book, we define symbiosis to include all such interactions, whether they are harmful, helpful, or neutral. Some biologists define symbiosis more narrowly as a synonym for mutualism, an interaction in which both species benefit.

Parasitism

Parasitism is a +/− symbiotic interaction in which one organism, the **parasite**, derives its nourishment from another organism, its **host**, which is harmed in the process. Parasites that live within the body of their host, such as tapeworms, are called **endoparasites**; parasites that feed on the external surface of a host, such as ticks and lice, are called **ectoparasites**. In one particular type of parasitism, parasitoid insects—usually small wasps—lay eggs on or in living hosts. The larvae then feed on the body of the host, eventually killing it. Some ecologists have estimated that at least one-third of all species on Earth are parasites.

Many parasites have complex life cycles involving multiple hosts. The blood fluke, which currently infects approximately 200 million people around the world, requires two hosts at different times in its development: humans and freshwater snails (see Figure 33.11). Some parasites change the behaviour of their hosts in a way that increases the probability of the parasite being transferred from one host to another. For instance, the presence of parasitic acanthocephalan (spiny-headed) worms leads their crustacean hosts to engage in a variety of atypical behaviours, including leaving protective cover and moving into the open. As a result of their modified behaviour, the crustaceans have a greater chance of being eaten by the birds that are the second host in the parasitic worm's life cycle.

Parasites can significantly affect the survival, reproduction, and density of their host population, either directly or indirectly. For example, ticks that live as ectoparasites on moose weaken their hosts by withdrawing blood and causing hair breakage and loss. In their weakened condition, the moose have a greater chance of dying from cold stress or predation by wolves.

Mutualism

Mutualistic symbiosis, or **mutualism**, is an interspecific interaction that benefits both species (+/+). We have described many examples of mutualism in previous chapters: nitrogen fixation by bacteria in the root nodules of legumes; the digestion of cellulose by microorganisms in the digestive systems of termites and ruminant mammals; the exchange of nutrients in mycorrhizae; associations of fungi and the roots of plants; and photosynthesis by unicellular algae in corals. The interaction between termites and the microorganisms in their digestive system is an example of *obligate mutualism*, in which at least one species has lost the ability to survive without its partner. In *facultative mutualism*, as in the acacia-ant example shown in **Figure 54.8**, each species can survive alone.

Mutualistic relationships sometimes involve the coevolution of related adaptations in both species, with changes in either species likely to affect the survival and reproduction of the other. For example, most flowering plants have adaptations such as nectar or fruit that attract animals that function in pollination or seed dispersal (see Chapter 38). In turn, many animals have adaptations that help them find and consume nectar.

Commensalism

An interaction between species that benefits one of the species but neither harms nor helps the other (+/0) is

(a) Certain species of acacia trees in Central and South America have hollow thorns that house stinging ants of the genus *Pseudomyrmex*. The ants feed on nectar produced by the tree and on protein-rich swellings along the bases of leaves.

(b) The acacia benefits because the pugnacious ants, which attack anything that touches the tree, remove fungal spores, small herbivores, and debris. They also clip vegetation that grows close to the acacia.

▲ Figure 54.8 **Mutualism between acacia trees and ants.**

called **commensalism**. Commensal interactions are difficult to document in nature because any close association between species likely affects both species, even if only slightly. For instance, "hitchhiking" species, such as algae that live on the shells of aquatic turtles or barnacles that attach to whales, are sometimes considered commensal. The hitchhikers gain a place to grow while having seemingly little effect on their ride. However, the hitchhikers may in fact slightly decrease the reproductive success of their hosts by reducing the hosts' efficiency of movement in searching for food or escaping from predators. Conversely, the hitchhikers may provide a benefit in the form of camouflage.

▲ Figure 54.9 **A possible example of commensalism between cattle egrets and water buffalo.**

Some associations that are possibly commensal involve one species obtaining food that is inadvertently exposed by another. Cowbirds and cattle egrets feed on insects flushed out of the grass by grazing bison, cattle, horses, and other herbivores. Because the birds increase their feeding rates when following the herbivores, they clearly benefit from the association. Much of the time, the herbivores may be unaffected by the relationship (**Figure 54.9**). However, they, too, may sometimes derive some benefit; the birds tend to be opportunistic feeders that occasionally remove and eat ticks and other ectoparasites from the herbivores.

Facilitation

Species can have positive effects (+/+ or 0/+) on the survival and reproduction of other species without necessarily living in the direct and intimate contact of a symbiosis. This type of interaction, called **facilitation**, is particularly common in plant ecology. For instance, the black rush *Juncus gerardi* makes the soil more hospitable for other plant species in some zones of New England salt marshes (**Figure 54.10a**). *Juncus* helps prevent salt build-up in the soil by shading the soil surface, which reduces evaporation. *Juncus* also prevents the salt marsh soils from becoming oxygen depleted as it transports oxygen to its belowground tissues. In one study, when *Juncus* was removed from areas in the upper middle intertidal zone, those areas supported 50% fewer plant species (**Figure 54.10b**).

All five types of interactions that we have discussed so far—competition, predation, herbivory, symbiosis, and facilitation—strongly influence the structure of

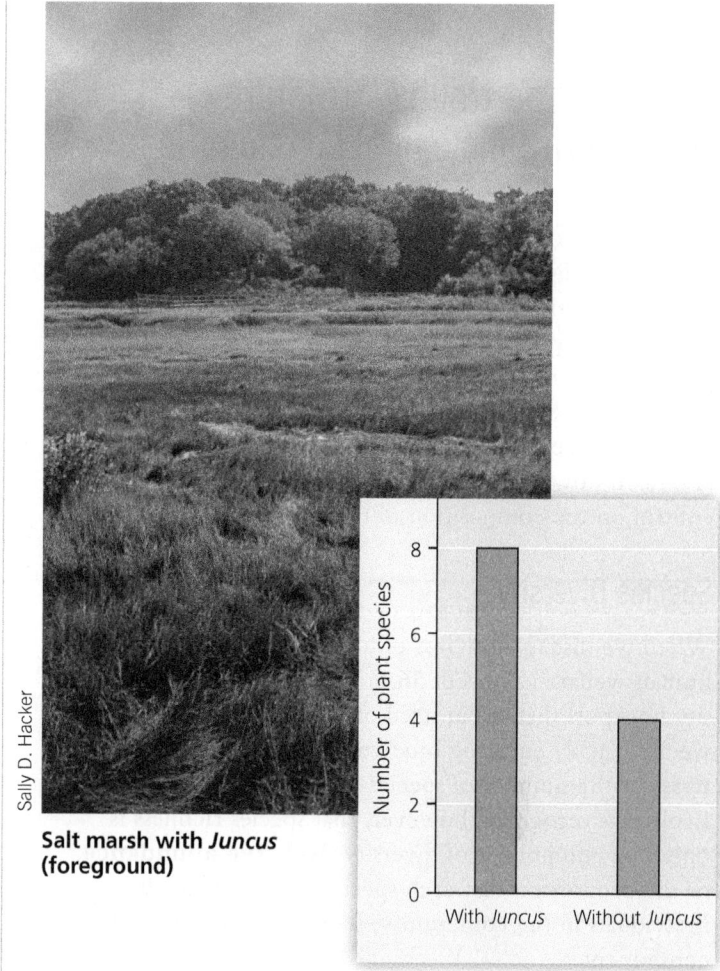

Salt marsh with *Juncus* (foreground)

▲ Figure 54.10 **Facilitation by black rush (*Juncus gerardi*) in New England salt marshes.** Black rush increases the number of plant species that can live in the upper middle zone of the marsh.

Source: Data from "Experimental Evidence for Factors Maintaining Plant Species Diversity in a New England Salt Marsh" by Sally D. Hacker and Mark D. Bertness, from *Ecology*, September 1999, Volume 80(6). © Jane B Reece.

communities. You will see other examples of these interactions throughout this chapter.

CONCEPT CHECK 54.1

1. Explain how interspecific competition, predation, and mutualism differ in their effects on the interacting populations of two species.

2. According to the principle of competitive exclusion, what outcome is expected when two species with identical niches compete for a limiting resource? Why?

3. **MAKE CONNECTIONS** Figure 24.13 illustrates the formation of and possible outcomes for a hybrid zone over time. Imagine that two finch species colonize a new island and are capable of hybridizing. The island contains two plant species, one with large seeds and one with small, growing in isolated habitats. If the two finch species specialize in eating different plant species, would reproductive barriers be reinforced, weakened, or unchanged in this hybrid zone? Explain.

For suggested answers, see Appendix A.

CONCEPT 54.2

Diversity and trophic structure characterize biological communities

A biological community is made up of species that potentially influence each other through one or more of the interactions discussed in the previous section. The nature of the interactions within a community depends on its **species composition**, that is, on the number of species present, their relative abundances, and their feeding relationships. In this section, you will read about various ways to characterize the composition of a community. You will also learn how a few species can sometimes exert strong control on the composition of their communities.

Species Diversity

When we discuss how loss of biodiversity may influence human welfare (Concept 56.1) or identify global biodiversity hot spots that are in need of protection (Concept 56.3), we are usually equating biodiversity with **species richness**, or the number of species present in a community. Ecologists recognize, however, that species richness is only one component of diversity. **Relative abundance**, or the proportion that each species represents of all individuals in the community, is an important second component.

Imagine two small forest communities, each with 100 individuals distributed among four tree species (A, B, C, and D) as follows:

Community 1: 25A, 25B, 25C, 25D
Community 2: 80A, 5B, 5C, 10D

The species richness is the same for both communities because they both contain four species of trees, but the relative abundance is very different (Figure 54.11). You would easily notice the four types of trees in community 1, but without looking carefully, you might see only the abundant species A in the second forest. Most observers would intuitively describe community 1 as the more diverse of the two communities.

Ecologists use many tools to quantitatively compare the diversity of different communities across time and space. They often calculate indexes of diversity based on species richness and relative abundance. One widely used index is **Shannon diversity** (H):

$$H = -(p_A \ln p_A + p_B \ln p_B + p_C \ln p_C + \cdots)$$

where A, B, C ... are the species in the community, p is the relative abundance of each species, and ln is the natural logarithm. A higher value of H indicates a more diverse community. Let's use this equation to calculate the Shannon diversity

Community 1
A: 25% B: 25% C: 25% D: 25%

Community 2
A: 80% B: 5% C: 5% D: 10%

▲ Figure 54.11 **Which forest is more diverse?** Ecologists would say that community 1 has greater species diversity, a measure that includes both species richness and relative abundance.

index of the two communities in Figure 54.11. For community 1, $p = 0.25$ for each species, so

$$H = -4(0.25 \ln 0.25) = 1.39.$$

For community 2,

$$H = -[0.8 \ln 0.8 + 2(0.05 \ln 0.05) + 0.1 \ln 0.1] = 0.71.$$

These calculations confirm our intuitive description of community 1 as more diverse.

Determining the number and relative abundance of species in a community is easier said than done. Many sampling techniques can be used, but since most species in a community are relatively rare, it may be hard to obtain a sample size large enough to be representative. It is also difficult to census the highly mobile or less visible or accessible members of communities, such as microorganisms, nematodes, deep-sea creatures, and nocturnal species. The small size of microorganisms makes them particularly difficult to sample, so ecologists sometimes use molecular tools to help determine microbial diversity. Advances in technology are also helping us to sample formerly inaccessible ecosystems. For example, exploration of the deep sea using submersibles and robots is revealing unexpectedly high levels of biodiversity (Figure 54.12). Measuring species diversity is often challenging but is essential for understanding community structure and for conserving diversity, as you will read in Chapter 56.

Diversity and Community Stability

In addition to measuring species diversity, ecologists manipulate diversity in experimental communities in nature

Bedford Institute of
Oceanography

Canadian Scientific Submersible Facility

▲ Figure 54.12 **Scientists are discovering the diversity of the deep ocean.** ROPOS is a remotely operated vehicle designed for scientific research. New species recently discovered on the seafloor east of Newfoundland include a purple octopus (left) and a sea pen (above left).

▲ Figure 54.13 **Study plots at the Cedar Creek Natural History Area, site of long-term experiments on manipulating plant diversity.**

Cedar Creek Ecosystem Science
Reserve, University of Minnesota, MN

and in the laboratory. They do this to examine the potential benefits of diversity, including increased productivity and stability of biological communities.

Researchers at the Cedar Creek Natural History Area, in Minnesota, have been manipulating plant diversity in experimental communities for more than two decades (Figure 54.13). Higher-diversity communities generally are more productive and are better able to withstand and recover from environmental stresses, such as droughts. More diverse communities are also more stable year to year in their productivity. In one decade-long experiment, for instance, researchers at Cedar Creek created 168 plots, each containing 1, 2, 4, 8, or 16 perennial grassland species. The most diverse plots consistently produced more **biomass** (the total mass of all organisms in a habitat) than the single-species plots each year.

Higher-diversity communities are often more resistant to **invasive species**, organisms that become established outside their natural range. Scientists working in Long Island Sound, off the coast of Connecticut, created communities of different diversity consisting of sessile marine invertebrates, including tunicates (see Figure 34.5). They then examined how vulnerable these experimental communities were to invasion by an exotic tunicate. They found that the exotic tunicate was four times more likely to survive in lower-diversity communities than in higher-diversity ones. The researchers concluded that relatively diverse communities captured more of the resources available in the system, leaving fewer resources for the invader and decreasing its survival.

Trophic Structure

Experiments like the ones just described often examine the importance of diversity within one trophic level. The structure and dynamics of a community also depend on

the feeding relationships between organisms—the **trophic structure** of the community. The transfer of food energy up the trophic levels from its source in plants and other autotrophic organisms (primary producers) through herbivores (primary consumers) to carnivores (secondary, tertiary, and quaternary consumers) and eventually to decomposers is referred to as a **food chain** (Figure 54.14).

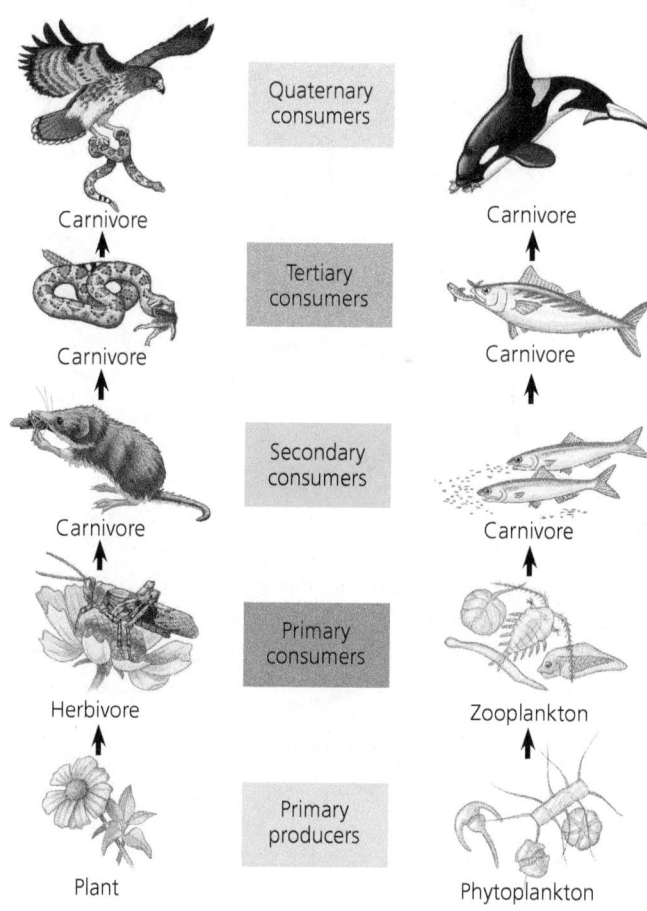

A terrestrial food chain   A marine food chain

▲ Figure 54.14 **Examples of terrestrial and marine food chains.** The arrows trace energy and nutrients that pass through the trophic levels of a community when organisms feed on one another. Decomposers, which "feed" on organisms from all trophic levels, are not shown here.

Food Webs

Food chains are not isolated units but are linked together in **food webs**. Ecologists summarize the trophic relationships of a community by diagramming a food web with arrows linking species according to who eats whom. In an Antarctic pelagic community, for example, the primary producers are phytoplankton, which serve as food for the dominant grazing zooplankton, especially euphausids (krill) and copepods, both of which are crustaceans (**Figure 54.15**). These zooplankton species are in turn eaten by various carnivores, including other plankton, penguins, seals, fishes, and baleen whales. Squid, which are carnivores that feed on fish and zooplankton, are another important link in these food webs, as they are in turn eaten by seals and toothed whales. During the time when whales were commonly hunted

for food, humans became the top predator in this food web. Having hunted many whale species to low numbers, humans are now harvesting at lower trophic levels, catching krill as well as fishes for food.

In the food web for an Arctic tundra community (**Figure 54.16**), we can see that some species have more trophic links than do other species. Lemmings, for example, are consumed by all vertebrate predators and eat most of the available plant types. Lemmings are particularly important in tundra communities, and a change in lemming abundance will affect many other species. Both the Antarctic marine and Arctic terrestrial food webs are "simplified" versions of the real communities. Species with similar trophic relationships have been grouped into broad functional groups. The phytoplankton group in Figure 54.15 is made up of more than 100 species and almost as many arthropod species are grouped together in Figure 54.16. **Omnivores**, species that feed at more than one trophic level, are found in many food webs. For example, krill feed on herbivores (copepods) as well as on phytoplankton, and ptarmigan eat insects as well as plants. Detritus, which is dead plant or animal matter, is an important component of most terrestrial food webs. In **Figure 54.17** on page 1286 you can read about the discovery that marine animal carcasses are an important source of energy for Arctic foxes.

Limits on Food Chain Length

Many food chains are embedded within a food web. Snowy owls are linked to willows through lemmings, but also through herbivorous birds (eiders and ptarmigan). If we count the number of links between primary producers and top predators, we can see that most food chains are quite short. The longest chains have four links in the Arctic terrestrial web (for example, willow–insects–passerines–rough-legged hawk) (Figure 54.16) and about seven links in the Antarctic marine web (Figure 54.15).

Why are food chains relatively short? The most common explanation, the **energetic hypothesis**, suggests that the length of a food chain is limited by the inefficiency of energy transfer along the chain. As you will read in Chapter 55, only about 10% of the energy stored in the organic matter of each trophic level is converted to organic matter at the next trophic level. Thus, a producer level consisting of 100 kg of plant material can support about 10 kg of herbivore biomass (the total mass of all individuals in a population) and 1 kg of carnivore biomass. The energetic hypothesis predicts that food chains should be relatively longer in habitats of higher photosynthetic production, since the starting amount of energy is greater than in habitats with lower photosynthetic production.

Ecologists tested the energetic hypothesis using tree-hole communities in tropical forests. Many trees have small

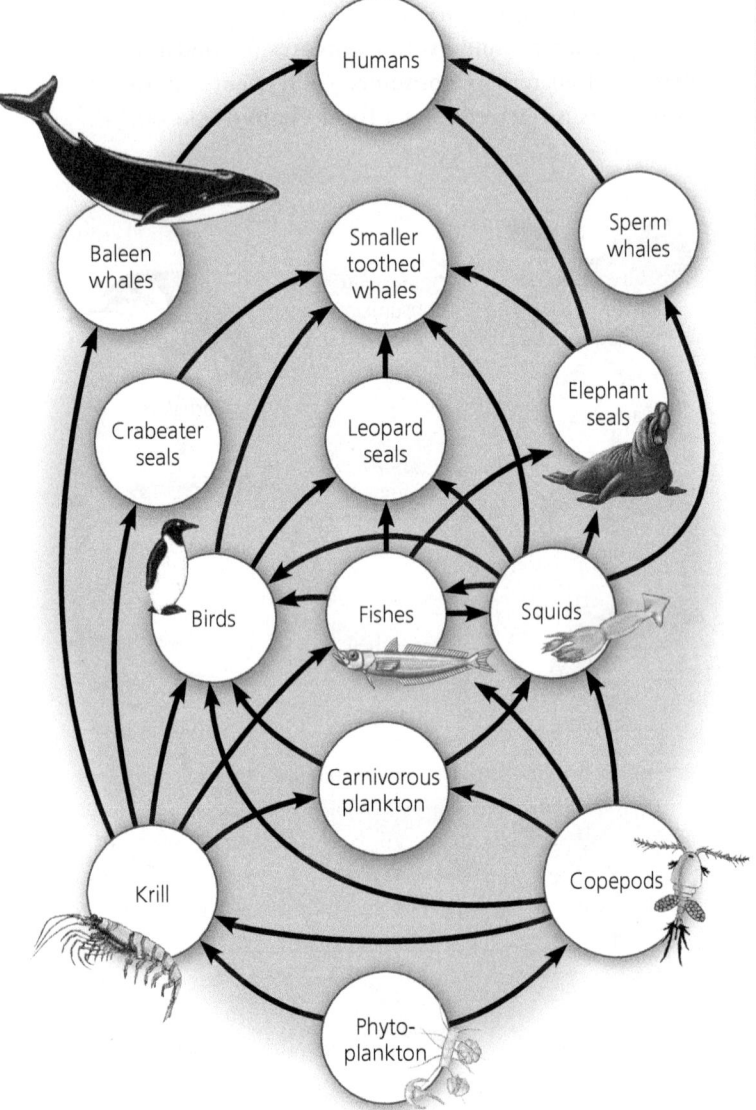

▲ **Figure 54.15 An Antarctic marine food web.** Arrows follow the transfer of food from the producers (phytoplankton) up through the trophic levels. For simplicity, this diagram omits decomposers.

Source: Based on "Antarctic Marine Ecosystems" by George A. Knox, from *Antarctic Ecology, Volume 1*, edited by Martin W. Holdgate. Academic Press, 1970. © Jane B Reece.

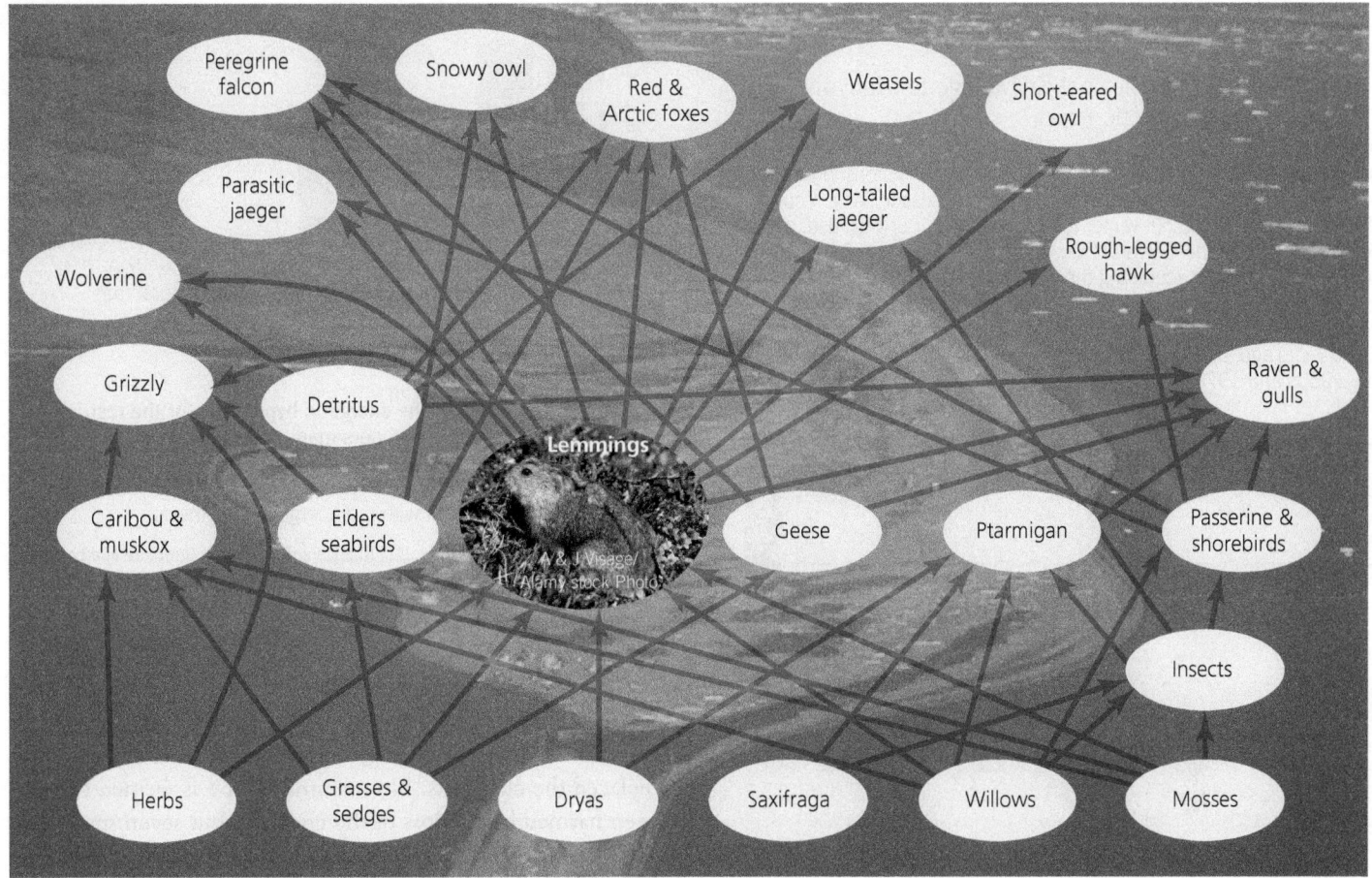

▲ **Figure 54.16 Tundra food web on Herschel Island, North Yukon.** The collared lemming (*Dicrostonyx groenlandicus*) is an important prey for most predators.

LOETSCHER CHLAUS/Alamy stock Photo

Source: Adapted from B. Jenkins. 1992. Productivity, disturbance and food web structure at a local spatial scale in experimental container habitats. *Oikos* 65: 252, Oikos, Sweden; 54.22 A.R. Townsend, et al. © Jane B Reece.

branch scars that rot, forming holes in the tree trunk. The holes hold water and provide a habitat for tiny communities consisting of microorganisms and insects that feed on leaf litter as well as predatory insects. **Figure 54.18** shows the results of experiments in which researchers manipulated productivity by varying the amount of leaf litter in tree holes. As predicted by the energetic hypothesis, holes with the most leaf litter, and hence the greatest total food supply at the producer level, supported the longest food chains.

Species with a Large Impact

Certain species have an especially large impact on the structure of entire communities because they are highly abundant or play a pivotal role in community dynamics. The impact of these species occurs through trophic interactions and their influence on the physical environment.

Dominant species in a community are the species that are the most abundant or that collectively have the highest biomass. As a result, dominant species exert a powerful control over the occurrence and distribution of other species. For example, the dominance of sugar maples in an eastern

North American forest community has a major impact on abiotic factors such as shading and soil nutrient availability, which in turn affect which other species live there.

There is no single explanation for why a species becomes dominant in a community. One hypothesis suggests that dominant species are competitively superior in exploiting limited resources such as water or nutrients. Another explanation is that dominant species are most successful at avoiding predation or the impact of disease. This latter idea could explain the high biomass attained in some environments by invasive species. Such species may not face the natural predators and agents of disease that would otherwise hold their populations in check.

One way to discover the impact of a dominant species is to remove it from the community. The American chestnut was a dominant tree in deciduous forests of eastern North America before 1910, making up more than 40% of mature trees. Then humans accidentally introduced the fungal disease chestnut blight to New York City via nursery stock imported from Asia. Between 1910 and 1950, this fungus killed almost all of the chestnut trees in eastern North America. In this case, removing the dominant species had

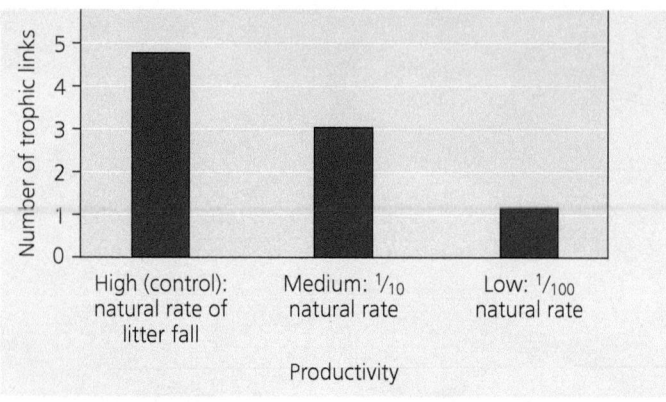

▲ **Figure 54.18 Test of the energetic hypothesis for the restriction of food chain length.** Researchers manipulated the productivity of tree-hole communities in Queensland, Australia, by providing leaf litter input at three levels. Reducing energy input reduced food chain length, a result consistent with the energetic hypothesis.

Source: Based on "Productivity, Disturbance and Food Web Structure at a Local Spatial Scale in Experimental Container Habitats" by B. Jenkins et al., from *Oikos*, November 1992, Volume 65(2). © Jane B Reece.

▼ Figure 54.17 | **Research Method**

Using Traditional Ecological Knowledge to Study the Winter Ecology of Arctic Foxes

Application Ecologists who study predator-prey interactions in the Arctic typically do their field work in the summer season. As a result, they may know little about winter foraging behaviour or prey use. Researchers from the Université du Québec à Rimouski began to fill one of these gaps by accessing the year-round knowledge of Arctic fox behaviour accumulated over decades by Inuit elders and hunters. Nomadic Inuit began to use the area (Bylot Island, Nunavut) over 4000 years ago, and almost all lived a traditional hunting lifestyle until the 1960s and 1970s.

Erni/Shutterstock

Technique Over a period of 7 months, Dominique Berteaux and doctoral student Catherine Gagnon conducted semi-directive interviews with 21 people who were considered local experts on Arctic foxes and snow geese (an important summer prey species for foxes). The interviewer started with set of topics to be discussed, but allowed the interviewee to direct the conversation so that new or unexpected information could more easily emerge. Interviews were conducted in Inuktitut, with a translator present, to reduce the likelihood of misunderstanding.

Results Berteaux and Gagnon learned that Arctic foxes on Bylot Island forage on both land and sea ice during the winter, and that some individuals spend most of their time out at sea while others stay closer to land. Marine prey includes the carcasses of beached sea mammals and leftovers from polar bear and hunter kills. In spring, large numbers of foxes migrate to the sea ice to prey on newborn ringed seal pups. In a follow-up study, Berteaux fitted foxes with satellite-tracking collars, and found that some individuals travel thousands of km over the ice during the winter!

The use of Traditional Ecological Knowledge (TEK) in ecological studies is growing. Inclusion of TEK enables ecologists to extend their studies to include additional locations or longer time periods (often reaching into the past). By providing new or different information, TEK can also help researchers refine their questions and hypotheses. TEK is a part of many environmental assessment studies and is used during the assessment of wildlife species that are of conservation concern (see Chapter 56).

Source: C. A. Gagnon, and D. Berteaux, Integrating traditional ecological knowledge and ecological science: A question of scale, *Ecology and Society* 14:19 (2009).

a relatively small impact on some species but severe effects on others. Oaks, hickories, beeches, and red maples that were already present in the forest increased in abundance and replaced the chestnuts. No mammals or birds seemed to have been harmed by the loss of the chestnut, but seven species of moths and butterflies that fed on the tree became extinct.

In contrast to dominant species, **keystone species** are not usually abundant in a community. They exert strong control on community structure not by numerical might but by their pivotal ecological roles, or niches. **Figure 54.19** highlights the importance of a keystone species, a sea star, in maintaining the diversity of an intertidal community.

The sea otter, a keystone predator in the North Pacific, offers another example. Sea otters feed on sea urchins, and sea urchins feed mainly on kelp. As we saw in the introduction to this chapter, sea urchins can eliminate kelp forests, destroying a habitat used by many fish and invertebrates. On the Pacific coast, sea otters **(Figure 54.20)** historically kept sea urchin populations in check. However, when overhunting had driven most otter populations extinct by the early 1900s, urchin populations expanded and kelp forests nearly disappeared. Protection and reintroduction led to a strong recovery of the sea otter and of the diverse kelp forest community.

Other organisms exert their influence on a community not through trophic interactions but by changing their physical environment. Species that dramatically alter their environment are called **ecosystem engineers** or, to avoid implying conscious intent, "foundation species." A familiar ecosystem engineer is the beaver **(Figure 54.21)**. The effects of ecosystem engineers on other species can be positive or negative, depending on the needs of the other species.

Inquiry

Is *Pisaster ochraceus* a keystone predator?

Experiment In rocky intertidal communities of western North America, the relatively uncommon sea star *Pisaster ochraceus* preys on mussels such as *Mytilus californianus*, a dominant species and strong competitor for space.

Genny Anderson

Robert Paine, of the University of Washington, removed *Pisaster* from an area in the intertidal zone and examined the effect on species richness.

Results In the absence of *Pisaster*, species richness declined as mussels monopolized the rock face and eliminated most other invertebrates and algae. In a control area where *Pisaster* was not removed, species richness changed very little.

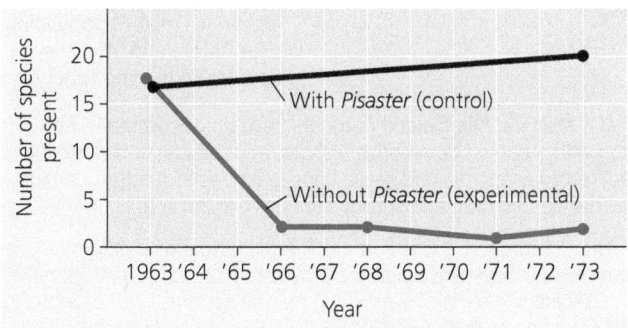

Conclusion *Pisaster* acts as a keystone species, exerting an influence on the community that is not reflected in its abundance.

Source: Based on R. T. Paine, Food web complexity and species diversity, *American Naturalist* 100:65–75 (1966). © Jane B Reece.

WHAT IF? *Suppose that an invasive fungus killed most individuals of* Mytilus *at these sites. Predict how species richness would be affected if* Pisaster *were then removed.*

Bottom-Up and Top-Down Controls

Ecologists frequently want to know what controls the abundance or biomass of a species or a particular trophic level. For example, we may want to know what limits

Alamy Stock Photo

▲ **Figure 54.20 The sea otter is a keystone predator in the North Pacific.** Without sea otter predation, sea urchins convert kelp forests to urchin barrens, a much less productive community with fewer species.

or controls the size of the Arctic lemming population in Figure 54.16. Is the limit set by the amount of edible vegetation available or do predators control lemming numbers? We can phrase this question in a more general way: Is the lemming population controlled from the bottom up (by food) or from the top down (by predators)? **Bottom-up control** means that an increase in food would lead to an increase in the number of lemmings. Under **top-down control**, reducing the number of predators would result in more lemmings.

The bottom-up model of community organization postulates a unidirectional influence from lower to higher trophic levels. Thus, nutrient levels control plant numbers or biomass, plants control herbivore numbers, herbivores control the number of predators, and so on. To change the community structure of a bottom-up community, you need to alter biomass at the lower trophic levels, allowing those changes to propagate up through the food web. For

Adam Welz

▲ **Figure 54.21 Beavers as ecosystem engineers.** By felling trees, building dams, and creating ponds, beavers can transform large areas of forest into flooded wetlands.

example, if you add mineral nutrients to stimulate growth of vegetation, then the higher trophic levels should also increase in biomass. If you add predators to or remove predators from a bottom-up community, however, the effect should not extend down to the lower trophic levels.

In contrast, the top-down model postulates the opposite: Predation mainly controls community organization because predators limit herbivores, herbivores limit plants, and plants limit nutrient levels through nutrient uptake. The top-down model is also known as the **trophic cascade model**. Often top-down effects are only noticed when top predators have been removed from communities by humans. We discussed one such example in the previous section. When sea otters were the top predators in Pacific kelp forest communities, they limited the abundance of herbivorous sea urchins, which allowed the kelp forest to flourish. About 20 years ago, orcas became a fourth trophic level in some Alaskan coastal communities, preying heavily on the sea otters. The sea otters can no longer control the sea urchin populations, and the kelp forests are disappearing once again (Figure 54.22). The overfishing that caused the collapse of the Atlantic cod fishery and greatly reduced the abundance of other ground fish also led to a trophic cascade that reaches all the way down to phytoplankton and their nutrient supply (Figure 54.23).

Communities vary in their degree of bottom-up and top-down control. To manage agricultural landscapes, parks, reservoirs, and fisheries, we need to understand each particular community's dynamics.

Pacific kelp forests

In the Pacific, kelp forests are abundant when sea otters control urchins, but are converted to barrens when sea otter numbers are low.

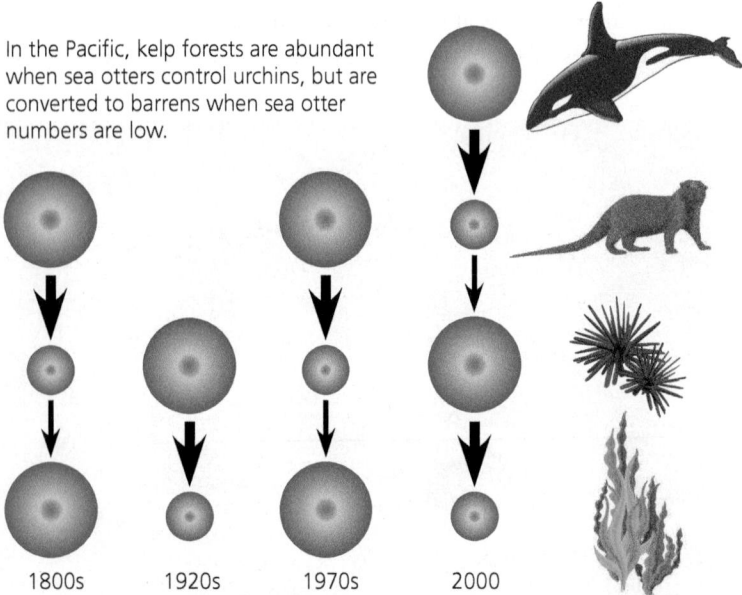

| 1800s | 1920s | 1970s | 2000 |

Period

▲ **Figure 54.22 The trophic cascade model explains historic transitions in Pacific kelp forest communities.** Kelp forests declined when sea otters were extirpated from much of the coast by hunters and are declining today where sea otters are preyed on by orcas.

▼ Figure 54.23

Impact

Overfishing and Trophic Cascades in the Sea

Large fish are the top predators in most ocean ecosystems. Cod were once so abundant in the coastal waters of eastern Canada that it was said they could be caught by dipping a bucket into the sea.

Overfishing in the 1980s and early 1990s caused the number of cod and other large predatory fish to collapse to such low numbers that the commercial cod fishery was closed in 1992.

Did the removal of so many predatory fish affect lower trophic levels? The answer appears to be *yes*. The abundance of smaller fish and large invertebrates such as snow crabs and northern shrimp increased several fold. The top-down effect even cascaded to lower trophic levels. There are fewer zooplankton and more phytoplankton, and the increased uptake of nutrients by the more abundant primary producers has led to a decline in the concentration of nutrients such as nitrate.

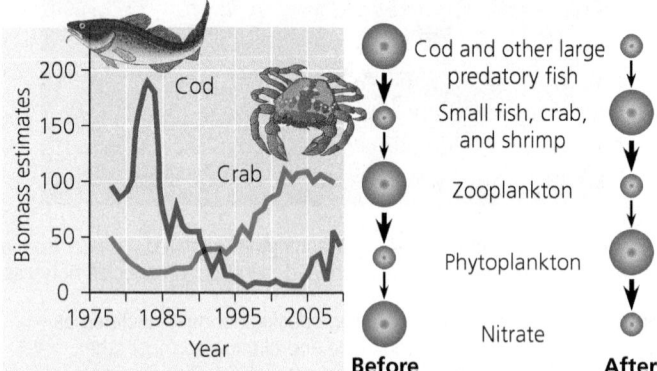

(a) Crab biomass increased as the cod fishery collapsed

(b) Change in ecosystem after overfishing. Circle size represents relative population sizes before and after the collapse of the cod fishery.

Why It Matters Atlantic cod numbers have not recovered in most areas even with a ban on commercial fishing, and the loss of the fishery has had severe economic and social consequences for eastern Canada. Meanwhile, the crab and shrimp fisheries are thriving.

Further Reading K.T. Frank et al., Trophic cascades in a formerly cod-dominated ecosystem, *Science* 308:1621–1623 (2005). M. Scheffer et al., Cascading effects of overfishing marine systems, *Trends in Ecology and Evolution* 11:579–581 (2005).

MAKE CONNECTIONS *There is currently an important debate as to whether grey seals, which consume various fish species, constitute a fifth trophic level in the coastal marine trophic cascade. If they are a significant fifth trophic level, how would an increase in the grey seal population affect the Atlantic cod and snow crab fisheries?*

CONCEPT CHECK 54.2

1. What two components contribute to species diversity? Explain how two communities with the same number of species can differ in species diversity.

2. How is a food chain different from a food web?

3. **WHAT IF?** Consider a grassland with five trophic levels: grasses, mice, snakes, raccoons, and bobcats. If you released additional bobcats into the grassland, how would grass biomass change if the bottom-up model applied? If the top-down model applied?

For suggested answers, see Appendix A.

Disturbance influences species diversity and composition

Decades ago, most ecologists favoured the traditional view that biological communities are at equilibrium, a more or less stable balance, unless seriously disturbed by human activities. The "balance of nature" view focused on interspecific competition as a key factor determining community composition and maintaining stability in communities. *Stability* in this context refers to a community's tendency to reach and maintain a relatively constant composition of species.

One of the earliest proponents of this view, the American ecologist F. E. Clements, argued that the community of plants at a site had only one state of equilibrium, controlled solely by climate. According to Clements, biotic interactions caused the species in this *climax community* to function as an integrated unit—in effect, as a superorganism. His argument was based on the observation that certain species of plants are consistently found together, such as the oaks, maples, birches, and beeches in deciduous forests of the northeastern United States.

Other ecologists questioned whether most communities were at equilibrium or functioned as integrated units. A. G. Tansley, of Oxford University, challenged the concept of a climax community, arguing that differences in soils, topography, and other factors created many potential communities that were stable within a region. H. A. Gleason, of the University of Chicago, saw communities not as superorganisms but more as chance assemblages of species found together because they happen to have similar abiotic requirements— for example, for temperature, rainfall, and soil type. Gleason and other ecologists also realized that disturbance keeps many communities from reaching a state of equilibrium in species diversity or composition. A **disturbance** is an event, such as a storm, fire, flood, drought, overgrazing, or human activity, that changes a community by removing organisms from it or altering resource availability.

This recent emphasis on change has produced the **nonequilibrium model**, which describes most communities as constantly changing after being affected by disturbances. Let's now take a look at the ways disturbances influence community structure and composition.

Characterizing Disturbance

The types of disturbances and their frequency and severity vary among communities. Storms disturb almost all communities, even those in the oceans, through the action of waves. Fire is a significant disturbance in most terrestrial communities; in fact, chaparral and some grassland biomes require regular burning to maintain their structure and species

composition. Freezing is a frequent occurrence in many rivers, lakes, and ponds, and many streams and ponds are disturbed by spring flooding and seasonal drying. A high level of disturbance is generally the result of a high intensity *and* high frequency of disturbance, while low disturbance levels can result from either a low intensity or low frequency of disturbance.

The **intermediate disturbance hypothesis** states that moderate levels of disturbance foster greater species diversity than do low or high levels of disturbance. High levels of disturbance reduce diversity by creating environmental stresses that exceed the tolerances of many species or by disturbing the community so often that slow-growing or slow-colonizing species are excluded. At the other extreme, low levels of disturbance can reduce species diversity by allowing competitively dominant species to exclude less competitive ones. Meanwhile, intermediate levels of disturbance can foster greater species diversity by opening up habitats for occupation by less competitive species. Such intermediate disturbance levels rarely create conditions so severe that they exceed the environmental tolerances or recovery rates of potential community members.

The intermediate disturbance hypothesis is supported by some terrestrial and aquatic studies. In one such study, ecologists in New Zealand compared the richness of invertebrate taxa living in the beds of streams exposed to different frequencies and intensities of flooding (**Figure 54.24**). When floods occurred either very frequently or rarely, invertebrate richness was low. Frequent floods made it difficult for some species to become established in the streambed, while rare floods resulted in species being displaced by superior competitors. Invertebrate richness peaked in streams that had an intermediate frequency or intensity of flooding, as predicted by the hypothesis.

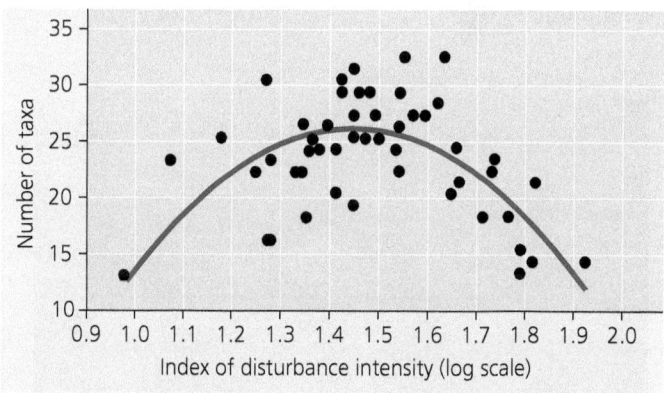

▲ Figure 54.24 **Testing the intermediate disturbance hypothesis.** Researchers identified the taxa (species or genera) of invertebrates at two locations in each of 27 New Zealand streams. They assessed the intensity of flooding at each location using an index of streambed disturbance. The number of invertebrate taxa peaked where the intensity of flooding was at intermediate levels.

Source: Adaptation of figure 2a from "The Intermediate Disturbance Hypothesis, Refugia, and Biodiversity in Streams" by Colin R. Townsend et al., from *Limnology and Oceanography*, 1997, Volume 42(5): 944. Copyright © 1997 by Association for the Sciences of Limnology and Oceanography, Inc.

Disturbance is an integral part of the lodgepole pine forest communities that blanket much of the Rocky Mountains. If the forest were to remain disturbance-free over a long period of time, pine would be replaced by more shade-tolerant species such as Douglas fir and Engelmann spruce. However, fires periodically sweep through parts of the forest, opening gaps in the forest canopy. Lodgepole pine is an aggressive colonizer, and burned areas are usually soon covered by a carpet of pine seedlings.

Insect outbreaks are another common and large-scale disturbance in lodgepole pine forests. Mountain pine beetle (MPB) outbreaks have occurred through known history, though a warmer and drier climate may be increasing their frequency and extent. The recent destruction of large areas of mature forest in British Columbia and Alberta (Figure 54.25) has had significant economic impacts. But the effects of the insect disturbance on the forest community are not necessarily all negative. After an MPB outbreak, many pine-dominated forests with trees all the same age become multi-aged forests with a much greater diversity of tree species. Some animal species benefit directly or indirectly from the MPB outbreaks. The outbreak provides a large pulse of food for many bird species, but especially benefits woodpeckers that specialize on bark beetles and other wood-boring insects. Large numbers of standing dead trees increase available habitat for cavity-dwellers, including woodpeckers, bats, and squirrels.

Studies of the lodgepole pine forest community and many others indicate that they are nonequilibrium communities, changing continually because of natural disturbances and the internal processes of growth and reproduction. Mounting evidence suggests that nonequilibrium conditions resulting from disturbance are in fact the norm for most communities.

Ecological Succession

Changes in the composition and structure of terrestrial communities are most apparent after some severe disturbance, such as a volcanic eruption or a glacier, strips away all the existing vegetation. The disturbed area may be colonized by a variety of species, which are gradually replaced by other species, which are in turn replaced by still other species—a process called **ecological succession**. This process is called **primary succession** when it begins in a virtually lifeless area where soil has not formed, such as on a new volcanic island or on the rubble (moraine) left by a retreating glacier.

During primary succession, often the only life forms initially present are prokaryotes and protists. Lichens and mosses, which grow from windblown spores, are commonly the first macroscopic photosynthesizers to colonize such areas. Soil develops gradually as rocks weather and organic matter accumulates from the decomposed remains of the early colonizers. Once soil is present, the lichens and mosses are usually overgrown by grasses, shrubs, and trees that sprout from seeds blown in from nearby areas or carried in by animals. Eventually, an area is colonized by plants that become the community's dominant form of vegetation. Producing such a community through primary succession may take hundreds or thousands of years.

Early-arriving species and later-arriving ones may be linked by one of three key processes. The early arrivals may *facilitate* the appearance of the later species by making the environment more favourable—for example, by increasing the fertility of the soil. Alternatively, the early species may *inhibit* establishment of the later species, so that successful colonization by later species occurs in spite of, rather than because of, the activities of the early species. Finally, the later species may be completely independent of the early species, which *tolerate* conditions created early in succession but are neither helped nor hindered by early species.

Ecologists have conducted some of the most extensive research on primary succession at Glacier Bay in southeastern Alaska, where glaciers have retreated more than 100 km since 1760 (Figure 54.26). By studying the communities at different distances from the mouth of the bay, ecologists can examine different stages in succession. The exposed glacial moraine is colonized

(a) A patchy landscape is created by a mountain pine beetle infestation in the Cariboo region of British Columbia.

(b) Lodgepole pine may recolonize after fire or insect disturbance (above), or a more diverse forest may develop.

▲ Figure 54.25 **Recovery of lodgepole pine following large-scale disturbance.** Mountain pine beetles and fire periodically destroy large expanses of pine forest in Alberta and British Columbia.

① Pioneer stage

Charles D. Winters/Science Source

② *Dryas* stage

Douglas W Veltre, Ph.D

1941
1907
1860

Glacier Bay

Alaska

1760

0 5 10 15
Kilometers

④ Spruce stage

Terry Donnelly

③ Alder stage

Glacier Bay National Park and Preserve

▲ Figure 54.26 **Glacial retreat and primary succession at Glacier Bay, Alaska.** The different shades of blue on the map show retreat of the glacier since 1760, based on historical descriptions.

Source: Based on "Soil Development in Relation to Vegetation and Surface Age at Glacier Bay, Alaska" by Robert L. Crocker and Jack Major, from *Journal of Ecology*, July 1955, Volume 43(2). © Jane B Reece.

first by pioneering species that include liverworts, mosses, fireweed, scattered *Dryas* (a mat-forming shrub), and willows. After about three decades, *Dryas* dominates the plant community. A few decades later, the area is invaded by alder, which forms dense thickets up to 9 m tall. In the next two centuries, these alder stands are overgrown first by Sitka spruce and later by western hemlock and mountain hemlock. In areas of poor drainage, the forest floor of this spruce-hemlock forest is invaded by sphagnum moss, which holds water and acidifies the soil, eventually killing the trees. Thus, by about 300 years after glacial retreat, the vegetation consists of sphagnum bogs on the poorly drained flat areas and spruce-hemlock forest on the well-drained slopes.

Succession on glacial moraines is related to changes in soil nutrients and other environmental factors caused by transitions in the vegetation. Because the bare soil after glacial retreat is low in nitrogen content, almost all the pioneer plant species begin succession with poor growth and yellow leaves. The exceptions are *Dryas* and alder, which have symbiotic bacteria that fix atmospheric nitrogen (see Chapter 37). Soil nitrogen content increases quickly during the alder stage of succession and keeps increasing during the spruce stage (**Figure 54.27**). By altering soil properties,

Soil nitrogen (g/m²) axis: 0, 10, 20, 30, 40, 50, 60

Pioneer ① → *Dryas* ② → Alder ③ → Spruce ④

Successional stage

▲ Figure 54.27 **Changes in soil nitrogen content during succession at Glacier Bay.**

Source: Adaptation of figure 6(e) from "Mechanisms of Primary Succession Following Deglaciation at Glacier Bay" by F. Stuart Chapin et al., from *Ecological Monographs*, May 1994, Volume 64(2). Copyright © 1994 by the Ecological Society of America. Reprinted with permission.

MAKE CONNECTIONS *Figures 37.10 and 37.11 illustrate two types of atmospheric nitrogen fixation by prokaryotes. At the earliest stages of primary succession, before any plants are present at a site, which type of nitrogen fixation would occur, and why?*

pioneer plant species can facilitate colonization by new plant species during succession.

In contrast to primary succession, **secondary succession** occurs when an existing community has been cleared by some disturbance that leaves the soil intact, as in lodgepole pine forests following fire or insect disturbance (see Figure 54.25) or a forested area that has been cleared for farming and later abandoned. Following the disturbance, the area often returns to something like its original state. The earliest plants to recolonize are often herbaceous species that grow from windblown or animal-borne seeds. Woody shrubs may in time replace most of the herbaceous species, and forest trees eventually replace most of the shrubs.

Human Disturbance

Ecological succession is a response to disturbance of the environment, and the strongest agent of disturbance today is human activity. Agricultural development has disrupted what were once the vast grasslands of the North American prairie. Logging and clearing for urban development, mining, and farming have reduced large tracts of forests to small patches of disconnected woodlots in many parts of North America and throughout Europe. Tropical rain forests are quickly disappearing as a result of clear-cutting for lumber, cattle grazing, and farmland. Centuries of overgrazing and agricultural disturbance have contributed to famine in parts of Africa by turning seasonal grasslands into vast barren areas.

Humans disturb marine ecosystems as well as terrestrial ones. The effects of ocean trawling, where boats drag weighted nets across the seafloor, are similar to those of clear-cutting a forest or plowing a field (Figure 54.28). The

◀ Before trawling

After ▶ trawling

Elliott A. Norse

▲ Figure 54.28 **Disturbance of the ocean floor by trawling.** These photos show the seafloor off northwestern Australia before (top) and after (bottom) deep-sea trawlers have passed.

trawls scrape and scour corals and other life on the seafloor. In a typical year, ships trawl an area about the size of South America and 150 times larger than the area of forests that are clear-cut annually.

In Chapter 56, we will take a closer look at how human-caused disturbance is affecting the diversity of life.

CONCEPT CHECK 54.3

1. Why do high and low levels of disturbance usually reduce species diversity? Why does an intermediate level of disturbance promote species diversity?

2. During succession, how might the early species facilitate the arrival of other species?

3. **WHAT IF?** Most prairies experience regular fires, typically every few years. If these disturbances were relatively modest, how would the species diversity of a prairie likely be affected if no burning occurred for 100 years? Explain your answer.

For suggested answers, see Appendix A.

CONCEPT 54.4

Biogeographic factors affect community diversity

So far, we have examined relatively small-scale or local factors that influence the diversity of communities, including the effects of species interactions, dominant species, and many types of disturbances. Ecologists also recognize that large-scale biogeographic factors contribute to the tremendous range of diversity observed in biological communities. The contributions of two biogeographic factors in particular—the latitude of a community and the area it occupies—have been investigated for more than a century.

Latitudinal Gradients

In the 1850s, both Charles Darwin and Alfred Wallace pointed out that plant and animal life was generally more abundant and diverse in the tropics than in other parts of the globe. Since that time, many researchers have confirmed this observation. One study found that a 6.6-hectare (1 ha = 10 000 m^2) plot in tropical Malaysia contained 711 tree species, while a 2-ha plot of deciduous forest in Michigan typically contained just 10 to 15 tree species. Moreover, there are only 50 tree species in all of western Europe north of the Alps. Many groups of animals show similar latitudinal gradients. There are more than 200 species of ants in Brazil but only 7 in Alaska, for instance.

The two key factors in latitudinal gradients of species richness are probably evolutionary history and climate. Over the course of evolutionary time, species richness may increase in a community as more speciation events occur (see Chapter 24). Tropical communities are generally older than temperate or polar communities because temperate and polar communities have repeatedly "started over" after major disturbances from glaciations. Also, the growing season in tropical forests is about five times as long as in the tundra communities of high latitudes. In effect, biological time runs about five times as fast in the tropics as near the poles, so intervals between speciation events are shorter in the tropics.

Climate is likely another cause of the latitudinal gradient in richness and diversity. In terrestrial communities, the two main climatic factors correlated with diversity are sunlight and precipitation, both of which are relatively abundant in the tropics. These factors can be considered together by measuring a community's rate of **evapotranspiration**, the evaporation of water from soil plus the transpiration of water from plants. Evapotranspiration, a function of solar radiation, temperature, and water availability, is much higher in hot areas with abundant rainfall than in areas with low temperatures or low precipitation. *Potential evapotranspiration*, a measure of potential water loss that assumes that water is readily available, is determined by the amount of solar radiation and temperature and is highest in regions where both are plentiful. The species richness of plants and animals correlates with both measures of evapotranspiration (**Figure 54.29**).

Area Effects

In 1807, naturalist and explorer Alexander von Humboldt described one of the first patterns of species richness to be recognized, the **species-area curve**: All other factors being equal, the larger the geographic area of a community, the more species it has, in part because larger areas offer a greater diversity of habitats and microhabitats. In conservation biology, developing species-area curves for the key taxa in a community helps ecologists predict how the loss of a certain area of habitat is likely to affect the community's diversity.

The first, and still widely used, mathematical description of the species-area relationship was proposed a century ago:

$$S = cA^z$$

where S is the number of species found in a habitat, c is a constant, and A is the area of the habitat. The exponent z tells you how many more species should be found in a habitat as its area increases. In a log-log plot of S versus A, z is the slope of the line through the data points. A value of $z = 1$ would indicate a linear relationship between species number and area, meaning that 10 times as many species would be found in a habitat that has 10 times the area.

In the 1960s, Robert MacArthur and E. O. Wilson tested the predictions of the species-area relationship by examining the number of animals and plants on different island chains.

▲ Figure 54.29 **Energy, water, and species richness.** Vertebrate species richness in North America increases most predictably with potential evapotranspiration, expressed as rainfall equivalents (mm/yr).

Source: Adaptation of Figure 7 from " Energy and Large-Scale Patterns of Animal- and Plant-Species Richness" by D. J. Currie, from *American Naturalist*, January 1991, Volume 137(1): 27–49. Copyright © 1991 by the University of Chicago Press. Reprinted with permission.

As one example, in the Sunda Islands of Malaysia, they found that the number of bird species increased with island size, with a value of $z = 0.4$ (**Figure 54.30**). Although the slopes of different species-area curves vary, the basic concept of diversity increasing with increasing area applies in many situations, from surveys of ant diversity in New Guinea to studies of plant species richness on islands of different sizes.

Island Equilibrium Model

Because of their isolation and limited size, islands provide excellent opportunities for studying the biogeographic factors that affect the species diversity of communities. By "islands," we mean not only oceanic islands, but also habitat islands on land, such as lakes, mountain peaks separated by lowlands, or natural woodland fragments surrounded by areas disturbed by humans—in other words, any patch surrounded by an environment not suitable for the "island" species. While studying the species-area relationship, MacArthur and Wilson developed a general model of island biogeography, identifying the key determinants of species diversity on an island with a given set of physical characteristics.

Consider a newly formed oceanic island that receives colonizing species from a distant mainland. Two factors that determine the number of species on the island are the rate at which new species immigrate to the island and the rate at which species become extinct on the island. At any given time, an island's immigration and extinction rates are affected by the number of species already present. As the number of species on the island increases, the immigration

▼ Figure 54.30 Inquiry

How does species richness relate to area?

Field Study Ecologists Robert MacArthur and E. O. Wilson studied the number of bird species on the Sunda Islands of Malaysia in relation to the area of the different islands.

Results

Source: Adaptation of figure 1 from "An Equilibrium Theory of Insular Zoogeography" by Robert H. MacArthur and Edward O. Wilson, from *Evolution*, December 1963, Volume 17(4). Copyright © 1963 by Society for the Study of Evolution. Reprinted with permission of John Wiley & Sons Ltd.

Conclusion Bird species richness increases with island size. The slope of the best-fit line through the data points (the parameter *z*) is about 0.4.

Source: R. H. MacArthur and E. O. Wilson, An equilibrium theory of insular zoogeography, *Evolution* 17:373–387 (1963).

WHAT IF? *Four islands in this study, ranging in area from about 100 to 800 square miles, each contained about 100 bird species. What does such variation tell you about the simple assumptions of the island equilibrium model?*

rate of new species decreases, because any individual reaching the island is less likely to represent a species that is not already present. At the same time, as more species inhabit an island, extinction rates on the island increase because of the greater likelihood of competitive exclusion.

Two physical features of the island further affect immigration and extinction rates: its size and its distance from the mainland. Small islands generally have lower immigration rates because potential colonizers are less likely to reach a small island. For instance, birds blown out to sea by a storm are more likely to land by chance on a large island than on a small one. Small islands also have higher extinction rates because they generally contain fewer resources, have less diverse habitats, and have smaller population sizes. Distance from the mainland is also important; for two islands of equal size, a closer island generally has a higher immigration rate and lower extinction rate, as arriving colonists help sustain the presence of a species on a near island and prevent its extinction.

MacArthur and Wilson's model is called the *island equilibrium model* because an equilibrium will eventually be reached where the rate of species immigration equals the rate of

species extinction. The number of species at this equilibrium point is correlated with the island's size and distance from the mainland. Like any ecological equilibrium, this species equilibrium is dynamic; immigration and extinction continue, and the exact species composition may change over time.

Studies of the diversity of plants and animals on many island chains (see Figure 54.30) support the prediction that species richness increases with island size, in keeping with the island equilibrium model. Species counts also fit the prediction that the number of species decreases with increasing remoteness of the island.

Over long periods, disturbances such as storms, adaptive evolutionary changes, and speciation generally alter the species composition and community structure on islands. Nonetheless, the island equilibrium model is widely applied in ecology. Conservation biologists, in particular, use it when designing habitat reserves or establishing a starting point for predicting the effects of habitat loss on species diversity.

CONCEPT CHECK 54.4

1. Describe two hypotheses that explain why species diversity is greater in tropical regions than in temperate and polar regions.
2. Describe how an island's size and distance from the mainland affect the island's species richness.
3. **WHAT IF?** Based on MacArthur and Wilson's island equilibrium model, how would you expect the richness of birds on islands to compare with the richness of snakes and lizards? Explain.

For suggested answers, see Appendix A.

CONCEPT **54.5**

Pathogens alter community structure locally and globally

We will close the chapter by examining less visible but extremely important community interactions involving **pathogens**—disease-causing microorganisms, viruses, viroids, or prions. (Viroids and prions are infectious RNA molecules and proteins, respectively; see Chapter 19.) Pathogens face the same fundamental life challenge as do larger organisms—to acquire the resources needed to reproduce. Pathogens typically associate very closely with larger "host" organisms to obtain required nutrients. But since hosts do not live forever, the growth (spread) of a pathogen population is often limited by its ability to find and infect new hosts. As a result, pathogens have evolved a plethora of ways to move, from manipulating the behaviour of its host (for example, making it sneeze) to hitching a ride on intermediate species known as **vectors**. Ecologists are coming to appreciate how widespread and significant the effects of pathogens are in ecological communities, and disease epidemiologists are realizing the critical role that species interactions play in the emergence and spread of pathogens.

For example, rinderpest, an infectious viral disease, was transported to Africa in shipments of infected cattle during the 19th century. The disease spread from cattle to native herbivores, decimating wild buffalo, giraffe, and wildebeest populations across the continent. Recovery took decades, and loss of the huge herds of native herbivores led to landscape-scale changes in savannah ecosystems, with trees invading large areas of grassland. A different disease is currently transforming North American grasslands. The plague bacterium *Yersinia pestis*, best known for the human deaths it caused in Europe during the Middle Ages, came to North America over 100 years ago (probably carried by ship rats and their fleas). The disease spread to native prairie dogs, causing up to 95% mortality in affected colonies. Loss of prairie dogs affects not only specialist predators such as the endangered black-footed ferret, but the reduced burrowing activity is altering soil chemistry, water availability, and plant growth on the prairies.

Humans are similarly vulnerable to the effects of emerging diseases spread by our increasingly global economy. H1N1, the virus that causes "swine flu" in humans, was first detected in Veracruz, Mexico, in early 2009. It quickly spread around the world when infected individuals flew on airplanes to other countries. By 2011, the world's first flu pandemic in 40 years had killed more than 18 000 people.

Pathogens and Communities

In spite of the potential of disease to limit populations, pathogens have until recently been the subject of relatively few ecological studies. This imbalance is now being addressed as events highlight the ecological importance of disease.

Several times in this chapter we have discussed how Pacific kelp forest communities persist only if sea urchin populations are kept in check by sea otters. But sea otters do not live in the Atlantic Ocean. What controls sea urchins in eastern Canadian kelp forests? Historically, east coast sea urchins were also limited by predators, including the ferocious-looking wolf fish (Figure 54.31). Today, however, a tiny, disease-causing amoeba plays that role in the coastal waters of Nova Scotia. Overfishing during the past century released the sea urchins from control by predatory fish, turning kelp forests into barrens (see Figure 54.1). However, in 1980, a disease decimated the super-abundant urchins. Robert Scheibling from Dalhousie University has discovered that disease outbreaks in urchins are linked to warm water masses carried north as hurricanes move up the Atlantic coast. The collapse of the sea urchin population allows the kelp forest community to recover. The pathogen disappears once the water cools, and the sea urchin population begins to grow again. Without top predators, the

▲ Figure 54.31 **Alternating communities in the Atlantic Ocean.** Kelp was abundant historically, and urchins were limited by predators such as the wolf fish (above). Without top predators, disease now causes the community to oscillate between barrens and kelp forest.

community is expected to continue to oscillate between a sea urchin-dominated barrens and a dense kelp forest with few urchins, a dynamic driven by disease.

Disease also affects terrestrial communities. For example, sudden oak death, a disease caused by the fungus-like protist *Phytophthora ramorum*, has killed more than a million oaks and other trees from California to Oregon. At least five bird species have declined in abundance, including the acorn woodpecker that relies on oaks for food and habitat. Plant diseases also significantly affect the human food supply—10% to 15% of global crop production is lost to disease each year.

Community Ecology and Zoonotic Diseases

Three-quarters of emerging human diseases and many of the most devastating diseases are caused by **zoonotic pathogens**, pathogens that are transferred to humans from other animals. Zoonotic pathogens do not need humans to complete their life cycles—in most cases we are just accidental (and unfortunate) hosts. The pathogen normally resides in an animal "reservoir," a species where the pathogen can multiply, often without causing major harm to its host. Small mammals, especially rodents and bats, are common reservoirs for diseases that spillover to humans.

Like other pathogens, zoonotic pathogens may move directly between hosts or they may be transported by a vector species. Hantavirus, which can cause a rare but deadly disease known as Hantavirus Pulmonary Syndrome, is found in deer mice and a few other rodent species. Hantavirus is transmitted from mouse to mouse by direct contact, a strategy that works well with social animals that live in burrows. Transmission to humans is rare because we generally do not socialize much with wild rodents, but can occur if a person accidentally comes into contact with an infected rodent or its droppings. West Nile virus, a disease that can cause serious flu-like symptoms in humans, resides in a variety of different bird species. It, however, uses a vector, *Culex* mosquitoes, to disperse from infected to uninfected bird (or to an unlucky human). From the virus' point of view humans are an undesirable host, a dead end, since *Culex* mosquitoes rarely carry West Nile virus from humans to another host. Vectors that spread zoonotic diseases are often parasites, including ticks, lice, and mosquitoes.

Identification of the animal reservoir is key to preventing and controlling zoonotic diseases. We need to know which species the pathogen requires for it to persist in the environment, we need to know how the pathogen is transmitted from host to host, and we need to know which ecological factors limit the abundance and distribution of the host and vector species. Only then can we begin to propose and implement effective measures to minimize contact between humans and the pathogen. In other words, zoonotic diseases are truly ecological problems.

In Chapter 52 we saw that the black-legged tick, which is the vector for the pathogen that causes Lyme disease, has been extending its range in Canada. The disease can cause serious and long-term disability in humans if not treated immediately, and the number of human cases has been rising rapidly. Migratory birds carry infected black-legged ticks to new habitats, and the ticks persist if abiotic conditions allow for survival and reproduction, and if hosts suitable for the tick are present. In **Figure 54.32** you will see how ecological research has led to a better understanding of the dynamics of Lyme disease.

▼ Figure 54.32

Impact

Lyme Disease Dynamics—Understanding Ecological Complexity

Pathogens such as *Borrelia burgdorferi*, the bacterium that causes Lyme disease, reside in complex ecological communities. The pathogen is transported from host to host by a vector, the black-legged tick, which must take blood meals from three different animal hosts to complete its life cycle. Pathogen abundance is thus influenced by numerous species interactions involving the tick vector and its various host species.

A researcher collects ticks from a white-footed mouse.

of small mammal hosts. Tick larvae and nymphs require a blood meal to moult to the next stage. Higher densities of small mammals thus result in more ticks. Ecologists are now examining the factors that influence host abundance, and have found that the populations of small mammals and deer are influenced by both bottom-up (food availability) and top-down (predation) factors.

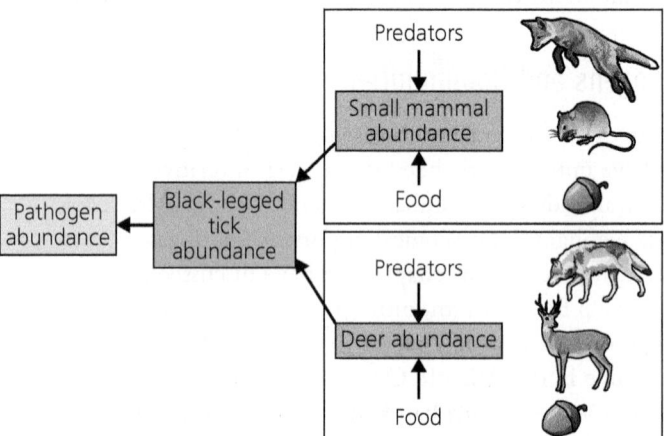

Why It Matters Understanding species interactions helps us explain an important but non-intuitive result: Moderate reduction of deer populations has little or no impact on tick numbers because the tick population is more limited by the availability of small mammal hosts. We can use this knowledge to predict that the incidence of Lyme disease is most likely to rise if weather or habitat alteration increases food supply or depresses predation rates on small mammals.

Further Reading R. S. Ostfeld, C. D. Canham, K. Oggenfuss, R. J. Winchcombe, F. Keesing, Climate, deer, rodents, and acorns as determinants of variation in Lyme-disease risk, *PLOS Biology* 4:6:145 (2006).

MAKE CONNECTIONS *Organisms rely on their immune systems to recognize and respond to pathogens (Chapter 43). Is a small mammal with a strong immune response to the Lyme pathogen,* Borrelia burgdorferi, *likely to be a good reservoir species? Why or why not?*

What Influences the Incidence of Lyme Disease? The number of human Lyme disease cases in an area rises with the density of infected ticks. Like many other organisms, the size of a tick population is limited by its food supply—in this case, available host animals. Deer are necessary for tick reproduction, but tick populations can persist in areas with low densities of deer. Most often, tick populations are limited by the supply

Community ecology provides the foundation for understanding the life cycles of pathogens and their interactions with hosts. Pathogen interactions are also greatly influenced by changes in the physical environment. To control pathogens and the diseases they cause, scientists need an ecosystem perspective—an intimate knowledge of how the pathogens interact with other species and with all aspects of their environment. Ecosystems are the subject of Chapter 55.

54 Chapter Review

SUMMARY OF KEY CONCEPTS

CONCEPT 54.1

Community interactions are classified by whether they help, harm, or have no effect on the species involved (pp. 1274–1281)

- A variety of **interspecific interactions** affect the survival and reproduction of the species that engage in them. These interactions include interspecific competition, predation, herbivory, symbiosis, and facilitation.
- Competitive exclusion states that two species competing for the same resource cannot coexist permanently in the same place. **Resource partitioning** is the differentiation of **ecological niches** that enables species to coexist in a community.

Interspecific Interaction	Description
Interspecific competition (−/−)	Two or more species compete for a resource that is in short supply.
Predation (+/−)	One species, the predator, kills and eats the other, the prey. Predation has led to diverse adaptations, including mimicry.
Herbivory (+/−)	An herbivore eats part of a plant or alga.
Symbiosis	Individuals of two or more species live in close contact with one another. Symbiosis includes parasitism, mutualism, and commensalism.
Parasitism (+/−)	The **parasite** derives its nourishment from a second organism, its **host**, which is harmed.
Mutualism (+/+)	Both species benefit from the interaction.
Commensalism (+/0)	One species benefits from the interaction, while the other is unaffected by it.
Facilitation (+/+ or 0/+)	Species have positive effects on the survival and reproduction of other species without the intimate contact of a symbiosis.

? *Give an example of a pair of species that exhibit each interaction listed in the table above.*

CONCEPT 54.2

Diversity and trophic structure characterize biological communities (pp. 1282–1288)

- **Species diversity** measures the number of species in a community— its **species richness**—and their **relative abundance**.
- More diverse communities typically produce more **biomass** and show less year-to-year variation in growth than less diverse communities and are more resistant to invasion by exotic species.

- **Trophic structure** is a key factor in community dynamics. **Food chains** link the trophic levels from producers to top carnivores. Branching food chains and complex trophic interactions form **food webs**.
- **Dominant species** are the most abundant species in a community. **Keystone species** are usually less abundant species that exert a disproportionate influence on community structure.
- The **bottom-up model** proposes a unidirectional influence from lower to higher trophic levels, in which nutrients and other abiotic factors primarily determine community structure. The **top-down model** proposes that control of each trophic level comes from the trophic level above, with the result that predators control herbivores, which in turn control primary producers.

? *Based on indexes such as Shannon diversity, is a community of higher species richness always more diverse than a community of lower species richness? Explain.*

CONCEPT 54.3

Disturbance influences species diversity and composition (pp. 1289–1292)

- Increasing evidence suggests that **disturbance** and lack of equilibrium, rather than stability and equilibrium, are the norm for most communities. According to the **intermediate disturbance hypothesis**, moderate levels of disturbance can foster higher species diversity than can low or high levels of disturbance.
- **Ecological succession** is the sequence of community and ecosystem changes after a disturbance. **Primary succession** occurs where no soil exists when succession begins; **secondary succession** begins in an area where soil remains after a disturbance.

? *Is the disturbance pictured in Figure 54.28 more likely to initiate primary or secondary succession? Explain.*

CONCEPT 54.4

Biogeographic factors affect community diversity (pp. 1292–1294)

- Species richness generally declines along a latitudinal gradient from the tropics to the poles. The greater age of tropical environments may account for their greater species richness.
- Species richness is directly related to a community's geographic size, a principle formalized in the **species-area curve**.
- Species richness on islands depends on island size and distance from the mainland. The island equilibrium model maintains that species richness on an ecological island reaches an equilibrium where new immigrations are balanced by extinctions.

? *How have periods of glaciation influenced latitudinal patterns of diversity?*

Pathogens alter community structure locally and globally (pp. 1294–1297)

- Recent work has highlighted the role that **pathogens** play in structuring terrestrial and marine communities.
- **Zoonotic pathogens** are transferred from other animals to humans and cause the largest class of emerging human diseases. Community ecology provides the framework for identifying key species interactions associated with such pathogens and for helping us track and control their spread.

? *In what way can a* **vector** *of a zoonotic pathogen differ from a host of the pathogen?*

TEST YOUR UNDERSTANDING

LEVEL 1: KNOWLEDGE/COMPREHENSION

1. The feeding relationships among the species in a community determine the community's
   a. secondary succession.
   b. ecological niche.
   c. species richness.
   d. trophic structure.

2. The principle of competitive exclusion states that
   a. two species cannot coexist in the same habitat.
   b. competition between two species always causes extinction or emigration of one species.
   c. two species that have exactly the same niche cannot coexist in a community.
   d. two species will stop reproducing until one species leaves the habitat.

3. Based on the intermediate disturbance hypothesis, a community's species diversity is increased by
   a. frequent massive disturbance.
   b. stable conditions with no disturbance.
   c. moderate levels of disturbance.
   d. human intervention to eliminate disturbance.

4. According to the island equilibrium model, species richness would be greatest on an island that is
   a. large and remote.
   b. small and remote.
   c. large and close to a mainland.
   d. small and close to a mainland.

LEVEL 2: APPLICATION/ANALYSIS

5. Predators that are keystone species can maintain species diversity in a community if they
   a. competitively exclude other predators.
   b. prey on the community's dominant species.
   c. reduce the number of disruptions in the community.
   d. prey only on the least abundant species in the community.

6. Food chains are sometimes short because
   a. only a single species of herbivore feeds on each plant species.
   b. local extinction of a species causes extinction of the other species in its food chain.
   c. most of the energy in a trophic level is lost as energy passes to the next higher level.
   d. most producers are inedible.

7. Which of the following could qualify as a top-down control on a grassland community?
   a. limitation of plant biomass by rainfall amount
   b. influence of temperature on competition among plants
   c. influence of soil nutrients on the abundance of grasses versus wildflowers
   d. effect of grazing intensity by bison on plant species diversity

8. The most plausible hypothesis to explain why species richness is higher in tropical than in temperate regions is that
   a. tropical communities are younger.
   b. tropical regions generally have more available water and higher levels of solar radiation.
   c. higher temperatures cause more rapid speciation.
   d. diversity increases as evapotranspiration decreases.

9. Community 1 contains 100 individuals distributed among four species: 5A, 5B, 85C, and 5D. Community 2 contains 100 individuals distributed among three species: 30A, 40B, and 30C. Calculate the Shannon diversity (H) for each community. Which community is more diverse?

LEVEL 3: SYNTHESIS/EVALUATION

10. **DRAW IT** The vector for Lyme disease, the black-legged tick, is influenced by species interactions within its ecological community. Ticks take blood meals from small mammals such as the white-footed mouse and from deer. Mice eat seeds and acorns and are preyed upon by owls and foxes. Deer eat acorns, grass, and shrubs and are preyed upon by coyotes. Draw a food web that includes the black-legged tick and these interactions. If the control of white-footed mouse abundance is primarily top-down, how would you expect a decline in fox numbers to affect the abundance of ticks?

11. **EVOLUTION CONNECTION**
    Explain why adaptations of particular organisms to interspecific competition may not necessarily represent instances of character displacement. What would a researcher have to demonstrate about two competing species to make a convincing case for character displacement?

12. **SCIENTIFIC INQUIRY**
    An ecologist studying plants in the desert performed the following experiment. She staked out two identical plots, each of which included a few sagebrush plants and numerous small annual wildflowers. She found the same five wildflower species in roughly equal numbers on both plots. She then enclosed one of the plots with a fence to keep out kangaroo rats, the most common grain-eaters of the area. After two years, four of the wildflower species were no longer present in the fenced plot, but one species had increased drastically. The control plot had not changed in species diversity. Using the principles of community ecology, propose a hypothesis to explain her results. What additional evidence would support your hypothesis?

13. **WRITE ABOUT A THEME: INTERACTIONS**
    In Batesian mimicry, a palatable species gains protection by mimicking an unpalatable one. Imagine that individuals of a palatable, brightly coloured fly species are blown to three remote islands. The first island has no predators of that species; the second has predators but no similarly coloured, unpalatable species; and the third has both predators and a similarly coloured, unpalatable species. In a short essay (100–150 words), predict what might happen to the colouration of the palatable species on each island through evolutionary time if colouration is a genetically controlled trait. Explain your predictions.

14. **SYNTHESIZE YOUR KNOWLEDGE**

    Describe two types of interspecific interactions that you can observe in this photo. What morphological adaptation can be seen in the species that is at the highest trophic level in this scene?

    Jacques Roses/Science Source

For selected answers, see Appendix A.

55

Ecosystems and Restoration Ecology

KEY CONCEPTS

55.1 Physical laws govern energy flow and chemical cycling in ecosystems

55.2 Energy and other limiting factors control primary production in ecosystems

55.3 Energy transfer between trophic levels is typically only 10% efficient

55.4 Biological and geochemical processes cycle nutrients and water in ecosystems

55.5 Restoration ecologists help return degraded ecosystems to a more natural state

Science Source

▲ Figure 55.1 **Giant tube worms, anemones and mussels live near hydrothermal vents**

In the Deep, Dark Sea

Deep in the ocean, west of Vancouver Island, two large underwater plates are slowly pulling apart. Hot magma rises to the surface of the ocean floor and continually adds new material to an underwater volcanic mountain chain, the Juan de Fuca Ridge. Hydrothermal vents are found along the ridge where seawater percolates down through cracks, is heated by the hot magma below, and then spews back out at temperatures exceeding 200°C. The hot water carries black sulphur-containing particles, which settle around the vents. To the surprise of the first scientists exploring such hydrothermal vents, many strange and wonderful creatures live in and around the vents (Figure 55.1). Verena Tunnicliffe, from the University of Victoria, has been studying these unique communities for more than 25 years (see the interview at the start of Unit Eight). The first big question scientists had was, What energy source sustains communities that live at depths no sunlight ever reaches? They first thought that surface organisms must somehow be transported to the ocean depths to provide an energetic base for hydrothermal vent communities. But further research led to the discovery that vent microbes were capable of using the chemical energy stored in compounds of sulphur to build organic compounds (chemosynthesis) and did not need to rely on energy derived from sunlight as do photosynthetic organisms.

These chemoautotrophic microbes, together with consumer organisms (protists, crustaceans, molluscs, and other invertebrates) and the surrounding physical

Science Source

◀ **A hydrothermal vent community on the floor of the Pacific Ocean**

environment, make up an **ecosystem**, the sum of all the organisms living in a given area and the physical environment with which they interact. An ecosystem can encompass a vast area, such as a lake, forest, or island, or can be a microcosm, such as the space under a fallen log or a desert spring (Figure 55.2). As with populations and communities, the boundaries of ecosystems are not always discrete. Many ecologists view the entire biosphere as a global ecosystem, a composite of all the local ecosystems on Earth.

Regardless of an ecosystem's size, its dynamics involve two processes that cannot be fully described by population or community phenomena: energy flow and chemical cycling. Energy enters most ecosystems as sunlight. It is converted to chemical energy by autotrophs, passed to heterotrophs in the organic compounds of food, and dissipated as heat. Chemical elements, such as carbon and nitrogen, are cycled among abiotic and biotic components of the ecosystem. Photosynthetic and chemosynthetic organisms assimilate these elements in inorganic form from the air, soil, and water and incorporate them into their biomass, some of which is consumed by animals. The elements are returned in inorganic form to the environment by the metabolism of plants and animals and by organisms such as bacteria and fungi that break down organic wastes and dead organisms.

Both energy and matter are transformed in ecosystems through photosynthesis and feeding relationships. But unlike matter, energy cannot be recycled. An ecosystem must be powered by a continuous influx of energy from an external

source—in most cases, the sun. Energy flows through ecosystems, whereas matter cycles within and through ecosystems.

Resources critical to human survival and welfare, ranging from the food we eat to the oxygen we breathe, are products of ecosystem processes. In this chapter, we will explore the dynamics of energy flow and chemical cycling, emphasizing the results of ecosystem experiments. One way to study ecosystem processes is to alter environmental factors, such as temperature or the abundance of nutrients, and study how ecosystems respond. We will also consider some of the impacts of human activities on energy flow and chemical cycling. Finally, we will explore the growing science of restoration ecology, which focuses on returning degraded ecosystems to a more natural state.

CONCEPT 55.1

Physical laws govern energy flow and chemical cycling in ecosystems

Cells transform energy and matter subject to the laws of thermodynamics (see Concept 8.1). Cell biologists study these transformations within organelles and cells and measure the amounts of energy and matter that cross the cells' boundaries. Ecosystem ecologists do the same thing, except in their case the "cell" is a complete ecosystem. By studying the dynamics of populations (see Chapter 53) and by grouping the species in a community into trophic levels of feeding relationships (see Chapter 54), ecologists can follow the transformations of energy in an ecosystem and map the movements of chemical elements.

Conservation of Energy

Because ecosystem ecologists study the interactions of organisms with the physical environment, many ecosystem approaches are based on laws of physics and chemistry. The first law of thermodynamics states that energy cannot be created or destroyed but only transferred or transformed (see Concept 8.1). Plants and other photosynthetic organisms convert solar energy to chemical energy, but the total amount of energy does not change: The amount of energy stored in organic molecules must equal the total solar energy intercepted by the plant minus the amounts reflected and dissipated as heat. Ecosystem ecologists often measure transfers within and across ecosystems, in part to understand how many organisms a habitat can support and the amount of food humans can harvest from a site.

One implication of the second law of thermodynamics, which states that every exchange of energy increases the entropy of the universe, is that energy conversions are inefficient. Some energy is always lost as heat (see Concept 8.1). We can measure the efficiency of ecological energy conversions just as we measure the efficiency of lightbulbs and car engines. Because energy flowing through ecosystems is ultimately

Anne Morkill/U.S. Fish and Wildlife Service

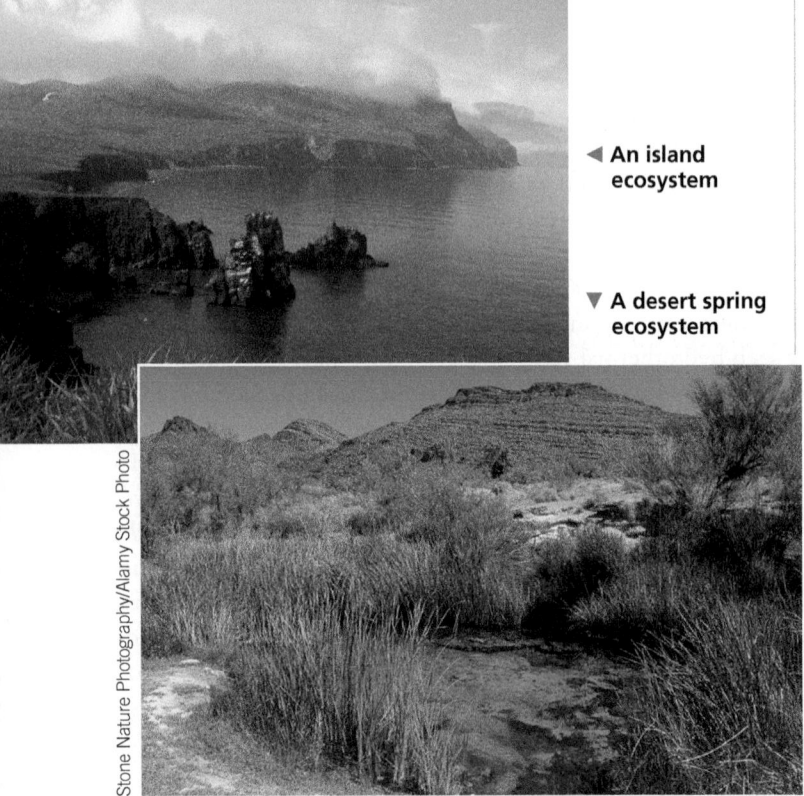

◀ An island ecosystem

▼ A desert spring ecosystem

Stone Nature Photography/Alamy Stock Photo

▲ Figure 55.2 **Ecosystems at different scales.**

dissipated into space as heat, most ecosystems would vanish if the sun were not continuously providing energy to Earth.

Conservation of Mass

Matter, like energy, cannot be created or destroyed. This **law of conservation of mass** is as important for ecosystems as the laws of thermodynamics. Because mass is conserved, we can determine how much of a chemical element cycles within an ecosystem or is gained or lost by that ecosystem over time.

Unlike energy, chemical elements are continually recycled within ecosystems. A carbon atom in CO_2 is released from the soil by a decomposer, taken up by a grass through photosynthesis, consumed by a bison or other grazer, and returned to the soil in the bison's waste. Measurement and analysis of chemical cycling are important in ecosystem ecology.

Although most elements are not gained or lost on a global scale, they can be gained by or lost from a particular ecosystem. In a forest ecosystem, most mineral nutrients—the essential elements that plants obtain from soil—enter as dust or as solutes dissolved in rainwater or leached from rocks in the ground. Nitrogen is also supplied through the biological process of nitrogen fixation (see Figure 37.10). In terms of losses, some elements return to the atmosphere as gases, and others are carried out of the ecosystem by moving water. Like organisms, ecosystems are open systems, absorbing energy and mass and releasing heat and waste products.

In nature, most gains and losses to ecosystems are small compared to the amounts recycled within them. Still, the balance between inputs and outputs determines whether an ecosystem is a source or a sink for a given element. If a mineral nutrient's outputs exceed its inputs, it will eventually limit production in that system. Human activities often change the balance of inputs and outputs considerably, as we will see later in this chapter and in Chapter 56.

Energy, Mass, and Trophic Levels

Ecologists group species into trophic levels based on their main source of nutrition and energy (see Concept 54.2). The trophic level that ultimately supports all others consists of autotrophs, also called the **primary producers** of the ecosystem. Most autotrophs are photosynthetic organisms that use light energy to synthesize sugars and other organic compounds, which they then use as fuel for cellular respiration and as building material for growth. Plants, algae, and photosynthetic prokaryotes are the biosphere's main autotrophs, although chemosynthetic prokaryotes are the primary producers in ecosystems such as deep-sea hydrothermal vents (see Figure 52.14) and places deep under the ground or ice.

Organisms in trophic levels above the primary producers are heterotrophs, which depend directly or indirectly on the outputs of primary producers for their source of energy. Herbivores, which eat plants and other primary producers,

▼ Fungi decomposing a dead tree

▲ Rod-shaped (bacillus) and spherical (coccus) bacteria in compost (colourized SEM)

▲ Figure 55.3 Detritivores.

are **primary consumers**. Carnivores that eat herbivores are **secondary consumers**, and carnivores that eat other carnivores are **tertiary consumers**.

Another group of heterotrophs is the **detritivores**, or **decomposers**, terms we use synonymously in this text to refer to consumers that get their energy from detritus. **Detritus** is nonliving organic material, such as the remains of dead organisms, feces, fallen leaves, and wood. Many detritivores are in turn eaten by secondary and tertiary consumers. Two important groups of detritivores are prokaryotes and fungi (Figure 55.3). These organisms secrete enzymes that digest organic material; they then absorb the breakdown products, linking the consumers and primary producers in an ecosystem. In a forest, for instance, birds eat earthworms that have been feeding on leaf litter and its associated prokaryotes and fungi.

Detritivores also play a critical role in recycling chemical elements back to primary producers. Detritivores convert organic matter from all trophic levels to inorganic compounds usable by primary producers, closing the loop of an ecosystem's chemical cycling. Producers recycle these elements into organic compounds. If decomposition stopped, life would cease as detritus piled up and the supply of ingredients needed to synthesize new organic matter was exhausted. Figure 55.4 summarizes the trophic relationships in an ecosystem.

CONCEPT CHECK 55.1

1. Why is the transfer of energy in an ecosystem referred to as energy flow, not energy cycling?

2. **WHAT IF?** You are studying nitrogen cycling on the Serengeti Plain in Africa. During your experiment, a herd of migrating wildebeests grazes through your study plot. What would you need to know to measure their effect on nitrogen balance in the plot?

3. **MAKE CONNECTIONS** How does the second law of thermodynamics explain why an ecosystem's energy supply must be continually replenished (see Concept 8.1)?

For suggested answers, see Appendix A.

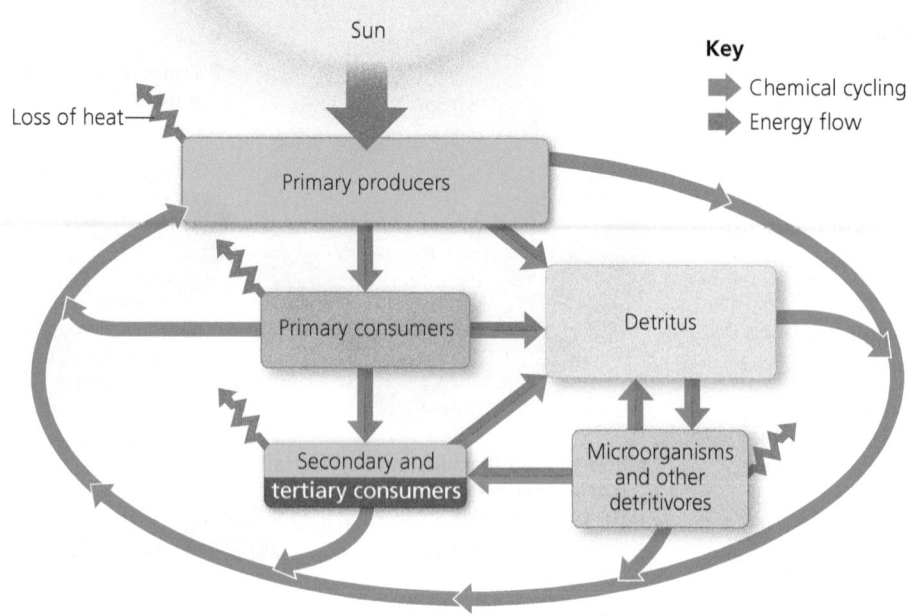

Sun

Loss of heat

Primary producers

Primary consumers

Detritus

Secondary and tertiary consumers

Microorganisms and other detritivores

▲ **Figure 55.4 An overview of energy and nutrient dynamics in an ecosystem.** Energy enters, flows through, and exits an ecosystem, whereas chemical nutrients cycle primarily within it. In this generalized scheme, energy (dark orange arrows) enters from the sun as radiation, moves as chemical energy transfers through the food web, and exits as heat radiated into space. Most transfers of nutrients (blue arrows) through the trophic levels lead eventually to detritus; the nutrients then cycle back to the primary producers.

Source: Based on figure 1.2 from *Dynamics of Nutrient Cycling and Food Webs* by Donald L. DeAngelis. Taylor & Francis, 1992. © Jane B Reece.

CONCEPT 55.2

Energy and other limiting factors control primary production in ecosystems

The theme of energy transfer underlies all biological interactions (see Concept 1.1). In most ecosystems, the amount of light energy converted to chemical energy—in the form of organic compounds—by autotrophs during a given time period is the ecosystem's **primary production**. These photosynthetic products are the starting point for most studies of ecosystem metabolism and energy flow. In ecosystems where the primary producers are chemoautotrophs, the initial energy input is chemical, and the initial products are the organic compounds synthesized by the microorganisms.

Ecosystem Energy Budgets

Since most primary producers use light energy to synthesize energy-rich organic molecules, consumers acquire their organic fuels secondhand (or even third- or fourth-hand) through food webs (see Figure 54.15). Therefore, the total amount of photosynthetic production sets the spending limit for the entire ecosystem's energy budget.

The Global Energy Budget

Each day, Earth's atmosphere is bombarded by about 10^{22} joules of solar radiation. This is enough energy to

supply the demands of the entire human population for approximately 18 years at 2014 energy consumption levels. The intensity of the solar energy striking Earth varies with latitude, with the tropics receiving the greatest input (see Figure 52.3). Most incoming solar radiation is absorbed, scattered, or reflected by clouds and dust in the atmosphere. The amount of solar radiation that ultimately reaches Earth's surface sets an upper limit to the possible photosynthetic output of ecosystems.

Only a small fraction of the sunlight that reaches Earth's surface is actually used in photosynthesis. Much of the radiation strikes materials that don't photosynthesize, such as ice and soil. Of the radiation that does reach photosynthetic organisms, only certain wavelengths are absorbed by photosynthetic pigments (see Figure 10.9); the rest is transmitted, reflected, or lost as heat. As a result, only about 1% of the visible light that strikes photosynthetic organisms is converted to chemical energy. Nevertheless, Earth's primary producers create about 105 billion metric tonnes (1.05×10^{14} kg) of organic material each year.

Gross and Net Production

Total primary production in an ecosystem is known as that ecosystem's **gross primary production (GPP)**—the amount of energy from light (or chemicals, in chemoautotrophic systems) converted to the chemical energy of organic molecules per unit time. Not all of this production is stored as organic material in the primary producers, because they use some of the molecules as fuel in their own cellular respiration. **Net primary production (NPP)** is equal to gross primary production minus the energy used by the primary producers for their "autotrophic respiration" (R_a):

$$NPP = GPP - R_a$$

On average, NPP is about one-half of GPP. To ecologists, net primary production is the key measurement because it represents the storage of chemical energy that will be available to consumers in the ecosystem.

Net primary production can be expressed as energy per unit area per unit time ($J/m^2 \cdot yr$) or as biomass (mass of vegetation) added per unit area per unit time ($g/m^2 \cdot yr$). (Note that biomass is usually expressed in terms of the dry mass of organic material.) An ecosystem's NPP should not be confused with the total biomass of photosynthetic autotrophs present, a measure called the *standing crop*. Net primary production is the amount of *new* biomass added in a given period of time. Although a forest has a large standing crop, its net primary production may actually be less than that of some grasslands; grasslands do not accumulate as much biomass as forests because animals consume the plants rapidly and because grasses and herbs usually have shorter life spans than trees.

Satellites provide a powerful tool for studying global patterns of primary production (Figure 55.5). Images produced from satellite data show that different ecosystems vary considerably in their net primary production. Tropical rain forests are among the most productive terrestrial ecosystems and contribute a large portion of the planet's net primary production. Estuaries and coral reefs also have very high net primary production, but their contribution to the global total is smaller because these ecosystems cover only about one-tenth the area covered by tropical rain forests. In contrast, while the oceans are relatively unproductive (Figure 55.6), their vast size means that together they contribute as much to total global net primary production as terrestrial systems do.

Whereas net primary production can be stated as the amount of new biomass added in a given period of time, **net ecosystem production (NEP)** is a measure of the *total biomass accumulation* during that time. Net ecosystem production is defined as gross primary production minus the total respiration of all organisms in the system (R_T)—not just primary producers, as for the calculation of NPP, but decomposers and other heterotrophs as well:

$$NEP = GPP - R_T$$

NEP is useful to ecologists because its value determines whether an ecosystem is gaining or losing carbon over time. A forest may have a positive NPP but still lose carbon if heterotrophs release it as CO_2 more quickly than primary producers incorporate it into organic compounds. In the Scientific Skills Exercise, you will explore the links between NEP and global warming.

The most common way to estimate NEP is to measure the net flux (flow) of CO_2 or O_2 entering or leaving the ecosystem. If more CO_2 enters than leaves, the system is storing carbon. Because O_2 flux is directly coupled to photosynthesis

▼ Figure 55.5 | **Research Method**

Determining Primary Production with Satellites

Application Because chlorophyll captures visible light (see Figure 10.9), photosynthetic organisms absorb more light at visible wavelengths (about 380–750 nm) than at near-infrared wavelengths (750–1100 nm). Scientists use this difference in absorption to estimate the rate of photosynthesis in different regions of the globe using satellites.

Technique Most satellites determine what they "see" by comparing the ratios of wavelengths reflected back to them. Vegetation reflects much more near-infrared radiation than visible radiation, producing a reflectance pattern very different from that of snow, clouds, soil, and liquid water.

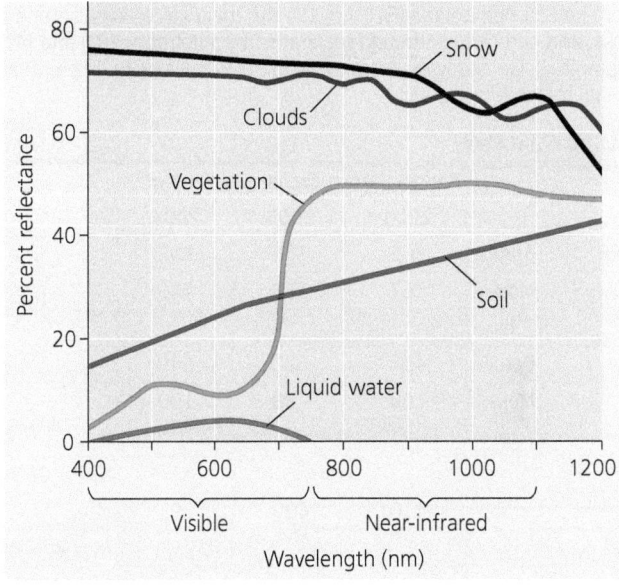

Results Scientists use the satellite data to help produce maps of primary production like the one in Figure 55.6.

and respiration (see Figure 9.2), a system that is giving off O_2 is also storing carbon. On land, ecologists typically measure only the net flux of CO_2 from ecosystems; detecting small changes in O_2 in a large atmospheric O_2 pool is difficult. In

► Figure 55.6 **Global net primary production.** The map is based on data collected by satellites, such as amount of sunlight absorbed by vegetation. Note that tropical land areas have the highest rates of production (yellow and red on the map).

? *Does this global map accurately reflect the importance of some highly productive habitats, such as wetlands, coral reefs, and coastal zones? Explain.*

Net primary production (kg carbon/m^2·yr)

Using Tabular Data to Calculate Net Ecosystem Production

How Will Global Warming Affect Carbon Cycling in Canadian Forests? In ecosystems, plants take up carbon through photosynthesis, and plants, animals, and microbes release carbon through respiration. The ecosystem is a net *carbon sink* if uptake exceeds respiration, or a *carbon source* if respiration exceeds uptake. Since temperature affects both photosynthesis and respiration rates, ecologists have wondered whether global warming will lead to increased uptake of carbon by our northern forests or whether warmer forest ecosystems will release more CO_2 to the atmosphere.

How the Study Was Done Ecosystem ecologists measured the uptake and release of CO_2 in a black spruce forest in northern Saskatchewan. They estimated carbon uptake (GPP) by the two main autotrophs, spruce and moss, and carbon lost through respiration by autotrophs (R_a) and heterotrophs (R_h). The study ran from 2004 to 2006, years with different mean annual temperatures.

MShieldsPhotos/Alamy Stock Photo

Data from the Study

		Annual Carbon Exchange (gCm^{-2}yr^{-1})			
		2004	**2005**	**2006**	
GPP	Spruce	766	835	893	
	Moss	167	220	249	
	Total				
R_a	Spruce	457	520	549	
	Moss	69	88	100	
	Total				
NPP					NPP = GPP − R_a
R_h		410	409	391	
R_T					$R_T = R_a + R_h$
NEP					NEP = GPP = R_T
Mean temp (°C)		−0.10	1.83	2.40	

Interpret the Data

1. Use the data in the table to calculate total GPP, total R_a, and NPP (highlighted boxes in table). Make a scatterplot of GPP and NPP versus temperature. Does spruce or moss contribute most to total NPP? What do the data suggest about the effect of warmer temperatures on plant growth?

2. Make a scatterplot of autotroph, heterotroph, and total respiration versus temperature. Which is greater, plant or heterotroph respiration? Did autotroph and heterotroph respiration show the same pattern with temperature?

3. Use the data to calculate NEP for each year. Make a bar graph of NEP versus year. In which year(s) was the ecosystem a carbon source and in which year(s) was it a carbon sink? Explain how you came to your answers.

4. The 30-year average for mean annual temperature at the study site is 0.40°C, about 2°C less than the mean annual temperature observed in 2006. Do these data suggest that global warming of 2°C is likely to make the black spruce forests of northern Saskatchewan a net carbon sink or source? Explain in terms of effects on photosynthesis and respiration.

Data from R.F. Grant, H.A. Margolis, A.G. Barr, T.A. Black, A.L. Dunn, P.Y Bernier, and O. Bergeron, Changes in net ecosystem productivity of boreal black spruce stands in response to changes in temperature at diurnal and seasonal time scales, *Tree Physiology* 29:1-17 (2008).

---

the oceans, researchers use both approaches. New marine research using O_2 measurements has revealed surprisingly high NEP in some of the nutrient-poor waters that cover much of the open ocean. This result is causing biologists to reevaluate regional and global estimates of ocean productivity and to examine the constraints to marine productivity.

What limits production in ecosystems? To ask this question another way, what factors could we change to increase production for a given ecosystem? We'll address this question first for aquatic ecosystems.

Primary Production in Aquatic Ecosystems

In aquatic (marine and freshwater) ecosystems, both light and nutrients are important in controlling primary production.

Light Limitation

Because solar radiation drives photosynthesis, you would expect light to be a key variable in controlling primary production in oceans. Indeed, the depth of light penetration affects

primary production throughout the photic zone of an ocean or lake (see Figure 52.12). About half of the solar radiation is absorbed in the first 15 m of water. Even in "clear" water, only 5–10% of the radiation may reach a depth of 75 m.

If light were the main variable limiting primary production in ocean surface waters, we would expect production to increase along a gradient from the poles toward the equator, which receives the greatest intensity of light. However, you can see in Figure 55.6 that there is no such gradient. Another factor must strongly influence primary production in the ocean.

Nutrient Limitation

More than light, nutrients limit primary production in most oceans and lakes. A **limiting nutrient** is the element that must be added for production to increase. The nutrient most often limiting marine production is either nitrogen or phosphorus. Concentrations of these nutrients are typically low in the photic zone because they are rapidly taken up by phytoplankton and because detritus tends to sink.

As detailed in **Figure 55.7**, nutrient enrichment experiments confirmed that nitrogen was limiting phytoplankton growth off the south shore of Long Island, New York. One practical application of this work was to identify the nutrient that had to be reduced to prevent algal "blooms" in coastal waters.

The macronutrients nitrogen and phosphorus are not the only nutrients that limit aquatic production. The Sargasso Sea, a subtropical region of the Atlantic Ocean, has some of the clearest water in the world because of its low phytoplankton density. The Sea has very low concentrations of both nitrogen and phosphorus. However, experiments have shown that primary producers in the Sargasso Sea are also limited by a critical micronutrient—iron (**Table 55.1**). Windblown dust from the land supplies iron to the oceans, and iron is scarce in this and many other areas of the ocean that are far from land.

▼ Figure 55.7 | **Inquiry**

Which nutrient limits phytoplankton production along the coast of Long Island?

Experiment Pollution from duck farms adds both nitrogen and phosphorus to the coastal water off Long Island, New York. To determine which nutrient limits phytoplankton growth in this area, ecologists cultured the phytoplankton *Nannochloris atomus* with water collected from several sites, identified as A–G. They added either ammonium (NH_4^+) or phosphate (PO_4^{3-}) to some of the cultures.

Results The addition of ammonium caused heavy phytoplankton growth in the cultures, but the addition of phosphate did not.

Source: Adaptation of figure 2 from "Nitrogen, Phosphorus, and Eutrophication in the Coastal Marine Environment" by John H. Ryther and William M. Dunstan, from *Science*, March 1971, Volume 171(3975). Copyright © 1971 by AAAS. Reprinted with permission

Conclusion Since adding phosphorus, which was already in rich supply, did not increase *Nannochloris* growth, whereas adding nitrogen increased phytoplankton density dramatically, the researchers concluded that nitrogen is the nutrient that limits phytoplankton growth in this ecosystem.

Source: J. H. Ryther and W. M. Dunstan, Nitrogen, phosphorus, and eutrophication in the coastal marine environment, *Science* 171:1008–1013 (1971).

WHAT IF? *How would you expect the results of this experiment to change if new duck farms substantially increased the amount of pollution in the water? Explain your reasoning.*

Table 55.1 Nutrient Enrichment Experiment for Sargasso Sea Samples

Nutrients Added to Experimental Culture	Relative Uptake of ^{14}C by Cultures*
None (controls)	1.00
Nitrogen (N) + phosphorus (P) only	1.10
N + P + metals excluding iron (Fe)	1.08
N + P + metals including Fe	12.90
N + P + Fe	12.00

*^{14}C uptake by cultures measures primary production.

Source: D. W. Menzel and J. H. Ryther, Nutrients limiting the production of phytoplankton in the Sargasso Sea, with special reference to iron, *Deep Sea Research* 7:276–281 (1961).

INTERPRET THE DATA *The element molybdenum (Mo) is another micronutrient that can limit primary production in the oceans. If the researchers found the following results for additions of Mo, what would you conclude about its relative importance for growth?*

N + P + Mo	6.0
N + P + Fe + Mo	72.0

Several large areas of the ocean have low phytoplankton densities despite relatively high nitrogen concentrations. The finding that iron limits production in some oceanic ecosystems encouraged marine scientists to carry out large-scale ocean fertilization experiments in the Pacific and Antarctic Oceans—research that might also shed light on ocean fertilization as a tool to remove the greenhouse gas carbon dioxide from the atmosphere. In one study, researchers spread low concentrations of dissolved iron over 72 km² of ocean. A massive phytoplankton bloom occurred. However, to effectively remove carbon dioxide from the atmosphere, the extra primary production must sink into deep ocean water and sediments. Unfortunately, this does not appear to occur. Instead, the extra carbon is recycled by secondary consumers and decomposers in shallow waters and returned to the atmosphere. Ecologists also have concerns about the overall effects of large-scale fertilization on marine communities. Iron fertilization is therefore unlikely to be widely applied anytime soon.

Areas of upwelling, where deep, nutrient-rich waters circulate to the ocean surface, have exceptionally high primary production. Because upwelling stimulates growth of the phytoplankton that form the base of marine food webs, upwelling areas typically host highly productive, diverse ecosystems and are prime fishing locations. The largest areas of upwelling occur in the Southern Ocean (also called the Antarctic Ocean), along the equator, and in the coastal waters off Peru, California, and parts of western Africa. Economically important fisheries depend on nutrients brought to the surface by upwelling in the Juan de Fuca Strait south of Vancouver Island and over the Grand Banks of Newfoundland.

Excessive algal growth also occurs in freshwater lakes when large amounts of nutrients are added. Many lakes became choked with cyanobacteria and algae in the 1970s due to nutrients from

Figure 55.8

▼ Figure 55.8 | **Impact**

Lake Erie—A Near Death Experience

In the 1960s, excessive growth or blooms of algae occurred each year in Lake Erie due to nutrient inputs from untreated human sewage and runoff from agricultural fields. Large mats of algae and dead fish washed up and rotted on the beaches. Some people even declared the lake "dead."

Experiments were conducted by David Schindler and colleagues at the Experimental Lakes Area, Ontario, to determine which nutrient limits primary production in lakes. In one test, they divided a small lake with a curtain, fertilized one side with carbon, nitrogen, and phosphorus, and added only carbon and nitrogen to the other side. The result was dramatic: a massive algal bloom occurred, but only on the side with phosphorus added. They had identified the limiting nutrient, and legislation soon reduced the phosphorus content of sewage discharge into the Great Lakes.

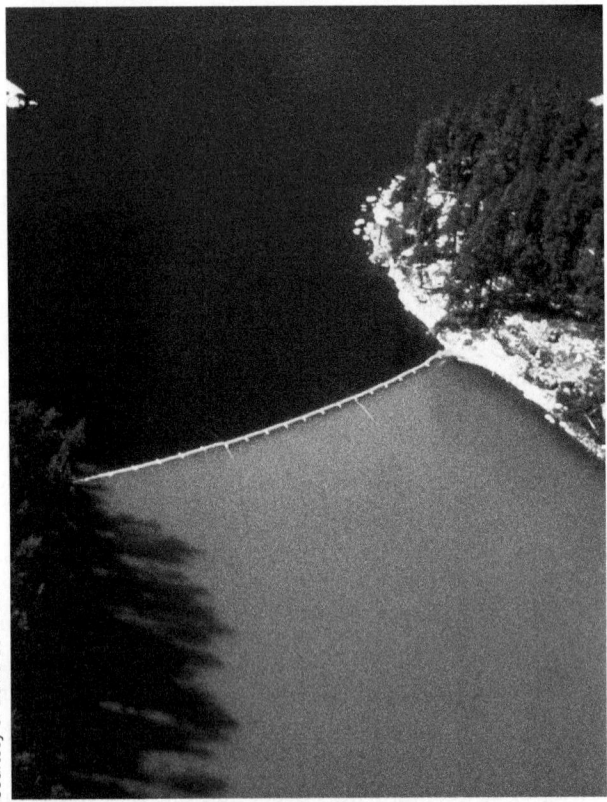

Courtesy of David Schindler

Why It Matters Eutrophication causes ecological and economic damage. The excess primary production sinks and decomposes on the lake bottom, depleting the dissolved oxygen in deep waters. Large fish kills occur, and species may be lost. Phosphorus inputs remain a problem in freshwater lakes around the world. Even Lake Erie, which recovered after phosphorus inputs were reduced, has begun to experience algal blooms again, due to increased input from agriculture.

Further Reading D. Schindler, Eutrophication and recovery in Experimental Lakes: Implication of lake management, *Science* 184:897–899 (1974); V. Smith & D. Schindler, Eutrophication science: Where do we go from here? *Trends in Ecology & Evolution* 24:201–207 (2009).

MAKE CONNECTIONS *Primary production in lakes is usually not limited by nitrogen because blooms become dominated by cyanobacteria, organisms that can fix nitrogen from the air (see Concept 27.3). Why is carbon not likely to be limiting?*

---

human sewage and runoff from agricultural and lawn fertilizers. The ecological impacts of this process, known as **eutrophication** (from the Greek *eutrophos*, well nourished), include the loss of many fish species from the lakes (see Figure 52.14).

Controlling eutrophication requires knowing which polluting nutrient is responsible. David Schindler of the University of Alberta led a set of elegant experiments that clearly demonstrated that phosphorus limits primary production in temperate freshwater lakes (**Figure 55.8**). These and other similar results led to legislation requiring phosphate-free detergents and some changes in agricultural practices.

Primary Production in Terrestrial Ecosystems

At regional and global scales, temperature and moisture are the main factors controlling primary production in terrestrial ecosystems. Tropical rain forests, with their warm, wet conditions that promote plant growth, are the most productive of all terrestrial ecosystems (see Figure 55.6). In contrast, low-productivity systems are generally hot and dry, like many deserts, or cold and dry, like arctic tundra. Between these extremes lie the temperate forest and grassland ecosystems, which have moderate climates and intermediate productivity.

The climate variables of moisture and temperature are very useful for predicting NPP in terrestrial ecosystems. Primary production is greater in wetter ecosystems, as shown for the plot of NPP and annual precipitation in **Figure 55.9**.

Nutrient Limitation

EVOLUTION Soil nutrients limit primary production in terrestrial ecosystems. As in aquatic systems, nitrogen and phosphorus are the nutrients that most commonly limit terrestrial production. Globally, nitrogen limits plant growth most. Phosphorus limitations are common in older soils where phosphate

▲ **Figure 55.9 A global relationship between net primary production and mean annual precipitation for terrestrial ecosystems.**

Source: Figure adapted from Robert H. Whittaker, *Communities and Ecosystems*, 1st edition, Copyright © 1970, p.82. Adapted and electronically reproduced by permission of Pearson Education, Inc., Upper Saddle River, New Jersey.

Biophoto Associates/Science Source

▲ Root nodules containing nitrogen-fixing bacteria

molecules have been leached away by water, such as in many tropical ecosystems. Phosphorus availability is also often low in soils of deserts and other ecosystems with a basic pH, where some phosphorus precipitates and becomes unavailable to plants. Adding a nonlimiting nutrient, even one that is scarce, will not stimulate production. Conversely, adding more of the limiting nutrient will increase production until some other nutrient becomes limiting.

Various adaptations have evolved in plants that can increase their uptake of limiting nutrients. One important mutualism that you have already studied is the symbiosis between plant roots and nitrogen-fixing bacteria (see Figure 37.11 and photo above). Another important mutualism is mycorrhizal association between plant roots and fungi that supply phosphorus and other limiting elements to plants (see Figure 37.13). Plants have root hairs and other anatomical features that increase the area of the soil that roots contact, increasing the rate at which nutrients can be absorbed (see Figure 35.3).

Studies relating nutrients to terrestrial primary production have practical applications in agriculture. For example, application of an optimal balance of nutrients can help farmers maximize crop yields, while reducing total fertilizer use, which not only lowers costs for the farmer, but may reduce damage to nearby ecosystems. This knowledge of limiting nutrients helps feed billions of people.

CONCEPT CHECK 55.2

1. Why is only a small portion of the solar energy that strikes Earth's atmosphere stored by primary producers?

2. How can ecologists experimentally determine the factor that limits primary production in an ecosystem?

3. **MAKE CONNECTIONS** Concept 10.3 describes the Calvin cycle of photosynthesis. Explain how nitrogen and phosphorus, the nutrients that most often limit primary production, are necessary for the Calvin cycle to function.

For suggested answers, see Appendix A.

CONCEPT 55.3

Energy transfer between trophic levels is typically only 10% efficient

The amount of chemical energy in consumers' food that is converted to their own new biomass during a given period is called the **secondary production** of the ecosystem.

Consider the transfer of organic matter from primary producers to herbivores, the primary consumers. In most ecosystems, herbivores eat only a small fraction of plant material produced; globally, they consume only about one-sixth of total plant production. Moreover, they cannot digest all the plant material that they *do* eat, as anyone who has walked through a dairy farm will attest. Most of an ecosystem's production is eventually consumed by detritivores. Next, we will analyze the process of energy transfer and cycling more closely.

Production Efficiency

First we will examine secondary production in an individual organism—a caterpillar. When a caterpillar feeds on a plant leaf, only about 33 J out of 200 J, or one-sixth of the potential energy in the leaf, is used for secondary production, or growth (Figure 55.10). The caterpillar uses some of the remaining energy (stored in organic compounds) for cellular respiration and excretes the rest in its feces. The energy contained in the feces remains in the ecosystem temporarily, but most of it is lost as heat after the feces are consumed by detritivores. The energy used for the caterpillar's respiration is also eventually lost from the ecosystem as heat. This is why energy is said to flow through, not cycle within, ecosystems. Only the chemical energy stored by herbivores as biomass, through growth or the production of offspring, is available as food to secondary consumers.

We can measure the efficiency of animals as energy transformers using the following equation:

$$\text{Production efficiency} = \frac{\text{Net secondary production} \times 100\%}{\text{Assimilation of primary production}}$$

Net secondary production is the energy stored in biomass represented by growth and reproduction. Assimilation

Plant material eaten by caterpillar

200 J

Feces — 100 J — Not assimilated

33 J — Growth (new biomass; secondary production)

67 J — Cellular respiration — Assimilated

▲ Figure 55.10 **Energy partitioning within a link of the food chain.**

INTERPRET THE DATA *What percentage of the energy in the caterpillar's food is actually used for secondary production (growth)?*

consists of the total energy taken in, not including losses in feces, used for growth, reproduction, and respiration. **Production efficiency**, therefore, is the percentage of energy stored in assimilated food that is *not* used for respiration. For the caterpillar in Figure 55.10, production efficiency is 33%; 67 J of the 100 J of assimilated energy is used for respiration. (The 100 J of energy lost as undigested material in feces does not count toward assimilation.) Birds and mammals typically have low production efficiencies, in the range of 1–3%, because they use so much energy in maintaining a constant, high body temperature. Fishes, which are ectotherms (see Concept 40.3), have production efficiencies around 10%. Insects and microorganisms are even more efficient, with production efficiencies averaging 40% or more.

Trophic Efficiency and Ecological Pyramids

Let's scale up now from the production efficiencies of individual consumers to the flow of energy through trophic levels.

Trophic efficiency is the percentage of production transferred from one trophic level to the next. Trophic efficiencies must always be less than production efficiencies because they take into account not only the energy lost through respiration and contained in feces, but also the energy in organic material in a lower trophic level that is not consumed by the next trophic level. Trophic efficiencies are generally only about 10% and range from approximately 5% to 20%, depending on the type of ecosystem. In other words, 90% of the energy available at one trophic level typically is *not* transferred to the next. This loss is multiplied over the length of a food chain. For example, if 10% of available energy is transferred from primary producers to primary consumers, such as caterpillars, and 10% of that energy is transferred to secondary consumers, called carnivores, then only 1% of net primary production is available to secondary consumers (10% of 10%).

The progressive loss of energy along a food chain severely limits the abundance of top-level carnivores that an ecosystem can support. Only about 0.1% of the chemical energy fixed by photosynthesis can flow all the way through a food web to a tertiary consumer, such as a snake or a shark. This explains why most food webs include only about four or five trophic levels (see Chapter 54).

The loss of energy with each transfer in a food chain can be represented by a *pyramid of net production*, in which the trophic levels are arranged in tiers (Figure 55.11). The width of each tier is proportional to the net production, expressed in joules, of each trophic level. The highest level, which represents top-level predators, contains relatively few individuals.

One important ecological consequence of low trophic efficiencies is represented in a *biomass pyramid*, in which

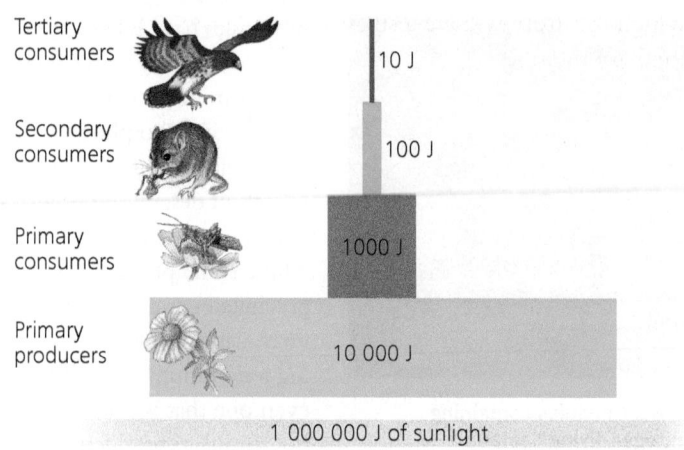

▲ **Figure 55.11 An idealized pyramid of net production.** This example assumes a trophic efficiency of 10% for each link in the food chain. Notice that primary producers convert only about 1% of the energy available to them to net primary production.

each tier represents the standing crop (the total dry mass of all organisms) in one trophic level. Most biomass pyramids narrow sharply from primary producers at the base to top-level carnivores at the apex because energy transfers between trophic levels are so inefficient (Figure 55.12a). Certain aquatic ecosystems, however, have inverted biomass pyramids: Primary consumers outweigh the producers (Figure 55.12b). Such inverted biomass pyramids occur because the producers—phytoplankton—grow, reproduce, and are consumed so quickly by the zooplankton that they never develop a large population size, or standing crop. In other words, the phytoplankton have a short **turnover time**,

Trophic level	Dry mass (g/m²)
Tertiary consumers	1.5
Secondary consumers	11
Primary consumers	37
Primary producers	809

(a) Most biomass pyramids show a sharp decrease in biomass at successively higher trophic levels, as illustrated by data from a Florida bog.

Trophic level	Dry mass (g/m²)
Primary consumers (zooplankton)	21
Primary producers (phytoplankton)	4

(b) In some aquatic ecosystems, such as the English Channel, a small standing crop of primary producers (phytoplankton) supports a larger standing crop of primary consumers (zooplankton).

▲ **Figure 55.12 Pyramids of biomass (standing crop).** Numbers denote the dry mass of all organisms at each trophic level.

which means they have a small standing crop compared to their production:

$$\text{Turnover time} = \frac{\text{Standing crop (g/m}^2)}{\text{Production} \left[\text{g/(m}^2 \cdot \text{day)} \right]}$$

Because the phytoplankton continually replace their biomass at such a rapid rate, they can support a biomass of zooplankton bigger than their own biomass. Nevertheless, because phytoplankton have much higher production than zooplankton, the pyramid of *production* for this ecosystem is still bottom-heavy, like the one in Figure 55.11.

The dynamics of energy flow through ecosystems have important implications for humans. Eating meat is a relatively inefficient way of tapping photosynthetic production. The same kilogram of soybeans that a person could eat for protein produces 200 g of beef or less when fed to a cow. Worldwide agriculture could, in fact, successfully feed many more people and require less cultivated land if humans all fed more efficiently—as primary consumers, eating mostly plant material. Consequently, estimates of Earth's human carrying capacity (see Chapter 53) depend greatly on our dietary choices.

In the next section, we will look at how the transfer of nutrients and energy through food webs is part of a larger picture of chemical cycling in ecosystems.

CONCEPT CHECK 55.3

1. If an insect that eats plant seeds containing 100 J of energy uses 30 J of that energy for respiration and excretes 50 J in its feces, what is the insect's net secondary production? What is its production efficiency?

2. Tobacco leaves contain nicotine, a poisonous compound that is energetically expensive for the plant to make. What advantage might the plant gain by using some of its resources to produce nicotine?

3. **WHAT IF?** Detritivores are consumers that obtain their energy from detritus. How many joules of energy are potentially available to detritivores in the ecosystem represented in Figure 55.11?

For suggested answers, see Appendix A.

CONCEPT 55.4

Biological and geochemical processes cycle nutrients and water in ecosystems

Although most ecosystems receive an abundant supply of solar energy, chemical elements are available only in limited amounts. Life on Earth therefore depends on the recycling of essential chemical elements. Much of an organism's chemical stock is replaced continuously as nutrients are assimilated and waste products released. When the organism dies, the atoms in its complex molecules are returned in simpler compounds to the atmosphere, water, or soil by the action of decomposers. Decomposition replenishes the pools of inorganic nutrients that plants and other autotrophs use to build new organic matter. Because nutrient cycles involve both biotic and abiotic components, they are called **biogeochemical cycles**.

Biogeochemical Cycles

An element's specific route through a biogeochemical cycle depends on the element and the trophic structure of the ecosystem. For convenience, we can recognize two general categories of biogeochemical cycles: global and local. Gaseous forms of carbon, oxygen, sulphur, and nitrogen occur in the atmosphere, and cycles of these elements are essentially global. For example, some of the carbon and oxygen atoms a plant acquires from the air as CO_2 may have been released into the atmosphere by the respiration of an organism in a distant locale. Other elements, including phosphorus, potassium, and calcium, are too heavy to occur as gases at Earth's surface, although they are transported in dust. In terrestrial ecosystems, these elements cycle more locally, absorbed from the soil by plant roots and eventually returned to the soil by decomposers. In aquatic systems, however, they cycle more broadly as dissolved forms carried in currents.

Figure 55.13 provides a detailed look at the cycling of water, carbon, nitrogen, and phosphorus. When you study each cycle, consider which steps are driven primarily by biological processes. For the carbon cycle, for instance, plants, animals, and other organisms control most of the key steps, including photosynthesis and decomposition. For the water cycle, however, purely physical processes control many key steps, such as evaporation from the oceans.

How have ecologists worked out the details of chemical cycling in various ecosystems? Two common methods use isotopes. One method is to follow the movement of naturally occurring, nonradioactive isotopes through the biotic (organic) and abiotic (inorganic) components of an ecosystem. The other method involves adding tiny amounts of radioactive isotopes of specific elements and tracing their progress. Scientists have also been able to make use of radioactive carbon (^{14}C) released into the atmosphere during atom bomb testing in the 1950s and early 1960s. This "spike" of ^{14}C can reveal where and how quickly carbon flows into ecosystem components, including plants, soils, and ocean water.

Decomposition and Nutrient Cycling Rates

The diagrams in Figure 55.13 illustrate the essential role that decomposers (detritivores) play in recycling carbon,

Exploring Water and Nutrient Cycling

Examine each cycle closely, considering the major reservoirs of water, carbon, nitrogen, and phosphorus and the processes that drive each cycle. The widths of the arrows in the diagrams approximately reflect the relative contribution of each process to the movement of water or a nutrient in the biosphere.

The Water Cycle

Biological importance Water is essential to all organisms, and its availability influences the rates of ecosystem processes, particularly primary production and decomposition in terrestrial ecosystems.

Forms available to life All organisms can exchange water directly with their environment. Liquid water is the primary physical phase in which water is used, though some organisms can harvest water vapour. Freezing of soil water can limit water availability to terrestrial plants.

Reservoirs The oceans contain 97% of the water in the biosphere. Approximately 2% is bound in glaciers and polar ice caps and the remaining 1% is in lakes, rivers, and groundwater. A negligible amount is in the atmosphere.

Key processes The main processes driving the water cycle are evaporation of liquid water by solar energy, condensation of water vapour into clouds, and precipitation. Transpiration by terrestrial plants also moves large volumes of water into the atmosphere. Surface and groundwater flow returns water to the oceans, completing the water cycle.

The Carbon Cycle

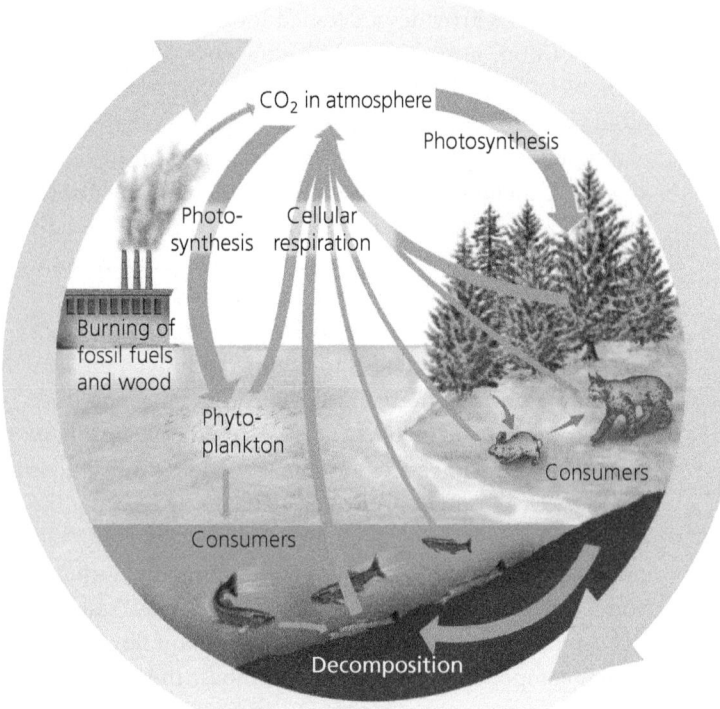

Biological importance Carbon forms the framework of the organic molecules essential to all organisms.

Forms available to life Photosynthetic organisms utilize CO_2 during photosynthesis and convert the carbon to organic forms that are used by consumers, including animals, fungi, and heterotrophic protists and prokaryotes. All organisms can return carbon directly to their environment as CO_2 through respiration.

Reservoirs The major reservoirs of carbon include fossil fuels, soils, the sediments of aquatic ecosystems, the oceans (dissolved carbon compounds), plant and animal biomass, and the atmosphere (CO_2). The largest reservoir is sedimentary rocks such as limestone; however, this pool turns over very slowly.

Key processes Photosynthesis by plants and phytoplankton removes substantial amounts of atmospheric CO_2 each year. This quantity is approximately equalled by CO_2 added to the atmosphere through cellular respiration by producers and consumers. The burning of fossil fuels and wood is adding significant amounts of additional CO_2 to the atmosphere. Over geologic time, volcanoes are also a substantial source of CO_2.

Source: Adaptation of figure 7.4 from The *Economy of Nature*, 5th edition, by Robert E. Ricklefs. Copyright © 2001 by W.H. Freeman and Company. Reprinted with permission.

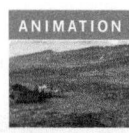

ANIMATION **BioFlix** Visit the Study Area in **MasteringBiology** for the BioFlix® 3-D Animation on The Carbon Cycle. BioFlix Tutorials can also be assigned in MasteringBiology.

The Phosphorus Cycle

Biological importance Organisms require phosphorus as a major constituent of nucleic acids, phospholipids, and energy storing molecules, such as ATP, and as a mineral constituent of bones and teeth.

Forms available to life The most biologically important inorganic form of phosphorus is phosphate (PO_4^{3-}), which plants absorb and use in the synthesis of organic compounds.

Reservoirs The largest accumulations of phosphorus are in sedimentary rocks of marine origin. There are also large quantities of phosphorus in soil, in the oceans (in dissolved form), and in organisms. Because soil particles bind PO_4^{3-}, the recycling of phosphorus tends to be quite localized in ecosystems.

Key processes Weathering of rocks gradually adds PO_4^{3-} to soil; some leaches into groundwater and surface water and may eventually reach the sea. Phosphate taken up by producers and incorporated into biological molecules may be eaten by consumers. Phosphate is returned to soil or water by either decomposition of biomass or excretion by consumers. Because there are no significant phosphorus-containing gases, only relatively small amounts of phosphorus move through the atmosphere, usually in the forms of dust and sea spray.

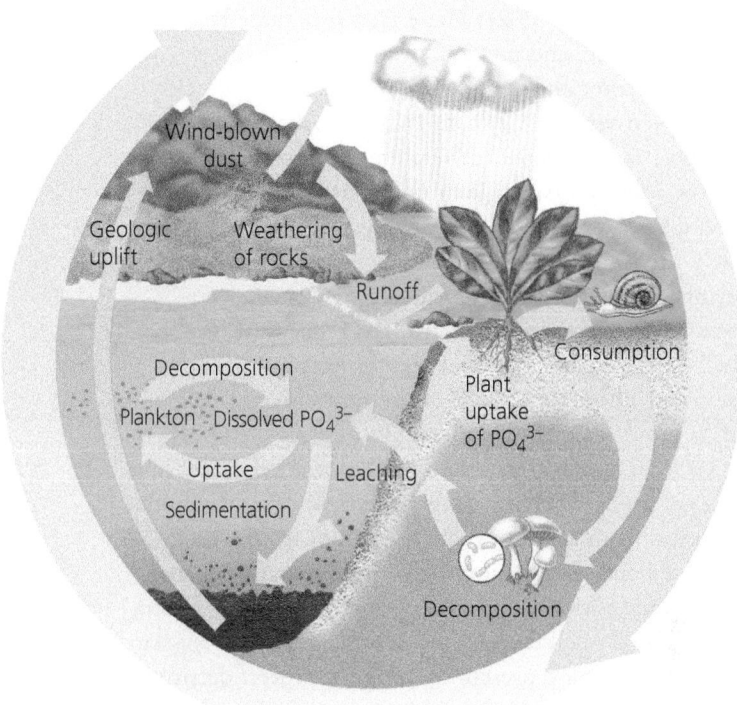

The Nitrogen Cycle

Biological importance Nitrogen is part of amino acids, proteins, and nucleic acids and is often a limiting plant nutrient.

Forms available to life Plants can assimilate (use) two inorganic forms of nitrogen—ammonium (NH_4^+) and nitrate (NO_3^-)—and some organic forms, such as amino acids. Various bacteria can use all of these forms as well as nitrite (NO_2^-). Animals can use only organic forms of nitrogen.

Reservoirs The main reservoir of nitrogen is the atmosphere, which is 78% free nitrogen gas (N_2). The other reservoirs of inorganic and organic nitrogen compounds are soils and the sediments of lakes, rivers, and oceans; surface water and groundwater; and the biomass of living organisms.

Key processes The major pathway for nitrogen to enter an ecosystem is via nitrogen fixation, the conversion of N_2 to forms that can be used to synthesize organic nitrogen compounds. Certain bacteria, as well as lightning and volcanic activity, fix nitrogen naturally (see Figures 37.10–37.12). Nitrogen inputs from human activities now outpace natural inputs on land. Two major contributors are industrially produced fertilizers and legume crops, such as soybeans, that fix nitrogen via bacteria in their root nodules. Other bacteria in soil convert nitrogen to different forms. Some bacteria carry out denitrification, the reduction of nitrate to nitrogen gases. Human activities also release large quantities of reactive nitrogen gases, such as nitrogen oxides, to the atmosphere.

nitrogen, and phosphorus. The rates at which these nutrients cycle in different ecosystems are extremely variable, mostly as a result of differences in rates of decomposition.

Decomposition is controlled by the same factors that limit primary production in aquatic and terrestrial ecosystems (see Concept 55.2). These factors include temperature, moisture, and nutrient availability. Decomposers usually grow faster and decompose material more quickly in warmer ecosystems (Figure 55.14). In tropical rain forests, for instance, most organic material decomposes in a few months to a few years, while in temperate forests, decomposition takes four to six years, on average. The difference is largely the result of the higher temperatures and more abundant precipitation in tropical rain forests.

Because decomposition in a tropical rain forest is rapid, relatively little organic material accumulates as leaf litter on the forest floor; about 75% of the nutrients in the ecosystem is present in the woody trunks of trees, and only about 10% is contained in the soil. Thus, the relatively low concentrations of some nutrients in the soil of tropical rain forests result from a short cycling time, not from a lack of these elements in the ecosystem. In temperate forests, where decomposition is much slower, the soil may contain as much as 50% of all the organic material in the ecosystem. The nutrients that are present in temperate forest detritus and soil may remain there for fairly long periods before plants assimilate them.

Decomposition on land is also slower when conditions are either too dry for decomposers to thrive or too wet to supply them with enough oxygen. Ecosystems that are both cold and wet, such as peatlands, store large amounts of organic matter (see Figure 29.10). Decomposers grow poorly there, and net primary production greatly exceeds decomposition.

In aquatic ecosystems, detritus sinks from the surface waters to the bottom sediments where decomposition occurs. Aquatic primary production is often limited by nutrients, because decomposition on the bottom is often slow due to low temperatures or lack of oxygen, and because the nutrients released at the bottom of the lake or ocean must be transported back to the surface. Aquatic ecosystems are thus usually very productive where deep nutrient-rich water is brought to the surface, as occurs in regions of upwelling.

Field Study: Nutrient Cycling in the Hubbard Brook Experimental Forest

Since 1963, ecologists have been studying nutrient cycling at the Hubbard Brook Experimental Forest in the White Mountains of the northeastern United States. The research site is a deciduous forest that grows in six small valleys, each drained by a single creek. Impenetrable bedrock underlies the soil of the forest.

▼ Figure 55.14 | Inquiry

How does temperature influence decomposition rates in Canadian soils?

Experiment Researchers with the Canadian Forest Service placed identical samples of organic material—litter—on the ground in 18 sites across Canada (marked by letters on the map below). Three years later, they returned to see how much of each sample had decomposed.

Source: Figure adapted from "The Canadian Intersite Decomposition Experiment: Project and Site Establishment Report" (Information Report BC-X-378) by J. A. Trofymow and the CIDET Working Group. Copyright © 1998 by Natural Resources Canada, Canadian Forest Service, Pacific Forestry Centre; and "Ecoclimatic Regions of Canada," from *Ecological Land Classification Series*, Number 23, Copyright © 1989 by Environment Canada. Reprinted with permission from the Minister of Public Works and Government Services, Canada, 2013.

Results The mass of litter decreased four times faster in the warmest ecosystem than in the coldest ecosystem.

Source: Adaptation of figure 2 from "Litter Decomposition Rates in Canadian Forests" by T. R. Moore, from *Global Change Biology*, January 1999, Volume 5(1). Copyright © 1999 by John Wiley & Sons Ltd. Reprinted with permission.

Conclusion Decomposition rate increases with temperature across much of Canada.

Source: T. R. Moore et al., Litter decomposition rates in Canadian forests, *Global Change Biology* 5:75–82 (1999).

WHAT IF? *What factors other than temperature might also have varied across these 18 sites? How might this variation have affected the interpretation of the results?*

US Forest Service

The research team first determined the mineral budget for each of six valleys by measuring the input and outflow of several key nutrients. They collected rainfall at several sites to measure the amount of water and dissolved minerals added to the ecosystem. To monitor the loss of water and minerals, they constructed a small concrete dam with a V-shaped spillway across the creek at the bottom of each valley. They found that about 60% of the water added to the ecosystem as rainfall and snow exits through the stream, and the remaining 40% is lost by evapotranspiration.

Preliminary studies confirmed that internal cycling conserved most of the mineral nutrients in the system. For example, only about 0.3% more calcium (Ca^{2+}) leaves a valley via its creek than is added by rainwater, and this small net loss is probably replaced by chemical decomposition of the bedrock. During most years, the forest even registers small net gains of a few mineral nutrients, including nitrogen.

Experimental deforestation of a watershed dramatically increased the flow of water and minerals leaving the watershed (Figure 55.15a). Over three years, water runoff from the newly deforested watershed was 30–40% greater than in a control watershed, apparently because there were no plants to absorb and transpire water from the soil. Most remarkable was the loss of nitrate, whose concentration in the creek increased 60-fold, reaching levels considered unsafe for drinking water (Figure 55.15b). The Hubbard Brook deforestation study showed that the amount of nutrients leaving an intact forest ecosystem is controlled mainly by the plants. Retaining nutrients in ecosystems helps to maintain the productivity of the systems and avoid problems, such as algal "blooms," caused by excess nutrient runoff.

(a) One watershed was clear-cut to study the effects of the loss of vegetation on drainage and nutrient cycling. All of the cut plant material was left in place to decompose.

US Forest Service

(b) The concentration of nitrate in runoff from the deforested watershed was 60 times greater than in a control (unlogged) watershed.

▲ Figure 55.15 **Nutrient cycling in the Hubbard Brook Experimental Forest: an example of long-term ecological research.**

(MB) *See the related experimental inquiry tutorial in MasteringBiology.*

CONCEPT CHECK 55.4

1. **DRAW IT** For each of the four biogeochemical cycles detailed in Figure 55.13, draw a simple diagram that shows one possible path for an atom of that chemical from abiotic to biotic reservoirs and back.

2. Why does deforestation of a watershed increase the concentration of nitrates in streams draining the watershed?

3. **WHAT IF?** Why is nutrient availability in a tropical rain forest particularly vulnerable to logging?

For suggested answers, see Appendix A.

CONCEPT 55.5

Restoration ecologists help return degraded ecosystems to a more natural state

Ecosystems can recover naturally from most disturbances (including the experimental deforestation at Hubbard Brook) through the stages of ecological succession (see Concept 54.3). Sometimes that recovery takes centuries, though, particularly when humans have degraded the environment. Tropical areas that are cleared for farming may quickly become unproductive because of nutrient losses. Mining activities may last for several decades, and the lands are often abandoned in a degraded state. Ecosystems can also be damaged by salts that build up in soils from irrigation and by toxic chemicals or oil spills. Biologists increasingly are called on to help restore and repair ecosystem damage.

Restoration ecologists seek to initiate or speed up the recovery of degraded ecosystems. One of the basic assumptions is that environmental damage is at least partly reversible. This optimistic view must be balanced by the knowledge that ecosystems are not infinitely resilient. Restoration ecologists therefore work to identify and manipulate the processes that most limit recovery of ecosystems from disturbances. Where disturbance is so severe that restoring all of a habitat is impractical, ecologists try to reclaim as much of a habitat or ecological process as possible, within the limits of the time and money available to them.

In extreme cases, the physical structure of an ecosystem may need to be restored before biological restoration can occur. If a stream was straightened to channel water quickly through a suburb, restoration ecologists may reconstruct a meandering channel to slow down the flow of water eroding the stream bank. To restore an open-pit mine or a landfill site, engineers may first grade the site with heavy equipment to reestablish a gentle slope, spreading topsoil when the slope is in place.

Once physical reconstruction of the ecosystem is complete—or when it is not needed—biological restoration is the next step. Two key strategies in biological restoration are bioremediation and biological augmentation.

Bioremediation

Using organisms—usually prokaryotes, fungi, or plants—to detoxify polluted ecosystems is known as **bioremediation** (see Chapter 27). Some plants and lichens adapted to soils containing heavy metals can accumulate high concentrations of potentially toxic metals such as zinc, nickel, lead, and cadmium in their tissues. Restoration ecologists can introduce such species to sites polluted by mining and other human activities and then harvest these organisms to remove the metals from the ecosystem. For instance, researchers in the United Kingdom have discovered a lichen species that grows on soil polluted with uranium dust left over from mining. The lichen concentrates uranium in a dark pigment, making it useful as a biological monitor and potentially as a remediator.

One of the biggest restoration challenges of the next few decades will be the oil sands region of northern Alberta. The scale of physical and biological reconstruction that will be required has led some ecologists to suggest that we will need to *re-create* these ecosystems rather than just restore them. **Figure 55.16** describes how the new landscape will compare to the pre-disturbance ecosystem. The large quantities of water mixed with fine sediments (tailings) produced during the processing of the oil sands remain an unsolved problem. The tailings contain organic acids known as naphthenic acids (NAs) that are highly toxic to most aquatic life, from zooplankton to amphibians and fish. The water is currently stored in enormous tailings ponds, and there is concern that nearby rivers and lakes are being contaminated. Perhaps microorganisms can be used to help "clean up" the sites. Bacteria and unicellular algae can metabolize many NAs, but some of the organic acids produced during bitumen extraction do not degrade easily. Microbiologists and biochemists continue to look for

▼ Figure 55.16 | **Impact**

Can this ecosystem be restored?

The contrast between an intact boreal ecosystem, with its landscape of forests and wetlands, and the aftermath of oil sands surface mining (below) could not be starker. Can the land be returned to a sustainable landscape equivalent to pre-disturbance conditions?

Ashley Cooper pics/Alamy Stock Photo

Bayne Stanley/Alamy Stock Photo

The boreal ecosystem of northern Alberta is a mosaic of conifer trees and wetlands.

In surface mines, the bitumen contained in the oil sands is accessed by removing all vegetation, soils, and rock to depths of up to 70 m.

During reclamation the mining pit is refilled with the gravel, sand, and shale that had been removed to access the bitumen below. Tailings, the contaminated liquid and sand left over once the oil is removed from the oil sand, may also be used to fill mine pits. The surface is then graded to build a drainage system with ponds. Topsoil is added and the area planted with grasses, shrubs, and trees.

Reclaimed and pre-disturbance landscapes look very different, mostly because much of the former peatland is converted to upland habitat and tailings lakes. As a result, the new landscapes store less carbon and are dominated by terrestrial plants rather than wetland mosses. The soils and water are saline, which favours salt-tolerant plants and can slow plant growth rates. Chemicals such as naphthenic acids in tailings are toxic to many aquatic species.

Only a tiny proportion (much less than 1%) of the mined area has been reclaimed thus far. But it is already clear that reclaimed ecosystems will differ from pre-disturbance landscapes in function (water and carbon cycling) and in the plants, animals, and microbes they contain.

Why It Matters The area disturbed by mining in northern Alberta is huge. It is critical that reclaimed ecosystems preserve the biodiversity of the region and provide services that are functionally equivalent to the former ecosystem.

Further Reading R. C. Rooney, S. E. Bayley, and D. W. Schindler, Oil sands mining and reclamation cause massive loss of peatland and stored carbon, *PNAS* 109:4933–4937 (2011).

MAKE CONNECTIONS *Why might plants grow more slowly in saline soil? See Concept 39.4.*

more effective prokaryote species and are testing chemical processes that may increase bacterial efficiency. Solving the problem is urgent; by 2025, there could be up to 1 billion m^3 of tailings pond water in need of remediation.

Biological Augmentation

In contrast to bioremediation, which is a strategy for removing harmful substances from an ecosystem, **biological augmentation** uses organisms to *add* essential materials to a degraded ecosystem. To augment ecosystem processes, restoration ecologists need to determine which factors, such as chemical nutrients, have been lost from a system and are limiting its recovery.

Encouraging the growth of plants that thrive in nutrient-poor soils often speeds up succession and ecosystem recovery. In alpine ecosystems, nitrogen-fixing plants such as lupines are often planted to raise nitrogen concentrations in soils disturbed by mining and other activities. Once these nitrogen-fixing plants become established, other native species are better able to obtain enough soil nitrogen to survive. In other systems where the soil has been severely disturbed or where topsoil is missing entirely, plant roots may lack the mycorrhizal symbionts that help them meet their nutritional needs (see Chapter 31). For example, during restoration of a large gold and copper mine in northern British Columbia, the area was seeded with a native seed mix, and a compost tea infused with mycorrhizae was added to promote the eventual establishment of conifers.

Restoring the physical structure and plant community of an ecosystem does not necessarily ensure that animal species will recolonize a site and persist there. Because animals aid critical ecosystem services, including pollination, seed dispersal, and herbivory, restoration ecologists sometimes help wildlife reach and establish in restored ecosystems. They might release animals in the restored site or establish habitat corridors that connect a restored site to other places where the animals are found. They sometimes establish artificial perches for birds or dig burrows for other animals to use at the site. These and other efforts can improve the biodiversity of restored ecosystems and help the community persist.

Restoration Projects Worldwide

Because restoration ecology is a relatively new discipline and because ecosystems are complex, restoration ecologists generally learn as they go. Many restoration ecologists advocate adaptive management: experimenting with several promising types of management to learn what works best.

Grasslands National Park in Saskatchewan is a good example of how ecologists have learned and adopted new strategies while restoring an ecosystem (Figure 55.17). Only tiny fragments of the tall, short, and mixed-grass prairie that once covered southern Alberta, Saskatchewan, and Manitoba remain today. In 1988, Parks Canada began to acquire and restore an area of former mixed-grass prairie in southern Saskatchewan. Land that had been cultivated was seeded with native grasses, and all cattle were removed from the new park. However, the importance of animal grazers and fire disturbance soon became evident. A bison herd was established in 2005, and cattle are now allowed to graze in part of the park. Grazing is expected to enhance nitrogen cycling and to increase ecosystem productivity. Prescribed fires are set to mimic natural fire disturbance, which helps native plants compete with invasive species. Much remains to be done, but prairie species such as burrowing owls,

Large grazers such as bison are key to restoring ecosystem processes in temperate grasslands.

Burrowing owl   Black-footed ferret

▲ Figure 55.17 **Restoration of a mixed-grass prairie ecosystem in Grasslands National Park, Saskatchewan.** This restoration required reestablishing natural disturbance regimes of fire and animal grazing. Native species, such as the burrowing owl, are increasing in abundance. Others, such as the bison and black-footed ferret, have been reintroduced.

prairie dogs. and pronghorn antelope are already recovering. And in 2009, 30 black-footed ferrets were released in the park; a year later, their offspring were the first wild-born ferrets in Canada in 70 years. The long-term objective of restoration is to return an ecosystem as much as possible to its pre-disturbance state. Figure 55.18, on the next two pages, identifies several ambitious and successful restoration projects around the world. The great number of such projects, the dedication of the people engaged in them, and the successes that have been achieved suggest that restoration ecology will continue to grow as a discipline for many years.

CONCEPT CHECK 55.5

1. Identify the main goal of restoration ecology.

2. **WHAT IF?** In what way is the Kissimmee River project a more complete ecological restoration than the Maungatautari project (see Figure 55.18)?

For suggested answers, see Appendix A.

Exploring Restoration Ecology Worldwide

The examples highlighted on these pages are just a few of the many restoration ecology projects taking place around the world. The colour-coded dots on the map indicate the locations of the projects.

■ Kissimmee River, Florida

The Kissimmee River was converted from a meandering river to a 90-km canal, threatening many fish and wetland bird populations. Kissimmee River restoration has filled 12 km of drainage canal and reestablished 24 km of the original 167 km of natural river channel. Pictured here is a section of the Kissimmee canal that has been plugged (wide, light strip on the right side of the photo), diverting flow into remnant river channels (centre of the photo). The project will also restore natural flow patterns, which will foster self-sustaining populations of wetland birds and fishes.

Universal Images Group Limited/Alamy Stock Photo

South Florida Water Management District

■ From log to canoe, La Mauricie National Park, Quebec

To accommodate timber harvesting between 1850 and 1970, lakes and streams in La Mauricie were modified, allowing logs to be floated downstream. Dams were built to raise water levels, and streams were diverted and straightened, damaging riparian (riverside) habitat. Non-native fish were introduced. To restore the ecosystem, old dams and road structures were taken down, and logging debris removed from stream channels (over 13 000 hemlock logs!). Water levels are returning to normal, and the riparian habitat is recovering. Non-native fish have been removed from several lakes and native brook trout reintroduced. Loons and beavers have returned to these lakes.

Daniel H. Janzen

■ Tropical dry forest, Costa Rica

Clearing for agriculture, mainly for livestock grazing, eliminated approximately 98% of tropical dry forest in Central America and Mexico. Reversing this trend, tropical dry forest restoration in Costa Rica has used domestic livestock to disperse the seeds of native trees into open grasslands. The photo shows one of the first trees (right centre), dispersed as seed by livestock, to colonize former pastureland. This project is a model for joining restoration ecology with the local economy and educational institutions.

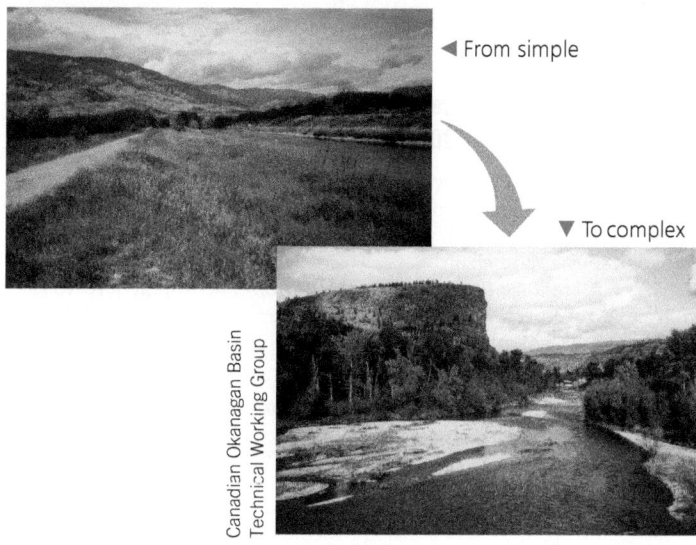

◄ From simple

▼ To complex

Canadian Okanagan Basin Technical Working Group

■ Okanagan River, British Columbia

To control flooding, the Okanagan River was channelized (straightened) and dykes were built on its banks. The result was a much shorter and wider river, without the pools and riffles used by salmon and trout for feeding and spawning. Meandering channels have been reestablished on a wider floodplain, and the riparian zone has been restored using native plants such as dogwood, willow, and cottonwood. Aquatic habitat diversity has increased, and the quality of spawning habitat for native fishes has improved. Native riparian (riverside) vegetation keeps summer temperatures cool for salmon and trout and provides critical habitat for terrestrial species such as the endangered western screech owl.

Kenji Morita

■ Coastal Japan

Seaweed and seagrass beds are important nursery grounds for a wide variety of fishes and shellfish. Once extensive but now reduced by development, these beds are being restored in the coastal areas of Japan. Techniques include constructing suitable seafloor habitat, transplanting from natural beds using artificial substrates, and hand seeding (shown in this photograph).

Jean Hall/Science Source

■ Succulent Karoo, South Africa

In this desert region of southern Africa, as in many arid regions, over-grazing by livestock has damaged vast areas. Private landowners and government agencies in South Africa are restoring large areas of this unique region, revegetating the land and employing more sustainable resource management. The photo shows a small sample of the exceptional plant diversity of the Succulent Karoo; its 5000 plant species include the highest diversity of succulent plants in the world.

Xcluder Pest Proof Fencing Ltd

■ Maungatautari, New Zealand

Weasels, rats, pigs, and other introduced species pose a serious threat to New Zealand's native plants and animals, including kiwis, a group of flightless, ground-dwelling bird species. The goal of the Maungatautari restoration project is to exclude all exotic mammals from a 3400-ha reserve located on a forested volcanic cone. A specialized fence around the reserve eliminates the need to continue setting traps and using poisons that can harm native wildlife. In 2006, a pair of critically endangered takahe (a species of flightless rail) were released into the reserve in hopes of reestablishing a breeding population of this colourful bird on New Zealand's North Island.

55 Chapter Review

Go to **MasteringBiology**® for Assignments, the eText, and the Study Area with Animations, Activities, Vocab Self-Quiz, and Practice Tests.

SUMMARY OF KEY CONCEPTS

CONCEPT 55.1

Physical laws govern energy flow and chemical cycling in ecosystems (pp. 1300–1302)

- An **ecosystem** consists of all the organisms in a community and all the abiotic factors with which they interact. The laws of physics and chemistry apply to ecosystems, particularly in regard to the conservation of energy. Energy is conserved but degraded to heat during ecosystem processes.
- Chemical elements enter and leave an ecosystem and cycle within it, subject to the **law of conservation of mass**. Inputs and outputs are generally small compared to recycled amounts, but their balance determines whether the ecosystem gains or loses an element over time.

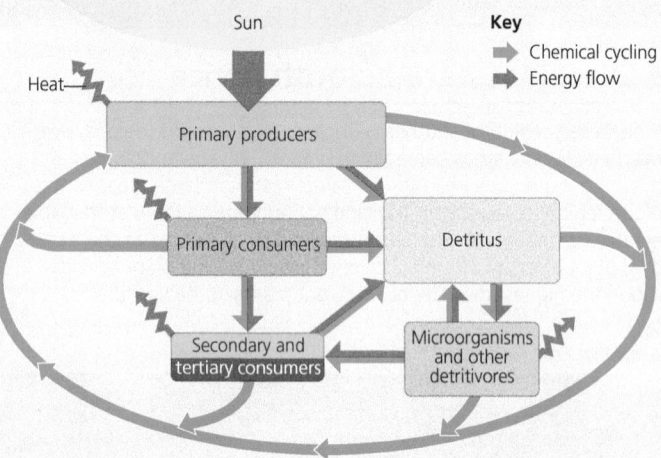

Source: Based on figure 1.2 from *Dynamics of Nutrient Cycling and Food Webs* by Donald L. DeAngelis. Taylor & Francis, 1992. © Jane B Reece.

? *Considering the second law of thermodynamics, would you expect the typical biomass of primary producers in an ecosystem to be greater than or less than the biomass of secondary consumers in the system? Explain your reasoning.*

CONCEPT 55.2

Energy and other limiting factors control primary production in ecosystems (pp. 1302–1307)

- **Primary production** sets the spending limit for the global energy budget. **Gross primary production** is the total energy assimilated by an ecosystem in a given period. **Net primary production**, the energy accumulated in autotroph biomass, equals gross primary production minus the energy used by the primary producers for respiration. **Net ecosystem production** is the total biomass accumulation of an ecosystem, defined as the difference between gross primary production and total ecosystem respiration.
- In aquatic ecosystems, light and nutrients limit primary production. In terrestrial ecosystems, climatic factors such as temperature and moisture affect primary production at large scales, but a soil nutrient is often the limiting factor locally.

? *If you know NPP, what additional variable do you need to know to estimate NEP? Why might measuring this variable be difficult, for instance, in a sample of ocean water?*

CONCEPT 55.3

Energy transfer between trophic levels is typically only 10% efficient (pp. 1307–1309)

- The amount of energy available to each trophic level is determined by the net primary production and the **production efficiency**, the efficiency with which food energy is converted to biomass at each link in the food chain.
- The percentage of energy transferred from one trophic level to the next, called **trophic efficiency**, is generally 5–20%, with 10% being the typical value. Pyramids of net production and biomass reflect low trophic efficiency.

? *Why would runners have a lower production efficiency when running a long-distance race than when they are sedentary?*

CONCEPT 55.4

Biological and geochemical processes cycle nutrients and water in ecosystems (pp. 1309–1313)

- Water moves in a global cycle driven by solar energy. The carbon cycle primarily reflects the reciprocal processes of photosynthesis and cellular respiration. Nitrogen enters ecosystems through atmospheric deposition and nitrogen fixation by prokaryotes.
- The proportion of a nutrient in a particular form and its cycling in that form vary among ecosystems, largely because of differences in the rate of decomposition.
- Nutrient cycling is strongly regulated by vegetation. The Hubbard Brook case study showed that logging increases water runoff and can cause large losses of minerals.

? *If decomposers usually grow faster and decompose material more quickly in warmer ecosystems, why is decomposition in hot deserts so slow?*

CONCEPT 55.5

Restoration ecologists help return degraded ecosystems to a more natural state (pp. 1313–1317)

- Restoration ecologists harness organisms to detoxify polluted ecosystems through the process of **bioremediation**.
- In **biological augmentation**, ecologists use organisms to add essential materials to ecosystems.

? *In preparing a site for surface mining and later restoration, what would be the advantage of removing the shallow topsoil first and setting it aside separately from the deeper soil, rather than removing all soil at once and mixing it in a single pile?*

TEST YOUR UNDERSTANDING

LEVEL 1: KNOWLEDGE/COMPREHENSION

1. Which of the following organisms is *incorrectly* paired with its trophic level?
   a. cyanobacterium—primary producer
   b. grasshopper—primary consumer
   c. zooplankton—primary producer
   d. fungus—detritivore

2. Which of these ecosystems has the *lowest* net primary production per square metre?
   a. a salt marsh
   b. open ocean
   c. a coral reef
   d. a tropical rain forest

3. The discipline that applies ecological principles to returning degraded ecosystems to a more natural state is known as
   a. restoration ecology.
   b. thermodynamics.
   c. eutrophication.
   d. biogeochemistry.

LEVEL 2: APPLICATION/ANALYSIS

4. Nitrifying bacteria participate in the nitrogen cycle mainly by
   a. converting nitrogen gas to ammonia.
   b. releasing ammonium from organic compounds, thus returning it to the soil.
   c. converting ammonium to nitrate, which plants absorb.
   d. incorporating nitrogen into amino acids and organic compounds.

5. Which of the following has the greatest effect on the rate of chemical cycling in an ecosystem?
   a. the production efficiency of the ecosystem's consumers
   b. the rate of decomposition in the ecosystem
   c. the trophic efficiency of the ecosystem
   d. the location of the nutrient reservoirs in the ecosystem

6. The Hubbard Brook watershed deforestation experiment yielded all of the following results *except*:
   a. Most minerals were recycled within a forest ecosystem.
   b. Calcium levels remained high in the soil of deforested areas.
   c. Deforestation increased water runoff.
   d. The nitrate concentration in waters draining the deforested area became dangerously high.

7. Which of the following would be considered an example of bioremediation?
   a. adding nitrogen-fixing microorganisms to a degraded ecosystem to increase nitrogen availability
   b. using a bulldozer to regrade a strip mine
   c. reconfiguring the channel of a river
   d. adding seeds of a chromium-accumulating plant to soil contaminated by chromium

8. If you applied a fungicide to a cornfield, what would you expect to happen to the rate of decomposition and net ecosystem production (NEP)?
   a. Both decomposition rate and NEP would decrease.
   b. Neither would change.
   c. Decomposition rate would increase and NEP would decrease.
   d. Decomposition rate would decrease and NEP would increase.

LEVEL 3: SYNTHESIS/EVALUATION

9. INTERPRET THE DATA Draw a simplified global water cycle showing ocean, land, atmosphere, and runoff from the land to the ocean. Add these annual water fluxes to the figure: ocean evaporation, 425 km^3; ocean evaporation that returns to the ocean as precipitation, 385 km^3; ocean evaporation that falls as precipitation on land, 40 km^3; evapotranspiration from plants and soil that falls as precipitation on land, 70 km^3; runoff to the oceans, 40 km^3. Based on these global numbers, how much precipitation falls on land in a typical year?

10. **EVOLUTION CONNECTION**
    Some biologists have suggested that ecosystems are emergent, "living" systems capable of evolving. One manifestation of this idea is environmentalist James Lovelock's Gaia hypothesis, which views Earth itself as a living, homeostatic entity—a kind of super-organism. If ecosystems are capable of evolving, would this be a form of Darwinian evolution? Why or why not?

11. **SCIENTIFIC INQUIRY**
    Using two neighbouring ponds in a forest as your study site, design a controlled experiment to measure the effect of falling leaves on net primary production in a pond.

12. **WRITE ABOUT A THEME: ENERGY TRANSFER**
    As described in Concept 55.4, decomposition typically occurs quickly in moist tropical forests. However, the waterlogged soil of some moist tropical forests results in a build-up of organic matter ("peat"; see Figure 29.10) over time. In a short essay (100–150 words), discuss the relationship of net primary production, net ecosystem production, and decomposition for such an ecosystem. Are NPP and NEP likely to be positive? What do you think would happen to NEP if a landowner drained the water from a tropical peatland, exposing the organic matter to air?

13. SYNTHESIZE YOUR KNOWLEDGE

This dung beetle (genus *Scarabaeus*) is burying a ball of dung it has collected from a large mammalian herbivore in Kenya. Explain why this process is important for the cycling of nutrients and for primary production.

For selected answers, see Appendix A.

56

Conservation Biology and Global Change

KEY CONCEPTS

56.1 Human activities threaten Earth's biodiversity

56.2 Population conservation focuses on population size, genetic diversity, and critical habitat

56.3 Landscape and regional conservation help sustain biodiversity

56.4 Earth is changing rapidly as a result of human actions

56.5 Sustainable development can improve human lives while conserving biodiversity

melissaf84/Shutterstock

▲ Figure 56.1 **Are seahorses in need of protection?**

An Odd Fish

It is early morning on a coral reef in the Indian Ocean. A little seahorse sits very still, holding on to a branch of coral with its tail. A few minutes later, another (female) seahorse swims up, and the two begin to dance, holding tails and changing colour. Amanda Vincent, of the University of British Columbia, has observed this and many other aspects of seahorse behaviour over the past 25 years. Seahorses (Figure 56.1) are fish and they live on coral reefs, among the roots of mangrove trees, and in seagrass beds. As she began to study seahorses, Vincent became aware of the threats that they face: shrimp trawlers accidentally catch large numbers of seahorses, and many are intentionally captured for the aquarium trade or for use in traditional Chinese medicine. However, it was not known if seahorses needed protection; no one knew if abundances were stable or declining, or even how many species there were. In 1996, Vincent co-founded Project Seahorse, an organization that sponsors research on seahorse taxonomy, behaviour, and ecology, and uses the information to lobby for conservation measures that will protect vulnerable seahorses. Strategies include establishing marine protected areas and developing sustainable harvesting practices for species that are economically valuable. Scientists are still arguing about how many species of seahorse there are, however!

Image Quest Marine

◀ **Diver observing a Caribbean seahorse**

To date, scientists have described and formally named about 1.8 million species of organisms. Biologists estimate that about 10 million species of eukaryote organisms exist on our planet. Some of the greatest concentrations of species are found in the tropics. Unfortunately, tropical forests are being cleared at an alarming rate to make room for and support a burgeoning human population, and tropical oceans are threatened by pollution and ocean acidification (see Figure 3.13).

Throughout the biosphere, human activities are altering trophic structures, energy flow, chemical cycling, and natural disturbance—ecosystem processes on which we and all other species depend (see Chapter 55). We have physically altered nearly half of Earth's land surface, and we use over half of all accessible surface fresh water. In the oceans, stocks of most major fisheries are shrinking because of overharvesting. By some estimates, we may be pushing more species toward extinction than the large asteroid that triggered the mass extinctions at the close of the Cretaceous period 65.5 million years ago (see Figure 25.19).

Biology is the science of life. Thus, it is fitting that our final chapter focuses on a discipline that seeks to preserve life. **Conservation biology** integrates ecology, physiology, molecular biology, genetics, and evolutionary biology to conserve biological diversity at all levels. Efforts to sustain ecosystem processes and stem the loss of biodiversity also connect the life sciences with the social sciences, economics, and humanities.

In this chapter, we will take a closer look at the biodiversity crisis and examine some of the conservation strategies being adopted to slow the rate of species loss. We will also examine how human activities are altering the environment through climate change, ozone depletion, and other global processes, and we will consider how these alterations could affect life on Earth.

Genetic diversity in a vole population

Species diversity in a coastal redwood ecosystem

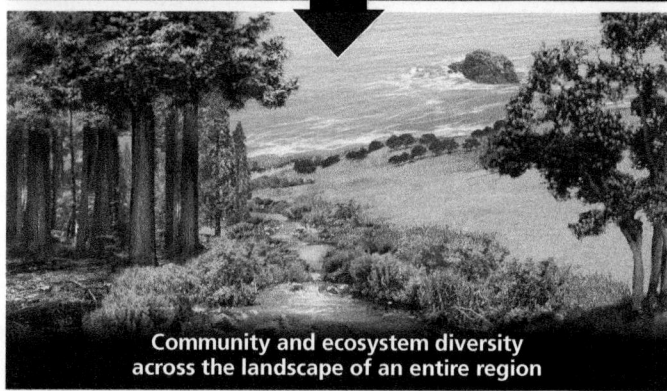

Community and ecosystem diversity across the landscape of an entire region

▲ Figure 56.2 **Three levels of biodiversity.** The oversized chromosomes in the top diagram symbolize the genetic variation within the population.

CONCEPT 56.1

Human activities threaten Earth's biodiversity

Extinction is a natural phenomenon that has been occurring since life first evolved; it is the high *rate* of extinction that is responsible for today's biodiversity crisis (see Concept 25.4). Because we can only estimate the number of species currently existing, we cannot determine the exact rate of species loss. However, we do know that the extinction rate is high and that human activities threaten Earth's biodiversity at all levels.

Three Levels of Biodiversity

Biodiversity—short for biological diversity—can be considered at three main levels: genetic diversity, species diversity, and ecosystem diversity (Figure 56.2).

Genetic Diversity

Genetic diversity comprises not only the individual genetic variation *within* a population, but also the genetic variation *between* populations that is often associated with adaptations to local conditions (see Chapter 23). If one population becomes extinct, then a species may have lost some of the genetic diversity that makes microevolution possible. This erosion of genetic diversity in turn reduces the adaptive potential of the species.

Species Diversity

Public awareness of the biodiversity crisis centres on species diversity—the variety of species in an ecosystem or across the biosphere. As more species are lost to extinction, species diversity decreases. Extinction of species may be local; for example, a species may be lost in one river system but survive in an adjacent one. Local extinction is known as **extirpation**. Global extinction of a species means that it is lost from all the ecosystems.

According to the International Union for Conservation of Nature and Natural Resources (IUCN), 12% of the 10 000 known species of birds and 21% of the 5500 known species of mammals are threatened, and some are dangerously close to disappearing forever **(Figure 56.3)**. The IUCN assesses the global conservation status of species and maintains a Red List of Threatened Species.

The Committee on the Status of Endangered Wildlife in Canada (COSEWIC) is a panel of Canadian scientists charged with the task of assessing the conservation status of species found in Canada and recommending to the federal government which should be given protected status. Five mammal and five bird species, known to be present when Europeans arrived, were extinct or extirpated as of 2015, including the greater prairie chicken (*Tympanuchus cupido*) that was extirpated from Canada in the 1980s (see Figure 56.12), and the sea mink (*Mustela macradon*) and great auk (*Pinguinus impennis*) that were globally extinct by the end of the 19th century. Approximately one-third of all Canadian mammals are listed as endangered, threatened, or of special concern.

COSEWIC uses quantitative criteria (declining abundance, limited distribution, small population size) and qualitative information (threats, life history traits) to assess a species' status. **Extinct** and extirpated species are those that are already gone (globally or from Canada, respectively), an **endangered species** is one that is facing imminent extirpation or extinction, and a **threatened species** is likely to become endangered if nothing is done to reverse the factors causing its decline.

The species designations recommended by COSEWIC are forwarded to the federal government each year, which then decides if the species will receive protection under SARA, the Species at Risk Act.

The beluga population in eastern Hudson Bay **(Figure 56.4a)** is listed as *endangered* because its numbers have declined by 50% since 1985, a rate of decline that could lead to extinction within 20 years. As a species recovers, its status is revised. For example, the swift fox **(Figure 56.4b)** was extirpated in 1928. Seventy years later, it was reintroduced to southern Saskatchewan, and the tiny population was listed as endangered. There are now over 600 individuals in the population, and its status has been upgraded to threatened.

Ecosystem Diversity

The variety of the biosphere's ecosystems is a third level of biological diversity. Human activities have already

(a)

Philippine eagle

Yangtze River dolphin

▲ **Figure 56.3 A hundred heartbeats from extinction.** These are just two members of what E. O. Wilson calls the Hundred Heartbeat Club, species with fewer than 100 individuals remaining on Earth. The Yangtze River dolphin was even thought to be extinct, but a few individuals were reportedly sighted in 2007.

? *To document that a species has actually become extinct, what spatial and temporal factors would you need to consider?*

(b)

▲ **Figure 56.4 Species at risk in Canada. (a)** The beluga whale (*Delphinapterus leucas*), an endangered species, and **(b)** the swift fox (*Vulpes velox*), a threatened species.

disrupted many ecosystems, and others are being altered at a rapid pace. The IUCN has recently developed criteria for assessing the status of ecosystems and has begun to produce a Red List for ecosystems that are threatened by human activity. Categories include collapsed (equivalent to extinct for species), critically endangered, endangered, and vulnerable. The goal is to identify ecosystems that are at risk of losing species and/or ecological functions and services, using information on decline in distribution, level of environmental degradation, and disruption of biotic processes and interactions.

Caribbean coral reef ecosystems are *endangered* (Figure 56.5). Major declines in coral abundance have occurred over the past 50 years, and large fleshy algae now occupy vast areas of reef. The shift is due to loss of important herbivores; historic overharvesting of large fish and the decimation of herbivorous seastars by disease is allowing algae to outcompete corals. Other continuing threats include coral diseases, pollution, and climate change. Raised bog ecosystems in Germany are *critically endangered*. Raised bogs now occupy only 2% of their former distribution due to historic peat mining (for use as fuel) and drainage to convert the land to agriculture. The Aral Sea ecosystem in central Asia is assessed as *collapsed*. Extraction of water for irrigation of agricultural land has fragmented the ecosystem into separate lakes that are becoming saline, resulting in major losses of plant, fish, and invertebrate biodiversity.

Biodiversity and Human Welfare

Why should we care about the loss of biodiversity? One reason is what Harvard biologist E. O. Wilson calls *biophilia*, our sense of connection to nature and all life. The belief that other species are entitled to life is a pervasive theme of many religions and the basis of a moral argument that we should protect biodiversity. There is also a concern

for future human generations. Paraphrasing an old proverb, G. H. Brundtland, a former prime minister of Norway, said: "We must consider our planet to be on loan from our children, rather than being a gift from our ancestors." In addition to such philosophical and moral justifications, species and genetic diversity bring us many practical benefits.

Benefits of Species and Genetic Diversity

Many species that are threatened could potentially provide food, fibres, and medicines for human use, making biodiversity a crucial natural resource. If we lose wild populations of plants closely related to agricultural species, we lose genetic resources that could be used to improve crop qualities. For instance, plant breeders responded to devastating outbreaks of the grassy stunt virus in rice (*Oryza sativa*) by screening 7000 populations of this species and its close relatives for resistance to the virus. A relative, Indian rice (*Oryza nivara*), was found to be resistant to the virus, and scientists succeeded in breeding the resistance trait into commercial rice varieties. Today, the original disease-resistant population has apparently become extinct in the wild.

Plant chemicals have been key to the development of many modern drugs, and many more may be waiting to be discovered. In the 1970s, researchers discovered that the rosy periwinkle, which grows on the island of Madagascar, off the coast of Africa, contains alkaloids that inhibit cancer cell growth (Figure 56.6). This discovery led to treatments for several deadly forms of cancer, including Hodgkin's lymphoma and childhood leukemia. Madagascar is home to five other species of periwinkles, one of which is approaching extinction. The loss of these species would mean the loss of any possible medicinal benefits they might offer.

Each loss of a species means the loss of unique genes, some of which may code for enormously useful proteins. The enzyme Taq polymerase was first extracted from a bacterium, *Thermus aquaticus*, found in hot springs at Yellowstone National Park. This enzyme is essential for the polymerase

▲ **Figure 56.5 Endangered ecosystem.** Loss of corals in Caribbean reef ecosystems puts many other species at risk.

◀ Figure 56.6
The rosy periwinkle (*Catharanthus roseus*), a plant that saves lives.

chain reaction (PCR) because it is stable at the high temperatures required for automated PCR (see Figure 20.8). DNA from many other species of prokaryotes, living in a variety of environments, is used in the mass production of proteins for new medicines, foods, petroleum substitutes, other industrial chemicals, and other products. If species become extinct before we discover them, we stand to lose the valuable genetic potential held in their unique libraries of genes.

Ecosystem Services

The benefits that individual species provide to humans are substantial, but saving individual species is only part of the reason for preserving ecosystems. Humans evolved in Earth's ecosystems, and we rely on these systems and their inhabitants for our survival. **Ecosystem services** encompass all the processes through which natural ecosystems help sustain human life. Ecosystems purify our air and water. They detoxify and decompose our wastes and reduce the impacts of extreme weather and flooding. The organisms in ecosystems pollinate our crops, control pests, and create and preserve our soils. Moreover, these diverse services are provided for free.

Perhaps because we don't attach a monetary value to the services of natural ecosystems, we generally undervalue them. In 1997, ecologist Robert Costanza and his colleagues estimated the value of Earth's ecosystem services at $33 trillion per year, nearly twice the gross national product of all the countries on Earth at the time ($18 trillion). It may be more realistic to do the accounting on a smaller scale. In 1996, New York City invested more than $1 billion to buy land and restore habitat in the Catskill Mountains, the source of much of the city's fresh water. This investment was spurred by increasing pollution of the water by sewage, pesticides, and fertilizers. By harnessing ecosystem services to purify its water naturally, the city saved $8 billion it would have otherwise spent to build a new water-treatment plant and $300 million a year to run the plant.

There is growing evidence that the functioning of ecosystems, and hence their capacity to perform services, is linked to biodiversity. As human activities reduce biodiversity, we are reducing the capacity of the planet's ecosystems to perform processes critical to our own survival.

Threats to Biodiversity

Many different human activities threaten biodiversity on local, regional, and global scales. The threats posed by these activities are of three major types: habitat loss, introduced species, and overharvesting.

Habitat Loss

Human alteration of habitat is currently the single greatest threat to biodiversity throughout the biosphere. Habitat loss has been brought about by agriculture, urban development, forestry, mining, and pollution. Global climate change is also altering habitats and will have an even larger effect later this century. When no alternative habitat is available or a species is unable to move, habitat loss may mean extinction. The IUCN implicates destruction of physical habitat for 73% of the species that have become extinct, endangered, vulnerable, or rare in the last few hundred years.

Habitat loss and fragmentation are occurring over immense regions. Approximately 98% of the tropical dry forests of Central America and Mexico have been cut down. Southeast Asian tropical forests are currently being destroyed at a rate of about 1% each year as native forests are converted to cash crops (Figure 56.7). Agriculture is also responsible for most of the habitat loss in Canada; 97% of prairie grassland habitat and 88% of the mixed woodland of southern Ontario have been converted to human use, with only small patches of the original habitat left intact. These two ecosystem types make up 6% of Canada's land area, but contain more than half of all the species listed as at risk. Populations in fragmented habitats may be more likely to go extinct because population sizes are small, or because the abiotic environment, food availability, or predation risk have been altered. For example, the fragmented landscape left by logging and oil sands development in northern Alberta has led to increased predation on endangered woodland caribou populations, increasing their risk of extinction (see the Scientific Skills Exercise in Chapter 54).

Habitat loss is also a major threat to aquatic biodiversity. Human activities have caused major declines in coral reefs, which provide habitat to one-third of the world's marine

▲ Figure 56.7 **Tropical deforestation in Vietnam.** Conversion of forests to agriculture is one of the leading causes of habitat loss worldwide.

fish species. Freshwater habitats are lost as a result of dams, reservoirs, and channel modification, or degraded by inputs of nutrients, pharmaceuticals, and the toxic by-products of industrial processes.

Introduced Species

Introduced species, also called non-native or exotic species, are those that humans move intentionally or accidentally from the species' native locations to new geographic regions. Human travel by ship and airplane has accelerated the transplant of species. Free from the predators, parasites, and pathogens that limit their populations in their native habitats, such transplanted species may spread rapidly through a new region.

Some introduced species disrupt their new community, often by preying on native organisms or outcompeting them for resources. The brown tree snake was accidentally introduced to the island of Guam from other parts of the South Pacific after World War II: It was a "stowaway" in military cargo. Since then, 12 species of birds and 6 species of lizards that the snakes preyed upon have become extinct on Guam, which had no native snakes.

Introduced species have also damaged aquatic ecosystems. Of the more than 180 species known to have invaded the Great Lakes since European colonization, one of the most destructive is the parasitic sea lamprey. The sea lamprey entered Lake Ontario and spread throughout the Great Lakes when new shipping canals were constructed. It devastated several freshwater fisheries; for example, catches of lake trout in Lake Michigan fell from 2.5 million kg in 1946 to less than 200 kg in 1953. Since 1960, the majority of new species enter the Great Lakes when ocean-going ships discharge their ballast water. Most famous is the zebra mussel, discovered in 1988. Zebra mussels form dense colonies on hard surfaces, displacing native aquatic species. They also clog water intake structures, causing billions of dollars in damage to domestic and industrial water supplies. Recent regulations for cargo ships appear to be reducing the rate at which new species invade the Great Lakes (Figure 56.8).

The majority of extinctions caused by introduced species have occurred on islands and have been due to introduced predators. For example, introduced rats and feral cats have been responsible for the loss of many species of island-nesting birds. Introduced species are now a worldwide problem, and the magnitude of their eventual impacts on communities and the long-term consequences of the resulting loss of native species are not yet known.

Overharvesting

The term *overharvesting* refers generally to the human harvesting of wild organisms at rates exceeding their ability to rebound. Species with restricted habitats, such as small

▼ **Figure 56.8** | **Inquiry**

Can we slow species invasions?

Experiment Since 1960, the majority of species invading the Great Lakes were introduced by ships discharging ballast water while in port. Since 1993, ships have been required to replace their ballast water with ocean water while at sea. In 2005 ships began to actively flush their tanks with seawater before entering the lakes. The goal is to remove most potential freshwater invaders and to kill any remaining individuals with highly saline water. But do the regulations actually work?

Methods Hugh MacIsaac from the University of Windsor and colleagues sampled the invertebrates present in the ballast water of ships entering the lakes, and compared abundances before and after 2005. They also examined the trend in number of new species discovered each year in the Great Lakes.

Ships have introduced many new species while discharging ballast water (above) including the zebra mussel shown below.

Results The abundance of freshwater invertebrates in ship ballast water decreased dramatically after 2005 (below left). The rate of discovery of new ship-vectored species in the Great Lakes was highest before 1993 and lowest after 2005 (below right). No new species were discovered between 2005 and 2010.

Conclusion Flushing tanks with seawater is highly effective, and removes well over 99% of potential invaders from ballast tanks. The program appears to have greatly reduced the risk of new invasive species entering the Great Lakes in the ballast water of ships.

Source: Based on S. Bailey et al., Evaluating efficacy of an environmental policy to prevent biological invasions, *Environmental Science & Technology* 45:2554–2561 (2011). © Jane B Reece.

WHAT IF? *Species are also carried by ships from lake to lake. Would a regulation requiring ships to flush their ballast tanks before sailing from Lake Erie to Lake Ontario reduce the transfer of organisms between the two lakes?*

islands, are particularly vulnerable to overharvesting. One such species was the great auk, a large, flightless seabird found on islands in the North Atlantic Ocean. By the 1840s, humans had hunted the great auk to extinction to satisfy demand for its feathers, eggs, and meat.

Also susceptible to overharvesting are large organisms with low reproductive rates, such as elephants, whales, and rhinoceros. Poaching (illegal hunting) decimated elephant populations in eastern Africa in the 1970s and 1980s. For example, the number of elephants in Tsavo National Park, one of Kenya's largest wildlife reserves, dropped from 35 000 in 1967 to under 6000 in 1988 (Figure 56.9). The population has been recovering since trading in ivory was banned in 1989, though poaching has not completely stopped.

Many commercially important fish populations, once thought to be inexhaustible, have been decimated by overfishing. Demands for protein-rich food from an increasing human population, coupled with new harvesting technologies, such as long-line fishing and modern trawlers, have reduced these fish populations to levels that cannot sustain further exploitation. Overharvested populations do not always recover quickly after exploitation ends. For example, there is little sign of recovery more than 20 years after the collapse of eastern Canadian cod populations despite a moratorium on commercial fishing (see Figure 54.23).

Can Extinct Species Be Resurrected?

To the best of our knowledge, extinction has always been forever. Some scientists are nevertheless trying to use cloning to resurrect species that have become extinct. Resurrecting species is at least theoretically possible because of recent progress in cloning living animals. The most famous case of cloning resulted in the birth of "Dolly" the lamb in 1997 (see Figure 20.17). To create Dolly, Scottish researchers took an egg cell from an adult sheep, removed its nucleus, fused the egg cell with a mammary cell from another sheep, and implanted the fused cell into a surrogate mother.

Spanish researchers used a similar approach on the Pyrenean ibex (*Capra pyrenaica pyrenaica*), one of four subspecies of wild goat endemic to Spain and other countries of the Iberian Peninsula. In 1999, researchers removed a small skin sample from the ear of the last living individual, a female, and froze it. When that individual died a year later, its subspecies became extinct. Using cells from the frozen tissue, the scientists then attempted to resurrect the ibex. Out of hundreds of fused cells and approximately 60 embryos implanted into surrogate mothers (either another species of ibex or a domestic goat), one individual ibex was born in 2009. Sadly, it lived for only 7 minutes before succumbing to lung defects similar to those observed in other cloned animals, including sheep. Nonetheless, this research demonstrated that species recovery may be possible in cases where frozen tissue is available.

Tissue from an extinct species need not be new to be used in cloning. A team of Russian and Japanese scientists is trying to revive the extinct woolly mammoth (*Mammuthus primigenius*) using well-preserved bone marrow from the thigh of a mammoth frozen in Arctic ice (Figure 56.10). Will they succeed? No one knows yet, but eventually someone likely will, with this species and with others. In fact, scientists are already banking frozen tissues from many endangered species so that cells will be available for cloning if those species become extinct. Other scientists are examining whether they can obtain viable cells from museum specimens, such as pelts or feathers. And, of course, some are trying to isolate ancient DNA in soft tissue from dinosaur fossils. Thus far, such attempts have failed.

The quest to resurrect extinct species raises a host of ethical questions. Should scientists be free to resurrect any species for which viable cells or DNA are available? If not, who will decide which species are off limits? What rules

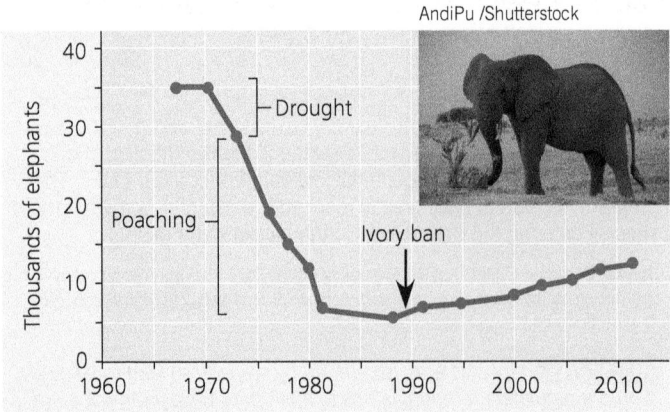

AndiPu /Shutterstock

▲ Figure 56.9 **Decline and partial recovery of the elephant population of Tsavo National Park in eastern Kenya.**

▲ Figure 56.10 **Collecting a frozen woolly mammoth.** Such specimens are being used in an attempt to resurrect the species through biotechnology.

should be put in place before resurrection occurs? Should the species eventually be restored to the wild? Note that, for the Pyrenean ibex, frozen tissue exists for only one female. No males of that subspecies may ever exist again.

Although resurrecting species might soon be possible, we still need to preserve species across Earth. For many reasons, including the issue of genetic diversity discussed in Concept 56.2, preservation remains the scientifically and ethically prudent course of action.

CONCEPT CHECK 56.1

1. Explain why it is too narrow to define the biodiversity crisis as simply a loss of species.

2. Identify the three main threats to biodiversity and explain how each damages diversity.

3. **WHAT IF?** Imagine two populations of a fish species, one in the Mediterranean Sea and one in the Caribbean Sea. Now imagine two scenarios: (1) The populations breed separately, and (2) adults of both populations migrate yearly to the North Atlantic to interbreed. Which scenario would result in a greater loss of genetic diversity if the Mediterranean population were harvested to extinction? Explain your answer.

For suggested answers, see Appendix A.

CONCEPT 56.2

Population conservation focuses on population size, genetic diversity, and critical habitat

Biologists who work on conservation at the population and species levels use two main approaches. One approach focuses on populations that are small and hence often vulnerable. The other emphasizes populations that are declining rapidly, even if they are not yet small.

Small-Population Approach

If overharvesting or habitat loss reduces a population to a small number of individuals, the small size itself can push the population to extinction. Conservation biologists who adopt the small population approach study the processes that cause extinctions once population sizes have been severely reduced.

The Extinction Vortex: Evolutionary Implications of Small Population Size

EVOLUTION A small population is vulnerable to inbreeding and genetic drift, which can draw the population down an **extinction vortex** toward smaller and smaller population size until no individuals survive (**Figure 56.11**). Inbreeding often reduces fitness because the offspring produced by close relatives are more likely to be homozygous

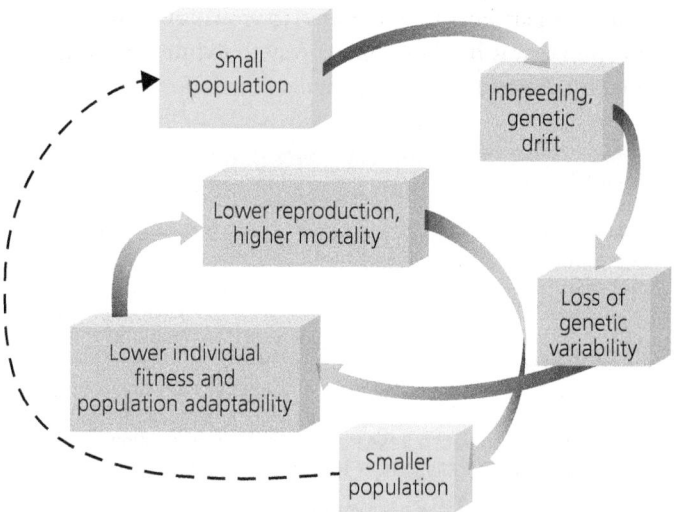

▲ Figure 56.11 **Processes driving an extinction vortex.**

Source: Krebs, Charles J., *Ecology: The Experimental Analysis Of Distribution And Abundance*, 5th ed., © 2001. Reprinted and Electronically reproduced by permission of Pearson Education, Inc., Upper Saddle River, New Jersey.

for harmful recessive traits (see Concept 14.4). In small populations, genetic drift can lead to loss of the genetic variation that enables evolutionary responses to environmental change such as the appearance of new pathogen strains. Thus small population size causes inbreeding and genetic drift, which can reduce fitness and lead to a smaller population with even more inbreeding and drift—a downward spiral ending in extinction.

Not all small populations are doomed by low genetic diversity, and low genetic variability does not automatically lead to permanently small populations. For instance, overhunting of northern elephant seals in the 1890s reduced the species to only 20 individuals—clearly a bottleneck with reduced genetic variation. Since that time, however, the northern elephant seal populations have rebounded to about 150 000 individuals today, though their genetic variation remains relatively low. Thus, low genetic diversity does not always impede population growth.

Field Study: *The Greater Prairie Chicken and the Extinction Vortex*

When Europeans arrived in North America, the greater prairie chicken (*Tympanuchus cupido*) inhabited tall-grass prairie habitat from Alberta in the north to Texas in the south. The conversion of native prairie to agricultural land led to the extirpation of the greater prairie chicken in Canada, and left small, fragmented populations within its former range in the United States. The state of Illinois had millions of greater prairie chickens in the 19th century but fewer than 50 by 1993. Researchers found that the decline in the Illinois population was associated with a decrease in fertility. As a test of the extinction vortex hypothesis, scientists increased genetic variation by importing 271 birds from larger populations elsewhere (Figure 56.12). The Illinois population rebounded, confirming that it had been on its way to extinction until rescued by the transfusion of genetic variation.

▼ **Figure 56.12** | **Inquiry**

What caused the near-extirpation of the Illinois greater prairie chicken population?

Experiment Researchers had observed that the decline of the greater prairie chicken was accompanied by lower fertility, as measured by the hatching rate of eggs. Genetic variation in the population was known to be low compared with historic, larger populations (see Figure 23.10). To increase genetic variation, researchers began translocating prairie chickens from other populations in 1992.

Results After translocation began (black arrow), the viability of eggs rapidly increased, and the population rebounded.

(a) Population dynamics

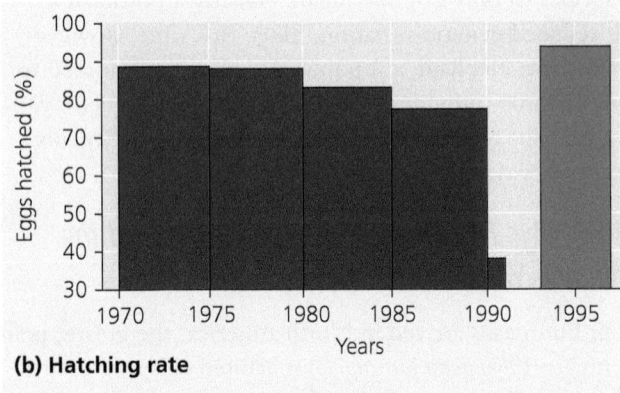

(b) Hatching rate

Conclusion Low levels of genetic variation had pushed the prairie chicken population into an extinction vortex.

Source: Based on R. L. Westemeier et al., Tracking the long-term decline and recovery of an isolated population, *Science* 282:1695–1698 (1998). © Jane B Reece.

Inquiry in Action Read and analyze the original paper in *Inquiry in Action: Interpreting Scientific Papers.*

WHAT IF? *Given the success of using transplanted birds as a tool for increasing the percentage of hatched eggs in Illinois, why wouldn't you transplant additional birds immediately to Illinois?*

Minimum Viable Population Size

How small does a population have to be before it starts down an extinction vortex? The answer depends on the type of organism and other factors. Large predators that feed high on the food chain usually require extensive individual ranges, resulting in low population densities. Therefore, not all rare species concern conservation biologists. All populations, however, require some minimum size to remain viable.

The minimal population size at which a species is able to sustain its numbers is known as the **minimum viable population (MVP)**. MVP is usually estimated for a given species using computer models that integrate many factors that affect population growth rate. The calculation may include, for instance, the effect of year-to-year variation in winter temperature on mortality rate. The smaller a population is, the more likely it is that a natural catastrophe such as a storm, or several years of bad weather, will finish off the population.

Effective Population Size

Genetic variation is the key issue in the small-population approach. The *total* size of a population may be misleading because only certain members of the population breed successfully and pass their alleles on to offspring. Therefore, a meaningful estimate of MVP requires the researcher to determine the **effective population size**, which is based on the breeding potential of the population.

The following formula incorporates the sex ratio of breeding individuals into the estimate of effective population size, abbreviated N_e:

$$N_e = \frac{4N_f N_m}{N_f + N_m}$$

where N_f and N_m are, respectively, the number of females and the number of males that successfully breed. If we apply this formula to an idealized population whose total size is 1000 individuals, N_e will also be 1000 if every individual breeds and the sex ratio is 500 females to 500 males. In this case, $N_e = (4 \times 500 \times 500)/(500 + 500) = 1000$. Any deviation from these conditions (not all individuals breed or there is not a 1:1 sex ratio) reduces N_e. For instance, if the total population size is 1000 but only 400 females and 400 males breed, then $N_e = (4 \times 400 \times 400)/(400 + 400) = 800$, or 80% of the total population size. Numerous life history traits can influence N_e, and alternative formulas for estimating N_e take into account factors such as family size, age at maturation, genetic relatedness among population members, the effects of gene flow between geographically separated populations, and population fluctuations.

In actual study populations, N_e is always some fraction of the total population. Thus, simply determining the total number of individuals in a small population does not provide a good measure of whether the population is large enough to avoid extinction. Whenever possible, conservation programs attempt to sustain total population sizes that include at least the minimum viable number of *reproductively active* individuals. The conservation goal of sustaining effective population size (N_e) above MVP stems from the concern that populations retain enough genetic diversity to adapt as their environment changes.

The MVP of a population is often used in population viability analysis. The objective of this analysis is to predict a population's chances for survival, usually expressed as a specific probability of survival, such as a 95% chance, over a particular time interval, perhaps 100 years. Such modelling approaches allow conservation biologists to explore the potential consequences of alternative management plans.

Field Study: *Analysis of Grizzly Bear Populations*

One of the first population viability analyses was conducted in 1978 by Mark Shaffer, of Duke University, as part of a long-term study of grizzly bears in Yellowstone National Park and its surrounding areas (**Figure 56.13**).

The grizzly population had declined dramatically after park garbage dumps were closed in 1971, and there was concern that the population might be too small to survive. Shaffer used data on year-to-year variation in birth and death rates obtained for individual Yellowstone bears and built mathematical models to estimate viable population sizes for the population. His models predicted that a Yellowstone grizzly bear population of 70–90 individuals would have about a 95% chance of surviving for 100 years. A slightly larger population of 100 bears would have a 95% chance of surviving for twice as long, about 200 years. Current estimates put the total grizzly bear population in the greater Yellowstone ecosystem at more than 500 individuals, well above Schaffer's estimates.

CRAIGHEAD ENVIORNMENTAL RESEARCH INSTITUTE

▲ **Figure 56.13 Long-term monitoring of a grizzly bear population.** The ecologist is fitting this tranquilized bear with a radio collar so that the bear's movements can be compared with those of other grizzlies in the Yellowstone National Park population.

Is the population large enough to conserve its genetic variation? Effective population size, N_e, depends on the number of males and females that actually breed. Because a few males dominate the breeding, and female reproduction depends on food abundance, N_e is only about 25% of the total population size, or about 125 bears. The Yellowstone grizzly population has less genetic variability than most grizzly populations. Immigration from other populations could be used to increase the genetic variation of the population; the introduction of only two unrelated individuals per decade would reduce the rate at which genetic variation is lost by about half. For the grizzly bear, and probably for many other species with small populations, finding ways to promote dispersal among populations may be one of the most urgent conservation needs.

This field study and that of the greater prairie chicken bridge small-population models and practical applications in conservation. Next, we look at an alternative approach to understanding the biology of extinction.

Declining-Population Approach

The declining-population approach focuses on threatened and endangered populations that show a downward trend, even if the population is far above its minimum viable population. The distinction between a declining population (which is not always small) and a small population (which is not always declining) is less important than the different priorities of the two approaches. The small-population approach emphasizes smallness itself as the cause of a population's extinction, through the loss of genetic diversity or through chance events such as winter storms or hurricanes. In contrast, the declining-population approach emphasizes the environmental factors that caused a population decline in the first place. If, for instance, an area is deforested, then species that depend on trees will decline in abundance and become locally extinct, whether or not they retain genetic variation.

Steps for Analysis and Intervention

The declining-population approach requires that population declines be evaluated on a case-by-case basis, with researchers carefully dissecting the causes of a decline before taking steps to correct it. If an invasive species such as the brown tree snake in Guam is harming a native bird species, then managers need to reduce or eliminate the invader to restore vulnerable populations of the bird. Although most situations are more complex, we can use the following steps for analyzing declining populations:

1. Confirm, using population data, that the species was more widely distributed or abundant in the past.
2. Study the natural history of this and related species, including reviewing the research literature, to determine the species' environmental needs.

3. Develop hypotheses for all possible causes of the decline, including human activities and natural events, and list the predictions of each hypothesis.

4. Because many factors may be correlated with the decline, test the most likely hypothesis first. For example, remove the suspected agent of decline to see if the experimental population rebounds compared to a control population.

5. Apply the results of the diagnosis to manage the threatened species and monitor its recovery.

The following field study is one example of how the declining-population approach has been applied to the conservation of an endangered species.

Field Study: *Decline of the Rufa Red Knot*

The rufa red knot (*Calidris canutus rufa*) is a medium-sized shorebird that undertakes one of the most remarkable long-distance migrations of any animal species. Red knots breed on Arctic islands in northern Canada and "winter" on the beaches of Tierra del Fuego at the southern tip of South America, an annual round trip of over 27 000 kilometres. Recently, very small electronic devices (geolocators) have been used to track the migration paths of individual birds. **Figure 56.14** shows the route taken by a red knot tagged in May 2009 and recaptured in May 2010. This male flew nonstop for 6 days from southern Brazil to the United States, a distance of 8000 kilometres.

The red knot population has declined precipitously over the past decade, and is listed as endangered by COSEWIC. Counts of red knots are made each year in the south, where the birds spend several months feeding on intertidal clams. At least 50 000 red knots came to Tierra del Fuego each year until 2000, but then numbers began to fall. In 2011, fewer than 10 000 red knots arrived at the southern feeding grounds.

Three general hypotheses could explain the decline: (1) Red knots could be dying or failing to reproduce while nesting in Arctic Canada; (2) Mortality rates might have increased on the southern feeding grounds; (3) Habitat might have been lost or degraded, increasing mortality during migration. To select the most likely hypothesis, ecologists examined the population trends of other species of birds that use the same habitats and migration routes. They found that other species nesting on the same Arctic islands or feeding in the same southern intertidal areas had stable, rather than declining, populations. But several species that

KEVIN ELSBY/Alamy stock Photo

Geolocator attached 11-May

1500 km N in 1 day

1500 km S in 8 days

8000 km N in 6 days

3300 km S in 3 days

3 (a) Nesting red knot on Arctic island (Nunavut) June–Aug.

Brad Winn

Barrie Britton/Nature Picture Library

1 (b) Spawning horseshoe crabs (Delaware Bay) Late May

8 (c) Red knots eating clams (Tierra del Fuego) Oct.–Mar.

Brad Winn

▲ **Figure 56.14 Route flown by a shorebird (*Calidrus canuta rufa*) fitted with a geolocator.** The abundance of this long-distance migrant is declining due to the overexploitation of horseshoe crabs at its critical stopover site in Delaware Bay, USA.

used the same stopover site as red knots on their way north were also declining. Researchers focused on this site, Delaware Bay on the eastern coast of the United States.

Delaware Bay is the last major feeding site before red knots fly to their Arctic breeding grounds. Here the birds gorge on the eggs of spawning horseshoe crabs (*Limulus polyphemus*) and can double their weight in just a couple of weeks. They need these fat stores. Food is scarce and the weather unpredictable in the Arctic spring, and an individual arriving without fat reserves may not survive and is almost certain to "skip" reproduction that year. Surveys at Delaware Bay showed that horseshoe crab egg abundances were down by 90% and that many red knots were beginning their flights north without enough fat. Annual mortality rate rose from 15% to over 40%.

Horseshoe crab numbers in Delaware Bay were decimated in the early 1990s by an intense fishery (horseshoe crabs are used as bait for catching conch and eels). Regulation of the horseshoe crab harvest has increased crab numbers, but egg abundances have not yet recovered. Recovery may take years, because horseshoe crabs don't mature until they are 10 to 12 years old. Meanwhile, studies of other stopover sites may reveal additional ways that we can improve the survival rates of migrating red knots.

Weighing Conflicting Demands

Determining population numbers and habitat needs is only part of a strategy to save species. Scientists also need to weigh a species' needs against other conflicting demands. Conservation biology often highlights the relationship between science, technology, and society. For example, the goal of conserving habitat for the endangered woodland caribou in northern Alberta is pitted against the economic opportunities offered by exploitation of the oil sands.

Large, high-profile vertebrates are not always the focal point in such conflicts, but habitat use is almost always the issue. Should work proceed on a new highway bridge if it destroys the only remaining habitat of a species of fresh-water mussel? If you were the owner of a coffee plantation growing varieties that thrive in bright sunlight, would you be willing to change to shade-tolerant varieties that produce less coffee per hectare but can grow beneath trees that support large numbers of songbirds?

Another important consideration is the ecological role of a species. Because we cannot save every endangered species, we must determine which species are most important for conserving biodiversity as a whole. Identifying keystone species and finding ways to sustain their populations can be central to maintaining communities and ecosystems.

CONCEPT CHECK 56.2

1. How does the reduced genetic diversity of small populations make them more vulnerable to extinction?

2. If there were 100 greater prairie chickens in a population, and 30 females and 10 males bred, what would be the effective population size (N_e)?

3. **WHAT IF?** In 2005, at least ten grizzly bears in the greater Yellowstone ecosystem were killed through contact with people. Three things caused most of these deaths: collisions with automobiles, hunters (of other animals) shooting when charged by a female grizzly bear with cubs nearby, and conservation managers killing bears that attacked livestock repeatedly. If you were a conservation manager, what steps might you take to minimize such encounters in Yellowstone?

For suggested answers, see Appendix A.

CONCEPT 56.3

Landscape and regional conservation help sustain biodiversity

Although conservation efforts historically focused on saving individual species, efforts today often seek to sustain the biodiversity of entire communities, ecosystems, and landscapes. Such a broad view requires applying not just the principles of community, ecosystem, and landscape ecology but aspects of human population dynamics and economics

as well. The goals of landscape ecology (see Chapter 52) include projecting future patterns of landscape use and making biodiversity conservation part of land-use planning.

Landscape Structure and Biodiversity

The biodiversity of a given landscape is in large part a function of the structure of the landscape. Understanding landscape structure is critically important in conservation because many species use more than one kind of ecosystem, and many live on the borders between ecosystems.

Fragmentation and Edges

The boundaries, or *edges*, between ecosystems—such as between a bog and the surrounding forest or between cropland and suburban housing tracts—are defining features of landscapes (Figure 56.15). An edge has its own set of physical conditions, which differ from those on either side of it. The soil surface of an edge between a forest patch and a burned area receives more sunlight and is usually hotter and drier than the forest interior, but it is cooler and wetter than the soil surface in the burned area.

Some organisms thrive in edge communities because they gain resources from both adjacent areas. The ruffed grouse (*Bonasa umbellus*) is a bird that needs forest habitat for nesting, winter food, and shelter, but it also needs forest openings with dense shrubs and herbs for summer food. White-tailed deer also thrive in edge habitats, where they can browse on woody shrubs; deer populations often expand when forests are logged and more edges are generated.

Ecosystems in which edges arise from human alterations often have reduced biodiversity and a preponderance of edge-adapted species. The brown-headed cowbird

▲ Figure 56.15 **Natural edges between ecosystems.** Boreal forest gives way to bog and wetland habitat in Northern Ontario.

(*Molothrus ater*) is an edge-adapted species that lays its eggs in the nests of other birds, often migratory songbirds. Cowbirds need forests, where they can parasitize the nests of other birds, and open fields, where they forage on seeds and insects. Consequently, their populations are growing where forests are being cut and fragmented, creating more edge habitat and open land. Increasing cowbird parasitism and habitat loss are correlated with declining populations of several of the cowbird's host species.

The influence of fragmentation on the structure of communities has been explored since 1979 in the long-term Biological Dynamics of Forest Fragments Project. Located in the heart of the Amazon River basin, the study area consists of isolated fragments of tropical rain forest separated from surrounding continuous forest by distances of 80–1000 m (Figure 56.16). Numerous researchers working on this project have clearly documented the effects of this fragmentation on organisms ranging from bryophytes to beetles to birds. They have consistently found that species adapted to forest interiors show the greatest declines when patches are the smallest, suggesting that landscapes dominated by small fragments will support fewer species.

Corridors That Connect Habitat Fragments

In fragmented habitats, the presence of a **movement corridor**, a narrow strip or series of small clumps of habitat connecting otherwise isolated patches, can be extremely important for conserving biodiversity. Riparian habitats often serve as corridors, and in some nations, government policy prohibits altering these habitats. In areas of heavy human use, artificial corridors are sometimes constructed.

Fences along the busy Trans-Canada highway near Banff, Alberta have greatly reduced wildlife-vehicle collisions. Wildlife overpasses (Figure 56.17) and underpasses are used by deer, elk, grizzlies, and even cougars, and such movement helps maintain habitat connectivity.

Movement corridors can also promote dispersal and reduce inbreeding in declining populations. Corridors have been shown to increase the exchange of individuals among populations of many organisms, including butterflies, voles, and aquatic plants. Corridors are especially important to species that migrate between different habitats seasonally. However, a corridor can also be harmful—for example, by allowing the spread of disease. In a 2003 study, a scientist at the University of Zaragoza, Spain, showed that habitat corridors facilitate the movement of disease-carrying ticks among forest patches in northern Spain. All the effects of corridors are not yet understood, and their impact is an area of active research in conservation biology.

Establishing Protected Areas

Conservation biologists are applying their understanding of landscape dynamics in establishing protected areas to slow biodiversity loss. Globally, governments have set aside about 7% of the world's land in various forms of reserves. Canada now has nearly 10% of its land under some form of protection. Choosing where to place nature reserves and determining how to design them poses many challenges. Should the reserve be managed to reduce risks to particular threatened species, by eliminating fires or removing predators, for example? Or should the reserve be left as natural as possible, with such processes as fires ignited by lightning allowed to play out on their own? This is just one of the debates that arise among people who share an interest in the health of national parks and other protected areas.

▲ Figure 56.16 **Amazon rain forest fragments created as part of the Biological Dynamics of Forest Fragments Project.**

▲ Figure 56.17 **An artificial corridor.** This bridge in Banff National Park, Canada, helps animals cross a human-created barrier.

Preserving Biodiversity Hot Spots

In deciding which areas are of highest conservation priority, biologists often focus on hot spots of biodiversity. A **biodiversity hot spot** is a relatively small area with numerous endemic species (species found nowhere else in the world) and a large number of endangered and threatened species (Figure 56.18). Nearly 30% of all bird species can be found in hot spots that make up only about 2% of Earth's land area. Approximately 50 000 plant species, or about one-sixth of all known plant species, inhabit just 18 hot spots covering 0.5% of the global land surface. Together, the "hottest" of the terrestrial biodiversity hot spots total less than 1.5% of Earth's land but are home to more than a third of all species of plants, amphibians, reptiles, birds, and mammals. Aquatic ecosystems also have hot spots, such as coral reefs and certain river systems.

Biodiversity hot spots are good choices for nature reserves, but identifying them is not always simple. One problem is that a hot spot for one taxonomic group, such as butterflies, may not be a hot spot for some other taxonomic group, such as birds. Designating an area as a biodiversity hot spot is often biased toward saving vertebrates and plants, with less attention paid to invertebrates and microorganisms. Some biologists are also concerned that the hot-spot strategy places too much emphasis on such a small fraction of Earth's surface.

Global change makes the task of preserving hot spots even more challenging because the conditions that favour a particular community may not be found in the same location in the future. The biodiversity hot spot in the southwest corner of Australia (see Figure 56.18) holds thousands of species of endemic plants and numerous endemic vertebrates. Researchers recently concluded that between 5% and 25% of the plant species they examined may become extinct by 2080 because the plants will be unable to tolerate the increased dryness predicted for this region.

Philosophy of Nature Reserves

Nature reserves are often protected "islands" of biodiversity in a sea of habitat altered or degraded by human activity. An earlier policy—that protected areas should be set aside to remain unchanged forever—was based on the concept that ecosystems are balanced, self-regulating units. As we saw in Chapter 54, however, disturbance is common in all ecosystems, and management policies that ignore natural disturbances or attempt to prevent them have generally failed. For instance, setting aside an area of a fire-dependent community, such as a portion of a tallgrass prairie, chaparral, or dry pine forest, with the intention of saving it is unrealistic if periodic burning is excluded. Without the dominant disturbance, the fire-adapted species are usually outcompeted and biodiversity is reduced.

An important conservation question is whether to create fewer large reserves or more numerous small reserves. One argument for large reserves is that large, far-ranging animals with low-density populations, such as the grizzly bear, require extensive habitats. Large reserves also have proportionately smaller perimeters than small reserves and are therefore less affected by edges.

As conservation biologists have learned more about the requirements for achieving minimum viable populations for endangered species, they have realized that most national parks and other reserves are far too small. The area needed for the long-term survival of the Yellowstone grizzly bear population is more than 10 times the combined area of Yellowstone and Grand Teton National Parks. Areas of private and public land surrounding reserves will likely have to contribute to biodiversity conservation.

Zoned Reserves

Several nations have adopted a zoned reserve approach to landscape management. A **zoned reserve** is an extensive region that includes areas relatively undisturbed by humans surrounded by areas that have been changed by human activity and are used for economic gain. The key challenge of the

▶ Figure 56.18 **Earth's terrestrial and marine biodiversity hot spots.**

Source: Adaptation of Figure 1 from "Biodiversity Hotspots for Conservation Priorities" by Norman Myers et al., from *Nature*, February 24, 2000, Volume 403(6772). Copyright © 2000 by Macmillan Publishers Ltd. Reprinted with permission.

■ Terrestrial biodiversity hot spots

▲ Marine biodiversity hot spots

Equator

zoned reserve approach is to develop a social and economic climate in the surrounding lands that is compatible with the long-term viability of the protected core. These surrounding areas continue to support human activities, but regulations prevent the types of extensive alterations likely to harm the protected area. As a result, the surrounding habitats serve as buffer zones against further intrusion into the undisturbed area.

The small Central American nation of Costa Rica has become a world leader in establishing zoned reserves. An agreement initiated in 1987 reduced Costa Rica's international debt in return for land preservation there. The country is now divided into 11 Conservation Areas, which include national parks and other protected areas, both on land and in the ocean (Figure 56.19). Costa Rica is making progress toward managing its zoned reserves, and the buffer zones provide a steady, lasting supply of forest products, water, and hydroelectric power while also supporting sustainable agriculture and tourism.

Costa Rica relies on its zoned reserve system to maintain at least 80% of its native species, but the system is not without problems. A 2003 analysis of land cover change between 1960 and 1997 showed negligible deforestation within Costa Rica's national parks and a gain in forest cover in the 1-km buffer around the parks. However, significant losses in forest cover were discovered in the 10-km buffer zones around all national parks, threatening to turn the parks into isolated habitat islands.

Marine ecosystems have also been heavily affected by human exploitation, and efforts to protect marine habitat are now under way in many countries. Canada is establishing a network of ocean reserves, or Marine Protected Areas (MPA). First to be protected (2003) were the Endeavour Hydrothermal Vents west of Vancouver Island. Here, new seafloor is continually being created more than 2000 m below the ocean surface, and a unique biota that can withstand temperatures of 121°C is present. Also protected is the Bowie Seamount off the coast of northern British Columbia, where an extinct underwater volcano extends 3000 m from the ocean floor to within 25 m of the water surface. Seamounts are highly productive and diverse ecosystems, and the abundant fish attract seabirds and marine mammals (Figure 56.20). The Gully, which is a submarine canyon on the Atlantic coast, is also an MPA. Here one finds a high diversity (over 20 species) of cold water corals as well as an endangered population of northern bottlenose whales, a whale that feeds on squid at depths of over 1400 m.

Marine Protected Areas are often established in areas that contain economic resources such as petroleum or fish. To integrate economic activity with conservation goals, Canadian MPAs are usually divided into three management zones. In the central and most restricted zone, no activities that disturb, damage, or remove marine organisms or their habitat can occur. Surrounding that is a fishing-only zone, with restrictions

(a) Boundaries of the Conservation Areas are indicated by black outlines.

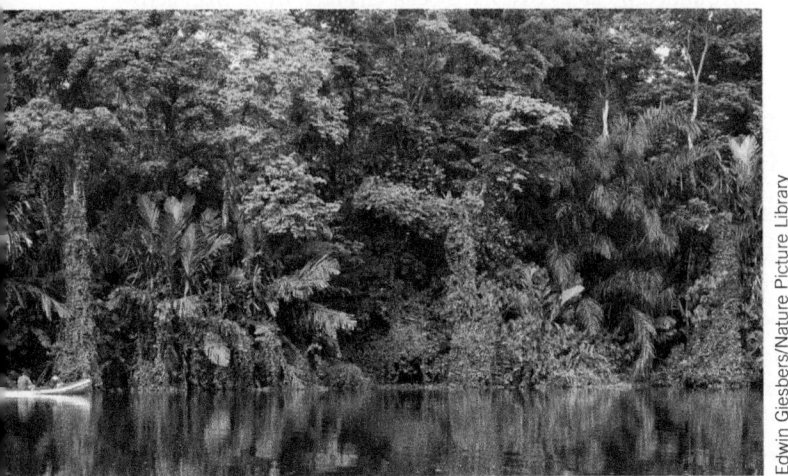

(b) Tourists marvel at the diversity of life in one of Costa Rica's protected areas.

▲ Figure 56.19 **Zoned reserves in Costa Rica.**

(a) More than 50 species of fish are found on the Bowie seamount.

(b) Northern bottlenose whales socialize at the water surface in the Gully.

▲ Figure 56.20 **Marine Protected Areas.** The Bowie seamount, an underwater mountain in the Pacific Ocean, and the Gully, an Atlantic submarine canyon, have been designated Marine Protected Areas under Canada's Oceans Act.

Urban Ecology

The zoned reserves that you just read about combine habitats that are relatively undisturbed by human activity with those that are used extensively by people for economic gain. Increasingly, ecologists are looking at species preservation even in the context of cities. The field of **urban ecology** examines organisms and their environment in urban settings.

For the first time in history, more than half of the people on Earth live in cities. By the year 2030, 5 billion people are expected to be living in urban environments. As cities expand in number and size, protected areas that were once outside city boundaries become incorporated into urban landscapes. Ecologists are now studying cities as ecological laboratories, seeking to balance species preservation and other ecological needs with the needs of people.

One critical area of research centres on urban streams, including the quality and flow of their water and the organisms living in them. Urban streams tend to rise and fall more quickly after rain than natural streams. This rapid change in water level occurs because of the concrete and other impervious surfaces in cities as well as the drainage systems that route water out of cities as quickly as possible to avoid flooding. Urban streams also tend to have higher concentrations of nutrients and contaminants and channels are often straightened, or even directed underground.

Near Vancouver, British Columbia, ecologists and volunteers worked to restore a degraded urban stream, Guichon Creek, by planting trees and shrubs along the creek and stabilizing its banks. Their efforts restored the water flow, and the invertebrate communities have largely recovered. A few years ago, ecologists reestablished cutthroat trout in the stream, and the trout are now thriving.

As cities continue to expand into the landscapes around them, understanding the ecological effects of this expansion will only increase in importance. Integrating cities into ecological research will grow as a research and conservation field over the coming decades.

CONCEPT CHECK 56.3

1. What is a biodiversity hot spot?
2. How do zoned reserves provide economic incentives for long-term conservation of protected areas?
3. **WHAT IF?** Suppose a developer proposes to clear-cut a forest that serves as a corridor between two parks. To compensate, the developer also proposes to add the same area of forest to one of the parks. As a professional ecologist, how might you argue for retaining the corridor?

For suggested answers, see Appendix A.

Earth is changing rapidly as a result of human actions

Landscape and regional conservation help protect habitats and preserve species. Today, however, many human activities are altering the fabric of Earth's ecosystems at regional to global scales. Global change includes alterations in climate, atmospheric chemistry, and broad ecological systems that may reduce the capacity of Earth to sustain life.

The rest of this section describes five types of large scale environmental change that humans are bringing about: acid precipitation, nutrient enrichment, bioaccumulation of toxic compounds, climate change, and ozone depletion. The impacts of these and other changes are evident, not just in human-dominated ecosystems such as cities and farms, but also in the most remote ecosystems on Earth.

Acid Precipitation

One of the first types of large-scale global change to cause global concern was *acid precipitation*, which is rain, snow, sleet, or fog with a pH less than 5.2. The burning of wood and fossil fuels releases oxides of sulphur and nitrogen that react with water in air, forming sulphuric and nitric acids. The acids eventually fall to Earth's surface, harming some aquatic and terrestrial organisms.

In the 1960s, ecologists determined that lake-dwelling organisms in eastern Canada were dying because of air pollution from factories in Ontario and the midwestern United States. In Nova Scotia, Atlantic salmon populations were extirpated from 14 rivers that had pH values less than 4.7. Lakes and streams in southern Norway and Sweden were also losing fish because of pollution generated in Great Britain and central Europe. (To review pH, see Concept 3.3.)

Environmental regulations and new technologies have enabled many countries to reduce sulphur dioxide emissions in recent decades. In North America, sulphur dioxide emissions have decreased by more than 60% since the 1970s, gradually reducing the acidity of precipitation. Some lakes have begun to recover. After the copper smelter in Sudbury, Ontario, reduced its emissions, pH of the water in nearby Clearwater Lake rose, and fish reappeared after decades of absence (Figure 56.21). However, further reductions in emissions will likely be necessary for the recovery of other lakes, such as Kejimkujik Lake in Nova Scotia.

Nutrient Enrichment

Human activity often removes nutrients from one part of the biosphere and adds them to another. Someone eating an orange in Calgary consumes nutrients that only weeks

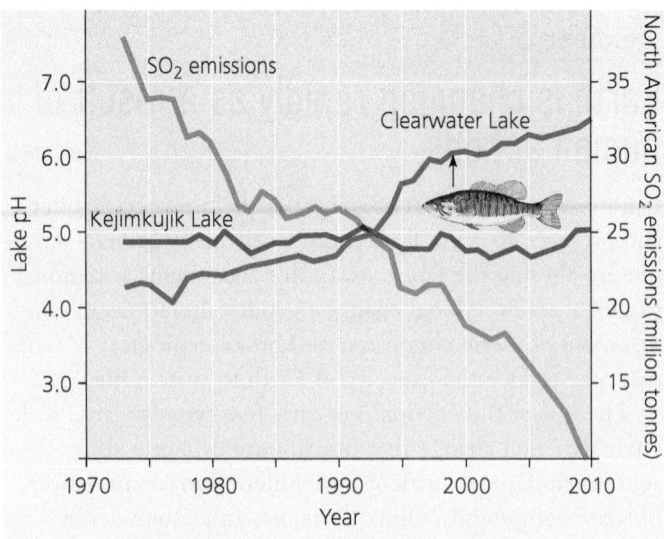

▲ Figure 56.21 **Recovery of acidic lakes.** North American sulphur emissions have declined since the 1970s. The pH of some lakes, such as Clearwater Lake near Sudbury, Ontario, has risen sufficiently to allow fish populations to recover (arrow). However, many other Canadian lakes, including Kejimkujik Lake in Nova Scotia, show little sign of recovery.

▲ Figure 56.22 **Fertilization of a corn (maize) crop.** To replace the nutrients removed in crops, farmers must apply fertilizers—either organic, such as manure or mulch, or synthetic, as shown here.

before were in the soil in California; a short time later, some of these nutrients will be in the Bow River, having passed through the person's digestive system and a local sewage treatment facility.

Agriculture has had an enormous impact on the movement and storage of nutrients in terrestrial ecosystems. Nutrients are lost from an ecosystem when land is cleared of its natural vegetation, and nutrients are removed from the soil each time a crop is harvested. If nutrients are not replaced, agriculture eventually exhausts the nutrients stored in soils. Rich soils, such as those of the North American grasslands, can be "mined" for their nutrients for decades, whereas poorer soils, such as those found in the tropics, can sustain intensive agriculture for only a few years before soil nutrients are depleted.

Nitrogen is perhaps the nutrient element that has been most affected by agriculture. Soil nitrogen taken up by crops is removed through harvesting, along with other nutrients. But we, as humans, are now adding nitrogen back into our agricultural and non-agricultural ecosystems at rates unprecedented in history. Organic amendments (manure, compost) are used to return nitrogen to the soil. The application of inorganic fertilizers to soils (**Figure 56.22**) has more than doubled the amount of nitrogen entering terrestrial ecosystems on a global scale.

Humans are also increasing nitrogen inputs through the burning of fossil fuels, which enter the atmosphere and dissolve in rainwater; the nitrogen ultimately enters ecosystems as nitrate. Increased cultivation of legumes, with their

nitrogen-fixing symbionts, is a third way in which humans increase the amount of nitrogen in the soil.

A problem arises when the nutrient level in an ecosystem exceeds the **critical load**, the amount of added nutrient, usually nitrogen or phosphorus, that can be absorbed by plants without damaging ecosystem integrity. For example, nitrogenous minerals in the soil that exceed the critical load eventually leach into ground water or run off into freshwater and marine ecosystems, contaminating water supplies and killing fish. Nitrate concentrations in ground water are increasing in most agricultural regions, sometimes reaching levels that are unsafe for drinking.

Many rivers contaminated with nitrates and ammonium from agricultural runoff and sewage drain into the Atlantic Ocean, with the highest inputs coming from northern Europe and the central United States. The Mississippi River carries nitrogen pollution to the Gulf of Mexico, fuelling a phytoplankton bloom each summer. When the phytoplankton die, their decomposition by oxygen-using organisms creates an extensive "dead zone" of low oxygen levels along the coast (**Figure 56.23**). Fishes and other marine animals disappear from the coastal waters, with impacts on economically important shrimp and oyster fisheries. To reduce the size of the dead zone, farmers have begun using fertilizers more efficiently, and managers are restoring wetlands in the Mississippi watershed, two changes stimulated by the results of ecosystem experiments.

Nutrient runoff can also lead to the eutrophication of lakes (see Concept 55.2). The bloom and subsequent die-off of algae and cyanobacteria and the ensuing depletion of oxygen are similar to what occurs in a marine dead zone. Such conditions threaten the survival of organisms. For example, eutrophication of Lake Erie coupled with overfishing wiped

◄ Figure 56.23 **A phytoplankton bloom arising from nitrogen pollution in the Mississippi basin that leads to a dead zone.** In this satellite image from 2004, red and orange represent high concentrations of phytoplankton in the Gulf of Mexico.

NASA/Goddard Space Flight Center/Pearson Education, Inc.

▲ Figure 56.24 **Biological magnification of PCBs in a Great Lakes food web.**

INTERPRET THE DATA *If a typical smelt weighs 225 g, what is the total mass of PCBs in a smelt in the Great Lakes? If an average lake trout weighs 4500 g, what is the total mass of PCBs in a trout in the Great Lakes? Assume that a lake trout from an unpolluted source is introduced into the Great Lakes and smelt are the only source of PCBs in the trout's diet. How many smelt would the new trout have to consume to attain a pcb level equivalent to existing trout in the Great Lakes? (Assume that the trout retains 100% of the PCBs it consumes.)*

out commercially important fishes such as blue pike, whitefish, and lake trout by the 1960s (Figure 55.8). Tighter regulations on waste dumping into the lake enabled fish populations to rebound. However, recently, blooms of cyanobacteria began to occur again and the dead zone is growing. Research indicates that nutrient inputs from agriculture are too high.

Toxic Compounds in the Environment

Humans release an immense variety of toxic chemicals, including thousands of synthetic compounds previously unknown in nature, with little regard for the ecological consequences. Organisms acquire toxic substances from the environment along with nutrients and water. Some of the poisons are metabolized or excreted, but others accumulate in specific tissues, often fat. One of the reasons accumulated toxins are particularly harmful is that they become more concentrated in successive trophic levels of a food web. This phenomenon, called **biological magnification**, occurs because the biomass at any given trophic level is produced from a much larger biomass ingested from the level below (see Concept 55.3). As a result, top-level carnivores tend to be most severely affected by toxic compounds in the environment.

One class of industrially synthesized compounds that have demonstrated biological magnification are the chlorinated hydrocarbons, which include the industrial chemicals called PCBs (polychlorinated biphenyls) and many pesticides, such as DDT. Current research implicates many of these compounds in endocrine system disruption in a large number of animal species, including humans (see pp. 1066–1067). Biological magnification of PCBs has been found in the food web of the Great Lakes, where the concentration of PCBs in herring gull eggs, at the top of the food web, is nearly 5000 times that in phytoplankton, at the base of the food web (Figure 56.24).

An infamous case of biological magnification that harmed top-level carnivores involved DDT, a chemical used to control insects such as mosquitoes and agricultural

pests. In the decade after World War II, the use of DDT grew rapidly; its ecological consequences were not yet fully understood. By the 1950s, scientists were learning that DDT persists in the environment and is transported by water to areas far from where it is applied. One of the first signs that DDT was a serious environmental problem was a decline in the populations of pelicans, ospreys, and eagles, birds that feed at the top of food webs. The accumulation of DDT (and DDE, a product of its breakdown) in the tissues of these birds interfered with the deposition of calcium in their eggshells. When the birds tried to incubate their eggs, the weight of the parents broke the shells of affected eggs, resulting in catastrophic declines in the birds' reproduction rates. Rachel Carson's book *Silent Spring* helped

◄ Figure 56.25 **Rachel Carson.** Through her writing and her testimony before the U.S. Congress, biologist and author Carson helped promote a new environmental ethic. Her efforts led to a ban on DDT use in the United States and stronger controls on the use of other chemicals.

bring the problem to public attention (Figure 56.25), resulting in the banning of DDT. A dramatic recovery in populations of the affected bird species followed.

In much of the tropics, DDT is still used to control the mosquitoes that spread malaria and other diseases. Societies there face a trade-off between saving human lives and protecting other species. The best approach seems to be to apply DDT sparingly and to couple its use with mosquito netting and other low-technology solutions. The complicated history of DDT illustrates the importance of understanding the ecological connections between diseases and communities (see Concept 54.5).

Pharmaceuticals make up another group of toxic compounds in the environment, one that is of growing concern among ecologists. The use of over-the-counter and prescription drugs has risen in recent years, particularly in industrialized nations. People who consume such products excrete residual chemicals in their waste and may also dispose of unused drugs improperly, such as in their toilets or sinks. Drugs that are not broken down in sewage treatment plants may then enter rivers and lakes with the material discharged from these plants. Growth-promoting drugs given to farm animals can also enter rivers and lakes with agricultural runoff. As a consequence, many pharmaceuticals are spreading in low concentrations across the world's freshwater ecosystems (Figure 56.26).

Among the pharmaceuticals that ecologists are studying are the sex steroids, especially estrogen and estrogen mimics (other chemicals that bind to estrogen receptors). Estrogens and their mimics are used in birth control pills and also to produce dairy products, soy milk, and biodiesel. Some fish species are so sensitive to certain estrogens that concentrations of a few parts per trillion in their water can cause males to acquire female characteristics. Researchers in Ontario conducted a seven-year experiment in which they applied the synthetic estrogen used in contraceptives to a lake in very low concentrations (5–6 ng/L). They found that chronic exposure of the fathead minnow (*Pimephales promelas*) to the estrogen led to feminization of males and a near extinction of the species from the lake. Feminization of male fish is widespread in Europe and parts of the United States, and intersex fish are present in the Grand River downstream of Kitchener-Waterloo, Ontario, and in Hamilton Harbour, Lake Ontario.

Many toxic chemicals cannot be degraded by microorganisms and persist in the environment for years or even decades. In other cases, chemicals released into the environment may be relatively harmless but are converted to more toxic products by reaction with other substances, by exposure to light, or by the metabolism of microorganisms. Mercury, a by-product of plastic production and coal-fired power generation, has been routinely expelled into rivers and the sea in an insoluble form. Bacteria in the bottom mud convert the waste to methylmercury (CH_3Hg^+), an extremely toxic water-soluble compound that accumulates in the tissues of organisms, including humans who consume fish from the contaminated waters.

Greenhouse Gases and Climate Change

Human activities release a variety of gaseous waste products. People once thought that the vast atmosphere could absorb these materials indefinitely, but we now know that such additions can cause fundamental changes to the atmosphere and to its interactions with the rest of the biosphere. For more than a century, scientists have studied how greenhouse gases affect the Earth's climate and how human activities such as burning fossil fuels and converting forests to agricultural or urban land are contributing to global warming. In Figure 56.27 and the Scientific Skills Exercise we examine how increasing carbon dioxide and global warming affect species and ecosystems.

▲ Figure 56.26 **Sources and movements of pharmaceuticals in the environment.**

Exploring Climate Change

An atmosphere in flux

The concentration of gases in the atmosphere fluctuates over time due to physical and biological processes. For example, there was more much carbon dioxide and less oxygen in the atmosphere before plants evolved (see Figure 25.9). Atmospheric carbon has risen dramatically over the past 50 years (graph at right). Scientists have been able to quantify the movement of carbon on a global scale, and the recent increase in atmospheric carbon is directly linked to emissions from burning fossil fuels. A doubling of current CO_2 levels is expected by the end of the 21st century.

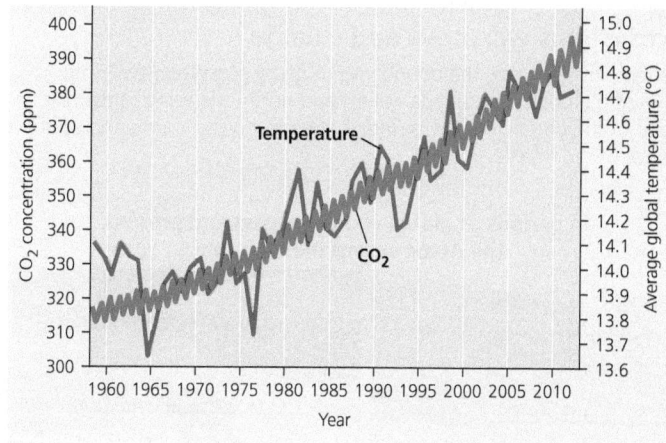

A greener planet?

CO_2 influences primary productivity

Increasing CO_2 is expected to increase productivity by plants. When CO_2 levels are raised in a greenhouse, most plants grow faster. However, natural ecosystems are less predictable, and ecologists are using field experiments to determine how or if rising CO_2 levels will affect primary productivity.

In one experiment, scientists exposed trees in a pine forest to elevated levels of CO_2. Plots of trees were ringed by towers that emitted CO_2-enriched air. Temperature, precipitation, and wind were similar in experimental and adjacent control plots. Primary productivity did increase: Trees in the experimental plots produced about 15% more wood each year. However, in this and other similar experiments, growth rates were lower than predicted from greenhouse experiments, probably because nutrients such as nitrogen limit growth in most natural ecosystems.

A warmer planet?

CO_2 influences climate

Rising concentrations of CO_2 and other greenhouse gases are changing Earth's heat budget. The solar radiation that strikes the planet is reflected back as infrared radiation. Greenhouse gases intercept and re-reflect some of this radiation back toward Earth. This process helps retain solar heat. If it were not for this greenhouse effect, the average air temperature of Earth's surface would be a frigid −18°C, and most life as we know it could not exist.

The marked rise in atmospheric CO_2 concerns scientists because of its link to increased global temperature. For more than a century, scientists have studied how greenhouse gases influence the Earth's climate. Most scientists are convinced that such warming is already occurring (see above graph) and that it will continue.

Global climate models predict that a doubling of atmospheric CO_2 will raise average global temperature by 1 to 4°C. Supporting these models is a correlation between CO_2 levels and temperature in prehistoric times. Past CO_2 concentrations can be measured in bubbles of air trapped in glacial ice, some of which is 700 000 years old. Prehistoric temperatures are inferred by several methods, including analysis of fossils and the chemical isotopes in sediments and corals. Temperatures were 3–4°C higher than preindustrial levels 4.5 million years ago, the last time that CO_2 levels were higher than today.

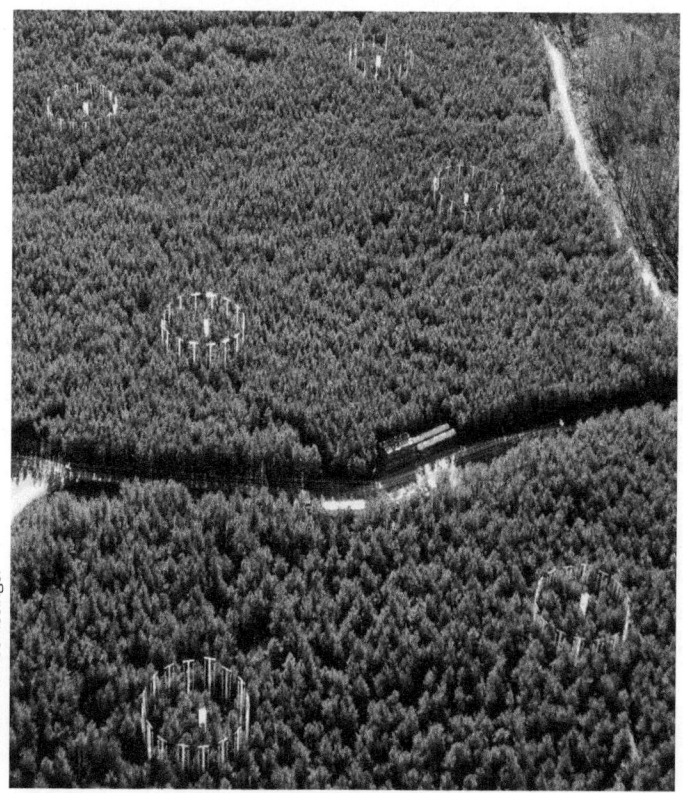

CO₂-enriched plots in a long-term experiment on plant productivity

An international team including scientists from Queen's University, Ontario, use sediment cores from lakes in the Arctic to track the climate of the past 200 000 years.

Continued on next page

Exploring Climate Change

The future

Ecosystems will move and change

As temperatures rise, the boundaries of many ecosystems will shift toward the poles. Grasslands will expand north, replacing forest. The edge of the boreal forest (treeline) is already moving north, and up the slopes of mountains.

In periods of global warming, past and present, the Arctic warms most rapidly.

Treeline has moved 60–80 m upslope in Kluane National Park, Yukon, during the 20th century.

Polar bear on ice flow, Nunavut. Scientists do not know if polar bears will be able to adapt to an ice-free Arctic.

Many plant and animal populations will track climate change, migrating north as it warms. Some will adapt to a warmer and drier or wetter environment. However, many species may not be able to move or adapt as quickly as the environment changes. Species with limited dispersal ability or little genetic variation will be most at risk. In addition, some habitat types, such as polar sea ice, may disappear completely. Polar bears depend on sea ice to hunt seals, their main prey. Time will tell if polar bears will be able to adapt to an ice-free Arctic.

Humans may also have to migrate or alter behaviour. Some cropland may become unsuitable for agriculture, especially regions that become drier. In addition, changing CO_2 and temperatures may affect productivity. Plants with C_3 photosynthesis are more limited by CO_2 availability than are C_4 plants (see Concept 10.4). In a CO_2-enriched environment, wheat or soybeans (C_3 plants) might become more productive than corn (maize), a C_4 plant.

Greenhouse gas emissions

Most CO_2 and nitrogen emissions come from burning fossil fuels, but significant amounts are also released by deforestation. Most human-related methane emissions come from the extraction of fossil fuels, agriculture, and landfills.

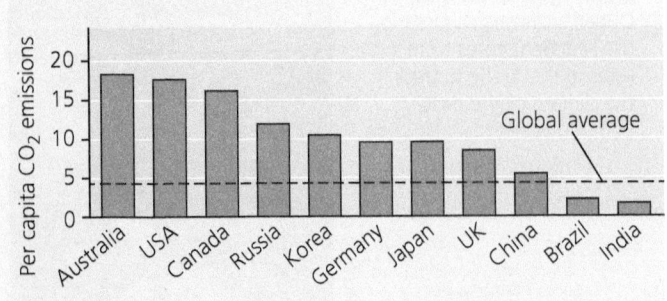

Canada has one of the highest per capita rates of CO_2 emissions in the world.

Insect pests and disease may be more common

Population growth rates (Concept 53.2) increase with temperature for most insects. Some species become serious pests when temperatures rise. For example, an outbreak of mountain pine beetle (*Dendroctonus ponderosae*) has damaged large areas of pine forest in British Columbia and Alberta. Insect outbreaks are expected to become more common with global warming.

Chris Harris/All Canada Photos

Forest near Prince George, BC, destroyed by the mountain pine beetle

As plants and animals expand their ranges, pathogens often tag along. For example, black-legged ticks (*Ixodes scapularis*) were first discovered in southern Ontario in the early 1990s, but the ticks are now established in all provinces east of Manitoba. Warmer temperatures and habitat change are helping the tick survive further north. Range expansion of black-legged ticks is of medical importance because the ticks carry the bacteria responsible for Lyme disease (see Figure 27.21).

Black-legged tick

Solutions

We will need many approaches to slow global warming. Coal, natural gas, wood, and other organic fuels cannot be burned without releasing CO_2. Emissions can be reduced by using energy more efficiently and perhaps by replacing fossil fuels with renewable solar and wind power and, more controversially, with nuclear power. Could CO_2 emissions be captured and buried? Perhaps this will be possible in the future, but current methods are far too expensive.

Reducing methane emissions would also help slow global warming. A molecule of methane is 21 times more effective at retaining heat than a molecule of CO_2. Improvements to and regulation of natural gas extraction methodology could greatly reduce industry emissions of methane. Careful management of cattle and manure, and the aeration of rice paddies would reduce inputs from agriculture. And emissions from landfills could be reduced by diverting organic waste, and by capturing the released methane to use as fuel.

Windmill farm in southern Alberta

Graphing Cyclic Data

How Does the Atmospheric CO₂ Concentration Change during a Year and from Decade to Decade? The blue curve in Figure 56.27 shows how the concentration of CO_2 in Earth's atmosphere has changed over a span of more than 50 years. For each year in that span, two data points are plotted, one in May and one in November. A more detailed picture of the change in CO_2 concentration can be obtained by looking at measurements made at more frequent intervals. In this exercise, you'll graph monthly CO_2 concentrations for three years over three decades.

Data from the Study The data in the table below are average CO_2 concentrations (in parts per million) at the Mauna Loa monitoring station for each month in 1990, 2000, and 2010.

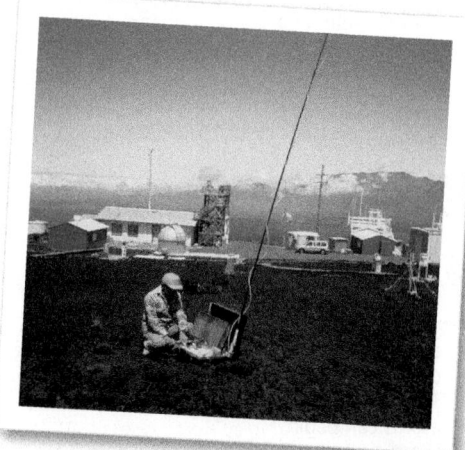

▶ A researcher sampling the air at the Mauna Loa monitoring station, Hawaii.

Hank Morgan/Science Source

Month	1990	2000	2010
January	353.79	369.25	388.45
February	354.88	369.50	389.82
March	355.65	370.56	391.08
April	356.27	371.82	392.46
May	359.29	371.51	392.95
June	356.32	371.71	392.06
July	354.88	369.85	390.13
August	352.89	368.20	388.15
September	351.28	366.91	386.80
October	351.59	366.91	387.18
November	353.05	366.99	388.59
December	354.27	369.67	389.68

Interpret the Data

1. Plot the data for all three years on one graph. Select a type of graph that is appropriate for these data, and choose a vertical axis scale that allows you to clearly see the patterns of CO_2 concentration changes,

both during each year and from decade to decade. (For additional information about graphs, see the Scientific Skills Review in Appendix E and in the Study Area in MasteringBiology.)

2. Within each year, what is the pattern of change in CO_2 concentration? Why does this pattern occur?

3. The measurements taken at Mauna Loa represent average atmospheric CO_2 concentrations for the Northern Hemisphere. Suppose you could measure CO_2 concentrations under similar conditions in the Southern Hemisphere. What pattern would you expect to see in those measurements over the course of a year? Explain.

4. In addition to the changes within each year, what changes in CO_2 concentration occurred between 1990 and 2010? Calculate the average CO_2 concentration for the 12 months of each year. By what percentage did this average change from 1990 to 2000 and from 1990 to 2010?

Data from National Oceanic & Atmospheric Administration, Earth System Research Laboratory, Global Monitoring Division.

Depletion of Atmospheric Ozone

Like carbon dioxide and other greenhouse gases, atmospheric ozone (O_3) has also changed in concentration because of human activities. Life on Earth is protected from the damaging effects of ultraviolet (UV) radiation by a layer of ozone located in the stratosphere 17–25 km above Earth's surface. However, satellite studies of the atmosphere show that the springtime ozone layer over Antarctica has thinned substantially since the mid-1970s **(Figure 56.28)**. The destruction of atmospheric ozone results primarily from the accumulation of chlorofluorocarbons (CFCs), chemicals once widely used in refrigeration and manufacturing. In the stratosphere, chlorine atoms released from CFCs react with ozone, reducing it to molecular O_2 **(Figure 56.29)**. Subsequent chemical reactions liberate the chlorine, allowing it to react with other ozone molecules in a catalytic chain reaction.

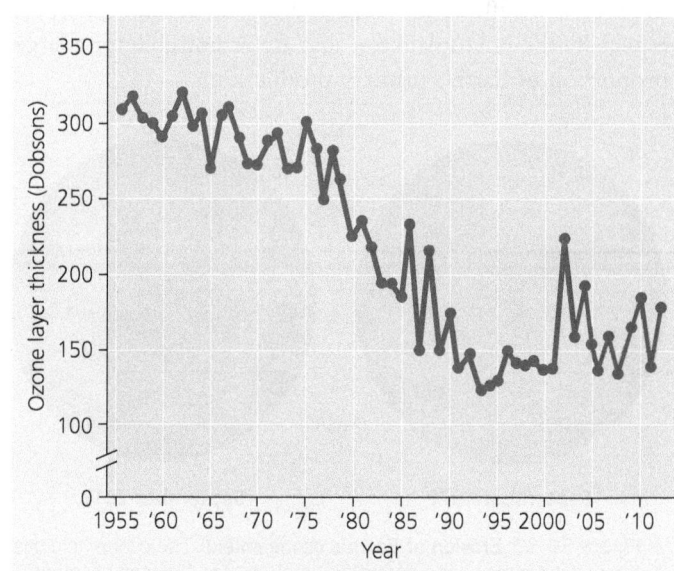

▲ Figure 56.28 **Thickness of the October ozone layer over Antarctica in units called Dobsons.**

① Chlorine from CFCs interacts with ozone (O_3), forming chlorine monoxide (ClO) and oxygen (O_2).

Chlorine atom

Chlorine O_3

O_2

O_2

ClO

ClO

③ Sunlight causes Cl_2O_2 to break down into O_2 and free chlorine atoms. The chlorine atoms can begin the cycle again.

Sunlight

Cl_2O_2

② Two ClO molecules react, forming chlorine peroxide (Cl_2O_2).

▲ Figure 56.29 **How free chlorine in the atmosphere destroys ozone.**

The thinning of the ozone layer is most apparent over Antarctica in spring, where cold, stable air allows the chain reaction to continue. The magnitude of ozone depletion and the size of the ozone hole have generally increased in recent years, and the hole sometimes extends as far as the southernmost portions of Australia, New Zealand, and South America (Figure 56.30). At the more heavily populated middle latitudes, ozone levels have decreased 2–10% during the past 20 years.

Decreased ozone levels in the stratosphere increase the intensity of UV rays reaching Earth's surface. The consequences of ozone depletion for life on Earth may be severe for plants, animals, and microorganisms. Some scientists expect increases in both lethal and nonlethal forms of skin cancer and in cataracts among humans, as well as unpredictable effects on crops and natural communities, especially the phytoplankton that are responsible for a large proportion of Earth's primary production.

NASA

September 1979   September 2012

▲ Figure 56.30 **Erosion of Earth's ozone shield.** The ozone hole over Antarctica is visible as the dark blue patch in these images based on atmospheric data.

To study the consequences of ozone depletion, ecologists have conducted field experiments in which they use filters to decrease or block the UV radiation in sunlight. One such experiment, performed on a scrub ecosystem near the tip of South America, showed that when the ozone hole passed over the area, the amount of UV radiation reaching the ground increased sharply, causing more DNA damage in plants that were not protected by filters. Scientists have shown similar DNA damage and a reduction in phytoplankton growth when the ozone hole opens over the Southern Ocean each year.

The good news about the ozone hole is how quickly many countries have responded to it. Since 1987, more than 190 nations have signed the Montreal Protocol, a treaty that regulates the use of ozone-depleting chemicals. Most nations have ended the production of CFCs. As a consequence of these actions, chlorine concentrations in the stratosphere have stabilized and ozone depletion is slowing. Even though CFC emissions are close to zero today, however, chlorine molecules already in the atmosphere will continue to influence stratospheric ozone levels for at least 50 years.

The partial destruction of Earth's ozone shield is one more example of how much humans have been able to disrupt the dynamics of ecosystems and the biosphere. It also highlights our ability to solve environmental problems when we set our minds to it.

CONCEPT CHECK 56.4

1. How can the addition of excess mineral nutrients to a lake threaten its fish population?

2. **MAKE CONNECTIONS** There are vast stores of organic matter in the soils of northern coniferous forests and tundra around the world. Suggest an explanation for why scientists who study global warming are closely monitoring these stores (see Figure 55.15).

3. **MAKE CONNECTIONS** Mutagens are chemical and physical agents that induce mutations in DNA (see Concept 17.5). How does reduced ozone concentration in the atmosphere increase the likelihood of mutations in various organisms?

For suggested answers, see Appendix A.

CONCEPT 56.5

Sustainable development can improve human lives while conserving biodiversity

With the increasing loss and fragmentation of habitats, changes in Earth's climate and physical environment, and pressures from an increasing human population, we face difficult trade-offs in managing the world's resources. Preserving all habitat patches isn't feasible, so biologists must help societies set conservation priorities by identifying which habitat patches are most crucial. Ideally, implementing these priorities should also improve the quality of life for local people. Ecologists use the concept of *sustainability* as a tool to establish long-term conservation priorities.

Sustainable Development

We need to understand the interconnections of the biosphere if we are to protect species from extinction and improve the quality of human life. To this end, many nations, scientific societies, and other groups have embraced the concept of **sustainable development**, economic development that meets the needs of people today without limiting the ability of future generations to meet their needs.

Achieving sustainable development is an ambitious goal. To sustain ecosystem processes and stem the loss of biodiversity, we must connect life science with the social sciences, economics, and the humanities. We must also reassess our personal values. Those of us living in wealthier nations have a larger ecological footprint than do people living in developing nations (see Concept 53.6). By including the long-term costs of consumption in our decision-making processes, we can learn to value the ecosystem services that sustain us. The following field study illustrates how the combination of scientific and personal efforts can make a significant difference in creating a truly sustainable world.

Field Study: *Sustainable Development in Costa Rica*

The success of conservation in Costa Rica that we discussed in Concept 56.3 has required a partnership between the national government, nongovernment organizations (NGOs), and private citizens. Many nature reserves established by individuals have been recognized by the government as national wildlife reserves and are given significant tax benefits. However, achieving and sustaining the conservation and restoration of biodiversity is closely linked to the other half of sustainable development—the human condition.

Can conservation be compatible with the socio-economic goals of developing countries? Costa Rica is renowned for the system of nature reserves it established in the 1980s. It has successfully used its conservation efforts to promote international "ecotourism," and today over 10% of the country's GDP is linked to the

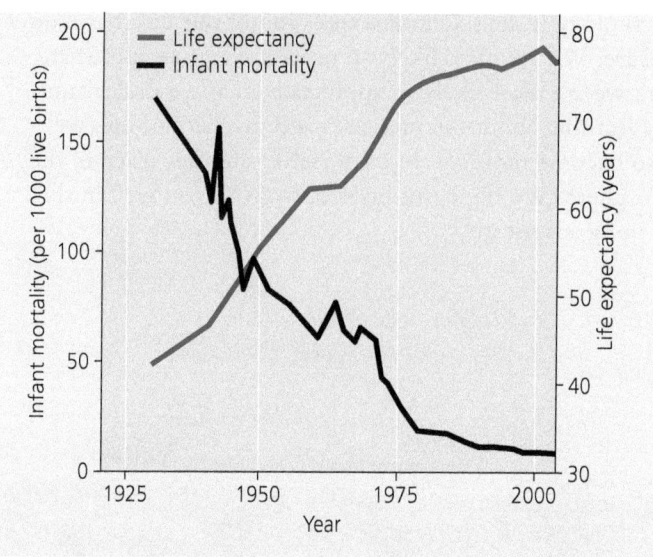

▲ Figure 56.31 **Infant mortality and life expectancy at birth in Costa Rica.**

tourism industry. Regionally, tourism can be even more important. For example, almost 100% of local employment is tourism-related in communities near Tortuguero National Park, a reserve on the Atlantic coast that contains one of the world's most important nesting sites for green turtles. However, it is important to recognize that conservation efforts in Costa Rica were implemented after the country had reached some important socioeconomic goals. By the 1980s, the infant mortality rate had declined and life expectancy had already increased to levels comparable to much of the developed world **(Figure 56.31)** as a result of public health initiatives begun in the 1940s (immunization, disease control, and education). Implementing and sustaining conservation programs in countries without such social supports is likely to be more difficult; however, the principles remain the same: In addition to sound ecological knowledge, community engagement and benefit are essential to successful sustainable development.

The Future of the Biosphere

Our appreciation of life, from the fundamentals of molecular biology, to the complexities of interconnected ecosystems, guides the field of biology today. We celebrate life by deciphering the genetic code that makes each species unique. We embrace life by using fossils and DNA to chronicle evolution through time. We preserve life through our efforts to classify and protect the millions of species on Earth. We respect life by using nature responsibly to improve human welfare.

Biology is the scientific expression of our desire to know nature. We are most likely to protect what we appreciate, and we are most likely to appreciate what we understand. By learning about the processes and diversity of life, we also become more aware of ourselves and our place in the biosphere. We hope this book has served you well in this lifelong adventure.

CONCEPT CHECK 56.5

1. What is meant by the term *sustainable development*?

2. **WHAT IF?** Suppose a new fish stock was discovered and a decision was made to harvest these fish, and you are put in charge of developing it sustainably. What ecological data might you want on the fish population? What criteria would you apply for the fishery's development?

For suggested answers, see Appendix A.

Gabriel Rojo/Nature Picture Library

Hans Reinhard/Getty Images

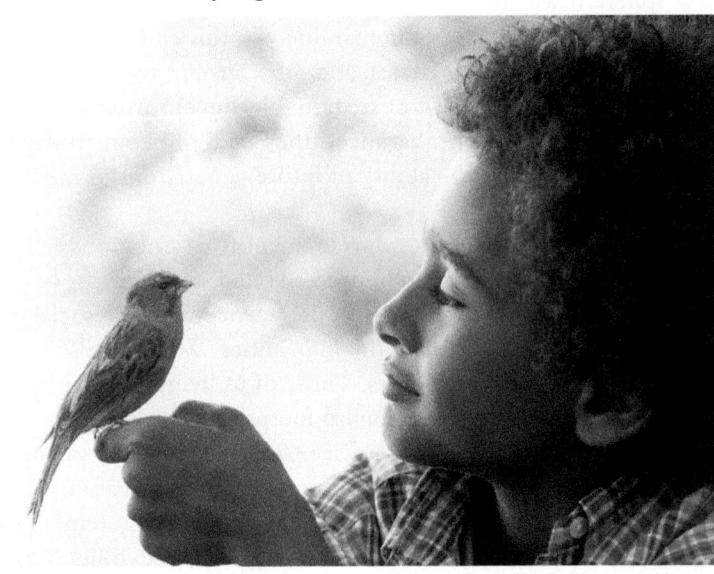

(a) Nature lovers on a wildlife-watching expedition

(b) A young biologist holding a songbird

▲ Figure 56.32 **Biophilia, past and present.**

56 Chapter Review

Go to **MasteringBiology**® for Assignments, the eText, and the Study Area with Animations, Activities, Vocab Self-Quiz, and Practice Tests.

SUMMARY OF KEY CONCEPTS

CONCEPT 56.1

Human activities threaten Earth's biodiversity (pp. 1321–1327)

- Biodiversity can be considered at three main levels:

Genetic diversity: source of variations that enable populations to adapt to environmental changes

Species diversity: important in maintaining structure of communities and food webs

Ecosystem diversity: provides life-sustaining services such as nutrient cycling and waste decomposition

- Our own biophilia enables us to recognize the value of biodiversity for its own sake. Other species also provide humans with food, fibre, medicines, and **ecosystem services**.
- Four major threats to biodiversity are habitat loss, **introduced species**, overharvesting, and global change.

? *Give at least three examples of key ecosystem services that nature provides for people.*

CONCEPT 56.2

Population conservation focuses on population size, genetic diversity, and critical habitat (pp. 1327–1331)

- When a population drops below a **minimum viable population (MVP)** size, its loss of genetic variation due to nonrandom mating and genetic drift can trap it in an **extinction vortex**.
- The declining-population approach focuses on the environmental factors that cause decline, regardless of absolute population size. It follows a step-by-step conservation strategy.
- Conserving species often requires resolving conflicts between the habitat needs of **endangered species** and human demands.

? *Why is the minimum viable population size smaller for a population that is more genetically diverse than it is for a less genetically diverse population?*

CONCEPT 56.3

Landscape and regional conservation help sustain biodiversity (pp. 1331–1335)

- The structure of a landscape can strongly influence biodiversity. As habitat fragmentation increases and edges become more extensive, biodiversity tends to decrease. **Movement corridors** can promote dispersal and help sustain populations.
- **Biodiversity hot spots** are also hot spots of extinction and thus prime candidates for protection. Sustaining biodiversity in parks and reserves requires management to ensure that human activities in the surrounding landscape do not harm the protected habitats. The **zoned reserve** model recognizes that conservation efforts often involve working in landscapes that are greatly affected by human activity.
- **Urban ecology** is the study of organisms and their environment in urban settings.

? *Give two examples that show how habitat fragmentation can harm species in the long term.*

CONCEPT 56.4

Earth is changing rapidly as a result of human actions (pp. 1335–1342)

- Burning wood and fossil fuels leads to the formation of acids in the atmosphere which then fall to the ground. Environmental regulations led to decreased sulphur dioxide emissions, allowing some freshwater ecosystems to recover.
- Agriculture removes plant nutrients from ecosystems, so large supplements are usually required. The nutrients in fertilizer can pollute groundwater and surface-water aquatic ecosystems, where they can stimulate excess algal growth (eutrophication).
- The release of toxic wastes and pharmaceuticals has polluted the environment with harmful substances that often persist for long periods and become increasingly concentrated in successively higher trophic levels of food webs (**biological magnification**).
- Because of human activities, the atmospheric concentration of CO_2 and other greenhouse gases has been steadily increasing. The ultimate effects may include significant climate change.
- The ozone layer reduces the penetration of UV radiation through the atmosphere. Human activities, notably the release of chlorine-containing pollutants, have eroded the ozone layer, but government policies are helping to solve the problem.

? *In the face of biological magnification of toxins, is it healthier to feed at a lower or higher trophic level? Explain.*

CONCEPT 56.5

Sustainable development aims to improve human lives while conserving biodiversity (pp. 1342–1344)

- **Sustainable development** is economic development that meets the needs of people today without limiting the ability of future generations to meet their needs.
- The success of Costa Rica's efforts to conserve tropical biodiversity is linked to improvements to human living conditions.
- By learning about biological processes and the diversity of life, we become more aware of our close connection to the environment and the value of other organisms that share it.

? *Why is sustainability such an important goal for conservation biologists?*

TEST YOUR UNDERSTANDING

LEVEL 1: KNOWLEDGE/COMPREHENSION

1. One characteristic that distinguishes a population in an extinction vortex from most other populations is that
   a. it is a rare, top-level predator.
   b. its effective population size is much lower than its total population size.
   c. its genetic diversity is very low.
   d. it is not well adapted to edge conditions.

2. The main cause of the increase in the amount of CO_2 in Earth's atmosphere over the past 150 years is
   a. increased worldwide primary production.
   b. increased worldwide standing crop.
   c. an increase in the amount of infrared radiation absorbed by the atmosphere.
   d. the burning of larger amounts of wood and fossil fuels.

3. What is the single greatest threat to biodiversity?
   a. overharvesting of commercially important species
   b. habitat alteration, fragmentation, and destruction
   c. introduced species that compete with native species
   d. pollution of Earth's air, water, and soil

LEVEL 2: APPLICATION/ANALYSIS

4. Which of the following is a consequence of biological magnification?
   a. Toxic chemicals in the environment pose greater risk to top-level predators than to primary consumers.
   b. Populations of top-level predators are generally smaller than populations of primary consumers.
   c. The biomass of producers in an ecosystem is generally higher than the biomass of primary consumers.
   d. Only a small portion of the energy captured by producers is transferred to consumers.

5. Which of the following strategies would most rapidly increase the genetic diversity of a population in an extinction vortex?
   a. Establish a reserve that protects the population's habitat.
   b. Introduce new individuals transported from other populations of the same species.
   c. Sterilize the least fit individuals in the population.
   d. Control populations of the endangered population's predators and competitors.

6. Of the following statements about protected areas that have been established to preserve biodiversity, which one is *not* correct?
   a. About 25% of Earth's land area is now protected.
   b. National parks are one of many types of protected areas.
   c. Management of a protected area should be coordinated with management of the land surrounding the area.
   d. It is especially important to protect biodiversity hot spots.

LEVEL 3: SYNTHESIS/EVALUATION

7. **DRAW IT** (a) Referring to Figure 56.27, estimate the average CO_2 concentration in 1975 and in 2012. (b) What was the rate of CO_2 concentration increase (ppm/yr) from 1975 to 2012? (c) Assuming that the CO_2 concentration continues to rise as fast as it did from 1975 to 2012, what will be the approximate CO_2 concentration in 2100? (d) Draw a graph of average CO_2 concentration from 1975 to 2012 and then use a dashed line to extrapolate the graph to the year 2100. (e) What ecological factors and human decisions will influence the actual rise in CO_2 concentration? (f) How might additional scientific data help societies predict this value?

8. **EVOLUTION CONNECTION**
   The fossil record indicates that there have been five mass extinction events in the past 500 million years (see Concept 25.4). Many ecologists think we are currently entering a sixth mass extinction event because of the threats to biodiversity described in this chapter. Briefly discuss the history of mass extinctions and the length of time it typically takes for species diversity to recover through the process of evolution. Explain why this should motivate us to slow the loss of biodiversity today.

9. **SCIENTIFIC INQUIRY**
   DRAW IT Suppose that you are managing a forest reserve, and one of your goals is to protect local populations of woodland birds from parasitism by the brown-headed cowbird. You know that female cowbirds usually do not venture more than about 100 m into a forest and that nest parasitism is reduced when woodland birds nest away from forest edges. The reserve you manage extends about 6000 m from east to west and 1000 m from north to south. It is surrounded by a deforested pasture on the west, an agricultural field for 500 m in the southwest corner, and intact forest everywhere else. You must build a road, 10 m by 1000 m, from the north to the south side of the reserve and construct a maintenance building that will take up 100 m^2 in the reserve. Draw a map of the reserve, showing where you would put the road and the building to minimize cowbird intrusion along edges. Explain your reasoning.

10. **WRITE ABOUT A THEME: INTERACTIONS**
    One factor favouring rapid population growth by an introduced species is the absence of the predators, parasites, and pathogens that controlled its population in the region where it evolved. In a short essay (100–150 words), explain how evolution by natural selection would influence the rate at which native predators, parasites, and pathogens in a region of introduction attack an introduced species.

11. **SYNTHESIZE YOUR KNOWLEDGE**

Edwin Giesbers/Nature Public Library

Big cats, such as the Siberian tiger (*Panthera tigris altaica*) shown here, are one of the most endangered groups of mammals in the world. Based on what you've learned in this chapter, discuss some of the approaches you would use to help preserve them.

For selected answers, see Appendix A.

Chapter 1

Figure Questions

Concept Check 1.1

1. Examples: A molecule consists of *atoms* bonded together. Each organelle has an orderly arrangement of *molecules*. Photosynthetic plant cells contain *organelles* called chloroplasts. A tissue consists of a group of similar *cells*. Organs such as the heart are constructed from several *tissues*. Organ systems, such as the cardiovascular system, are made up of multiple different organs, such as the heart and blood vessels. A complex multicellular organism, such as an animal, consists of multiple organ systems, such as the cardiovascular system, the digestive system, and the nervous system. A population is a set of *organisms* of the same species. A community consists of *populations* of the various species inhabiting a specific area. An ecosystem consists of a biological *community* along with the nonliving factors important to life, such as air, soil, and water. The biosphere is made up of all of Earth's *ecosystems*. 2. New properties emerge at successive levels of biological organization: (a) Structure and function are correlated. (b) Cells are an organism's basic units, *and* the continuity of life is based on heritable information in the form of DNA. (c) Organisms interact with other organisms and with the physical environment, *and* life requires energy transfer and transformation. 3. Some possible answers: *Emergent properties*: The ability of a human heart to pump blood requires an intact heart; it is not a capability of any of the heart's tissues or cells working alone. *Environmental interactions*: A mouse eats food, such as nuts or grasses, and deposits some of the food material as feces and urine. Construction of a nest rearranges the physical environment and may hasten degradation of some of its components. The mouse may also act as food for a predator. *Energy transfer*: A plant, such as a grass, absorbs energy from the sun and transforms it into molecules that act as stored fuel. Animals can eat parts of the plant and use the food for energy to carry out their activities. *Structure and function*: The strong, sharp teeth of a wolf are well suited to grasping and dismembering its prey. *The cellular basis of life*: The digestion of food is made possible by chemicals (chiefly enzymes) made by cells of the digestive tract. *The genetic basis of life*: Human eye colour is determined by the combination of genes inherited from the two parents. *Feedback regulation*: When your stomach is full, it signals your brain to decrease your appetite. *Evolution*: All plants have chloroplasts, indicating their descent from a common ancestor.

Concept Check 1.2

1. An address pinpoints a location by tracking from broader to narrower categories—a province, city, postal code, street, and building number. This is analogous to the groups-subordinate-to-groups structure of biological taxonomy. 2. The naturally occurring heritable variation in a population is "edited" by natural selection because individuals with heritable traits better suited to the environment survive and reproduce more successfully than others. Over time, better-suited individuals persist and their percentage in the population increases, while less suited individuals become less prevalent—a type of population editing.
3.

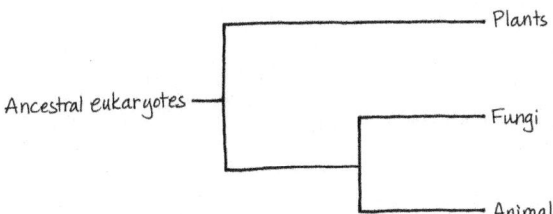

Concept Check 1.3

1. Inductive reasoning derives generalizations from specific cases; deductive reasoning predicts specific outcomes from general premises. 2. The fur coat colour of the mouse models is the independent variable because this is the variable that was changed intentionally by the researchers. Predation is the dependent variable, measured by the investigators and recorded as the proportion of the total number of attacked models. 3. Compared to a hypothesis, a scientific theory is usually more general and substantiated by a much greater amount of evidence. Natural selection is an explanatory idea that applies to all kinds of organisms and is supported by vast amounts of evidence of various kinds. 4. Based on the mouse colouration in Figure 1.28, you might expect that the mice that live on the sandy soil would be lighter in colour and those that live on the lava rock would be much darker. And in fact, that is what researchers have found. You would predict that each colour of mouse would be less preyed upon in its native habitat than it would be in the other habitat. (Research results also support this prediction.) You could repeat the Hoekstra experiment with coloured models, painted to resemble these two types of mice. Or you could try transplanting some of each population to its non-native habitat and counting how many you can recapture over the next few days, then comparing the four samples as was done in Hoekstra's experiment. (The painted models are easier to recapture, of course!) In the live mouse transplantation experiment, you would have to do controls to eliminate the variable represented by the transplanted mice being in a new, unknown territory. You could control for the transplantation process by transplanting some dark mice from one area of lava rock to one far distant, and some light mice from one area of sandy soil to a distant area.

Concept Check 1.4

1. Science aims to understand natural phenomena and how they work, while technology involves application of scientific discoveries for a particular purpose or to solve a specific problem. 2. Natural selection could be operating. Malaria is present in sub-Saharan Africa, so there might be an advantage to people with the sickle-cell disease form of the gene that makes them more able to survive and pass on their genes to offspring. Among those of African descent living in North America, where malaria is absent, there would be no advantage, so they would be selected against more strongly, resulting in fewer individuals with the sickle-cell disease form of the gene.

Summary of Key Concepts Questions

1.1 Evolution explains the most fundamental aspects of all life on Earth. It accounts for the common features shared by all forms of life due to descent from a common ancestor, while also providing an explanation for how the great diversity of living organisms on the planet has arisen. 1.2 Jackrabbits that, due to their genes, were better at controlling blood flow to their ears would be better able to maintain an ideal body temperature when exposed to changes in the temperature of their environment. These jackrabbits would survive and reproduce more than other jackrabbits that were less able to regulate body temperature using their ears. 1.3 Gathering and interpreting data are core activities in the scientific process, and they are affected by, and affect in turn, three other arenas of the scientific process: exploration and discovery, community analysis and feedback, and societal benefits and outcomes. 1.4 Different approaches taken by scientists studying natural phenomena at different levels complement each other, so more is learned about each problem being studied. A diversity of backgrounds among scientists may lead to fruitful ideas in the same way that important innovations have often arisen where a mix of cultures coexist.

Test Your Understanding

1. b 2. d 3. a 4. c 5. c 6. c 7. b 8. c 9. a 10. d
11. Your figure should show: (1) For the biosphere, the Earth with an arrow coming out of a tropical ocean; (2) for the ecosystem, a distant view of a coral reef; (3) for the community, a collection of reef animals and algae, with corals, fishes, some seaweed, and any other organisms you can think of; (4) for the population, a group of fish of the same species; (5) for the organism, one fish from your population; (6) for the organ, the fish's stomach, and for the organ system, the whole digestive tract (see Chapter 41 for help); (7) for a tissue, a group of similar cells from the stomach; (8) for a cell, one cell from the tissue, showing its nucleus and a few other organelles; (9) for an organelle, the nucleus, where most of the cell's DNA is located; and (10) for a molecule, a DNA double helix. Your sketches can be very rough!

Chapter 2

Figure Questions

Figure 2.7 Atomic number = 12; 12 protons, 12 electrons; 3 electron shells; 2 valence electrons. Figure 2.14 One possible answer:

Figure 2.17 The plant is submerged in water (H_2O), in which the CO_2 is dissolved. The sun's energy is used to make sugar, which is found in the plant and can act as food for the plant itself, as well as for animals that eat the plant. The oxygen (O_2) is present in the bubbles.

Concept Check 2.1

1. Table salt (sodium chloride) is made up of sodium and chlorine. We are able to eat the compound, showing that it has different properties from those of a metal (sodium) and a poisonous gas (chlorine). 2. Yes, because an organism requires trace elements, even though only in small amounts. 3. A person with an iron deficiency will probably show fatigue and other effects of a low oxygen level in the blood. (The condition is called anemia and can also result from too few red blood cells or abnormal hemoglobin.) 4. Variant ancestral plants that could tolerate the toxic elements could grow and reproduce in serpentine soils. (Plants that were well adapted to nonserpentine soils would not be expected to survive in serpentine areas.) The offspring of the variants would also vary, with those most capable of thriving under serpentine conditions growing best and reproducing most. Over many generations, this probably led to the serpentine-adapted species we see today.

Concept Check 2.2

1. 7 2. $^{15}_{7}N$ 3. 9 electrons; two electron shells; $1s$, $2s$, $2p$ (three orbitals); 1 electron is needed to fill the valence shell. 4. The elements in a row all have the same number of electron shells. In a column, all the elements have the same number of electrons in their valence shells.

Concept Check 2.3

1. Each carbon atom has only three covalent bonds instead of the required four. 2. The attraction between oppositely charged ions, forming ionic bonds 3. If you could synthesize molecules that mimic these shapes, you might be able to treat diseases or conditions caused by the inability of affected individuals to synthesize such molecules.

Concept Check 2.4

1.

2. At equilibrium, the forward and reverse reactions occur at the same rate. 3. $C_6H_{12}O_6 + 6\ O_2 \rightarrow 6\ CO_2 + 6\ H_2O$ + Energy. Glucose and oxygen react to form carbon dioxide and water, releasing energy. We breathe in oxygen because we need it for this reaction to occur, and we breathe out carbon dioxide because it is a by-product of this reaction. (This reaction is called cellular respiration, and you will learn more about it in Chapter 9.)

Summary of Key Concepts Questions

2.1 Iodine (part of a thyroid hormone) and iron (part of hemoglobin in blood) are both trace elements, required in minute quantities. Calcium and phosphorus (components of bones and teeth) are needed by the body in much greater quantities. 2.2

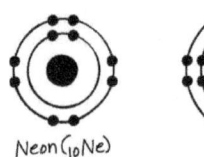

Neon ($_{10}$Ne)   Argon ($_{18}$Ar)

Both neon and argon have completed valence shells, containing 8 electrons. They do not have unpaired electrons that could participate in chemical bonds. 2.3 Electrons are shared equally between the two atoms in a nonpolar covalent bond. In a polar covalent bond, the electrons are drawn closer to the more electronegative atom. In the formation of ions, an electron is completely transferred from one atom to a much more electronegative atom. 2.4 The concentration of products would increase as the added reactants were converted to products. Eventually, an equilibrium would again be reached in which the forward and reverse reactions were proceeding at the same rate and the relative concentrations of reactants and products returned to where they were before the addition of more reactants.

Test Your Understanding

1. a 2. d 3. b 4. a 5. d 6. b 7. c 8. d
9.

a. This structure makes sense because all valence shells are complete, and all bonds have the correct number of electrons.

b. This structure doesn't make sense because H has only 1 electron to share, so it cannot form bonds with 2 atoms.

Chapter 3

Figure Questions

Figure 3.2 One possible answer:

Hydrogen bond
Polar covalent bonds

Figure 3.6 Without hydrogen bonds, water would behave like other small molecules, and the solid phase (ice) would be denser than liquid water. The ice would sink to the bottom and would no longer insulate the whole body of water, which would eventually freeze because the average annual temperature at the South Pole is −50°C. The krill could not survive. Figure 3.8 Heating the solution would cause the water to evaporate faster than it is evaporating at room temperature. At a certain point, there wouldn't be enough water molecules to dissolve the salt ions. The salt would start coming out of solution and re-forming crystals. Eventually, all the water would evaporate, leaving behind a pile of salt like the original pile. Figure 3.13 By causing the loss of coral reefs, a decrease in the ocean's carbonate concentration would have a ripple effect on noncalcifying organisms. Some of these organisms depend on the reef structure for protection, while others feed on species associated with reefs.

Concept Check 3.1

1. Electronegativity is the attraction of an atom for the electrons of a covalent bond. Because oxygen is more electronegative than hydrogen, the oxygen atom in H_2O pulls electrons toward itself, resulting in a partial negative charge on the oxygen atom and partial positive charges on the hydrogen atoms. Atoms in neighbouring water molecules with opposite partial charges are attracted to each other, forming a hydrogen bond. 2. The hydrogen atoms of one molecule, with their partial positive charges, would repel the hydrogen atoms of the adjacent molecule. 3. The covalent bonds of water molecules would not be polar, and water molecules would not form hydrogen bonds with each other.

Concept Check 3.2

1. Hydrogen bonds hold neighbouring water molecules together. This cohesion helps the chain of water molecules move upward against gravity in water-conducting cells as water evaporates from the leaves. Adhesion between water molecules and the walls of the water-conducting cells also helps counter gravity. 2. High humidity hampers cooling by suppressing the evaporation of sweat. 3. As water freezes, it expands because water molecules move farther apart in forming ice crystals. When there is water in a crevice of a boulder, expansion due to freezing may crack the boulder. 4. The hydrophobic substance repels water, perhaps helping to keep the ends of the legs from becoming coated with water and breaking through the surface. If the legs were coated with a hydrophilic substance, water would be drawn up them, possibly making it more difficult for the water strider to walk on water. 5. A litre of blood would contain 7.8×10^{13} molecules of ghrelin [(1.3×10^{-10} moles per litre) $\times (6.02 \times 10^{23}$ molecules per mole)].

Concept Check 3.3

1. 10^5, or 100 000 2. [H^+] = 0.01; $M = 10^{-2}\ M$, so pH = 2. 3. $CH_3COOH \rightarrow CH_3COO^- + H^+$. CH_3COOH is the acid (the H^+ donor), and CH_3COO^- is the base (the H^+ acceptor). 4. The pH of the water should decrease from 7 to about 2; the pH of the acetic acid solution will decrease only a small amount, because the reaction shown for question 3 will shift to the left, with CH_3COO^- accepting the influx of H^+ and becoming CH_3COOH molecules.

Summary of Key Concepts Questions

3.1

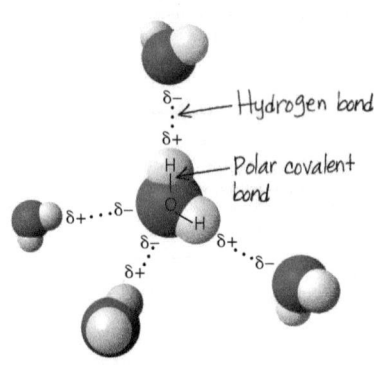

Hydrogen bond
Polar covalent bond

No. A covalent bond is a strong bond in which electrons are shared between two atoms. A hydrogen bond is a weak bond, which does not involve electron sharing, but is simply an attraction between two partial charges on neighbouring atoms. 3.2 Ions dissolve in water when polar water molecules form a hydration shell around them. Polar molecules dissolve as water molecules form hydrogen bonds with them and surround them. Solutions are homogeneous mixtures of solute and solvent. 3.3 CO_2 reacts with H_2O to form carbonic acid (H_2CO_3), which dissociates into H^+ and bicarbonate (HCO_3^-). Although the carbonic acid–bicarbonate reaction is a buffering system, adding CO_2 drives the reaction to the right, releasing more H^+ and lowering pH. The excess protons combine with CO_3^{2-} to form bicarbonate, lowering the concentration of carbonate available for the formation of calcium carbonate (calcification) by corals.

Test Your Understanding

1. c 2. d 3. c 4. a 5. d

6.

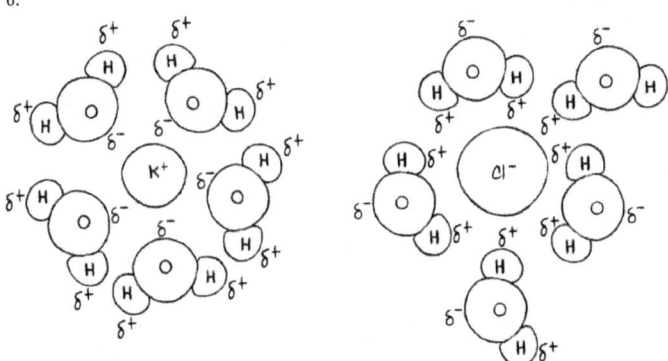

7. Both global warming and ocean acidification are caused by increasing levels of carbon dioxide in the atmosphere, the result of burning fossil fuels. 8. Due to intermolecular hydrogen bonds, water has a high specific heat (the amount of heat required to increase the temperature of water by 1°C). When water is heated, much of the heat is absorbed in breaking hydrogen bonds before the water molecules increase their motion and the temperature increases. Conversely, when water is cooled, many H bonds are formed, which releases a significant amount of heat. This release of heat can provide some protection against freezing of the plants' leaves, thus protecting the cells from damage.

Chapter 4

Figure Questions
Figure 4.2 Because the concentration of the reactants influences the equilibrium (as discussed in Chapter 2), there might have been more HCN relative to CH_2O, since there would have been a higher concentration of the reactant gas containing nitrogen.
Figure 4.4

$$Na\cdot \quad \cdot\overset{\cdot\cdot}{\underset{\cdot}{P}}\cdot \quad \cdot\overset{\cdot\cdot}{\underset{\cdot\cdot}{S}}: \quad \cdot\overset{\cdot\cdot}{\underset{\cdot\cdot}{Cl}}:$$

Figure 4.6 The tails of fats contain only carbon-hydrogen bonds, which are relatively nonpolar. Because the tails occupy the bulk of a fat molecule, they make the molecule as a whole nonpolar and therefore incapable of forming hydrogen bonds with water.
Figure 4.7

$$
\begin{array}{c}
H \\
| \\
H-C-H \\
H\;|\;H \\
|\;\;|\;\;| \\
H-C-C-C-H \\
H\;|\;H \\
| \\
H-C-H \\
| \\
H
\end{array}
$$

Concept Check 4.1
1. Prior to Wöhler's experiment, the prevailing view was that only living organisms could synthesize "organic" compounds. Wöhler made urea, an organic compound, without the involvement of living organisms. 2. The spark provided energy needed for the inorganic molecules in the atmosphere to react with each other. (You'll learn more about energy and chemical reactions in Chapter 8.)

Concept Check 4.2
1.

a.
$$H\!\!\diagdown \qquad \diagup H$$
$$C=C$$
$$H\!\!\diagup \qquad \diagdown H$$

b.
$$H\!\!\diagdown \qquad \diagup Cl$$
$$C=C$$
$$Cl\!\!\diagup \qquad \diagdown H$$

2. The forms of C_4H_{10} in (b) are structural isomers, as are the butenes in (c). 3. Both consist largely of hydrocarbon chains and are relatively nonpolar. 4. No. There is not enough diversity in the atoms. It can't form structural isomers because there is only one way for three carbons to attach to each other (in a line). There are no double bonds, so cis-trans isomers are not possible. Each carbon has at least two hydrogens attached to it, so the molecule is symmetrical and cannot have enantiomers.

Concept Check 4.3
1. It has both an amino group (—NH_2), which makes it an amine, and a carboxyl group (—COOH), which makes it a carboxylic acid. 2. The ATP molecule loses a phosphate, becoming ADP. 3. A chemical group that can act as a base has been replaced with a group that can act as an acid, increasing the acidic properties of the molecule. The shape of the molecule would also change, likely changing the molecules with which it can interact. The original cysteine molecule has an asymmetric carbon in the centre. After replacement of the amino group with a carboxyl group, this carbon is no longer asymmetric.

Summary of Key Concepts Questions
4.1 Miller showed that organic molecules could form under the physical and chemical conditions estimated to have been present on early Earth. This abiotic synthesis of organic molecules would have been a first step in the origin of life. 4.2 Acetone and propanal are structural isomers. Acetic acid and glycine have no asymmetric carbons, whereas glycerol phosphate has one. Therefore, glycerol phosphate can exist as forms that are enantiomers, but acetic acid and glycine cannot. 4.3 The methyl group is nonpolar and not reactive. The other six groups are called functional groups. They are each hydrophilic, increasing the solubility of organic compounds in water, and can participate in chemical reactions.

Test Your Understanding
1. b 2. b 3. c 4. c 5. a 6. b 7. a 8. The molecule on the right; the middle carbon is asymmetric.
9.

$$\cdot\overset{\cdot}{\underset{}{Si}}\cdot$$

Si has 4 valence electrons, the same number as carbon. Therefore, silicon would be able to form long chains, including branches, that could act as skeletons for large molecules. It would clearly do this much better than neon (with no valence electrons) or aluminum (with 3 valence electrons).

Chapter 5

Figure Questions
Figure 5.3 Glucose and fructose are structural isomers.
Figure 5.4

Note that the oxygen on carbon 5 lost its proton and that the oxygen on carbon 2, which used to be the carbonyl oxygen, gained a proton. Four carbons are in the fructose ring, and two are not. (The latter two carbons are attached to carbons 2 and 5, which are in the ring.) The fructose ring differs from the glucose ring, which has five carbons in the ring and one that is not. (Note that the orientation of this fructose molecule is flipped relative to that of the one in Figure 5.5b.)
Figure 5.5

Figure 5.11

Figure 5.12

Figure 5.15

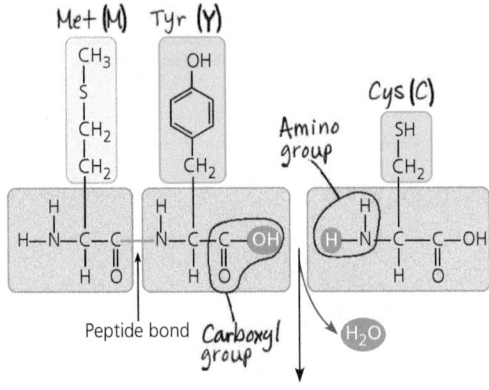

Figure 5.19 The R group on glutamic acid is acidic and hydrophilic, whereas that on valine is nonpolar and hydrophobic. Therefore, it is unlikely that valine can participate in the same intramolecular interactions that glutamic acid can. A change in these interactions causes a disruption of molecular structure. Figure 5.22 The helical stretches are α helices; these can be seen clearly in many places in the RNA polymerase II model, such as the bottom middle, the upper right, and the lower right areas. Although β pleated sheets may be present, they are not as easy to see. Figure 5.26 Using a genomics approach allows us to use gene sequences to identify species, and to learn about evolutionary relationships among any two species. This is because all species are related by their evolutionary history, and the evidence is in the DNA sequences. Proteomics—looking at proteins that are expressed—allows us to learn how organisms or cells are functioning at a given time, or in an association with another species.

Concept Check 5.1
1. The four main classes are proteins, carbohydrates, lipids, and nucleic acids. Lipids are not polymers. 2. Nine, with one water molecule required to hydrolyze each connected pair of monomers 3. The amino acids in the fish protein must be released in hydrolysis reactions and incorporated into other proteins in dehydration reactions.

Concept Check 5.2
1. $C_3H_6O_3$ 2. $C_{12}H_{22}O_{11}$ 3. The antibiotic treatment is likely to have killed the cellulose-digesting prokaryotes in the cow's stomach. The absence of these prokaryotes would hamper the cow's ability to obtain energy from food and could lead to weight loss and possibly death. Thus, prokaryotic species are reintroduced, in appropriate combinations, in the gut culture given to treated cows.

Concept Check 5.3
1. Both have a glycerol molecule attached to fatty acids. The glycerol of a fat has three fatty acids attached, whereas the glycerol of a phospholipid is attached to two fatty acids and one phosphate group. 2. Human sex hormones are steroids, a type of hydrophobic compound. 3. The oil droplet membrane could consist of a single layer of phospholipids rather than a bilayer, because an arrangement in which the hydrophobic tails of the membrane phospholipids were in contact with the hydrocarbon regions of the oil molecules would be more stable.

Concept Check 5.4
1. The function of a protein is a consequence of its specific shape, which is lost when a protein becomes denatured. 2. Secondary structure involves hydrogen bonds between atoms of the polypeptide backbone. Tertiary structure involves interactions between atoms of the side chains of the amino acid subunits. 3. These are all nonpolar amino acids, so you would expect this region to be located in the interior of the folded polypeptide, where it would not contact the aqueous environment inside the cell.

Concept Check 5.5
1.

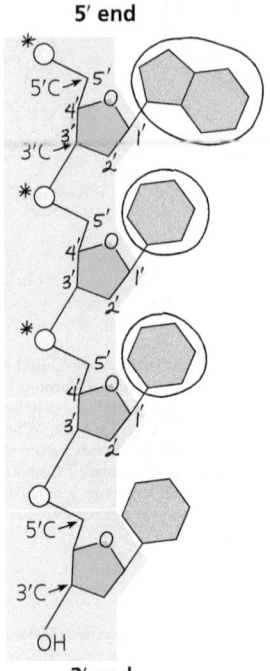

2.
5'-T A G G C C T-3'
3'-A T C C G G A-5'

Concept Check 5.6
1. The DNA of an organism encodes all of its proteins, and proteins are the molecules that carry out the work of cells, whether an organism is unicellular or multicellular. By knowing the DNA sequence of an organism and comparing it to genomes of known organisms, scientists would be able to catalogue the protein sequences as well. 2. Ultimately, the DNA sequence carries the information necessary to make the proteins that determine the traits of a particular species, so given that the traits of the two species are similar, one would expect the proteins to be similar too, and therefore the gene sequences would be expected to share a high degree of similarity.

Summary of Key Concepts Questions
5.1 The polymers of carbohydrates, proteins, and nucleic acids are built from three different types of monomers: monosaccharides, amino acids, and nucleotides, respectively. 5.2 Both starch and cellulose are polymers of glucose, but the glucose monomers are in the α configuration in starch and the β configuration in cellulose. The glycosidic linkages thus have different geometries, giving the polymers different shapes and thus different properties. Starch is an energy-storage compound in plants; cellulose is a structural component of plant cell walls. Humans can hydrolyze starch to provide energy but cannot hydrolyze cellulose. Cellulose aids in the passage of food through the digestive tract. 5.3 Lipids are not polymers because they do not exist as a chain of linked monomers. They are not considered macromolecules because they do not reach the giant size of many polysaccharides, proteins, and nucleic acids. 5.4 Proteins, in comparison to nucleic acids and carbohydrates, have many more monomers that can form the basis of their primary sequence. Also, a polypeptide, which may consist of hundreds of amino acids in a specific sequence (primary structure), has regions of helices and pleats (secondary structure), which are then folded into irregular contortions (tertiary structure) and may be associated with other polypeptides either covalently or noncovalently (quaternary structure). The linear order of amino acids, with the varying properties of their side chains (R groups), determines what secondary and tertiary structures will form to produce a protein. The resulting unique three-dimensional shapes of proteins are key to their specific and diverse functions. 5.5 The complementary base pairing of the two strands of DNA makes possible the precise replication of DNA every time a cell divides, ensuring that genetic information is faithfully transmitted. In some types of RNA, complementary base pairing enables RNA molecules to assume specific three-dimensional shapes that facilitate diverse functions. 5.6 You would expect the human gene sequence to be most similar to that of the mouse (another mammal), than to that of the fish (another vertebrate), and least similar to that of the fruit fly (an invertebrate).

Test Your Understanding
1. d 2. a 3. b 4. a 5. b 6. b 7. c

8.

	Monomers or Components	Polymer or larger molecule	Type of linkage
Carbohydrates	Monosaccharides	Polysaccharides	Glycosidic linkages
Lipids	Fatty acids	Triacylglycerols	Ester linkages
Proteins	Amino acids	Polypeptides	Peptide bonds
Nucleic acids	Nucleotides	Polynucleotides	Phosphodiester linkages

9.

Original Strand   Complementary strand

Chapter 6

Figure Questions

Figure 6.6 A phospholipid is a lipid, consisting of a glycerol molecule joined to two fatty acids and one phosphate group. Together, the glycerol and phosphate end of the phospholipid form the "head," which is hydrophilic, while the hydrocarbon chains on the fatty acids form hydrophobic "tails." The presence in a single molecule of both a hydrophilic and a hydrophobic region makes the molecule ideal as the main building block of a membrane. Figure 6.9 The DNA in a chromosome dictates synthesis of a messenger RNA (mRNA) molecule, which then moves out to the cytoplasm. There, the information is used for the production, on ribosomes, of proteins that carry out cellular functions. Figure 6.10 Any of the bound ribosomes (attached to the endoplasmic reticulum) could be circled, because any could be making a protein that will be secreted. Figure 6.22 Each centriole has 9 sets of 3 microtubules, so the entire centrosome (two centrioles) has 54 microtubules. Each microtubule consists of a helical array of tubulin dimers (as shown in Table 6.1).

1 microtubule

Triplet of microtubules

Figure 6.24

Central pair of microtubules

They terminate here

The two central microtubules terminate above the basal body, so they aren't present at the level of the cross section through the basal body, indicated by the lower red rectangle in (a).

Concept Check 6.1
1. Stains used for light microscopy are coloured molecules that bind to cell components, affecting the light passing through, while stains used for electron microscopy involve heavy metals that affect the beams of electrons passing through. 2. (a) Light microscope, (b) scanning electron microscope

Concept Check 6.2
1. See Figure 6.8.
2.

This cell would have the same volume as the cells in columns 2 and 3 but proportionally more surface area than that in column 2 and less than that in column 3. Thus, the surface-to-volume ratio should be greater than 1.2 but less than 6. To obtain the surface area, you would add the area of the six sides (the top, bottom, sides, and ends): $125 + 125 + 125 + 125 + 1 + 1 = 502$. The surface-to-volume ratio equals 502 divided by a volume of 125, or 4.0.

Concept Check 6.3
1. Ribosomes in the cytoplasm translate the genetic message, carried from the DNA in the nucleus by mRNA, into a polypeptide chain. 2. Nucleoli consist of DNA and the ribosomal RNA (rRNA) made according to its instructions, as well as proteins imported from the cytoplasm. Together, the rRNA and proteins are assembled into large and small ribosomal subunits. (These are exported through nuclear pores to the cytoplasm, where they will participate in polypeptide synthesis.) 3. Each chromosome consists of one long DNA molecule attached to numerous protein molecules, a combination called chromatin. As a cell begins division, each chromosome becomes "condensed" as its diffuse mass of chromatin coils up.

Concept Check 6.4
1. The primary distinction between rough and smooth ER is the presence of bound ribosomes on the rough ER. Both types of ER make phospholipids, but membrane proteins and secretory proteins are all produced on the ribosomes of the rough ER. The smooth ER also functions in detoxification, carbohydrate metabolism, and storage of calcium ions. 2. Transport vesicles move membranes and substances they enclose between other components of the endomembrane system. 3. The mRNA is synthesized in the nucleus and then passes out through a nuclear pore to be translated on a bound ribosome, attached to the rough ER. The protein is synthesized into the lumen of the ER and perhaps modified there. A transport vesicle carries the protein to the Golgi apparatus. After further modification in the Golgi, another transport vesicle carries it back to the ER, where it will perform its cellular function.

Concept Check 6.5
1. Both organelles are involved in energy transformation, mitochondria in cellular respiration and chloroplasts in photosynthesis. They both have multiple membranes that separate their interiors into compartments. In both organelles, the innermost membranes—cristae, or infoldings of the inner membrane, in mitochondria, and the thylakoid membranes in chloroplasts—have large surface areas with embedded enzymes that carry out their main functions. 2. Yes. Plant cells are able to make their own sugar by photosynthesis, but mitochondria in these eukaryotic cells are the organelles that are able to generate energy from sugars, a function required in all cells. 3. Mitochondria and chloroplasts are not derived from the ER, nor are they connected physically or via transport vesicles to organelles of the endomembrane system. Mitochondria and chloroplasts are structurally quite different from vesicles derived from the ER, which are bounded by a single membrane.

Concept Check 6.6
1. Both systems of movement involve long filaments that are moved in relation to each other by motor proteins that grip, release, and grip again adjacent polymers. 2. Such individuals have defects in the microtubule-based movement of cilia and flagella. Thus, the sperm can't move because of malfunctioning or nonexistent flagella, and the airways are compromised because cilia that line the trachea malfunction or don't exist, and so mucus cannot be cleared from the lungs.

Concept Check 6.7
1. The most obvious difference is the presence of direct cytoplasmic connections between cells of plants (plasmodesmata) and animals (gap junctions). These connections result in the cytoplasm being continuous between adjacent cells.
2. The cell would not be able to function properly and would probably soon die, as the cell wall or ECM must be permeable to allow the exchange of matter between the cell and its external environment. Molecules involved in energy production and use must be allowed entry, as well as those that provide information about the cell's environment. Other molecules, such as products synthesized by the cell for export and the by-products of cellular respiration, must be allowed to exit. 3. The parts of the protein that face aqueous regions would be expected to have polar or charged (hydrophilic) amino acids, while the parts that go through the membrane would be expected to have nonpolar (hydrophobic) amino acids. You would predict polar or charged amino acids at each end (tail), in the region of the cytoplasmic

loop, and in the regions of the two extracellular loops. You would predict nonpolar amino acids in the four regions that go through the membrane between the tails and loops.

Summary of Key Concepts Questions

6.1 Both light and electron microscopy allow cells to be studied visually, thus helping us understand internal cellular structure and the arrangement of cell components. Cell fractionation techniques separate out different groups of cell components, which can then be analyzed biochemically to determine their function. Performing microscopy on the same cell fraction helps to correlate the biochemical function of the cell with the cell component responsible. 6.2 The separation of different functions in different organelles has several advantages. Reactants and enzymes can be concentrated in one area instead of spread throughout the cell. Reactions that require specific conditions, such as a lower pH, can be compartmentalized. And enzymes for specific reactions are often embedded in the membranes that enclose or partition an organelle. 6.3 The nucleus contains the genetic material of the cell in the form of DNA, which codes for messenger RNA, which in turn provides instructions for the synthesis of proteins (including the proteins that make up part of the ribosomes). DNA also codes for ribosomal RNA, which is combined with proteins in the nucleolus into the subunits of ribosomes. Within the cytoplasm, ribosomes join with mRNA to build polypeptides, using the genetic information in the mRNA. 6.4 Transport vesicles move proteins and membranes synthesized by the rough ER to the Golgi for further processing and then to the plasma membrane, lysosomes, or other locations in the cell, including back to the ER. 6.5 According to the endosymbiont theory, mitochondria originated from an oxygen-using prokaryotic cell that was engulfed by an ancestral eukaryotic cell. Over time, the host and endosymbiont evolved into a single organism. Chloroplasts originated when at least one of these eukaryotic cells containing mitochondria engulfed and then retained a photosynthetic prokaryote. 6.6 Inside the cell, motor proteins interact with components of the cytoskeleton to move cellular parts. Motor proteins may "walk" vesicles along microtubules. The movement of cytoplasm within a cell involves interactions of the motor protein myosin and microfilaments (actin filaments). Whole cells can be moved by the rapid bending of flagella or cilia, which is caused by the motor-protein-powered sliding of microtubules within these structures. Cell movement can also occur when pseudopodia form at one end of a cell (caused by actin polymerization into a filamentous network), followed by contraction of the cell toward that end; this is powered by interactions of microfilaments with myosin. Interactions of motor proteins and microfilaments in muscle cells can propel whole organisms. 6.7 A plant cell wall is primarily composed of microfibrils of cellulose embedded in other polysaccharides and proteins. The ECM of animal cells is primarily composed of collagen and other protein fibres, such as the glycoprotein fibronectins. These fibres are embedded in a network of carbohydrate-rich proteoglycans. A plant cell wall provides structural support for the cell and, collectively, for the plant body. In addition to giving support, the ECM of an animal cell allows for communication of environmental changes into the cell.

Test Your Understanding

1. b 2. c 3. b 4. a 5. a 6. c 7. c 8. See Figure 6.8.

Chapter 7

Figure Questions
Figure 7.2

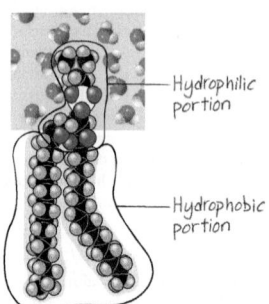

The hydrophilic portion is in contact with an aqueous environment (cytosol or extracellular fluid), and the hydrophobic portion is in contact with the hydrophobic portions of other phospholipids and membrane proteins in the interior of the bilayer. Figure 7.4 You couldn't rule out movement of proteins within membranes of the same species. You might propose that the membrane lipids and proteins from one species weren't able to mingle with those from the other species because of some incompatibility. You might also propose that the type of membrane proteins you labelled might be the type that are held immobile by the cytoskeleton. Figure 7.7 A transmembrane protein like the dimer in (f) might change its shape upon binding to a particular ECM molecule. The new shape might enable the interior portion of the protein to bind to a second, cytoplasmic protein that would relay the message to the inside of the cell, as shown in (c). Figure 7.8 The shape of a protein on the HIV surface is likely to be complementary to the shape of the receptor (CD4) and also to that of the co-receptor (CCR5). A molecule that was a similar shape to the HIV surface protein could bind CCR5, blocking HIV binding. (Another alternative would be a molecule that bound to CCR5 and changed the shape of CCR5 so it could no longer bind HIV.)

Figure 7.9

The protein would contact the extracellular fluid. Figure 7.11 The orange dye would be evenly distributed throughout the solution on both sides of the membrane. The solution levels would not be affected because the orange dye can diffuse through the membrane and equalize its concentration. Thus, no additional osmosis would take place in either direction. Figure 7.16 The diamond solutes are moving into the cell (down), and the round solutes are moving out of the cell (up); both are moving against their concentration gradient.

Concept Check 7.1
1. They are on the inner side of the transport vesicle membrane. 2. The grasses living in the cooler region would be expected to have more unsaturated fatty acids in their membranes because those fatty acids remain fluid at lower temperatures. The grasses living immediately adjacent to the hot springs would be expected to have more saturated fatty acids, which would allow the fatty acids to "stack" more closely, making the membranes less fluid and therefore helping them to stay intact at higher temperatures. (Cholesterol could not be used to moderate the effects of temperature on membrane fluidity because it is not found within plant cell membranes.)

Concept Check 7.2
1. O_2 and CO_2 are both nonpolar molecules that can easily pass through the hydrophobic interior of a membrane. 2. Water is a polar molecule, so it cannot pass very rapidly through the hydrophobic region in the middle of a phospholipid bilayer. 3. The hydronium ion is charged, while glycerol is not. Charge is probably more significant than size as a basis for exclusion by the aquaporin channel.

Concept Check 7.3
1. CO_2 is a nonpolar molecule that can diffuse through the plasma membrane. As long as it diffuses away so that the concentration remains low outside the cell, it will continue to exit the cell in this way. (This is the opposite of the case for O_2, described in this section.) 2. The activity of *Paramecium caudatum*'s contractile vacuole will decrease. The vacuole pumps out excess water that accumulates in the cell; this accumulation occurs only in a hypotonic environment.

Concept Check 7.4
1. The pump uses ATP. To establish a voltage, ions have to be pumped against their gradients, which requires energy. 2. Each ion is being transported against its electrochemical gradient. If either ion were transported down its electrochemical gradient, this *would* be considered cotransport. 3. The internal environment of a lysosome is acidic, so it has a higher concentration of H^+ than does the cytoplasm. Therefore, you might expect the membrane of the lysosome to have a proton pump such as that shown in Figure 7.18 to pump H^+ into the lysosome.

Concept Check 7.5
1. Exocytosis. When a transport vesicle fuses with the plasma membrane, the vesicle membrane becomes part of the plasma membrane.
2.

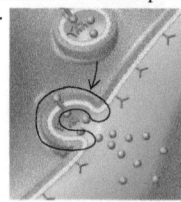

3. The glycoprotein would be synthesized in the ER lumen, then travel in a vesicle to the Golgi apparatus. From there, the glycoprotein would take another vesicle to the plasma membrane, where it would undergo exocytosis and become part of the ECM.

Summary of Key Concepts Questions

7.1 Plasma membranes define the cell by separating the cellular components from the external environment. This allows conditions inside cells to be controlled by membrane proteins, which regulate entry and exit of molecules and even cell function (see Figure 7.7). The processes of life can be carried out inside the controlled environment of the cell, so membranes are crucial. In eukaryotes, membranes also function to subdivide the cytoplasm into different compartments where distinct processes can occur, even under differing conditions such as pH. **7.2** Aquaporins are channel proteins that greatly increase the permeability of a membrane to water molecules, which are polar and therefore do not readily diffuse through the hydrophobic interior of the membrane. **7.3** There will be a net diffusion of water out of a cell into a hypertonic solution. The free water concentration is higher inside the cell than in the solution (where water molecules are not free, but are clustered around the higher concentration of solute particles). **7.4** One of the solutes moved by the cotransporter is transported against its concentration gradient. The energy for this transport comes from the concentration gradient of the other solute, which was established by an electrogenic pump that used energy to transport the other solute across the membrane. **7.5** In receptor-mediated endocytosis, specific molecules act as ligands when they bind to receptors on the plasma membrane. The cell can acquire bulk quantities of those molecules when a coated pit forms a vesicle and carries the bound molecules into the cell.

Test Your Understanding

1. b 2. c 3. a 4. c 5. b
6. (a)

(b) The solution outside is hypotonic. It has less sucrose, which is a nonpenetrating solute. (c) See answer for (a). (d) The artificial cell will become more turgid. (e) Eventually, the two solutions will have the same solute concentrations. Even though sucrose can't move through the membrane, water flow (osmosis) will lead to isotonic conditions.

Chapter 8

Figure Questions

Figure 8.5 With a proton pump (Figure 7.17), the energy stored in ATP is used to pump protons across the membrane and build up a higher (nonrandom) concentration outside of the cell, so this process results in higher free energy. When solute molecules (analogous to H^+ ions) are uniformly distributed, similar to the random distribution in the bottom of (b), the system has less free energy than it does in the top of (b). The system in the bottom can do no work. Because the concentration gradient created by a proton pump (Figure 7.17) represents higher free energy, this system has the potential to do work (as you will see in Chapter 9). **Figure 8.10** Glutamic acid has a carboxyl group at the end of its R group. Glutamine has exactly the same structure as glutamic acid, except that there is an amino group in place of the −OH on the R group. (The O atom on the R group leaves during the synthesis reaction.)
Figure 8.13

Figure 8.16

Figure 8.17

Concept Check 8.1

1. The second law is the trend toward randomness, or increasing entropy. When the concentrations of a substance on both sides of a membrane are equal, the distribution is more random than when they are unequal. Diffusion of a substance to a region where it is initially less concentrated increases entropy, making it an energetically favourable (spontaneous) process as described by the second law. This explains the process seen in Figure 7.11. 2. The apple has potential energy in its position hanging on the tree, and the sugars and other nutrients it contains have chemical energy. The apple has kinetic energy as it falls from the tree to the ground. Finally, when the apple is digested and its molecules broken down, some of the chemical energy is used to do work, and the rest is lost as thermal energy. 3. The sugar crystals become less ordered (entropy increases) as they dissolve and become randomly spread out in the water. Over time, the water evaporates, and the crystals form again because the water volume is insufficient to keep them in solution. While the reappearance of sugar crystals may represent a "spontaneous" increase in order (decrease in entropy), it is balanced by the decrease in order (increase in entropy) of the water molecules, which changed from a relatively compact arrangement as liquid water to a much more dispersed and disordered form as water vapour.

Concept Check 8.2

1. Cellular respiration is a spontaneous and exergonic process. The energy released from glucose is used to do work in the cell or is lost as heat. 2. Catabolism breaks down organic molecules, releasing their chemical energy and resulting in smaller products with more entropy, as when moving from the top to the bottom of part (c). Anabolism consumes energy to synthesize larger molecules 3. The reaction is exergonic because it releases energy—in this case, in the form of light. (This is a nonbiological version of the bioluminescence seen in Figure 8.1.)

Concept Check 8.3

1. ATP usually transfers energy to endergonic processes by phosphorylating (adding phosphate groups to) other molecules. (Exergonic processes phosphorylate ADP to regenerate ATP.) 2. A set of coupled reactions can transform the first combination into the second. Since this is an exergonic process overall, ΔG is negative and the first combination must have more free energy (see Figure 8.10). 3. Active transport: The solute is being transported against its concentration gradient, which requires energy, provided by ATP hydrolysis.

Concept Check 8.4

1. A spontaneous reaction is a reaction that is exergonic. However, if it has a high activation energy that is rarely attained, the rate of the reaction may be low. 2. Only the specific substrate(s) will fit properly into the active site of an enzyme, the part of the enzyme that carries out catalysis. 3. In the presence of malonate, increase the concentration of the normal substrate (succinate) and see whether the rate of reaction increases. If it does, malonate is a competitive inhibitor. 4. If lactose were not present in the environment as a source of food and the fucose-containing disaccharide were available, bacteria that could digest the latter would be better able to grow and multiply than those that could not.

Concept Check 8.5

1. The activator binds in such a way that it stabilizes the active form of an enzyme, whereas the inhibitor stabilizes the inactive form. 2. A catabolic pathway breaks down organic molecules, generating energy which is stored in ATP molecules. In feedback inhibition of such a pathway, ATP (one product) would act as an allosteric inhibitor of an enzyme catalyzing an early step in the catabolic process. When ATP is plentiful, the pathway would be turned off, and no more would be made.

Summary of Key Concepts Questions

8.1 The process of "ordering" a cell's structure is accompanied by an increase in the entropy or disorder of the universe. For example, an animal cell takes in highly ordered organic molecules as the source of matter and energy used to build and maintain its structures. In the same process, however, the cell releases heat and the simple molecules of carbon dioxide and water to the surroundings. The increase in entropy of the latter process offsets the entropy decrease in the former. **8.2** A spontaneous reaction has a negative ΔG and is exergonic. For a chemical reaction to proceed with a net release of free energy ($-\Delta G$), the enthalpy or total energy of the system must decrease ($-\Delta H$), and/or the entropy or disorder must increase (yielding a more negative term, $-T\Delta S$). Spontaneous reactions supply the energy to perform cellular work. **8.3** The free energy released from the hydrolysis of ATP may drive endergonic reactions through the transfer of a phosphate group to a reactant molecule, forming a more reactive phosphorylated intermediate. ATP hydrolysis also powers the mechanical and transport work of a cell, often by powering shape changes in the relevant motor proteins. Cellular respiration, the catabolic breakdown of glucose, provides the energy for the endergonic regeneration of ATP from ADP and P_i. **8.4** Activation energy barriers prevent the complex molecules of the cell, which are rich in free energy, from spontaneously breaking down to less ordered, more stable molecules. Enzymes permit a regulated metabolism by binding to specific substrates and forming enzyme-substrate complexes that selectively lower the E_A for the chemical reactions in a cell. 8.5 A cell tightly regulates its metabolic pathways in response to fluctuating needs for energy and materials. The binding of activators or inhibitors to regulatory sites on allosteric enzymes stabilizes either the active or inactive form of the subunits. For example, the binding of ATP to a catabolic enzyme in a cell with excess ATP would inhibit that pathway. Such types of feedback inhibition preserve chemical resources within a cell. If ATP supplies are depleted, binding of ADP to the regulatory site of catabolic enzymes would activate that pathway.

Test Your Understanding
1. b 2. c 3. b 4. a 5. c 6. d 7. c

9.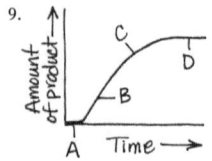

A. The substrate molecules are entering the cells, so no product is made yet.
B. There is sufficient substrate, so the reaction is proceeding at a maximum rate.
C. As the substrate is used up, the rate decreases (the slope is less steep).
D. The line is flat because no new substrate remains and thus no new product appears.

Chapter 9

Figure Questions
Figure 9.4 The reduced form has an extra hydrogen, along with 2 electrons, bound to the carbon shown at the top of the nicotinamide (opposite the N). There are different numbers and positions of double bonds in the two forms: The oxidized form has three double bonds in the ring, while the reduced form has only two. (In organic chemistry you may have learned, or will learn, that three double bonds in a ring are able to "resonate," or act as a ring of electrons.) In the oxidized form there is a + charge on the N (because it is sharing 4 electron pairs), whereas in the reduced form it is only sharing 3 electron pairs (having a pair of electrons to itself). Figure 9.7 Because there is no external source of energy for the reaction, it must be exergonic, and the reactants must be at a higher energy level than the products. Figure 9.9 The removal would probably stop glycolysis, or at least slow it down, since it would push the equilibrium for step 5 toward the left. If less (or no) glyceraldehyde 3-phosphate were available, step 6 would slow down (or be unable to occur). Figure 9.14 The parts of the body that are the most susceptible to energy deprivation are the nervous system and the muscles. Thus, most mitochondrial diseases primarily affect these systems. For example, mitochondrial myopathy causes weakness, intolerance of exercise and muscle deterioration. Refer to Chapters 48–50. Figure 9.16 At first, some ATP could be made, since electron transport could proceed as far as complex III, and a small H^+ gradient could be built up. Soon, however, no more electrons could be passed to complex III because it could not be reoxidized by passing its electrons to complex IV. Figure 9.17 First, there are 2 NADH from the oxidation of pyruvate plus 6 NADH from the citric acid cycle (CAC); 8 NADH $\times$ 2.5 ATP/NADH = 20 ATP. Second, there are 2 $FADH_2$ from the CAC; 2 $FADH_2$ $\times$ 1.5 ATP/$FADH_2$ = 3 ATP. Third, the 2 NADH from glycolysis enter the mitochondrion through one of two types of shuttle. They pass their electrons either to 2 FAD, which become $FADH_2$ and result in 3 ATP, or to 2 NAD^+, which become NADH and result in 5 ATP. Thus, 20 + 3 + 3 = 26 ATP, or 20 + 3 + 5 = 28 ATP from all NADH and $FADH_2$.

Concept Check 9.1
1. Both processes include glycolysis, the citric acid cycle, and oxidative phosphorylation. In aerobic respiration, the final electron acceptor is molecular oxygen (O_2); in anaerobic respiration, the final electron acceptor is a different substance. 2. $C_4H_6O_5$ would be oxidized and NAD^+ would be reduced.

Concept Check 9.2
1. NAD^+ acts as the oxidizing agent in step 6, accepting electrons from glyceraldehyde 3-phosphate, which thus acts as the reducing agent.

Concept Check 9.3
1. NADH and $FADH_2$; they will donate electrons to the electron transport chain. 2. CO_2 is released during the oxidation of pyruvate that is the end product of glycolysis, and CO_2 is also released during the citric acid cycle. 3. In both cases, the precursor molecule loses a CO_2 molecule and then donates electrons to an electron carrier in an oxidation step. Also, the product has been activated due to the attachment of a CoA group.

Concept Check 9.4
1. Oxidative phosphorylation would eventually stop entirely, resulting in no ATP production by this process. Without oxygen to "pull" electrons down the electron transport chain, H^+ would not be pumped into the mitochondrion's intermembrane space and chemiosmosis would not occur. 2. Decreasing the pH means addition of H^+. This would establish a proton gradient even without the function of the electron transport chain, and we would expect ATP synthase to function and synthesize ATP. (In fact, it was experiments like this that provided support for chemiosmosis as an energy-coupling mechanism.) 3. One of the components of the electron transport chain, ubiquinone (Q), must be able to diffuse within the membrane. It could not do so if the membrane were locked rigidly into place.

Concept Check 9.5
1. A derivative of pyruvate, such as acetaldehyde during alcohol fermentation, or pyruvate itself during lactic acid fermentation; oxygen 2. The cell would need to consume glucose at a rate about 16 times the consumption rate in the aerobic environment (2 ATP are generated by fermentation versus up to 32 ATP by cellular respiration).

Concept Check 9.6
1. The fat is much more reduced; it has many —CH_2— units, and in all these bonds the electrons are equally shared. The electrons present in a carbohydrate molecule are already somewhat oxidized (shared unequally in bonds), as quite a few of them are bound to oxygen. 2. When we consume more food than necessary for metabolic processes, our body synthesizes fat as a way of storing energy for later use. 3. AMP will accumulate, stimulating phosphofructokinase, and thus increasing the rate of glycolysis. Since oxygen is not present, the cell will convert pyruvate to lactate in lactic acid fermentation, providing a supply of ATP. 4. When oxygen is present, the fatty acid chains containing most of the energy of a fat are oxidized and fed into the citric acid cycle and the electron transport chain. During intense exercise, however, oxygen is scarce in muscle cells, so ATP must be generated by glycolysis alone. A very small part of the fat molecule, the glycerol backbone, can be oxidized via glycolysis, but the amount of energy released by this portion is insignificant compared to that released by the fatty acid chains. (This is why moderate exercise, staying below 70% maximum heart rate, is better for burning fat—because enough oxygen remains available to the muscles.)

Summary of Key Concepts Questions
9.1 Most of the ATP produced in cellular respiration comes from oxidative phosphorylation, in which the energy released from redox reactions in an electron transport chain is used to produce ATP. In substrate-level phosphorylation, an enzyme directly transfers a phosphate group to ADP from an intermediate substrate. All ATP production in glycolysis occurs by substrate-level phosphorylation; this form of ATP production also occurs at one step in the citric acid cycle. 9.2 The oxidation of the three-carbon sugar, glyceraldehyde 3-phosphate, yields energy. In this oxidation, electrons and H^+ are transferred to NAD^+, forming NADH, and a phosphate group is attached to the oxidized substrate. ATP is then formed by substrate-level phosphorylation when this phosphate group is transferred to ADP. The oxidation of phosphoenol-pyruvate (PEP) is a second energy-yielding reaction, where a phosphate group is transferred from PEP to ADP, forming ATP and pyruvate. 9.3 The release of six molecules of CO_2 represents the complete oxidation of glucose. During the processing of two pyruvates to acetyl CoA, the fully oxidized carboxyl group (—COO^-) is given off as CO_2. The remaining four carbons are released as CO_2 in the citric acid cycle as citrate is oxidized back to oxaloacetate. 9.4 The flow of H^+ through the ATP synthase complex causes the rotor and attached rod to rotate, exposing catalytic sites in the knob portion that produce ATP from ADP and $\textcircled{P}_i$. ATP synthases are found in the inner mitochondrial membrane, the plasma membrane of prokaryotes, and membranes within chloroplasts. 9.5 Anaerobic respiration yields more ATP. The 2 ATP produced by substrate-level phosphorylation in glycolysis represent the total energy yield of fermentation. NADH passes its "high-energy" electrons to pyruvate or a derivative of pyruvate, recycling NAD^+ and allowing glycolysis to continue. Anaerobic respiration uses an electron transport chain to capture the energy of the electrons in NADH via a series of redox reactions; ultimately, the electrons are transferred to an electronegative molecule other than oxygen. And additional molecules of NADH are produced in anaerobic respiration as pyruvate is oxidized. 9.6 The ATP produced by catabolic pathways is used to drive anabolic pathways. Also, many of the intermediates of glycolysis and the citric acid cycle are used in the biosynthesis of a cell's molecules.

Test Your Understanding
1. c 2. c 3. b 4. a 5. d 6. a 7. b
8. Since the overall process of glycolysis results in net production of ATP, it would make sense for the process to slow down when ATP levels have increased substantially. Thus, we would expect ATP to allosterically inhibit phosphofructokinase.
9. The proton pump in Figure 7.17 is carrying out active transport, using ATP hydrolysis to pump protons against their concentration gradient. Because ATP is required, this is active transport of protons. The ATP synthase in Figure 9.14 is using the flow of protons down their concentration gradient to power ATP synthesis. Because the protons are moving down their concentration gradient, no energy is required, and this is passive transport. 10. H^+ would continue to be pumped across the membrane into the intermembrane space, increasing the difference between the matrix pH and the intermembrane space pH. H^+ would not be able to flow back through ATP synthase, since the enzyme is inhibited by the poison, so rather than maintaining a constant difference across the membrane, the difference would continue to increase. (Ultimately, the H^+ concentration in the intermembrane space would be so high that no more H^+ would be able to be pumped against the gradient, but this isn't shown in the graph.)
11.

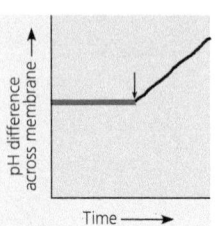

Chapter 10

Figure Questions

Figure 10.3 Situating containers of algae near sources of CO_2 emissions makes sense because algae need CO_2 to carry out photosynthesis. The higher their rate of photosynthesis, the more plant oil they will produce. At the same time, algae would be absorbing the CO_2 emitted from industrial plants or from car engines, reducing the amount of CO_2 entering the atmosphere. Figure 10.10 Red, but not violet-blue, wavelengths would pass through the filter, so the bacteria would not congregate where the violet-blue light normally comes through. Therefore, the left "peak" of bacteria would not be present, but the right peak would be observed because the red wavelengths passing through the filter would be used for photosynthesis. Figure 10.12 In the leaf, most of the chlorophyll electrons excited by photon absorption are used to power the reactions of photosynthesis. Figure 10.16 The person at the top of the photosystem I tower would not turn and throw his electron into the bucket. Instead, he would throw it onto the top of the ramp right next to the photosystem II tower. The electron would then roll down the ramp, get energized by a photon, and return to him. This cycle would continue as long as light was available. (This is why it's called cyclic electron flow.) Figure 10.22 Yes, plants can break down the sugar (in the form of glucose) by cellular respiration, producing ATPs for various cellular processes such as endergonic chemical reactions, transport of substances across membranes, and movement of molecules in the cell. ATPs are also used for the movement of chloroplasts during cellular streaming in some plant cells (see Figure 6.26).

Concept Check 10.1

1. CO_2 enters leaves via stomata, and water and minerals enters via roots and is carried to leaves through veins. 2. Using ^{18}O, a heavy isotope of oxygen, as a label, researchers were able to confirm van Niel's hypothesis that the oxygen produced during photosynthesis originates in water, not in carbon dioxide. 3. The light reactions could *not* keep producing NADPH and ATP without the NADP$^+$, ADP, and (P)$_i$ that the Calvin cycle generates. The two cycles are interdependent.

Concept Check 10.2

1. Green, because green light is mostly transmitted and reflected—not absorbed—by photosynthetic pigments 2. In chloroplasts, light-excited electrons are trapped by a primary electron acceptor, which prevents them from dropping back to the ground state. In isolated chlorophyll, there is no electron acceptor, so the photoexcited electrons immediately drop back down to the ground state, with the emission of light and heat. 3. Water (H_2O) is the initial electron donor; NADP$^+$ accepts electrons at the end of the electron transport chain, becoming reduced to NADPH. 4. In this experiment, the rate of ATP synthesis would slow and eventually stop because the added compound would not allow a proton gradient to build up across the membrane; ATP synthase could not catalyze ATP production.

Concept Check 10.3

1. 6, 18, 12 2. The more potential energy a molecule stores, the more energy and reducing power is required for the formation of that molecule. Glucose is a valuable energy source because it is highly reduced, storing lots of potential energy in its electrons. To reduce CO_2 to glucose, much energy and reducing power are required in the form of large numbers of ATP and NADPH molecules, respectively. 3. The light reactions require ADP and NADP$^+$, which would not be formed in sufficient quantities from ATP and NADPH if the Calvin cycle stopped.
4.

$$3 \times 1 (=3)$$

$$3 \times 6 (=18)$$

$$3 \times 5 (=15)$$

$$6 \times 3 (=18)$$

$$6 \times 3 (=18)$$

$$5 \times 3 (=15)$$

$$6 \times 3 (=18)$$

$$1 \times 3 (=3)$$

Three carbon atoms enter the cycle, one by one, as individual CO_2 molecules, and leave the cycle in one three-carbon molecule (G3P) per three turns of the cycle. 5. In glycolysis, G3P acts as an intermediate. The 6-carbon sugar fructose 1,6-bisphosphate is cleaved into two 3-carbon sugars, one of which is G3P. The other is an isomer called dihydroxyacetone phosphate, which can be converted to G3P by an isomerase. Because G3P is the substrate for the next enzyme, it is constantly removed, and the reaction equilibrium is pulled in the direction of conversion of dihydroxyacetone phosphate to more G3P. In the Calvin cycle, G3P acts as both an intermediate and a product. For every three CO_2 molecules that enter the cycle, six G3P molecules are formed, five of which must remain in the cycle and become rearranged to regenerate three 5-carbon RuBP molecules. The one remaining G3P is a product, which can be thought of as the result of "reducing" the three CO_2 molecules that entered the cycle into a 3-carbon sugar that can later be used to generate energy.

Concept Check 10.4

1. Photorespiration decreases photosynthetic output by adding oxygen, instead of carbon dioxide, to the Calvin cycle. As a result, no sugar is generated (no carbon is fixed), and O_2 is used rather than generated. 2. Without PS II, no O_2 is generated in

bundle-sheath cells. This avoids the problem of O_2 competing with CO_2 for binding to rubisco in these cells. 3. Both problems are caused by a drastic change in Earth's atmosphere due to burning of fossil fuels. The increase in CO_2 concentration affects ocean chemistry by decreasing pH, thus affecting calcification by marine organisms. On land, CO_2 concentration and air temperature are conditions that plants have become adapted to, and changes in these characteristics have a strong effect on photosynthesis by plants. Thus, alteration of these two fundamental factors could have critical effects on organisms all around the planet, in all different habitats. 4. C_4 and CAM species would replace many of the C_3 species.

Summary of Key Concepts Questions

10.1 CO_2 and H_2O are the products of respiration; they are the reactants in photosynthesis. In respiration, glucose is oxidized to CO_2 as electrons are passed through an electron transfer chain from glucose to O_2, producing H_2O. In photosynthesis, H_2O is the source of electrons, which are energized by light, temporarily stored in NADPH, and used to reduce CO_2 to carbohydrate. 10.2 The action spectrum of photosynthesis shows that some wavelengths of light that are not absorbed by chlorophyll *a* are still effective at promoting photosynthesis. The light-harvesting complexes of photosystems contain accessory pigments such as chlorophyll *b* and carotenoids, which absorb different wavelengths and pass the energy to chlorophyll *a*, broadening the spectrum of light useful for photosynthesis. 10.3

In the reduction phase of the Calvin cycle, ATP phosphorylates a 3-carbon compound, and NADPH then reduces this compound to G3P. ATP is also used in the regeneration phase, when five molecules of G3P are converted to three molecules of the 5-carbon compound RuBP. Rubisco catalyzes the first step of carbon fixation—the addition of CO_2 to RuBP. 10.4 Both C_4 and CAM photosynthesis involve initial fixation of CO_2 to produce a 4-carbon compound (in mesophyll cells in C_4 plants and at night in CAM plants). These compounds are then broken down to release CO_2 (in the bundle-sheath cells in C_4 plants and during the day in CAM plants). ATP is required for recycling the molecule that is used initially to combine with CO_2. These pathways avoid the photorespiration that consumes ATP and reduces the photosynthetic output of C_3 plants when they close stomata on hot, dry, bright days. Thus, hot, arid climates would favour C_4 and CAM plants.

Test Your Understanding

1. d 2. b 3. c 4. a 5. c 6. b 7. c
10.

The ATP would end up outside the thylakoid. The thylakoids were able to make ATP in the dark because the researchers set up an artificial proton concentration gradient across the thylakoid membrane; thus, the light reactions were not necessary to establish the H$^+$ gradient required for ATP synthesis by ATP synthase.

Chapter 11

Figure Questions

Figure 11.6 Epinephrine is a signalling molecule; presumably, it binds to a cell-surface receptor protein. Figure 11.8 This is a case of passive transport, because the ions are flowing down their electrochemical gradient. In addition, no ATP is used, meaning that this cannot be an example of active transport. Figure 11.9 The aldosterone molecule is hydrophobic and can therefore pass directly through the lipid bilayer of the plasma membrane into the cell. (Hydrophilic molecules cannot do this.) Figure 11.10 The mutation would prevent phosphorylation and cause the purple protein to remain in the inactive form resulting in lack of a cellular response. Figure 11.11 The signalling molecule (cAMP) would remain in its active form and would continue to signal. Figure 11.16 100,000,000 (one hundred million or 10_8) glucose molecules are released. The first step results in 100✴ amplification (one epinephrine activates 100 G proteins); the next step does not amplify the response; the next step is a 100✴ amplification (10_2 active adenylyl cyclase molecules to 10_4 cyclic AMPs); the next step does not amplify; the next two steps are each 10^* amplifications, and the final step is a 100✴ amplification. Figure 11.17 The signalling pathway shown in Figure 11.14 leads to the splitting of PIP_2 into the second messengers DAG and IP_3, which produce different responses. (The response elicited by DAG is mentioned but not shown.) The pathway shown for cell B is similar in that it branches and leads to two responses.

Concept Check 11.1

1. The two cells of opposite mating type (a and α) each secrete a certain signalling molecule, which can only be bound by receptors carried on cells of the opposite mating type. Thus, the **a** mating factor cannot bind to another **a** cell and cause it to grow toward the first **a** cell. Only an α cell can "receive" the signalling molecule and respond by directed growth. 2. The secretion of neurotransmitter molecules at a synapse is an example of local signalling. The electrical signal that travels along a very long nerve cell and is passed to the next nerve cell can be considered an example of long-distance signalling. (Note, however, that local signalling at the synapse between two cells is necessary for the signal to pass from one cell to the next.) 3. Glucose 1-phosphate is not generated, because the activation of the enzyme requires an intact cell, with an intact receptor in the membrane and an intact signal transduction pathway. The enzyme cannot be activated directly by interaction with the signalling molecule in the test tube. 4. Glycogen phosphorylase acts in the third stage, the response to epinephrine signalling.

Concept Check 11.2

1. NGF is water-soluble (hydrophilic), so it cannot pass through the lipid membrane to reach intracellular receptors, as steroid hormones can. Therefore, you'd expect the NGF receptor to be in the plasma membrane—which is, in fact, the case. 2. The cell with the faulty receptor would not be able to respond appropriately to the signalling molecule when it was present. This would most likely have dire consequences for the cell, since regulation of the cell's activities by this receptor would not occur appropriately. 3. Binding of a ligand to a receptor changes the shape of the receptor, altering the ability of the receptor to transmit a signal. Binding of an allosteric regulator to an enzyme changes the shape of the enzyme, either promoting or inhibiting enzyme activity. 4. When the receptor is actively transmitting a signal to the inside of the cell, it is bound to a G protein. To determine a structure corresponding to that state, it might be useful to crystallize the receptor in the presence of many copies of the G protein. (In fact, a research group used this approach successfully with a G protein-coupled receptor related to the one shown in Figure 11.7.)

Concept Check 11.3

1. A protein kinase is an enzyme that transfers a phosphate group from ATP to a protein, usually activating that protein (often a second type of protein kinase). Many signal transduction pathways include a series of such interactions, in which each phosphorylated protein kinase in turn phosphorylates the next protein kinase in the series. Such phosphorylation cascades carry a signal from outside the cell to the cellular protein(s) that will carry out the response. 2. Protein phosphatases reverse the effects of the kinases by removing phosphate groups resulting in the protein returning to the inactive form. 3. The signal that is being transduced is the information that a signalling molecule is bound to the cell-surface receptor. Information is transduced by way of sequential protein-protein interactions that change protein shapes, causing them to function in a way that passes the signal along. 4. The IP_3-gated channel opens, allowing calcium ions to flow out of the ER, which raises the cytosolic Ca^{2+} concentration resulting in a cellular response.

Concept Check 11.4

1. At each step in a cascade of sequential activations, one molecule or ion may activate numerous molecules functioning in the next step (Figure 11.16). 2. Scaffolding proteins hold molecular components of signalling pathways in a complex with each other. Different scaffolding proteins would assemble different collections of proteins, leading to different cellular responses in the two cells. 3. A malfunctioning protein phosphatase would not be able to dephosphorylate a particular receptor or relay protein. As a result, the signalling pathway, once activated, would not be able to be terminated. (In fact, one study found altered protein phosphatases in cells from 25% of colorectal tumours.)

Concept Check 11.5

1. In formation of the hand or paw in mammals, cells in the regions between the digits are programmed to undergo apoptosis. This serves to shape the digits of the hand or paw so that they are not webbed. 2. If a receptor protein for a death-signalling molecule were defective such that it was activated even in the absence of the death signal, this would lead to apoptosis when it wouldn't normally occur. Similar defects in any of the proteins in the signalling pathway, which would activate these relay or response proteins in the absence of interaction with the previous protein or second messenger in the pathway, would have the same effect. Conversely, if any protein in the pathway were defective in its ability to respond to an interaction with an early protein or other molecule or ion, apoptosis would not occur when it normally should. For example, a receptor protein for a death-signalling ligand might not be able to be activated, even when ligand was bound. This would stop the signal from being transduced into the cell.

Summary of Key Concepts Questions

11.1 A cell is able to respond to a hormone only if it has a receptor protein on the cell surface or inside the cell that can bind to the hormone. The response to a hormone depends on the specific cellular activity that a signal transduction pathway

triggers within the cell. The response can vary for different types of cells. 11.2 Both GPCRs and RTKs have an extracellular binding site for a signalling molecule (ligand) and an α helix region of the polypeptide that spans the membrane. GPCRs usually trigger a single transduction pathway, whereas the multiple activated tyrosines on an RTK dimer may trigger several different transduction pathways at the same time. 11.3 A protein kinase is an enzyme that adds a phosphate group to another protein. Protein kinases are often part of a phosphorylation cascade that transduces a signal. A second messenger is a small, nonprotein molecule or ion that rapidly diffuses and relays a signal throughout a cell. Both protein kinases and second messengers can operate in the same pathway. For example, the second messenger cAMP often activates protein kinase A, which then phosphorylates other proteins. 11.4 In G protein-coupled pathways, the GTPase portion of a G protein converts GTP to GDP and inactivates the G protein. Protein phosphatases remove phosphate groups from activated proteins, thus stopping a phosphorylation cascade of protein kinases. Phosphodiesterase converts cAMP to AMP, thus reducing the effect of cAMP in a signal transduction pathway. 11.5 The basic mechanism of controlled cell suicide evolved early in eukaryotic evolution, and the genetic basis for these pathways has been conserved during animal evolution. Such a mechanism is essential to the development and maintenance of all animals.

Test Your Understanding

1. d 2. a 3. b 4. a 5. c 6. c 7. c. 8. This is one possible drawing of the pathway. (Similar drawings would also be correct.)

Chapter 12

Figure Questions

Figure 12.4

Circling the other chromatid instead would also be correct. Figure 12.5 The chromosome has four arms. Figure 12.7 12; 2; 2; 1. Figure 12.8

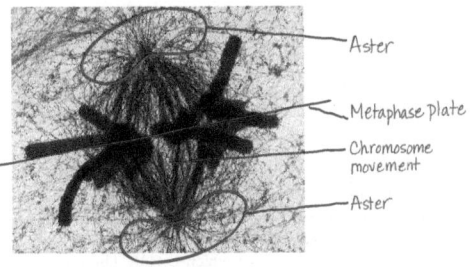

Figure 12.9 The mark would have moved toward the nearer pole. The lengths of fluorescent microtubules between that pole and the mark would have decreased, while the lengths between the chromosomes and the mark would have remained the same. Figure 12.14 In both cases, the G_1 nucleus would have remained in G_1 until the time it normally would have entered the S phase. Chromosome condensation and spindle formation would not have occurred until the S and G_2 phases had been completed. Figure 12.16 Passing the G_2 checkpoint in the diagram corresponds to the beginning of the "Time" axis of the graph, and entry into the mitotic phase (yellow background on the diagram) corresponds to the peaks of MPF activity and cyclin concentration on the graph (see the yellow M banner over the peaks). During G_1 and S phase in the diagram, Cdk is present without cyclin, so on the graph both cyclin concentration and MPF activity are low. The

curved purple arrow in the diagram shows increasing cyclin concentration, seen on the graph during the end of S phase and throughout G_2 phase. Then the cell cycle begins again. Figure 12.17 The cell would divide under conditions where it was inappropriate to do so, possibly producing daughter cells with an abnormal chromosome complement and/or missing organelles. If the daughter cells and their descendants also ignored the checkpoint and divided, there would soon be an abnormal mass of cells. (This type of inappropriate cell division can contribute to the development of cancer.) Figure 12.18 The cells in the vessel with PDGF would not be able to respond to the growth factor signal and thus would not divide. The culture would resemble that without the added PDGF. Figure 12.21 If genes that encode proteins involved in the cell cycle control system (see Figures 12.15 and 12.16) were disrupted, cancer could result. (You'll learn more about tumour suppressor genes in Chapters 18.) In addition, mutations to receptor proteins (such as receptor-tyrosine kinases) involved in recognizing growth factors could also cause cancer.

Concept Check 12.1
1. 1; 1; 2 2. 39; 39; 78

Concept Check 12.2
1. 6 chromosomes, duplicated; 12 chromatids 2. Following mitosis, cytokinesis results in two genetically identical daughter cells in both plant cells and animal cells. However, the mechanism of dividing the cytoplasm is different in animals and plants. In an animal cell, cytokinesis occurs by cleavage, which divides the parent cell in two with a contractile ring of actin filaments. In a plant cell, a cell plate forms in the middle of the cell and grows until its membrane fuses with the plasma membrane of the parent cell. Material inside the cell plate thus becomes the new cell wall. 3. From the end of S phase in interphase through the end of metaphase in mitosis 4. During eukaryotic cell division, tubulin is involved in spindle formation and chromosome movement, while actin functions during cytokinesis. In bacterial binary fission, it's the opposite: Tubulin-like molecules are thought to act in daughter cell separation, and actin-like molecules are thought to move the daughter bacterial chromosomes to opposite ends of the cell. 5. In this case, the chromosome is the cargo to be moved, and it is the motor proteins attached to the microtubules that generate the force to move them. Since the microtubules attach to the chromosomes at the kinetochore, the kinetochore is the "coupling device" that links the chromosome "cargo" to the motor protein "motors." 6. Microtubules made up of tubulin in the cell provide "rails" along which vesicles and other organelles can travel, based on interactions of motor proteins with tubulin in the microtubules. In muscle cells, actin in microfilaments interacts with myosin filaments to cause muscle contraction.

Concept Check 12.3
1. The nucleus on the right was originally in the G_1 phase; therefore, it had not yet duplicated its chromosome. The nucleus on the left was in the M phase, so it had already duplicated its chromosome. 2. A sufficient amount of MPF has to exist for a cell to pass the G_2 checkpoint; this occurs through the accumulation of cyclin proteins, which combine with Cdk to form MPF. 3. The intracellular estrogen receptor, once activated, would be able to act as a transcription factor in the nucleus, turning on genes that may cause the cell to pass a checkpoint and divide. The HER2 receptor, when activated by a ligand, would form a dimer, and each subunit of the dimer would phosphorylate the other. This would lead to a series of signal transduction steps, ultimately turning on genes in the nucleus. As in the case of the estrogen receptor, the genes would code for proteins necessary to commit the cell to divide.

Summary of Key Concepts Questions
12.1 The DNA of a eukaryotic cell is packaged into structures called *chromosomes*. Each chromosome is a long molecule of DNA, which carries hundreds to thousands of genes, with associated proteins that maintain chromosome structure and help control gene activity. This DNA-protein complex is called *chromatin*. The chromatin of each chromosome is long and thin when the cell is not dividing. Prior to cell division, each chromosome is duplicated, and the resulting sister *chromatids* are attached to each other by proteins at the centromeres and, for many species, all along their lengths (sister chromatid cohesion). 12.2 Chromosomes exist as single DNA molecules in G_1 of interphase and in anaphase and telophase of mitosis. During S phase, DNA replication produces sister chromatids, which persist during G_2 of interphase and through prophase, prometaphase, and metaphase of mitosis. 12.3 Checkpoints allow cellular surveillance mechanisms to determine whether the cell is prepared to go to the next stage. Internal and external signals move a cell past these checkpoints. The G_1 checkpoint, called the "restriction point" in mammalian cells, determines whether a cell will complete the cell cycle and divide or switch into the G_0 phase. The signals to pass this checkpoint often are external—such as growth factors. Passing the G_2 checkpoint requires sufficient numbers of active MPF complexes, which in turn orchestrate several mitotic events. MPF also initiates degradation of its cyclin component, terminating the M phase. The M phase will not begin again until sufficient cyclin is produced during the next S and G_2 phases. The signal to pass the M phase checkpoint is not activated until all chromosomes are attached to kinetochore fibres and are aligned at the metaphase plate. Only then will sister chromatid separation occur.

Test Your Understanding
1. b 2. a 3. c 4. c 5. a 6. b 7. a 8. d
9. See Figure 12.7 for a description of major events.

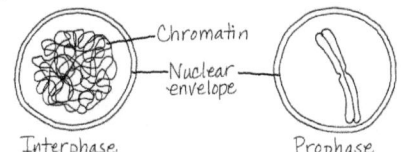

Only one cell is indicated for each stage, but other correct answers are also present in this micrograph.

10.

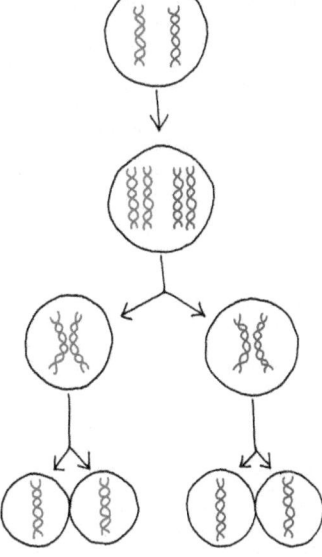

Chapter 13

Figure Questions
Figure 13.4 Two sets of chromosomes and three pairs of homologous chromosomes are present.
Figure 13.7

(A short strand of DNA is shown here for simplicity, but each chromosome or chromatid contains a very long coiled and folded DNA molecule.) Figure 13.8 If the two cells in Figure 12.7 underwent another round of mitosis, each of the four resulting cells would have six chromosomes, while the four cells resulting from meiosis in Figure 13.8 each have three chromosomes. In mitosis, DNA replication (and thus chromosome duplication) precedes each prophase, ensuring that daughter cells have the same number of chromosomes as the parent cell. In meiosis, in contrast, DNA replication occurs only before prophase I (not prophase II). Thus, in two rounds of mitosis, the chromosomes duplicate twice and divide twice, while in meiosis, the chromosomes duplicate once and divide twice. Figure 13.10 Yes. Each of the six chromosomes (three per cell) shown in telophase I has one nonrecombinant chromatid and one recombinant chromatid. Therefore, eight possible sets of chromosomes can be generated for the cell on the left and eight for the cell on the right.

Concept Check 13.1

1. Parents pass genes to their offspring; the genes are expressed to make specific enzymes and other proteins, whose cumulative action produces an individual's inherited traits. 2. Such organisms reproduce by mitosis, which generates offspring whose genomes are exact copies of the parent's genome (in the absence of mutation). 3. She should clone it by taking cuttings. Cross-breeding it with another plant would generate offspring that have additional variation, which she no longer desires now that she has obtained her ideal orchid.

Concept Check 13.2

1. Each of the six chromosomes is duplicated, so each contains two DNA double helices. Therefore, there are 12 DNA molecules in the cell. The haploid number, n, is 3. A set is always haploid. 2. 23 pairs of chromosomes and 2 sets of chromosomes are present. 23 pairs of chromosomes; 2 sets of chromosomes. 3. This organism has the life cycle shown in Figure 13.6c. Therefore, it must be a fungus or a protist, perhaps an alga.

Concept Check 13.3

1. The chromosomes are similar in that each is composed of two sister chromatids, and the individual chromosomes are positioned similarly at the metaphase plate. The chromosomes differ in that in a mitotically dividing cell, sister chromatids of each chromosome are genetically identical, but in a meiotically dividing cell, sister chromatids are genetically distinct because of crossing over in meiosis I. Moreover, the chromosomes in metaphase of mitosis can be a diploid set or a haploid set, but the chromosomes in metaphase of meiosis II always consist of a haploid set. 2. If crossing over did not occur, the two homologues would not be associated in any way. This might result in incorrect arrangement of homologues during metaphase I and ultimately in formation of gametes with an abnormal number of chromosomes. Improper or insufficient crossing over during prophase I is believed to contribute to aneuploidy (abnormal chromosome numbers) in humans.

Concept Check 13.4

1. Mutations in a gene lead to the different versions (alleles) of that gene. 2. Without crossing over, independent assortment of chromosomes during meiosis I theoretically can generate 2^n possible haploid gametes, and random fertilization can produce $2^n \times 2^n$ possible diploid zygotes. Because the haploid number (n) of grasshoppers is 23 and that of fruit flies is 4, two grasshoppers would be expected to produce a greater variety of zygotes than would two fruit flies. 3. If the segments of the maternal and paternal chromatids that undergo crossing over are genetically identical and thus have the same two alleles for every gene, then the recombinant chromosomes will be genetically equivalent to the parental chromosomes. Crossing over contributes to genetic variation only when it involves the rearrangement of different alleles.

Summary of Key Concepts Questions

13.1 Genes program specific traits, and offspring inherit their genes from each parent, accounting for similarities in their appearance to one or the other parent. Humans reproduce sexually, which ensures new combinations of genes (and thus traits) in the offspring. Consequently, the offspring are not clones of their parents (which would be the case if humans reproduced asexually). 13.2 Animals and plants both reproduce sexually, alternating meiosis with fertilization. Both have haploid gametes that unite to form a diploid zygote, which then goes on to divide mitotically, forming a diploid multicellular organism. In animals, haploid cells become gametes and don't undergo mitosis, while in plants, the haploid cells resulting from meiosis undergo mitosis to form a haploid multicellular organism, the gametophyte. This organism then goes on to generate haploid gametes. (In plants such as trees, the gametophyte is quite reduced in size and not obvious to the casual observer.) 13.3 At the end of meiosis I, the two members of a homologous pair end up in different cells, so they cannot pair up and undergo crossing over. 13.4 First, during independent assortment in metaphase I, each pair of homologous chromosomes lines up independently of each other pair at the metaphase plate, so a daughter cell of meiosis I randomly inherits either a maternal or paternal chromosome. Second, due to crossing over, each chromosome is not exclusively maternal or paternal, but includes regions at the ends of the chromatid from a nonsister chromatid (a chromatid of the other homologue). (The nonsister segment can also be in an internal region of the chromatid if a second crossover occurs beyond the first one before the end of the chromatid.) This provides much additional diversity in the form of new combinations of alleles. Third, random fertilization ensures even more variation, since any sperm of a large number containing many possible genetic combinations can fertilize any egg of a similarly large number of possible combinations.

Test Your Understanding

1. a 2. b 3. a 4. d 5. c

6. (a)

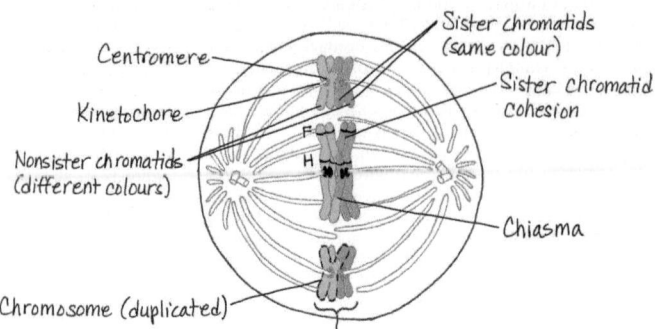

The chromosomes of one colour make up a haploid set.
All red and blue chromosomes together make up a diploid set.

(b) The chromosomes of one colour make up a haploid set. (In cases where crossovers have occurred, a haploid set of one colour may include segments of chromatids of the other colour.) All red and blue chromosomes together make up a diploid set. (c) Metaphase I 7. This cell must be undergoing meiosis because homologous chromosomes are associated with each other at the metaphase plate and chiasmata are present; this does not occur in mitosis.

Chapter 14

Figure Questions

Figure 14.3 All offspring would have purple flowers. (The ratio would be one purple to zero white.) The P generation plants are true-breeding, so mating two purple-flowered plants produces the same result as self-pollination: All the offspring have the same trait.
Figure 14.8

Yes, this cross would also have allowed Mendel to make different predictions for the two hypotheses, thereby allowing him to distinguish the correct one. Figure 14.10 Your classmate would probably point out that the F_1 generation hybrids show an intermediate phenotype between those of the homozygous parents, which supports the blending hypothesis. You could respond that crossing the F_1 hybrids results in the reappearance of the white phenotype, rather than identical pink offspring, which fails to support the idea of traits blending during inheritance. Figure 14.11 Both the I^A and I^B alleles are dominant to the i allele, which results in no attached carbohydrate. The I^A and I^B alleles are codominant; both are expressed in the phenotype of $I^A I^B$ heterozygotes, who have type AB blood. Figure 14.16 In the Punnett square, two of the three individuals with normal colouration are carriers, so the probability is $^2/_3$. (Note that you must take into account everything you know when you calculate probability: You know she is not aa, so there are only three possible genotypes to consider.) Figure 14.19 If one parent tests negative for the recessive allele, then the probability is zero that the offspring will have the disease and ½ that the offspring will be a carrier.

If the first child is a carrier, the probability of the next child being a carrier is still ½ because the two births are independent events. (Note: Assume autosomal and not sex-linked disorder.) Genetic screening can currently be used to predict the risk for certain types of cancer (such as breast, ovarian, or colon cancer), and it can also be used on specific cancer cells to identify preferential treatments.

Concept Check 14.1

1. According to the law of independent assortment, 25 plants (¹/₁₆ of the offspring) are predicted to be *aatt*, or recessive for both characters. The actual result is likely to differ slightly from this value.

Parents
AaTt × *AaTt*

Sperm from *AaTt* plant

	AT	At	aT	at
AT	AATT	AATt	AaTT	AaTt
At	AATt	AAtt	AaTt	Aatt
aT	AaTT	AaTt	aaTT	aaTt
at	AaTt	Aatt	aaTt	aatt

Eggs from *AaTt* plant

2. The plant could make eight different gametes (*YRI*, *YRi*, *YrI*, *Yri*, *yRI*, *yRi*, *yrI*, and *yri*). To fit all the possible gametes in a self-pollination, a Punnett square would need 8 rows and 8 columns. It would have spaces for the 64 possible unions of gametes in the offspring. 3. Self-pollination is sexual reproduction because meiosis is involved in forming gametes, which unite during fertilization. As a result, the offspring in self-pollination are genetically different from the parent. (As mentioned in the footnote on p. 283, we have simplified the explanation in referring to the single pea plant as a parent. Technically, the gametophytes in the flower are the two "parents.")

Concept Check 14.2

1. ½ homozygous dominant (*AA*), 0 homozygous recessive (*aa*), and ½ heterozygous (*Aa*) 2. ¼ *BBDD*; ¼ *BbDD*; ¼ *BBDd*; ¼ *BbDd* 3. The genotypes that fulfill this condition are *ppyyIi*, *ppYyii*, *Ppyyii*, *ppYYii*, and *ppyyii*. Use the multiplication rule to find the probability of getting each genotype, and then use the addition rule to find the overall probability of meeting the conditions of this problem:

ppyy Ii	½ (probability of *pp*) × ¼ (*yy*) × ½ (*Ii*) =	$\frac{1}{16}$
pp Yy ii	½ (*pp*) × ½ (*Yy*) × ½ (*ii*)	= $\frac{2}{16}$
Pp yy ii	½ (*Pp*) × ¼ (*yy*) × ½ (*ii*)	= $\frac{1}{16}$
pp YY ii	½ (*pp*) × ¼ (*YY*) × ½ (*ii*)	= $\frac{1}{16}$
pp yy ii	½ (*pp*) × ¼ (*yy*) × ½ (*ii*)	= $\frac{1}{16}$

Fraction predicted to have at least two recessive traits = $\frac{6}{16}$ or ⅜

Concept Check 14.3

1. Incomplete dominance describes the relationship between two alleles of a single gene, whereas epistasis relates to the genetic relationship between two genes (and the respective alleles of each). 2. Half of the children would be expected to have type A blood and half type B blood. 3. The black and white alleles are incompletely dominant, with heterozygotes being grey in colour. A cross between a grey rooster and a black hen should yield approximately equal numbers of grey and black offspring.

Concept Check 14.4

1. ⅛ (Since cystic fibrosis is caused by a recessive allele, Beth and Tom's siblings who have CF must be homozygous recessive. Therefore, each parent must be a carrier of the recessive allele. Since neither Beth nor Tom has CF, this means they each have a ⅔ chance of being a carrier. If they are both carriers, there is a ¼ chance that they will have a child with CF. ⅔ × ⅔ × ¼ = ⅑); 0 (Both Beth and Tom would have to be carriers to produce a child with the disease.) 2. In normal hemoglobin, the sixth amino acid is glutamic acid (Glu), which is acidic (has a negative charge on its side chain). In sickle-cell hemoglobin, Glu is replaced by valine (Val), which is a nonpolar amino acid, very different from Glu. The primary structure of a protein (its amino acid sequence) ultimately determines the shape of the protein and thus its function. The substitution of Val for Glu enables the hemoglobin molecules to interact with each other and form long fibres, leading to the protein's deficient function and the deformation of the red blood cell. 3. Joan's genotype is *Dd*. Because the allele for polydactyly (*D*) is dominant to the allele for five digits per appendage (*d*), the trait is expressed in people with either the *DD* or *Dd* genotype. But because Joan's father does not have polydactyly, his genotype must be *dd*, which means that Joan inherited a *d* allele from him. Therefore Joan, who does have the trait, must be heterozygous. 4. In the monohybrid cross involving flower colour, the ratio is 3.15 purple : 1 white, while in the human family in the pedigree, the ratio in the third generation is 1 PTC taster : 1 PTC non-taster. The difference is due to the small sample size (two offspring) in the human family. If the second-generation couple in this pedigree were

able to have 929 offspring as in the pea plant cross, the ratio would likely be closer to 3:1. (Note that none of the pea plant crosses in Table 14.1 yielded *exactly* a 3:1 ratio.)

Summary of Key Concepts Questions

14.1 Alternative versions of genes, called alleles, are passed from parent to offspring during sexual reproduction. In a cross between purple- and white-flowered homozygous parents, the F₁ offspring are all heterozygous, each inheriting a purple allele from one parent and a white allele from the other. Because the purple allele is dominant, it determines the phenotype of the F₁ offspring to be purple, and the expression of the white allele is masked. Only in the F₂ generation is it possible for a white allele to exist in a homozygous state, which causes the white trait to be expressed.
14.2

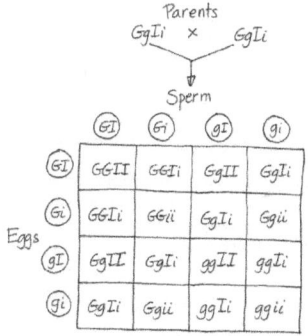

¾ yellow × ¾ round = ⁹/₁₆ yellow-round
¾ yellow × ¼ wrinkled = ³/₁₆ yellow-wrinkled
¼ green × ¾ round = ³/₁₆ green-round
¼ green × ¼ wrinkled = ¹/₁₆ green-wrinkled

= 9 yellow-round : 3 yellow-wrinkled : 3 green-round : 1 green-wrinkled

14.3 The ABO blood group is an example of multiple alleles because this single gene has more than two alleles (I^A, I^B, and i). Two of the alleles, I^A and I^B, exhibit codominance, since both carbohydrates (A and B) are present when these two alleles exist together in a genotype. I^A and I^B each exhibit complete dominance over the *i* allele. This situation is not an example of incomplete dominance because each allele affects the phenotype in a distinguishable way, so the result is not intermediate between the two phenotypes. Because this situation involves a single gene, it is not an example of epistasis or polygenic inheritance. 14.4 The chance of the fourth child having cystic fibrosis is ¼, as it was for each of the other children, because each birth is an independent event. We already know both parents are carriers, so whether their first three children are carriers or not has no bearing on the probability that their next child will have the disease. The parents' genotypes provide the only relevant information.

Test Your Understanding

1.

Parents
GgIi × *GgIi*

Sperm

	GI	Gi	gI	gi
GI	GGII	GGIi	GgII	GgIi
Gi	GGIi	GGii	GgIi	Ggii
gI	GgII	GgIi	ggII	ggIi
gi	GgIi	Ggii	ggIi	ggii

Eggs

9 green-inflated : 3 green-constricted : 3 yellow-inflated : 1 yellow-constricted

2. Man $I^A i$; woman $I^B i$; child *ii*. Genotypes for future children are predicted to be ¼ $I^A I^B$, ¼ $I^A i$, ¼ $I^B i$, ¼ *ii*. 3. ½ 4. A cross of *Ii* × *ii* would yield offspring with a genotypic ratio of 1 *Ii* : 1 *ii* (2:2 is an equivalent answer) and a phenotypic ratio of 1 inflated : 1 constricted (2:2 is equivalent).

Parents
Ii × *ii*

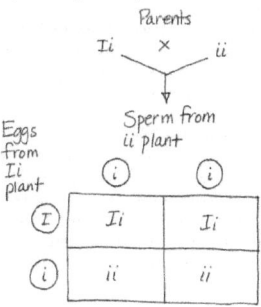

Sperm from *ii* plant

Genotypic ratio 1 *Ii* : 1 *ii*
(2:2 is equivalent)

Phenotypic ratio 1 inflated : 1 constricted
(2:2 is equivalent)

5. (a) $\frac{1}{64}$; (b) $\frac{1}{64}$; (c) $\frac{1}{8}$; (d) $\frac{1}{32}$ 6. (a) $\frac{3}{4} \times \frac{3}{4} \times \frac{3}{4} = \frac{27}{64}$; (b) $1 - \frac{27}{64} = \frac{37}{64}$; (c) $\frac{1}{4} \times \frac{1}{4} \times \frac{1}{4} = \frac{1}{64}$; (d) $1 - \frac{1}{64} = \frac{63}{64}$ 7. (a) $\frac{1}{256}$; (b) $\frac{1}{16}$; (c) $\frac{1}{256}$; (d) $\frac{1}{64}$; (e) $\frac{1}{128}$ 8. (a) 1; (b) $\frac{1}{32}$; (c) $\frac{1}{8}$; (d) $\frac{1}{2}$ 9. $\frac{1}{9}$ 10. Matings of the original mutant cat with true-breeding noncurl cats will produce both curl and noncurl F_1 offspring if the curl allele is dominant, but only noncurl offspring if the curl allele is recessive. You would obtain some true-breeding offspring homozygous for the curl allele from matings between the F_1 cats resulting from the original curl $\times$ noncurl crosses whether the curl trait is dominant or recessive. You know that cats are true-breeding when curl $\times$ curl matings produce only curl offspring. As it turns out, the allele that causes curled ears is dominant. 11. 25%, or $\frac{1}{4}$, will be cross-eyed; all (100%) of the cross-eyed offspring will also be white. 12. The dominant allele I is epistatic to the P/p locus, and thus the genotypic ratio for the F_1 generation will be 9 I–P– (colourless) : 3 I–pp (colourless): 3 iiP– (purple) : 1 iipp (red). Overall, the phenotypic ratio is 12 colourless : 3 purple : 1 red. 13. Recessive. All affected individuals (Arlene, Tom, Wilma, and Carla) are homozygous recessive aa. George is Aa, since some of his children with Arlene are affected. Sam, Ann, Daniel, and Alan are each Aa, since they are all unaffected children with one affected parent. Michael also is Aa, since he has an affected child (Carla) with his heterozygous wife Ann. Sandra, Tina, and Christopher can each have either the AA or Aa genotype. 14. $\frac{1}{6}$.

Chapter 15

Figure Questions

Figure 15.2 The ratio would be 1 yellow-round : 1 green-round : 1 yellow-wrinkled : 1 green-wrinkled. Figure 15.4 About $\frac{3}{4}$ of the F_2 offspring would have red eyes and about $\frac{1}{4}$ would have white eyes. About half of the white-eyed flies would be female and half would be male; similarly, about half of the red-eyed flies would be female and half would be male. Figure 15.7 All the males would be colour-blind, and all the females would be carriers. Figure 15.9 The two largest classes would still be the parental-type offspring (offspring with the phenotypes of the true-breeding P generation flies), but now they would be grey-vestigial and black-normal because those were the specific allele combinations in the P generation. Figure 15.10 The two chromosomes below, left, are like the two chromosomes inherited by the F_1 female, one from each P generation fly. They are passed by the F_1 female intact to the offspring and thus could be called "parental" chromosomes. The other two chromosomes result from crossing over during meiosis in the F_1 female. Because they have combinations of alleles not seen in either of the F_1 female's chromosomes, they can be called "recombinant" chromosomes. (Note that in this example, the alleles on the recombinant chromosomes, $b^+ vg^+$ and $b\ vg$, are the allele combinations that were on the parental chromosomes in the cross shown in Figures 15.9 and 15.10. The basis for calling them parental chromosomes is the combination of alleles that was present on the P generation chromosomes.)

Parental chromosomes   Recombinant chromosomes

Figure 15.13 Search to see if mutations in the genes and regions identified as candidate genes/regions in chromosome 7 are found in patients (and families of patients) with autism. Future research could include experiments focused on identifying the functions of the proteins encoded by candidate-autism genes.

Concept Check 15.1

1. The law of segregation relates to the inheritance of alleles for a single character. The law of independent assortment of alleles relates to the inheritance of alleles for two characters. 2. The physical basis for the law of segregation is the separation of homologues in anaphase I. The physical basis for the law of independent assortment is the alternative arrangements of homologous chromosome pairs in metaphase I. 3. To show the mutant phenotype, a male needs to possess only one mutant allele. If this gene had been on a pair of autosomes, *two* mutant alleles would have had to be present for an individual to show the recessive mutant phenotype, a much less probable situation.

Concept Check 15.2

1. Because the gene for this eye-colour character is located on the X chromosome, all female offspring will be red-eyed and heterozygous ($X^{w+}\ X^w$); all male offspring will inherit a Y chromosome from the father and be white-eyed ($X^w Y$). 2. $\frac{1}{4}$ ($\frac{1}{2}$ chance that the child will inherit a Y chromosome from the father and be male $\times$ $\frac{1}{2}$ chance that he will inherit the X carrying the disease allele from his mother). If the child is a boy, there is a $\frac{1}{2}$ chance he will have the disease; a female would have zero chance (but $\frac{1}{2}$ chance of being a carrier). 3. With a disorder caused by a dominant allele, there is no such thing as a "carrier," since those with the allele have the disorder. Because the allele is dominant, the females lose any "advantage" in having two X chromosomes, since one disorder-associated allele is sufficient to result in the disorder. All fathers who have the dominant allele will pass it along to *all* their daughters, who will also have the disorder. A mother who has the allele (and thus the disorder) will pass it to half of her sons and half of her daughters.

Concept Check 15.3

1. Crossing over during meiosis I in the heterozygous parent produces some gametes with recombinant genotypes for the two genes. Offspring with a recombinant phenotype arise from fertilization of the recombinant gametes by homozygous recessive gametes from the double-mutant parent. 2. In each case, the alleles

contributed by the female parent determine the phenotype of the offspring because the male in this cross contributes only recessive alleles. 3. No. The order could be A-C-B or C-A-B. To determine which possibility is correct, you need to know the recombination frequency between B and C.

Concept Check 15.4

1. In meiosis, a combined 14-21 chromosome will behave as one chromosome. If a gamete receives the combined 14-21 chromosome and a normal copy of chromosome 21, trisomy 21 will result when this gamete combines with a normal gamete during fertilization. 2. No. The child can be either $I^A I^A i$ or $I^A ii$. A sperm of genotype $I^A I^A$ could result from nondisjunction in the father during meiosis II, while an egg with the genotype ii could result from nondisjunction in the mother during either meiosis I or meiosis II. 3. Activation of this gene could lead to the production of too much of this kinase. If the kinase is involved in a signalling pathway that triggers cell division, too much of it could trigger unrestricted cell division, which in turn could contribute to the development of a cancer (in this case, a cancer of one type of white blood cell).

Concept Check 15.5

1. Inactivation of an X chromosome in females and genomic imprinting. Because of X inactivation, the effective dose of genes on the X chromosome is the same in males and females. As a result of genomic imprinting, only one allele of certain genes is phenotypically expressed. 2. The genes for leaf colouration are located in plastids within the cytoplasm. Normally, only the maternal parent transmits plastid genes to offspring. Since variegated offspring are produced only when the female parent is of the B variety, we can conclude that variety B contains both the wild-type and mutant alleles of pigment genes, producing variegated leaves. (Variety A contains only the wild-type allele of pigment genes.) 3. The situation is similar to that for chloroplasts. Each cell contains numerous mitochondria, and in affected individuals, most cells contain a variable mixture of normal and mutant mitochondria. The normal mitochondria carry out enough cellular respiration for survival.

Summary of Key Concepts Questions

15.1 Because the sex chromosomes are different from each other and because they determine the sex of the offspring, Morgan could use the sex of the offspring as a phenotypic characteristic to follow the parental chromosomes. (He could also have followed them under a microscope, as the X and Y chromosomes look different.) At the same time, he could record eye colour to follow the eye-colour alleles. 15.2 Males have only one X chromosome, along with a Y chromosome, while females have two X chromosomes. The Y chromosome has very few genes on it, while the X has about 1000. When a recessive X-linked allele that causes a disorder is inherited by a male on the X from his mother, there isn't a second allele present on the Y (males are hemizygous), so the male has the disorder. Because females have two X chromosomes, they must inherit two recessive alleles in order to have the disorder, a rarer occurrence. 15.3 Crossing over results in new combinations of alleles. Crossing over is a random occurrence, and the more distance there is between two genes, the more chances there are for crossing over to occur, leading to a new allele combination. 15.4 In inversions and reciprocal translocations, the same genetic material is present in the same relative amount but just organized differently. In aneuploidy, duplications, deletions, and nonreciprocal translocations, the balance of genetic material is upset, as large segments are either missing or present in more than one copy. Apparently, this type of imbalance is very damaging to the organism. (Although it isn't lethal in the developing embryo, the reciprocal translocation that produces the Philadelphia chromosome can lead to a serious condition, cancer, by altering the expression of important genes.) 15.5 In these cases, the sex of the parent contributing an allele affects the inheritance pattern. For imprinted genes, either the paternal or the maternal allele is expressed, depending on the imprint. For mitochondrial and chloroplast genes, only the maternal contribution will affect offspring phenotype because the offspring inherit these organelles from the mother, via the egg cytoplasm.

Test Your Understanding

1. 0; $\frac{1}{2}$; $\frac{1}{16}$ 2. Recessive; if the disorder were dominant, it would affect at least one parent of a child born with the disorder. The disorder's inheritance is sex-linked because it is seen only in boys. For a girl to have the disorder, she would have to inherit recessive alleles from both parents. This would be very rare, since males with the recessive allele on their X chromosome die in their early teens. 3. 17%. 4. Between T and A, 12%; between A and S, 5% 5. Between T and S, 18%; sequence of genes is T–A–S 6. 6%; wild-type heterozygous for normal wings and red eyes recessive homozygous for vestigial wings and purple eyes 7. Fifty percent of the offspring will show phenotypes resulting from crossovers. These results would be the same as those from a cross where A and B were not on the same chromosome, and you would interpret the results to mean that the genes are unlinked. (Further crosses involving other genes on the same chromosome would reveal the genetic linkage and map distances.) 8. 450 each of blue-oval and white-round (parentals) and 50 each of blue-round and white-oval (recombinants) 9. About one-third of the distance from the vestigial-wing locus to the brown-eye locus 10. Because bananas are triploid, homologous pairs cannot line up during meiosis. Therefore, it is not possible to generate gametes that can fuse to produce a zygote with the triploid number of chromosomes. 12. (a) For each pair of genes, you had to generate an F_1 dihybrid fly; let's use the A and B genes as an example. You obtained homozygous parental flies, either the first with dominant alleles of the two genes ($AABB$) and the second with recessive alleles ($aabb$), or the first with dominant alleles of gene A and recessive alleles of gene B ($AAbb$) and the second with recessive alleles of gene A and dominant alleles of gene B ($aaBB$). Breeding either of these pairs of P generation flies gave you an F_1 dihybrid, which you then testcrossed with a doubly homozygous recessive fly ($aabb$). You classed the offspring as parental or recombinant, based on the genotypes of the P generation parents (either of the two pairs described above). You added up the number of recombinant types and then divided by the total number of offspring.

This gave you the recombination percentage (in this case, 8%), which you can translate into map units (8 map units) to construct your map.

(b)

Chapter 16

Figure Questions

Figure 16.2 The living S cells found in the blood sample were able to reproduce to yield more S cells, indicating that the S trait is a permanent, heritable change, rather than just a one-time use of the dead S cells' capsules. Figure 16.4 The radioactivity would have been found in the pellet when proteins were labelled (batch 1) because proteins would have had to enter the bacterial cells to program them with genetic instructions. It's hard for us to imagine now, but the DNA might have played a structural role that allowed some of the proteins to be injected while it remained outside the bacterial cell (thus no radioactivity in the pellet in batch 2). Figure 16.11 The tube from the first replication would look the same, with a middle band of hybrid ^{15}N-^{14}N DNA, but the second tube would not have the upper band of two light blue strands. Instead it would have a bottom band of two dark blue strands, like the bottom band in the result predicted after one replication in the conservative model. Figure 16.12 In the bubble at the top in (b), arrows should be drawn pointing left and right to indicate the two replication forks. Figure 16.14 Looking at any of the DNA strands, we see that one end is called the 5′ end and the other the 3′ end. If we proceed from the 5′ end to the 3′ end on the left-most strand, for example, we list the components in this order: phosphate group → 5′ C of the sugar → 3′ C → phosphate → 5′ C → 3′ C. Going in the opposite direction on the same strand, the components proceed in the reverse order: 3′ C → 5′ C → phosphate. Thus, the two directions are distinguishable, which is what we mean when we say that the strands have directionality. (Review Figure 16.5 if necessary.)
Figure 16.17

Figure 16.18

Figure 16.22 **Make Connections** Any cell that divides indefinitely would need high levels of telomerase to maintain telomere integrity. This would include germ cells and cancer cells. **What If?** Lack of telomerase can lead to telomere shortening, which could lead to genome instability and the accumulation of genetic alterations associated with cancer development. Of note, approximately 90% of human tumours show high levels of telomerase expression, which helps them to divide indefinitely. Figure 16.24 The two members of a homologous pair (which would be the same colour) would be associated tightly together at the metaphase plate. In metaphase of mitosis, however,

each chromosome would be lined up individually, so the two chromosomes of the same colour would be in different places at the metaphase plate.

Concept Check 16.1

1. You can't tell which end is the 5′ end. You need to know which end has a phosphate group on the 5′ carbon (the 5′ end) or which end has an —OH group on the 3′ carbon (the 3′ end). 2. He was expecting that the mouse injected with the mixture of heat-killed S cells and living R cells would survive, since neither type of cell alone would kill the mouse.

Concept Check 16.2

1. Complementary base pairing ensures that the two daughter molecules are exact copies of the parental molecule. When the two strands of the parental molecule separate, each serves as a template on which nucleotides are arranged, by the base-pairing rules, into new complementary strands.
2.

Protein	Function
Helicase	Unwinds parental double helix at replication forks
Single-strand binding protein	Binds to and stabilizes single-stranded DNA until it can be used as a template
Topoisomerase	Relieves "overwinding" strain ahead of replication forks by breaking, swivelling, and rejoining DNA strands
Primase	Synthesizes an RNA primer at 5′ end of leading strand and at 5′ end of each Okazaki fragment of lagging strand
DNA pol III	Using parental DNA as a template, synthesizes new DNA strand by covalently adding nucleotides to 3′ end of a pre-existing DNA strand or RNA primer
DNA pol I	Removes RNA nucleotides of primer from 5′ end and replaces them with DNA nucleotides
DNA ligase	Joins 3′ end of DNA that replaces primer to rest of leading strand and joins Okazaki fragments of lagging strand

3. In the cell cycle, DNA synthesis occurs during the S phase, between the G_1 and G_2 phases of interphase. DNA replication is therefore complete before the mitotic phase begins. 4. Synthesis of the leading strand is initiated by an RNA primer, which must be removed and replaced with DNA, a task that could not be performed if the cell's DNA pol I were nonfunctional. In the overview box in Figure 16.17, just to the left of the top origin of replication, a functional DNA pol I would replace the RNA primer of the leading strand (shown in red) with DNA nucleotides (blue).

Concept Check 16.3

1. A nucleosome is made up of eight histone proteins, two each of four different types, around which DNA is wound. Linker DNA runs from one nucleosome to the next. 2. Euchromatin is chromatin that becomes less compacted during interphase and is accessible to the cellular machinery responsible for gene activity. Heterochromatin, on the other hand, remains quite condensed during interphase and contains genes that are largely inaccessible to this machinery. 3. The nuclear lamina is a netlike array of protein filaments that provides mechanical support just inside the nuclear envelope and thus maintains the shape of the nucleus. Considerable evidence also supports the existence of a nuclear matrix, a framework of protein fibres extending throughout the nuclear interior.

Summary of Key Concepts Questions

16.1 Each strand in the double helix has polarity, the end with a phosphate group on the 5′ carbon of the sugar being called the 5′ end, and the end with an —OH group on the 3′ carbon of the sugar being called the 3′ end. The two strands run in opposite directions, so each end of the molecule has both a 5′ and a 3′ end. This arrangement is called "antiparallel." If the strands were parallel, they would both run 5′ → 3′ in the same direction, so one end of the molecule would have either two 5′ ends or two 3′ ends. 16.2 On both the leading and lagging strands, DNA polymerase adds onto the 3′ end of an RNA primer synthesized by primase, synthesizing DNA in the 5′ → 3′ direction. Because the parental strands are antiparallel, however, only on the leading strand does synthesis proceed continuously into the replication fork. The lagging strand is synthesized bit by bit in the direction away from the fork as a series of shorter Okazaki fragments, which are later joined together by DNA ligase. Each fragment is initiated by synthesis of an RNA primer by primase as soon as a given stretch of single-stranded template strand is opened up. Although both strands are synthesized at the same rate, synthesis of the lagging strand is delayed because initiation of each fragment begins only when sufficient template strand is available. 16.3 Most of the chromatin in an interphase nucleus is uncondensed. Much is present as the 30-nm fibre, with some in the form of the 10-nm fibre and some as looped domains of the 30-nm fibre. (These different levels of chromatin packing may reflect differences in gene expression occurring in these regions.) Also, a small percentage of the chromatin, such as that at the centromeres and telomeres, is highly condensed heterochromatin.

Test Your Understanding

1. c 2. c 3. b 4. d 5. a 6. d 7. b 8. a
9. Like histones, the *E. coli* proteins would be expected to contain many basic (positively charged) amino acids, such as lysine and arginine, which can form weak bonds with the negatively charged phosphate groups on the sugar-phosphate backbone of the DNA molecule.

12.

New DNA strand (olive)
Parental DNA strand (purple)
Sliding clamp
DNA pol III
Single-strand binding protein
Direction of replication

Chapter 17

Figure Questions

Figure 17.2 The previously presumed pathway would have been wrong. The new results would support this pathway: precursor → citrulline → ornithine → arginine. They would also indicate that class I mutants have a defect in the second step and class II mutants have a defect in the first step. Figure 17.4 The mRNA sequence (5′-UGGUUUGGCUCA-3′) is the same as the nontemplate DNA strand sequence (5′-TGGTTTGGCTCA-3′), except there is U in the mRNA and T in the DNA. Figure 17.7 The processes are similar in that polymerases form polynucleotides complementary to an antiparallel DNA template strand. In replication, however, both strands act as templates, whereas in transcription, only one DNA strand acts as a template. Figure 17.8 The RNA polymerase would bind directly to the promoter, rather than depending on the previous binding of other factors. Figure 17.21 It would be packaged in a vesicle, transported to the Golgi apparatus for further processing, and then transported via a vesicle to the plasma membrane. The vesicle would fuse with the membrane, releasing the protein outside the cell. Figure 17.23 The mRNA farthest to the right (the longest one) started transcription first. The ribosome at the top, closest to the DNA, started translating first and thus has the longest polypeptide. Figure 17.26 Both the proposed CF-mutation specific treatments and the tailored breast cancer chemotherapy treatments are versions of personalized medicine. However, the CF treatment is dependent upon the specific mutation leading to the CF phenotype, while the targeted breast cancer treatment is dependent upon a specific phenotype of the cancerous cells. Note that different mutations can lead to similar cancerous cell phenotypes. For example, several mutations have been identified that will lead to increased expression of HER2 on breast cancer cells. You will learn in Chapters 18 about the mutations that lead to cancer development and progression. Another difference between the two treatment modalities is that the targeted CF treatments are trying to increase and/or restore CFTR function, whereas the targeted breast cancer treatments are trying to limit cell division or destroy cancerous cells.

Concept Check 17.1

1. Recessive 2. A polypeptide made up of 10 Gly (glycine) amino acids
3.

Template sequence (from problem): 3′-TTCAGTCGT-5′

Nontemplate sequence: 5′-AAGTCAGCA-3′

mRNA sequence: 5′-AAGUCAGCA-3′

The nontemplate and mRNA nucleotide sequences are the same except that there is T in the nontemplate strand of DNA wherever there is U in the mRNA.

4. "Template sequence" (from nontemplate sequence in problem, written 3′ → 5′): 3′-ACGACTGAA-5′

mRNA sequence: 5′-UGCUGACUU-3′

Translated: Cys-STOP-Leu

(Remember that the mRNA is antiparallel to the DNA strand.) A protein translated from the nontemplate sequence would have a completely different amino acid sequence and would most likely be nonfunctional. (It would also be shorter because of the stop signal shown in the mRNA sequence above—and possibly others earlier in the mRNA sequence.)

Concept Check 17.2

1. The promoter is the region of DNA to which RNA polymerase binds to begin transcription, and it is at the upstream end of the gene (transcription unit). 2. In a bacterial cell, RNA polymerase recognizes the gene's promoter and binds to it. In a eukaryotic cell, transcription factors mediate the binding of RNA polymerase to the promoter. In both cases, sequences in the promoter bind precisely to the RNA polymerase, so the enzyme is in the right location and orientation. 3. The transcription factor that recognizes the TATA sequence would be unable to bind, so RNA polymerase could not bind and transcription of that gene probably would not occur.

Concept Check 17.3

1. Due to alternative splicing of exons, each gene can result in multiple different mRNAs and can thus direct synthesis of multiple different proteins. 2. In editing a video, segments are cut out and discarded (like introns), and the remaining segments are joined together (like exons) so that the regions of joining ("splicing") are not noticeable. 3. The cap helps direct the mRNA for export from the nucleus. In addition, once the mRNA has exited the nucleus, the cap prevents it from being degraded by hydrolytic enzymes and facilitates its attachment to ribosomes. If the cap were removed from all mRNAs, the cell would no longer be able to synthesize any proteins and would probably die.

Concept Check 17.4

1. First, each aminoacyl-tRNA synthetase specifically recognizes a single amino acid and attaches it only to an appropriate tRNA. Second, a tRNA charged with its specific amino acid binds only to an mRNA codon for that amino acid. 2. The structure and function of the ribosome seem to depend more on the rRNAs than on the ribosomal proteins. Because it is single-stranded, an RNA molecule can hydrogen-bond with itself and with other RNA molecules. RNA molecules make up the interface between the two ribosomal subunits, so presumably RNA-RNA binding helps hold the ribosome together. The binding site for mRNA in the ribosome includes rRNA that can bind the mRNA. Also, complementary bonding within an RNA molecule allows it to assume a particular three-dimensional shape and, along with the RNA's functional groups, presumably enables rRNA to catalyze peptide bond formation during translation. 3. A signal peptide on the leading end of the polypeptide being synthesized is recognized by a signal-recognition particle that brings the ribosome to the ER membrane. There the ribosome attaches and continues to synthesize the polypeptide, depositing it in the ER lumen. 4. Because of wobble, the tRNA could bind to either 5′-GCA-3′ or 5′-GCG-3′, both of which code for alanine (Ala). Alanine would be attached to the tRNA.

Ala
3′ CGU 5′
GCA
5′⌐ΙΙΙ⌐3′
GCG
5′⌐ΙΙΙ⌐3′

5. When one ribosome terminates translation and dissociates, the two subunits would be very close to the cap. This could facilitate their rebinding and initiating synthesis of a new polypeptide, thus increasing the efficiency of translation.

Concept Check 17.5

1. In the mRNA, the reading frame downstream from the deletion is shifted, leading to a long string of incorrect amino acids in the polypeptide, and in most cases, a stop codon will arise, leading to premature termination. The polypeptide will most likely be nonfunctional. 2. Heterozygous individuals, said to have sickle-cell trait, have a copy each of the wild-type allele and the sickle-cell allele. Both alleles will be expressed, so these individuals will have both normal and sickle-cell hemoglobin molecules. Apparently, having a mix of the two forms of β-globin has no effect under most conditions, but during prolonged periods of low blood oxygen (such as at higher altitudes), these individuals can show some signs of sickle-cell disease.
3.

Normal DNA sequence (template strand is on top):
3′-TACTTGTCCGATATC-5′
5′-ATGAACAGGCTATAG-3′

mRNA sequence: 5′-AUGAACAGGCUAUAG-3′

Amino acid sequence: Met-Asn-Arg-Leu-STOP

Mutated DNA sequence (template strand is on top):
3′-TACTTGTCCAATATC-5′
5′-ATGAACAGGTTATAG-3′

mRNA sequence: 5′-AUGAACAGGUUAUAG-3′

Amino acid sequence: Met-Asn-Arg-Leu-STOP

No effect: The amino acid sequence is Met-Asn-Arg-Leu both before and after the mutation because the mRNA codons 5′-CUA-3′ and 5′-UUA-3′ both code for Leu. (The fifth codon is a stop codon.)

Summary of Key Concepts Questions

17.1 A gene contains genetic information in the form of a nucleotide sequence. The gene is first transcribed into an RNA molecule, and a messenger RNA molecule is ultimately translated into a polypeptide. The polypeptide makes up part or all of a protein, which performs a function in the cell and contributes to the phenotype of the organism. 17.2 Both bacterial and eukaryotic genes have promoters, regions where RNA polymerase ultimately binds and begins transcription. In bacteria, RNA polymerase binds directly to the promoter; in eukaryotes, transcription factors bind first to the promoter, and then RNA polymerase binds to the transcription factors and promoter together. 17.3 Both the 5′ cap and the poly-A tail help the mRNA exit from the nucleus and then, in the cytoplasm, help ensure mRNA stability and allow it to bind to ribosomes. 17.4 tRNAs function as translators between the nucleotide-based language of mRNA and the amino-acid-based language of polypeptides. A tRNA carries a specific amino acid, and the anticodon on the tRNA is complementary to the codon on the mRNA that codes for that amino acid. In the ribosome, the tRNA binds to the A site, where the polypeptide being synthesized is joined to the new amino acid, which becomes the new (C-terminal) end of the polypeptide. Next, the tRNA moves to the P site. When the next amino acid is added via transfer of the polypeptide to the new tRNA, the now empty tRNA moves to the E site, where it exits the ribosome. 17.5 When a nucleotide base is altered chemically, its base-pairing characteristics may be changed. When that happens, an incorrect nucleotide is likely to be incorporated into the complementary strand during the next replication of the DNA, and successive rounds of replication will perpetuate the mutation. Once the gene is transcribed, the mutated codon may code for a different amino acid that inhibits or changes the function of a protein. If the chemical change in the base is detected and repaired by the DNA repair system before the next replication, no mutation will result.

Test Your Understanding
1. b 2. c 3. a 4. a 5. b 6. c 7. d
8. No, transcription and translation are separated in space and time in a eukaryotic cell, as a result of the eukaryotyic cell's nuclear membrane.
9.

Type of RNA	Functions
Messenger RNA (mRNA)	Carries information specifying amino acid sequences of proteins from DNA to ribosomes
Transfer RNA (tRNA)	Serves as translator molecule in protein synthesis; translates mRNA codons into amino acids
Ribosomal RNA (rRNA)	Plays catalytic (ribozyme) roles and structural roles in ribosomes
Primary transcript	Is a precursor to mRNA, rRNA, or tRNA, before being processed; some intron RNA acts as a ribozyme, catalyzing its own splicing
Small nuclear RNA (snRNA)	Plays structural and catalytic roles in spliceosomes, the complexes of protein and RNA that splice pre-mRNA

Chapter 18

Figure Questions
Figure 18.3 As the concentration of tryptophan in the cell falls, eventually there will be none bound to repressor molecules. These will then take on their inactive shapes and dissociate from the operator, allowing transcription of the operon to resume. The enzymes for tryptophan synthesis will be made, and they will begin to synthesize tryptophan again in the cell. Figure 18.11 The albumin gene enhancer has the three control elements coloured yellow, grey, and red. The sequences in the liver and lens cells would be identical, since the cells are in the same organism. Figure 18.18 Even if the mutant MyoD protein couldn't activate the *myoD* gene, it could still turn on genes for the other proteins in the pathway (other transcription factors, which would turn on the genes for muscle-specific proteins, for example). Therefore, some differentiation would occur. But unless there were other activators that could compensate for the loss of the MyoD protein's activation of the *myoD* gene, the cell would not be able to maintain its differentiated state. Figure 18.22 Normal Bicoid protein would be made in the anterior end and compensate for the presence of mutant *bicoid* mRNA put into the egg by the mother. Development should be normal, with a head present. Figure 18.25 The mutation is likely to be recessive because it is more likely to have an effect if both copies of the gene are mutated and code for nonfunctional proteins. If one normal copy of the gene is present, its product could inhibit the cell cycle. (However, there are also known cases of dominant *p53* mutations.) Figure 18.27 Cancer is a disease in which cell division occurs without its usual regulation. Cell division can be stimulated by growth factors (see Figure 12.18), which bind to cell-surface receptors (see Figure 11.8). Cancer cells evade these normal controls and can often divide in the absence of growth factors (see Figure 12.19). This suggests that the receptor proteins or some other components in a signalling pathway are abnormal in some way (see, for example, the mutant Ras protein in Figure 18.24) or are expressed at abnormal levels, as seen for the receptors in this figure. Under some circumstances in the mammalian body, steroid hormones such as estrogen and progesterone can also promote cell division. These molecules also use cell-signalling pathways, as described in Chapters 11 (see Figure 11.9). Because signalling receptors are involved in triggering cells to undergo cell division, it is not surprising that altered

genes encoding these proteins might play a significant role in the development of cancer. Genes might be altered either through a mutation that changes the function of the protein product or a mutation that causes the gene to be expressed at abnormal levels that disrupt the overall regulation of the signalling pathway. Figure 18.28 It is possible that Mutation B happened earlier in the genomic evolution of the clonal samples. Depending on the data, Mutation B could be considered a founder mutation. Mutation A, which is detected at a lower frequency, could have occurred later in the progression of the tumour.

Concept Check 18.1
1. Binding by the *trp* corepressor (tryptophan) activates the *trp* repressor, shutting off transcription of the *trp* operon; binding by the *lac* inducer (allolactose) inactivates the *lac* repressor, leading to transcription of the *lac* operon. 2. When glucose is scarce, cAMP is bound to CAP and CAP is bound to the promoter, favouring the binding of RNA polymerase. However, in the absence of lactose, the repressor is bound to the operator, blocking RNA polymerase binding to the promoter. Therefore, the operon genes are not transcribed. 3. The cell would continuously produce β-galactosidase and the two other enzymes for lactose utilization, even in the absence of lactose, thus wasting cell resources.

Concept Check 18.2
1. Histone acetylation is generally associated with gene expression, while DNA methylation is generally associated with lack of expression. 2. General transcription factors function in the transcription initiation complex at the promoters for all genes. Specific transcription factors bind to control elements associated with a particular gene and, once bound, either increase (activators) or decrease (repressors) transcription of that gene. 3. The three genes should have some similar or identical sequences in the control elements of their enhancers. Because of this similarity, the same specific transcription factors in muscle cells could bind to the enhancers of all three genes and stimulate their expression coordinately. 4. Degradation of the mRNA, regulation of translation, activation of the protein (by chemical modification, for example), and protein degradation.

Concept Check 18.3
1. Both miRNAs and siRNAs are small, single-stranded RNAs that associate with a complex of proteins and then can base-pair with mRNAs that have a complementary sequence. This base pairing leads to either degradation of the mRNA or blockage of its translation. Some siRNAs, in association with other proteins, can bind back to the chromatin in a certain region, causing chromatin changes that affect transcription. Both miRNAs and siRNAs are processed from double-stranded RNA precursors, but have subtle variations in the structure of those precursors. 2. The mRNA would persist and be translated into the cell division–promoting protein, and the cell would probably divide. If the intact miRNA is necessary for inhibition of cell division, then division of this cell might be inappropriate. Uncontrolled cell division could lead to formation of a mass of cells (tumour) that prevents proper functioning of the organism and could contribute to the development of cancer.

Concept Check 18.4
1. Cells undergo differentiation during embryonic development, becoming different from each other; in the adult organism, there are many highly specialized cell types. 2. By binding to a receptor on the receiving cell's surface and triggering a signal transduction pathway, involving intracellular molecules such as second messengers and transcription factors that affect gene expression 3. Their products, made and deposited into the egg by the mother, determine the head and tail ends, as well as the back and belly, of the embryo (and eventually the adult fly). 4. The lower cell is synthesizing signalling molecules because the gene encoding them is activated, meaning that the appropriate specific transcription factors are binding to the gene's enhancer. The genes encoding these specific transcription factors are also being expressed in this cell because the transcriptional activators that can turn them on were expressed in the precursor to this cell. A similar explanation also applies to the cells expressing the receptor proteins. This scenario began with specific cytoplasmic determinants localized in specific regions of the egg. These cytoplasmic determinants were distributed unevenly to daughter cells, resulting in cells going down different developmental pathways.

Concept Check 18.5
1. Apoptosis is signalled by p53 protein when a cell has extensive DNA damage, so apoptosis plays a protective role in eliminating a cell that might contribute to cancer. If mutations in the genes in the apoptotic pathway blocked apoptosis, a cell with such damage could continue to divide and might lead to tumour formation. 2. When an individual has inherited an oncogene or a mutant allele of a tumour-suppressor gene 3. A cancer-causing mutation in a proto-oncogene usually makes the gene product overactive, whereas a cancer-causing mutation in a tumour-suppressor gene usually makes the gene product nonfunctional.

Summary of Key Concepts Questions
18.1 A corepressor and an inducer are both small molecules that bind to the repressor protein in an operon, causing the repressor to change shape. In the case of a corepressor (like tryptophan), this shape change allows the repressor to bind to the operator, blocking transcription. In contrast, an inducer causes the repressor to dissociate from the operator, allowing transcription to begin. 18.2 The chromatin must not be tightly condensed because it must be accessible to transcription factors. The appropriate specific transcription factors (activators) must bind to the control elements in the enhancer of the gene, while repressors must not be bound. The DNA must be bent by a bending protein so the activators can contact the mediator proteins and form a complex with general transcription factors at the promoter. Then RNA polymerase must bind and begin transcription. 18.3 miRNAs do not "code" for the amino acids of a protein—they are never translated. Each miRNA is cleaved from

its hairpin RNA structure and then trimmed by Dicer. Next, one strand is degraded while the other associates with a group of proteins to form a complex. Binding of the complex to an mRNA with a complementary sequence causes that mRNA to be degraded or blocks its translation. This is considered gene regulation because it controls the amount of a particular mRNA that can be translated into a functional protein. 18.4 The first process involves cytoplasmic determinants, including mRNAs and proteins, placed into specific locations in the egg by the mother. The cells that are formed from different regions in the egg during early cell divisions will have different proteins in them, which will direct different programs of gene expression. The second process involves the cell in question responding to signalling molecules secreted by neighbouring cells. The signalling pathway in the responding cell also leads to a different pattern of gene expression. The coordination of these two processes results in each cell following a unique pathway in the developing embryo. 18.5 The protein product of a proto-oncogene is usually involved in a pathway that stimulates cell division. The protein product of a tumour-suppressor gene is usually involved in a pathway that inhibits cell division.

Test Your Understanding
1. c 2. a 3. b 4. a 5. c 6. d 7. a 8. d 9. b 10. b
11. a.

The purple, blue, and red activator proteins would be present.
b.

Only gene 4 would be transcribed.
c. In nerve cells, the orange, blue, green, and black activators would have to be present, thus activating transcription of genes 1, 2, and 4. In skin cells, the red, black, purple, and blue activators would have to be present, thus activating genes 3 and 5.

Chapter 19

Figure Questions
Figure 19.3 Beijerinck might have concluded that the agent was a toxin produced by the plant that was able to pass through a filter but that became more and more dilute. In this case, he would have concluded that the infectious agent could not replicate. Figure 19.5 Top vertical arrow: Infection. Left upper arrow: Replication. Right upper arrow: Transcription. Right middle arrow: Translation. Lower left and right arrows: Self-assembly. Bottom middle arrow: Exit. Figure 19.9 Any class V virus, including the viruses that cause influenza (flu), measles, and mumps. Figure 19.10 The main protein on the cell surface that HIV binds to is called CD4. However, HIV also requires a "co-receptor," which in many cases is a protein called CCR5. HIV binds to both of these proteins together and then is taken into the cell. Researchers discovered this requirement by studying individuals who seemed to be resistant to HIV infection, despite multiple exposures. These individuals turned out to have mutations in the gene that encodes CCR5 such that the protein apparently cannot act as a co-receptor, and so HIV can't enter and infect cells. Figure 19.11 DNA viruses usually have lower mutation rates compared to RNA viruses. This is because viral RNA polymerases do not possess the same proofreading ability of DNA polymerases, and thus more mutations tend to occur in RNA viral genomes, thus making vaccine development more difficult.

Concept Check 19.1
1. TMV consists of one molecule of RNA surrounded by a helical array of proteins. The influenza virus has eight molecules of RNA, each surrounded by a helical array of proteins, similar to the arrangement of the single RNA molecule in TMV. Another difference between the viruses is that the influenza virus has an outer envelope and TMV does not. 2. The T2 phages were an excellent choice for use in the Hershey-Chase experiment because they consist of only DNA surrounded by a protein coat, and DNA and protein were the two candidates for macromolecules that carried genetic information. Hershey and Chase were able to radioactively label each type of molecule alone and follow it during separate infections of *E. coli* cells with T2. Only

the DNA entered the bacterial cell during infection, and only labelled DNA showed up in some of the progeny phage. Hershey and Chase concluded that the DNA must carry the genetic information necessary for the phage to reprogram the cell and produce progeny phages.

Concept Check 19.2
1. Lytic phages can only carry out lysis of the host cell, whereas lysogenic phages may either lyse the host cell or integrate into the host chromosome. In the latter case, the viral DNA (prophage) is simply replicated along with the host chromosome. Under certain conditions, a prophage may exit the host chromosome and initiate a lytic cycle. 2. Both the CRISPR system and miRNAs involve RNA molecules bound in a protein complex and acting as "homing devices" that enable the complex to bind a complementary sequence, but miRNAs are involved in regulating gene expression (by affecting mRNAs) and the CRISPR system protects bacterial cells from foreign invaders (infecting phages). Thus the CRISPR system is more like an immune system than are miRNAs. 3. Both the viral RNA polymerase and the RNA polymerase in Figure 17.9 synthesize an RNA molecule complementary to a template strand. However, the RNA polymerase in Figure 17.9 uses one of the strands of the DNA double helix as a template, whereas the viral RNA polymerase uses the RNA of the viral genome as a template. 4. Because it synthesizes DNA from its RNA genome. This is the reverse ("retro") of the usual DNA → RNA information flow. 5. There are many steps that could be interfered with: binding of the virus to the cell, reverse transcriptase function, integration into the host cell chromosome, genome synthesis (in this case, transcription of RNA from the integrated provirus), assembly of the virus inside the cell, and budding of the virus. (Many of these, if not all, are targets of actual medical strategies to block progress of the infection in HIV-infected people.)

Concept Check 19.3
1. Mutations can lead to a new strain of a virus that can no longer be effectively fought by the immune system, even if an animal had been exposed to the original strain; a virus can jump from one species to a new host; and a rare virus can spread if a host population becomes less isolated. 2. In horizontal transmission, a plant is infected from an external source of virus, which could enter through a break in the plant's epidermis due to damage by herbivores. In vertical transmission, a plant inherits viruses from its parent either via infected seeds (sexual reproduction) or via an infected cutting (asexual reproduction). 3. Humans are not within the host range of TMV, so they can't be infected by the virus.

Summary of Key Concepts Questions
19.1 Viruses are generally considered nonliving, because they are not capable of replicating outside of a host cell. To replicate, they depend completely on host enzymes and resources. 19.2 Single-stranded RNA viruses require an RNA polymerase that can make RNA using an RNA template. (Cellular RNA polymerases make RNA using a DNA template.) Retroviruses require reverse transcriptases to make DNA using an RNA template. (Once the first DNA strand has been made, the same enzyme can promote synthesis of the second DNA strand.) 19.3 The mutation rate of RNA viruses is higher than that of DNA viruses because RNA polymerase has no proofreading function, so errors in replication are not corrected. Their higher mutation rate means that RNA viruses change faster than DNA viruses, leading to their being able to have an altered host range and to evade immune defences in possible hosts.

Test Your Understanding
1. c 2. d 3. c 4. c 5. b
6. As shown below, the viral genome would be translated into capsid proteins and envelope glycoproteins directly, rather than after a complementary RNA copy was made. A complementary RNA strand would still be made, however, that could be used as a template for many new copies of the viral genome.

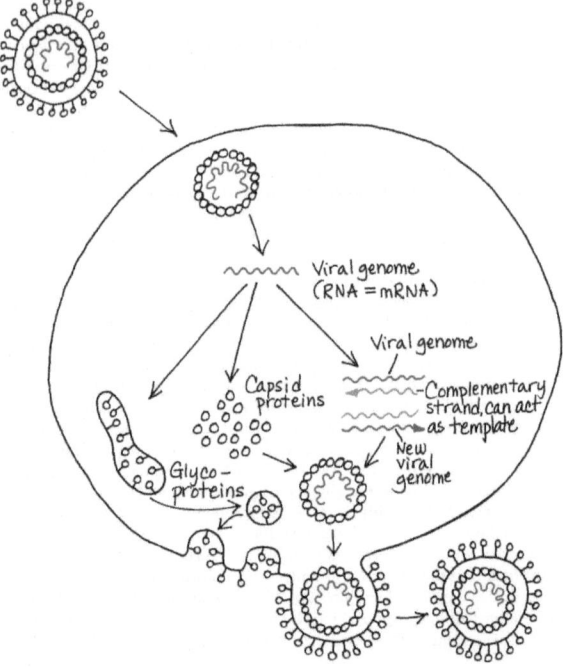

Chapter 20

Figure Questions

Figure 20.6

Figure 20.15 Crossing over, which causes recombination, is a random event. The chance of crossing over occurring between two loci increases as the distance between them increases. The SNP is located very close to an unknown disease-causing allele, and therefore crossing over rarely occurs between the SNP and the allele, so the SNP is a genetic marker indicating the presence of the particular allele. Figure 20.16 None of the eggs with the transplanted nuclei from the four-cell embryo at the upper left would have developed into a tadpole. Also, the result might include only some of the tissues of a tadpole, which might differ, depending on which nucleus was transplanted. (This assumes that there was some way to tell the four cells apart, as one can in some frog species.) Figure 20.19 Stem cell-based therapies are currently used to treat burn victims, and to replenish bone marrow in leukemia patients. Stem cells could be used to generate specific cells and/or tissues, resulting in cell-based therapies to replace defective or missing cells as needed. This could be applied to many diseases including neurodegenerative diseases such as Alzheimer's, cardiovascular disease, stroke, and spinal cord injury. Figure 20.22 Converted iPS cells would not carry the same risk, which is their major advantage. Because the donor cells would come from the patient, they would be perfectly matched. The patient's immune system would recognize them as "self" cells and would not mount an attack (which is what leads to rejection). On the other hand, cells that are rapidly dividing might carry a risk of inducing some type of tumour or contributing to development of cancer. Figure 20.23 The treatment described in Figure 20.23 uses a protein to stimulate stem cell growth inside the human body, whereas converted iPS cells are stimulated to grow and divide outside the human body and are then transplanted back into the patient. Using either the protein injection or converted iPS cells would not carry the same risk as conventional transplantation, which is a major advantage of these therapies. Because the protein injection would stimulate the patient's own cells and because the iPS donor cells would come from the patient, they would be perfectly matched. The patient's immune system would recognize them as "self" cells and would not mount an attack (which is what leads to rejection).

Concept Check 20.1

1. The covalent sugar-phosphate bonds of the DNA strands 2. Yes, *Pvu* I will cut the molecule.

3. Bacterial cells lack the means to process RNA transcripts into mRNA, and even if the need for RNA processing is avoided by using cDNA, bacteria lack enzymes to catalyze the post-translational processing that many human proteins require to function properly. 4. During the replication of the ends of linear DNA molecules (see Figure 16.20), an RNA primer is used at the 5′ end of each new strand. The RNA must be replaced by DNA nucleotides, but DNA polymerase is incapable of starting from scratch at the 5′ end of a new DNA strand. During PCR, the primers are made of DNA nucleotides already, so they don't need to be replaced—they just remain as part of each new strand. Therefore, there is no problem with end replication during PCR, and the fragments don't shorten with each replication.

Concept Check 20.2

1. In RT-PCR, the primers must base pair with their target sequences in the DNA mixture, locating one specific region among many. In microarray analysis, the labelled probe binds only to the specific target sequence due to complementary nucleic acid hybridization (DNA-DNA hybridization), During CRISPR-Cas9 editing, a guide RNA in the CRISPR-Cas9 complex must base pair with its complementary sequence in the genome (in the target gene) before editing can occur. The repair system also uses complementarity of bases when using a template strand to repair breaks. 2. As a researcher interested in cancer development, you would want to study genes represented by spots that are clearly green or red because these are genes for which the expression level differs between the two types of tissues. Some of these genes may be expressed differently as a result of cancer, but others might play a role in causing cancer.

Concept Check 20.3

1. The state of chromatin modification in the nucleus from the intestinal cell was undoubtedly less similar to that of a nucleus from a fertilized egg, explaining why many fewer of these nuclei were able to be reprogrammed. In contrast, the chromatin in a nucleus from a cell at the four-cell stage would have been much more like that of a nucleus in a fertilized egg and therefore much more easily programmed to direct development. 2. No, primarily because of subtle (and perhaps not so subtle) differences in the environment in which the clone develops and lives from that in which the original pet lived (see the differences noted in Figure 20.18). This does provoke ethical questions. To produce Dolly, also a mammal, several hundred embryos

were cloned but only one survived to adulthood. If any of the "reject" dog embryos survived to birth as defective dogs, would they be killed? Is it ethical to produce living animals that may be defective? You can probably think of other ethical issues as well. 3. Given that muscle cell differentiation involves a master regulatory gene (MyoD), you might start by introducing either the MyoD protein or an expression vector carrying the *myoD* gene into stem cells. (This is not likely to work, because the embryonic precursor cell in Figure 18.18 is more differentiated than the stem cells you are working with, and some other changes would have to be introduced as well. But it's a good way to start! And you may be able to think of others.)

Concept Check 20.4

1. Stem cells continue to reproduce themselves, ensuring that the corrective gene product will continue to be made. 2. Herbicide resistance, pest resistance, disease resistance, salinity resistance, and delayed ripening 3. Because hepatitis A is an RNA virus, you could isolate RNA from the blood and try to detect copies of hepatitis A RNA. Using RT-PCR, you would reverse-transcribe the blood RNA into cDNA and then use PCR to amplify the cDNA, using primers specific to hepatitis A sequences. If you then ran the products on an electrophoretic gel, the presence of a band would support your hypothesis.

Summary of Key Concepts Questions

20.1 A plasmid vector and a source of foreign DNA to be cloned are both cut with the same restriction enzyme, generating restriction fragments with sticky ends. These fragments are mixed together, ligated, and reintroduced into bacterial cells, which are then grown on an appropriate antibiotic such as ampicillin. The plasmid has a gene for antibiotic resistance that allows selection of recombinant clones. This gene only allows cells to grow on the antibiotic if they have taken up a plasmid. 20.2 The genes that are expressed in a given tissue or cell type determine the proteins (and noncoding RNAs) that are the basis of the structure and functions of that tissue or cell type. Understanding which groups of interacting genes establish particular structures and allow certain functions will help us learn how the parts of an organism work together and help us treat diseases that occur when faulty gene expression leads to malfunctioning tissues. 20.3 Cloning a mouse involves transplanting a nucleus from a differentiated mouse cell into a mouse egg cell that has had its own nucleus removed. Fertilizing the egg cell and promoting its development into an embryo in a surrogate mother results in a mouse that is genetically identical to the mouse that donated the nucleus. In this case, the differentiated nucleus has been reprogrammed by factors in the egg cytoplasm. Mouse ES cells are generated from inner cells in mouse blastocysts, so in this case the cells are "naturally" reprogrammed by the process of reproduction and development. (Cloned mouse embryos can also be used as a source of ES cells.) iPS cells can be generated without the use of embryos from a differentiated adult mouse cell, by adding certain transcription factors into the cell. In this case, the transcription factors are reprogramming the cells to become pluripotent. 20.4 First, the disease must be caused by a single gene, and the molecular basis of the problem must be understood. Second, the cells that are going to be introduced into the patient must be cells that will integrate into body tissues and continue to multiply (and provide the needed gene product). Third, the gene must be able to be introduced into the cells in question in a safe way, as there have been instances of cancer resulting from some gene therapy trials. (Note that this will require testing the procedure in mice; moreover, the factors that determine a safe vector are not yet well understood. Maybe one of you will go on to solve this problem!)

Test Your Understanding

1. d 2. b 3. c 4. b 5. c 6. b 7. a 8. b
9. You would use PCR to amplify the gene. This could be done from genomic DNA. Alternatively, mRNA could be isolated from lens cells and reverse-transcribed by reverse transcriptase to make cDNA. This cDNA could then be used for PCR.
10.

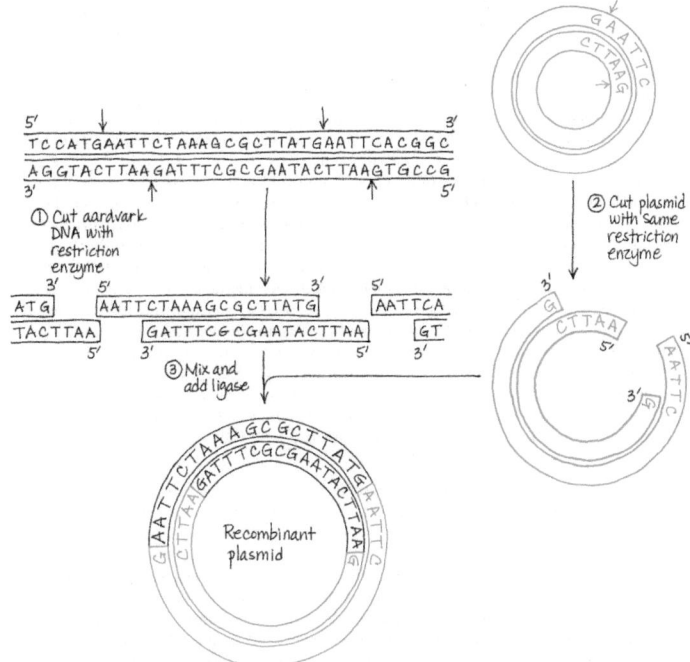

Chapter 21

Figure Questions

Figure 21.2 In stage 2 of this figure, the order of the fragments relative to each other is not known and will be determined later by computer. **Figure 21.9** The transposon would be cut out of the DNA at the original site rather than copied, so the figure would show the original stretch of DNA without the transposon after the mobile transposon had been cut out. **Figure 21.11** The RNA transcripts extending from the DNA in each transcription unit are shorter on the left and longer on the right. This means that RNA polymerase must be starting on the left end of the unit and moving toward the right. **Figure 21.13**

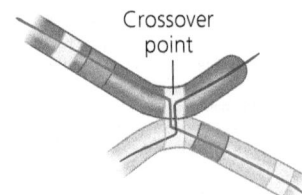

Crossover point

Figure 21.14 Pseudogenes are nonfunctional. They could have arisen by any mutations in the second copy that made the gene product unable to function. Examples would be base changes that introduce stop codons in the sequence, alter amino acids, or change a region of the gene promoter so that the gene can no longer be expressed. **Figure 21.16** Let's say a transposable element (TE) existed in the intron to the left of the indicated EGF exon in the EGF gene, and the same TE was present in the intron to the right of the indicated F exon in the fibronectin gene. During meiotic recombination, these TEs could cause nonsister chromatids on homologous chromosomes to pair up incorrectly, as seen in Figure 21.13. One gene might end up with an F exon next to an EGF exon. Further mistakes in pairing over many generations might result in these two exons being separated from the rest of the gene and placed next to a single or duplicated K exon. In general, the presence of repeated sequences in introns and between genes facilitates these processes because it allows incorrect pairing of nonsister chromatids, leading to novel exon combinations. **Figure 21.18** Since you know that chimpanzees do not speak but humans do, you'd probably want to know how many amino acid differences there are between the human wild-type FOXP2 protein and that of the chimpanzee and whether these changes affect the function of the protein. (As we explain later in the text, there are two amino acid differences.) You know that humans with mutations in this gene have severe language impairment. You would want to learn more about the human mutations by checking whether they affect the same amino acids in the gene product that the chimpanzee sequence differences affect. If so, those amino acids might play an important role in the function of the protein in language. Going further, you could analyze the differences between the chimpanzee and mouse FOXP2 proteins. You might ask: Are they more similar than the chimpanzee and human proteins? (It turns out that the chimpanzee and mouse proteins have only one amino acid difference and thus are more similar than the chimpanzee and human proteins, which have two differences, and more similar than the human and mouse proteins, which have three differences.)

Concept Check 21.1

1. In the whole-genome shotgun approach, short fragments generated by multiple restriction enzymes are cloned and sequenced and then ordered by computer programs that identify overlapping regions (see Figure 21.2).

Concept Check 21.2

1. The Internet allows centralization of databases such as GenBank and software resources such as BLAST, making them freely accessible. Having all the data in a central database, easily accessible on the Internet, minimizes the possibility of errors and of researchers working with different data. It streamlines the process of science, since all researchers are able to use the same software programs, rather than each having to obtain their own, possibly different, software. It speeds up dissemination of data and ensures as much as possible that errors are corrected in a timely fashion. These are just a few answers; you can probably think of more. 2. Cancer is a disease caused by multiple factors. To focus on a single gene or a single defect would ignore other factors that might influence the cancer and even the behaviour of the single gene being studied. The systems approach, because it takes into account many factors at the same time, is more likely to lead to an understanding of the causes and most useful treatments for cancer. 3. Some of the transcribed region is accounted for by introns. The rest is transcribed into noncoding RNAs, including small RNAs, such as microRNAs (miRNAs). These RNAs help regulate gene expression by blocking translation, causing degradation of mRNA, binding to the promoter and repressing transcription, or causing remodelling of chromatin structure. The functions of the remainder are not yet known. 4. Genome-wide association studies are the systems biology approach in that they consider the correlation of many single nucleotide polymorphisms (SNPs) with particular diseases, such as heart disease and diabetes, in an attempt to find patterns of SNPs that correlate with each disease.

Concept Check 21.3

1. Alternative splicing of RNA transcripts from a gene and post-translational processing of polypeptides 2. At the top of the web page, you can see the number of genomes completed and those considered permanent drafts in a bar graph by year. Scrolling down, you can see the number of complete and incomplete sequencing projects by year, the number of projects by domain by year (the genomes of viruses and metagenomes are counted too, even though these are not "domains"), the phylogenetic distribution of bacterial genome projects, and projects by sequencing centre. Finally, near the bottom, you can see a pie chart of the "Project Relevance of Bacterial Genome Projects," which shows that about 47% have medical relevance. The web page ends with another pie chart showing the sequencing centres for archaeal and bacterial projects. 3. Prokaryotes are generally smaller cells than eukaryotic cells, and they reproduce by binary fission. The evolutionary process involved is natural selection for more quickly reproducing cells: The faster they can replicate their DNA and divide, the more likely they will be able to dominate a population of prokaryotes. The less DNA they have to replicate, then, the faster they will reproduce.

Concept Check 21.4

1. The number of genes is higher in mammals, and the amount of noncoding DNA is greater. Also, the presence of introns in mammalian genes makes them larger, on average, than prokaryotic genes. 2. In the copy-and-paste transposon mechanism and in retrotransposition 3. In the rRNA gene family, identical transcription units for the three different RNA products are present in long, tandemly repeated arrays. The large number of copies of the rRNA genes enable organisms to produce the rRNA for enough ribosomes to carry out active protein synthesis, and the single transcription unit ensures that the relative amounts of the different rRNA molecules produced are correct. Each globin gene family consists of a relatively small number of nonidentical genes. The differences in the globin proteins encoded by these genes result in production of hemoglobin molecules adapted to particular developmental stages of the organism. 4. The exons would be classified as exons (1.5%); the enhancer region containing the distal control elements, the region closer to the promoter containing the proximal control elements, and the promoter itself would be classified as regulatory sequences (5%); and the introns would be classified as introns (20%).

Concept Check 21.5

1. If meiosis is faulty, two copies of the entire genome can end up in a single cell. Errors in crossing over during meiosis can lead to one segment being duplicated while another is deleted. During DNA replication, slippage backward along the template strand can result in segment duplication. 2. For either gene, a mistake in crossing over during meiosis could have occurred between the two copies of that gene, such that one ended up with a duplicated exon. This could have happened several times, resulting in the multiple copies of a particular exon in each gene. 3. Homologous transposable elements scattered throughout the genome provide sites where recombination can occur between different chromosomes. Movement of these elements into coding or regulatory sequences may change expression of genes. Transposable elements also can carry genes with them, leading to dispersion of genes and in some cases different patterns of expression. Transport of an exon during transposition and its insertion into a gene may add a new functional domain to the originally encoded protein, a type of exon shuffling. (For any of these changes to be heritable, they must happen in germ cells, cells that will give rise to gametes.) 4. Because more offspring are born to women who have this inversion, it must provide some advantage. It would be expected to persist and spread in the population. (In fact, evidence in the study allowed the researchers to conclude that it has been increasing in proportion in the population. You'll learn more about population genetics in the next unit.)

Concept Check 21.6

1. Because both humans and macaques are primates, their genomes are expected to be more similar than the macaque and mouse genomes are. The mouse lineage diverged from the primate lineage before the human and macaque lineages diverged. 2. Homeotic genes differ in their *non*homeobox sequences, which determine the interactions of homeotic gene products with other transcription factors and hence which genes are regulated by the homeotic genes. These nonhomeobox sequences differ in the two organisms, as do the expression patterns of the homeobox genes. 3. *Alu* elements must have undergone transposition more actively in the human genome for some reason. Their increased numbers may have then allowed more recombination errors in the human genome, resulting in more or different duplications. The divergence of the organization and content of the two genomes presumably made the chromosomes of each genome less homologous to those of the other, thus accelerating divergence of the two species by making matings less and less likely to result in fertile offspring.

Summary of Key Concepts Questions

21.1 One focus of the Human Genome Project was to improve sequencing technology in order to speed up the process. During the project, many advances in sequencing technology allowed faster reactions, which were therefore less expensive. **21.2** The most significant finding was that more than 90% of the human genomic region studied was transcribed, which suggested that the transcribed RNA (and thus the DNA from which it was produced) was performing some unknown functions. The project has been expanded to include other species because to determine the functions of these transcribed DNA elements, it is necessary to carry out this type of analysis on the genomes of species that can be used in laboratory experiments. **21.3** (a) In general, bacteria and archaea have smaller genomes, lower numbers of genes, and higher gene density than eukaryotes. (b) Among eukaryotes, there is no apparent systematic relationship between genome size and phenotype. The number of genes is often lower than would be expected from the size of the genome—in other words, the gene density is often lower in larger genomes. (Humans are an example.) **21.4** Transposable element-related sequences can move from place to place in the genome, and a subset of these sequences make a new copy of themselves when they do so. Thus, it is not surprising that they make up a significant percentage of the genome, and this percentage might be expected to increase over evolutionary time. **21.5** Chromosomal rearrangements within a species lead to some individuals having different chromosomal arrangements. Each of these individuals could still undergo meiosis and produce gametes, and fertilization involving gametes with different chromosomal arrangements could result in viable offspring. However, during meiosis in the offspring, the maternal and paternal chromosomes might not be able to pair up, causing gametes with incomplete sets of chromosomes to form. Most often, when zygotes are produced from such gametes, they do not survive. Ultimately, a new species could form if two different chromosomal arrangements became prevalent within a population and individuals could mate successfully only with other individuals having the same arrangement. 21.6 Comparing the genomes of two closely related species can reveal information about more recent evolutionary events, perhaps events that resulted in the distinguishing characteristics of the two species. Comparing the genomes of very distantly related species can tell us about evolutionary events that occurred a very long time ago. For example, genes that are shared between two distantly related species must have arisen before the two species diverged.

Test Your Understanding

1. b 2. a 3. c

4.

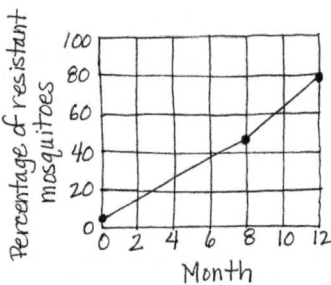

1. ATETI...PKSSD...TSSTT...NARRD
2. ATETI...PKSSE...TSSTT...NARRD
3. ATETI...PKSSD...TSSTT...NARRD
4. ATETI...PKSSD...TSSNT...SARRD
5. ATETI...PKSSD...TSSTT...NARRD
6. VTETI...PKSSD...TSSTT...NARRD

(a) Lines 1, 3, and 5 are the C, G, R species. (b) Line 4 is the human sequence. (c) Line 6 is the orangutan sequence. (d) There is one amino acid difference between the mouse (the E on line 2) and the C, G, R species (which have a D in that position). There are three amino acid differences between the mouse and the human. (The E, T, and N in the mouse sequence are instead D, N, and S, respectively, in the human sequence.) (e) Because only one amino acid difference arose during the 60–100 million years since the mouse and C, G, R species diverged, it is somewhat surprising that two additional amino acid differences resulted during the 6 million years since chimpanzees and humans diverged. This indicates that the *FOXP2* gene has been evolving faster in the human lineage than in the lineages of other primates.

Chapter 22

Figure Questions

Figure 22.6 The cactus-eater is more closely related to the seed-eater; Figure 1.23 shows that they share a more recent common ancestor (a seed-eater) than the cactus-eater shares with the insect-eater. Figure 22.8 More than 5.5 million years ago. Figure 22.12 The colours and body forms of these mantids allow them to blend into their surroundings, providing an example of how organisms are well matched to life in their environments. The mantids also share features with one another (and with all other mantids), such as six legs, grasping forelimbs, and large eyes. These shared features illustrate another key observation about life: the unity of life that results from descent from a common ancestor. Over time, as these mantids diverged from a common ancestor, they accumulated different adaptations that made them well suited for life in their different environments. Eventually, these differences may have become large enough that new species were formed, thus contributing to the great diversity of life. Figure 22.13 These results show that being reared from the egg stage on one plant species or the other did not result in the adult having a beak length appropriate for that host; instead, adult beak lengths were determined primarily by the population from which the eggs were obtained. Because an egg from a balloon vine population likely had long-beaked parents, while an egg from a goldenrain tree population likely had short-beaked parents, these results indicate that beak length is an inherited trait. Figure 22.14 Both strategies should increase the time it takes *S. aureus* to become resistant to a new drug. If a drug that harms *S. aureus* does not harm other bacteria, natural selection will not favour resistance to that drug in the other species. This would decrease the chance that *S. aureus* would acquire resistance genes from other bacteria—thus slowing the evolution of resistance. Similarly, selection for resistance to a drug that slows the growth but does not kill *S. aureus* is much weaker than selection for resistance to a drug that kills *S. aureus*—again slowing the evolution of resistance. Figure 22.17 Based on this evolutionary tree, crocodiles are more closely related to birds than to lizards because they share a more recent common ancestor with birds (ancestor 5) than with lizards (ancestor 4). Figure 22.20 Hind limb structure changed first. *Rodhocetus* lacked flukes, but its pelvic bones and hind limbs had changed substantially from how those bones were shaped and arranged in *Pakicetus*. For example, in *Rodhocetus*, the pelvis and hind limbs appear to be oriented for paddling, whereas they were oriented for walking in *Pakicetus*.

Concept Check 22.1

1. Hutton and Lyell proposed that events in the past were caused by the same processes operating today. This principle suggested that Earth must be much older than a few thousand years, the age that was widely accepted at that time. Hutton and Lyell also thought that geologic change occurs gradually, stimulating Darwin to reason that the slow accumulation of small changes could ultimately produce the profound changes documented in the fossil record. In this context, the age of Earth was important to Darwin, because unless Earth was very old, he could not envision how there would have been enough time for evolution to occur. 2. By this criterion, Cuvier's explanation of the fossil record and Lamarck's hypothesis of evolution are both scientific. Cuvier thought that species did not evolve over time. He also suggested that catastrophes and the resulting extinctions were usually confined to local regions and that such regions were later repopulated by a different set of species that immigrated from other areas. These assertions can be tested against the fossil record, and his assertion that species do not evolve has been found to be false. With respect to Lamarck, his principle of use and disuse can be used to make testable predictions for fossils of groups such as whale ancestors as they adapted to a new habitat.

Lamarck's principle of use and disuse and his associated principle of the inheritance of acquired characteristics can also be tested directly in living organisms (these principles have been found to be false).

Concept Check 22.2

1. Organisms share characteristics (the unity of life) because they share common ancestors; the great diversity of life occurs because new species have repeatedly formed when descendant organisms gradually adapted to different environments, becoming different from their ancestors. 2. The fossil mammal species (or its ancestors) would most likely have colonized the Andes from within South America, whereas ancestors of mammals currently found in African mountains would most likely have colonized those mountains from other parts of Africa. As a result, the Andes fossil species would share a more recent common ancestor with South American mammals than with mammals in Africa. Thus, for many of its traits, the fossil mammal species would probably more closely resemble mammals that live in South American jungles than mammals that live on African mountains. It is also possible, however, that the fossil mammal species could resemble the African mountain mammals by convergent evolution (even though they were only distantly related to one another). 3. As long as the white phenotype (encoded by the genotype *pp*) continues to be favoured by natural selection, the frequency of the *p* allele will likely increase over time in the population. The explanation is that if the proportion of white individuals increases relative to purple individuals, the frequency of the recessive *p* allele will also increase relative to that of the *P* allele, which only appears in purple individuals (some of whom also carry a *p* allele).

Concept Check 22.3

1. An environmental factor such as a drug does not create new traits, such as drug resistance, but rather selects for traits among those that are already present in the population. 2. (a) Despite their different functions, the forelimbs of different mammals are structurally similar because they all represent modifications of a structure found in the common ancestor. (b) Convergent evolution: The similarities between the sugar glider and flying squirrel indicate that similar environments selected for similar adaptations despite different ancestry. 3. At the time that dinosaurs originated, Earth's landmasses formed a single large continent, Pangaea. Because many dinosaurs were large and mobile, it is likely that early members of these groups lived on many different parts of Pangaea. When Pangaea broke apart, fossils of these organisms would have moved with the rocks in which they were deposited. As a result, we would predict that fossils of early dinosaurs would have a broad geographic distribution (this prediction has been upheld).

Summary of Key Concepts Questions

22.1 Darwin thought that descent with modification occurred as a gradual, steplike process. The age of Earth was important to him because if Earth were only a few thousand years old (as conventional wisdom suggested), there wouldn't have been sufficient time for major evolutionary change. 22.2 All species have the potential to produce more offspring (overreproduce) than can be supported by the environment. This ensures that there will be what Darwin called a "struggle for existence" in which many of the offspring are eaten, starved, diseased, or unable to reproduce for a variety of other reasons. Members of a population exhibit a range of heritable variations, some of which make it likely that their bearers will leave more offspring than other individuals (for example, the bearer may escape predators more effectively or be more tolerant of the physical conditions of the environment). Over time, natural selection resulting from factors such as predators, lack of food, or the physical conditions of the environment can increase the proportion of individuals with favourable traits in a population (evolutionary adaptation). 22.3 The hypothesis that cetaceans originated from a terrestrial mammal and are closely related to even-toed ungulates is supported by several lines of evidence. For example, fossils document that early cetaceans had hind limbs, as expected for organisms that descended from a land mammal; these fossils also show that cetacean hind limbs became reduced over time. Other fossils show that early cetaceans had a type of ankle bone that is otherwise found only in even-toed ungulates, providing strong evidence that even-toed ungulates are the land mammals to which cetaceans are most closely related. DNA sequence data also indicate that even-toed ungulates are the land mammals to which cetaceans are most closely related.

Test Your Understanding

1. b 2. d 3. c 4. b 5. a

7. (a)

(b) The rapid rise in the percentage of mosquitoes resistant to DDT was most likely caused by natural selection in which mosquitoes resistant to DDT could survive and reproduce while other mosquitoes could not. (c) In India—where DDT resistance first appeared—natural selection would have caused the frequency of resistant mosquitoes to increase over time. If resistant mosquitoes then migrated from India (for example, transported by wind or in planes, trains, or ships) to other parts of the world, the frequency of DDT resistance would increase there as well.

Chapter 23

Figure Questions

Figure 23.3 The genetic code is redundant, meaning that more than one codon can specify the same amino acid. As a result, a substitution at a particular site in a coding region of the *Adh* gene might change the codon but not the translated amino acid, and thus not the resulting protein encoded by the gene. One way an insertion in an exon would not affect the gene produced is if it occurs in an untranslated region of the exon. (This is the case for the insertion at location 1,703.) Figure 23.7 The predicted frequencies are 36% $C^R C^R$, 48% $C^R C^W$, and 16% $C^W C^W$. Figure 23.12 Directional selection. Goldenrain tree has smaller fruit than does the native host, balloon vine. Thus, in soapberry bug populations feeding on goldenrain tree, bugs with shorter beaks had an advantage, resulting in directional selection for shorter beak length. Figure 23.15 Crossing a single female's eggs with both an SC and an LC male's sperm allowed the researchers to directly compare the effects of the males' contribution to the next generation, since both batches of offspring had the same maternal contribution. This isolation of the male's impact enabled researchers to draw conclusions about differences in genetic "quality" between the SC and LC males. Figure 23.17 The researchers measured the percentages of successfully reproducing adults in the breeding adult population that had each phenotype. This approach of determining which phenotype was favoured by selection assumes that reproduction was a sufficient indicator of relative fitness (as opposed to counting the number of eggs laid or offspring hatched, for example) and that mouth phenotype was the driving factor determining the fish's ability to reproduce.

Concept Check 23.1

1. (a) Within a population, genetic differences among individuals provide the raw material on which natural selection and other mechanisms can act. Without such differences, allele frequencies could not change over time—and hence the population could not evolve. (b) Genetic differences between separate populations can result from natural selection if different alleles are favoured in different populations; this might occur, for example, if the different populations experienced different environmental conditions (as in Figure 23.4). Genetic differences between populations can also result from chance events (genetic drift) if the genetic changes have few or no phenotypic effects (as in Figure 23.3). 2. Many mutations occur in somatic cells, which do not produce gametes and so are lost when the organism dies. Of mutations that do occur in cell lines that produce gametes, many do not have a phenotypic effect on which natural selection can act. Others have a harmful effect and are thus unlikely to increase in frequency because they decrease the reproductive success of their bearers. 3. Its genetic variation (whether measured at the level of the gene or at the level of nucleotide sequences) would probably drop over time. During meiosis, crossing over and the independent assortment of chromosomes produce many new combinations of alleles. In addition, a population contains a vast number of possible mating combinations, and fertilization brings together the gametes of individuals with different genetic backgrounds. Thus, via crossing over, independent assortment of chromosomes, and fertilization, sexual reproduction reshuffles alleles into fresh combinations each generation. Without sexual reproduction, the rate of forming new combinations of alleles would be vastly reduced, likely causing the overall amount of genetic variation to drop. (The action of genetic drift or selection on an asexually reproducing population would lead to a drop in variation. You'll learn about both genetic drift and natural selection in Section 23.3.)

Concept Check 23.2

1. Each individual has two alleles, so the total number of alleles is 1400. To calculate the frequency of allele *A*, note that each of the 85 individuals of genotype *AA* has two *A* alleles, each of the 320 individuals of genotype *Aa* has one *A* allele, and each of the 295 individuals of genotype *aa* has zero A alleles. Thus, the frequency (p) of allele A is:

$$p = \frac{(2 \times 85) + (1 \times 320) + (0 \times 295)}{1400} = 0.35$$

There are only two alleles (*A* and *a*) in our population, so the frequency of allele a must be $q = 1 = p = 0.65$. 2. Because the frequency of allele a is 0.45, the frequency of allele A must be 0.55. Thus, the expected genotype frequencies are $p^2 = 0.3025$ for genotype *AA*, $2pq = 0.495$ for genotype *Aa*, and $q^2 = 0.2025$ for genotype *aa*. 3. There are 120 individuals in the population, so there are 240 alleles. Of these, there are 124 *A* alleles—32 from the 16 *AA* individuals and 92 from the 92 *Aa* individuals. Thus, the frequency of the *A* allele is $p = {}^{124}/_{240} = 0.52$; hence, the frequency of the *a* allele is $q = 0.48$. Based on the Hardy-Weinberg equation, if the population were not evolving, the frequency of genotype *AA* should be $p^2 = 0.52 \times 0.52 = 0.27$; the frequency of genotype *Aa* should be $2pq = 2 \times 0.52 \times 0.48 = 0.5$; and the frequency of genotype *aa* should be $q^2 = 0.48 \times 0.48 = 0.23$. In a population of 120 individuals, these expected genotype frequencies lead us to predict that there would be 32 *AA* individuals (0.27 × 120), 60 *Aa* individuals (0.5 × 120), and 28 *aa* individuals (0.23 × 120). The actual numbers for the population (16 *AA*, 92 *Aa*, 12 aa) deviate from these expectations (fewer homozygotes and more heterozygotes than expected). This indicates that the population is not in Hardy-Weinberg equilibrium and hence may be evolving at this locus.

Concept Check 23.3

1. Natural selection is more "predictable" in that it alters allele frequencies in a nonrandom way: It tends to increase the frequency of alleles that increase the organism's reproductive success in its environment and decrease the frequency of alleles that decrease the organism's reproductive success. Alleles subject to genetic drift increase or decrease in frequency by chance alone, whether or not they are advantageous. 2. Genetic drift results from chance events that cause allele frequencies to fluctuate at random from generation to generation; within a population, this process tends to decrease genetic variation over time. Gene flow is the exchange of alleles between populations, a process that can introduce new alleles to a population and hence may increase its genetic variation (albeit slightly, since rates of gene flow are often low). 3. Selection is not important at this locus; furthermore, the populations are not small,

and hence the effects of genetic drift should not be pronounced. Gene flow is occurring via the movement of pollen and seeds. Thus, allele and genotype frequencies in these populations should become more similar over time as a result of gene flow.

Concept Check 23.4

1. Zero, because fitness includes reproductive contribution to the next generation, and a sterile mule cannot produce offspring. 2. Although both gene flow and genetic drift can increase the frequency of advantageous alleles in a population, they can also decrease the frequency of advantageous alleles or increase the frequency of harmful alleles. Only natural selection *consistently* results in an increase in the frequency of alleles that enhance survival or reproduction. Thus, natural selection is the only mechanism that consistently causes adaptive evolution. 3. The three modes of natural selection (directional, stabilizing, and disruptive) are defined in terms of the selective advantage of different *phenotypes*, not different genotypes. Thus, the type of selection represented by heterozygote advantage depends on the phenotype of the heterozygotes. In this question, because heterozygous individuals have a more extreme phenotype than either homozygote, heterozygote advantage represents directional selection.

Summary of Key Concepts Questions

23.1 Much of the nucleotide variability at a genetic locus occurs within introns. Nucleotide variation at these sites typically does not affect the phenotype because introns do not code for the protein product of the gene. (Note: In certain circumstances, it is possible that a change in an intron could affect RNA splicing and ultimately have some phenotypic effect on the organism, but such mechanisms are not covered in this introductory text.) There are also many variable nucleotide sites within exons. However, most of the variable sites within exons reflect changes to the DNA sequence that do not change the sequence of amino acids encoded by the gene (and hence may not affect the phenotype). 23.2 No, this is not an example of circular reasoning. Calculating p and q from observed genotype frequencies does not imply that those genotype frequencies must be in Hardy-Weinberg equilibrium. Consider a population that has 195 individuals of genotype *AA*, 10 of genotype *Aa*, and 195 of genotype *aa*. Calculating p and q from these values yields $p = q = 0.5$. Using the Hardy-Weinberg equation, the predicted equilibrium frequencies are $p^2 = 0.25$ for genotype *AA*, $2pq = 0.5$ for genotype *Aa*, and $q^2 = 0.25$ for genotype *aa*. Since there are 400 individuals in the population, these predicted genotype frequencies indicate there should be 100 *AA* individuals, 200 *Aa* individuals, and 100 *aa* individuals—numbers that differ greatly from the values that we used to calculate p and q. 23.3 It is unlikely that two such populations would evolve in similar ways. Since their environments are very different, the alleles favoured by natural selection would probably differ between the two populations; although genetic drift may have important effects in each of these small populations, drift causes unpredictable changes in allele frequencies, so it is unlikely that drift would cause the populations to evolve in similar ways; both populations are geographically isolated, suggesting that little gene flow will occur between them (again making it less likely that they will evolve in similar ways). 23.4 Compared to males, it is likely that the females of such species would be larger, more colourful, endowed with more elaborate ornamentation (for example, a large morphological feature such as the peacock's tail), and more apt to engage in behaviours intended to attract mates or prevent other members of their sex from obtaining mates.

Test Your Understanding

1. d 2. c 3. d 4. b 5. a 6. c
7. Although natural selection can improve the match between organisms and their environments, the evolutionary process can also lead to imperfections in organisms. A central reason for this is that evolution does not design organisms from scratch to match their environments and ways of life but works instead by a process of descent with modification: Organisms inherit a basic form from their ancestors, and that form is modified by natural selection over time. As a result, a flying mammal such as a bat has wings that are not perfectly designed, but rather represent modifications of forelimbs that bat ancestors used for walking. Imperfections in organisms result from a variety of other constraints, such as a lack of genetic variation for the trait in question, and the fact that adaptations often represent compromises (since organisms must do many different things, and a "perfect" design for one activity might impair the performance of another activity). 8. The frequency of the *lap*[94] allele forms a cline, increasing as one moves from southwest to northeast across Long Island Sound.

Site	1	2	3	4	5	6
lap[94] %	13	16	16	25	36	37

Site	7	8	9	10	11
lap[94] %	39	55	59	59	59

A hypothesis that explains the cline and accounts for the observations stated in the question is that the cline is maintained by an interaction between selection and gene flow. Under this hypothesis, in the southwest portion of the Sound, salinity is relatively low, and selection against the lap^{94} allele is strong. Moving toward the northeast and into the open ocean, where salinity is relatively high, selection favours a high frequency of the lap^{94} allele. However, because mussel larvae disperse long distances, gene flow prevents the lap^{94} allele from becoming fixed in the open ocean or from declining to zero in the southwestern portion of Long Island Sound.

Chapter 24

Figure Questions

Figure 24.7 This was done to remove the possibility that the flies could differentiate among potential mates by detecting what those potential mates had eaten as larvae. If this had not been done, the strong preference of "starch flies" and "maltose flies" to mate with like-adapted flies could have occurred simply because the flies could detect (for example, by sense of smell) what their potential mates had eaten as larvae—and they preferred to mate with flies that had a similar smell to their own. Figure 24.11 In murky waters where females distinguish colours poorly, females of each species might mate more often with males of the other species. Hence, since hybrids between these species are viable and fertile, the gene pools of the two species would become more similar over time. Figure 24.12 The graph suggests there has been gene flow of some fire-bellied toad alleles into the range of the yellow-bellied toad. Otherwise, all individuals located to the left of the hybrid zone portion of the graph would have allele frequencies close to 1.0. Figure 24.13 Because the populations had only just begun to diverge from one another at this point in the process, it is likely that any existing barriers to reproduction would weaken over time. Figure 24.18 It is unlikely that the observed rise in fertility of the experimental hybrids was due to selection for life under laboratory conditions. Over time, the chromosomes of the experimental hybrids came to resemble those of *H. anomalus*. This occurred even though conditions in the laboratory differed greatly from conditions in the field, where *H. anomalus* is found, suggesting that selection for laboratory conditions was not strong. Figure 24.19 The presence of *M. cardinalis* plants that carry the *M. lewisii yup* allele would make it more likely that bumblebees would transfer pollen between the two monkey flower species. As a result, we would expect the number of hybrid offspring to increase.

Concept Check 24.1

1. (a) All except the biological species concept can be applied to both asexual and sexual species because they define species on the basis of characteristics other than ability to reproduce. In contrast, the biological species concept can be applied only to sexual species. (b) The easiest species concept to apply in the field would be the morphological species concept because it is based only on the appearance of the organism. Additional information about its ecological habits, evolutionary history, and reproduction are not required. 2. Because these birds live in fairly similar environments and can breed successfully in captivity, the reproductive barrier in nature is probably prezygotic; given the species' differences in habitat preference, this barrier could result from habitat isolation.

Concept Check 24.2

1. In allopatric speciation, a new species forms while in geographic isolation from its parent species; in sympatric speciation, a new species forms in the absence of geographic isolation. Geographic isolation greatly reduces gene flow between populations, whereas ongoing gene flow is more likely in sympatric populations. As a result, sympatric speciation is less common than allopatric speciation. 2. Gene flow between subsets of a population that live in the same area can be reduced in a variety of ways. In some species—especially plants—changes in chromosome number can block gene flow and establish reproductive isolation in a single generation. Gene flow can also be reduced in sympatric populations by habitat differentiation (as seen in the apple maggot fly, *Rhagoletis*) and sexual selection (as seen in Lake Victoria cichlids). 3. Allopatric speciation would be less likely to occur on a nearby island than on an isolated island of the same size. The reason we expect this result is that continued gene flow between mainland populations and those on a nearby island reduces the chance that enough genetic divergence will take place for allopatric speciation to occur. 4. If all of the homologues failed to separate during anaphase I of meiosis, some gametes would end up with an extra set of chromosomes (and others would end up with no chromosomes). If a gamete with an extra set of chromosomes fused with a normal gamete, a triploid would result; if two gametes with an extra set of chromosomes fused with each other, a tetraploid would result.

Concept Check 24.3

1. Hybrid zones are regions in which members of different species meet and mate, producing some offspring of mixed ancestry. Such regions can be viewed as "natural laboratories" in which to study speciation because scientists can directly observe factors that cause (or fail to cause) reproductive isolation. 2. (a) If hybrids consistently survive and reproduce poorly compared to the offspring of intraspecific matings, reinforcement could occur. If it did, natural selection would cause prezygotic barriers to reproduction between the parent species to strengthen over time, decreasing the production of unfit hybrids and leading to a completion of the speciation process. (b) If hybrid offspring survived and reproduced as well as the offspring of intraspecific matings, indiscriminate mating between the parent species would lead to the production of large numbers of hybrid offspring. As these hybrids mated with each other and with members of both parent species, the gene pools of the parent species could fuse over time, reversing the speciation process.

Concept Check 24.4

1. The time between speciation events includes (1) the length of time that it takes for populations of a newly formed species to begin diverging reproductively from one another and (2) the time it takes for speciation to be complete once this divergence begins. Although speciation can occur rapidly once populations have begun to diverge

from one another, it may take millions of years for that divergence to begin. 2. Investigators transferred alleles at the *yup* locus (which influences flower colour) from each parent species to the other. *M. lewisii* plants with an *M. cardinalis yup* allele received many more visits from hummingbirds than usual; hummingbirds usually pollinate *M. cardinalis* but avoid *M. lewisii*. Similarly, *M. cardinalis* plants with an *M. lewisii yup* allele received many more visits from bumblebees than usual; bumblebees usually pollinate *M. lewisii* and avoid *M. cardinalis*. Thus, alleles at the *yup* locus can influence pollinator choice, which in these species provides the primary barrier to interspecific mating. Nevertheless, the experiment does not prove that the *yup* locus alone controls barriers to reproduction between *M. lewisii* and *M. cardinalis*; other genes might enhance the effect of the *yup* locus (by modifying flower colour) or cause entirely different barriers to reproduction (for example, gametic isolation or a postzygotic barrier). 3. Crossing over. If crossing over did not occur, each chromosome in an experimental hybrid would remain as in the F₁ generation: composed entirely of DNA from one parent species or the other.

Summary of Key Concepts Questions

24.1 According to the biological species concept, a species is a group of populations whose members interbreed and produce viable, fertile offspring; thus, gene flow occurs between populations of a species. In contrast, members of different species do not interbreed and hence no gene flow occurs between their populations. Overall, then, in the biological species concept, species can be viewed as designated by the *absence* of gene flow—making gene flow of central importance to the biological species concept. 24.2 Sympatric speciation can be promoted by factors such as polyploidy, habitat shifts, and sexual selection, all of which can reduce gene flow between the subpopulations of a larger population. But such factors can also occur in allopatric populations and hence can also promote allopatric speciation. 24.3 If the hybrids are selected against, the hybrid zone could persist if individuals from the parent species regularly travel into the zone, where they mate to produce hybrid offspring. If hybrids are not selected against, there is no cost to the continued production of hybrids, and large numbers of hybrid offspring may be produced. However, natural selection for life in different environments may keep the gene pools of the two parent species distinct—thus preventing the loss (by fusion) of the parent species and once again causing the hybrid zone to be stable over time. 24.4 As the goatsbeard plant, Bahamas mosquitofish, and apple maggot fly examples illustrate, speciation continues to happen today. A new species can begin to form whenever gene flow is reduced between populations of the parent species. Such reductions in gene flow can occur in many ways: A new, geographically isolated population may be founded by a few colonists; some members of the parent species may begin to utilize new habitat; and sexual selection may isolate formerly connected populations or subpopulations. These and many other such events are happening today.

Test Your Understanding

1. b   2. c   3. b   4. a   5. d   6. c   7. d
10. Here is one possibility:

Chapter 25

Figure Questions

Figure 25.2 Proteins are almost always composed of the 20 amino acids shown in Figure 5.14. However, many other amino acids could potentially form in this or any other experiment. For example, any molecule that had a different R group than those listed in Figure 5.14 (yet still contained an α carbon, an amino group, and a carboxyl group) would be an amino acid—yet it would not be one of the 20 amino acids commonly found in nature. Figure 25.6 Because uranium-238 has a half-life of 4.5 billion years, the x-axis would be relabelled (in billions of years) as 4.5, 9, 13.5, and 18. Figure 25.11 You should have circled the node, shown in the tree diagram at approximately 580 million years ago (mya), that leads to the echinoderm/chordate lineage and to the lineage that gave rise to brachiopods, annelids, molluscs, and arthropods. Although the 580 mya date is estimated, this common ancestor must be at least as old as any of its descendants. Since fossil molluscs date to about 555 mya, the common ancestor represented by the circled branch point must be at least 555 million years old. Figure 25.17 The blue curve is for marine animal families. Families often contain many species, so we would expect the percentage of families that became extinct to be lower than the percentage of species that became extinct. Figure 25.18 Elevated global temperatures combined with a decrease in oxygen concentrations (from increases in bacterial decomposers) would likely have contributed to the extinction of land organisms. Recall from Chapter 3 that ocean acidification due to rising atmospheric carbon dioxide levels could result in death of marine organisms. When CO_2 dissolves in sea water, it reacts with water to form carbonic acid, which lowers ocean pH. As sea water acidifies, the extra hydrogen ions combine with carbonate ions to form bicarbonate ions, thus decreasing carbonate concentration. This means that less carbonate will be available to marine organisms that depend on it to make calcium carbonate (what corals and shells are made of). Figure 25.27 The coding sequence of the *Pitx1* gene would differ between the marine and lake populations, but patterns of gene expression would not.

Concept Check 25.1

1. The hypothesis that conditions on early Earth could have permitted the synthesis of organic molecules from inorganic ingredients 2. In contrast to random mingling of molecules in an open solution, segregation of molecular systems by membranes could concentrate organic molecules, assisting biochemical reactions. 3. Today, genetic information usually flows from DNA to RNA, as when the DNA sequence of a gene is used as a template to synthesize the mRNA encoding a particular protein. However, the life cycle of retroviruses such as HIV shows that genetic information can flow in the reverse direction (from RNA to DNA). In these viruses, the enzyme reverse transcriptase uses RNA as a template for DNA synthesis, suggesting that a similar enzyme could have played a key role in the transition from an RNA world to a DNA world.

Concept Check 25.2

1. 22 920 years (four half-lives: 5730×4) 2. The fossil record shows that different groups of organisms dominated life on Earth at different points in time and that many organisms once alive are now extinct; specific examples of these points can be found in Figure 25.5. The fossil record also indicates that new groups of organisms can arise via the gradual modification of previously existing organisms, as illustrated by fossils that document the origin of mammals from their cynodont ancestors. 3. The discovery of such a (hypothetical) fossil organism would indicate that aspects of our current understanding of the origin of mammals are not correct because mammals are thought to have originated much more recently (see Figure 25.7). For example, such a discovery could suggest that the dates of previous fossil discoveries are not correct or that the lineages shown in Figure 25.7 shared features with mammals but were not their direct ancestors. Such a discovery would also suggest that radical changes in multiple aspects of the skeletal structure of organisms could arise suddenly—an idea that is not supported by the known fossil record.

Concept Check 25.3

1. Free oxygen attacks chemical bonds and can inhibit enzymes and damage cells. As a result, prokaryotes that had thrived in anaerobic environments would have survived and reproduced poorly in oxygen-rich environments, driving many species to extinction. 2. All eukaryotes have mitochondria or remnants of these organelles, but not all eukaryotes have plastids. 3. A fossil record of life today would include many organisms with hard body parts (such as vertebrates and many marine invertebrates), but might not include some species we are very familiar with, such as those that have small geographic ranges and/or small population sizes (for example, endangered species such as the giant panda, tiger, and several rhinoceros species).

Concept Check 25.4

1. Continental drift alters the physical geography and climate of Earth, as well as the extent to which organisms are geographically isolated. Because these factors affect extinction and speciation rates, continental drift has a major impact on life on Earth. 2. Mass extinctions; major evolutionary innovations; the diversification of another group of organisms (which can provide new habitat or sources of food); migration to new locations where few competitor species exist 3. In principle, fossils of both common and rare species would be present right up to the time of the catastrophic event, then disappear. Reality is more complicated because the fossil record is not perfect. So the most recent fossil for a species might be a million years before the mass extinction—even though the species did not become extinct *until* the mass extinction. This complication is especially likely for rare species because few of their fossils will form and be discovered. Hence, for many rare species, the fossil record would not document that the species was alive immediately before the extinction (even if it was).

Concept Check 25.5

1. Heterochrony can cause a variety of morphological changes. For example, if the onset of sexual maturity changes, a retention of juvenile characteristics (paedomorphosis) may result. Paedomorphosis can be caused by small genetic changes that result in large changes in morphology, as seen in the axolotl salamander. 2. In animal embryos, *Hox* genes influence the development of structures such as limbs and feeding appendages. As a result, changes in these genes—or in the regulation of these genes—are likely to have major effects on morphology. 3. From genetics, we know that gene regulation is altered by how well transcription factors bind to noncoding DNA sequences called control elements. Thus, if changes in morphology are often caused by changes in gene regulation, portions of noncoding DNA that contain control elements are likely to be strongly affected by natural selection.

Concept Check 25.6

1. Complex structures do not evolve all at once, but in increments, with natural selection selecting for adaptive variants of the earlier versions. 2. Although the myxoma virus is highly lethal, initially some of the rabbits are resistant (0.2% of infected rabbits are not killed). Thus, assuming resistance is an inherited trait, we would expect the rabbit population to show a trend for increased resistance to the

virus. We would also expect the virus to show an evolutionary trend toward reduced lethality. We would expect this trend because a rabbit infected with a less lethal virus would be more likely to live long enough for a mosquito to bite it and hence potentially transmit the virus to another rabbit. (A virus that kills its rabbit host before a mosquito transmits the virus to another rabbit dies with its host.)

Summary of Key Concepts Questions

25.1 Particles of montmorillonite clay may have provided surfaces on which organic molecules became concentrated and hence were more likely to react with one another. Montmorillonite clay particles may also have facilitated the transport of key molecules, such as short strands of RNA, into vesicles. These vesicles can form spontaneously from simple precursor molecules, "reproduce" and "grow" on their own, and maintain internal concentrations of molecules that differ from those in the surrounding environment. These features of vesicles represent key steps in the emergence of protocells and (ultimately) the first living cells. 25.2 One challenge is that organisms do not use radioisotopes that have long half-lives to build their bones or shells. As a result, fossils older than 75 000 years cannot be dated directly. Fossils are often found in sedimentary rock, but those rocks typically contain sediments of different ages, again posing a challenge when trying to date old fossils. To circumvent these challenges, geologists date layers of volcanic rock that surround old fossils and that use radioisotopes with long half-lives. This approach provides minimum and maximum estimates for the ages of fossils sandwiched between two layers of volcanic rock. 25.3 The "Cambrian explosion" refers to a relatively short interval of time (535–525 million years ago) during which large forms of many present-day animal phyla first appear in the fossil record. The evolutionary changes that occurred during this time, such as the appearance of large predators and well-defended prey, were important because they set the stage for many of the key events in the history of life over the last 500 million years. 25.4 The broad evolutionary changes documented by the fossil record reflect the rise and fall of major groups of organisms. In turn, the rise or fall of any particular group results from a balance between speciation and extinction rates: A group increases in size when the rate at which its members produce new species is greater than the rate at which its member species are lost to extinction, while a group shrinks in size if extinction rates are greater than speciation rates. 25.5 A change to the sequence or regulation of a developmental gene can produce major morphological changes. In some cases, such morphological changes may enable organisms to perform new functions or live in new environments—thus potentially leading to an adaptive radiation and the formation of a new group of organisms. 25.6 Evolutionary change results from interactions between organisms and their current environments. No goal is involved in this process. As environments change over time, the features of organisms favoured by natural selection may also change. When this happens, what once may have seemed like a "goal" of evolution (for example, improvements in the function of a feature previously favoured by natural selection) may cease to be beneficial or may even be harmful.

Test Your Understanding

1. b 2. a 3. d 4. b 5. c
6.

7. c 8. a

Chapter 26

Figure Questions

Figure 26.3 The lizard and snake lineage is the most basal taxon shown (closest to the root of the tree). Among the descendants of the common ancestor indicated by the blue dot, the crocodilian lineage is the most basal. **Figure 26.5** The branching pattern of the tree indicates that the beaver and the rat share a common ancestor that is more recent than the ancestor these two animals share with the squirrel. **Figure 26.6** This new version does not alter any of the evolutionary relationships shown in Figure 26.6. For example, B and C remain sister taxa, taxon A is still as closely related to taxon B as it is to taxon C, and so on.

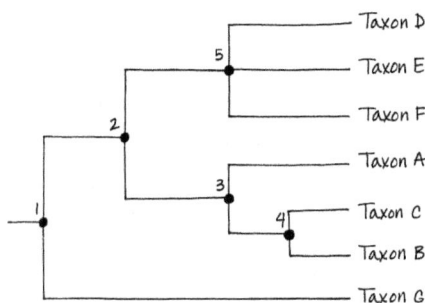

Figure 26.11 You should have circled the branch point that is drawn farthest to the left (the common ancestor of all taxa shown). Both cetaceans and seals descended from terrestrial lineages of mammals, indicating that the cetacean-seal common ancestor lacked a streamlined body form and hence would not be part of the cetacean-seal group. **Figure 26.12** You should have drawn a box around the bass, frog, turtle, and leopard lineages, along with their most recent common ancestor (bass). **Figure 26.18** The molecular clock indicates that the divergence time is roughly 45–50 million years. **Figure 26.20** The chloroplast and mitochondria are eukaryotic organelles that contain DNA. When this DNA is sequenced and compared to the DNA of existing organisms, they group within two different clades of bacteria, as shown in the tree. Chloroplasts group with cyanobacteria and mitochondria with proteobacteria. This indicates two things: 1) these organelles evolved through an symbiosis between a eukaryotic cell and intracellular bacteria (endosymbiosis), and 2) these events occurred independently, meaning on separate occasions with different bacteria. In the case of chloroplasts, its closest living relatives are the cyanobacteria, a group of bacteria that produce energy and release oxygen via photosynthesis, just like chloroplasts.

Concept Check 26.1

1. We are classified the same from the domain level to the class level; both the beaver and human are mammals. Beavers belong to order Rodentia, whereas humans do not.
2.

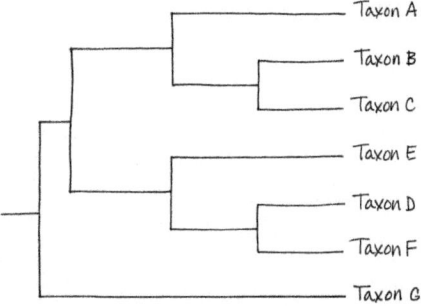

Concept Check 26.2

1. (a) Analogy, since porcupines and cacti are not closely related and since most other animals and plants do not have similar structures; (b) homology, since cats and humans are both mammals and have homologous forelimbs, of which the hand and paw are the lower part; (c) analogy, since owls and hornets are not closely related and since the structure of their wings is very different. 2. Species B and C are more likely to be closely related. Small genetic changes (as between species B and C) can produce divergent physical appearances, but if many genes have diverged greatly (as in species A and B), then the lineages have probably been separate for a long time.

Concept Check 26.3

1. No; when comparing groups of mammals, hair is a shared ancestral character common to all mammals and thus is not helpful in distinguishing different mammalian subgroups. 2. The tree in (c) shows a different pattern of evolutionary relationships. In (c), C and B are sister taxa, whereas C and D are sister taxa in (a) and (b). 3. The traditional classification provides a poor match to evolutionary history, thus violating the basic principle of cladistics—that classification should be based on common descent. Both birds and mammals originated from groups traditionally designated as reptiles, making reptiles (as traditionally delineated) a paraphyletic group. These problems can be addressed by removing *Dimetrodon*

and cynodonts from the reptiles and by considering birds as a group of reptiles (specifically, as a group of dinosaurs).

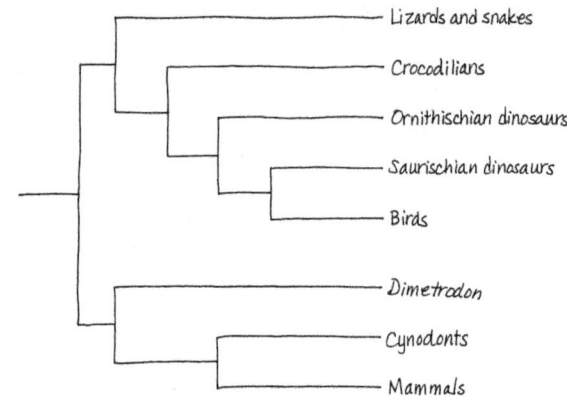

Concept Check 26.4

1. Proteins are gene products. Their amino acid sequences are determined by the nucleotide sequences of the DNA that codes for them. Thus, differences between comparable proteins in two species reflect underlying genetic differences that have accumulated as the species diverged from one another. As a result, differences between the proteins can reflect the evolutionary history of the species. 2. These observations suggest that the evolutionary lineages leading to species 1 and species 2 diverged from one another before a gene duplication event in species 1 produced gene B from gene A. 3. In RNA processing, the exons or coding regions of a gene can be spliced together in different ways, yielding different mRNAs and hence different protein products. As a result, different proteins could potentially be produced from the same gene in different tissues, thereby enabling the gene to perform different functions in these different tissues.

Concept Check 26.5

1. A molecular clock is a method of estimating the actual time of evolutionary events based on numbers of base changes in orthologous genes. It is based on the assumption that the regions of genomes being compared evolve at constant rates. 2. There are many portions of the genome that do not code for genes; many base changes in these regions could accumulate through drift without affecting an organism's fitness. Even in coding regions of the genome, some mutations may not have a critical effect on genes or proteins. 3. The gene (or genes) used for the molecular clock may have evolved more slowly in these two taxa than in the species used to calibrate the clock; as a result, the clock would underestimate the time at which the taxa diverged from each other.

Concept Check 26.6

1. The kingdom Monera included bacteria and archaea, but we now know that these organisms are in separate domains. Kingdoms are subsets of domains, so a single kingdom (like Monera) that includes taxa from different domains is not valid. 2. Because of horizontal gene transfer, some genes in eukaryotes are more closely related to bacteria, while others are more closely related to archaea; thus, depending on which genes are used, phylogenetic trees constructed from DNA data can yield conflicting results.
3.

The fossil record indicates that prokaryotes originated long before eukaryotes. This suggests that the third tree, in which the eukaryotic lineage diverged first, is not accurate and hence is not likely to receive support from genetic data.

Summary of Key Concepts Questions

26.1 The fact that humans and chimpanzees are sister species indicates that we share a more recent common ancestor with chimpanzees than we do with any other living primate species. But that does not mean that humans evolved from chimpanzees, or vice versa; instead, it indicates that both humans and chimpanzees are descendants of that common ancestor. **26.2** Homologous characters result from shared ancestry. As organisms diverge over time, some of their homologous characters will also diverge. The homologous characters of organisms that diverged long ago typically differ more than do the homologous characters of organisms that diverged more recently. As a result, differences in homologous characters can be used to infer phylogeny. In contrast, analogous characters result from convergent evolution, not shared ancestry, and hence can give misleading estimates of phylogeny. **26.3** All features of organisms arose at some point in the history of life. In the group in which a new feature first arises, that feature is a shared derived character that is unique to that clade. The group in which each shared derived character first appears can be determined, and the resulting nested pattern can be used to infer evolutionary history. **26.4** Orthologous genes should be used; for such genes, the homology results from speciation and hence reflects evolutionary history. **26.5** A key assumption of molecular clocks is that nucleotide substitutions occur at fixed rates and hence the number of nucleotide differences between two DNA sequences is proportional to the time since the sequences diverged from each other. Some limitations of molecular clocks: No gene marks time with complete precision; natural selection can favour certain DNA changes over others; nucleotide substitution rates can change over long periods of time (causing molecular clocks estimates of when events in the distant past occurred to be highly uncertain); and the same gene can evolve at different rates in different organisms 26.6 Genetic data indicated that many prokaryotes differed as much from each other as they did from eukaryotes. This indicated that organisms should be grouped into three "super-kingdoms," or domains (Archaea, Bacteria, Eukarya). These data also indicated that the previous kingdom Monera (which had contained all the prokaryotes) did not make biological sense and should be abandoned. Later genetic and morphological data also indicated that the former kingdom Protista (which had primarily contained single-celled organisms) should be abandoned because it was polyphyletic.

Test Your Understanding
1. b 2. c 3. a 4. d 5. c 6. c
8.

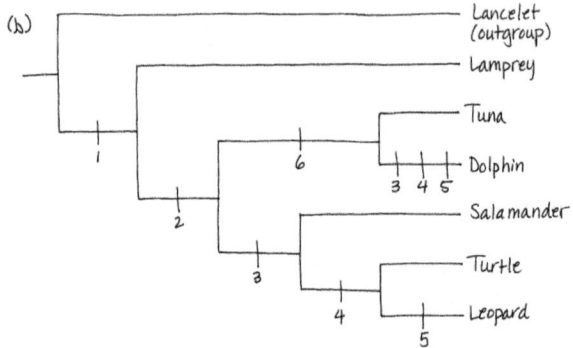

(c) The tree in (a) requires seven evolutionary changes, while the tree in (b) requires nine evolutionary changes. Thus, the tree in (a) is more parsimonious, since it requires fewer evolutionary changes.

Chapter 27

Figure Questions
Figure 27.10 It is likely that the expression or sequence of genes that affect glucose metabolism may have changed; genes for metabolic processes no longer needed by the cell also may have changed. Figure 27.11 Transduction results in horizontal gene transfer when the host and recipient cells are members of different species. Figure 27.15 Eukarya Figure 27.17 Thermophiles live in very hot environments, so it is likely that their enzymes can continue to function normally at much higher temperatures than do the enzymes of other organisms. At low temperatures, however, the enzymes of thermophiles may not function as well as the enzymes of other organisms. Figure 27.18 From the graph, plant uptake can be estimated as 0.7, 0.6, and 0.95 (mg K) for strains 1, 2, and 3, respectively. These values average to 0.75 mg K. If bacteria had no effect, the average plant uptake of potassium for strains 1, 2, and 3 should be close to 0.5 mg K, the value observed for plants grown in bacteria-free soil. Figure 27.20 While antibiotic treatment may be a vital and life-saving treatment, it is not specific to the targeted, disease-causing bacteria. Your intestinal tract, for instance, is an ecosystem housing many different species of bacteria. This microbiome is dynamic and different depending on diet and location. However, upon antibiotic treatment, this community is suppressed and the genetic diversity declines. While much of the microbiome will recover within a week or two, it is often incomplete with a reduced diversity. Suppression of the gut microbiome by antibiotic treatment may also provide opportunities for undesirable bacterial strains, like *C. difficile,* to grow and cause disease.

Concept Check 27.1
1. Adaptations include the capsule (shields prokaryotes from host's immune system) and endospores (enable cells to survive harsh conditions and to revive

when the environment becomes favourable). 2. Prokaryotic cells lack the complex compartmentalization associated with the membrane-enclosed organelles of eukaryotic cells. Prokaryotic genomes have much less DNA than eukaryotic genomes, and most of this DNA is contained in a single ring-shaped chromosome located in the nucleoid rather than within a true membrane-enclosed nucleus. In addition, many prokaryotes also have plasmids, small ring-shaped DNA molecules containing a few genes. 3. Plastids such as chloroplasts are thought to have evolved from an endosymbiotic photosynthetic prokaryote. More specifically, the phylogenetic tree shown in Figure 26.20 indicates that plastids are closely related to cyanobacteria. Hence, we can hypothesize that the thylakoid membranes of chloroplasts resemble those of cyanobacteria because chloroplasts evolved from a cyanobacterium endosymbiont.

Concept Check 27.2
1. Prokaryotes can have extremely large population sizes, in part because they have short generation times. The large number of individuals in prokaryotic populations makes it likely that in each generation there will be thousands of individuals that have new mutations at any particular gene, thereby adding considerable genetic diversity to the population. 2. In transformation, naked, foreign DNA from the environment is taken up by a bacterial cell. In transduction, phages carry bacterial genes from one bacterial cell to another. In conjugation, a bacterial cell directly transfers plasmid or chromosomal DNA to another cell via a mating bridge that temporarily connects the two cells. 3. The population that includes individuals capable of conjugation would probably be more successful, since some of its members could form recombinant cells whose new gene combinations might be advantageous in a novel environment. 4. Yes. Genes for antibiotic resistance could be transferred (by transformation, transduction, or conjugation) from the nonpathogenic bacterium to a pathogenic bacterium; this could make the pathogen an even greater threat to human health. In general, transformation, transduction, and conjugation tend to increase the spread of resistance genes.

Concept Check 27.3
1. A phototroph derives its energy from light, while a chemotroph gets its energy from chemical sources. An autotroph derives its carbon from a form of CO_2, while a heterotroph gets its carbon from organic nutrients such as glucose. Thus, there are four nutritional modes: photoautotrophic, photoheterotrophic (unique to prokaryotes), chemoautotrophic (unique to prokaryotes), and chemoheterotrophic. 2. Chemoheterotrophy; the bacterium must rely on chemical sources of energy, since it is not exposed to light, and it must be a heterotroph if it requires a source of carbon other than CO_2 (or a related compound, such as bicarbonate). 3. If humans could fix nitrogen, we could build proteins using atmospheric N_2 and hence would not need to eat high-protein foods such as meat, fish, or soy. Our diet would, however, need to include a source of carbon, along with minerals and water. Thus, a typical meal might consist of carbohydrates as a carbon source, along with fruits and vegetables to provide essential minerals (and additional carbon).

Concept Check 27.4
1. Before molecular systematics, taxonomists classified prokaryotes according to phenotypic characters that did not clarify evolutionary relationships. Molecular comparisons—of DNA in particular—indicate key divergences in prokaryotic lineages. 2. By not requiring that organisms be cultured in the laboratory, genetic prospecting has revealed an immense diversity of previously unknown prokaryotic species. Over time, the ongoing discovery of new species by genetic prospecting is likely to alter our understanding of prokaryotic phylogeny greatly. 3. The argument arose from the comparison of molecular features of the three domains of life: Eukarya, Archaea, and Bacteria. From these analyses, the Archaea and Eukarya are sister groups, separate from the Bacteria. The key point is that Bacteria and Archaea are not monophyletic and thus "prokaryote" not a valid taxonomic term. However, in our Eukarya-centric view of the world, prokaryote will likely remain a convenient tag for all those little things that lack a nuclear envelope and membrane-bound organelles! 4. At present, all known methanogens are archaea in the clade Euryarchaeota; this suggests that this unique metabolic pathway probably arose in ancestral species within Euryarchaeota. Since Bacteria and Archaea have been separate evolutionary lineages for billions of years, the discovery of a methanogen from the domain Bacteria would suggest that adaptations that enabled the use of CO_2 to oxidize H_2 may have evolved twice—once in Archaea (within Euryarchaeota) and once in Bacteria. (It is also possible that a newly discovered bacterial methanogen could have acquired the genes for this metabolic pathway by horizontal gene transfer from a methanogen in domain Archaea. However, horizontal gene transfer is not a likely explanation because of the large number of genes involved and because gene transfers between species in different domains are rare.)

Concept Check 27.5
1. Although prokaryotes are small, their large numbers and metabolic abilities enable them to play key roles in ecosystems by decomposing wastes, recycling chemicals, and affecting the concentrations of nutrients available to other organisms 2. Ultimately, N_2-fixing plants reduce the need to apply ammonia-based fertilizers that are becoming increasingly expensive and are responsible for pollution of waterways as a result of runoff from the fields following rains. Legumes, like alfalfa, are also used in crop rotations to replenish the fixed nitrogen content in soils in preparation for growing a non-legume (like canola or wheat) the following year.

Concept Check 27.6
1. Sample answers: eating fermented foods such as yogurt, sourdough bread, or cheese; receiving clean water from sewage treatment; taking medicines produced by bacteria 2. No. If the poison is secreted as an exotoxin, live bacteria could be transmitted to another person. But the same is true if the poison is an

endotoxin—only in this case, the live bacteria that are transmitted may be descendants of the (now-dead) bacteria that produced the poison. 3. Some of the many different species of prokaryotes that live in the human gut compete with one another for resources (in the food you eat). Because different prokaryotic species have different adaptations, a change in diet may alter which species can grow most rapidly, thus altering species abundance.

Summary of Key Concepts Questions
27.1 Prokaryotes are small, they have short generation times, and their populations can consist of trillions of individuals. As a result, populations of prokaryotes can evolve substantially in short periods of time, enabling them to adapt to a wide range of environments. Specific structural features that enable prokaryotes to thrive in diverse environments include their cell walls (which provide shape and protection), flagella (which function in directed movement), and ability to form endospores (which enable tolerance of harsh conditions). Prokaryotes also possess biochemical adaptations for growth in varied conditions, such as those that enable them to tolerate extremely hot or salty environments. 27.2 Prokaryotes reproduce extremely rapidly, and their populations can number in the trillions. As a result, even though mutations are rare, every day thousands of offspring are produced that have new mutations at particular gene loci. In addition, even though prokaryotes reproduce asexually and hence the vast majority of offspring are genetically identical to their parent, the genetic variation of their populations can be increased by transduction, transformation, and conjugation. Each of these (nonreproductive) processes can increase genetic variation by transferring DNA from one cell to another—even among cells that are of different species. 27.3 Prokaryotes have an exceptionally broad range of metabolic adaptations. As a group, prokaryotes perform all four modes of nutrition (photoautotrophy, chemoautotrophy, photoheterotrophy, and chemoheterotrophy), whereas eukaryotes perform only two of these (photoautotrophy and chemoheterotrophy). Prokaryotes are also able to metabolize nitrogen in a wide variety of forms (again unlike eukaryotes), and they frequently cooperate with other prokaryotic cells of the same or different species. 27.4 Phenotypic criteria such as shape, motility, and nutritional mode do not provide a clear picture of the evolutionary history of the prokaryotes. In contrast, molecular data have elucidated relationships among major groups of prokaryotes. Molecular data have also allowed researchers to sample genes directly from the environment; using such genes to construct phylogenies has led to the discovery of major new groups of prokaryotes. 27.5 Prokaryotes play key roles in the chemical cycles on which life depends. For example, prokaryotes are important decomposers, breaking down corpses and waste materials, thereby releasing nutrients to the environment where they can be used by other organisms. Prokaryotes also convert inorganic compounds to forms that other organisms can use. With respect to their ecological interactions, many prokaryotes form life-sustaining mutualisms with other species. In some cases, such as hydrothermal vent communities, the metabolic activities of prokaryotes provide an energy source on which hundreds of other species depend; in the absence of the prokaryotes, the community collapses. 27.6 Human well-being depends on our associations with mutualistic prokaryotes, such as the many species that live in our intestines and digest food that we cannot. Humans also can harness the remarkable metabolic capabilities of prokaryotes to produce a wide range of useful products. Negative effects of prokaryotes result primarily from bacterial pathogens that cause disease.

Test Your Understanding
1. d 2. a 3. c 4. c 5. b 6. a
8. (a)

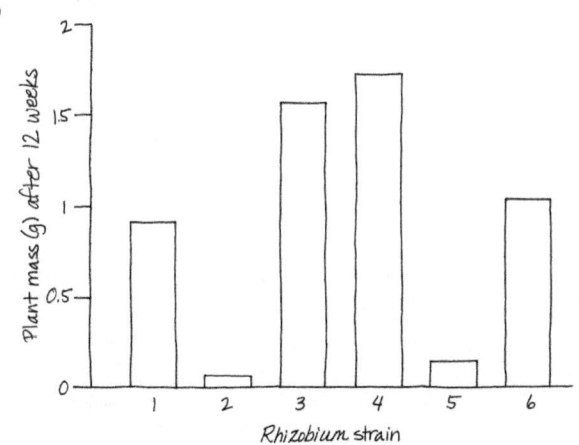

(b) Some *Rhizobium* strains are much more effective at promoting plant growth than other *Rhizobium* strains; the most ineffective strains have little positive effect (plant growth with these strains differs little from plant growth in the absence of *Rhizobium*). The ineffective strains may transfer relatively little nitrogen to their plant host, limiting plant growth. 10. Human sweat contains a number of important metabolites that can ultimately be metabolized by bacteria, such as *Staphylococcus epidermidis* and *Propionibacteria acnes*, which are part of your normal skin microbiota. With a warm, moist environment plus a source of carbon (in the form of lactate, pyruvate, and amino acids) and nitrogen (in the form of urea, amino acids, and NH_4^+), bacteria transferred from your skin to your equipment can grow. These bacteria can produce volatile organic compounds as a by-product of metabolism, thus causing an odour. To prevent this, the easiest thing to do is to hang up your gear to dry after each use to make it an inhospitable place for bacteria to grow!

Chapter 28

Figure Questions
Figure 28.3 Four. The first (and primary) genome is the DNA located in the chlorarachniophyte nucleus. A chlorarachniophyte also contain remnants of a green alga's nuclear DNA, located in the nucleomorph. Finally, mitochondria and chloroplasts contain DNA from the (different) bacteria from which they evolved. These two prokaryotic genomes comprise the third and fourth genomes contained within a chlorarachniophyte. Figure 28.13 The sperm cells in the diagram are produced by the asexual (mitotic) division of cells in a single male gametophyte, which was itself produced by the asexual (mitotic) division of a single zoospore. Thus, the sperm cells are all derived from a single zoospore and so are genetically identical to one another. Figure 28.16 Merozoites are produced by the asexual (mitotic) cell division of haploid sporozoites; similarly, gametocytes are produced by the asexual cell division of merozoites. Hence, it is likely that individuals in these three stages have the same complement of genes and that morphological differences between them result from changes in gene expression. Figure 28.17 The most recognized function of the chloroplast is photosynthesis, but there are many other functions associated with the organelle. Amongst these are nitrogen assimilation, fatty acid and amino acid biosynthesis, plus the synthesis of essential cofactors such as heme. The retention of the apicoplast and the presence of plastids in non-photosynthetic, parasitic plants is due to the requirement of these other metabolic functions. Figure 28.24 The following stage should be circled: step 6, where a mature cell undergoes mitosis and forms four or more daughter cells. In step 7, the zoospores eventually grow into mature haploid cells, but they do not produce new daughter cells. Likewise, in step 2, a mature cell develops into a gamete, but it does not produce new daughter cells. Figure 28.25 If the assumption is correct, then their results indicate that the DHFR-TS gene fusion may be a derived trait shared by members of three supergroups of eukaryotes (Excavata, SAR clade and Archaeplastida). However, if the assumption is not correct, the presence or absence of the gene fusion may tell little about phylogenetic history. For example, if the genes fused multiple times, groups could share the trait because of convergent evolution rather than common descent. If the genes were secondarily split, a group with such a split could be placed (incorrectly) in Unikonta rather than its correct placement in one of the other three supergroups. Figure 28.31 If diatom populations decrease in size as global temperatures warm, less carbon dioxide would be "pumped" from surface waters to the deep ocean floor. Atmospheric carbon dioxide levels might increase as a result, thereby potentially causing further warming. If this process continues, a positive-feedback loop would result in which warming causes diatom populations to drop, thereby causing additional warming, further drops in diatom populations, and so on.

Concept Check 28.1
1. Sample response: Protists include unicellular, colonial, and multicellular organisms; photoautotrophs, heterotrophs, and mixotrophs; species that reproduce asexually, sexually, or both ways; and organisms with diverse physical forms and adaptations. 2. Strong evidence shows that eukaryotes acquired mitochondria after an early eukaryote first engulfed and then formed an endosymbiotic association with an alpha proteobacterium. Similarly, chloroplasts in red and green algae appear to have descended from a photosynthetic cyanobacterium that was engulfed by an ancient heterotrophic eukaryote. Secondary endosymbiosis also played an important role: Various protist lineages acquired plastids by engulfing unicellular red or green algae. 3. The modified tree would look as follows:

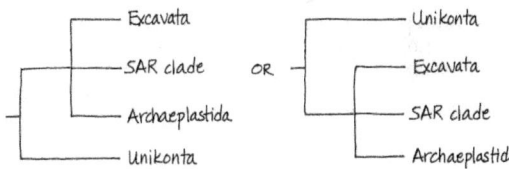

Concept Check 28.2
1. Their mitochondria do not have an electron transport chain and so cannot function in aerobic respiration. 2. Since the unknown protist is more closely related to diplomonads than to euglenids, it must have originated after the diplomonads and parabasalids diverged from the euglenozoans. In addition, since the unknown species has fully functional mitochondria—yet both diplomonads and parabasalids do not—it is likely that the unknown species originated *before* the last common ancestor of the diplomonads and parabasalids.

Concept Check 28.3
1. Because foram tests are hardened with calcium carbonate, they form long-lasting fossils in marine sediments and sedimentary rocks. 2. The plastid DNA would likely be more similar to the chromosomal DNA of cyanobacteria based on the well-supported hypothesis that eukaryotic plastids (such as those found in the eukaryotic groups listed) originated by an endosymbiosis event in which a eukaryote engulfed a cyanobacterium. If the plastid is derived from the cyanobacterium, its DNA would be derived from the bacterial DNA. 3. Figure 13.6b. Algae and plants with alternation of generations have a multicellular haploid stage and a multicellular diploid stage. In the other two life cycles, either the haploid stage or the diploid stage is unicellular. 4. During photosynthesis, aerobic algae produce O_2 and use CO_2. O_2 is produced as a by-product of the light reactions, while CO_2 is used as an input to the Calvin cycle (the end products of which are sugars). Aerobic algae also perform cellular respiration, which uses O_2 as an input and produces CO_2 as a waste product.

Concept Check 28.4

1. Many red algae contain an accessory pigment called phycoerythrin, which gives them a reddish colour and allows them to carry out photosynthesis in relatively deep coastal water. Also unlike brown algae, red algae have no flagellated stages in their life cycle and must depend on water currents to bring gametes together for fertilization. 2. *Ulva* contains many cells and is differentiated into leaflike blades and a rootlike holdfast. *Caulerpa*'s body is composed of multinucleate filaments without cross-walls, so it is essentially one large cell. 3. Red algae have no flagellated stages in their life cycle and hence must depend on water currents to bring their gametes together. This feature of their biology might increase the difficulty of reproducing on land. In contrast, the gametes of green algae are flagellated, making it possible for them to swim in thin films of water. In addition, a variety of green algae contain compounds in their cytoplasm, cell wall, or zygote coat that protect against intense sunlight and other terrestrial conditions. Such compounds may have increased the chance that descendants of green algae could survive on land.

Concept Check 28.5

1. Amoebozoans have lobe-shaped pseudopodia, whereas forams have threadlike pseudopodia. 2. Slime moulds are fungus-like in that they produce fruiting bodies that aid in the dispersal of spores, and they are animal-like in that they are motile and ingest food. However, slime moulds are more closely related to gymnamoebas and entamoebas than to fungi or animals. 3. Support. Unikonts lack the unique cytoskeletal features shared by many excavates (see Concept 28.2). Thus, if the unikonts were the first group of eukaryotes to diverge from other eukaryotes (as shown in Figure 28.25), it would be unlikely that the eukaryote common ancestor had the cytoskeletal features found today in many excavates. Such a result would strengthen the case that many excavates share cytoskeletal features because they are members of a monophyletic group, the Excavata.

Concept Check 28.6

1. Because photosynthetic protists constitute the base of aquatic food webs, many aquatic organisms depend on them for food, either directly or indirectly. (In addition, a substantial percentage of the oxygen produced in photosynthesis on Earth is made by photosynthetic protists.) 2. Protists form mutualistic and parasitic associations with other organisms. Examples include photosynthetic dinoflagellates that form a mutualistic symbiosis with coral polyps, and parabasalids that form a mutualistic symbiosis with termites, and the malaria-causing parasite, *Plasmodium*. 3. Corals depend on their dinoflagellate symbionts for nourishment, so coral bleaching would be expected to cause the corals to die. As the corals die, less food will be available for fishes and other species that eat coral. As a result, populations of these species may decline, and that, in turn, might cause populations of their predators to decline. 4. The two approaches differ in the evolutionary changes they may bring about. A strain of *Wolbachia* that confers resistance to infection by *Plasmodium* and does not harm mosquitoes would spread rapidly through the mosquito population. In this case, natural selection would favor any *Plasmodium* individuals that could overcome the resistance to infection conferred by *Wolbachia*. If insecticides are used, mosquitoes that are resistant to the insecticide would be favoured by natural selection. Hence, use of *Wolbachia* could cause evolution in *Plasmodium* populations, while using insecticides could cause evolution in mosquito populations.

Summary of Key Concepts Questions

28.1 There are several lines of evidence that indicate plastids evolved via an endosymbiosis with eukaryotic algae: (1) There are additional membranes surrounding the plastids (for a total of 3 or 4) in many protists that is believed to be remnants of the host endomembrane system (E.R. and/or vacuole) and the endosymbiont plasma membrane. (2) The presence of a vestigial nucleus sandwiched between the two sets of plastid membranes provides solid evidence for an algal ancestry. (3) Analyses of the genes encoding the plastid proteins often show they are related to free-living red or green algae. 28.2 Unique cytoskeletal features are shared by many excavates. In addition, some members of Excavata have an "excavated" feeding groove for which the group was named. DNA evidence does not strongly support or refute Excavata as a group. Overall, evidence for the group is relatively weak. 28.3 Stramenopiles and alveolates are hypothesized to have originated by secondary endosymbiosis. Under this hypothesis, we can infer that the common ancestor of these two groups had a plastid, in this case of red algal origin. Thus, we would expect that apicomplexans (and alveolate or stramenopile protists) either would have plastids or would have lost their plastids over the course of evolution. 28.4 Red algae, green algae, and land plants are placed in the same supergroup because considerable evidence indicates that these organisms all descended from the same ancestor, an ancient heterotrophic protist that acquired a cyanobacterial endosymbiont. 28.5 The unikonts are a diverse group of eukaryotes that includes many protists, along with animals and fungi. Most of the protists in Unikonta are amoebozoans, a clade of amoebas that have lobe- or tube-shaped pseudopodia (as opposed to the threadlike pseudopodia of rhizarians). Other protists in Unikonta include several groups that are closely related to fungi and several other groups that are closely related to animals. 28.6 Sample response: Ecologically important protists include photosynthetic dinoflagellates that provide essential sources of energy to their symbiotic partners, the corals that build coral reefs. Other important protistan symbionts include those that enable termites to digest wood and *Plasmodium*, the pathogen that causes malaria. Photosynthetic protists such as diatoms are among the most important producers in aquatic communities; as such, many other species in aquatic environments depend on them for food.

Test Your Understanding

1. d 2. b 3. b 4. b 5. d 6. c

7.

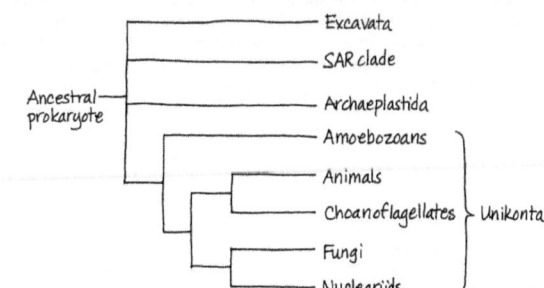

Pathogens that share a relatively recent common ancestor with humans should also share metabolic and structural characteristics with humans. Because drugs target the pathogen's metabolism or structure, developing drugs that harm the pathogen but not the patient should be most difficult for pathogens with whom we share the most recent evolutionary history. Working backward in time, we can use the phylogenetic tree to determine the order in which humans shared a common ancestor with pathogens in different taxa. This process leads to the prediction that it should be hardest to develop drugs to combat animal pathogens, followed by choanoflagellate pathogens, fungal and nucleariid pathogens, amoebozoans, other protists, and finally prokaryotes. 10. The picture shows the reproductive structure (fruiting body) of the dog-vomit fungus (*Fuligo septica*). *Fuligo septica* produces the largest fruiting body (aethalium) of the plasmodial slime moulds (mycetozoans). It can be up to 20 cm across, and will eventually produce spores (sexual reproduction) that will be released as it dries. After that, evidence of the slime mould will disappear, as the remaining parts of the life cycle are less visible. Molecular evidence has supported the inclusion of the slime moulds with the amoebozoans rather than the fungi, despite some superficial similarities to the latter. Unlike fungi, slime moulds have a flagellated stage and lack chitin in their cell walls, which is common in true fungi. The slime moulds are also unicellular, unlike fungi that produce fruiting bodies, and they acquire nutrition through phagocytosis rather than absorption as do true fungi.

Chapter 29

Figure Questions

Figure 29.3 In Figure 29.3, land plants are shown as a sister group to the charophytes, not as members of the charophyte lineage. However, current evidence indicates that land plants emerged from within the charophyte algae, indicating that land plants descended from the common ancestor that gave rise to the charophytes. Hence, when land plants are excluded from the charophytes, the charophytes are a paraphyletic group. Figure 29.4 The life cycle in Figure 13.6b has alternation of generations; the others do not. Unlike the animal life cycle (Figure 13.6a), in alternation of generations, meiosis produces spores, not gametes. These spores then divide repeatedly by mitosis, ultimately forming a multicellular haploid individual that produces gametes. There is no multicellular haploid stage in the animal life cycle. An alternation of generations life cycle also has a multicellular diploid stage, whereas the life cycle shown in Figure 13.6c does not. Figure 29.7 Yes. As shown in the diagram, the sperm cell and the egg cell that fuse each resulted from the mitotic division of spores produced by the same sporophyte. However, these spores would differ genetically from one another because they were produced by meiosis, a cell division process that generates genetic variation among the offspring cells. Figure 29.8 The basis for this is not known but the researchers hypothesized that the fertile shoots may be a source of food. It is also possible that fertile shoots release a compound/ odour that attracts the microarthropods. Either way, a mutualistic relationship was proposed. Figure 29.12 A fern that had wind-dispersed sperm would not require water for fertilization, thus removing a difficulty that ferns face when they live in arid environments. The fern would also be under strong selection to produce sperm above ground (as opposed to the current situation, where some fern gametophytes are located below ground). Figure 29.15 The Carboniferous was a dramatic time of climate change, extinction, and animal diversification. The supercontinent called Pangaea was forming during the Carboniferous and there were cyclic changes in water levels from shallow warm waters on the continents to a drier period. At the start of the Carboniferous, amphibians were abundant and bony fishes and sharks were diversifying in the oceans and fresh water. The first tetrapods (like *Hylonomus*) with amniotic eggs adapted to survival on land were present and later became abundant. Significantly, reptiles diversified during the Carboniferous. Arthropods were also abundant (and often quite large!) during the Carboniferous period.

Concept Check 29.1

1. Land plants share some key traits only with charophytes: rings of cellulose-synthesizing complexes, presence of peroxisome enzymes, similarity in sperm structure, and the formation of a phragmoplast in cell division. Comparisons of nuclear and chloroplast genes also point to a common ancestry. 2. Spore walls toughened by sporopollenin (protects against harsh environmental conditions); multicellular, dependent embryos (provides nutrients and protection to the developing embryo); cuticle (reduces water loss); stomata (control gas exchange and reduce water loss) 3. The multicellular diploid stage of the life cycle would not produce gametes. Instead, both males and females would produce haploid spores by meiosis. These spores would give rise to multicellular male and female haploid stages—a major change from the single-celled haploid stages (sperm and eggs) that we actually have. The multicellular haploid stages would produce gametes and reproduce sexually. An individual at the multicellular haploid stage of the human life cycle might look like us, or it might look completely different. 4. To prevent excessive water loss, many

animals have evolved a tough skin (tetrapods) or thick, waxy cuticle (invertebrates). Plants have also developed a number of strategies to reduce water loss, such as a waxy cuticle. For gas exchange, while most land plants have stomata, animals have a variety of strategies including lungs (tetrapods) or tracheal tubes (arthropods) for gas exchange rather than gills that are efficient in aquatic settings. To counter the effects of gravity and increase height, plants developed lignified cell walls and a vascular system (xylem) for water transport. Many animals, however, have developed limbs and stronger skeletal elements to support the body on land and to facilitate efficient movement.

Concept Check 29.2

1. Bryophytes do not have a vascular transport system, and their life cycle is dominated by gametophytes rather than sporophytes. 2. Answers may include the following: Large surface area of protonema enhances absorption of water and minerals; the vase-shaped archegonia protect eggs during fertilization and transport nutrients to the embryos via placental transfer cells; the stalk-like seta conducts nutrients from the gametophyte to the capsule, where spores are produced; the peristome enables gradual spore discharge; stomata enable CO_2/O_2 exchange while minimizing water loss; lightweight spores are readily dispersed by wind. 3. Effects of global warming on peatlands could result in positive feedback, which occurs when an end product of a process increases its own production. In this case, global warming is expected to lower the water levels of some peatlands. This would expose peat to air and cause it to decompose, thereby releasing stored CO_2 to the atmosphere. The release of more stored CO_2 to the atmosphere could cause additional global warming, which in turn could cause further drops in water levels, the release of still more CO_2 to the atmosphere, additional warming, and so on: an example of positive feedback.

Concept Check 29.3

1. Lycophytes have microphylls, whereas seed plants and monilophyte (ferns and their relatives) have megaphylls. Monilophytes and seed plants also share other traits not found in lycophytes, such as overtopping growth and the initiation of new root branches at various points along the length of an existing root. 2. Both seedless vascular plants and bryophytes have flagellated sperm that require moisture for fertilization; this shared similarity poses challenges for these species in arid regions. With respect to key differences, seedless vascular plants have lignified, well-developed vascular tissue, a trait that enables the sporophyte to grow tall and that has transformed life on Earth (via the formation of forests). Seedless vascular plants also have true leaves and roots, which, when compared with bryophytes, provide increased surface area for photosynthesis and improve their ability to extract nutrients from soil. 3. If lycophytes and monilophytes formed a clade, the traits shared by monilophytes and seed plants might have been present in the common ancestor of all vascular plants, but lost in the lycophytes. Alternatively, the common ancestor of all vascular plants may have lacked the traits shared by monilophytes and seed plants; in this case, monilophytes and seed plants would share these traits as a result of convergent evolution. 4. Three mechanisms contribute to the production of genetic variation in sexual reproduction: independent assortment of chromosomes, crossing over, and random fertilization. If fertilization were to occur between gametes from the same gametophyte, all of the offspring would be genetically identical. This would be the case because all of the cells produced by a gametophyte—including its sperm and egg cells—are the descendants of a single spore and hence are genetically identical. Genetic variation would continue to be generated by the first two mechanisms mentioned, but overall, the amount of genetic variation produced by sexual reproduction would drop.

Summary of Key Concepts Questions

29.1

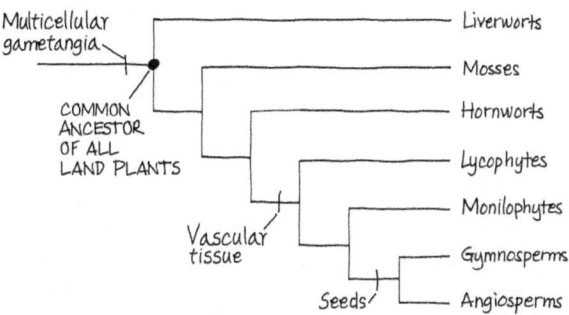

29.2 Some mosses colonize bare, sandy soils, leading to the increased retention of nitrogen in these otherwise low-nitrogen environments. Other mosses harbour nitrogen-fixing cyanobacteria that increase the availability of nitrogen in the ecosystem. The moss *Sphagnum* is often a major component of deposits of peat (partially decayed organic material). Boggy regions with thick layers of peat, known as peatlands, cover broad geographic regions and contain large reservoirs of carbon. By storing large amounts of carbon—in effect, removing CO_2 from the atmosphere—peatlands affect the global climate, making them of considerable ecological importance. 29.3 Lignified vascular tissue provided the strength needed to support a tall plant against gravity, as well as a means to transport water and nutrients to plant parts located high above ground. Roots were another key trait, anchoring the plant to the ground and providing additional structural support for plants that grew tall. Tall plants could shade shorter plants, thereby outcompeting them for light. Because the spores of a tall plant disperse farther than the spores of a short plant, it is also likely that tall plants could colonize new habitats more rapidly than short plants.

Test Your Understanding

1. b 2. d 3. d 4. b 5. a 6. b 7. a. diploid; b. haploid; c. haploid; d. diploid; e. haploid 8. Based on our current understanding of the evolution of major plant groups, the phylogeny has the four branch points shown here:

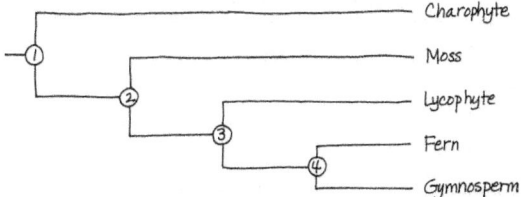

Derived characters unique to the charophyte and land plant clade (indicated by branch point 1) include rings of cellulose-synthesizing complexes, peroxisome enzymes, flagellated sperm structure, and a phragmoplast. Derived characters unique to the land plant clade (branch point 2) include apical meristems, alternation of generations, walled spores produced in sporangia, and multicellular gametangia. Derived characters unique to the vascular plant clade (branch point 3) include life cycles with dominant sporophytes, complex vascular systems (xylem and phloem), and well-developed roots and leaves. Derived characters unique to the monilophyte and seed plant clade (branch point 4) include megaphylls and overtopping growth.

9. (a)

(b) In the first 40 years after a fire, nitrogen fixation rates were below 0.01 kg per ha per yr, which was less than 1% of the amount of nitrogen deposited from the atmosphere. Thus, in the initial decades after a fire, the moss *Pleurozium* and the nitrogen-fixing bacteria it harbours had relatively little effect on the amount of nitrogen added to the forest. With time, however, *Pleurozium* and its symbiotic, nitrogen-fixing bacteria became increasingly important. By 170 years after a fire, the percentage of the ground surface covered by the moss had increased to about 70%, leading to a corresponding increase in populations of the symbiotic bacteria. As would be predicted from this result, in older forests considerably more nitrogen (130–300%) was added by nitrogen fixation than was deposited from the atmosphere.

Chapter 30

Figure Questions

Figure 30.2 Retaining the gametophyte within the sporophyte shields the egg-containing gametophyte from UV radiation. UV radiation is a mutagen. Hence, we would expect fewer mutations to occur in the egg cells produced by a gametophyte retained within the body of a sporophyte. Most mutations are harmful. Thus, the fitness of embryos should increase because fewer embryos would carry harmful mutations. Figure 30.3 Three generations: (1) the current sporophyte (cells of ploidy $2n$, found in the seed coat and in the megasporangium remnant that surrounds the spore wall); (2) the female gametophyte (cells of ploidy n, found in the food supply); and (3) the sporophyte of the next generation (cells of ploidy $2n$, found in the embryo) Figure 30.5 Mitosis. A single haploid megaspore divides by mitosis to produce a multicellular, haploid female gametophyte. Likewise, a single haploid microspore divides by mitosis to produce a multicellular male gametophyte.)
Figure 30.14 No. The branching order shown could still be correct if *Amborella* and other early angiosperms had originated prior to 150 million years ago, but angiosperm fossils of that age had not yet been discovered. In such a situation, the 140-million-year-old date for the origin of the angiosperms shown on the phylogeny would be incorrect. Figure 30.18 Many insect pollinators (such as bees) can visit and pollinate many different plant species, but others have specialized to pollinate one or a few plants (as in Figure 38.6). Under this latter scenario, declines in the population of the plant would be expected to lead to declines in the insect pollinator that acquires food from the flower. Declines in the insect could lead to declines in fertilization success of the plant, and hence affect population numbers.

Concept Check 30.1

1. To reach the eggs, the flagellated sperm of seedless plants must swim through a film of water, usually over a distance of no more than a few centimetres. In contrast, the sperm of seed plants do not require water because they are produced within pollen grains that can be transported long distances by wind or by animal pollinators. Although flagellated in some species, the sperm of seed plants do not require mobility because pollen tubes convey them from the point at which the pollen grain is deposited (near the ovules) directly to the eggs. 2. The reduced gametophytes of seed plants are nurtured by sporophytes and protected from stress, such as drought conditions and UV radiation. Pollen grains, with walls containing sporopollenin, provide protection during transport by wind or animals. Seeds have one or two layers of protective tissue, the seed coat, that improve survival by providing more protection from environmental stresses than do the walls of spores. Seeds also contain a stored supply of food, which provides nourishment for growth after dormancy is broken and the embryo emerges as a seedling. 3. If a seed could not enter dormancy, the embryo would continue to grow after it was fertilized. As a result, the embryo might rapidly become too large to be dispersed, thus limiting its transport. The embryo's chance of survival might also be reduced because it could not delay growth until conditions become favourable.

Concept Check 30.2

1. Although gymnosperms are similar in not having their seeds enclosed in ovaries and fruits, their seed-bearing structures vary greatly. For instance, cycads have large cones, whereas some gymnosperms, such as *Ginkgo* and *Gnetum*, have small cones that look somewhat like berries, even though they are not fruits. Leaf shape also varies greatly, from the needles of many conifers to the palmlike leaves of cycads to *Gnetum* leaves that look like those of flowering plants. 2. The pine life cycle illustrates heterospory, as ovulate cones produce megaspores and pollen cones produce microspores. The reduced gametophytes are evident in the form of the microscopic pollen grains that develop from microspores and the microscopic female gametophyte that develops from the megaspore. The egg is shown developing within an ovule, and a pollen tube is shown conveying the sperm. The figure also shows the protective and nutritive features of a seed. 3. No. Fossil evidence indicates that gymnosperms originated at least 305 million years ago, but this does not mean that angiosperms are that old—only that the most recent common ancestor of gymnosperms and angiosperms must be that old.

Concept Check 30.3

1. In the oak's life cycle, the tree (the sporophyte) produces flowers, which contain gametophytes in pollen grains and ovules; the eggs in ovules are fertilized; the mature ovaries develop into dry fruits called acorns. We can view the oak's life cycle as starting when the acorn seeds germinate, resulting in embryos giving rise to seedlings and finally to mature trees, which produce flowers—and then more acorns. 2. Pine cones and flowers both have sporophylls, modified leaves that produce spores. Pine trees have separate pollen cones (with pollen grains) and ovulate cones (with ovules inside cone scales). In flowers, pollen grains are produced by the anthers of stamens, and ovules are within the ovaries of carpels. Unlike pine cones, many flowers produce both pollen and ovules. In flowers, the fertilized ovule matures into a fruit, which is not the case for the ovulate cones of pine trees. 3. There are a number of considerations. A key one would be to consider the type of flower the tree produces, especially if for decorative purposes. Apples, cherries and magnolias have beautiful spring flowers. However, it is important to consider the production of nuisance fruit that litters city streets. This could be from fruits (e.g., chestnuts that produce spiny seed pods) to the production of wind-dispersed seeds (e.g., poplars that produce cotton-like fluff for dispersal). For trees with separate male and female plants (dioecious), planting only males can prevent this. Another issue is pollen production, which can be a nuisance simply by the amount of pollen produced, but can contribute to seasonal allergies within cities. Finally, one has to be mindful that when using non-native species, there is the potential for them becoming invasive. Spreading to native habitats via seed dispersal or asexual reproduction is increasingly a concern because of the potential to out-compete native plant varieties (e.g., buckthorn).

Concept Check 30.4

1. Plant diversity can be considered a resource because plants provide many important benefits to humans; as a resource, plant diversity is nonrenewable because if a species is lost to extinction, that loss is permanent. 2. A detailed phylogeny of the seed plants would identify many different monophyletic groups of seed plants. Using this phylogeny, researchers could look for clades that contained species in which medicinally useful compounds had already been discovered. Identification of such clades would allow researchers to concentrate their search for new medicinal compounds among clade members—as opposed to searching for new compounds in species that were selected at random from the more than 250 000 existing species of seed plants.

Summary of Key Concepts Questions

30.1 The integument of an ovule develops into the protective seed coat of a seed. The ovule's megaspore develops into a haploid female gametophyte, and two parts of the seed are related to that gametophyte: The food supply of the seed is derived from haploid gametophyte cells, and the embryo of the seed develops after the female gametophyte's egg cell is fertilized by a sperm cell. A remnant of the ovule's megasporangium surrounds the spore wall that encloses the seed's food supply and embryo. 30.2 Gymnosperms arose about 305 million years ago, making them a successful group in terms of their evolutionary longevity. Gymnosperms have the five derived traits common to all seed plants (reduced gametophytes, heterospory, ovules, pollen, and seeds), making them well adapted for life on land. Finally, because gymnosperms dominate immense geographic regions today, the group is also highly successful in geographic distribution. 30.3 Darwin was troubled by the relatively sudden and geographically widespread appearance of angiosperms in the fossil record.

Fossil evidence shows that angiosperms arose and began to diversify over a period of 20–30 million years, a less rapid event than was suggested by the fossils known during Darwin's lifetime. Fossil discoveries have also uncovered extinct lineages of woody seed plants that may have been closely related to angiosperms; one such group, the Bennettitales, had flowerlike structures that may have been pollinated by insects. Phylogenetic analyses have identified Amborella as the most basal angiosperm lineage; Amborella is woody, and hence its basal position supports the conclusion (from fossils) that the angiosperm common ancestor was likely woody. 30.4 Ultimately, humans are dependent on plants for many products including lumber, oils, textiles, and a wide variety of secondary products that are effective medicines. Our major dependence on plants is for food, both for ourselves and for the animals we eat. Plants, however, are often dependent on insects for reproduction (pollination) and plants and insects have been co-evolving for millions of years. So, for modern food production, we have created co-dependent interactions between us, the plants we use, and the insects that facilitate plant reproduction.

Test Your Understanding

1. c 2. a 3. b 4. a 5. c
6.

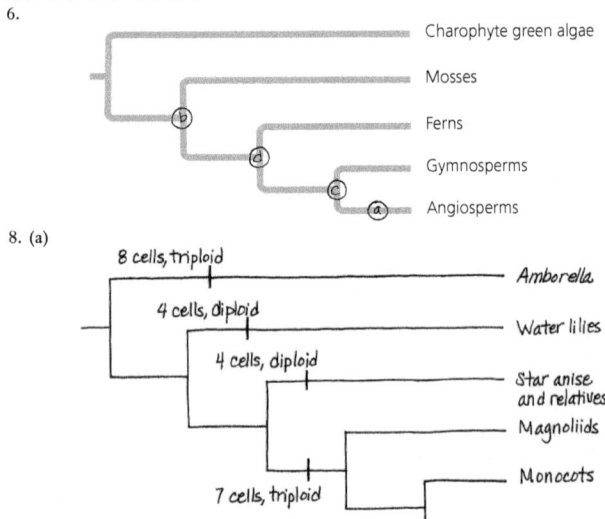

8. (a)

(b) The phylogeny indicates that basal angiosperms differed from other angiosperms in terms of the number of cells in female gametophytes and the ploidy of the endosperm. The ancestral state of the angiosperms cannot be determined from these data alone. It is possible that the common ancestor of angiosperms had seven-celled female gametophytes and triploid endosperm and hence that the eight-celled and four-celled conditions found in basal angiosperms represent derived traits for those lineages. Alternatively, either the eight-celled or four-celled condition may represent the ancestral state. 10. Some tree ferns can grow upwards of 20 m tall. The ability to grow tall is due to the presence of lignin in the cell wall, which gives strength to the "trunk," which is similar to gymnosperms and angiosperms. However, tree ferns are still vascular, seedless plants that reproduce through spores. The spores give rise to the gametophytes that produce gametes (egg and sperm) for sexual reproduction. This is quite different from gymnosperms and angiosperms that produce seeds. Seed plants retain the female gametophyte and become fertilized by pollen from the male gametophyte. From this a seed develops. Seeds have a tough outer coat and contain a food supply (endosperm) for the developing embryo. Seeds may also have adaptations for dispersal. The ability of seeds to disperse and survive harsh conditions accounts for their success.

Chapter 31

Figure Questions

Figure 31.2 DNA from each of these mushrooms would be identical if each mushroom is part of a single hyphal network, as is likely. Figure 31.5 The haploid spores produced in the sexual portion of the life cycle develop from haploid nuclei that were produced by meiosis; because genetic recombination occurs during meiosis, these spores will differ genetically from one another. In contrast, the haploid spores produced in the asexual portion of the life cycle develop from nuclei that were produced by mitosis; as a result, these spores are genetically identical to one another. Figure 31.15 One or both of the following would apply to each species: DNA analyses would reveal that it is a member of the ascomycete clade, or aspects of its sexual life cycle would indicate that it is an ascomycete (for example, it would produce asci and ascospores). Figure 31.20 Two possible controls would be E–P– and E+P–. Results from an E–P+ control could be compared with results from the E+P+ experiment, and results from an E+P– control could be compared with results from the E+P+ experiment. Together, these two comparisons would indicate whether the addition of the pathogen causes an increase in leaf mortality. Results from an E–P– experiment could also be compared with results from the second control (E+P–) to determine whether adding the endophytes has a negative effect on the plant.

Concept Check 31.1

1. Both a fungus and a human are heterotrophs. Many fungi digest their food externally by secreting enzymes into the food and then absorbing the small molecules

that result from digestion. Other fungi absorb such small molecules directly from their environment. In contrast, humans (and most other animals) ingest relatively large pieces of food and digest the food within their bodies. 2. The ancestors of such a mutualist most likely secreted powerful enzymes to digest the body of their insect host. Since such enzymes would harm a living host, it is likely that the mutualist would not produce such enzymes or would restrict their secretion and use. 3. Carbon that enters the plant through stomata is fixed into sugar through photosynthesis. Some of these sugars are absorbed by the fungus that partners with the plant to form mycorrhizae; others are transported within the plant body and used in the plant. Thus, the carbon may be deposited in either the body of the plant or the body of the fungus.

Concept Check 31.2

1. The majority of the fungal life cycle is spent in the haploid stage, whereas the majority of the human life cycle is spent in the diploid stage. 2. The two mushrooms might be reproductive structures of the same mycelium (the same organism). Or they might be parts of two separate organisms that have arisen from a single parent organism through asexual reproduction and thus carry the same genetic information.

Concept Check 31.3

1. DNA evidence indicates that fungi, animals, and their protistan relatives form a clade, the opisthokonts. Furthermore, an early-diverging fungal lineage, the chytrids, have posterior flagella, as do most other opisthokonts. This suggests that other fungal lineages lost their flagella after diverging from chytrids. 2. This indicates that fungi had already established mutualistic relationships with plants by the date the fossils of the earliest vascular plants had formed. 3. Fungi are heterotrophs. Prior to the colonization of land by plants, terrestrial fungi would have lived where other organisms (or their remains) were present and provided a source of food. Thus, if fungi had colonized land before plants, they could have fed on any prokaryotes or protists that lived on land or by the water's edge—but not on the plants or animals on which many fungi feed today.

Concept Check 31.4

1. Flagellated spores; molecular evidence also suggests that chytrids are an early-diverging fungal lineage. 2. Possible answers include the following: In zygomycetes, the sturdy, thick-walled zygosporangium can withstand harsh conditions and then undergo karyogamy and meiosis when the environment is favourable for reproduction. In glomeromycetes, the hyphae have a specialized morphology that enables the fungi to form arbuscular mycorrhizae with plant roots. In ascomycetes, the asexual spores (conidia) are often produced in chains or clusters at the tips of conidiophores, where they are easily dispersed by wind. The often cup-shaped ascocarps house the sexual spore-forming asci. In basidiomycetes, the basidiocarp supports and protects a large surface area of basidia, from which spores are dispersed. 3. Such a change to the life cycle of an ascomycete would reduce the number and genetic diversity of ascospores that result from a mating event. Ascospore number would drop because a mating event would lead to the formation of only one ascus. Ascospore genetic diversity would also drop because in ascomycetes, one mating event leads to the formation of asci by many different dikaryotic cells. As a result, genetic recombination and meiosis occur independently many different times—which could not happen if only a single ascus was formed. It is also likely that if such an ascomycete formed an ascocarp, the shape of the ascocarp would differ considerably from that found in its close relatives.

Concept Check 31.5

1. A suitable environment for growth, retention of water and minerals, protection from intense sunlight, and protection from being eaten 2. A hardy spore stage enables dispersal to host organisms through a variety of mechanisms; their ability to grow rapidly in a favourable new environment enables them to capitalize on the host's resources. 3. Many different outcomes might have occurred. Organisms that currently form mutualisms with fungi might have gained the ability to perform the tasks currently done by their fungal partners, or they might have formed similar mutualisms with other organisms (such as bacteria). Alternatively, organisms that currently form mutualisms with fungi might be less effective at living in their present environments. For example, the colonization of land by plants might have been more difficult. And if plants did eventually colonize land without fungal mutualists, natural selection might have favoured plants that formed more highly divided and extensive root systems (in part replacing mycorrhizae).

Summary of Key Concepts Questions

31.1 The body of a multicellular fungus typically consists of thin filaments called hyphae. These filaments form an interwoven mass (mycelium) that penetrates the substrate on which the fungus grows and feeds. Because the individual filaments are thin, the surface-to-volume ratio of the mycelium is maximized, making nutrient absorption highly efficient.
31.2

31.3 Phylogenetic analyses show that fungi and animals are more closely related to each other than either is to other multicellular eukaryotes (such as plants or multicellular algae). These analyses also show that fungi are more closely related to single-celled protists called nucleariids than they are to animals, whereas animals are more closely related to a different group of single-celled protists, the choanoflagellates, than they are to fungi. In combination, these results indicate that multicellularity evolved in fungi and animals independently, from different single-celled ancestors.
31.4

31.5 As decomposers, fungi break down the bodies of dead organisms, thereby recycling elements between the living and nonliving environments. Without the activities of fungi and bacterial decomposers, essential nutrients would remain tied up in organic matter, and life would cease. As an example of their key role as mutualists, fungi form mycorrhizal associations with plants. These associations improve the growth and survival of plants, thereby indirectly affecting the many other species (humans included) that depend on plants. As pathogens, fungi harm other species. In some cases, fungal pathogens have caused their host populations to decline across broad geographic regions, as seen for the American chestnut.

Test Your Understanding

1. b 2. d 3. a 4. d
5.

As indicated by the raw data and bar graph, grass plants with endophytes (E+) produced more new shoots and had greater biomass than did grass plants that lacked endophytes (E–). These differences were especially pronounced at the highest soil temperature, where E– grass plants produced no new shoots and had a biomass of zero (indicating they were dead). 8. The size of *Prototaxites* is indeed curious. In fact, it's the size of this organism that is problematic in the interpretation. Why would it be so large, much larger than the ankle-high land plants that were also present at this time? Plants, for instance, grew tall in response to a competition for light, leading to the dominant lycopod forests of the Carboniferous over 100 million years after the appearance of *Prototaxites*. That is one reason why the fossils are interpreted as a lichen or some other photosynthetic organism. If it were a lichen, the size could be related to competition for sunlight. However, if the fossil is a sporophyte structure of a fungus, then the height may have facilitated the dispersal of spores, especially if the environment was patchy. Unfortunately, no spore-producing structure or fossil spores have been identified. The size of this structure also begs the question of what nutritional sources would allow the fungus to produce such a structure! It likely relied on decaying plant biomass having an extensive network of hyphae.

Chapter 32

Figure Questions

Figure 32.3 As described in ❶ and ❷, choanoflagellates and a broad range of animals have collar cells. Since collar cells have never been observed in plants, fungi, or non-choanoflagellate protists, this suggests that choanoflagellates may be more closely related to animals than to other eukaryotes. If choanoflagellates are more closely related to animals than to any other group of eukaryotes, choanoflagellates and animals should share other traits that are not found in other eukaryotes. The data described in ❸ are consistent with this prediction. Figure 32.7 The Cambrian period represented by the Burgess Shale site was well before the appearance of plants, so one wouldn't predict any aquatic plants. One would predict that there may be red or green algae, since these groups diverged early, around that time frame. One would expect the presence of cyanobacteria as well, the earliest photosynthetic organisms. Though not as commonly discussed, there are abundant algal (potentially green and red) and filamentous cyanobacteria-like fossils at the Burgess Shale site. Figure 32.10 The cells of an early embryo with deuterostome development typically are not committed to a particular developmental fate, whereas the cells of an early embryo with protostome development typically are committed to a particular developmental fate. As a result, an embryo with deuterostome development would be more likely to contain stem cells that could give rise to cells of any type. Figure 32.11 Cnidaria is the sister phylum in this figure.

Concept Check 32.1

1. In most animals, the zygote undergoes cleavage, which leads to the formation of a blastula. Next, in gastrulation, one end of the embryo folds inward, producing layers of embryonic tissue. As the cells of these layers differentiate, a wide variety of animal forms result. Despite the diversity of animal forms, animal development is controlled by a similar set of *Hox* genes across a broad range of taxa. 2. The imaginary plant would require tissues composed of cells that were analogous to the muscle and nerve cells found in animals: "Muscle" tissue would be necessary for the plant to chase prey, and "nerve" tissue would be required for the plant to coordinate its movements when chasing prey. To digest captured prey, the plant would need to either secrete enzymes into one or more digestive cavities (which could be modified leaves, as in a Venus flytrap) or secrete enzymes outside of its body and feed by absorption. To extract nutrients from the soil—yet be able to chase prey—the plant would need something other than fixed roots, perhaps retractable "roots" or a way to ingest soil. To conduct photosynthesis, the plant would require chloroplasts. Overall, such an imaginary plant would be very similar to an animal that had chloroplasts and retractable roots.

Concept Check 32.2

1. c, b, a, d 2. We cannot infer whether animals originated before or after fungi. If correct, the date provided for the most recent common ancestor of fungi and animals would indicate that animals originated some time within the last billion years. The fossil record indicates that animals originated at least 565 million years ago. Thus, we could conclude only that animals originated sometime between 1 billion years ago and 565 million years ago.

Concept Check 32.3

1. Grade-level characteristics are those that multiple lineages share regardless of evolutionary history. Some grade-level characteristics may have evolved multiple times independently. Features that unite clades are derived characteristics that originated in a common ancestor and were passed on to the various descendants. 2. A snail has a spiral and determinate cleavage pattern; a human has radial, indeterminate cleavage. In a snail, the coelomic cavity is formed by splitting of mesoderm masses; in a human, the coelom forms from folds of archenteron. In a snail, the mouth forms from the blastopore; in a human, the anus develops from the blastopore. 3. Most coelomate triploblasts have two openings to their digestive tract, a mouth and an anus. As such, their bodies have a structure that is analogous to that of a doughnut: The digestive tract (the hole of the doughnut) runs from the mouth to the anus and is surrounded by various tissues (the solid part of the doughnut). The doughnut analogy is most obvious at early stages of development (see Figure 32.10c).

Concept Check 32.4

1. Cnidarians possess true tissues, while sponges do not. Also unlike sponges, cnidarians exhibit body symmetry, though it is radial and not bilateral as in other animal phyla. 2. Under the hypothesis that ctenophores are basal metazoans, sponges (which lack true tissues) would be nested within a clade whose other members all have true tissues.

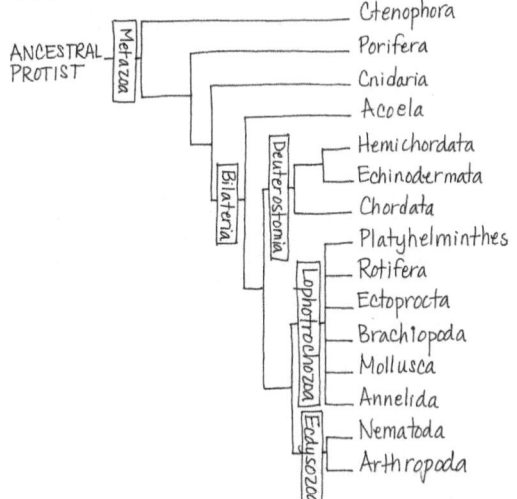

3. The phylogeny in Figure 32.11 indicates that molluscs are members of Lophotrochozoa, one of the three main groups of bilaterians (the others being Deuterostomia and Ecdysozoa). As seen in Figure 25.11, the fossil record shows that molluscs were present tens of millions of years before the Cambrian explosion. Thus, long before the Cambrian explosion, the lophotrochoan clade had formed and was evolving independently of the evolutionary lineages leading to Deuterostomia and Ecdysozoa. Based on the phylogeny in Figure 32.11, we can also conclude that the lineages leading to Deuterostomia and Ecdysozoa were independent of one another before the Cambrian explosion. Since the lineages leading to the three main clades

of bilaterians were evolving independently of one another prior to the Cambrian explosion, that explosion could be viewed as consisting of three "explosions," not one.

Summary of Key Concepts Questions

32.1 Unlike animals, which are heterotrophs that ingest their food, plants are autotrophs, and fungi are heterotrophs that grow on their food and feed by absorption. Animals lack cell walls, which are found in both plants and fungi. Animals also have muscle tissue and nerve tissue, which are not found in either plants or fungi. In addition, the sperm and egg cells of animals are produced by meiotic division, unlike what occurs in plants and fungi (where reproductive cells such as sperm and eggs are produced by mitotic division). Finally, animals regulate the development of body form with *Hox* genes, a unique group of genes that is not found in either plants or fungi. 32.2 Current hypotheses about the cause of the Cambrian explosion include new predator-prey relationships, an increase in atmospheric oxygen, and an increase in developmental flexibility provided by the origin of *Hox* genes and other genetic changes. 32.3 Body plans provide a helpful way to compare and contrast key features of organisms. However, phylogenetic analyses show that similar body plans have arisen independently in different groups of organisms. As such, similar body plans may have arisen by convergent evolution and hence may not be informative about evolutionary relationships. 32.4 Listed in order from the most to the least inclusive clade, humans belong to Metazoa, Eumetazoa, Bilateria, Deuterostomia, and Chordata.

Test Your Understanding

1. a 2. c 3. d 4. c 5. b

7.

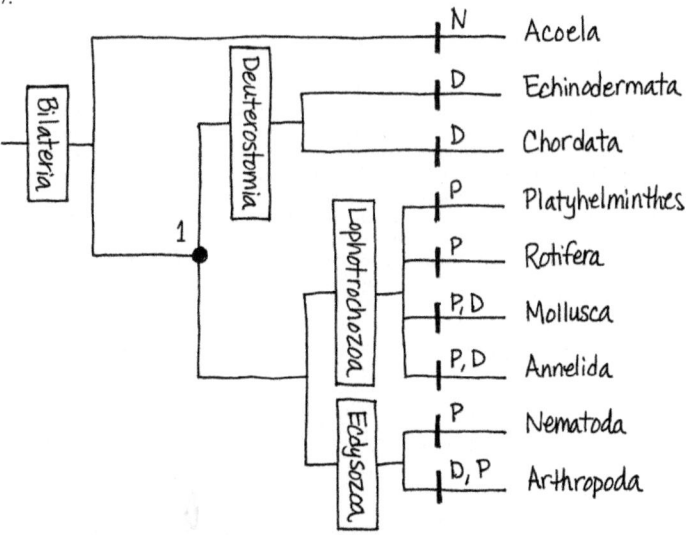

Based on the phylogeny, the ancestral condition in bilaterians may have been similar to that in Acoela, where the blastopore closes and the mouth forms elsewhere (N); however, it is also possible that blastopore fate in Acoela is a derived trait and hence is not informative about the ancestral condition. Although the phylogeny indicates that blastopore fate has changed multiple times over the course of evolution, a precise estimate cannot be made. For example, if we assume that the common ancestor of all non-Acoela bilaterians (marked with a 1 on the tree) exhibited protostomy, then blastopore fate has changed at least five times: once in common ancestor 1, once in Deuterostomia, at least once in Mollusca, at least once in Annelida, and at least once in Arthropoda. Other assumptions would lead to different estimates.

Chapter 33

Figure Questions

Figure 33.8 Within a reproductive polyp, a cell that gives rise to a medusa would have to divide by meiosis. A resulting haploid cell would then divide repeatedly (by mitosis), forming a haploid medusa. Later, cells in the medusa's gonads would divide by mitosis, forming the haploid eggs and sperm. Figure 33.11 Adding fertilizer to the water supply would probably increase the abundance of algae, and that, in turn, would likely increase the abundance of snails (which eat algae). If the water were also contaminated with infected human feces, an increase in the number of snails would likely lead to an increase in the abundance of blood flukes (which require snails as an intermediate host). As a result, the occurrence of schistosomiasis might increase. Figure 33.22 The extinctions of freshwater bivalves might lead to an increase in the abundance of photosynthetic protists and bacteria. Because these organisms are at the base of aquatic food webs, increases in their abundance could have major effects on aquatic communities (including both increases and decreases in the abundance of other species). Figure 33.30 Such a result would be consistent with the *Ubx* and *abd-A Hox* genes having played a major role in the evolution of increased body segment diversity in arthropods. However, by itself, such a result would simply show that the presence of the *Ubx* and *abd-A Hox* genes was *correlated with* an increase in body segment diversity in arthropods; it would not provide direct experimental evidence that the acquisition of the *Ubx* and *adb-A* genes *caused* an increase in arthropod body segment diversity. Figure 33.36 You should have circled the clade that includes the insects, remipedians, and other crustaceans, along with the branch point that represents their most recent common ancestor.

Concept Check 33.1

1. The flagella of choanocytes draw water through their collars, which trap food particles. The particles are engulfed by phagocytosis and digested, either by choanocytes or by amoebocytes. 2. The collar cells of sponges (and some other animals—see Chapters 32) bear a striking resemblance to a choanoflagellate cell. This suggests that the last common ancestor of animals and their protist sister group may have resembled a choanoflagellate. Nevertheless, mesomycetozoans could still be the sister group of animals. If this is the case, the lack of collar cells in mesomycetozoans would indicate that over time their structure evolved in ways that caused it to no longer resemble a choanoflagellate cell. It is also possible that choanoflagellates and sponges share similar-looking collar cells as a result of convergent evolution.

Concept Check 33.2

1. Both the polyp and the medusa are composed of an outer epidermis and an inner gastrodermis separated by a gelatinous layer, the mesoglea. The polyp is a cylindrical form that adheres to the substrate by its aboral end; the medusa is a flattened, mouth-down form that moves freely in the water. 2. Cnidarian stinging cells (cnidocytes) function in defence and prey capture. They contain capsule-like organelles (cnidae), which in turn contain coiled threads. The threads either inject a toxin or stick to and entangle small prey. 3. Evolution is not goal oriented; hence, it would not be correct to argue that cnidarians were not "highly evolved" simply because their form had changed relatively little over the past 560 million years. Instead, the fact that cnidarians have persisted for hundreds of millions of years indicates that the cnidarian body plan is a highly successful one.

Concept Check 33.3

1. Tapeworms can absorb food from their environment and release ammonia into their environment through their body surface because their body is very flat, due in part to the lack of a coelom. 2. The inner tube is the alimentary canal, which runs the length of the body. The outer tube is the body wall. The two tubes are separated by the coelom. 3. All molluscs have inherited a foot from their common ancestor. However, in different groups of molluscs, the structure of the foot has been modified over time (by natural selection) in ways that reflect how the foot is used in locomotion by members of each clade. In gastropods, the foot is used as a holdfast or to move slowly on the substrate. In cephalopods, the foot has been modified into part of the tentacles and into an excurrent siphon, through which water is propelled (resulting in movement in the opposite direction).

Concept Check 33.4

1. Nematodes lack body segments and a true coelom; annelids have both. 2. The arthropod exoskeleton, which had already evolved in the ocean, allows terrestrial species to retain water and support their bodies on land. Wings allow them to disperse quickly to new habitats and to find food and mates. The tracheal system allows for efficient gas exchange despite the presence of an exoskeleton. 3. Yes. Under the traditional hypothesis, we would expect body segmentation to be controlled by similar *Hox* genes in annelids and arthropods. However, if annelids are in Lophotrochozoa and arthropods are in Ecdysozoa, body segmentation may have evolved independently in these two groups. In such a case, we might expect that different *Hox* genes would control the development of body segmentation in the two clades.

Concept Check 33.5

1. Each tube foot consists of an ampulla and a podium. When the ampulla squeezes, it forces water into the podium, which causes the podium to expand and contact the substrate. Adhesive chemicals are then secreted from the base of the podium, thereby attaching the podium to the substrate. 2. Both insects and nematodes are members of Ecdysozoa, one of the three major clades of bilaterians. Therefore, a characteristic shared by *Drosophila* and *Caenorhabditis* may be informative for other members of their clade—but not necessarily for members of Deuterostomia. Instead, Figure 33.2 suggests that a species within Echinodermata (Deuterostomia) might be a more appropriate invertebrate model organism from which to draw inferences about humans and other vertebrates. 3. Echinoderms include species with a wide range of body forms. However, even echinoderms that look very different from one another, such as sea stars and sea cucumbers, share characteristics unique to their phylum, including a water vascular system and tube feet. The differences between echinoderm species illustrate the diversity of life, while the characteristics they share illustrate the unity of life. The match between organisms and their environments can be seen in such echinoderm features as the eversible stomachs of sea stars (enabling them to digest prey that are larger than their mouth) and the complex, jaw-like structure that sea urchins use to eat seaweed.

Summary of Key Concepts Questions

33.1 The sponge body consists of two layers of cells, both of which are in contact with water. As a result, gas exchange and waste removal occur as substances diffuse into and out of the cells of the body. Choanocytes and amoebocytes ingest food particles from the surrounding water. Choanocytes also release food particles to amoebocytes, which then digest the food particles and deliver nutrients to other cells. 33.2 The cnidarian body plan consists of a sac with a central digestive compartment, the gastrovascular cavity. The single opening to this compartment serves as both a mouth and an anus. The two main variations on this body plan are sessile polyps (which adhere to the substrate at the end of the body opposite to the mouth/anus) and motile medusae (which move freely through the water and resemble flattened, mouth-down versions of polyps). 33.3 No. Some lophotrochozoans have a crown of ciliated tentacles that function in feeding (called a lophophore), while others go through a distinctive developmental stage known as trochophore larvae. Many other lophotrochozoans do not have either of these features. As a result, the clade is defined primarily by DNA similarities, not morphological similarities. 33.4 Many nematode species live in soil and in sediments on the bottom of bodies of water. These free-living species play important roles in decomposition and nutrient

cycling. Other nematodes are parasites, including many species that attack the roots of plants and some that attack animals (including humans). Arthropods have profound effects on all aspects of ecology. In aquatic environments, crustaceans play key roles as grazers (of algae), scavengers, and predators, and some species, such as krill, are important sources of food for whales and other vertebrates. On land, it is difficult to think of features of the natural world that are not affected in some way by insects and other arthropods, such as spiders and ticks. There are more than 1 million species of insects, many of which have enormous ecological effects as herbivores, predators, parasites, decomposers, and vectors of disease. Insects are also key sources of food for many organisms, including humans in some regions of the world. 33.5 Echinoderms and chordates are both members of Deuterostomia, one of the three main clades of bilaterian animals. As such, chordates (including humans) are more closely related to echinoderms than we are to animals in any of the other phyla covered in this chapter. Nevertheless, echinoderms and chordates have evolved independently for over 500 million years. This statement does not contradict the close relationship of echinoderms and chordates, but it does make clear that "close" is a relative term indicating that these two phyla are more closely related to each other than either is to animal phyla not in Deuterostomia.

Test Your Understanding

1. a 2. c 3. b 4. d 5. c 6. d
7.

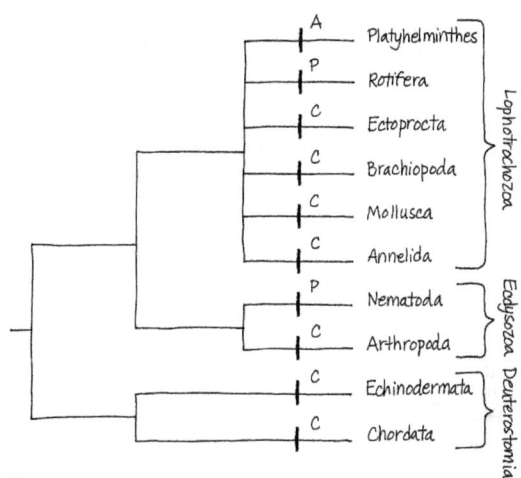

(a) Both phyla in Deuterostomia are coelomates, suggesting that their most recent common ancestor had a true coelom. Lophotrochozoa contains one phylum of acoelomates (Platyhelminthes), one phylum of pseudocoelomates (Rotifera), and four phyla of coelomates (Ectoprocta, Brachiopoda, Mollusca, Annelida); thus, we cannot, from this information alone, infer the condition of the most recent common ancestor shared by these phyla. Similarly, since Ecdysozoa contains one phylum of pseudocoelomates (Nematoda) and one phylum of coelomates (Arthropoda), we cannot infer whether their most recent common ancestor had a true coelom or not.
(b) Depending on whether or not the last common ancestor of Bilateria had a true coelom, the presence of a true coelom has either been lost or gained multiple times during the evolutionary history of bilaterians. Thus, the presence of a true coelom appears to have changed over the course of evolution.

Chapter 34

Figure Questions

Figure 34.2 Based on the phylogeny in Figure 34.2 you would expect the ray-finned fish, coelacanths, lungfishes, amphibians, reptiles, and mammals to have lungs or lung derivatives. These groups all have the shared, derived character of lungs or lung derivatives. Figure 34.6 Results in these figures suggest that specific *Hox* genes, as well as the order in which they are expressed, have been highly conserved over the course of evolution. Figure 34.20 *Tiktaalik* was a lobe-fin fish that had both fish and tetrapod characters. Like a fish, *Tiktaalik* had fins, scales, and gills. As described by Darwin's concept of descent with modification, such shared characters can be attributed to descent from ancestral species—in this case, *Tiktaalik*'s descent from fish ancestors. *Tiktaalik* also had traits that were unlike a fish, but like a tetrapod, including a flat skull, a neck, a full set of ribs, and the skeletal structure of its fin. These characters illustrate the second part of descent with modification, showing how ancestral features had become modified over time. Figure 34.21 Sometime between 380 mya and 340 mya. We can infer this because amphibians must have originated after the most recent common ancestor of *Tulerpeton* and living tetrapods (and that ancestor originated 380 mya), but no later than the date of the earliest known fossils of amphibians (shown in the figure as 340 mya). Figure 34.25 Pterosaurs did not descend from the dinosaur common ancestor; hence, pterosaurs are not dinosaurs. However, birds are descendants of the common ancestor of the dinosaurs. As a result, a monophyletic clade of dinosaurs must include birds. In that sense, birds are dinosaurs. Figure 34.37 In general, the process of exaptation occurs as a structure that had one function acquires a different function via a series of intermediate stages. Each of these intermediate stages typically has some function in the organism in which it is found. The incorporation of articular and quadrate bones into the mammalian ear illustrates exaptation because these bones originally evolved as part of the jaw, where they functioned as the jaw hinge, but over time they became co-opted for another function, namely the transmission of sound. Figure 34.43 The phylogeny shows humans as the sister group to the lineage that contains chimpanzees and bonobos. This relationship is not consistent with humans as having descended from either chimpanzees or bonobos. If humans had descended from chimpanzees, for example, the human lineage would be nested within the chimpanzee lineage, much as birds are nested within the reptile clade (see Figure 34.25). Figure 34.50 Fossil evidence indicates that Neanderthals did not live in Africa; hence there would have been little opportunity for mating (gene flow) between Neanderthals and humans in Africa. However, as humans migrated from Africa, mating may have occurred between Neanderthals and humans in the first region where the two species encountered one another: the Middle East. Humans carrying Neanderthal genes may then have migrated to other locations, explaining why Neanderthals are equally related to humans from France, China, and Papua New Guinea.

Concept Check 34.1
1. The four characters are a notochord; a dorsal, hollow nerve chord; pharyngeal slits or clefts; and a muscular, post-anal tail. 2. In humans, these characters are present only in the embryo. The notochord becomes disks between the vertebrae, the tail is almost completely lost, and the pharyngeal clefts develop into various adult structures. 3. Not necessarily. It would be possible that the chordate common ancestor had this gene, which was then lost in the lancelet lineage and retained in other chordates. However, it would also be possible that the chordate common ancestor lacked this gene; this could occur if the gene originated after lancelets diverged from other chordates but before tunicates diverged from other chordates.

Concept Check 34.2
1. Lampreys have a round, rasping mouth, which they use to attach to fish. Conodonts had two sets of mineralized dental elements, which may have been used to impale prey and cut it into smaller pieces. 2. Such a finding suggests that early organisms with a head were favoured by natural selection in several different evolutionary lineages. However, while a logical argument can be made that having a head was advantageous, fossils alone do not constitute proof. 3. In armoured jawless vertebrates, bone served as external armour that may have provided protection from predators. Some species also had mineralized mouthparts, which could be used for either predation or scavenging. Still others had mineralized fin rays, which may have enabled them to swim more rapidly and with greater steering control.

Concept Check 34.3
1. Both are gnathostomes and have jaws, four clusters of *Hox* genes, enlarged forebrains, and lateral line systems. Shark skeletons consist mainly of cartilage, whereas cod have bony skeletons. Sharks also have a spiral valve. Cod have an operculum and a swim bladder, as well as flexible rays supporting their fins. 2. Aquatic gnathostomes have jaws (an adaptation for feeding) and paired fins and a tail (adaptations for swimming). Aquatic gnathostomes also typically have streamlined bodies for efficient swimming and swim bladders or other mechanisms (such as oil storage in sharks) for buoyancy.
3.

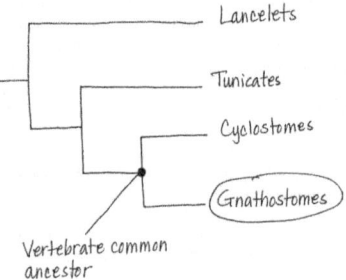

4. Yes, that could have happened. The paired appendages of aquatic gnathostomes other than the lobe-fins could have served as a starting point for the evolution of limbs. The colonization of land by aquatic gnathostomes other than the lobe-fins might have been facilitated in lineages that possessed lungs, as that would have enabled those organisms to breathe air.

Concept Check 34.4
1. Tetrapods are thought to have originated about 365 million years ago when the fins of some lobe-fins evolved into the limbs of tetrapods. In addition to their four limbs with digits—a key derived trait for which the group is named—other derived traits of tetrapods include a neck (consisting of vertebrae that separate the head from the rest of the body), a pelvic girdle that is fused to the backbone, and a lack of gill slits. 2. Some fully aquatic species are paedomorphic, retaining larval features for life in water as adults. Species that live in dry environments may avoid dehydration by burrowing or living under moist leaves, and they protect their eggs with foam nests, viviparity, and other adaptations. 3. Many amphibians spend part of their life cycle in aquatic environments and part on land. Thus, they may be exposed to a wide range of environmental problems, including water and air pollution and the loss or degradation of aquatic and/or terrestrial habitats. In addition, amphibians have highly permeable skin, providing relatively little protection from external conditions, and their eggs do not have a protective shell.

Concept Check 34.5
1. The amniotic egg provides protection to the embryo and allows the embryo to develop on land, eliminating the necessity of a watery environment for reproduction. Another key adaptation is rib cage ventilation, which improves the efficiency of air intake and may have allowed early amniotes to dispense with breathing through their skin. Finally, not breathing through their skin allowed amniotes to develop relatively

impermeable skin, thereby conserving water. 2. Yes. Although snakes lack limbs, they descended from lizards with legs. Some snakes retain vestigial pelvic and leg bones, providing evidence of their descent from an ancestor with legs. 3. Birds have weight-saving modifications, including the absence of teeth, a urinary bladder, and a second ovary in females. The wings and feathers are adaptations that facilitate flight, and so are efficient respiratory and circulatory systems that support a high metabolic rate. 4.

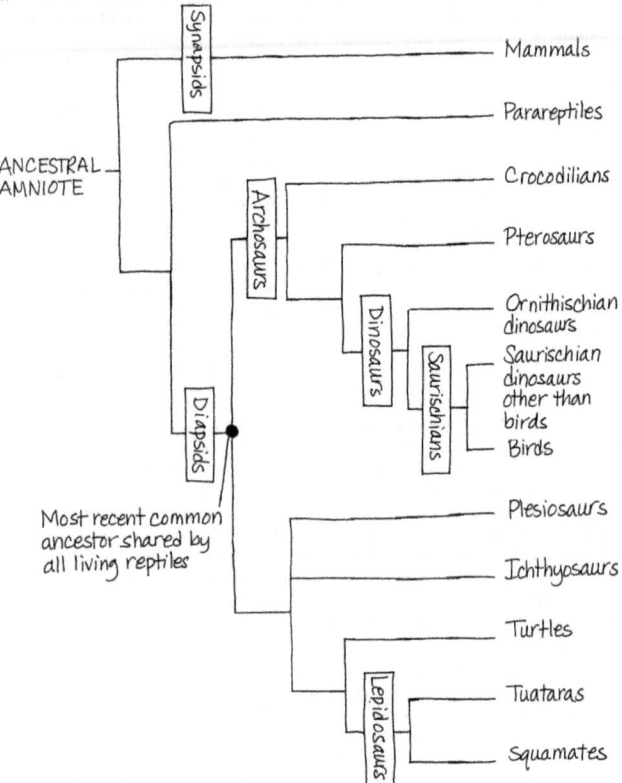

Under this convention, the reptiles would consist of all groups in Figure 34.25 except parareptiles and mammals.

Concept Check 34.6
1. Monotremes lay eggs. Marsupials give birth to very small live young that attach to a nipple in the mother's pouch, where they complete development. Eutherians give birth to more developed live young. 2. Hands and feet adapted for grasping, flat nails, large brain, forward-looking eyes on a flat face, parental care, and movable big toe and thumb 3. Mammals are endothermic, enabling them to live in a wide range of habitats. Milk provides young with a balanced set of nutrients, and hair and a layer of fat under the skin help mammals retain heat. Mammals have differentiated teeth, enabling them to eat many different kinds of food. Mammals also have relatively large brains, and many species are capable learners. Following the mass extinction at the end of the Cretaceous period, the absence of large terrestrial dinosaurs may have opened many new ecological niches to mammals, promoting their adaptive radiation. Continental drift also isolated many groups of mammals from one another, promoting the formation of many new species.

Concept Check 34.7
1. Hominins are a clade within the ape clade that includes humans and all species more closely related to humans than other apes. The derived characters of hominins include bipedal locomotion and relatively larger brains. 2. In hominins, bipedal locomotion evolved long before large brain size. *Homo ergaster*, for example, was fully upright, bipedal, and as tall as modern humans, but its brain was significantly smaller than that of modern humans. 3. Yes, both can be correct. *Homo sapiens* may have established populations outside of Africa as early as 115 000 years ago, as indicated by the fossil record. However, those populations may have left few or no descendants today. Instead, all living humans may have descended from Africans that spread from Africa roughly 50 000 years ago, as indicated by genetic data.

Summary of Key Concepts Questions
34.1 Lancelets are the most basal group of living chordates, and as adults they have key derived characters of chordates. This suggests that the chordate common ancestor may have resembled a lancelet in having an anterior end with a mouth along with the following four derived characters: a notochord; a dorsal, hollow nerve cord; pharyngeal slits or clefts; and a muscular, post-anal tail. 34.2 Conodonts, among the earliest vertebrates in the fossil record, were very abundant for over 300 million years. While jawless, their well-developed teeth provide early signs of bone formation. Other species of jawless vertebrates developed armour on the outside of their bodies, which probably helped protect them from predators. Like lampreys, these species had paired fins for locomotion and an inner ear with semicircular canals that provided a sense of balance. There were many species of these armoured jawless vertebrates, but they all became extinct by the close of the Devonian period, 359 million years ago. 34.3 The origin of jaws altered how fossil gnathostomes obtained food, which in

turn had large effects on ecological interactions. Predators could use their jaws to grab prey or remove chunks of flesh, stimulating the evolution of increasingly sophisticated means of defence in prey species. Evidence for these changes can be found in the fossil record, which includes fossils of 10-m-long predators with remarkably powerful jaws, as well as lineages of well-defended prey species whose bodies were covered by armoured plates. 34.4 Amphibians require water for reproduction; their bodies can lose water rapidly through their moist, highly permeable skin; and amphibian eggs do not have a shell and hence are vulnerable to desiccation. 34.5 Birds are descended from theropod dinosaurs, and dinosaurs are nested within the archosaur lineage, one of the two main reptile lineages. Thus, the other living archosaur reptiles, the crocodilians, are more closely related to birds than they are to non-archosaur reptiles such as lizards. As a result, birds are considered reptiles. (Note that if reptiles were defined as excluding birds, the reptiles would not form a clade; instead, the reptiles would be a paraphyletic group.) 34.6 Mammals are members of a group of amniotes called synapsids. Early (nonmammalian) synapsids laid eggs and had a sprawling gait. Fossil evidence shows that mammalian features arose gradually over a period of more than 100 million years. For example, the jaw was modified over time in nonmammalian synapsids, eventually coming to resemble that of a mammal. By 180 million years ago, the first mammals had appeared. There were many species of early mammals, but most of them were small, and they were not abundant or dominant members of their community. Mammals did not rise to ecological dominance until after the extinction of the dinosaurs. 34.7 The fossil record shows that from 4.5 to 2.5 million years ago, a wide range of hominin species walked upright but had relatively small brain sizes. About 2.5 million years ago, the first members of genus *Homo* emerged. These species used tools and had larger brains than those of earlier hominins. Fossil evidence indicates that multiple members of our genus were alive at any given point in time. Furthermore, until about 1.3 million years ago, these various *Homo* species also coexisted with members of earlier hominin lineages, such as *Paranthropus*. The different hominins alive at the same periods of time varied in body size, body shape, brain size, dental morphology, and the capacity for tool use. Ultimately, except for *Homo sapiens*, all of these species became extinct. Thus, human evolution is viewed not as an evolutionary path leading to *H. sapiens*, but rather as an evolutionary tree with many branches—the only surviving lineage of which is our own.

Test Your Understanding

1. d 2. c 3. b 4. c 5. d 6. a 8. (a) Because brain size tends to increase consistently in such lineages, we can conclude that natural selection favoured the evolution of larger brains and hence that the benefits outweighed the costs. (b) As long as the benefits of brains that are large relative to body size are greater than the costs, large brains can evolve. Natural selection might favour the evolution of brains that are large relative to body size because such brains confer an advantage in obtaining mates and/or an advantage in survival.
(c)

Adult mortality tends to be lower in birds with larger brains.

Chapter 35

Figure Questions

Figure 35.17 Pith and cortex are defined, respectively, as ground tissue that is internal and ground tissue that is external to vascular tissue. Since vascular bundles of monocot stems are scattered throughout the ground tissue, there is no clear distinction between internal and external relative to the vascular tissue. Figure 35.19 The vascular cambium produces growth that increases the diameter of a stem or root. The tissues that are exterior to the vascular cambium cannot keep pace with the growth because their cells no longer divide. As a result, these tissues rupture. Fig. 35.32 Every root epidermal cell would develop a root hair. Fig. 35.34 Another example of homeotic gene mutation is the *Drosophila* mutation depicted in Figure 18.20, in which a mutation in a *Hox* gene causes legs to form in place of antennae. Fig. 35.35 The flower would consist of nothing but carpels.

Concept Check 35.1

1. The vascular tissue system connects leaves and roots, allowing sugars to move from leaves to roots in the phloem and allowing water and minerals to move to the leaves in the xylem. 2. To get sufficient energy from photosynthesis, we would need lots of surface area exposed to the sun. This large surface-to-volume ratio, however, would create a new problem—evaporative water loss. We would have to be permanently connected to a water source—the soil, also our source of minerals. In short, we

would probably look and behave very much like plants. 3. As plant cells enlarge, they typically form a huge central vacuole that contains a dilute watery sap. Central vacuoles enable plant cells to become large with only a minimal investment of new cytoplasm. The orientation of the cellulose microfibrils in plant cell walls affects the growth pattern of cells.

Concept Check 35.2

1. Yes. In a woody plant, secondary growth is occurring in the older parts of the stem and root, while primary growth is occurring at the root and shoot tips. 2. The largest, oldest leaves would be lowest on the shoot. Since they would probably be heavily shaded, they would not photosynthesize much regardless of their size. 3. No, the carrot roots will probably be smaller at the end of the second year because the food stored in the root will be used to produce flowers, fruits, and seeds.

Concept Check 35.3

1. In roots, primary growth occurs in three successive stages, moving away from the tip of the root: the zones of cell division, elongation, and differentiation. In shoots, it occurs at the tip of apical and axillary buds, with leaf primordia arising along the sides of an apical meristem. Most growth in length occurs in older internodes below the shoot tip. 2. No. Because vertically oriented leaves, such as maize, can capture light equally on both sides of the leaf, you would expect them to have mesophyll cells that are not differentiated into palisade and spongy layers. This is typically the case. Also, vertical leaves usually have stomata on both leaf surfaces. 3. Root hairs are cellular extensions that increase the surface area of the root epidermis, thereby enhancing the absorption of minerals and water. Microvilli are extensions that increase the absorption of nutrients by increasing the surface area of the gut.

Concept Check 35.4

1. The sign will still be 2 m above the ground because this part of the tree is no longer growing in length (primary growth); it is now growing only in thickness (secondary growth). 2. Stomata must be able to close because evaporation is much more intensive from leaves than from the trunks of woody trees as a result of the higher surface-to-volume ratio in leaves. 3. Since there is little temperature variation in the tropics, the growth rings of a tree from the tropics would be difficult to discern unless the tree came from an area that had pronounced wet and dry seasons. 4. Girdling removes an entire ring of secondary phloem (part of the bark), completely preventing transport of sugars and starches from the shoots to the roots.

Concept Check 35.5

1. Although all the living vegetative cells of a plant have the same genome, they differentiate to have different forms and functions because of differential gene expression. 2. Plants show indeterminate growth; juvenile and mature phases are found on the same individual plant; cell differentiation in plants is more dependent on final position than on lineage. 3. In theory, tepals could arise if *B* gene activity were present in all three of the outer whorls of the flower.

Summary of Key Concepts Questions

35.1 Here are a few examples: The cuticle of leaves and stems protects these structures from desiccation. Collenchyma and sclerenchyma cells have thick walls that provide support for plants. Strong, branching root systems help anchor the plant in the soil. 35.2 All plant organs and tissues are ultimately derived from meristematic activity. 35.3 Lateral roots emerge from the pericycle and destroy plant cells as they emerge. In stems, branches arise from axillary buds and do not destroy any cells. 35.4 With the evolution of secondary growth, plants were able to grow taller and shade competitors. 35.5 The orientation of cellulose microfibrils in the innermost layers of the cell wall causes this growth along one axis. Microtubules play a key role in regulating the plane of cell expansion. It is the orientation of microtubules in the cell's outermost cytoplasm that determines the orientation of cellulose microfibrils.

Test Your Understanding

1. d 2. c 3. c 4. a 5. b 6. d 7. d
8.

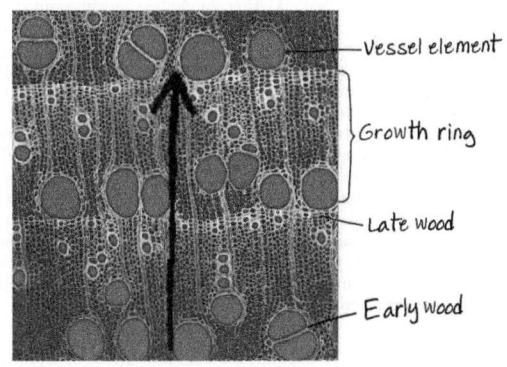

Chapter 36

Figure Questions

Figure 36.3 The leaves are being produced in a counterclockwise spiral. Figure 36.4 A higher leaf area index will not necessarily increase photosynthesis because of upper leaves shading lower leaves. Figure 36.6 A proton pump inhibitor would depolarize the membrane potential because fewer H^+ ions would be pumped out across the plasma membrane. The immediate effect of an inhibitor of the H^+/sucrose transporter would be to hyperpolarize the membrane potential because fewer H^+ ions would be leaking back into the cell through these cotransporters. An inhibitor of the H^+/NO_3^- cotransporter would have no effect on the membrane potential because the simultaneous cotransport of a positively charged ion and a negatively charged ion has no net effect on charge difference across the membrane. An inhibitor of the K^+ ion channels would decrease the membrane potential because additional positively charged ions would not be accumulating outside the cell. Figure 36.8 The Casparian strip blocks water and minerals from moving between endodermal cells or moving around an endodermal cell via the cell's wall. Therefore, water and minerals must pass through an endodermal cell's plasma membrane. Figure 36.18 Because the xylem is under negative pressure (tension), excising a stylet that had been inserted into a tracheid or vessel element would probably introduce air into the cell. No xylem sap would exude unless positive root pressure was predominant.

Concept Check 36.1
1. Vascular plants must transport minerals and water absorbed by the roots to all the other parts of the plant. They must also transport sugars from sites of production to sites of use. 2. Many features of plant architecture affect self-shading, including leaf arrangement, leaf and stem orientation, and leaf area index. 3. Increased stem elongation would raise the plant's upper leaves. Erect leaves and reduced lateral branching would make the plant less subject to shading by the encroaching neighbours. 4. As discussed in Chapter 35, pruning shoot tips removes apical dominance, resulting in axillary buds growing into lateral shoots (branches). This branching produces a bushier plant with a higher leaf area index. 5. Fungal hyphae are long, thin filaments that form a large interwoven network in the soil. Their high surface-to-volume ratio is an adaptation that enhances the absorption of materials from the soil.

Concept Check 36.2
1. The cell's Ψ_P is 0.7 MPa. In a solution with a Ψ of –0.4 MPa, the cell's Ψ_P at equilibrium would be 0.3 MPa. 2. The cells would still adjust to changes in their osmotic environment, but their responses would be slower. Although aquaporins do not affect the water potential gradient across membranes, they allow for more rapid osmotic adjustments. 3. If tracheids and vessel elements were alive at maturity, their cytoplasm would impede water movement, preventing rapid long-distance transport. 4. The protoplasts would burst. Because the cytoplasm has many dissolved solutes, water would enter the protoplast continuously without reaching equilibrium. (When present, the cell wall prevents rupturing by excessive expansion of the protoplast.)

Concept Check 36.3
1. Because water-conducting xylem cells are dead at maturity and form essentially hollow tubes, they offer little resistance to water flow, and their thick walls prevent the cells from collapsing from the negative pressure inside. 2. At dawn, a drop is exuded because the xylem is under positive pressure due to root pressure. At noon, the xylem is under negative pressure tension when it is cut and the xylem sap is pulled away from the cut surface up into the stem. Root pressure cannot keep pace with the increased rate of transpiration at noon. 3. The endodermis regulates the passage of water-soluble solutes by requiring all such molecules to cross a selectively permeable membrane. Presumably, the inhibitor never reaches the plant's photosynthetic cells. 4. Perhaps greater root mass helps compensate for the lower water permeability of the plasma membranes. 5. The Casparian strip and tight junctions both prevent movement of fluid between cells.

Concept Check 36.4
1. Stomatal opening at dawn is controlled mainly by light, CO_2 concentrations, and a circadian rhythm. Environmental stresses such as drought, high temperature, and wind can stimulate stomata to close during the day. Water deficiency can trigger release of the plant hormone abscisic acid, which signals guard cells to close stomata. 2. The activation of the proton pump of stomatal cells would cause the guard cells to take up K^+. The increased turgor of the guard cells would lock the stomata open and lead to extreme evaporation from the leaf. 3. After the flowers are cut, transpiration from any leaves and from the petals (which are modified leaves) will continue to draw water up the xylem. If cut flowers are transferred directly to a vase, air pockets in xylem vessels prevent delivery of water from the vase to the flowers. Cutting stems again underwater, a few centimetres from the original cut, will sever the xylem above the air pocket. The water droplets prevent another air pocket from forming while placing the flowers in a vase. 4. Water molecules are in constant motion, travelling at different rates. The average speed of these particles depends on the water's temperature. If water molecules gain enough energy, the most energetic molecules near the liquid's surface will impart sufficient speed, and therefore sufficient kinetic energy, to cause water molecules to propel away from the liquid in the form of gaseous molecules or, more simply, as water vapour. As the particles with the highest kinetic energy levels evaporate, the average kinetic energy of the remaining liquid decreases. Because a liquid's temperature is directly related to the average kinetic energy of its molecules, the liquid cools as it evaporates.

Concept Check 36.5
1. In both cases, the long-distance transport is a bulk flow driven by a pressure difference at opposite ends of tubes. Pressure is generated at the source end of a sieve tube by the loading of sugar and resulting osmotic flow of water into the phloem, and this pressure *pushes* sap from the source end to the sink end of the tube. In contrast, transpiration generates a negative pressure potential (tension) as a force that *pulls* the ascent of xylem sap. 2. The main sources are fully grown leaves (by photosynthesis) and fully developed storage organs (by breakdown of starch). Roots, buds, stems, expanding leaves, and fruits are powerful sinks because they are actively growing. A storage organ may be a sink in the summer when accumulating carbohydrates, but a source in the spring when breaking down starch into sugar for growing shoot tips. 3. Positive pressure, whether it be in the xylem when root pressure predominates or in

the sieve-tube elements of the phloem, requires active transport. Most long-distance transport in the xylem depends on bulk flow driven by negative pressure potential generated ultimately by the evaporation of water from the leaf and does not require living cells. 4. The spiral slash prevents optimal bulk flow of the phloem sap to the root sinks. Therefore, more phloem sap can move from the source leaves to the fruit sinks, making them sweeter.

Concept Check 36.6
1. Plasmodesmata, unlike gap junctions, have the ability to pass RNA, proteins, and viruses from cell to cell. 2. Long-distance signalling is critical for the integrated functioning of all large organisms, but the speed of such signalling is much less critical to plants because their response to the environment, unlike those of animals, do not typically involve rapid movements. 3. Although this strategy would eliminate the systemic spread of viral infections, it would also severely impact the development of the plants.

Summary of Key Concepts Questions
36.1 Plants with tall shoots and elevated leaf canopies generally had an advantage over shorter competitors. A consequence of the selective pressure for tall shoots was the further separation of leaves from roots. This separation created problems for the transport of materials between root and shoot systems. Plants with xylem cells were more successful at supplying their shoot systems with soil resources (water and minerals). Similarly, those with phloem cells were more successful at supplying sugar sinks with carbohydrates. 36.2 Xylem sap is usually pulled up the plant by transpiration, much more often than it is pushed up the plant by root pressure. 36.3 Hydrogen bonds are necessary for the cohesion of water molecules to each other and for the adhesion of water to other materials, such as cell walls. Both adhesion and cohesion of water molecules are involved in the ascent of xylem sap under conditions of negative pressure. 36.4 Although stomata account for most of the water lost from plants, they are necessary for exchange of gases—for example, for the uptake of carbon dioxide needed for photosynthesis. 36.5 Although the movement of phloem sap depends on bulk flow, the pressure gradient that drives phloem transport depends on the osmotic uptake of water in response to the loading of sugars into sieve-tube elements at sugar sources. Phloem loading depends on H^+ cotransport processes that ultimately depend on H^+ gradients established by active H^+ pumping. 36.6 Voltage between cells, cytoplasmic pH, cytoplasmic calcium concentration, and viral movement proteins all affect symplastic communication, as do developmental changes in the number of plasmodesmata.

Test Your Understanding
1. c 2. a 3. b 4. b 5. b 6. d 7. c 8. a 9. c
10.

Chapter 37

Figure Questions
Figure 37.3 Anions. Because cations are bound to soil particles, they are less likely to be lost from the soil following heavy rains. Table 37.1 During photosynthesis, CO_2 is fixed into carbohydrates, which contribute to the dry mass. In cellular respiration, O_2 is reduced to H_2O and does not contribute to the dry mass. Figure 37.11 The legume plants benefit because the bacteria fix nitrogen that is absorbed by their roots. The bacteria benefit because they acquire photosynthetic products from the plants. Figure 37.12 All three plant tissue systems are affected. Root hairs (dermal tissue) are modified to allow *Rhizobium* penetration. The cortex (ground tissue) and pericycle (vascular tissue) proliferate during nodule formation. The vascular tissue of the nodule connects to the vascular cylinder of the root to allow for efficient nutrient exchange. Figure 37.14 The nodulating bacteria are able to use their nitrogen fixing system to reduce N_2 gas into organic nitrogen. The organic nitrogen can then be transported around the plant to where it is needed for the production of amino acids and nucleotides. In barren or contaminated sites, there is often a lack of nutrients available to help support plant growth. In these situations fertilizer could be added, but would add extra cost to cleaning up the soil. Instead, if nodulating plants were grown, they would naturally enrich the soil with nitrogen, the nutrient which is most frequently limiting for plant growth. Thus planting seeds of nodulating plants, in the presence of nodulating bacteria, on barren or contaminated soil would allow both the nodulating plant, and subsequent plants grown on the site, to be better nourished.

Concept Check 37.1
1. Overwatering deprives roots of oxygen. Overfertilizing is wasteful and can lead to soil salinization and water pollution. 2. As lawn clippings decompose, they restore mineral nutrients to the soil. If they are removed, the minerals lost from the soil must be replaced by fertilization. 3. Because of their small size and negative charge, clay particles would increase the number of binding sites for cations and water molecules and would therefore increase cation exchange and water retention in the soil. 4. Due to hydrogen bonding between water molecules, water expands when it freezes, and this causes mechanical fracturing of rocks. Water also coheres to many objects,

and this cohesion combined with other forces, such as gravity, can help tug particles from rock. Finally, water, because it is polar, is an excellent solvent that allows many substances, including ions, to become dissolved in solution.

Concept Check 37.2

1. No, because even though macronutrients are required in greater amounts, all essential elements are necessary for the plant to complete its life cycle. 2. No. The fact that the addition of an element results in an increase in the growth rate of a crop does not mean that the element is strictly required for the plant to complete its life cycle. 3. Waterlogging displaces air from the soil, leading to low O_2 conditions. Such conditions promote the anaerobic process of alcoholic fermentation in plants, the end product of which is ethanol.

Concept Check 37.3

1. The rhizosphere is a narrow zone in the soil immediately adjacent to living roots. This zone is especially rich in both organic and inorganic nutrients and has a microbial population that is many times greater than the bulk of the soil. 2. Soil bacteria and mycorrhizae enhance plant nutrition by making certain minerals more available to plants. For example, many types of soil bacteria are involved in the nitrogen cycle, and the hyphae of mycorrhizae provide a large surface area for the absorption of nutrients, particularly phosphate ions. 3. Mixotrophy refers to the strategy of using photosynthesis and heterotrophy for nutrition. Euglenids are well-known mixotrophic protists. 4. Saturating rainfall may deplete the soil of oxygen. A lack of soil oxygen would inhibit nitrogen fixation by the peanut root nodules and decrease the nitrogen available to the plant. Alternatively, heavy rain may leach nitrate from the soil. A symptom of nitrogen deficiency is yellowing of older leaves.

Summary of Key Concepts Questions

37.1 The term *ecosystem* refes to the communities of organisms within a given area and their interactions with the physical environment around them. Soil is teeming with many communities of organisms, including bacteria, fungi, animals, and the root systems of plants. The vigour of these individual communities depends on nonliving factors in the soil environment, such as minerals, oxygen, and water, as well as on interactions, both positive and negative, between different communities of organisms. 37.2 No, plants can complete their life cycle when grown hydroponically, that is, in aerated salt solutions containing the proper ratios of all the minerals needed by plants. 37.3 No, some parasitic plants obtain their energy by siphoning off carbon nutrients from other organisms.

Test Your Understanding

1. b 2. b 3. a 4. d 5. b 6. b 7. d 8. c 9. d
10.

Chapter 38

Figure Questions

Figure 38.5 Having a specific pollinator is more efficient because less pollen gets delivered to flowers of the wrong species. However, it is also a risky strategy: If the pollinator population suffers to an unusual degree from predation, disease, or climate change, then the plant may not be able to produce seeds. Figure 38.8 In addition to having a single cotyledon, monocots have leaves with parallel leaf venation, scattered vascular bundles in their stems, a fibrous root system, floral parts in threes or multiples of threes, and pollen grains with only one opening. In contrast, dicots have two cotyledons, netlike leaf venation, vascular bundles in a ring, taproots, floral parts in fours or fives or multiples thereof, and pollen grains with three openings. Figure 38.9 Beans use a hypocotyl hook to push through the soil. The delicate leaves and shoot apical meristem are also protected by being sandwiched between two large cotyledons. The coleoptile of maize seedlings helps protect the emerging leaves. Figure 38.19 Cellulosic biofuel is generally digested, using fungi or bacteria, into simpler sugars and then fermented to produce ethanol. The greater the amount of biomass produced in a given growing season, the greater the amount of ethanol produced. Thus, first and foremost the given plant must have rapid growth characteristics. Secondly, any treatments that plants require will increase the production costs. The need for fertilization, irrigation, or spraying of pesticides all add significantly to the cost of production. Thus, a good model plant would be pest resistant and able to maintain high rates of growth without supplemental water or fertilization. Thirdly, an often overlooked cost is diversion of land from other uses. For example, if a high-quality, high-value crop can be grown on a field, then producing a lower-value biofuel crop has an associated cost. Thus, a good model plant for biofuel production would grow well on poorer quality land. Summing up these qualities, an ideal candidate for cellulosic biofuel research would grow rapidly on poor quality land without the need for maintenance or fertilization.

Concept Check 38.1

1. In angiosperms, pollination is the transfer of pollen from an anther to a stigma. Fertilization is the fusion of the egg and sperm to form the zygote; it cannot occur until after the growth of the pollen tube from the pollen grain. 2. Seed dormancy prevents the premature germination of seeds. A seed will germinate only when the environmental conditions are optimal for the survival of its embryo as a young seedling. 3. Long styles help to weed out pollen grains that are genetically inferior and not capable of successfully growing long pollen tubes. 4. No. The haploid (gametophyte) generation of plants is multicellular and arises from spores. The haploid phase of the animal life cycle is a single-celled gamete (egg or sperm) that arises directly from meiosis: There are no spores.

Concept Check 38.2

1. Asexually propagated crops lack genetic diversity. Genetically diverse populations are less likely to become extinct in the face of an epidemic because there is a greater likelihood that a few individuals in the population are resistant. 2. In the short term, selfing may be advantageous in a population that is so dispersed and sparse that pollen delivery is unreliable. In the long term, however, selfing is an evolutionary dead end because it leads to a loss of genetic diversity that may preclude adaptive evolution. 3. This might be possible, but satisfactory results would be very unlikely. Both tubers and fruits are tremendous energy sinks. Each plant has only a finite amount of energy to divide between sexual and asexual reproduction. Although a tomato-potato hybrid could, in theory, produce an offspring that makes fruits and tubers equally, these fruits and tubers would be of inferior quality or low yielding.

Concept Check 38.3

1. Traditional breeding and genetic engineering both involve artificial selection for desired traits. However, genetic engineering techniques facilitate faster gene transfer and are not limited to transferring genes between closely related varieties or species. 2. GM crops may be more nutritious and less susceptible to insect damage or pathogens that invade insect-damaged plants. They also may not require as much chemical spraying. However, unknown risks may include adverse effects on human health and nontarget organisms and the possibility of transgene escape. 3. *Bt* maize suffers less insect damage; therefore, *Bt* maize plants are less likely to be infected by fumonisin-producing fungi that infect plants through wounds. 4. In such species, engineering the transgene into the chloroplast DNA would not prevent its escape in pollen; such a method requires that the chloroplast DNA be found only in the egg. An entirely different method of preventing transgene escape would therefore be needed, such as male sterility, apomixis, or self-pollinating closed flowers.

Summary of Key Concepts Questions

38.1 After pollination, a flower typically changes into a fruit. The petals, sepals, and stamens typically fall off the flower. The stigma of the pistil withers and the ovary begins to swell. The ovules (embryonic seeds) inside the ovary begin to mature. 38.2 Asexual reproduction can be advantageous in a stable environment because individual plants that are well suited to that environment pass on all their genes to offspring. Also, asexual reproduction generally results in offspring that are less fragile than the seedlings produced by sexual reproduction. However, sexual reproduction offers the advantage of dispersal of tough seeds. Moreover, sexual reproduction produces genetic variety, which may be advantageous in an unstable environment. The likelihood is better that at least one offspring of sexual reproduction will survive in a changed environment. 38.3 "Golden Rice" has been engineered to produce more vitamin A, thereby raising the nutritional value of rice. A protoxin gene from a soil bacterium has been engineered into *Bt* maize. This protoxin is lethal to invertebrates but harmless to vertebrates. *Bt* crops require less pesticide spraying and have lower levels of fungal infection. The nutritional value of cassava is being increased in many ways by genetic engineering. Enriched levels of protein, iron, and beta-carotene (a vitamin A precursor) have been achieved, and cyanide-producing chemicals have been almost eliminated from the roots.

Test Your Understanding

1. b 2. a 3. c 4. d 5. b 6. c 7. d 8. d
9.

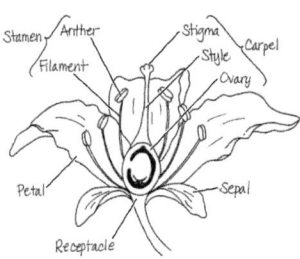

Chapter 39

Figure Questions

Figure 39.4 Panel B in Figure 11.17 shows a branching signal transduction pathway that resembles the branching phytochrome-dependent pathway involved in de-etiolation. Figure 39.5 To determine which wavelengths of light are most effective in phototropism, you could use a glass prism to split white light into its component colours and see which colours cause the quickest bending (the answer is blue; see Figure 39.15). Figure 39.6 No. Polar auxin transport depends on the distribution of auxin transport proteins at the basal ends of cells. Figure 39.16 Yes. The white light, which contains red light, would stimulate seed germination in all treatments. Figure 39.20 The short-day plant would not flower. The long-day plant would flower. Figure 39.21 If this were true, florigen would be an inhibitor of flowering, not an inducer.

Concept Check 39.1

1. Dark-grown seedlings are etiolated: They have long stems, underdeveloped root systems, and unexpanded leaves, and their shoots lack chlorophyll. Etiolated growth is beneficial to seeds sprouting under the dark conditions they would encounter underground. By devoting more energy to stem elongation and less to leaf expansion and root growth, a plant increases the likelihood that the shoot will reach the sunlight before its stored foods run out. 2. Cycloheximide should inhibit de-etiolation by preventing the synthesis of new proteins necessary for de-etiolation. 3. No. Applying Viagra, like injecting cyclic GMP as described in the text, should cause only a partial de-etiolation response. Full de-etiolation would require activation of the calcium branch of the signal transduction pathway.

Concept Check 39.2

1. Because cytokinins delay leaf senescence and floral parts are modified leaves, cytokinins also delay the senescence of cut flowers.   2. Fusicoccin's ability to cause an increase in plasma H⁺ pump activity has an auxin-like effect and promotes stem cell elongation.   3. The plant will exhibit a constitutive triple response. Because the kinase that normally prevents the triple response is dysfunctional, the plant will undergo the triple response regardless of whether ethylene is present or the ethylene receptor is functional.   4. Since ethylene often stimulates its own synthesis, it is under positive-feedback regulation.

Concept Check 39.3

1. Not necessarily. Many environmental factors, such as temperature and light, change over a 24-hour period in the field. To determine whether the enzyme is under circadian control, a scientist would have to demonstrate that its activity oscillates even when environmental conditions are held constant.   2. Flowering of the species may have been day-neutral or required multiple exposures to short nights.   3. It is impossible to say. To establish that this species is a short-day plant, it would be necessary to establish the critical night length for flowering and that this species only flowers when the night is longer than the critical night length.   4. According to the action spectrum of photosynthesis, red and blue light are the most effective in photosynthesis. Thus, it is not surprising that plants assess their light environment using blue- and red-light-absorbing photoreceptors.

Concept Check 39.4

1. A plant that overproduces ABA would undergo less evaporative cooling because its stomata would not open as widely.   2. Plants close to the aisles may be more subject to mechanical stresses caused by passing workers and air currents. The plants nearer to the centre of the bench may also be taller as a result of shading and less evaporative stress.   3. No. Because root caps are involved in sensing gravity, roots that have their root caps removed are almost completely insensitive to gravity.

Concept Check 39.5

1. Some insects increase plants' productivity by eating harmful insects or aiding in pollination.   2. Mechanical damage breaches a plant's first line of defence against infection, its protective dermal tissue.   3. No. Pathogens that kill their hosts would soon run out of victims and might themselves go extinct.   4. Perhaps the breeze dilutes the local concentration of a volatile defence compound that the plants produce.

Summary of Key Concepts Questions

39.1 Signal transduction pathways often activate protein kinases, enzymes that phosphorylate other proteins. Protein kinases can directly activate certain preexisting enzymes by phosphorylating them, or they can regulate gene transcription (and enzyme production) by phosphorylating specific transcription factors.   39.2 Yes, there is truth to the old adage that one bad apple spoils the whole bunch. Ethylene, a gaseous hormone that stimulates ripening, is produced by damaged, infected, or overripe fruits. Ethylene can diffuse to healthy fruit in the "bunch" and stimulate their rapid ripening.   39.3 Plant physiologists proposed the existence of a floral-promoting factor (florigen) based on the fact that a plant induced to flower could induce flowering in a second plant to which it was grafted, even though the second plant was not in an environment that would normally induce flowering in that species.   39.4 Plants subjected to drought stress are often more resistant to freezing stress because the two types of stress are quite similar. Freezing of water in the extracellular spaces causes free water concentrations outside the cell to decrease. This, in turn, causes free water to leave the cell by osmosis, leading to the dehydration of cytoplasm, much like what is seen in drought stress.   39.5 Chewing insects make plants more susceptible to pathogen invasion by disrupting the waxy cuticle of shoots, thereby creating an opening for infection. Moreover, substances released from damaged cells can serve as nutrients for the invading pathogens.

Test Your Understanding

1. b   2. c   3. c   4. d   5. b   6. b   7. c
8.

Chapter 40

Figure Questions

Figure 40.4 Such exchange surfaces are internal in the sense that they are inside the body. However, they are also continuous with openings on the external body surface that contact the environment. Figure 40.8 An example of a stimulus is an open window on a cold day. The response would be a room temperature decrease. The change would cause the sensor/control centre to increase heat production.

The air conditioner would form a second control circuit, cooling the house when air temperature exceeded the set point. Such opposing, or antagonistic, pairs of control circuits increase the effectiveness of a homeostatic mechanism. Figure 40.15 The experiment focused on how acclimation temperature affected the tolerance of high water temperature. Two outcomes would be possible if the experiment tested tolerance of low temperature. First, it is possible that a similar pattern would exist if cold temperature exposure were used. That is, warm-acclimated lobsters would succumb at higher low temperatures than cold-acclimated lobsters. However, it is also possible that, regardless of acclimation, the lobsters would all tolerate the lowest temperature until the point where their body fluids froze. Figure 40.16 The ice water would cool tissues in your head, including blood that would then circulate throughout your body. This effect would accelerate the return to a normal body temperature. If, however, the ice water reached the eardrum and cooled the blood vessel that supplies the hypothalamus, the hypothalamic thermostat would respond by inhibiting sweating and constricting blood vessels in the skin, slowing cooling elsewhere in the body. Figure 40.17 The transport of nutrients across membranes and the synthesis of RNA and protein are coupled to ATP hydrolysis. These processes proceed spontaneously because there is an overall drop in free energy, with the excess energy given off as heat. Similarly, less than half of the free energy in glucose is captured in the coupled reactions of cellular respiration. The remainder of the energy is released as heat. Figure 40.19 Each ground squirrel is about 10/100th the mass of the dog in this figure. So 100 ground squirrels would have about the same mass as the dog. However, the dog has less than 100x greater metabolic rate than the ground squirrel. So, the first observer is wrong, and the second observer is correct in disagreeing. Figure 40.20 Nothing. Although genes that show a circadian variation in expression during euthermia exhibit constant RNA levels during hibernation, a gene that shows constant expression during hibernation might also show constant expression during euthermia.

Concept Check 40.1

1. All types of epithelia consist of cells that line a surface, are tightly packed, are situated on top of a basal lamina, and form an active and protective interface with the external environment.   2. By flattening its ears along its body, the jackrabbit can reduce the exposed surface area of its body and hence the amount of heat lost. However, by placing its ears flat, the jackrabbit reduces its ability to detect potential predators.   3. You need the nervous system to perceive the danger and provoke a split-second muscular response to keep from falling. The nervous system, however, does not make a direct connection with blood vessels or glucose-storing cells in the liver. Instead, the nervous system triggers the release of a hormone (called epinephrine, or adrenaline) by the endocrine system, bringing about a change in these tissues in just a few seconds.

Concept Check 40.2

1. In the enzyme-catalyzed biosynthetic process, the product of a pathway (in this case, isoleucine) inhibits the pathway that generated it. In thermoregulation, the product of the pathway (a change in temperature) decreases pathway activity by reducing the stimulus.   2. You would want to put the thermostat close to where you would be spending time, where it would be protected from environmental perturbations, such as direct sunshine, and not right in the path of the output of the heating system. Similarly, the sensors for homeostasis located in the human brain are separated from environmental influences and can monitor conditions in a vital and sensitive tissue.   3. In convergent evolution, the same biological trait arises independently in two or more species. Gene analysis can provide evidence for an independent origin. In particular, if the genes responsible for the trait in one species lack significant sequence similarity to the corresponding genes in another species, scientists conclude that there is a separate genetic basis for the trait in the two species and thus an independent origin. In the case of circadian rhythms, the clock genes in cyanobacteria appear unrelated to those in humans.

Concept Check 40.3

1. "Wind chill" involves heat loss through convection, as the moving air contributes to heat loss from the skin surface.   2. The hummingbird, being a very small endotherm, has a very high metabolic rate. If by absorbing sunlight certain flowers warm their nectar, a hummingbird feeding on these flowers is saved the metabolic expense of warming the nectar to its body temperature.   3. When an infection triggers an immune response, the internal thermometer is reprogrammed to a higher set point. This means that the normal body temperature is perceived to be too cool, and the body launches efforts to warm, including shivering thermogenesis.

Concept Check 40.4

1. The mouse would consume oxygen at a higher rate because it is an endotherm, so its basal metabolic rate is higher than the ectothermic lizard's standard metabolic rate.   2. The house cat; smaller animals have a higher metabolic rate per unit body mass and a greater demand for food per unit body mass.   3. The alligator would cool its body temperature and metabolic rate would decline. The lion would initiate thermogenesis and its metabolic rate would increase, keeping the body at a near constant temperature.

Summary of Key Concepts Questions

40.1 Animals exchange materials with their environment across their body surface, and a spherical shape has the minimum surface area per unit volume. As body size increases, the ratio of surface area to body volume decreases.   40.2 No; even though an animal regulates some aspects of its internal environment, the internal environment fluctuates slightly around set points. Homeostasis is a dynamic state. Furthermore, there are sometimes programmed changes in set points, such as those resulting in radical increases in hormone levels at particular times in development.   40.3 Heat exchange across the skin is a primary mechanism for the regulation of body core temperature, with the result that the skin is cooler than the body core.   40.4 Because small animals have the highest ratio of BMR per unit mass, they have the greatest energetic savings per unit mass during hibernation. Consequently, the selective pressure favouring hibernation during evolution is especially strong for small animals.

Test Your Understanding

1. b 2. c 3. a 4. b 5. c 6. c 7. d
8.

Chapter 41

Figure Questions

Figure 41.2 Though the researchers examined the profiles of the prey, it is possible that the prey species may differ regionally, or seasonally, depending on what they eat. It is possible that the diet of walruses and bearded seals also differs regionally. If polar bears were eating the same foods, but those foods differed in their fatty acid profile, it could be interpreted as differences in the diets of the bears. Male and female bears also likely differ in the hormones that influence metabolism. They differ in sex steroids (testosterone, estrogens), as well as other hormones that affect interactions between nutrition and stress (glucocorticoids). Any of these hormones have the potential to alter metabolism in sex-specific ways. If, for example, female bears have lower levels of cortisol than male bears, this might influence fatty acid metabolism in sex-specific ways. One way to test the hypothesis would be to artificially increase the levels of a hormone, such as cortisol. Cortisol implants could be used to increase the levels, and subsequent analyses could detect if the changed hormone levels affected how the animals treated dietary fatty acids. This would be a long-term experiment, and challenging to accomplish but, in principle, could test the hypothesis. Figure 41.11 Since enzymes are proteins, and proteins are hydrolyzed in the small intestine, the digestive enzymes in that compartment need to be resistant to enzymatic cleavage other than the cleavage required to activate them. Figure 41.12 None. Since digestion is completed in the small intestine, tapeworms simply absorb predigested nutrients through their large body surface. Figure 41.20 The regulation shown in these regulatory circuits is negative feedback, acting on both insulin and glucose.

Concept Check 41.1

1. The only essential amino acids are those that an animal cannot synthesize from other molecules. 2. Many vitamins serve as enzyme cofactors, which, like enzymes themselves, are unchanged by the chemical reactions in which they participate. Therefore, only very small amounts of vitamins are needed. 3. To identify the essential nutrient missing from an animal's diet, a researcher could supplement the diet with individual nutrients and determine which nutrient eliminates the signs of malnutrition.

Concept Check 41.2

1. A gastrovascular cavity is a digestive pouch with a single opening that functions in both ingestion and elimination; an alimentary canal is a digestive tube with a separate mouth and anus at opposite ends. 2. As long as nutrients are within the cavity of the alimentary canal, they are in a compartment that is continuous with the outside environment via the mouth and anus and have not yet crossed a membrane to enter the body. 3. Just as food remains outside the body in a digestive tract, gasoline moves from the fuel tank to the engine, and waste products exit through the exhaust without ever entering the passenger compartment of the automobile. In addition, gasoline, like food, is broken down in a specialized compartment, so that the rest of the automobile (or body) is protected from disassembly. In both cases, high-energy fuels are consumed, complex molecules are broken down into simpler ones, and waste products are eliminated.

Concept Check 41.3

1. By peristalsis, which can squeeze food through the esophagus even without the help of gravity 2. Because parietal cells in the stomach pump hydrogen ions to produce HCl, a proton pump inhibitor reduces the acidity of chyme and thus the irritation that occurs when chyme enters the esophagus. 3. Proteins would be denatured and digested into peptides. Further digestion, to individual amino acids, would require enzymatic secretions found in the small intestine. No digestion of carbohydrates or lipids would occur.

Concept Check 41.4

1. The increased time for transit through the alimentary canal allows for more extensive processing, and the increased surface of the canal area provides greater opportunity for absorption. 2. A mammal's digestive system provides mutualistic microbes with an environment that is protected against other microbes by saliva and gastric juice, that is held at a constant temperature conducive to enzyme action, and that provides a steady source of nutrients. 3. For the yogurt treatment to be effective, the bacteria from yogurt would have to establish a mutualistic relationship with the small intestine, where disaccharides are broken down and sugars are absorbed. Conditions in the small intestine are likely to be very different from those in a yogurt culture. The bacteria might be killed before they reach the small intestine, or they might not be able to grow there in sufficient numbers to aid in digestion.

Concept Check 41.5

1. Over the long term, the body stores excess calories in fat, whether those calories come from fat, carbohydrate, or protein in food. 2. In normal individuals, leptin levels decline during fasting. Individuals in the group with low levels of leptin are likely to be defective in leptin production, so leptin levels would remain low regardless of food intake. Individuals in the group with high leptin levels are likely to be defective in responding to leptin, but they still should shut off leptin production as fat stores are used up. 3. Insulin will not be subjected to negative feedback, and insulin levels will continue to rise. This will at first drive glucose levels down as tissues are induced to take up glucose for storage (as glycogen and lipid) and oxidation. Liver will increase glycogen levels and lipid storage, leading to a condition known as fatty liver.

Summary of Key Concepts Questions

41.1 Since collagen is found in all mammals, a likely explanation is that mammals other than primates and guinea pigs can synthesize vitamin C from other organic molecules. 41.2 A liquid diet containing glucose, amino acids, and other building blocks could be ingested and absorbed without the need for mechanical or chemical digestion. 41.3 The small intestine has a much larger surface area than the stomach. 41.4 The assortment of teeth in our mouth and the short length of our cecum suggest that our ancestors' digestive systems were not specialized for digesting plant material. 41.5 When mealtime arrives, nervous inputs from the brain signal the stomach to prepare to digest food through secretions and churning.

Test Your Understanding

1. b 2. c 3. b 4. c 5. d 6. b
7.

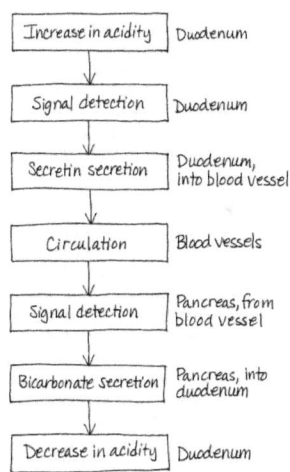

Chapter 42

Figure Questions

Figure 42.2 Although gas exchange might be improved by a steady, one-way flow of fluid, there would likely be inadequate time for food to be digested and nutrients absorbed if fluid flowed through the cavity in this manner. Figure 42.5 When salmon return to their natal rivers, there is a chance over many generations that the physiology evolves in ways that fine-tune physiological performance. Because the populations have had some period of separation, it is possible that evolutionary events in the history of one population enable a different trajectory for evolution of the trait. In other words, each population may take a different route for physiological evolution and therefore the solutions found in one population may be unique to that population. If an individual with a genetic predisposition to making, for example, a big heart, would find itself in a river where that heart was not needed, it is possible the individual would have an inferior physiology as a result of the enlarged heart and that this would be selected against. However, it is also possible that the individual with a genetically larger heart would possess advantages that the native population lacks, permitting positive selection. Figure 42.9 Each feature of the ECG recording, such as the sharp upward spike, occurs once per cardiac cycle. Using the x-axis to measure the time in seconds between successive spikes and dividing that number into

60 would yield the heart rate as the number of cycles per minute. Figure 42.21 The three main lineages are Deuterostomia, Lophotrochozoa, and Ecdysozoa. All three are represented by the animals shown in Figure 42.21: Polychaetes (phylum Annelida) are lophotrochozoans, crayfish (phylum Arthropoda) are ecdysozoans, and sea stars (phylum Echinodermata) are deuterostomes. Figure 42.26 Since exhalation is largely passive, the recoil of the elastic fibres in alveoli helps force air out of the lungs. When alveoli lose their elasticity, as occurs in the disease emphysema, less air is exhaled. Because more air is left in the lungs, less fresh air can be inhaled. With a smaller volume of air exchanged, there is a decrease in the partial pressure gradient that drives gas exchange. Figure 42.27 Breathing at a rate greater than that needed to meet metabolic demand (hyperventilation) would lower blood CO_2 levels. Sensors in major blood vessels and the medulla would signal the breathing control centres to decrease the rate of contraction of the diaphragm and rib muscles, decreasing the breathing rate and restoring normal CO_2 levels in the blood and other tissues. Figure 42.30 If the Hb properties of mammoths are important adaptations, then it is possible that other lineages in the same environment would coevolve similar mechanisms. Thus, musk ox might be less affected by the cold than are their relatives from temperature regions, such as sheep.

Concept Check 42.1

1. In both an open circulatory system and a fountain, fluid is pumped through a tube and then returns to the pump after collecting in a pool. 2. The fish pattern is a single circuit, simple in organization. The most important feature is position of the heart, before the gills. This means that it receives deoxygenated blood returning from the systemic circulation. The amphibian circuit permits separation of flow into skin and lung loops, with partial separation of flow in the ventricle. Whether the blood in these loops is oxygenated or not depends on whether the animal is breathing through the skin (in water) or lungs (on land). Reptiles have greater separation of pulmonary and systemic blood, which improves efficiency, and in some species incorporates a shunt that can alter flow through the body. The most complete separation occurs in birds and mammals, with two completely separate loops. This permits the independent regulation of blood pressure in pulmonary and systemic circulation. 3. The O_2 content would be abnormally low because some oxygen-depleted blood returned to the right atrium from the systemic circuit would mix with the oxygen-rich blood in the left atrium.

Concept Check 42.2

1. The pulmonary veins carry blood that has just passed through capillary beds in the lungs, where it accumulated O_2. The venae cavae carry blood that has just passed through capillary beds in the rest of the body, where it lost O_2 to the tissues. 2. The delay allows the atria to empty completely, filling ventricles fully before they contract. 3. The heart, like any other muscle, becomes stronger through regular exercise. You would expect a stronger heart to have a greater stroke volume, which would allow for the decrease in heart rate.

Concept Check 42.3

1. Though the capillaries have a narrower diameter, there are a great many capillaries, providing a large total cross-sectional area. 2. An increase in blood pressure and cardiac output combined with the diversion of more blood to the skeletal muscles would increase the capacity for action by increasing the rate of blood circulation and delivering more O_2 and nutrients to the skeletal muscles. 3. Additional hearts could be used to improve blood return from the legs. However, it might be difficult to coordinate the activity of multiple hearts and to maintain adequate blood flow to hearts far from the gas exchange organs.

Concept Check 42.4

1. An increase in the number of white blood cells (leukocytes) may indicate that the person is combating an infection. 2. Clotting factors do not initiate clotting but are essential steps in the clotting process. Also, the clots that form a thrombus typically result from an inflammatory response to an atherosclerotic plaque, not from clotting at a wound site. 3. The chest pain results from inadequate blood flow in coronary arteries. Vasodilation promoted by nitric oxide from nitroglycerin increases blood flow, providing the heart muscle with additional oxygen and thus relieving the pain. 4. When a mutant allele is codominant with the wild-type allele, the phenotype of heterozygotes is intermediate between that of wild-type and mutant homozygotes. Therefore, in the presence of wild-type Hb, the aggregation of Hb^S that causes sickling must be significantly reduced. Based on this fact, some therapies for sickle-cell disease are aimed at boosting adult expression of another hemoglobin gene in the body, such as that normally expressed only in the fetus. 5. Embryonic stem cells are pluripotent rather than multipotent, meaning that they can give rise to many rather than a few different cell types.

Concept Check 42.5

1. Their interior position helps them stay moist. If the respiratory surfaces of lungs extended out into the terrestrial environment, they would quickly dry out, and diffusion of O_2 and CO_2 across these surfaces would stop. 2. Earthworms need to keep their skin moist for gas exchange, but they need air outside this moist layer. If they stay in their waterlogged tunnels after a heavy rain, they will suffocate because they cannot get as much O_2 from water as from air. 3. In the extremities of some vertebrates, blood flows in opposite directions in neighbouring veins and arteries; this countercurrent arrangement maximizes the recapture of heat from blood leaving the body core in arteries, which is important for thermoregulation in cold environments. Similarly, in the gills of fish, water passes over the gills in the direction opposite to that of blood flowing through the gill capillaries, maximizing the extraction of oxygen from the water along the length of the exchange surface.

Concept Check 42.6

1. An increase in blood CO_2 concentration causes an increase in the rate of CO_2 diffusion into the cerebrospinal fluid, where the CO_2 combines with water to form carbonic acid. Dissociation of carbonic acid releases hydrogen ions, decreasing the pH

of the cerebrospinal fluid. 2. Increased heart rate increases the rate at which CO_2-rich blood is delivered to the lungs, where CO_2 is removed. 3. A hole would allow air to enter the space between the inner and outer layers of the double membrane, resulting in a condition called a pneumothorax. The two layers would no longer stick together, and the lung on the side with the hole would collapse and cease functioning.

Concept Check 42.7

1. Differences in partial pressure; gases diffuse from a region of higher partial pressure to a region of lower partial pressure. 2. The Bohr shift causes hemoglobin to release more O_2 at a lower pH, such as found in the vicinity of tissues with high rates of cellular respiration and CO_2 release. 3. The doctor is assuming that the rapid breathing is the body's response to low blood pH. Metabolic acidosis, the lowering of blood pH, can have many causes, including complications of certain types of diabetes, shock (extremely low blood pressure), and poisoning.

Summary of Key Concepts Questions

42.1 In a closed circulatory system, an ATP-driven muscular pump generally moves fluids in one direction on a scale of millimetres to metres. Exchange between cells and their environment relies on diffusion, which involves random movements of molecules. Concentration gradients of molecules across exchange surfaces can drive rapid net diffusion on a scale of 1 mm or less. 42.2 Replacement of a defective valve should increase stroke volume. A lower heart rate would therefore be sufficient to maintain the same cardiac output. 42.3 Blood pressure in the arm would fall by 25–30 mm Hg, the same difference as is normally seen between your heart and your brain. 42.4 One microlitre of blood contains about 5 million erythrocytes and 5000 leukocytes, so leukocytes make up only about 0.1% of the cells in the absence of infection. 42.5 Because CO_2 is such a small fraction of atmospheric gas (0.29 mm Hg/760 mm Hg, or less than 0.04%), the partial pressure gradient of CO_2 between the respiratory surface and the environment always strongly favours the release of CO_2 to the atmosphere. 42.6 Because the lungs do not empty completely with each breath, incoming and outgoing air mix, so not all of the tidal volume represents fresh air. 42.7 An enzyme speeds up a reaction without changing the equilibrium and without being consumed. Similarly, a respiratory pigment speeds up the movement of gases in the body without changing the equilibrium and without being consumed.

Test Your Understanding

1. c 2. a 3. d 4. c 5. c 6. a 7. a
8.

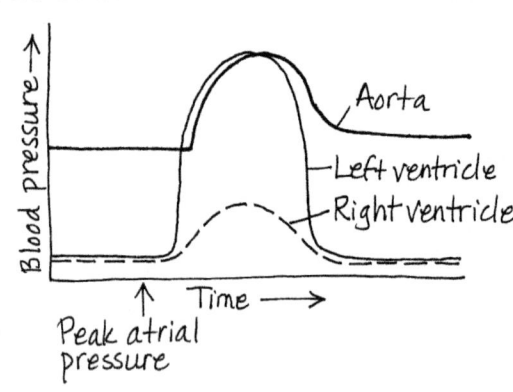

Chapter 43

Figure Questions

Figure 43.5 The seemingly inactive peptides might offer protection against pathogens other than those studied. Also, some antimicrobial peptides might work best in combination. Figure 43.6 Cell-surface TLRs recognize pathogens identifiable by surface molecules, whereas TLRs in vesicles recognize pathogens identifiable by internal molecules after the pathogens are broken down. Figure 43.10 Part of the enzyme or antigen receptor provides a structural "backbone" that maintains overall shape, while interaction occurs at a surface with a close fit to the substrate or antigen. The combined effect of multiple noncovalent interactions at the active site or binding site is a high-affinity interaction of tremendous specificity. Figure 43.13 After gene rearrangement, a lymphocyte and its daughter cells make a single version of the antigen receptor. In contrast, alternative splicing is not heritable and can give rise to diverse gene products in a single cell. Figure 43.16 Other cell types in the immune system are able to carry out the phagocytotic responsibilities of dendritic cells, so if they lost their capacity for phagocytosis, but retained other functions, it is possible that there would be few consequences. Figure 43.19 These receptors enable memory cells to present antigen on their cell surface to a helper T cell. This presentation of antigen is required to activate memory cells in a secondary immune response. Figure 43.21 Primary response: arrows extending from Antigen (1st exposure), Antigen-presenting cell, Helper T cell, B cell, Plasma cells, Cytotoxic T cell, and Active cytotoxic T cells; secondary response: arrows extending from Antigen (2nd exposure), Memory helper T cells, Memory B cells, and Memory cytotoxic T cells.

Concept Check 43.1

1. Because pus contains white blood cells, fluid, and cell debris, it indicates an active and at least partially successful inflammatory response against invading microbes. 2. Whereas the ligand for the TLR receptor is a foreign molecule, the ligand for many signal transduction pathways is a molecule produced by the animal itself. 3. Bacteria with a human host would be likely to grow optimally at normal body temperature or, if fever were often induced, at a temperature a few degrees higher.

Concept Check 43.2

1. See Figure 43.9. The transmembrane regions lie within the C regions, which also form the disulphide bridges. In contrast, the antigen-binding sites are in the V regions. 2. Generating memory cells ensures both that a receptor specific for a particular epitope will be present and that there will be more lymphocytes with this specificity than in a host that had never encountered the antigen. 3. If each B cell produced two different light and heavy chains for its antigen receptor, different combinations would make four different receptors. If any one were self-reactive, the lymphocyte would be eliminated in the generation of self-tolerance. For this reason, many more B cells would be eliminated, and those that could respond to a foreign antigen would be less effective at doing so due to the variety of receptors (and antibodies) they express.

Concept Check 43.3

1. A child lacking a thymus would have no functional T cells. Without helper T cells to help activate B cells, the child would be unable to produce antibodies against extracellular bacteria. Furthermore, without cytotoxic T cells or helper T cells, the child's immune system would be unable to kill virus-infected cells. 2. Since the antigen-binding site is intact, the antibody fragments could neutralize viruses and opsonize bacteria. 3. If the handler developed immunity to proteins in the antivenin, another injection could provoke a severe immune response. The handler's immune system might also now produce antibodies that could neutralize the venom.

Concept Check 43.4

1. Myasthenia gravis is considered an autoimmune disease because the immune system produces antibodies against self molecules (certain receptors on muscle cells). 2. A person with a cold is likely to produce oral and nasal secretions that facilitate viral transfer. In addition, since sickness can cause incapacitation or death, a virus that is programmed to exit the host when there is a physiological stress has the opportunity to find a new host at a time when the current host may cease to function. 3. A person with a macrophage deficiency would have frequent infections. The causes would be poor innate responses, due to diminished phagocytosis and inflammation, and poor adaptive responses, due to the lack of macrophages to present antigens to helper T cells.

Summary of Key Concepts Questions

43.1 Lysozyme in saliva destroys bacterial cell walls; the viscosity of mucus helps trap bacteria; acidic pH in the stomach kills many bacteria; and the tight packing of cells lining the gut provides a physical barrier to infection. 43.2 Sufficient numbers of cells to mediate an innate immune response are always present, whereas an adaptive response requires selection and proliferation of an initially very small cell population specific for the infecting pathogen. 43.3 No. Immunological memory after a natural infection and after vaccination are very similar. There may be minor differences in the particular antigens that can be recognized in a subsequent infection. 43.4 No. AIDS refers to a loss of immune function that can occur over time in an individual infected with HIV, not to the viral infection itself. For individuals infected with HIV, certain multidrug combinations ("cocktails") or rare genetic variations usually prevent progression to AIDS.

Test Your Understanding

1. b 2. c 3. c 4. d 5. b 6. b 7. c
8. One possible answer:

Chapter 44

Figure Questions

Figure 44.2 Aquaporins, which act as water channels. Figure 44.8 It is likely that the Lake Magadi fish are physiologically committed to living at an extreme pH. They may survive as individual transplants, using physiological processes to cope with the different water conditions. Over the short term, they may retain the propensity of producing urea as a waste product, though they may down-regulate the activities of the enzymes of the urea cycle. Over the long term, the costs of this excretory pattern, both in terms of synthesis of urea and urea cycle enzymes, would represent a cost that would likely be a factor in natural selection. Over generations, these Lake Magadi tilapia might evolve urea cycle genes with lower expression, which would be accelerated should they interbreed. Figure 44.14 You would expect to find these cells lining tubules where they pass through the renal medulla. Because the extracellular fluid of the renal medulla has a very high osmolarity, production of solutes by tubule cells in this region keeps intracellular osmolarity high, with the result that these cells maintain normal volume. Figure 44.15 Furosemide increases urine volume. The absence of ion transport in the ascending limb leaves the filtrate too concentrated for substantial volume reduction in the distal tubule and collecting duct. Figure 44.18 If a charged molecule is given a chance to cross the cell membrane, the direction it moves depends upon both the concentration gradient for the chemical and the electrical gradient or membrane potential. For instance, when a sodium channel opens, there is an inward Na^+ gradient, which tends to drive Na^+ into the cell. There is also an inward electrical gradient (more negative inside). Since both forces favour Na^+ movement into the cell, Na^+ would move rapidly into the cell when a channel opens. Figure 44.21 The ADH levels would likely be elevated in both sets of patients with mutations because either defect prevents the recapture of water that restores blood osmolarity to normal levels.

Concept Check 44.1

1. Because the salt is moved against its concentration gradient, from low concentration (fresh water) to high concentration (blood) 2. A freshwater osmoconformer would

have body fluids too dilute to carry out life's processes. 3. Without a layer of insulating fur, the camel must use the cooling effect of evaporative water loss to maintain body temperature, thus linking thermoregulation and osmoregulation.

Concept Check 44.2

1. Because uric acid is largely insoluble in water, it can be excreted as a semisolid paste, thereby reducing an animal's water loss. 2. Humans produce uric acid from purine breakdown, and reducing purines in the diet often lessens the severity of gout. Birds, however, produce uric acid as a waste product of general nitrogen metabolism. They would therefore need a diet low in all nitrogen-containing compounds, not just purines.

Concept Check 44.3

1. In flatworms, ciliated cells draw interstitial fluids containing waste products into protonephridia. In earthworms, waste products pass from interstitial fluids into the coelom. From there the cilia move the wastes into metanephridia via a funnel surrounding an internal opening to the metanephridia. In insects, the Malpighian tubules pump fluids from the hemolymph, which receives waste products during exchange with interstitial fluids in the course of circulation. 2. Filtration produces a fluid for exchange processes that is free of cells and large molecules, which are of benefit to the animal and could not readily be reabsorbed. 3. The presence of Na^+ and other ions (electrolytes) in the dialysate would limit the extent to which they would be removed from the filtrate during dialysis. Adjusting the electrolytes in the starting dialysate can thus lead to the restoration of proper electrolyte concentrations in the plasma. Similarly, the absence of urea and other waste products in the starting dialysate results in their efficient removal from the filtrate.

Concept Check 44.4

1. The numerous nephrons and well-developed glomeruli of freshwater fishes produce urine at a high rate, while the small numbers of nephrons and smaller glomeruli of marine fishes produce urine at a low rate. 2. The kidney medulla would absorb less water; thus, the drug would increase the amount of water lost in the urine. 3. A decline in blood pressure in the afferent arteriole would reduce the rate of filtration by moving less material through the vessels.

Concept Check 44.5

1. Alcohol inhibits the release of ADH, causing an increase in urinary water loss and increasing the chance of dehydration. 2. The consumption of a large amount of water in a very short period of time, coupled with an absence of solute intake, can reduce sodium levels in the blood below tolerable levels. This condition, called hyponatremia, leads to disorientation and, sometimes, respiratory distress. It has occurred in some marathon runners who drink water rather than sports drinks. (It has also caused the death of a fraternity pledge as a consequence of a water hazing ritual and the death of a contestant in a water-drinking competition.) 3. High blood pressure 4. Each molecule of renin or ACE activates multiple molecules of the next protein in the pathway. The same is true for the protein kinases. The proteases differ from the protein kinases in at least two ways. First, their action is irreversible. Second, they do not require activation by another enzyme molecule.

Summary of Key Concepts Questions

44.1 Water moves into a cell by osmosis when the fluid outside the cells is hypoosmotic (has a lower solute concentration than the cytosol).
44.2

Waste Attribute	Ammonia	Urea	Uric Acid
Toxicity	High	Very low	Low
Energy content	Low	Moderate	High
Water loss in excretion	High	Moderate	Low

44.3 Filtration retains large molecules that would be difficult to transport across membranes. 44.4 Both types of nephrons have proximal tubules that can reabsorb nutrients, but only juxtamedullary nephrons have loops of Henle that extend deep into the renal medulla. Thus, only kidneys containing juxtamedullary nephrons can produce urine that is more concentrated than the blood. 44.5 Patients who don't produce ADH have symptoms relieved by treatment with the hormone, but many patients with diabetes insipidus lack functional receptors for ADH.

Test Your Understanding

1. d 2. a 3. c 4. d 5. d 6. b
7.

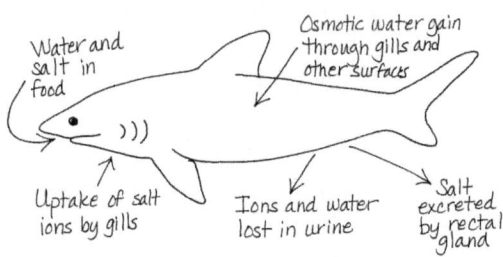

Chapter 45

Figure Questions

Figure 45.4 Synthesizing epinephrine requires breaking the bond between the carboxyl group (–COOH) and the α-carbon in tyrosine. Figure 45.5 The hormone is water soluble and has a cell-surface receptor. Such receptors, unlike those for lipid-soluble hormones, can cause observable changes in cells without hormone-dependent gene transcription. Figure 45.13 Insulin is a protein, encoded by a gene. The sequence of the gene, and consequently the sequence and structure of the protein, differs among species. This structural evolution likely occurs in parallel with evolution of the insulin receptors. When a species is given insulin purified from another species, it is possible that there is a structural mismatch between the non-native insulin and the native receptor.

Concept Check 45.1

1. Water-soluble hormones, which cannot penetrate the plasma membrane, bind to cell-surface receptors. This interaction triggers an intracellular signal transduction pathway that ultimately alters the activity of a preexisting protein in the cytoplasm and/or changes transcription of specific genes in the nucleus. Steroid hormones are lipid-soluble and can cross the plasma membrane into the cell interior, where they bind to receptors located in the cytosol or nucleus. The hormone-receptor complex then functions directly as a transcription factor that changes transcription of specific genes. 2. Prostaglandins in semen that induce contractions in the uterus are acting as signalling molecules that are transferred from one individual to another of the same species (like pheromones), thus aiding in reproduction. 3. Both hormones produce opposite effects in different target tissues. In the fight-or-flight response, epinephrine increases blood flow to skeletal muscles and reduces blood flow to smooth muscles in the digestive system. In establishing apical dominance, auxin promotes the growth of apical buds and inhibits the growth of lateral buds.

Concept Check 45.2

1. In a healthy person, insulin released in response to the initial rise in blood glucose stimulates uptake of glucose by body cells. In a person with diabetes, however, inadequate production of insulin or nonresponsiveness of target cells decreases the body's ability to clear excess glucose from the blood. The initial increase in blood glucose is therefore greater in a person with diabetes, and it remains high for a prolonged period. 2. If the function of the pathway is to provide a transient response, a short-lived stimulus would be less dependent on negative feedback. 3. Since patients with type 2 diabetes produce insulin but fail to maintain normal glucose levels, you might predict that there could be mutations in the genes for the insulin receptor or the signal transduction pathway it activates. Such mutations have in fact been found in type 2 patients.

Concept Check 45.3

1. The adrenal medulla is derived from neural tissue during development. Reflecting this origin, it is an endocrine organ that produces two molecules—epinephrine and norepinephrine—that act both as hormones and as neurotransmitters. 2. The levels of these hormones in the blood would become very high. This would be due to the diminished negative feedback on the hypothalamic neurons that secrete the releasing hormone that stimulates the secretion of ACTH by the anterior pituitary. 3. By applying glucocorticoids to tissue by local injection, you exploit their anti-inflammatory activity. Local injection avoids the effects on glucose metabolism that would occur if glucocorticoids were taken orally and transported throughout the body in the bloodstream.

Summary of Key Concepts Questions

45.1 Because receptors for water-soluble hormones are located on the cell surface, facing the extracellular space, injecting the hormone into the cytoplasm would not trigger a response. 45.2 It would lessen the symptoms. Glucagon acts antagonistically with insulin, so lowering the effects of glucagon would be similar to increasing the levels or activity of insulin. 45.3 Both the pituitary and the adrenal glands are formed by fusion of neural and nonneural tissue. ADH is secreted by the neurosecretory portion of the pituitary gland, and epinephrine is secreted by the neurosecretory portion of the adrenal gland.

Test Your Understanding

1. c 2. a 3. d 4. c 5. c 6. b 7. a 8. a
9.

Chapter 46

Figure 46.4 The total gestational time includes all the events between fertilization and birth. It is feasible that the earlier birth date could correspond to an earlier mating time. Seals come into estrous after lactation is complete, so if lactation supporting a previous pup is completed sooner, the female will be ready to mate earlier in the year. The implantation could occur sooner, though this is usually thought to be dependent on photoperiod. If the embryonic diapause was unchanged, development could be induced to occur at a faster rate; utero development is usually well choreographed such that there is limited capacity to grow to a given stage at a faster rate. Birth could occur at a smaller or younger stage. The cause of these changes could be due to warming conditions, and may be linked to effects of global warming on food webs. For example, increases in the abundance of food could improve milk quality or quantity, or support faster embryonic growth rates. It has also been suggested that hunting practices have contributed to a change in the average size of females; smaller females tend to give birth to smaller pups, though the pups are generally not born any sooner to smaller females. Figure 46.9 According to the graph, about one-third of the females rid themselves of all sperm from the first mating. Thus, two-thirds retain some sperm from the first mating. We would therefore predict that two-thirds of the females would have some offspring exhibiting the small-eye phenotype of the dominant mutation carried by the males with which the females mated first. Figure 46.12 The analysis would be informative because the polar bodies contain all of the maternal chromosomes that don't end up in the mature egg. For example, finding two copies of the disease gene in the polar bodies would indicate its absence in the egg. This method of genetic testing is sometimes carried out when oocytes collected from a female are fertilized with sperm in a laboratory dish. Figure 46.16 Testosterone can pass from fetal blood to maternal blood via the placental circulation, temporarily upsetting the hormonal balance in the mother. Figure 46.18 Oxytocin would most likely induce labour, starting a positive-feedback loop that would direct labour to completion. Synthetic oxytocin is in fact frequently used to induce labour when prolonged pregnancy might endanger the mother or fetus.

Concept Check 46.1

1. The offspring of sexual reproduction are more genetically diverse. However, asexual reproduction can produce more offspring over multiple generations. 2. Unlike other forms of asexual reproduction, parthenogenesis involves gamete production. By controlling whether or not haploid eggs are fertilized, species such as honeybees can readily switch between asexual and sexual reproduction. 3. No. Owing to random assortment of chromosomes during meiosis, the offspring may receive the same copy or different copies of a particular parental chromosome from the sperm and the egg. Furthermore, genetic recombination during meiosis will result in reassortment of genes between pairs of parental chromosomes. 4. Both fragmentation and budding in animals have direct counterparts in the asexual reproduction of plants.

Concept Check 46.2

1. Internal fertilization allows the sperm to reach the egg without either gamete drying out. 2. (a) Animals with external fertilization tend to release many gametes at once, resulting in the production of enormous numbers of zygotes. This increases the chances that some will survive to adulthood. (b) Animals with internal fertilization produce fewer offspring but generally exhibit greater care of the embryos and the young. 3. Like the uterus of an insect, the ovary of a plant is the site of fertilization. Unlike the plant ovary, the uterus is not the site of egg production, which occurs in the insect ovary. In addition, the fertilized insect egg is expelled from the uterus, whereas the plant embryo develops within a seed in the ovary.

Concept Check 46.3

1. Spermatogenesis occurs normally only when the testicles are cooler than normal body temperature. Extensive use of a hot tub (or of very tight-fitting underwear) can cause a decrease in sperm quality and number. 2. In humans, the secondary oocyte combines with a sperm before it finishes the second meiotic division. Thus, oogenesis is completed after, not before, fertilization. 3. The only effect of sealing off each vas deferens is an absence of sperm in the ejaculate. Sexual response and ejaculate volume are unchanged. The cutting and sealing off of these ducts, a *vasectomy*, is a common surgical procedure for men who do not wish to produce any (more) offspring.

Concept Check 46.4

1. In the testis, FSH stimulates the Sertoli cells, which nourish developing sperm. LH stimulates the production of androgens (mainly testosterone), which in turn stimulate sperm production. In both females and males, FSH encourages the growth of cells that support and nourish developing gametes (follicle cells in females and Sertoli cells in males), and LH stimulates the production of sex hormones that promote gametogenesis (estrogens, primarily estradiol, in females and androgens, especially testosterone, in males). 2. In estrous cycles, which occur in most female mammals, the endometrium is reabsorbed (rather than shed) if fertilization does not occur. Estrous cycles often occur just one or a few times a year, and the female is usually receptive to copulation only during the period around ovulation. Menstrual cycles are found only in humans and some other primates. 3. The combination of estradiol and progesterone would have a negative-feedback effect on the hypothalamus, blocking release of GnRH. This would interfere with LH secretion by the pituitary, thus preventing ovulation. This is in fact one basis of action of the most common hormonal contraceptives. 4. In the viral reproductive cycle, the production of new viral genomes is coordinated with capsid protein expression and with the production of phospholipids for viral coats. In the case of the human female, there is hormonally based coordination of egg maturation with the development of support tissues of the uterus.

Concept Check 46.5

1. hCG secreted by the early embryo stimulates the corpus luteum to make progesterone, which helps maintain the pregnancy. During the second trimester, however, hCG production drops, the corpus luteum disintegrates, and the placenta completely takes over progesterone production. 2. Both tubal ligation and vasectomy block the movement of gametes from the gonads to a site where fertilization could take place. 3. By introducing a spermatid nucleus directly into an oocyte, ICSI bypasses the sperm's acquisition of motility in the epididymis, its swimming to meet the egg in the oviduct, and its fusion with the egg.

Summary of Key Concepts Questions

46.1 No. Because parthenogenesis involves meiosis, the mother would pass on to each offspring a random and therefore typically distinct combination of the chromosomes she inherited from her mother and father. 46.2 None. 46.3 The small size and lack of cytoplasm characteristic of a sperm are adaptations well suited to its function as a delivery vehicle for DNA. The large size and rich cytoplasmic contents of eggs support the growth and development of the embryo. 46.4 Circulating anabolic steroids mimic the feedback regulation of testosterone, turning off pituitary signalling to the testes and thereby blocking release of signals required for spermatogenesis. 46.5 Oxygen-rich blood in maternal arteries flows into pools in the endometrium, passes into fetal capillaries in the chorionic villi of the placenta, and from there travels throughout the circulatory system of the fetus.

Test Your Understanding

1. d 2. b 3. a 4. c 5. a 6. b 7. c 8. d
9.

(a)

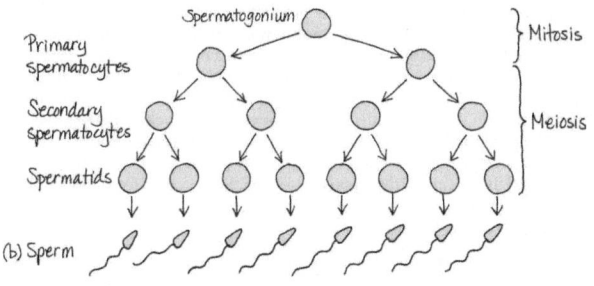

(c) The supply of stem cells would be used up and spermatogenesis would not be able to continue.

Chapter 47

Figure Questions

Figure 47.4 You could inject the compound into an unfertilized egg, expose the egg to sperm, and see whether the fertilization envelope forms. Figure 47.22 The researchers allowed normal cortical rotation to occur, resulting in activation of the "back-forming" determinants. Then they forced the opposite rotation to occur, which established the back on the opposite side as well. Because the molecules on the normal side were already activated, forcing the opposite rotation apparently did not "cancel out" the establishment of the back side by the first rotation. Figure 47.23 In Spemann's control, the two blastomeres were physically separated, and each grew into a whole embryo. In Roux's experiment, remnants of the dead blastomere were still contacting the live blastomere, which developed into a half-embryo. Therefore, molecules present in the dead cell's remnants may have been signalling to the live cell, inhibiting it from making all the embryonic structures. Figure 47.24 You could inject the isolated protein or an mRNA encoding it into ventral cells of an earlier gastrula. If dorsal structures form on the ventral side, that would support the idea that the protein is the signalling molecule secreted or presented by the dorsal lip. You should also do a control experiment to make sure the injection process alone did not cause dorsal structures to form. Figure 47.26 You could remove the AER and look for Sonic hedgehog mRNA or protein as a marker of the ZPA. If either was absent, that would support your hypothesis. You could also block FGF function and see whether the ZPA formed (by looking for Sonic hedgehog).

Concept Check 47.1

1. The fertilization envelope forms after cortical granules release their contents outside the egg, causing the vitelline membrane to rise and harden. The fertilization envelope serves as a barrier to fertilization by more than one sperm. 2. The increased Ca^{2+} concentration in the egg would cause the cortical granules to fuse with the plasma membrane, releasing their contents and causing a fertilization envelope to form, even though no sperm had entered. This would prevent fertilization. 3. You

would expect it to fluctuate. The fluctuation of MPF drives the transition between DNA replication (S phase) and mitosis (M phase), which is still required in the abbreviated cleavage cell cycle.

Concept Check 47.2

1. The cells of the notochord migrate toward the midline of the embryo (converge), rearranging themselves so there are fewer cells across the notochord, which thus becomes longer overall (extends; see Figure 47.17). 2. Because microfilaments would not be able to contract and decrease the size of one end of the cell, both the inward bending in the middle of the neural tube and the outward bending of the hinge regions at the edges would be blocked. Therefore, the neural tube probably would not form. 3. Dietary intake of the vitamin folic acid dramatically reduces the frequency of neural tube defects.

Concept Check 47.3

1. Axis formation establishes the location and polarity of the three axes that provide the coordinates for development. Pattern formation positions particular tissues and organs in the three-dimensional space defined by those coordinates. 2. Morphogen gradients act by specifying cell fates across a field of cells through variation in the level of a determinant. Morphogen gradients thus act more globally than cytoplasmic determinants or inductive interactions between pairs of cells. 3. Yes, a second embryo could develop because inhibiting BMP-4 activity would have the same effect as transplanting an organizer. 4. The limb that developed probably would have a mirror-image duplication, with the most posterior digits in the middle and the most anterior digits at either end.

Summary of Key Concepts Questions

47.1 The binding of a sperm to a receptor on the egg surface is very specific and likely would not occur if the two gametes were from different species. Without sperm binding, the sperm and egg membranes would not fuse. 47.2 The neural tube forms when the neural plate, a band of ectodermal tissue oriented along the anterior-posterior axis on the dorsal side of the embryo, rolls into a tube and pinches off from the rest of the ectoderm. Neural crest cells arise as groups of cells in the regions between the edges of the neural tube and the surrounding ectoderm migrate away from the neural tube. 47.3 Mutations that affected both limb and kidney development would be more likely to alter the function of monocilia because these organelles are important in several signalling pathways. Mutations that affected limb development but not kidney development would more likely alter a single pathway, such as Hedgehog signalling.

Test Your Understanding

1. a 2. b 3. d 4. a 5. d 6. c 7. b
8.

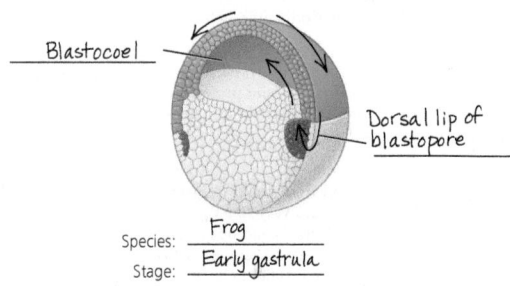

Species: Frog
Stage: Early gastrula

Chapter 48

Figure Questions

Figure 48.7 Adding chloride channels makes the membrane potential less positive. Adding sodium or potassium channels would have no effect, because sodium movement is already at equilibrium and there are no potassium ions present. Figure 48.9

Figure 48.15 The production and transmission of action potentials would be unaffected. However, action potentials arriving at chemical synapses would be unable

to trigger release of neurotransmitter. Signalling at such synapses would thus be blocked. Figure 48.16 If only a fraction of animals recovered, this still demonstrates that animals are able to reform connections. It would be possible that refinements in either removing the interneuron from the donor or transplanting it to the recipient might increase the probability of a successful recovery.

Concept Check 48.1

1. Sensors in your ear transmit information to your brain. There the activity of interneurons in processing centres enables you to recognize your name. In response, signals transmitted via motor neurons cause contraction of muscles that turn your neck. 2. Increased branching would allow control of a greater number of postsynaptic cells, enhancing coordination of responses to nervous system signals. 3. Communication by bacteria involves all the cells in a colony, whereas communication by neurons involves just a few cells in the animal body. In addition, neurons direct signals from one location to another, whereas bacterial cells communicate in all directions. 4. Synaptic signalling refers to a signal emanating from a neuron and going to other cells. If the signal affects the same neuron that released it, this would be consistent with autocrine signalling. If the target cell is a different nerve or a muscle, this would be similar to paracrine signalling, which occurs between two different cells. In either situation, the signal is being transmitted locally, across very small distances, which is a criterion for both autocrine and paracrine signalling.

Concept Check 48.2

1. Ions can flow against a chemical concentration gradient if there is an opposing electrical gradient of greater magnitude. 2. A decrease in permeability to K^+, an increase in permeability to Na^+, or both 3. The activity of the sodium-potassium pump is essential to maintain the resting potential. With the pump inactivated, the sodium and potassium concentration gradients would gradually disappear, resulting in a greatly reduced resting potential. 4. Charged dye molecules could equilibrate only if other charged molecules could also cross the membrane. If not, a membrane potential would develop that would counterbalance the chemical gradient.

Concept Check 48.3

1. A graded potential has a magnitude that varies with stimulus strength, whereas an action potential has an all-or-none magnitude that is independent of stimulus strength. 2. Loss of the insulation provided by myelin sheaths leads to a disruption of action potential propagation along axons. Voltage-gated sodium channels are restricted to the nodes of Ranvier, and without the insulating effect of myelin, the inward current produced at one node during an action potential cannot depolarize the membrane to the threshold at the next node. 3. The maximum frequency would decrease because the refractory period would be extended.

Concept Check 48.4

1. It can bind to different types of receptors, each triggering a specific response in postsynaptic cells. 2. These toxins would prolong the EPSPs that acetylcholine produces because the neurotransmitter would remain longer in the synaptic cleft. 3. Membrane fusion and depolarization.

Summary of Key Concepts Questions

48.1 It would prevent information from being transmitted away from the cell body along the axon. 48.2 There are very few open sodium channels in a resting neuron, so the resting potential either would not change or would become slightly more negative (hyperpolarization). 48.3 Positive feedback is responsible for the rapid opening of many voltage-gated sodium channels, causing the rapid outflow of sodium ions responsible for the rising phase of the action potential. As the membrane potential becomes positive, voltage-gated potassium channels open in a form of negative feedback that helps bring about the falling phase of the action potential. 48.4 A given neurotransmitter can have many receptors that differ in their location and activity. Drugs that target receptor activity rather than neurotransmitter release or stability are therefore likely to exhibit greater specificity and potentially have fewer undesirable side effects.

Test Your Understanding

1. c 2. c 3. c 4. b 5. a 6. d. 7. By inhibiting the Na K ATPase, the cell membrane would lose the ability to build a membrane potential and the membrane would slowly depolarize. 8. GABA is usually an inhibitory neurotransmitter making it more difficult to trigger an action potential. The neurons become less excitable. 9. As shown in this pair of drawings, a pair of action potentials would move outward in both directions from each electrode. (Action potentials are unidirectional only if they begin at one end of an axon.) However, because of the refractory period, the two action potentials between the electrodes both stop where they meet. Thus, only one action potential reaches the synaptic terminals.

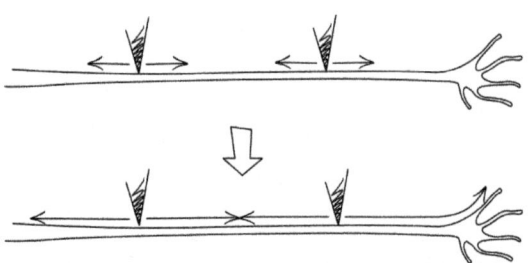

Chapter 49

Figure Questions

Figure 49.7 During swallowing, muscles along the esophagus alternately contract and relax, resulting in peristalsis. One model to explain this alternation is that each section of muscle receives nerve impulses that alternate between excitation and inhibition, just as the quadriceps and hamstring receive opposing signals in the knee-jerk reflex. Figure 49.15 Regions you would expect to be active regardless of the type of music played would include ones that are important for processing and interpreting sounds. Figure 49.21 Under Canadian law, any human experimentation requires the "informed consent" of the subject. The subject must be fully advised of the nature, purpose, and risk of the proposed experiment in order to obtain a valid informed consent. Any deception invalidates consent. A human ethics review process can help determine how consent should be obtained from subjects and to verify the required full and frank disclosure. If a subject cannot provide express consent because he or she lacks the capacity to appreciate the nature and consequences of the treatment, the researcher may seek consent from a substitute decision maker. The laws of each province determine how a substitute decision maker may be appointed. A substitute decision maker must act in the best interests of the incapacitated subject. Therefore, substitute decision makers cannot give consent on behalf of an incapacitated subject for enrollment in medical research unless such participation can be expected to result in some direct therapeutic benefit to the subject. Figure 49.24 If the depolarization brings the membrane potential to or past threshold, it should initiate action potentials that cause dopamine release from the VTA neurons. This should mimic natural stimulation of the brain reward system, resulting in positive and perhaps pleasurable sensations.

Concept Check 49.1

1. The sympathetic division would likely be activated. It mediates the "fight-or-flight" response in stressful situations. 2. Nerves contain bundles of axons, some that belong to motor neurons, which send signals outward from the CNS, and some that belong to sensory neurons, which bring signals into the CNS. Therefore, you would expect effects on both motor control and sensation. 3. Neurosecretory cells of the adrenal medulla secrete the hormones epinephrine and norepinephrine in response to preganglionic input from sympathetic neurons. These hormones travel in the circulation throughout the body, triggering responses in many tissues.

Concept Check 49.2

1. The cerebral cortex on the left side of the brain initiates voluntary movement of the right side of the body. 2. Alcohol diminishes function of the cerebellum. 3. Paralysis reflects an inability to carry out motor commands transmitted from the cerebrum to the spinal cord. You would expect these patients to have injuries in the portion of the CNS extending from the spinal cord up to but not including the reticular formation. A coma reflects a disruption in the cycles of sleep and arousal regulated by communication between the reticular formation and the cerebrum. You would expect these patients to have injuries in the reticular formation or in the portion of the brain on the opposite side of the reticular formation from the spinal cord.

Concept Check 49.3

1. Brain damage that disrupts behaviour, cognition, memory, or other functions provides evidence that the portion of the brain affected by the damage is important for the normal activity that is blocked or altered. 2. Broca's area, which is active during the generation of speech, is located near the part of the primary motor cortex that controls muscles in the face. Wernicke's area, which is active when speech is heard, is located near the part of the temporal lobe that is involved in hearing. 3. Each cerebral hemisphere is specialized for different parts of this task—the right for face recognition and the left for language. Without an intact corpus callosum, neither hemisphere can take advantage of the other's processing abilities.

Concept Check 49.4

1. There can be an increase in the number of synapses between the neurons or an increase in the strength of existing synaptic connections. 2. If consciousness is an emergent property resulting from the interaction of many different regions of the brain, then it is unlikely that localized brain damage will have a discrete effect on consciousness. 3. The hippocampus is responsible for organizing newly acquired information. Without hippocampal function, the links necessary to retrieve information from the neocortex will be lacking, and no functional memory, short- or long-term, will be formed.

Concept Check 49.5

1. Both are progressive brain diseases whose risk increases with advancing age. Both result from the death of brain neurons and are associated with the accumulation of peptide or protein aggregates. 2. The symptoms of schizophrenia can be mimicked by a drug that stimulates dopamine-releasing neurons. The brain's reward system, which is involved in drug addiction, is composed of dopamine-releasing neurons that connect the ventral tegmental area to regions in the cerebrum. Parkinson's disease results from the death of dopamine-releasing neurons. 3. Not necessarily. It might be that the plaques, tangles, and missing regions of the brain seen at death reflect secondary effects, the consequence of other unseen changes that are actually responsible for the alterations in brain function.

Summary of Key Concepts Questions

49.1 Because reflex circuits involve only a few neurons—the simplest consist of a sensory neuron and a motor neuron—the path for information transfer is short and simple, increasing the speed of the response. 49.2 The pons and medulla (the midbrain) coordinate visual reflexes; the cerebellum controls coordination of movement that depends on visual input; the thalamus serves as a routing centre for visual information; and the cerebrum is essential for converting visual input to a visual image. 49.3 You would expect the right side of the body to be paralyzed because it is controlled by the left cerebral hemisphere, where language generation and interpretation are localized. 49.4 Learning a new language likely requires the maintenance of synapses that are formed during early development but are otherwise lost prior to adulthood. 49.5 Whereas amphetamines stimulate dopamine release, PCP blocks glutamate receptors, suggesting that schizophrenia does not reflect a defect in the function of just one neurotransmitter.

Test Your Understanding
1. b 2. a 3. d 4. c 5. c 6. d
7.

Chapter 50

Figure Questions
Figure 50.12 In the brain. Each note is detected separately in the ear, with each causing vibration of the basilar membrane and deflection of hair cells in a distinct location. Sensory neurons in each location provide output in the form of action potentials that travel along distinct axons in the auditory nerve. It is not until the information reaches the brain that the individual notes are detected and the perception of the chord is generated. Figure 50.15 There is quite a bit of electromagnetic "noise" in any area with significant construction and mechanical activity. The noise is often great enough to influence the detection of small electromagnetic signals. Figure 50.20 Each of the three types of cones is most sensitive to a different wavelength of light. A cone might be fully depolarized when there is light present if the light is of a wavelength far from its optimum. Figure 50.24 The results of the experiment would have been identical. What matters is the activation of particular sets of neurons, not the manner in which they are activated. Any signal from a bitter cell will be interpreted by the brain as a bitter taste, regardless of the nature of the compound and the receptor involved. Figure 50.26 Only perception. Binding of an odourant to its receptor will cause action potentials to be sent to the brain. Although an excess of that odourant might cause a diminished response through adaptation, another odourant can mask the first only at the level of perception in the brain. Figure 50.29 Hundreds of myosin heads participate in sliding each pair of thick and thin filaments past each other. Because cross-bridge formation and breakdown are not synchronized, many myosin heads are exerting force on the thin filaments at all times during muscle contraction. Figure 50.33 By causing all of the motor neurons that control the muscle to generate action potentials at a rate high enough to produce tetanus in all of the muscle fibres Figure 50.40 Since a duck is more specialized for flying than for swimming, you might expect that it would consume more energy per unit body mass and distance in swimming than would, for example, a fish. (In fact, if the value for a 10^3-g swimming duck were plotted on this graph, it would appear well above the line for swimmers and just above the line for runners.)

Concept Check 50.1
1. Electromagnetic receptors in general detect only external stimuli. Nonelectromagnetic receptors, such as chemoreceptors or mechanoreceptors, can act as either internal or external sensors. 2. The capsaicin present in the peppers activates the thermoreceptor for high temperatures. In response to the perceived high temperature, the nervous system triggers sweating to achieve evaporative cooling. 3. You would perceive the electrical stimulus as if the sensory receptors that regulate that neuron had been activated. For example, electrical stimulation of the sensory neuron controlled by the thermoreceptor activated by menthol would likely be perceived as a local cooling.

Concept Check 50.2
1. Statocysts detect the animal's orientation with respect to gravity, providing information that is essential in environments such as these, where light cues are absent. 2. As a sound that changes gradually from a very low to a very high pitch. 3. The stapes and the other middle ear bones transmit vibrations from the tympanic membrane to the oval window. Fusion of these bones (as occurs in a disease called otosclerosis) would block this transmission and result in hearing loss.

Concept Check 50.3
1. Planarians have ocelli that cannot form images but can sense the intensity and direction of light, providing enough information to enable the animals to find protection in shaded places. Flies have compound eyes that form images and excel at detecting movement. 2. The person can focus on distant objects but not close objects (without glasses) because close focusing requires the lens to become almost spherical. This problem is common after age 50. 3. Close each eye in turn. An object floating on the surface of an eyeball will appear only when that eye is open. 4. Absorption of light by retinal converts a structure isomer in the *cis* configuration to the isomer in the *trans* configuration, initiating the process of light detection. In contrast, a photon absorbed by chlorophyll does not bring about isomerization, but instead boosts an electron to a higher energy orbital, initiating the electron flow that generates ATP and NADPH.

Concept Check 50.4
1. Both taste cells and olfactory cells have receptor proteins in their plasma membrane that bind certain substances, leading to membrane depolarization through a signal transduction pathway involving a G protein. However, olfactory cells are sensory neurons, whereas taste cells are not. 2. Since animals rely on chemical signals for behaviours that include finding mates, marking territories, and avoiding dangerous substances, it is adaptive for the olfactory system to have a robust response to a very small number of molecules of a particular odourant. 3. Because the sweet, bitter, and umami tastes involve GPCR proteins but the sour taste does not, you might predict that the mutation is in a molecule that acts in the signal transduction pathway common to the different GPCRs.

Concept Check 50.5
1. In a skeletal muscle fibre, Ca^{2+} binds to the troponin complex, which moves tropomyosin away from the myosin-binding sites on actin and allows cross-bridges to form. In a smooth muscle cell, Ca^{2+} binds to calmodulin, which activates an enzyme that phosphorylates the myosin head and thus enables cross-bridge formation. 2. *Rigor mortis*, a Latin phrase meaning "stiffness of death," results from the complete depletion of ATP in skeletal muscle. Since ATP is required to release myosin from actin and to pump Ca^{2+} out of the cytosol, muscles become chronically contracted beginning about 3–4 hours after death. 3. A competitive inhibitor binds to the same site as the substrate for the enzyme. In contrast, the troponin and tropomyosin complex masks, but does not bind to, the myosin-binding sites on actin.

Concept Check 50.6
1. Septa provide the divisions of the coelom that allow for peristalsis, a form of locomotion requiring independent control of different body segments. 2. The main problem in swimming is drag; a fusiform body minimizes drag. The main problem in flying is overcoming gravity; wings shaped like airfoils provide lift, and adaptations such as air-filled bones reduce body mass. 3. When you grasp the sides of the chair, you are using a contraction of the triceps to keep your arms extended against the pull of gravity on your body. As you lower yourself slowly into the chair, you gradually decrease the number of motor units in the triceps that are contracted. Contracting your biceps would jerk you down, since you would no longer be opposing gravity.

Summary of Key Concepts Questions
50.1 Nociceptors overlap with other classes of receptors in the type of stimulus they detect. They differ from other receptors only in how a particular stimulus is perceived. 50.2 The direction of displacement of a hair cell is determined by stimulus intensity, which is encoded by the frequency of action potentials transmitted to the brain. 50.3 The major difference is that neurons in the retina integrate information from multiple sensory receptors (photoreceptors) before transmitting information to the central nervous system. 50.4 Our olfactory sense is responsible for most of what we describe as distinct tastes. A head cold or other source of congestion blocks odourant access to receptors lining portions of the nasal cavity. 50.5 Hydrolysis of ATP is required to convert myosin to a high-energy configuration for binding to actin and to power the Ca^{2+} pump that removes cytosolic Ca^{2+} during muscle relaxation. 50.6 Human body movements rely on the contraction of muscles anchored to a rigid endoskeleton. Tendons attach muscles to bones, which in turn are composed of fibres built up from a basic organizational unit, the sarcomere. The thin and thick filaments have separate points of attachment within the sarcomere. In response to nervous system motor output, the formation and breakdown of cross-bridges between myosin heads and actin ratchet the thin and thick filaments past each other. Because the filaments are anchored, this sliding movement shortens the muscle fibres. Furthermore, because the fibres themselves are part of the muscles attached at each end to bones, muscle contraction moves bones of the body relative to each other. In this way, the structural anchoring of muscles and filaments enables muscle function, such as the bending of an elbow by contraction of the biceps.

The answer shows the actual distribution of rods and cones in the human eye. Your graph may differ but should have the following properties: Only cones at the fovea; fewer cones and more rods at both ends of the *x*-axis; no photoreceptors in the optic disk.

Chapter 51

Figure Questions

Figure 51.2 The fixed action pattern based on the sign stimulus of a red belly ensures that the male will chase away any invading males of his species. By chasing away such males, the defender decreases the chance that another male will fertilize eggs laid in his nesting territory. **Figure 51.7** There should be no effect. Imprinting is an innate behaviour that is carried out anew in each generation. Assuming the nest was not disturbed, the offspring of the Lorenz followers would imprint on the mother goose. **Figure 51.8** Perhaps the wasp doesn't use visual cues. It might also be that wasps recognize objects native to their environment, but not foreign objects, such as the pinecones. Tinbergen addressed these ideas before carrying out the pinecone study. When he swept away the pebbles and sticks around the nest, the wasps could no longer find their nests. If he shifted the natural objects in their natural arrangement, the shift in the landmarks caused a shift in the site to which the wasps returned. Finally, if natural objects around the nest site were replaced with pinecones while the wasp was in the burrow, the wasp nevertheless found her way back to the nest site. **Figure 51.24** It might be that the birds require stimuli during flight to exhibit their migratory preference. If this were true, the birds would show the same orientation in the funnel experiment despite their distinct genetic programming. **Figure 51.26** It holds true for some, but not all individuals. If a parent has more than one reproductive partner, the offspring of different partners will have a coefficient of relatedness less than 0.5.

Concept Check 51.1

1. The proximate explanation for this fixed action pattern might be that nudging and rolling are released by the sign stimulus of an object outside the nest, and the behaviour is carried to completion once initiated. The ultimate explanation might be that ensuring that eggs remain in the nest increases the chance of producing healthy offspring. 2. In both cases, the detection of periodic variation in the environment results in a reproductive cycle timed to environmental conditions that optimize the opportunity for success. 3. There might be selective pressure for other prey fish to detect an injured fish because the source of the injury might threaten them as well. Among predators, there might be selection for those that are attracted to the alarm substance because they would be more likely to encounter crippled prey. Fish with adequate defences might show no change because they have a selective advantage if they do not waste energy responding to the alarm substance.

Concept Check 51.2

1. Natural selection would tend to favour convergence in colour pattern because a predator learning to associate a pattern with a sting or bad taste would avoid all other individuals with that same colour pattern, regardless of species. 2. You might move objects around to establish an abstract rule, such as "past landmark A, the same distance as A is from the starting point," while maintaining a minimum of fixed metric relationships, that is, avoiding having the food directly adjacent to or a set distance from a landmark. As you might surmise, designing an informative experiment of this kind is not easy. 3. Learned behaviour, just like innate behaviour, can contribute to reproductive isolation and thus to speciation. For example, learned bird songs contribute to species recognition during courtship, thereby helping ensure that only members of the same species mate.

Concept Check 51.3

1. Certainty of paternity is higher with external fertilization. 2. Balancing selection could maintain the two alleles at the *forager* locus if population density fluctuated from one generation to another. At times of low population density, the energy-conserving sitter larvae (carrying the *for^s* allele) would be favoured, while at higher population density, the more mobile Rover larvae (*for^R* allele) would have a selective advantage.

3. Because females would now be present in much larger numbers than males, all three types of males should have some reproductive success. Nevertheless, since the advantage that the blue-throats rely on—a limited number of females in their territory—will be absent, the yellow-throats are likely to increase in frequency in the short term.

Concept Check 51.4

1. Because this geographic variation corresponds to differences in prey availability between two garter snake habitats, it seems likely that snakes with characteristics enabling them to feed on the abundant prey in their locale would have had increased survival and reproductive success. In this way, natural selection would have resulted in the divergent foraging behaviours. 2. Yes. Kin selection does not require any recognition or awareness of relatedness. 3. The older individual cannot be the beneficiary because he or she cannot have extra offspring. However, the cost is low for an older individual performing the altruistic act because that individual has already reproduced (but perhaps is still caring for a child or grandchild). There can therefore be selection for an altruistic act by a postreproductive individual that benefits a young relative.

Summary of Key Concepts Questions

51.1 Circannual rhythms are typically based on the cycles of light and dark in the environment. As the global climate changes, animals that migrate in response to these rhythms may shift to a location before or after local environmental conditions are optimal for reproduction and survival. 51.2 For the goose, all that is acquired is an object at which the behaviour is directed. In the case of the sparrow, learning takes place that will give shape to the behaviour itself. 51.3 Because feeding the female is likely to improve her reproductive success, the genes from the sacrificed male are likely to appear in a greater number of progeny. 51.4 You would likely have missed the idea that changes in a single gene can have large-scale effects on even complex behaviours.

Test Your Understanding

1. c 2. b 3. d 4. a 5. c 6. a
7.

You could measure the size of mussels that oystercatchers successfully open and compare that with the size distribution in the habitat.

Chapter 52

Figure Questions

Figure 52.9 The amount of moisture available for plant growth depends on precipitation and on temperature. Warm temperatures lead to moisture loss, through plant transpiration and evaporation. Thus there can be less moisture available for plant growth in hot deserts than in cold tundra, even though precipitation may be similar. **Figure 52.16** Some factors, such as fire, are relevant only for terrestrial systems. At first glance, water availability is primarily a terrestrial factor, too. However, species living along the intertidal zone of oceans or along the edge of lakes also suffer desiccation. Salinity stress is important for species in some aquatic and terrestrial systems. Oxygen availability is an important factor primarily for species in some aquatic systems and in soils and sediments. **Figure 52.17** There is no easy answer to this question. According to the Biological Species Concept, reproductive barriers define species (see Concept 24.1). However, wolves, coyotes, and domestic dogs can and do interbreed, yet we consider them separate species due to morphological and ecological differences. Perhaps coy-wolves, which are genetically mostly coyote, are in the very early stages of speciation, and may eventually diverge further as they adapt to a different ecological niche.

Concept Check 52.1

1. In the tropics, high temperatures evaporate water and cause warm, moist air to rise. The rising air cools and releases much of its water as rain over the tropics. The remaining dry air descends at approximately 30° north and south, causing deserts to occur in those regions. 2. The microclimate around the stream will be cooler, moister, and have more shade than that around the unplanted agricultural field. 3. Trees that require a long time to reach reproductive age are likely to evolve more slowly than annual plants in response to climate change, constraining the potential ability of such trees to respond to rapid climate change. 4. Plants with C_4 photosynthesis are likely to expand their range globally as Earth's climate warms. As described in Concept 10.4, C_4 photosynthesis minimizes photorespiration and enhances sugar production, an advantage that is especially useful in warmer regions where C_4 plants are found today.

Concept Check 52.2

1. Temperate broadleaf forests have higher mean annual precipitation. 2. Answers will vary by location but should be based on the information and maps in Figure 52.11.

How much your local area has been altered from its natural state will influence how much it reflects the expected characteristics of your biome, particularly the expected plants and animals. 3. Northern coniferous forest is likely to replace tundra along the boundary between these biomes. To see why, note that northern coniferous forest is adjacent to tundra throughout North America, northern Europe, and Asia (see Figure 52.8) and that the temperature range for northern coniferous forest is just above that for tundra (see Figure 52.9).

Concept Check 52.3

1. In the oceanic pelagic zone, the ocean bottom lies below the photic zone, so there is too little light to support benthic algae or rooted plants. 2. Aquatic organisms either gain or lose water by osmosis if the osmolarity of their environment differs from their internal osmolarity. Water gain can cause cells to swell, and water loss can cause them to shrink. To avoid excessive changes in cell volume, organisms that live in estuaries must be able to compensate for both water gain (under freshwater conditions) and water loss (under saltwater conditions). 3. In a river below a dam, the fish are more likely to be species that prefer colder water. In summer, the deep layers of a reservoir are colder than the surface layers, so a river below a dam will be colder than an undammed river.

Concept Check 52.4

1. (a) Humans might transplant a species to a new area that it could not previously reach because of a geographic barrier. (b) Humans might eliminate a predator or herbivore species, such as coyotes, from an area. 2. One test would be to build a fence around a plot of land in an area that has trees of that species, excluding all deer from the plot. You could then compare the abundance of tree seedlings inside and outside the fenced plot over time. 3. Because the ancestor of the silverswords reached isolated Hawaii early in the islands' existence, it likely faced little competition and was able to occupy many unfilled niches. The cattle egret, in contrast, arrived in the Americas only recently and has to compete with a well-established group of species. Thus, its opportunities for adaptive radiation are probably much more limited.

Summary of Key Concepts Questions

52.1 Because dry air would descend at the equator instead of at 30° north and south latitude (where deserts exist today), deserts would be more likely to exist along the equator (see Figure 52.3). 52.2 The dominant plants in savanna ecosystems tend to be adapted to fire and tolerant of seasonal droughts. The savanna biome is maintained by periodic fires, both natural and set by humans, but humans are also clearing savanna for agriculture and other uses. 52.3 An aphotic zone is most likely to be found in the deep waters of a lake, the oceanic pelagic zone, or the marine benthic zone. 52.4 You could arrange a flowchart that begins with abiotic limitations— first determining the physical and chemical conditions under which a species could survive—and then moves through the other factors listed in the flowchart.

Test Your Understanding

1. b 2. b 3. c 4. c 5. d 6. c 7. a 8. a 9. b

Chapter 53

Figure Questions

Figure 53.4 The dispersion of the albatrosses would likely appear clumped as you flew over densely populated islands and sparsely populated ocean. Figure 53.13 In years with little disease, survival is not lower for females that lay more eggs. Females adjust clutch size to match their physical condition, that is, healthy, fat females lay more eggs while those with lower fat supplies lay fewer eggs. As a result, in the absence of disease, survival rates are high for all females, regardless of the number of eggs they lay.

Figure 53.15
The equilibrium density will be smaller with a higher death rate.

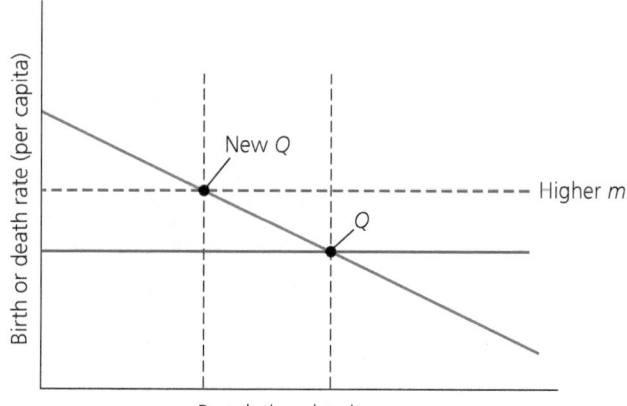

Figure 53.19 Peak numbers of hares and lynx are not always the same, and the most recent hare peak was much smaller than the previous peaks. Researchers are not sure why this is, but suspect that recent increases in other predators, such as the marten, may have suppressed hare numbers. Figure 53.20 Glucocortinoids provide additional "ready" energy by allowing the body to make glucose from non-carbohydrates such as muscle protein. This is useful if hares need to escape from a threat such as a predator. However, stress depletes energy reserves and weakens the hare, and she therefore

provides less nourishment to her unborn young. The young grow more slowly or do not survive.

Concept Check 53.1

1.

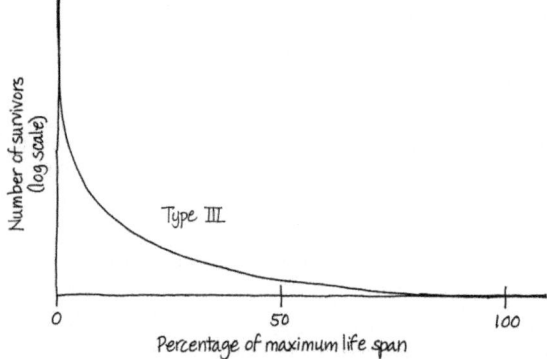

A Type III survivorship curve is most likely because very few of the young probably survive. 2. If an animal is captured by attracting it with food, it may be more likely to be recaptured if it seeks the same food. The number of marked animals captured (x) would be an overestimate, and because the population size (N) is equal to sn/x, N would be an underestimate. Alternatively, if an animal has a negative experience during capture and learns from that experience, it may be less likely to be recaptured. In this case, x would be an underestimate and N would be an overestimate. 3. Male sticklebacks would likely have a uniform pattern of dispersion, with antagonistic interactions maintaining a relatively constant spacing between them.

Concept Check 53.2

1. Though r_{max} is constant, N, the population size, is increasing. As r_{max} is applied to an increasingly large N, population growth ($r_{max}N$) accelerates, producing the J-shaped curve. 2. Exponential growth is more likely in the area where a forest was destroyed by fire. The first plants that found suitable habitat there would encounter an abundance of space, nutrients, and light. In the undisturbed forest, competition among plants for these resources would be intense. 3. The net population growth due to births and deaths was $\Delta N/\Delta t = bN - mN$. The annual birth rate (b) was $^{10}/_{1000}$ or 0.010 and the mortality rate (m) was $^8/_{1000}$ or 0.008. Therefore the net growth due to births and deaths was:

$$\Delta N/\Delta t = (0.010 \times 34\ 000\ 000) - (0.008 \times 34\ 000\ 000)$$

or 68 000 people. If we include net migration (0.006 × 34 000 000), the population grew by another 204 000 people, for a total of 272 000 new people.

Concept Check 53.3

1. When N (population size) is small, there are relatively few individuals producing offspring. When N is large, near the carrying capacity, the per capita growth rate is relatively small because it is limited by available resources. The steepest part of the logistic growth curve corresponds to a population with a number of reproducing individuals that is substantial but not yet near carrying capacity. 2. All else being equal, you would expect a plant species to have a larger carrying capacity at the equator than at high latitudes because there is more incident sunlight near the equator. 3. If a population becomes too crowded, the likelihood of disease and mortality may increase because of the effects of pathogens. Thus, pathogens can reduce the equilibrium abundance of a population.

Concept Check 53.4

1. The constant, spring-fed stream. In more constant physical conditions, populations are more stable and competition for resources is more likely. In such conditions, larger, well-provisioned young typical of iteroparous species have a better chance of surviving. 2. By preferentially investing in the eggs it lays in the nest, the peacock wrasse increases their probability of survival. The eggs it disperses widely and does not provide care for are less likely to survive, at least some of the time, but require a lower investment by the adults. (In this sense, the adults avoid the risk of placing all their eggs in one basket.) 3. If a parent's survival is compromised greatly by bearing young during times of stress, the animal's fitness may increase if it abandons its current young and survives to produce healthier young at a later time.

Concept Check 53.5

1. Three attributes are the size, quality, and isolation of patches. A patch that is larger or of higher quality is more likely to attract individuals and to be a source of individuals for other patches. A patch that is relatively isolated will undergo less exchange of individuals with other patches. 2. You would need to study the population for more than one cycle (longer than 10 years and probably at least 20) before having sufficient data to examine changes through time. Otherwise, it would be impossible to know whether an observed decrease in the population size reflected a long-term trend or was part of the normal cycle. 3. In negative feedback, the output, or product, of a process slows that process. In populations that have a density-dependent birth rate, such as dune fescue grass, an accumulation of product (more individuals, resulting in a higher population density) slows the process (population growth) by decreasing the birth rate.

Concept Check 53.6

1. A bottom-heavy age structure, with a disproportionate number of young people, portends continuing growth of the population as these young people begin reproducing. In contrast, a more evenly distributed age structure predicts a more stable population size, and a top-heavy age structure predicts a decrease in population size because relatively fewer young people are reproducing. 2. The growth rate of Earth's human population has dropped by half since the 1960s, from 2.2% in 1962 to 1.2% today. Nonetheless, growth has not slowed much because the smaller growth rate is counterbalanced by increased population size; the number of extra people on Earth each year remains enormous—approximately 79 million. 3. Each of us influences our ecological footprint by how we live—what we eat, how much energy we use, and the amount of waste we generate—as well as by how many children we have. Making choices that reduce our demand for resources makes our ecological footprint smaller.

Summary of Key Concepts Questions

53.1 Ecologists can potentially estimate birth rates by counting the number of young born each year, and they can estimate death rates by seeing how the number of adults changes each year. 53.2 Under the exponential model, both populations will continue to grow to infinite size, regardless of the specific value of r_{max} (see Figure 53.7). 53.3 There are many things you can do to increase the carrying capacity of the species, including increasing its food supply, protecting it from predators, and providing more sites for nesting or reproduction. 53.4 Two key factors appear to be the survival rate of the offspring and the chance that adults will live long enough to reproduce again. 53.5 An example of a biotic factor would be disease caused by a pathogen; natural disasters, such as floods and storms, are examples of abiotic factors. 53.6 Humans are unique in our potential ability to reduce global population through contraception and family planning. Humans also are capable of consciously choosing their diet and personal lifestyle, and these choices influence the number of people Earth can support.

Test Your Understanding

1. b 2. a 3. a 4. d 5. c 6. b 7. c 8. d 9. b 10. a

Chapter 54

Figure Questions

Figure 54.3 Its realized and fundamental niches would be similar, unlike those of *Chthamalus*. Figure 54.19 The death of individuals of *Mytilus*, a dominant species, should open up space for other species and increase species richness even in the absence of *Pisaster*. Figure 54.23 If grey seals do exert top-down control on cod and other large ground fish, an increase in their abundance would have a negative effect on the cod fishery but a positive effect on the snow crab fishery. Figure 54.27 At the earliest stages of primary succession, free-living prokaryotes in the soil would reduce atmospheric N_2 to NH_3. Symbiotic nitrogen fixation could not occur until plants were present at the site. Figure 54.32 A species with a strong immune response is a poor reservoir species. After infecting its host, the pathogen must be able to multiply to a high enough density that it is likely to be ingested by another feeding tick. A strong immune response will slow the growth rate of the pathogen.

Concept Check 54.1

1. Interspecific competition has negative effects on both species (−/−). In predation, the predator population benefits at the expense of the prey population (+/−). Mutualism is a symbiosis in which both species benefit (+/+). 2. One of the competing species will become locally extinct because of the greater reproductive success of the more efficient competitor. 3. By specializing in eating seeds of a single plant species, individuals of the two finch species may be less likely to come into contact in the separate habitats, reinforcing a reproductive barrier to hybridization.

Concept Check 54.2

1. Species richness, the number of species in the community, and relative abundance, the proportions of the community represented by the various species, both contribute to species diversity. Compared to a community with a very high proportion of one species, one with a more even proportion of species is considered more diverse. 2. A food chain presents a set of one-way transfers of food energy up to successively higher tropic levels. A food web documents how food chains are linked together, with many species weaving into the web at more than one trophic level. 3. According to the bottom-up model, adding extra predators would have little effect on lower trophic levels, particularly vegetation. If the top-down model applied, increased bobcat numbers would decrease raccoon numbers, increase snake numbers, decrease mouse numbers, and increase grass biomass.

Concept Check 54.3

1. High levels of disturbance are generally so disruptive that they eliminate many species from communities, leaving the community dominated by a few tolerant species. Low levels of disturbance permit competitively dominant species to exclude other species from the community. But moderate levels of disturbance can facilitate coexistence of a greater number of species in a community by preventing competitively dominant species from becoming abundant enough to eliminate other species from the community. 2. Early successional species can facilitate the arrival of other species in many ways, including increasing the fertility or water-holding capacity of soils or providing shelter to seedlings from wind and intense sunlight. 3. The absence of fire for 100 years would represent a change to a low level of disturbance. According to the intermediate disturbance hypothesis, this change should cause diversity to decline as competitively dominant species gain sufficient time to exclude less competitive species.

Concept Check 54.4

1. Ecologists propose that the greater species richness of tropical regions is the result of their longer evolutionary history and the greater solar energy input and water availability in tropical regions. 2. Immigration of species to islands declines with distance from the mainland and increases with island area. Extinction of species is lower on larger islands and on less isolated islands. Since the number of species on islands is largely determined by the difference between rates of immigration and extinction, the number of species will be highest on large islands near the mainland and lowest on small islands far from the mainland. 3. Because of their greater mobility, birds disperse to islands more often than snakes and lizards, so birds should have greater richness.

Concept Check 54.5

1. Pathogens are microorganisms, viruses, viroids, or prions that cause disease. 2. To keep the rabies virus out, you could ban imports of all mammals, including pets. Potentially, you could also attempt to vaccinate all dogs in the British Isles against the virus. A more practical approach might be to quarantine all pets brought into the country that are potential carriers of the virus, the approach the British government actually takes.

Summary of Key Concepts Questions

54.1 Interspecific competition: a fox and a bobcat competing for prey. Predation: an orca eating a sea otter. Herbivory: a bison grazing in a prairie. Parasitism: a parasitoid wasp that lays its eggs on a caterpillar. Mutualism: a fungus and an alga that make up a lichen. Commensalism: a remora attached to a whale. Facilitation: a flowering plant and its pollinator. 54.2 Not necessarily if the more species-rich community is dominated by only one or a few species. 54.3 Because of the presence of species initially, the disturbance would initiate secondary succession in spite of its severe appearance. 54.4 Glaciations have severely reduced diversity in northern temperate, boreal, and Arctic ecosystems, compared to tropical ecosystems. 54.5 A host is required to complete the pathogen's life cycle, but a vector is not. Vectors are intermediate species that merely transport a pathogen to its host.

Test Your Understanding

1. d 2. c 3. c 4. c 5. b 6. c 7. d 8. b 9. Community 1: $H = -(0.05 \ln 0.05 + 0.05 \ln 0.05 + 0.85 \ln 0.85 + 0.05 \ln 0.05) = 0.59$. Community 2: $H = -(0.30 \ln 0.30 + 0.40 \ln 0.40 + 0.30 \ln 0.30) = 1.1$. Community 2 is more diverse. 10. If the number of foxes declines, white-footed mice will increase and the abundance of ticks will also increase.

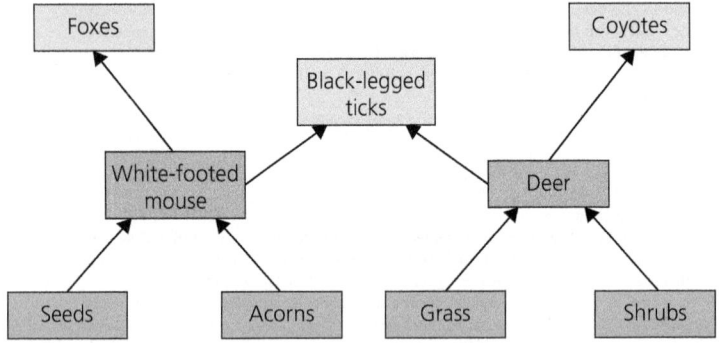

Chapter 55

Figure Questions

Figure 55.6 Wetlands, coral reefs, and coastal zones cover areas too small to show up clearly on global maps. Figure 55.7 If the new duck farms made nitrogen available in rich supply, as phosphorus already is, then adding extra nitrogen in the experiment would not increase phytoplankton density. Figure 55.8 A balance is maintained between carbon dioxide in the atmosphere and carbonates dissolved in water (see Figure 3.12). As carbonates are used by aquatic photosynthetic organisms, more CO_2 enters the water from the atmosphere. Figure 55.14 Water availability is probably another factor that varied across the sites. Such factors not included in the experimental design could make the results more difficult to interpret. Multiple factors can also covary in nature, so ecologists must be careful that the factor they are studying is actually causing the observed response and is not just correlated with it. Figure 55.16 High salt concentrations in the soil water lower the potential gradient between plant cells and soil water, reducing the rate of water uptake. Plants in saline soils can experience water deficit even if there is plenty of water.

Concept Check 55.1

1. Energy passes through an ecosystem, entering as sunlight and leaving as heat. It is not recycled within the ecosystem. 2. You would need to know how much biomass the wildebeests ate from your plot and how much nitrogen was contained in that biomass. You would also need to know how much nitrogen they deposited in urine or feces. 3. The second law states that the total entropy of a system increases over time, meaning that in any energy transfer or transformation, some of the energy is dissipated to the surroundings as heat. This "escape" of energy from an ecosystem is offset by the continuous influx of solar radiation.

Concept Check 55.2

1. Only a fraction of solar radiation strikes plants or algae, only a portion of that fraction is of wavelengths suitable for photosynthesis, and much energy is lost as a result of reflection or heating of plant tissue. 2. By manipulating the level of the factors of interest, such as phosphorus availability or soil moisture, and measuring responses by primary producers 3. The enzyme rubisco, which catalyzes the first step in the Calvin cycle, is the most abundant protein on Earth. Photosynthetic organisms require considerable nitrogen to make rubisco. Phosphorus is also needed as a component of several metabolites in the Calvin cycle and as a component of both ATP and NADPH (see Figure 10.19).

Concept Check 55.3

1. 20 J; 40% 2. Nicotine protects the plant from herbivores. 3. Total net primary production is 10 000 + 1000 + 100 + 10 J = 11 110 J. This is the amount of energy theoretically available to detritivores.

Concept Check 55.4

1. For example, for the carbon cycle:

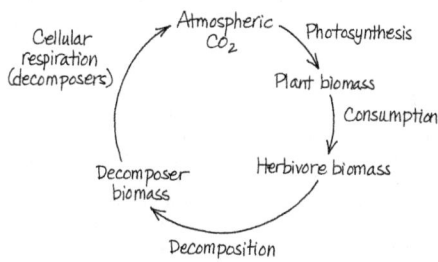

Cycling of a carbon atom

2. Removal of the trees stops nitrogen uptake from the soil, allowing nitrate to accumulate there. The nitrate is washed away by precipitation and enters the streams. 3. Most of the nutrients in a tropical rain forest are contained in the trees, so removing the trees by logging rapidly depletes nutrients from the ecosystem. The nutrients that remain in the soil are quickly carried away into streams and groundwater by the abundant precipitation.

Concept Check 55.5

1. The main goal is to restore degraded ecosystems to a more natural state. 2. The Kissimmee River project returns the flow of water to the original channel and restores natural flow, a self-sustaining outcome. Ecologists at the Maungatautari reserve will need to maintain the integrity of the fence indefinitely, an outcome that is not self-sustaining in the long term.

Summary of Key Concepts Questions

55.1 Because energy conversions are inefficient, with some energy inevitably lost as heat, you would expect that a given mass of primary producers would support a smaller biomass of secondary consumers. 55.2 For estimates of NEP, you need to measure the respiration of all organisms in an ecosystem, not just the respiration of primary producers. In a sample of ocean water, primary producers and other organisms are usually mixed together, making their respective respirations hard to separate. 55.3 The runner would typically burn many more calories through respiration, reducing his or her production efficiency. 55.4 Factors other than temperature, including a shortage of water and nutrients, slow decomposition in hot deserts. 55.5 If the topsoil and deeper soil are kept separate, you could return the deeper soil to the site first and then apply the more fertile topsoil to improve the success of revegetation and other restoration efforts.

Test Your Understanding

1. c 2. b 3. a 4. c 5. b 6. b 7. d 8. d
9.

Based on these global numbers, approximately 110 km³ of precipitation falls over land each year.

Chapter 56

Figure Questions

Figure 56.3 You would need to know the complete range of the species and that it is missing across all of that range. You would also need to be certain that the species isn't hidden, as might be the case for an animal that is hibernating underground or a plant that is present in the form of seeds or spores. Figure 56.8 Several factors reduced the effectiveness of the initial (1993) ballast exchange program. First, not all the water and none of the sediment in the tanks was removed when ships pumped ballast water out at sea. The result was weak to moderately saline water in the tanks that allowed some organisms to survive. Active flushing removes almost all the water and the sediments, where the eggs and resting stages of many species are found, and ensures that any remaining organisms are exposed to high salinities. Second, and even more important, prior to 2005, ships entering with only a small amount of ballast water had not been required to exchange at sea. It was determined that these ships were a significant source of potential invaders, and now all ships must flush tanks before entering the lakes. Figure 56.12 Because the population of Illinois birds has a different genetic makeup than birds in other regions, you would want to maintain to the greatest extent possible the frequency of beneficial genes or alleles found only in that population. In restoration, preserving genetic diversity in a species is as important as increasing organism numbers.

Concept Check 56.1

1. In addition to species loss, the biodiversity crisis includes the loss of genetic diversity within populations and species and the degradation of entire ecosystems. 2. Habitat destruction, such as deforestation, channelizing of rivers, or conversion of natural ecosystems to agriculture or urban development deprives species of places to live. Introduced species, which are transported by humans to regions outside their native range, where they are not controlled by their natural pathogens or predators, often reduce the population sizes of native species through competition or predation. Overharvesting has reduced populations of plants and animals or driven them to extinction. 3. If both populations breed separately, then gene flow between the populations would not occur and genetic differences between them would be greater. As a result, the loss of genetic diversity would be greater than if the populations interbreed.

Concept Check 56.2

1. Reduced genetic variation decreases the capacity of a population to evolve in the face of change. 2. The effective size, Ne, would be 4(30 × 10)/(30 + 10)) = 30 birds. 3. Because millions of people use the greater Yellowstone ecosystem each year, it would be impossible to eliminate all contact between people and bears. Instead, you might try to reduce the kinds of encounters where bears are killed. You might recommend lower speed limits on roads in the park, adjust the timing or location of hunting seasons (where hunting is allowed outside the park) to minimize contact with mother bears and cubs, and provide financial incentives for livestock owners to try alternative means of protecting livestock, such as using guard dogs.

Concept Check 56.3

1. A small area supporting numerous endemic species as well as a large number of endangered and threatened species 2. Zoned reserves may provide sustained supplies of forest products, water, hydroelectric power, educational opportunities, and income from tourism. 3. Habitat corridors can increase the rate of movement or dispersal of organisms between habitat patches and thus the rate of gene flow between subpopulations. They thus help prevent a decrease in fitness attributable to inbreeding. They can also minimize interactions between organisms and humans as the organisms disperse; in cases involving potential predators, such as bears or large cats, minimizing such interactions is desirable.

Concept Check 56.4

1. Adding nutrients causes population explosions of algae and the organisms that feed on them. Increased respiration by algae and consumers, including detrivorous, depletes the lake's oxygen, which the fish require. 2. Because higher temperatures lead to faster decomposition, organic matter in these soils could be quickly decomposed to CO_2, speeding up global warming. 3. Reduced concentrations of ozone in the atmosphere increase the amount of UV radiation that reaches Earth's surface and the organisms living there. UV radiation can cause mutations by producing disruptive thymine dimers in DNA.

Concept Check 56.5

1. Sustainable development is an approach to development that works toward the long-term prosperity of human societies and the ecosystems that support them, which requires linking the biological sciences with the social sciences, economics, and humanities. 2. At a minimum, you would want to know the size of the population and the average reproductive rate of individuals in it. To develop the fishery sustainably, you would seek a harvest rate that maintains the population near its original size and maximizes its harvest in the long term rather than the short term.

Summary of Key Concepts Questions

56.1. Nature provides us with many beneficial services, including a supply of reliable, clean water, the production of food and fibre, and the dilution and detoxification of our pollutants. 56.2 A more genetically diverse population is better able to withstand pressures from disease or environmental change, making it less likely to become extinct over a given period of time. 56.3 Habitat fragmentation can isolate populations, leading to inbreeding and genetic drift, and it can make populations more susceptible to local extinctions resulting from the effects of pathogens, parasites, or predators. 56.4 It is healthier to feed at a lower trophic level because biological magnification increases the concentration of toxins at higher levels. 56.5 One goal of conservation biology is to preserve as many species as possible. Sustainable approaches that maintain the quality of habitats are required for the long-term survival of organisms.

Test Your Understanding

1. c 2. d 3. b 4. a 5. b 6. a 7. (a) The average CO_2 concentration was approximately 330 ppm in 1975 and approximately 394 ppm in 2012. (b) The rate of CO_2 concentration increase was (394 ppm − 330 ppm)/(2012 − 1975) = 64 ppm/37 years = 1.73 ppm/yr. (c) If this rate continues, the concentration in 2100 will be approximately 550 ppm (1.73 ppm/yr * 88 yr = 152 ppm for the increase from 2012–2100 + 394 ppm in 2012 = 546 ppm, rounded off to 550 ppm).

7 (d).

(e) The actual rise in CO_2 concentration could be larger or smaller, depending on Earth's human population, per capita energy use, and the extent to which societies take steps to reduce CO_2 emissions, including replacing fossil fuels with renewable or nuclear fuels. (f) Additional scientific data will be important for many reasons, such as determining how quickly greenhouse gases such as CO_2 are removed from the atmosphere by the biosphere.

9.

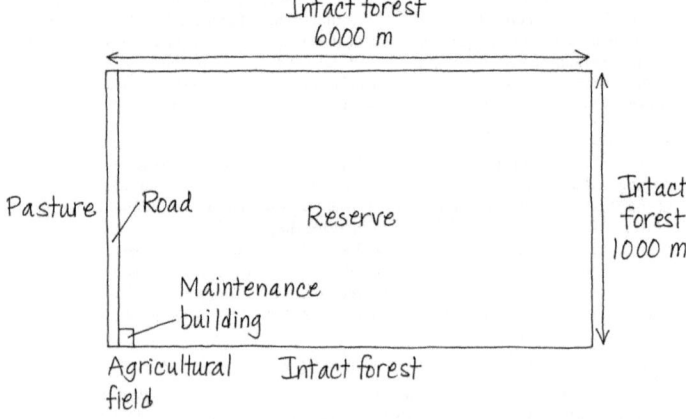

To minimize the area of forest into which the cowbirds penetrate, you should locate the road along one edge of the reserve. Any other location would increase the area of affected habitat. Similarly, the maintenance building should be in a corner of the reserve to minimize the area susceptible to cowbirds.

Unit Openers

Unit 1 Make Connections

The heat capacity of ocean water is much higher than the air (about four times of air), meaning it takes more energy to heat ocean water than it does to heat air. The fact that the ocean temperatures have increased by one-tenth of a degree means a very large amount of energy has been absorbed by the oceans.

Unit 2 Make Connections

The gene encoding hexokinase is part of the DNA of a chromosome in the nucleus. There, the gene is transcribed into mRNA, which is transported to the cytoplasm where it is translated on a free ribosome into a polypeptide. The polypeptide folds into a functional protein with secondary and tertiary structure. Once functional, it carries out the first reaction of glycolysis in the cytoplasm.

Unit 3 Make Connections

The location and type of mutation will impact CF disease. For example, a missense mutation may cause severe, mild, or no disease depending on the amino acid change. A mutation that inserts a stop codon can result in a truncated protein. Severity can also be impacted if the mutation occurs in an exon or an intro. These are just some examples, and many more exist.

Unit 4 Make Connections

Under prolonged low-oxygen conditions, some of the red blood cells of a heterozygote may sickle, leading to harmful effects. This does not occur in individuals with two wild-type hemoglobin alleles, suggesting that there may be selection against heterozygotes in malaria-free regions (where heterozygote advantage does not occur). However, since heterozygotes are healthy under most conditions, selection against them is unlikely to be strong.

Unit 5 Make Connections

The vertebrate circulatory system is responsible for transport of fluids, gases, and nutrients in circuits around the body. In plants, these internal transport functions fall to the xylem and phloem. The xylem carries water and minerals from the roots to the leaves. The phloem carries sugars and other organic nutrients throughout the plant. The vertebrate circulatory system also ensures that cells are bathed in extracellular fluids with an osmolarity that permits cells to maintain an appropriate volume. Plant cell volume is determined in large part by regulation of the volume of the intracellular vacuole, but is also constrained by the cell wall. The respiratory system of vertebrates ensures that gases are exchanged across a layer of respiratory epithelial cells. In plants, gas exchange occurs locally and the circulatory system of plants has little role in gas transport. Leaves have relatively low potential for gas exchange except through the stomata, much like the spiracles control gas exchange in insects. Whereas animals consume organic nutrients and transport them across the epithelium of the gastrointestinal tract, plants make their own "food" through the process of photosynthesis.

Unit 6 Make Connections

Photosynthetic adaptations can occur at the molecular level, as is apparent in the fact that C_3 plants use rubisco to fix carbon dioxide initially, whereas C_4 and CAM plants use PEP carboxylase. An adaptation at the tissue level is that plants have different stomatal densities based on their genotype and environmental conditions. At the organismal level, plants alter their shoot architectures to make photosynthesis more efficient. For example, self-pruning removes branches and leaves that respire more than they photosynthesize.

Unit 7 Make Connections

The ciliates are part of a larger clade of organisms (the Alveolates) that contain many photosynthetic members (or members with plastid-like organelles). There are two simple hypotheses to explain the lack of plastids in the ciliates. The first suggests that the common ancestor of the Alveolates was not photosynthetic. This implies that the ciliates diverged from the other Alveolates before plastids evolved via endosymbiosis in the branches leading to the dinoflagellates and apicomplexans. The second is a little more controversial and predicts that the common ancestor of all Alveolates (ciliates, dinoflagellates, and apicomplexans) was once photosynthetic but that this capability was lost (along with the organelle and associated genes) in the lineage leading to the ciliates. The pattern of plastid gain and loss within Alveolates (and the SAR clade) is unclear but it remains an active field of research. Studying these events, however, is important to understand the processes responsible for the evolution of eukaryotes and the important role of endosymbiosis.

Unit 8 Make Connections

The lichen symbiosis allows the photosynthetic symbiont to photosynthesize and, in cases where it is a cyanobacterium, to fix nitrogen. The fungal symbiont provides the photosynthetic symbiont with a protective environment as well as phosphorus and other soil nutrients. Lichens are particularly abundant in nutrient-poor habitats such as those found in the Arctic tundra.

Atomic number (number of protons)
Element symbol

6
C
12.01

Atomic mass (number of protons plus number of neutrons averaged over all isotopes)

Metals   Metalloids   Nonmetals

Representative elements

Groups: Elements in a vertical column have the same number of electrons in their valence (outer) shell and thus have similar chemical properties.

Periods: Each horizontal row contains elements with the same total number of electron shells. Across each period, elements are ordered by increasing atomic number.

Alkali metals   Alkaline earth metals

Halogens   Noble gases

Period number

Transition elements

Period	Group 1A	Group 2A	3 3B	4 4B	5 5B	6 6B	7 7B	8	9 8B	10	11 1B	12 2B	13 Group 3A	14 Group 4A	15 Group 5A	16 Group 6A	17 Group 7A	18 Group 8A
1	1 H 1.008																	2 He 4.003
2	3 Li 6.941	4 Be 9.012											5 B 10.81	6 C 12.01	7 N 14.01	8 O 16.00	9 F 19.00	10 Ne 20.18
3	11 Na 22.99	12 Mg 24.31											13 Al 26.98	14 Si 28.09	15 P 30.97	16 S 32.07	17 Cl 35.45	18 Ar 39.95
4	19 K 39.10	20 Ca 40.08	21 Sc 44.96	22 Ti 47.87	23 V 50.94	24 Cr 52.00	25 Mn 54.94	26 Fe 55.85	27 Co 58.93	28 Ni 58.69	29 Cu 63.55	30 Zn 65.41	31 Ga 69.72	32 Ge 72.64	33 As 74.92	34 Se 78.96	35 Br 79.90	36 Kr 83.80
5	37 Rb 85.47	38 Sr 87.62	39 Y 88.91	40 Zr 91.22	41 Nb 92.91	42 Mo 95.94	43 Tc (98)	44 Ru 101.1	45 Rh 102.9	46 Pd 106.4	47 Ag 107.9	48 Cd 112.4	49 In 114.8	50 Sn 118.7	51 Sb 121.8	52 Te 127.6	53 I 126.9	54 Xe 131.3
6	55 Cs 132.9	56 Ba 137.3	57* La 138.9	72 Hf 178.5	73 Ta 180.9	74 W 183.8	75 Re 186.2	76 Os 190.2	77 Ir 192.2	78 Pt 195.1	79 Au 197.0	80 Hg 200.6	81 Tl 204.4	82 Pb 207.2	83 Bi 209.0	84 Po (209)	85 At (210)	86 Rn (222)
7	87 Fr (223)	88 Ra (226)	89† Ac (227)	104 Rf (261)	105 Db (262)	106 Sg (266)	107 Bh (264)	108 Hs (269)	109 Mt (268)	110 Ds (271)	111 Rg (272)	112 Cn (285)	113 Uut (284)	114 Fl (289)	115 Uup (288)	116 Lv (293)	117 Uus (292)	118 Uuo (294)

*Lanthanides

58 Ce 140.1	59 Pr 140.9	60 Nd 144.2	61 Pm (145)	62 Sm 150.4	63 Eu 152.0	64 Gd 157.3	65 Tb 158.9	66 Dy 162.5	67 Ho 164.9	68 Er 167.3	69 Tm 168.9	70 Yb 173.0	71 Lu 175.0

†Actinides

90 Th 232.0	91 Pa 231.0	92 U 238.0	93 Np (237)	94 Pu (244)	95 Am (243)	96 Cm (247)	97 Bk (247)	98 Cf (251)	99 Es 252	100 Fm 257	101 Md 258	102 No 259	103 Lr 260

Name (Symbol)	Atomic Number	Name (Symbol)	Atomic Number	Name (Symbol)	Atomic Number	Name (Symbol)	Atomic Number	Name (Symbol)	Atomic Number
Actinium (Ac)	89	Copper (Cu)	29	Iron (Fe)	26	Phosphorus (P)	15	Sulphur (S)	16
Aluminum (Al)	13	Curium (Cm)	96	Krypton (Kr)	36	Platinum (Pt)	78	Tantalum (Ta)	73
Americium (Am)	95	Darmstadtium (Ds)	110	Lanthanum (La)	57	Plutonium (Pu)	94	Technetium (Tc)	43
Antimony (Sb)	51	Dubnium (Db)	105	Lawrencium (Lr)	103	Polonium (Po)	84	Tellurium (Te)	52
Argon (Ar)	18	Dysprosium (Dy)	66	Lead (Pb)	82	Potassium (K)	19	Terbium (Tb)	65
Arsenic (As)	33	Einsteinium (Es)	99	Lithium (Li)	3	Praseodymium (Pr)	59	Thallium (Tl)	81
Astatine (At)	85	Erbium (Er)	68	Livermorium (Lv)	116	Promethium (Pm)	61	Thorium (Th)	90
Barium (Ba)	56	Europium (Eu)	63	Lutetium (Lu)	71	Protactinium (Pa)	91	Thulium (Tm)	69
Berkelium (Bk)	97	Fermium (Fm)	100	Magnesium (Mg)	12	Radium (Ra)	88	Tin (Sn)	50
Beryllium (Be)	4	Flerovium (Fl)	114	Manganese (Mn)	25	Radon (Rn)	86	Titanium (Ti)	22
Bismuth (Bi)	83	Fluorine (F)	9	Meitnerium (Mt)	109	Rhenium (Re)	75	Tungsten (W)	74
Bohrium (Bh)	107	Francium (Fr)	87	Mendelevium (Md)	101	Rhodium (Rh)	45	Ununtrium	113
Boron (B)	5	Gadolinium (Gd)	64	Mercury (Hg)	80	Roentgenium (Rg)	111	Ununpentium	115
Bromine (Br)	35	Gallium (Ga)	31	Molybdenum (Mo)	42	Rubidium (Rb)	37	Ununseptium	117
Cadmium (Cd)	48	Germanium (Ge)	32	Neodymium (Nd)	60	Ruthenium (Ru)	44	Ununoctium	118
Calcium (Ca)	20	Gold (Au)	79	Neon (Ne)	10	Rutherfordium (Rf)	104	Uranium (U)	92
Californium (Cf)	98	Hafnium (Hf)	72	Neptunium (Np)	93	Samarium (Sm)	62	Vanadium (V)	23
Carbon (C)	6	Hassium (Hs)	108	Nickel (Ni)	28	Scandium (Sc)	21	Xenon (Xe)	54
Cerium (Ce)	58	Helium (He)	2	Niobium (Nb)	41	Seaborgium (Sg)	106	Ytterbium (Yb)	70
Cesium (Cs)	55	Holmium (Ho)	67	Nitrogen (N)	7	Selenium (Se)	34	Yttrium (Y)	39
Chlorine (Cl)	17	Hydrogen (H)	1	Nobelium (No)	102	Silicon (Si)	14	Zinc (Zn)	30
Chromium (Cr)	24	Indium (In)	49	Osmium (Os)	76	Silver (Ag)	47	Zirconium (Zr)	40
Cobalt (Co)	27	Iodine (I)	53	Oxygen (O)	8	Sodium (Na)	11		
Copernicium (Cn)	112	Iridium (Ir)	77	Palladium (Pd)	46	Strontium (Sr)	38		

Appendix B Periodic Table

Appendix C Microscopes

Light Microscope

In light microscopy, light is focused on a specimen by a glass condenser lens; the image is then magnified by an objective lens and an ocular lens for projection on the eye, digital camera, digital video camera, or photographic film.

Electron Microscope

In electron microscopy, a beam of electrons (top of the microscope) is used instead of light, and electromagnets are used instead of glass lenses. The electron beam is focused on the specimen by a condenser lens; the image is magnified by an objective lens and a projector lens for projection on a digital detector, fluorescent screen, or photographic film.

This appendix presents a taxonomic classification for the major extant groups of organisms discussed in this text; not all phyla are included. The classification presented here is based on the three-domain system, which assigns the two major groups of prokaryotes, bacteria and archaea, to separate domains (with eukaryotes making up the third domain).

Various alternative classification schemes are discussed in Unit Five of the text. The taxonomic turmoil includes debates about the number and boundaries of kingdoms and about the alignment of the Linnaean classification hierarchy with the findings of modern cladistic analysis. In this review, asterisks (★) indicate currently recognized phyla thought by some systematists to be paraphyletic.

DOMAIN BACTERIA

- **Proteobacteria**
- **Chlamydia**
- **Spirochetes**
- **Gram-Positive Bacteria**
- **Cyanobacteria**

DOMAIN ARCHAEA

- **Korarchaeota**
- **Euryarchaeota**
- **Crenarchaeota**
- **Nanoarchaeota**

DOMAIN EUKARYA

In the phylogenetic hypothesis we present in Chapter 28, major clades of eukaryotes are grouped together in the four "supergroups" listed in bold type below and on the next page. Formerly, all the eukaryotes generally called protists were assigned to a single kingdom, Protista. However, advances in systematics have made it clear that some protists are more closely related to plants, fungi, or animals than they are to other protists. As a result, the kingdom Protista has been abandoned.

Excavata
- Diplomonadida (diplomonads)
- Parabasala (parabasalids)
- Euglenozoa (euglenozoans)
  Kinetoplastida (kinetoplastids)
  Euglenophyta (euglenids)

"SAR" Clade
- Stramenopila (stramenopiles)
  Chrysophyta (golden algae)
  Phaeophyta (brown algae)
  Bacillariophyta (diatoms)

- Alveolata (alveolates)
  Dinoflagellata (dinoflagellates)
  Apicomplexa (apicomplexans)
  Ciliophora (ciliates)
- Rhizaria (rhizarians)
  Radiolaria (radiolarians)
  Foraminifera (forams)

  Cercozoa (cercozoans)

Archaeplastida
- Rhodophyta (red algae)
- Chlorophyta (green algae: chlorophytes)
- Charophyta (green algae: charophytes)
- Plantae
  Phylum Hepatophyta (liverworts)   ⎫
  Phylum Bryophyta (mosses)   ⎬ Nonvascular plants (bryophytes)
  Phylum Anthocerophyta (hornworts) ⎭
  Phylum Lycophyta (lycophytes)   ⎫ Seedless vascular plants
  Phylum Monilophyta (ferns, horsetails, whisk ferns) ⎭
  Phylum Ginkgophyta (ginkgo)   ⎫
  Phylum Cycadophyta (cycads)   ⎬ Gymnosperms ⎫
  Phylum Gnetophyta (gnetophytes)   ⎬   ⎬ Seed plants
  Phylum Coniferophyta (conifers)   ⎭   ⎬
  Phylum Anthophyta (flowering plants) ⎬ Angiosperms ⎭

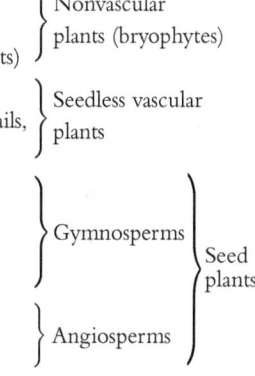

Unikonta

- Amoebozoa (amoebozoans)
  - Myxogastrida (plasmodial slime moulds)
  - Dictyostelida (cellular slime moulds)
  - Tubulinea (tubulinids)
  - Entamoeba (entamoebas)
- Nucleariida (nucleariids)
- Fungi
  - ★Phylum Chytridiomycota (chytrids)
  - ★Phylum Zygomycota (zygomycetes)
  - Phylum Glomeromycota (glomeromycetes)
  - Phylum Ascomycota (ascomycetes)
  - Phylum Basidiomycota (basidiomycetes)

- Choanoflagellata (choanoflagellates)
- Animalia
  - Phylum Porifera (sponges)
  - Phylum Ctenophora (comb jellies)
  - Phylum Cnidaria (cnidarians)
    - Medusozoa (hydrozoans, jellies, box jellies)
    - Anthozoa (sea anemones and most corals)
  - Phylum Acoela (acoel flatworms)
  - Phylum Placozoa (placozoans)
  - Lophotrochozoa (lophotrochozoans)
  - Phylum Platyhelminthes (flatworms)
    - Catenulida (chain worms)
    - Rhabditophora (planarians, flukes, tapeworms)
  - Phylum Nemertea (proboscis worms)
  - Phylum Ectoprocta (ectoprocts)
  - Phylum Brachiopoda (brachiopods)
  - Phylum Rotifera (rotifers)
  - Phylum Cycliophora (cycliophorans)
  - Phylum Mollusca (molluscs)
    - Polyplacophora (chitons)
    - Gastropoda (gastropods)
    - Bivalvia (bivalves)
    - Cephalopoda (cephalopods)
  - Phylum Annelida (segmented worms)
    - Errantia (errantians)
    - Sedentaria (sedentarians)
  - Phylum Acanthocephala (spiny-headed worms)

Ecdysozoa (ecdysozoans)
- Phylum Loricifera (loriciferans)
- Phylum Priapula (priapulans)
- Phylum Nematoda (roundworms)
- Phylum Arthropoda (This survey groups arthropods into a single phylum, but some zoologists now split the arthropods into multiple phyla.)
  - Chelicerata (horseshoe crabs, arachnids)
  - Myriapoda (millipedes, centipedes)
  - Pancrustacea (crustaceans, insects)
- Phylum Tardigrada (tardigrades)
- Phylum Onychophora (velvet worms)

Deuterostomia (deuterostomes)
- Phylum Hemichordata (hemichordates)
- Phylum Echinodermata (echinoderms)
  - Asteroidea (sea stars, sea daisies)
  - Ophiuroidea (brittle stars)
  - Echinoides (sea urchins, sand dollars)
  - Crinoidea (sea lilies)
  - Holothuroidea (sea cucumbers)
- Phylum Chordata (chordates)
  - Cephalochordata (cephalochordates: lancelets)
  - Urochordata (urochordates: tunicates)
  - Cyclostomata (cyclostomes)
    - Myxini (hagfishes)
    - Petromyzontida (lampreys)
- Gnathostomata (gnathostomes)
  - Chondrichthyes (sharks, rays, chimaeras)
  - Actinopterygii (ray-finned fishes)
  - Actinistia (coelacanths)
  - Dipnoi (lungfishes)
  - Amphibia (amphibians: frogs, salamanders, caecilians)
  - Reptilia (reptiles: tuataras, lizards, snakes, turtles, crocodilians, birds)
  - Mammalia (mammals)

} Vertebrates

Graphs

Graphs provide a visual representation of numerical data. They may reveal patterns or trends in the data that are not easy to recognize in a table. A graph is a diagram that shows how one variable in a data set is related (or perhaps not related) to another variable. If one variable is dependent on the other, the dependent variable is typically plotted on the y-axis and the independent variable on the x-axis. Types of graphs that are frequently used in biology include scatter plots, line graphs, bar graphs, and histograms.

▶ A **scatter plot** is used when the data for all variables are numerical and continuous. Each piece of data is represented by a point. In a **line graph**, each data point is connected to the next point in the data set with a straight line, as in the graph to the right. (To practise making and interpreting scatter plots and line graphs, see the Scientific Skills Exercises in Chapters 2, 3, 7, 8, 10, 13, 19, 24, 34, 43, 47, 49, 50, 52, 54, and 56.)

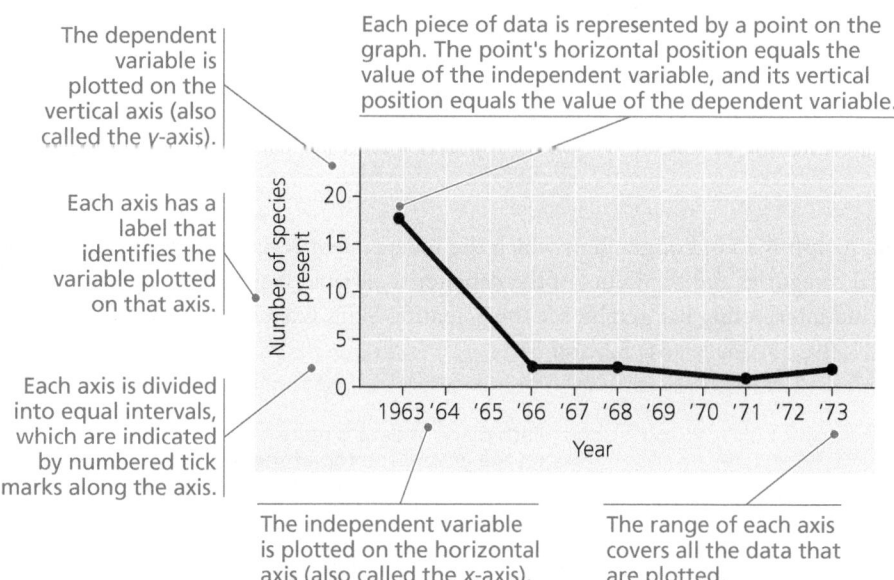

The dependent variable is plotted on the vertical axis (also called the y-axis).

Each axis has a label that identifies the variable plotted on that axis.

Each axis is divided into equal intervals, which are indicated by numbered tick marks along the axis.

Each piece of data is represented by a point on the graph. The point's horizontal position equals the value of the independent variable, and its vertical position equals the value of the dependent variable.

The independent variable is plotted on the horizontal axis (also called the x-axis).

The range of each axis covers all the data that are plotted.

▼ Two or more data sets can be plotted on the same line graph to show how two dependent variables are related to the same independent variable. (To practise making and interpreting line graphs with two or more data sets, see the Scientific Skills Exercises in Chapters 7, 43, 47, 49, 50, 52, and 56.)

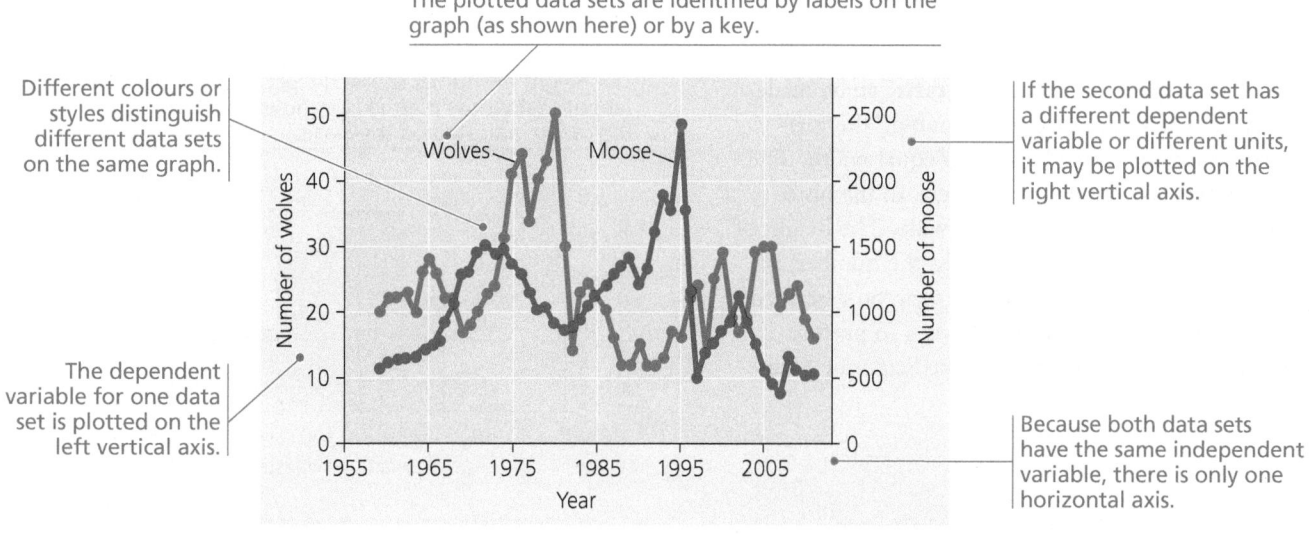

The plotted data sets are identified by labels on the graph (as shown here) or by a key.

Different colours or styles distinguish different data sets on the same graph.

The dependent variable for one data set is plotted on the left vertical axis.

If the second data set has a different dependent variable or different units, it may be plotted on the right vertical axis.

Because both data sets have the same independent variable, there is only one horizontal axis.

▼ In some scatter plot graphs, a straight or curved line is drawn through the entire data set to show the general trend in the data. A straight line that mathematically fits the data best is called a *regression line*. Alternatively, a mathematical function that best fits the data may describe a curved line, often termed a *best-fit curve*. (To practise making and interpreting regression lines, see the Scientific Skills Exercises in Chapters 3, 10, and 34.)

The regression line can be expressed as a mathematical equation. It allows you to predict the value of the dependent variable for any value of the independent variable within the range of the data set and, less commonly, beyond the range of the data.

▼ A **bar graph** is a kind of graph in which the independent variable represents groups or non-numerical categories and the values of the dependent variable(s) are shown by bars. (To practise making and interpreting bar graphs, see the Scientific Skills Exercises in Chapters 1, 9, 18, 20, 22, 25, 27, 29, 33, 35, 39, 51, 52, and 54.)

As in a line graph or scatter plot, the vertical axis is usually used for the dependent variable.

The axis for the dependent variable is labelled and divided into equal intervals indicated by numbered tick marks.

Each piece of data is represented by a bar on the graph. The top of the bar aligns with the value of the dependent variable.

If multiple data sets are plotted on the same bar graph, they are distinguished by bars of different colours or styles and identified by labels or a key.

The groups or categories of the independent variable are usually spaced equally along the horizontal axis. (In some bar graphs, the horizontal axis is used for the dependent variable and the vertical axis for the independent variable.)

▶ A variant of a bar graph called a **histogram** can be made for numeric data by first grouping, or "binning," the variable plotted on the *x*-axis into intervals of equal width. The "bins" may be integers or ranges of numbers. In the histogram at right, the intervals are 25 mg/dL wide. The height of each bar shows the percent (or alternatively, the number) of experimental subjects whose characteristics can be described by one of the intervals plotted on the *x*-axis. (To practise making and interpreting histograms, see the Scientific Skills Exercises in Chapters 12, 14, and 42.)

The height of this bar shows the percent of individuals (about 4%) whose plasma LDL cholesterol levels are in the range indicated on the *x*-axis.

This interval runs from 50 to 74 mg/dL.

Glossary of Scientific Inquiry Terms

See Concept 1.3 for more discussion of the process of scientific inquiry.

control group In a controlled experiment, a set of subjects that lacks (or does not receive) the specific factor being tested. Ideally, the control group should be identical to the experimental group in other respects.

controlled experiment An experiment in which an experimental group is compared with a control group that varies only in the factor being tested.

data Recorded observations.

deductive reasoning A type of logic in which specific results are predicted from a general premise.

dependent variable A variable whose value is measured during an experiment or other test to see whether it is influenced by changes in another variable (the independent variable).

experiment A scientific test, carried out under controlled conditions, involving manipulation of one or more factors in a system in order to see the effects of those changes.

experimental group A set of subjects that has (or receives) the specific factor being tested in a controlled experiment.

hypothesis A testable explanation for a set of observations based on the available data and guided by inductive reasoning. A hypothesis is narrower in scope than a theory.

independent variable A variable whose value is manipulated or changed during an experiment or other test to reveal possible effects on another variable (the dependent variable).

inductive reasoning A type of logic in which generalizations are based on a large number of specific observations.

inquiry The search for information and explanation, often focusing on specific questions.

model A physical or conceptual representation of a natural phenomenon.

prediction In deductive reasoning, a forecast that follows logically from a hypothesis. By testing predictions, experiments may allow certain hypotheses to be rejected.

theory An explanation that is broader in scope than a hypothesis, generates new hypotheses, and is supported by a large body of evidence.

variable A factor that varies in an experiment or other test.

Chi-Square (χ^2) Distribution Table

To use the table, find the row that corresponds to the degrees of freedom in your data set. (The degrees of freedom is the number of categories of data minus 1.) Move along that row to the pair of values that your calculated χ^2 value lies between. Move up from those numbers to the probabilities at the top of the columns to find the probability range for your χ^2 value. A probability of 0.05 or less is generally considered significant. (To practise using the chi-square test, see the Scientific Skills Exercise in Chapter 15.)

Degrees of Freedom (df)	Probability										
	0.95	0.90	0.80	0.70	0.50	0.30	0.20	0.10	0.05	0.01	0.001
1	0.004	0.02	0.06	0.15	0.45	1.07	1.64	2.71	3.84	6.64	10.83
2	0.10	0.21	0.45	0.71	1.39	2.41	3.22	4.61	5.99	9.21	13.82
3	0.35	0.58	1.01	1.42	2.37	3.66	4.64	6.25	7.82	11.34	16.27
4	0.71	1.06	1.65	2.19	3.36	4.88	5.99	7.78	9.49	13.28	18.47
5	1.15	1.61	2.34	3.00	4.35	6.06	7.29	9.24	11.07	15.09	20.52
6	1.64	2.20	3.07	3.83	5.35	7.23	8.56	10.64	12.59	16.81	22.46
7	2.17	2.83	3.82	4.67	6.35	8.38	9.80	12.02	14.07	18.48	24.32
8	2.73	3.49	4.59	5.53	7.34	9.52	11.03	13.36	15.51	20.09	26.12
9	3.33	4.17	5.38	6.39	8.34	10.66	12.24	14.68	16.92	21.67	27.88
10	3.94	4.87	6.18	7.27	9.34	11.78	13.44	15.99	18.31	23.21	29.59

Mean and Standard Deviation

The **mean** is the sum of all data points in a data set divided by the number of data points. The mean (or average) represents a "typical" or central value around which the data points are clustered. The mean of a variable x (denoted by $\bar{x}$) is calculated from the following equation:

$$\bar{x} = \frac{1}{n}\sum_{i=1}^{n} x_i$$

In this formula, n is the number of observations, and x_i is the value of the ith observation of variable x; the "$\sum$" symbol indicates that the n values of x_i are to be summed. (To practise calculating the mean, see the Scientific Skills Exercises in Chapters 32 and 34.)

The **standard deviation** provides a measure of the variation found in a set of data points. The standard deviation of a variable x (denoted s_x) is calculated from the following equation:

$$s = \sqrt{\frac{\sum_{i=1}^{n}(x_i - \bar{x})^2}{n - 1}}$$

In this formula, n is the number of observations, x_i is the value of the ith observation of variable x, and $\bar{x}$ is the mean of x; the "$\sum$" symbol indicates that the n values of $(x_i - \bar{x})^2$ are to be summed. (To practise calculating standard deviation, see the Scientific Skills Exercises in Chapters 32 and 34.)

GLOSSARY

5′ cap A modified form of guanine nucleotide added onto the 5′ end of a pre-mRNA molecule.

A site One of a ribosome's three binding sites for tRNA during translation. The A site holds the tRNA carrying the next amino acid to be added to the polypeptide chain. (A stands for amino-acyl tRNA.)

ABC hypothesis A model of flower formation identifying three classes of organ identity genes that direct formation of the four types of floral organs.

abiotic (ā′-bī-ot′-ik) Nonliving; referring to the physical and chemical properties of an environment.

abortion The termination of a pregnancy in progress.

abscisic acid (ABA) (ab-sis′-ik) A plant hormone that slows growth, often antagonizing the actions of growth hormones. Two of its many effects are to promote seed dormancy and facilitate drought tolerance.

absorption The third stage of food processing in animals: the uptake of small nutrient molecules by an organism's body.

absorption spectrum The range of a pigment's ability to absorb various wavelengths of light; also a graph of such a range.

abyssal zone (uh-bis′-ul) The part of the ocean's benthic zone between 2000 and 6000 m deep.

acanthodian (ak′-an-thō′-dē-un) Any of a group of ancient jawed aquatic vertebrates from the Silurian and Devonian periods.

accessory fruit A fruit, or assemblage of fruits, in which the fleshy parts are derived largely or entirely from tissues other than the ovary.

acclimation (uh-klī′-mā′-shun) Physiological adjustment to a change in a single environmental factor.

acclimatization (uh-klī′-muh-tī-zā′-shun) Physiological adjustment to changes in complex environmental factors.

acetyl CoA Acetyl coenzyme A; the entry compound for the citric acid cycle in cellular respiration, formed from a fragment of pyruvate attached to a coenzyme.

acetylcholine (as′-uh-til-kō′-lēn) One of the most common neurotransmitters; functions by binding to receptors and altering the permeability of the postsynaptic membrane to specific ions, either depolarizing or hyperpolarizing the membrane.

acid A substance that increases the hydrogen ion concentration of a solution.

acoelomate (uh-sē′-lō-māt) A solid-bodied animal lacking a cavity between the gut and outer body wall.

acrosomal reaction (ak′-ruh-sōm′-ul) The discharge of hydrolytic enzymes from the acrosome, a vesicle in the tip of a sperm, when the sperm approaches or contacts an egg.

acrosome (ak′-ruh-sōm) A vesicle in the tip of a sperm containing hydrolytic enzymes and other proteins that help the sperm reach the egg.

actin (ak′-tin) A globular protein that links into chains, two of which twist helically about each other, forming microfilaments (actin filaments) in muscle and other kinds of cells.

action potential An electrical signal that propagates (travels) along the membrane of a neuron or other excitable cell as a nongraded (all-or-none) depolarization.

action spectrum A graph that profiles the relative effectiveness of different wavelengths of radiation in driving a particular process.

activation energy The amount of energy that reactants must absorb before a chemical reaction will start; also called free energy of activation.

activator A protein that binds to DNA and stimulates gene transcription. In prokaryotes, activators bind in or near the promoter; in eukaryotes, activators generally bind to control elements in enhancers.

active immunity Long-lasting immunity conferred by the action of B cells and T cells and the resulting B and T memory cells specific for a pathogen. Active immunity can develop as a result of natural infection or immunization.

active site The specific region of an enzyme that binds the substrate and that forms the pocket in which catalysis occurs.

active transport The movement of a substance across a cell membrane against its concentration or electrochemical gradient, mediated by specific transport proteins and requiring an expenditure of energy.

adaptation Inherited characteristic of an organism that enhances its survival and reproduction in a specific environment.

adaptive immunity A vertebrate-specific defence that is mediated by B lymphocytes (B cells) and T lymphocytes (T cells). It exhibits specificity, memory, and self-nonself recognition. Also called acquired immunity.

adaptive radiation Period of evolutionary change in which groups of organisms form many new species whose adaptations allow them to fill different ecological roles in their communities.

addition rule A rule of probability stating that the probability of any one of two or more mutually exclusive events occurring can be determined by adding their individual probabilities.

adenosine triphosphate *See* ATP (adenosine triphosphate).

adenylyl cyclase (uh-den′-uh-lil) An enzyme that converts ATP to cyclic AMP in response to an extracellular signal.

adhesion The clinging of one substance to another, such as water to plant cell walls by means of hydrogen bonds.

adipose tissue A connective tissue that insulates the body and serves as a fuel reserve; contains fat-storing cells called adipose cells.

adrenal gland (uh-drē′-nul) One of two endocrine glands located adjacent to the kidneys in mammals. Endocrine cells in the outer portion (cortex) respond to adrenocorticotropic hormone (ACTH) by secreting steroid hormones that help maintain homeostasis during long-term stress. Neurosecretory cells in the central portion (medulla) secrete epinephrine and norepinephrine in response to nerve signals triggered by short-term stress.

adrenocorticotropic hormone (ACTH) A tropic hormone that is produced and secreted by the anterior pituitary and that stimulates the production and secretion of steroid hormones by the adrenal cortex.

aerobic respiration A catabolic pathway for organic molecules, using oxygen (O_2) as the final electron acceptor in an electron transport chain and ultimately producing ATP. This is the most efficient catabolic pathway and is carried out in most eukaryotic cells and many prokaryotic organisms.

age structure The relative number of individuals of each age in a population.

aggregate fruit A fruit derived from a single flower that has more than one carpel.

AIDS (acquired immunodeficiency syndrome) The symptoms and signs present during the late stages of HIV infection, defined by a specified reduction in the number of T cells and the appearance of characteristic secondary infections.

alcohol fermentation Glycolysis followed by the reduction of pyruvate to ethyl alcohol, regenerating NAD^+ and releasing carbon dioxide.

aldosterone (al-dos′-tuh-rōn) A steroid hormone that acts on tubules of the kidney to regulate the transport of sodium ions (Na^+) and potassium ions (K^+).

algae A diverse grade of photosynthetic protists, including unicellular and multicellular forms. Algal species are included in four of the five eukaryote supergroups (Excavata, Chromalveolata, Rhizaria, and Archaeplastida).

alimentary canal (al′-uh-men′-tuh-rē) A complete digestive tract, consisting of a tube running between a mouth and an anus.

allele (uh-lē′-ul) Any of the alternative versions of a gene that may produce distinguishable phenotypic effects.

allergen An antigen that triggers an exaggerated immune response.

allopatric speciation (al′-uh-pat′-rik) The formation of new species in populations that are geographically isolated from one another.

allopolyploid (al′-ō-pol′-ē-ployd) A fertile individual that has more than two chromosome sets as a result of two different species interbreeding and combining their chromosomes.

allosteric regulation The binding of a regulatory molecule to a protein at one site that affects the function of the protein at a different site.

alpha (α) helix (al′-fuh hē′-liks) A coiled region constituting one form of the secondary structure of proteins, arising from a specific pattern of hydrogen bonding between atoms of the polypeptide backbone (not the side chains).

alternation of generations A life cycle in which there is both a multicellular diploid form, the sporophyte, and a multicellular haploid form, the gametophyte; characteristic of plants and some algae.

alternative RNA splicing A type of eukaryotic gene regulation at the RNA-processing level in which different mRNA molecules are produced from the same primary transcript, depending on which RNA segments are treated as exons and which as introns.

altruism (al′-trū-iz-um) Selflessness; behaviour that reduces an individual's fitness while increasing the fitness of another individual.

alveolate (al-vē′-uh-let) A protist with membrane-bounded sacs (alveoli) located just under the plasma membrane.

alveolus (al-vē′-uh-lus) (plural, **alveoli**) One of the dead-end air sacs where gas exchange occurs in a mammalian lung.

Alzheimer's disease (alts′-hī-merz) An age-related dementia (mental deterioration) characterized by confusion and memory loss.

amino acid (uh-mēn′-ō) An organic molecule possessing both a carboxyl and an amino group. Amino acids serve as the monomers of polypeptides.

amino group A chemical group consisting of a nitrogen atom bonded to two hydrogen atoms; can act as a base in solution, accepting a hydrogen ion and acquiring a charge of 1+.

aminoacyl-tRNA synthetase An enzyme that joins each amino acid to the appropriate tRNA.

ammonia A small, toxic molecule (NH_3) produced by nitrogen fixation or as a metabolic waste product of protein and nucleic acid metabolism.

ammonite A member of a group of shelled cephalopods that were important marine predators for hundreds of millions of years until their extinction at the end of the Cretaceous period (65.5 million years ago).

amniocentesis (am′-nē-ō-sen-tē′-sis) A technique associated with prenatal diagnosis in which amniotic fluid is obtained by aspiration from a needle inserted into the uterus. The fluid and the fetal cells it contains are analyzed to detect certain genetic and congenital defects in the fetus.

amniote (am′-nē-ōt) Member of a clade of tetrapods named for a key derived character, the amniotic egg, which contains specialized membranes, including the fluid-filled amnion, that protect the embryo. Amniotes include mammals as well as birds and other reptiles.

amniotic egg An egg that contains specialized membranes that function in protection, nourishment, and gas exchange. The amniotic egg was a major evolutionary innovation, allowing embryos to develop on land in a fluid-filled sac, thus reducing the dependence of tetrapods on water for reproduction.

amoeba (uh-mē′-buh) A protist grade characterized by the presence of pseudopodia.

amoebocyte (uh-mē′-buh-sīt′) An amoeba-like cell that moves by pseudopodia and is found in most animals. Depending on the species, it may digest and distribute food, dispose of wastes, form skeletal fibres, fight infections, or change into other cell types.

amoebozoan (uh-mē′-buh-zō′-an) A protist in a clade that includes many species with lobe- or tube-shaped pseudopodia.

amphibian Member of the tetrapod class Amphibia, including salamanders, frogs, and caecilians.

amphipathic (am′-fē-path′-ik) Having both a hydrophilic region and a hydrophobic region.

amplification The strengthening of stimulus energy during transduction.

amygdala (uh-mig′-duh-luh) A structure in the temporal lobe of the vertebrate brain that has a major role in the processing of emotions.

anabolic pathway (an′-uh-bol′-ik) A metabolic pathway that consumes energy to synthesize a complex molecule from simpler molecules.

anaerobic respiration (an-er-ō′-bik) A catabolic pathway in which inorganic molecules other than oxygen accept electrons at the "downhill" end of electron transport chains.

analogous Having characteristics that are similar because of convergent evolution, not homology.

analogy (an-al′-uh-jē) Similarity between two species that is due to convergent evolution rather than to descent from a common ancestor with the same trait.

anaphase The fourth stage of mitosis, in which the chromatids of each chromosome have separated and the daughter chromosomes are moving to the poles of the cell.

anatomy The structure of an organism.

anchorage dependence The requirement that a cell must be attached to a substratum in order to initiate cell division.

androgen (an′-drō-jen) Any steroid hormone, such as testosterone, that stimulates the development and maintenance of the male reproductive system and secondary sex characteristics.

aneuploidy (an′-yū-ploy′-dē) A chromosomal aberration in which one or more chromosomes are present in extra copies or are deficient in number.

angiosperm (an′-jē-ō-sperm) A flowering plant, which forms seeds inside a protective chamber called an ovary.

angiotensin II A peptide hormone that stimulates constriction of precapillary arterioles and increases reabsorption of NaCl and water by the proximal tubules of the kidney, increasing blood pressure and volume.

anhydrobiosis (an-hī′-drō-bī-ō′-sis) A dormant state involving loss of almost all body water.

animal pole The point at the end of an egg in the hemisphere where the least yolk is concentrated; opposite of vegetal pole.

anion (an′-ī-on) A negatively charged ion.

anterior Pertaining to the front, or head, of a bilaterally symmetrical animal.

anterior pituitary A portion of the pituitary that develops from nonneural tissue; consists of endocrine cells that synthesize and secrete several tropic and nontropic hormones.

anther In an angiosperm, the terminal pollen sac of a stamen, where pollen grains containing sperm-producing male gametophytes form.

antheridium (an-thuh-rid′-ē-um) (plural, **antheridia**) In plants, the male gametangium, a moist chamber in which gametes develop.

anthropoid (an′-thruh-poyd) Member of a primate group made up of the monkeys and the apes (gibbons, orangutans, gorillas, chimpanzees, bonobos, and humans).

antibody A protein secreted by plasma cells (differentiated B cells) that binds to a particular antigen; also called immunoglobulin. All antibodies have the same Y-shaped structure and in their monomer form consist of two identical heavy chains and two identical light chains.

anticodon (an′-tī-kō′-don) A nucleotide triplet at one end of a tRNA molecule that base-pairs with a particular complementary codon on an mRNA molecule.

antidiuretic hormone (ADH) (an′-tī-dī-yū-ret′-ik) A peptide hormone, also known as vasopressin, that promotes water retention by the kidneys. Produced in the hypothalamus and released from the posterior pituitary, ADH also functions in the brain.

antigen (an'-ti-jen) A substance that elicits an immune response by binding to receptors of B cells, antibodies, or of T cells.

antigen presentation The process by which an MHC molecule binds to a fragment of an intracellular protein antigen and carries it to the cell surface, where it is displayed and can be recognized by a T cell.

antigen-presenting cell A cell that upon ingesting pathogens or internalizing pathogen proteins generates peptide fragments that are bound by class II MHC molecules and subsequently displayed on the cell surface to T cells. Macrophages, dendritic cells, and B cells are the primary antigen-presenting cells.

antigen receptor The general term for a surface protein, located on B cells and T cells, that binds to antigens, initiating adaptive immune responses. The antigen receptors on B cells are called B cell receptors, and the antigen receptors on T cells are called T cell receptors.

antiparallel Referring to the arrangement of the sugar-phosphate backbones in a DNA double helix (they run in opposite $5' \rightarrow 3'$ directions).

aphotic zone (ā'-fō'-tik) The part of an ocean or lake beneath the photic zone, where light does not penetrate sufficiently for photosynthesis to occur.

apical bud (ā'-pik-ul) A bud at the tip of a plant stem; also called a terminal bud.

apical dominance (ā'-pik-ul) Tendency for growth to be concentrated at the tip of a plant shoot, because the apical bud partially inhibits axillary bud growth.

apical ectodermal ridge (AER) A thickened area of ectoderm at the tip of a limb bud that promotes outgrowth of the limb bud.

apical meristem (ā'-pik-ul mār'-uh-stem) Embryonic plant tissue in the tips of roots and buds of shoots. The dividing cells of an apical meristem enable the plant to grow in length.

apicomplexan (ap'-ē-kom-pleks'-un) A protist in a clade that includes many species that parasitize animals. Some apicomplexans cause human disease.

apomixis (ap'-uh-mik'-sis) The ability of some plant species to reproduce asexually through seeds without fertilization by a male gamete.

apoplast (ap'-ō-plast) Everything external to the plasma membrane of a plant cell, including cell walls, intercellular spaces, and the space within dead structures such as xylem vessels and tracheids.

apoptosis (ā-puh-tō'-sus) A type of programmed cell death, which is brought about by activation of enzymes that break down many chemical components in the cell.

aposematic colouration (ap'-ō-si-mat'-ik) The bright warning colouration of many animals with effective physical or chemical defences.

appendix A small, finger-like extension of the vertebrate cecum; contains a mass of white blood cells that contribute to immunity.

aquaporin A channel protein in the plasma membrane of a plant, animal, or microorganism cell that specifically facilitates osmosis, the diffusion of free water across the membrane.

aqueous solution (ā'-kwē-us) A solution in which water is the solvent.

arachnid A member of a major arthropod group, the chelicerates. Arachnids include spiders, scorpions, ticks, and mites.

arbuscular mycorrhiza (ar-bus'-kyū-lur mī'-kō-rī'-zuh) Association of a fungus with a plant root system in which the fungus causes the invagination of the host (plant) cells' plasma membranes.

arbuscular mycorrhizal fungus A symbiotic fungus whose hyphae grow through the cell wall of plant roots and extend into the root cell (enclosed in tubes formed by invagination of the root cell plasma membrane).

Archaea (ar'-kē'-uh) One of two prokaryotic domains, the other being Bacteria.

Archaeplastida (ar'-kē-plas'-tid-uh) One of five supergroups of eukaryotes proposed in a current hypothesis of the evolutionary history of eukaryotes. This monophyletic group, which includes red algae, green algae, and land plants, descended from an ancient protist ancestor that engulfed a cyanobacterium. *See also* Excavata, Chromalveolata, Rhizaria, and Unikonta.

archegonium (ar-ki-gō'-nē-um) (plural, **archegonia**) In plants, the female gametangium, a moist chamber in which gametes develop.

archenteron (ar-ken'-tuh-ron) The endoderm-lined cavity, formed during gastrulation, that develops into the digestive tract of an animal.

archosaur (ar'-kō-sōr) Member of the reptilian group that includes crocodiles, alligators and dinosaurs, including birds.

Archosauria (ar'-kō-sōr-ē-uh) The archosaur clade.

arteriole (ar-ter'-ē-ōl) A vessel that conveys blood between an artery and a capillary bed.

artery A vessel that carries blood away from the heart to organs throughout the body.

arthropod A segmented ecdysozoan with a hard exoskeleton and jointed appendages. Familiar examples include insects, spiders, millipedes, and crabs.

artificial selection The selective breeding of domesticated plants and animals to encourage the occurrence of desirable traits.

ascocarp The fruiting body of a sac fungus (ascomycete).

ascomycete (as'-kuh-mī'-sēt) Member of the fungal phylum Ascomycota, commonly called sac fungus. The name comes from the saclike structure in which the spores develop.

ascus (plural, **asci**) A saclike spore capsule located at the tip of a dikaryotic hypha of a sac fungus.

asexual reproduction The generation of offspring from a single parent that occurs without the fusion of gametes (by budding, division of a single cell, or division of the entire organism into two or more parts). In most cases, the offspring are genetically identical to the parent.

associative learning The acquired ability to associate one environmental feature (such as a colour) with another (such as danger).

aster A radial array of short microtubules that extends from each centrosome toward the plasma membrane in an animal cell undergoing mitosis.

astrobiologists Biologists who look for life elsewhere in the universe.

astrocyte A glial cell with diverse functions, including providing structural support for neurons, regulating the interstitial environment, facilitating synaptic transmission, and assisting in regulating the blood supply to the brain.

atherosclerosis A cardiovascular disease in which fatty deposits called plaques develop in the inner walls of the arteries, obstructing the arteries and causing them to harden.

atom The smallest unit of matter that retains the properties of an element.

atomic mass The total mass of an atom, which is the mass in grams of 1 mole of the atom.

atomic nucleus An atom's dense central core, containing protons and neutrons.

atomic number The number of protons in the nucleus of an atom, unique for each element and designated by a subscript to the left of the elemental symbol.

ATP (adenosine triphosphate) (a-den'-ō-sēn trī-fos'-fāt) An adenine-containing nucleoside triphosphate that releases free energy when its phosphate bonds are hydrolyzed. This energy is used to drive endergonic reactions in cells.

ATP synthase A complex of several membrane proteins that functions in chemiosmosis with adjacent electron transport chains, using the energy of a hydrogen ion (proton) concentration gradient to make ATP. ATP synthases are found in the inner mitochondrial membranes of eukaryotic cells and in the plasma membranes of prokaryotes.

atrial natriuretic peptide (ANP) (ā'-trē-ul na'-trē-yū-ret'-ik) A peptide hormone secreted by cells of the atria of the heart in response to high blood pressure. ANP's effects on the kidney alter ion and water movement and reduce blood pressure.

atrioventricular (AV) node A region of specialized heart muscle tissue between the left and right atria where electrical impulses are delayed for about 0.1 second before spreading to both ventricles and causing them to contract.

atrioventricular (AV) valve A heart valve located between each atrium and ventricle that prevents a backflow of blood when the ventricle contracts.

atrium (ā'-trē-um) (plural, **atria**) A chamber of the vertebrate heart that receives blood from the veins and transfers blood to a ventricle.

autocrine Referring to a secreted molecule that acts on the cell that secreted it.

autoimmune disease An immunological disorder in which the immune system turns against self.

autonomic nervous system (ot'-ō-nom'-ik) An efferent branch of the vertebrate peripheral nervous system that regulates the internal environment; consists of the sympathetic, parasympathetic, and enteric divisions.

autopolyploid (ot′-ō-pol′-ē-ployd) An individual that has more than two chromosome sets that are all derived from a single species.

autosome (ot′-ō-sōm) A chromosome that is not directly involved in determining sex; not a sex chromosome.

autotroph (ot′-ō-trōf) An organism that obtains organic food molecules without eating other organisms or substances derived from other organisms. Autotrophs use energy from the sun or from oxidation of inorganic substances to make organic molecules from inorganic ones.

auxin (ôk′-sin) A term that primarily refers to indoleacetic acid (IAA), a natural plant hormone that has a variety of effects, including cell elongation, root formation, secondary growth, and fruit growth.

axillary bud (ak′-sil-ār-ē) A structure that has the potential to form a lateral shoot, or branch. The bud appears in the angle formed between a leaf and a stem.

axon (ak′-son) A typically long extension, or process, of a neuron that carries nerve impulses away from the cell body toward target cells.

B cells The lymphocytes that complete their development in the bone marrow and become effector cells for the humoral immune response.

BACI (Before-After-Control-Impact) design Experimental design often used in environmental impact assessment.

Bacteria One of two prokaryotic domains, the other being Archaea.

bacteriophage (bak-tĕr′-ē-ō-fāj) A virus that infects bacteria; also called a phage.

bacteroid A form of the bacterium *Rhizobium* contained within the vesicles formed by the root cells of a root nodule.

balancing selection Natural selection that maintains two or more phenotypic forms in a population.

bark All tissues external to the vascular cambium, consisting mainly of the secondary phloem and layers of periderm.

Barr body A dense object lying along the inside of the nuclear envelope in cells of female mammals, representing a highly condensed, inactivated X chromosome.

basal body (bā′-sul) A eukaryotic cell structure consisting of a "9 + 0" arrangement of microtubule triplets. The basal body may organize the microtubule assembly of a cilium or flagellum and is structurally very similar to a centriole.

basal metabolic rate (BMR) The metabolic rate of a resting, fasting, and nonstressed endotherm at a comfortable temperature.

basal taxon In a specified group of organisms, a taxon whose evolutionary lineage diverged early in the history of the group.

base A substance that reduces the hydrogen ion concentration of a solution.

basidiocarp Elaborate fruiting body of a dikaryotic mycelium of a club fungus.

basidiomycete (buh-sid′-ē-ō-mī′-sēt) Member of the fungal phylum Basidiomycota, commonly called club fungus. The name comes from the club-like shape of the basidium.

basidium (plural, **basidia**) (buh-sid′-ē-um, buh-sid′-ē-ah) A reproductive appendage that produces sexual spores on the gills of mushrooms (club fungi).

basilar membrane The membrane in the cochlea of the vertebrate inner ear.

Batesian mimicry (bāt′-zē-un mim′-uh-krē) A type of mimicry in which a harmless species looks like a species that is poisonous or otherwise harmful to predators.

behaviour Individually, an action carried out by muscles or glands under control of the nervous system in response to a stimulus; collectively, the sum of an animal's responses to external and internal stimuli.

behavioural ecology The study of the evolution of and ecological basis for animal behaviour.

benign tumour A mass of abnormal cells with specific genetic and cellular changes such that the cells are not capable of surviving at a new site and generally remain at the site of the tumour's origin.

benthic zone The bottom surface of an aquatic environment.

benthos (ben′-thōz) The communities of organisms living in the benthic zone of an aquatic biome.

beta oxidation A metabolic sequence that breaks fatty acids down to two-carbon fragments that enter the citric acid cycle as acetyl CoA.

beta (β) pleated sheet One form of the secondary structure of proteins in which the polypeptide chain folds back and forth. Two regions of the chain lie parallel to each other and are held together by hydrogen bonds between atoms of the polypeptide backbone (not the side chains).

bicoid A maternal effect gene that codes for a protein responsible for specifying the anterior end in *Drosophila melanogaster*.

bilateral symmetry Body symmetry in which a central longitudinal plane divides the body into two equal but opposite halves.

bilaterian (bī′-luh-ter′-ē-uhn) Member of a clade of animals with bilateral symmetry and three germ layers.

bile A mixture of substances that is produced in the liver and stored in the gallbladder; enables formation of fat droplets in water as an aid in the digestion and absorption of fats.

binary fission A method of asexual reproduction by "division in half." In prokaryotes, binary fission does not involve mitosis, but in single-celled eukaryotes that undergo binary fission, mitosis is part of the process.

binomial The two-part, latinized format for naming a species, consisting of the genus and specific epithet; a binomen.

biodiversity hot spot A relatively small area with numerous endemic species and a large number of endangered and threatened species.

bioenergetics (1) The overall flow and transformation of energy in an organism. (2) The study of how energy flows through organisms.

biofilm A surface-coating colony of one or more species of prokaryotes that engage in metabolic cooperation.

biofuel A fuel produced from dry organic matter or combustible oils produced by plants.

biogenic amine A neurotransmitter derived from an amino acid.

biogeochemical cycle Any of the various chemical cycles, which involve both biotic and abiotic components of ecosystems.

biogeography The study of the past and present geographic distribution of species.

bioinformatics The use of computers, software, and mathematical models to process and integrate biological information from large data sets.

biological augmentation An approach to restoration ecology that uses organisms to add essential materials to a degraded ecosystem.

biological clock An internal timekeeper that controls an organism's biological rhythms. The biological clock marks time with or without environmental cues but often requires signals from the environment to remain tuned to an appropriate period. *See also* circadian rhythm.

biological community *See* community.

biological magnification A process in which retained substances become more concentrated at each higher trophic level in a food chain.

biological species concept Definition of a species as a group of populations whose members have the potential to interbreed in nature and produce viable, fertile offspring, but do not produce viable, fertile offspring with members of other such groups.

biology The scientific study of life.

biomass The total mass of organic matter comprising a group of organisms in a particular habitat.

biome (bī′-ōm) Any of the world's major ecosystem types, often classified according to the predominant vegetation for terrestrial biomes and the physical environment for aquatic biomes and characterized by adaptations of organisms to that particular environment.

bioremediation The use of organisms to detoxify and restore polluted and degraded ecosystems.

biosphere The entire portion of Earth inhabited by life; the sum of all the planet's ecosystems.

biotechnology The manipulation of organisms or their components to produce useful products.

biotic (bī-ot′-ik) Pertaining to the living factors—the organisms—in an environment.

bipolar disorder A depressive mental illness characterized by swings of mood from high to low; also called manic-depressive disorder.

birth control pill A chemical contraceptive that inhibits ovulation, retards follicular development, or alters a woman's cervical mucus to prevent sperm from entering the uterus.

blade (1) A leaflike structure of a seaweed that provides most of the surface area for photosynthesis. (2) The flattened portion of a typical leaf.

blastocoel (blas'-tuh-sēl) The fluid-filled cavity that forms in the centre of a blastula.

blastocyst (blas'-tuh-sist) The blastula stage of mammalian embryonic development, consisting of an inner cell mass, a cavity, and an outer layer, the trophoblast. In humans, the blastocyst forms 1 week after fertilization.

blastomere An early embryonic cell arising during the cleavage stage of an early embryo.

blastopore (blas'-tō-pōr) In a gastrula, the opening of the archenteron that typically develops into the anus in deuterostomes and the mouth in protostomes.

blastula (blas'-tyū-luh) A hollow ball of cells that marks the end of the cleavage stage during early embryonic development in animals.

blood A connective tissue with a fluid matrix called plasma in which red blood cells, white blood cells, and cell fragments called platelets are suspended.

blood vessels Part of the circulatory system, transport blood through the body, and are comprised of arteries, capillaries, and veins.

blue-light photoreceptor A type of light receptor in plants that initiates a variety of responses, such as phototropism and slowing of hypocotyl elongation.

body cavity A fluid- or air-filled space between the digestive tract and the body wall.

body plan In animals, a set of morphological and developmental traits that are integrated into a functional whole—the living animal.

Bohr shift A lowering of the affinity of hemoglobin for oxygen, caused by a drop in pH. It facilitates the release of oxygen from hemoglobin in the vicinity of active tissues.

bolus A lubricated ball of chewed food.

bone A connective tissue consisting of living cells held in a rigid matrix of collagen fibres embedded in calcium salts.

book lung An organ of gas exchange in spiders, consisting of stacked plates contained in an internal chamber.

bottleneck effect Genetic drift that occurs when the size of a population is reduced, as by a natural disaster or human actions. Typically, the surviving population is no longer genetically representative of the original population.

bottom-up control A model of community organization in which mineral nutrients influence community organization by controlling plant or phytoplankton numbers, which in turn control herbivore numbers, which in turn control predator numbers.

Bowman's capsule (bō'-munz) A cup-shaped receptacle in the vertebrate kidney that is the initial, expanded segment of the nephron where filtrate enters from the blood.

brachiopod (bra'-kē-uh-pod') A marine lophophorate with a shell divided into dorsal and ventral halves. Brachiopods are also called lamp shells.

brain Organ of the central nervous system where information is processed and integrated.

brainstem A collection of structures in the vertebrate brain, including the midbrain, the pons, and the medulla oblongata; functions in homeostasis, coordination of movement, and conduction of information to higher brain centres.

branch point The representation on a phylogenetic tree of the divergence of two or more taxa from a common ancestor. A branch point is usually shown as a dichotomy in which a branch representing the ancestral lineage splits (at the branch point) into two branches, one for each of the two descendant lineages.

brassinosteroid A steroid hormone in plants that has a variety of effects, including inducing cell elongation, retarding leaf abscission, and promoting xylem differentiation.

breathing Ventilation of the lungs through alternating inhalation and exhalation.

bronchiole (brong'-kē-ōl') A fine branch of the bronchi that transports air to alveoli.

bronchus (brong'-kus) (plural, **bronchi**) One of a pair of breathing tubes that branch from the trachea into the lungs.

brown alga A multicellular, photosynthetic protist with a characteristic brown or olive colour that results from carotenoids in its plastids. Most brown algae are marine, and some have a plant-like body (thallus).

bryophyte (brī'-uh-fīt) An informal name for a moss, liverwort, or hornwort; a nonvascular plant that lives on land but lacks some of the terrestrial adaptations of vascular plants.

budding A sexual reproduction in which outgrowths from the parent form and pinch off to live independently or else remain attached to eventually form extensive colonies.

buffer A solution that contains a weak acid and its corresponding base. A buffer minimizes changes in pH when acids or bases are added to the solution.

bulk feeder An animal that eats relatively large pieces of food.

bulk flow The movement of a fluid due to a difference in pressure between two locations.

bundle-sheath cell In C_4 plants, a type of photosynthetic cell arranged into tightly packed sheaths around the veins of a leaf.

C_3 plant A plant that uses the Calvin cycle for the initial steps that incorporate CO_2 into organic material, forming a three-carbon compound as the first stable intermediate.

C_4 plant A plant in which the Calvin cycle is preceded by reactions that incorporate CO_2 into a four-carbon compound, the end product of which supplies CO_2 for the Calvin cycle.

calcitonin (kal'-si-tō'-nin) A hormone secreted by the thyroid gland that lowers blood calcium levels by promoting calcium deposition in bone and calcium excretion from the kidneys; nonessential in adult humans.

callus A mass of dividing, undifferentiated cells growing in culture.

Calvin cycle The second of two major stages in photosynthesis (following the light reactions), involving fixation of atmospheric CO_2 and reduction of the fixed carbon into carbohydrate.

CAM plant A plant that uses crassulacean acid metabolism, an adaptation for photosynthesis in arid conditions. In this process, carbon dioxide entering open stomata during the night is converted to organic acids, which release CO_2 for the Calvin cycle during the day, when stomata are closed.

Cambrian explosion A relatively brief time in geologic history when many present-day phyla of animals first appeared in the fossil record. This burst of evolutionary change occurred about 535–525 million years ago and saw the emergence of the first large, hard-bodied animals.

cAMP *See* cyclic AMP.

canopy The uppermost layer of vegetation in a terrestrial biome.

capillary (kap'-il-ār'-ē) A microscopic blood vessel that penetrates the tissues and consists of a single layer of endothelial cells that allows exchange between the blood and interstitial fluid.

capillary bed A network of capillaries in a tissue or organ.

capsid The protein shell that encloses a viral genome. It may be rod-shaped, polyhedral, or more complex in shape.

capsule (1) In many prokaryotes, a dense and well-defined layer of polysaccharide or protein that surrounds the cell wall and is sticky, protecting the cell and enabling it to adhere to substrates or other cells. (2) The sporangium of a bryophyte (moss, liverwort, or hornwort).

carbohydrate (kar'-bō-hī'-drāt) A sugar (monosaccharide) or one of its dimers (disaccharides) or polymers (polysaccharides).

carbon fixation The initial incorporation of carbon from CO_2 into an organic compound by an autotrophic organism (a plant, another photosynthetic organism, or a chemoautotrophic prokaryote).

carbonyl group (kar-buh-nēl') A chemical group present in aldehydes and ketones and consisting of a carbon atom double-bonded to an oxygen atom.

carboxyl group (kar-bok'-sil) A chemical group present in organic acids and consisting of a single carbon atom double-bonded to an oxygen atom and also bonded to a hydroxyl group.

cardiac cycle (kar'-dē-ak) The alternating contractions and relaxations of the heart.

cardiac muscle A type of striated muscle that forms the contractile wall of the heart. Its cells are joined by intercalated disks that relay the electrical signals underlying each heartbeat.

cardiac output The volume of blood pumped per minute by each ventricle of the heart.

cardiovascular system A closed circulatory system with a heart and branching network of arteries, capillaries, and veins. The system is characteristic of vertebrates.

carnivore An animal that mainly eats other animals.

carotenoid (kuh-rot'-uh-noyd') An accessory pigment, either yellow or orange, in the chloroplasts of plants and in some prokaryotes. By absorbing wavelengths of light that chlorophyll cannot, carotenoids broaden the spectrum of colours that can drive photosynthesis.

carpel (kar′-pul) The ovule-producing reproductive organ of a flower, consisting of the stigma, style, and ovary.

carrier In genetics, an individual who is heterozygous at a given genetic locus for a recessively inherited disorder. The heterozygote is generally phenotypically normal for the disorder but can pass on the recessive allele to offspring.

carrying capacity The maximum population size that can be supported by the available resources, symbolized as *K*.

cartilage (kar′-til-ij) A flexible connective tissue with an abundance of collagenous fibres embedded in chondroitin sulphate.

Casparian strip (ka-spār′-ē-un) A water-impermeable ring of wax in the endodermal cells of plants that blocks the passive flow of water and solutes into the stele by way of cell walls.

catabolic pathway (kat′-uh-bol′-ik) A metabolic pathway that releases energy by breaking down complex molecules to simpler molecules.

catalyst (kat′-uh-list) A chemical agent that selectively increases the rate of a reaction without being consumed by the reaction.

catecholamine (kat′-uh-kōl′-uh-mēn) Any of a class of neurotransmitters and hormones, including the hormones epinephrine and norepinephrine, that are synthesized from the amino acid tyrosine.

cation (cat′-ī-on) A positively charged ion.

cation exchange A process in which positively charged minerals are made available to a plant when hydrogen ions in the soil displace mineral ions from the clay particles.

cecum (sē′-kum) (plural, **ceca**) The blind pouch forming one branch of the large intestine.

cell body The part of a neuron that houses the nucleus and most other organelles.

cell cycle An ordered sequence of events in the life of a cell, from its origin in the division of a parent cell until its own division into two. The eukaryotic cell cycle is composed of interphase (including G_1, S, and G_2 subphases) and M phase (including mitosis and cytokinesis).

cell cycle control system A cyclically operating set of molecules in the eukaryotic cell that both triggers and coordinates key events in the cell cycle.

cell differentiation See differentiation.

cell division The reproduction of cells.

cell fractionation The disruption of a cell and separation of its parts by centrifugation at successively higher speeds.

cell plate A membrane-bounded, flattened sac located at the midline of a dividing plant cell, inside which the new cell wall forms during cytokinesis.

cell wall A protective layer external to the plasma membrane in the cells of plants, prokaryotes, fungi, and some protists. Polysaccharides such as cellulose (in plants and some protists), chitin (in fungi), and peptidoglycan (in bacteria) are important structural components of cell walls.

cell-mediated immune response The branch of adaptive immunity that involves the activation of cytotoxic T cells, which defend against infected cells.

cellular respiration The catabolic pathways of aerobic and anaerobic respiration, which break down organic molecules and use an electron transport chain for the production of ATP.

cellular slime mould A type of protist characterized by unicellular amoeboid cells and aggregated reproductive bodies in its life cycle.

cellulose (sel′-yū-lōs) A structural polysaccharide of plant cell walls, consisting of glucose monomers joined by β glycosidic linkages.

central canal The narrow cavity in the centre of the spinal cord that is continuous with the fluid-filled ventricles of the brain.

central nervous system (CNS) The portion of the nervous system where signal integration occurs; in vertebrate animals, the brain and spinal cord.

central vacuole In a mature plant cell, a large membranous sac with diverse roles in growth, storage, and sequestration of toxic substances.

centriole (sen′-trē-ōl) A structure in the centrosome of an animal cell composed of a cylinder of microtubule triplets arranged in a $9 + 0$ pattern. A centrosome has a pair of centrioles.

centromere (sen′-trō-mēr) In a duplicated chromosome, the region on each sister chromatid where they are most closely attached to each other by proteins that bind to specific DNA sequences; this close attachment causes a constriction in the condensed chromosome. (An uncondensed, unduplicated chromosome has a single centromere, identified by its DNA sequence.)

centrosome (sen′-trō-sōm) A structure present in the cytoplasm of animal cells that functions as a microtubule-organizing centre and is important during cell division. A centrosome has two centrioles.

cephalization (sef′-uh-luh-zā′-shun) An evolutionary trend toward the concentration of sensory equipment at the anterior end of the body.

cercozoan An amoeboid or flagellated protist that feeds with threadlike pseudopodia.

cerebellum (sār′-ruh-bel′-um) Part of the vertebrate hindbrain located dorsally; functions in unconscious coordination of movement and balance.

cerebral cortex (suh-rē′-brul) The surface of the cerebrum; the largest and most complex part of the mammalian brain, containing nerve cell bodies of the cerebrum; the part of the vertebrate brain most changed through evolution.

cerebral hemisphere The right or left side of the cerebrum.

cerebrospinal fluid (suh-rē′-brō-spī′-nul) Blood-derived fluid that surrounds, protects against infection, nourishes, and cushions the brain and spinal cord.

cerebrum (suh-rē′-brum) The dorsal portion of the vertebrate forebrain, composed of right and left hemispheres; the integrating centre for memory, learning, emotions, and other highly complex functions of the central nervous system.

cervix (ser′-viks) The neck of the uterus, which opens into the vagina.

chaparral A scrubland biome of dense, spiny evergreen shrubs found at midlatitudes along coasts where cold ocean currents circulate offshore; characterized by mild, rainy winters and long, hot, dry summers.

chaperonin (shap′-er-ō′-nin) A protein complex that assists in the proper folding of other proteins.

character An observable heritable feature that may vary among individuals.

character displacement The tendency for characteristics to be more divergent in sympatric populations of two species than in allopatric populations of the same two species.

checkpoint A control point in the cell cycle where stop and go-ahead signals can regulate the cycle.

chelicera (kē-lih′-suh-ruh) (plural, **chelicerae**) One of a pair of clawlike feeding appendages characteristic of chelicerates.

chelicerate (kē-lih-suh′-rāte) An arthropod that has chelicerae and a body divided into a cephalothorax and an abdomen. Living chelicerates include sea spiders, horseshoe crabs, scorpions, ticks, and spiders.

chemical bond An attraction between two atoms, resulting from a sharing of outer-shell electrons or the presence of opposite charges on the atoms. The bonded atoms gain complete outer electron shells.

chemical energy Energy available in molecules for release in a chemical reaction; a form of potential energy.

chemical equilibrium In a chemical reaction, the state in which the rate of the forward reaction equals the rate of the reverse reaction, so that the relative concentrations of the reactants and products do not change with time.

chemical reaction The making and breaking of chemical bonds, leading to changes in the composition of matter.

chemiosmosis (kem′-ē-oz-mō′-sis) An energy-coupling mechanism that uses energy stored in the form of a hydrogen ion gradient across a membrane to drive cellular work, such as the synthesis of ATP. Under aerobic conditions, most ATP synthesis in cells occurs by chemiosmosis.

chemoautotroph (kē′-mō-ot′-ō-trōf) An organism that obtains energy by oxidizing inorganic substances and needs only carbon dioxide as a carbon source.

chemoheterotroph (kē′-mō-het′-er-ō-trōf) An organism that requires organic molecules for both energy and carbon.

chemoreceptor A sensory receptor that responds to a chemical stimulus, such as a solute or an odorant.

chiasma (plural, **chiasmata**) (kī-az′-muh, kī-az′-muh-tuh) The X-shaped, microscopically visible region where crossing over has occurred earlier in prophase I between homologous nonsister chromatids. Chiasmata become visible after synapsis ends, with the two homologues remaining associated due to sister chromatid cohesion.

chitin (kī′-tin) A structural polysaccharide, consisting of amino sugar monomers, found in many fungal cell walls and in the exoskeletons of all arthropods.

chlorophyll (klōr′-ō-fil) A green pigment located in membranes within the chloroplasts of plants and algae and in the membranes of certain prokaryotes. Chlorophyll *a* participates directly in the light reactions, which convert solar energy to chemical energy.

chlorophyll *a* A photosynthetic pigment that participates directly in the light reactions, which convert solar energy to chemical energy.

chlorophyll *b* An accessory photosynthetic pigment that transfers energy to chlorophyll *a*.

chloroplast (klōr′-ō-plast) An organelle found in plants and photosynthetic protists that absorbs sunlight and uses it to drive the synthesis of organic compounds from carbon dioxide and water.

choanocyte (kō-an′-uh-sīt) A flagellated feeding cell found in sponges. Also called a collar cell, it has a collar-like ring that traps food particles around the base of its flagellum.

cholesterol (kō-les′-tuh-rol) A steroid that forms an essential component of animal cell membranes and acts as a precursor molecule for the synthesis of other biologically important steroids, such as many hormones.

chondrichthyan (kon-drik′-thē-an) Member of the class Chondrichthyes, vertebrates with skeletons made mostly of cartilage, such as sharks and rays.

chondrocyte A connective tissue cell that comprises cartilage.

chordate Member of the phylum Chordata, animals that at some point during their development have a notochord; a dorsal, hollow nerve cord; pharyngeal slits or clefts; and a muscular, post-anal tail.

chorionic villus sampling (CVS) (kōr′-ē-on′-ik vil′-us) A technique associated with prenatal diagnosis in which a small sample of the fetal portion of the placenta is removed for analysis to detect certain genetic and congenital defects in the fetus.

chromatin (krō′-muh-tin) The complex of DNA and proteins that makes up eukaryotic chromosomes. When the cell is not dividing, chromatin exists in its dispersed form, as a mass of very long, thin fibres that are not visible with a light microscope.

chromosome (krō′-muh-sōm) A cellular structure carrying genetic material, found in the nucleus of eukaryotic cells. Each chromosome consists of one very long DNA molecule and associated proteins. (A bacterial chromosome usually consists of a single circular DNA molecule and associated proteins. It is found in the nucleoid region, which is not membrane bounded.) *See also* chromatin.

chromosome theory of inheritance A basic principle in biology stating that genes are located at specific positions (loci) on chromosomes and that the behaviour of chromosomes during meiosis accounts for inheritance patterns.

chylomicron (kī′-lō-mī′-kron) A lipid transport globule composed of fats mixed with cholesterol and coated with proteins.

chyme (kīm) The mixture of partially digested food and digestive juices formed in the stomach.

chytrid (kī′-trid) Member of the fungal phylum Chytridiomycota, mostly aquatic fungi with flagellated zoospores that represent an early-diverging fungal lineage.

ciliate (sil′-ē-it) A type of protist that moves by means of cilia.

cilium (sil′-ē-um) (plural, **cilia**) A short appendage containing microtubules in eukaryotic cells. A motile cilium is specialized for locomotion or moving fluid past the cell; it is formed from a core of nine outer doublet microtubules and two inner single microtubules (the "9 + 2" arrangement) ensheathed in an extension of the plasma membrane. A primary cilium is usually nonmotile and plays a sensory and signalling role; it lacks the two inner microtubules (the "9 + 0" arrangement).

circadian rhythm (ser-kā′-dē-un) A physiological cycle of about 24 hours that persists even in the absence of external cues.

cis-trans **isomer** One of several compounds that have the same molecular formula and covalent bonds between atoms but differ in the spatial arrangements of their atoms owing to the inflexibility of double bonds; formerly called a geometric isomer.

citric acid cycle A chemical cycle involving eight steps that completes the metabolic breakdown of glucose molecules begun in glycolysis by oxidizing acetyl CoA (derived from pyruvate) to carbon dioxide; occurs within the mitochondrion in eukaryotic cells and in the cytosol of prokaryotes; together with pyruvate oxidation, the second major stage in cellular respiration.

clade (klayd) A group of species that includes an ancestral species and all of its descendants.

cladistics (kluh-dis′-tiks) An approach to systematics in which organisms are placed into groups called clades based primarily on common descent.

cladogram A branching diagram that is used to show phylogenetic relationships among organisms.

class In Linnaean classification, the taxonomic category above the level of order.

cleavage (1) The process of cytokinesis in animal cells, characterized by pinching of the plasma membrane. (2) The succession of rapid cell divisions without significant growth during early embryonic development that converts the zygote to a ball of cells.

cleavage furrow The first sign of cleavage in an animal cell; a shallow groove around the cell in the cell surface near the old metaphase plate.

climate The long-term prevailing weather conditions at a given place.

climate change Increase in temperature and change in weather patterns all around the planet, due mostly to increasing atmospheric CO_2 levels from the burning of fossil fuels. The increase in temperature, called global warming, is a major aspect of global climate change.

clitoris (klit′-uh-ris) An organ at the upper intersection of the labia minora that engorges with blood and becomes erect during sexual arousal.

cloaca (klō-ā′-kuh) A common opening for the digestive, urinary, and reproductive tracts found in many nonmammalian vertebrates but in few mammals.

clonal selection The process by which an antigen selectively binds to and activates only those lymphocytes bearing receptors specific for the antigen. The selected lymphocytes proliferate and differentiate into a clone of effector cells and a clone of memory cells specific for the stimulating antigen.

clone (1) A lineage of genetically identical individuals or cells. (2) In popular usage, an individual that is genetically identical to another individual. (3) As a verb, to make one or more genetic replicas of an individual or cell. *See also* gene cloning.

cloning vector In genetic engineering, a DNA molecule that can carry foreign DNA into a host cell and replicate there. Cloning vectors include plasmids and bacterial artificial chromosomes (BACs), which move recombinant DNA from a test tube back into a cell, and viruses that transfer recombinant DNA by infection.

closed circulatory system A circulatory system in which blood is confined to vessels and is kept separate from the interstitial fluid.

cnidocyte (nī′-duh-sīt) A specialized cell unique to the phylum Cnidaria; contains a capsule-like organelle housing a coiled thread that, when discharged, explodes outward and functions in prey capture or defence.

cochlea (kok′-lē-uh) The complex, coiled organ of hearing that contains the organ of Corti.

codominance The situation in which the phenotypes of both alleles are exhibited in the heterozygote because both alleles affect the phenotype in separate, distinguishable ways.

codon (kō′-don) A three-nucleotide sequence of DNA or mRNA that specifies a particular amino acid or termination signal; the basic unit of the genetic code.

coefficient of relatedness The fraction of genes that, on average, are shared by two individuals.

coelom (sē′-lōm) A body cavity lined by tissue derived only from mesoderm.

coelomate (sē′-lō-māt) An animal that possesses a true coelom (a body cavity lined by tissue completely derived from mesoderm).

coenocytic fungus (sē′-no-si′-tic) A fungus that lacks septa and hence whose body is made up of a continuous cytoplasmic mass that may contain hundreds or thousands of nuclei.

coenzyme (kō-en′-zīm) An organic molecule serving as a cofactor. Most vitamins function as coenzymes in metabolic reactions.

coevolution The joint evolution of two interacting species, each in response to selection imposed by the other.

cofactor Any nonprotein molecule or ion that is required for the proper functioning of an enzyme. Cofactors can be permanently bound to the active site or may bind loosely and reversibly, along with the substrate, during catalysis.

cognition The process of knowing that may include awareness, reasoning, recollection, and judgment.

cognitive map A neural representation of the abstract spatial relationships between objects in an animal's surroundings.

cohesion The linking together of like molecules, often by hydrogen bonds.

cohesion-tension hypothesis The leading explanation of the ascent of xylem sap. It states that transpiration exerts pull on xylem sap, putting the sap under negative pressure or tension, and that the cohesion of water molecules transmits this pull along the entire length of the xylem from shoots to roots.

cohort A group of individuals of the same age in a population.

coitus (kō′-uh-tus) The insertion of a penis into a vagina; also called sexual intercourse.

coleoptile (kō′-lē-op′-tul) The covering of the young shoot of the embryo of a grass seed.

coleorhiza (kō′-lē-uh-rī′-zuh) The covering of the young root of the embryo of a grass seed.

collagen A glycoprotein in the extracellular matrix of animal cells that forms strong fibres, found extensively in connective tissue and bone; the most abundant protein in the animal kingdom.

collecting duct The location in the kidney where processed filtrate, called urine, is collected from the renal tubules.

collenchyma cell (kō-len′-kim-uh) A flexible plant cell type that occurs in strands or cylinders that support young parts of the plant without restraining growth.

colon (kō′-len) The largest section of the vertebrate large intestine; functions in water absorption and formation of feces.

commensalism (kuh-men′-suh-lizm) A symbiotic relationship in which one organism benefits but the other is neither helped nor harmed.

communication In animal behaviour, a process involving transmission of, reception of, and response to signals. The term is also used in connection with other organisms, as well as individual cells of multicellular organisms.

community All the organisms that inhabit a particular area; an assemblage of populations of different species living close enough together for potential interaction.

community ecology The study of how interactions between species affect community structure and organization.

companion cell A type of plant cell that is connected to a sieve-tube element by many plasmodesmata and whose nucleus and ribosomes may serve one or more adjacent sieve-tube elements.

competitive exclusion The concept that when populations of two similar species compete for the same limited resources, one population will use the resources more efficiently and have a reproductive advantage that will eventually lead to the elimination of the other population.

competitive inhibitor A substance that reduces the activity of an enzyme by entering the active site in place of the substrate, whose structure it mimics.

complement system A group of about 30 blood proteins that may amplify the inflammatory response, enhance phagocytosis, or directly lyse extracellular pathogens.

complementary DNA (cDNA) A double-stranded DNA molecule made *in vitro* using mRNA as a template and the enzymes reverse transcriptase and DNA polymerase. A cDNA molecule corresponds to the exons of a gene.

complete dominance The situation in which the phenotypes of the heterozygote and dominant homozygote are indistinguishable.

complete flower A flower that has all four basic floral organs: sepals, petals, stamens, and carpels.

complete metamorphosis The transformation of a larva into an adult that looks very different, and often functions very differently in its environment, than the larva.

compound A substance consisting of two or more different elements combined in a fixed ratio.

compound eye A type of multifaceted eye in insects and crustaceans consisting of up to several thousand light-detecting, focusing ommatidia.

concentration gradient A region along which the density of a chemical substance increases or decreases.

conception The fertilization of an egg by a sperm in humans.

condom A thin, latex rubber or natural membrane sheath that fits over the penis to collect semen.

conduction The direct transfer of thermal motion (heat) between molecules of objects in direct contact with each other.

cone A cone-shaped cell in the retina of the vertebrate eye, sensitive to colour.

conformer An animal for which an internal condition conforms to (changes in accordance with) changes in an environmental variable.

conidium (plural, **conidia**) A haploid spore produced at the tip of a specialized hypha in ascomycetes during asexual reproduction.

conifer Member of the largest gymnosperm phylum. Most conifers are cone-bearing trees, such as pines and firs.

conjugation (kon′-jū-gā′-shun) (1) In prokaryotes, the direct transfer of DNA between two cells that are temporarily joined. When the two cells are members of different species, conjugation results in horizontal gene transfer.

(2) In ciliates, a sexual process in which two cells exchange haploid micronuclei but do not reproduce.

connective tissue Animal tissue that functions mainly to bind and support other tissues, having a sparse population of cells scattered through an extracellular matrix.

conodont An early, soft-bodied vertebrate with prominent eyes and dental elements.

conservation biology The integrated study of ecology, evolutionary biology, physiology, molecular biology, and genetics to sustain biological diversity at all levels.

contraception The deliberate prevention of pregnancy.

contractile vacuole A membranous sac that helps move excess water out of certain freshwater protists.

control element A segment of noncoding DNA that helps regulate transcription of a gene by serving as a binding site for a transcription factor. Multiple control elements are present in a eukaryotic gene's enhancer.

controlled experiment An experiment in which an experimental group is compared with a control group that varies only in the factor being tested.

convection The mass movement of warmed air or liquid to or from the surface of a body or object.

convergent evolution The evolution of similar features in independent evolutionary lineages.

convergent extension A process in which the cells of a tissue layer rearrange themselves in such a way that the sheet of cells becomes narrower (converges) and longer (extends).

cooperativity A kind of allosteric regulation whereby a shape change in one subunit of a protein caused by substrate binding is transmitted to all the other subunits, facilitating binding of additional substrate molecules to those subunits.

copepod (cō′-puh-pod) Any of a group of small crustaceans that are important members of marine and freshwater plankton communities.

coral reef Typically a warm-water, tropical ecosystem dominated by the hard skeletal structures secreted primarily by corals. Some coral reefs also exist in cold, deep waters.

corepressor A small molecule that binds to a bacterial repressor protein and changes the protein's shape, allowing it to bind to the operator and switch an operon off.

cork cambium (kam′-bē-um) A cylinder of meristematic tissue in woody plants that replaces the epidermis with thicker, tougher cork cells.

corpus callosum (kor′-pus kuh-lō′-sum) The thick band of nerve fibres that connects the right and left cerebral hemispheres in mammals, enabling the hemispheres to process information together.

corpus luteum (kor′-pus lū′-tē-um) A secreting tissue in the ovary that forms from the collapsed follicle after ovulation and produces progesterone.

cortex (1) The outer region of cytoplasm in a eukaryotic cell, lying just under the plasma membrane, that has a more gel-like consistency than the inner regions due to the presence of multiple microfilaments. (2) In plants, ground tissue that is between the vascular tissue and dermal tissue in a root or eudicot stem.

cortical nephron In mammals and birds, a nephron with a loop of Henle located almost entirely in the renal cortex.

corticosteroid Any steroid hormone produced and secreted by the adrenal cortex.

cotransport The coupling of the "downhill" diffusion of one substance to the "uphill" transport of another against its own concentration gradient.

cotyledon (kot'-uh-lē'-dun) A seed leaf of an angiosperm embryo. Some species have one cotyledon, others two.

countercurrent exchange The exchange of a substance or heat between two fluids flowing in opposite directions. For example, blood in a fish gill flows in the opposite direction of water passing over the gill, maximizing diffusion of oxygen into and carbon dioxide out of the blood.

countercurrent multiplier system A countercurrent system in which energy is expended in active transport to facilitate exchange of materials and generate concentration gradients.

covalent bond (kō-vā'-lent) A type of strong chemical bond in which two atoms share one or more pairs of valence electrons.

crassulacean acid metabolism (CAM) An adaptation for photosynthesis in arid conditions, first discovered in the family Crassulaceae. In this process, a plant takes up CO_2 and incorporates it into a variety of organic acids at night; during the day, CO_2 is released from organic acids for use in the Calvin cycle.

crista (plural, **cristae**) (kris'-tuh, kris'-tē) An infolding of the inner membrane of a mitochondrion. The inner membrane houses electron transport chains and molecules of the enzyme catalyzing the synthesis of ATP (ATP synthase).

critical load The amount of added nutrient, usually nitrogen or phosphorus, that can be absorbed by plants without damaging ecosystem integrity.

crop rotation The practice of planting nonlegumes one year and legumes in alternating years to restore concentrations of fixed nitrogen in the soil.

cross-fostering study A behavioural study in which the young of one species are placed in the care of adults from another species.

crossing over The reciprocal exchange of genetic material between nonsister chromatids during prophase I of meiosis.

cross-pollination In angiosperms, the transfer of pollen from an anther of a flower on one plant to the stigma of a flower on another plant of the same species.

cryptic colouration Camouflage that makes a potential prey difficult to spot against its background.

culture A system of information transfer through social learning or teaching that influences the behaviour of individuals in a population.

cuticle (kyū'-tuh-kul) (1) A waxy covering on the surface of stems and leaves that prevents desiccation in terrestrial plants. (2) The exoskeleton of an arthropod, consisting of layers of protein and chitin that are variously modified for different functions. (3) A tough coat that covers the body of a nematode.

cyclic AMP (cAMP) Cyclic adenosine monophosphate, a ring-shaped molecule made from ATP that is a common intracellular signalling molecule (second messenger) in eukaryotic cells. It is also a regulator of some bacterial operons.

cyclic electron flow A route of electron flow during the light reactions of photosynthesis that involves only photosystem I and that produces ATP but not NADPH or O_2.

cyclin (sī'-klin) A cellular protein that occurs in a cyclically fluctuating concentration and that plays an important role in regulating the cell cycle.

cyclin-dependent kinase (Cdk) A protein kinase that is active only when attached to a particular cyclin.

cyclostome Member of the vertebrate subgroup lacking jaws. Cyclostomes include hagfishes and lampreys.

cystic fibrosis (sis'-tik fī-brō'-sis) A human genetic disorder caused by a recessive allele for a chloride channel protein; characterized by an excessive secretion of mucus and consequent vulnerability to infection; fatal if untreated.

cytochrome (sī'-tō-krōm) An iron-containing protein that is a component of electron transport chains in the mitochondria and chloroplasts of eukaryotic cells and the plasma membranes of prokaryotic cells.

cytokine (sī'-tō-kīn') Any of a group of small proteins secreted by a number of cell types, including macrophages and helper T cells, that regulate the function of other cells.

cytokinesis (sī'-tō-kuh-nē'-sis) The division of the cytoplasm to form two separate daughter cells immediately after mitosis, meiosis I, or meiosis II.

cytokinin (sī'-tō-kī'-nin) Any of a class of related plant hormones that retard aging and act in concert with auxin to stimulate cell division, influence the pathway of differentiation, and control apical dominance.

cytoplasm (sī'-tō-plaz'-um) The contents of the cell bounded by the plasma membrane; in eukaryotes, the portion exclusive of the nucleus.

cytoplasmic determinant A maternal substance, such as a protein or RNA, that when placed into an egg influences the course of early development by regulating the expression of genes that affect the developmental fate of cells.

cytoplasmic streaming A circular flow of cytoplasm, involving interactions of myosin and actin filaments, that speeds the distribution of materials within cells.

cytoskeleton A network of microtubules, microfilaments, and intermediate filaments that extend throughout the cytoplasm and serve a variety of mechanical, transport, and signalling functions.

cytosol (sī'-tō-sol) The semifluid portion of the cytoplasm.

cytotoxic T cell A type of lymphocyte that, when activated, kills infected cells as well as certain cancer cells and transplanted cells.

dalton A measure of mass for atoms and subatomic particles; the same as the atomic mass unit, or amu.

data Recorded observations.

day-neutral plant A plant in which flower formation is not controlled by photoperiod or day length.

decapod A member of the group of crustaceans that includes lobsters, crayfishes, crabs, and shrimps.

decomposer An organism that absorbs nutrients from nonliving organic material such as corpses, fallen plant material, and the wastes of living organisms and converts them to inorganic forms; a detritivore.

deductive reasoning A type of logic in which specific results are predicted from a general premise.

deep-sea hydrothermal vent A dark, hot, oxygen-deficient environment associated with volcanic activity on or near the seafloor. The producers in a vent community are chemoautotrophic prokaryotes.

de-etiolation The changes a plant shoot undergoes in response to sunlight; also known informally as greening.

dehydration reaction A chemical reaction in which two molecules become covalently bonded to each other with the removal of a water molecule.

deletion (1) A deficiency in a chromosome resulting from the loss of a fragment through breakage. (2) A mutational loss of one or more nucleotide pairs from a gene.

demographic transition In a stable population, a shift from high birth and death rates to low birth and death rates.

demography The study of changes over time in the vital statistics of populations, especially birth rates and death rates.

denaturation (dē-nā'-chur-ā'-shun) In proteins, a process in which a protein loses its native shape due to the disruption of weak chemical bonds and interactions, thereby becoming biologically inactive; in DNA, the separation of the two strands of the double helix. Denaturation occurs under extreme (noncellular) conditions of pH, salt concentration, or temperature.

dendrite (den'-drīt) One of usually numerous, short, highly branched extensions of a neuron that receive signals from other neurons.

dendritic cell An antigen-presenting cell, located mainly in lymphatic tissues and skin, that is particularly efficient in presenting antigens to helper T cells, thereby initiating a primary immune response.

density The number of individuals per unit area or volume.

density dependent Referring to any characteristic that varies with population density.

density-dependent inhibition The phenomenon observed in normal animal cells that causes them to stop dividing when they come into contact with one another.

density independent Referring to any characteristic that is not affected by population density.

deoxyribonucleic acid see DNA.

deoxyribose (dē-ok′-sē-rī′-bōs) The sugar component of DNA nucleotides, having one fewer hydroxyl group than ribose, the sugar component of RNA nucleotides.

dependent variable A variable whose value is measured during an experiment or other test to see whether it is influenced by changes in another variable (the independent variable).

depolarization A change in a cell's membrane potential such that the inside of the membrane is made less negative relative to the outside. For example, a neuron membrane is depolarized if a stimulus decreases its voltage from the resting potential of 70 mV in the direction of zero voltage.

dermal tissue system The outer protective covering of plants.

desert A terrestrial biome characterized by very low precipitation.

desmosome A type of intercellular junction in animal cells that functions as a rivet, fastening cells together.

determinate cleavage A type of embryonic development in protostomes that rigidly casts the developmental fate of each embryonic cell very early.

determinate growth A type of growth characteristic of most animals and some plant organs, in which growth stops after a certain size is reached.

determination The progressive restriction of developmental potential in which the possible fate of each cell becomes more limited as an embryo develops. At the end of determination, a cell is committed to its fate.

detritivore (deh-trī′-tuh-vōr) A consumer that derives its energy and nutrients from nonliving organic material such as corpses, fallen plant material, and the wastes of living organisms; a decomposer.

detritus (di-trī′-tus) Dead organic matter.

deuterostome development (dū′-tuh-rō-stōm′) In animals, a developmental mode distinguished by the development of the anus from the blastopore; often also characterized by radial cleavage and by the body cavity forming as outpockets of mesodermal tissue.

Deuterostomia (dū·-tuh-rō-stōm′-ē-uh) One of the three main lineages of bilaterian animals. *See also* Ecdysozoa and Lophotrochozoa.

development The events involved in an organism's changing gradually from a simple to a more complex or specialized form.

diabetes mellitus (dī′-uh-bē′-tis mel′-uh-tus) An endocrine disorder marked by an inability to maintain glucose homeostasis. The type 1 form results from autoimmune destruction of insulin-secreting cells; treatment usually requires daily insulin injections. The type 2 form most commonly results from reduced responsiveness of target cells to insulin; obesity and lack of exercise are risk factors.

diacylglycerol (DAG) (dī-a′-sil-glis′-er-ol) A second messenger produced by the cleavage of the phospholipid PIP_2 in the plasma membrane.

diaphragm (dī′-uh-fram′) (1) A sheet of muscle that forms the bottom wall of the thoracic cavity in mammals. Contraction of the diaphragm pulls air into the lungs. (2) A dome-shaped rubber cup fitted into the upper portion of the vagina before sexual intercourse. It serves as a physical barrier to the passage of sperm into the uterus.

diapsid (dī-ap′-sid) Member of an amniote clade distinguished by a pair of holes on each side of the skull. Diapsids include the lepidosaurs and archosaurs.

diastole (dī-as′-tō-lē) The stage of the cardiac cycle in which a heart chamber is relaxed and fills with blood.

diastolic pressure Blood pressure in the arteries when the ventricles are relaxed.

diatom A unicellular or colonial algae with a silicon-rich cell wall.

dicot A term traditionally used to refer to flowering plants that have two embryonic seed leaves, or cotyledons. Recent molecular evidence indicates that dicots do not form a clade; species once classified as dicots are now grouped into eudicots, magnoliids, and several lineages of basal angiosperms.

differential gene expression The expression of different sets of genes by cells with the same genome.

differentiation The process by which a cell or group of cells become specialized in structure and function.

diffusion The spontaneous movement of a substance down its concentration or electrochemical gradient, from a region where it is more concentrated to a region where it is less concentrated.

digestion The second stage of food processing in animals: the breaking down of food into molecules small enough for the body to absorb.

dihybrid (dī′-hī′-brid) An organism that is heterozygous with respect to two genes of interest. All the offspring from a cross between parents doubly homozygous for different alleles are dihybrids. For example, parents of genotypes *AABB* and *aabb* produce a dihybrid of genotype *AaBb*.

dihybrid cross A cross between two organisms that are each heterozygous for both of the characters being followed (or the self-pollination of a plant that is heterozygous for both characters).

dikaryotic (dī′-kār-ē-ot′-ik) Referring to a fungal mycelium with two haploid nuclei per cell, one from each parent.

dinoflagellate (dī′-nō-flaj′-uh-let) Member of a group of mostly unicellular photosynthetic algae with two flagella situated in perpendicular grooves in cellulose plates covering the cell.

dinosaur Member of an extremely diverse clade of reptiles varying in body shape, size, and habitat. Birds are the only extant dinosaurs.

dioecious (dī-ē′-shus) In plant biology, having the male and female reproductive parts on different individuals of the same species.

diploblastic Having two germ layers.

diploid cell (dip′-loyd) A cell containing two sets of chromosomes (2*n*), one set inherited from each parent.

diplomonad A protist that has modified mitochondria, two equal-sized nuclei, and multiple flagella.

directional selection Natural selection in which individuals at one end of the phenotypic range survive or reproduce more successfully than do other individuals.

disaccharide (dī-sak′-uh-rīd) A double sugar, consisting of two monosaccharides joined by a glycosidic linkage formed by a dehydration reaction.

dispersal The movement of individuals or gametes away from their parent location. This movement sometimes expands the geographic range of a population or species.

dispersion The pattern of spacing among individuals within the boundaries of a population.

disruptive selection Natural selection in which individuals on both extremes of a phenotypic range survive or reproduce more successfully than do individuals with intermediate phenotypes.

distal tubule In the vertebrate kidney, the portion of a nephron that helps refine filtrate and empties it into a collecting duct.

disturbance A natural or human-caused event that changes a biological community and usually removes organisms from it. Disturbances, such as fires and storms, play a pivotal role in structuring many communities.

disulphide bridge A strong covalent bond formed when the sulphur of one cysteine monomer bonds to the sulphur of another cysteine monomer.

DNA (deoxyribonucleic acid) (dē-ok′-sē-rī′-bō-nū-klā′-ik) A double-stranded, helical nucleic acid molecule, consisting of nucleotide monomers with a deoxyribose sugar and the nitrogenous bases adenine (A), cytosine (C), guanine (G), and thymine (T); capable of being replicated and determining the inherited structure of a cell's proteins.

DNA cloning Several molecular biology techniques that are used to produce many copies of a DNA sequence or specific gene of interest.

DNA ligase (lī′-gās) A linking enzyme essential for DNA replication; catalyzes the covalent bonding of the 3′ end of one DNA fragment (such as an Okazaki fragment) to the 5′ end of another DNA fragment (such as a growing DNA chain).

DNA methylation The presence of methyl groups on the DNA bases (usually cytosine) of plants, animals, and fungi. (The term also refers to the process of adding methyl groups to DNA bases.)

DNA microarray assay A method to detect and measure the expression of thousands of genes at one time. Tiny amounts of a large number of single-stranded DNA fragments representing different genes are fixed to a glass slide and tested for hybridization with samples of labelled cDNA.

DNA polymerase (puh-lim′-er-ās) An enzyme that catalyzes the elongation of new DNA (for example, at a replication fork) by the addition of nucleotides to the 3′ end of an existing chain. There are several different DNA polymerases; DNA polymerase III and DNA polymerase I play major roles in DNA replication in *E. coli*.

DNA replication The process by which a DNA molecule is copied; also called DNA synthesis.

DNA sequencing Several techniques that are used to identify the nucleotide sequence of a gene or segment of DNA.

DNA synthesis *See* DNA replication.

DNA technology: Techniques for sequencing and manipulating DNA.

domain (1) A taxonomic category above the kingdom level. The three domains are Archaea, Bacteria, and Eukarya. (2) A discrete structural and functional region of a protein.

dominant allele An allele that is fully expressed in the phenotype of a heterozygote.

dominant species A species with substantially higher abundance or biomass than other species in a community. Dominant species exert a powerful control over the occurrence and distribution of other species.

dopamine A neurotransmitter that is a catecholamine, like epinephrine and norepinephrine.

dormancy A condition typified by extremely low metabolic rate and a suspension of growth and development.

dorsal Pertaining to the top of an animal with radial or bilateral symmetry.

dorsal lip The region above the blastopore on the dorsal side of the amphibian embryo.

double bond A double covalent bond; the sharing of two pairs of valence electrons by two atoms.

double circulation A circulatory system consisting of separate pulmonary and systemic circuits, in which blood passes through the heart after completing each circuit.

double fertilization A mechanism of fertilization in angiosperms in which two sperm cells unite with two cells in the female gametophyte (embryo sac) to form the zygote and endosperm.

double helix The form of native DNA, referring to its two adjacent antiparallel polynucleotide strands wound around an imaginary axis into a spiral shape.

Down syndrome A human genetic disease usually caused by the presence of an extra chromosome 21; characterized by developmental delays and heart and other defects that are generally treatable or non-life-threatening.

Duchenne muscular dystrophy (duh-shen′) A human genetic disease caused by a sex-linked recessive allele; characterized by progressive weakening and a loss of muscle tissue.

duodenum (dū′-uh-dēn′-um) The first section of the small intestine, where chyme from the stomach mixes with digestive juices from the pancreas, liver, and gallbladder as well as from gland cells of the intestinal wall.

duplication An aberration in chromosome structure due to fusion with a fragment from a homologous chromosome, such that a portion of a chromosome is duplicated.

dynein (dī′-nē-un) In cilia and flagella, a large motor protein extending from one microtubule doublet to the adjacent doublet. ATP hydrolysis drives changes in dynein shape that lead to bending of cilia and flagella.

E site One of a ribosome's three binding sites for tRNA during translation. The E site is the place where discharged tRNAs leave the ribosome. (E stands for exit.)

Ecdysozoa (ek′-dē-sō-zō′-uh) One of the three main lineages of bilaterian animals; many ecdysozoans are moulting animals. *See also* Deuterostomia and Lophotrochozoa.

ecdysteroid A steroid hormone, secreted by the prothoracic glands, that triggers moulting in arthropods.

echinoderm (i-kī′-nō-derm) A slow-moving or sessile marine deuterostome with a water vascular system and, in larvae, bilateral symmetry. Echinoderms include sea stars, brittle stars, sea urchins, feather stars, and sea cucumbers.

ecological footprint The aggregate land and water area required by a person, city, or nation to produce all of the resources it consumes and to absorb all of the wastes it generates.

ecological niche (nich) The sum of a species' use of the biotic and abiotic resources in its environment.

ecological species concept A definition of species in terms of ecological niche, the sum of how members of the species interact with the nonliving and living parts of their environment.

ecological succession Transition in the species composition of a community following a disturbance; establishment of a community in an area virtually barren of life.

ecology The study of how organisms interact with each other and their environment.

ecosystem All the organisms in a given area as well as the abiotic factors with which they interact; one or more communities and the physical environment around them.

ecosystem ecology The study of energy flow and the cycling of chemicals among the various biotic and abiotic components in an ecosystem.

ecosystem engineer An organism that influences community structure by causing physical changes in the environment.

ecosystem service A function performed by an ecosystem that directly or indirectly benefits humans.

ecotone The transition from one type of habitat or ecosystem to another, such as the transition from a forest to a grassland.

ectoderm (ek′-tō-durm) The outermost of the three primary germ layers in animal embryos; gives rise to the outer covering and, in some phyla, the nervous system, inner ear, and lens of the eye.

ectomycorrhiza (ek′-tō-mī′-kō-rī′-zuh) Association of a fungus with a plant root system in which the fungus surrounds the roots but does not cause invagination of the host (plant) cells' plasma membranes.

ectomycorrhizal fungus A symbiotic fungus that forms sheaths of hyphae over the surface of plant roots and also grows into extracellular spaces of the root cortex.

ectoparasite A parasite that feeds on the external surface of a host.

ectopic Occurring in an abnormal location.

ectoproct A sessile, colonial lophophorate; also called a bryozoan.

ectotherm An animal that utilizes an ectothermic strategy to determine body temperature.

ectothermic The thermal strategy whereby body temperature is determined primarily by the external environment.

Ediacaran biota (ē′-dē-uh-keh′-run bī-ō′-tuh) An early group of soft-bodied, multicellular eukaryotes known from fossils that range in age from 565 million to 550 million years old.

effective population size An estimate of the size of a population based on the numbers of females and males that successfully breed; generally smaller than the total population.

effector Pathogen-encoded protein that cripples the host's innate immune system.

effector cell (1) A muscle cell or gland cell that performs the body's response to stimuli as directed by signals from the brain or other processing centre of the nervous system. (2) A lymphocyte that has undergone clonal selection and is capable of mediating an adaptive immune response.

egg The female gamete.

egg-polarity gene A gene that helps control the orientation (polarity) of the egg; also called a maternal effect gene.

ejaculation The propulsion of sperm from the epididymis through the muscular vas deferens, ejaculatory duct, and urethra.

ejaculatory duct In mammals, the short section of the ejaculatory route formed by the convergence of the vas deferens and a duct from the seminal vesicle. The ejaculatory duct transports sperm from the vas deferens to the urethra.

electrocardiogram (ECG or EKG) A record of the electrical impulses that travel through heart muscle during the cardiac cycle.

electrochemical gradient The diffusion gradient of an ion, which is affected by both the concentration difference of an ion across a membrane (a chemical force) and the ion's tendency to move relative to the membrane potential (an electrical force).

electrogenic pump An active transport protein that generates voltage across a membrane while pumping ions.

electromagnetic receptor A receptor of electromagnetic energy, such as visible light, electricity, or magnetism.

electromagnetic spectrum The entire spectrum of electromagnetic radiation, ranging in wavelength from less than a nanometre to more than a kilometre.

electron A subatomic particle with a single negative electrical charge and a mass about 1/2000 that of a neutron or proton. One or more electrons move around the nucleus of an atom.

electron microscope (EM) A microscope that uses magnets to focus an electron beam on or through a specimen, resulting in a practical resolution of a hundredfold greater than that of a light microscope using standard techniques. A transmission electron microscope (TEM) is used to study the internal structure of thin sections of cells. A scanning electron microscope (SEM) is used to study the fine details of cell surfaces.

electron shell An energy level of electrons at a characteristic average distance from the nucleus of an atom.

electron transport chain A sequence of electron carrier molecules (membrane proteins) that shuttle electrons down a series of redox reactions that release energy used to make ATP.

electronegativity The attraction of a given atom for the electrons of a covalent bond.

electroporation A technique to introduce recombinant DNA into cells by applying a brief electrical pulse to a solution containing the cells. The pulse creates temporary holes in the cells' plasma membranes, through which DNA can enter.

element Any substance that cannot be broken down to any other substance by chemical reactions.

elimination The fourth and final stage of food processing in animals: the passing of undigested material out of the body.

embryo sac (em′-brē-ō) The female gametophyte of angiosperms, formed from the growth and division of the megaspore into a multicellular structure that typically has eight haploid nuclei.

embryonic lethal A mutation with a phenotype leading to death of an embryo or larva.

embryophyte Alternate name for land plants that refers to their shared derived trait of multicellular, dependent embryos.

emergent properties New properties that arise with each step upward in the hierarchy of life, owing to the arrangement and interactions of parts as complexity increases.

emigration The movement of individuals out of a population.

enantiomer (en-an′-tē-ō-mer) One of two compounds that are mirror images of each other and that differ in shape due to the presence of an asymmetric carbon.

endangered species A species that is in danger of extinction throughout all or a significant portion of its range.

endemic (en-dem′-ik) Referring to a species that is confined to a specific geographic area.

endergonic reaction (en′-der-gon′-ik) A nonspontaneous chemical reaction, in which free energy is absorbed from the surroundings.

endocrine gland (en′-dō-krin) A ductless gland that secretes hormones directly into the

interstitial fluid, from which they diffuse into the bloodstream.

endocrine system The internal system of communication involving hormones, the ductless glands that secrete hormones, and the molecular receptors on or in target cells that respond to hormones; functions in concert with the nervous system to effect internal regulation and maintain homeostasis.

endocytosis (en′-dō-sī-tō′-sis) Cellular uptake of biological molecules and particulate matter via formation of vesicles from the plasma membrane.

endoderm (en′-dō-durm) The innermost of the three primary germ layers in animal embryos; lines the archenteron and gives rise to the liver, pancreas, lungs, and the lining of the digestive tract in species that have these structures.

endodermis In plant roots, the innermost layer of the cortex that surrounds the vascular cylinder.

endomembrane system The collection of membranes inside and surrounding a eukaryotic cell, related either through direct physical contact or by the transfer of membranous vesicles; includes the plasma membrane, the nuclear envelope, the smooth and rough endoplasmic reticulum, the Golgi apparatus, lysosomes, vesicles, and vacuoles.

endometriosis (en′-dō-mē-trē-ō′-sis) The condition resulting from the presence of endometrial tissue outside of the uterus.

endometrium (en′-dō-mē′-trē-um) The inner lining of the uterus, which is richly supplied with blood vessels.

endoparasite A parasite that lives within a host.

endophyte A fungus that lives inside a leaf or other plant part without causing harm to the plant.

endoplasmic reticulum (ER) (en′-dō-plaz′-mik ruh-tik′-yū-lum) An extensive membranous network in eukaryotic cells, continuous with the outer nuclear membrane and composed of ribosome-studded (rough) and ribosome-free (smooth) regions.

endorphin (en-dōr′-fin) Any of several hormones produced in the brain and anterior pituitary that inhibit pain perception.

endoskeleton A hard skeleton buried within the soft tissues of an animal.

endosperm In angiosperms, a nutrient-rich tissue formed by the union of a sperm with two polar nuclei during double fertilization. The endosperm provides nourishment to the developing embryo in angiosperm seeds.

endospore A thick-coated, resistant cell produced by some bacterial cells when they are exposed to harsh conditions.

endosymbiont theory The theory that mitochondria and plastids, including chloroplasts, originated as prokaryotic cells engulfed by an ancestral eukaryotic cell. The engulfed cell and its host cell then evolved into a single organism.

endothelium (en′-dō-thē′-lē-um) The simple squamous layer of cells lining the lumen of blood vessels.

endotherm An animal that utilizes an endothermic strategy to determine body temperature.

endothermic The thermal strategy whereby body temperature is warmed by heat generated by their own metabolism. This heat usually maintains a relatively stable body temperature higher than that of the external environment.

endotoxin A toxic component of the outer membrane of certain gram-negative bacteria that is released only when the bacteria die.

energetic hypothesis The concept that the length of a food chain is limited by the inefficiency of energy transfer along the chain.

energy The capacity to cause change, especially to do work (to move matter against an opposing force).

energy coupling In cellular metabolism, the use of energy released from an exergonic reaction to drive an endergonic reaction.

enhancer A segment of eukaryotic DNA containing multiple control elements, usually located far from the gene whose transcription it regulates.

enteric division One of three divisions of the autonomic nervous system; consists of networks of neurons in the digestive tract, pancreas, and gallbladder; normally regulated by the sympathetic and parasympathetic divisions of the autonomic nervous system.

entropy A measure of disorder, or randomness.

enzyme (en′-zīm) A macromolecule serving as a catalyst, a chemical agent that increases the rate of a reaction without being consumed by the reaction. Most enzymes are proteins.

enzyme-substrate complex A temporary complex formed when an enzyme binds to its substrate molecule(s).

eosinophil A type of white blood cell that contains granules.

epicotyl (ep′-uh-kot′-ul) In an angiosperm embryo, the embryonic axis above the point of attachment of the cotyledon(s) and below the first pair of miniature leaves.

epidemic A general outbreak of a disease.

epidermis (1) The dermal tissue system of nonwoody plants, usually consisting of a single layer of tightly packed cells. (2) The outermost layer of cells in an animal.

epididymis (ep′-uh-did′-uh-mus) A coiled tubule located adjacent to the mammalian testis where sperm are stored.

epigenetic inheritance Inheritance of traits transmitted by mechanisms not directly involving the nucleotide sequence of a genome.

epinephrine (ep′-i-nef′-rin) A catecholamine that, when secreted as a hormone by the adrenal medulla, mediates "fight-or-flight" responses to short-term stresses; also released by some neurons as a neurotransmitter; also known as adrenaline.

epiphyte (ep′-uh-fīt) A plant that nourishes itself but grows on the surface of another plant for support, usually on the branches or trunks of trees.

epistasis (ep′-i-stā′-sis) A type of gene interaction in which the phenotypic expression of one gene alters that of another independently inherited gene.

epithelial tissue (ep′-uh-thē′-lē-ul) Sheets of tightly packed cells that line organs and body cavities as well as external surfaces.

epithelium An epithelial tissue.

epitope A small, accessible region of an antigen to which an antigen receptor or antibody binds; also called an antigenic determinant.

EPSP *See* excitatory postsynaptic potential.

equilibrium potential (E$_{ion}$) The magnitude of a cell's membrane voltage at equilibrium; calculated using the Nernst equation.

erythrocyte (eh-rith′-ruh-sīt) A blood cell that contains hemoglobin, which transports oxygen; also called a red blood cell.

erythropoietin (EPO) (eh-rith′-rō-poy′-uh-tin) A hormone that stimulates the production of erythrocytes. It is secreted by the kidney when body tissues do not receive enough oxygen.

esophagus (eh-sof′-uh-gus) A muscular tube that conducts food, by peristalsis, from the pharynx to the stomach.

essential amino acid An amino acid that an animal cannot synthesize itself and must be obtained from food in prefabricated form.

essential element A chemical element required for an organism to survive, grow, and reproduce.

essential fatty acid An unsaturated fatty acid that an animal needs but cannot make.

essential nutrient A substance that an organism cannot synthesize from any other material and therefore must absorb in preassembled form.

estradiol (es′-truh-dī′-ol) A steroid hormone that stimulates the development and maintenance of the female reproductive system and secondary sex characteristics; the major estrogen in mammals.

estrogen (es′-trō-jen) Any steroid hormone, such as estradiol, that stimulates the development and maintenance of the female reproductive system and secondary sex characteristics.

estrous cycle (es′-trus) A reproductive cycle characteristic of female mammals except humans and certain other primates, in which the non-pregnant endometrium is reabsorbed rather than shed, and sexual response occurs only during mid-cycle at estrus.

estuary The area where a freshwater stream or river merges with the ocean.

ethylene (eth′-uh-lēn) A gaseous plant hormone involved in responses to mechanical stress, programmed cell death, leaf abscission, and fruit ripening.

etiolation Plant morphological adaptations for growing in darkness.

euchromatin (yū-krō′-muh-tin) The less condensed form of eukaryotic chromatin that is available for transcription.

eudicot (yū-dī′-kot) Member of a clade that contains the vast majority of flowering plants that have two embryonic seed leaves, or cotyledons.

euglenid (yū′-glen-id) A protist, such as *Euglena* or its relatives, characterized by an anterior pocket from which one or two flagella emerge.

euglenozoan Member of a diverse clade of flagellated protists that includes predatory heterotrophs, photosynthetic autotrophs, and pathogenic parasites.

Eukarya (yū-kar′-ē-uh) The domain that includes all eukaryotic organisms.

eukaryotic cell (yū′-ker-ē-ot′-ik) A type of cell with a membrane-enclosed nucleus and membrane-enclosed organelles. Organisms with eukaryotic cells (protists, plants, fungi, and animals) are called eukaryotes.

eumetazoan (yū′-met-uh-zō′-un) Member of a clade of animals with true tissues. All animals except sponges and a few other groups are eumetazoans.

eurypterid (yur-ip′-tuh-rid) An extinct carnivorous chelicerate; also called a water scorpion.

Eustachian tube (yū-stā′-shun) The tube that connects the middle ear to the pharynx.

eutherian (yū-thēr′-ē-un) Placental mammal; mammal whose young complete their embryonic development within the uterus, joined to the mother by the placenta.

eutrophication A process by which nutrients, particularly phosphorus and nitrogen, become highly concentrated in a body of water, leading to increased growth of organisms such as algae or cyanobacteria.

evaporation The process by which a liquid changes to a gas.

evaporative cooling The process in which the surface of an object becomes cooler during evaporation, a result of the molecules with the greatest kinetic energy changing from the liquid to the gaseous state.

evapotranspiration The total evaporation of water from an ecosystem, including water transpired by plants and evaporated from a landscape, usually measured in millimetres and estimated for a year.

evo-devo Evolutionary developmental biology; a field of biology that compares developmental processes of different multicellular organisms to understand how these processes have evolved and how changes can modify existing organismal features or lead to new ones.

evolution Descent with modification; the idea that living species are descendants of ancestral species that were different from the present-day ones; also defined more narrowly as the change in the genetic composition of a population from generation to generation.

evolutionary tree A branching diagram that reflects a hypothesis about evolutionary relationships among groups of organisms.

Excavata One of five supergroups of eukaryotes proposed in a current hypothesis of the evolutionary history of eukaryotes. Excavates have unique cytoskeletal features, and some species have an "excavated" feeding groove on one side of the cell body. *See also* Chromalveolata, Rhizaria, Archaeplastida, and Unikonta.

excitatory postsynaptic potential (EPSP) An electrical change (depolarization) in the membrane of a postsynaptic cell caused by the binding of an excitatory neurotransmitter from a presynaptic cell to a postsynaptic receptor; makes it more likely for a postsynaptic cell to generate an action potential.

excretion The disposal of nitrogen-containing metabolites and other waste products.

exergonic reaction (ek′-ser-gon′-ik) A spontaneous chemical reaction, in which there is a net release of free energy.

exocytosis (ek′-sō-sī-tō′-sis) The cellular secretion of biological molecules by the fusion of vesicles containing them with the plasma membrane.

exon A sequence within a primary transcript that remains in the RNA after RNA processing; also refers to the region of DNA from which this sequence was transcribed.

exoskeleton A hard encasement on the surface of an animal, such as the shell of a mollusc or the cuticle of an arthropod, that provides protection and points of attachment for muscles.

exotoxin (ek′-sō-tok′-sin) A toxic protein that is secreted by a prokaryote or other pathogen and that produces specific symptoms, even if the pathogen is no longer present.

expansin Plant enzyme that breaks the cross-links (hydrogen bonds) between cellulose microfibrils and other cell wall constituents, loosening the wall's fabric.

experiment A scientific test, carried out under controlled conditions, involving manipulation of one or more factors in a system in order to see the effects of those changes.

exponential population growth Growth of a population in an ideal, unlimited environment, represented by a J-shaped curve when population size is plotted over time.

expression vector A cloning vector that contains a highly active bacterial promoter just upstream of a restriction site where a eukaryotic gene can be inserted, allowing the gene to be expressed in a bacterial cell. Expression vectors are also available that have been genetically engineered for use in specific types of eukaryotic cells.

external fertilization The fusion of gametes that parents have discharged into the environment.

extinct Refers to a species that is no longer found alive and has "died out."

extinction vortex A downward population spiral in which inbreeding and genetic drift combine to cause a small population to shrink and, unless the spiral is reversed, become extinct.

extirpation The local extinction of a species in a certain geographical area.

extracellular matrix (ECM) The meshwork surrounding animal cells, consisting of glycoproteins, polysaccharides, and proteoglycans synthesized and secreted by the cells.

extraembryonic membrane One of four membranes (yolk sac, amnion, chorion, and allantois) located outside the embryo that support the developing embryo in reptiles and mammals.

extreme halophile An organism that lives in a highly saline environment, such as the Great Salt Lake or the Dead Sea.

extreme thermophile An organism that thrives in hot environments (often 60–80°C or hotter).

extremophile An organism that lives in environmental conditions so extreme that few other species can survive there. Extremophiles include extreme halophiles ("salt lovers") and extreme thermophiles ("heat lovers").

F factor In bacteria, the DNA segment that confers the ability to form pili for conjugation and associated functions required for the transfer of DNA from donor to recipient. The F factor may exist as a plasmid or be integrated into the bacterial chromosome.

F plasmid The plasmid form of the F factor.

F₁ generation The first filial, hybrid (heterozygous) offspring arising from a parental (P generation) cross.

F₂ generation The offspring resulting from interbreeding (or self-pollination) of the hybrid F₁ generation.

facilitated diffusion The passage of molecules or ions down their electrochemical gradient across a biological membrane with the assistance of specific transmembrane transport proteins, requiring no energy expenditure.

facilitation An interaction in which one species has a positive effect on the survival and reproduction of another species without the intimate association of a symbiosis.

facultative anaerobe (fak'-ul-tā'-tiv an'-uh-rōb) An organism that makes ATP by aerobic respiration if oxygen is present but that switches to anaerobic respiration or fermentation if oxygen is not present.

family In Linnaean classification, the taxonomic category above genus.

fast block to polyspermy The depolarization of the egg plasma membrane that begins within 1–3 seconds after a sperm binds to an egg membrane protein. The depolarization lasts about 1 minute and prevents additional sperm from fusing with the egg during that time.

fast-twitch fibre A muscle fibre used for rapid, powerful contractions.

fat A lipid consisting of three fatty acids linked to one glycerol molecule; also called a triacylglycerol or triglyceride.

fate map A territorial diagram of embryonic development that displays the future derivatives of individual cells and tissues.

fatty acid A carboxylic acid with a long carbon chain. Fatty acids vary in length and in the number and location of double bonds; three fatty acids linked to a glycerol molecule form a fat molecule, also known as a triacylglycerol or triglyceride.

feces (fē'-sēz) The wastes of the digestive tract.

feedback inhibition A method of metabolic control in which the end product of a metabolic pathway acts as an inhibitor of an enzyme within that pathway.

feedback regulation The regulation of a process by its output or end product.

fermentation A catabolic process that makes a limited amount of ATP from glucose (or other organic molecules) without an electron transport chain and that produces a characteristic end product, such as ethyl alcohol or lactic acid.

fertilization (1) The union of haploid gametes to produce a diploid zygote. (2) The addition of mineral nutrients to the soil.

fetus (fē'-tus) A developing mammal that has all the major structures of an adult. In humans, the fetal stage lasts from the 9th week of gestation until birth.

fibre A lignified cell type that reinforces the xylem of angiosperms and functions in mechanical support; a slender, tapered sclerenchyma cell that usually occurs in bundles.

fibroblast (fī'-brō-blast) A type of cell in loose connective tissue that secretes the protein ingredients of the extracellular fibres.

fibronectin An extracellular glycoprotein secreted by animal cells that helps them attach to the extracellular matrix.

filament In an angiosperm, the stalk portion of the stamen, the pollen-producing reproductive organ of a flower.

filter feeder *See* suspension feeder.

filtrate Cell-free fluid extracted from the body fluid by the excretory system.

filtration In excretory systems, the extraction of water and small solutes, including metabolic wastes, from the body fluid.

fimbria (plural, **fimbriae**) A short, hairlike appendage of a prokaryotic cell that helps it adhere to the substrate or to other cells.

first law of thermodynamics The principle of conservation of energy: Energy can be transferred and transformed, but it cannot be created or destroyed.

fission The separation of an organism into two or more individuals of approximately equal size.

fixed action pattern In animal behaviour, a sequence of unlearned acts that is essentially unchangeable and, once initiated, usually carried to completion.

flaccid (flas'-id) Limp. Lacking turgor (stiffness or firmness), as in a plant cell in surroundings where there is a tendency for water to leave the cell. (A walled cell becomes flaccid if it has a higher water potential than its surroundings, resulting in the loss of water.)

flagellum (fluh-jel'-um) (plural, **flagella**) A long cellular appendage specialized for locomotion. Like motile cilia, eukaryotic flagella have a core with nine outer doublet microtubules and two inner single microtubules (the "9 + 2" arrangement) ensheathed in an extension of the plasma membrane. Prokaryotic flagella have a different structure.

florigen A flowering signal, probably a protein, that is made in leaves under certain conditions and that travels to the shoot apical meristems, inducing them to switch from vegetative to reproductive growth.

flower In an angiosperm, a specialized shoot with up to four sets of modified leaves, bearing structures that function in sexual reproduction.

fluid feeder An animal that lives by sucking nutrient-rich fluids from another living organism.

fluid mosaic model The currently accepted model of cell membrane structure, which envisions the membrane as a mosaic of protein molecules drifting laterally in a fluid bilayer of phospholipids.

follicle (fol'-uh-kul) A microscopic structure in the ovary that contains the developing oocyte and secretes estrogens.

follicular phase That part of the ovarian cycle during which follicles are growing and oocytes maturing.

food chain The pathway along which food energy is transferred from trophic level to trophic level, beginning with producers.

food vacuole A membranous sac formed by phagocytosis of microorganisms or particles to be used as food by the cell.

food web The interconnected feeding relationships in an ecosystem.

foot (1) The portion of a bryophyte sporophyte that gathers sugars, amino acids, water, and minerals from the parent gametophyte via transfer cells. (2) One of the three main parts of a mollusc; a muscular structure usually used for movement. *See also* mantle, visceral mass.

foraging The seeking and obtaining of food.

foram (foraminiferan) An aquatic protist that secretes a hardened shell containing calcium carbonate and extends pseudopodia through pores in the shell.

forebrain One of three ancestral and embryonic regions of the vertebrate brain; develops into the thalamus, hypothalamus, and cerebrum.

fossil A preserved remnant or impression of an organism that lived in the past.

founder effect Genetic drift that occurs when a few individuals become isolated from a larger population and form a new population whose gene pool composition is not reflective of that of the original population.

fovea (fō'-vē-uh) The place on the retina at the eye's centre of focus, where cones are highly concentrated.

fragmentation A means of asexual reproduction whereby a single parent breaks into parts that regenerate into whole new individuals.

frameshift mutation A mutation occurring when nucleotides are inserted in or deleted from a gene and the number inserted or deleted is not a multiple of three, resulting in the improper grouping of the subsequent nucleotides into codons.

free energy The portion of a biological system's energy that can perform work when temperature and pressure are uniform throughout the system. The change in free energy of a system $\Delta(\Delta G)$ is calculated by the equation $\Delta G = \Delta H - T\Delta S$, where ΔH is the change in enthalpy (in biological systems, equivalent to total energy), T is the absolute temperature, and ΔS is the change in entropy.

frequency-dependent selection Selection in which the fitness of a phenotype depends on how common the phenotype is in a population.

fruit A mature ovary of a flower. The fruit protects dormant seeds and often aids in their dispersal.

functional group A specific configuration of atoms commonly attached to the carbon skeletons of organic molecules and involved in chemical reactions.

fundamental niche The ecological space occupied by a species when there are not any competitors in that species' habitat.

fungus (fungi) A eukaryotic lineage of organisms that get their nutrients through absorption and usually possess a filamentous body.

G protein A GTP-binding protein that relays signals from a plasma membrane signal receptor, known as a G protein-coupled receptor, to other signal transduction proteins inside the cell.

G protein-coupled receptor (GPCR) A signal receptor protein in the plasma membrane that responds to the binding of a signalling molecule by activating a G protein. Also called a G protein-linked receptor.

G_0 phase A nondividing state occupied by cells that have left the cell cycle, sometimes reversibly.

G_1 phase The first gap, or growth phase, of the cell cycle, consisting of the portion of interphase before DNA synthesis begins.

G_2 phase The second gap, or growth phase, of the cell cycle, consisting of the portion of interphase after DNA synthesis occurs.

gallbladder An organ that stores bile and releases it as needed into the small intestine.

game theory An approach to evaluating alternative strategies in situations where the outcome of a particular strategy depends on the strategies used by other individuals.

gametangium (gam′-uh-tan′-jē-um) (plural, **gametangia**) Multicellular plant structure in which gametes are formed. Female gametangia are called archegonia, and male gametangia are called antheridia.

gamete (gam′-ēt) A haploid reproductive cell, such as an egg or sperm. Gametes unite during sexual reproduction to produce a diploid zygote.

gametogenesis The process by which gametes are produced.

gametophore (guh-mē′-tō-fōr) The mature gamete-producing structure of a moss gametophyte.

gametophyte (guh-mē′-tō-fīt) In organisms (plants and some algae) that have alternation of generations, the multicellular haploid form that produces haploid gametes by mitosis. The haploid gametes unite and develop into sporophytes.

gamma-aminobutyric acid (GABA) An amino acid that functions as a CNS neurotransmitter in the central nervous system of vertebrates.

ganglia (gang′-glē-uh) (singular, **ganglion**) Clusters (functional groups) of nerve cell bodies in a centralized nervous system.

gap junction A type of intercellular junction in animal cells, consisting of proteins surrounding a pore that allows the passage of materials between cells.

gas exchange The uptake of molecular oxygen from the environment and the discharge of carbon dioxide to the environment.

gastric juice A digestive fluid secreted by the stomach.

gastrovascular cavity A central cavity with a single opening in the body of certain animals, including cnidarians and flatworms, that functions in both the digestion and distribution of nutrients.

gastrula (gas′-trū-luh) An embryonic stage in animal development encompassing the formation of three layers: ectoderm, mesoderm, and endoderm.

gastrulation (gas′-trū-lā′-shun) In animal development, a series of cell and tissue movements in which the blastula-stage embryo folds inward, producing a three-layered embryo, the gastrula.

gated channel A transmembrane protein channel that opens or closes in response to a particular stimulus.

gated ion channel A gated channel for a specific ion. The opening or closing of such channels may alter a cell's membrane potential.

gel electrophoresis (ē-lek′-trō-fōr-ē′-sis) A technique for separating nucleic acids or proteins on the basis of their size and electrical charge, both of which affect their rate of movement through an electric field in a gel made of agarose or another polymer.

gene A discrete unit of hereditary information consisting of a specific nucleotide sequence in DNA (or RNA, in some viruses).

gene annotation Analysis of genomic sequences to identify protein-coding genes and determine the function of their products.

gene cloning The production of multiple copies of a gene.

gene expression The process by which information encoded in DNA directs the synthesis of proteins or, in some cases, RNAs that are not translated into proteins and instead function as RNAs.

gene flow The transfer of alleles from one population to another, resulting from the movement of fertile individuals or their gametes.

gene pool The aggregate of all copies of every type of allele at all loci in every individual in a population. The term is also used in a more restricted sense as the aggregate of alleles for just one or a few loci in a population.

gene therapy The introduction of genes into an afflicted individual for therapeutic purposes.

genetically modified (GM) organism An organism that has acquired one or more genes by artificial means; also known as a transgenic organism.

genetic drift A process in which chance events cause unpredictable fluctuations in allele frequencies from one generation to the next. Effects of genetic drift are most pronounced in small populations.

genetic engineering The direct manipulation of genes for practical purposes.

genetic map An ordered list of genetic loci (genes or other genetic markers) along a chromosome.

genetic profile An individual's unique set of genetic markers, detected most often today by PCR or, previously, by electrophoresis and nucleic acid probes.

genetic recombination General term for the production of offspring with combinations of traits that differ from those found in either parent.

genetics The scientific study of heredity and hereditary variation.

genetic variation Differences among individuals in the composition of their genes or other DNA segments.

genome (jē′-nōm) The genetic material of an organism or virus; the complete complement of an organism's or virus's genes along with its noncoding nucleic acid sequences.

genome-wide association study A large-scale analysis of the genomes of many people having a certain phenotype or disease, with the aim of finding genetic markers that correlate with that phenotype or disease.

genomic imprinting A phenomenon in which expression of an allele in offspring depends on whether the allele is inherited from the male or female parent.

genomics (juh-nō′-miks) The study of whole sets of genes and their interactions within a species, as well as genome comparisons between species.

genotype (jē′-nō-tīp) The genetic makeup, or set of alleles, of an organism.

genus (jē′-nus) (plural, **genera**) A taxonomic category above the species level, designated by the first word of a species' two-part scientific name.

geologic record The division of Earth's history into time periods, grouped into three eons—Archaean, Proterozoic, and Phanerozoic—and further subdivided into eras, periods, and epochs.

germ layer One of the three main layers in a gastrula that will form the various tissues and organs of an animal body.

gestation (jes-tā′-shun) Pregnancy; the state of carrying developing young within the female reproductive tract.

gibberellin (jib′-uh-rel′-in) Any of a class of related plant hormones that stimulate growth in the stem and leaves, trigger the germination of seeds and breaking of bud dormancy, and (with auxin) stimulate fruit development.

glans The rounded structure at the tip of the clitoris or penis that is involved in sexual arousal.

glia (glial cells) Cells of the nervous system that support, regulate, and augment the functions of neurons.

global ecology The study of the functioning and distribution of organisms across the biosphere and how the regional exchange of energy and materials affects them.

glomeromycete (glō′-mer-ō-mī′-sēt) Member of the fungal phylum Glomeromycota, characterized by a distinct branching form of mycorrhizae called arbuscular mycorrhizae.

glomerulus (glō-mār′-yū-lus) A ball of capillaries surrounded by Bowman's capsule in the nephron and serving as the site of filtration in the vertebrate kidney.

glucagon (glū′-kuh-gon) A hormone secreted by pancreatic alpha cells that raises blood glucose levels. It promotes glycogen breakdown and release of glucose by the liver.

glucocorticoid A steroid hormone that is secreted by the adrenal cortex and that influences glucose metabolism and immune function.

glutamate An amino acid that functions as a neurotransmitter in the central nervous system.

glyceraldehyde 3-phosphate (G3P) (glis′-er-al′-de-hīd) A three-carbon carbohydrate that is the direct product of the Calvin cycle; it is also an intermediate in glycolysis.

glycogen (glī′-kō-jen) An extensively branched glucose storage polysaccharide found in the liver and muscle of animals; the animal equivalent of starch.

glycolipid A lipid with one or more covalently attached carbohydrates.

glycolysis (glī-kol′-uh-sis) A series of reactions that ultimately splits glucose into pyruvate. Glycolysis occurs in almost all living cells, serving as the starting point for fermentation or cellular respiration.

glycoprotein A protein with one or more covalently attached carbohydrates.

glycosidic linkage A covalent bond formed between two monosaccharides by a dehydration reaction.

gnathostome (na′-thu-stōm) Member of the vertebrate subgroup possessing jaws.

golden alga A biflagellated, photosynthetic protist named for its colour, which results from its yellow and brown carotenoids.

Golgi apparatus (gol′-jē) An organelle in eukaryotic cells consisting of stacks of flat membranous sacs that modify, store, and route products of the endoplasmic reticulum and synthesize some products, notably noncellulose carbohydrates.

gonads (gō′-nadz) The male and female sex organs; the gamete-producing organs in most animals.

grade A group of organisms that share the same level of organizational complexity or share a key adaptation.

graded potential In a neuron, a shift in the membrane potential that has an amplitude proportional to signal strength and that decays as it spreads.

Gram stain A staining method that distinguishes between two different kinds of bacterial cell walls; may be used to help determine medical response to an infection.

gram-negative Describing the group of bacteria that have a cell wall that is structurally more complex and contains less peptidoglycan than the cell wall of gram-positive bacteria. Gram-negative bacteria are often more toxic than gram-positive bacteria.

gram-positive Describing the group of bacteria that have a cell wall that is structurally less complex and contains more peptidoglycan than the cell wall of gram-negative bacteria.

Gram-positive bacteria are usually less toxic than gram-negative bacteria.

granum (gran′-um) (plural, **grana**) A stack of membrane-bounded thylakoids in the chloroplast. Grana function in the light reactions of photosynthesis.

gravitropism (grav′-uh-trō′-pizm) A response of a plant or animal to gravity.

green alga A photosynthetic protist, named for green chloroplasts that are similar in structure and pigment composition to those of land plants. Green algae are a paraphyletic group, some of whose members are more closely related to land plants than they are to other green algae.

grey matter Regions of dendrites and clustered neuron cell bodies within the CNS.

gross primary production (GPP) The total primary production of an ecosystem.

ground tissue system Plant tissues that are neither vascular nor dermal, fulfilling a variety of functions, such as storage, photosynthesis, and support.

growth An irreversible increase in size or biomass.

growth factor (1) A protein that must be present in the extracellular environment (culture medium or animal body) for the growth and normal development of certain types of cells. (2) A local regulator that acts on nearby cells to stimulate cell proliferation and differentiation.

growth hormone (GH) A hormone that is produced and secreted by the anterior pituitary and that has both direct (nontropic) and tropic effects on a wide variety of tissues.

guard cells The two cells that flank the stomatal pore and regulate the opening and closing of the pore.

gustation The sense of taste.

guttation The exudation of water droplets from leaves, caused by root pressure in certain plants.

gymnosperm (jim′-nō-sperm) A vascular plant that bears naked seeds—seeds not enclosed in protective chambers.

hagfish Aquatic, jawless vertebrates in the class Myxini that have highly reduced vertebrae and a skull made of cartilage.

hair cell A mechanosensory cell that alters output to the nervous system when hairlike projections on the cell surface are displaced.

half-life The amount of time it takes for 50% of a sample of a radioactive isotope to decay.

Hamilton's rule The principle that for natural selection to favour an altruistic act, the benefit to the recipient, devalued by the coefficient of relatedness, must exceed the cost to the altruist.

haploid cell (hap′-loyd) A cell containing only one set of chromosomes (n).

Hardy-Weinberg equilibrium The state of a population in which frequencies of alleles and genotypes remain constant from generation to generation, provided that only Mendelian segregation and recombination of alleles are at work.

haustorium (plural, **haustoria**) (ho-stōr′-ē-um, ho-stōr′-ē-uh) In certain symbiotic fungi, a specialized hypha that can penetrate the tissues of host organisms.

heart A muscular pump that uses metabolic energy to elevate the hydrostatic pressure of the circulatory fluid (blood or hemolymph). The fluid then flows down a pressure gradient through the body and eventually returns to the heart.

heart attack The damage or death of cardiac muscle tissue resulting from prolonged blockage of one or more coronary arteries.

heart murmur A hissing sound that most often results from blood squirting backward through a leaky valve in the heart.

heart rate The frequency of heart contraction (in beats per minute).

heat The total amount of kinetic energy due to the random motion of atoms or molecules in a body of matter; also called thermal energy. Heat is energy in its most random form.

heat of vaporization The quantity of heat a liquid must absorb for 1 g of it to be converted from the liquid to the gaseous state.

heat-shock protein A protein that helps protect other proteins during heat stress. Heat-shock proteins are found in plants, animals, and microorganisms.

heavy chain One of the two types of polypeptide chains that make up an antibody molecule and B cell receptor; consists of a variable region, which contributes to the antigen-binding site, and a constant region.

helicase An enzyme that untwists the double helix of DNA at replication forks, separating the two strands and making them available as template strands.

helper T cell A type of T cell that, when activated, secretes cytokines that promote the response of B cells (humoral response) and cytotoxic T cells (cell-mediated response) to antigens.

hemoglobin (hē′-mō-glō′-bin) An iron-containing protein in red blood cells that reversibly binds oxygen.

hemolymph (hē′-mō-limf′) In invertebrates with an open circulatory system, the body fluid that bathes tissues.

hemophilia (hē′-muh-fil′-ē-uh) A human genetic disease caused by a sex-linked recessive allele resulting in the absence of one or more blood-clotting proteins; characterized by excessive bleeding following injury.

hepatic portal vein A large vessel that conveys nutrient-laden blood from the small intestine to the liver, which regulates the blood's nutrient content.

herbivore (hur′-bi-vōr′) An animal that mainly eats plants or algae.

herbivory An interaction in which an organism eats parts of a plant or alga.

heredity The transmission of traits from one generation to the next.

hermaphrodite (hur-maf′-ruh-dīt′) An individual that functions as both male and female in sexual reproduction by producing both sperm and eggs.

hermaphroditism (hur-maf′-rō-dī-tizm) A condition in which an individual has both female and male gonads and functions as both a male and female in sexual reproduction by producing both sperm and eggs.

heterochromatin (het′-er-ō-krō′-muh-tin) Eukaryotic chromatin that remains highly compacted during interphase and is generally not transcribed.

heterochrony (het′-uh-rok′-ruh-nē) Evolutionary change in the timing or rate of an organism's development.

heterocyst (het′-er-ō-sist) A specialized cell that engages in nitrogen fixation in some filamentous cyanobacteria; also called a *heterocyte*.

heterokaryon (het′-er-ō-kār′-ē-un) A fungal mycelium that contains two or more haploid nuclei per cell.

heteromorphic (het′-er-ō-mōr′-fik) Referring to a condition in the life cycle of plants and certain algae in which the sporophyte and gametophyte generations differ in morphology.

heterosporous (het-er-os′-pōr-us) Referring to a plant species that has two kinds of spores: microspores, which develop into male gametophytes, and megaspores, which develop into female gametophytes.

heterotroph (het′-er-ō-trōf) An organism that obtains organic food molecules by eating other organisms or substances derived from them.

heterozygote advantage Greater reproductive success of heterozygous individuals compared with homozygotes; tends to preserve variation in a gene pool.

heterozygous (het′-er-ō-zī′-gus) Having two different alleles for a given gene.

hexapod An insect or closely related wingless, six-legged arthropod.

hibernation A long-term physiological state in which metabolism decreases, the heart and respiratory system slow down, and body temperature is maintained at a lower level than normal.

high-density lipoprotein (HDL) A particle in the blood made up of thousands of cholesterol molecules and other lipids bound to a protein. HDL scavenges excess cholesterol.

hindbrain One of three ancestral and embryonic regions of the vertebrate brain; develops into the medulla oblongata, pons, and cerebellum.

histamine (his′-tuh-mēn) A substance released by mast cells that causes blood vessels to dilate and become more permeable in inflammatory and allergic responses.

histone (his′-tōn) A small protein with a high proportion of positively charged amino acids that binds to the negatively charged DNA and plays a key role in chromatin structure.

histone acetylation The attachment of acetyl groups to certain amino acids of histone proteins.

HIV (human immunodeficiency virus) The infectious agent that causes AIDS. HIV is a retrovirus.

holdfast A rootlike structure that anchors a seaweed.

holoblastic (hō′-lō-blas′-tik) Referring to a type of cleavage in which there is complete division of the egg; occurs in eggs that have little yolk

(such as those of the sea urchin) or a moderate amount of yolk (such as those of the frog).

homeobox (hō′-mē-ō-boks′) A 180-nucleotide sequence within homeotic genes and some other developmental genes that is widely conserved in animals. Related sequences occur in plants and yeasts.

homeostasis (hō′-mē-ō-stā′-sis) The steady-state physiological condition of the body.

homeotic gene (hō-mē-o′-tik) Any of the master regulatory genes that control placement and spatial organization of body parts in animals, plants, and fungi by controlling the developmental fate of groups of cells.

hominin (hō′-mi-nin) A member of the human branch of the evolutionary tree. Hominins include *Homo sapiens* and our ancestors, a group of extinct species that are more closely related to us than to chimpanzees.

homologous chromosomes (hō-mol′-uh-gus) A pair of chromosomes of the same length, centromere position, and staining pattern that possess genes for the same characters at corresponding loci. One homologous chromosome is inherited from the organism's father, the other from the mother. Also called homologues, or a homologous pair.

homologous structures Structures in different species that are similar because of common ancestry.

homology (hō-mol′-ō-jē) Similarity in characteristics resulting from a shared ancestry.

homoplasy (hō′-muh-play′-zē) A similar (analogous) structure or molecular sequence that has evolved independently in two species.

homosporous (hō-mos′-puh-rus) Referring to a plant species that has a single kind of spore, which typically develops into a bisexual gametophyte.

homozygous (hō′-mō-zī′-gus) Having two identical alleles for a given gene.

horizontal gene transfer The transfer of genes from one genome to another through mechanisms such as transposable elements, plasmid exchange, viral activity, and perhaps fusions of different organisms.

hormone In multicellular organisms, one of many types of secreted chemicals that are formed in specialized cells, travel in body fluids, and act on specific target cells in other parts of the body, changing the target cells' functioning. Hormones are thus important in long-distance signalling.

hornwort A small, herbaceous, nonvascular plant that is a member of the phylum Anthocerophyta.

host The larger participant in a symbiotic relationship, often providing a home and food source for the smaller symbiont.

host range The limited number of species whose cells can be infected by a particular virus.

human chorionic gonadotropin (hCG) (kōr′-ē-on′-ik gō-na′-dō-trō′-pin) A hormone secreted by the chorion that maintains the corpus luteum of the ovary during the first three months of pregnancy.

Human Genome Project An international collaborative effort to map and sequence the DNA of the entire human genome.

humoral immune response (hyū′-mer-ul) The branch of adaptive immunity that involves the activation of B cells and that leads to the production of antibodies, which defend against bacteria and viruses in body fluids.

humus (hyū′-mus) Decomposing organic material that is a component of topsoil.

Huntington's disease A human genetic disease caused by a dominant allele; characterized by uncontrollable body movements and degeneration of the nervous system; usually fatal 10 to 20 years after the onset of symptoms.

hybrid Offspring that results from the mating of individuals from two different species or from two true-breeding varieties of the same species.

hybridization In genetics, the mating, or crossing, of two true-breeding varieties.

hybrid zone A geographic region in which members of different species meet and mate, producing at least some offspring of mixed ancestry.

hydration shell The sphere of water molecules around a dissolved ion.

hydraulic failure A condition in which xylem sap can no longer flow because of cavitations and air bubble formation within xylem elements due to drought stress.

hydrocarbon An organic molecule consisting only of carbon and hydrogen.

hydrogen bond A type of weak chemical bond that is formed when the slightly positive hydrogen atom of a polar covalent bond in one molecule is attracted to the slightly negative atom of a polar covalent bond in another molecule or in another region of the same molecule.

hydrogen ion A single proton with a charge of 1+. The dissociation of a water molecule (H_2O) leads to the generation of a hydroxide ion (OH^-) and a hydrogen ion (H^+); in water, H^+ is not found alone but associates with a water molecule to form a hydronium ion.

hydrolysis (hī-drol′-uh-sis) A chemical reaction that breaks bonds between two molecules by the addition of water; functions in disassembly of polymers to monomers.

hydronium ion A water molecule that has an extra proton bound to it; H_3O^+, commonly represented as H^+.

hydrophilic (hī′-drō-fil′-ik) Having an affinity for water.

hydrophobic (hī′-drō-fō′-bik) Having no affinity for water; tending to coalesce and form droplets in water.

hydrophobic interaction A type of weak chemical interaction caused when molecules that do not mix with water coalesce to exclude water.

hydroponic culture A method in which plants are grown in mineral solutions rather than in soil.

hydrostatic skeleton A skeletal system composed of fluid held under pressure in a closed body compartment; the main skeleton of most cnidarians, flatworms, nematodes, and annelids.

hydroxide ion A water molecule that has lost a proton; OH^-.

hydroxyl group (hī-drok′-sil) A chemical group consisting of an oxygen atom joined to a hydrogen atom. Molecules possessing this group are soluble in water and are called alcohols.

hymen A thin membrane that partly covers the vaginal opening in the human female. The hymen is ruptured by sexual intercourse or other vigorous activity.

hyperpolarization A change in a cell's membrane potential such that the inside of the membrane becomes more negative relative to the outside. Hyperpolarization reduces the chance that a neuron will transmit a nerve impulse.

hypersensitive response A plant's localized defence response to a pathogen, involving the death of cells around the site of infection.

hypertension A disorder in which blood pressure remains abnormally high.

hypertonic Referring to a solution that, when surrounding a cell, will cause the cell to lose water.

hypha (plural, **hyphae**) (hī′-fuh, hī′-fē) One of many connected filaments that collectively make up the mycelium of a fungus.

hypocotyl (hī′-puh-cot′-ul) In an angiosperm embryo, the embryonic axis below the point of attachment of the cotyledon(s) and above the radicle.

hypothalamus (hī′-pō-thal′-uh-mus) The ventral part of the vertebrate forebrain; functions in maintaining homeostasis, especially in coordinating the endocrine and nervous systems; secretes hormones of the posterior pituitary and releasing factors that regulate the anterior pituitary.

hypothesis (hī-poth′-uh-sis) A testable explanation for a set of observations based on the available data and guided by inductive reasoning. A hypothesis is narrower in scope than a theory.

hypotonic Referring to a solution that, when surrounding a cell, will cause the cell to take up water.

imbibition The physical adsorption of water onto the internal surfaces of structures.

immigration The influx of new individuals into a population from other areas.

immune system An animal body's system of defences against agents that cause disease.

immunization The process of generating a state of immunity by artificial means. In active immunization, also called vaccination, an inactive or weakened form of a pathogen is administered, inducing B and T cell responses and immunological memory. In passive immunization, antibodies specific for a particular microbe are administered, conferring immediate but temporary protection.

immunodeficiency A disorder in which the ability of an immune system to protect against pathogens is defective or absent.

immunoglobulin (Ig) (im′-yū-nō-glob′-yū-lin) Any of the class of proteins that function as antibodies. Immunoglobulins are divided into five major classes that differ in their distribution in the body and antigen disposal activities.

imprinting In animal behaviour, the formation at a specific stage in life of a long-lasting behavioural response to a specific individual or object. *See also* genomic imprinting.

inclusive fitness The total effect an individual has on proliferating its genes by producing its own offspring and by providing aid that enables other close relatives to increase production of their offspring.

incomplete dominance The situation in which the phenotype of heterozygotes is intermediate between the phenotypes of individuals homozygous for either allele.

incomplete flower A flower in which one or more of the four basic floral organs (sepals, petals, stamens, or carpels) are either absent or nonfunctional.

incomplete metamorphosis A type of development in certain insects, such as grasshoppers, in which the young (called nymphs) resemble adults but are smaller and have different body proportions. The nymph goes through a series of moults, each time looking more like an adult, until it reaches full size.

independent variable A variable whose value is manipulated or changed during an experiment or other test to reveal possible effects on another variable (the dependent variable).

indeterminate cleavage A type of embryonic development in deuterostomes in which each cell produced by early cleavage divisions retains the capacity to develop into a complete embryo.

indeterminate growth A type of growth characteristic of plants, in which the organism continues to grow as long as it lives.

induced fit Caused by entry of the substrate, the change in shape of the active site of an enzyme so that it binds more snugly to the substrate.

inducer A specific small molecule that binds to a bacterial repressor protein and changes the repressor's shape so that it cannot bind to an operator, thus switching an operon on.

induction The process in which one group of embryonic cells influences the development of another, usually by causing changes in gene expression.

inductive reasoning A type of logic in which generalizations are based on a large number of specific observations.

inflammatory response An innate immune defence triggered by physical injury or infection of tissue involving the release of substances that promote swelling, enhance the infiltration of white blood cells, and aid in tissue repair and destruction of invading pathogens.

inflorescence A group of flowers tightly clustered together.

ingestion The first stage of food processing in animals: the act of eating.

ingroup A species or group of species whose evolutionary relationships we seek to determine.

inhibin A hormone produced in the male and female gonads that functions in part by regulating the anterior pituitary by negative feedback.

inhibitory postsynaptic potential (IPSP) An electrical change (usually hyperpolarization) in the membrane of a postsynaptic neuron caused by the binding of an inhibitory neurotransmitter from a presynaptic cell to a postsynaptic receptor; makes it more difficult for a postsynaptic neuron to generate an action potential.

innate behaviour Animal behaviour that is developmentally fixed and under strong genetic control. Innate behaviour is exhibited in virtually the same form by all individuals in a population despite internal and external environmental differences during development and throughout their lifetimes.

innate immunity A form of defence common to all animals that is active immediately upon exposure to pathogens and that is the same whether or not the pathogen has been encountered previously.

inner cell mass An inner cluster of cells at one end of a mammalian blastocyst that subsequently develops into the embryo proper and some of the extraembryonic membranes.

inner ear One of three main regions of the vertebrate ear; includes the cochlea (which in turn contains the organ of Corti) and the semicircular canals.

inositol trisphosphate (IP₃) (in-ō′-suh-tol) A second messenger that functions as an intermediate between certain signalling molecules and a subsequent second messenger, Ca^{2+}, by causing a rise in cytoplasmic Ca^{2+} concentration.

inquiry The search for information and explanation, often focusing on specific questions.

insertion A mutation involving the addition of one or more nucleotide pairs to a gene.

***in situ* hybridization** A technique using nucleic acid hybridization with a labelled probe to detect the location of a specific mRNA in an intact organism.

insulin (in′-suh-lin) A hormone secreted by pancreatic beta cells that lowers blood glucose levels. It promotes the uptake of glucose by most body cells and the synthesis and storage of glycogen in the liver and also stimulates protein and fat synthesis.

integral protein A transmembrane protein with hydrophobic regions that extend into and often completely span the hydrophobic interior of the membrane and with hydrophilic regions in contact with the aqueous solution on one or both sides of the membrane (or lining the channel in the case of a channel protein).

integrin In animal cells, a transmembrane receptor protein with two subunits that interconnects the extracellular matrix and the cytoskeleton.

integument (in-teg′-yū-ment) Layer of sporophyte tissue that contributes to the structure of an ovule of a seed plant.

integumentary system The outer covering of a mammal's body, including skin, hair, and nails, claws, or hooves.

intercalated disk (in-ter′-kuh-lā′-ted) A specialized junction between cardiac muscle cells that provides direct electrical coupling between the cells.

interferon (in′-ter-fēr′-on) A protein that has antiviral or immune regulatory functions. Interferon-α and interferon-β, secreted by virus-infected cells, help nearby cells resist viral infection; interferon-γ, secreted by T cells, helps activate macrophages.

intermediate disturbance hypothesis The concept that moderate levels of disturbance can foster greater species diversity than low or high levels of disturbance.

intermediate filament A component of the cytoskeleton that includes filaments intermediate in size between microtubules and microfilaments.

internal fertilization The fusion of eggs and sperm within the female reproductive tract. The sperm are typically deposited in or near the tract.

interneuron An association neuron; a nerve cell within the central nervous system that forms synapses with sensory and/or motor neurons and integrates sensory input and motor output.

internode A segment of a plant stem between the points where leaves are attached.

interphase The period in the cell cycle when the cell is not dividing. During interphase, cellular metabolic activity is high, chromosomes and organelles are duplicated, and cell size may increase. Interphase often accounts for about 90% of the cell cycle.

intersexual selection Selection whereby individuals of one sex (usually females) are choosy in selecting their mates from individuals of the other sex; also called mate choice.

interspecific competition Competition for resources between individuals of two or more species when resources are in short supply.

interspecific interaction A relationship between individuals of two or more species in a community.

interstitial fluid The fluid filling the spaces between cells in most animals.

intertidal zone The shallow zone of the ocean adjacent to land and between the high- and low-tide lines.

intrasexual selection Selection in which there is direct competition among individuals of one sex for mates of the opposite sex.

introduced species A species moved by humans, either intentionally or accidentally, from its native location to a new geographic region; also called non-native or exotic species.

intron (in′-tron) A noncoding, intervening sequence within a primary transcript that is removed from the transcript during RNA processing; also refers to the region of DNA from which this sequence was transcribed.

invasive species A species, often introduced by humans, that takes hold outside its native range.

inversion An aberration in chromosome structure resulting from reattachment of a chromosomal fragment in a reverse orientation to the chromosome from which it originated.

invertebrate An animal without a backbone. Invertebrates make up 95% of animal species.

in vitro **fertilization (IVF)** (vē′-trō) Fertilization of oocytes in laboratory containers followed by artificial implantation of the early embryo in the mother's uterus.

in vitro **mutagenesis** A technique used to discover the function of a gene by cloning it, introducing specific changes into the cloned gene's sequence, reinserting the mutated gene into a cell, and studying the phenotype of the mutant.

ion (ī′-on) An atom or group of atoms that has gained or lost one or more electrons, thus acquiring a charge.

ion channel A transmembrane protein channel that allows a specific ion to diffuse across the membrane down its concentration or electrochemical gradient.

ionic bond (ī-on′-ik) A chemical bond resulting from the attraction between oppositely charged ions.

ionic compound A compound resulting from the formation of an ionic bond; also called a salt.

IPSP *See* inhibitory postsynaptic potential.

iris The coloured part of the vertebrate eye, formed by the anterior portion of the choroid.

isomer (ī′-sō-mer) One of several compounds with the same molecular formula but different structures and therefore different properties. The three types of isomers are structural isomers, *cis-trans* isomers, and enantiomers.

isomorphic Referring to alternating generations in plants and certain algae in which the sporophytes and gametophytes look alike, although they differ in chromosome number.

isopod A member of one of the largest groups of crustaceans, which includes terrestrial, freshwater, and marine species. Among the terrestrial isopods are the pill bugs, or wood lice.

isotonic (ī′-sō-ton′-ik) Referring to a solution that, when surrounding a cell, causes no net movement of water into or out of the cell.

isotope (ī′-sō-tōp′) One of several atomic forms of an element, each with the same number of protons but a different number of neutrons, thus differing in atomic mass.

iteroparity Reproduction in which adults produce offspring over many years; also known as repeated reproduction.

jasmonate Any of a class of plant hormones that regulate a wide range of developmental processes in plants and play a key role in plant defense against herbivores.

juxtaglomerular apparatus (JGA) (juks′-tuh-gluh-mār′-yū-ler) A specialized tissue in nephrons that releases the enzyme renin in response to a drop in blood pressure or volume.

juxtamedullary nephron In mammals and birds, a nephron with a loop of Henle that extends far into the renal medulla.

karyogamy (kār′-ē-og′-uh-mē) In fungi, the fusion of haploid nuclei contributed by the two parents; occurs as one stage of sexual reproduction, preceded by plasmogamy.

karyotype (kār′-ē-ō-tīp) A display of the chromosome pairs of a cell arranged by size and shape.

keystone species A species that is not necessarily abundant in a community yet exerts strong control on community structure by the nature of its ecological role or niche.

kidney In vertebrates, one of a pair of excretory organs where blood filtrate is formed and processed into urine.

kilocalorie (kcal) A thousand calories; the amount of heat energy required to raise the temperature of 1 kg of water by 1°C.

kin selection Natural selection that favours altruistic behaviour by enhancing the reproductive success of relatives.

kinetic energy (kuh-net′-ik) The energy associated with the relative motion of objects. Moving matter can perform work by imparting motion to other matter.

kinetochore (kuh-net′-uh-kōr) A structure of proteins attached to the centromere that links each sister chromatid to the mitotic spindle.

kinetoplastid A protist, such as a trypanosome, that has a single large mitochondrion that houses an organized mass of DNA.

*K***-selection** Selection for life history traits that are sensitive to population density; also called density-dependent selection.

labia majora A pair of thick, fatty ridges that encloses and protects the rest of the vulva.

labia minora A pair of slender skin folds that surrounds the openings of the vagina and urethra.

labour A series of strong, rhythmic contractions of the uterus that expels a baby out of the uterus and vagina during childbirth.

lactation The continued production of milk from the mammary glands.

lacteal (lak′-tē-ul) A tiny lymph vessel extending into the core of an intestinal villus and serving as the destination for absorbed chylomicrons.

lactic acid fermentation Glycolysis followed by the reduction of pyruvate to lactate, regenerating NAD⁺ with no release of carbon dioxide.

lagging strand A discontinuously synthesized DNA strand that elongates by means of Okazaki fragments, each synthesized in a $5' \rightarrow 3'$ direction away from the replication fork.

lamprey Aquatic, jawless vertebrates in the class Petromyzontida with vertebrae and skeleton made of cartilage.

lancelet Member of the clade Cephalochordata, small blade-shaped marine chordates that lack a backbone.

landscape An area containing several different ecosystems linked by exchanges of energy, materials, and organisms.

landscape ecology The study of how the spatial arrangement of habitat types affects the distribution and abundance of organisms and ecosystem processes.

large intestine The portion of the vertebrate alimentary canal between the small intestine and the anus; functions mainly in water absorption and the formation of feces.

larva (lar′-vuh) (plural, **larvae**) A free-living, sexually immature form in some animal life cycles that may differ from the adult animal in morphology, nutrition, and habitat.

larynx (lar′-inks) The portion of the respiratory tract containing the vocal cords; also called the voice box.

lateral geniculate nucleus One of a pair of structures in the brain that are the destination for most of the ganglion cell axons that form the optic nerves.

lateral inhibition A process that sharpens the edges and enhances the contrast of a perceived image by inhibiting receptors lateral to those that have responded to light.

lateral line system A mechanoreceptor system consisting of a series of pores and receptor units along the sides of the body in fishes and aquatic amphibians; detects water movements made by the animal itself and by other moving objects.

lateral meristem (mār′-uh-stem) A meristem that thickens the roots and shoots of woody plants. The vascular cambium and cork cambium are lateral meristems.

lateral root A root that arises from the pericycle of an established root.

law of conservation of mass A physical law stating that matter can change form but cannot be created or destroyed. In a closed system, the mass of the system is constant.

law of independent assortment Mendel's second law, stating that each pair of alleles segregates, or assorts, independently of each other pair during gamete formation; applies when genes for two characters are located on different pairs of homologous chromosomes or when they are far enough apart on the same chromosome to behave as though they are on different chromosomes.

law of segregation Mendel's first law, stating that the two alleles in a pair segregate (separate from each other) into different gametes during gamete formation.

leading strand The new complementary DNA strand synthesized continuously along the template strand toward the replication fork in the mandatory $5' \rightarrow 3'$ direction.

leaf The main photosynthetic organ of vascular plants.

leaf primordium A finger-like projection along the flank of a shoot apical meristem, from which a leaf arises.

learning The modification of behaviour based on specific experiences.

lens The structure in an eye that focuses light rays onto the photoreceptors.

lenticel (len′-ti-sel) A small raised area in the bark of stems and roots that enables gas exchange between living cells and the outside air.

lepidosaur (leh-pid′-uh-sōr) Member of the reptilian group that includes lizards, snakes, and two species of New Zealand animals called tuataras.

leptin A hormone produced by adipose (fat) cells that acts as a satiety factor in regulating appetite.

leukocyte (lū′-kō-sīt′) A blood cell that functions in fighting infections; also called a white blood cell.

Leydig cell (lī′-dig) A cell that produces testosterone and other androgens and is located between the seminiferous tubules of the testes.

lichen The mutualistic association between a fungus and a photosynthetic alga or cyanobacterium.

life cycle The generation-to-generation sequence of stages in the reproductive history of an organism.

life history The traits that affect an organism's schedule of reproduction and survival.

life table An age-specific summary of the survival pattern of a population.

ligament A fibrous connective tissue that joins bones together at joints.

ligand (lig′-und) A molecule that binds specifically to another molecule, usually a larger one.

ligand-gated ion channel A transmembrane protein containing a pore that opens or closes as it changes shape in response to a signalling molecule (ligand), allowing or blocking the flow of specific ions; also called an ionotropic receptor.

light chain One of the two types of polypeptide chains that make up an antibody molecule and B cell receptor; consists of a variable region, which contributes to the antigen-binding site, and a constant region.

light-harvesting complex A complex of proteins associated with pigment molecules (including chlorophyll *a*, chlorophyll *b*, and carotenoids) that captures light energy and transfers it to reaction-centre pigments in a photosystem.

light microscope (LM) An optical instrument with lenses that refract (bend) visible light to magnify images of specimens.

light reactions The first of two major stages in photosynthesis (preceding the Calvin cycle). These reactions, which occur on the thylakoid membranes of the chloroplast or on membranes of certain prokaryotes, convert solar energy to the chemical energy of ATP and NADPH, releasing oxygen in the process.

lignin (lig′-nin) A hard material embedded in the cellulose matrix of vascular plant cell walls that provides structural support in terrestrial species.

limiting nutrient An element that must be added for production to increase in a particular area.

limnetic zone In a lake, the well-lit, open surface waters far from shore.

linear electron flow A route of electron flow during the light reactions of photosynthesis that involves both photosystems (I and II) and produces ATP, NADPH, and O_2. The net electron flow is from H_2O to $NADP^+$.

linkage map A genetic map based on the frequencies of recombination between markers during crossing over of homologous chromosomes.

linked genes Genes located close enough together on a chromosome that they tend to be inherited together.

lipid (lip′-id) Any of a group of large biological molecules, including fats, phospholipids, and steroids, that mix poorly, if at all, with water.

littoral zone In a lake, the shallow, well-lit waters close to shore.

liver A large internal organ in vertebrates that performs diverse functions, such as producing bile, maintaining blood glucose level, and detoxifying poisonous chemicals in the blood.

liverwort A small, herbaceous, nonvascular plant that is a member of the phylum Hepatophyta.

loam The most fertile soil type, made up of roughly equal amounts of sand, silt, and clay.

lobe-fin Member of the vertebrate clade Sarcopterygii, osteichthyans with rod-shaped muscular fins, including coelacanths, lungfishes, and tetrapods.

local regulator A secreted molecule that influences cells near where it is secreted.

locomotion Active motion from place to place.

locus (lō′-kus) (plural, **loci**) A specific place along the length of a chromosome where a given gene is located.

logistic population growth Population growth that levels off as population size approaches carrying capacity.

long-day plant A plant that flowers (usually in late spring or early summer) only when the light period is longer than a critical length.

long-term memory The ability to hold, associate, and recall information over one's lifetime.

long-term potentiation (LTP) An enhanced responsiveness to an action potential (nerve signal) by a receiving neuron.

loop of Henle The hairpin turn, with a descending and ascending limb, between the proximal and distal tubules of the vertebrate kidney; functions in water and salt reabsorption.

lophophore (lof′-uh-fōr) In some lophotrochozoan animals, including brachiopods, a crown of ciliated tentacles that surround the mouth and function in feeding.

Lophotrochozoa (lo-phah′-truh-kō-zō′-uh) One of the three main lineages of bilaterian animals; lophotrochozoans include organisms that have lophophores or trochophore larvae. *See also* Deuterostomia and Ecdysozoa.

low-density lipoprotein (LDL) A particle in the blood made up of thousands of cholesterol molecules and other lipids bound to a protein. LDL transports cholesterol from the liver for incorporation into cell membranes.

lung An infolded respiratory surface of a terrestrial vertebrate, land snail, or spider that connects to the atmosphere by narrow tubes.

luteal phase That portion of the ovarian cycle during which endocrine cells of the corpus luteum secrete female hormones.

lycophyte (lī′-kuh-fīt) An informal name for a member of the phylum Lycophyta, which includes club mosses, spike mosses, and quillworts.

lymph The colourless fluid, derived from interstitial fluid, in the lymphatic system of vertebrates.

lymphatic system A system of vessels and nodes, separate from the circulatory system, that returns fluid, proteins, and cells to the blood.

lymph node An organ located along a lymph vessel. Lymph nodes filter lymph and contain cells that attack viruses and bacteria.

lymphocyte A type of white blood cell that mediates immune responses. The two main classes are B cells and T cells.

lysogenic cycle (lī′-sō-jen′-ik) A type of phage replicative cycle in which the viral genome becomes incorporated into the bacterial host chromosome as a prophage, is replicated along with the chromosome, and does not kill the host.

lysosome (lī′-suh-sōm) A membrane-enclosed sac of hydrolytic enzymes found in the cytoplasm of animal cells and some protists.

lysozyme (lī′-sō-zīm) An enzyme that destroys bacterial cell walls; in mammals, found in sweat, tears, and saliva.

lytic cycle (lit′-ik) A type of phage replicative cycle resulting in the release of new phages by lysis (and death) of the host cell.

macroclimate Large-scale patterns in climate; the climate of an entire region.

macroevolution Evolutionary change above the species level. Examples of macroevolutionary change include the origin of a new group of organisms through a series of speciation events and the impact of mass extinctions on the diversity of life and its subsequent recovery.

macromolecule A giant molecule formed by the joining of smaller molecules, usually by a dehydration reaction. Polysaccharides, proteins, and nucleic acids are macromolecules.

macronutrient An essential element that an organism must obtain in relatively large amounts. *See also* micronutrient.

macrophage (mak′-rō-fāj) A phagocytic cell present in many tissues that functions in innate immunity by destroying microbes and in acquired immunity as an antigen-presenting cell.

magnoliid Member of the angiosperm clade that is most closely related to the combined eudicot and monocot clades. Extant examples are magnolias, laurels, and black pepper plants.

major depressive disorder A mood disorder characterized by feelings of sadness, lack of self-worth, emptiness, or loss of interest in nearly all things.

major histocompatibility complex (MHC) molecule A host protein that functions in antigen presentation. Foreign MHC molecules on transplanted tissue can trigger T cell responses that may lead to rejection of the transplant.

malignant tumour A cancerous tumour containing cells that have significant genetic and cellular changes and are capable of invading and surviving in new sites. Malignant tumours can impair the functions of one or more organs.

Malpighian tubule (mal-pig′-ē-un) A unique excretory organ of insects that empties into the digestive tract, removes nitrogenous wastes from the hemolymph, and functions in osmoregulation.

mammal Member of the class Mammalia, amniotes that have hair and mammary glands (glands that produce milk).

mammary gland An exocrine gland that secretes milk to nourish the young. Mammary glands are characteristic of mammals.

mandible One of a pair of jaw-like feeding appendages found in myriapods, hexapods, and crustaceans.

mantle One of the three main parts of a mollusc; a fold of tissue that drapes over the mollusc's visceral mass and may secrete a shell. *See also* foot, visceral mass.

mantle cavity A water-filled chamber that houses the gills, anus, and excretory pores of a mollusc.

map unit A unit of measurement of the distance between genes. One map unit is equivalent to a 1% recombination frequency.

marine benthic zone The ocean floor.

mark-recapture method A sampling technique used to estimate the size of animal populations.

marsupial (mar-sū′-pē-ul) A mammal, such as a koala, kangaroo, or opossum, whose young complete their embryonic development inside a maternal pouch called the marsupium.

mass extinction The elimination of a large number of species throughout Earth, the result of global environmental changes.

mass number The sum of the number of protons and neutrons in an atom's nucleus.

mast cell A vertebrate body cell that produces histamine and other molecules that trigger inflammation in response to infection and in allergic reactions.

mate-choice copying Behaviour in which individuals in a population copy the mate choice of others, apparently as a result of social learning.

maternal effect gene A gene that, when mutant in the mother, results in a mutant phenotype in the offspring, regardless of the offspring's genotype. Maternal effect genes, also called egg-polarity genes, were first identified in *Drosophila melanogaster*.

matter Anything that takes up space and has mass.

maximum likelihood As applied to molecular systematics, a principle that states that when considering multiple phylogenetic hypotheses, one should take into account the hypothesis that reflects the most likely sequence of evolutionary events, given certain rules about how DNA changes over time.

maximum parsimony A principle that states that when considering multiple explanations for an observation, one should first investigate the simplest explanation that is consistent with the facts.

mechanoreceptor A sensory receptor that detects physical deformation in the body's environment associated with pressure, touch, stretch, motion, or sound.

medulla oblongata (meh-dul′-uh ōb′-long-go′-tuh) The lowest part of the vertebrate brain, commonly called the medulla; a swelling of the hindbrain anterior to the spinal cord that controls autonomic, homeostatic functions, including breathing, heart and blood vessel activity, swallowing, digestion, and vomiting.

medusa (plural, **medusae**) (muh-dū′-suh) The floating, flattened, mouth-down version of the cnidarian body plan. The alternate form is the polyp.

megapascal (MPa) (meg′-uh-pas-kal′) A unit of pressure equivalent to about 10 atmospheres of pressure.

megaphyll (meh′-guh-fil) A leaf with a highly branched vascular system, characteristic of the vast majority of vascular plants. *See* microphyll.

megaspore A spore from a heterosporous plant species that develops into a female gametophyte.

meiosis (mī-ō′-sis) A modified type of cell division in sexually reproducing organisms consisting of two rounds of cell division but only one round of DNA replication. It results in cells with half the number of chromosome sets as the original cell.

meiosis I The first division of a two-stage process of cell division in sexually reproducing organisms that results in cells with half the number of chromosome sets as the original cell.

meiosis II The second division of a two-stage process of cell division in sexually reproducing organisms that results in cells with half the number of chromosome sets as the original cell.

melanocyte-stimulating hormone (MSH) A hormone produced and secreted by the anterior pituitary with multiple activities, including regulating the behaviour of pigment-containing cells in the skin of some vertebrates.

melatonin A hormone that is secreted by the pineal gland and that is involved in the regulation of biological rhythms and sleep.

membrane potential The difference in electrical charge (voltage) across a cell's plasma membrane due to the differential distribution of ions. Membrane potential affects the activity of excitable cells and the transmembrane movement of all charged substances.

memory cell One of a clone of long-lived lymphocytes, formed during the primary immune response, that remains in a lymphoid organ until activated by exposure to the same antigen that triggered its formation. Activated memory cells mount the secondary immune response.

menopause The cessation of ovulation and menstruation marking the end of a human female's reproductive years.

menstrual cycle (men′-strū-ul) In humans and certain other primates, a type of reproductive cycle in which the nonpregnant endometrium is shed through the cervix into the vagina; also called the uterine cycle.

menstrual flow phase That portion of the uterine (menstrual) cycle when menstrual bleeding occurs.

menstruation The shedding of portions of the endometrium during a uterine (menstrual) cycle.

meristem (mār′-uh-stem) Plant tissue that remains embryonic as long as the plant lives, allowing for indeterminate growth.

meristem identity gene A plant gene that promotes the switch from vegetative growth to flowering.

meroblastic (mār′-ō-blas′-tik) Referring to a type of cleavage in which there is incomplete division of a yolk-rich egg, characteristic of avian development.

mesoderm (mez′-ō-derm) The middle primary germ layer in a triploblastic animal embryo; develops into the notochord, the lining of the coelom, muscles, skeleton, gonads, kidneys, and most of the circulatory system in species that have these structures.

mesohyl (mez'-ō-hīl) A gelatinous region between the two layers of cells of a sponge.

mesophyll (mez'-ō-fil) Leaf cells specialized for photosynthesis. In C_3 and CAM plants, mesophyll cells are located between the upper and lower epidermis; in C_4 plants, they are located between the bundle-sheath cells and the epidermis.

messenger RNA (mRNA) A type of RNA, synthesized using a DNA template, that attaches to ribosomes in the cytoplasm and specifies the primary structure of a protein. (In eukaryotes, the primary RNA transcript must undergo RNA processing to become mRNA.)

metabolic pathway A series of chemical reactions that either builds a complex molecule (anabolic pathway) or breaks down a complex molecule to simpler molecules (catabolic pathway).

metabolic rate The total amount of energy an animal uses in a unit of time.

metabolism (muh-tab'-uh-lizm) The totality of an organism's chemical reactions, consisting of catabolic and anabolic pathways, which manage the material and energy resources of the organism.

metabolomics The systematic study of sets of metabolites within a cell, tissue, or organism under defined growth conditions.

metagenomics The collection and sequencing of DNA from a group of species, usually an environmental sample of microorganisms. Computer software sorts partial sequences and assembles them into genome sequences of individual species making up the sample.

metamorphosis (met'-uh-mōr'-fuh-sis) A developmental transformation that turns an animal larva into either an adult or an adult-like stage that is not yet sexually mature.

metanephridium (met'-uh-nuh-frid'-ē-um) (plural, **metanephridia**) An excretory organ found in many invertebrates that typically consists of tubules connecting ciliated internal openings to external openings.

metaphase The third stage of mitosis, in which the spindle is complete and the chromosomes, attached to microtubules at their kinetochores, are all aligned at the metaphase plate.

metaphase plate An imaginary structure located at a plane midway between the two poles of a cell in metaphase on which the centromeres of all the duplicated chromosomes are located.

metapopulation A group of spatially separated populations of one species that interact through immigration and emigration.

metastasis (muh-tas'-tuh-sis) The spread of cancer cells to locations distant from their original site.

methanogen (meth-an'-ō-jen) An organism that produces methane as a waste product of the way it obtains energy. All known methanogens are in domain Archaea.

methyl group A chemical group consisting of a carbon bonded to three hydrogen atoms. The methyl group may be attached to a carbon or to a different atom.

microbiome The community of microorganisms that live on and in the human body.

microclimate Climate patterns on a very fine scale, such as the specific climatic conditions underneath a log.

microevolution Evolutionary change below the species level; change in the allele frequencies in a population over generations.

microfilament A cable composed of actin proteins in the cytoplasm of almost every eukaryotic cell, making up part of the cytoskeleton and acting alone or with myosin to cause cell contraction; also known as an actin filament.

micronutrient An essential element that an organism needs in very small amounts. *See also* macronutrient.

microphyll (mī'-krō-fil) In lycophytes, a small leaf with a single unbranched vein. *See* megaphyll.

micropyle A pore in the integuments of an ovule.

microRNA (miRNA) A small, single-stranded RNA molecule, generated from a hairpin structure on a precursor RNA transcribed from a particular gene. The miRNA associates with one or more proteins in a complex that can degrade or prevent translation of an mRNA with a complementary sequence.

microspore A spore from a heterosporous plant species that develops into a male gametophyte.

microtubule A hollow rod composed of tubulin proteins that makes up part of the cytoskeleton in all eukaryotic cells and is found in cilia and flagella.

microvillus (plural, **microvilli**) One of many fine, finger-like projections of the epithelial cells in the lumen of the small intestine that increase its surface area.

midbrain One of three ancestral and embryonic regions of the vertebrate brain; develops into sensory integrating and relay centres that send sensory information to the cerebrum.

middle ear One of three main regions of the vertebrate ear; in mammals, a chamber containing three small bones (the malleus, incus, and stapes) that convey vibrations from the eardrum to the oval window.

middle lamella (luh-mel'-uh) In plants, a thin layer of adhesive extracellular material, primarily pectins, found between the primary walls of adjacent young cells.

migration A regular, long-distance change in location.

mineral In nutrition, a simple nutrient that is inorganic and therefore cannot be synthesized in the body.

mineralocorticoid A steroid hormone secreted by the adrenal cortex that regulates salt and water homeostasis.

minimum viable population (MVP) The smallest population size at which a species is able to sustain its numbers and survive.

mismatch repair The cellular process that uses specific enzymes to remove and replace incorrectly paired nucleotides.

missense mutation A nucleotide-pair substitution that results in a codon that codes for a different amino acid.

mitochondrial matrix The compartment of the mitochondrion enclosed by the inner membrane and containing enzymes and substrates for the citric acid cycle, as well as ribosomes and DNA.

mitochondrion (mī'-tō-kon'-drē-un) (plural, **mitochondria**) An organelle in eukaryotic cells that serves as the site of cellular respiration; uses oxygen to break down organic molecules and synthesize ATP.

mitosis (mī-tō'-sis) A process of nuclear division in eukaryotic cells conventionally divided into five stages: prophase, prometaphase, metaphase, anaphase, and telophase. Mitosis conserves chromosome number by allocating replicated chromosomes equally to each of the daughter nuclei.

mitotic (M) phase The phase of the cell cycle that includes mitosis and cytokinesis.

mitotic spindle An assemblage of microtubules and associated proteins that is involved in the movement of chromosomes during mitosis.

mixotroph An organism that is capable of both photosynthesis and heterotrophy.

model organism A particular species chosen for research into broad biological principles because it is representative of a larger group and usually easy to grow in a lab.

molarity A common measure of solute concentration, referring to the number of moles of solute per litre of solution.

mole (mol) The number of grams of a substance that equals its molecular weight in daltons and contains Avogadro's number of molecules.

molecular characteristics Features based on the macromolecular composition of an organism, most notably the content and sequence of DNA and proteins.

molecular clock A method for estimating the time required for a given amount of evolutionary change, based on the observation that some regions of genomes evolve at constant rates.

molecular mass The sum of the masses of all the atoms in a molecule; sometimes called molecular weight.

molecular systematics A scientific discipline that uses nucleic acids or other molecules to infer evolutionary relationships between different species.

molecule Two or more atoms held together by covalent bonds.

monilophyte An informal name for a member of the phylum Monilophyta, which includes ferns, horsetails, and whisk ferns and their relatives.

monoclonal antibody (mon'-ō-klōn'-ul) Any of a preparation of antibodies that have been produced by a single clone of cultured cells and thus are all specific for the same epitope.

monocot Member of a clade consisting of flowering plants that have one embryonic seed leaf, or cotyledon.

monogamous (muh-nog'-uh-mus) Referring to a type of relationship in which one male mates with just one female.

monohybrid An organism that is heterozygous with respect to a single gene of interest. All the offspring from a cross between parents homozygous for different alleles are monohybrids. For example, parents of genotypes *AA* and *aa* produce a monohybrid of genotype *Aa*.

monohybrid cross A cross between two organisms that are heterozygous for the character being followed (or the self-pollination of a heterozygous plant).

monomer (mon′-uh-mer) The subunit that serves as the building block of a polymer.

monophyletic (mon′-ō-fī-let′-ik) Pertaining to a group of taxa that consists of a common ancestor and all of its descendants. A monophyletic taxon is equivalent to a clade.

monosaccharide (mon′-ō-sak′-uh-rīd) The simplest carbohydrate, active alone or serving as a monomer for disaccharides and polysaccharides. Also known as simple sugars, monosaccharides have molecular formulas that are generally some multiple of CH_2O.

monosomic Referring to a diploid cell that has only one copy of a particular chromosome instead of the normal two.

monotreme An egg-laying mammal, such as a platypus or echidna. Like all mammals, monotremes have hair and produce milk, but they lack nipples.

morphogen A substance, such as Bicoid protein in *Drosophila*, that provides positional information in the form of a concentration gradient along an embryonic axis.

morphogenesis (mōr′-fō-jen′-uh-sis) The cellular and tissue-based processes by which an animal body takes shape.

morphological characteristics Relating to the outward appearance of structural features of an organism or its parts. Includes a description of characteristics such as size, shape, colour, number, and arrangement of any other visible feature.

morphological species concept A definition of species in terms of measurable anatomical criteria.

moss A small, herbaceous, nonvascular plant that is a member of the phylum Bryophyta.

motor neuron A nerve cell that transmits signals from the brain or spinal cord to muscles or glands.

motor protein A protein that interacts with cytoskeletal elements and other cell components, producing movement of the whole cell or parts of the cell.

motor system The collection of neurons that sends signals to skeletal muscles.

motor unit A single motor neuron and all the muscle fibres it controls.

mould Informal term for a fungus that grows as a filamentous fungus, producing haploid spores by mitosis and forming a visible mycelium.

moulting A process in ecdysozoans in which the exoskeleton is shed at intervals, allowing growth by the production of a larger exoskeleton.

movement corridor A series of small clumps or a narrow strip of quality habitat (usable by organisms) that connects otherwise isolated patches of quality habitat.

MPF Maturation-promoting factor (or M-phase-promoting factor); a protein complex required for a cell to progress from late interphase to mitosis. The active form consists of cyclin and a protein kinase.

mucous cell An epithelial cell that produces mucus.

mucus A viscous and slippery mixture of glycoproteins, cells, salts, and water that moistens and protects the membranes lining body cavities that open to the exterior.

Müllerian mimicry (myū-lār′-ē-un) Reciprocal mimicry by two unpalatable species.

multifactorial Referring to a phenotypic character that is influenced by multiple genes and environmental factors.

multigene family A collection of genes with similar or identical sequences, presumably of common origin.

multiple fruit A fruit derived from an entire inflorescence.

multiplication rule A rule of probability stating that the probability of two or more independent events occurring together can be determined by multiplying their individual probabilities.

muscle tissue Tissue consisting of long muscle cells that can contract, either on its own or when stimulated by nerve impulses.

mutagen (myū′-tuh-jen) A chemical or physical agent that interacts with DNA and can cause a mutation.

mutation (myū-tā′-shun) A change in the nucleotide sequence of an organism's DNA or in the DNA or RNA of a virus.

mutualism (myū′-chū-ul-izm) An ecological interaction that benefits each of the interacting species.

mycelium (mī-sē′-lē-um) The densely branched network of hyphae in a fungus.

mycetozoa A group of slime moulds.

mycorrhiza (mī′-kō-rī′-zuh) (plural, **mycorrhizae**) A mutualistic association of plant roots and fungus.

mycosis (mī-kō′-sis) General term for a fungal infection.

myelin sheath (mī′-uh-lin) Wrapped around the axon of a neuron, an insulating coat of cell membranes from Schwann cells or oligodendrocytes. It is interrupted by nodes of Ranvier, where action potentials are generated.

myofibril (mī′-ō-fī′-bril) A longitudinal bundle in a muscle cell (fibre) that contains thin filaments of actin and regulatory proteins and thick filaments of myosin.

myoglobin (mī′-uh-glō′-bin) An oxygen-storing, pigmented protein in muscle cells.

myosin (mī′-uh-sin) A type of motor protein that associates into filaments that interact with actin filaments to cause cell contraction.

myotonia (mī′-uh-tō′-nī-uh) Increased muscle tension, characteristic of sexual arousal in certain human tissues.

myriapod (mir′-ē-uh-pod′) A terrestrial arthropod with many body segments and one or two pairs of legs per segment. Millipedes and centipedes are the two major groups of living myriapods.

NAD+ Nicotinamide adenine dinucleotide, a coenzyme that cycles easily between oxidized (NAD^+) and reduced (NADH) states, thus acting as an electron carrier.

NADP+ Nicotinamide adenine dinucleotide phosphate, an electron acceptor that, as NADPH, temporarily stores energized electrons produced during the light reactions.

natural family planning A form of contraception that relies on refraining from sexual intercourse when conception is most likely to occur; also called the rhythm method.

natural killer cell A type of white blood cell that can kill tumour cells and virus-infected cells as part of innate immunity.

natural range expansion Expansion of a species' range in response to natural events.

natural selection A process in which individuals that have certain inherited traits tend to survive and reproduce at higher rates than other individuals *because of* those traits.

negative feedback A form of regulation in which accumulation of an end product of a process slows the process; in physiology, a primary mechanism of homeostasis, whereby a change in a variable triggers a response that counteracts the initial change.

negative pressure breathing A breathing system in which air is pulled into the lungs.

nematocyst (nem′-uh-tuh-sist′) In a cnidocyte of a cnidarian, a capsule-like organelle containing a coiled thread that when discharged can penetrate the body wall of the prey.

nephron (nef′-ron) The tubular excretory unit of the vertebrate kidney.

neritic zone The shallow region of the ocean overlying the continental shelf.

nerve A fibre composed primarily of the bundled axons of PNS neurons.

nerve net A weblike system of neurons, characteristic of radially symmetrical animals, such as hydras.

nervous system The fast-acting internal system of communication involving sensory receptors, networks of nerve cells, and connections to muscles and glands that respond to nerve signals; functions in concert with the endocrine system to effect internal regulation and maintain homeostasis.

nervous tissue Tissue made up of neurons and supportive cells.

net ecosystem production (NEP) The gross primary production of an ecosystem minus the energy used by all autotrophs and heterotrophs for respiration.

net primary production (NPP) The gross primary production of an ecosystem minus the energy used by the producers for respiration.

neural crest In vertebrates, a region located along the sides of the neural tube where it pinches off from the ectoderm. Neural crest cells migrate to various parts of the embryo and form pigment cells in the skin and parts of the skull, teeth, adrenal glands, and peripheral nervous system.

neural plasticity The capacity of a nervous system to change with experience.

neural tube A tube of infolded ectodermal cells that runs along the anterior-posterior axis of a vertebrate, just dorsal to the notochord. It will give rise to the central nervous system.

neurohormone A molecule that is secreted by a neuron, travels in body fluids, and acts on specific target cells, changing their functioning.

neuron (nyūr′-on) A nerve cell; the fundamental unit of the nervous system, having structure and properties that allow it to conduct signals by taking advantage of the electrical charge across its plasma membrane.

neuropeptide A relatively short chain of amino acids that serves as a neurotransmitter.

neurotransmitter A molecule that is released from the synaptic terminal of a neuron at a chemical synapse, diffuses across the synaptic cleft, and binds to the postsynaptic cell, triggering a response.

neutral variation Genetic variation that does not provide a selective advantage or disadvantage.

neutron A subatomic particle having no electrical charge (electrically neutral), with a mass of about 1.7×10^{-24} g, found in the nucleus of an atom.

neutrophil The most abundant type of white blood cell. Neutrophils are phagocytic and tend to self-destruct as they destroy foreign invaders, limiting their life span to a few days.

nitric oxide (NO) A gas produced by many types of cells that functions as a local regulator and as a neurotransmitter.

nitrogen cycle The natural process by which nitrogen, either from the atmosphere or from decomposed organic material, is converted by soil bacteria to compounds assimilated by plants. This incorporated nitrogen is then taken in by other organisms and subsequently released, acted on by bacteria, and made available again to the nonliving environment.

nitrogen fixation The conversion of atmospheric nitrogen (N_2) to ammonia (NH_3). Biological nitrogen fixation is carried out by certain prokaryotes, some of which have mutualistic relationships with plants.

nociceptor (nō′-si-sep′-tur) A sensory receptor that responds to noxious or painful stimuli; also called a pain receptor.

node A point along the stem of a plant at which leaves are attached.

node of Ranvier (ron′-vē-ā′) Gap in the myelin sheath of certain axons where an action potential may be generated. In saltatory conduction, an action potential is regenerated at each node, appearing to "jump" along the axon from node to node.

nodule A swelling on the root of a legume. Nodules are composed of plant cells that contain nitrogen-fixing bacteria of the genus *Rhizobium*.

noncompetitive inhibitor A substance that reduces the activity of an enzyme by binding to a location remote from the active site, changing the enzyme's shape so that the active site no longer effectively catalyzes the conversion of substrate to product.

nondisjunction An error in meiosis or mitosis in which members of a pair of homologous chromosomes or a pair of sister chromatids fail to separate properly from each other.

nonequilibrium model A model that maintains that communities change constantly after being buffeted by disturbances.

nonpolar covalent bond A type of covalent bond in which electrons are shared equally between two atoms of similar electronegativity.

nonsense mutation A mutation that changes an amino acid codon to one of the three stop codons, resulting in a shorter and usually nonfunctional protein.

nonshivering thermogenesis A process that occurs in brown adipose tissue that results in the production of heat.

norepinephrine A catecholamine that is chemically and functionally similar to epinephrine and acts as a hormone or neurotransmitter; also known as noradrenaline.

northern coniferous forest A terrestrial biome characterized by long, cold winters and dominated by cone-bearing trees.

no-till agriculture A plowing technique that minimally disturbs the soil, thereby reducing soil loss.

notochord (nō′-tuh-kord′) A longitudinal, flexible rod made of tightly packed mesodermal cells that runs along the anterior-posterior axis of a chordate in the dorsal part of the body.

nuclear envelope In a eukaryotic cell, the double membrane that surrounds the nucleus, perforated with pores that regulate traffic with the cytoplasm. The outer membrane is continuous with the endoplasmic reticulum.

nucleariid Member of a group of unicellular, amoeboid protists that are more closely related to fungi than they are to other protists.

nuclear lamina A netlike array of protein filaments that lines the inner surface of the nuclear envelope and helps maintain the shape of the nucleus.

nuclease An enzyme that cuts DNA or RNA, either removing one or a few bases or hydrolyzing the DNA or RNA completely into its component nucleotides.

nucleic acid (nū-klā′-ik) A polymer (polynucleotide) consisting of many nucleotide monomers; serves as a blueprint for proteins and, through the actions of proteins, for all cellular activities. The two types are DNA and RNA.

nucleic acid hybridization The process of base pairing between a gene and a complementary sequence on another nucleic acid molecule.

nucleic acid probe In DNA technology, a labelled single-stranded nucleic acid molecule used to locate a specific nucleotide sequence in a nucleic acid sample. Molecules of the probe hydrogen-bond to the complementary sequence wherever it occurs; radioactive, fluorescent, or other labelling of the probe allows its location to be detected.

nucleoid (nū′-klē-oyd) A non-membrane-bounded region in a prokaryotic cell where the DNA is concentrated.

nucleolus (nū-klē′-ō-lus) (plural, **nucleoli**) A specialized structure in the nucleus, consisting of chromosomal regions containing ribosomal RNA (rRNA) genes along with ribosomal

proteins imported from the cytoplasm; site of rRNA synthesis and ribosomal subunit assembly. *See also* ribosome.

nucleomorph Vestigial eukaryotic nuclei that are found between some plastids' inner and outer membranes.

nucleosome (nū′-klē-ō-sōm′) The basic, bead-like unit of DNA packing in eukaryotes, consisting of a segment of DNA wound around a protein core composed of two copies of each of four types of histone.

nucleotide (nū′-klē-ō-tīd′) The building block of a nucleic acid, consisting of a five-carbon sugar covalently bonded to a nitrogenous base and one or more phosphate groups.

nucleotide excision repair A repair system that removes and then correctly replaces a damaged segment of DNA using the undamaged strand as a guide.

nucleotide-pair substitution A type of point mutation in which one nucleotide in a DNA strand and its partner in the complementary strand are replaced by another pair of nucleotides.

nucleus (1) An atom's central core, containing protons and neutrons. (2) The organelle of a eukaryotic cell that contains the genetic material in the form of chromosomes, made up of chromatin. (3) A cluster of neurons.

nutrition The process by which an organism takes in and makes use of food substances.

obligate aerobe (ob′-lig-et ār′-ōb) An organism that requires oxygen for cellular respiration and cannot live without it.

obligate anaerobe (ob′-lig-et an′-uh-rōb) An organism that only carries out fermentation or anaerobic respiration. Such organisms cannot use oxygen and in fact may be poisoned by it.

ocean acidification Decreasing pH of ocean waters due to absorption of excess atmospheric CO_2 from the burning of fossil fuels.

oceanic pelagic zone Most of the ocean's waters far from shore, constantly mixed by ocean currents.

odorant A molecule that can be detected by sensory receptors of the olfactory system.

Okazaki fragment (ō′-kah-zah′-kē) A short segment of DNA synthesized away from the replication fork on a template strand during DNA replication. Many such segments are joined together to make up the lagging strand of newly synthesized DNA.

olfaction The sense of smell.

oligodendrocyte A type of glial cell that forms insulating myelin sheaths around the axons of neurons in the central nervous system.

ommatidium (ōm′-uh-tid′-ē-um) (plural, **ommatidia**) One of the facets of the compound eye of arthropods and some polychaete worms.

omnivore An animal that regularly eats animals as well as plants or algae.

oncogene (on′-kō-jēn) A gene found in viral or cellular genomes that is involved in triggering molecular events that can lead to cancer.

oocyte A cell in the female reproductive system that differentiates to form an egg.

oogenesis (ō′-uh-jen′-uh-sis) The process in the ovary that results in the production of female gametes.

oogonium (ō′-uh-gō′-nē-em) (plural, **oogonia**) A cell that divides mitotically to form oocytes.

open circulatory system A circulatory system in which fluid called hemolymph bathes the tissues and organs directly and there is no distinction between the circulating fluid and the interstitial fluid.

operator In bacterial and phage DNA, a sequence of nucleotides near the start of an operon to which an active repressor can attach. The binding of the repressor prevents RNA polymerase from attaching to the promoter and transcribing the genes of the operon.

operculum (ō-per′-kyuh-lum) In aquatic osteichthyans, a protective bony flap that covers and protects the gills.

operon (op′-er-on) A unit of genetic function found in bacteria and phages, consisting of a promoter, an operator, and a coordinately regulated cluster of genes whose products function in a common pathway.

opisthokont (uh-pis′-thuh-kont′) Member of the diverse clade Opisthokonta, organisms that descended from an ancestor with a posterior flagellum, including fungi, animals, and certain protists.

opposable thumb A thumb that can touch the ventral surface of the fingertips of all four fingers.

opsin A membrane protein bound to a light-absorbing pigment molecule.

optic chiasm The place where the two optic nerves meet and axons representing distinct sides of the visual field are segregated from one another before reaching the brain.

optimal foraging model The basis for analyzing behaviour as a compromise between feeding costs and feeding benefits.

oral cavity The mouth of an animal.

orbital The three-dimensional space where an electron is found 90% of the time.

order In Linnaean classification, the taxonomic category above the level of family.

organ A specialized centre of body function composed of several different types of tissues.

organ identity gene A plant homeotic gene that uses positional information to determine which emerging leaves develop into which types of floral organs.

organ of Corti The actual hearing organ of the vertebrate ear, located in the floor of the cochlear duct in the inner ear; contains the receptor cells (hair cells) of the ear.

organ system A group of organs that work together in performing vital body functions.

organelle (ōr-guh-nel′) Any of several membrane-enclosed structures with specialized functions, suspended in the cytosol of eukaryotic cells.

organic chemistry The study of carbon compounds (organic compounds).

organismal ecology The branch of ecology concerned with the morphological, physiological, and behavioural ways in which individual organisms meet the challenges posed by their biotic and abiotic environments.

organogenesis (ōr-gan′-ō-jen′-uh-sis) The process in which organ rudiments develop from the three germ layers after gastrulation.

orgasm Rhythmic, involuntary contractions of certain reproductive structures in both sexes during the human sexual response cycle.

origin of replication Site where the replication of a DNA molecule begins, consisting of a specific sequence of nucleotides.

orthologous genes Homologous genes that are found in different species because of speciation.

osculum (os′-kyuh-lum) A large opening in a sponge that connects the spongocoel to the environment.

osmoconformer An animal that is isoosmotic with its environment.

osmolarity (oz′-mō-lār′-uh-tē) Solute concentration expressed as molarity.

osmoregulation Regulation of solute concentrations and water balance by a cell or organism.

osmoregulator An animal that controls its internal osmolarity independent of the external environment.

osmosis (oz-mō′-sis) The diffusion of free water across a selectively permeable membrane.

osteichthyan (os′-tē-ik′-thē-an) Member of a vertebrate clade with jaws and mostly bony skeletons.

outer ear One of three main regions of the ear in reptiles (including birds) and mammals; made up of the auditory canal and, in many birds and mammals, the pinna.

outgroup A species or group of species from an evolutionary lineage that is known to have diverged before the lineage that contains the group of species being studied. An outgroup is selected so that its members are closely related to the group of species being studied, but not as closely related as any study-group members are to each other.

oval window In the vertebrate ear, a membrane-covered gap in the skull bone, through which sound waves pass from the middle ear to the inner ear.

ovarian cycle (ō-vār′-ē-un) The cyclic recurrence of the follicular phase, ovulation, and the luteal phase in the mammalian ovary, regulated by hormones.

ovary (ō′-vuh-rē) (1) In flowers, the portion of a carpel in which the egg-containing ovules develop. (2) In animals, the structure that produces female gametes and reproductive hormones.

oviduct (ō′-vuh-duct) A tube passing from the ovary to the vagina in invertebrates or to the uterus in vertebrates, where it is also known as a fallopian tube.

oviparous (ō-vip′-uh-rus) Referring to a type of development in which young hatch from eggs laid outside the mother's body.

ovoviviparous (ō′-vō-vī-vip′-uh-rus) Referring to a type of development in which young hatch from eggs that are retained in the mother's uterus.

ovulation The release of an egg from an ovary. In humans, an ovarian follicle releases an egg during each uterine (menstrual) cycle.

ovule (o′-vyūl) A structure that develops within the ovary of a seed plant and contains the female gametophyte.

oxidation The complete or partial loss of electrons from a substance involved in a redox reaction.

oxidative phosphorylation (fos′-fōr-uh-lā′-shun) The production of ATP using energy derived from the redox reactions of an electron transport chain; the third major stage of cellular respiration.

oxidizing agent The electron acceptor in a redox reaction.

oxytocin (ok′-si-tō′-sen) A hormone produced by the hypothalamus and released from the posterior pituitary. It induces contractions of the uterine muscles during labour and causes the mammary glands to eject milk during nursing.

P generation The true-breeding (homozygous) parent individuals from which F_1 hybrid offspring are derived in studies of inheritance; P stands for "parental."

P site One of a ribosome's three binding sites for tRNA during translation. The P site holds the tRNA carrying the growing polypeptide chain. (P stands for peptidyl tRNA.)

***p53* gene** A tumour-suppressor gene that codes for a specific transcription factor that promotes the synthesis of proteins that inhibit the cell cycle.

paedomorphosis (pē′-duh-mōr′-fuh-sis) The retention in an adult organism of the juvenile features of its evolutionary ancestors.

pain receptor A sensory receptor that responds to noxious or painful stimuli; also called a nociceptor.

paleoanthropology The study of human origins and evolution.

paleontology (pā′-lē-un-tol′-ō-jē) The scientific study of fossils.

pancreas (pan′-krē-us) A gland with exocrine and endocrine tissues. The exocrine portion functions in digestion, secreting enzymes and an alkaline solution into the small intestine via a duct; the ductless endocrine portion functions in homeostasis, secreting the hormones insulin and glucagon into the blood.

pancrustacean A member of a diverse arthropod clade that includes lobsters, crabs, barnacles and other crustaceans, as well as insects and their six-legged terrestrial relatives.

pandemic A global epidemic.

Pangaea (pan-jē′-uh) The supercontinent that formed near the end of the Paleozoic era, when plate movements brought all the landmasses of Earth together.

parabasalid A protist, such as a trichomonad, with modified mitochondria.

paracrine Referring to a secreted molecule that acts on a neighbouring cell.

paralogous genes Homologous genes that are found in the same genome as a result of gene duplication.

paraphyletic (pār'-uh-fī-let'-ik) Pertaining to a group of taxa that consists of a common ancestor and some, but not all, of its descendants.

parareptile A basal group of reptiles, consisting mostly of large, stocky quadrupedal herbivores. Parareptiles died out in the late Triassic period.

parasite (par'-uh-sīt) An organism that feeds on the cell contents, tissues, or body fluids of another species (the host) while in or on the host organism. Parasites harm but usually do not kill their host.

parasitism (par'-uh-sit-izm) A symbiotic relationship in which one organism, the parasite, benefits at the expense of another, the host, by living either within or on the host.

parasympathetic division One of three divisions of the autonomic nervous system; generally enhances body activities that gain and conserve energy, such as digestion and reduced heart rate.

parathyroid gland One of four small endocrine glands, embedded in the surface of the thyroid gland, that secrete parathyroid hormone.

parathyroid hormone (PTH) A hormone secreted by the parathyroid glands that raises blood calcium level by promoting calcium release from bone and calcium retention by the kidneys.

parenchyma cell (puh-ren'-ki-muh) A relatively unspecialized plant cell type that carries out most of the metabolism, synthesizes and stores organic products, and develops into a more differentiated cell type.

parental type An offspring with a phenotype that matches one of the true-breeding parental (P generation) phenotypes; also refers to the phenotype itself.

parietal cell An epithelial cell of the stomach that secretes acid.

Parkinson's disease A progressive brain disease characterized by difficulty in initiating movements, slowness of movement, and rigidity.

parthenogenesis (par'-thuh-nō'-jen'-uh-sis) A form of asexual reproduction in which females produce offspring from unfertilized eggs.

partial pressure The pressure exerted by a particular gas in a mixture of gases (for instance, the pressure exerted by oxygen in air).

passive immunity Short-term immunity conferred by the transfer of antibodies, as occurs in the transfer of maternal antibodies to a fetus or nursing infant.

passive transport The diffusion of a substance across a biological membrane with no expenditure of energy.

pathogen An organism, virus, viroid, or prion that causes disease.

pathogen-associated molecular patterns (PAMPs) Short molecular sequences that typify certain groups of pathogens and that are recognized by cells of the innate immune system.

pattern formation The development of a multicellular organism's spatial organization, the arrangement of organs and tissues in their characteristic places in three-dimensional space.

peat Extensive deposits of partially decayed organic material often formed primarily from the wetland moss *Sphagnum*.

pedigree A diagram of a family tree with conventional symbols, showing the occurrence of heritable characters in parents and offspring over multiple generations.

pelagic zone The open-water component of aquatic biomes.

penis The copulatory structure of male mammals.

PEP carboxylase An enzyme that adds CO_2 to phosphoenolpyruvate (PEP) to form oxaloacetate in mesophyll cells of C_4 plants. It acts prior to photosynthesis.

pepsin An enzyme present in gastric juice that begins the hydrolysis of proteins.

pepsinogen The inactive form of pepsin secreted by chief cells located in gastric pits of the stomach.

peptide bond The covalent bond between the carboxyl group on one amino acid and the amino group on another, formed by a dehydration reaction.

peptidoglycan (pep'-tid-ō-glī'-kan) A type of polymer in bacterial cell walls consisting of modified sugars cross-linked by short polypeptides.

perception The interpretation of sensory system input by the brain.

pericycle The outermost layer in the vascular cylinder, from which lateral roots arise.

periderm (par'-uh-derm') The protective coat that replaces the epidermis in woody plants during secondary growth, formed of the cork and cork cambium.

peripheral nervous system (PNS) The sensory and motor neurons that connect to the central nervous system.

peripheral protein A protein loosely bound to the surface of a membrane or to part of an integral protein and not embedded in the lipid bilayer.

peristalsis (par'-uh-stal'-sis) (1) Alternating waves of contraction and relaxation in the smooth muscles lining the alimentary canal that push food along the canal. (2) A type of movement on land produced by rhythmic waves of muscle contractions passing from front to back, as in many annelids.

peristome A ring of interlocking, tooth-like structures on the upper part of a moss capsule (sporangium), often specialized for gradual spore discharge.

peritubular capillary One of the tiny blood vessels that form a network surrounding the proximal and distal tubules in the kidney.

peroxisome (puh-rok'-suh-sōm') An organelle containing enzymes that transfer hydrogen atoms from various substrates to oxygen (O_2), producing and then degrading hydrogen peroxide (H_2O_2).

petal A modified leaf of a flowering plant. Petals are the often colourful parts of a flower that advertise it to insects and other pollinators.

petiole (pet'-ē-ōl) The stalk of a leaf, which joins the leaf to a node of the stem.

pH A measure of hydrogen ion concentration equal to $-\log [H^+]$ and ranging in value from 0 to 14.

phage (fāj) A virus that infects bacteria; also called a bacteriophage.

phagocytosis (fag'-ō-sī-tō'-sis) A type of endocytosis in which large particulate substances or small organisms are taken up by a cell. It is carried out by some protists and by certain immune cells of animals (in mammals, mainly macrophages, neutrophils, and dendritic cells).

pharyngeal cleft (fuh-rin'-jē-ul) In chordate embryos, one of the grooves that separate a series of pouches along the sides of the pharynx and may develop into a pharyngeal slit.

pharyngeal slit (fuh-rin'-jē-ul) In chordate embryos, one of the slits that form from the pharyngeal clefts and communicate to the outside, later developing into gill slits in many vertebrates.

pharynx (far'-inks) (1) An area in the vertebrate throat where air and food passages cross. (2) In flatworms, the muscular tube that protrudes from the ventral side of the worm and ends in the mouth.

phase change A shift from one developmental phase to another.

phenotype (fē'-nō-tīp) The observable physical and physiological traits of an organism, which are determined by its genetic makeup.

pheromone (far'-uh-mōn) In animals and fungi, a small molecule released into the environment that functions in communication between members of the same species. In animals, it acts much like a hormone in influencing physiology and behaviour.

phloem (flō'-em) Vascular plant tissue consisting of living cells arranged into elongated tubes that transport sugar and other organic nutrients throughout the plant.

phloem sap The sugar-rich solution carried through a plant's sieve tubes.

phosphate group A chemical group consisting of a phosphorus atom bonded to four oxygen atoms; important in energy transfer.

phospholipid (fos'-fō-lip'-id) A lipid made up of glycerol joined to two fatty acids and a phosphate group. The hydrocarbon chains of the fatty acids act as nonpolar, hydrophobic tails, while the rest of the molecule acts as a polar, hydrophilic head. Phospholipids form bilayers that function as biological membranes.

phosphorylated intermediate A molecule (often a reactant) with a phosphate group covalently bound to it, making it more reactive (less stable) than the unphosphorylated molecule.

photic zone (fō'-tic) The narrow top layer of an ocean or lake, where light penetrates sufficiently for photosynthesis to occur.

photoautotroph (fō'-tō-ot'-ō-trōf) An organism that harnesses light energy to drive the synthesis of organic compounds from carbon dioxide.

photoheterotroph (fō'-tō-het'-er-ō-trōf) An organism that uses light to generate ATP but must obtain carbon in organic form.

photomorphogenesis Effects of light on plant morphology.

photon (fō'-ton) A quantum, or discrete quantity, of light energy that behaves as if it were a particle.

photoperiodism (fō'-tō-pēr'-ē-ō-dizm) A physiological response to photoperiod, the relative lengths of night and day. An example of photoperiodism is flowering.

photophosphorylation (fō'-tō-fos'-fōr-uh-lā'-shun) The process of generating ATP from ADP and phosphate by means of chemiosmosis, using a proton-motive force generated across the thylakoid membrane of the chloroplast or the membrane of certain prokaryotes during the light reactions of photosynthesis.

photoreceptor An electromagnetic receptor that detects the radiation known as visible light.

photorespiration A metabolic pathway that consumes oxygen and ATP, releases carbon dioxide, and decreases photosynthetic output. Photorespiration generally occurs on hot, dry, bright days, when stomata close and the O_2/CO_2 ratio in the leaf increases, favouring the binding of O_2 rather than CO_2 by rubisco.

photosynthesis (fō'-tō-sin'-thi-sis) The conversion of light energy to chemical energy that is stored in sugars or other organic compounds; occurs in plants, algae, and certain prokaryotes.

photosystem A light-capturing unit located in the thylakoid membrane of the chloroplast or in the membrane of some prokaryotes, consisting of a reaction-centre complex surrounded by numerous light-harvesting complexes. There are two types of photosystems, I and II; they absorb light best at different wavelengths.

photosystem I (PS I) A light-capturing unit in a chloroplast's thylakoid membrane or in the membrane of some prokaryotes; it has two molecules of P700 chlorophyll *a* at its reaction centre.

photosystem II (PS II) One of two light-capturing units in a chloroplast's thylakoid membrane or in the membrane of some prokaryotes; it has two molecules of P680 chlorophyll *a* at its reaction centre.

phototropism (fō'-tō-trō'-pizm) Growth of a plant shoot toward or away from light.

phragmoplast (frag'-mō-plast') An alignment of cytoskeletal elements and Golgi-derived vesicles that forms across the midline of a dividing plant cell.

phyllotaxy (fil'-uh-tak'-sē) The pattern of leaf attachment to the stem of a plant.

phylogenetic species concept A definition of species as the smallest group of individuals that share a common ancestor, forming one branch on the tree of life.

phylogenetic tree A branching diagram that represents a hypothesis about the evolutionary history of a group of organisms.

phylogeny (fī-loj'-uh-nē) The evolutionary history of a species or group of related species.

phylogram A phylogenetic tree wherein the branch lengths are proportional to the amount of change seen in species' characteristics.

phylum (fī'-lum) (plural, **phyla**) In Linnaean classification, the taxonomic category above class.

physiology The processes and functions of an organism.

phytochrome (fī'-tuh-krōm) A type of light receptor in plants that mostly absorbs red light and regulates many plant responses, such as seed germination and shade avoidance.

phytoremediation An emerging technology that seeks to reclaim contaminated areas by taking advantage of some plant species' ability to extract heavy metals and other pollutants from the soil and to concentrate them in easily harvested portions of the plant.

pilus (plural, **pili**) (pī'-lus, pī'-lī) In bacteria, a structure that links one cell to another at the start of conjugation; also known as a sex pilus or conjugation pilus.

pineal gland (pī'-nē-ul) A small gland on the dorsal surface of the vertebrate forebrain that secretes the hormone melatonin.

pinocytosis (pī'-nō-sī-tō'-sis) A type of endocytosis in which the cell ingests extracellular fluid and its dissolved solutes.

pistil A single carpel or a group of fused carpels.

pith Ground tissue that is internal to the vascular tissue in a stem; in many monocot roots, parenchyma cells that form the central core of the vascular cylinder.

pituitary gland (puh-tū'-uh-tār'-ē) An endocrine gland at the base of the hypothalamus; consists of a posterior lobe, which stores and releases two hormones produced by the hypothalamus, and an anterior lobe, which produces and secretes many hormones that regulate diverse body functions.

placenta (pluh-sen'-tuh) A structure in the pregnant uterus for nourishing a viviparous fetus with the mother's blood supply; formed from the uterine lining and embryonic membranes.

placoderm A member of an extinct group of fishlike vertebrates that had jaws and were enclosed in a tough outer armour.

planarian A free-living flatworm found in ponds and streams.

plasma (plaz'-muh) The liquid matrix of blood in which the blood cells are suspended.

plasma cell The antibody-secreting effector cell of humoral immunity. Plasma cells arise from antigen-stimulated B cells.

plasma membrane The membrane at the boundary of every cell that acts as a selective barrier, regulating the cell's chemical composition.

plasmid (plaz'-mid) A small, circular, double-stranded DNA molecule that carries accessory genes separate from those of a bacterial chromosome; in DNA cloning, used as vectors carrying up to about 10 000 base pairs (10 kb) of DNA. Plasmids are also found in some eukaryotes, such as yeasts.

plasmodesma (plaz'-mō-dez'-muh) (plural, **plasmodesmata**) An open channel through the cell wall that connects the cytoplasm of adjacent plant cells, allowing water, small solutes, and some larger molecules to pass between the cells.

plasmodial slime mould (plaz-mō'-dē-ul) A type of protist that has amoeboid cells, flagellated cells, and a plasmodial feeding stage in its life cycle.

plasmodium A single mass of cytoplasm containing many diploid nuclei that forms during the life cycle of some slime moulds.

plasmogamy (plaz-moh'-guh-mē) In fungi, the fusion of the cytoplasm of cells from two individuals; occurs as one stage of sexual reproduction, followed later by karyogamy.

plasmolysis (plaz-mol'-uh-sis) A phenomenon in walled cells in which the cytoplasm shrivels and the plasma membrane pulls away from the cell wall; occurs when the cell loses water to a hypertonic environment.

plastid One of a family of closely related organelles that includes chloroplasts, chromoplasts, and amyloplasts. Plastids are found in cells of photosynthetic eukaryotes.

platelet A pinched-off cytoplasmic fragment of a specialized bone marrow cell. Platelets circulate in the blood and are important in blood clotting.

plate tectonics The theory that the continents are part of great plates of Earth's crust that float on the hot, underlying portion of the mantle. Movements in the mantle cause the continents to move slowly over time.

pleiotropy (plī'-o-truh-pē) The ability of a single gene to have multiple effects.

pluripotent Describing a cell that can give rise to many, but not all, parts of an organism.

point mutation A change in a single nucleotide pair of a gene.

polar covalent bond A covalent bond between atoms that differ in electronegativity. The shared electrons are pulled closer to the more electronegative atom, making it slightly negative and the other atom slightly positive.

polarity A lack of symmetry; structural differences in opposite ends of an organism or structure, such as the root end and shoot end of a plant.

polar molecule A molecule (such as water) with an uneven distribution of charges in different regions of the molecule.

pollen grain In seed plants, a structure consisting of the male gametophyte enclosed within a pollen wall.

pollen tube A tube that forms after germination of the pollen grain and that functions in the delivery of sperm to the ovule.

pollination (pol'-uh-nā'-shun) The transfer of pollen to the part of a seed plant containing the ovules, a process required for fertilization.

poly-A tail A sequence of 50–250 adenine nucleotides added onto the 3' end of a pre-mRNA molecule.

polygamous Referring to a type of relationship in which an individual of one sex mates with several of the other.

polygenic inheritance (pol'-ē-jen'-ik) An additive effect of two or more genes on a single phenotypic character.

polymer (pol'-uh-mer) A long molecule consisting of many similar or identical monomers linked together by covalent bonds.

polymerase chain reaction (PCR) (puh-lim'-uh-rās) A technique for amplifying DNA *in vitro* by incubating it with specific primers, a heat-resistant DNA polymerase, and nucleotides.

polynucleotide (pol'-ē-nū'-klē-ō-tīd) A polymer consisting of many nucleotide monomers in a chain. The nucleotides can be those of DNA or RNA.

polyp The sessile variant of the cnidarian body plan. The alternate form is the medusa.

polypeptide (pol'-ē-pep'-tīd) A polymer of many amino acids linked together by peptide bonds.

polyphyletic (pol'-ē-fī-let'-ik) Pertaining to a group of taxa derived from two or more different ancestors.

polyploidy (pol'-ē-ploy'-dē) A chromosomal alteration in which the organism possesses more than two complete chromosome sets. It is the result of an accident of cell division.

polyribosome (polysome) (pol'-ē-rī'-buh-sōm') A group of several ribosomes attached to, and translating, the same messenger RNA molecule.

polysaccharide (pol'-ē-sak'-uh-rīd) A polymer of many monosaccharides, formed by dehydration reactions.

polytomy (puh-lit'-uh-mē) In a phylogenetic tree, a branch point from which more than two descendant taxa emerge. A polytomy indicates that the evolutionary relationships between the descendant taxa are not yet clear.

pons A portion of the brain that participates in certain automatic, homeostatic functions, such as regulating the breathing centres in the medulla.

population A group of individuals of the same species that live in the same area and interbreed, producing fertile offspring.

population dynamics The study of how complex interactions between biotic and abiotic factors influence variations in population size.

population ecology The study of populations in relation to their environment, including environmental influences on population density and distribution, age structure, and variations in population size.

positional information Molecular cues that control pattern formation in an animal or plant embryonic structure by indicating a cell's location relative to the organism's body axes. These cues elicit a response by genes that regulate development.

positive feedback A form of regulation in which an end product of a process speeds up that process; in physiology, a control mechanism in which a change in a variable triggers a response that reinforces or amplifies the change.

positive pressure breathing A breathing system in which air is forced into the lungs.

posterior Pertaining to the rear, or tail end, of a bilaterally symmetrical animal.

posterior pituitary An extension of the hypothalamus composed of nervous tissue that secretes oxytocin and antidiuretic hormone made in the hypothalamus; a temporary storage site for these hormones.

postzygotic barrier (pōst'-zī-got'-ik) A reproductive barrier that prevents hybrid zygotes produced by two different species from developing into viable, fertile adults.

potential energy The energy that matter possesses as a result of its location or spatial arrangement (structure).

predation An interaction between species in which one species, the predator, eats the other, the prey.

pregnancy The condition of carrying one or more embryos in the uterus.

prepuce (prē'-pyūs) A fold of skin covering the head of the clitoris or penis.

pressure potential (Ψ_p) A component of water potential that consists of the physical pressure on a solution, which can be positive, zero, or negative.

prezygotic barrier (prē'-zī-got'-ik) A reproductive barrier that impedes mating between species or hinders fertilization if interspecific mating is attempted.

primary cell wall In plants, a relatively thin and flexible layer that surrounds the plasma membrane of a young cell.

primary consumer An herbivore; an organism that eats plants or other autotrophs.

primary electron acceptor In the thylakoid membrane of a chloroplast or in the membrane of some prokaryotes, a specialized molecule that shares the reaction-centre complex with a pair of chlorophyll *a* molecules and that accepts an electron from them.

primary endosymbiosis The process whereby one bacterium is engulfed by another organism.

primary growth Growth produced by apical meristems, lengthening stems and roots.

primary immune response The initial adaptive immune response to an antigen, which appears after a lag of about 10 to 17 days.

primary oocyte (ō'-uh-sīt) An oocyte prior to completion of meiosis I.

primary producer An autotroph, usually a photosynthetic organism. Collectively, autotrophs make up the trophic level of an ecosystem that ultimately supports all other levels.

primary production The amount of light energy converted to chemical energy (organic compounds) by the autotrophs in an ecosystem during a given time period.

primary structure The level of protein structure referring to the specific linear sequence of amino acids.

primary succession A type of ecological succession that occurs in an area where there were originally no organisms present and where soil has not yet formed.

primary transcript An initial RNA transcript from any gene; also called pre-mRNA when transcribed from a protein-coding gene.

primary visual cortex The destination in the occipital lobe of the cerebrum for most of the axons from the lateral geniculate nuclei.

primase An enzyme that joins RNA nucleotides to make a primer during DNA replication, using the parental DNA strand as a template.

primer A short stretch of RNA with a free 3' end, bound by complementary base pairing to the template strand and elongated with DNA nucleotides during DNA replication.

primitive streak A thickening along the future anterior-posterior axis on the surface of an early avian or mammalian embryo, caused by a piling up of cells as they congregate at the midline before moving into the embryo.

prion An infectious agent that is a misfolded version of a normal cellular protein. Prions appear to increase in number by converting correctly folded versions of the protein to more prions.

problem solving The cognitive activity of devising a method to proceed from one state to another in the face of real or apparent obstacles.

producer An organism that produces organic compounds from CO_2 by harnessing light energy (in photosynthesis) or by oxidizing inorganic chemicals (in chemosynthetic reactions carried out by some prokaryotes).

product A material resulting from a chemical reaction.

production efficiency The percentage of energy stored in assimilated food that is not used for respiration or eliminated as waste.

progesterone A steroid hormone that prepares the uterus for pregnancy; the major progestin in mammals.

progestin Any steroid hormone with progesterone-like activity.

progymnosperm (prō'-jim'-nō-sperm) An extinct seedless vascular plant that may be ancestral to seed plants.

prokaryotic cell (prō-kār'-ē-ot'-ik) A type of cell lacking a membrane-enclosed nucleus and membrane-enclosed organelles. Organisms with prokaryotic cells (bacteria and archaea) are called prokaryotes.

prolactin A hormone produced and secreted by the anterior pituitary with a great diversity of effects in different vertebrate species. In mammals, it stimulates growth of and milk production by the mammary glands.

proliferative phase That portion of the uterine (menstrual) cycle when the endometrium regenerates and thickens.

prometaphase The second stage of mitosis, in which the nuclear envelope fragments and the spindle microtubules attach to the kinetochores of the chromosomes.

promiscuous Referring to a type of relationship in which mating occurs with no strong pair-bonds or lasting relationships.

promoter A specific nucleotide sequence in the DNA of a gene that binds RNA polymerase, positioning it to start transcribing RNA at the appropriate place.

prophage (prō'-fāj) A phage genome that has been inserted into a specific site on a bacterial chromosome.

prophase The first stage of mitosis, in which the chromatin condenses into discrete chromosomes visible with a light microscope, the mitotic spindle begins to form, and the nucleolus disappears but the nucleus remains intact.

prostaglandin (pros'-tuh-glan'-din) One of a group of modified fatty acids secreted by virtually all tissues and performing a wide variety of functions as local regulators.

prostate gland (pros'-tāt) A gland in human males that secretes an acid-neutralizing component of semen.

protease An enzyme that digests proteins by hydrolysis.

proteasome A giant protein complex that recognizes and destroys proteins tagged for elimination by the small protein ubiquitin.

protein (prō'-tēn) A biologically functional molecule consisting of one or more poly-peptides folded and coiled into a specific three-dimensional structure.

protein kinase An enzyme that transfers phosphate groups from ATP to a protein, thus phosphorylating the protein.

protein phosphatase An enzyme that removes phosphate groups from (dephosphorylates) proteins, often functioning to reverse the effect of a protein kinase.

proteoglycan (prō'-tē-ō-glī'-kan) A large molecule consisting of a small core protein with many carbohydrate chains attached, found in the extracellular matrix of animal cells. A proteoglycan may consist of up to 95% carbohydrate.

proteome The entire set of proteins expressed by a given cell or group of cells.

proteomics (prō'-tē-ō'-miks) The systematic study of the full protein sets (proteomes) encoded by genomes.

protist An informal term applied to any eukaryote that is not a plant, animal, or fungus. Most protists are unicellular, though some are colonial or multicellular.

protocell An abiotic precursor of a living cell that had a membrane-like structure and that maintained an internal chemistry different from that of its surroundings.

proton (prō'-ton) A subatomic particle with a single positive electrical charge, with a mass of about 1.7×10^{-24} g, found in the nucleus of an atom.

proton pump An active transport protein in a cell membrane that uses ATP to transport hydrogen ions out of a cell against their concentration gradient, generating a membrane potential in the process.

protonema (plural, **protonemata**) A mass of green, branched, one-cell-thick filaments produced by germinating moss spores.

protonephridium (prō'-tō-nuh-frid'-ē-uhm) (plural, **protonephridia**) An excretory system, such as the flame bulb system of flatworms, consisting of a network of tubules lacking internal openings.

proton-motive force The potential energy stored in the form of a proton electrochemical gradient, generated by the pumping of hydrogen ions (H^+) across a biological membrane during chemiosmosis.

proto-oncogene (prō'-tō-on'-kō-jēn) A normal cellular gene that has the potential to become an oncogene.

protoplast The living part of a plant cell, which also includes the plasma membrane.

protostome development In animals, a developmental mode distinguished by the development of the mouth from the blastopore; often also characterized by spiral cleavage and by the body cavity forming when solid masses of mesoderm split.

provirus A viral genome that is permanently inserted into a host genome.

proximal tubule In the vertebrate kidney, the portion of a nephron immediately downstream from Bowman's capsule that conveys and helps refine filtrate.

pseudocoelomate (sū'-dō-sē'-lō-māt) An animal whose body cavity is lined by tissue derived from mesoderm and endoderm.

pseudogene (sū'-dō-jēn) A DNA segment very similar to a real gene but which does not yield a functional product; a DNA segment that formerly functioned as a gene but has become inactivated in a particular species because of mutation.

pseudopodium (sū'-dō-pō'-dē-um) (plural, **pseudopodia**) A cellular extension of amoeboid cells used in moving and feeding.

pterosaur Winged reptile that lived during the Mesozoic era.

pulmocutaneous circuit A branch of the circulatory system in many amphibians that supplies the lungs and skin.

pulmonary circuit The branch of the circulatory system that supplies the lungs.

pulse The rhythmic bulging of the artery walls with each heartbeat.

punctuated equilibria In the fossil record, long periods of apparent stasis, in which a species undergoes little or no morphological change, interrupted by relatively brief periods of sudden change.

Punnett square A diagram used in the study of inheritance to show the predicted genotypic results of random fertilization in genetic crosses between individuals of known genotype.

pupil The opening in the iris, which admits light into the interior of the vertebrate eye. Muscles in the iris regulate its size.

purine (pyū'-rēn) One of two types of nitrogenous bases found in nucleotides, characterized by a six-membered ring fused to a five-membered ring. Adenine (A) and guanine (G) are purines.

pyrimidine (puh-rim'-uh-dēn) One of two types of nitrogenous bases found in nucleotides, characterized by a six-membered ring. Cytosine (C), thymine (T), and uracil (U) are pyrimidines.

quantitative character A heritable feature that varies continuously over a range rather than in an either-or fashion.

quaternary structure (kwot-er-nār'-ē) The particular shape of a complex, aggregate protein, defined by the characteristic three-dimensional arrangement of its constituent subunits, each a polypeptide.

radial cleavage A type of embryonic development in deuterostomes in which the planes of cell division that transform the zygote into a ball

of cells are either parallel or perpendicular to the vertical axis of the embryo, thereby aligning tiers of cells one above the other.

radial symmetry Symmetry in which the body is shaped like a pie or barrel (lacking a left side and a right side) and can be divided into mirror-imaged halves by any plane through its central axis.

radiation The emission of electromagnetic waves by all objects warmer than absolute zero.

radicle An embryonic root of a plant.

radioactive isotope An isotope (an atomic form of a chemical element) that is unstable; the nucleus decays spontaneously, giving off detectable particles and energy.

radiolarian A protist, usually marine, with a shell generally made of silica and pseudopodia that radiate from the central body.

radiometric dating A method for determining the absolute age of rocks and fossils, based on the half-life of radioactive isotopes.

radula A straplike scraping organ used by many molluscs during feeding.

ras **gene** A gene that codes for Ras, a G protein that relays a growth signal from a growth factor receptor on the plasma membrane to a cascade of protein kinases, ultimately resulting in stimulation of the cell cycle.

ratite (rat'-īt) Member of the group of flightless birds.

ray-finned fish Member of the class Actinopterygii, aquatic osteichthyans with fins supported by long, flexible rays, including tuna, bass, and herring.

reabsorption In excretory systems, the recovery of solutes and water from filtrate.

reactant A starting material in a chemical reaction.

reaction-centre complex A complex of proteins associated with a special pair of chlorophyll *a* molecules and a primary electron acceptor. Located centrally in a photosystem, this complex triggers the light reactions of photosynthesis. Excited by light energy, the pair of chlorophylls donates an electron to the primary electron acceptor, which passes an electron to an electron transport chain.

reading frame On an mRNA, the triplet grouping of ribonucleotides used by the translation machinery during polypeptide synthesis.

realized niche The ecological space occupied by a species when that species' competitors are present.

receptacle The base of a flower; the part of the stem that is the site of attachment of the floral organs.

reception In cellular communication, the first step of a signaling pathway in which a signaling molecule is detected by a receptor molecule on or in the cell.

receptor-mediated endocytosis (en'-dō-sī-tō'-sis) The movement of specific molecules into a cell by the inward budding of vesicles containing proteins with receptor sites specific to the molecules being taken in; enables a cell to acquire bulk quantities of specific substances.

receptor potential An initial response of a receptor cell to a stimulus, consisting of a change in voltage across the receptor membrane proportional to the stimulus strength.

receptor tyrosine kinase (RTK) A receptor protein spanning the plasma membrane, the cytoplasmic (intracellular) part of which can catalyze the transfer of a phosphate group from ATP to a tyrosine on another protein. Receptor tyrosine kinases often respond to the binding of a signalling molecule by dimerizing and then phosphorylating a tyrosine on the cytoplasmic portion of the other receptor in the dimer. The phosphorylated tyrosines on the receptors then activate other signal transduction proteins within the cell.

recessive allele An allele whose phenotypic effect is not observed in a heterozygote.

reciprocal altruism Altruistic behaviour between unrelated individuals, whereby the altruistic individual benefits in the future when the beneficiary reciprocates.

recombinant chromosome A chromosome created when crossing over combines DNA from two parents into a single chromosome.

recombinant DNA molecule A DNA molecule made *in vitro* with segments from different sources.

recombinant type (recombinant) An offspring whose phenotype differs from that of the true-breeding P generation parents; also refers to the phenotype itself.

rectum The terminal portion of the large intestine, where the feces are stored prior to elimination.

red alga A photosynthetic protist, named for its colour, which results from a red pigment that masks the green of chlorophyll. Most red algae are multicellular and marine.

redox reaction (rē′-doks) A chemical reaction involving the complete or partial transfer of one or more electrons from one reactant to another; short for reduction-oxidation reaction.

reducing agent The electron donor in a redox reaction.

reduction The complete or partial addition of electrons to a substance involved in a redox reaction.

reflex An automatic reaction to a stimulus, mediated by the spinal cord or lower brain.

refractory period (rē-frakt′-ōr-ē) The short time immediately after an action potential in which the neuron cannot respond to another stimulus, owing to the inactivation of voltage-gated sodium channels.

regulator An animal for which mechanisms of homeostasis moderate internal changes in a particular variable in the face of external fluctuation of that variable.

regulatory gene A gene that codes for a protein, such as a repressor, that controls the transcription of another gene or group of genes.

reinforcement In evolutionary biology, a process in which a process in which natural selection strengthens prezygotic barriers to reproduction, thus reducing the chances of hybrid formation. Such a process is likely to occur only if hybrid

offspring are less fit than members of the parent species.

relative abundance The proportional abundance of different species in a community.

relative fitness The contribution an individual makes to the gene pool of the next generation, relative to the contributions of other individuals in the population.

renal cortex The outer portion of the vertebrate kidney.

renal medulla The inner portion of the vertebrate kidney, beneath the renal cortex.

renal pelvis The funnel-shaped chamber that receives processed filtrate from the vertebrate kidney's collecting ducts and is drained by the ureter.

renin-angiotensin-aldosterone system (RAAS) A hormone cascade pathway that helps regulate blood pressure and blood volume.

repetitive DNA Nucleotide sequences, usually noncoding, that are present in many copies in a eukaryotic genome. The repeated units may be short and arranged tandemly (in series) or long and dispersed in the genome.

replication fork A Y-shaped region on a replicating DNA molecule where the parental strands are being unwound and new strands are being synthesized.

repressor A protein that inhibits gene transcription. In prokaryotes, repressors bind to the DNA in or near the promoter. In eukaryotes, repressors may bind to control elements within enhancers, to activators, or to other proteins in a way that blocks activators from binding to DNA.

reproductive isolation The existence of biological factors (barriers) that impede members of two species from producing viable, fertile offspring.

reproductive table An age-specific summary of the reproductive rates in a population.

reptile Member of the clade of amniotes that includes tuataras, lizards, snakes, turtles, crocodilians, and birds.

residual volume The amount of air that remains in the lungs after forceful exhalation.

resource partitioning The division of environmental resources by coexisting species such that the niche of each species differs by one or more significant factors from the niches of all coexisting species.

respiratory pigment A protein that transports oxygen in blood or hemolymph.

response (1) In cellular communication, the change in a specific cellular activity brought about by a transduced signal from outside the cell. (2) In feedback regulation, a physiological activity triggered by a change in a variable.

resting membrane potential The membrane potential characteristic of a nonconducting excitable cell, with the inside of the cell more negative than the outside.

restriction enzyme An endonuclease (type of enzyme) that recognizes and cuts DNA molecules foreign to a bacterium (such as phage genomes). The enzyme cuts at specific nucleotide sequences (restriction sites).

restriction fragment A DNA segment that results from the cutting of DNA by a restriction enzyme.

restriction site A specific sequence on a DNA strand that is recognized and cut by a restriction enzyme.

reticular formation (re-tik′-yū-ler) A diffuse network of neurons in the core of the brainstem that filters information travelling to the cerebral cortex.

retina (ret′-i-nuh) The innermost layer of the vertebrate eye, containing photoreceptor cells (rods and cones) and neurons; transmits images formed by the lens to the brain via the optic nerve.

retinal The light-absorbing pigment in rods and cones of the vertebrate eye.

retrotransposon (re′-trō-trans-pō′-zon) A transposable element that moves within a genome by means of an RNA intermediate, a transcript of the retrotransposon DNA.

retrovirus (re′-trō-vī′-rus) An RNA virus that replicates by transcribing its RNA into DNA and then inserting the DNA into a cellular chromosome; an important class of cancer-causing viruses.

reverse transcriptase (tran-skrip′-tās) An enzyme encoded by certain viruses (retroviruses) that uses RNA as a template for DNA synthesis.

reverse transcriptase–polymerase chain reaction (RT-PCR) A technique for determining expression of a particular gene. It uses reverse transcriptase and DNA polymerase to synthesize cDNA from all the mRNA in a sample and then subjects the cDNA to PCR amplification using primers specific for the gene of interest.

Rhizaria (rī-za′-rē-uh) One of five supergroups of eukaryotes proposed in a current hypothesis of the evolutionary history of eukaryotes; a morphologically diverse protist clade that is defined by DNA similarities. *See also* Excavata, Chromalveolata, Archaeplastida, and Unikonta.

rhizobacterium A soil bacterium whose population size is much enhanced in the rhizosphere, the soil region close to a plant's roots.

rhizoid (rī′-zoyd) A long, tubular single cell or filament of cells that anchors bryophytes to the ground. Unlike roots, rhizoids are not composed of tissues, lack specialized conducting cells, and do not play a primary role in water and mineral absorption.

rhizosphere The soil region close to plant roots and characterized by a high level of microbiological activity.

rhodopsin (rō-dop′-sin) A visual pigment consisting of retinal and opsin. Upon absorbing light, the retinal changes shape and dissociates from the opsin.

rhythm method A form of contraception that relies on refraining from sexual intercourse when conception is most likely to occur; also called natural family planning.

ribonucleic acid (RNA) (rī′-bō-nū-klā′-ik) A type of nucleic acid consisting of a polynucleotide made up of nucleotide monomers with a ribose sugar and the nitrogenous bases adenine (A), cytosine (C), guanine (G), and uracil (U); usually single-stranded; functions in protein synthesis, gene regulation, and as the genome of some viruses.

ribose The sugar component of RNA nucleotides.

ribosomal RNA (rRNA) (rī′-buh-sō′-mul) RNA molecules that, together with proteins, make up ribosomes; the most abundant type of RNA.

ribosome (rī′-buh-sōm′) A complex of rRNA and protein molecules that functions as a site of protein synthesis in the cytoplasm; consists of a large and a small subunit. In eukaryotic cells, each subunit is assembled in the nucleolus. *See also* nucleolus.

ribozyme (rī′-buh-zīm) An RNA molecule that functions as an enzyme, such as an intron that catalyzes its own removal during RNA splicing.

RNA interference (RNAi) A technique used to silence the expression of selected genes. RNAi uses synthetic double-stranded RNA molecules that match the sequence of a particular gene to trigger the breakdown of the gene's messenger RNA.

RNA polymerase An enzyme that links ribonucleotides into a growing RNA chain during transcription, based on complementary binding to nucleotides on a DNA template strand.

RNA processing Modification of RNA primary transcripts, including splicing out of introns, joining together of exons, and alteration of the 5′ and 3′ ends.

RNA splicing After synthesis of a eukaryotic primary RNA transcript, the removal of portions of the transcript (introns) that will not be included in the mRNA and the joining together of the remaining portions (exons).

rod A rodlike cell in the retina of the vertebrate eye, sensitive to low light intensity.

root An organ in vascular plants that anchors the plant and enables it to absorb water and minerals from the soil.

root cap A cone of cells at the tip of a plant root that protects the apical meristem.

rooted Describing a phylogenetic tree that contains a branch point (often, the one farthest to the left) representing the most recent common ancestor of all taxa in the tree.

root hair A tiny extension of a root epidermal cell, growing just behind the root tip and increasing surface area for absorption of water and minerals.

root pressure Pressure exerted in the roots of plants as the result of osmosis, causing exudation from cut stems and guttation of water from leaves.

root system All of a plant's roots, which anchor it in the soil, absorb and transport minerals and water, and store food.

rough ER That portion of the endoplasmic reticulum with ribosomes attached.

round window In the mammalian ear, the point of contact where vibrations of the stapes create a travelling series of pressure waves in the fluid of the cochlea.

R plasmid A bacterial plasmid carrying genes that confer resistance to certain antibiotics.

r-selection Selection for life history traits that maximize reproductive success in uncrowded environments; also called density-independent selection.

rubisco (rū-bis′-kō) Ribulose bisphosphate (RuBP) carboxylase, the enzyme that catalyzes the first step of the Calvin cycle (the addition of CO_2 to RuBP).

ruminant (rū′-muh-nent) An animal, such as a cow or a sheep, with multiple stomach compartments specialized for an herbivorous diet.

S phase The synthesis phase of the cell cycle; the portion of interphase during which DNA is replicated.

saccule In the vertebrate ear, a chamber in the vestibule behind the oval window that participates in the sense of balance.

salicylic acid (sal′-i-sil′-ik) A signalling molecule in plants that may be partially responsible for activating systemic acquired resistance to pathogens.

salivary amylase (am′-uh-lās′) An enzyme that hydrolyzes starch (a glucose polymer from plants) and glycogen (a glucose polymer from animals) into smaller polysaccharides and the disaccharide maltose.

salivary gland A gland associated with the oral cavity that secretes substances that lubricate food and begin the process of chemical digestion.

salt A compound resulting from the formation of an ionic bond; also called an ionic compound.

saltatory conduction (sol′-tuh-tōr′-ē) Rapid transmission of a nerve impulse along an axon, resulting from the action potential jumping from one node of Ranvier to another, skipping the myelin-sheathed regions of membrane.

saprotroph Saprotrophic fungi that get their nutrition from dead plant material and other non-living organic materials.

SAR clade One of four major eukaryotic supergroups. SAR is an acronym derived from the names of the three main groups making up the clade: stramenopiles, alveolates, and rhizarians.

sarcomere (sar′-kō-mēr) The fundamental, repeating unit of striated muscle, delimited by the Z lines.

sarcoplasmic reticulum (SR) (sar′-kō-plaz′-mik ruh-tik′-yū-lum) A specialized endoplasmic reticulum that regulates the calcium concentration in the cytosol of muscle cells.

saturated fatty acid A fatty acid in which all carbons in the hydrocarbon tail are connected by single bonds, thus maximizing the number of hydrogen atoms that are attached to the carbon skeleton.

savanna A tropical grassland biome with scattered individual trees and large herbivores and maintained by occasional fires and drought.

scaffolding protein A type of large relay protein to which several other relay proteins are simultaneously attached, increasing the efficiency of signal transduction.

scanning electron microscope (SEM) A microscope that uses an electron beam to scan the surface of a sample, coated with metal atoms, to study details of its topography.

schizophrenia (skit′-suh-frē′-nē-uh) A severe mental disturbance characterized by psychotic episodes in which patients have a distorted perception of reality.

Schwann cell A type of glial cell that forms insulating myelin sheaths around the axons of neurons in the peripheral nervous system.

science An approach to understanding the natural world.

scion (sī′-un) The twig grafted onto the stock when making a graft.

sclereid (sklār′-ē-id) A short, irregular sclerenchyma cell in nutshells and seed coats. Sclereids are scattered throughout the parenchyma of some plants.

sclerenchyma cell (skluh-ren′-kim-uh) A rigid, supportive plant cell type usually lacking a protoplast and possessing thick secondary walls strengthened by lignin at maturity.

scrotum A pouch of skin outside the abdomen that houses the testes; functions in maintaining the testes at the lower temperature required for spermatogenesis.

second law of thermodynamics The principle stating that every energy transfer or transformation increases the entropy of the universe. Usable forms of energy are at least partly converted to heat.

secondary cell wall In plant cells, a strong and durable matrix that is often deposited in several laminated layers around the plasma membrane and provides protection and support.

secondary consumer A carnivore that eats herbivores.

secondary endosymbiosis A process in eukaryotic evolution in which a heterotrophic eukaryotic cell engulfed a photosynthetic eukaryotic cell, which survived in a symbiotic relationship inside the heterotrophic cell.

secondary growth Growth produced by lateral meristems, thickening the roots and shoots of woody plants.

secondary immune response The adaptive immune response elicited on second or subsequent exposures to a particular antigen. The secondary immune response is more rapid, of greater magnitude, and of longer duration than the primary immune response.

secondary oocyte (ō′-uh-sīt) An oocyte that has completed the first of the two meiotic divisions.

secondary production The amount of chemical energy in consumers' food that is converted to their own new biomass during a given time period.

secondary structure Regions of repetitive coiling or folding of the polypeptide backbone of a protein due to hydrogen bonding between constituents of the backbone (not the side chains).

secondary succession A type of succession that occurs where an existing community has been cleared by some disturbance that leaves the soil or substrate intact.

second messenger A small, nonprotein, water-soluble molecule or ion, such as a calcium ion (Ca^{2+}) or cyclic AMP, that relays a signal to a cell's interior in response to a signalling molecule bound by a signal receptor protein.

secretion (1) The discharge of molecules synthesized by a cell. (2) The discharge of wastes from the body fluid into the filtrate.

secretory phase That portion of the uterine (menstrual) cycle when the endometrium continues to thicken, becomes more vascularized, and develops glands that secrete a fluid rich in glycogen.

seed An adaptation of some terrestrial plants consisting of an embryo packaged along with a store of food within a protective coat.

seed coat A tough outer covering of a seed, formed from the outer coat of an ovule. In a flowering plant, the seed coat encloses and protects the embryo and endosperm.

seedless vascular plant An informal name for a plant that has vascular tissue but lacks seeds. Seedless vascular plants form a paraphyletic group that includes the phyla Lycophyta (club mosses and their relatives) and Pterophyta (ferns and their relatives).

selective permeability A property of biological membranes that allows them to regulate the passage of substances across them.

self-incompatibility The ability of a seed plant to reject its own pollen and sometimes the pollen of closely related individuals.

semelparity Reproduction in which an organism produces all of its offspring in a single event; also known as big-bang reproduction.

semen (sē'-mun) The fluid that is ejaculated by the male during orgasm; contains sperm and secretions from several glands of the male reproductive tract.

semicircular canals A three-part chamber of the inner ear that functions in maintaining equilibrium.

semiconservative model Type of DNA replication in which the replicated double helix consists of one old strand, derived from the parental molecule, and one newly made strand.

semilunar valve A valve located at each exit of the heart, where the aorta leaves the left ventricle and the pulmonary artery leaves the right ventricle.

seminal vesicle (sem'-i-nul ves'-i-kul) A gland in males that secretes a fluid component of semen that lubricates and nourishes sperm.

seminiferous tubule (sem'-i-nif'-er-us) A highly coiled tube in the testis in which sperm are produced.

senescence (se-nes'-ens) The growth phase in a plant or plant part (as a leaf) from full maturity to death.

sensitive period A limited phase in an animal's development when learning of particular behaviours can take place; also called a critical period.

sensor In homeostasis, a receptor that detects a stimulus.

sensory adaptation The tendency of sensory neurons to become less sensitive when they are stimulated repeatedly.

sensory neuron A nerve cell that receives information from the internal or external environment and transmits signals to the central nervous system.

sensory reception The detection of a stimulus by sensory cells.

sensory receptor An organ, cell, or structure within a cell that responds to specific stimuli from an organism's external or internal environment.

sensory transduction The conversion of stimulus energy to a change in the membrane potential of a sensory receptor cell.

sepal (sē'-pul) A modified leaf in angiosperms that helps enclose and protect a flower bud before it opens.

septum (plural, **septa**) One of the cross-walls that divide a fungal hypha into cells. Septa generally have pores large enough to allow ribosomes, mitochondria, and even nuclei to flow from cell to cell.

serial endosymbiosis A hypothesis for the origin of eukaryotes consisting of a sequence of endosymbiotic events in which mitochondria, chloroplasts, and perhaps other cellular structures were derived from small prokaryotes that had been engulfed by larger cells.

serotonin (ser'-uh-tō'-nin) A neurotransmitter, synthesized from the amino acid tryptophan, that functions in the central nervous system.

seta (sē'-tuh) (plural, **setae**) The elongated stalk of a bryophyte sporophyte.

set point In homeostasis in animals, a value maintained for a particular variable, such as body temperature or solute concentration.

sex chromosome A chromosome responsible for determining the sex of an individual.

sex-linked gene A gene located on either sex chromosome. Most sex-linked genes are on the X chromosome and show distinctive patterns of inheritance; there are very few genes on the Y chromosome.

sexual dimorphism (dī-mōr'-fizm) Differences between the secondary sex characteristics of males and females.

sexual reproduction A type of reproduction in which two parents give rise to offspring that have unique combinations of genes inherited from both parents via the gametes.

sexual selection A form of selection in which individuals with certain inherited characteristics are more likely than other individuals to obtain mates.

Shannon diversity An index of community diversity symbolized by H and represented by the equation $H = -(p_A \ln p_A + p_B \ln p_B + p_C \ln p_C + ...)$, where A, B, C ... are species, p is the relative abundance of each species, and ln is the natural logarithm.

shared ancestral character A character, shared by members of a particular clade, that originated in an ancestor that is not a member of that clade.

shared derived character An evolutionary novelty that is unique to a particular clade.

shoot system The aerial portion of a plant body, consisting of stems, leaves, and (in angiosperms) flowers.

short tandem repeat (STR) Simple sequence DNA containing multiple tandemly repeated units of two to five nucleotides. Variations in STRs act as genetic markers in STR analysis, used to prepare genetic profiles.

short-day plant A plant that flowers (usually in late summer, fall, or winter) only when the light period is shorter than a critical length.

short-term memory The ability to hold information, anticipations, or goals for a time and then release them if they become irrelevant.

sickle-cell disease A recessively inherited human blood disorder in which a single nucleotide change in the β-globin gene causes hemoglobin to aggregate, changing red blood cell shape and causing multiple symptoms in afflicted individuals.

sieve plate An end wall in a sieve-tube element, which facilitates the flow of phloem sap in angiosperm sieve tubes.

sieve-tube element A living cell that conducts sugars and other organic nutrients in the phloem of angiosperms; also called a sieve-tube member. Connected end to end, they form sieve tubes.

sign stimulus An external sensory cue that triggers a fixed action pattern by an animal.

signal In animal behaviour, transmission of a stimulus from one animal to another. The term is also used in the context of communication in other kinds of organisms and in cell-to-cell communication in all multicellular organisms.

signal peptide A sequence of about 20 amino acids at or near the leading (amino) end of a polypeptide that targets it to the endoplasmic reticulum or other organelles in a eukaryotic cell.

signal-recognition particle (SRP) A protein-RNA complex that recognizes a signal peptide as it emerges from a ribosome and helps direct the ribosome to the endoplasmic reticulum (ER) by binding to a receptor protein on the ER.

signal transduction The linkage of a mechanical, chemical, or electromagnetic stimulus to a specific cellular response.

signal transduction pathway A series of steps linking a mechanical, chemical, or electrical stimulus to a specific cellular response.

silent mutation A nucleotide-pair substitution that has no observable effect on the phenotype; for example, within a gene, a mutation that results in a codon that codes for the same amino acid.

simple fruit A fruit derived from a single carpel or several fused carpels.

simple sequence DNA A DNA sequence that contains many copies of tandemly repeated short sequences.

single bond A single covalent bond; the sharing of a pair of valence electrons by two atoms.

single circulation A circulatory system consisting of a single pump and circuit, in which blood passes from the sites of gas exchange to the rest of the body before returning to the heart.

single-lens eye The camera-like eye found in some jellies, polychaete worms, spiders, and many molluscs.

single nucleotide polymorphism (SNP) A single base-pair site in a genome where nucleotide variation is found in at least 1% of the population.

single-strand binding protein A protein that binds to the unpaired DNA strands during DNA replication, stabilizing them and holding them apart while they serve as templates for the synthesis of complementary strands of DNA.

sinoatrial (SA) node A region in the right atrium of the heart that sets the rate and timing at which all cardiac muscle cells contract; the pacemaker.

sister chromatids Two copies of a duplicated chromosome attached to each other by proteins at the centromere and, sometimes, along the arms. While joined, two sister chromatids make up one chromosome. Chromatids are eventually separated during mitosis or meiosis II.

sister taxa Groups of organisms that share an immediate common ancestor and hence are each other's closest relatives.

skeletal muscle A type of striated muscle that is generally responsible for the voluntary movements of the body.

sliding-filament model The idea that muscle contraction is based on the movement of thin (actin) filaments along thick (myosin) filaments, shortening the sarcomere, the basic unit of muscle organization.

slow block to polyspermy The formation of the fertilization envelope and other changes in an egg's surface that prevent fusion of the egg with more than one sperm. The slow block begins about 1 minute after fertilization.

slow-twitch fibre A muscle fibre that can sustain long contractions.

small interfering RNA (siRNA) One of multiple small, single-stranded RNA molecules generated by cellular machinery from a long, linear, double-stranded RNA molecule. The siRNA associates with one or more proteins in a complex that can degrade or prevent translation of an mRNA with a complementary sequence. In some cases, siRNA can also block transcription by promoting chromatin modification.

small intestine The longest section of the alimentary canal, so named because of its small diameter compared with that of the large intestine; the principal site of the enzymatic hydrolysis of food macromolecules and the absorption of nutrients.

smooth ER That portion of the endoplasmic reticulum that is free of ribosomes.

smooth muscle A type of muscle lacking the striations of skeletal and cardiac muscle because of the uniform distribution of myosin filaments in the cells; responsible for involuntary body activities.

social learning Modification of behaviour through the observation of other individuals.

sociobiology The study of social behaviour based on evolutionary theory.

sodium-potassium pump A transport protein in the plasma membrane of animal cells that actively transports sodium out of the cell and potassium into the cell.

soil horizon A soil layer with physical characteristics that differ from those of the layers above or beneath.

solute (sol′-yūt) A substance that is dissolved in a solution.

solute potential (Ψ_S) A component of water potential that is proportional to the molarity of a solution and that measures the effect of solutes on the direction of water movement; also called osmotic potential, it can be either zero or negative.

solution A liquid that is a homogeneous mixture of two or more substances.

solvent The dissolving agent of a solution. Water is the most versatile solvent known.

somatic cell (sō-mat′-ik) Any cell in a multicellular organism except a sperm or egg or their precursors.

somite One of a series of blocks of mesoderm that exist in pairs just lateral to the notochord in a vertebrate embryo.

soredium (plural, **soredia**) In lichens, a small cluster of fungal hyphae with embedded algae.

sorus (plural, **sori**) A cluster of sporangia on a fern sporophyll. Sori may be arranged in various patterns, such as parallel lines or dots, which are useful in fern identification.

spatial learning The establishment of a memory that reflects the environment's spatial structure.

spatial summation A phenomenon of neural integration in which the membrane potential of the postsynaptic cell is determined by the combined effect of EPSPs or IPSPs produced nearly simultaneously by different synapses.

speciation (spē′-sē-ā′-shun) An evolutionary process in which one species splits into two or more species.

species (spē′-sēz) A population or group of populations whose members have the potential to interbreed in nature and produce viable, fertile offspring, but do not produce viable, fertile offspring with members of other such groups.

species-area curve The biodiversity pattern that shows that the larger the geographic area of a community is, the more species it has.

species composition The number and variety of species that make up a community.

species richness The number of species in a biological community.

species transplant experiment An experiment that can be conducted to determine if a species' potential range is greater than its actual range. The experiment involves transplanting some organisms from one area to another area.

specific heat The amount of heat that must be absorbed or lost for 1 g of a substance to change its temperature by 1°C.

spectrophotometer An instrument that measures the proportions of light of different wavelengths absorbed and transmitted by a pigment solution.

sperm The male gamete.

spermatheca (sper′-muh-thē′-kuh) In many insects, a sac in the female reproductive system where sperm are stored.

spermatogenesis The continuous and prolific production of mature sperm cells in the testis.

spermatogonium (plural, **spermatogonia**) A cell that divides mitotically to form spermatocytes.

sphincter (sfink′-ter) A ringlike band of muscle fibres that controls the size of an opening in the body, such as the passage between the esophagus and the stomach.

spiral cleavage A type of embryonic development in protostomes in which the planes of cell division that transform the zygote into a ball of cells are diagonal to the vertical axis of the embryo. As a result, the cells of each tier sit in the grooves between cells of adjacent tiers.

spliceosome (splī′-sō-sōm) A large complex made up of proteins and RNA molecules that splices RNA by interacting with the ends of an RNA intron, releasing the intron and joining the two adjacent exons.

spongocoel (spon′-jō-sēl) The central cavity of a sponge.

spontaneous process A process that occurs without an overall input of energy; a process that is energetically favourable.

sporangium (spōr-an′-jē-um) (plural, **sporangia**) A multicellular organ in fungi and plants in which meiosis occurs and haploid cells develop.

spore (1) In the life cycle of a plant or alga undergoing alternation of generations, a haploid cell produced in the sporophyte by meiosis. A spore can divide by mitosis to develop into a multicellular haploid individual, the gametophyte, without fusing with another cell. (2) In fungi, a haploid cell, produced either sexually or asexually, that produces a mycelium after germination.

sporocyte A diploid cell, also known as a spore mother cell, that undergoes meiosis and generates haploid spores.

sporophyll (spō′-ruh-fil) A modified leaf that bears sporangia and hence is specialized for reproduction.

sporophyte (spō-ruh-fīt′) In organisms (plants and some algae) that have alternation of generations, the multicellular diploid form that results from the union of gametes. The sporophyte produces haploid spores by meiosis that develop into gametophytes.

sporopollenin (spōr-uh-pol′-eh-nin) A durable polymer that covers exposed zygotes of charophyte algae and forms the walls of plant spores, preventing them from drying out.

stabilizing selection Natural selection in which intermediate phenotypes survive or reproduce more successfully than do extreme phenotypes.

stamen (stā′-men) The pollen-producing reproductive organ of a flower, consisting of an anther and a filament.

standard metabolic rate (SMR) Metabolic rate of a resting, fasting, and nonstressed ectotherm at a particular temperature.

starch A storage polysaccharide in plants, consisting entirely of glucose monomers joined by α glycosidic linkages.

start point In transcription, the nucleotide position on the promoter where RNA polymerase begins synthesis of RNA.

statocyst (stat′-uh-sist′) A type of mechanoreceptor that functions in equilibrium in invertebrates by use of statoliths, which stimulate hair cells in relation to gravity.

statolith (stat′-uh-lith′) (1) In plants, a specialized plastid that contains dense starch grains and may play a role in detecting gravity. (2) In invertebrates, a dense particle that settles in response to gravity and is found in sensory organs that function in equilibrium.

stele (stēl) The vascular tissue of a stem or root.

stem A vascular plant organ consisting of an alternating system of nodes and internodes that support the leaves and reproductive structures.

stem cell Any relatively unspecialized cell that can produce, during a single division, one identical daughter cell and one more specialized daughter cell that can undergo further differentiation.

steroid A type of lipid characterized by a carbon skeleton consisting of four fused rings with various chemical groups attached.

sticky end A single-stranded end of a double-stranded restriction fragment.

stigma (plural, **stigmata**) The sticky part of a flower's carpel, which receives pollen grains.

stimulus In feedback regulation, a fluctuation in a variable that triggers a response.

stipe A stemlike structure of a seaweed.

stock The plant that provides the root system when making a graft.

stoma (stō′-muh) (plural, **stomata**) A microscopic pore surrounded by guard cells in the epidermis of leaves and stems that allows gas exchange between the environment and the interior of the plant.

stomach An organ of the digestive system that stores food and performs preliminary steps of digestion.

stramenopile A protist in which a "hairy" flagellum (one covered with fine, hairlike projections) is paired with a shorter, smooth flagellum.

stratum (strah′-tum) (plural, **strata**) A rock layer formed when new layers of sediment cover older ones and compress them.

striated muscle Muscle in which the regular arrangement of filaments creates a pattern of light and dark bands.

strigolactones A class of plant hormone that inhibits shoot branching, triggers the germination of parasitic plant seeds, and stimulates the association of plant roots with mycorrhizal fungi.

strobilus (strō-bī′-lus) (plural, **strobili**) The technical term for a cluster of sporophylls known commonly as a cone, found in most gymnosperms and some seedless vascular plants.

stroke The death of nervous tissue in the brain, usually resulting from rupture or blockage of arteries in the head.

stroke volume The volume of blood pumped by a heart ventricle in a single contraction.

stroma (strō′-muh) The dense fluid within the chloroplast surrounding the thylakoid membrane and containing ribosomes and DNA; involved in the synthesis of organic molecules from carbon dioxide and water.

stromatolite Layered rock that results from the activities of prokaryotes that bind thin films of sediment together.

structural isomer One of several compounds that have the same molecular formula but differ in the covalent arrangements of their atoms.

style The stalk of a flower's carpel, with the ovary at the base and the stigma at the top.

substrate The reactant on which an enzyme works.

substrate feeder An animal that lives in or on its food source, eating its way through the food.

substrate-level phosphorylation The enzyme-catalyzed formation of ATP by direct transfer of a phosphate group to ADP from an intermediate substrate in catabolism.

sugar sink A plant organ that is a net consumer or storer of sugar. Growing roots, shoot tips, stems, and fruits are examples of sugar sinks supplied by phloem.

sugar source A plant organ in which sugar is being produced by either photosynthesis or the breakdown of starch. Mature leaves are the primary sugar sources of plants.

sulfhydryl group A chemical group consisting of a sulphur atom bonded to a hydrogen atom.

summation The phenomenon of an additive effect of individual postsynaptic potentials at a nerve cell, resulting in several stimulations below the threshold adding to cause an action potential.

suprachiasmatic nucleus (SCN) A group of neurons in the hypothalamus of mammals that functions as a biological clock.

surface tension A measure of how difficult it is to stretch or break the surface of a liquid. Water has a high surface tension because of the hydrogen bonding of surface molecules.

surfactant A substance secreted by alveoli that decreases surface tension in the fluid that coats the alveoli.

survivorship curve A plot of the number of members of a cohort that are still alive at each age; one way to represent age-specific mortality.

suspension feeder An aquatic animal, such as a sponge, clam, or baleen whale, that feeds by sifting small organisms or food particles from the water.

sustainable agriculture Long-term productive farming methods that are environmentally safe.

sustainable development Development that meets the needs of people today without limiting the ability of future generations to meet their needs.

swim bladder In aquatic osteichthyans, an air sac that enables the animal to control its buoyancy in the water.

symbiont (sim′-bē-ont) The smaller participant in a symbiotic relationship, living in or on the host.

symbiosis An ecological relationship between organisms of two different species that live together in direct and intimate contact.

sympathetic division One of three divisions of the autonomic nervous system; generally increases energy expenditure and prepares the body for action.

sympatric speciation (sim-pat′-rik) The formation of new species in populations that live in the same geographic area.

symplast In plants, the continuum of cytoplasm connected by plasmodesmata between cells.

synapse (sin′-aps) The junction where a neuron communicates with another cell across a narrow gap via a neurotransmitter or an electrical coupling.

synapsid Member of an amniote clade distinguished by a single hole on each side of the skull. Synapsids include the mammals.

synapsis (si-nap′-sis) The pairing and physical connection of duplicated homologous chromosomes during prophase I of meiosis.

systematics A scientific discipline focused on classifying organisms and determining their evolutionary relationships.

systemic acquired resistance A defensive response in infected plants that helps protect healthy tissue from pathogenic invasion.

systemic circuit The branch of the circulatory system that supplies oxygenated blood to and carries deoxygenated blood away from organs and tissues throughout the body.

systems biology An approach to studying biology that aims to model the dynamic behaviour of whole biological systems based on a study of the interactions among the system's parts.

systole (sis′-tō-lē) The stage of the cardiac cycle in which a heart chamber contracts and pumps blood.

systolic pressure Blood pressure in the arteries during contraction of the ventricles.

T cells The class of lymphocytes that mature in the thymus; they include both effector cells for the cell-mediated immune response and helper cells required for both branches of adaptive immunity.

taproot A main vertical root that develops from an embryonic root and gives rise to lateral (branch) roots.

tastant Any chemical that stimulates the sensory receptors in a taste bud.

taste bud A collection of modified epithelial cells on the tongue or in the mouth that are receptors for taste in mammals.

TATA box A DNA sequence in eukaryotic promoters crucial in forming the transcription initiation complex.

taxis (tak′-sis) An oriented movement toward or away from a stimulus.

taxon (plural, **taxa**) A named taxonomic unit at any given level of classification.

taxonomy (tak-son′-uh-mē) A scientific discipline concerned with naming and classifying the diverse forms of life.

Tay-Sachs disease A human genetic disease caused by a recessive allele for a dysfunctional enzyme, leading to accumulation of certain lipids in the brain. Seizures, blindness, and degeneration of motor and mental performance usually become manifest a few months after birth, followed by death within a few years.

technology The application of scientific knowledge for a specific purpose, often involving industry or commerce but also including uses in basic research.

telomerase An enzyme that catalyzes the lengthening of telomeres in eukaryotic germ cells.

telomere (tel´-uh-mēr) The tandemly repetitive DNA at the end of a eukaryotic chromosome's DNA molecule. Telomeres protect the organism's genes from being eroded during successive rounds of replication. *See also* repetitive DNA.

telophase The fifth and final stage of mitosis, in which daughter nuclei are forming and cytokinesis has typically begun.

temperate broadleaf forest A biome located throughout midlatitude regions where there is sufficient moisture to support the growth of large, broadleaf deciduous trees.

temperate grassland A terrestrial biome that exists at midlatitude regions and is dominated by grasses and forbs.

temperate phage A phage that is capable of replicating by either a lytic or lysogenic cycle.

temperature A measure of the intensity of heat in degrees, reflecting the average kinetic energy of the molecules.

template strand The DNA strand that provides the pattern, or template, for ordering, by complementary base pairing, the sequence of nucleotides in an RNA transcript.

temporal summation A phenomenon of neural integration in which the membrane potential of the postsynaptic cell in a chemical synapse is determined by the combined effect of EPSPs or IPSPs produced in rapid succession.

tendon A fibrous connective tissue that attaches muscle to bone.

terminator In bacteria, a sequence of nucleotides in DNA that marks the end of a gene and signals RNA polymerase to release the newly made RNA molecule and detach from the DNA.

territoriality A behaviour in which an animal defends a bounded physical space against encroachment by other individuals, usually of its own species.

tertiary consumer (ter-shē-ār´-ē) A carnivore that eats other carnivores.

tertiary structure The overall shape of a protein molecule due to interactions of amino acid side chains, including hydrophobic interactions, ionic bonds, hydrogen bonds, and disulphide bridges.

test The porous shell of a foram.

testcross Breeding an organism of unknown genotype with a homozygous recessive individual to determine the unknown genotype. The ratio of phenotypes in the offspring reveals the unknown genotype.

testis (plural, **testes**) The male reproductive organ, or gonad, in which sperm and reproductive hormones are produced.

testosterone A steroid hormone required for development of the male reproductive system, spermatogenesis, and male secondary sex characteristics; the major androgen in mammals.

tetanus (tet´-uh-nus) The maximal, sustained contraction of a skeletal muscle, caused by a very high frequency of action potentials elicited by continual stimulation.

tetrapod A vertebrate clade whose members have limbs with digits. Tetrapods include mammals, amphibians, and birds and other reptiles.

thalamus (thal´-uh-mus) An integrating centre of the vertebrate forebrain. Neurons with cell bodies in the thalamus relay neural input to specific areas in the cerebral cortex and regulate what information goes to the cerebral cortex.

theory An explanation that is broader in scope than a hypothesis, generates new hypotheses, and is supported by a large body of evidence.

thermal energy Kinetic energy due to the random motion of atoms and molecules; energy in its most random form. *See also* heat.

thermocline A narrow stratum of abrupt temperature change in the ocean and in many temperate-zone lakes.

thermodynamics (ther´-mō-dī-nam´-iks) The study of energy transformations that occur in a collection of matter. *See* first law of thermodynamics; second law of thermodynamics.

thermoreceptor A receptor stimulated by either heat or cold.

thermoregulation The maintenance of internal body temperature within a tolerable range.

theropod Member of a group of dinosaurs that were bipedal carnivores.

thick filament A filament composed of staggered arrays of myosin molecules; a component of myofibrils in muscle fibres.

thigmomorphogenesis A response in plants to chronic mechanical stimulation, resulting from increased ethylene production. An example is thickening stems in response to strong winds.

thigmotropism (thig-mo´-truh-pizm) A directional growth of a plant in response to touch.

thin filament A filament consisting of two strands of actin and two strands of regulatory protein coiled around one another; a component of myofibrils in muscle fibres.

threatened species A species that is considered likely to become endangered in the foreseeable future.

threshold The potential that an excitable cell membrane must reach for an action potential to be initiated.

thrombus A fibrin-containing clot that forms in a blood vessel and blocks the flow of blood.

thylakoid (thī´-luh-koyd) A flattened, membranous sac inside a chloroplast. Thylakoids often exist in stacks called grana that are interconnected; their membranes contain molecular "machinery" used to convert light energy to chemical energy.

thymus (thī´-mus) A small organ in the thoracic cavity of vertebrates where maturation of T cells is completed.

thyroid gland An endocrine gland, located on the ventral surface of the trachea, that secretes two iodine-containing hormones, triiodothyronine (T_3) and thyroxine (T_4), as well as calcitonin.

thyroxine (T_4) One of two iodine-containing hormones that are secreted by the thyroid gland and that help regulate metabolism, development, and maturation in vertebrates.

tidal volume The volume of air a mammal inhales and exhales with each breath.

tight junction A type of intercellular junction between animal cells that prevents the leakage of material through the space between cells.

tissue An integrated group of cells with a common structure, function, or both.

tissue system One or more tissues organized into a functional unit connecting the organs of a plant.

Toll-like receptor (TLR) A membrane receptor on a phagocytic white blood cell that recognizes fragments of molecules common to a set of pathogens.

tonicity The ability of a solution surrounding a cell to cause that cell to gain or lose water.

top-down control A model of community organization in which predation influences community organization by controlling herbivore numbers, which in turn control plant or phytoplankton numbers, which in turn control nutrient levels; also called the trophic cascade model.

topoisomerase A protein that breaks, swivels, and rejoins DNA strands. During DNA replication, topoisomerase helps to relieve strain in the double helix ahead of the replication fork.

topsoil A mixture of particles derived from rock, living organisms, and decaying organic material (humus).

torpor A physiological state in which activity is low and metabolism decreases.

totipotent (tō´-tuh-pōt´-ent) Describing a cell that can give rise to all parts of the embryo and adult, as well as extraembryonic membranes in species that have them.

trace element An element indispensable for life but required in extremely minute amounts.

trachea (trā´-kē-uh) The portion of the respiratory tract that passes from the larynx to the bronchi; also called the windpipe.

tracheal system In insects, a system of branched, air-filled tubes that extends throughout the body and carries oxygen directly to cells.

tracheid (trā´-kē-id) A long, tapered water-conducting cell found in the xylem of nearly all vascular plants. Functioning tracheids are no longer living.

trait One of two or more detectable variants in a genetic character.

trans **fat** An unsaturated fat, formed artificially during hydrogenation of oils, containing one or more *trans* double bonds.

transcription The synthesis of RNA using a DNA template.

transcription factor A regulatory protein that binds to DNA and affects transcription of specific genes.

transcription initiation complex The completed assembly of transcription factors and RNA polymerase bound to a promoter.

transcription unit A region of DNA that is transcribed into an RNA molecule.

transduction (1) A process in which phages (viruses) carry bacterial DNA from one bacterial cell to another. When these two cells are members of different species, transduction results in horizontal gene transfer. (2) In cellular communication, the conversion of a signal from outside the cell to a form that can bring about a specific cellular response; also called *signal transduction*.

transfer RNA (tRNA) An RNA molecule that functions as a translator between nucleic acid and protein languages by carrying specific amino acids to the ribosome, where they recognize the appropriate codons in the mRNA.

transformation (1) The conversion of a normal animal cell to a cancerous cell. (2) A change in genotype and phenotype due to the assimilation of external DNA by a cell. When the external DNA is from a member of a different species, transformation results in horizontal gene transfer.

transgenic Pertaining to an organism whose genome contains a gene introduced from another organism of the same or a different species.

translation The synthesis of a polypeptide using the genetic information encoded in an mRNA molecule. There is a change of "language" from nucleotides to amino acids.

translocation (1) An aberration in chromosome structure resulting from attachment of a chromosomal fragment to a nonhomologous chromosome. (2) During protein synthesis, the third stage in the elongation cycle, when the RNA carrying the growing polypeptide moves from the A site to the P site on the ribosome. (3) The transport of organic nutrients in the phloem of vascular plants.

transmission The passage of a nerve impulse along axons.

transmission electron microscope (TEM) A microscope that passes an electron beam through very thin sections stained with metal atoms and is primarily used to study the internal ultrastructure of cells.

transpiration The evaporative loss of water from a plant.

transport epithelium One or more layers of specialized epithelial cells that carry out and regulate solute movement.

transport protein A transmembrane protein that helps a certain substance or class of closely related substances to cross the membrane.

transport vesicle A small membranous sac in a eukaryotic cell's cytoplasm carrying molecules produced by the cell.

transposable element A segment of DNA that can move within the genome of a cell by means of a DNA or RNA intermediate; also called a transposable genetic element.

transposon A transposable element that moves within a genome by means of a DNA intermediate.

transverse (T) tubule An infolding of the plasma membrane of skeletal muscle cells.

triacylglycerol (trī-as′-ul-glis′-uh-rol) A lipid consisting of three fatty acids linked to one glycerol molecule; also called a fat or triglyceride.

triiodothyronine (T$_3$) (trī′-ī-ō′-dō-thī′-rō-nēn) One of two iodine-containing hormones that are secreted by the thyroid gland and that help regulate metabolism, development, and maturation in vertebrates.

trimester In human development, one of three 3-month-long periods of pregnancy.

triple response A plant growth maneuver in response to mechanical stress, involving slowing of stem elongation, thickening of the stem, and a curvature that causes the stem to start growing horizontally.

triplet code A genetic information system in which a set of three-nucleotide-long words specify the amino acids for polypeptide chains.

triploblastic Possessing three germ layers: the endoderm, mesoderm, and ectoderm. Most eumetazoans are triploblastic.

trisomic Referring to a diploid cell that has three copies of a particular chromosome instead of the normal two.

trochophore larva (trō′-kuh-fōr) Distinctive larval stage observed in some lophotrochozoan animals, including some annelids and molluscs.

trophic cascade model *See* top-down model.

trophic efficiency The percentage of production transferred from one trophic level to the next.

trophic structure The different feeding relationships in an ecosystem, which determine the route of energy flow and the pattern of chemical cycling.

trophoblast The outer epithelium of a mammalian blastocyst. It forms the fetal part of the placenta, supporting embryonic development but not forming part of the embryo proper.

tropic hormone A hormone that has an endocrine gland or cells as a target.

tropical dry forest A terrestrial biome characterized by relatively high temperatures and precipitation overall but with a pronounced dry season.

tropical rain forest A terrestrial biome characterized by relatively high precipitation and temperatures year-round.

tropics Latitudes between 23.5° north and south.

tropism A growth response that results in the curvature of whole plant organs toward or away from stimuli due to differential rates of cell elongation.

tropomyosin The regulatory protein that blocks the myosin-binding sites on actin molecules.

troponin complex The regulatory proteins that control the position of tropomyosin on the thin filament.

true-breeding Referring to organisms that produce offspring of the same variety over many generations of self-pollination.

tubal ligation A means of sterilization in which a woman's two oviducts (fallopian tubes) are tied closed to prevent eggs from reaching the uterus. A segment of each oviduct is removed.

tube foot One of numerous extensions of an echinoderm's water vascular system. Tube feet function in locomotion and feeding.

tumour-suppressor gene A gene whose protein product inhibits cell division, thereby preventing the uncontrolled cell growth that contributes to cancer.

tundra A terrestrial biome at the extreme limits of plant growth. At the northernmost limits, it is called arctic tundra, and at high altitudes, where plant forms are limited to low shrubby or mat-like vegetation, it is called alpine tundra.

tunicate Member of the clade Urochordata, sessile marine chordates that lack a backbone.

turgid (ter′-jid) Swollen or distended, as in plant cells. (A walled cell becomes turgid if it has a lower water potential than its surroundings, resulting in entry of water.)

turgor pressure The force directed against a plant cell wall after the influx of water and swelling of the cell due to osmosis.

turnover The mixing of waters as a result of changing water-temperature profiles in a lake.

turnover time The time required to replace the standing crop of a population or group of populations (for example, of phytoplankton), calculated as the ratio of standing crop to production.

twin study A behavioural study in which researchers compare the behaviour of identical twins raised apart with that of identical twins raised in the same household.

tympanic membrane Another name for the eardrum, the membrane between the outer and middle ear.

Unikonta (yū′-ni-kon′-tuh) One of five supergroups of eukaryotes proposed in a current hypothesis of the evolutionary history of eukaryotes. This clade, which is supported by studies of myosin proteins and DNA, consists of amoebozoans and opisthokonts. *See also* Excavata, Chromalveolata, Rhizaria, and Archaeplastida.

unsaturated fatty acid A fatty acid that has one or more double bonds between carbons in the hydrocarbon tail. Such bonding reduces the number of hydrogen atoms attached to the carbon skeleton.

urban ecology The study of organisms and their environment in urban and suburban settings.

urea A soluble nitrogenous waste produced in the liver by a metabolic cycle that combines ammonia with carbon dioxide.

ureter (yū-rē′-ter) A duct leading from the kidney to the urinary bladder.

urethra (yū-rē′-thruh) A tube that releases urine from the mammalian body near the vagina in females and through the penis in males; also serves in males as the exit tube for the reproductive system.

uric acid A product of protein and purine metabolism and the major nitrogenous waste product of insects, land snails, and many reptiles. Uric acid is relatively nontoxic and largely insoluble.

urinary bladder The pouch where urine is stored prior to elimination.

uterine cycle The changes that occur in the uterus during the reproductive cycle of the human female; also called the menstrual cycle.

uterus A female organ where eggs are fertilized and/or development of the young occurs.

utricle In the vertebrate ear, a chamber in the vestibule behind the oval window that opens into the three semicircular canals.

vaccination *See* immunization.

vaccine A harmless variant or derivative of a pathogen that stimulates a host's immune system to mount defences against the pathogen.

vacuole (vak′-yū-ōl′) A membrane-bounded vesicle whose specialized function varies in different kinds of cells.

vagina Part of the female reproductive system between the uterus and the outside opening; the birth canal in mammals. During copulation, the vagina accommodates the male's penis and receives sperm.

valence The bonding capacity of a given atom; usually equals the number of unpaired electrons required to complete the atom's outermost (valence) shell.

valence electron An electron in the outermost electron shell.

valence shell The outermost energy shell of an atom, containing the valence electrons involved in the chemical reactions of that atom.

van der Waals interactions Weak attractions between molecules or parts of molecules that result from transient local partial charges.

variable A factor that varies in an experiment or other test.

variation Differences between members of the same species.

vasa recta The capillary system in the kidney that serves the loop of Henle.

vascular cambium A cylinder of meristematic tissue in woody plants that adds layers of secondary vascular tissue called secondary xylem (wood) and secondary phloem.

vascular plant A plant with vascular tissue. Vascular plants include all living plant species except liverworts, mosses, and hornworts.

vascular tissue Plant tissue consisting of cells joined into tubes that transport water and nutrients throughout the plant body.

vascular tissue system A transport system formed by xylem and phloem throughout a vascular plant. Xylem transports water and minerals; phloem transports sugars, the products of photosynthesis.

vas deferens In mammals, the tube in the male reproductive system in which sperm travel from the epididymis to the urethra.

vasectomy The cutting and sealing of each vas deferens to prevent sperm from entering the urethra.

vasocongestion The filling of a tissue with blood, caused by increased blood flow through the arteries of that tissue.

vasoconstriction A decrease in the diameter of blood vessels caused by contraction of smooth muscles in the vessel walls.

vasodilation An increase in the diameter of blood vessels caused by relaxation of smooth muscles in the vessel walls.

vector An organism that transmits pathogens from one host to another.

vegetal pole The point at the end of an egg in the hemisphere where most yolk is concentrated; opposite of animal pole.

vegetative propagation/reproduction Cloning of plants by asexual means.

vein (1) In animals, a vessel that carries blood toward the heart. (2) In plants, a vascular bundle in a leaf.

ventilation The flow of air or water over a respiratory surface.

ventral Pertaining to the underside, or bottom, of an animal with radial or bilateral symmetry.

ventricle (ven′-tri-kul) (1) A heart chamber that pumps blood out of the heart. (2) A space in the vertebrate brain, filled with cerebrospinal fluid.

venule (ven′-yūl) A vessel that conveys blood between a capillary bed and a vein.

vernalization The use of cold treatment to induce a plant to flower.

vertebrate A chordate animal with a backbone, including sharks and rays, ray-finned fishes, coelacanths, lungfishes, amphibians, reptiles, and mammals.

vesicle (ves′-i-kul) A membranous sac in the cytoplasm of a eukaryotic cell.

vessel A continuous water-conducting micropipe found in most angiosperms and a few nonflowering vascular plants.

vessel element A short, wide water-conducting cell found in the xylem of most angiosperms and a few nonflowering vascular plants. Dead at maturity, vessel elements are aligned end to end to form micropipes called vessels.

vestigial structure A feature of an organism that is a historical remnant of a structure that served a function in the organism's ancestors.

villus (plural, **villi**) (1) A finger-like projection of the inner surface of the small intestine. (2) A finger-like projection of the chorion of the mammalian placenta. Large numbers of villi increase the surface areas of these organs.

viral envelope A membrane, derived from membranes of the host cell, that cloaks the capsid, which in turn encloses a viral genome.

virulent phage A phage that replicates only by a lytic cycle.

virus An infectious particle incapable of replicating outside of a cell, consisting of an RNA or DNA genome surrounded by a protein coat (capsid) and, for some viruses, a membranous envelope.

visceral mass One of the three main parts of a mollusc; the part containing most of the internal organs. *See also* foot, mantle.

visible light That portion of the electromagnetic spectrum that can be detected as various colours by the human eye, ranging in wavelength from about 380 nm to about 750 nm.

vital capacity The maximum volume of air that a mammal can inhale and exhale with each breath.

vitamin An organic molecule required in the diet in very small amounts. Many vitamins serve as coenzymes or parts of coenzymes.

viviparous (vī-vip′-uh-rus) Referring to a type of development in which the young are born alive after having been nourished in the uterus by blood from the placenta.

voltage-gated ion channel A specialized ion channel that opens or closes in response to changes in membrane potential.

vulva Collective term for the female external genitalia.

water potential (Ψ) The physical property predicting the direction in which water will flow, governed by solute concentration and applied pressure.

water vascular system A network of hydraulic canals unique to echinoderms that branches into extensions called tube feet, which function in locomotion and feeding.

wavelength The distance between crests of waves, such as those of the electromagnetic spectrum.

wetland A habitat that is inundated by water at least some of the time and that supports plants adapted to water-saturated soil.

white matter Tracts of axons within the CNS.

whole-genome shotgun approach An approach to sequencing a genome that involves breaking up a genome into small overlapping fragments that can be sequenced.

wild type The phenotype most commonly observed in natural populations; also refers to the individual with that phenotype.

wilting The drooping of leaves and stems as a result of plant cells becoming flaccid.

wobble Flexibility in the base-pairing rules in which the nucleotide at the 5′ end of a tRNA anticodon can form hydrogen bonds with more than one kind of base in the third position (3′ end) of a codon.

xerophyte A plant adapted to an arid climate.

X-linked gene A gene located on the X chromosome; such genes show a distinctive pattern of inheritance.

X-ray crystallography A technique used to study the three-dimensional structure of molecules. It depends on the diffraction of an X-ray beam by the individual atoms of a crystallized molecule.

xylem (zī′-lum) Vascular plant tissue consisting mainly of tubular dead cells that conduct most of the water and minerals upward from the roots to the rest of the plant.

xylem sap The dilute solution of water and dissolved minerals carried through vessels and tracheids.

yeast Single-celled fungus that reproduces asexually by binary fission or by the pinching of small buds off a parent cell. Some species exhibit cell fusion between different mating types.

yolk Nutrients stored in an egg.

zero population growth (ZPG) A period of stability in population size, when additions to the population through births and immigration are balanced by subtractions through deaths and emigration.

zona pellucida The extracellular matrix surrounding a mammalian egg.

zoned reserve An extensive region that includes areas relatively undisturbed by humans surrounded by areas that have been changed by human activity and are used for economic gain.

zone of polarizing activity (ZPA) A block of mesoderm located just under the ectoderm where the posterior side of a limb bud is attached to the body; required for proper pattern formation along the anterior-posterior axis of the limb.

zoonotic pathogen A disease-causing agent that is transmitted to humans from other animals.

zoospore Flagellated spore found in chytrid fungi and some protists.

zygomycete (zī′-guh-mī′-sēt) Member of the fungal phylum Zygomycota, characterized by the formation of a sturdy structure called a zygosporangium during sexual reproduction.

zygosporangium (zī′-guh-spōr-an′-jē-um) In zygomycete fungi, a sturdy multinucleate structure in which karyogamy and meiosis occur.

zygote (zī′-gōt) The diploid cell produced by the union of haploid gametes during fertilization; a fertilized egg.

INDEX

Numbers

2,4-dichlorophenoxyacetic acid (2,4-D), 895
3′ end, 361
5′ cap, 361*f*, **361**
30-nm fibre, 347*f*
300-nm fibre, 347*f*

A

Aardvarks, 787*f*
ABC hypothesis, 825*f*, **825**
Abiotic, **1230**
Abiotic factors, 1245–46
Abiotic stresses, 909
Abiotic synthesis, 551, 552, 553*f*
Abomasum, 959*f*
"Abominable mystery," 684, 868*f*
Aboriginal peoples, and diet, 947
Abortion, **1091**
Abscisic acid (ABA), **842**, 892*t*, 897–**98**
Abscission, 900, 900*f*, 901
Absorption, 948*f*, **950**
    of fats, 956*f*
    in large intestine, 956–57
    in small intestine, 955–56, 955*f*
Absorption spectrum, **204**, 205*f*
Abstinence, 1090
Abyssal zones, **1238**
Acacia koa, 824*f*
Acacia trees, 10, 10*f*, 1280*f*
Acanthocephala, 728*f*
Acanthocephalan worms, 1280
Acanthodians, 767
Acanthokara kaputensis, 747*f*
Accessory fruits, 876*f*, **877**
Accessory proteins, 1013
Acclimation, **930**, 935
Acclimatization, **930**, 935, 1028
Acer rubrum, 806
Acer saccharum, 1231
Acetycholine, 1144
Acetyl CoA, **181**–82, 182*f*
Acetylcholine, **1134**
Achondroplasia, 299, 299*f*
Acid growth hypothesis, 894, 895*f*
Acid precipitation, 1335
Acidification, 59
Acids, **56**

buffers, 58–59
    and the pH scale, 57–58
    review, 61
    and water, 56, 59
Acinonyx jubatus, 1265*f*
Acoel flatworms, 727*f*
Acoela, 727*f*
Acoelomate flatworms, 723–24
Acoelomates, **720**
Acorn woodpeckers, 1220*f*
Acorn worms, 729*f*
Acqueous humour, 1174*f*
Acquired immune response, 1000
Acquired immunodeficiency, 1019. *See also* AIDS (acquired immune deficiency syndrome)
Acquired traits, 495*f*
Acrosomal process, 1096
Acrosomal reaction, **1096**–97, 1097*f*
Acrosomes, **1080***f*, **1096**
Actias luna, 1050*f*
Actin, **127**
Actin filaments, 1108–9, 1181, 1183*f*
Action potentials, **908**, 1126*f*, **1127**
    of cardiac muscle, 1188
    conduction of, 1128–30, 1129*f*
    generation of, 1127–28, 1128*f*
    and graded potentials, 1126–27
    and muscle contraction, 1184, 1185*f*, 1186
    review, 1138
    in sensory systems, 1164
    and voltage-gated ion channels, 1127, 1128*f*
Action spectrum, 205*f*, **205**, 901, 902*f*
Activation energy, **165**, 166*f*
Activation energy barrier, 164–65
Activators, 171, 171*f*, **384**, 388–89, 389*f*
Active immunity, **1015**–17
Active site, **166**, 167, 167*f*
Active transport, 146–49, **147**, 148*f*, 152, 956, 1033
Activity, and metabolic rate, 938–39
Acyclovir, 426
Adaptation, 2*f*, **496**, **920**, 930
    of axon structure, 1129–30
    in bats, 16*f*
    in birds, 780–81
    and camouflage, 2*f*
    camouflage, 500*f*
    and compromise, 527
    Darwin's research focus on, 496–97
    defensive, 740
    dental, 957–58
    of digestive systems in vertebrates, 957–960
    and gene flow, 521*f*
    mutualistic, 958–960

of plants, enabling the move to land, 653–54
    in prokaryotes, 604–8
    as reproductive success, 2*f*
    respiratory adaptations, in diving mammals, 995–96
    sensory, 1164
    of stomach and intestines, 958
Adaptive evolution, 518, 522–27, 572
Adaptive immunity, **1000**
    and antibodies, 1013–15
    antibodies as tools, 1017
    and antibody function, 1013–15
    and antigen recognition by B cells and antibodies, 1006
    and antigen recognition by T cells, 1006–7
    and B cells, 1006, 1013–15
    cell-mediated immune response, **1011**, 1012, 1012*f*, 1015
    and cytotoxic T cells, 1012–13, 1013*f*
    and helper T cells, 1012, 1012*f*
    humoral immune response, **1011**, 1012, 1012*f*, 1014*f*, 1015
    and immune rejection, 1017–18
    and immunization, 1015–17
    and infection of body fluids and body cells, 1011–18
    vs. innate immunity, 1000
    overview, 1000*f*, 1016*f*
    and pathogen-specific recognition, 1005–11
    review, 1023
    and self-tolerance, 1008–9
    and T cells, 1006
Adaptive radiations, **568**–570, 570*f*, 752
Addition rule, **289**
Adejeania vexatrix, 753*f*
Adélie penguins, 939
Adenine, 334–35
Adenoids, 1004*f*
Adenomatous polyposis coli (APC), 407
Adenosine diphosphate (ADP). *See* ADP (adenosine diphosphate)
Adenosine monophosphate (AMP). *See* AMP (adenosine monophosphate)
Adenosine triphosphate (ATP). *See* ATP (adenosine triphosphate)
Adenoviruses, 417, 417*f*
Adenylyl cyclase, **231**
Adhesion, 51, 839–840
Adipose cells, 68*f*, 82
Adipose tissue, 925*f*, 934, 961
ADP (adenosine diphosphate),
    and ATP hydrolysis, 162–63
    and enzyme regulation, 171

Adrenal cortex, 1054f, 1064–65, 1065f
Adrenal glands, 1054f, 1064, 1064–65, 1065f, 1103
Adrenal medulla, 1064, 1065f
Adrenaline. *See* Epinephrine
Adrenocorticotropic hormone (ACTH), 1054f, 1066
Adult stem cells, 451–53, 452f
Adventitious, 804
Aerobic respiration, **176**, 192–93
Afferent, 1143
African acacia trees, 10f
African blood lily, 244f
African descent, 298–99, 484
African elephants, 787f
African grey parrots, 1153
African sleeping sickness, 754
African violets, 881
Afrotheria, 760
Agaves, 1260, 1260f
Age structure, **1268**, 1269f
Aggregate fruits, 876f, **876**
Aglantha digitale, 1120
Aglaophyton, 698
Aglaophyton major, 664f
Agonistic behaviour, 1211, 1212f
Agriculture
 DNA technology applications, 459
 and dynamics of energy flow through ecosystems, 1309
 and honeybee colony losses, 688
 as human disturbance, 1292
 hydroponic culture, 854f
 and mycorrhizae, 862
 and nitrogen fixation, 860–61
 and nutrient enrichment, 1336
 soil mismanagement, 851–52
 sustainable. *See* Sustainable agriculture
Agrilus planipennis, 1050
Agrobacterium tumefaciens, 442, 621, 820
AIDS (acquired immune deficiency syndrome), 140, 418, **423**, 457, 947, 1020–21, **1020**
Ailuropoda melanoleuca, 469t
Air
 circulation, and precipitation patterns, 1227f
 as respiratory medium, 986t
Air roots, 804f
Airfoils, 1192–93
Alarm substance, 1200, 1200f
Albinism, 297f
Albumin, 391f, 399
Albuterol, 69f
Alcohol, and smooth ER, 115
Alcohol dehydrogenase, 512
Alcohol fermentation, 192f, **192**
Alder trees, 860, 1291
Aldoses, 76, 76f
Aldosterone, 228–29, 229f, **1045**, 1064
Aleuria aurantia, 700f
Algae, 199f
 brown, 635–36, 635f, 636f
 charophyte, 655f

golden, 635, 635f
green, 625f, 626, 629f, 643, 669–670
identification of, 594f
and land plants, evolution of, 653–58
mutualism between fungi and, 707
red, 642–43, 642f
review, 650
sexual life cycles of, 270f, 271
viral particles in, 415f
Algal blooms, 1306, 1306f
Alimentary canal, **737**, 738, **950**, 951, 951f, 958, 958f
Alkaline vents, 552, 552f
Alkaptonuria, 352
Allanatois, 1106
Alleles, 271, 284f, **284**–86, 287, 288f, 289f
 correlating behaviour with chromosome pair, 310
 dominant, 291–92, 299–300
 formation of new, 513–14
 frequencies, 514
 and gene flow, **521**–22
 and genetic drift, 520–21
 genetic drift and frequencies in, 518–521
 multiple, 292, 292f
 new combinations of, 316–17
 random selection from gene pool, 515f
 recessive, 297–98
 S-alleles, 880
 sickle-cell allele, 490f–91f
Allergens, **1018**
Allergies, 1018–19, 1018f
Alligators, 779f
Allolactose, **383**, 384
Allopatric speciation, 535f, **535**–38, 536f, 537f, 539, 565
Allopolypoids, 538, 538f, 539f
Allosteric regulation, 170–72, 171f, **171**
Alpha (α) carbon, 83
Alpha cells, 222, 222f, 1056
Alpha proteobacteria, 616f
Alpine ecosystems, 1315
Alpine pennycress, 854
Alpine woodsorrel, 879f
Alsomitra macrocarpa, 878f
Alternating communities, 1295f
Alternation of generations, 270, **636**–37, 655f
Alternative fuels, 199f, 622f, 692–93. *See also* Biofuels
Alternative RNA splicing, **363**, 393f, **393**
Alternative splicing, 353
Altruism, 1216–17, 1217f
Altrusim, 1214–16, **1215**
Alu elements, 473, 481
Aluminum toxicity, 856
Alvarez, Luis, 567
Alvarez, Walter, 567
Alveolates, **637**–39
Alveoli, **990**
Alzheimer's disease, 240, 1159f, **1159**
Amacrine cells, 1174f, 1176

Amanita muscaria, 700f
Amborella trichopoda, 685, 687f
American alligators, 779f
American beech, 1231, 1231f
American black bears, 351–52
American chestnut, 1285
American eel, 1028
American flamingo, 15f
Amines, 1051, 1051f
Aminidase (N), 428
Amino acid polymers, 86
Amino acids, **83**, 944
 antimicrobial peptides, 1001
 bonds, 83
 in enzyme's active site, 167
 formula for, 83
 linary chain, 88f
 monomers of, 83–84
 and mutation, 170
 as neuotransmitters, 1135
 as polymers in proteins, 83
 of proteins, 85f
 sequence identity tables, 479f, 480f
 synthesis of, 552f
Amino group, 70, 71f, 83
Aminoacyl-tRNA synthetases, 365f, **365**
Amitochondriate protists, 627
Ammonia, 46, 56, 1031, 1031f, **1031**
Ammonifying Bacteria, 859f
Ammonites, **741**
Amniocentesis, 301, 302f, 1091
Amniotes, **775**, **1106**
 derived characters of, 775–76
 early evolution of, 776–77
 extraembryonic membranes in, 1106
 phylogeny of, 776f
 review, 797
Amniotic eggs, **775**, 777f
Amoeba, 127, 128f, 244f, 629f, **639**, 921, 922f
Amoeba proteus, 646
Amoebocytes, **731**
Amoebozoans, **645**–46
AMP (adenosine monophosphate), 195
Amphetamine, 1157
Amphibians, **773**. *See also* Frogs (anurans)
 axis formation in, 1113f
 breathing in, 990
 circulation in, 969–971, 970f
 developmental fate of, 1115f
 and extraembryonic membranes, 1106
 fertilization in, 1074
 forebrain in, 1145
 hearing in, 1172
 kidneys in, 1041
 lifestyle and ecology of, 774–75
 lungs in, 989
 and nitrogenous wastes, 1032
 parental care in, 1209
Amphipathic, **137**
Amplification, 404, 404f, **1164**
amu, 35

Amygdala, **1150**
α amylase, 897
Amylopectin, 78
Amyloplasts, 123
Amylose, 78
Amyotrophic lateral sclerosis (ALS), 1184
Anabaena, 613, 613*f*
Anableps anableps, 380
Anabolic pathways, 155, 194
Anabolic steroids, 1065
Anabrus simplex, 470
Anaerobic respiration, 192–93, **612**
Analogies, **586**–87
Analogous, 505
Anaphase, **246**, 248*f*, 250, 250*f*, 252*f*
Anaphase I, 272*f*, 275*f*
Anaphase II, 273*f*
Anaphylactic shock, 1018–19
Anarhichas lupus, 1273*f*
Anatomical homologies, 503–4, 503*f*
Anatomy. *See* Animal form and function, **920**
Anchiornis huxleyi, 582*f*
Anchorage dependence, 257*f*, **258**
Anchoring junctions, 132*f*
Androgens, 1054*f*, **1065**, 1082–83, 1085
Anemia, 983
Aneuploidy, **321**, 323
Angel dust, 1157
Angiosperms, **658**, 674*f*
    asexual reproduction in, 877–882
    biotechnology and genetic engineering,
        883–85
    characteristics of, 678–684
    diversity of, 686–88, 687*f*
    double fertilization in, 870
    evolution of, 684–85, 685*f*, 868*f*
    evolutionary links with animals, 685–86
    flower structure and function, 867
    flowers of, 678–681, 872–76
    as food source, 688–89
    fossil, 684
    fruit and seed dispersal, 878*f*
    fruit form and function, 876–77
    fruits of, 681–82
    gametophytes, development of, 869–870, 869*f*
    and genetic engineering, 882–86
    and leaf morphology, 805
    life cycle of, 682–84, 683*f*, 869–870
    phyllotaxy of, 830
    phylogeny of, 684–85, 685*f*
    pollination in, 870–72, 871*f*
    reproductive adaptations of, 678–688
    review, 690, 886–87
    seed development in, 870. *See also* Seeds
    translocation in, 844–45
    unusual morphology in, 827*f*
Angiotensin II, **1044**–45
Angraecum sesquipedale, 873*f*
Anguilla rostrata, 1028
Anhydrobiosis, 1028*f*, **1028**
Animal behaviour

altruism, 1214–16
    fixed action patterns, 1197
    foraging, **1206**–7, 1207*f*, 1208
    game theory applied to, 1212
    genetic basis of, 1213
    genetic variation and evolution of, 1213–14
    and human culture, 1217–18
    inclusive fitness, 1216–17
    and learning, 1201–6
    mating and mate choice, 1207–12
    migration, 1197–98
    review, 1218–19
    rhythms of, 1198
    sensory inputs as stimuli for simple and
        complex, 1197–1201
    signals and communication in, 1198–1201
    and survival and reproductive success, 1206–12
Animal cells, 112*f*
    cytokinesis in, 251*f*
    endocytosis in, 150*f*
    meiosis in, **272**/–73*f*
    mitosis in, 247*f*–48*f*
    structure and specialization, 713
    water balance in, 144*f*
Animal complexity, and miRNA diversity, 718
Animal development. *See also* Development
    cell fate determination and pattern formation
        of, by inductive signals, 1114–17
    cell fate specification by cytoplasmic
        determinants and inductive signals,
        1110–17
    embryonic, 713*f*
    mophogenesis in, 1102–10
Animal form and function
    basic principles, 920–940
    body plans, 921–23
    coordination and control, 927
    energy requirements and bioenergetics,
        936–940
    and evolution, 918*f*, 921
    and exchange with environment, 921–23, 922*f*
    feedback control and maintenance of internal
        environment, 928–930
    homeostatic processes for thermoregulation in,
        930–36
    organ systems, 923*t*
    review, 941
    tissue structure and function, 924*f*–26*f*
Animal nutrition
    dietary requirements, 944–48
    evolutionary adaptations of vertebrate digestive
        system and diets, 957–960
    feedback regulation of digestion, energy
        storage, and appetite, 960–63
    feeding mechanisms, 949*f*
    food processing, organs for, 951–57
    food processing, stages of, 948–951, 948*f*
    mode of, 713
    review, 964
Animal pole, 1100*f*, **1100**
Animal reproduction

asexual, 1071
    and development, 713–14
    fertilization in, 1074–76
    regulation by tropic and sex hormones,
        1082–86
    reproductive cycles in, 1072–73
    review, 1092–93
    sexual reproduction, an evolutionary enigma,
        1071–72
    sexual reproductive organs in, 1077–81
Animal reservoirs, 1295–96
Animal viruses, 421–25, 422*t*
Animalia, kingdom, 598, 599
Animals
    bipedal, 1191
    body plans of, 719–722
    cells of. *See* Animal cells
    circulation. *See* Circulatory systems
    cloning of, 449–451
    diversification of, 722–23
    diversity of, 712–13, 918*f*, 919*f*
    evolutionary history of, 714–18
    evolutionary links with angiosperms, 685–86
    in fossil record, 561*f*
    as multicellular, heterotrophic eukaryotes,
        713–14
    mutualism between fungi and, 706–7
    nocturnal, 1198
    "pharm" animals, 457, 457*f*
    phylogeny of, 722–24, 722*f*, 726*f*
    review, 724
    and seed dispersal, 878*f*
    sexual life cycles of, 270*f*
    systematics, 723–24
    transgenic, 457, 459
Anions, **42**
Ankle bones, 506*f*
Annelids (Annelida), 728*f*, 742–45, 969, 1034,
        1071, 1140*f*, 1189
Annual plants, 811
Anolis lizards, 1275*f*
Anomalocaridid, 716*f*
Anomalocaris canadensis, 716, 717*f*
Anopheles, 638
Anser anser, 1202
Antagonistic hormones, 1056–59
Antarctic marine food web, 1284*f*
Antarctic Ocean, 1305
Anteaters, 787*f*
Anterior pituitary glands, 1054*f*, 1060*f*, **1060**
Anterior pituitary hormones,
        1060–61, 1061*f*
Antheridia, **656***f*
Anthers, **681**, **867**
Anthoceros, 662*f*
Anthophyta, 678
Anthopleura elegantissima, 1071*f*
Anthozoans, 733–34
Anthrax, 606, 621
Anthropoids, **788**–89
Anti-aging effects, 896

Antibiotics
    from fungal sources, 709
    resistance to, 502, 611–12
    from sponges, 731
Antibodies, 981, **1006**, 1007*f*
    function of, 1013–15
    monoclonal, 1017
    polyclonal, 1017
    as tools, 1017
Antibody proteins, 87*f*
Anticodons, **364**–65
Antidiuretic hormone (ADH), 1043*f*, **1043**–44, 1044*f*, 1049, 1054*f*, **1060**
Antifreeze proteins, 911
Antigen fragments, 1007
Antigen presentation, **1007**, 1008*f*
Antigen receptors, 1006, **1006**, 1007*f*, 1009
Antigenic variation, 1020
Antigen-presenting cells, **1011**
Antigens, 1006*f*, **1006**
    antibody-mediated mechanism
        of disposal of, 1015*f*
    recognition by B cells, 1006, 1007*f*
    recognition by T cells, 1006–7, 1008*f*
Antihistamines, 1018
Anti-inflammatories, 1064
Antimicrobial peptides, 1001, 1003
Antiparallel, **95**, **334**, 356
Antiparallel elongation, 339–341
Antivenin, 1017
Ants, 706–7, 706*f*, 878*f*, 1071, 1179
    and mutualism, 1280*f*
    wood ants, 32
Anurans, 773–74, 774*f*. *See also* Frogs (anurans)
Anus, 957
APC gene, 407
Apes
    as anthropoid group, 789
    nonhuman, 789*f*
    and tool use, 792
Aphelocoma californica, 1153
Aphids, 600, 845*f*
Aphotic zones, **1238**
Apical buds, **805**
Apical dominance, **813**, 896, 896*f*
Apical ectodermal ridge (AER), **1116**
Apical meristems, **656***f*, **810**
Apical surface, of epithelia, 924*f*
Apicomplexans, 637–39, 638*f*
Apis mellifera, 1199
Apodans, 774*f*
Apomixis, **877**
Apoplast, 831–**32**
Apoplastic route, 832, 837*f*
Apoptosis, 221, **238**–240, 239*f*, 241, 406, **896**, 1009, **1109**–10
Aposematic colouration, 1278*f*, **1278**
Appendix, **956**, 1004*f*
Appetite, regulation of, 961–62, 963
Apple maggot flies, 538, 538*f*
Apples, 876*f*, 881, 900

Aptenodytes patagonicus, 782*f*
Aquaporins, 142, 145, 834–35, **1036**
Aquatic biomes, 1238–39, *f*–1239
    coral, 1243*f*
    estuaries, 1241*f*
    intertidal zones, 1242*f*
    lakes, 1240*f*
    marine benthic zone, 1243*f*
    oceanic pelagic zone, 1242*f*
    review, 1248
    rivers, 1241*f*
    streams, 1241*f*
    wetlands, **1240***f*
Aquatic communities, 649*f*
Aquatic ecosystems
    biomass pyramids in, 1308
    decomposition in, 1312
    light limitation in, 1304
    nutrient limitation in, 1304–6
    primary production in, 1304–6
Aqueous solutions, **54**, 58*f*
Arabidopsis mutants, 891, 901, 902
Arabidopsis thaliana (mustard plant)
    and auxin movement, 894*f*
    and axial polarity, 822*f*
    and cell differentiation, 823
    and circadian rhythm, 904
    and deficiency warnings, 857*f*
    flowers of, 824*f*
    gene expression, altering, 908*f*
    genes, number of, 469*t*
    genetically modified, 912
    and gravitropism, 908
    as model organism, 820–21
    and mutualism, 864
    phytochromes in, 902
    and secondary growth, 818
    triple response in, 899
Arachnids, **748**
Aral Sea ecosystem, 1323
Arbuscular mycorrhizae, 702*f*, 861*f*, **861**
Arbuscular mycorrhizal fungi, **694**
Arbuscule, 562*f*
Archaea, **12**
    compared to bacteria and eukarya, 614–15
    genomes, 469, 469*t*, 470
    methane-consuming, 613
Archaea, domain
    compared to bacteria and eukarya, 615*t*
    as domain of life, 13*f*
    as prokaryotes, 614
Archaean eon, 558*f*
Archaefructus, 684, 684*f*
Archaeoglobus fulgidus, 469*t*
Archaeognatha (bristletails), 753*f*
Archaeopteris, 652–53, 652*f*, 676
Archaeopteryx, 781, 781*f*
Archaeplastida, **627**, 629*f*, **642**
Archegonia, **656***f*
Archenteron, **721**, **1103**
Archibald, John, 626

Archosauria, **583**
Archosaurs, **778**
Archosaurs, birds as, 780
ARCTIC, 471*f*
Arctic foxes, 1286*f*
Arctic ground squirrels, 940
Arctic ice, 54*f*
Arctic lemmings, 1287
Arctic mammals, 1072*f*
Arctic tundra, 1222*f*–23*f*, 1284
"Ardi," 791*f*
Ardipithecus ramidus, 790, 791, 791*f*, 792
Area, and relationship to volume, 109*f*
Area effects, 1293
Arginine, 353*f*
Ariolimax, 1070
Ariolimax californicus, 1214
Aristotle, 494
Armadillos, 787*f*
Armillaria ostoyae, 692*f*
Arnold, A. Elizabeth, 706*f*
Arousal
    autonomic, 1150
    and hibernation, 940
    sleep and, 1148
Art, as human hallmark, 796*f*
Artemia, 572, 572*f*
Arteries, **969**, 975, 975*f*
Arterioles, **969**, 975*f*, 977
Arthrobotrys, 695*f*
Arthropleura, 749
Arthropods (Arthropoda), 562, 729*f*, **746**
    anatomy of, 747*f*
    body plan, 746, 747*f*
    characteristics of, 746–48
    chelicerates, 748–49
    crustaceans, 750
    in food chain, 1284
    insects, 751–54
    muscles of, 1188
    Myriapods, 749
    nervous system in, 1141
    origins and traits of, 746
    pancrustaceans, 749–750
Artificial selection, **498**, 499*f*, 688, 882, 882*f*
Artiodactyls, 787*f*
Ascocarps, 700*f*, **702**
Ascomycetes, 700*f*, 702*f*, **702**–4
Ascomycota, 702
Ascorbic acid (vitamin C), 944
Asexual reproduction, **267**, **877**, **1071**
    advantages/disadvantages of, 877–79
    in animals, 1071
    in aspen trees, 879*f*
    fission, 1071
    fragmentation, 877, 1071
    of fungi, 697
    of lichens, 707
    mechanisms of, 877, 1071
    in multicellular organisms, 267*f*
    parthenogenesis, 737, 1071, 1073*f*

review, 886–87
of rotifers, 737
of sea anemone, 1071*f*
and totipotency, 881–82
Asian ladybird beetles, 499*f*
A site (aminoacyl-tRNA binding site), **366**
Asix establishment, 402–3
Aspen trees, 877, 879*f*
Aspergillus, 708, 709
Aspidoscelis, 1071, 1073
Aspidoscelis uniparens, 1073*f*
Aspirin, 1167
Assessment of Risk for Colorectal Tumours in Canada, 471*f*
Associative learning, 1203–**4**
Asteroidea, 754–55
Asters, 247*f*, 249*f*, **249**
Astrobiologists, **56**
Astrocytes, 1141*f*, 1142
Asymmetrical cell division, 821, 822*f*
Atherosclerosis, **983**, 984, 984*f*
Athlete's foot, 708
Athyrium filix-femina, 667*f*
Atlantic cod, 1231, 1277, 1288
Atlantic lobsters, 1027
Atlantic wolffish, 1273*f*
Atmosphere of early Earth, 551–52
Atmospheric carbon, 1339*f*, 1341
Atmospheric oxygen, 559*f*, 560*f*
Atmospheric ozone, 1341–42
Atmospheric pressure, 985
Atomic mass, **35**
atomic mass unit, 35
Atomic nucleus, **34**
Atomic number, **35**
Atoms, **34**
and elements, 34–40
energy levels of electrons, 36*f*
and formation of molecules, 40–44
and photosynthesis, 201–2, 202*f*
ATP (adenosine triphosphate), **70**, **162**, 937, 1183*f*
and animal nutrition, 944
and catabolic pathways, 176
and cellular respiration, 188–191, 189*f*
cycle of, 164*f*
and DNA replication, 339
and enzyme regulation, 171
and glucose homeostasis, 961
hydrolysis of, 162–63, 162*f*
and muscle contraction, 1182–84
in photosynthesis, 202–3
powering cellular work, 161–64, 163*f*
production of without oxygen, 191–93
regeneration of, 164
review, 173
structure of, 162, 162*f*
synthesis of, 180, 180*f*
ATP synthases, 187*f*, **187**, 188*f*
Atria, **969**
Atrial natriuretic factor (ANP), 1049

Atrial natriuretic peptide (ANP), **1045**
Atrioventricular (AV) node, **974**
Atrioventricular (AV) valve, **973**
Auditory communication, 1199
AUG, 357
Aurea, 890, 891
Aurelia, 967*f*
Australia, 785, 1333
Australian hopping mice, 1038, 1040
Australian thorny devil lizard, 779*f*
Australopithecus afarensis, 791–92, 794
Australopithecus africanus, 791, 792*f*
Australopithecus anamensis, 791
Australopithecus deyrimeda, 792
Australopithecus garhi, 793
Austroraptor cabazai, 14*f*
Autism, 1154
Autocrine signalling, **1049**, 1050*f*
Autoimmune diseases, **1019**
Autonomic arousal, 1150
Autonomic nervous system, **1143**, 1144*f*
Autophagy, 118*f*, 119
Autopolyploid, **538**
Autosomes, **269**
Autotrophs, **198**, 612, 612*t*, 937, 1301
Auxin (IAA), 892*t*
and apical dominance, 896, 896*f*
vs. brassinosteroids, 901
and leaf abscission, 900
overview, **893**–94
polar movement of, 894*f*, 895, 896
practical uses for, 895–96
role of in cell elongation, 894, 895*f*
role of in plant development, 894–95
synthetic, 895
Auxin indolebutyric acid (IBA), 895
Avery, Oswald, 330
Aves. *See* Birds
Avian flu, 428
Avian respiratory system, 991*f*
Avogadro's number, 55
Axel, Richard, 1180
Axial polarity, 822*f*
Axillary buds, **805**
Axis formation, 1112–13, 1113*f*
Axolotl, 773
Axon hillocks, 1121
Axon terminal, 1121
Axons, 926*f*, **1121**, 1129–30
Azidothymidine (AZT), 426
Azolla, 860

B

B cells, 982*f*, 1005*f*, 1006*f*, **1006**, 1007*f*, 1010*f*
activation of, 1013, 1014*f*
development of, 1007–11
diversity, generation of, 1008
proliferation of, 1009–10
β chains, 1006–7
β globin, 393, 477, 478, 479, 481
β glucose ring structures, 79

β pleated sheets, **88***f*, 91
β polypeptide chain, 98
β tubulin, 124, 125
Baby boom, 1268
Bacilli, 604*f*
Bacillus anthracis, 606*f*
Bacillus thuringiensis, 883
Bacteria, **12**
ammonifying, 859*f*
binary fission in, 251–52, 252*f*, 253*f*
in colon, 957
communication among, 222–23, 222*f*
compared to archaea, 614
compared to archaea and eukarya, 615*t*
in compost, 1301*f*
coupled transcription and translation in, 372*f*
and DNA replication, 341*f*, 342*t*
DNA transformation of, 330
domain bacteria, 13*f*
drug-resistant, evolution of, 501–3
and genetic expression, 355*f*
genetic traits in, 330*f*
genomes, 469, 469*t*, 470
gram-negative/positive, 605*f*, 617*f*
groups of, 616*f*–17*f*
microbiome, 958
Micrococcus luteus, 1001, 1002*f*
mutualistic, 619–620
in nitrogen cycle, 858–59
nitrogen-fixing, 858, 859–860, 859*f*
as pathogen, 999
pathogenic, 620–21
and plant nutrition, 857–861, 858*f*, 859*f*
as prokaryotes, 614. *See also* Prokaryotes
purple sulphur bacteria, 199*f*
regulation of transcription in, 381–85, 410–11
RNA polymerase, 358
in soil, 618*f*, 851
Streptococcus pneumoniae, 1005
and stressful environment, 862*f*
in technology, 621–22
Thermus aquaticus, 1323
and virus infection, 330*f*
Bacterial chromosomes, 345–46
Bacterial expression systems, 441–42
Bacteriods, **859**
Bacteriophages, 330*f*
Bacteriophages (phages), **331**, 417*f*, **417**. *See also* Phages
Bacteriorhodopsin, 139*f*
Bacteroides thetaiotaomicron, 619
Bada, Jeffrey, 65
Balancing selection, 524–25
Balanus, 1275*f*, 1276
Baleen, 949*f*
Ball pythons, 939
Ball-and-socket joint, 1190*f*
Balloon vines, 501, 501*f*
Ballooning, 749
Balsam poplar trees, 803
Bamboo, 801*f*

Banana slugs, 1070, 1070*f*, 1073, 1214
Banded sea snakes, 1278
Bandicoots, 784*f*, 785
Banff Springs snail, 742, 742*f*
Banting, Frederick G., 1057*f*
Barbiturates, 115, 116
Bar-headed geese, **992**
Bark, **818**
Barley, 687*f*, 897*f*
Barnacles, 522, 750, 751*f*, 1275, 1275*f*
Barr, Murray, 313
Barr body, **313**
Bartlett pears, 881
Basal angiosperms, 687*f*
Basal animals, 730–31
Basal bodies, 126
Basal metabolic rate (BMR), **937**
Basal metazoans, 723
Basal nuclei, 1147*f*
Basal surface, of epithelia, 924*f*
Basal taxons, **585**
Basal-like subtype of cancer, 408*f*, 409*f*
Base pairing, 335–37, 335*f*
Bases, **56**
    nitrogenous bases, 93
    review, 61
    and water, 56
Basidiocarps, **704**
Basidiomycetes, 700*f*, 704*f*, **704**, 705*f*
Basidiomycota, 704
Basidium, **704**
Basilar membrane, **1168***f*, 1169
Bass, 928, 928*f*, 931
Bassham, James, 203
Batesian mimicry, 1278*f*, **1278**
Bathymodiolus septemdierum, 1221
Batrachochytrium dendrobatidis, 699
Bats, 1169, 1199
    characteristics of, 787*f*
    evolution of, 16, 16*f*, 571
    kidney function in, 1040–41, 1041*f*
    and pollination, 872*f*
    resemblance to cats vs. birds, 587
    and torpor, 940
    white-nose syndrome, 708, 709*f*
Bdelloid rotifer, 1071
Bdelloidea rotifers, 737
Beadle, George, 352–53
Beads on a string, 346*f*
Beaks, 782*f*, 1239, 1276
Beans, 874*f*, 875*f*, 903–4, 904*f*, 912
Bearded seals, 54*f*, 945*f*
Bears, 534, 534*f*, 543, 787*f*, 943, 943*f*, 945*f*, 1072*f*, 1085, 1329, 1329*f*, 1333, 1340*f*
Beavers, 584, 787*f*, 1029, 1040, 1279, 1286, 1287*f*
Bees, 871*f*, 934, 949*f*, 1071, 1166, 1173, 1179, 1200, 1203, 1205*f*, 1278*f*
Beetles (Coleoptera), 492*f*, 499*f*, 522, 708, 752*f*, 753*f*, 757*f*, 844, 913–14, 1200*f*, 1233, 1279, 1290, 1290*f*, 1319*f*, 1340*f*
Beets, 804*f*

Behaviour, **1196**
Behavioural defence, 1277
Behavioural ecology, **1197**
Behavioural isolation, 532*f*
Behavioural rhythms, 1198
Beijerinck, Martinus, 416
Belding's ground squirrels, 1217*f*, 1253, 1253*t*, 1254*f*, 1255
Belmonte, Mark, 799, 883
Belostoma, 1075*f*
Beluga whales, 1166*f*, 1322, 1322*f*
Benign tumours, **258**
Bennettitales, 685, 685*f*
Benson, Andrew, 203
Benthic zones, **1238**
Benthos, **1238**
Berteaux, Dominique, 1286*f*
Berthold, Peter, 1215*f*
Best, C., 1057*f*
Beta cells, 1056
Beta oxidation, 194
Beta proteobacteria, 616*f*
Beta-carotene, 884, 947
BGI, 465
β-globin, 393, 475, 475*f*, 477, 478, 478*f*, 479, 481
Biarmosuchus, 783*f*
The Bible, 494
Bicarbonate, 955
bicoid gene, 402*f*, **402**–3
Bicoid mRNA, 402
Bicoid product, 402
Bicoid protein, 402
Biennial plants, 811
Bighorn sheep, 1250, 1250*f*, 1255, 1258, 1259*f*, 1263
Bilateral symmetry, 681*f*, 688, 734, 868*f*
Bilateria clade, 722–23, 734
Bilaterians, **716**
Bilayers, 82–83
Bile, **955**
Bile salts, 956*f*
Binary fission, 251–52, 252*f*, 253*f*, 608
Binomial, **584**
Binomial format for naming species, 494
Binomial nomenclature, 584
Biochemical pathways, **155**
Biochemistry, 107
Biodiesel, 199*f*
Biodiversity
    benefits of, 1323–24
    ecosystem diversity, 1322–23
    and ecosystem services, 1324
    genetic diversity, 1321
    and habitat loss, 1324–25
    hot spots, preserving, 1333
    human activities threatening, 1321–27
    and human welfare, 1323–26
    and introduced species, 1325
    and landscape structure, 1331–32
    levels of, 1321–23, 1321*f*
    loss of, in invertebrates, 742

    and overharvesting, 1325–26
    review, 1345
    species diversity, 1321–22
    and species richness, 1282, 1282*f*
    and sustainable development, 1342–44
    threats to, 1324–26
Biodiversity hot spots, 1333*f*, **1333**
Bioenergetics, **155**, **936**
    energy allocation and use, 937
    energy budgets for terrestrial vertebrates, 939
    metabolic rate, influences on, 938–39, 938*f*
    metabolic rate, minimum, 937–38
    overview, 937*f*
    quantifying energy use in, 937
    and thermoregulation, 937–38
    torpor and energy conservation, 939–940
Bioethanol, 199*f*
Biofence, 199*f*
Biofilms, 223, **613**
Biofuels, 199*f*, 884*f*, **884**
Biogenic amines, **1135**
Biogeochemical cycles, **1309**
Biogeographic factors in community ecology
    area effects, 1293
    island equilibrium model, 1293–94
    latitudinal gradients, 1292–93
Biogeography, **506**–7
Bioinformatics, **8**, 92, 96, **464**
    to analyze genomes and their functions, 465–69
    identifying protein-coding genes and understanding their functions, 466–67
    Internet tools, 466*f*
    understanding genes and gene expression at the systems level, 467–69
Biological augmentation, **1314**–15
Biological clocks, 904–5, 929–930, 940, 1067, **1149**
Biological communities, **1273**. *See also* Communities
    characterized by diversity and tropic structure, 1282–88
    characterizing disturbance, 1289–90
    disturbance influencing species diversity and composition in, 1289–92
    diversity and community stability, 1282–83
    ecological succession, 1289–90
    and human disturbance, 1292, 1292*f*
    review, 1297
    species diversity in, 1282
    and species with large impact, 1285–87
Biological Dynamics of Forest Fragments Project, 1332, 1332*f*
Biological magnification, 1337*f*, **1337**
Biological molecules
    carbohydrates, 76–80
    classes of, 74
    macromolecules as polymers, built from monomers, 75–76
    proteins. *See* Proteins
Biological order and disorder, 157–58, 157*f*

Biological organization, 3–6, 4f, 26
Biological species concept, 531f, **531**–34
Biology, **1**
    and chemistry, connection to, 32–33
    conservation biology, 97f
    as information science, 8f
    molecular biology, 820–21
    systems biology, 3, 467–69, 468f, 820
    tools of, 105–8, 133
Biomass, **1283**
    and fuels, 884
    primary production of, 1302–3, 1302–7
    secondary production of, 1307–9
Biomass pyramid, 1308, 1308f
Biomes, **1231**. See also Aquatic biomes; Terrestrial biomes
Biophilia, 1323, 1344f
Bioremediation, **621**, 622f, **1314**
Biorhythms, 1067
Biosphere, **1226**f
    and climate change, 1230–31
    future of, 1343–44
    as level of biological organization, 4f
    process that feeds, 198–200
    prokaryotes, role in, 618–19
Biosphere 2, 60
Biosynthesis (anabolic pathways), 194
Biotechnology, **434**. See also DNA technology
    agricultural applications, 459
    environmental cleanup, 458–59
    forensic applications of, 457–58
    medical applications, 454–57
    plant. See Plant biotechnology
    review, 461
    safety and ethical issues, 459–460
Biotic, **1230**
Biotic factors, 1246
Biotic stresses, 909
Biotin, 957, 958
Bipedal animals, 1191
Bipedal saurischian dinosaurs, 781
Bipedalism, 792
Bipolar cells, 1174f
Bipolar disorder, **1158**
Birds
    acorn woodpeckers, 1220f
    adaptations for flight, 780–81
    alimentary canals in, 951f
    blackcaps, 1214, 1215f
    blue jays, 1203–4, 1203f
    breathing in, 990, 991f
    brown-headed cowbirds, 1331–32
    canaries, 1205
    cattle egrets, 1246, 1246f
    circulation in, 970f, 971
    Clark's nutcracker, 1203
    common yellowthroat, 1224
    communication among, 1199, 1205
    cowbirds, 1281
    crows, 1208
    derived characters of, 780–81

    and dinosaurs, 582–83
    diversity and unity, 15f
    early, 781f
    egrets, 1281
    finches, 17f, 522, 1210f, 1211f, 1239, 1276
    flightless, 781–82
    forebrain in, 1145
    great auks, 1322, 1326
    grey jays, 1203
    grouse, 1196, 1196f, 1331
    gulls, 1209f
    hearing in, 1172
    higher cognition in, 1153, 1153f
    kidneys in, 1041
    living, 781–82
    lungs in, 990
    and mate selection, 1210, 1211f
    maungatautari, 1317f
    migrating, 1198
    migratory patterns of, 1214, 1215f
    and nitrogenous wastes, 1032
    and nutrition, 944
    origin of, 781
    and osmoregulation, 1029
    pheasants, 1209
    phylogenetic tree, 583f
    and pollination, 872f
    and population cycles, 1263
    and predation, 1277
    ravens, 1203–4
    reproduction in, 781
    rufa red knots, 1330, 1330f
    sparrows, 1205
    and steroid hormones, 1053
    and transport epithelium, 1030
    vocalizations, 1082
    and weight, 1193
    wings and feathers, 780f
    zebra finches, 17f, 522, 1210, 1210f, 1211f
Birol, Inanc, 471f
Birth control, 1089–91, 1090f
Birth control pills, **1090**
Bison, 1274, 1315, 1315f
Bivalves, 740–41, 740f
Black bears, 351f, 943, 943f
Black blizzards, 851
Black poplar, 884f
Black rush, 1281
Black smokers, 552
Black spruce, 1304
Black urine, 352
Black-bellied seedcracker finches, 522
Blackcaps, 1214, 1215f
Black-footed ferrets, 1295, 1315, 1315f
Black-legged ticks, 1224, 1224f, 1296, 1296f, 1340f
Blacktip reef sharks, 768f
Bladderwort, 469t, 470
Blades, 635f, **635**
BLAST, 465
Blastocoel, **1100**

Blastocysts, **1086**, **1104**
Blastoderm, 1103
Blastomeres, **1099**
Blastopores, 721f, **721**, **1103**, 1115f
Blastula, **713**, 1100f, **1100**
Blind spots, 1174f
Blombos Cave, 796f
Blood, 748, 925f, **969**, 980f. See also Blood vessels; Circulatory systems
    cellular elements of, 980f, 981, 982–83
    clotting, 10, 981–82, 982f
    composition and function of, 980–83
    differential of blood cells, 982f
    and digestion, 956, 961f
    and heat exchange, 933, 933f
    osmolarity of, 1038, 1043–44
    plasma, 925f, 980–81, 980t, 1003
    review, 997
Blood calcium, 1063–64, 1063f
Blood filtrate, 1035–38, 1039–40
Blood flow, 975–76, 976f, 978f
Blood flukes, 736, 736f, 1280
Blood groups, 292f, 1017
Blood pressure, 976f
    cardiac cycle and changes in, 976
    and gravity, 977–78
    and hypertension, 984
    measurement of, 977f
    regulation of, 976–77
    review, 997
    and salt intake, 947
Blood sugar, 9
Blood vessels, **969**, 975, 975f, 976f
Blood-brain barrier, 1142
Bloodhounds, 1195f
Bloodroot, 868f
Blooms, 635, 637, 1305, 1306f, 1336, 1337f
Blubber, 932
Blue jays, 1203–4, 1203f
Blue pike, 1337
Blue stain fungus, 708, 844
Blue-footed boobies, 532f
Bluehead wrasse, 1073
Blue-light photoreceptors, **901**–2, 902f
Boa constrictors, 1191
Body cavities, 720f, **720**
Body plan, 400
Body plans, **719**
    angiosperms, 684
    animal, 719–722, 724, 921–23
    of arthropods, 746, 747f
    birds, 15f
    crustaceans, 486, 486f
    and evolution, 921
    hierarchical organization of, 923
    insects, 572f
    of molluscs, 738, 739f
    pattern formation, 400–403
    of tetrapods, 771–72
Body size, and metabolic rate, 938–39

Body temperature regulation. *See*
    Thermoregulation
Bohlmann, Joerg, 471*f*
Bohr shift, 994
Bolting, 897
Bolus, **952**
Bombardier beetles, 48*f*, 492
Bombina, 541, 541*f*, 544
Bombyx mori, 1166*f*
Bonasa umbellus, 1196, 1331
Bonding, 1202
Bone marrow, 244*f*, 452, 455, 1018
Bone morphogenetic protein 4 (BMP-4), 1114
Bones, 766, **925***f*
Bonnemaisonia hamifera, 642*f*
Bonobos, 481, 789, 789*f*
Bonsai trees, 495*f*, 828–29
Bony fishes, 1027, 1027*f*, 1029, 1032, 1041, 1192
Book lungs, **748**
Boone, Charles, 468*f*
Boone, Charlie, 263
Borisy, Gary, 250*f*
Borrelia, 1224
Borrelia burgdorferi, 1296*f*
Bottleneck effect, 519, 519*f*
Bottlenose dolphins, 933*f*, 1148, 1148*f*
Bottom-up control, **1287**
Botulism, 621
Bound ribosomes, 115
Boutin, Stan, 510
Bouzat, Juan, 520
Boveri, Theodor, 309
Bowie seamount, 1334, 1334*f*
Bowman's capsule, 1035, **1037***f*
Boysen-Jensen, Peter, 893, 893*f*
Brachiopods (Brachiopoda), 727*f*, 738*f*, **738**
Brain trauma, 1139–40
Brain volume, 793, 796
Brainbow technology, 1139
Brains, **1121**
    arousal and sleep function, 1148, 1148–50
    bird compared to human, 1153*f*
    cerebral cortex functions in, 1151–53
    cognition, evolution of, 1153
    components of, 1142*f*
    development of, 1146*f*
    and drug addiction, 1158–59, 1158*f*
    and emotions, 1150
    endocrine glands in, 1060*f*
    frontal lobe function, 1152–53
    functional imaging of, 1150
    glia in, 1122*f*
    and information processing, 1148, 1151–52,
        1153, 1177, 1178
    and language, 1152, 1152*f*
    long-term potentiation in, 1156, 1156*f*
    organization of, 1146*f*–47*f*
    regions of, 1145–48
    review, 1160–61
    and speech, 1152
    structure and evolution of, 1145*f*

visual information processing in, **1177**, 1178
Brainstem, **1146***f*, 1147*f*
Bramley orchid, 868*f*
Branch points, **585**, 586*f*
Branching, 830
Branchiostoma, 762*f*
Branta canadensis, 1202
Brassica napus, 866, 883
Brassinosteroids, 892*t*, **900–901**
Brazil trees, 1261
BRCA genes, 409–10
Bread mould, 352
Breast cancer
    development of, 258*f*
    and gene expression, 455, 468
    genomic evolution of cancer, 409*f*
    genomics and cell signalling in, 408*f*
    HER2 and, 260, 408*f*
    inherited predisposition to, 407
    subtypes of, 408*f*
    testing for mutations in BRCA, 409–10
    viruses, role of, 410
Breathing, **990**
    in amphibians, 990
    in birds, 990, 991*f*
    homeostatic control of, 992*f*
    humans, control of, 992
    in mammals, 990–92
    review, 997
Breathing control centres, 992
Breeding, plant, 882–83
Brenner, Sydney, 1110, 1112*f*
Brewer's yeast, 692–93, 1265*f*
Briggs, Robert, 449
Brightfield, 106*f*
Brine shrimp, 486*f*, 1029
Bristlecone pine, 680*f*
Brittle stars, 755, 755*f*
Broad-nosed pipefish, 524
Broca, Pierre, 1152
Broca's area, 1152
Bronchi, **989**
Bronchioles, **989**
Brood bodies, 660
Brown, Carissa, 1230*f*
Brown adipose tissue (BAT), 934
Brown algae, 635*f*, **635**–36, 636*f*
Brown bear, 156*f*
Brown tree snakes, 1325
Brown-headed cowbirds, 1331–32
Brundtland, G. H., 1323
Brunham, Robert, 427
Brush border, 955
Brushtail possums, 784*f*
Bryophytes, **658**
    diversity of, 662*f*–63*f*
    gametophytes, 659–660
Bt toxin, 883, 883*f*, 885
Bubo scandiacus, 1264*f*
Buchloe dactyloides, 831
Buck, Linda, 1180

Bud cells, 697
Budding, **1071**
Buffalo grass, 831
Buffers, 58–59
Bulbourethral glands, 1079
Bulk feeders, **949***f*
Bulk flow, **835**, 836–840, 840, 844–45, 845*f*
Bulk transport, 149–151, 152
Bundle sheaths, 814
Bundle-sheath cells, **214**–15, 215*f*
Burgess Shale, 716, 717*f*, 746
Burkholderia glathei, 618*f*
Burkitt's lymphoma, 410
Burrowing owls, 1315*f*
Bush babies, 788, 788*f*
Buttercups, 812*f*
Butterflies, 328*f*, 752*f*, 753*f*, 872*f*, 885, 919*f*, 1048,
    1048*f*, 1058–59, 1172*f*, 1203–4, 1203*f*
Buxbaum, Joseph, 483*f*
Byrophyte sporophytes, 660–61

C

C segments, 1008
C$_3$ plants, **214**
C$_4$ plants, **214**–16, 215*f*, 216*f*
Ca^{2+}, 890, 891
Cabomba caroliniana, 819, 819*f*
Cacao tree, 706, 706*f*
Cachexia, 1059
Cacti, 800*f*, 806*f*, 843*f*, 872*f*, 1233, 1233*f*, 1234*f*
Caecilians, 774, 774*f*
Caenorhabditis elegans, 239, 239*f*, 467, 469*t*, 470,
    471, 745, 1110–11, 1111*f*, 1112*f*, 1141
Calcitonin, 1054*f*, **1064**
Calcium, 946*t*
Calcium ions, 1063–64, 1063*f*
    and cell communication, 232–33, 233*f*
    in fertilization, 1097–98, 1098*f*
    in muscle contraction, 1184, 1184*f*
    and muscle contraction, 1187, 1188
    and sensory receptors, 1166
Calidris canutus rufa, 1330, 1330*f*
California mice, 1201, 1201*t*
Callus, **881**
Calories (cal), 51–52, 937
Calvin, Melvin, 203
Calvin cycle, 202*f*, **202**
    reducing CO$_2$ to sugar, 212–13
    review, 218*f*, 219
    three turns of, 213*f*
Calystegia septium, 868*f*
CAM, **216**
CAM plants, 216–17, **216**
Cambium, 815, 818
Cambrian explosion, 561–62, 716, 746
Cambrian period, 716*f*
Camels, 1029
Camouflage
    as example of evolutionary adaptation, 2*f*, 500*f*
    and predation on mice by owls, 24
cAMP, 231*f*, **231**–32, 232*f*, **384**, 1052, 1133

Campbell, Kevin, 995
Canada geese, 933*f*, 1202
Canaries, 1205
Canavalia ensiformis, 912
Canavanine, 912
Cancer
   brain cancer inhibitors, 259
   breast, 407, 408*f*, 409–10, 409*f*, 455, 468, 961
   cell cycle controls, loss of, 258–260
   colorectal, 406–7, 407*f*, 471*f*, 961
   environmental factors, 407–10
   and evolution, 456–57
   genes associated with, 404–5, 411–12
   and genomics and cell signalling, 408*f*
   growth and metastasis of malignant
      tumour, 258*f*
   and immune system suppression, 1019
   and immunity, 1022
   inherited predisposition to, 407–10
   International Cancer Genome
      Consortium, 260
   and Kaposi's sarcoma herpesvirus, 1022
   multistep model of development of, 406–7,
      407*f*
   mutations causing, 375, 404, 405–7, 468
   and the rosy periwinkle, 1323
   and viruses, 410, 426
Cancer Genome Atlas, 468
Cancer Genome Atlas Network, 407
Candida albicans, 709
Canis latrans, 1225, 1245*f*
Canis lycaon, 1245*f*
Canola, 866–67, 866*f*, 883
Canopy, **1233**
Canyon tree frogs, 1278*f*
Capacitation, 1099
Capecchi, Mario, 446
Capillaries, **969**, 975, 975*f*, 976, 978–79,
   979*f*, 986
Capillary beds, **969**, 978*f*
Capitanian extinction, 566
Capra pyrenaica pyrenaica, 1326
Capsaicin, 1166
Capsids, **416**–17
Capsomeres, 416
Capsules, 605*f*, **605**, **660**
Carbohydrates, **76**
   digestion of, 954*f*
   membrane carbohydrates, 141
   review, 99
   sugars. *See* Sugars
α carbon, 83
Carbon, 67*f*
   and acidification, 59, 59*f*, 60
   atmospheric, 1339*f*, 1341
   bonding, 63, 66–67, 72
   capture and burial of, 1340*f*
   as carbohydrates. *See* Carbohydrates
   emission rates in Canada, 1340*f*
   as essential element, 33
   importance of, 63

   isotopes of, 35
   and lipids, bonded to, 605
   molecular diversity and carbon skeletons,
      67–69
   and organic chemistry, 64–65
   in radiometric dating, 37
   skeletons, 67–69, 67*f*
Carbon cycle, 1310*f*
Carbon cycling, 1304
Carbon dioxide
   atmospheric, 10, 60, 216
   and cellular respiration, 176, 180
   and climate change, 1230, 1339*f*
   and covalent bonding, 66–67
   and diatoms and capture of, 634–35
   and forests, 689
   and gas exchange, 994–95. *See also* Gas
      exchange
   and global warming, 10, 566
   in human breathing, 992
   and ocean acidification, 60
   and ocean fertilization, 1305
   in photosynthesis, 200, 201, 212–13, 217
   in plants, 855
   as ripening agent, 900
   structural formula, 66–67
   transport of, 994–95
Carbon fixation, **203**, 212, 214–17, 219
Carbon monoxide, 1050, 1135
Carbon sink, 1304
Carbon source, 1304
Carboniferous period, 666, 668*f*, 669, 678
Carbonyl group, 70, 71*f*
Carboxyl group, 70, 71*f*, 83, 84
Cardiac cycle, 973*f*, **973**, 976
Cardiac muscle, **926***f*, **1187**–88
Cardiac output, **973**
Cardiovascular disease, 961, 983–84
Cardiovascular systems, **969**, 972–74, 972*f*
Caribou, 514*f*, 712*f*, 1072*f*, 1276, 1277, 1324
Carnivores (carnivora), 787*f*, **943**
   and alimentary canals, 958, 958*f*
   and dentition, 957*f*
   plant, 862–64, 863*f*
Caron, Jean-Bernard, 716
Carotenoids, **206**, 600
Carpels, 681*f*, **681**, **867**
Carrick, Bill, 1202
Carrier proteins, 142, 145*f*, 146
Carriers, genetic, 297–98, 300–301
Carroll, Scott, 501*f*
Carroll, Sean, 747*f*
Carrots, cloning, 449
Carrying capacity, **1257**, 1259, 1268–70
Carson, Rachel, 1337, 1338
Cartilage, **925***f*
Cas9. *See* CRISPR-Cas9 system
Case Study
   evolution of tolerance to toxic elements, 33–34
   kidney function in vampire bats, 1040–41
   mouse coat colouration, 21–23

   variation in migratory patterns, 1214
   variation in prey selection, 1214
Casparian strip, **836**
Cassava, 884*f*
Castor beans, 874, 874*f*
Castor canadensis, 584, 1029
Catabolic pathways, 155
   oxidizing organic fuels, 176–181
   and production of ATP, 176
   review, 196
Catabolic reaction, **155**
Catabolism, 193–94, 193*f*, 194*f*
Catabolite activator protein (CAP), 384–85, 384*f*
Catalysis, 167, 167*f*
Catalysts, **83**, **164**
Catecholamines, 1051, **1064**
Catenulida, 735
Caterpillars, 513*f*, 752, 912, 949*f*, 1048, 1048*f*,
   1307
Catfishes, 1171
Catharanthus roseus, 1323*f*
Cation exchange, 851*f*, **851**
Cations, **42**
Cats, 787*f*, 1165, 1325
   cloning, 450, 450*f*
   colour vision in, 1177
   drinking technique, 62*f*
   Siamese, 379*f*
   and X inactivation, 314*f*
Cattle, 787*f*
Cattle egrets, 1246, 1246*f*, 1281, 1281*f*
Caulerpa, 643, 643*f*
Cavalier-Smith, Thomas, 645*f*
Cavendish banana, 280
CD8, 1013, 1013*f*
Cdks. *See* Cyclin-dependent kinases (Cdks)
cDNA. *See* Complementary DNA (cDNA)
Cecum, **956**
Cedar Creek Natural History Area, 1283, 1283*f*
Celera Genomics, 464
Cell adhesion molecules, 1109
Cell body, **1121**
Cell communication. *See also* Signalling
   among bacteria, 222*f*
   apoptosis, 238–240
   by direct contact, 223*f*
   in endocrine system, 927
   evolution of, 222–23
   external signals, conversion of, 222–25
   introduced, 221
   local and long-distance, 223–24, 223*f*
   in nervous system, 927
   reception, 224*f*, 225–29
   response, 224*f*, 234–38
   review, 241
   stages of, 224–25, 224*f*
   transduction, 224*f*, 229–233
Cell cultures, protein production in, 457
Cell cycle, 244. *See also* Cell division; Cells
   binary fission in bacteria, 251–52
   in cancer cells, 258–260

Cell cycle (*Continued*)
  checkpoints, 254, 255–58, 256*f*
  clock, 255–58
  cytokinesis, **246**, 248*f*, 250–51, 251*f*
  inhibitors, 259
  mitotic spindles, 249–250
  molecular signals, 254*f*
  phases of, 246–49, 246*f*
  regulation of, 253–58
Cell cycle control system, 254*f*, **254**–58, 255*f*
Cell differentiation, 823, 823*f*, 896
Cell division, 243. *See also* Cell cycle
  anchorage dependence, 257, 257*f*
  asymmetrical, 821, 822*f*
  by binary fission, 251–52, 252*f*
  chromosomes, distribution of, 245–46
  daughter cells, 244–46
  density-dependent inhibition, 257, 257*f*
  eukaryotic, 245–46
  frequency of, 253
  functions of, 244*f*
  and gibberellins, 897
  mechanisms of, 253, 253*f*
  patterns of, 821*f*
  plane and symmetry of, 821–22, 821*f*
  review, 260–61
  roles of, 243–44
  zone of, in roots, 812
Cell elongation, 894, 895*f*
Cell expansion, 822, 822*f*
Cell fate
  and axis formation, 1112–13
  and cilia, 1117
  determination and differentiation, 1110
  determination and pattern formation of, by
      inductive signals, 1114–17
  developmental potential, restricting, 1113
  fate mapping, 1110–14
  review, 1118–19
Cell fractionation, 107*f*, **107**–8
Cell junctions, 223*f*
Cell migration, 1109
Cell motility, 125
Cell plates, 251*f*, **251**
Cell polarity, 1106*f*
Cell signalling
  cell-cell recognition, 223*f*
  by direct contact, 223*f*
  evolution of, 222–23
  external signals, conversion of, 223–25
  and genomics and cancer, 408*f*
  and homeostasis, 918*f*
  interference with, 405–6
  junctions, 223*f*
  local and long-distance, 223–24, 223*f*
  overview, 224*f*
  reception, 224
  response, 225
  stages of, 224–25
  termination in, 238
  transduction, 225

  transduction in, 224*f*
Cell walls, 113*f*, **129**–130, 144–45
Cell-cell recognition, 141, 223*f*
Cell-inhibiting pathway, normal and mutant, 406*f*
Cell-mediated immune response, **1011**, 1012,
      1012*f*, 1015
α cells. *See* Alpha cells
Cells
  activities of, 102*f*
  activities of, as theme in biology, 4–6
  alpha, 1056
  animal, 112*f*
  beta, 1056
  a/α cells, 222, 222*f*
  characteristics of, 4
  chief, 953
  chloride, 1027, 1028
  chromosomes in, 268–69
  cutaway view, 112*f*
  cytoskeleton, 123–29, 123*f*
  daughter cells, 244–46, 251*f*
  dendritic, 1003, 1011*f*
  effector, 1009
  endomembrane system, 115–19
  enzymes in, 172
  eukaryotic cells. *See* Eukaryotic cells
  extracellular components and connections
      between cells, 129–131
  fate mapping, 1111*f*
  foam, 984*f*
  forms of, 4, 6
  as fundamental units of life, 104
  fungal, 112*f*
  generative, 682
  genetic information in, 102*f*
  germ, 1110–11
  HeLa cells, 258
  junctions, 131
  as level of biological organization, 5*f*
  Leydig, 1078, 1085, 1085*f*
  lung cell dividing, 6*f*
  mast, 1004, 1018*f*
  mating, 222*f*
  memory, 1009
  mesenchyme, 1102–3
  mitochondria, 120–22
  natural killer, **1003**
  organization of genetic material, 244–45
  parietel, 953
  phagocytic, 1003
  photosynthetic cells, 214
  plant. *See* Plant cells
  in retina, 104*f*
  review, 133, 133–34
  Schwann, 1129, 1130*f*, 1141, 1141*f*
  Sertoli cells, 1085
  sister cells, 244
  size range of, 105*f*
  stem, 982–83, 982*f*
  study of, 105–8
  sugar-conducting, 809*f*

  tube, 682
  types of work, 161
  water-conducting, 809*f*
  with/without cell walls, 144–45
  work of, 175
  xylem, 689
Cell-stimulating pathway, normal and mutant, 405*f*
Cell-surface receptors, 225–28, 226–28*f*
Cellular defences, 1002–3
Cellular differentiation, and sequential regulation,
      398–400
Cellular elements of blood, 980*f*, 981, 982–83
Cellular mechanisms in morphogenesis, 1108–10
Cellular respiration, **176**
  and ATP production, 188–191, 189*f*
  and catabolic pathways, 176–181
  and catabolism, versatility of, 193–94
  citric acid cycle, 182–85
  control of, 195*f*
  and energy transformation, 103*f*
  glycolysis, 181
  overview, 180*f*
  oxydative phosphorylation, 185–191
  pyruvate oxidation, 181–82
  and redox reactions, **177**–79
  regulation of via feedback mechanisms, 194–95
  review, 196–97
  stages of, 179–181
Cellular response pathways, 1051–53
Cellular slime moulds, **645**–46
Cellulose, **79**
  overview, 79–80
  structure of, 78*f*, 79*f*
Cellulose-synthesizing proteins, rings of, 653
Cellulosic biofuels, 884*f*
Cenozoic era, 558*f*, 559, 717–18, 785
Centipedes, 749, 749*f*
Central canal, **1142**
Central dogma, 355
Central nervous system (CNS), **1122**
  brain. *See* Brains
  and neural plasticity, 1154–55, 1154*f*
  and peripheral nervous system, 1143
  role of, 1141
  and sensory reception, 1163–67
  vertebrate, 1143*f*
Central vacuoles, 113*f*, **119**
Centrifuge, 108
Centrioles, 125*f*, **125**, 249
Centromere, **245**, 247*f*, 272*f*
Centromeric DNA, 474
Centrosomes, 112*f*, 125*f*, **125**, 247*f*, 248*f*, 249*f*,
      249, 272*f*
Century plants, 1260, 1260*f*
Cephalization, 1141
Cephalocereus senilis, 843*f*
Cephalopods, 741–42, 741*f*, 969
Cephalorhynchus hectori, 1251
Ceratotherium simum, 1259
Cercozoans, **641**–42
Cerebellum, 1145, **1146***f*, 1147*f*

Cerebral cortex, **1147**f
    frontal lobe function, 1152–53
    information processing in, 1151–52, 1151f
    and language, 1152, 1152f
    and memory and learning, 1155–56
    review, 1160
    and speech, 1152
    and vision, 1177
Cerebral hemispheres, **1147**f
Cerebral palsy, 1147f
Cerebrospinal fluid, 992, **1142**, 1147f
Cerebrum, 1145, **1146**f, 1147f. See also Cerebral
    cortex
Certainty of paternity, 1209
Cervix, **1077**
Cetaceans, 505–6, 506f, 759, 787f, 1153
Cetartiodactyla, 787f
CFCs (chlorofluorocarbons), 1341, 1342
CFTR gene, **264**
CFTR protein, **265**
cGMP. See Cyclic GMP
Chaenomeles japonica, 868f
Chagas' disease, 633
α chains, 1006–7
Chamois, 947f
Channel proteins, 142, 145–46, 145f
Chaparral, 1233, **1235**f, 1289
Chaperonins, 91f, **91**
Chara species, 653
Character displacement, **1276**
Characters, **282**, 285
Chargaff, Erwin, 332, 333
Chargaff's rules, 332
Charophyte algae, 655f
Charophytes, 643, 653f, 654f
Charpentier, Emmanuelle, 447
Charter of Rights and Freedoms, 301
Chase, Martha, 331–32, 331f
"cheating," 1217
Checkpoints, **254**, 255–58, 256f
Cheetahs, 1265f
Chelicerae, **748**
Chelicerates, **748**–49
Chelydra serpentina, 777f
Chemical bonds, **40**
    covalent, 40–42
    hydrogen bonds, 43, 43f
    ionic bonds, 42–43
    molecular shape and function, 44
    van der Waals interactions, 43–44
    weak, 43–44
Chemical communication, 1199
Chemical cycling, 9f, 1301
Chemical defence, 1278, 1278f
Chemical defences, 1278, 1278f
Chemical digestion, 948–950, 953–55, 954f
Chemical energy, **155**
Chemical equilibrium, 46
Chemical groups
    biologically important groups, 71f
    most important to life, 69–70

    review, 72
    role of, 69
Chemical reactions, **45**
    making and breaking of chemical bonds, 45–46
    review, 47
Chemical recycling, 618
Chemical signals
    hormones as, 223f, 224, 1049
    intercellular signalling factors, 1050
    in myxobacteria, 222f
Chemical synapses, 1130, 1131f
Chemical work, 161
Chemiosmosis, **187**–88, 188f, 196
    in chloroplasts and mitochondria, comparison,
        210–12, 210f
    and light reactions, 211f
Chemistry
    and biology, connection to, 32–33
    organic chemistry, 64–65
Chemoautotrophic microbes, 1299
Chemoautotrophs, 612t
Chemoheterotrophs, 612t
Chemoreceptors, **1165**, 1166f
Chemosynthesis, 1299
Chemotaxis, 606
Chemotrophs, 612
Chen caerulescens, 1198f
Chen caerulescens caerulescens, 1279
Chestnut blight, 914, 1285–86
Chiasmata, 272f, **272**f, 276
Chickadees, 934, 940
Chicks
    axis formation in, 1112
    gastrulation in, 1103, 1105f
    limb development in, 1114–16, 1115f
    organogenesis in, 1108, 1108f
Chicxulub crater, 567, 568f
Chief cells, 953
Chikungunya, 430
Childbirth, 1051, 1056, 1060, 1088, 1089f
Childhood leukemia, 1323
Chimpanzees, 463, 463f, 481, 571, 571f, 787f,
    789, 789f, 793, 1203, 1205, 1205f
Chipmunks, 1029
Chiroptera, 787f
Chi-square tests, 318
Chitin, 80f, **80**, **693**, **1189**
Chitons, 738–39, 739f, 1140f, 1141
Chivers, Douglas, 1200
Chlamydias, 617f, 1092
Chlamydomonas, 113f, 643, 644f
Chlorarachniophytes, 625–26, 630, 630f, 641
Chloride, 945
Chloride cells, 1027, 1028
Chlorinated hydrocarbons, 1337
Chlorine, 33f, 946t, 1342, 1342f
Chlorocebus aethiops, 1206
Chlorofluorocarbons (CFCs), 1341, 1342
Chlorophyll, 122, **201**, 889
    chlorophyll *a*, **204**, 205–6, 207, 208
    chlorophyll *b*, **204**, 205–6

    excitation of by light, 206, 206f
    molecule of, 5f
    structure of in chloroplasts, 205f
Chlorophytes, 643, 643f, 644f, 654f
Chloroplasts, **120**
    in algal cell, 122f
    chemiosmosis in, 210–12, 210f
    diagram, 122f
    evolutionary origins of, 120–22, 121f
    and interaction of light, 122–23, 204f
    and photosynthesis, 5f, 113f, 200–201
    and plant biotechnology, 886
    and structure of chlorophyll, 205f
Chlorosis, 856
Choanocytes, **730**
Choanoflagellates, 715f
Cholecystokinin (CCK), 960f
Cholera, 232
Cholesterol, 83f, **83**, 138, 139f, 149–151, 983,
    985, 1051
Choline, 82
Chondrichthyans, **767**–69, 768f, 1027
Chondrocytes, **768**, 925f
Chondroitin sulphate, 925f
Chondromyces crocatus, 616f
Chordates (Chordata), 723, 729f, 756, **760**, 1103
    derived characters of, 761, 761f
    early evolution of, 762–63
    endoskeleton of, 1190
    fossil of, 765f
    hagfishes, 764, 764f
    kidneys in, 1035
    lampreys, 764–65, 765f
    lancelets, 761–62, 762f, 763f
    phylogeny of, 760f
    review, 797
    tunicates, 762, 763f
    vertebrates, 763–66
Chorion, 1106
Chorionic villus sampling (CVS), 301,
    302f, 1091
Choristoneura fumiferana, 1050
Christmas tree worm, 743, 743f
Chromatids, 247f
Chromatin, **111**, 112f, 114f, **244**–45, **347**–48
    in interphase nucleus, 392f
    regulation of structure of, 385–87
    remodelling by ncRNAs, 395–96, 396f
Chromatophores, 641f
Chromoplasts, 123
Chromosomal basis of inheritance
    behaviour of chromosomes as basis of
        Mendelian inheritance, 307, 308, 309
    chromosome numbers, 321–22
    chromosome structure, alterations in,
        322–24, 322f
    exceptions to standard Mendelian inheritance,
        324–26, 327
    linked genes, 314–321
    and Mendel's hereditary factors, 307
    Morgan's experimental evidence, 309–11

Chromosomal basis of inheritance (*Continued*)
  recombination of linked genes, 317*f*
  review, 326–27
  sex-linked genes in, 311–14, 311*f*
Chromosome 7, **264**, 320*f*
Chromosome theory of inheritance, **309**
Chromosomes, **108**, **111**, **244**
  alterations of structure, 476
  bacterial, 253*f*
  bacterial chromosomes, 345–46
  in cell cycle, 247*f*, 249*f*
  daughter chromosomes, 248*f*
  describing, 269*f*
  distribution of during cell division, 245–46, 245*f*
  division of, 243*f*
  duplication of, 476, 514
  eukaryotic, 244*f*
  F factor in, 610
  and heredity, 267–68, 279
  human chromosome 2, 476
  independent assortment of, 277, 277*f*
  in interphase nucleus, 392*f*
  locating genes along, 307–9
  and Mendel's laws, 308*f*
  metaphase chromosomes, 347*f*
  numbers, abnormal, 321–22, 327
  painting, 348*f*
  of prokaryotic cells, 608*f*
  sets of in human cells, 268–69
  sex chromosomes, 269
  sister chromatids, 245*f*
  structure, alteration of, 322–24, 322*f*, 327
Chronic inflammation, 1005
Chronic myelogenous leukemia (CML), 323, 324*f*, 456
Chrysanthemums, 905
Chthamalus, 1275*f*, 1276
Chutter, 1206
Chylomicrons, **956**
Chyme, **953**, 955, 960*f*
Chymotripsin, 955
Chytridiomycota, 699
Chytrids, **699**, 700*f*
Cichlid fish, 538–39, 539*f*, 543, 543*f*, 545
Cilia, 14*f*, **125**–27, 126*f*, 127*f*, 949*f*, 990, 1117, 1165
Ciliated protists, 1274
Ciliates, **639**, 640*f*
Cinnebar, 319
Circadian rhythms, **842**, 903–**4**, **929**–930, 930*f*, 940, 1149, 1198
Circannual rhythms, 1198
Circulatory adaptations, 932–33
Circulatory systems, 923*t*
  blood in, 980–84. *See also* Blood
  blood pressure, blood vessels, and blood flow, 975–980, 976*f*
  and cardiovascular disease, 983–84
  cells and exchange surfaces, 967–972
  closed, 741
  coordination of, 993

double circulation, 969, 972–74
evolution of, in vertebrates, 969–971
evolutionary variation in, 968–69
exchange surfaces of, 922
and exchange with environment, 923
and gas exchange, 985–990. *See also* Gas exchange organs
gastrovascular cavities, 967–68
general properties of, 968
mammalian, 972–74
open/closed, 748, 968–69, 968*f*
review, 996–97
single circulation, 969
vertebrates, evolutionary variation in, 970*f*, 971
Cis double bonds, in fatty acids, 81
Cis face, 117–18
Cis-retinal arrangement, 1175, 1175*f*
Cisternal maturation model, 118
Cis-trans isomers, 68*f*, **68**–69
Citric acid cycle, 180*f*, **180**, 182–85, 183*f*, 184*f*, 193–95
Clades, taxonomy, **588**, 629*f*, 634–642, 639, 650
Cladistics, 588–89, 588*f*, **588**–89
Cladograms, 592*f*, **592**
Clams, 741*f*, 949*f*, 986, 1073, 1141, 1188, 1189
Clark's nutcracker, 1203
Classes, **584**
Classical conditioning, 1203
Classification of life. *See* Taxonomy
Claviceps purpurea, 708
Clayoquot Sound, 198*f*
Clear-cutting, 689, 689*f*, 1292, 1313
Cleavage, **250**, **713**, 721, 721*f*, **1086**, **1099**
  in echinoderm embryo, 1099*f*
  in frogs, 1100*f*, 1101
  patterns of, 1100–1101
  regulation of, 1101
  review, 1118
Cleavage furrow, 248*f*, **250**, 251*f*, 272*f*, 1100
Clements, F. E., 1289
Climate, **1225**. *See also* Climate change
  and bodies of water, 1225
  and latitudinal gradients, 1293
  and mountains, 1228, 1229*f*
  review, 1248
  seasonality of, 1225
  and terrestrial biomes, 1231–32, 1232*f*
Climate change, 10. *See also* Global warming
  atmosphere in flux, 1339*f*
  and bodies of water, 1229*f*
  and brewer's yeast, 692–93
  and continental drift, 565
  and dendrochronology, 817*f*
  and ecosystems, 1340*f*
  elements of, 10–11
  and fertility of plant species, 870
  and the future, 1340*f*
  and a greener planet, 1339*f*
  and greenhouse gases, 1338
  and insect pests, 1340*f*
  overview, 1230–31

solutions for, 1340*f*
and a warmer planet, 1339*f*
and water potential, 839
Climax community, 1289
Clitoris, **1078**
Cloaca, **769**, **1075**
Clonal selection, **1009**, 1010*f*
Clones, **267**
  Dolly the sheep, 450, 1326
  garlic, 881*f*
  Pando aspen, 877
Cloning
  of extinct species, 1326
  test-tube cloning of plants, 881–82
Cloning, DNA. *See* DNA cloning
Cloning, genes. *See* Gene cloning
Cloning, organismal. *See* Organismal cloning
Cloning, therapeutic. *See* Therapeutic cloning
Cloning vectors, **437**
Closed circulatory systems, 968*f*, **969**
Clostridium botulinum, 621
Clostridium difficile, 620
Clotting, 10, 981–82, 982*f*
Club fungi, 700*f*, 704, 704*f*
Club mosses, 658, 666
Clumped dispersion, 1252, 1252*f*
Cn3D, 466*f*
Cnidaria, 727*f*
Cnidarians, 731–32, 731*f*, 732*f*, 950, 967, 967*f*, 1071, 1140, 1140*f*, 1189, 1192
Cnidocytes, 732*f*, **732**
CNVs, 484–85
Coal, 668*f*
Coastal redwood ecosystem, 1321*f*
Coat protein, 150*f*
Cocci, 604*f*
Coccidioidomycosis, 708
Coccosteus cuspidatus, 555*f*
Cochlea, **1168***f*, 1169, 1170, 1170*f*, 1172
Cockleburs, 682*f*, 905
Cockroaches, 1167
Coconuts, 873, 895
Cod, 101, 770, 1027, 1277, 1288, 1326
Coding strands, 356
Codominance, 291
Codon recognition, 369*f*
Codons, 356, **356**, 357*f*, 364–65
Coefficient of relatedness, 1216*f*, **1216**–17
Coelacanths, 771, 771*f*
Coelom, **720**, 721, 721*f*, 738
Coelomates, **720**
Coencytic fungi, **694**
Coenocytic hyphae, 694*f*
Coenzyme Q (CoQ), 197*f*
Coenzymes, **169**
Coevolution, **871**, 873*f*
Cofactors, **169**
Cognition, 1153, 1153*f*, **1203**
Cognitive maps, **1203**
Cohesins, **245**, 274
Cohesion, **50**–51, 839–840

Cohesion-tension hypothesis, **838**
Cohn, Z. A., 1011*f*
Coho salmon, 1260
Coitus, **1086**
Coitus interruptus, 1090
Cold stress, plant, 911
Coleochaete orbicularis, 653, 653*f*
Coleoptera (beetles), 753*f*
Coleoptiles, **874**, 893, 893*f*, 898*f*, 902*f*
Coleorhiza, **874**
Coleus, 325*f*, 813*f*
Collagen, 89*f*, **130**, 925*f*
Collagenous fibres, 925*f*
Collared flycatcher, 542
Collared lemmings, 1264*f*
Collared pika, 1266, 1266*f*
Collecting ducts, **1037**, **1037***f*, 1038*f*
Collenchyma cells, **808***f*
Collip, J., 1057*f*
Colocasia esculenta, 800*f*
Colon, **956**
Colonization of land, 562
Colony Collapse Disorder, 688
Colorectal cancer, 406–7, 407*f*, 471*f*
Colour blindness, 1178, 1178*f*
Colour vision, 1173, 1175*f*, 1177–78
Colour-blindness, 312*f*
Columbine flowers, 872*f*
Comb jelly, 154*f*, 723, 727*f*
Combinatorial control of gene activation, 390–91
Commensalism, **619**, **1280–81**
Committee on the Status of Endangered Wildlife in Canada (COSEWIC), 742, 1322
Common arrowhead, 879*f*
Common cold, 1019
Common eiders, 1261*f*
Common juniper, 680*f*
Common yellowthroat, 1224
Communication
 among birds, 1199, 1205
 among monkeys, 1206
 animal forms of, 1198–99, 1199*f*
 auditory, 1199
 chemical, 1199
 intercellular. *See* Intercellular communication
 by pheremones, 1199–1201
 synaptic, 1130–35, 1138
 tactile, 1199
 visual communication, 1199
Communities
 biological. *See* Biological communities
 and ecology, **1226***f*
 as level of biological organization, 4*f*
Community analysis and feedback, 20*f*
Community ecology, **1226***f*
 biogeographic factors affecting diversity in, 1292–94
 and competition, 1274–76
 complexity of, 1296*f*
 disturbances in, 1289–92
 interspecific interactions, 1274–81

pathogens in, 1294–97
 and predation, 1276–78
 review, 1297–98
 and zoonotic diseases, 1295–97
Companion cells, 809*f*
Competition for resources, 1264*f*
Competitive exclusion, 1274–75
Complement system, **1003**, 1014
Complementary DNA (cDNA), 442, 444*f*, **444**
Complete digestive tract, 950
Complete dominance, **291**
Complete flowers, **867**
Complete medium, 352
Complete metamorphosis, **752**, 753*f*
Compost, 1301*f*
Compound eyes, 1173*f*, **1173**
Compound leaves, 805*f*
Compounds, 33*f*, **33**
Concentration gradient, **143**, 148
Conception, **1086**
Concussion, 1139–40
Condoms, **1090**
Conduction, 932*f*
Condulura cristata, 1162, 1162*f*
Cones, 104, **1175***f*, 1176–77, 1178
Confocal, 106*f*
Conformers, **928**
Conidia, **702**
Coniferophyta, 680*f*
Conifers, **676**, 680*f*
Conjugation, 610*f*, **610–12**, **639**
Connective tissue, 923, **925***f*
Connell, Joseph, 1275*f*
Conodonts, 766, 766*f*
Consanguineous, 298
Conservation areas, 1334, 1334*f*. *See also* Protected areas
Conservation biology, 97*f*, **1321**
 biodiversity and, 1321–27
 and grizzly bears, 1329
 landscape and regional conservation in, 1331–35
 population conservation in, 1327–31
 protected areas, establishing, 1332–35
 and urban ecology, 1335
Conservation of developmental genes among animals, 485–86
Conservation of mass, **1301**
Conservation of soil, 851–52
Conservative model, 336, 336*f*
Conserved Domain Database, (CDD), 466*f*
Constant (C) region, 1006
Constitutive triple-response (*ctr*) mutants, 899
Consumers, **8**
Consumption, regulation of, 961–62
Continental drift, 563–65, 565*f*
Contour tillage, 854*f*
Contraception, **1089–91**, 1090*f*
Contractile and motor proteins, 84*f*
Contractile vacuoles, **119**
Control centre, 929

Control elements, **387**
Controlled experiments, **22–23**
Convection, 932*f*
Convergent evolution, 505*f*, **505**
 of analogous burrowing characteristics, 586, 586*f*
 in cacti and euphorbs, 1233*f*
 in fast swimmers, 921*f*
 of marsupials and eutherians, 785, 785*f*
Convergent extension, 1109*f*, **1109**
Cooksonia sporangium, 654, 654*f*
Cooper, Vaughn, 609*f*
Cooperation, in scientific process, 23–25, 29, 263
Cooperativity, 171*f*, **171**
Coordinately controlled genes, 381, 391–92
Copepods, **750**, 1284
Coprophagy, 959
Copy-number variants (CNVs), 484–85
Coral reefs, 60, 60*f*, **1243***f*, 1303, 1323, 1323*f*
Corals, 731, 732*f*, 733–34, 1071
Corepressor, **382**
Cork cambium, **810**, 818
Corkscrew carnivore, 849
Cormorants, 530
Corn, 216*f*, 463, 469*t*, 473, 473*f*, 481, 688
Corneas, 1174*f*
Corpse flowers, 686*f*
Corpus callosum, **1147***f*
Corpus luteum, **1077**, 1084
Correns, Karl, 325
Corridors, 1332, 1332*f*
Cortex, **127**, **807**, 812, 1097
Cortical microfilaments, 127
Cortical nephrons, **1036***f*
Cortical reaction, 1097–98, 1097*f*, 1099
Cortical rotation, 1112
Corticosteroids, **1064**
Cortisol, 1064
Corvids, 1203, 1204
Corvus caurinus, 1208
Corvus moneduloides, 1153
Corylus avellana, 871*f*
Costa Rica, 1316*f*, 1334, 1334*f*, 1343, 1343*f*
Costanza, Robert, 1324
Cotransport, **148–49**, 149*f*, 832, 833*f*
Cotton, 898
Cotyledons, **683**, 874, 874*f*
Cougars, 1258
Countercurrent exchange, 933*f*, **933**, **986**, 987*f*, 988
Countercurrent multiplier system, **1039**
Courtship. *See also* Mating
 in fruit flies, 1198–99, 1199*f*, 1213
 in guppies, 1210
 and mate competition by males, 1211–12
 and mate selection by females, 1210
Covalent bonds, 40*f*, **40–42**, 41*f*
Cowbirds, 1281, 1331–32
Cowpox, 1015
Cows, 959*f*
Coyotes, 787*f*, 958, 958*f*, 1225, 1245*f*
Crabs, 748, 748*f*, 750, 750*f*, 1196*f*, 1254, 1278, 1288*f*, 1330*f*

"Crank," 69f
Crassulacean acid metabolism (CAM), **216**, 842
Crawling, 1189, 1191
Crayfishes, 750, 986, 987f, 1167
C-reactive protein (CRP), 984
Crenarchaeota, 615, 618
Cretacious mass extinction, 566, 567, 568f, 569f
Cretacious period, 684, 784
Creutzfeldt-Jakob disease, 430
Cri du chat, 323
Cricetus cricetus, 940
Crick, Francis, 3, 329f, 333–35, 335–36, 355
Crickets, 470, 753f
Crinoidea, 756, 756f
CRISPR-Cas system, 421, 421f
CRISPR-Cas9 system, **446**–47, 447f, 456, 467
Cristae, **122**
Critical load, 1336
Critical night length, 905
Crocodiles, 489
Crocodilians, 780
Crohn's disease, 1005
Crop, digestive organ, 959
Crop plants, 459
Crop rotations, 851, 860
Cross-fostering studies, 1201t, **1201**
Crossing over, **272**f, 274–76, 274f, 277–78, 278f, **316**, 477, 477f
Cross-pollination, 282–83, 289–290, **682**
Crows, 1208
Crustaceans, 750
    compound eyes of, 1173
    in food chain, 1284
    Hox gene expression in, 486f
    and osmoregulation, 1029
    and parasites, 1280
Crustose lichens, 707f
Cryolophosaurus, 551
Cryptic colouration, 1278f, **1278**
Cryptochromes, 901–2
Cryptococcus gattii, 709
Cryptomonads, 630, 631
Cryptomycota, 698, 699
Crystallin, 391f, 399
Ctenophora, 727f
Ctenophores, 723
C-terminus, 367
Cuboidal epithelium, 924f
Cubozoans (box jellies), 733
Cuckoo bee, 1278f
Cud, 959f
Culex mosquitoes, 1296
Culex pipiens, 521
Culture, **1206**
Cupulate seed, 676f, 1170
Currie, Philip, 14f
Currie, Suzie, 917
Cuscuta, 888–89
Cuticle, **654**, **745**, 746–47, **806**, 1028, 1190
Cuttings, 821
Cuttlefish, 523

Cuvier, Georges, 494, 495
Cyanobacteria, 199f, 562, 617f, 618, 627
Cyanocitta cristata, 1203–4, 1203f
Cycadophyta, 679f
Cycads, 679f
Cyclic AMP (cAMP). *See* cAMP
Cyclic electron flow, 209f, **209**–10
Cyclic GMP, 232, 890–91, 1175
Cyclin-dependent kinases (Cdks), **255**
Cyclins, 255f, **255**
Cycliophora, 728f
Cyclostomes, **764**
Cynodonts, 557f
Cystic fibrosis, **264**, **298**
    genetic transmission of, 265
    and mutations, 374
    and mutations and inheritance, 264–65
    testing for, 301
    treatment of, 264, 375f
Cytochrome *c*, 240
Cytochrome oxidase (CO1), 593, 594f
Cytochromes, **186**
Cytogenetic maps, 320
Cytokines, 1049, 1051
Cytokinesis, **246**, 248f, 250–51, 251f, 272f, 273f, **1004**, 1013
Cytokinins, 892t, **895**–96
Cytology, 107
Cytoplasm, **109**, 110
Cytoplasmic determinants, **398**
Cytoplasmic genes, 325
Cytoplasmic responses, 234, 235f
Cytoplasmic streaming, 128f, **128**
Cytosine, 334–35, 335f
Cytoskeleton, **123**
    components of, 125–29
    cutaway view, 112f, 113f
    in fluorescence micrograph, 123f
    and motor proteins, 124f
    review, 134
    roles of, 124–25
    structure and function of, 124t
Cytosol, **108**
Cytotoxic T cells, 1010, 1010f, **1012**–13, 1013f

D

Daffodils, 681f, 883, 884
Dalmatian dogs, 1032
Dalton, John, 35
Daltons, **35**
Damselfish, 1278
Damselflies, 2f
Danaus plexippus, 1203–4, 1203f
Dance language, 1199, 1200f
Dandelions, 672, 672f, 871f
Daphnia, 1073, 1259f
Daphnia pulex, 469t
D'Arcy, Ryan, 1140
D'Arrigo, Rosanne, 817f
Darwin, Charles
    on adaptation, 496–97

on angiosperms, 684
barnacles as inspiration, 750
Beagle voyage and field research of, 495–96, 496f
on classification of species, 494
on earthworms, 744
on flowering plants, 868f
in Galápagos Islands, 16, 20, 496, 530
and genetic variation, 278, 279
"I think." sketch, 498f
intellectual context of his ideas, 493f
on Lamarck's hypothesis of evolution, 495
on latitudinal gradients, 1292
mystery of mysteries, 530
on natural selection, 498–500
observations on life, 493
photo, 14f
on phototropism, 893, 893f
publication of *Origin of Species*, 493, 497
on swim bladders, 770
theory of descent with modification by, 495–500
and theory of natural selection, 13–16
on theory of young Earth with unchanging species, 493–95
Darwin, Francis, 893, 893f
Dasyatis americana, 768f
Data, **18**
Dating, radiometric, 36, 554–56, 556f
Daughter cells, 244, 244–46, 251f
Daughter chromosomes, 248f
Davidson, William, 470f
Dawson, William, 777
Day-neutral plants, **905**
db genes, 963
DDE, 1337
DDT, 1337–38
de Bold, Adolfo, 1049
Dead Sea, 614
Deanimation, 194
Death signal, apoptosis, 239f, 240
Decapods, 750f, **750**
Declining-population approach, population conservation, 1329–30
Decomposers, **618**, 700f, 704f, **704**, 705–6, **1301**
Decomposition, 1309–13, 1312f
Deconvolution, 106f
Dedifferentiation, 449
Deductive reasoning, 19
Deep sea ecosystem, 1221
Deep-sea mining, 1221
Deep-sea vents, 552, 552f
Deer, 787f, 1207, 1279, 1331
Deer mice, 939, 947
DEET, 1179
De-etiolation (greening), 889f, **889**, 890–91, 890f, 891
Defences
    barrier, 1002
    behavioural, 1277
    chemical, 1278f

internal, 1002f
mechanical, 1278f
against pathogens, 912
plant defences against herbivores, 800f–801f
Defensive proteins, 84f
Deforestation, 1230, 1313, 1324, 1324f, 1340f
Dehydration, 1028
Dehydration reaction, 75f, **75**, 81f
Dehydrogenases, 178
Deinococcus radiodurans, 604
Deletions, 322f, **322**, **374–75**
Delphinapterus leucas, 1322f
Delta proteobacteria, 616f
Dementias, 1159
Demographic transition, **1267**
Demographics, 1253–55
Demography, **1253**
Denaturation, 90f, **90–91**
Dendrites, 926f, **1121**
Dendritic cells, **1003**, 1011f
Dendrochronology, 817, 817f, 828
Dendroctonus ponderosae, 11, 1233, 1340f
Dengue fever, 430
Denisova cave, 795
Density, population, **1251**
and carrying capacity, 1257–59, 1259
dynamics of, 1251
equilibrium, determining, 1263f
and offspring survival, 1263f
Density dependent, **1262**, 1264f–65f
Density independent, **1262**
Density-dependent inhibition, 257f, **257**, 258
Dentition, 957–58, 957f
Deoxyribonucleic acid (DNA). *See* DNA
    (deoxyribonucleic acid)
Deoxyribose, **93**, 94f
Department of Fisheries and Oceans, 935f
Dependent variables, **23**
Dephosphorylation, 230–31
Depolarization, 1097, 1123, 1124, 1125–**26**,
    1126f, 1127, 1128f
Depression, 1158
Derivatives cells, 810
Derived traits, 654
Dermal tissue systems, **806**, 807f
Descamps, Sébastien, 1261f
Descent with modification theory, 497. *See also*
    Evolution; Natural selection
    Darwin on, 13
    as definition of evolution, 493
    evolutionary tree of elephants, 498f
    explained, 11, 16
    Galápagos finches, 17f
    Lamarck's hypothesis of evolution, 495
    natural selection, adaptations, and unity and
        diversity of life, 495–500
    review, 508–9
    tree of life, 497–98
Desert animals, 1029
Deserts, **1234f**
Desiccation, 1028

Desmosomes, 131, **132f**
Desynchronization, 904
Determinate cleavage, **721**
Determinate growth, **810**
Determination, **398**, 399f, **1110**
Detoxification, 116
Detritivores, 1301f, **1301**
Detritus, **1238**, 1284, **1301**
Deuterostome development, **720–21**, 721f
Deuterostomes (Deuterostomia), 729f, 754–56
Deuterostomia clade, 722, **723**, 725f
Development, **819**
    of angiosperms, 658
    in animals, 713–14, 713f
    apoptosis during, 240f
    cell division as function, 244f
    evolution of, 571–73
    of human brain, 1146f
    of learned behaviours, 1205
    modes of, 720–21
    of nervous system, 240
    paw development in mice, 240f
    protostome and deuterostome, 720–21, 721f
    sustainable, 1242–1344, 1345
Developmental confusion, 803
Developmental genes
    changes in, 572
    effects of, 570–71
    in lancelets and vertebrates, 763f
Developmental plasticity, 819, 819f
Developmental potential, 1113, 1114f
Devonian period, 669, 699, 717, 771
d'Hérelle, Félix, 414
Diabetes
    insipidus, 1044f
    mellitus, 470f, 1057–58
    type 1, 453, 457, 1019, 1058
    type 2, 470f, 947, 961, 1058
Diacodexis, 505f, 506
Diacylglycerol (DAG), **233**
Diadromous fishes, 1028
Diaphragm, **991**
Diaphragm contraceptives, **1090**
Diapsids, **778**
Diarrhea, 620
Diastole, 973f, **973**
Diastolic pressure, **976**
Diatom diversity, 629f
Diatomaceous earth, 634
Diatoms, 253f, 634f, **634–35**
Dickinsonia costata, 555f
Dicots, **686**
Dicrostonyx groenlandicus, 1264f, 1285f
Dictyostelium, 647f
Dictyostelium discoideum, 646
Dideoxy sequencing, 434, 435f
Dideoxyribonucleotide (or dideoxy) chain
    termination sequencing, 434, 435f
Diencephalon, 1147f
Diethylstilbestrol (DES), 1066
Diets. *See also* Animal nutrition; Nutrition

deficiencies in, 947
    and dentition, 957–58, 957f
    essential nutrients, 944–47
    vegetarian, 944
Differential gene expression, **385**, 411
    cytoplasmic determinants and inductive signals
        in, 397–98
    and determination, 399f
    and embryonic development, 397, 397f
    pattern formation, 400–403
    regulation of, 385–87
    sequential regulation of, 398–400
Differential-interference-contrast (Nomarski), 106f
Differentiation, **397**, 449, **819**, **1110**
    and gene expression, 823, 823f
    zone of, in roots, 812
Diffusion, 143f, **143–46**, 834–35, 967, 976
Digestion, 948f, **948**, **950**. *See also* Digestive
        system
    absorption in large intestine, 956–57
    absorption in small intestine, 955–56, 955f
    chemical, 953–55, 954f
    and endocrine system, 960
    extracellular, 950
    hormonal control of, 960f
    in hydras, 950, 950f
    intracellular, 950
    regulation of, 960
    ruminant, 959, 959f
    in small intestine, 954–55
    in the stomach, 953–54, 953f
    summary, 964
Digestive compartments, 950
Digestive system, 923t
    esophagus, 952
    evolution of, 957
    evolutionary adaptations of, in vertebrates,
        957–960
    exchange surfaces of, 922, 922f
    human, 952f
    and human airway, 952f
    oral cavity, 951–52
    organization of, 923
    organs, mammalian, 951–57
    pharynx, 952
    summary, 964
Digger wasps, 1203, 1203f
Digits, 773f
Dihybrid cross, **287**, 289–290
Dihybrids, **287**
Dihydroxyacetone, 76f
Dikaryotic mycelium, **696**
Dimer, 125
Dimetrodon, 555f
Dinobryon, 635, 635f
Dinoflagellates, 253f, 637f, **637**
Dinosaurs, 489
    and birds, 582–83
    and blood pressure, 977
    conceptual drawing of, 550f
    as early reptiles, **778**

Dinosaurs (*Continued*)
    feathered, 550*f*, 582*f*, 583, 583*f*, 781
    therapods, 781
Dioecious species, **879**
Dionaea muscipula, 846, 863*f*, 908
Diploblastic, **719**
Diploblasts, 1102
Diploid cells, **269**, 275*f*
Diplomonads, **632**
Dipodomys ordii, 1029
Diptera, 753*f*
Direct exchange, 921–22, 922*f*
Directional cell growth, 237
Directional selection, **522**, 523*f*
Disa watsonii, 868*f*
Disaccharides, 77*f*, **77**–78, 950
Discovery, in scientific process, 20*f*
Diseases, animal
    density-dependent transmission of, 1264*f*
    and global warming, 1340*f*
    spread of, 1332
    and viruses, 426
Diseases, plant, viral, 430
Diseases and disorders, human
    Alzheimer's disease, 1159, 1159*f*
    amyotrophic lateral sclerosis (ALS), 1184
    athlete's foot, 708
    autoimmune diseases, 1019
    avian flu, 428
    bipolar disorder, 1158
    cancer, 961
    cardiovascular disease, 983–84
    cerebral palsy, 1147*f*
    Chagas' disease, 633
    chikungunya, 430
    childhood leukemia, 1323
    chronic myelogenous leukemia, 456
    coccidioidomycosis, 708
    Creutzfeldt-Jakob disease, 430
    Crohn's disease, 1005
    Cryptococcus gattii, 709
    dengue fever, 430
    density-dependent transmission of, 1264*f*
    depression, 1158
    diabetes. *See* Diabetes
    diagnosis and treatment of, 454–55
    Down syndrome, 453
    Ebola, 426
    encephalitis, 426
    ergotism, 708
    glaucoma, 1174*f*
    Graves' disease, 1061
    H1N1 virus, 427–28, 429*f*
    Hantavirus Pulmonary Syndrome, 1295–96
    heart attacks, 457
    Hemorrhagic fever, 426
    hepatitis C, 426, 1003
    HIV/AIDS. *See* AIDS (acquired immune
        deficiency syndrome); HIV (human
        immunodeficiency virus)
    Hodgkin's disease, 1019, 1323

    Huntington's disease, 453
    influenza viruses, 417*f*, 427–28, 427*f*, 429*f*
    kuru, 430
    leukemia, 323, 324, 410, 1018, 1323
    Lou Gehrig's disease, 1184
    lupus, 1019
    lyme disease, 620, 620*f*, 1224–25, 1296, 1296*f*,
        1340*f*
    malaria, 526*f*, 638, 638*f*, 639, 1001
    measles, 1016–17
    multiple sclerosis, 1019
    myasthenia gravis, 1184
    Parkinson's disease, 453, **1159**
    and population regulation, 1264*f*
    rheumatoid arthritis, 1019, 1019*f*
    ringworm, 708
    SARS, 427, 427*f*
    schizophrenia, 1157–58
    sickle-cell disease, 454
    sleeping sickness, 633, 633*f*, 754
    smallpox, 426, 1015
    strokes, 457
    trichinosis, 745
    tuberculosis, 620, 1005
    typhoid fever, 621
    ulcerative colitis, 1005
    West Nile virus, 426
    yeast infections, 709
Disorder, 157–58
Dispersal, **1244**–45
Dispersion, population, **1251**, 1252, 1252*f*
Dispersive model, 336, 336*f*
Disposaurus dorsalis, 936
Disruptive selection, **522**, 523*f*
Distal control elements, 387*f*, 388
Distal tubules, **1037**, **1037***f*
Distance vision, 1178*f*
Disturbance, **1233**
Disturbances, **1289**
    characterizing disturbance, 1289–90
    ecological succession, 1289–90
    human, 1292, 1292*f*
    review, 1297
Disulphide bridges, **89***f*
Divergence, 698
Diversity. *See also* Biodiversity
    of animals, 712–13
    cilia in eukaryotes, 14*f*
    and evolution, 580*f*–81*f*
    and extinction, 563*f*
    of insects, 753*f*
    of life, classifying, 11–16, 12*f*
    and mass extinction, 566*f*
    of plastids, 630*f*
    of polymers, 75
    and speciation, 563*f*
    unity within, 12–13, 15*f*
Diving bell spider (*Argyroneta aquatica*), 998*f*
Diving mammals, respiratory adaptations of,
    995–96
Dixon, Henry, 838

Dizygotic twins, 1088
DNA (deoxyribonucleic acid), **6**, **92**. *See also*
    Biotechnology
    aligning, 587, 587*f*
    alterations of, 476
    applications of, 25
    and bacteria, transformation of, 330
    base pairing in, 335*f*
    cellular organization of, 244–45
    centromeric, 474
    and chromosomes, 111
    and crime scene investigation, 25*f*
    and damage from ozone depletion, 1342
    and development of an organism, 7*f*
    divergence of, 477–78
    double helix, 7*f*, 346
    duplication of, 476, 477–78, 477*f*
    in early life, 552
    evidence for as genetic materials, 330–33, 349
    and evolution, 96–98
    flow of, in cells, 102*f*
    and genetic variation, 511–12
    and genome evolution, 476–482
    and inherited information, 267
    "junk," 472
    as level of biological organization, 6–8
    life's operating instructions, 329
    molecular structure of, 3, 6
    and programming cells, 330–32
    of prokaryotic cells, 607–8
    prokaryotic genetic recombination of, 609–12
    and receptor diversity, 1008
    repetitive, 474
    replication of, 6
    role of, 6, 92–93, 93*f*
    sequencing of, 96
    simple sequence, 474
    single strand, 7*f*
    staggered ends of, 344
    structural model of, 333–35
    structural role for chromosomes, 474
    structure of, 94–95, 95*f*, 329*f*, 332, 332*f*, 334*f*
    and TAL protein, 350*f*
    telomeric, 474
    transposable elements and related sequences,
        473–74, 480–81
    and viruses, 415
DNA barcode, 593
DNA chips, 446, 469*f*
DNA cloning, **437**
    amplifying DNA using the polymerase chain
        reaction, 440–41
    gene cloning, 437
    making multiple copies of a gene or other
        DNA segment, 437–38
    using restriction enzymes to make a
        recombinant DNA plasmid, 438–440, 439*f*
DNA Data Bank of Japan, 465
DNA ligases, **341**, **438**, 439*f*
DNA methylation, **386**
DNA microarray assays, 446*f*, **446**

DNA polymerases, **339**, 341, 342*t*
DNA replication, 329, 337
   antiparallel elongation, 339–341
   bacterial proteins and their functions, 342*t*
   basic principle, 335–37, 336*f*
   of ends of DNA molecules, 343–45, 344*f*
   evolutionary significance of altered DNA
      nucleotides, 342
   models of, 336, 336*f*
   origins of, 337, 338*f*
   proofreading and repair, 342–43, 343*f*
   proteins involved in, 339*f*
   review, 349
   summary, 341*f*
   synthesis of lagging strand, 340*f*
   synthesis of leading strand, 340*f*
   synthesizing a new DNA strand, 338–39
DNA replication complex, 341–42, 342*f*
DNA sequences
   in human genome, 472*f*
   identical, 475
   noncoding DNA, 472–75
   nonidentical, 475
   review, 487
   short tandem repeat, 474
   simple sequence DNA, 474
   types of in human genome, 472*f*, 474
DNA sequencing, **434**
   lab, 434*f*
   machines for, 434
   of Neanderthals, 794–95, 795*f*
   next-generation sequencing, 434–37, 436*f*
   techniques for, 434–37
   third-generation sequencing, 437
DNA technology, **433**. *See also* DNA sequencing
   ethical issues, 459–460
   high-throughput technology, 437
   practical applications of, 454–460
   review, 460–61
   in study of gene expression, 442–48
   in study of gene function, 446–48
DNA toolbox, 433–34
Dobsons, 1341*f*
Dobzhansky, Theodosius, 96
Dodd, Diane, 536*f*
Dodder, 888–89
Dog roses, 687*f*
Dog vomit fungus, 651*f*
Dogs, 62*f*, 787*f*, 1032, 1169, 1195*f*
Dolly the sheep, 450, 1326
Dolphins, 787*f*, 921, 933*f*, 1148, 1148*f*, 1251,
   1322*f*
Domains, **363**, **584**
   comparison of, 615*t*
   exon and protein, 363*f*
   taxonomy, 12, 13*f*, 598–99, 598*f*
Dominance, 291–92
Dominant species, **1285–86**
Dominant traits, 284, 284*t*
Dominantly inherited disorders, 299–300, 299*f*
Domoic acid, 634

Dopamine, **1135**, 1157
Dormancy, **874–75**, 898
Dorsal, hollow nerve cords, 761
Dorsal lip, **1103**, 1115*f*
Double bonds, **41**
Double circulation, **969**, 996–97
Double fertilization, **683**–84, **870**
Double helix, **94–95**, 95*f*, 334*f*, **334**, 346*f*
Doudna, Jennifer, 447
Douglas, Carl Douglas, Carl, 884*f*
Douglas, Susan, 630
Douglas fir, 680*f*
Doves, 1187
Down syndrome, 321, **322**–23, 323*f*, 453
Downey, R. Keith, 866
Downstream, 358
Dragonflies, 934, 934*f*
Drip irrigation, 853
Dromaius novaehollandiae, 781*f*
Drooping trillium, 868*f*
Drosera, 863*f*
Drosophila melanogaster (fruit fly)
   abnormal pattern formation in, 401*f*
   alteration of allele frequencies in, 518
   and alternative RNA splicing, 393
   axis establishment, 402–3
   bicoid gene, effect of, 402–3, 402*f*, 403*f*
   and chromosomes, 269
   conservation of homeotic genes, 485–86, 485*f*
   courtship in, 1198–99, 1199*f*, 1213
   and directional natural selection, 597
   divergence of allopatric populations leading to
      reproductive isolation, 536*f*
   embryo development in, 1095–96
   foraging behaviour, **1206**–7, 1207*f*
   gastrulation in, 1109
   and gene expression, 443–44, 443*f*
   genetic analysis of early development,
      400–402
   and genetic variation, 511
   genome sequencing, 463, 467
   genomes, 469*t*, 470
   and hybrid sterility, 546–47
   immunity in, 1001*f*
   life cycle of, 400, 401*f*
   linkage map, 319*f*
   as model organism, 25, 1096
   and Morgan's inheritance research, 309–10,
      309*f*, 310*f*, 315*f*, 317*f*
   and mutations, 352, 375
   reproduction in, 1076*f*
   and RNA splicing, 363
   and study of human disorders, 484
   Ubx gene, 572, 572*f*
   yolk in, 1101
Drought
   abscisic acid tolerance to, 898
   American Dust Bowl, 852, 852*f*
   plant responses to, 909–10
   stomatal opening and closing and, 840
   tolerance to, 898

Drug-resistant bacteria, 501–3
Drugs
   addictive, effects on brain, 1158–59, 1158*f*
   antivirals, 426
   mimicking schizophrenia, 1157–58
   synthesis of small molecules for use as,
      456–57
   to treat nervous system disorders, 1158
Dryas, 1291
Dual organisms, 707
Duchenne muscular dystrophy, **313**, 453, 454
Duckweed, 113*f*
Dueterostomes, 1103
Dugesia, 735, 967*f*
Dugongs, 787*f*
Dulse, 642*f*
Dune fescue grass, 1262
Dung beetles, 1319*f*
Duodenum, **955**
Duplication, 322*f*, **322**
Dust Bowl, 852
Dust mites, 749*f*
Dust storms, 851, 852*f*
Dutch elm disease, 708
Dwarfism, 299, 457
Dyneins, 126

E
E site (exit site), **366**
Eagles, 1075, 1322*f*
Earl Washington, 458*f*
Ears, 556, 574
   and equilibrium, 1170–71, 1171*f*
   human, structure of, 1168*f*
Earth. *See also* Biosphere
   and axis of rotation, 1225, 1227*f*, 1228*f*
   Cambrian explosion, 561–62
   carrying capacity, 1268–70
   cutaway view, 563*f*
   early, conditions on, 551–54, 576
   early atmosphere, 551–52
   Ediacaran period, 561
   eons and eras of, 556–59, 558*f*
   geologic record of, 556, 558*f*
   greening of, 652–53
   history of life on. *See* Evolution;
      Macroevolution
   key events in history, 559*f*, 576
   and plate tectonics, 563–570, 564*f*
   synthesis of organic compounds on, 551–52
   trauma for, 568*f*
Earthworms, 744–45, 744*f*, 851, 951*f*, 968*f*, 969,
   1034, 1034*f*, 1189, 1191
Eastern box turtle, 778*f*
Eastern chipmunks, 1029
Eastern grey kangaroos, 1212*f*
Eastern meadowlarks, 531*f*
Eastern white cedar trees, 828*f*
Ebola virus, 426, 427
Ecdysis, 723, 723*f*
Ecdysozoa clade, 722, **723**

Ecdysozoans (Ecdysozoa), 728*f*
    arthropods, 746–754
    nematodes, 745–46
Ecdysteroid, **1059**
ECG, **974**
Echidnas, 787*f*, 1106
Echinodermata, 729*f*, 1096
Echinoderms, **754**–56, 755*f*, 1140*f*
Echinoidea, 756, 756*f*
Echo generation, 1268
Ecological communities
    prokaryotes, role in, 619
    protists, role in, 647–49, 649*f*, 650
Ecological footprints, **1269**
Ecological niches, **1275**–76
Ecological species concept, **534**
Ecological succession, 1291–92, 1291*f*
Ecological time, 1239
Ecology, **1225**
    aquatic biomes and, 1238–39, 1240*f*–43
    and evolution, 564
    and mass extinctions, 569*f*
    and mycorrhizae, 862
    of populations. *See* Population ecology
    and prokaryotes, 618–19
    research, scope of, 1226*f*–27*f*
    and species distribution, 1239, 1244–47
    terrestrial biomes and, 1231–37
Ecosystem diversity, 1322–23
Ecosystem ecology, **1226***f*
Ecosystem engineers, **1286**, 1287*f*
Ecosystem services, **1324**
Ecosystems, **1226***f*, **1300**, 1309. *See also* Biosphere
    Alpine, 1315
    aquatic, 1304–6
    Arctic tundra, 1222*f*–23
    biogeochemical cycles in, 1309
    and climate change, 1340*f*
    conservation of mass in, 1301
    desert spring, 1300*f*
    edges between, 1331–32, 1331*f*
    energy and nutrient dynamics in, 1302*f*
    energy budgets in, 1302–4
    energy conservation in, 1300–1301
    energy flow and chemical cycling in, 176*f*,
        1300–1301
    interactions, 10–11
    island, 1300*f*
    as level of biological organization, 4*f*
    marine, 1334
    nutrient cycling and biogeochemical cycles in,
        1309–13, 1310*f*–11*f*
    nutrient enrichment in, 1305*t*
    overview, 1300
    primary production in, 1301, 1302–7
    restoration of degraded, 1313–15, 1314*f*
    review, 1318
    secondary production in, 1307–9
    of soil, 850–54
    trophic levels in, 1301
    water and nutrient cycling in, 1310*f*–11*f*

Ecotone, **1232**
Ectoderm, **719**, 720*f*, **1102**, 1103*f*
Ectomycorrhizae, 861*f*, **861**
Ectomycorrhizal fungi, **694**, 700*f*
Ectoparasites, **1279**
Ectopic tissue, 1084
Ectoprocta, 727*f*
Ectoprocts, **738**
Ectothermic, 777
Ectotherms, 931*f*, **931**, 933, 934, 935, 1246
Ediacaran biota, **714**–16
Ediacaran period, 561
Edomorphosis, **571**
Eels, 1028
Effective population size, **1328**–29
Effector cells, **1009**
Effectors, **913**
Efferent, 1143
Egg activation, 1098
Egg yolks, 100*f*
Egg-polarity genes, **402**
Eggs, **1071**
    activation of, in embryonic development, 1098
    fertilization in. *See* Fertilization
    human, 1103
    and nitrogenous wastes, 1032
    in seed plants, 673
Egrets, 1246, 1246*f*, 1281*f*
Eiders, 1284
Ein mutants, 899
Eisner, Thomas, 754
Ejaculation, **1079**
Ejaculatory duct, **1079**
EKG, **974**
Elastic fibres, 925*f*
Eldredge, Niles, 544
Electrical signalling, 846–47
Electrical synapses, 1130
Electrically charged side chains, 85*f*
Electrocardiogram (ECG), 974*f*, **974**
Electrochemical gradient, **148**
Electroencephalogram (EEG), 1148
Electrogenic pump, **148**
Electromagnetic energy, 203
Electromagnetic radiation, 203
Electromagnetic receptors, **1165**–66, 1166*f*
Electromagnetic spectrum, 203*f*, **203**
Electron microscope (EM), 105, 106*f*
Electron shells, **38**
Electron transport chain, 178–**79**, 178*f*, 179*f*,
    185–86, 188*f*
Electronegativities, 41–42
Electrons, **34**
    chemical properties of, 38–39
    distribution of, 38–39, 38*f*
    energy levels of, 36–38, 36*f*
    ionic bonding, 42*f*
    orbitals, 39–40, 39*f*
    transfer, 42*f*
Electroporation, **442**
Elements, **33**

atomic mass, 35
atomic number, 35
atomic structure and properties of, 34–40
    essential, 33
    essential to life, 70
    in human body, 34*t*
    isotopes, 35–36
    review, 46–47
    subatomic particles, 34–35
    trace, 33
Elephant seals, 995, 1327
Elephants, 497–98, 498*f*, 787*f*, 938, 959, 995,
    1085, 1279, 1326, 1326*f*
Elimination, 948*f*, **950**
Elk, 1209*f*
Elm bark beetles, 708
Elodea, 45*f*
Elongation, 339–341, 359, 359*f*, 360*f*
    and auxin, role of, 894, 895*f*
    as cycle of translation, 369*f*
    of polypeptide chain, 367
    of stems, 897
    zone of, in roots, 812
Elongation factors, 367
Embryo sacs, **682**, 869*f*, **870**
Embryonic development, 397*f*
    animal, 713*f*
    body-building plan, 1096
    of brain, 1146*f*
    cytoplasmic determinants and inductive signals
        in, 398*f*
    differential gene expression in, 397
    fertilization as initiation of, 1096–99
    of frogs, 1096*f*
    of fruit flies, 1095–96
    human, 1104–5, 1105*f*
    of nervous system, 1154
    review, 1118
    in seeds, 873–74, 873*f*
Embryonic development, human,
    1086–89, 1095*f*
    human, 1093
    maternal immune tolerance of embryo and
        fetus, 1089
    review, 1093
Embryonic lethals, **401**
Embryonic stem (ES) cells, 451–53, 452*f*
Embryophytes, 654*f*, **655***f*
Embryos, 1075. *See also* Embryonic development
    multicellular, dependent, 655*f*
    primary sex characteristics in, 1082
Emerald ash borer, 1050
Emergent properties, **3**, 923
Emerging viruses, 426–430
Emigration, **1252**, 1265–66
Emotions, 1150
Emus, 781*f*
Enantiomers, 68*f*, 69*f*, **69**
Encephalitis, 426, 1016
ENCODE (Encyclopedia of DNA Elements),
    467, 473

Endangered species, 742, **1322**
Endeavour Hydrothermal Vents, 1334
Endemic, **507**
Endergonic reactions, 159–**160**, 160*f*
Endocrine (hormonal) signalling, 223*f*, 224, 927, 927*f*, 1049–51, 1050*f*
Endocrine disruptors, 1066–67
Endocrine glands, 1060*f*
Endocrine systems, 923*t*, 927, 927*f*, 960, **1049**
    antagonistic hormones controlling blood glucose in, 1056–59
    disruption of, 1066–67
    feedback regulation, 1055–56
    glands of, 1054*f*
    hormones as chemical signals, 1049
    intercellular communication, 1049–51
    review, 1067–68
    signalling in. *See* Endocrine (hormonal) signalling
    and thyroid regulation, 1061–62, 1062*f*
Endocytosis, 149, **149**–151, 150*f*
Endoderm, **719**, 720*f*, **1102**, 1103*f*
Endodermis, **812**, 837*f*
Endomembrane system, **115**–19, 120*f*
Endometriosis, 1084
Endometrium, **1077**
Endoparasites, **1279**
Endophytes, 706*f*, **706**, **857**
Endoplasmic reticulum (ER), 112*f*, **115**–16, 116*f*
Endorphins, 44, 45*f*, **1135**
Endoskeletons, **1190**
Endosperm, **683**, **870**, 873
Endospores, 606*f*, **606**
Endosymbiont, **120**
Endosymbiont theory, **120**, 121*f*, **560**
Endosymbiosis, 580*f*–81*f*
    and diversity of plastids, 630*f*
    in eukaryotic evolution, 631–32
    organelles created through, 627, 631–32
    and spread of photosynthesis during protist evolution, 627–631
Endothelin, 977
Endothelium, **975**, 979
Endothermic, **778**, 781
Endotherms, 931*f*, **931**, 934, 935, 936
Endotoxins, **621**
End-Permian mass extinction, 567*f*
Energetic hypothesis, **1284**
Energy, 37, **155**
    bioenergetics, 936–940
    dietary deficiency, 947
    ecosystem energy budgets, 1302–4
    in ecosystems, 1300–1301
    flow of, in ecosystems, 176*f*
    forms of, 155–56
    global energy budget, 1302
    gross and net production, 1302–4
    harvesting from organic molecules. *See* Cellular respiration
    in hydrothermal vents, 1299
    of life, 154
    and locomotion, 1192
    metabolic rate, 937
    and nitrogenous wastes, 1032
    and osmoregulation, 1029
    per capita use, 1270*f*
    production in muscles, 1182–84
    regulation of storage, 961
    stepwise energy harvest, 178–79
    thermal, 1238
    transfer and transformation of, as theme in biology, 8, 27
    transformation, laws of, 156–58
    transformation of, 103*f*
Energy barriers, 164–65, 173
Energy conservation, in bioenergetics, 939–940
Energy coupling, **161**
Energy flow
    in ecosystems, 1300–1301, 1302*f*
    in photosynthesis, 9*f*
Energy partitioning, 1307*f*
Energy processing, as property of life, 2*f*
Engelmann, Theodor W., 205
Enhancers, **388**–390, 389*f*, 391*f*
Entamoeba histolytica, 646
Entamoebas, 646
Enteric division, 960, **1143**
Entropy, **157**
Enucleated eggs, 449
Environment
    animal exchanges with, 921–23, 922*f*, 967–972
    effect on phenotype, 295, 295*f*
    internal, in animals, 928–930
    and nitrogenous wastes, 1032
Environmental cleanup, 458–59
Environmental stresses, 908–11
Enzymatic hydrolysis, 950
Enzymatic proteins, 84*f*
Enzyme inhibitors, 169*f*, **169**
Enzymes, 75, **164**
    and activation energy barrier, 164–65
    catalysis in, 167, 167*f*
    chymotripsin, 955
    cofactors in structure of, 945
    effect on activation energy, 166*f*
    evolution of, 170, 170*f*
    and genes, 352–53
    and local conditions, 168–170
    location of, 172
    lysozyme, 1001
    and metabolic reactions, 164–170
    pancreatic, 955
    PCSK9, 985
    pepsin, 953
    and pH, 168–69, 169*f*
    in photosynthesis, 891
    and reactions, speeding up, 165–66
    regulation of, 170–72, 173
    review, 173
    of the smooth ER, 115
    and starch, 79
    substrate specificity of, 166–67
    Taq polymerase, 1323
    and temperature, 168, 169*f*
    trypsin, 955
Enzyme-substrate complex, **166**
Eosinophils, **1003**
Ependymal cells, 1141*f*
Ephedra, 679*f*
Ephrussi, Boris, 352
Epiblast, 1103, 1105
Epicotyl, **874**
Epidemics, **427**
Epidemiology, 948
Epidermis, **806**
Epididymis, **1078**
Epigenetic inheritance, **386**–87, 467
Epigenome, 467
Epiglottis, 952*f*, 989
Epinephrine, 1051, 1052, **1052**, 1054*f*, 1135
    in fight-or-flight response, 221, 1053*f*, 1144
    and glycogen, 224, 236*f*
    and glycogen breakdown, 231
    and liver, 231
    multiple effects of, 1053–54, 1053*f*, 1065*f*
    and signal transduction pathways, 1052
Epiphytes, 667*f*, 862–64, **863***f*
Epistasis, **293**
Epithalamus, 1147*f*
Epithelial cells, 135*f*
Epithelial tissue (epithelia), 923, **924***f*
Epitopes, **1006**, 1009, 1020
Epsilon proteobacteria, 616*f*
Epstein-Barr virus, 410
Equational division, 276
Equilibrium, 1123
    chemical, 46
    and free energy, 159
    island equilibrium model, 1293–94
    in isolated hydroelectric system, 160*f*
    in mammals, 1170–71, 1171*f*
    and metabolism, 160–61
    in open system, 161*f*
    in other vertebrates, 1171–72
    for population density, 1263*f*
Equilibrium potential, **1124**
Equine encephalitis, 418
Equinox, 1228*f*
Equisetum, 669
Equisetum telmateia, 667*f*
Equus, 575, 576*f*
ER lumen, 115
Erectile dysfunction, 1079, 1135
Ergotism, 708
Ergots, 708, 709
Erosion of soil, 853
Errantians, 743, 743*f*
Erythrocytes, 925*f*, **981**, 983
Erythropoietin (EPO), **983**
Escherichia coli, 25, 91, 91*f*, 170, 251–52, 252*f*, 331–32, 338*f*

Escherichia coli (*Continued*)
  adaptations in, 609*f*
  chromosomal DNA, 346
  in digestive system, 957
  in DNA cloning, 437
  and DNA replication, 337–38, 337*f*, 339
  in gene cloning, 621
  and gene expression, 381–82, 385
  genetic recombination and conjugation in,
    610–12, 610*f*, 611*f*
  genetic variation in, 608
  genome sequence, 463, 467
  genome size, 469, 469*t*
  infection by phage λ, 419–420
  lac operons in, 383, 383*f*
  and mutualistic symbiosis, 958
  pathogenic strains, 621
  prokaryotic chromosome and plasmids, 608*f*
  reproduction in, 608, 608–9
  and *trp* operon, 382, 382*f*
  viruses infecting, 417
Esophageal pouch, 959
Esophagus, 952*f*, **952**, 989
Essential amino acids, **944**, 947
Essential elements, **33**, 855*t*, **855**–56
Essential fatty acids, **944**
Essential nutrients, **944**–47, 947*f*
Estivation, 940
Estradiol, 69–70, 1053, **1065**, 1077, 1082, 1084
Estrogen, 1338
Estrogen mimics, 1338
Estrogens, 1053, 1054, 1054*f*, **1065**, 1082,
  1083, 1091
Estrous cycles, 1085
Estrus, 1085
ESTs, 466
Estuaries, **1241***f*, 1303
Ethane, 66*f*
Ethanol, 622*f*, 692–93
Ethene (ethylene), 66*f*
Ethical issues
  diagnosing genetic diseases in fetuses, 1091
  DNA technology, 459–460
  gene therapy, 456
  study of human nutrition, 947–48
Ethyl alcohol
  mass of, 56
  specific heat of, 52
Ethylene, 66*f*, 892*t*, **898**–900
Etiolation, **889**
Eucalyptus, 958
Euchromatin, **348**
Eudicots, 686*f*, **686**, 687*f*, 812*f*, 814*f*, 873–74, 895
Euglena gracilis, 121*f*
Euglenids, 633*f*, **633**
Euglenozoan flagella, 633*f*
Euglenozoans, **632**–33, 633*f*
Eukarya, **12**
  compared to bacteria and archaea, 615*t*
  taxonomy, 13*f*
Eukaryotes

diversity of, 626–632
  early, 560
  evolution of, 627–631
  multicellular, 560–61
  multicellular, noncoding DNA and many
    multigene families in, 472–75
  number of genes in, 469, 469*t*
  numbers of genes, 470
  origin through serial endosymbiosis, 561*f*
  phylogenetic tree, 628*f*
  vs. prokaryotes, 606, 607–8
  protists. *See* Protists
  supergroups of, 626–27, 628*f*–29*f*
Eukaryotic cells, 4, 6, 6*f*, **108**, 261
  binary fission in, 251–52
  cell cycle regulation, 253–58
  evolution of, 631–32
  exploration of, 112–13*f*
  and gene expression regulation, 385–394,
    386*f*, 411
  and genetic expression, 355*f*
  internal membranes, 108–10
  modifying RNA after transcription, 361–63
  nucleus, 111–15
  origins of replication in, 338*f*
  panoramic view of, 110
  and prokaryotic cells, comparison, 108–10
  review, 133–34
  ribosomes, 111, 115
Eukaryotic DNA cloning and expression systems,
  442
Eukaryotic genes
  coordinately controlled, 391–92
  differential expression of genes, 385
  expressing cloned eukaryotic genes, 441–42
  and gene expression regulation,
    385–394, 386*f*
  mechanism of post-transcriptional regulation,
    392–94
  organization of, 387
  regulation of chromatin structure, 385–87
  regulation of transcript initiation, 387–392
  transcript of, 387, 388*f*
Eukaryotic genome, 393
Eukaryotic tree, 644–45, 645*f*
Eulipotyphla, 787*f*
Eumatazoans, 722, 731–32
Eumetazoa clade, 722
Euphausids, 1284
Euphorbs, 1233, 1233*f*
European hamsters, 940
European honeybee, 1199, 1200*f*
European larch, 680*f*
European Molecular Biology Laboratory, 465
European robin, 15*f*
Euryarchaeota, 615
Euryhaline osmoregulators, 1026, 1028*f*
Eurypterids, **748**
Eustachian tubes, **1168***f*
Eusthenopteron, 771
Eusthenopteron foordi, 771*f*

Eutherians (placental mammals), 505, 586,
  785–790, **785**
Eutrophication, 1306*f*, **1306**
Evans, Martin, 446
Evaporation, 31, 52
Evaporative cooling, 52–53, **53**, 933–34
Evaporative water loss, 842
Evapotranspiration, 1293*f*, **1293**
Even-toed ungulates, 506, 506*f*
Evo-Devo (evolutionary developmental biology),
  403, **485**
Evolution, **1**, 493. *See also* Darwin, Charles;
  Natural selection
  adaptive evolution, 518
  and altered DNA nucleotides, 342
  of angiosperms, 684–85, 868*f*
  of animal behaviour, 1213–14
  and animal form and function, 921
  of animals, 714–18
  of antifreeze proteins, 911
  and asexual reproduction, 877–79
  of axon structure, 1129–30
  of bacterial flagella, 606
  biogeography, 506–7
  of cell signalling, 222–23
  and character displacement, 1276
  of chordates, 762–63
  of circulatory systems, 968–69, 970*f*
  of cognition in vertebrates, 1153
  convergent, 505, 586, 586*f*, 1233*f*
  and creation of organelles through
    endosymbiosis, 631–32
  cross-species gene expression and evolutionary
    ancestry, 442
  of development, 571–73
  of digestive systems, 957–960
  direct observations of evolutionary change,
    501–3
  and diversity of life, 580*f*–81*f*
  DNA as measure of, 96–98
  and ecological factors, 564
  ecological niches, 1275–76
  of enzymes, 170, 170*f*
  of eukaryotic cells, 631–32
  evolutionary developmental biology, 403
  evolutionary relationships of the three domains
    of life, 481*f*
  and extinction vortex, 1327–29, 1327*f*
  and extraembryonic membranes, 1106
  of flower and pollinator, 871–72, 873*f*
  of flowers, 868*f*
  fossil record, 505–6
  of genes with novel functions, 478
  of genes with related functions, 477–78
  of genetic code, 357–58
  and genetic variation, 278–79, 511–13
  of genomes, 476–482, 481–86, 596
  of genomic evolution of cancer, 409*f*
  and genomics, 97*f*
  and glycolysis, significance of, 193
  of gymnosperms, 677–78

of *Homo sapiens*, 795–96
and homology, 503–5
of hormone function, 1059
and human culture, 1217–18
and introns, importance of, 362–63
of jawbones, 767, 767*f*
key events in history, 559*f*
kidneys, adaptations of, 1040–41
Lamarck's hypothesis of, 494–95
of land plants, 657*f*
of leaves, 666, 806*f*
and life history diversity, 1260–61
of mammalian ear bones, 783*f*
of mammals, 783–84
of marsupials and eutherians, 785*f*
of membrane lipids, 139
of mitosis, 252–53
new combinations of, 316–17
and nitrogenous wastes, 1032
and nutrient limitation, 1306–7
and obesity, 962–63
on other planets, 56
of pathogens, 1020–22
and photosynthesis, 214
of plant immunity, 913
and plant responses, 907
of populations. *See* Microevolution
proteins as measure of, 96–98
of reptiles, 778
resource partitioning, 1275–76, 1275*f*
of respiratory systems, 995–96
of roots, 665
scientific evidence for, 500–508, 508–9
of secondary growth, 818
of seeds, 676
sexual reproduction, an evolutionary enigma,
1071–72
and sickle-cell disease, 298–99
and small ncRNAs, significance of, 396
of stems, 805*f*
as theme in biology, 11–16, 27
as theory, 507–8
transition of life in the sea, 506*f*
tree of life, 16
of vascular plants, 829–830
vertebrate, organization of, 969–971
of vertebrates, 765–66
of viruses, 425, 429*f*
Evolutionary adaptation. *See* Adaptation
Evolutionary biology, 97, 493
Evolutionary developmental biology (Evo-Devo),
403
Evolutionary time, 1239
Evolutionary tree, **504**, **583**. *See also* Tree of life
of cetaceans, 506*f*
of elephants, 498*f*
explained, 504–5
and homologies, 504–5
information provided in, 504*f*
Exaptations, 574
Excavata, 628*f*, **632**–33, 650

Exchange surfaces, animal, 921–22, 922*f*, 967–972
Excitatory postsynaptic potential (EPSP), **1132**
Excretion, **1026**, 1033*f*
of ammonia, 1031
by freshwater animals, 1027–28
guano, 1032
by land animals, 1029
by marine animals, 1027
Excretory organs, 1036*f*
Excretory systems, 923*t*. *See also* Osmoregulation
excretory processes, 1033
filtrate processing, 1035–41
hormonal regulation of, 1043–45
ion movement and gradients, 1042*f*
kidneys in, 1035
Malpighian tubules in, 1034–35, 1034*f*
mammalian, 1036*f*
metanephrida in, 1034, 1034*f*
and nitrogenous wastes, 1030–32
overview, 1033*f*
protonephridia in, 1033–34
review, 1046
solute gradients and water conservation,
1038–40
survey of, 1033–35
and tubular networks, 1033–35
Exercise, 1019
Exergonic reactions, 159–**160**, 160*f*, 165*f*
Exertion, and immune system, 1019
Exit tunnel, 366
Exocrine glands, 1055
Exocytosis, **149**
Exon duplication, 478–480
Exon shuffling, 363, 478–480, 480*f*
Exons, **362**, 363*f*
Exoskeletons, 80, **733**, 745, 746–47, 1001, 1028,
1189–90
Exotoxins, **620**
Expansins, **894**
Experience, and behaviour, 1201
Experimental Lakes Area, 649
Experiments, **18**, 237
Exploration, 20*f*, **22**
Exponential population growth, **1256**, 1257*f*,
1271
Expressed sequence tags (ESTs), 466
Expression vectors, **441**
External fertilization, 1074*f*, **1074**
External skeletons, 923
Extinct species, **1322**
Extinction
and continental drift, 565
and diversity, 563*f*
of frogs, 775
and island equilibrium model, 1293–94
mass. *See* Mass extinction
of plant species, 689
rates, rising, 742
and resurrecting, 1326–27
of synapsids, 783
and temperature, 568*f*

Extinction vortex, 1327*f*, **1327**–29
Extirpation, **1322**
Extracellular concentration, 1123*t*
Extracellular digestion, 950
Extracellular matrix (ECM), 130*f*, **130**–31, 134,
1109
Extraembryonic membranes, 775, 777*f*, **1105**,
1106
Extranuclear genes, 325
Extreme halophiles, **614**
Extreme thermophiles, **615**, 618*f*
Extremophiles, **614**
Eyes
complexity of, among molluscs, 575*f*
compound, 1173, 1173*f*
cones, 104, 1175*f*, 1176–77, 1178
evolution of, 574
focusing, 1178*f*
human, 1173, 1174*f*–75*f*
in planarians, 735, 1173, 1173*f*
retinas, 104*f*, 574, **1174***f*, 1176–77, 1178
rods, 104, 1175–76, **1175***f*, 1176–77, 1176*f*,
1178
sensory transduction in, 1175–76
Eyespots, 1173

F

F factors, **610**
F plasmids, **610**
F_1 generation, 283*f*, **283**, 284*t*, 285*f*, 286–87, 288*f*
F_2 generation, 283*f*, **283**, 285*f*, 287, 288*f*
Facilitated diffusion, **145**–46
Facilitation, **1281**, 1290
Facultative anaerobes, **193**
Facultative anaerobes, **612**
Facultative mutualism, 1280
Fagus grandifolia, 1231
Fairy ring, 704, 705*f*
Falling phase, 1127, 1128*f*
Fallopian tubes, **1077**
Familial hypercholesterolemia, **151**
Families, **584**
Family resemblance. *See* Genetics; Heredity
Fanworts, 819, 819*f*
Farrell, Tony, 971*f*
Fast block to polyspermy, **1097**, 1099
Fast-twitch fibres, **1187**
Fate maps, **1110**–14, 1111*f*
Fathead minnows, 1338
Fats, **80**
absorption of by, 956*f*
as adipose tissue, 925*f*
digestion of, 954*f*
hydrocarbons in, 68*f*
saturated and unsaturated, 81, 81*f*
synthesis and structure of, 81*f*
trans, 82, 984
Fat-soluble vitamins, 945, 946*t*
Fatty acid signature, 944
Fatty acids, **80**, 81*f*, 944, 945*f*
Feather stars, 756, 756*f*

Feathers, 583, 780*f*
Feces, **957**
Feedback control, 928–930, 941
Feedback inhibition, 172*f*, **172**, 194–95, 381
Feedback mechanisms
    regulation by, 9, 9*f*
    and regulation of cellular respiration, 194
Feedback regulation, **9**. *See also* Negative feedback;
    Positive feedback
    of animal digestion, energy storage, and
        appetite, 960–63, 964
    in endocrine systems, 1055–56
    and population dynamics, 1263
Feeding mechanisms, 949*f*
Feldmann, Heinz, 427
Female condoms, 1090
Females
    fruit fly bias in sperm usage, 1076*f*
    mate choice by, 1210–11
    reproductive anatomy, 1077–78, 1077*f*
    reproductive cycles in, 1083–85, 1083*f*
    reproductive rates of, 1254–55
    sex determination in, 269
Feminization, 1338
Fermentation, **176**, 196
    and anaerobic and aerobic respiration, 192–93
    and ATP production, 191–93
    types of, 191–92, 192*f*
Ferns, 664–69, 665*f*, 667*f*, 670, 674*f*, 676*f*, 691*f*
Ferrets, 428, 1295, 1315, 1315*f*
Fertility replacement, 1268
Fertilization, **269**, **853**, **870**, **1074**, **1096**
    acrosomal reaction, 1096–97, 1097*f*
    calcium ions in, 1097–98
    cell surface events in, 1096
    as chance events, 289*f*
    cortical reaction, 1097–98, 1097*f*, 1099
    double, 870
    double fertilization, 683–84
    egg activation, 1098
    ensuring offspring survival, 1074–75
    external, 1074, 1074*f*
    in frogs, 775, 1074
    gamete production and delivery, 1075–76
    and genetic engineering, 856
    in gymnosperm, 674*f*
    human, 1103–4
    internal/external, 1074
    in mammals, 1098–99, 1099*f*
    random fertilization, 278
    review, 1092–93, 1118
    self-fertilization, 879–881, 879*f*
    in sexual life cycles, 269–271, 270*f*
    in sponges, 731
    steps in, 1096
    in vitro, 1092, 1092*f*
Fertilization envelope, 1097, 1098*f*
Festa-Bianchet, Marco, 1250
Fetal development, 1088*f*
Fetal testing, 301–2, 302*f*
Fetoscopy, 302

Fetus, **1088**
Fever, 936, 1004
Fibre, insoluble, 79
Fibre cells, **808***f*
Fibrin, 981, 982*f*
Fibrinogen, 981
Fibroblasts, 124*t*, 257, 617*f*, **925***f*
Fibronectin, **130**
Fibrous connective tissue, 925*f*
Fibrous proteins, 86
Fibrous root system, 804
Fiddler crabs, 1196*f*
Fight-or-flight response, 221, 1053*f*, 1144
Figs, 804*f*
Filaments, **681**
Filopodia, 625–26
Filter feeders, **949***f*
Filtrate, **1033**, 1035–38, 1039–40
Filtration, 1033*f*, **1033**
Fimbriae, 606*f*, **606**
Finches, 17*f*, 522, 1210*f*, 1211*f*, 1239, 1276
Finlay, Brett, 427
Fire-bellied toads, 541, 541*f*
Fireflies, 358*f*
Fires, 1289
First law of thermodynamics, 156*f*, **156**–57
First trimester, 1086–88
Fisheries Research Board of Canada, 935*f*
Fishes
    Atlantic cod, 1231, 1277
    bass, 928, 931
    bluehead wrasse, 1073
    bony fishes. *See* Bony fishes
    broad-nosed pipefish, 524
    cichlid fish, 538–39, 539*f*, 543, 543*f*, 545
    circulation in, 969, 970*f*
    and climate change, 1231
    cod, 101, 770, 1027, 1277, 1288, 1326
    communication among, 1200, 1200*f*
    cuttlefish, 523
    damselfish, 1278
    diadromous, 1028
    and extraembryonic membranes, 1106
    eyes of, 1174
    feminization of, 1338
    flashlight fish, 413*f*
    forebrain in, 1145
    freshwater, 1041
    gills, 986–88, 987*f*
    hagfishes, 764, 764*f*, 1035
    and heat exchange, 933
    herring, 1231
    jawfish, 1210*f*
    jellyfish. *See* Jellies
    kidneys in, 1041
    lake trout, 1325
    lateral line system in, 1171*f*
    lobe-fins, 770–71, 771*f*
    lungfish, 504, 771, 989
    Mangrove rivulus, 917, 918*f*
    minnows, 1200*f*

    mosquitofish, 535–36, 536*f*
    nile perch, 543
    nitrogenous waste in fishes in alkaline lakes,
        1031*f*
    and nutrient enrichment, 1337
    overfishing, 1288, 1288*f*, 1326
    parental care in, 1209, 1210*f*
    ray-finned, 770, 770*f*, 1145, 1152
    regulating and conforming in, 928
    salmon, 1028, 1166, 1335
    scale-eating fish, 526, 526*f*
    stickleback, 919*f*
    and thermoregulation, 928, 931, 935
    threespine stickleback fish, 572–73, 573*f*, 1197,
        1197*f*, 1276, 1276*f*
    toadfish, 1187, 1187*f*
    trout, 769*f*
    wolf fish, 1295, 1295*f*
    zebrafish, 25
Fission, **1071**
Fitness, 1216–17
FitzRoy, Robert, 495
Fixed action patterns, 1197*f*, **1197**
Flaccid, **145**, **834**
Flagella, 112*f*, **125**–27, 126*f*, 127*f*, 606–7, 607*f*,
    701*f*
    euglenozoan, 633*f*
    eukaryotic vs prokaryotic, 632
    and plant immunity, 913
    stramenopile flagella, 634*f*
Flagellated sperm, 653
Flaggelin, 1002
Flame bulbs, 735, 1033–34, 1033*f*
Flamingoes, 782, 782*f*
Flashlight fish, 413*f*
Flatworms (Platyhelminthes), 734–37, 950, 967*f*,
    1033–34, 1075
    acoelomate flatworms, 723–24, 727*f*
    free-living species, 735, 735*f*
    nervous system in, 1140*f*
    parasitic species, 735–37
    skeletal system of, 1189
    tapeworms, 736–37, 736*f*
    trematodes, 735–36
Fleas, 1035, 1073, 1258
Flemming, Walther, 246
Flesh-eating disease, 502
Flies
    and cloned mice genes, 442
    compound eyes of, 1173*f*
    and mate selection, 1210, 1210*f*
    mayflies, 1252
    and pollination, 872*f*
Flight, 587
Flooding, 909, 909*f*, 1289*f*, **1289**
Floral meristem, 875
Flores fossils, 796
Florida manatee, 759*f*
Florigen, 906*f*, **906**–7
FLOWERING LOCUS T (FT), 907
Flowering plants

categories of, 811

Darwin's description of, 868f

overview, 803f

reproduction in, 877–882

Flowers, **678**

ABC hypothesis of formation, 825, 825f

Acacia koa, 824f

coevolution of, 871–72, 873f

complete/incomplete, 867

early flowering plant, 684f

evolution of, 868f, 871–72

formation of, 875–76

fruit, transition to, 876f

genetic control of formation of, 824–25

monkey flowers, 880

and photoperiodism, 905–7, 906f

pollination of, 678, 871f, 872f

review, 886–87

structure and function of, 867, 867f

structure of, 678–681, 681f

symmetry of, and pollination, 685–86, 686f

Flu virus, 87f

Fluid feeders, **949f**

Fluid mosaic model, 137

Fluid return by lymphatic system, 979–980

Fluorescence, 106f, 206f

Fluorine, 946t

Fluoxetine, 1158

Fly agaric, 700f

Fly Away Home, 1202

Flycatchers, 542, 543f

Flying, 1192–93

Flying frogs, 493f

Flying squirrels, 505, 505f

Foam cells, 984f

Folic acid, 948, 957, 958

Foliose lichens, 707f

Follicles, **1077**, 1081f

Follicle-stimulating hormone (FSH), 1054f, 1081f, 1082, 1083–84, 1085, 1085f

Follicular phase, **1084**

Fon, Edward A., 74

Food

processing, stages of, 948–951, 948f, 964

sources of, 501f, 688–89

Food chains, 1283f, **1283**, 1284–85, 1286f, 1308

Food vacuoles, 118, **119**, 950

Food webs, 1284f, **1284**, 1285f, 1337, 1337f

Food-shortage hypothesis, 1264

Foolish seedling disease, 896–97

Foot, **660**, **738**

Forager gene, 1206–7

Foraging, **1206**–7, 1207f, 1208

Foraminiferans, **641**

Forams, 641f, **641**

Forebrain, **1145**

Forelimbs, mammalian, 16

Forensic science, 457–58

Forests

boreal, 1331f, 1340f

clear-cutting in, 689, 689f, 1292, 1313

and climate, 1229

northern coniferous, 1233, 1236f

temperate broadleaf, 1237f

tropical, 1234f

Formin, 237

Fossil angiosperms, 684

Fossil extinctions, 568f

Fossil forams, 641f

Fossil fuels

burning of, 1230

photosynthesis as source of, 199

replacing, 1340f

transgenic crops reducing dependency on, 884–85

unsustainable reliance on, 1270

Fossil records, 544, **553**

of amniotes, 777

of animal groups, 561f, 562

animals in, 715, 718

and defensive adaptation, 740

of early reptiles, 777

of gnathostomes, 767

as history of life, 550–51, 554–56, 555f, 576

of hominins, 791

of *Homo sapiens*, 795

of insects, 751

of of monkeys, 788

Fossils, 494f, **494**

and colonization of land, 652f

Cooksonia sporangium, 654f

dating of, 554–56

of early chordate, 765f

from Ediacaran period, 714–16, 715f

as evidence for evolution, 505–6

Flores fossils, 796

of fungi, 698, 698f

of gnathostomes, 767f

of hominins, 791f

of *Homo ergaster*, 794f

of *Homo sapiens*, 795f

Kimberella, 562

living, 669, 748

and origin of mammals, 557f

of primates, 788

radiometric dating of, 36

snail, 726f

spores, 657f

Tiktaalik, 772–73

trilobite, 746f

Founder effect, **518**–19

Fouquieria splendens, 843f

Fovea, **1178**

Foxes, 1274, 1286f, 1322f

FOXP2, 483–84, 483f

Fragmentation

habitat, 1332, 1332f

reproductive, **877**, **1071**

Frameshift Mutation, **374**–75

Franco, Eduardo, 426

Franklin, Rosalind, 333–34

Fratercula arctica, 1025

Free energy, **158**

of activation, 165

change during electron transport, 185f

change of, 158, 163f

in exergonic and endergonic reactions, 159–160, 160f

and metabolism, 159–161

relationship to stability, work capacity, and spontaneous change, 159f

review, 173

and stability and equilibrium, 158–59

Free ribosomes, 115

Free-living rhabditophorans, 735, 735f

Freezing, 911, 1289

Frequency-dependent selection, **525**–26, 526f

Freshwater animals, 1027–28, 1027f, 1029

Freshwater biomes, 1238

Frog-eating bat, 787f

Frogs (anurans), 397, 397f

axis formation in, 1112, 1113f

breathing in, 990

canyon tree, 1278f

circulation in, 969–971

cleavage in, 1100, 1100f, 1101

and cloned mice genes, 442

"dual life" of, 774f

and elanocyte-stimulating hormone (MSH), 1069f

embryo development in, 1096f

fate map of, 1111f

fertilization in, 1074

flying frogs, 493f

gastrulation in, 1103, 1104f

grey tree frogs, 524, 525f, 538

hearing in, 1172

mating calls, 1082

metamorphorsis in, Frogs (anurans)

neurulation in, 1107f

overview, 773–74

poison dart, 1278f

and programmed cell death, 1109

somatic cell nuclear transfer, 449f

and steroid hormones, 1053

strawberry poison dart frogs, 549f

wood frogs, 918f

Frontal lobotomy, 1153

Frontonia leucas, 625f, 627

Frost, Barrie, 1172f

Fru genes, 1213

Fructose, 76, 76f, 956

Fruit flies. *See Drosophila melanogaster* (fruit fly)

Fruits, **681**, **876**

developmental origin of, 876f

form and function, 876–77

and gibberellins and growth, 897

ripening, 900

and seed dispersal, 878f

seed dispersal, 681, 682f

Fruticose lichens, 707f

Fuels
    alternative fuels, 199f, 622f, 692–93
    fossil fuels. See Fossil fuels
    wood, 689
Fumonisin, 885
Functional groups, **70**
Functional imaging, 1150, 1150f
Functional magnetic resonance imaging (fMRI),
    1150
Fundamental niche, 1245, **1275**
Fungal cells, 112f
Fungi, **693**, 694f, 697f
    asexual reproduction, 697
    and biotechnology, 883
    blue stain, 844
    chytrids, 699, 700f
    and colonization of land, 562
    as decomposers, 705–6
    diversity of, 699–704, 700f, 711
    dog vomit fungus, 651f
    early-diverging groups, 698
    fossils of, 698, 698f
    Fusarium, 885
    genetically modified, 710
    genomic analysis of, 696
    as hetertrophs that feed by absorption, 693–95
    impact on other organisms, 704
    land colonization by, 698–99
    life cycle of, 697f, 701f
    and mutualism, 706–7, 1307
    mycorrhizal, 694–95, 697f
    Neurospora crassa, 1001, 1002f
    nutrition and ecology, 693, 704–10
    as pathogens, 708–9
    phylogeny of, 698f, 700f
    and plant nutrition, 861–62
    Pneumocystis carinii, 1022
    protist ancestor or, 698–99
    review, 710–11
    sexual life cycles of, 270f, 271, 695–97
    structure of, 693–94, 694f
    uses of, 709–10
Fungi, kingdom, 598, 599
Fus3 kinase, 237
Fusarium, 883f
Fusion, 543–44, 543f
Fusion, of floral parts, 868f

G

G protein, **226f**
G protein-coupled receptors (GPCRs), 225, 225f,
    226–28f, 231, 232, 232f, 1179
G_0 phase, **256**
G_1 phase, **246**, 254
G_2 phase, **246**, 247f, 254
GABA, 1051
Gadhus morhua, 1231
Gadus morhua, 770
Gage, Phineas, 1152–53
Gagnon, Catherine, 1286f
Galactose, 76, 76f

Galápagos finches, 16, 17f, 20, 23, 496, 497f,
    1239, 1276
Galápagos Islands, 496
Gallbladder, **955**
Gälweiler, Leo, 894f
Game theory, **1212**, 1217
Gametangia, **656f**
Gametes, **245**, **267**, 1079
Gametic isolation, 533f
Gametogenesis, **1079**, 1080f–81f, 1082, 1083
Gametophores, **660**
Gametophytes, 270, 637, **655f**
    bryophyte, 659–660
    development of, 869–870, 869f
    and sporophyte relationships in plant groups,
        674f
Gametophytic self-incompatibility, 880
Gamma proteobacteria, 616f
Gamma-aminobutyric acid (GABA), **1135**
Ganglia, **1121**, **1141**
Ganglion cells, 1174f, 1176
Gap junctions, 131, **132f**
Garden pea plants. See Pea plants
Garlic, 881f
Garrod, Archibald, 352
Garter snakes, 532f
Gas exchange, **985**. See also Respiratory systems
    across specialized respiratory surfaces, 985–990
    and breathing and lung ventilations, 990–92
    carbon dioxide transport, 994–95
    coordination of, 993
    gills for, 986–88, 987f
    ion movement and gradients, 1042f
    loading and unloading of respiratory gases, 993f
    lungs, 988–990
    partial pressure in, 985
    respiratory adaptations of diving mammals,
        995–96
    respiratory media, 986
    respiratory pigments and, 993–95
    respiratory surfaces, 986
    review, 997
    tracheal systems in insects, 988
Gas exchange organs, 748, 922f
Gaseous signalling factors, 1050–51
Gases, as neurotransmitters, 1135
Gasterosterus sp, 1276f
Gasterosteus aculeatus, 1197, 1197f
Gastric juices, 953f, **953**, 960
Gastric ulcers, 954
Gastrin, 960f
Gastrodermis, 950f
Gastropods, 739, 739f
Gastrovascular cavities, **731**, **950**, 967–68
Gastrula, **714**, **1102**
Gastrulation, 719, **1102**
    in chicks, 1103, 1105f
    in frogs, 1103, 1104f
    in fruit flies, 1109
    in humans, 1103–6
    in sea urchins, 1102–3, 1102f

Gated channels, **146**
Gated ion channels, **1125**
Gause, G. F., 1274
Gecko lizards, 28f, 43–44, 599f
Geckskin, 44
Geese, 1198f, 1202, 1279, 1286f
Gehring, Kalle, 74
Gel electrophoresis, 439f, **439**–440
GenBank, 465
Gender, 312
Gene activation, combinatorial control of, 390–91
Gene annotation, **466**
Gene chips, 468, 469f
Gene cloning, **437**
    and Escherichia coli, 621
    eukaryotic DNA cloning and expression
        systems, 442
    and gene expression, 441–42
    use of restriction enzymes and PCR in, 441f
    uses of, 437–38, 438f
Gene duplications, 595–96
Gene expression, **6**, **27**, **352**, 360f. See also
        Genetics; Transcription; Translation
    altering, 908f
    analyzing data, 445
    and auxin, role of, 894
    bacterial expression systems, 441–42
    and cell differentiation, 823, 823f
    cloned eukaryotic genes, 441–42
    cross-species gene expression and evolutionary
        ancestry, 442
    of developmental genes, 763f
    from different species, 358f
    eukaryotic DNA cloning and expression
        systems, 442
    flow of information, 351–52, 355, 355f
    gene specification of proteins via transcription
        and translation, 352–58
    of interacting groups of genes, 445–46
    mutations and, 372–76
    and nuclear architecture, 392
    products of, 353
    of prophage genes, 420
    and protein production, 7f
    review, 377–78
    RNA modification after transcription by
        eukaryotic cells, 361–63
    of single genes, 443–44
    systems approach, 445–46
    at the systems level, 467–69
    vs. transcription, 385
    use of DNA technology, 442–48
Gene expression, regulation of. See also Genetics
    in bacterial transcription, 381–85
    cancer and genetic changes affecting cell cycle
        control, 404–10
    differential expression of genes, 380, 385,
        397–403
    faulty gene regulation in clones animals, 450
    and initiation of translation, 393–94
    by miRNAs, 395f

mPGES-1, 390
negative gene regulation, 383–84
noncoding RNAs and role in, 394–96
positive gene regulation, 384–85
post-transcriptional regulation, 392–94
and protein processing and degradation, 394
review, 411
and RNA processing, 392–93
stages of, 385–394, 386*f*
and steroid hormone receptors, 1053*f*
of transcription initiation, 387–392
Gene families, 474–75, 475*f*, 595–96
Gene flow, 521*f*, **521**, 523–24, 531
and alteration of allele frequencies in
population, 521–22
and biological species concept, 534
Gene function, 446–48, 447*f*
Gene identification
duchenne muscular dystrophy, 454
hemophilia, 454
huntington's disease, 454
Gene pools, **514**, 515*f*
Gene regulation, 382, 572–73
Gene therapy, 455*f*, **455**–56, 1178*f*
Gene transfer, horizontal, 599, 600, 600*f*
General transcription factors, 387–88
Generative cells, 682, 869
Genes, **6**, **267**, **377**. *See also* Heredity
altering number or position, 514
amplification of, 404, 404*f*
analysis of, 443–46
changes in, evolutionary, 572
on chromosomes, 307–9
conservation of developmental genes among
animals, 485–86
cytoplasmic genes, 325
db, 963
developmental, 572
duplication of, 477–78, 477*f*
editing, 446–47
egg-polarity genes, **402**
and enzymes, 352–53
evolution of genes with related functions,
477–78
extranuclear genes, 325
forager, 1206–7
FOXP2, 483–84, 483*f*
fru, 1213
GLABRA-2, 823
homeotic, 401, 571, 823*f*
Hox, 485–86, 486*f*, 571, 714, 716, 746, 747*f*,
823, 1116
human globin genes, 477–78, 479*f*
inheritance of, 267
for insulin-like growth factor2, 324, 325*f*
KNOTTED-1, 823, 823*f*
linked, 314–321
MADS-box, 571, 823
maternal effect gene, 402
Mendel's gene idea, 281–305
meristem identity genes, 824

multigene families, 474–75
with novel functions, 478
ob, 963
organ identity genes, 824, 824*f*, 825*f*
and protein production, 6
protein-coding genes, 466–67
rearrangement of parts of: exon duplication
and exon shuffling, 478–480
regulatory genes, 382
reporter, 856
review, 376–77
sex-linked genes, 311–14, 312
S-genes, 880
split genes and RNA splicing, **361**–63
suicide genes, 406
sym genes, 698
tinman, 1096
V, J, and *C* segments, 1008, 1009*f*
vocabulary, 286
Genetic assimilation, 562
Genetic code
codons, 356, 357*f*
cracking, 357
evolution of, 357–58
triplet code, 356, 356*f*
Genetic counselling, 300
Genetic diversity, 1321
Genetic drift, **518**
and alteration of allele frequencies in
population, 518–521, 523
bottleneck effect, 519, 519*f*
founder effect, 518–19
greater prairie chicken, impact on,
519–520, 520*f*
in wildflower population, 519*f*
Genetic engineering, **434**, 459
of angiosperms, 882–86
and plant biotechnology, 883–85
and plant nutrition, 856
and plant tissue culture, 881–82
review, 887
Genetic information, expression and transmission
of, as theme in biology, 6–8, 26–27
Genetic interactions, 263
Genetic map, **317**
Genetic markers, 448, 448*f*
Genetic mutants, 1149
Genetic profiles, 455, **457**–58
Genetic recombination, **315**, 316–17,
610–12
Genetic testing, 300–303, 302*f*
Genetic variation, 278–79, 280, **511**
altering gene number or position, 514
and genetic drift, 520, 520*f*
at molecular level, 511–12, 512*f*
nonheritable variation, 513*f*
in prokaryotes, 608
rapid reproduction, 514
review, 527
and sexual reproduction, 514
sources of, 512–13

Genetically modified organisms
(GMOs), **459**
Arabidopsis thaliana, 912
canola, 867
and cloning, 437
debate over, 885–86
ethical issues, 459–460
fungi, 710
smart plants, 857, 857*f*
Genetics, **266**
and animal behaviour, 1213, 1219
and biotechnology. *See* Biotechnology
and colour blindness, 1178
diagnosing genetic diseases in fetuses, 1091
effects of, 520–21
in embryonic development, 397
ethical issues in, 1091
flow of information, 351–52, 355, 355*f*
and loss of genetic variation, 520*f*
and nervous system disorders, 1157
and schizophrenia, 1157*f*
Genlisea, 849, 864
Genome, **8**
Genome sequencing
centralized resources for, 465–66, 466*f*
development of, 433
Human Genome Project. *See* Human Genome
Project
model of, 433*f*
of Neanderthals, 795, 795*f*
next-generation techniques, 434–37,
436*f*, 465
sequences completed, 463
whole-genome shotgun approach, 464*f*
Genomes, **244**. *See also* Genetics
analyzing using bioinformatics, 465–69
comparing closely related species, 481–83
comparing distantly related species, 481
comparing within species, 484–85
conservation of developmental genes among
animals, 485–86
editing, 446–47
eukaryotic, 472–75
evolution of, 476–482, 481–86, 596
as evolutionary history of an organism,
595–96
evolutionary relationships, 481*f*
genes and multigene families, 474–75
Human Genome Project. *See* Human Genome
Project
numbers of genes, 469*t*, 470–71
repetitive DNA, including simple sequence
DNA, 474
review, 487–88
sizes of, 469–470, 469*t*
transposable elements and related sequences,
473–74, 480–81
variations in, 469–472
viral, 416
Genome-wide association studies, **448**
Genomic imprinting, **324**–25, 325*f*, 386

Genomics, **8**, **96**, 97*f*, 99, **464**, 471–72
    and cancer, 409*f*
    and cell signalling and cancer, 408*f*
    and crops, 883
    nucleotides in, 333
    overview, 8
    research in Canada, 470*f*–71*f*
    single cell genomics, research into, 470*f*
    single-base pair variations, 448
    stem cell genomics, 471*f*
    systems level approach, 467–69
Genomics Research on Atlantic Salmon Project, 470*f*
Genotype, 286*f*, **286**, 295
Gentoo penguin, 15*f*
Genus, **584**
Geococcyx californianus, 1041*f*
Geographic separation, 535–540, 548
Geologic record, **556**, 558*f*
Geometric isomers, 68
Geothlypis trichas, 1224
Germ cells, 270, 1110–11, 1112*f*
Germ layers, 719, **1102**, 1103*f*
Germination, 875, 875*f*
    and gibberellins, 897, 897*f*
    and phytochromes, 902–3
    precocious, 898*f*
    and red and far-red illumination, 903*f*
Gesner, Abraham Actinistia, 771
Gestation, **1086**. *See also* Pregnancy
Ghost crabs, 750*f*
Ghrelin, 962
Giant mussels, 1221
Giant panda, 469*t*
Giant tubeworm, 959*f*
Giant water bugs, 1075*f*
Giardia intestinalis, 628*f*, 632
Gibberella, 896
Gibberellins, 892*t*, 896–**97**, 897*f*
Gibbons, 98, 789, 789*f*
Gibbs, J. Willard, 158
Gigantism, 1063
Gills, 969, 986–88, 987*f*, 1027, 1031
Ginkgo biloba, 679*f*
Ginkgophyta, 679*f*
Giraffes, 495, 787*f*, 977, 1249*f*
GLABRA-2 genes, 823
Glacial retreat, 1290–91, 1291*f*
Glands
    adrenal, 1064–65, 1065*f*, 1103
    bulbourethral, 1079
    endocrine, 1054*f*
    exocrine, 1055
    mammary, 1055, 1056, 1060
    nasal salt, 1030, 1030*f*
    parathyroid, 1063
    pineal, 1060*f*, 1067, 1147*f*
    pituitary, 1054*f*, 1060
    prostate, 1079
    salivary, 951, 1055
    thyroid, 33, 927

Glans, **1078**
Glaucoma, 1174*f*
Gleason, H. A., 1289
Gleevec, 456
Glia, **1121**, 1122*f*, 1141–42, 1141*f*
Glial cells (glia), **926***f*, **1121**, 1122*f*, 1141–42, 1141*f*
Glick, Bernie, 862*f*
Gliocladium roseum, 710
Global change. *See also* Climate change; Global warming
    acid precipitation, 1335
    depletion of atmospheric ozone, 1341–42
    greenhouse gases and climate change, 1338
    and nutrient enrichment, 1335–37, 1336*f*
    review, 1345
    and toxic compounds in the environment, 1337–38
Global climate change. *See* Climate change
Global climate patterns, 1225
Global ecology, **1226***f*
Global energy budgets, 1302
Global net primary production, 1303*f*
Global warming. *See also* Climate change
    and Arctic mammals, 1072*f*
    and carbon cycling, 1304
    and CO_2, 10, 1230
    and protists, 649, 649*f*
    and sugar maples, 1230*f*
Globigerina, 629*f*
α globin, 393
α globin, 475
α-globin, 475
α globin, 475*f*
α globin, 477, 478
α globin, 478*f*
α globin, 479
α-globin, 479
α globin, 481
Globin genes, 477–78, 479*f*
Globular proteins, 86
Glomeromycetes, 700*f*, **701**–2
Glomeromycota, 701
Glomerulus, **1037***f*
Glottis, 989
Glucagon, 1051, 1054*f*, **1056**–57, 1057*f*
Glucocorticoids, 1051, 1054*f*, **1064**, 1065*f*
Glucose
    and age, 146
    in cellulose, 79
    control of by antagonistic hormones, 1056–59
    glycolysis of, 181, 182–83*f*
    homeostasis of, 1057*f*
    and *lac* operons, 384–85, 384*f*
    linear forms, 77*f*
    in photosynthesis, 201–2
    regulation of, 961*f*
    ring forms, 77*f*, 79, 79*f*
    in starches, 78
    structure of, 76–77, 76*f*

Glucose 6-phosphatase, 168
Glucose homeostasis, 961
α glucose ring structures, 79, 79*f*
Glutamate, 1051, **1135**
Glutamate receptor, 242*f*
Glutamate signalling, 1157
Glutamic acid, 163*f*
Glutamine, 163*f*
Glyceraldehyde, 76*f*
Glyceraldehyde 3-phosphate (G3P), **212**
Glycerol, 80, 81*f*
Glycogen, 78*f*, **78**–79, 224, 961
Glycolipids, 141
Glycolysis, 180*f*, 181, 181*f*, 182–83*f*, 193–95, 196–97
Glycolytic fibres, 1187
Glycoproteins, **116**, 141, 417, 422
Glycosidic linkage, **77**
Glycosis, **180**
Glyoxysomes, 123
Glyptemys insculpta, 1225, 1244, 1244*f*
GMOs. *See* Genetically modified organisms (GMOs)
Gnathostomes, **767**
    chondrichthyans, 767–69
    derived characters of, 767
    fossil, 767
    lobe-fins, 770–71, 771*f*
    osteichthyans, 769–770
    ray-finned fishes, 770, 770*f*
    review, 797
    tetrapods, 771–782
Gnetophyta, 679*f*, 684
Gnetum, 679*f*
Goats, 457*f*
Goatsbeard plants, 539
Gobi Desert, 1228
Goiter, 33, 1062
Golden algae, 635*f*, **635**
Golden lion tamarins, 787*f*
Golden Rice, 884, 947
Goldenrain trees, 501, 501*f*
Golgi apparatus, 112*f*, 113*f*, **116**–18, 117*f*
Gonadotropin-releasing hormone (GnRH), 1066, 1082, 1083, 1084, 1085, 1085*f*
Gonadotropins (FSH and LH), 1066, 1082, 1083–84
Gonads, 1065, **1075**, 1082
Gonorrhea, 606, 1092
Goodall, Jane, 18, 18*f*
Gorillas, 787*f*, 789, 789*f*, 794
Gormley, Andrew, 1251
Gould, Stephen Jay, 544
Gout, 1032
Graded potentials, 1126–27, 1126*f*, **1126**
Grades, **658**, **720**
Graft versus host reaction, 1018
Gram, Hans Christian, 605
Gram staining, 605*f*, **605**
Gram-Positive Bacteria, 617*f*
Grana, **122**, 201

Grant, Peter, 23
Grant Rosemary, 23
Granzymes, 1013f
Grapefruits, 682f
The Grapes of Wrath (Steinbeck), 852
Grasby, Stephen, 566
GRASP, 470f
Grasses, 893, 893f
Grasshoppers, 486f, 751f, 753f, 951f, 968f, 1188, 1188f, 1272f, 1274
Grasslands, 1232, 1233, 1289
Grasslands National Park, 1315, 1315f
Grastulation, **714**
Graves' disease, 1061
Gravitropism, 907f, **907**
Gravity, 907–8
    and flying, 1192–93
    and locomotion, 1191
    sensing, in invertebrates, 1167
Gray, Michael, 630
Graylag geese, 1202
Great auks, 1322, 1326
Great Basin, 1228
Great Lakes, 1325f
Great Lakes food web, 1337, 1337f
Great Salt Lake, 604, 614
Great tit, 782f
Greater prairie chickens, 519–520, 520f, 1322, 1327–29, 1328f
Green, Richard, 795f
Green algae, 113f, 122f, 643, 650, 653–58, 669–670
Green manure, 860
Green parrot snake, 1278f
Green roots, 804f
Greenberg, Bruce, 862f
Greenhouse effect, 613, 689
Greenhouse gases, 613, 1230, 1338, 1340f
Greening, 889, 890, 890f, 891
Gregory, Patrick, 1214
Grey jays, 1203
Grey matter, 1142, 1142f
Grey seals, 1276
Grey tree frogs, 524, 525f, 538
Griffith, Frederick, 330, 330f
Grizzly bears, 543, 1329, 1329f, 1333
Grolar bears, 534, 534f
Grosmannia clavigera, 708
Gross primary production (GPP), **1302**
Ground squirrels, 1252
Ground tissue systems, 807f, **807**
Grouse, 1196, 1196f, 1331
Growth, **819**
    and abscisic acid, 898
    cell division and cell expansion, 821–22
    as property of life, 2f
Growth factors, 223, **257**, **1051**
Growth hormone (GH), 1054f, **1062**–63, 1063f
Growth rings, 817
Grubs, 752
Grus americana, 1202
Grus canadensis, 1202

Guanine, 334–35, 335f
Guano, 1032
Guard cells, **814**, 821, 840–42, 841f
!Gubi, 484–85
Guderley, Helga, 101, 137
Guichon Creek, 1335
Guinea pigs, 146, 944
Gulls, 1202, 1209f, 1337
The Gully, 1334, 1334f
Guppies, 507f, 1210, 1211f
Gurdon, John, 449–50, 449f, 452
Gustation, **1179**–80, 1180f, 1193–94
Gutenberg, Johannes, 26
Guttation, 837f, **837**
Guy, Rob, 803
Gymnosperms, **658**, 674f, 675
    diversity of, 678, 679f–680f
    evolution of, 677–78

H
H1N1 virus, 427–28, 427f, 429f, 1020, 1295
H5N1 virus, 428
Habitat differentiation, 538–39
Habitat isolation, 532f
Habitat loss, 1324–25, 1324f
Habitats, riparian, 1332
Hadean eon, 558f
Haeckel, Ernst, 625
Haemophilus influenzae, 469t
Hagfishes, 764f, **764**, 1035
Haikouella, 765, 765f
Hair cells, **1168**f, 1169f, **1169**, 1170
Hairs
    and equilibrium, 1170
    and soundwaves, 1167, 1168f, 1169f
    and tasting, 1179
Hala trees, 804f
Haldane, J. B. S., 551, 1217
Half-life, 36, **554**, 556f
Halifax Consciousness Scanner (HCS), 1140
Hallucigenia, 555f, 716, 716f, 746
Halobacterium, 614
Hamilton, William, 1216
Hamilton's Rule, **1216**
Hammerhead sharks, 1071
Hamsters, 940, 1149
Hansen, Carl, 470f
Hantavirus Pulmonary Syndrome, 1295–96
Haplo-diploid system, 311f
Haploid cells, **269**, 272f, 273f, 476
Harbour seals, 1072f
Hardy-Weinberg equation, 514–15, 516–17, 527
Hardy-Weinberg equilibrium, **515**–16, 516f
Hares, 221f, 787f, 1263–65, 1265f, 1266f, 1274
Harley, Calvin, 344, 345f
Harp seals, 49f, 54f
Haustoria, **694**, 695f
Hawaiian archipelago, 569, 570f
Hawkmoths (*Manduca sexta*), 801f, 873f, 935f, 1278, 1278f
Hay fever, 1018

Hazel, 871f
Hazelnuts, 682f
Health
    and human microbiome, 620f
    and plant biotechnology, 885
Hearing
    human ear, structure of, 1168f
    in mammals, 1167–70
    mechanoreceptors responsible for, in vertebrate and mammal bodies, 1167–72
    in other vertebrates, 1171–72, 1171f
    transduction in the cochlea, 1170f
Heart, **968**
    chambers of, 969, 971
    mammalian, 972–73, 973f
    rhythmic beat of, 974, 974f
Heart attacks, 457, **983**
Heart murmur, **973**
Heart rate, **973**
Heartburn, 954
Heartwood, 818
Heat, 51–52, **51**, 155
    by conduction, 932f
    measurement of, 51–52
    specific heat of water, 52
    and thermodynamics, 157
Heat (estrus), 1085
Heat exchange, 932–34. *See also* Thermoregulation
    behavioural responses, 934, 934f
    circulatory adaptations, 932–33
    by convection, 932f
    evaporative cooling, 933–34
    and insulation, 932
    metabolic heat production, adjusting, 934
Heat of vaporization, **52**
Heat stress, plant, 910–11
Heat-shock proteins, 911
Heavy chains, **1006**, 1008
Hebert, Paul, 470f, 593
Hector's dolphins, 1251
Hedge bindweed, 868f
HeLa cells, 258, 262f
Helical viruses, 417
Helicases, **338**, 342t
Helicobacter pylori, 616f, 954, 958, 959f
Helium, 35, 35f, 39
α helix, 88f, 91, 139, 388f
Helper T cells, 1010, 1010f, **1012**
Hemagglutinin (H), 428
Hemeroplanes ornatus, 1278
Hemichordates (hemichordata), 723, 729f
Hemings, Sally, 458
Hemiptera, 753f
Hemizygous, 313
Hemlock trees, 1291
Hemochromatosis, 948
Hemocoel, 748
Hemocyanin, 993
Hemocytes, 1001
Hemoglobin, 89f, 90f, 98, **981**, 993f, 995
    amino acid sequences, 479f

Hemoglobin (*Continued*)
  and cooperativity, 171–72
  and gas exchange, 993–94, 994*f*
  as nonidentical multigene family, 475, 475*f*
  polypeptides in, 353
Hemolymph, 748, 968*f*, **968**
Hemophilia, **313**, 454, 981–82
Hemorrhagic fever, 426
Henderson, Charles, 567*f*
Hens and chicks, 216, 216*f*
Henslow, John, 495
Hepatic portal vein, **956**
Hepatitis B, 1022
Hepatitis C, 426, 1003
HER2, 228, 260, 408*f*
Herbicide resistance, 885
Herbicides, 883, 895
Herbivores, **943**, 947
  and alimentary canals, 958, 958*f*
  and dentition, 957*f*
  mutualistic adaptations in, 958–960
  plant defences against, 800*f*–801*f*
  plant responses to, 912
Herbivory, **1279**
Heredity, **266**, 279. *See also* Genetics; Inheritance
  and autoimmune disorders, 1019
  and cardiovascular disease, 984
  and chromosomes, 267–68
  complexity of, 290–96
  dominantly inherited disorders, 299–300
  laws of inheritance, 282–88
  Mendel's model, 284–86
  multifactorial disorders, 300
  pedigree analysis, 296–97, 297*f*
  recessively inherited disorders, 297–99
  and variation, 295–96
Heredity distance, 1216–17
Hermaphrodites, **731**, 735, 745, 1110
Hermaphroditism, **1073**
Herpesviruses, 422, 426, 1020
Herring, 1231
Herring gulls, 1337
Hershey, Alfred, 331–32, 331*f*
Heterocephalus glaber, 1215, 1215*f*
Heterochromatin, **348**
Heterochrony, **570**–71
Heterocysts, **613**
Heterokaryon mycelium, **696**
Heteromorphic generations, **637**
Heterosporous, **666**, 673
Heterotherms, 934
Heterotrophic protists, 625*f*
Heterotrophs, 199, 612*t*, 937, 1240*f*–43*f*, 1301
Heterozygote advantage, **525**
Heterozygote protection, 513
Heterozygous, **286**, 313, 511
Hexapods, **748**
Hexoses, 76, 76*f*
Hfr cells, 610, 611*f*
hGH. *See* Human growth hormone (hGH)
Hibernation, **940**

High-density lipoprotein (HDL), **983**
Hindbrain, **1145**
Hindlimbs, 506*f*
Hinge joint, 1190*f*
Hippocampus, 1150
Hippocrates, 689
Hippopotamus, 97*f*
Hirudinea (leeches), 742
Histamine, **1004**
Histograms, 259, 294
Histone acetylation, **386**, 387*f*
Histone modifications, 386, 387*f*
Histone tails, 386, 387*f*
Histones, **346***f*
Hitchhikers, 1280
HIV (human immunodeficiency virus), 140–41, 140*f*, **423**
  drugs for, 426
  emergence of, 426
  generation span of, 514
  and immune system, **1020**–21
  origin of, 597, 598*f*
  replicative cycle of, 424*f*
  untreated, 1022*f*
HM, 1155*f*
Hoatzins, 959
Hodgkin, Alan, 1127
Hodgkin's disease, 1019, 1323
Hoekstra, Hopi, 22, 22*f*, 24, 25
Holdfast, 635*f*, **635**
Holly flowers, 681*f*
Holoblastic, **1100**
Holothuroidea, 756, 756*f*
Homeoboxes, **485**–86, 714
Homeodomain, 485–86
Homeostasis, **928**
  alterations in, 929–930
  feedback control in, 929
  glucose, 961
  in kidneys, 1045
  mechanisms of, 928–29
  and nervous systems, 1144
  and regulation of cellular fuel, 961*f*
  review, 941
  and signalling, 918*f*
Homeostatic control of breathing, 992*f*
Homeotherms, 931
Homeotic genes, **401**, **571**, 823*f*
Homing pigeons, 1198
Hominins, **790**–91
  Australopiths, 791–92
  bipedalism in, 792, 792*f*
  brain volume in, 793
  Homo sapiens, 794. *See also* Humans
  Neanderthals, 794–95
  skeleton of, 791*f*
  timeline of, 791*f*
  tool use, 792–94
Homo, 789
Homo erectus, 794
Homo ergaster, 794, 794*f*

Homo floresiensis, 796
Homo habilis, 794
Homo neanderthalensis, 37, 463, 484, 794
Homo sapiens, 469*t*, 484, 790. *See also* Humans
  evolution of, 795–96
  fossil record of, 795
  and Neanderthals, 794, 795*f*
Homologies, **503**, **586**
  vs. analogies, 586–87
  anatomical, 503–4, 503*f*
  and convergent evolution, 505, 505*f*
  as evidence for evolution, 503
  molecular, 503–4, 503*f*, 587–88
  and phylogenies, 586
  and tree thinking, 504–5
Homologous chromosomes, **268**, 271, 272*f*, 274–76, 276, 277
Homologous genes, 595*f*
Homologous structures, **503**
Homoplasies, **587**, 588*f*
Homosporous, **666**, 673
Homozygous, **286**, 313, 511
Homunculus, 1151
Honey mushrooms, 693, 694
Honeybees, 688, 934, 1071, 1196, 1199, 1200, 1200*f*, 1215
Honig, Lawrence, 1116*f*
Hooke, Robert, 105
Hopping, 1191
Hori, Michio, 526*f*
Horizontal cells, 1174*f*
Horizontal gene transfer, **599**, 600, 600*f*
Horizontal transmission, 430
Hormonal contraceptives, 1090–91
Hormonal proteins, 84*f*
Hormonal signalling, 223*f*, 224, 927, 1067
Hormone cascade pathway, 1062*f*
Hormone therapy, 1092
Hormones, **224**, **892**, **927**, **1048**
  adrenocorticotropic hormone (ACTH), 1054*f*
  aldosterone, 228–29, 229*f*, 1045
  androgens, 1054*f*
  angiostensin II acting as, 1044–45
  antagonistic, 1056–59
  antidiuretic, 1043–44, 1043*f*, 1044*f*, 1049, 1054*f*
  atrial natriuretic factor, 1049
  calcitonin, 1054*f*
  cellular response pathways, 1051–53
  and digestion, 960, 960*f*
  effects of, 1053–55, 1053*f*
  as endocrine signals. *See* Endocrine (hormonal) signalling
  of endocrine system, 1054*f*
  epinephrine, 1054*f*
  estrogen, 1054*f*
  evolution of, 1059
  and female reproductive cycles, 1083–85
  follicle-stimulating hormone (FSH), 1054*f*
  ghrelin, 962

glucagon, 1054f
glucocorticoids, 1054f
growth hormone (GH), 1054f
hydrophilic, 1050, 1051, 1051f
hydrophobic, 1050
inhibiting, 1060
insulin, 1054f
interactions regulating complex processes, 1058–59
leptin, 962
lipid-soluble, 1050, 1051f, 1052–53, 1052f, 1054
luteinizing hormone (LH), 1054f
and male reproductive system, 1085, 1085f
melanocyte-stimulating hormone (MSH), 1059
melatonin, 930, 930f, 1054f
mineralocorticoids, 1054f
neurohoromones, 1049, 1055
nonpolar, 1050
norepinephrine, 1054f
oxytocin, 1054f
parathyroid hormone (PTH), 1054f
plant. See Plant hormones
progestin, 1054f
prolactin, 1054f, 1059
as proteins, 1051
PYY, 962
regulation of homeostasis, development, and behaviour in vertebtates, 1059–67
releasing, 1060
sex, 69, 1065–67, 1082–86
and sex determination, 1082
simple hormone pathways, 1055
solubility of, 1051f
steroids. See Steroid hormones
structure and solubility of, 1050
testosterone, 69–70
thyroid, 1051, 1054f, 1059
thyroid-stimulating, 927, 1054f
tropic, 1060
vasopressin, 1054f
water-soluble, 1051f, 1052, 1052f
Hornworts (phylum Anthocerophyta), **658**
Horowitz, Norman, 353, 353f
Horses, 511f, 575, 576f, 787f, 959
Horseshoe crabs, 748, 748f, 1330, 1330f
Horsetails, 666, 667f, 669, 671f
Horvitz, Robert, 1110, 1112f
Hosken, David, 1076f
Host ranges, 418
Hosts, **1279**
Hot spots, of biodiversity, 1333, 1333f
Houghton, Michael, 426
Hox genes, 445, 485–86, 486f, 571, 572f, 714, 716, 746, 747f, 823, 1116
HPV (human papillomavirus), 426
HTLV-1 virus, 410
Hubbard Brook Experimental Forest, 1312–13, 1313f
Hudson, Thomas, 260

Hudson, Tom, 471f
Human chorionic gonadotropin (hCG), 1017, **1086**
Human culture, and evolution, 1217–18
Human genetics
dominantly inherited disorders, 299–300
multifactorial disorders, 300
pedigree analysis, 296–97, 297f
recessively inherited disorders, 297–99
review, 304
Human genome. *See also* Genomes
and alternative RNA splicing, 393
compared to chimpanzee genome, 481
components of, 472, 472f
DNA sequences in, 472f
Human Genome Project, 96, 363, 464–65
Human globin genes, 477–78, 479f
Human growth hormone (hGH), 457
Human immunodeficiency virus (HIV). *See* HIV (human immunodeficiency virus)
Human impact
and acid precipitation, 1335
on aquatic biomes, 1240f–43f
on biodiversity, 1321–27
on biological communities, 1292, 1292f
and greenhouse gases, 1338
on marine ecosystems, 1334
and nutrient enrichment, 1335–37, 1336f
and possible sixth mass extinction, 567–68
review, 1345
on terrestrial biomes, 1234f–37f
and toxic compounds in the environment, 1337–38
on wolf predation, 1277
Human Metabolome Database, 96
Human papillomavirus (HPV), 426, 1022, 1022f
Human population
and age structure, 1268, 1269f
carrying capacity, 1268–70
and energy use, 1270f
growth of, 1267, 1267f
and infant mortality, 1268
and life expectancy, 1268
limits on, 1269
regional patterns of change, 1267–68
review, 1271
Human reproduction
conception, embryonic development and birth, 1086–89
fetal development, 1088f
gametogenesis, 1079, 1080f–81f, 1082, 1083
hormonal regulation of, 1083–84
maternal immune tolerance of embryo and fetus, 1089
and modern reproductive technologies, 1091–92
prevention of, 1089–91, 1090f
reproductive organs, 1066f, 1077–81, 1077f, 1078f
sexual response, 1085–86

Human Reproductive and Genetic Technologies Act, 301
Human sexual response, 1085–86
Humans
affected by climate change, 1340f
aging in, 745
Australopiths, 791–92
bipedalism, 792
birth weight, 522
brain volume in, 793
characteristics of, 787f
classification of, 789
colour vision in, 1173, 1175f, 1177–78
communication among, 1199
derived characters of, 790
earliest hominins, 790–91
early *Homo*, 794
embryo development in, 1105f
eyes of, 1174f–75f
forearm, 1188f
gastrulation in, 1103–6
gene flow between Neanderthals and, 795f
and global change, 1335–42
infertility, treating, 1091–92
magnetite in, 1166
night vision in, 1175–76, 1176f
review, 798
and species distribution, 1246, 1247
thermorerceptors in, 1166
and tool use, 792–94
Hummingbird hawkmoth, 753f
Hummingbirds, 2f, 4, 782, 801f, 872f, 880, 940, 949f, 965f
Humoral immune response, **1011**, 1012, 1012f, 1014f, 1015
Humpback whales, 949f
Humus, **850**, 851
Hundred Heartbeat Club, 1322f
Hunger, transgenic crops reducing, 883–84
Huntington's disease, **300**, 453, 454
Hutton, James, 494
Huxley, Andrew, 1127
Hybrid breakdown, 533f
Hybrid orbitals, 44f
Hybrid zones, **540**, 548
formation of, 542f
over time, 542–44, 542f
patterns in, 541–42, 541f
and reproductive isolation, 540–44
Hybridization, **283**, 534f, 546f, 882, 885–86
Hybrids, 533f, **534**
Hydras, 267f, 731, 732f, 921, 922f, 950, 950f, 967, 1140, 1140f, 1179, 1189
Hydration shells, 55
Hydraulic failure, **840**
Hydrocarbon Metagenome Project, 604
Hydrocarbon tails, 138, 139f
Hydrocarbons, 67–68. *See also* Fossil fuels
Hydrochloric acid, 56, 953
Hydroelectric systems, 160f, 161f

Hydrogen
  atomic number of, 35
  bonding, 50, 50f, 52, 53, 53f, 61
  covalent bonding, 41, 41f
  electron distribution of, 39
  as essential element, 33
  molecular structure of, 40
  and monomers, 75
  valence of, 67f
Hydrogen bonds, 43f, **43**
Hydrogen ions, **56**
Hydrogen peroxide, 123
Hydrogen sulphide (H$_2$S), 1050
Hydrogenated vegetable oils, 81, 82
Hydrogenosomes, 632
Hydrolagus colliei, 768f
Hydrolysis, 75f, **75**, 950
  of ATP, 162–63, 162f, 163f
  enzymatic, 950
  of fats, 956
Hydrolytic enzymes, 118
Hydronium ions, **56**
Hydrophilic hormones, 1050, 1051
Hydrophilic substances, **55**, 82–83, 84, 85f
Hydrophobic hormones, 1050, 1051
Hydrophobic interaction, 89f
Hydrophobic substances, **55**, 80, 82–83, 84, 85f
Hydroponic culture, 854f, **855**
Hydrostatic skeletons, **1189**
Hydrothermal vents, 552, 615, 619, 1221, 1299–1300, 1334
Hydroxide ions, **56**
Hydroxyl group, 70, 71f, 75
Hydrozoans, 733, 733f
Hylobates, 789
Hylonomus lyelli, 777, 777f
Hymen, **1078**
Hymenoptera, 753f
Hyperosmotic, 1026, 1026f
Hyperosmotic urine, 1038
Hyperpolarization, 1123, 1124, 1125–**26**, 1126f
Hypersensitive response, **913**, 914f
Hypertension, **984**, 1049
Hyperthyroidism, 1061
Hypertonic solution, 144f, **144**
Hyphae, **693**, 694–95, 694f, 695f, 700f
Hypoblast, 1103, 1105
Hypocotyl, **874**
Hypoosmotic, 1026, 1026f
Hypothalamus, **935**, 936f, 1054f, **1059**, 1060f, **1147**f
Hypothalamus-pituitary axis, 1059–61
Hypotheses, **18**
  forming and testing, 18–19, 20f, 21
  vs. theories, 23
Hypothesis of dependent/independent assortment, 288f
Hypothyroidism, 1061, 1062
Hypotonic solution, 144f, **144**
Hyracoidea, 787f

Hyracotherium, 575, 576f
Hyraxes, 787f

I

Ibexes, 1326
Ibuprofen, 69f, 1167
Ice
  Arctic ice, 54f
  crystalline structure and floating barrier, 53f
  floating on water, 53–54
  properties of, 31
Icosahedral viruses, 417
Idioblasts, **800**f
"If… then" logic, 19
Iguanas, 493f, 933, 936, 1030, 1047f
Ileum, 955
Imatinib, 456
imbibition, **875**
Immigration, **1252**, 1265–66, 1293–94
Immune reject, 1017–18
Immune responses
  allergies, 1018–19
  autoimmune diseases, 1019
  cell-mediated, **1011**, 1012, 1012f, 1015
  exaggerated, self-directed, and diminished, 1018–20
  and exertion and stress, 1019
  humoral, **1011**, 1012, 1012f, 1014f, 1015
  immunodeficiency diseases, 1019–20
  plants and epiphytes, parasites, and carnivores, 912–**13**
  primary and secondary, 1010, 1011f
Immune systems, 426, 923t, 958, **999**
  attack on: HIV, 1020–21
  and changing pathogens, 1021
  disruptions in, 1018–22
  and evolutionary adaptations of pathogens, 1020–22
  exaggerated, self-directed, and diminished immune responses, 1018–20
  and exertion and stress, 1019
  innate, 958
  innate immunity. *See* Innate immunity
  review, 1023–24
Immunity, 956
  adaptive immunity. *See* Adaptive immunity
  and cancer, 1022
  innate immunity. *See* Innate immunity
  overview, 1000f
Immunization, 1015–17, **1015–17**
Immunodeficiency, **1019–20**
Immunoglobins, 981
Immunoglobulin (Ig), **1006**, 1008, 1009f, 1014, 1018, 1018f
Immunological memory, 1007, 1010–11, 1011f
Impact figures
  alternative fuels, 199f
  breast cancer, genomic evolution of, 409f
  Burgess Shale and *Anomalocaris canadensis*, 717f
  cellulosic biofuels, 884f
  chromosome 7 decoded, 320f

  coyotes, 1245f
  dendritic cells, discovery of, 1011f
  discovery of a "fishapod": *Tiktaalik*, 772f
  end-Permian mass extinction, 567f
  global warming and arctic mammals, 1072f
  human microbiome and health, 620f
  inducing stem cell growth to treat disease, 454f
  International Cancer Genome Consortium, 260f
  invertebrates, loss of biodiversity, 742
  Lake Erie, 1306f
  Leber's Hereditary Optic Neuropathy, 186f
  Lyme disease, 1296f
  marine protists in a warmer world, 649f
  modern agriculture and honeybee colony losses, 688
  mutation-specific disease treatment, 375f
  overfishing and trophic cascades, 1288f
  oxidative phosphorylation, improperly functioning, 186f
  painting chromosomes, 348f
  prenatal genetic testing, 301f
  protist diversity and malaria, 639
  purified insulin, 1057f
  range expansion, 1245f
  restoration ecology, 1314f
  rise of MRSA, 502f
  seedless vascular plants that became coal, 668f
  sequencing the SARS genome, 427f
  short-term memory, 1155f
  stem cells, 451f
  threat of ocean acidification to marine life, 60f
  ticking telomere clock, 345f
  white-nose syndrome, 709f
Implantation, 1104–5
Imprinting, 1202f, **1202**, 1210, 1211f
Inborn errors of metabolism, 352
Inborn immunodeficiency, 1019
Inclusive fitness, **1216**–17
inclusive fitness, 1219
Incomplete dominance, 291f, **291**
Incomplete flowers, **867**
Incomplete metamorphosis, **752**, 753f
Independent assortment, 277, 277f, 316
Independent variables, **23**
Indeterminate cleavage, **721**
Indeterminate growth, **810**
Indian corn, 473, 473f, 481
Indian pipe, 863f
Indian rhinoceros, 787f
Induced fit, 166f, **167**
Induced pluripotent stem (iPS) cells, 452–53
Inducers, **383**
Inducible enzymes, 383f, 384
Inducible operons, 383–84
Induction, **398**
Inductive reasoning, **18**
Inductive signals, and cell fate, 1114–17
  formation of vertebrate limbs, 1114–17
  Spemann's organizer, 1114
Infant mortality, 1268, 1343f

Infection, defences against. *See* Immune systems
Infection thread, 860
Infertility, 1091–92
Inflammation, 983, 984, 1167
Inflammatory response, **1003**–5, 1005f
Inflorescences, **867**
Influenza viruses, 417f, 427–28, 427f, 429f, 1020
Information processing, 1042f
    in birds, 1153
    in the brain, 1148, 1151–52, 1153
    of nervous system, 1203
    and neurons, 1122, 1144, 1144f
    of visual information, 1176–77
Ingestion, 948f, **948**
Ingroups, **589**
Inheritance. *See also* Heredity; Human genetics
    and acquired traits, 495f
    and cancer, 407–10
    chromosomal basis of. *See* Chromosomal basis
        of inheritance
    chromosome theory of, 309
    epigenetic, 386–87
    of genes, 267
    laws of, 282–88, 303
    and linked genes, 314–15, 315f
    molecular basis of. *See* Molecular basis of
        inheritance
    and mutations, 264–65
    of organelle genes, 325–26
    and origin of self-replication molecules, 551
    polygenic, 293, **293**–94, 294f
    of X-linked genes, 312–13
Inheritance of acquired characteristics, 495
Inhibin, **1085**
Inhibited germination, 902
Inhibiting hormones, 1060
Inhibition, 1290
Inhibitors, 171–72, 171f
Inhibitory postsynaptic potential (IPSP), **1132**
Initial cells, 810
Initiation, 359, 359f, 360f, 367f
Initiation factors, 367
Innate behaviour, **1201**
Innate immunity, **1000**
    vs. adaptive immunity, 1000
    antimicrobial peptides and proteins, 1003
    barrier defences, 1002
    cellular defences, 1002–3
    inducible, 1001f
    inflammatory response, 1003–5, 1005f
    of invertebrates, 1001
    overview, 1000f
    pathogens, evasion by, 1005
    review, 1023
    of vertebrates, 1001–5
Inner cell mass, **1104**
Inner ear, **1168**f
The Innocence Project, 458
Inorganic components of topsoil, 850–51
Inositol trisphosphate (IP$_3$), 233f, **233**
Inquiry, **17**. *See also* Scientific process

Inquiry figures
    3-D shape of RNA polymerase II, 92f
    alleles for characters, 288f
    aquaporin mutations and diabetes, 1044f
    arthropod body plan, 747f
    bacterial communities and roots, 858f
    bicoid gene, 403f
    calcium ions in fertilization, 1098f
    camouflage and predation rates on mice, 22f
    circadian clock and hibernation, 940
    common eiders, 1261f
    crossing fruit flies for eye colour, 310f
    deprogramming differentiated human cells,
        453f
    developmental fate of amphibians, 1115f
    developmental potential, 1114f
    divergence of allopatric populations leading to
        reproductive isolation, 536f
    DNA replication models, 337f
    endophytes and woody plants, 706f
    eukaryotic tree, root of, 645f
    fertilization in mosses, 661f
    function of FOXP2, 483f
    gene flow between Neanderthals and humans,
        795f
    gene linkage, 315f
    gene specification in enzymes that function in
        a biochemical pathway, 353f
    genetic traits in bacteria, 330f
    grass coleoptiles, 893f
    greater prairie chicken, 1328f
    hybridization in sunflowers, 546f
    infection in fruit flies, 1002f
    interspecific competition, 1275f
    kinetochore microtubules, 250f
    light wavelengths and photosynthesis, 205f
    limb pattern formation in vertebrates, 1116f
    limiting nutrients and phytoplankton, 1305f
    mammoth hemoglobin, 995
    membrane proteins, 138f
    migratory patterns, 1215f
    molecular signals and cell cycle regulation, 254f
    monarch butterflies, 1172f
    natural selection and food source, 501f
    nitrogenous waste in fishes in alkaline lakes,
        1031f
    organic molecules, conditions for
        forming, 64f
    phage T2, genetic material of, 331f
    phloem sap and sugar sources and sinks, 845f
    Pisaster ochraceus as keystone predator,
        1287f
    polar bear diet, 945f
    polar movement of auxin, 894f
    prokaryotes evolving in response to
        environmental change, 609f
    red and far-red illumination and seed
        germination, 903f
    sexual selection, 525f, 539f
    snowshoe hares, 1266f
    soil bacteria and stressful environment, 862f

    somatic cell nuclear transfer, 449f
    species invasions, 1325f
    species richness, 1294f
    sperm usage bias in fruit flies, 1076f
    stickleback fish, 573f
    sugar maples and global warming, 1230f
    synaptic connections and damaged neurons,
        1132f
    taste, 1180f
    temperature adaptation in salmon, 971f
    thermal history and thermal
        tolerance, 935f
    tobacco mosaic disease, 416f
    traits in F$_2$ generation, 283f
    wasps using landmarks, 1203f
    zone of polarizing activity (ZPA), 1116f
Insecticides, 883
Insects (Hexapoda)
    anatomy of, 751f
    blacklegged ticks, 1224, 1224f
    chemoreceptors in, 1166f
    and climate change, 1340f
    clumping in, 1252
    colour vision in, 1173
    compound eyes of, 1173
    diversity of, 753f
    Hox gene expression in, 486f, 488f
    innate immunity of, 1001
    Malpighian tubules in, 1034f
    muscles of, 1188
    nervous system in, 1140f
    and nitrogenous wastes, 1032
    and osmoregulation, 1028
    overview, 751–54
    parasitoid, 1279–80
    phylogenitic position of, 750f
    regulation of development and metamorphosis,
        1058f
    reproduction in, 752, 1075, 1076f
    sound detection, 1167
    taste receptors in, 1179
    tracheal systems in, 988, 988f
    tympanic membranes of, 1167f
    winged, 753f
Insertions, **374**–75
Insoluble fibre, 79
Insulation, 932
Insulin, 9, 962, 1051, 1054f, **1056**–57, 1057f
    and diabetes mellitus, 1057–58
    growing insulin-producing cells, 453
    as nonenzymatic protein, 353
    purified, 1057f
    research on, 86
    synthetic production of, 457
Insulin-like growth factors (IGFs), 324,
        325f, 1062
Integral proteins, 139
Integration, sensory, 1163f, 1164
Integrins, **130**, 140
Integumentary systems, 923, 923t, **932**
Integuments, **673**, 870

Interactions
  interspecific, 1274–81
  within organisms, 9–10
  with other organisms, 10–11
  as theme in biology, 9–11, 27
Intercalary meristems, 813
Intercalated disks, **1188**
Intercellular communication, 1049–51, 1050*f*
Interferons, **1003**
Intermediate disturbance hypothesis, 1289*f*, **1289**
Intermediate filaments, 112*f*, 113*f*, **128**–29
Internal fertilization, **1074**
International Barcode of Life Network, 470*f*
International Cancer Genome Consortium, 260
International Union for Conservation of Nature and Natural Resources (IUCN), 1322, 1323
Interneurons, 1122*f*, **1122**
Internodes, **805**
Interphase, **246**, 249
Interphase nucleus, 392*f*
Intersex fish, 1338
Intersexual selection, **524**, 1210
Interspecific competition, **1274**
  character displacement, 1276
  Competitive exclusion, 1274–**75**
  ecological niches, 1275–76
  resource partitioning, 1275*f*
Interspecific interactions, **1274**
  competition, 1275–76
  facilitation, 1281
  herbivory, 1279
  predation, 1276–78
  review, 1297
  symbiosis, 1279–81
Interstitial fluid, **922**, 968, 969, 979*f*
Intertidal zones, **1242***f*
Intestines, 956*f*, 958
  large, 956–57
  small, 954–56
Intracellular concentration, 1123*t*
Intracellular digestion, 950
Intracellular recording, 1126
Intrasexual selection, **524**, 1210
Intrauterine devices (IUDs), 1090
Intrinsic factors, of population regulation, 1265*f*
Intrinsically disordered proteins, 92
Introduced species, **1325**
Introns, 362–63, **362**, 363*f*
Invagination, 1103
Invasive species, **1283**
Inversion, 322*f*, **322**
Invertebrates, **723**, **726**
  anthozoans, 733–34
  biodiversity, loss of, 742
  chordates. *See* Chordates (Chordata)
  cnidarians, 731–32
  deuterostomes, 754–56
  diversity of, 727*f*–29*f*

  ecdysozoans, 745–754
  echinoderms, 754–56
  eyes of, 1173–74
  fragmentation in, 1071
  innate immunity of, 1001
  kidneys in, 1035
  light-detecting organs, 1173
  lophotrochozoans, 734–745
  medusozoans, 732–33
  muscles of, 1188
  organogenesis in, 1108
  parental care in, 1075*f*
  parthenogenesis in, 1071
  as proportion of animal species, 730
  reproduction in, 1075
  sponges, 730–31, 730*f*
  summary, 757
Involution, 1103
Iodine, 946*t*, 1061
Ion channel receptors, 228*f*
Ion channels, **146**, 832, 833*f*
  gated, 1125, 1127, 1128, 1128*f*, 1132
  and resting membrane potential, 1124–25
  review, 1138
  in sensory transduction, 1175
  stretch-activated, 1125
Ion concentrations, 1123*t*
Ion gradients, 1124–25, 1124*f*, 1138
Ion pumps, 147–48, 1123
Ionic bonds, 42*f*, **42**–43
Ionic compounds, **42**
Ionotropic receptor, 1132
Ions, **42**, **43**
  movement and gradients, 1042*f*
  as second messengers, 231
Iridium, 567
Irises, 805*f*, **1173**, 1174*f*
Irish mossess, 658
Iron
  as dietary nutrient, 945, 946*t*, 947
  and hemochromatosis, 948
  in plants, 856
Irrigation, 852–53, 852*f*
Island equilibrium model, 1293–94
Isoetes gunnii, 667*f*
Isolated system, 156
Isolation, reproductive. *See* Reproductive isolation
Isoleucine, 172
Isomers, 68*f*, **68**–69
Isomorphic generations, **637**
Isopods, **750**
Isotonic solution, 144*f*, **144**
Isotopes, **35**–36, 1309
Iteroparity, 1260*f*, **1260**–61
Ivanowsky, Dimitri, 416
Iverson, Sarah, 944, 945*f*
Ivory gull, 10–11, 11*f*
Ixodes pacificus, 1224
Ixodes scapularis, 1224, 1340*f*

J
J segments, 1008, 1009*f*
Jackbeans, 912
Jackrabbits, 2*f*, 787*f*, 920*f*, 932
Jacob, François, 381, 383, 574
Jacoby, G. C., 817*f*
Japan, 1317*f*
Japanese canopy plants, 469*t*, 470
Japanese quince, 868*f*
Jaragua lizard, 779
Jasminum grandiflorum, 901
Jasmonates, 892*t*
Jasmonates (JA), **901**
Jaundice, 955
Jawbones, 767, 767*f*
Jawfish, 1210*f*
Jawless vertebrates, 766, 766*f*
Jaws, 556
Jefferson, Thomas, 458
Jejunum, 955
Jellies, 358*f*, 654, 727*f*, 731, 732–33, 732*f*, 967, 967*f*, 1120, 1120*f*, 1140, 1173
Jellyfish genes, in transgenic pig, 358*f*
Jenner, Edward, 1015
Jet-propelled locomotion, 1192
Jews, 298
Joggins Fossil Cliffs, 668*f*, 749
Joints, 1190*f*
Joly, John, 838
Jones, Steven, 471*f*
Jost, Alfred, 1082
Joules (J), 51–52, 937
Jumping genes, 473
Junctions
  in animal cells, 131, 132*f*
  and cell polarity, 1106*f*
  and cellular messaging, 223*f*
  types of, in animal tissues, 132*f*
Juncus gerardi, 1281, 1281*f*
Juniper, 680*f*
Junk DNA, 394, 472
Jurassic period, 684, 784
Juvenile hormones, 1059
Juxtaglomerular apparatus (JGA), **1044**
Juxtamedullary nephrons, **1036***f*, 1039, 1040

K
Kalanchoë, 877
Kangaroo rats, 1029, 1040
Kangaroos, 784, 787*f*, 991, 1075, 1191, 1191*f*, 1212*f*
Kaposi's sarcoma herpesvirus, 1022
Karenia brevis, 637
Kartagener's syndrome, 1117
Karyogamy, **696**–97
Karyotypes, 268*f*, **268**
Kaufman, D. W., 24
Keeling, Patrick, 579
Kelp, 199*f*, 1273, 1273*f*, 1286
Kelp forest communities, 1273, 1288, 1288*f*, 1295, 1295*f*

Keratin, 353, **777**
Kermode bears, 351–52, 351f
Ketoses, 76, 76f
Keystone species, **1286**, 1287f
Kidd, Karen, 1091
Kidneys, 922f, 1031, **1036f**
  adaptations to diverse environments, 1040–41
  antidiuretic hormones in, 1043–44, 1043f, 1044f
  Bowman's capsule in, 1035
  homeostatic regulation of, 1045
  mammalian, 1040–41
  physiology of, 1039–40
  and renin-angiotensin-aldosterone system (RAAS), 1044–45, 1045f
  review, 1046–47
  solute gradients and conservation of, 1038–40
  structure of, 1036f
  two-solute model and urine concentration, 1039–40, 1039f
  in vampire bats, 1040–41
  volume of blood processed, 1037
Killer whales, 759
Kilocalorie (kcal), **52**, 937
Kilojoules (kJ), 937
Kimberella, 562
Kin selection, **1216**–17, 1217f
Kinases. *See* Protein kinases
Kinetic energy, **51**, **155**, 156f
Kinetochore microtubules, 247f, 249f, 250f, 253f
Kinetochores, 247f, 249f, **249**
Kinetoplastids, **632**–33, 633f
King, Mary-Claire, 409
King, Thomas, 449
King of the forest, 692f
Kingdom Animalia, 13f
Kingdom Fungi, 13f
Kingdom Plantae, 13f
Kingdoms, **584**, 598–99
  animalia, 727f
  of life, classifying, 12, 13f, 625
  of plants, 654f
Kingsley, David, 573f
Kissimmee River, Florida, 1316f
Klinefelter syndrome, 323
Knee-jerk reflex, 1143f, 1165
Knocking out, 467, 468, 484
"Knock-out mutants," 820
KNOTTED-1 genes, 823, 823f
Koalas, 787f, 958, 958f, 959
Kobinger, Gary, 427
Komodo dragons, 779, 1071, 1094f
Koop, Ben, 470f
Korarchaeota, 615
Kornberg, Roger, 92
Krill, 751f, 1284
K-selection, **1261**
Kung, Sam, 1000
Kuru, 430

L
La Mauricie National Park, 1316f
Labia majora, **1078**
Labia minora, **1078**
Labour, **1088**, 1089f
Labrador retrievers, 293
lac operons, 383–84, 383f, 384–85, 384f
lac repressors, 383
Laccaria bicolor, 696
Lacks, Henrietta, 258
α-lactalbumin, 478, 480f
Lactation, **1088**
Lacteals, **956**
Lactic acid fermentation, 192f, **192**
Lactose, 78, 383, 383f, 384f
Lady fern, 667f
Ladybird beetles, 499f, 752f
Laetoli footprints, 792f
Lagging strands, 340f, **340**
Lagomorpha, 787f
Lake Erie, 1306f, 1336–37
Lake trout, 1325, 1337
Lakes, 1238, 1239f, 1240f
Lamarck, Jean-Baptiste de, 494–95
Lambs, 1263f
Laminaria, 636–37
Lamp shells, **738**
Lampreys, **764**–65, 765f
Lancelets, **761**–62, 762f, 763f, 1034
Land. *See also* Terrestrial biomes
  colonization of, 562, 652f, 698–99, 707, 747
  decomposition on, 1312
  locomotion on, 1191–92, 1191f
Land plants. *See also* Plants
  and bryophyte gametophytes, 659–660
  and byrophyte sporophytes, 660–61
  derived traits of, 654, 655f–56f
  evolution of, 657f
  evolved from green algae, 653–58
  morphological and molecular evidence, 653
  mosses and other novascular plants, 658–661
  movement to land, 653–54, 698–99
  origin and diversification of, 654
  phyla of, 657t
  review, 669–670
  seedless vascular. *See* Seedless vascular plants
Land snails, 739f, 989
Landscape, **1226f**
Landscape ecology, **1226f**
  biodiversity hot spots in, 1333
  landscape fragmentation and edges in, 1331–32
  movement corridors in, 1332
  philosophy of nature reserves, 1333
  protected areas, establishing, 1332–35
  review, 1345
  zoned reserves, 1333–35

Landscape structure, and biodiversity, 1331–32
Language, 1152, 1152f
Large intestine, **956**
  absorption in, 956–57
  junction with small intestine, 956f
Larson, Doug, 828
Larsson, Hans, 489, 562
Larvae, **714**, 752, 752f
Larynx, **989**
Latency, 1020
Lateral geniculate nuclei, **1177**
Lateral inhibition, **1176**
Lateral line systems, **767**, 1171f, **1171**
Lateral meristems, **810**
Lateral roots, **804**, 813f
Latimeria, 771f
Latitudes, 1227f
Latitudinal gradients, 1292–93
Law of conservation of mass, **1301**
Law of independent assortment, 286–88, **287**, 308f
Law of segregation, 283–86, 285f, **285**, 308f
Laws of inheritance, 282–88, 303
Laws of probability, 288–290
Leaching, 850
Leading strands, 340f, **340**
Leaf abscission, 900, 900f, 901
Leaf area index, 830, 831f
Leaf primordia, 813f, **813**
Leaf-cutter ants, 706–7, 706f
Learning, **1201**
  and animal behaviour, 1201–6
  associative, 1203–4
  cognition, 1203
  cognitive maps, 1203
  development of learned behaviours, 1205
  imprinting, 1202
  and neural plasticity, 1155
  problem solving, 1203–4
  review, 1218
  social, 1205–6, 1205f
  spatial, 1202–3
  and synaptic connections, 1154–56
Leaves, **666**
  blades, **805**
  evolution of, 666
  evolutionary adaptations of, 806f
  orientation of, 831
  rapid leaf movements, 908
  simple vs. compound, 805f
  size and structure, 830
  tissue organization of, 814
  tissues of, 815f
Leber's congenital amaurosis (LCA), 1178
Leber's Hereditary Optic Neuropathy (LHON), 186f, 326
Leeches, 743–44, 743f, 1140f
Leefructus, 684
Leghemoglobin, 859

Legislation
  Charter of Rights and Freedoms, 301
  Human Reproductive and Genetic Technologies Act, 301
  Ocean's Act, 1334*f*
  Personal Information Protection and Electronic Documents Act, 301
  Species at Risk Act (SARA), 520
Legs, 1191
Legumes, 859, 859*f*, 860
Lemaitre, Bruno, 1001, 1002*f*
Lemmings, 1264*f*, 1284, 1285*f*, 1287
Lemurs, 524, 787*f*, 788, 788*f*
Lens cells, 391*f*, 399
Lenses, **1174***f*
Lenski, Richard, 609*f*
Lenticels, **818**
Lepidoptera, 753*f*
Lepidosaurs, **778**, 779–780
Leptin, **962**
Leptospira, 617*f*
Lepus americanus, 1263–65
Lepus townsendii, 920–21
Lettuce, 903*f*
Leukemia, 323, 324*f*, 410, 1018, 1323
Leukocytes, 925*f*, **981**, 983
Levy, Eugene and Dan, 266
Lewis, Edward B., 400
Lewis dot structure, 40
Leydig cells, **1078**, 1085, 1085*f*
Lichens, 658, 707*f*, **707**, 1290, 1314
Life
  and adaptive radiations, 569
  cells as fundamental units of, 104
  chemical elements of, 70
  chemical groups most important to, 69–70
  colonization of land, 562
  diversity of, classifying, 11–16, 12*f*
  domains of, 12
  energy of, 154
  fossil record of, 550–51, 554–56, 555*f*
  multicellularity, origin of, 560–62
  operating instructions, 329
  origin of on early Earth, 551–54
  on other planets, 56
  and the oxygen revolution, 559–560
  properties and processes of, 2
  rise and fall of organisms, 563–570
  single-celled organisms, early, 559–560
  themes of, 3–11, 26–27
  three observations on, 492–93
  variety of sexual life cycles, 270–71
  as work, 175
Life cycles, **268**
  of angiosperms, 682–84, 683*f*, 869–870
  of blood flukes, 736*f*
  of *drosophila melanogaster* (fruit fly), 400, 401*f*
  of fungi, 697*f*, 701*f*
  human, 269–270, 269*f*
  of hydrozoan *Obelia*, 733*f*

  of lichens, 707*f*
  of mosses (phylum Bryophyta), 659*f*
  of nonvascular plants, 658–661
  of pine trees, 676–77, 677*f*
Life expectancy at birth, 1268, 1343*f*
Life history, **1260**–62, 1271
Life tables, 1253–54, 1253*t*
Ligaments, 925*f*
Ligand-gated ion channel, **228***f*, 1125, **1132**
Ligands, **151**, **225**
Ligase, 342*t*
Light
  and colour vision, 1177–78
  red and far-red, 902, 903, 905, 906*f*
  visible light, 203*f*, **203**
Light, plant responses to
  action spectrum, 901, 902*f*
  biological clocks and circadian rhythms, 903–5
  blue-light photoreceptors, **901**–2
  photoperiodism and responses to seasons, 905–7
  phytochromes as photoreceptors, 902–3
  review, 915
Light capture, and shoot architecture, 830–31
Light chains, **1006**, 1008
Light microscope (LM), 105, 106*f*
Light reactions, 202*f*, **202**
  and the Calvin cycle, 202*f*
  and chemiosmosis, 210–12, 210*f*, 211*f*
  and chlorophyll, excitation of, 206, 206*f*
  and chloroplasts, 204*f*
  cyclic electron flow, 209*f*, **209**–10
  light receptors, 204–6
  linear electron flow, 208*f*, **208**–9, 209*f*
  photosystems, 206–8
  review, 218*f*, 219
  sunlight, nature of, 203–4
Light receptors, 204–6, 901–2
Light-detecting organs, 1173
Light-harvesting complex, **207**
Light-induced de-etiolation, 889, 889*f*
Lignin, **665**
Likelihood, 589–590
Lilacs, 815*f*
Lilly, John, 1148
Lima beans, 801*f*
Limb buds, 1115–16, 1115*f*
Limbic systems, 1150
Limbs
  development of, in vertebrates, 1114–16, 1115*f*, 1116*f*
  with digits, 773*f*
  in tetrapods, 771
Limenitis arthemis, 1048
Limiting nutrients, **1304**–6
Limpets, 574, 574*f*
Limulus polyphemus, 1330
Line graphs, 276
LINE-1, 474
Lineage-based mechanisms, 823
Linear electron flow, 208*f*, **208**–9, 209*f*

Lingula, 738
Linkage groups, 319
Linkage maps, 317–321, 319*f*, **319**
Linked genes, **314**
  and chi-square tests, 318
  and genetic recombination, 316–17, 317*f*
  and inheritance, 314–15, 315*f*
  mapping, 317–321
Linnaean system of taxonomy, 12*f*, 584, 584*f*
Linnaeus, Carolus, 494, 584
Lions, 958, 1209
Lipid bilayer, 139, 142
Lipid signalling factors, 1051
Lipids, **80**
  and carbohydrates, bonded to, 605
  fats, 80–82
  membrane lipids, 101, 137, 137*f*, 139
  phospholipids, 82–83
  review, 99
  steroids, 83
Lipid-soluble hormones, 1050, 1051*f*, 1052–53, 1052*f*, 1054
Lipopolysaccharides, 605, 1002
Lipoproteins, 983, 984*f*
Lishman, Bill, 1202
Lithops sp., 868*f*
Liver, **955**, 984, 1032
  bile production in, 955
  cell type–specific transcription, 391*f*, 399
  damage to, 947
  and epinephrine, 1054
  and glucose homeostasis, 961
  role of, 956
  as target for glucagon and insulin, 1057
Liverworts (phylum Hepatophyta), 656*f*, **658**, 661, 662*f*, 699
Living fossils, 669, 748
Lizards, 779, 931, 932*f*, 936, 1071, 1073, 1073*f*, 1212, 1212*f*, 1275, 1275*f*
Loams, **850**
Lobe-fins, **770**–71, 771*f*
Lobopods, 746
Lobotomy, 1153, 1155*f*
Lobsters, 750, 935*f*, 986, 1027, 1130
Local regulators, **223**, **1049**
Loci, **267**
"Lock-and-key" recognition, 1097
Locomotion, 1042*f*, 1073, **1191**
  and breathing, 991
  energy costs of, 1192
  of flagellum, 1042*f*
  flying, 1192–93
  jet-propelled, 1192
  on land, 1191–92, 1191*f*
  swimming, 1192
  types of, 1191–93
Locusts, 1272*f*
Lodgepole pine, 1, 2*f*, 708, 1233, 1290, 1290*f*
Logistic population growth model, **1257**–59, 1258*f*, 1259*f*, 1271
Lokiarchaeota, 615

Long Island, 1305f
Long Island Sound, 1283
Long-day plants, **905**, 906f
Long-distance transport, 835
Long-nosed bandicoots, 784f
Long-term memory, **1155**
Long-term potentiation (LTP), 1156f, **1156**
Loop of Henle, **1036**–37, **1037**f, 1039, 1039f, 1040
Looped domains, 347f
Loose connective tissue, 925f
Lophophorates, 738, 738f
Lophophore, 723f, **723**, 725f, 734, 738, 738f
Lophotrochozoans (Lophotrochozoa), 722, 723f, **723**, 727f
    annelids, 742–45
    flatworms, 734–37
    lophophorates, 738
    molluscs, 738–742
    overview, 734
    rotifers, 737
Lorenz, Konrad, 1197, 1202
Loricifera, 728f
Lorises, 788, 788f
"Lost City," 552f
Lou Gehrig's disease, 1184
Low-density lipoprotein (LDL), **983**, 985
"Lucy," 791
Luminal subtypes of cancer, 408f
Luna moths, 1050f
Lungfishes, 504, 771, 989
Lungs, 922f, **988**–990
    avian, 990
    book, 748
    breathing and ventilation, 990–92
    structure of, 991
Lupines, 1315
Lupus, 1019
Luteal phase, **1084**
Luteinizing hormone (LH), 1054f, 1082
Lycophytes (lycophyta), **658**, 666, 667f
Lycopods, 658
Lyctic cycle, **419**
Lyell, Charles, 494, 496, 497, 777
Lyme disease, 620, 620f, 1224–25, 1296, 1296f, 1340f
Lymnea stagnalis, 1132f
Lymph, **979**, 1003
Lymph nodes, 979f, **979**, 1003
Lymphatic systems, 923t, **979**–980, 1003, 1004f
Lymphocytes, **1005**–6
Lymphoid stem cells, 982f
Lynx, 1263–65, 1265f, 1274
Lynx canadensis, 1264–65
Lyon, Mary, 313
Lysogenic cycle, **419**–420, 420f
Lysogeny, 420
Lysosomal membranes, 118
Lysosomes, 112f, 118–19, 118f, 1002–3
Lysozyme, 55f, 87f, 478, 480f, **1001**, 1002
Lytic cycle, 419f, 420f

M

M lines, 1182
M phase. *See* Mitotic (M) phase
Macaca fuscata, 942f
Macaques, 942f
MacArthur, Robert, 1293, 1294f
MacIsaac, Hugh, 1325f
Mackie, Gerry, 1120
MacLeod, Colin, 330
Macleod, J.J.R., 1057f
Macroclimate, **1225**
Macroevolution, 530, **551**
    and adaptive radiations, 568–570
    conditions on early Earth that made origin of life possible, 551–54
    and development as major changes in body form, 570–74
    as field of research, 489
    fossil record as history of life, 550–51
    key events in, 556–563, 559f
    new groups of organisms, origin of, 556
    novelties in, 574
    review, 576–77
    rise and fall of organisms, 563–570
    and speciation, 547
    trends in, 575
Macromolecules, **74**
    abiotic synthesis of, 551, 552
    carbohydrates as, 76–80
    as polymers, built from monomers, 75–76
Macronutrients, 855f, **855**
Macrophages, 118f, 119, **925**f, 984f, 999, **1003**
Macropus giganteus, 1212f
Madagascar orchids, 873f
MADS-box genes, 571, 823
Maggots, 752
Magnesium, 42–43, 945, 946t
Magnetite, 1166, 1198
Magnification, 105
Magnolias, 687f
Magnoliids, **686**, 687f
Maiden veil fungus, 704f
Maize (corn), 688, 896. *See also* Corn
    action spectrum for, 902f
    and *Bt* toxin, 883f, 885
    germination in, 875f
    and KNOTTED-1, 836
    and mutants, 821f, 898f
    phenotypic characters in, 511
    as product of artificial selection, 882, 882f
    response to flooding, 909f
    and response to herbivores, 912
    root organization in, 812f
    structure of, 874f
    tangled-1 mutant of, 821
    transgenic, 885
    transpiration in, 836
    transposable elements and, 473
Major depressive disorder, **1158**
Mak, Tak Wah, 1007

Malaria, 526f, 638, 638f, 639, 754, 1001
Male contraceptives, 1091
Males
    hormonal control of reproductive system, 1085, 1085f
    with Kartagener's syndrome, 1117
    and life tables, 1253
    and mate selection, 1211–12
    reproductive anatomy, 1078–79, 1078f
    sex determination in, 270
Malignant tumours, 258f, **258**
Malnutrition, 883–84, 947, 1061
Malpighian tubules, 1034–35, 1034f
Malt sugar, 77
Malthus, Thomas, 499
Maltose, 77, 77f
Malva moschata, 868f
Mammals, **783**
    and adaptive radiations, 569, 569f
    Arctic, 1072f
    axis formation in, 1112–13
    body temperature of, 931
    breathing in, 990–92
    cardiovascular system, 972f
    chromosomes in, 313
    circulation in, 970f, 971, 972–74
    derived characters of, 783
    digestive system, 951–57
    diversity of, 786f–87f
    diving, 995–96
    ear bones, evolution of, 783f
    early evolution of, 783–84
    eutherians, 785–790
    excretory system, 1036f
    eyes of, 1178f
    fertilization in, 1098–99, 1099f
    forebrain in, 1145
    forelimbs in, 503f
    hearing in, 1167–70
    heart in, 972–73, 973f
    humans. *See* Humans
    innate immunity of, 1002–5
    kidneys, adaptations of, 1040–41
    marine mammals, 54f
    marsupials, 784–85
    molecular clock for, 596f
    monotremes, 784
    and nitrogenous wastes, 1032
    organ systems in, 923t
    origin of, 557f
    and osmoregulation, 1029
    phylogeny of, 786f–87f
    primates, 785–790
    reproduction regulation by tropic and sex hormones, 1082–86
    reproductive cloning of, 450
    respiratory systems, 989–990, 989f
    review, 797–98
    skeleton of, 1190
    taste in, 1179–80, 1180f
    thermorerceptors in, 1166

Mammary glands, 1055, 1056, 1059, 1060, **1078**

Mammoths, 995

Mammuthus primigenius, 995, 1326

Manatees, 759, 787*f*, 1279*f*

Mandibles, **749**

Manduca sexta, 801*f*, 873*f*, 935*f*

Mangold, Hilde, 1114, 1115*f*

Mangrove rivulus, 917, 918*f*

Mangroves, 804*f*, 898*f*

Manic-depressive disorder, 1158

Manihot esculenta, 884*f*

Mantle, **738**

Mantle cavity, **738**

Map units, 319

Maple trees, 295, 806, 878*f*, 900*f*, 1230*f*, 1231*f*, 1285

maraviroc, 140

Marchantia, 656*f*, 662*f*

Marella, 716*f*

Marine animals, osmoregulation in, 1026, 1027, 1027*f*

Marine benthic zone, **1243***f*

Marine biodiversity hot spots, 1333*f*

Marine biomes, 1238

Marine birds, 1030, 1030*f*

Marine bony fishes, 1041

Marine ecosystems, 1334

Marine iguanas, 493*f*, 1030, 1047*f*

Marine life
  and ocean acidification, 60
  and specific heat of water, 52

Marine mammals, 54*f*, 932

Marine Protected Areas (MPA), 1334, 1334*f*

Marine worms, 987*f*

Mark-recapture method, 1251, **1251**

Marra, Marco, 470*f*

Mars, 56, 56*f*

Marsh gas, 615

Marshall, Barry, 954

Marsupials (Marsupialia), 505, 565, 586, 784*f*, **784**–85, 787*f*, 1038, 1075

Marsupium, 784

Maryland Mammoth tobacco, 905

Mass, **33**

Mass extinction, **566**
  adaptive radiations after, 568–570
  "big five," 566–67, 566*f*
  consequences of, 568
  and diversity of life, 566*f*
  and ecological factors, 569*f*
  end-Permian mass extinction, 567*f*
  sixth, possible, 567–68

Mass number, **35**

Mast cells, **1004**, 1018*f*

Master regulatory genes, 399

Masting, 801*f*

Mate choice, 524, 1210–12

Mate recognition, 532*f*

Mate-choice copying, **1210**, 1211*f*

Maternal chromosomes, 277

Maternal effect gene, **402**

Maternal immune tolerance of embryo and fetus, 1089

Mating. *See also* Animal reproduction; Mate choice; Reproduction
  of banana slugs, 1070, 1070*f*, 1073
  of cells, 222, 222*t*, 1082
  of fungi, 695–97
  reproductive barriers to, 532*f*–33*f*
  research of, pea plants, 282*f*

Mating behaviour
  and game theory, 1212
  and genetics, 1213
  mating systems and parental care, 1209
  mating systems and sexual dimorphism, 1207–8
  sexual selection and mate choice, 1210–12

Mating bridge, 610

Mating cells, 222, 222*f*

Mating systems, 1207–8, 1209*f*

Matter, **33**
  review, 46
  transfer and transformation of, as theme in biology, 8, 27

Maungatautari, 1317*f*

Mawsonites spriggi, 715*f*

Maximum likelihood, 589–**590**

Maximum parsimony, 589–**590**

Mayer, Adolf, 415

Mayflies, 1252

Mazes, 1203, 1205*f*

McCarty, Maclyn, 330

McClintock, Barbara, 473, 481

McConnell, Richard, 717*f*

McCulloch, Ernest, 451, 451*f*

McLeese, D.W., 935*f*

McLellan, Bruce, 943

Meadow voles, 1213

Meadowlarks, 531*f*

Measles, 418, 1016–17

Meat, 1309

Mechanical defences, 1277–78, 1278*f*

Mechanical digestion, 948

Mechanical isolation, 532*f*

Mechanical stimuli, 908

Mechanical stress, 898–99

Mechanical work, 161, 163, 163*f*

Mechanoreceptors, **1165**, 1167–72, 1169, 1193

Mediator proteins, 389

Medical science, 97*f*

Medicine, and systems biology, 468–69

Medicines
  from fungal sources, 709–10
  leeches, use of, 743–44
  from plants, 689, 689*t*

Mediterranean climate, 1228

Mediterranean house gecko, 599*f*

Medulla, 992, 1148

Medulla oblongata, **1147***f*

Medusa, 731*f*, **731**

Medusozoans, 732–33

Megapascal, **833**

Megaphyll leaves, 666*f*, **666**

Megaspores, **666**, 673, **870**

Megasporocytes, 870

Meiosis, 244, 246, **270**, 1080*f*–81*f*
  errors leading to duplication of chromosomal regions, 477, 514
  in fungi reproduction, 697
  and independent assortment, 277*f*
  vs. mitosis, 274–76, 275*f*
  and number of chromosome sets, 271–77, 271*f*
  prophase I, 274–76
  review, 279
  in sexual life cycles, 270–71, 270*f*
  stages of, 271
  summary, 275*f*
  in yeast, 276

Meiosis I, **271**, 272*f*, 275*f*, 276

Meiosis II, **271**, 273*f*, 275*f*, 276

Meiotic nondisjunction, 321*f*

Melanerpes formicivorus, 1220*f*

Melanocortin 1 receptor gene (MC1R), 351–52

Melanocyte-stimulating hormone (MSH), **1059**, 1069*f*

Melatonin, 930, 930*f*, 1054*f*, **1067**, 1147*f*, 1148

Membrane attack complex, 1014

Membrane carbohydrates, 141

Membrane lipids, 101, 137, 139

Membrane potential, **147**, 833*f*, **1123**
  and ion gradients, 1124–25, 1124*f*
  and ion pumps, 147–48
  resting, determination of, 1124–25
  resting, formation of, 1123–24

Membrane proteins, 137, 138*f*, 139–141, 140*f*

Membranes
  active transport, 146–49, 148*f*, 152
  bulk transport across plasma membrane, 149–151, 152
  cotransport, 148–49, 149*f*
  in eukaryotic cells, 108–11
  fluidity of, 137–39, 139*f*
  of the mitochondria, 121–22
  as mosaic of lipids and proteins, 137–141, 151
  movement across, 103*f*
  in nuclear envelope, 111
  overview, 136–37
  passive transport, 143–46, 148*f*, 151–52
  plasma. *See* Plasma membranes
  of prokaryotic cells, 607*f*
  review, 151–52
  and selective permeability, 136, 142, 151
  sidedness of, 141
  structure of, 142
  synthesis of, 141*f*

Memory, 1154–56

Memory cells, **1009**

Mendel, Gregor, 279, 281–82, 281*f*, 303, 316, 511

Mendelian genetics
  and chromosomes, 308*f*
  exceptions to, 324–26, 327
  experimental, quantitative approach, 282–83
  and genetic counselling, 300
  heredity and variation, 295–96

and human traits, 296–303
law of independent assortment, 286–88, 308f
law of segregation, 283–86, 308f
and probability laws, 288–290
review, 303–4
for single gene, 290–93
for two or more genes, 293–94
Mendel's gene idea, 281–305
Menopause, **1084**–85
Menstrual cycles, **1083**, 1084, 1085
Menstrual flow phase, 1084
Menstruation, **1083**
Mercury, 1338
Meristem identity genes, **824**
Meristems, **810**–11
Meroblastic, **1101**
Meselson, Matthew, 337, 337f
Mesenchyme cells, 1102–3
Mesocricetus auratus, 1149
Mesoderm, 720f, **720**, **1102**, 1103f
Mesohyl, **731**
Mesophyll, **200**
Mesophyll cells, 214–15, 215f, **814**
Mesozoic era, 558f, 559, 717
Messenger RNA (mRNA), **353**
  bicoid, 402–3
  codon table for, 357f
  degradation of, 393–94
  detection techniques, 443–44
  effects of microRNAs and small interfering
    RNAs, 394–95
  ends, alternation of, 361
  and small-scale mutations, 376f
  transcription of, 93, 93f, 355, 356, 358–59
Metabolic cooperation, 613
Metabolic defects, 352–53
Metabolic pathways, **155**, 381, 381f
Metabolic rate, **937**–39, 938f
Metabolism, **155**, 161f
  and ATP, 161–64
  and enzymes, 164–170
  and equilibrium, 160–61
  and free energy, 158–161
  metabolic pathways, 155
  nitrogen, role of, 612–13
  and organelles, 172f
  oxygen, role of, 612
  review, 173
  transformation of matter and energy, 155–58
Metabolomics, **96**
Metabotropic receptors, 1133
Metagenomics, **465**, 614, **620**
Metamorphosis, **714**, 1048
  complete/incomplete, 752, 752f, 753f
  of frogs, 774f, 1059f
  of insects, 752f, 1058f, 1059
Metanephridia, 1034, 1034f
Metaphase, **246**, 248f, 249f, 252f
Metaphase chromosomes, 347f
Metaphase I, 272f, 275f
Metaphase II, 273f

Metaphase plate, 248f, 249f, **249**, 272f
Metapopulations, 1265–**66**, 1266, 1266f
Metastasis, **259**
Metazoa clade, 722
Methamphetamine, 69f
Methane, 66f, 1340f
  archaea consumption of, 613
  combustion of, 177f, **177**
  covalent bonding, 41, 41f, 44
  from tailings, 603–4, 613
Methanogens, **615**
Methanosarcina barkeri, 469t
Methanotophic prokaryotes, 613
Methicillin, 502
Methicillin-resistant Staphylococcus aureus
    (MRSA), 502–3, 502f
Methyl group, 70, 71f
Methyl jasmonate (MeJA), 901
Methylation, 386
Methyljasmonic acid, 912
Methylmercury, 1338
Methylsalicylic acid, 913
MHC (major histocompatibility complex)
    molecule, **1007**, 1008f, 1012, 1017–18
Mice
  and apoptosis, 240f
  Australian hopping mice, 1038, 1040
  and bioenergetics, 939
  characteristics of, 787f
  cloning, 442, 450
  coat colouration, 21–23, 21f, 22f
  conservation of homeotic genes, 485–86, 485f
  correcting a genetic defect with CRISPR-Cas9
    technology, 456
  and cross-fostering studies, 1201, 1201t
  disabling of genes, 446
  and Duchenne muscular dystrophy, 453
  and embryonic development, 1105–6, 1106f
  and experiments with genetic mutants, 963
  FOXP2 gene in, 484
  gene for insulin-like growth factor2, 324, 325f
  genome sequence, 463
  globin gene regulation, 389
  and Hantavirus Pulmonary Syndrome,
    1295–96
  hindlimb muscles in, 101
  limb development in, 1116
  and metabolic rate, 938
  as model organism, 25
  mutations of nervous system, 1117
  neurons in brain, 1139f
  oogonia in, 1081f
  and predation by owls, 24
  stem cells in, 1142, 1142f
  taste in, 1180f
  white-footed, 1265f
  whole-genome sequence, 476
Michael Smith Genome Sciences Centre, 434f,
    471f
Microarray chips, 468, 469f
Microbiome, 958, 959f

Microbiome, human, 619, 620f
Microclimate, **1225**, 1229–30
Micrococcus luteus, 1001, 1002f
Microevolution, **511**, **530**
  and gene flow, 521–22
  and genetic variation, 511–14
  and the Hardy-Weinberg equation, 514–18
  natural selection, genetic drift, and gene flow
    in alteration of allele frequencies in a
    population, 518–522
  review, 527–28
Microfilaments (actin filaments), 112f, 113f,
    127–28, 128f, 1181
Microglia, 1141f
Micronutrients, 855f, **855**–56
Microorganisms, soil, 621, 622
Microphyll leaves, 666f, **666**
Micropyles, **682**, 870
MicroRNAs (miRNAs), **394**–95, 395f
Microscopy, 105–7
Microspores, **666**, 673, **869**
Microsporocytes, 869
Microtubules, 112f, 113f, **125**, 247f, 249, 249f,
    253f, 272f
Microtus ochrogaster, 1213, 1213f
Microtus pennsylvanicus, 1213
Microvilli, 109, 112f, **955**
Midbrain, **1145**
Middle ear, **1168**f
Middle lamella, **130**
Mifepristone (RU486), 1091
Migration, 1197–**98**, 1198f, 1214
Miguasha National Park, 652, 771
Milgaard, David, 25f
Milk, 945
Milkweed, 682f, 885, 1203
Miller, Stanley, 64, 65, 551, 552f
Millipedes, 749, 749f
Milner, Brenda, 1155, 1155f
Mimic octopus, 1278, 1279f
Mimicry, 1278
Mimivirus, 425
Mimosa pudica, 846, 908, 909f
Mimulus, 880
Mineralocorticoids, 1051, 1054f, **1064**,
    1065f
Minerals, **945**
  absorption of by root epidermal cells, 836
  as essential nutrient, 945–47
  human requirements, 946t
  in plants, 856, 857
  root architecture and acquisition of, 831
  transport into the xylem, 836, 837f
Minimal medium, 352
Minimum viable population (MVP), **1328**
Minnows, 1171, 1200f, 1338
Miramichi River, 917
miRNAs, **394**–95, 395f, 718
Miscarriage, 1091
Mismatch repair, **342**
Missense Mutation, **374**

Mississippi watershed, 1336, 1337f
Mistletoe, 863f
Mitchell, P., 188
Mitochondria, 101, 112f, 113f, **120**
    and apoptotic pathways, 240
    chemical energy conversion, 121–22
    chemiosmosis in, 210–12, 210f
    disorders of, 326
    evolutionary origins of, 120–22, 121f
    mutations in, 122, 186f
    origin of, 560
    review, 134
    as site of cellular respiration, 121f
Mitochondrial matrix, **122**
Mitochondrial myopathy, 326
Mitosis, **245**
    in animal cells, 247f–48f
    drawing of, 307f
    evolution of, 252–53
    vs. meiosis, 274–76, 275f
    in plant cells, 252f
    in sexual life cycles, 270f
    stages of, 246, 252f
    summary, 275f
Mitosomes, 632
Mitotic (M) phase, **246**–253, 254, 261, 1099, 1101
Mitotic spindles, 247f, 249f, **249**
Mixotrophs, **626**
Mobile genetic elements, 425
Mockingbirds, 496
Model organisms, **24**–25, 820–21, **1096**
Modern reproductive technologies, 1091–92
Mojave Desert, 1228
Molaison, Henry, 1155f
Molar mass, 55
Molarity, **56**
Mole (mol), **55**–56
Molecular basis of inheritance. *See also* DNA
        (deoxyribonucleic acid)
    chromatin packing in a eukaryotic
        chromosome, 345–48
    discover of double helix structure of DNA,
        333–35
    DNA as genetic material, 330–35
    DNA as life's operating system, 329
    DNA replication and repair, 335–345
    evidence for DNA as genetic materials,
        330–33
    review, 349
Molecular biology, 820–21
Molecular characteristics, **583**
Molecular clocks, 596f, **596**–97, 601, 698
Molecular diversity, 67–69
Molecular genealogy, 96
Molecular homologies, 503–4, 504, 586, 587–88
Molecular homoplasy, 588f
Molecular markers, 594f
Molecular mass, **55**–56
Molecular recognition, 1000
Molecular systematics, **588**, 591f, 595
Molecules, **40**

and cell cycle control system, 254–58, 254f,
        255f
formation and function of, 40–44
interactions within organisms, 9–10
large biological molecules. *See* Biological
        molecules
as level of biological organization, 5f
MHC (major histocompatibility complex)
        molecule, 1007, 1008f
mimicking, 45f
nitrogenous, 1026
organic molecules. *See* Organic molecules
review, 47
as second messengers, 231
secreted, 1050f
shape and function, 44, 44f
signalling, 1117
Moles, 586f, 787f, 1162, 1162f, 1163, 1163f
Moll, 739f
Molluscs (Mollusca), 728f, 1166
    bivalves, 740–41, 740f
    body plan, 738, 739f
    cephalopods, 741–42, 741f
    chitons, 738–39, 739f
    exoskeleton of, 1189
    eyes, 574, 575f
    eyes of, 1173
    gastropods, 739
    nervous system in, 1140f, 1141
    and osmoregulation, 1029
    protecting freshwater and terrestrial, 742
    protonephridia in, 1034
    and selection for defensive adaptations, 740
Moloch horridus, 779f
Molothrus ater, 1332
Molybdenum, 856
Monarch butterflies, 885, 919f, 1172f, 1203–4,
        1203f
Monera, kingdom, 598, 599
Monilophyta, 666, 667f, 669
Monilophytes, **658**, 666, 667f
Monkey flowers, 546, 547f, 880
Monkeys, 98, 787f, 1205–6, 1206f
    macaques, 942f
    new and old world, 788–89, 788f, 789f
    squirrel monkeys, 1178
Monocilia, 1117
Monoclonal antibodies, **1017**
Monocots, 686f, **686**, 687f, 812f, 814f, 874, 895
Monod, Jacques, 381, 383
Monogamy, 1076, **1208**
Monogo, 1209f
Monohybrid cross, **286**
Monohybrids, **286**
Monomers, **75**
Monophyletic groups, 588f, **588**
Monosaccharides, 76f, **76**–77
Monosodium glutamate (MSG), 1179
Monosomic, **321**
Monotremata, 787f
Monotremes, 784f, **784**, 1106

Monotropa uniflora, 863f
Monozygotic twins, 1088, 1113
Montmorillonite, 553
Montreal Protocol, 1342
Moose, 73f, 1263, 1264f, 1279
Moray eels, 770f
Morchella esculenta, 702f
Morels, 709
Morgan, Thomas Hunt, 309–10, 314–15, 315f,
        326, 330
"Morning after" pills, 1090
Morning sickness, 1088
Morphine, 45f
Morphogen gradient hypothesis, 402
Morphogenesis, **397**, **819**–825, 822–23,
        1102
    cell migration in, 1109
    cell shape, changes in, 1108–9, 1109f
    cellular mechanisms in, 1108–10
    and extraembryonic membranes, 1106
    gastrulation in, 1102–6
    organogenesis in, 1106–8
    review, 1118
Morphogens, **402**
Morphological characteristics, **582**
Morphological homologies, 586
Morphological species concept, **534**
Mosaic, of cells, 313
Mosquitoes, 521, 949f, 1167, 1296
Mosquitofish, 535–36, 536f
Mosses (phylum Bryophyta), **658**–661, 662f
    ecological and economic importance of, 661
    and ecological succession, 1290, 1291
    fertilization in, 661f
    gametophyte-sporophyte relationships in plant
        groups, 674f
    life cycle of, 659f
    review, 670
    spores as survival mechanism, 675
"Mother cells," 821
Moths, 513f, 522, 872f, 935f, 1050f, 1165, 1166f,
        1200, 1278
Motility, 128f, 606–7
Motor cortex, 1151–52, 1152f
Motor neurons, 1122f, **1122**, 1184, 1185f, 1186
Motor output, 1163f
Motor proteins, 124f, **125**
Motor system, **1143**
Motor units, 1186f, **1186**
Moulds, 352, 353f, **697**, 699, 701f, 702, 703f, 709,
        883f
Moulting, **745**, 1059
Mountain hemlock, 1291
Mountain lions, 1207
Mountain pine beetles, 492f, 708, 1233
    as characterizing disturbance, 1290, 1290f
    and climate change, 11, 1340f
    and lodgepole pines, 1
    and sugar transport, 845f
    system genomics, 471f
    and systemic acquired resistance, 913–14

Mountains, and climate, 1228, 1229*f*

Mouritsen, Henrik, 1172*f*

Movement corridors, 1332*f*, **1332**

MPF, 255*f*, **255**

mPGES-1, 390

mRNA. *See* Messenger RNA (mRNA)

MRSA, 502–3, 502*f*

Mucor, 700*f*

Mucosa, 1002

Mucus, **951**, 990, **1002**

Mucus escalator, 990

Mudpuppies, 966–67, 966*f*

Mueller, Ken, 1180*f*

Mukhametov, Lev, 1148

Mule deer, 916*f*, 1207

Mules, 533*f*

Muller, Hermann, 375

Müllerian mimicry, 1278*f*, **1278**

Multicellular, dependent embryos, 655*f*

Multicellular alga, 199*f*

Multicellular gametangia, 656*f*

Multicellularity, origin of, 560–62

Multifactorial, 295

Multifactorial disorders, 300

Multigene families, 474–**75**

Multiple fruits, 876*f*, **877**

Multiple sclerosis, 1019

Multiplication rule, **289**

Murchison meteorite, 552

Mus musculus, 463, 469*t*

Muscle contraction

    and calcium and regulatory proteins, 1184–85, 1184*f*

    energy production for, 1182–84

    and nervous control of muscle tension, 1186–87

    regulation of, 1185*f*

    sliding-filament model of, 1182, 1183*f*

Muscle tissue, 923, **926*f***

Muscles

    cell function of, 1181

    contraction of, 1183*f*, 1185*f*

    of invertebrates, 1188

    review, 1194

    skeletal. *See* Skeletal muscle

    types of, 1187–88

Muscular systems, 923*t*

Mushrooms, 693, 694*f*, 704, 705*f*, 709. *See also* Fungi

    and clumping, 1252

    energy production in, 1182–84

    in kingdom fungi, 13*f*

Musk mallow, 868*f*

Muskox, 175*f*

Muskrats, 1029, 1040

Mussels, 986, 1287*f*, 1325, 1325*f*

Mustard plant, 25, 469*t*, 820–21

Mustela macradon, 1322

Mutagens, **375**

Mutant phenotypes, 309, 309*f*, 319*f*

Mutation, **372**, 985

affecting protein structure and function, 372–76

and alleles, 278

aquaporin mutations and diabetes, 1044*f*

Arabidopsis mutants, 891

and arginine, 353*f*

BRCA, 409–10

cancer-causing, 375, 404, 405–7, 468

causes of, 375

and cell-inhibiting pathways, 406*f*

and cell-stimulating pathways, 405*f*

constitutive triple-response (*ctr*) mutants, 899

and cystic fibrosis, 264–65

and disease treatment, mutation-specific, 375*f*

disease-causing, 454

and DNA replication, 343

in *Drosophila melanogaster*, 1002*f*

ein mutants, 899

embryonic lethals, 401

in enzymes, 170

in *Escherichia coli*, 608–9

eto mutants, 899

experiments with, 963

frameshift, 374–75

in fruit flies, 401–2

and genetic variation, 514

and heritability, 513

insertions and deletions, 374–75, 376*f*

and Kermode bears, 351

"knock-out mutants," 820

maize, 898*f*

mangroves, 898*f*

melanocortin 1 receptor gene (MC1R), 351–52

missense, 374

in mitochondrial genes, 122, 186*f*

and monocilia, 1117

and Morgan's inheritance research, 309, 310*f*

nonsense, 374

nutritional mutants in neurospora, 352–53

organ identity mutations in flowers, 825*f*

point, 372, 374*f*

in prokaryotes, 608–9

review, 378

silent, 374

small-scale, 374–75, 376*f*

substitutions, 374, 376*f*

tangled-1mutants, 821

and viruses, 428

Mutualisms, **619**, **1280**

    between acacia trees and ants, 1280*f*

    bacteria-plant, 857–861

    evolutionary adaptations, 958–960

    flower-pollinator, 871, 873*f*

    fungus-algal, 707

    fungus-animal, 706–7

    fungus-plant, 706, 861–62, 862*f*

    in herbivores, 958–960

    as interspecific interactions, 1274

    between plant roots and fungi, 1307

    between plant roots and nitrogen-fixing bacteria, 1307

    plants and epiphytes, parasites, and carnivores, 862–64

    as symbiosis, 1280

Mutualistic bacteria, **619–620**

Mutualists, **704**, 706–7

Myasthenia gravis, 1184

Myblasts, 399

Mycelia, **694**

Mycobacterium tuberculosis, 620

Mycoplasmas, 617*f*

Mycorrhizae, 654, **694**–95, 702*f*, **831**, 861–62, 861*f*

Mycosis, **708**–9

Myelin sheath, **1129**, 1130*f*

Myeloid stem cells, 982*f*

Myglobin, **995**

Myllokunmingia, 765, 765*f*

Myocardial infarction, 983

myoD, 388*f*, 399–400

Myofibrils, **1182**

Myoglobin, **1187**

Myosin, **127**, 128*f*, 1182, 1183*f*

Myotonia, **1085**

Myriapods, **748**, 749, 749*f*

"Mystery of mysteries," 530–31

Mytilus californianus, 1287*f*

Myxobacteria, 222*f*

N

NAD$^+$ (nicotinamide adenine dinucleotide), 178*f*, **178**, 179

NADH, 178, 179

NADP$^+$ (nicotinamide adenine dinucleotide), **202**

NADPH, 202–3

Naked mole rats, 1199, 1215, 1215*f*, 1217

Nanoarchaeota, 615

Nanopores, 437

Nanulak bears, 534, 534*f*

Naphthenic acids (NAs), 1314

Nasal cavity, 989

Nasal salt glands, 1030, 1030*f*

Nash, John, 1212

National Cancer Institute, 468

National Center for Biotechnology Information (NCBI), 465, 466*f*, 484

National Institutes of Health (NIH), 465, 468

National Library of Medicine, 465

Natural family planning, **1089**

Natural killer cells, **1003**

Natural range expansion, **1244**

Natural selection, **15**, **496**

    and adaptive evolution, 518, 522–27, 572

    alleles, new combinations of, 316–17

    and alteration of allele frequencies in population, 518

    balancing selection, 524–**25**

    beetles example, 15*f*

Natural selection (*Continued*)
    and chance, 527
    for colour in guppies, 507*f*
    Darwin's theory of, 13–16, 498–500
    directional selection, 522, 523*f*
    disruptive selection, 522, 523*f*
    and the environment, 527
    evolution of drug-resistant bacteria, 501–3
    and food source, 501*f*
    frequency-dependent selection,
        525–26, 526*f*
    heterozygote advantage, 525
    historical constraints, 526
    and life history traits, 1260–62
    modes of, 523*f*
    perfect organisms not fashioned by,
        526–27
    relative fitness, 522
    in response to introduced plant
        species, 501
    review, 527–28
    and self-replicating RNA, 553–54
    sexual dimorphism, 1210
    and sexual selection, 524
    species selection, 575
    stabilizing selection, 522, 523*f*
    summary, 500
Nature and nurture, 295
Nature reserves, 1333
Nautiluses, 741*f*
ncRNAs, 394–96, 395–96
Neanderthals, 37, 463, 484, 794–95
Near vision, 1178*f*
Nectarines, 682*f*
Neel, James, 963
Negative feedback, 9, **929**, **1056**
Negative gene regulation, 382–83
Negative pressure breathing, **990**, 991*f*
Nematocysts, **732**
Nematodes (Nemadoda), 469*t*, 470, 484, 729*f*,
    745–46, 745*f*, 1028, 1110, 1189
Nemertea, 728*f*
Nemoria arizonaria, 513*f*
Neocortex, 1153
Neodenticula seminae, 1231
Neoproterozoic era, 714–16
Neornithes, 781
Nepenthes, 863*f*
Nephrons, **1036***f*
    blood filtrate, processing of, 1035–41
    collecting duct and, 1038*f*
    juxtamedullary, 1036*f*, 1039, 1040
    organization of, 1037*f*
    review, 1046
    types of, 1036*f*
Nereimyra punctata, 743*f*
Nerium oleander, 843*f*
Nernst equation, 1124
Nerve cords, 761
Nerve nets, **1140**
Nerves, **1122**, **1140**

Nervous systems, **1049**. *See also* Central nervous
    system (CNS); Peripheral nervous system
    (PNS)
    circuits of neurons and supporting cells,
        1140–41
    development of, 1154
    disorders of, 1157–59
    glia in, 1141–42
    and muscle contraction, 1186
    neural plasticity of, 1154–55, 1154*f*
    organization of, 1140*f*
    organization of, vertebrate, 1142–43, 1143*f*
    review, 1160–61
    signalling in, 927, 927*f*
Nervous tissue, 923, **926***f*
Net ecosystem production (NEP), **1303**
Net primary production (NPP), **1302**, 1303*f*, 1306*f*
Neural crests, **1107**
Neural pathways for vision, 1177*f*
Neural plasticity, 1154*f*, **1154**–55
Neural plates, 1107, 1107*f*
Neural tubes, 948, 1107*f*, **1107**
Neuroendocrine signalling, 1049, 1050*f*
Neurohormones, **1049**, 1055
Neuromuscular junction, 1134
Neuronal receptors, 1163*f*
Neurons, **926***f*, 927*f*, **1120**
    action potentials as signals conducted by axons,
        1125–30
    communication with cells at synapses, 1130–35
    graded potentials and action potential in,
        1126–27, 1126*f*
    identifying, 1139
    and information processing, 1122
    ion concentrations in, 1123*t*
    ion gradients, ion channels and resting
        membrane potential of, 1123–25
    modelling mammalian, 1125*f*
    and nervous system development, 1154
    number of, in human brain, 1139
    post-synaptic, 1131*f*
    review, 1137–38
    in sensory systems, 1163*f*, 1164
    signalling in, 1154
    structural diversity of, 1122*f*
    structure and organization, 1121–22, 1121*f*
Neuropeptides, **1135**
Neurospora, 352–53
Neurospora crassa, 353*f*, 702–4, 703*f*, 1001, 1002*f*
Neurotransmitters, **1049**, **1121**, 1133–35, 1134*f*
Neurulation, 1106, 1107*f*, 1108–9
Neutral variation, **514**
Neutralization, 1014, 1015*f*
Neutrons, **34**
Neutrophils, **1003**
New Caledonian crows, 1153
New World monkeys, 788–89, 788*f*, 789*f*
New Zealand, 1317*f*
Newborn screening, 302–3
Newton, Isaac, 23
Newts, 247*f*–48*f*, 1115*f*, 1214

Next-generation sequencing, 434–37, 436*f*, 465
Nicotiana attenuata, 801*f*
Nicotine, 1279
Nile crocodiles, 2*f*, 582
Nile perch, 543
Nirenberg, Marshall, 357
Nitric oxide (NO), 977, **1051**, 1135
Nitrification, 858
Nitrifying bacteria, 858
Nitrogen
    as essential element, 33
    and nutrient enrichment, 1336
    role of, in metabolism, 612–13
    soil, 1291, 1291*f*
    valence of, 67*f*
Nitrogen cycle, **858**–59, 1311*f*
Nitrogen fixation, **613**, **859**, 860–61, 1301
Nitrogenase, 859
Nitrogen-fixing bacteria, 858, 859–860, 859*f*,
    1307
Nitrogen-fixing plants, 1315
Nitrogenous bases, 93, 94*f*, 332*f*, 334–35
Nitrogenous molecules, 1026
Nitrogenous wastes
    ammonia, 1030, 1031, 1031*f*
    forms of, 1031, 1031*f*
    influence of evolution and environment on,
        1032
    review, 1046
    urea, 1031–32, 1031*f*
    uric acid, 1031*f*, 1032
Nitrosomonas, 616*f*
Nitrous oxides, 1340*f*
Nobel prizes
    Axel, Richard, 1180
    Banting, Frederick G., 1057*f*
    Beadle, George, 353
    Best, C., 1057*f*
    Brenner, Sydney, 1112*f*
    Buck, Linda, 1180
    Capecchi, Mario, 446
    Collip, J., 1057*f*
    Crick, Francis, 335
    Evans, Martin, 446
    Gurdon, John, 450, 452
    Hodgkin, Alan, 1127
    Horvitz, Robert, 1112*f*
    Huxley, Andrew, 1127
    Jacob, François, 574
    Kornberg, Roger, 92
    Lorenz, Konrad, 1197
    Macleod, J.J.R., 1057*f*
    Marshall, Barry, 954
    McClintock, Barbara, 473
    Mitchell, P., 188
    Sanger, Frederick, 434
    Smithies, Oliver, 446
    Steinman, Ralph M., 1011*f*
    Sulston, John, 1112*f*
    Sutherland, Earl W., 224
    Tatum, Edward, 353

von Frisch, Karl, 1197
Warren, Robin, 954
Watson, James, 335
Wilkins, Maurice, 335
Yamanaka, Shinya, 452
Nociceptors, **1166**–67
Nocturnal animals, 1198
Nodes, **805**
Nodes of Ranvier, **1129**
Nodules, 859–860, 859f, 860f, 1307f
Noncoding DNA, 472–75
Noncoding RNAs (ncRNAs)
    and gene density, 471–72
    and gene expression, 394–96, 395–96, 411
Noncompetitive inhibitors, 169f, **169**
Nondisjunction, 321f, **321**
Nonequilibrium model, **1289**
Nonheritable variation, 513f
Nonkinetochore microtubules, 247f, 249f
Non-neuronal receptors, 1163f
Nonpolar covalent bonds, **41**
Nonpolar hormones, 1050
Nonpolar side chains, 85f
Nonsense Mutation, **374**
Non-shivering thermogenesis, **934**
Nonsteroidal anti-inflammatory drugs (NSAIDs), 1064
Nontemplate strands, 356
Nonvascular plants, 657t, 658
    gametophyte-sporophyte relationships in plant
        groups, 674f
    life cycles dominated by gametophytes, 658–661
    and weathering of rocks and climate damage
        during Ordovician period, 663
Norepinephrine, 1054f, **1064**, 1065f, 1133, **1135**,
    1144
Nori, 642f, 643
North Star, 1198
Northern bottlenose whales, 1334f
Northern coniferous forests, 1233, **1236f**
Northern Hemisphere, 1228
Northern red maples, 806
Norway spruce trees, 830f
No-till agriculture, **853**
Notochords, **761**, **1106**
N-P-K ratio, **853**
N-terminus, 367
Nucifraga columbiana, 1203
Nuclear architecture, 392
Nuclear envelope, **111**, 112f, 114f, 247f, 248f,
    253f, 272f
Nuclear lamina, **111**, 114f
Nuclear magnetic resonance (NMR) spectroscopy,
    92
Nuclear matrix, 111
Nuclear responses, 234, 234f
Nuclear transplantation, 449–451
Nucleariids, **698**
Nuclease, **342**
Nucleic acid hybridization, **434**
Nucleic acid probe, **443**
Nucleid acids, **92**

components of, 93–94, 94f
    digestion of, 954f
    polymers of, 94
    roles of, 92–93
Nucleoids, **108**, **346**, **607**
Nucleoli, **111**
Nucleolus, 112f, 247f, 248f
Nucleomorphs, 626, 630f, **630**
Nucleosides, 93, 94f
Nucleosomes, **346f**
Nucleotide excision repair, **342**, 343f
Nucleotide variability, 511
Nucleotide-pair substitution, **374**, 376f
Nucleotides, **93**
    in genomes, 333
    sequencing of, 6
    triplets of, 356
Nucleus, **111**, 113f
    cutaway view, 112f
    envelope of, 114f
Nucleus accumbens, 1158
Nudibranchs, 739f
Nurture and nature, 295
Nüsslein-Volhard, Christiane, 401–2,
    402, 403f
Nutrient cycling, 1309–13, 1313f, 1318
Nutrient enrichment, 1305t, 1335–37, 1336f
Nutrient limitation, 1304–6, 1306–7
Nutrition, **943**. *See also* Animal nutrition
    absorption, 922f
    of fungi, 693
    overnourishment, 961–62
    study of, 948
Nutritional modes, 612t

O

O>N>C»H, **42**
O157:H7, 621
Oak trees, 687f, 1295
ob genes, 963
Obelia, 733, 733f
Obesity, 947, 961–62, 962–63
Obligate aerobes, **612**
Obligate anaerobes, **193**, **612**
Obligate mutualism, 1280
Observations, as scientific process, 18
Occam's razor, 590
Ocean acidification, 59, 59f, 60
Ocean Networks Canada, 619
Ocean reserves, 1334
Oceanic pelagic zone, **1242f**
Oceans
    and biomass production, 1303
    and climate, 1225–28, 1229f, 1238
    global circulation of, 1229f
    as marine biome, 1238
    and species diversity, 1283f
Ocean's Act, 1334f
Ocelli, 1173, 1173f
Ochotona collaris, 1266, 1266f
Ocotillo, 843f, 910

Octopuses, 574, 728f, 741, 741f, 986, 1141, 1173,
    1278, 1279f, 1283f
Odocoileus hemionus, 1207
Odorants, **1179**
Offspring
    of common eiders, 1261f
    survival of, 1074–75, 1209, 1263f
    trade-off between number and size, 1261–62
Oil sands, 603, 1314, 1314f
Oils
    as fats, 81–82
    human secretions, 1002
Okanagan River, 1317f
Okazaki, Reiji, 340
Okazaki fragments, **340**–41
Old World monkeys, 788–89, 788f, 789f
Olea europaea, 800f
Oleander, 843f
Olfaction, **1179**, 1180–81, 1181f, 1193–94
Olfactory bulb, 1145
Olfactory receptor genes, 514
Oligochaeta (oligochaetes), 742, 743
Oligodendrocytes, **1129**, 1141f
Olive leaf, 800f
Ommatidia, **1173**
Omnivores, **943**, **1284**
    and alimentary canals, 958
    and dentition, 957f
Oncogenes, 404f, **404**, 405
Oncorhynchus nerka, 1028f
One gene–one enzyme hypothesis, 352, 353
Onions, 806f
Onychophora, 729f, 747f
Oocytes, **1077**
Oogenesis, **1079**, 1081f
Oogonia, **1081f**
Oparin, A.I., 551
Oparin-Haldane hypothesis, 551
Open circulatory systems, **748**, 968, 968f
Open system, 156, 161f
Operant conditioning, 1203
Operation Migration, 1202
Operators, **381**
Operculum, **769**
Operon model, 381
Operons, **382**
    basic concept, 381–83
    repressible and inducible, 383–84
Ophiostoma ulmi, 708
Ophiuroidea, 755, 755f
Opiate receptors, 1136
Opiates, 44, 45f, 87
Opisthokonts, **646**–47, **698**
Opium poppies, 800f
Opossums, 784f, 787f, 1075
Opposable thumbs, **788**
Opsin, **1175f**
Opsonization, 1014, 1015f
Optic chiasm, **1177**
Optimal foraging model, **1207**
Oral cavities, **951**–52

Orange peel fungus, 700*f*

Orangutans, 463, 789, 789*f*, 792, 794

Orbitals, 39*f*, **39**–40, 44*f*

Orcas, 1288, 1288*f*

Orchids, 681*f*, 687*f*, 868*f*, 873*f*, **874**, 881

Order, 157–58, 157*f*

Orders, in taxonomy, **584**

Ordovician period, 663, 698, 717

Organ identity genes, 824*f*, **824**, 825*f*

Organ of Corti, **1168***f*

Organ pipe cacti, 1234*f*

Organ systems, **923**

    as level of biological organization, 5*f*

    in mammals, 923*t*

Organelles, 105

    of endomembrane system, relationships among, 120*f*

    evolution of, 580*f*

    inheritance of, 325–26

    as level of biological organization, 5*f*

    lysosomes breaking down, 118*f*

    and structural order in metabolism, 172*f*

Organic chemistry, **64**, 72

Organic components of topsoil, 851

Organic compounds. *See also* Organic molecules

    and alkaline vents, 552*f*

    synthesis of, 551–52

Organic fertilizers, **853**

Organic molecules. *See also* Organic compounds

    carbohydrates. *See* Carbohydrates

    and isomers, 68–69

    lipids. *See* Lipids

    nucleic acids, 92–96

    and origin of life, 64, 64*f*, 65

    review, 99–100

    shapes of, 66*f*

    valences of, 67*f*

Organismal cloning, **448**, 449–451

    faulty gene regulation in clones animals, 450

    of plants, 449

    research and applications of, 448–454

    review, 461

    stem cells of animals, 451–53

Organismal ecology, 1226*f*, 1246

Organisms

    evolutionary history of, in genomes, 595–96

    as level of biological organization, 4*f*

    rise and fall of groups of, 563–570

    single-celled, early, 559–560

Organogenesis, **1088**, **1102**, 1106–8, 1108*f*, 1109

Organs, 5*f*, **803**, **923**

Orgasm, **1086**

Origin of replication, **251**–52

On the Origin of Species by Means of Natural Selection (Darwin), 13, 14*f*, 497, 508

Origins of replication, **337**, 338*f*

Ornithogalum arabicum, 868*f*

Orthologous genes, 595*f*, **595**

Orthoptera, 753*f*

Oryza nivara, 1323

Oryza sativa, 1323

Oscillatoria, 617*f*

Osculum, **730**

Oseltamivir (Tamiflu), 432*f*

Osmoconformer, **1026**

Osmolarity, **1026**, 1036

Osmoreceptors, 1165

Osmoregulation, **145**, **1025**. *See also* Excretory systems

    in animals living in temporary waters, 1028

    in animals moving between fresh and seawater, 1028

    in earthworms, 1034

    energetics of, 1029

    in freshwater animals, 1027–28, 1027*f*

    hormonal management of, 1043–44

    ion movement and gradients, 1042*f*

    in land animals, 1028–2019

    in marine animals, 1026, 1027, 1027*f*

    osmosis and osmolarity in, 1026

    osmotic challenges, 1026–29

    review, 1046

    transport epithelia in, 1030

Osmoregulator, **1026**

Osmosis, **144**, **832**, **1026**

    in excretory system, 1036

    movement of water across plasma membranes, 143–45, 144*f*

    and solute concentration, 1026*f*

Osmotic potential, 833

Osmotic pressure, 979

Osmotic stress, 1029

Osteichthyans, **769**–770

Osteoblasts, 925*f*

Osteons, 925*f*

Otoliths, 1170

Otters, 787*f*, 928, 928*f*, 931, 1286, 1287*f*, 1295

Outer ear, **1168***f*

Outgroups, **589**

Oval window, **1168***f*

Ovarian cycle, **1083**–84

Ovaries, **867**

    in flowers, **681**, 868*f*

    human, 1054*f*, 1077

Overfishing, 1242*f*, 1288, 1288*f*, 1295, 1336–37

Overnourishment, 961–62

Overreproduction, 499, 499*f*

Oviducts, **1077**

Oviparous, **769**

Ovis canadensis, 1250

Ovoviviparous, **769**

Ovulation, **1072**, 1083, 1084, 1090

Ovules, **673**, 674*f*, **867**

Owls, 24, 1264*f*, 1277, 1284, 1315*f*

Oxalis alpina, 879*f*

Oxidation, 123, 177–78, **177**

Oxidation-reduction reactions. *See* Redox reactions

Oxidative fibres, 1187

Oxidative phosphorylation, 180*f*, **180**, 185–191, 186*f*, 188*f*, 196

Oxidizing agent, **177**

Oxygen

    atmospheric, 559*f*, 560*f*

    covalent bonding, 41–42, 41*f*

    as essential element, 33

    and gas exchange, 993–95. *See also* Gas exchange

    measuring consumption of, 937*f*

    molecular structure of, 40

    and photosynthesis, 201–2

    role of, in metabolism, 612

    valence of, 67*f*

Oxygen revolution, 559–560

Oxytocin, 1054*f*, **1055**, 1056, 1060

Oysters, 949*f*, 1073, 1254

Ozone layer, 1341–42, 1341*f*, 1342*f*

P

P generation, 283*f*, **283**, 285*f*, 288*f*

P granules, 1110–11, 1112*f*

P site (peptidyl-tRNA binding site), **366**

p53 genes, **405**–6

Paabo, Svante, 795*f*

Pacific white-sided porpoise, 787*f*

"Pac-man" mechanism, 250

Paedomorphosis, 571*f*, 773

Pain receptors, **1166**–67

Paine, Robert, 1287*f*

Painted nettle coleus plants, 325*f*

Pair-bonds, 1202

Paleoanthropology, **790**

Paleogene period, 785

Paleontology, 97*f*, **494**

Paleozoic era, 558*f*, 559, 716–17

Palisade mesophyll, 814

Pallium, 1153

Palm seeds, **874**

Palm trees, 687*f*

Palolo, 1075

PAMP-triggered immunity, 912–13

Pan, 789

Panagea, **565**

Pancreas, 923, **955**, 1051, 1054*f*, 1056

Pancreatic islets, 1056

Pancrustaceans, **748**, 749–750

Pandemics, 427, 427*f*, 1020

Pando aspen, 877

Pangea, **506**, 785

Panicum virgatum, 884

Panthera tigris altaica, 1346*f*

Papaver somniferum, 800*f*

Papaya, 883

Paper wasp, 753*f*

Papillae, 1180*f*

Papillomaviruses, 410

Parabasalids, **632**

Paracrine signalling, 223, 223*f*, **1049**, 1050*f*

Parahippus, 575, 576*f*

Paralogous genes, 595*f*, **595**

Paramecium aurelia, 1274

Paramecium caudatum, 145, 640*f*, 1274, 1274*f*

Paranthropus boisei, 792

Paraphyletic groups, 588*f*, **588**, 589*f*
Parapodia, 987*f*
Parareptiles, **778**
Parasites, **619**, **1279**
    apicomplexans, 637–39
    Batrachochytrium dendrobatidis, 699
    dodder (*Cuscuta*), 888–89
    ectoparasites, 1279
    endoparasites, 1279
    flatworms, 735–37, 1034
    Giardia intestinalis, 628*f*
    nematodes, 745–46
    plant, 862–64, 863*f*, 888–89, 901
    Plasmodium falciparum, 579, 638, 638*f*
    and sleeping sickness, 1020, 1021
    as symbiosis, 1279
    tapeworms, 736–37, 736*f*, 922
    trematodes, 735–36
    Trichomonas vaginalis, 632, 632*f*
    Trypanosoma, 1021
    wasps, 801*f*, 912
Parasitism, **619**, **1279**
Parasympathetic division, 1143–**44**, 1144*f*
Parathyroid glands, 1054*f*, **1063**
Parathyroid hormone (PTH), 1054*f*, 1063*f*, **1063**
Parenchyma cells, **808***f*, 812*f*
Parental care, 1209, 1210*f*, 1213, 1213*f*
Parental molecule, 336
Parental types, **316**
Parietal cells, 953
Paris japonica, 469*t*, 470
Parkin, 74*f*
Parkinson's disease, 240, 453, **1159**
Parrots, 782
Parsimony, 589–590, 591*f*
Parthenogenesis, **737**, **1071**, 1073*f*
Partial pressure, **985**, 994*f*
Particles, 296
Parus major, 782*f*
Parus major (Great tit), 521*f*, 521*f*
Passiflora, 800*f*
Passion flowers, 800*f*
Passive immunity, **1015**–17
Passive transport, **143**–46, 148*f*, 151–52, 956
Paternal chromosomes, 277
Paternity, 1209
Pathogen-associated molecular patterns (PAMPs),
    912–**13**
Pathogenic bacteria, 620–21
Pathogens, **619**, **704**, **999**, 1001, **1294**
    antigenic variation, 1020
    and community ecology, 1294–97
    defences against. *See* Immune systems
    evolutionary adaptations of, 1020–22
    extracellular, 1013–15
    fungi as, 708–9
    and innate immunity, 1005
    latency, 1020
    plant response to, 912, 914*f*
    zoonotic, 1295–97
Pathway of electron transport, 185–86

Pattern formation, **400**, **822**–23, 894, **1116**
    abnormal, in fruit flies, 401*f*
    setting up the body plan, 400–403
Patzek, Tad, 884
Paulinella chromatophora, 641–42, 641*f*
Pauling, Linus, 333
Paungfoo-Lonhienne, Chanyarat, 864
Pavlov, Ivan, 1203
Paw development, 445
Pax-6 gene, 442
PCBs (polychlorinated biphenyls), 1337, 1337*f*
PCP, 1157
PCR. *See* Polymerase chain reaction (PCR)
PCSK9 Enzyme, 985
Pea plants, 281*f*, 806*f*
    crossing, 282*f*
    and drought, 910
    flower and fruit of, 876*f*
    and gibberellins, 897
    inheritance in, 511
    and Mendel's experimental approach, 282–88,
        284*t*
    seed shape, 292, 316
    snow peas, 687*f*
    traits in F_2 generation, 283*f*, 285*f*, 286*f*
Pears, 881
Peat, **661**, 663*f*
Pectinatella magnifica, 738
Pectins, 117, 130
Pedigree, **296**
Pedigree analysis, 296–97, 297*f*
Pedipalps, 748
Pel enhancer, 573
Pelagic zones, **1238**
Penfield, Wilder, 1151
Penguins, 174*f*, 782, 782*f*, 921, 939
Penicillin, 502, 605, 709
Penis, **1079**
Penny bun fungus, 694*f*
Pentoses, 76, 76*f*
PEP (phosphoenolpyruvate), 215
PEP carboxylase, **215**
Pepsin, **953**
Pepsinogen, **953**
Peptide bond formation, 369*f*
Peptide bonds, **83**
Peptides, 1001, 1003, 1051
Peptidoglycan, **604**
Perception, **1164**. *See also* Sensory systems
Perennial plants, 811
Pericarp, 876
Pericycle, **812**
Periderm, **807**, 818
Perilymph, 1169
Periodic table of elements, 38*f*
Peripheral nervous system (PNS), **1122**, 1141,
    1143–44, 1144*f*
Peripheral proteins, 139
Peripheral vision, 1178
Perisoreus canadensis, 1203
Perissodactyla, 787*f*

Peristalsis, **951**, 960, 1189, **1189**
Peristome, **660**
Peritubular capillaries, **1037***f*
Periwinkles, 740
Permeability, 136, 142, 151, 1123
Permian mass extinction, 566, 569*f*
Permian period, 678, 783
Peromyscus californicus, 1201
Peromyscus leucopus, 1201
Peroxisomes, 112*f*, 113*f*, 123*f*, **123**
Personal Information Protection and Electronic
    Documents Act, 301
Personalized medicine, 455
Pesticides, 1337
PET scans, 36*f*, 1150
Petals, **681**, **867**
Petioles, **805**
Petrels, 962, 962*f*
Pévet, Paul, 940
Peyer's patches, 1004*f*
Pfu polymerase, 441
pH, **58**
    of acid precipitation, 1335
    of blood, 980
    and buffers, 58–59
    and enzymes, 168–69, 169*f*
    of gastric juice, 953
    in soil, 853
pH scale, 56–57, 58*f*
PHA (polyhydroxyalkanoate), 621, 621*f*
Phage λ, 419–420, 420*f*
Phage T2, 331–32, 331*f*
Phages, **331**, **417**
    bacterial defences against, 420–21, 421*f*
    replicative cycles of, 419–421, 419*f*
    and transduction, 610*f*
Phagocytic cells, 1003
Phagocytosis, 118, 118*f*, 149, **150***f*, 1001*f*, **1001**,
    1002, 1014
Phalaropus lobatus, 1209*f*
Phanerozoic eon, 556, 558*f*, 559, 565*f*
"Pharm" animals, 457, 457*f*
Pharmaceutical products, 456–57. *See also* Drugs;
    Medicines
Pharmaceuticals, 1338, 1338*f*
Pharyngeal clefts, **761**
Pharyngeal slits, **761**
Pharyngolepis, 766*f*
Pharynx, **952**
Phase changes, 824, 824*f*
Phase-contrast, 106*f*
Phaseolus lunatus, 801*f*
Phaseolus vulgaris, 904*f*
Phases, 824
Pheasants, 1209
Phenobarbital, 115
Phenotypes, 286*f*, **286**, 291–92, 294, 295, 295*f*
Phenotypic plasticity, 917
Phenotypic variation, 511–12, 511*f*
Phenylalanine (Phe), 357
Phenylketonuria (PKU), 302–3, 516–17

Phenyl-ß-d-glucopyranoside (PBDG), 1180*f*
Pheremones, **1050**, 1074, 1165, **1199**–1201
Pheromone signalling, 1050*f*
Pheromones, **696**
Philadelphia chromosome, 323
Philanthus triangulum, 1203
Philippine eagles, 1322*f*
Phloem, **665**, **807**, 812*f*, 829, 835
    electrical signalling in, 846–47
    information superhighway, 846
    and transport of sugars, 843–45
Phloem sap, 829*f*, **843**–45, 845*f*
Phoca vitulina, 1072*f*
Phoenicopterus ruber, 782*f*
Phoradendron, 863*f*
Phosphate group, 70, 71*f*
Phosphoenolpyruvate (PEP), 215
Phosphofructokinase, 195
Phospholipids, 82*f*, **82**–83, 137, 137*f*
Phosphorus, 946*t*
Phosphorus cycle, 1311*f*
Phosphorylated intermediate, 162
Phosphorylation, 230–31
Phosphorylation cascade, 230*f*, 231
Photic zones, **1238**
Photoautotrophs, 198, 199*f*, 612*t*
Photobioreactor, 199*f*
Photoheterotrophs, 612*t*
Photomorphogenesis, **901**, 902*f*
Photons, **203**, 206
Photoperiod, 1198
Photoperiodism, **905**–7, 906*f*
Photophosphorylation, **202**
Photoprotection, 206
Photopsins, 1177
Photoreceptors, **1173**
    blue-light, 901–2
    human types of, 1175*f*
    phytochromes as, 902–3
    and sensory transduction, 1175
    in simple eyes, 574, 574*f*
Photorespiration, **214**
Photosynthates, 803
Photosynthesis, **198**
    atoms, tracking, 201–2, 202*f*
    Calvin cycle, 212–13
    CAM and C_4 compared, 216*f*
    carbon fixation, alternative mechanisms of, 214–17
    as chemical reaction, 45–46, 45*f*
    and chloroplasts, 122*f*
    and emergent properties, 3
    and endosymbiosis, 627–631
    energy flow in, 9*f*
    and energy transformation, 103*f*
    enzymes in, 891
    importance of, 217–18
    and leaves, 805–6
    light reactions. *See* Light reactions
    location of, 5*f*
    location of in plants, 200*f*

    measuring, 1303*f*
    origin of process, 200
    and the oxygen revolution, 559–560
    as redox process, 202
    review, 218*f*, 219
    stages of, 202–3
    and wavelengths, 205*f*
Photosynthetic pigments, 204–6
Photosynthetic prokaryotes, 569
Photosystem I (PS I), **207**
Photosystem II (PS II), **207**
Photosystems, 206–8, 207*f*, **207**
Phototrophs, 612
Phototropin, 902
Phototropism, 893*f*, **893**
Phragmoplasts, **653**
Phyla, **584**
Phyllotaxy, 830*f*, **830**, 894
Phylogenetic bracketing, 583
Phylogenetic species concept, **535**
Phylogenetic trees, **585**
    anatomy of, 586*f*
    based on rRNA sequence data, 598*f*
    of birds and close relatives, 583*f*
    and cladistics, 588–89
    constructing, 590*f*
    for eukaryotes, 628*f*
    eukaryotic, 645*f*
    interpreting, 590–93
    and maximum likelihood, 589–590
    and maximum parsimony, 589–590
    of prokaryotes, 614*f*
    review, 601–2
    shared characteristics used in construction of, 588–593
    types of, 592
Phylogenies, **583**. *See also* Phylogenetic trees
    of amniotes, 776*f*
    of angiosperms, 684–85, 685*f*
    animal, 722–24, 722*f*, 726*f*
    applying, 593
    of chordates, 760*f*
    and classification, 585–86, 585*f*
    derived characters used to infer, 589
    and evolutionary relationships, 584–86
    horizontal gene transfer, importance of, 599, 600*f*
    of mammals, 786*f*–87*f*
    molecular clocks and evolutionary time in, 596–97
    and molecular homologies, 586
    and morphological homologies, 586
    of primates, 788*f*
    review, 601–2
Phylograms, **592**, 593*f*
Physella johnsoni, 742, 742*f*
Physiological thermostats, 935–36, 936*f*
Physiology, **921**
Phytoalexins, 913
Phytochromes, **901**
    and de-etiolation, 890–91, 890*f*

    as photoreceptors, 902–3
    and seed germination, 902–3
    and shade avoidance, 903
Phytophthora ramorum, 1295
Phytoplankton, 1284, 1305, 1305*f*, 1308–9, 1336, 1337*f*, 1342
Phytoremediation, **854**
Picrophilus oshimae, 604
Pied flycatcher, 542
Pigeons, 934, 1166, 1198, 1203
Pigmentation, 293–94, 294*f*
Pigments, 204–6
    photosynthetic, 1302
    respiratory, 993–95
    visual, 1177–78
Pigs, 358*f*, 787*f*
Pikaia, 716*f*
Pikas, 787*f*
Pili, **606**
Pill bugs, 750
Pilobolus, 702*f*
Pimentel, David, 884
Pimephales promelas, 1338
Pin flower, 879*f*
Pinaceae, 585
Pine beetles, 522, 844, 845*f*
Pine trees, 1
    bristlecone pine, 680*f*
    life cycle of, 676–77, 677*f*
    lodgepole pine, 1, 2*f*, 708, 1290, 1290*f*
    wollemi pine, 680*f*
Pineal glands, 1054*f*, 1060*f*, **1067**, 1147*f*
Pineapples, 876*f*
Pinguinus impennis, 1322
Pinnipeds, 759, 760
Pinocytosis, 149, **150***f*
Pinus contorta latifolia, 1233
piRNAs, 395
Pistils, **867**
Pisum sativum, 910
Pit vipers, 1277
Pitch, 1169
Pitcher plants, 863*f*
Pith, **807**
Pithovirus sibericum, 425
Pits, 150*f*
Pituitary glands, 1054*f*, **1060**
Pitx1, 572–73, 573*f*
Pivot joint, 1190*f*
Piwi-interacting RNAs (piRNAs), 395
PKU, 516–17
Placenta, **784**, **1087**
Placental circulation, 1087*f*
Placoderms, 767
Placozoa, 727*f*
Placques, 82
Plague, 1295
Planarians, 735*f*, **735**, 967*f*, 968, 1140*f*, 1141, 1173*f*
Plane, of cell division, 821–22, 821*f*
Planets, life on, 56

Planktonic crustaceans, 750, 751f
Plant biotechnology
    debate over, 885–86
    and genetic engineering, 883–85
    and human health, 885
    and nontarget organisms, effects on, 885
    and transgene escape, 885–86
Plant cells
    cell plate formation in, 251f
    cutaway view, 113f
    cytokinesis in, 251f
    differentiated, 808f–9f
    division of, 821–22
    expansion of, 822
    meristem generation of cells, 810–11
    mitosis in, 252f
    types of, 807
    vacuoles, 119f
    water balance in, 144f
    water relations in, 835f
Plant development, **819**, 821
    auxin, role of, 894–95
    gene expression and control of cell
        differentiation, 823
    genetic control of flowering, 824–25
    and model organisms, 820–21
    morphogenesis and cell differentiation,
        819–825
    morphogenesis and pattern formation in,
        822–23
    review, 826
    shifts in, 823–24
Plant growth
    cell division and cell expansion, 821–22
    primary, 810–15
    review, 826
    secondary, 810, 810f, 815–19
    wood development, 818–19
Plant growth regulators, 224, 892. See also Plant
        hormones
Plant hormones, 915
    abscisic acid, 892t, 897–98
    auxin, 892t, 893
    brassinosteroids, 892t, 900–901
    cytokinins, 892t, 895–96
    in de-etiolation responses, 889
    ethylene, 892t, 898f
    flowering hormone, 906, 906f
    gibberellins, 892t
    jasmonates, 892t, 901
    overview, 892t
    strigolactones, 892t, 901
    survey of, 892
Plant nutrition
    and bacteria, 857–861, 858f, 859f
    and fungi, 861–62
    improvement by genetic modification, 856
    and mutualism, 857–864
    review, 864
    soil properties and quality for, 850–54
    vascular transport systems, 831–35

Plant responses
    to cold stress, 911
    to drought, 909–10
    environmental stresses, 908–11
    and evolution, 907
    to flooding, 909, 909f
    to gravity, 907–8
    to heat stress, 910–11
    to herbivores, 912
    and hormones. See Plant hormones
    hypersensitive response, 913
    immune responses, 912–13
    to light, 901–7
    to mechanical stimuli, 908, 909f
    to pathogens, 912, 914f
    review, 915–16
    to salt stress, 911
    and signal transduction pathways, 889–891
    systemic acquired resistance, 913–14
    triple response, 899
Plant structure
    cells. See Plant cells
    hierarchical organization of, 803–7
    meristem generation of cells for growth in,
        810–11
    organs, 803–6
    review, 826
Plant tissue culture, 881–82
Plantae, kingdom, 598, 599
Plants. See also Land plants
    breeding, 882–83
    C_3 plants, **214**
    C_4 plants, **214**–16, 215f, 216f
    CAM plants, 216–17
    carnivorous, 862–64, 863f
    cloning of, 449
    and colonization of land, 562
    compartment structure of, 832, 832f
    components of, 854–55
    defences against herbivores, 800f–801f, 1279
    disease epidemics, 914
    diversity of, manipulating, 1283, 1283f
    essential elements in, 854–57, 855–56, 855t,
        864
    evolution of, 829–830
    gametophyte-sporophyte relationships in plant
        groups, 674f
    and genetic engineering, 459
    growth directed by environmental cues, 802–3
    growth of, 810–15, 810f, 811f
    hydroponic culture, 854f
    kingdoms of, 654f
    and mineral deficiency, 856, 857
    mutualism between fungi and, 706
    nonvascular, 657t, 658, 658–661, 663
    nutrition of, 850
    nutritional adaptations, 863f
    overview, 803f
    parasitic, 863f
    polypoid speciation in, 538–39
    and season detection, 905

seed plants, 657t
    seedless vascular. See Seedless vascular plants
    sexual life cycles of, 270f
    smart, 856, 857f
    and soil pH, 853
    transgenic, 460, 820–f
    vascular. See Vascular plants
    water content of, 854
Plaque, **983**, 984f
Plasma, 925f, 980f, **980**–81, 1003
Plasma cells, **1013**
Plasma membranes, 108, 109f, **109**, 110,
        112f, 113f
    bulk transport across, 149–151, 152
    in cell cycle, 247f
    movement of water across, 143–45, 144f
    receptors in, 225–28
    selectively permeable, 836
    transport of substances across, 832–35
Plasmids, 425, **437**
    and conjugation, 610–12
    of prokaryotic cells, **607**, 608f
    recombinant material, 438–39
Plasmodesmata, 113f, **131**, 846, 846f
Plasmodial slime moulds, **645**, 646f
Plasmodium, **645**, 646f, 1001
Plasmodium falciparum, 579, 638, 638f, 754
Plasmogamy, **696**
Plasmolysis, **145**, **834**
Plasticity, 819f
Plastics, 621
Plastids, **123**, 560, **627**, 630f
Plate tectonics, 506, **563**–65, 564f
Platelet-derived growth factor (PDGF),
        257, 257f
Platelets, **981**
Platyhelminthes, 727f, 734
Platynereis, 743
Platypuses, 787f, 1106, 1165
Pleiotropy, **292**
Pleurozium, 661
Plummer, Frank, 427
Plumule, 874
Pluripotent, **452**
Pluripotent stem (iPS) cells, 452–53
Pneumatophores, 804f
Pneumocystis carinii, 1022
Pneumonia, 330, 609
Poecilia reticulata, 1210, 1211f
Poikilotherms, 931
Point mutation, **372**, 374f, 404, 513
Poison dart frogs, 1278f
Polar bears, 2f, 54f, 534, 534f, 543, 945f, 1072f,
        1340f
Polar covalent bonds, 31, 41f, **41**, **50**, 61
Polar factors, 1050
Polar molecules, **50**
Polar side chains, 85f
Polar transport, 894
Polarity, 821, 822f, 1106f
Polarity of epithelia, 924f

Polistes dominulus, 753*f*
Pollen, and sperm production, 673–75
Pollen grains, 673*f*, **673**, 678*f*, 690, 869–870, 869*f*, **869**, 887*f*
Pollen sacs, 869*f*
Pollen tubes, 675, **870**
Pollination, **675**, **870**
   angiosperm, 678, 685–86
   flowers and angiosperm, 686*f*
   of flowers and angiosperms, 870–72, 871*f*, 872*f*
   methods of, 870–72
   and wind, 871*f*
Pollinator choice, 546, 547*f*
Poly-A tail, 361*f*, **361**
Polyadenylation signal, 360
Polyandry, 1208, 1209*f*
Polychaeta (polychaetes), 742, 743, 1075
Polychaos dubium, 470
Polychlorinated biphenyls (PCBs), 1337
polychlorinated biphenyls (PCBs), 1337*f*
Polyclonal antibodies, 1017
Polygamy, **1208**
Polygenic inheritance, 293, **293**–94, 294*f*
Polygyny, 1208, 1209*f*
Polymerase chain reaction (PCR), **440**
   amplifying DNA using, 440–41, 440*f*
   in gene cloning, 441*f*
Polymers, 75*f*, **75**–76
Polymorphisms, 448
Polynucleotides, **93**, 94, 94*f*
Polypeptide backbone, 86, 88*f*
Polypeptide chain, 86*f*
Polypeptide sequence data, 98
Polypeptides, **83**
   amino acid polymers, 86
   antigen receptor chains, 1006–7
   building, 366–69
   elongation of, 367
   making multiples, 371–72
   targeting to specific locations, 370, 371*f*
   transfer RNA, role of, 364–65
   as water-soluble hormones, 1051*f*
Polyphyletic groups, 588*f*, **588**, 589*f*
Polyploidy, 321–22, **538**
Polyps, 731*f*, **731**
Polyribosomes, 371*f*, **371**
Polysaccharides, **78**
   digestion of, 950
   storage polysaccharides, 78–79
   structural polysaccharides, 79–80
   structure of, 78*f*
Polysomes, **371**
Polyspermy, 1096
Polyterus, 562
Polytomy, **586**
Polytrichum commune, 662*f*
Poly-U, 357
Pongo, 789
Pongo pygmaeus, 463
Pons, 992, **1147***f*, 1148
POPCAN, 884*f*

Poplar trees, 802*f*, 803, 884
Population conservation, 1327
   declining-population approach, 1329–30
   and the greater prairie chicken, 1327–29
   and grizzly bears, 1329*f*
   review, 1345
   rufa red knots, 1330, 1330*f*
   small-population approach, 1327
   weight conflicting demands in, 1331
Population cycles, 1263–65
Population dynamics, **1263**
   and cycles, 1263–65
   and immigration, emigration, and metapopulations, 1265–66
   stability and fluctuation, 1263
Population ecology, **1251**
   density-dependent regulation in, 1264*f*–65*f*
   and density-dependent selection, 1261
   and density-independent selection, 1262
   exponential growth model in, 1255–56, 1256*f*
   human population growth in, 1267–70
   life history traits produced by natural selection in, 1260–62
   population density, dispersion, and demographics, 1251–55
   review, 1270–71
Population growth, 1271
   and density-dependent selection, 1262
   and density-independent selection, 1262
   exponential model of, 1255–56, 1256*f*
   factors regulating, 1262–66
   logistic model of, 1257–59, 1258*f*, 1259*f*
Populations, **514**, **1251**
   carrying capacity, 1257–59, 1259
   demographics, 1253–55
   density and dispersion, 1251–53
   density of, 1251, **1251**, 1257–59, 1259, 1263*f*
   dynamics of, 1252*f*
   human, 1267–70
   immigration and emigration, 1252
   as level of biological organization, 4*f*
   within species, 514*f*
   survivorship curves, 1254
Populus trichocarpa, 884*f*
Porcupines, 787*f*, 798*f*, 1278*f*
Pore complexes, 111, 114*f*
Porifera, 723, 727*f*
Porphyra, 642*f*
Porpoises, 787*f*
Positional information, **400**, **1116**
Position-based mechanisms, 823
Positive feedback, 10, **929**, **1056**, 1089*f*, 1127
Positive gene regulation, 384–85
Positive gravitropism, 907*f*
Positive pressure breathing, **990**
Positron-emission tomography (PET). *See* PET scans
Post-anal tails, 761
Posterior pituitary glands, 1054*f*, 1060*f*, **1060**
Posterior pituitary hormones, 1060

Postganglionic neurons, 1144
Postsynaptic cells, 1121
Postsynaptic potentials, 1132, 1133*f*
Post-transcriptional regulation, 392–94
Post-translational modifications, 369–370, 891
Postzygotic barriers, 533*f*, **534**
Potassium
   functions of, 945, 946*t*
   and stomatal opening/closing, 841*f*
Potassium channels, 1126, 1126*f*, 1127
Potatoes, 805*f*, 889, 889*f*, 914
Potential energy, **37**, **155**, 156*f*
Potential evapotranspiration, 1293
Potential range, 1244
Prairie dogs, 1295
Prairie voles, 1213, 1213*f*
Precapillary sphincters, 978
Precipitation
   acid. *See* Acid precipitation
   and global air circulation, 1227*f*
   in terrestrial biomes, 1234*f*–37*f*
Precocious germination, 898*f*
Predation, 1264*f*, 1265, 1274, **1276**–78
Predation hypothesis, 1264
Preganglionic neurons, 1144
Pregnancy, **1086**
   and conception, 1086
   detecting disorders in, 1091
   first trimester, 1086–88
   maternal immune tolerance of embryo and fetus, 1089
   second trimester, 1088
   termination of, 1091
   third trimester, 1088–89
Pregnancy tests, 1017
Pre-mRNA, 355, 362*f*
Prenatal genetic testing, 301*f*
Prepophase bands, 821, 821*f*
Prepuce, **1078**
Pressure flow, 844–45
Pressure potential, **833**
Presynaptic cells, 1121
Prey
   defences of, 1278
   selection of, 1214
Prezygotic barriers, 532*f*–33*f*, **534**
Priapula, 728*f*
Primary cilium, 126
Primary consumers, **1301**
Primary electron acceptor, **207**
Primary endosymbiosis, 580*f*, **627**, 641*f*
Primary growth, **810**
   review, 826
   of roots, 811–13, 811*f*, 812*f*
   of shoots, 813–15
   of woody stems, 810*f*, 815
Primary immune response, **1010**
Primary oocytes, **1081***f*
Primary producers, **1301**
Primary production, **1302**, 1303*f*
   in aquatic ecosystems, 1304–6

determining with satellites, 1301, 1303*f*
and ecosystem energy budgets, 1302–4
in terrestrial ecosystems, 1306–7
Primary roots, 804
Primary structure, **88***f*, 90*f*
Primary succession, **1290**, 1291*f*
Primary transcript, **355**
Primary visual cortex, **1177**
Primase, **338**, 342*t*
Primates, 1153
characteristics of, 787*f*
derived characters of, 785–86
living, 788–7990
and nutrition, 944
phylogeny of, 788*f*
Primer, **338**
Primitive streak, **1103**
Principles of Geology (Lyell), 496
Priomordial germ cells, 1080*f*
Prions, **430**–31, 431*f*, 1294
Prisms, 203*f*
Probability laws, 288, 290, 300, 303
Problem solving, **1203**–4
Proboscidea, 787*f*
Proboscis worms, 728*f*
Producers, **8**, **647**
Production efficiency, 1307–**8**
Productive cycles, animal, 1072–73, 1083–85, 1083*f*
Products, **45**
Progesterone, **1065**, 1077, 1082, 1084
Progestin, 1054*f*, **1065**, 1090–91
Programmed cell death, 238, 406, 1109–10, 1154
Progymnosperms, **676**
Prohormone, 1051
Prokaryotes, 1166
adaptive abilities of, 604–8
and bacteria, mutualistic, 619–620
and bacteria, pathogenic, 620–21
and bioremediation, 621
biosphere, role in, 618–19
cells of. *See* Prokaryotic cells
and chemical recycling, 618
chemoheterotrophic, 618
diversity of, 614
and ecological interactions, 618–19
and endospores, 606
vs. eukaryotes, 606, 607–8
evolving in response to environmental change, 609*f*
genetic recombination in, 609–12
genetic variation in, 608
and humans, impact on, 619–622
lineages of, 613–15
metabolic cooperation in, 613, 613*f*
motility of, 606–7
nutritional and metabolic adaptations in, 612–13
photosynthetic, 569
phylogeny of, 614*f*

rapid reproduction and mutation, 608–9
in research and technology, 621–22
review, 623
shapes of, 604*f*
specialized membranes of, 607*f*
spiral, 604*f*
structural and functional adaptations of, 604–8
Prokaryotic cells, 4, 6, 6*f*, 108*f*, **108**–11, **180**.
See also Cells
binary fission in, 251–52
internal organization and DNA, 607–8
reproduction in, 608
structures of, 604–6
Prolactin, 1054*f*, 1059, **1060**
Prolactin-releasing hormones, 1060
Proliferative phase, 1084
Prometaphase, **246**, 247*f*, 249, 252*f*
Promiscuous, **1207**
Promoters, **358**, 360*f*
Proofreading DNA, 342–43
Prop roots, 804*f*
Prophages, **420**
Prophase, **246**, 247*f*, 252*f*
Prophase I, 272*f*, 274*f*, 275*f*
Prophase II, 273*f*, 274–76
Prostaglandins, **1051**, 1167
Prostate glands, **1079**
Prosthetic groups, 185
Protease, **953**
Protected areas
establishing, 1332–35
philosophy of nature reserves, 1333
preserving biodiversity hot spots, 1333
zoned reserves, 1333–35
Protein Data Bank, 465–66
Protein folding, 369–370
Protein kinase A, 232
Protein kinases, 230, 255, 456
Protein phosphatases, 231
Protein-coding genes, 466–67
Proteins, **83**, 86
accessory, 1013
activation of, 891
amino acid polymers, 86
amino acids of, 85*f*
antibody proteins, 87*f*
antifreeze, 911
carrier proteins, 142, 145*f*, 146
cellulose-synthesizing, 653
channel proteins, 142, 145–46, 145*f*
coat protein, 150*f*
complete/incomplete, 944
C-reactive, 984
dietary deficiency, 947
digestion of, 954*f*
in DNA molecules, 345–48
and DNA replication and repair, 335–345, 339*f*, 342*t*, 349
as eukaryotes, 626
and evolution, 96–98
folding of, in cells, 91–92

functions of, 84*f*, 86–92
heat-shock, 911
as hormones, 1051
integral proteins, 139
interferons, 1003
levels of structure, 87, 88–89*f*
mediator proteins, 389
membrane proteins, 137, 139–141, 140*f*
motor proteins, 124*f*, **125**
overview, 83
peripherial proteins, 139
phosphorylation and dephosphorylation, 230–31
polypeptides, 86
post-translational modification of, 891
prions, 430–31
processing and degradation of, 394
production of, 6, 457
regulatory, 1184, 1184*f*
review, 99
scaffolding, 236–38, 236*f*
sequencing of, 96
as signalling factor, 1051
structural determinants, 90–91
structure of, 74*f*, 86–92, 87*f*, 139*f*
and temperature, 101
tissue-specific proteins, 398
Toll, 1001
transport proteins, 142, 145
viral movement proteins, 846
water soluble, 55*f*
Proteobacteria, 616*f*, 959*f*
Proteoglycans, **130**
Proteomes, **8**, **467**
Proteomics, **8**, **96**, 97*f*, 99, **467**
Proterozoic eon, 558*f*
Prothoracicotropic hormone (PTTH), 1058
Protista, kingdom, 598, 599, 627
Protists, **108**, 1166, 1259*f*. *See also* Eukaryotes
and algae, 642–43
alveolates, 637–39
as ancestor of fungi, 698–99, 698*f*
ciliates, 639
classification of, 12, 13*f*
diversity of, 626, 628*f*–29*f*, 639
and ecological communities, 647–49, 649*f*, 650
evolution of, 627–631
and Excavata, 632–33
flagellated, 698
heterotrophic, 625*f*
and malaria, 639
origin of term, 625
review, 650–51
rhizarians, 639–642
SAR clade, 634–642
sexual life cycles of, 270*f*, 271
stramenopiles, 634–37
structural and functional diversity of, 626
supergroups of, 626–27, 628*f*–29*f*
unikonts, 644–47
Protocells, **551**, 552–53

Proton pump, 148*f*, **148**, 894
Protonema, **660**
Protonephridia, **735**, 1033*f*, **1033**–34
Proton-motive force, **187**
Protons, **34**
Proto-oncogenes, 404*f*, **404**, 405
Protoplast, **833**
Protostome development, 720–21, 721*f*
Prototaxites, 699, 711*f*
Prototype, 16
Proviruses, **423**
Proximal control elements, 387*f*, 388
Proximal tubules, **1035**–36, **1037***f*
Proximate causation, 1197
Prozac, 1158
Pseudocoelomates, **720**
Pseudogenes, **472**, 504
Pseudogymnoascus destructans, 708, 709*f*
Pseudomyrmex, 1280*f*
Pseudopodia, **128**, **639**
Pseudostratified columnar epithelium, 924*f*
Psilotum nudum, 667*f*
Psittacus erithacus, 1153
Ptarmigans, 1263, 1284
Pteraspis, 766*f*
Pterosaurs, **778**, 1192
Puberty, 1082–83
Puffball fungus, 499*f*, 695, 704*f*
Puffins, 1025, 1025*f*
Pulmocutaneous circuits, **969**, 970*f*
Pulmonary circuits, **969**, 970*f*
Pulse, **976**
Puma concolour, 1207
Punctuated equilibria, **544**
Puncture vine, 878*f*
Punnett square, 285*f*, **285**, 289–290, 293*f*
Pupa, 752*f*
Pupils, **1173**
Purine metabolism, 1032
Purines, **93**, 94*f*, 334–35
Purple sulphur bacteria, 199*f*
Pus, 1004
Pygmy date palms, 687*f*
Pygmy marsupial frog, 775*f*
Pygmy weeds, 830
Pyramid of net production, 1308, 1308*f*
Pyrenean ibexes, 1326
Pyrenean oak, 687*f*
Pyrimidines, **93**, 94*f*, 334–35
Pyrococcus furiosus, 441, 615
Pyruvate
    in catabolism, 193*f*
    conversion to ethanol, 192
    oxidation of, 180*f*, 181–82, 182*f*, 183*f*, 196
Pythons, 949*f*, 1191
PYY, 962

Q

Qualitative data, 18
Quantitative characters, **293**
Quantitative data, **18**

Quantitative PCR (real-time PCR), 444
Quaternary structure, **89***f*
Quillworts, 666, 667*f*
Quorum sensing, 222

R

R groups, 83–84, 85*f*
R plasmids, 611–12
Rabbits, 787*f*, 920–21, 932, 959, 1082
Raccoons, 1079
Radial cleavage, **721**
Radial symmetry, 681*f*, 688
Radicle, **874**
Radioactive isotopes, **35**, 36*f*, 37, 554, 556
Radioactive tracers, 36
Radiolarians, **640**–41, 641*f*
Radiometric dating, 36, **554**–56, 556*f*
Radishes, 804*f*
Radula, **738**
Rafflesia arnoldii, 686*f*, 863*f*
Rain forests, 689, 689*f*
Rain shadow, 1228
Raised bog ecosystems, 1323
Rana sylvatica, 918*f*
Randall, Dave, 1031*f*
Random dispersion, 1252*f*, 1253
Random fertilization, 278
Rangeomorphs, 715, 715*f*
Ranger tarandus, 1072*f*
Ranunculus, 812*f*
Raoellids, 759
Rapaport, Anatol, 1217
Raphia regalis palm, 830
Ras genes, **405**
Ras protein, 405
Raspberries, 876*f*
Rat kangaroo cells, 243*f*
Ratites, **781**
Rats, 787*f*, 1085, 1203, 1215, 1215*f*, 1217, 1325
Rattlesnakes, 1139, 1166*f*, 1187, 1277
Ravens, 1203–4
Ray-finned fishes (Actinopterygii), 770*f*, **770**, 1145, 1152
Rays, 768, 769
Reabsorption, 1033*f*, **1033**, 1035
Reactants, **45**–46, 167
Reaction-centre complex, **207**
Reading frame, 357
Realized niche, **1275**
Real-time PCR, 444
Receptacles, **867**
Reception, in cellular messaging, 224, 224*f*, 225–29, 241
Receptive fields, 1176
Receptor potentials, **1164**, 1176*f*
Receptor proteins, 84*f*
Receptor tyrosine kinases (RTKs), **227***f*, 228, 230
Receptor-mediated endocytosis, 149, **150***f*
Receptors
    intracellular receptors, 228–29
    in plasma membrane, 225–28

toll-like, 913
Recessive traits, 284
Recessively inherited disorders, 297–99, 297*f*
Reciprocal altruism, **1217**
Recombinant bacteria, 437
Recombinant chromosomes, 278
Recombinant DNA, **437**
    ethical issues with, 459
    and HGD production, 1063
    and hirudin from leeches, 744
    using restriction enzymes to make, 438–440, 439*f*
    and viruses, 428
Recombinant types, **316**
Recombinants, **316**
Recombinase, 1008
Recombination frequency, 317
Recombination of linked genes, 317*f*
Rectum, **957**
Red algae, 642*f*, **642**–43, 650, 654*f*
Red and far-red light, 902, 903*f*
Red blood cells, 89*f*, 90, 90*f*
Red Delicious apples, 881
Red kangaroos, 784
Red List of Threatened Species, 1322, 1323
Red maples, 806
Red spruce, 1233
Red squirrels, 510–11, 510*f*, 787*f*
Red tachinid, 753*f*
Red tide, 637*f*
Red wood ants, 32
Red-necked phalaropes, 1209*f*
Redox reactions, **177**
    photosynthesis as, 202
    principle of, 176–79
Red-spotted Purple butterfly, 1048
Reduced hybrid fertility, 533*f*
Reduced hybrid viability, 533*f*
Reducing agent, **177**
Reduction, **177**, 212
Reduction, of floral parts, 868*f*
Reductional division, 276
Reductionism, 3
Redwood trees, 267*f*
Reflexes, **1142**–43, 1143*f*, 1165
Refractory period, **1127**
Regenerative medicine, 453
Regulation
    of animal digestion, energy storage, and appetite, 960–63
    of appetite and consumption, 961–62, 963
    of blood flow, 2*f*
    of cellular fuel, 961*f*
    of energy storage, 961
    of enzymes, 170–72, 171*f*
    as property of life, 2*f*
Regulation feedback, 9*f*, **9**–10
Regulators, **928**
Regulatory genes, **382**
Regulatory proteins, 1184, 1184*f*

Reindeer moss, 658
Reinforcement, **542**, 543*f*
Relative abundance, 1282*f*, **1282**
Relative fitness, **522**
Relay molecules, 225
Release factors, 367
Releasing hormones, 1060
Renal cortex, **1036***f*
Renal medulla, **1036***f*
Renal pelvis, **1036***f*
Renaturation, 90*f*
Renin-angiotensin-aldosterone system (RAAS), **1044**–45, 1045*f*
Renne, Paul, 567
Repairing DNA, 342–43
Repenomamus giganticus, 569
Replacement cells, 453
Replication fork, **338**
Replicative cycles
    of animal viruses, 421–25
    of enveloped RNA virus, 423*f*
    general features of, 418–19
    of HIV, 424*f*
    simplified viral, 419*f*
Reporter genes, 856
Repressible enzymes, 384
Repressible operons, 383–84
Repressors, **382**, 390
Reproduction. *See also* Animal reproduction; Asexual reproduction; Human reproduction; Sexual reproduction
    asexual vs. sexual, 267
    in birds, 781
    circulation in, 971
    of echinoderms, 754
    in fish, 770
    in flowering plants, 877–882
    of frogs, 774*f*, 775, 775*f*
    hermaphroditism, 731, 745
    in insects, 752
    in planarians, 735
    in prokaryotes, 608–9
    as property of life, 2*f*
    trade-off with survival, 1261
    vegetative propagation, 881
Reproductive barriers
    breakdown of, 543–44, 543*f*
    exploring, 532*f*–33*f*
    reinforcement, 542, 543*f*
    weakening, 542–43
Reproductive cloning, 450
Reproductive cycles, 1072–73
Reproductive handicap, 1071
Reproductive isolation, **531**, 536*f*
    and divergence of allopatric populations, 536–37, 536*f*
    and hybrid zones, 540–44
    interpreting data, 537
    reproductive barriers, 531–34
    review, 547
Reproductive leaves, 806*f*

Reproductive organs, 1066*f*, 1077–79, 1077*f*, 1078, 1093
Reproductive success, 1207–12, 1219
Reproductive systems, 923*t*
Reptiles (Reptilia), **777**
    amniotic eggs, **775**, 777*f*
    birds, 780–82
    circulation in, 970*f*
    crocodilians, 780
    and evolution of mammalian ear bones, 783*f*
    hatching, 777*f*
    hearing in, 1172
    kidneys in, 1041
    lepidosaurs, 779–780
    and nitrogenous wastes, 1032
    origin and evolutionary radiation of, 778
    and osmoregulation, 1029
    turtles, 778–79
Research methods
    absorption spectrum, 204*f*
    applying parsimony to molecular systematics, 591*f*
    cell fractionation, 107*f*
    crossing (mating), 282*f*
    determining population size using the mark-recapture method, 1251
    determining primary production with satellites, 1303*f*
    dideoxy sequencing, 435*f*
    hydroponic culture, 854*f*
    intracellular recording, 1126
    karyotypes, 268*f*
    linkage map, 319*f*
    polymerase chain reaction, 440*f*
    testcross, 287*f*
    Traditional Ecological Knowledge (TEK), 1286*f*
    using a molecular marker for universal species identification, 594*f*
    using dendrochronology to study climate, 817*f*
    using the Ti plasmid to produce transgenic plants, 820–*f*
    using traditional ecological knowledge to study Arctic foxes, 1286*f*
Residual volume, **991**
Resistance genes, 611
Resolution, 105
Resource acquisition, vascular plants
    evolution of, 829–830
    review, 847–48
    root architecture and acquisition of water and minerals, 831
    shoot architecture and light capture, 830–31
    transport mechanisms, 831–35
Resource partitioning, 1275*f*, **1275**–76
Respiratory media, 986, 986*t*
Respiratory pigments, **993**–95, 997
Respiratory surfaces, 986, 997
Respiratory systems, 923*t*. *See also* Gas exchange
    components of, 989–990

    evolution of, 995–96
    exchange surfaces of, 922
    mammalian, 989–990, 989*f*
Responses, **929**
    animal, to the environment, 919*f*
    as cell signalling stage, 224*f*, 225
    to mechanical stress, 898–99
    nuclear and cytoplasmic, 234, 234*f*
    regulation of, 234–38
    review, 241
    scaffolding proteins and signalling complexes, 236–38
    and signal amplification, 235
    specificity and coordination of, 235–36
    termination of signal, 238
"Rest and digest," 1144
Resting membrane potential
    determination of, 1124–25
    formation of, 1123–24
Restoration ecology
    biological augmentation, 1314–15
    bioremediation, 1314
    review, 1318
    worldwide projects, 1315, 1316*f*–17*f*
Restriction enzymes, **438**, 439*f*, 441*f*
Restriction fragments, **438**
Restriction point, 256
Restriction sites, **438**
Resurrection of extinct species, 1326–27
Reticular fibres, 925*f*
Reticular formation, 1148*f*, **1148**
Reticulum, 959*f*
Retinal molecules, **1175***f*
Retinas, 104*f*, 574, **1174***f*, 1176–77, 1178
Retinitis pigmentosa, 519
Retrotransposon movement, 473*f*
Retrotransposons, **473**
Retroviral vector, 455*f*
Retroviruses, **423**, 455
Reverse transcriptase, **423**
Reverse transcriptase—polymerase chain reaction (RT-PCR), **443**
Rhabditophora, 735
Rhabditophorans, 735, 736
Rhesus monkeys, 98
Rheumatoid arthritis, 1019, 1019*f*
Rhiastus lasternus, 753*f*
Rhinoceroses, 787*f*
Rhizarians, **639**–642
Rhizobacteria, **857**
Rhizobium, 859–860
Rhizobium, 616*f*
Rhizoids, **660**
Rhizomes, 805*f*
Rhizopus stolonifer, 699
Rhizopus stolonifer, 699–701, 701*f*
Rhizosphere, 622, **857**
Rhodopsin, **1175***f*
Rhomaleosaurus victor, 555*f*
Rhythm method, **1089**
Ribbon model, 87*f*

Ribonucleic acid (RNA). *See* RNA (ribonucleic acid)

Ribose, 76*f*, **93**, 94*f*

Ribosomal RNA (rRNA), **366**, 475*f*

Ribosomes, **108**, **111**, 112*f*, 113*f*, 114*f*, 115
    anatomy of, 366*f*
    as component of translation, 365–66
    and initiation of translation, 367
    using a sequence logo to identify binding sites, 368

Ribozymes, **362**, **553**

Ribulose, 76*f*

Rice, 459, 533*f*, 860, 883, 884, 896–97, 947, 1323

Richardson's ground squirrel, 1215

Ricinus communis, 874

Rickets, 945

Rieseberg, Loren, 546*f*

Rinderpest, 1295

Ring-tailed lemurs, 524

Ringworm, 708

Riparian habitats, 1332

Rising phase, 1127, 1128*f*

Ritland, Kermit, 351

Rivers, 1241*f*

RNA (ribonucleic acid), **92**
    evolution of, 595
    modification after transcription, 361–63
    and protein production, 6
    role of, 8, 93
    self-replicating, 553–54
    structure of, 95, 95*f*
    synthesis of RNA transcript, 358–360
    synthesization of, 111
    as viral genetic material, 422–23, 423*f*

RNA interference (RNAi), **395**, **447**–48

RNA polymerase, 92, **358**, 359–360, 360*f*, 912*f*

RNA processing, 361*f*, **361**, 392–93

RNA sequencing, 446

RNA splicing, 361*f*, **361**–63, **393**

RNAi. *See* RNA interference (RNAi), **395**

Roadmap Epigenomics Project, 467, 468

Roadrunners, 1041*f*

"Robbers," 868*f*

Rock pythons, 949*f*

Rocks, dating of, 554–56

Rodentia, 787*f*

Rodents, 959, 1029, 1079, 1165, 1213, 1213*f*

Rods, 104, 1175–76, **1175***f*, 1176–77, 1176*f*, 1178

Root caps, **811**

Root epidermal cells, 836

Root hairs, 804*f*, **804**, 823*f*

Root pressure, **837**

Root systems, 803*f*, **803**

Rooted, **585**

Roots, **665**, **804**
    and absorption of water and minerals, 836
    architecture and acquisition of water and minerals, 831
    evolution of, 665

growth of, 811–13, 811*f*
    and mutualism with nitrogen-fixing bacteria, 1307
    nodules on, 859–860, 859*f*, 860*f*, 1307*f*
    organization of primary tissues in, 812*f*
    role of in vascular plants, 804

ROPOS, 1283*f*

Rossant, Janet, 1105

Rosy periwinkle, 1323, 1323*f*

Rotifers (Rotifera), 727*f*, 737, 737*f*, 1034, 1071

Rough ER, **115**, 116

Rough-skinned newt, 1214

Round dance, 1199, 1200*f*

Round window, **1169**

Roundworms, 729*f*, 745–46, 745*f*, 1028, 1110, 1189

Rous, Peyton, 410

Rowan, William, 1198

Rozella, 698

rRNA. *See* Ribosomal RNA (rRNA)

r-selection, 1262

RT-PCR, **443**

RU486, 1091

Rubisco, **212**

Rudnicki, Michael, 453, 454*f*, 471*f*

Rufa red knots, 1330, 1330*f*

Ruffed grouse, 1196, 1196*f*, 1263, 1331

Rumen, 959*f*

Ruminants, 959*f*, **959**

Rundle, Howard, 1199

Running, 1191

Rupicapra rupicapra, 947*f*

Rutgers University, 465

Ryba, Nick, 1180*f*

Rye plants, 708

S

S phase, **246**, 395, 1099, 1101

Sac fungi, 700*f*, 702*f*

Saccharomyces cerevisiae, 110, 468, 468*f*, 469, 469*t*, 692, 697*f*, 709–10, 1265*f*. *See also* Yeast

Saccule, **1170**

Safran, Bernard, 712

Sagittaria latifolia, 879*f*

Sahelanthropus tchadensis, 790

Saimiri sciureus, 1178

Salamanders, 533*f*, 534, 537, 571, 571*f*, 773, 774*f*, 966, 966–67, 1140*f*, 1252

Salicylic acid, **913**

Salinity, 1245

Salivary amylase, **951**, 1002

Salivary glands, **951**

S-alleles, 880

Salmon, 917, 919*f*, 971*f*, 1028, 1028*f*, 1166, 1260, 1335

Salmonella, 621

Salt, table, 33, 54*f*, 177, 947

Salt glands, 1030, 1030*f*

Salt marsh, 1281, 1281*f*

Salt stress, plant, 911

Saltatory conduction, 1130*f*, **1130**

Salts, **42**
    dissolving in water, 54*f*
    table salt, 33, 54*f*, 177, 947

Sand dollars, 244*f*, 756

Sandhill cranes, 1202

Sanger, Frederick, 86, 434

Sanguinaria canadensis, 868*f*

Saprotrophs, **704**, 705–6

Sapwood, 818

SAR clade, 629*f*, 634–642, **634**, 639, 650

SARA (Species at Risk Act), 1322

Sarcomeres, 926*f*, **1182**

Sarcoplasmic reticulum (SR), **1184**

Sargasso Sea, 1305, 1305*t*

Sarracenia, 863*f*

SARS (severe acute respiratory syndrome), 427, 427*f*

Satellites, 1303, 1303*f*

Satiety centre, 962

Saturated enzymes, 167

Saturated fats, 81, 81*f*

Saturated fatty acid, 81, 81*f*

Savannas, 1233, **1235***f*

Saxena, Praveen, 708

Scaffolding proteins, 236*f*, **236**–38

Scala naturae, 494

Scale-eating fish, 526, 526*f*

Scallops, 101, 1192

Scanning electron microscope (SEM), 105–7, 106*f*

Scans, 367

Scarabaeus, 1319*f*

Scatter plots, 60, 146

Schatten, Gerald, 1098*f*

Scheibling, Robert, 1295

Schemske, Douglas, 546

Schindler, David, 1306, 1306*f*

Schistosoma, 736, 736*f*

Schizophrenia, 1157*f*, **1157**–58

Schmidt-Nielsen, Knut, 1192

Schwann cells, **1129**, 1130*f*, 1141, 1141*f*

SCID, 455

Science, **17**
    diverse viewpoints, value of, 26
    goal of, 25
    and society, 25–26
    and technology, 25–26
    theories in, 23

Scientific inquiry. *See* Scientific process

Scientific method. *See* Scientific process

Scientific process
    case study, 21–23
    cooperative approach, 23–25, 27–28, 29
    deductive reasoning, 19
    flexibility of, 20–21
    hypotheses, 18–19
    limitations of, 19
    making observations, 18
    model of, 20*f*
    process of, 18
    review, 27

simplified view of, 19f
"textbook" scientific method, 20
Scientific Skills Exercise
  amino acid sequence identity tables, 479f
  bar graphs, 24, 190, 622, 663, 806, 910
  change in slope, 1101
  chi-square tests, 318
  comparing variables on a common
      X-axis, 1021
  comparisons of genetic sequences, 631
  controlled experiments, 1066
  correlation coefficients, 718
  cyclic data, 1341
  data in tables, 333
  data values expressed in scientific
      notation, 1136
  distribution patters, 294
  DNA deletion experiments, 390
  equations of regression lines, 793
  estimating quantitative data, 564
  experimental data, 1277
  experimental design, 740
  experiments to test a model, 237
  experiments with genetic mutants, 963, 1149
  genomic data, 696
  graphs with log scales, 1192
  Hardy-Weinberg equation, 517
  histograms, 259, 294, 985
  inferences and experiment design, 1082
  line and scatterplot graphs, 1247
  line graph and slope, 168
  line graphs, 276
  logistic equations, 1259
  making observations, 857
  moles and molar ratios, 65
  natural logarithms, 675
  pie charts, 939
  polypeptide sequence data, 98
  population growth models, 1259
  positive and negative correlations, 880
  predictions, 507f
  protein sequence data, 600
  quantitative and spatial gene expression data, 445
  quantitative data, 1029
  quantitative date from graphs, 564
  quantitative models, 1208
  scale bars, 110
  scatter plots, 60, 146, 216
  sequence logos, 368
  sequence-based phylogenetic trees, 429f
  sex determination, 1082
  standard radioactive isotope decay curve, 37
  tabular data, 1304
  temperature coefficients, 834
  variables and scatter plots, 537
Scions, **881**
Sclera, 1174f
Sclereid cells, **808**f
Sclerenchyma cells, **808**f
Scorpions, 749f
Scottish broom, 686f

Scoville, William, 1155f
Scriver, Charles, 945
Scrotum, **1078**
Scutellum, 874
Scyphozoans (jellies), 732–33
Sea anemones, 732f, 733, 1071f
Sea cucumbers, 756, 756f
Sea daisies, 755, 755f
Sea lampreys, 1325
Sea lilies, 756
Sea minks, 1322
Sea otters, 1256, 1257f, 1286, 1287f, 1288,
      1288f, 1295
Sea palm, 635f
Sea pen, 1283f
Sea slugs, 739f
Sea snails, 1208
Sea squirts, 763f
Sea stars, 754, 755f, 987f, 1140f, 1141, 1252, 1287f
Sea surface temperature (SST), 649f
Sea turtles, 1030, 1166
Sea urchins, 157f, 332, 533f, 721, 729f, 756f,
      1096–97, 1097f, 1098, 1102–3, 1102f,
      1273, 1273f, 1279, 1286, 1295
Sea wasps, 732f, 733
Seahorses, 2f, 770f, 1320, 1320f
Seals, 787f, 921, 945f, 995–96, 995f, 1072f, 1276
Seamounts, 1334
Seasonality, 1225, 1228f, 1239f
Seawater, 59, 60, 1027
Seaweeds, 635f, 642f. See also Algae
Second law of thermodynamics, 156f, **157**, 1300
Second messengers, **231**–33, **890**, 891, 1052
Second trimester, 1088
Secondary cell walls, **130**
Secondary consumers, **1301**
Secondary endosymbiosis, 581f, **627**
Secondary growth, **810**
  cork cambium and production
      of periderm, 818
  evolution of, 818
  produced by vascular cambium, 815–18, 817f
  review, 826
  of woody stems, 810f, 815, 816f
Secondary immune response, **1010**
Secondary oocytes, **1081**f
Secondary production, **1307**
  production efficiency in, 1307–8
  trophic efficiency and ecological pyramids,
      1308–9
Secondary structure, **88**f, 90f
Secondary succession, **1292**
Secretin, 960f, 1056
Secretion, 1033f
Secretions, **1033**
  as defence against pathogens, 1002
  digestive juices, 957
  of pancreas, 955
  of small intestine, 955
  stomach gastric juice, 953
Secretory phase, 1084

Sedentarians, 743–45
Seed coats, **874**
Seed ferns, 676f
Seed plants
  adaptations for life on land, 673–76
  angiosperms, 678–688
  diversity, threats to, 689
  gametophyte reduction, advantages of, 673
  gametophyte-sporophyte relationships in plant
      groups, 674f
  gymnosperms, 676–78
  heterospory among, 673
  human welfare dependent on, 688–89
  ovules and production of eggs, 673
  phyla of, 657t
  pollen and production of sperm, 673–75
  products from, 688–89
  review, 690
Seedless vascular plants, **658**
  classification of, 666–69, 667f
  coal, producing, 668f
  first plants to grow tall, 664
  origins and traits of, 664–66
  significance of, 669
Seeds, **658**, **672**
  cupulate, 676f
  development of, 870
  dispersal of, 878f
  dispersal of, in fruits, 681, 682f
  dormancy, 675, 874–75, 898
  embryo development, 873–74, 873f
  endosperm development, 873
  evolution of, 676
  evolutionary advantage of, 675
  germination, 875, 875f, 902–3
  seedling development, 875
  structure of, 874, 874f
Seehausen, Ole, 539f, 540f
Seeing. See Visual systems
Segregation, 289f
Selaginella moellendorffii, 667f
Selasphorus platycercus, 880
Selective permeability, **136**, 142, 151
Selectively permeable plasma membranes, 836
Self-fertilization, 879–881, 879f
Self-incompatibility, **880**–81
Self-pruning, 831
Self-thinning, 845
Self-tolerance, 1008–9
Selzentry, 141
Semelparity, 1260f, **1260**
Semen, 1051, **1079**
Semi-aquatic, 1029
Semicircular canals, **1168**f
Semiconservative model, 336f, **336**
Semilunar valves, **973**
Seminal vesicles, **1079**
Seminiferous tubules, **1078**, 1085
Senescence, **899**–900
Sensitive period, **1202**
Sensors, **929**

Sensory adaptation, **1164**
Sensory input, 1163*f*, 1197–1201, 1218
Sensory neurons, 1122*f*, **1122**
Sensory pathways, 1163–64
Sensory reception, **1163**, 1169*f*
Sensory receptors, **1163**
    chemoreceptors, 1165, 1166*f*
    classes of, 1163*f*
    and coding of stimulus intensity, 1164*f*
    electromagnetic receptors, 1166, 1166*f*
    hair cells, 1168*f*, 1169, 1169*f*, 1170
    mechanoreceptors, 1165, 1167–72
    olfactory receptors, 1180–81, 1181*f*
    osmoreceptors, 1165
    pain receptors, 1166–67
    photoreceptors, 1173, 1175*f*
    review, 1193–94
    in skin, 1165*f*
    taste receptors, 1179–80, 1180*f*
    thermoreceptors, 1166, 1166*f*
    transmission of signals to central nervous
        system, 1163–67
    types of, 1165–67
Sensory systems
    in fish, 1171*f*
    mechanoreceptors for hearing and
        equilibrium, 1167–72
    muscle function in, 1181–88
    sensory pathways in, 1163–64
    sensory receptors in, 1163–67, 1163*f*,
        1165–67
    smell receptors in, 1180–81
    taste receptors in, 1179–80
    visual receptors in, 1172–79
Sensory transduction, **1164**, 1175–76
Sepals, **681**, **867**
Separase, 250
Septa, **694**
Septate hyphae, 694*f*
Septic shock, 1004–5
Sequence logos, 368
Sequencing, of DNA, 96
Sequencing by synthesis, 434
Sequential regulation, 398–400
Sequoia, 680*f*, 818*f*
Serial endosymbiosis, **560**, 561*f*
Serial transfers, 609*f*
Serotinin, **1135**
Serpentine plant community, 34*f*
Sertoli cells, 1085
Serum, 981
Sessile animals, 1073
Set points, **929**
Seta, **660**
Severe acute respiratory syndrome (SARS),
    427, 427*f*
Severe combined immunodeficiency (SCID),
    455, 1019
Sex
    of cells, 222
    chromosomal basis of, 311–14, 311*f*

and size and weight, 794
Sex bias, 1019
Sex chromosomes, **269**
Sex determination, 269–270
Sex hormones, 1065–67, 1066*f*
    and functional groups, 69
    mammalian reproduction regulated
        by, 1082–86
    review, 1093
Sex reversal, 1073–74
Sex steroids, 1338
Sex-linked genes, 311–14, 311*f*, **312**, 326–27
Sexual dimorphism, 524*f*, **524**, 794, 1208, 1210
Sexual life cycles
    and evolution, 277–79
    fertilization and meiosis in, 268–271
    genetic variations, 277–79
    review, 279
    variety of, 270–71, 270*f*
Sexual reproduction, **267**, 514, **1071**
    animal, 713–14
    of echinoderms, 754
    of fungi, 695–97, 697
    human reproductive organs, 1077–81, 1077*f*,
        1078*f*
    regulation by tropic and sex hormones,
        1082–86
    review, 1092–93
    of rotifers, 737
    and sex reversal, 1073–74
    variation in, 1073–74
Sexual selection, 524*f*, **524**, 525*f*, 538–39,
    1210–12, 1211*f*
Sexually transmitted diseases (STIs), 1092
S-genes, 880
Shade avoidance, 903
Shaffer, Mark, 1329
Shannon diversity, **1282**
Shapiro, Michael, 573*f*
Shared ancestral characters, **589**
Shared derived characters, **589**
Sharks, 768, 768*f*, 917, 921, 933, 937*f*, 1027,
    1032, 1071, 1192
Sheep, 787*f*, 1072, 1250, 1255, 1258, 1259*f*, 1263
Shelf fungi, 704*f*
Sheriff, Michael, 1266*f*
Shigella, 611
"Shirt-striping," 306*f*
Shmoo, 237
Shoot architecture, and light capture, 830–31
Shoot systems, 803*f*, **803**
Shoots, 813–15, 813*f*
Short, Steven, 415
Short tandem repeats (STRs), 458*f*, **458**, **474**
Short-beaked echidna, 784*f*
Short-day plants, **905**, 906*f*
Short-finned pilot whale, 97*f*
Short-term memory, 1155*f*, **1155**
Shoubridge, Eric, 186*f*
Shrews, 787*f*
Shrimp, 486*f*, 536–37, 537*f*, 750, 1029, 1288*f*

Siberian tigers, 1346*f*
Siblings, coefficient of relatedness in, 1216–17,
    1216*f*
Sickle-cell disease, 90*f*, **90**, **298**–99, 299*f*, **981**
    allele of, 490*f*–91*f*
    and connections among levels of biology, 25
    gene identification for, 454
    and heterozygote advantage, 525, 526*f*
    molecular basis of, 374*f*
    and mutations, 513
    testing for, 301
Sickle-cell trait, 299, 299*f*
Side chains, 83–84, 85*f*
Side-blotched lizards, 1212, 1212*f*
Sieve plates, **809***f*
Sieve-tube elements, **809***f*
Sight. *See* Visual systems
Sign stimuli, 1197*f*, **1197**
Signal amplification, 235
Signal peptides, **370**, 371*f*
Signal transduction, **1052**
Signal transduction pathway, 222
Signal transduction pathways, **225**, 229–230,
    889–891, 889*f*
    general model of, 889*f*
    linking signal reception to plant
        response, 889–891
    phytochrome, role of, 890*f*
    reception, 890
    response, 891
    review, 915
    second messengers, 890, 891
Signalling
    electrical, 846–47, 927
    and hormones, 223*f*, 224, 927
Signalling molecules, 1117
Signal-recognition particles (SRPs), **370**, 371*f*
Silent mutation, **374**
Silent Spring (Carson), 1337
Silkworm moths, 1165, 1166*f*
Silurian period, 717
Silversword alliance, 570*f*, 586
Simard, Suzanne, 695
Similicaudipteryx, 583*f*
Simple columnar epithelium, 924*f*
Simple endocrine pathways, 1055, 1055*f*
Simple fruits, 876*f*, **876**
Simple leaves, 805*f*
Simple neuroendocrine pathways, 1055, 1056*f*
Simple sequence DNA, **474**
Simple squamous epithelium, 924*f*
Single bonds, **40**
Single circulation, **969**
Single nucleotide polymorphism (SNP), 448*f*,
    448, 454–55, 484
Single-base pair variations, 448
Single-celled organisms, 559–560
Single-lens eyes, **1173**–74
Single-strand binding protein, 342*t*
Single-strand binding proteins, **338**
Sinoatrial (SA) node, **974**

Sirenia, 787f
Sirenians, 760
siRNAs, **395**
Sirtalis, 1214
Sister cells, 244
Sister chromatid cohesion, 271
Sister chromatids, **245**, 247f, 249f, 272f, 273f
Sister taxa, **585**
Sitka spruce, 1291
In situ hybridization, 443f, **443**
Situs inversus, 1117, 1117f
Skates, 768–69
Skeletal development, 489
Skeletal muscle, **926f, 1181**
    fibres of, 1182, 1187
    and interaction with skeleton
        in movement, 1188f
    motor units in, 1186f, **1186**
    nervous system control of, 1186
    specialization of, 1187f
    structure of, 1182f
    vertebrate, 1181–88
Skeletal systems, 923t
    endoskeletons, 1190
    exoskeleton, 1189–90
    hydrostatic, 1189
    and muscle contraction transformed into
        locomotion, 1188–92, 1188f
    review, 1194
    types of, 1189–91
Skeletons
    external, 923
    human, 1190f
    joints of, 1190f
    mammalian, 1190
    size and scale of, 1191
Skin, 923
    genetic damage to, 342
    pH of, 1002
    pigmentation of, 293–94, 294f
    as respiratory organ, 986
    sensory receptors in, 1165f
    thermorerceptors in, 1166
Skinner, B. F., 1203
Skull growth rates, 571f
Skunks, 532f, 1278f
Sladek, Robert, 470f
Sleep
    and adrenocorticotropic hormone (ACTH), 1066
    and arousal, 1148
    cycles of, 1148, 1149
    and immune system, 1019
    and melatonin, 1067, 1148
Sleeping sickness, 633, 633f, 754, 1020, 1021
Sliding-filament model, **1182**, 1183f
Slime layers, 605
Slime moulds, 645–46, 647f
Sloths, 787f
Slow block to polyspermy, **1097**
Slow-twitch fibres, **1187**
Slugs, 1070, 1070f, 1073

Small interfering RNAs (siRNAs), **395**
Small intestine
    absorption in, 955–56, 955f
    digestion in, **954**–55
    junction with large intestine, 956f
Small ncRNAs, 394, 395, 396
Small-population approach, population
        conservation, 1327
Smallpox, 426, 1015
Smallwood, Joey, 712
Smart plants, 856, 857f
Smell, 1179, 1180–81, 1181f, 1193–94
Smithies, Oliver, 446
Smoking
    and cardiovascular disease, 984, 1091
    and lung capacity, 990
    and oral contraceptives, 1090
Smoltificatioin, 1028
Smooth ER, **115**–16
Smooth muscle, **926f, 1188**
Snails, 532f, 546, 564, 726f, 739f, 742, 1028, 1032,
        1132f, 1208, 1279
Snakebite, 1017
Snakes, 532f, 779–780, 939, 949f, 1139, 1191,
        1277, 1325
    and mimicry, 1278, 1278f
    movable jaw bones in, 523, 524f
    and nutrition, 944
    and prey selection, 1214
    thermorerceptors in, 1166, 1166f
Snapdragons, 291f
Snapping shrimp, 536–37, 537f
Snapping turtles, 777f
Snook, Rhonda, 1076f
Snout weevils, 753f
Snow crabs, 1288f
Snow geese, 1198f, 1279, 1286f
Snow peas, 687f
Snowflake plant, 800f
Snowshoe hares, 221f, 1263–65, 1265f,
        1266f, 1274
Snowy owls, 1264f, 1284
SNP. *See* Single nucleotide polymorphism (SNP)
Soapberry bugs, 501, 501f
Social learning, 1205f, **1205**–6
Societal benefits and outcomes, in scientific
        process, 20f
Sociobiology, **1217**–18
Sociobiology: The New Synthesis (Wilson), 1217
Socium hydroxide, 56
Sodium, 33f, 35, 945, 946t, 947
Sodium channels, 1126, 1126f, 1127, 1129
Sodium chloride, 33, 33f, 42f, 54f, 177
Sodium-potassium pump, 147f, **147**, 1126f
Soil
    adjusting pH in, 853
    bacteria in, 618f, 851
    composition of, 850–51
    conservation of, 851–52
    ecosystem of, 850–54
    and erosion, 853

    review, 864
    salinity, 911
    and sustainable agriculture, 852–54
    texture of, 850
Soil horizons, 850f, **850**
Soil microorganisms, 621, 622
Soil nitrogen, 1291
Soil worms
    apoptosis in, 239, 239f
    information about aging, 484
    as model organism, 25
Solar radiation, 1302
Solstice, 1228f
Solute concentration, 1026f
Solute potential, **833**
Solutes, **54**
    concentrations in aqueous solutions, 55–56
    in excretory system, 1038–40, 1039f
    short-distance transport of, across plasma
        membranes, 832, 833f
Solutions, **54**
Solvents, **54**
Somatic cell nuclear transfer, 449–451
Somatic cells, **245**, **267**
Somatic sensory receptors, 1151
Somatosensory cortex, 1151, 1152f
Somites, 762, 1107f, **1107**–8
Sonic hedgehog, 1116
Soredia, **707**
Sori, **666**
Sorophyte, 636
Sound
    pitch and volume, 1169
    sense of, 1167–72
South Africa, 1317f
South America, 785
Southern magnolias, 687f
Southern Ocean, 1305
Southern red maples, 806
Southern stingray, 768f
Soybeans, 517, 860f, 1309
Space-filling model, 87f
Spacer DNA, 421
Spanish flu, 428
Spanish mosses, 658
Sparrows, 1205
Spatial heterotherms, 934
Spatial learning, 1202–**3**
Spatial patterns, 571
Spatial summation, **1132**
Spawning, 1074
Speciation, **530**. *See also* Evolution
    allopatric, 535–38, 535f, 537f, 539
    allopolyploid, 538f
    biological concept of, 531–34
    and continental drift, 565
    Darwin on, 530
    and divergence of allopatric populations, 545
    and diversity, 563f
    genetics of, 546–47
    and geographic separation, 535–540, 535f

Speciation (*Continued*)
    and habitat differentiation, 539
    hybrid zones, and reproductive isolation, 540–44
    and macroevolution, 547
    patterns in fossil record, 544
    polypoid, 538–39
    rates of, 544–46, 545*f*
    review, 547–48
    and rise and fall of organisms, 563–570
    and sexual selection, 538–39
    sympatric, 538–540, 539
    Sympatric speciation, 535*f*
    time course of, 544–46
Species, **531**
    allopatric, 536*f*
    biological concept of, 531–34
    classification of, 494
    and climate change, 1231
    definitions of, 534–35
    dominant, 1285–86
    ecological species concept of, 534
    grouping of, 11–12
    interactions of, 97*f*
    invasive, 1283
    keystone species, 1286
    with large impact, 1285–86
    morphological species concept of, 534
    phylogenetic species concept of, 535
    similarity and diversity within, 531*f*
    threatened, 1322
    universal identification, 594*f*
Species at Risk Act (SARA), 520, 1322
Species composition, **1282**
Species distribution
    abiotic factors, 1245–46
    biotic factors, 1246
    and dispersal factors, 1244–45
    geographic factors limiting, 1244*f*
    and interactions between organisms and environment, 1239, 1244
    review, 1248
Species diversity, 1321–22
    and community stability, 1282–83
    manipulation of, 1283, 1283*f*
    quantifying, 1282
Species richness, 1282*f*, **1282**, 1293*f*, 1294*f*
Species selection, 575
Species transplant experiment, **1244**
Species-area curve, **1293**
Specific heat, **52**
Specific transcription
    cell type, 391*f*
    factors of, 388, 388*f*, 891
Specificity, 1006
Spectrophotometer, **204**
Speech, 1152
"Speed," 1157
Spemann, Hans, 1113, 1114, 1114*f*, 1115*f*
Spemann's organizer, 1114, 1115*f*

Sperm, **1071**, 1078–79
    flagellated, 653, 675
    and pollen, in seed plants, 673–75
Spermathecae, **1075**
Spermatogenesis, **1079**, 1080*f*, 1085
Spermatogonia, **1080***f*
Spermidical foam, 1090
Spermocytes, 1080*f*
Spermophilus beldingi, 1252, 1253, 1253*t*, 1254*f*
Spermophilus parryii, 940
Sphagnum, 656*f*, 661, 663*f*
Sphagnum moss, 1291
Sphenisciformes, 782
Sphincters, **951**, 957, 978, 978*f*
Sphygmomanometer, 977*f*
Spider mites, 912
Spiders, 89*f*, 748–49, 749*f*, 947, 969, 989, 998*f*, 1173
Spiderworts, 815*f*
Spike mosses, 666, 667*f*
SPIN, 599*f*
Spina bifida, 1108
Spindles, 248*f*, 272*f*
Spines, 806*f*
Spiral cleavage, **721**
Spiral valves, 768
Spirilla, 604*f*
Spirobranchus giganteus, 743*f*
Spirochetes, 617*f*
Spirogyra crassa, 122*f*
Spleen, 1004*f*
Spliceosome, 362*f*, **362**
Sponges (Porifera), 714, 722, 723, 727*f*, 730–31, 730*f*, 923, 950, 1071, 1191
Spongocoel, **730**
Spongy mesophyll, 814
Spontaneous change, 159*f*
Spontaneous Mutation, 375
Spontaneous process, **157**, 159
Sporangia, **656***f*, 702*f*
Spores, **655***f*–56*f*, **695**
    compared to seeds, 675
    fossilized, 657*f*
    production of, in fungi, 695–97
    as survival mechanism, 675
    tetrads, 654
Sporocytes, **656***f*
Sporophyll leaves, **666**
Sporophytes, 270, **655***f*, 664*f*
    characteristics of, 667*f*
    dominant, 664
    fossilized tissue of, 664*f*
    and gametophyte relationships in plant groups, 674*f*
    pine tree as, 676–77
    of vascular plants, 664
Sporophytic self-incompatibility, 880–81
Sporopollenin, **653**
Sporozites, 637
Spotted ratfish, 768*f*
Spriggina floundersi, 715*f*

Spruce budworm, 1050, 1200
Spruce forest, 1304
Squamates, 779
Squids, 574, 575*f*, 741, 741*f*, 986, 1130, 1140*f*, 1141, 1173, 1192, 1284
Squirrel monkeys, 1178
Squirrels, 787*f*, 878*f*
    flying squirrels, 505, 505*f*
    ground squirrels, 1252, 1253, 1253*t*, 1254*f*, 1255
    and hibernation, 940
    red squirrels, 510–11, 510*f*
    Richardson's ground squirrel, 1215
Srb, Adrian, 353, 353*f*
ß pleated sheets, 91
ß-amyloid, 1159
ß-galactosidase, 383
ß-thalassemia gene, 456
ß-tubulin, 124*f*, 125
Stability, 1289
Stabilizing selection, **522**, 523*f*
Stahl, Franklin, 337, 337*f*
"Stair-stepped" curves, 1254
Stalk-eyed flies, 1210, 1210*f*
Stamens, 681*f*, **681**, **867**
Standard metabolic rate (SMR), **938**
Standing crop, 1302, 1308, 1308*f*
Stanley, Steven, 575
Stanley, Wendell, 416
Stapelia sp., 872*f*
Stapes, 1169
Staphylococcus aureus, 502, 605
Star anise, 687*f*
Star corals, 732*f*
Star fish, 754
Star of Bethlehem, 868*f*
Starches, 78*f*, **78**, 79*f*
Starfish, 754, 755*f*
Star-nosed moles, 787*f*, 1162, 1162*f*, 1163, 1163*f*
Start points, **359**
Statocysts, 1167*f*, **1167**
Statoliths, 907*f*, **907**, **1167**
Stechmann, Alexandra, 645*f*
Stefansson, Baldur, 866
Steinbeck, John, 852
Steinhardt, Rick, 1098*f*
Steinman, Ralph M., 1011*f*
Stele, **807**
Stem cell genomics, 471*f*
Stem Cell Genomics Project, 471*f*
Stem cells, **449**, 982*f*, **982–83**
    discovery of, 451*f*
    maintenance of own population of, and generation of differentiated cells, 451*f*
    of plants, 810
    radial glia and astrocytes as, 1142
Stem cells of animals
    deprogramming differentiated human cells, 453*f*
    embryonic and adult stem cells, 451–53
    inducing stem cell growth to treat disease, 454*f*

working with, 452*f*

Stem elongation, 897

Stems, **805**
  anatomy of a tree trunk, 818*f*
  evolutionary adaptations of, 805*f*
  growth of, 810*f*, 816*f*
  purposes of, 830
  tissue organization of, 813–14, 814*f*

Stenohaline osmoregulators, 1026

Stepwise energy harvest, 178–79

Sterilization, 1090, 1091

Steroid hormones, 69, 83*f*, **83**, 891, 1051, 1051*f*, 1064–65, 1082
  anabolic, 1065
  and coordinate regulation, 392
  and hormone signalling, 1052–53, 1053*f*
  and smooth ER, 115

Steward, F. C., 449

Stickleback fish, 572–73, 573*f*, 919*f*

Sticky ends, **438**

Stigma, **681**

Stigmas, **867**

Stimulated state, 909*f*

Stimuli, **929**

Stimulus-response chain, 1198–99

Stink bugs, 753*f*

Stipe, 635*f*, **635**

Stirling, Ian, 945*f*

STIs, 1092

Stock, **881**

Stolons, 805*f*

Stomach, 953*f*, **953–54**
  evolutionary adaptations of, 958
  microbiome, 959*f*

Stomata, **200**, 660, 671*f*, **814**
  opening and closing, 841–42, 841*f*
  as pathways for water loiss, 841
  and transpiration, 214, 838, 840–42, 847

Stomatal development, 822*f*

Stone plants, 868*f*

Stony corals, 1071

Storage leaves, 806*f*

Storage polysaccharides, 78–79

Storage proteins, 84*f*

Storey, Ken, 918*f*

Storks, 582, 582*f*

Storms, 1289

Stramenopiles, 634*f*, **634–642**

"Strangling" aerial roots, 804*f*

Strasburger, Eduard, 838

Strata, 494*f*, **494**, 554

Stratified squamous epithelium, 924*f*

Strawberry plants, 805*f*

Strawberry poison dart frogs, 549*f*

Streams, 1241*f*

Streptococcus, 605*f*, 731

Streptococcus pneumoniae, 1005

Streptomyces, 617*f*

Stress
  and the adrenal gland, 1065*f*
  and immune system, 1019

mechanical, 898–99

Stretch receptors, 1165

Stretch-activated ion channels, 1125

Striated muscle, 926*f*, **1182**

Strickland, Dan, 1203

Striga, 901

Strigolactones, 892*t*, 896, **901**

Strobili, **666**, 667*f*

Stroke volume, **973**

Strokes, 457, **983**

Stroma, **122**, **201**

Stromatolites, **559**

STRs, 458*f*, **458**, **474**

Structural formula, 40

Structural isomers, 68*f*, **68**

Structural polysaccharides, 79–80

Structural proteins, 84*f*

Structure, as property of life, 2*f*

Structure and function, as theme in biology, 3–4

Struthioniformes, 781

Strychnine, 1279

Strychnos, 1279

Sturtevant, Alfred H., 317, 319

Styles, **681**, **867**

Subatomic particles, 34–35

Suberin, 818

Substance P, 1135

Substrate feeders, **949***f*

Substrate-level phosphorylation, 180*f*, **180**

Substrates, 166*f*, **166**, 171

Succulent Karoo, 1317*f*

Succulent plants, 157*f*

Sucrase, 166

Sucrose. *See also* Sugars
  dehydration reation in synthesis of, 77*f*
  hydrolyzation of, 164
  monomers of, 77
  transport into phloem, 844*f*

Sudden oak death, 914, 1295

Sugar gliders, 505, 505*f*

Sugar maple trees, 295, 1230*f*, 1231*f*, 1285

Sugar sinks, **843–45**, 845*f*

Sugar sources, **843–45**, 845*f*

Sugar-phosphate backbone, 94, 332*f*

Sugars. *See also* Sucrose
  deoxyribose, 93, 94*f*
  disaccharides, 77–78
  monosaccharides, 76–77, 76*f*
  polysaccharides, 78–80
  ribose, 93, 94*f*
  table sugar, molecular mass of, 55
  transport in vascular plants, 843–45, 845*f*

Suicide genes, 406

Sulfhydryl group, 70, 71*f*

Sulfolobus, 615

Sulphur, 946*t*
  as dietary nutrient, 945
  and photosynthesis, 201–2

Sulphur dioxide emissions, 1335, 1336*f*

Sulston, John, 1110, 1112*f*

Summation, 1132, 1133*f*, 1186*f*, **1186**

Summer torpor, 940

Summerbell, Dennis, 1116*f*

Sumner, Francis Bertody, 22

Sunda islands, 1293, 1294*f*

Sundews, 863*f*

Sunflowers, 2*f*, 545, 545*f*, 546*f*

Sunlight, 1227*f*, 1228*f*, 1238
  nature of, 203–4
  and primary production, 1302
  and secondary production, 1308*f*
  and species distribution, 1245

Super weeds, 460

Supergroups, of eukaryotes, 626–27, 628*f*–29*f*

Super-resolution, 106*f*, 107

Superweed, 885

Suprachiasmatic nucleus (SCN), 1067, 1149, **1149**

Surface tension, **51**

Surfactant, **990**

Survival
  and beak size, 1239
  behaviour for, 1206–12, 1219
  and population density, 1263*f*

Survivorship curves, 1254*f*, **1254**

Suspension feeders, **730**, **949***f*

Suspensors, 873

Sustainable agriculture, **852**
  adjusting soil pH for, 853
  and fertilization, 853
  and irrigation, 852–53, 852*f*
  and phytoremediation, 854
  and soil erosion, 853

Sustainable development, 1342–44, **1343**, 1345

Sutherland, Earl W., 224, 231

Sutherland, John, 552

Sutton, Walter S., 309

Swallowing, 952, 952*f*

Sweat, human, 624*f*, 1002

Swift foxes, 1322*f*

Swim bladders, **769**–770, 1171, 1187

Swimming, 1192

Swine flu. *See* H1N1 virus

Switchgrass, 884

Syed, Naweed, 1131, 1132*f*

Sylvia atricapilla, 1214, 1215*f*

Sym genes, 698

Symbion pandora, 728*f*

Symbiont, **618**

Symbiosis, 562*f*, **618**, **1279**
  commensalism, 1280–81
  mutualism, 1280
  parasitism, 1279–80

Symmetry
  bilateral, 681*f*, 688, 734, 868*f*
  in body plans, 719
  of cell division, 821–22
  of chordates, 760
  of flowers, 681*f*
  and plant-pollinator interactions, 685–86, 686*f*
  radial, 681*f*, 688
  and speciation, 686–88

Sympathetic division, 1143–**44**, 1144*f*

Sympatric speciation, 535f, **538**–540, 539
Symplast, 831–**32**, 848
Symplastic domains, 846
Symplastic route, 832, 837f
Synapses, **1121**
    elimination of, 1154
    and memory and learning, 1154–56
    modulated signalling at, 1133
    and neural communication, 1130–35
    and neural plasticity, 1154, 1154f
    review, 1160
    terminals, 1131f
Synapsids, 557f, 783f, **783**
Synapsis, 274f, **274**–76
Synaptic cleft, 1131
Synaptic signalling, 223f, 224, 1049, 1176f
Synaptic vesicles, 1130
Synaptonemal complex, 274
Synthesis, 552f
Syringa, 815f
Systematics, **583**
    animal, future directions in, 723–24
    applying parsimony to, 591f
    cladistics, 588–89
    molecular, **588**
Systemic acquired resistance, **913**–14, 914f
Systemic circuits, **969**, 970f
Systemic lupus erythematosus, 1019
Systems, open and closed, 156
Systems biology, **3**, 467–69, 468f, 820
Systole, 973f
Systolic pressure, **976**
Szent-Györgyi, Albert, 945

T

T2, 331–32, 331f
T4 bacteriophage, 414, 414f
Table salt. *See* Sodium chloride
Table sugar, 55, 77
Tachyglossus aculeatus, 784f
Tactile communication, 1199
Tadpoles, 1059f, 1109–10
Tailings, 603–4, 613, 615, 1314, 1314f
Tails, 761
TAL protein, 350f
Tamanduas, 787f
Tamias striatus, 1029
Tamiflu, 432f
Tangled-1 mutants, 821
Tannins, 1279
Tansley, A. G., 1289
Tapeworms, 736–37, 736f, 922, 1073
Tapirs, 787f
Taproots, **804**
Taq polymerase, 441, 1323
Taraxacum vulgare, 871f
Tardigrades (Tardigrada), 729f, 1028, 1028f
Target cells, 1049
Taricha granulosa, 1214
Taro, 800f
Tastants, **1179**

Taste, 1179–80, 1180f, 1193–94
Taste buds, **1179**
TATA box, **359**
Tattersall, Glen, 918f
Tatum, Edward, 352–53
Tau, 1159
Taxa, **584**
Taxis, **606**
Taxonomy, **584**, 598–99. *See also* Systematics
    binomial nomenclature, 584
    grouping of species, 11–12
    hierarchical classification, 584–85
    Linnaean system, 12f, 584, 584f
    and phylogeny, 585–86, 585f
    of trees, 585
Taylor, Eric, 1276
Tay-Sachs disease, **292**, 298, 301, 302
T cells, 982f, 1005f, 1006–7, **1006**, 1007f,
    1010f
    cytotoxic, 1010, 1010f, 1012–13, 1013f
    development of, 1007–11
    diversity, generation of, 1008
    helper T cells, 1010, 1010f, 1012, 1012f
    proliferation of, 1009–10
Tears, 1002
Technology
    and bacteria, 621–22
    brain imaging, 1150
    brainbow, 1139
    goal of, 25
    and prokaryotes, 621–22
    and science, 25–26
Tectonic plates. *See* Plate tectonics
Tectorial membranes, 1169
Teeth, 556, 957f
    in mammals, 783
    origins of, 766
    in reptiles, 778, 780
Telomerase, **344**–45
Telomeres, 344f, **344**, 345f
Telomeric DNA, 474
Telophase, **246**, 248f, 252f
Telophase I, 272f, 275f
Telophase II, 273f
Temperate broadleaf forest, **1237f**
Temperate grasslands, 1232, **1236f**
Temperate phages, **419**
Temperature, **51**. *See also* Thermoregulation
    adaptation, in salmon, 971f
    and climate change, 1339f
    and decomposition rates, 1312f
    and enzymes, 168, 169f
    and extinction, 568f
    and fever, 1004
    and heat, 51–52
    and melatonin, 930f
    and membrane fluidity, 137–39
    mountain effects on, 1228
    and nervous systems, 1144
    ocean effects on, 1228
    of Pacific Ocean and Southern California, 52f

    and plant stress, 910–11
    and protein structures, 101
    regulating and conforming relative to, 928,
        928f, 929f
    and species distribution, 1245–46
    for sperm production, 1078
    in terrestrial biomes, 1234f–37f
    variation in, 931
    water's moderating effect, 31, 51–53
    and wilting, 842
Temperature coefficients, 834
Template strands, **356**
Temporal heterotherms, 934
Temporal isolation, 532f
Temporal summation, **1132**
Tendons, **925f**
Tendrils, 806f
Teosinte, 882f
Termination
    in cell signalling, 238
    of translation, 359–360, 359f, 367, 370f
Terminators, **358**
Terrapene carolina carolina, 778f
Terrestrial biodiversity hot spots, 1333f
Terrestrial biomes
    chaparral, 1233, 1235f
    and climate, 1231–32, 1232f
    deserts, 1234f
    distribution of, 1232
    and disturbance, 1233
    features of, 1232–33
    northern coniferous forest, 1233, 1236f
    review, 1248
    savanna, 1233, 1235f
    temperate broadleaf forest, 1237f
    temperate grasslands, 1233, **1236f**
    tropical forest, 1234f
    tundra, 1222f–23f, 1231, 1237f
Terrestrial ecosystems
    decomposition in, 1312
    primary production in, 1306–7, 1306f
Territoriality, **1253**, 1265f
Tertiary consumers, **1301**
Tertiary structure, 90f
Testability, 19
Testcross, **286**, 287f, 315f, 316, 317f
Testes, 1054f, **1078**, 1085f
Testing, genetic, 301–2
Testosterone, 69–70, **1065**, 1066f, 1078,
    1082, 1085
Tests, **641**
Tetanus, **1186**
Tetany, 1063
Tetrahymena, 362
Tetraploids, 321, 538
Tetrapods, 504, 556, 557f, 562, **771**
    amniotes, 775–782
    amphibians, 773–75
    derived characters of, 771–72
    origin of, 772–73
    review, 797

"Textbook" scientific method, 20
Thalamus, **1147**f, 1150
Thalassoma bifasciatum, 1073
Thamnophis elegans, 1214
Thamnophis sirtalis, 1214
Thaumoctopus mimicus, 1278
Theobroma cacao, 706, 706f
Theories, **23**
Theories vs. hypotheses, 23, 507–8
Therapeutic cloning, 452
    inducing stem cell growth to treat disease, 454f
    insulin-producing cells, 453
    replacement cells, 453
Therapods, **778**, 781
Therapsids, 557f
Thermal energy, **51**, **155**, 1238
Thermoclines, **1238**
Thermodynamics, 156f, **156**, **157**, 1300
Thermogenesis, 934
Thermoreceptors, 1166f, **1166**
Thermoregulation, **930**
    acclimation and acclimatization, 934–35
    in aquatic animals, 928, 928f
    balancing heat loss and gain, 932–34
    behavioural responses, 934, 934f
    and endothermic and ectothermic animals, 931
    and minimum metabolic rate, 937–38
    physiological thermostats and fever, 935–36, 936f
    review, 941
    and variation in body temperature, 931
Thermus aquaticus, 440, 1323
Thick filaments, **1182**
Thigmomorphogenesis, **908**
Thigmotropism, **908**
Thin filaments, 1181, **1182**
Thiomargarita namibiensis, 604, 616f
Third trimester, 1088–89
Third-generation sequencing, 437
Thlaspi caerulescens, 854
Thompson seedless grapes, 897
Thoracic cavity, 991
Threatened species, **1322**
Threespine stickleback fish, 572–73, 573f, 1197, 1197f, 1276, 1276f
Threonine, 172
Thresholds, **1127**
Thrifty gene hypothesis, 963
Thrombin, 981
Thrombus, **982**, 984
Thrum flower, 879f
Thucydides, 1010
Thuja occidentalis, 828f
Thuja plicata, 836
Thylakoids, **122**, **201**, 210–12, 211f
Thymine, 334–35
Thymine dimers, 342
Thymus, **1005**
Thyroid glands, 33, 927, 1054f, **1061**, 1062f

Thyroid hormones, 190, 1051, 1054f, 1059, 1061–62
Thyroid-stimulating hormone (TSH), 927, 1054f, 1061, 1062
Thyrotropin, 1061
Thyroxine (T$_4$), 1051, 1059f, **1061**
Thysanura (silverfish), 753f
Ti plasmids, 820–f
Tiburon Mariposa lily, 34f
Ticks, 1224, 1224f, 1296, 1296f, 1332, 1340f
Tidal volume, **991**
Tigers, 1346f
Tight junctions, 131, **132**f, 1106f
Tiktaalik, 554, 555f, 772–73
Till, James, 451, 451f
Tinbergen, Niko, 1197, 1203, 1203f
Tinman gene, 1096
Tissue culture, 881–82
Tissue plasminogen activator (tPA), 457
Tissue systems, **806**, 807f
Tissues, **714**, **803**, **923**
    and body plans, 719–720
    as level of biological organization, 5f
    plant, 806–7
    in plant roots, 812f
    structure and function of, 924f–26f
    types of, 923
Tissue-specific proteins, 398
Tit for tat, 1217
T lymphocytes, 984f
Tmesipteris, 667f, 669
Toadfish, 1187, 1187f
Toads, 541, 541f, 773, 1172
Tobacco, 801f, 895, 905
Tobacco mosaic virus (TMV), 415–16, 416f, 417f, 430
Tobacco plants, 358f
Tolerance, 33–34, 1290
Toll, 1001
Toll-like receptors (TLR), 913, **1002**, 1003f
Tollund man, 661, 663f
Tomatoes, 682f, 864, 890, 891, 895
Tonicity, **144**
Tonsils, 1004f
Tool use, 792–94
Top-down control, **1287**
Topoisomerase, **338**, 342t
Topsoil, 850–51, **850**
Torpor, 939–940
Tortoiseshell cats, 314f
Total biomass accumulation, 1303
Total fertility rate, 1268f
Totipotency, **881**–82
Totipotent, **449**, **1113**
Toucans, 918f
Touch, sense of, 1165
Touch specialists, 908
Toxic compounds in the environment, 1337–38
Toxic elements, tolerance to, 33–34
Toxic wastes, 1265f
tPA, 457

Trace elements, **33**
Tracers, 36
Trachea, 952f, **989**
Tracheal system, 988f, **988**
Tracheid cells, **809**f
Tracheids, **664**
Tracheoles, 988f
Trade-offs, 1261–62
Tradescantia, 815f
Traditional Ecological Knowledge (TEK), 1286f
Tragopogon, 539, 539f
Traits, **282**
    land plant derived, 654, 655f–56f
    life history, 1260–62
Trans double bonds, in fatty acids, 81, 82
Trans face, 117–18
Trans fats, 82, 984
Transcription, **353**, 377–78
    basic principles, 353–55
    cell type-specific, 391f
    coupled, in bacteria, 372f
    as DNA-directed synthesis of RNA, 358–360
    of eukaryotic genes, 388f
    vs. gene expression, 385
    genetic code, 355–58
    molecular components of, 358
    regulation of, 381–85, 387–392, 891
    review, 410–11
    roles of, 355f
    stages of, 358, 359f
    summary, 373f
    synthesis of RNA transcript, 358–360
Transcription activators, 388–89, 389f
Transcription factories, 392
Transcription factors, 229, **359**
    general, 387–88
    roles of, 387–392
    specific, 388–390
Transcription initiation complex, **359**, 387
Transcription repressors, 388, 390
Transcription units, **358**
Transcriptional regulation, 891
Transduction, **609**–10, 610f, 1052f. *See also* Signal transduction pathways
    in cell signalling, 224f
    and cellular mating, 222
    in the cochlea, 1170f
    explained, 225
    protein phosphorylation and dephosphorylation, 230–31, 230f
    review, 241
    second messengers, 231–33
    sensory, 1175–76
Transfer DNA, 95f
Transfer RNA (tRNA), **363**
    aminoacyl-tRNA synthetase joining a specific amino acid to, 365f
    structure and function of, 363–65, 364f
Transformation, **258**, **330**, **609**
Transgene escape, 885–86

Transgenes, 457
Transgenic, **882**, **883**
Transgenic animals, **457**, 459
Transgenic crops. *See also* Genetically modified organisms (GMOs)
    biotechnology and genetic engineering, 883
    canola, 867
    reducing fossil fuel dependency, 884–85
    reducing malnutrition and hunger, 883–84
    review, 887
Transgenic plants, 460, 820–f, 881–82
Transition site, 165
Transition state, 165
Translation, **353**
    basic principles, 353–55, 364f
    completing and targeting the functional protein, 369–371
    coupled, in bacteria, 372f
    elongation cycle, 369f
    initiation of, 393–94
    molecular components of, 363–66
    post-transcriptional regulation, 392–94
    review, 377, 378
    and ribosome association, 367
    as RNA-directed synthesis of polypeptides, 363–372
    roles of, 355f
    summary, 373f
    termination of, 367, 370f
Translation initiation complex, 367f
Translocation, 322f, **322**, 324f, 369f, 404, 404f, **843**, 844–45
Transmembrane glycoproteins, 1109
Transmembrane proteins, 139–140, 139f
Transmembrane route, 832, 837f
Transmission, sensory, **1164**
Transmission electron microscope (TEM), 106f, 107
Transpiration, 829f, **836**
    review, 847
    and stomata, 214, 838, 840–42
    and temperature, 842
    transport of water and minerals, 836–840
    and wilting, 842
Transpirational pull, 838–39, 838f
Transplants, 1017–18
Transport epithelia, **1030**, 1034, 1035, 1036, 1037, 1038
Transport in vascular plants
    apoplast, 831–32
    long-distance transport, 835
    review, 847–48
    short-distance transport of solutes across plasma membranes, 832, 832f, 833f
    short-distance transport of water across plasma membranes, 832–35
    sugar transport via phloem, 843–45
    symplast, 831–32, 846–47
Transport proteins, 84f, 142, 145
Transport vesicles, **116**
Transport work, 161, 163, 163f

Transposable elements, 473f, **473**–74, 480–81
Transposase, 473
Transposition, 473
Transposon movement, 473f
Transposons, 425, **473**, 599f
Trans-retinal arrangement, 1175, 1175f
Transthyretin, 88f
Transverse (T) tubules, **1184**
Tree ferns, 691f
Tree of life. *See also* Evolutionary tree; Phylogenetic trees
    and descent with modification, 16
    of finches, 17f
    genomes and their evolution, 463–64
    investigating, 582–83
    understanding based on new data, 598–99
Tree topology, 585
Trees
    acacia, 1280f
    alders, 860, 1291
    American beech, 1231, 1231f
    American chestnut, 1285
    anatomy of a tree trunk, 818f
    aspen, 877, 879f
    balsam poplars, 803
    black spruce, 1304
    bonsai, 828–29
    Brazil, 1261
    Eastern white cedar, 828f
    halas, 804f
    hemlock, 1291
    lodgepole pine, 1233
    maples, 806, 1230f, 1231f, 1285
    Norway spruce, 830f
    oaks, 687f, 1295
    palms, 687f
    pine. *See* Pine trees
    poplars, 802f, 803, 884, 884f
    red spruce, 1233
    Sitka spruce, 1291
    and systemic immune response, 913–14
    taxonomy of, 585
    walnut, 1261
    Western red cedar, 836
Trehalose, 1028
Trematodes, **735**–36
Trevesia palmata, 800f
Tria Project, 471f
Triacylglycerol, 80, 81f
Triassic period, 568, 783
Tribulus terrestris, 878f
Triceratium morlandii, 634f
Trichechus manatus, 759f, 1279f
Trichinella spiralis, 745–46, 746f
Trichinosis, 745
Trichomes, 800f–801f, 807
Trichomonas vaginalis, 632, 632f
Triiodothyronine (T_3), **1061**
Trillium flexipes, 868f
Trilobites, 746f
Trimesters, **1086**

Trimethylamine oxide (TMAO), 1027
Trioses, 76, 76f
Triple response, 899f, **899**
Triplet code, 356f, **356**
Triploblastic, **720**, 734
Triploblasts, 1102
Triploidy, 321
Trisomic, **321**
Trisomy 21 (Down Syndrome). *See* Down syndrome
Trisomy X, 323
Tristan da Cunha, 519
Triticum aestivum, 1264f
tRNA. *See* Transfer RNA (tRNA)
Trochophore larva, 723f, **723**, 734
Trophic cascade model, 1288f, **1288**
Trophic efficiency, 1308f, **1308**–9
Trophic structure, **1283**
    bottom-up and top-down controls in, 1287–88
    cascade model, 1288, 1288f
    dominant species in, 1285–86
    ecosystem engineers in, 1286, 1287f
    energy transfer between levels, 1307–9
    and food chains, 1283, 1284–85, 1286f
    and food webs, 1284, 1284f, 1285f
    keystone species in, 1286, 1287f
    levels of, 1301
    review, 1297
Trophoblast, **1086**, **1104**
Tropic hormones, **1060**
Tropical deforestation, 1324f
Tropical dry forests, **1234**f, 1316f
Tropical forests, 689, 689f
Tropical rain forests, **1234**f, 1303
Tropical tree lizard, 1275
Tropics, **1227**f
Tropidolaemus wagleri, 779f
Tropism, **893**
Tropomyosin, **1184**
Troponin complex, **1184**
Troponin T gene, 393f
Trout, 769f, 1325
trp operon, 382, 382f
trp repressor, 382
True-breeding, **283**
Truffles, 702f, 709
Tryglyceride, 80
Trypanosoma, 633, 633f, 754, 1021
Trypsin, 955
Tryptophan, 381–83, 381f, 382f, 1051
Tsavo National Park, 1326, 1326f
Tuataras, 779, 779f
Tubal ligation, **1091**
Tube cells, 682, 869
Tube feet, **754**
Tuber melanosporum, 702f
Tuberculosis, 620, 1005
Tubers, 805f
Tubules, 1033–35, 1035–36
Tubulidentata, 787f

α tubulin, 124, 124*f*, 125
Tubulin, 124*f*, 125, 1224
Tubulinids, 646
Tumbleweeds, 878*f*
Tumour viruses, 410
Tumour-suppressor genes, **405**
Tuna, 921, 1145
Tundra, 1222*f*–23*f*, 1231, 1237*f*, 1284, 1285*f*
Tunicates, 729*f*
Tunicates (Urochordata), **762**, 763*f*, 1071, 1111*f*
Tunnicliffe, Verena, 1221, 1299
Turgid, **145**, **834**
Turgor pressure, 145, **833**
Turner syndrome, 323
Turnover, **1238**, 1239*f*
Turnover time, **1308**
Turtles, 777*f*, 778–79, 778*f*, 931*f*, 989, 1030, 1032, 1119*f*, 1166, 1225, 1244, 1244*f*, 1246, 1247
Tutu, Desmond, 484–85
Twin studies, **1201**
Twins, 1088, 1113
Twitches, 1186*f*
Tympanic canal, 1169
Tympanic membranes, 1167, 1167*f*, **1168*f***
Tympanuchus cupido, 1322, 1327
Tyndall stone, 726
Type 1 diabetes mellitus, 453, 457, 1019
Type 2 diabetes mellitus, 470*f*, 947, 961
α-type epinephrine receptor, 1054
Typhoid fever, 621
Tyrannosaurus rex, 550, 778, 921, 1032
Tyrosine, 1051
Tyrosine kinases, 456
Tyrosinemia, 456

U

Ubx gene, 571, 572
Ulcerative colitis, 1005
Ulcers, 954
Ultimate causation, 1197
Ultrasound imaging, 1091
Ultrasound techniques, 302
Ultraviolet light, 342, 1173
Ulva, 643, 643*f*
Umbilical cord, 1106
Undernutrition, 947
Undersea volcanoes, 1221
Undershoot, 1127, 1128*f*
Ungulates, 506, 506*f*
Unicellular eukaryotes, 113*f*
Unicellular protists, 199*f*
Uniform dispersion, 1252*f*, 1253
Unikont amoeba, 629*f*
Unikonta, 629*f*, **644**–47, 650
Unisexual, 867
Unity within diversity, 12–13, 15*f*
Universal species identification, 594*f*
University of California, San Diego, 465
Unsaturated fats, 81, 81*f*
Unsaturated fatty acid, 81, 81*f*

Upstream, 358
Upwelling, 1238–39, 1305
Uranium-238, 36
Urban ecology, **1335**
Urchin barrens, 1273
Urea, 1031–**32**, 1031*f*, 1035, 1039*f*
Ureter, **1036*f***
Urethra, **1079**
Urey, Harold, 551
Uric acid, 1031*f*, **1032**
Urinary bladders, **1036*f***
Urine
    black, 352
    concentration of, 1038, 1039–40, 1039*f*
    formation of, 1037
    hyperosmotic, 1038, 1040
    nephron processing of blood filtrate in, 1035–38
Urocitellus richardsonii, 1215
Urodeles (Urodela), 773, 774*f*
Ursus americanus, 943, 943*f*
Ursus maritimus, 1072*f*
Utricularia gibba, 469*t*, 470
USA300, 502
Use and disuse, 495
Uta stansburiana, 1212, 1212*f*
Uterine cycle, **1083**, 1084
Uterus, 112*f*, **1077**
Utricle, **1170**

V

V segments, 1008, 1009*f*
Vaccination, **1015**–17
Vaccines, **426**
Vacuolar sap, 822
Vacuoles, 119*f*, **119**, 950, 1002
Vagina, **1077**
Vaginal pouches, 1090
Valence electrons, **39**
Valence shells, **39**
Valences, **41**, 67*f*
Valves, of circulatory system, 973, 975
Vampire bats, 1040–41, 1041*f*
Vampire plants, 888*f*
van Alphen, Jacques, 539*f*, 540*f*
van der Waals interactions, **43**–44
van Leeuwenhoek, Antoni, 105, 625, 1269
van Niel, C. B., 201
Vaporization, 31, 52
Varanus komodoensis, 1094*f*
Variable (V) region, 1006
Variables, **22**–23
Variation, **266**
    and heredity, 295–96
    in population, 499*f*
Vas deferens, **1079**
Vasa recta, **1037*f***
Vascular bundles, 807
Vascular cambium, **810**, 815, 817*f*, 895
Vascular cylinder, 807
Vascular plants, 562, **658**, 829–830

gametophyte-sporophyte relationships in plant groups, 674*f*
    phyla of, 657*t*
    resource acquisition, 829–831, 829*f*
    review, 847–48
    seedless. *See* Seedless vascular plants
    transport mechanisms, 831–35
Vascular rays, 817
Vascular tissue, **657**
Vascular tissue systems, 807*f*, **807**
Vasectomy, **1091**
Vasocongestion, **1085**
Vasoconstriction, **932**, **977**
Vasodilation, **932**, **977**
Vasopressin, 1043, 1049, 1054*f*, 1060, 1213
Vectors, **1294**, 1296
    cloning, 437
    retroviral, 455*f*
Vegetal pole, **1100**
Vegetarian diets, 944
Vegetative propagation, **881**
Vegetative reproduction, **879**
Veins, **805**, **969**, 975, 978*f*
Venter, J. Craig, 464
Ventilation, **986**, 990–92. *See also* Breathing
Ventral tegmental area (VTA), 1158
Ventricles, **969**, 1142*f*, **1142**
Vents, 552, 552*f*, 615
Venules, **969**, 975*f*
Venus flytrap, 846, 863*f*, 908
Vernalization, **906**
Vertebrate stretch receptors, 1165
Vertebrates, **723**, **759**
    amniotes, 775–782
    and anatomical homology, 503*f*
    brain in, 1145–51, 1145*f*
    chordates, 760–63, 763–66
    circulatory systems, 969–971, 970*f*
    cognition, evolution of, 1153
    derived characters of, 764
    digestive systems and diet, 957–960
    disparity of, 760
    diversity of, 760
    early evolution of, 765–66
    embryonic germ layers in, 1103*f*
    evolution of, 717, 759–760
    eyes of, 1174
    forebrain in, 1145
    gnathostomes, 767–771
    hormone regulation of homeostasis, development, and behaviour, 1059–67
    innate immunity of, 1001–5
    jawless, 766, 766*f*
    kidneys in, 1035, 1040–41
    limb development in, 1114–16, 1115*f*, 1116*f*
    male vocalizations, 1082
    mammals. *See* Mammals
    nervous system in, 1141, 1142–43, 1143*f*
    and nutrition, 945
    organogenesis in, 1107–8
    and osmoregulation, 1028

Vertebrates (*Continued*)
parthenogenesis in, 1071
peripheral nervous systems, 1144f
reproduction in, 1075
review, 797–98
skeletal muscle in, 1181–87
tetrapods, 771–782
and vestigial structures, 504
visual system in, 1174–79
Vertical transmission, 430
Vervet monkeys, 1205–6, 1206f
Vesicles, **115**, 553, 553f
Vessel elements, **809**f
Vessels, **809**f
Vestibular canals, 1169
Vestigial structures, **504**
Viagra, 232, **1079**, 1135
Vibrio cholerae, 232
Victoria (queen), and transmission of hemophilia, 313
Villi, **955**
Vincent, Amanda, 1320
Vines, 908
Viral envelopes, 417, 422
Viral genomes, 416
Viral movement proteins, 846, 846f
Virchow, Rudolf, 243
Viroids, 1294
Virulent phages, **419**
Viruses, **331**, **414**, 430. *See also* Genetics
algal, 415, 415f
in bacteria. *See* Bacteriophages (phages)
and cancer, 410, 426
as cause of diseases, 425
classes of, animal, 422t
discovery of, 415–16
diseases in animals, 426
diseases in plants, 430
and DNA, 415
elements of, 415–17
emergence of, 426–430
evolution of, 425, 429f
and genetic variation, 514
H1N1, 427–28, 427f, 429f, 1020, 1295
H5N1, 428
Hepatitis B, 1022
herpes, 422, 426, 1020
HIV (human immunodeficiency virus). *See* HIV (human immunodeficiency virus)
infected cell, 414f
influenza viruses, 417f, 427–28, 427f, 429f, 1020
and innate immunity, 1003
introduced, 414–15
and latency, 1020
and mutations, 428
and prions, 430–31, 431f
replication of, in host cells, **418–425**, 431
replicative cycles, general features, 418–19, 418f

replicative cycles of animal, 421–25
replicative cycles of phages, 419–421
review, 431–32
rinderpest, 1295
RNA as viral genetic material, 422–23, 423f
structure of, 416–17, 417f
West Nile, 418, 426, 1296
Visceral mass, **738**
Visible light, 203f, **203**
Visual communication, 1199
Visual fields, 1178–79
Visual perception, evolution of, 1172–74
Visual receptors, 1172–79
Visual systems
compound eyes, 1173
light-detecting organs, 1173
review, 1193
single-lens eyes, 1173–74
Visual systems, vertebrate, 1174–79
colour vision in, 1177–78
light-detecting organs, 574
neural pathways, 1177f
sensory transduction in, 1175–76
visual fields, 1178–79
visual processing in brain, 1177
visual processing in retina, 1176–77
Vital capacity, **991**
Vitamin A, 947
Vitamin B$_2$, 945
Vitamin B$_9$, 948
Vitamin C, 944
Vitamin D, 945, 1063
Vitamin K, 945, 957, 958
Vitamins
as essential nutrient, 945
human requirements, 946t
Vitelline layer, 1097
Vitellogenin, 1054
Vitreous humour, 1174f
In vitro cloning, 881–82
In vitro fertilization (IVF), 1092f, **1092**
In vitro mutagenesis, **446**
Viviparous, **769**
Vocal cords, 989
Vocal folds, 989
Vogt, Walther, 1110
Volcanic eruptions, 578f
and mass extinctions, 566
simulated, 552f
Voles, 1213, 1321f
Voltage-gated ion channels, 1125, **1127**, 1128f
Voltages, 147
Volume, 109f, 1169
Volvox, 629f, 643
von Frisch, Karl, 1197, 1199
von Humboldt, Alexander, 1293
Vulpes velox, 1322f

Vulpia fasciculata, 1262
Vulva, **1077**

W

Wadlow, Robert, 1063f
Waggle dance, 1199
Wagler's pit viper, 779f
Walking, 1191
Walking fish, 489f
Wallace, Alfred Russel, 497, 1292
Walnut trees, 1261
Walruses, 54f, 787f, 931f, 932, 945f, 1079
Warren, Robin, 954
Wasps, 801f, 912, 1071, 1203, 1203f, 1279–80
Water
absorption of by root epidermal cells, 836
acidification of, 59
and acids and bases, 56
adaptations that reduce evaporative loss, 842
and animal shapes, 921
balance in cells, 144–45, 144f
and climate, 1225–28, 1229f
cohesion of molecules, 50–51
covalent bonding, 41, 41f, 44
cycling in ecosystems, 1310f
diffusion into cells, 103f
diffusion of, 834–35
in digestion, 957
dissociation of, 55–56
emergent properties of, 50–56, 61
evaporative cooling, 53
global circulation of, 1229f
heat of vaporization, 52
hydrogen bonds, 50f
hydrophilic and hydrophobic substances, 55
ice, floating on, 53–54
importance of, 49
and irrigation, 852–53, 852f
on Mars, 56f
and moderation of temperature, 31, 51–53
movement across plant cell membranes, 834
movement across plasma membranes, 143–45, 832–35
in plants, 854
polar covalent bonds, 50
properties of, 30–31
relations in plant cells, 835f
as respiratory medium, 986t
root architecture and acquisition of, 831
and seed dispersal, 878f
and seed germination, 875
solute concentrations in aqueous solutions, 55–56
solute gradients and conservation of, 1038–40

as solvent, 54–56
specific heat of, 52
splitting of, in photosynthesis, 201–2
transport into the xylem, 836, 837f
transport within plants, 51f
walking on, 51f
Water bears, 1028, 1028f
Water breaking, in childbirth, 1106
Water buffalo, 1281f
Water cycle, 1310f
Water fleas, 469t, 922, 1073, 1258, 1259f
Water lilies, 687f
Water potential, **832**–34, 838–39
Water vascular system, **754**
Waterfowl, 1202
Watermelon snow, 220f
Water-soluble, 1050
Water-soluble hormones, 1051f, 1052, 1052f
Water-soluble protein, 55f
Water-soluble vitamins, 945, 946t
Watson, James, 3, 329f, 333–35, 335–36, 465
Wavelength, **203**, 205f
Wawona Sequoia, 818f
WD40 domain, 466f, 467
Weasels, 787f
Weddell seals, 995–96, 995f
Weeds, 885–86, 1274
Weight, **33**
Welch, Allison, 525f
Welwitschia, 679f
Wernicke, Karl, 1152
Wernicke's area, 1152
West Indies manatees, 1279f
West Nile virus, 418, 426, 1296
Western garter snakes, 1214
Western hemlock, 1291
Western meadowlarks, 531f
Western Red Cedar trees, 836
Western scrub jays, 1153
Wetlands, 1240f
Whales, 571, 787f, 922, 932, 949f, 1079, 1166f, 1284, 1322, 1322f
Wheat, 539, 882, 906, 1264f
Whelks, 1208
Whiptail lizard, 1071, 1073, 1073f
Whisk ferns, 666, 667f, 669
Whiskers, 1165
White blood cells, 239f
White matter, 1142f, **1142**
White rhinoceros, 1259, 1260f
White-crowned sparrows, 1205
Whitefish, 1337
White-footed mice, 1201, 1201t, 1265f
White-nose syndrome, 708, 709f
White-tailed deer, 1331
White-tailed jackrabbits, 2f, 920–21
Whole-genome shotgun approach, **464**–65
Whooping cranes, 1202, 1202f
Widow's peak, 296, 297f
Wieschaus, Eric, 401–2

Wild type, **309**, 319f, 898f
Wildfires, 1233, 1289
Wildlife DNA Forensic Laboratory, 593
Wildlife overpasses/underpasses, 1332, 1332f
Wilkins, Maurice, 333, 335
William of Occam, 590
Williams, Rebecca, 458f
Willow, 689
Wilson, E. O., 1293, 1294f, 1322f, 1323
Wilson, E.O., 1217
Wilting, **834**, 842
Wind
    and pollination, 871f
    and seed dispersal, 878f
Winged insects, 753f
Wings, 587, 780f, 1192–93
Wireframe model, 87f
Wishart, David, 29, 96
Wiskott-Aldrich syndrome (WAS), 238
Witchweed, 901
WNT4 genes, 312
Wobble, **365**
Wöhler, Friedrich, 64
Wolf fish, 1295, 1295f
Wolffia, 664
Wollemi pine, 680f
Wolves, 787f, 918f, 934, 1085, 1245f, 1263, 1264f, 1276, 1277
Wood, 689, 884f
Wood ants, 32
Wood development, 818–19
Wood frogs, 918f
Wood lice, 750
Wood turtles, 1225, 1244, 1244f, 1246, 1247
Woodland caribou, 712f
Woolly mammoth, 433
Woolly mammoths, 995, 1326, 1326f
Workplace Hazardous Materials Information
    System (WHMIS), 375
Worms, 729f
    acanthocephalan, 1280
    acoel flatworms, 727f
    acoelomate flatworms, 723–24
    acorn worms, 729f
    earthworms, 744–45, 744f, 851, 951f, 968f, 1034, 1034f, 1189, 1191
    flatworms, 727f, 734–37, 950, 967f, 1033–34, 1075, 1140f, 1189
    fragmentation in, 1071
    giant tubeworms, 959f
    marine worms, 987f
    nervous system in, 1141
    palolo, 1075
    peristalsis in, 1189
    proboscis worms, 728f
    roundworms, 729f, 745–46, 745f, 1028, 1110, 1189
    skeletal system of, 1189
    soil worms, 25, 239, 239f, 484
    tapeworms, 1073

X

X chromosome inactivation, 395–96
X inactivation, 313–14, 314f
X-0 System, 311f
Xanthium strumarium, 905
Xanthomonas, 350f
Xanthopan morganii praedicta, 873f
Xenarthra, 787f
Xenopsylla, 1035
Xeroderma pigmentosum (XP), 342
Xerophytes, **842**
XIST genes, 395–96
X-linked genes, 312f, **312–14**
X-ray crystallography, 87f, **92**, 333
X-ray diffraction photography, 333, 333f
X-Y system, 311f
Xylem, **664**, 689, **807**, 812f, 829, 835, 836, 837f
Xylem sap, 829f, **836**, 837–840, 839–840, 839f

Y

Yamanaka, Shinya, 452, 453f
Yangtze River dolphins, 1322f
Yeast, 110, 112f, 222, 237, 1265f
    cell division in, 253f
    and chromatin remodelling by ncRNAs, 395–96, 396f
    and climate change, 692–93
    and cloning and expressing eukaryotic genes, 442
    as cultured fungi, 709
    DNA content, 276
    genetic interactions, 263
    genomes, 469f, 469t
    mapping protein interaction network, 468, 468f
    meiosis in, 276
    structure of, 693
Yeast infections, 709
Yeat, 222f
Yellow jackets, 1278f
Yellow-bellied toads, 541, 541f
Yellow-billed storks, 582, 582f
Yellowstone National Park, 462f, 615
Yersinia pestis, 1295
Y-linked genes, 312
Yolk, **1100**–1101, 1106
Yolk sac, 1106
Yucca flowers, 872f

Z

Z lines, 1182
Zanke, Brent, 471f
Zea mays, 463, 469t, 812f, 896. See also Maize (corn)
Zeatin, 896
Zebra finches, 1210, 1210f, 1211f
Zebra mussels, 1325, 1325f
Zebrafish, 25

Zebras, 787f
Zelenitsky, Darla, 550
Zinc, 856
Zona pellucida, **1099**
Zonation in aquatic biomes, 1238–39, f–1239
Zone of cell division, 812
Zone of differentiation, 812
Zone of elongation, 812
Zone of polarizing activity (ZPA), 1116f, **1116**
Zoned reserves, **1333**–35
Zonotrichia leucophrys, 1205
Zoonotic pathogens, **1295**–97
Zooplankton, 1284, 1308–9
Zoospsores, **699**, 701f
Zuker, Charles, 1180f
Z-W system, 311f
Zygomycetes, **699**–701, 700f
Zygomycota, 699
Zygosporangium, **701**
Zygotes, **269**, 1071, 1075